A COMPREHENSIVE TREATISE ON
INORGANIC AND THEORETICAL CHEMISTRY

VOLUME IX
As, Sb, Bi, V, Cb, Ta

The complete work

A COMPREHENSIVE TREATISE ON
INORGANIC AND THEORETICAL CHEMISTRY

In Sixteen Volumes.   With Diagrams.

SUPPLEMENT TO MELLOR'S COMPREHENSIVE
TREATISE ON INORGANIC AND THEORETICAL CHEMISTRY

Other volumes in preparation.

By the same author
MODERN INORGANIC CHEMISTRY

A COMPREHENSIVE TREATISE ON

INORGANIC
AND THEORETICAL
CHEMISTRY

BY

J. W. MELLOR, D.Sc., F.R.S.

VOLUME IX

WITH 161 DIAGRAMS

LONGMANS

LONGMANS, GREEN AND CO LTD
48 Grosvenor Street, London W.1

*Associated companies, branches and representatives
throughout the world*

First published 1929
New impression 1964

*Made and printed in Great Britain by
William Clowes and Sons, Limited, London and Beccles*

Dedicated

TO THE

PRIVATES IN THE GREAT ARMY
OF WORKERS IN CHEMISTRY

THEIR NAMES HAVE BEEN FORGOTTEN
THEIR WORK REMAINS

PREFACE

I AM greatly indebted to my friends and colleagues—Dr. A. Scott, Mr. H. V. Thompson, M.A., Mr. A. T. Green, F.Inst.P., Mr. A. Rigby, Mr. L. S. Theobald, B.Sc., Mr. F. H. Clews, M.Sc., and Mr. A. J. Dale, B.Sc., for help and suggestions in the proof-reading of Vols. VII, VIII, and IX; Mr. P. Roche and Miss Schoett, for help with the references; and Misses Till, Littler, and Stubbs, for help with the typing, indexing, etc.

J. W. M.

CONTENTS

CHAPTER LI

ARSENIC

CHAPTER LII

ANTIMONY

CHAPTER LIII

BISMUTH

CHAPTER LIV

VANADIUM

CHAPTER LV

COLUMBIUM

CHAPTER LVI

TANTALUM

ABBREVIATIONS

aq. = aqueous

atm. = atmospheric or atmosphere(s)

at. vol. = atomic volume(s)

at. wt. = atomic weight(s)

$T°$ or $°K$ = absolute degrees of temperature

b.p. = boiling point(s)

$θ°$ = centigrade degrees of temperature

coeff. = coefficient

conc. = concentrated or concentration

dil. = dilute

eq. = equivalent(s)

f.p. = freezing point(s)

m.p. = melting point(s)

$\text{mol(s)} = \begin{cases} \text{gram-molecule(s)} \\ \text{gram-molecular} \end{cases}$

$\text{mol(s)}. = \begin{cases} \text{molecule(s)} \\ \text{molecular} \end{cases}$

mol. ht. = molecular heat(s)

mol. vol. = molecular volume(s)

mol. wt. = molecular weight(s)

press. = pressure(s)

sat. = saturated

soln. = solution(s)

sp. gr. = specific gravity (gravities)

sp. ht. = specific heat(s)

sp. vol. = specific volume(s)

temp. = temperature(s)

vap. = vapour

In the cross references the first number in clarendon type is the number of the volume ; the second number refers to the chapter; and the succeeding number refers to the "§," section. Thus **5.** 38, 24 refers to § 24, chapter 38, volume 5.

The oxides, hydrides, halides, sulphides, sulphates, carbonates, nitrates, and phosphates are considered with the basic elements ; the other compounds are taken in connection with the acidic element. The double or complex salts in connection with a given element include those associated with elements previously discussed. The carbides, silicides, titanides, phosphides, arsenides, etc., are considered in connection with carbon, silicon, titanium, etc. The intermetallic compounds of a given element include those associated with elements previously considered.

The use of triangular diagrams for representing the properties of three-component systems was suggested by G. G. Stokes (*Proc. Roy. Soc.*, **49.** 174, 1891). The method was immediately taken up in many directions and it has proved of great value. With practice it becomes as useful for representing the properties of ternary mixtures as squared paper is for binary mixtures. The principle of triangular diagrams is based on the fact that in an equilateral triangle the sum of the perpendicular distances of any point from the three sides is a constant. Given any three substances A, B, and C, the composition of any possible combination of these can be represented by a point in or on the triangle. The apices of the triangle represent the single components A, B, and C, the sides of the triangle represent binary mixtures of A and B, B and C, or C and A; and points within the triangle, ternary mixtures. The compositions of the mixtures can be represented in percentages, or referred to unity, 10, etc. In Fig. 1, pure A will be represented by a point at the apex marked A. If 100 be the

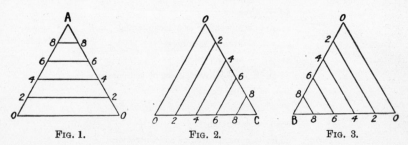

FIG. 1.   FIG. 2.   FIG. 3.

standard of reference, the point A represents 100 per cent. of A and nothing else; mixtures containing 80 per cent. of A are represented by a point on the line 88, 60 per cent. of A by a point on the line 66, etc. Similarly with B and C—Figs. 3 and 2 respectively. Combine Figs. 1, 2, and 3 into one diagram by superposition, and Fig. 4 results. Any point in this

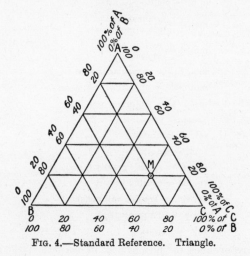

FIG. 4.—Standard Reference.   Triangle.

diagram, Fig. 4, thus represents a ternary mixture. For instance, the point M represents a mixture containing 20 per cent. of A, 20 per cent. of B, and 60 per cent. of C.

CHAPTER LI

ARSENIC

§ 1. The History of Arsenic

T. BERGMAN,[1] in his *De arsenico* (Upsala, 1777), said that it is probable that arsenic was first discovered by those who wrought in the roasting and fusing of ores, for it would betray itself by its white smoke, its garlic smell, and its pernicious effects in depraving metals, and destroying life. In the fourth century B.C., arsenic sulphide was designated σανδαράκη, *sandarach*, by Aristotle, in his Μηχανικὰ Προβλήματα (**33**. 2) ; ἀρρενικόν, arrhenicum, by Theophrastos in his Περὶ Λίθων ; and in the first century of our era, Dioscorides, in his Περὶ Ὕλης Ἰατρικῆς (**5**. 10), called the mineral suphide ἀρσενικόν, *arsenicon*. In the first century of our era, Pliny, in his *Historia naturalis* (**33**. 22 ; and **34**. 55 and 56), said :

Sandarach is found in gold and silver mines. The redder it is, the more powerful its odour, the better its quality. . . . *Arsenicum* is composed of the same matter as *sandarach ;* the best in quality has the same colour as that of the best gold, and that which is pale in colour resembling sandarach is of inferior quality.

Pliny also confused white arsenic with ceruse ; and the context of the Olympio-dorus references to the preparation of alum shows that white arsenic was meant. Pliny also seems to have confused red-lead with realgar. The yellow *auripigmentum*, or orpiment of Pliny is the yellow arsenic sulphide ; M. P. Vitruvius, in his *De architectura* (**7**. 7), added that *auripigmentum* is a mineral called by the Greeks *arsenicum*. The *sandarach* of these early writers was probably the mineral now known as *realgar*, AsS ; and *arsenicum* and *auripigmentum*, the mineral *orpiment*, As$_2$S$_3$. The observations of Aristotle, and many early references to arsenic, were discussed by E. O. von Lippmann. J. H. Pott wrote on the orpiment, and J. G. Lehmann, on the sandarach of the ancients. The term *arsenic* is derived from the Greek ἀρσενικός=ἀρρενικός, meaning valiant or bold, in allusion, said R. J. Haüy, to the great energy with which it acts on other metals. F. von Kobell said the Greek term was derived from the Arabian *arsa naki ;* S. Fraenkel, however, said that this term does not occur in the Arabian language ; rather was the Greek term derived from the Persian word for arsenic, *zarnich*, *zirnuk*, or *zirne*.

It is rather surprising that these early writers—Dioscorides, Pliny, A. C. Celsus,[2] and C. Galen—should mention several medicinal qualities of arsenical preparations, but did not mention the toxic properties of white arsenic—*i.e.* arsenic trioxide. They must have had an impure form of this oxide since Pliny said that in order to increase the energy of arsenicum, it was heated in a new earthen vessel until it changed its colour ; and Dioscorides said that sandarach was mixed with carbon and calcined until it changed its colour.

The thirteenth-century Latin translation of Geber's *Summa perfectionis magisterii* shows that *arsenicum album* or white arsenic was obtained as a sublimate from arsenicum. He said that the product which has been sublimed cannot be inflamed like the impure raw arsenicum, because, when heated, it merely sublimes without inflammation. According to T. Bergman's *De arsenico* (Upsala, 1777), the eleventh-century Arabian writer Avicenna said that there are three forms of *arsenicum*—white, yellow, and red—and that the white is obtained from the other forms by sublimation. He also mentioned the poisonous properties of white arsenic. In the *Breve breviarium de dono Dei* attributed to Roger Bacon, of the thirteenth century, it is stated that white arsenic is prepared by calcining orpiment with iron scales. The iron would have taken the sulphur, and the arsenic vap. set free would be oxidized to white arsenic. Both Geber, and Avicenna recognized that *arsenicum* has many of the properties of sulphur ; and A. Libavius, in his *Commentationum metallicarum* (Francofurti, 1597), said :

> Arsenicum is a rich, inflammable mineral juice which is akin to sulphur, yet more virulent because of the salt combined with it ; it is composed of a sulphurous richness with a little mercury and spirit of salt.

Somewhat similar views were held by N. Lemery,[3] J. Kunckel, and N. Sokoloff. J. J. Becher regarded *arsenicum* as a combination of *terra sulphuris*, common salt, and a metal ; and C. Neumann said that it contains an acid of sulphur. According to M. Berthelot, metallic arsenic is first mentioned in a fragmental writing attributed to Zosimos of the third or fourth century ; and the preparation of white arsenic is described by Olympiodorus, a writer of the fifth century. Geber, in his *De fornacibus*, supposed that arsenicum contains a metal ; and Albertus Magnus, in his thirteenth-century work *De alchymia*, said that arsenicum becomes metallic when heated with twice its weight of soap. Basil Valentine called *arsenicum metallinum* a bastard metal ; and in the seventeenth century, N. Lemery obtained reguline arsenic—metallic arsenic—by heating white arsenic with potash and soap ; and it was also made by J. Schröder, and J. F. Henkel. G. Brandt said that reguline arsenic must be regarded as a semimetal, and white arsenic, as the calx of reguline arsenic. This was supported by the work of J. Browall, and A. G. Monnet. In modern language, this means white arsenic is an oxide of the metal arsenic. The history of the different combinations of arsenic is indicated in connection with the individual compounds. The stoichiometrical relations of arsenic with other elements were worked out by J. J. Berzelius in 1817. In the Middle Ages, arsenic received various names—*Scherbenkobold, Näpchenkobold, Goblet-fiend, Bowl-sprite, Cobaltum,* etc. M. Muccioli discussed the history of arsenic in ancient China.

> F. B. Fittica [4] stated that arsenic is not an element, but rather a compound of phosphorus, nitrogen, and oxygen, PN_2O ; but C. Winkler, A. C. Christomanos, C. R. Gyzander, and E. Noelting and W. Feuerstein showed that F. B. Fittica erred grievously in his speculation.

REFERENCES.

[1] T. Bergman, *De arsenico*, Upsala, 1777 ; E. O. von Lippmann, *Arch. Geschichte Naturwiss. Tech.*, 233, 1910 ; *Abhandlungen und Vorträge*, Leipzig, 2. 103, 1913 ; *Entstehung und Aussbreitung der Alchemie*, Berlin, 1919 ; J. H. Pott, *De sulphuribus metallorum*, Halæ, 1716 ; J. G. Lehmann, *Physikalischechemische Schriften*, Berlin, 1761 ; Olympiodorus, Manuscript No. 2250 in the Bibliothèque Royale de Paris ; R. J. Haüy, *Traité de minéralogie*, Paris, 4. 220, 1801 ; F. von Kobell, *Geschichte der Mineralogie*, München, 536, 1864 ; S. Fraenkel in C. Hintze, *Handbuch der Mineralogie*, Leipzig, 1. 106, 1904.

[2] A. C. Celsus, *De medicinia*, 5. 7, first century ; C. Galen, *De simplicibus medicamentis*, 10. 3, second century.

[3] N. Lemery, *Cours de chymie*, Paris, 1675 ; J. Kunckel, *Philosophia chemica experimentes confirmata*, Amstelædami, 1694 ; London, 1730 ; C. Neumann, *Chymia medica*, Züllichau, 1749 ; J. J. Becher, *Physica subterranea*, Lipsæ, 1669 ; Basil Valentine, *Von dem grossen Stein der Uhralten*, Strassburg, 1651 ; J. F. Henkel, *Pyritologia*, Leipzig, 1725 ; G. Brandt, *Arch. Akad. Upsala*, 3. 39, 1733 ; J. Browall, *Rön om Arsenik och dess metalliska natur*, Stockholm, 1744 ; A. G. Monnet, *Dissertation sur l'arsenic*, Berlin, 1774 ; N. Sokoloff, *De natura arsenici*, St. Petersburg, 1782 ; M. Berthelot, *Ann. Chim. Phys.*, (6), 13. 430, 1888 ; *Collection des anciens alchimistes grecs*, Paris, 1. 75, 1887 ; *Introduction à l'étude de la chimie des anciens et du moyen age*, Paris, 281, 1889 ; J. Schröder, *Pharmacopœa medico-chymica*, Ulmæ, 1641 ; Olympiodorus, Manuscript No. 2250 in the Bibliothèque Royale de Paris ; J. J. Berzelius, *Ann. Chim. Phys.*, (2), 5. 179. 1817 ; (2), 11. 225, 1819 ; *Schweigger's Journ.*, 34. 46, 1822 ; *Pogg. Ann.*, 7. 1, 137, 1826 ; M. Muccioli, *Notiz. Chim. Ind.*, 2. 699, 1927.

[4] F. B. Fittica, *Leopoldina*, 36. 3, 40, 1900 ; *Chem. Ztg.*, 24. 483, 561, 991, 1900 ; 25. 41,

259, 1901 ; A. C. Christomanos, *ib.*, 24. 943, 1900 ; C. Winkler, *Ber.*, 33. 1693, 1900 ; E. Noelting and W. Feuerstein, *ib.*, 33. 2684, 1900 ; C. Arnold and F. Murach, *ib.*, 25. 131, 1901 ; C. R. Gyzander, *Chem. News*, 82. 210, 1900.

§ 2. The Occurrence of Arsenic

Arsenic is ubiquitous. Every particle of coal dust or ashes, every tin-tack and every metal cooking vessel, is slightly arsenical. Few manufactured food materials or food ingredients are entirely free from it. The glass of white bottles contains it and gives it up to some of the substances stored in them, whence it also enters into food. The Royal Commission on Arsenical Poisoning, recognizing this ubiquity, limited the permissible quantity to $\frac{1}{100}$th grain per pound in solid and $\frac{1}{100}$th grain per gallon in liquid foods.— ANON.

Arsenic occurs very widely diffused in nature, and traces of it are common in most organic matter. Traces of the element are common in natural waters. F. W. Clarke and H. S. Washington [1] estimate that the igneous rocks of the earth contain $n \times 10^{-6}$ per cent. of this element ; and J. H. L. Vogt, $n \times 10^{-5}$ per cent. F. W. Clarke and G. Steiger found 0·00074 per cent. As₂O₅ to be present in a composite sample of 329 rocks from the United States. W. Vernadsky gave 0·0₄11 for the percentage amount, and 0·0₄5 for the atomic proportion of arsenic in the earth's crust. H. A. Rowland,[2] and M. N. Saha reported no arsenic lines in the solar spectrum ; but arsenic has been reported in a number of meteorites by A. Daubrée, C. Rumler, N. W. Fischer and A. Duflos, B. Silliman and F. S. Hunt, J. A. Antipoff, and L. H. Borgström.

Elemental arsenic occurs in veins in crystalline rocks and schists, and it commonly accompanies ores of antimony, silver, arsenic, zinc, and other metal sulphides. J. B. L. Romé de l'Isle [3] agreed that the *Scherbenkobalt* of the German miners, mentioned by J. H. G. Justi, and the *Cobatum testaceum*, mentioned by R. A. Vogel, are forms of arsenic. L. A. Emmerling referred to the synonyms—*Fliegelkobelt*, *Fliegelstein*, *Fliegengift*, *Näpfchenkobelt*, *Löffebikobelt*, and *Schirlkobelt*—for the mineral arsenic. The crystals were described by A. Breithaupt. The arsenic occurring near Marienberg, Saxony, was at first supposed to be galena. J. C. Freiesleben regarded it as molybdenite, and A. Breithaupt, as arsenic glance ; but C. M. Kersten showed that it contained scarcely a trace of sulphur, and A. Breithaupt thereupon called it bismuthiferous arsenic glance, and *hypotyphite*— from ὑποτύφομαι, to glow or burn slowly—in allusion to its behaviour when heated. F. von Kobell supposed bismuth to be the chief impurity. A. Frenzel showed that arsenic is the chief constituent, and he regarded the mineral as *eine besondere Modification* of arsenic. The following analysis of native arsenic from Joachimstahl is by J. V. Janowsky ; from Marienberg, by A. Frenzel ; from Montreal, by N. Norton ; from Ophir (California), by F. A. Genth ; and from Saltash (Cornwall), by A. Russell and H. F. Harwood :

Origin.	As	Sb	Bi	Fe	Ni	S	SiO₂
Joachimstahl .	90·91	1·56	—	2·07	4·64	—	0·55
Marienberg .	95·86	—	1·61	1·01	—	0·99	—
Montreal .	98·14	1·65	—	—	—	0·16	0·15
Ophir . .	90·82	9·18	—	—	—	—	—
Cornwall .	94·80	5·15	—	0·15	—	0·11	0·10

C. Hintze found a Chilean mineral closely resembling that from Saxony, and he called it *arsenolamprite*—from λαμπρός, lustrous—J. W. Retgers regarded arseno-lamprite as a distinct mineral species ; and analyses—ranging from 95·86 to 98·43 per cent. As, up to 3·0 per cent. Bi, up to 1·01 per cent. of S, and up to 0·55 per cent. SiO₂—were published by C. Hintze, C. M. Kersten, and A. Frenzel.

The occurrence of elemental arsenic in Germany was described by A. Madelung,[4] C. Hintze, G. Leonhard, L. A. Emmerling, F. Sandberger, O. Luedecke, J. C. L. Zincken, E. Reidemeister, A. Frenzel, J. F. John, M. Websky, H. Traube, V. R. von Zepharovich, A. E. Reuss, A. Eschka, and F. Babanek ; in Austria-Hungary, by V. R. von Zepharovich, A. Frenzel, G. Benkö, G. Rose, C. F. Peters, E. Hatle, A. Höfer, J. V. Janowsky, and

E. Fugger ; in Italy, by G. Jervis, and D. Bizzarri and G. Campani ; in Spain, by A. Orio ; in England, by H. Dewey, A. Russell and H. F. Harwood, and R. P. Greg and W. G. Lettsom ; in Norway, by G. Leonhard, C. Bugge and S. Foslie, and A. Erdmann ; in Russia, by P. N. Tschirwinsky ; in Siberia, by J. D. Dana, and G. Leonhard ; in Japan, by R. Scheibe, and A. Frenzel ; in Australasia, by A. Liversidge, and J. D. Dana ; in Chili and Peru, by I. Domeyko, and A. Raimondi ; in Mexico, by C. F. de Landero, and A. del Castillo and M. Barcena ; in Colorado, by C. Hersey ; in New Hampshire, by G. Leonhard ; in Maine, by J. D. Dana ; in Arizona, by C. H. Warren ; and in Canada, by G. C. Hoffmann, W. Gatt, M. E. Hurst, and N. N. Evans.

The world's production of arsenic—including the oxide and sulphide—in 1896 was 3674 metric tons for the United Kingdom ; 2632 metric tons for Germany ; 320 for Italy ; 6 for Japan ; and 271 for Spain, in 1907, 1913, and 1921. In 1926 there were 48 metric tons of white arsenic produced in Southern Rhodesia ; 38, in the Union of South Africa ; 1220, in Australia ; 1000, in Greece ; and 6354, in Mexico. The results, in metric tons, so far as they are available, are :

	Canada.	Germany.	Italy.	Japan.	Portugal.	Spain.	United Kingdom.	United States.	France (ore).
1907 .	317	2904	73	7	1538	2400	1523	916	7,900
1913 .	1538	5008	—	21	925	47	1723	2.158	70,613
1921 .	1353	—	—	1406	268	—	1049	4 342	580
1926 .	1779	—	136	—	—	—	3207	10,540	49,100

The chief minerals containing arsenic are the two sulphides, numerous arsenides, sulpharsenides, and arsenates of the heavy metals. Arsenopyrite or mispickel is perhaps the commonest mineral containing this element. The trioxide also occurs as the minerals *arsenolite*, and *claudetite*. The arsenical minerals include :

Arsenides.—*Algodonite*, Cu_6As ; *arsenargentite*, or *huntilite*, Ag_3As ; *arsenical copper*, or *domeykite*, Cu_3As ; *chloanthite*, or *white nickel ore*, $NiAs_2$, or, $(Ni,Co,Fe)As_2$; *huntilite* (see arsenargentite) ; *leucopyrite*, Fe_3As_4 ; *löllingite*, $FeAs_2$; *niccolite*, *nickeline*, or *red nickel ore*, $NiAs$; *nickeline* (see niccolite) ; *rammelsbergite*, $(Ni,Co,Fe)As_2$; *red nickel ore* (see niccolite) : *safflorite*, $(Co,Fe,Ni)As_2$; *skutterudite*, $CoAs_3$; *smaltite*, $CoAs_2$; *speiss cobalt*, $(Co,Fe,Ni)As_3$; *white nickel ore* (see chloanthite) ; *whitneyite*, Cu_9As. Mixed arsenides and antimonides.—*Arite*, Ni(As,Sb), and *sperrylite*, $(Pt,Rh)(As,Sb)_2$. Sulphides. —*Orpiment*, As_2S_3 ; and *realgar*, AsS. Mixed arsenides and sulphides.—*Alloclasite* (Co,Fe)S(As,Bi) ; *annivite* (see fahlerz) ; *arsenical nickel*, (Ni,Fe)AsS ; *arsenopyrites* (see mispickel) ; *baumhauerite*, $Pb_4As_6S_{13}$; *binnite*, $Cu_6As_4S_9$; *clarite* (see enargite) ; *cobalt glance*, (Co,Fe)AsS ; *cobaltite*, CoAsS ; *corynite*, (Ni,Fe)(As,Sb)S ; *danaite*, or *glaucodote*, (Fe,Co)(AsS) ; *dufrenoysite*, $Pb_2As_2S_5$; *enargite*, *clarite*, and *luzonite*, Cu_3AsS_4 ; *epigenite*, or *regnolite*, $Cu_8Fe_3As_2S_{12}$; *fahlerz*, *tetrahedrite*, *annivite*, *sandbergerite*, and *julianite*, $(As,Sb)_2S_7(Cu_2,Ag_2,Fe,Zn)_4$; *gersdorffite*, NiSAs ; *glaucodote* (see danaite) ; *guitermanite*, $Pb_3As_2S_7$; *hermesite* (see mercury fahlerz) ; *hutchinsonite*, $(Tl,Ag)_2Pb(AsS_2)_4$; *jordanite*, $Pb_4.As_2S_7$; *julianite* (see fahlerz) ; *lengenbachite*, $Pb_6(Ag,Cu)_2As_4S_{13}$; *light red silver ore* (see proustite) ; *liveingite*, $Pb_5As_8S_{17}$; *lorandite*, TlAsS₂ ; *mercury fahlerz*, *schwatzite*, or *hermesite*, $(Sb,As)_2S_7(Cu_2,Hg_2,Fe,Zn)_4$; *hermesite* (see mercury fahlerz) ; *mispickel*, or *arsenopyrites*, FeAsS ; *pearceite*, $(Ag,Cu)_{16}(Sb,As)_2S_{11}$; *polybasite*, $(Sb,As)_2S_{12}(Ag,Cu)_{18}$; *proustite*, or *light red silver ore*, Ag_3AsS_3 ; *rathite*, $Pb_3As_4S_9$; *regnolite* (see epigenite) ; *sandbergerite* (see fahlerz) ; *sartorite*, $Pb(AsS_2)_2$; *scleroclase*, $PbAs_2S_4$; *schwatzite* (see mercury fahlerz) ; *seligmannite*, PbCuAsS₃ ; *tennantite*, $Cu_8As_2S_7$; *tetrahedrite* (see fahlerz) ; *wolfachite*, (Ni,Fe)(As,S,Sb)₂ ; *xanthoconite*, Ag_3AsS_4.

Arsenites and arsenates.—*Adamite*, Zn(ZnOH)AsO₄ ; *allactite*, $Mn_3Mn(OH)_{24}(AsO_4)_2$; *annabergite* (see nickel bloom) ; *ardennite*, $10SiO_2(As,V,P)_2O_5.5(Al,Fe)_2O_3.10(Mn,Mg,Ca,Cu)O$ $6H_2O$; *armangite*, $Mn(AsO_3)_2$; *arseniopleite*, $(MnFe)_3(Mn,Ca,Pb,Mg)_3(MnOH)_6(AsO_4)_6$; *arseniosiderite*, $Fe_4Ca_3(OH)_9(AsO_4)_3$; *atelestite*, $(BiO)_2.Bi(OH)_2.AsO_4$; *bayldonite*, $(Pb,Cu)_2$- $(OH)AsO_4.\frac{1}{2}H_2O$; *berzeliite*, $(Ca,Mg,Mn,Na_2)_3(AsO_4)_2$; *beudantite*, $(Cu,Pb)_2Fe_2O_5(SO_3)$- $(P,As)_2O_5.H_2O$; *brandtite*, $Mn,Ca_2(AsO_4)_2.2H_2O$; *cabrerite*, $(Ni,Mg,Co)_3(AsO_4)_2.8H_2O$; *campylite*, $Pb_5Cl(As,P)O_{43}$; *carmine spar* (see carminite) ; *carminite*, or *carmine spar*, $Fe_{10}Pb_3(AsO_4)_{12}$; *caryinite*, $(Mn,Ca,Pb,Mg)_3(AsO_4)_2$; *chalcophyllite* (see copper mica) ; *chenevixite* (see henwoodite) ; *chlorotile*, $(CuOH)_3Cu(OH)_2AsO_4$; *chondrarsenite*, (Mn,Ca,Mg)- $(MnOH)_4(AsO_4)_2.\frac{1}{2}H_2O$; *clinoclasite*, $(CuOH)_3AsO_4$; *cobalt bloom*, or *erythrite*, $Co_3(AsO_4)_2.$ $8H_2O$; *conichalcite*, $(Cu,Ca)(CuOH)(As,P,V)O_4.\frac{1}{2}H_2O$; *copper mica*, or *chalcophyllite*, $(CuOH)_5AsO_4.3\frac{1}{2}H_2O$; *cornwallite*, $Cu(CuOH)_4(AsO_4)_2.3H_2O$; *cube ore*, or *pharmacosiderite*, $Fe(FeOH)_3(AsO_4)_3.6H_2O$; *diadelphite* (see hæmatolite) ; *discenite*, $(HOMn)_2Mn_3SiO_3$- $(AsO_3)_2$; *dixenite*, $Mn_3(AsO_3)_2.MnSiO_3.Mn(OH)_2$; *duftile*, $Pb_5(PbOH)(CuOH)_7(AsO_4)_6$; *durangite*, Na(Al,F)AsO₄ ; *ecdemite*, $Pb_3As_4O_{16}Cl_8$; *endlichite*, $Pb_5Cl\{(As,V)O_4\}_3$; *erinite*, $Cu(CuOH)_4(AsO_4)_2$; *erythrite* (see cobalt bloom) ; *euchroite*, $Cu(CuOH)AsO_4.3H_2O$; *fermorite*,

$(Cu,Sr)_5(F,OH)\{(P,As)O_4\}_3$; *finnemanite*, $Pb_3(AsO_3)_2.PbCl$; *flinkite*, $Mn\{Mn(OH)_2\}_2AsO_4$; *forbesite*, $(Ni,Co)H.AsO_4.3\frac{1}{2}H_2O$; *georgiadesite*, $Pb_5Cl_4(AsO_4)_2$; *hæmafibrite*, $(MnOH)_3AsO_4.$ H_2O ; *hæmatolite*, or *diadelphite*, $(Mn,Al)\{Mn(OH)_2\}_4AsO_4$; *haidingerite*, $CaHAsO_4.H_2O$; *hedyphane*, $(Pb,Ca,Ba)_5Cl(AsO_4)_3$; *henwoodite*, or *chenevixite*, $(FeO)_2Cu_3(AsO_4)_2.3H_2O$; *higginsite*, $Ca(CuOH)AsO_4$; *hœrnesite*, $Mg_3(AsO_4)_2.8H_2O$; *keottigite*, $(Zn,Co,Ni)_3(AsO_4)_2.$ $8H_2O$; *lavendulite*, $Cu_3(AsO_4)_2.2H_2O$; *leucochalcite*, $Cu_2(OH)AsO_4.H_2O$; *lindackerite*, $Ni_3Cu_6(OH)_4(AsO_4)_4(SO_4).5H_2O$; *liroconite*, $Al_4Cu_9(OH)_{15}(AsO_4)_5.20H_2O$; *liskeardite*, $(Al,Fe)_3.(OH)_6AsO_4.5H_2O$; *manganostibiite*, $Mn_2(Mn_2O_7)(Sb,As)O_4$; *mazapilite*, $Fe_4(OH)_6.$ $Ca_3(AsO_4)_4.3H_2O$; *mimetesite*, $Pb_4Cl(AsO_4)_3$; *mixite*, $BiCu_{10}(OH)_8(AsO_4)_5.7H_2O$; *nickel bloom*, or *annabergite*, $Ni_3(AsO_4)_2.8H_2O$; *olivenite*, $Cu(CuOH)AsO_4$; *pharmacolite*, $CaHAsO_4.2H_2O$; *pharmacosiderite* (see cube ore) ; *picropharmacolite*, $(Ca,Mg)_3(AsO_4)_2.$ $8H_2O$; *pitticite*, $Fe_{20}(OH)_{24}\{(As,P)O_4\}_{10}(SO_4)_3.9H_2O$; *polyarsenite* (see sarkinite) ; *rhagite*, $Bi(BiO)_9(AsO_4)_4.8H_2O$; *roesslerite*, $MgHAsO_4.\frac{1}{2}H_2O$; *roselite*, $(Ca,Co,Mg)_3(AsO_4)_2.2H_2O$; *sarkinite*, or *polyarsenite*, $Mn(MnOH)AsO_4$; *scorodite*, $FeAsO_4.2H_2O$; *svavite*, $Cu_5(F,OH,Cl)$- $(AsO_4)_3$; *symplesite*, $Fe_3(AsO_4)_2.8H_2O$; *synadelphite*, $(Mn,Al)\{Mn(OH)_2\}_5(AsO_4)_2$; *tilasite*, $Ca(MgF)AsO_4$; *trichalcite*, $Cu_3(AsO_4)_2.5H_2O$; *trigonite*, $MnHAsO_3.Pb_3(AsO_3)_2$; *trippkeite*, $nCuO.As_2O_3$; *trœgerite*, $(UO_2)_3(AsO_4)_2.12H_2O$; *tyrolite*, $Cu(CuOH)_4(AsO_4)_2.3\frac{1}{2}H_2O$; *urano-* *spinite*, $Ca(UO_2)_2(AsO_4)_2.8H_2O$; *veszelyite*, $\{(Cu,Zn)OH\}_3\{Cu(OH)_2\}(As,P)O_{42}.6H_2O$; *walpurgite*, $Bi_{10}(UO_2)_3(AsO_4)_7.10H_2O$; *wapplerite*, $(Ca,Mg)HAsO_4.3\frac{1}{2}H_2O$.

Small proportions of arsenic contaminate numerous minerals and earths. Most volcanic sulphur contains a small proportion of arsenic. T. L. Phipson [5] found 11·16 per cent. of arsenic sulphide in sulphur from the solfatara of Naples ; and F. Rinne, 29·22 per cent. of arsenic in the sulphur from Java to which he gave the name *sulphurite.* H. D. Gibbs and C. C. James found arsenic in a number of samples of sulphur. M. Vollhase and M. Berndt found that of 77 samples of potassium carbonate, 21 contained arsenic acid in amount varying from 0·241 to 0·841 per cent. As_2O_5. Arsenic also occurs in nearly all iron pyrites—*e.g.* A. Breithaupt and C. F. Plattner found up to 4·39 per cent. in the pyrites from Freiberg ; H. A. Smith, 0·944 per cent. in Belgian pyrites, 1·65–1·71 per cent. in Norwegian pyrites, 1·65–1·75 per cent. in Spanish pyrites, and 1·87 per cent. in Westphalian pyrites. H. Reguard found arsenic in malfinite. D. Campbell, R. A. Smith, A. Daubrée, W. M. Doherty, and H. Fischer and D. Rüst, reported arsenic in the pyrites of coal, and in coal ; hence, the presence of arsenic trioxide in the flue-gases from such coal observed by H. Ramage, etc. F. A. Walchner, H. Becker, E. Ludwig, and J. Mauthner, F. L. Sonnenschein, and M. Popp observed traces of arsenic in ferruginous earths, clays, and soils, from various sources ; A. J. Kunkel, A. Daubrée, and F. Sandberger, in various limestones and marls ; D. Campbell, and A. J. Kunkel, in sands from different localities. A. Daubrée observed 0·001 per cent. of arsenic in the basalt of Kaiserstuhl. F. Garrigou, indeed, found arsenic to be present in all the rocks and earths which he examined ; but A. Gautier considered this plausible generalization too sweeping. If arsenical ores and minerals be exposed to air and moisture for some time, soluble arsenic salts may be formed, and these find their way into brooks and spring waters. The wide distribution of arsenic in mineral deposits is one reason why traces of arsenic are so common in the waters of rivers which arise in hills containing mineral veins. According to W. H. Weed and L. V. Pirsson,[6] and A. Hague, the waters of some springs in the Yellowstone National Park, U.S.A., contain sulphur and arsenic ; and the deposits from the Norris Geyser basin contain sulphur, orpiment, realgar, and siliceous sinter. These same sulphides are common in old fissures through which thermal waters have arisen in former geological periods.

There has been an extraordinary number of reports of the presence of arsenic in mineral waters, and in deposits from mineral waters. Indeed, F. Garrigou found arsenic in all the natural waters he examined. The subject was discussed by L. J. Thénard, J. Glax, A. Gautier and P. Clausmann, M. Goy and W. Rudolph, etc. F. Taboury showed that arsenic had been previously mistaken for selenium in the mineral waters of La Roche-Posay. Arsenic was found in sea-water by G. Bertrand, and A. Daubrée. According to the latter, the evaporated residue contained 0·009 per cent. As. A. Gautier found water in a well, 30 metres from Brittany at a depth of 5 metres, with 0·010 mgrm. of arsenic per litre ; and from the

neighbourhood of the Azores at a depth of 10 metres, 0·025 mgrm. per litre, at a
depth of 1335 metres, 0·016 mgrm., and at a depth of 5943 metres (6–8 metres
from the bottom), 0·080 mgrm. per litre. W. R. G. Atkins and E. G. Wilson
found the amount of arsenic, principally as arsenite, in sea-water to be as great or
greater than that of the phosphate, and that reports of phosphates in sea-water
have included also arsenate. A. A. Bado observed arsenic in the subterranean
waters of Bellville, Cordoba, Argentine.

H. Kayser and C. Runge [7] said that arsenic lines can be nearly always detected
in the spectrum of the carbon arc-light ; W. Stein observed arsenic in the ashes
of and in the fumes from wood-charcoal. It was also observed in the ashes of many
plants by H. Marcelet, F. Jadin and A. Astruc, W. Stein, V. Legrip, A. Chatin,
J. E. Herberger, J. Girardin, F. Garrigou, and A. Gautier and P. Clausmann.
F. Jadin and A. Astruc found 0·006 mgrm. of arsenic in 100 grms. of mushrooms ;
0·007 to 0·025, in dry pears and beans ; 0·003 to 0·0023, in fresh vegetables ; 0·011
to 0·025, in nuts ; 0·005 to 0·012, in fruit. The highest proportions of arsenic were
found in red haricots, 0·025 ; almonds, 0·025 ; lettuce, 0·023 ; and celery, 0·020.
H. Marcelet observed no relation between the proportion of arsenic and manganese
in sea-water plants. It has also been reported in wines by M. Fermenti, and
A. Barthélemy. The maximum quantity of arsenic found by H. D. Gibbs and
C. C. James in California wines, was one part of arsenic in 2,500,000 parts of wine ;
the most probable sources of the arsenic were considered to be the arsenical sprays
used for the vines ; and the sulphur used for sulphuring the wine. A. Gautier,
and C. Husson found arsenic in wines coloured with aniline dyes. A. M. Peter
found arsenic in tobacco which had been sprayed with Paris green. The arsenic
found in beer is mainly derived from the glucose ; and the glucose obtains its arsenic
from the sulphuric acid used in its manufacture. The outbreak of arsenical poisoning in 1900, reported by T. N. Kelynack and W. Kirkby, and E. S. Reynolds, was
traced to the beer in which arsenic was introduced through the glucose. J. Clouet
found that caramel frequently contains large amounts of arsenic. A. P. Luff found
certain malts contained arsenic derived from the coke and anthracite coal used in
the drying operations. T. H. Barry said that most printing ink compositions contain arsenic. A. Gautier found arsenic in terrestrial and marine chlorophyllous
algæ. The occurrence of up to 0·1 grain of arsenic per pound of apples is due
to the spraying of the trees with arsenical preparations when the rainfall is not
sufficient to wash off the deposit. A. Hartzell and F. Wilcoxon found that
some sprayed apples contained a maximum of 0·704 mgrm. of As_2O_3 per
kilogram ; and that cider and jelly made from such apples contained only
traces of arsenic. R. Spallino found arsenic in snuff and tobacco ; and
R. E. Remington found arsenic invariably present in various kinds of smoking
and chewing tobacco—e.g. cigars, cigarettes, etc.—and from 6 to 30 parts of arsenic
per million were found in smoking and plug tobacco—i.e. about 0·05–0·27 grain
of arsenic trioxide per pound. Approximately half the arsenic in pipe tobacco is
evolved in the smoke, and about half of that in plug tobacco is soluble in water.
W. P. Headden reported that virgin soils contain from 2·5 to 5 parts of arsenic per
million, and the underlying marl, 4–15 parts per million. F. Rerchert and
R. A. Trelles also found arsenic in soils. According to E. F. von Gorup-Besanez,
plants grown on earth soaked with arsenious acids take up only an infinitesimal
quantity of arsenic ; while E. Davy, and A. Andouard found that superphosphate
fertilizers may contain arsenic, and plants to which the manure has been applied
may take up arsenic in their tissues. W. A. Lampadius said that a trace of arsenic
in soils has a beneficial influence on vegetation.

According to P. Brouardel and G. Pouchet,[8] the children of arsenic eaters—
vide infra—contain arsenic ; and that element can be detected in the placenta, and
in the mother's milk. According to P. Orfila and J. P. Couerbe, F. P. Danger and
C. Flandin, A. Gautier, A. Chevallier, C. H. Pfaff, N. Barbot and co-workers,
C. Steinberg, and V. A. Jacquelain, arsenic is a normal constituent of the human

body, but P. Orfila, **F. L.** Sonnenschein, E. Ziemke, and G. H. E. Schnedermann and W. Knop deny this. The literature has been summarized by **J. A.** Fordyce and co-workers, and by G. Bertrand. **F. L.** Sonnenschein said :

> I procured from the churchyard at Berlin the remnants of the body of a person killed twenty-five years previously, and investigated several others in a similar way, without finding the least trace of arsenic. Similar experiments in great numbers were repeated in my laboratory, but in no case was arsenic recognized.

A. Gautier found a small proportion of arsenic normally present in the thyroid glands of all the different animals ; 127 grms. of human thyroid gland gave 0·95 mgrm. of arsenic. The arsenic in the thyroid gland of a sheep was found to be present in the nucleins, not the peptones ; and hence it was inferred that arsenic may possibly form arsenic nucleins like those of phosphorus. Arsenic was also found in the thymus and brain, and only traces in the skin. No arsenic was detected in the liver of the dog, sheep, calf, or pig ; in the spleen of the dog or ox ; in the kidney of the pig ; in the flesh of the dog ; in the blood of the pig ; or in the testicle of man. Arsenic was not found in healthy blood except in the menstrual period when 0·28 mgrm. per kilogram of blood was present. According to W. H. Blömendal, and L. van Itallie and J. J. van Eck, the human liver does not normally contain arsenic, but G. Lechartier and F. Bellamy, and F. M. Raoult and H. Breton found arsenic. G. Bertrand, and M. Segale favoured the hypothesis that arsenic, along with carbon, nitrogen, sulphur, and phosphorus, is a normal constituent of protoplasm. A. J. Kunkel did not find arsenic to be present as a normal constituent in any animal organ including the thyroid gland. A. J. Kunkel, C. Hödlmoser, and K. Cerny denied that arsenic normally plays a physiological rôle in the human organism ; and, added D. Mann :

> It is possible that traces of arsenic may occasionally be found in some of the tissues without there being any obvious explanation of its presence ; but this does not constitute arsenic a physiological component of the human body. Until more evidence is forthcoming, arsenic must, as hitherto, still be regarded as not being a normal constituent of the human body.

The subject was also discussed by G. F. Schaefer, W. H. Blömendal, E. Ziemke, and A. Keilholz. A. Gautier found no arsenic in the muscles and adipose tissue of terrestrial animals. E. Marfurt stated that arsenic occurs normally in all parts of the human body he examined ; and the older the organism, the greater the proportion of arsenic present. If arsenic normally plays a part in the organism, this rôle is not confined to one special organ. D. Scolosuboff found that the arsenic concentrates principally in the nervous tissue. Thus, he found the following amounts of arsenic per 100 grms. of the tissue of a bull-dog, 0·00025 grm. in the muscles, 0·00271 grm. in the liver, 0·00885 grm. in the brain, and 0·00933 in the marrow. E. Ludwig, on the contrary, found in all cases of acute or chronic arsenical poisoning the liver is richer in arsenic than the other organs : thus, he found the following amounts of arsenic per 100 grms. of tissue : brain, 0·00004 grm., liver, 0·00338 grm. R. H. Chittenden found in a human body the following proportions of arsenic calculated in grains of As_2O_3 on the entire organs : stomach and oesophagus, 0·158 ; liver, 0·218 ; intestines, 0·314 ; kidneys, 0·020 ; heart, 0·112 ; lungs and spleen, 0·1719 ; brain, 0·075 ; trachea, larynx, and tongue, 0·081 ; and diaphragm, 0·010. He said that the entire body contained 3·1 grains As_2O_3 ; and that when the arsenic has been administered in a single dose, it is irregularly distributed in the muscular tissue, but when administered in long-continued, small doses, the distribution is regular. In a case of chronic arsenical poisoning, D. Mann found that arsenic is eliminated from the system viâ the kidneys as urine, the bowels, sweat, saliva, bronchial secretion, and, during lactation, in the milk. It also appears in the skin and its appendages—the nails and hair. He detected 0·013 per cent. of As_2O_3 in the exfoliated horny scales of the epiderm ; 0·008 per cent. in the hair ; and probably more in the nails.

He added that there thus appears to be a strong affinity between the keratin-tissues and arsenic. He found arsenic in the brain and spongy bone, but it was not prominently present in the brain substance or bone. This was confirmed by T. Stevenson. G. Bertrand said that arsenic occurs in fish from a depth of 1800 metres in the Atlantic Ocean. He also found it in all tissues and organs of animals —fishes, mussels, sponges, etc.—and in hen's eggs. A single egg contained 0·005 mgrm of arsenic—mostly in the yolk, but A. Gautier did not find arsenic in the eggs of fishes and birds. The Ministry of Agriculture and Fisheries on oyster mortality in 1920 reported finding oysters in certain beds containing 3·7 parts of arsenic per million, and H. E. Cox found up to 4 parts of arsenic per million in fish sold in the London market. According to A. C. Chapman, marine crustaceæ and shellfish have been found to contain from 10 to 174 parts of arsenic (as As_2O_3) per million of the wet edible portions ; native oysters contained from 5 to 10 parts, and Portuguese oysters from 33 to 70 parts per million. In fresh-water fish, shell-fish and crustaceæ, the amounts of arsenic ranged from only about 0·4 to 1·5 parts per million. The arsenic in the marine animals is therefore derived from the sea-water. Potted and canned crustaceæ and shellfish contained from 0·5 to 85 parts of arsenic per million. The arsenic in the urine of two experimental subjects was raised from the normal figure of about $\frac{1}{200}$th grain per gallon to half a grain in one case, and one-third of a grain in the other, after a meal of lobster. A. Gautier and P. Clausmann concluded that people take daily in their food 0·021 mgrm. of arsenic, *i.e.* 7·66 mgrms. per year. This subject was discussed by P. A. Meerburg.

Traces of arsenic occur in numerous commercial products—*e.g.* zinc, antimony, bismuth, nickel, etc. C. E. Schafhäutl[9] found it in commercial copper, tin, lead, and iron ; A. Loir, in most varieties of brass ; and J. J. H. Spirgatis, and F. A. Genth, in antique and other bronzes. Arsenic can be introduced into materials by the use of inadequately purified metal derived from arseniferous minerals. L. Grimbert, and T. Bosch found up to 127 mgrms. per litre in commercial hydrogen dioxide ; C. L. Bloxam, and A. Gautier, in hydrogen sulphide ; A. Scott, in hydro-bromic acid ; F. W. Richardson, C. Pedersen, T. E. Thorpe, A. S. Delépine, W. Thomson, etc., in beer—*vide infra* ; A. Chevallier, in vinegar ; A. Barthélemy, and C. Kippenberger, in wine—*vide infra* ; E. Bonjean, in sodium phosphate ; H. Fresenius, in precipitated calcium phosphate ; E. W. Davy, and A. Andouard, in superphosphates ; C. F. Bärwald, F. P. Dulk, C. Wittstock, H. W. F. Wacken-roder, J. von Liebig, E. Noelting and W. Feuerstein, and G. Denigès, in yellow phosphorus ; T. Husemann, and C. Winkler, in red phosphorus ; T. Husemann, in phosphoric acid ; M. Piron, C. R. Fresenius, E. Donath, and A. Gautier, in sodium sulphate and carbonate ; L. Garnier, in bleaching powder, calcium chloride, and potassium chlorate ; E. Buchner, in ferric chloride ; K. Scholvien, in chloroform ; A. Gautier, A. Latour de Trée and E. Lefrançois, and N. J. B. G. Guibourt, in sodium chloride—but G. S. Sérullas found none in the salt from Sézanne ; J. Marshall and C. S. Potts, in caustic alkalies ; J. Morland, T. Poleck and C. Thümmel, A. Glénard, W. B. Herapath, and J. W. Gunning, in bismuth preparations ; E. Seybel and H. Wikander, H. A. Smith, E. Filhol and M. Lacassin, A. Houzeau, H. W. F. Wackenroder, G. Hattensaur, G. C. Wittstein, A. Gautier, A. Dupasquier, etc., in hydrochloric acid ; G. Lockemann, and A. Gautier, in nitric acid, and in potassium nitrate ; O. Gottheil, and A. Gautier, in aq. ammonia and ammonium salts ; R. S. Morrell and C. I. Smyth, in printing inks ; and E. E. Hjelt, F. P. Dulk, F. Selmi, H. Hager, E. Seybel and H. Wikander, R. Kissling, A. Bussy and H. Buignet, N. Blondlot, F. M. Lyte, J. Loewe, A. Dupasquier, W. Tod, A. Gautier, N. Gräger, H. A. Smith, L. Ducher, W. Thorn, L. W. McCay, E. Buchner, A. Wagner, etc., in sulphuric acid. The two important acids—hydrochloric and sulphuric acids—being commonly arseniferous, and used in so many industrial processes, are *véritables distributeurs de ce métalloïde*. The fact that the presence of arsenic " poisons " the catalyst in the contact process

for sulphuric acid renders it necessary to clean the gases free from this agent
Hence sulphuric acid prepared by the contact process is free from arsenic, and is
consequently preferred for use in the manufacture of foodstuffs. M. Ritter and
M. Clouet, and O. Schweissinger found it in glucose, but O. Krey found none in
petroleum which had been treated with sulphuric acid; and W. Fresenius.
J. Marshall and C. S. Pott, E. T. Allen and E. G. Zies, L. Riedal, etc., in glass
Some iron enamels contain a high proportion of arsenic and antimony. E. Ritsert.
J. Galimard and E. Verdier, R. Engel and J. Bernhard, J. Lewkowitsch, B. H. Paul
and A. J. Cownley, J. Bougault, L. Barthe, A. C. Langmuir, and G. E. Barton found
arsenic in commercial glycerol. Many organic and inorganic colouring agents contain arsenic; in some—like king's yellow, As_2S_3; mineral blue, copper potassium
arsenite; Scheele's green, $CuHAsO_3$; and Schweinfurt's green, or *emerald green*,
or *Paris green*, $Cu(AsO_2)_2.Cu(C_2H_3O_2)_2$—it is an essential constituent; while in
others—like some of the aniline dyes—it is an impurity. In consequence, as shown
by F. Springmühl, and W. F. Gintl, articles—paper, and fabrics—coloured with
these agents may appear arseniferous. Thus, a non-fatal case of poisoning has
been reported through inhaling the fumes from burning candles coloured with
arsenical pigments; and F. W. Draper mentioned that poisoning has been produced
by the use of arsenical pigments for colouring artificial flowers, toys, confectionery,
and fancy papers used for wrapping confectionery. F. W. Draper, G. J. Warner,
A. W. Stokes, T. T. P. B. Warren, H. Grimshaw, H. Fleck, and J. Wolf found the
arsenical colours of tapestries or wall-papers may contaminate the air of a room and
produce arsenical poisoning; W. Harding reported a number of cases of poisoning
produced by the use of green baize curtains; and H. Vohl found arsenic in note-
paper. The arsenic contained in the air of rooms with arsenical wall-paper is
present as dust; or as diethylarsine, $(C_2H_5)_2AsH$; or, according to P. Klason, as
ethyl-cacodyl, $\{As(C_2H_5)_2\}O$, a gas produced by the action of common moulds on
organic matter in the presence of small amounts of arsenic. The *penicillium
glaucum*, and the *mucor ramosus* have either no action or but a slight one; the
mucor mucedo, and the *aspergillas glaucus* react well; while the *penicillium brevicaule*
is so well endowed with this quality that B. Gosio proposed its use as a reagent
for arsenic, the garlic odour being perceived when the fungus is made to grow in
soln. containing organic matter and only traces of arsenic. This reaction was
discussed by R. Abel and P. Buttenberg, O. Emmerling, P. Biginelli, and B. Galli-
Valerio and C. Strzyzowsky. Arsenical wall-papers, etc., were discussed by
G. Kirchgasser, M. Segale, W. Foster, H. Vohl, N. P. Hamberg, etc.

REFERENCES.

¹ F. W. Clarke and G. Steiger, *Proc. Nat. Acad. Sciences*, 4. 60, 1914; F. W. Clarke and
H. S. Washington, *ib.*, 8. 108, 1922; *The Composition of the Earth's Crust*, Washington, 1924;
J. H. L. Vogt, *Zeit. prakt. Geol.*, 6. 225, 314, 377, 413, 1898; 7. 10, 274, 1899; W. Vernadsky,
Centr. Min., 758, 1912; *Essai de minéralogie descriptive*, St. Petersburg, 1. 121, 740, 1914;
Geochimie, Paris, 16, 1924; A. E. Fersman, *Bull. Acad. St. Petersburg*, (6), 6. 367, 1912.
² H. A. Rowland, *Amer. Journ. Science*, (3), 41. 243, 1891; *Chem. News*, 63. 133, 1891;
Johns Hopkins Univ. Circular, 85, 1891; J. A. Antipoff, *Zeit. Kryst.*, 32. 426, 1900; L. H. Borg-
ström, *Bull. Geol. Finland*, 12, 1902; A. Daubrée, *Ann. Mines*, (4), 19. 669, 1851; *Compt.
Rend.*, 74. 1541, 1871; B. Silliman and F. S. Hunt, *Amer. Journ. Science*, (2), 2. 374, 1846;
C. Rumler, *Pogg. Ann.*, 49. 591, 1840; N. W. Fischer and A. Duflos, *ib.*, 72. 479, 1847; M. N. Saha,
Phil. Mag., (6), 40. 808, 1920.
³ J. B. L. Romé de l'Isle, *Cristallographie*, Paris, 3. 26, 1783; R. A. Vogel, *Practisches
Mineralsystem*, Leipzig, 294, 1762; L. A. Emmerling, *Lehrbuch der Mineralogie*, Giessen, 2.
548, 1796; A. Breithaupt, *Schweigger's Journ.*, 52. 167, 1828; *Vollständiges Charakteristik der
Mineralsystem*, Dresden, 129, 250, 1823; 261, 1832; *Journ. prakt. Chem.*, (1), 4. 249, 1835;
C. M. Kersten, *Schweigger's Journ.*, 53. 377, 1828; J. H. G. Justi, *Grundriss der gesammten
Mineralogie*, Göttingen, 180, 1757; J. W. Retgers, *Zeit. anorg. Chem.*, 4. 418, 1893; C. Hintze,
Zeit. Kryst., 11. 606, 1886; *Handbuch der Mineralogie*, Leipzig, 1. 110, 1904; F. von Kobell,
Charakteristik der Mineralien, Nürnberg, 1831; J. C. Freiesleben, *Geognostische Arbeiten*,
Freiberg, 6. 173, 1817; A. Russell and H. F. Harwood, *Min. Mag.*, 20. 299, 1925; A. Frenzel,
Neues Jahrb. Min., 25, 1873; 677, 1874; *Mineralogische Lexikon für des Kaiserthum Oesterreich,*

Wien, 26, 1874; *Neues Jahrb. Min.*, 677, 1874; J. V. Janowsky, *Sitzber. Akad. Wien*, 71. 276, 1875; N. Norton, *Amer. Journ. Science*, (4), 15. 92, 1903; F. A. Genth, *ib.*, (2), 33. 190, 1863.
⁴ C. Hintze, *Handbuch der Mineralogie*, Leipzig, 1. 102, 1904; L. A. Emmerling, *Lehrbuch der Mineralogie*, Giessen, 1796; A. Madelung, *Vorkommen des gediegenen Arsens*, Göttingen, 13, 1862; G. Leonhard, *Handwörterbuch der topographischen Mineralogie*, Heidelberg, 39, 1843; *Neues Jahrb. Min.*, 809, 1849; F. Sandberger, *Geologische Beschreibung der Renchbäder*, Heidelberg, 24, 1863; *Neues Jahrb. Min.*, i, 158, 1882; O. Luedecke, *Die Minerale des Harzes*, Berlin, 8, 1896; J. C. L. Zincken, *Der östliche Harz, mineralogisch und bergmannisch Betrachter*, Braunschweig, 134, 1825; E. Reidemeister, *Eine mineralogische Wanderung durch den östlichen Harz*, Magdeburg, 6, 1887; *Ber. Magdeburg Nat. Ver.*, 57, 1887; H. Traube, *Die Minerale Schlesiens*, Breslau, 19, 1888; E. Fugger, *Die Mineralien des Herzogthum Salzburg*, Salzburg, 1, 1878; A. Höfer, *Die Mineralien Karnthens*, Klagenfurt, 11, 1870; G. Jervis, *I Tesori sotterranei dell' Italia*, Turin, 1. 116, 1873; A. des Cloizeaux, *Manuel de minéralogie*, Paris, 342, 1893; A. Frenzel, *Mineralogisches Lexikon für das Königreich Sachsen*, Leipzig, 25, 1874; *Tschermak's Mitt.*, (2), 16. 529, 1897; *Neues Jahrb. Min.*, 25, 1873; V. R. von Zepharovich, *Mineralogisches Lexikon für das Kaiserthum Oesterreich*, Wien, 35, 1859; 37, 1873; *Sitzber. Akad. Wien*, 71. 272, 1875; A. E. Reuss, *ib.*, 47. 13, 1863; *Lotos*, 10. 211, 1860; *Neues Jahrb. Min.*, 325, 1861; C. F. Peters, *ib.*, 665, 1861; E. Hatle, *Die Minerale Steiermarks*, Graz, 4, 1885; G. Rose, *Das krystallo-chemischen Mineralsystem*, Leipzig, 54, 1852; A. Orio, *Elementos de mineralojia*, Madrid, 484, 1882; R. P. Greg and W. G. Lettsom, *Manual of the Mineralogy of Great Britain and Ireland*, London, 369, 1858; J. H. Collins, *A Handbook to the Mineralogy of Cornwall and Devon*, Falmouth, 10, 1876; J. D. Dana, *A System of Mineralogy*, New York, 12, 1892; A. Erdmann, *Lärobok i Mineralogien*, Stockholm, 178, 1853; I. Domeyko, *Elementos de Mineralojia*, Santiago, 273, 1879; *Journ. prakt. Chem.*, (1), 79. 62, 1860; *Ann. Mines*, (3), 20. 473, 1841; R. Scheibe, *Zeit. deut. geol. Ges.*, 47. 223, 1895; M. Websky, *ib.*, 19. 449, 1867; A. Liversidge, *The Minerals of New South Wales*, Sydney, 1882; A. Raimondi, *Minéraux du Pérou*, Paris, 184, 1878; C. F. de Landero, *Sinopsis Mineralogica o catalogo descriptivo de los minerales*, Mexico, 41, 1888; F. Field, *Journ. Chem. Soc.*, 12. 8, 1859; A. del Castillo and M. Barcena, *La Natturaleza*, 313, 1873; G. C. Hoffmann, *Ann. Rep. Geol. Sur. Canada*, Ottawa, 74, 1890; J. F. John, *Chemische Untersuchungen*, Berlin, 2. 288, 1810; A. Eschka, *Berg. Hütt. Ztg.*, 13. 23, 1862; F. Babanek, *Tschermak's Mitt.*, (1), 5. 83, 1875; G. Benkö, *Orvos Természet-tudomanyi Ertesito*, 14. 163, 1889; *Zeit. Kryst.*, 19. 199, 1891; D. Bizzarri and G. Campani, *ib.*, 12. 194, 1886; P. N. Tschirwinsky, *ib.*, 58. 386, 1923; *Bull. Acad. Bohème*, 23. 237, 1923; *Rozp. Ceske Akad.*, 31. 14, 1923; C. Hersey, *Amer. Journ. Science*, (3), 39. 161, 1890; N. N. Evans, *ib.*, (4), 15. 92, 1903; C. H. Warren, *ib.*, (4), 16. 337, 1903; J. V. Janowsky, *Sitzber. Akad. Wien*, 71. 276, 1875; A. Russell and H. F. Harwood, *Min. Mag.*, 20. 299, 1925; W. Gatt, *Canadian Chem. Journ.*, 4. 268, 1920; C. Bugge and S. Foslie, *Norg. Geol. Undersökelse*, 6, 1922; H. Dewey, *Arsenic and Antimony Ores*, London, 1920; M. E. Hurst, *Arsenic-bearing Deposits in Canada*, Ottawa, 1927.

⁵ T. L. Phipson, *Compt. Rend.*, 55. 108, 1862; F. Garrigou, *ib.*, 135. 1113, 1903; A. Gautier, *ib.*, 135. 1115, 1903; A. Daubrée, *ib.*, 47. 959, 1858; 74. 1541, 1871; *Ann. Mines*, (4), 19. 669, 1851; F. Rinne, *Centr. Min.*, 499, 1902; A. Breithaupt and C. F. Plattner, *Pogg. Ann.*, 77. 135, 1849; M. Popp, *Zeit. Unters. Nahr. Genuss.*, 14. 38, 1907; A. J. Kunkel, *Zeit. physiol. Chem.*, 44. 511, 1905; E. Ludwig, *Tschermak's Mitt.*, (2), 4. 173, 1881; E. Ludwig and H. Reguard, *Bull. Soc. Min.*, 5. 3, 1882; H. Ramage, *Nature*, 119. 783, 1927; J. Mauthner, *Wien. Klin. Wochschr.*, 3. 691, 1890; H. Becker, *Arch. Pharm.*, (2), 57. 129, 1849; F. L. Sonnenschein, *ib.*, (2), 143. 245, 1870; *Russ. Journ. Pharm.*, 9. 591, 1870; F. A. Walchner, *Liebig's Ann.*, 61. 205, 1847; F. Sandberger, *Neues Jahrb. Min.*, 158, 1882; W. M. Doherty, *Chem. News*, 73. 191, 1896; M. Vollhase and M. Berndt, *Pharm. Centrh.*, 66. 289, 1925; H. Fischer and D. Rüst, *Zeit. Kryst.*, 7. 209, 1882; H. A. Smith, *Proc. Manchester Lit. Phil. Soc.*, 10. 162, 1871; 11. 172, 1872; *Chem. News*, 23. 221, 1871; R. A. Smith, *Phil. Mag.*, (4), 20. 408, 1860; D. Campbell, *ib.*, (4), 20. 304, 1860; (4), 21. 318, 1860; *Chem. News*, 2. 218, 1860; H. D. Gibbs and C. C. James, *Journ. Amer. Chem. Soc.*, 27. 1484, 1905; W. H. Weed and L. V. Pirsson, *Amer. Journ Science*, (3), 42. 401, 1891.

⁶ F. Garrigou, *Compt. Rend.*, 135. 1113, 1903; L. J. Thénard, *ib.*, 38. 986, 1903, 1854; 39. 763, 1854; *Ann. Chim. Phys.*, (3), 42. 484, 1854; A. Gautier, *Bull. Soc. Chim.*, (3), 29. 31, 913, 1903; *Chem. News*, 88. 189, 1903; *Compt. Rend.*, 135. 1115, 1903; A. Gautier and P. Clausmann, *ib.*, 139. 101, 1904; H. Lemonnier, *ib.*, 24. 629, 1847; A. Grasset, *ib.*, 46. 182, 1858; C. A. de Gouvenain, *ib.*, 76. 1063, 1873; *Ann. Mines*, (7), 3. 26, 1873; L. J. Thénard, *Ann. Chim. Phys.*, (3), 42. 484, 1854; *Compt. Rend.*, 39. 763, 1854; *Ann. Chim. Phys.*, (3), 42. 484, 1854; E. Willm, *Bull. Soc. Chim.*, (2), 31. 3, 1879; (2), 33. 292, 1880; *Compt. Rend.*, 90. 630, 1880; M. Socquet, *ib.*, 46. 584, 1858; C. Blondeau, *ib.*, 31. 313, 1850; A. Monitessier, *ib.*, 51. 636, 1860; S. de Luca, *ib.*, 70. 408, 1870; R. Guyot, *ib.*, 77. 1384, 1873; B. Caury, *ib.*, 46. 1167, 1858; A. Bechamp, *ib.*, 62. 1034, 1866; 63. 559, 1866; L. Figuier, *ib.*, 23. 818, 1846; G. Bertrand, *ib.*, 134. 1434, 1902; *Bull. Soc. Chim.*, (3), 27. 843, 1902; F. Taboury, *ib.*, (4), 5. 865, 1909; H. Vohl, *Ber.*, 9. 987, 1876; 10. 1811, 1877; R. Meyer, *ib.*, 11. 1521, 1878; T. Poleck, *ib.*, 12. 1902, 1879; *Thermen und Warmbrunn*, Breslau, 1885; T. Poleck and A. Duflos, *Journ. prakt. Chem.*, (1), 52. 353, 1851; R. Wildenstein, *Journ. prakt. Chem.*, (1), 85. 100, 1863; E. F. von Gorup-Besanez, *Leibig's Ann.*, 79. 50, 1851; *Journ. prakt. Chem.*, (2), 17. 371, 1878; P. J. van Kerckhoff, *ib.*, (1), 43. 350, 1847; F. Keller, *ib.*, (1), 40. 442, 1847; *Repert. Pharm.*, (2), 48. 289, 1847;

C. Morelli, *Chem. Ztg.*, **5**. 815, 1881 ; R. Pribram, *Chem. Ztg.*, **10**. 145, 1886 ; E. Ebler, *Vehr. Nat. Ver. Heidelberg*, **8**. 435, 1907 ; *Ber.*, **40**. 1807, 1907 ; J. Lefort, *Journ. Chim. Pharm.*, (3), **21**. 340, 1852 ; (2), **27**. 341, 1855 ; (3), **32**. 264, 1857 ; S. Robinet and J. Lefort, *ib.*, (4), **1**. 340, 1865 ; E. Filhol, *ib.*, (3), **13**. 13, 1847 ; C. P. Kosmann, *ib.*, (3), **17**. 43, 1850 ; F. J. Hugi, *ib.*, (2), **74**. 19, 1853 ; N. W. Fischer, *ib.*, (2), **52**. 263, 1847 ; W. H. Weed and L. V. Pirsson, *Amer. Journ. Science*, (3), **42**. 401, 1891 ; A. Hague, *ib.*, (3), **34**. 171, 1887 ; J. Bouquet, *Ann. Chim. Phys.*, (3), **42**. 278, 1854 ; *Rép. Chim. Appl.*, **3**. 199, 1861 ; J. Glax, *Lehrbuch der Balneotherapie*, Stuttgart, 1900 ; G. Bizio, *Gazz. Chim. Ital.*, **10**. 43, 1800 ; H. D. Gibbs and C. C. James, *Journ. Amer. Chem. Soc.*, **27**. 1484, 1905 ; M. Braun, *Geol. Zeit.*, **24**. 34, 1872 ; T. L. Phipson, *Chem. News*, **60**. 67, 1889 ; F. J. Malaguti, *Bull. Soc. Chim.*, (1), **5**. 456, 1863 ; J. R. Blum, *Liebig's Ann.*, **73**. 217, 1850 ; L. Carius, *ib.*, **137**. 106, 1866 ; J. Hessel, *ib.*, **113**. 364, 1860 ; M. Popp, *ib.*, **155**. 344, 1870 ; C. F. Rammelsberg, *Pogg. Ann.*, **72**. 571, 1847 ; F. A. Walchner, *Liebig's Ann.*, **61**. 205, 1847 ; H. Will, *ib.*, **61**. 192, 1847 ; J. von Liebig, *ib.*, **63**. 221, 1847 ; C. R. Fresenius, *ib.*, **75**. 172, 1850 ; **82**. 249, 1851 ; *Jahrb. Nassau Ver. Nat.*, 7, 1851 ; 19, 20, 1866 ; *Untersuchung des Mineralwassers des Herzogthums Nassau*, Wiesbaden, 1850 ; *Journ. prakt. Chem.*, (1), **34**. 365, 1845 ; (1), **64**. 335, 1855 ; (1), **90**. 36, 1863 ; (1), **92**. 456, 1864 ; (1), **95**. 151, 1865 ; (1), **98**. 321, 1866 ; (2), **9**. 368, 1874 ; R. Bunsen in F. Sandberger, *Geologische Beschreibung der Renchbader*, Heidelberg, 16, 1863 ; R. W. Bunsen and G. Kirchhoff, *Pogg. Ann.*, **113**. 358, 1861 ; L. R. von Fellenberg, *Untersuchung des Schwefelwassers des Gurnigelbades*, Bern, 1849 ; G. Bauck, *Analyse der Salzsoolen von Colberg*, Göttingen, 1860 ; A. Wrany, *Chem. Centr.*, (2), **13**. 61, 1868 ; A. Daubrée, *Ann. Mines*, (4), **19**. 669, 1851 ; *Compt. Rend.*, **32**. 827, 1851 ; L. F. Bley, *Arch. Pharm.*, (2), **52**. 268, 1847 ; (2), **80**. 129, 1854 ; (2), **82**. 129, 1855 ; H. A. Wiggers, *ib.*, (2), **102**. 215, 1860 ; E. Ludwig, *ib.*, (2), **51**. 145, 1847 ; *Tschermak's Mitt.*, (2), **4**. 173, 1881 ; E. Ludwig and J. Mauthner, *ib.*, (2), **2**. 269, 1880 ; W. F. Gintl, *ib.*, (2), **5**. 82, 1882 ; *Verh. geol. Reichsanst. Wien*, 333, 1882 ; *Journ. prakt. Chem.*, (2), **20**. 356, 1879 ; (2), **24**. 25, 1881 ; E. Reichardt, *ib.*, (3), **2**. 124, 1873 ; B. Viale and V. Latini, *ib.*, (3), **33**. 174, 1858 ; F. L. Sonnenschein, *ib.*, (2), **143**. 245, 1870 ; M. Hugounenq, *Journ. Pharm. Chim.*, (3), **35**. 93, 1859 ; O. Henry, *Répert. Chim. Appl.*, **1**. 282, 1859 ; *Journ. Pharm. Chim.*, (3), **12**. 241, 1847 ; (3), **20**. 161, 1851 ; (3), **35**. 250, 1859 ; (4), **9**. 461, 1869 ; O. Henry and C. L. Lheritier, *ib.*, (3), **28**. 333, 1855 ; A. Andouard, *Journ. Chim. Méd.*, (3), **5**. 466, 1849 ; *Journ. Pharm. Chim.*, (4), **9**. 336, 1869 ; A. Chevalier and M. Gobley, *ib.*, (3), **13**. 324, 1847 ; A. Chevallier and M. Schaueffele, *Journ. Chim. Méd.*, (3), **4**. 401, 1847 ; A. Chevallier, *ib.*, (3), **7**. 193, 1851 ; (4), **5**. 257, 1859 ; F. M. Tripier, *ib.*, (2), **6**. 278, 1847 ; O. Henry and A. Chevallier, *ib.*, (3), **1**. 413, 1847 ; H. Braconnot, *ib.*, (3), **37**. 737, 1851 ; A. Ferreil, *ib.*, **96**. 1581, 1883 ; J. L. Lassaigne, *ib.*, (3), **5**. 489, 1849 ; A. B. Poggiale, (3), **9**. 81, 1853 ; J. Girardin, *ib.*, (3), **4**. 643, 1848 ; *Trav. Acad. Rouen*, 11, 1848 ; H. von Fehling, *Württemberg. Nat. Jahresb.*, **13**. 113, 1857 ; **22**. 129, 147, 1867 ; H. Göttl, *Oester. Zeit. Pharm.*, 353, 1853 ; *Viertelj. prakt. Pharm.*, **5**. 161, 1856 ; A. J. Kunkel, *Zeit. physiol. Chem.*, **44**. 511, 1905 ; J. Löwe, *Jahresb. phys. Ver. Frankfurt a. M.*, 58, 1854 ; W. T. Casselmann, *Jahrb. Nassau. Ver. Nat.*, 15, 1861 ; W. Uloth, *Neues Jahrb. Pharm.*, **36**. 82, 1871 ; G. Müller, *ib.*, **3**. 205, 1855 ; *Arch. Pharm.*, (2), **68**. 152, 1851 ; T. Hausemann, *Neues Jahrb. Pharm.*, **39**. 206, 1873 ; *Arch. Pharm.*, (3), **6**. 97, 395, 1875 ; (3), **7**. 204, 1875 ; C. A. Doremus, *Russ. Journ. Pharm.*, **9**. 546, 1870 ; *Pharm. Viertelj.*, **19**. 294, 1870 ; E. Adler, *Journ. prakt. Pharm.*, **24**. 216, 1852 ; F. Filipuzzi, *Sitzber. Akad. Wien*, **21**. 561, 1856 ; C. O. Buchner, *Anz. Gel. München*, **24**. 601, 1847 ; **25**. 1025, 1847 ; **26**. 756, 1848 ; *Journ. prakt. Chem.*, (1), **40**. 442, 1847 ; A. A. Bado and J. E. Zanetta, *Anal. Quim. Argentina*, **9**. 24, 1921 ; A. A. Bado, *Bol. Acad. Ciencias Cordoba*, **23**. 85, 1918 ; W. R. G. Atkins and E. G. Wilson, *Journ. Marine Biol. Assoc.*, **14**. 609, 1927 ; M. Goy and W. Rudolph, *Zeit. angew. Chem.* **40**. 945, 1927 ; A. Hartzell and F. Wilcoxon, *Journ. Econ. Entomol.*, **20**. 204, 1927.

[7] H. Kayser and C. Runge, *Wied. Ann.*, **52**. 93, 1893 ; W. Stein, *Journ. prakt. Chem.*, (1), **51**. 302, 1850 ; (1), **53**. 37, 1850 ; J. E. Herberger, *Ber. deut. Nat. Versl.*, 108, 1842 ; J. Girardin, *Journ. Chem. Méd.*, (3), **4**. 643, 1848 ; *Trav. Acad. Rouen*, 11, 1848 ; A. Chatin, *Ann. Chim. Phys.*, (3), **23**. 105, 1848 ; *Compt. Rend.*, **20**. 21, 1845 ; T. H. Barry, *Analyst*, **52**. 217, 1927 ; R. E. Remington, *Journ. Amer. Chem. Soc.*, **49**. 1410, 1927 ; R. Spallino, *Gazz. Chim. Ital.*, **43**. 475, 1913 ; W. P. Headden, *Proc. Colorado Scient. Soc.*, **9**. 345, 1910 ; F. Rerchert and R. A. Trelles, *Anal. Quim. Argentina*, **9**. 89, 1921 ; H. D. Gibbs and C. C. James, *Journ. Amer. Chem. Soc.*, **27**. 1484, 1905 ; A. Barthélemy, *Compt. Rend.*, **97**. 752, 1883 ; A. Gautier and P. Clausmann, *ib.*, **139**. 101, 1904 ; F. Garrigou, *ib.*, **135**. 1113, 1903 ; A. Gautier, *Bull. Soc. Chim.*, (2), **25**. 483, 530, 1876 ; *Compt. Rend.*, **135**. 812, 1902 ; A. Gautier and P. Clausmann, *ib.*, **139**. 101, 1904 ; C. Husson, *ib.*, **83**. 1113, 1876 ; F. Jadin and A. Astruc, *ib.*, **154**. 893, 1912 ; **156**. 2023, 1913 ; **159**. 268, 1914 ; H. Marcelet, *Bull. Soc. Pharmacol.*, **20**. 480, 1913 ; M. Fermenti, *Boll. Chim. Farm.*, **45**. 217, 1906 ; V. Legrip, *Dingler's Journ.*, **97**. 389, 1845 ; A. M. Peter, *Kentucky Agric. Station Rep.*, 14, 1893 ; C. H. Tattersall, *Report on Arsenical Poisoning, Borough of Salford*, Manchester, 1900 ; J. Niven, *Report of the Medical Officer of Health at Manchester*, Manchester, 1900 ; J. Clouet, *Ann. Hyg.*, 145, 1878 ; E. F. von Gorup-Besanez, *Liebig's Ann.*, **128**. 243, 1863 ; E. Davy, *Journ. Dublin. Soc.*, 2. 270, 1859 ; *Phil. Mag.*, (3), **18**. 108, 1859 ; A. Andouard, *Journ. Chim. Méd.*, (3), **5**. 466, 1849 ; *Journ. Pharm. Chim.*, (4), **9**. 336, 1869 ; W. A. Lampadius, *Journ. tech. ökon. Chem.*, **8**. 393, 1830 ; **9**. 316, 1830 ; T. N. Kelynack and W. Kirkby, *Arsenical Poisoning in Beer Drinkers*, London, 1901 ; E. S. Reynolds, *Brit. Med. Journ.*, 1769, 1900 ; A. P. Luff, *Royal Commission on Arsenical Poisoning*, London, 1901.

⁸ A. Gautier and P. Clausmann, *Compt. Rend.*, **139.** 101, 1904 ; A. Gautier, *ib.*, **129. 929,** 1899 ; **130.** 248, 1900 ; **131.** 361, 1900 ; 134. 1394, 1902 ; **135.** 812, 1902 ; *Chem. News*, **88. 189,** 1903 ; *Bull. Soc. Chim.*, (2), **25.** 483, 530, 1876 ; (3), **27.** 847, 1902 ; (3), **29.** 31, 913, 1903 ; G. Bertrand, *ib.*, (3). 27. 843, 1902 ; (3), **29.** 790, 1903 ; *Bull. Soc. Hyg.*, **8.** 49, 1920 ; *Ann. Pasteur Inst.*, **16.** 553, 1902 ; *Ann. Chim. Phys.*, (7), **29.** 245, 1903 ; *Compt. Rend.*, **134.** 1434, 1902 ; **135.** 809, 1902 ; **136.** 1083, 1903 ; F. Garrigou, *ib.*, **135.** 1113, 1903 ; V. A. Jacquelain, *ib.*, **16.** 30, 1843 ; C. Steinberg, *Journ. prakt. Chem.*, (1), **25.** 384, 1842 ; G. H. E. Schnedermann and W. Knop, *ib.*, (1), **36.** 471, 1845 ; C. H. Pfaff, *Repert. Pharm.*, **74.** 106, 1841 ; P. Orfila, *Ann. Chim. Phys.*, (3), **2.** 159, 1841 ; J. A. Fordyce, I. Rosen, and E. Myers, *Arch. Intern. Med.*, **31.** 739, 1923 ; P. Orfila and J. P. Couerbe, *Journ. Chim. Méd.*, (2), **5.** 462, 632, 1839 ; N. Barbot, J. Fauré, and H. Magonty, *ib.*, (2), 7. 654, 1841 ; A. Chevallier, *ib.*, (2), 84, 1841 ; F. P. Danger and C. Flandin, *Compt. Rend.*, **11.** 1038, 1840 ; **12.** 118, 1841 ; **16.** 136, 391, 1843 ; C. Hödlmoser, *Zeit. physiol. Chem.*, **33.** 329, 1901 ; M. Segale, *ib.*, **42.** 175, 1904 ; K. Cerny, *ib.*, **34.** 408, 1902 ; P. Brouardel and G. Pouchet, *Ann. Hyg.*, (3), **14.** 73, 1887 ; F. L. Sonnenschein, *Handbuch der gerichtlichen Chemie*, Berlin, 212, 1869 ; D. Scolosuboff, *Bull. Soc. Chim.*, (2), **24.** 124 1876 : E. Ludwig, *Anz. Akad. Wien*, **16.** 181, 1879 ; *Jahrb. Med.*, 501, 1877 ; 467, 1880 ; R. H. Chittenden, *Amer. Chem. Journ.*, **5. 8**, 1884 ; D. Mann, *Forensic Medicine and Toxicology*, London, 465, 1908 ; A. J. Kunkel, *Zeit. physiol. Chem.*, **44.** 511, 1905 ; T. Stevenson, *Royal Commission on Arsenical Poisoning*, London, 1901 ; E. Ziemke, *Viertelj. Ger. Med.*, (3), **22.** 231, 1901 ; (3), **23.** 51, 1902 ; G. F. Schaefer, *Ann. Chim. Anal.*, **12.** 52, 96, 1907 ; W. H. Blémendal, *Arch. Pharm.*, 246, 599, 1909 ; *Arsenicum in het dierlijk organisme*, London, 1908 ; L. van Itallie and J. J. van Eck, *Proc. Acad. Amsterdam*, **15.** 580, 1913 ; G. Lechartier and F. Bellamy, *Compt. Rend.*, **84.** 687, 1877 ; F. M. Raoult and H. Breton, *ib.*, **85.** 40, 1877 ; A. Keilholz, *Pharm. Weekbl.*, **58.** 1482, 1922 ; E. Marfurt, *Contribution à la recherche de minimes quantités d'arsenic ; et de la teneur normale en arsenic dans le corps humain*, Bale, 1923 ; H. E. Cox, *Analyst*, **49.** 484, 1924 ; *Nature*, **115.** 51, 1925 ; *Report on the Ministry of Agriculture and Fisheries*, (2), **6.** 4, 1924 ; P. A. Meerburg, *Chem. Weekbl.*, **19.** 54, 1922 ; A. C. Chapman, *Analyst*, **51.** 548, 1926.

⁹ C. L. Bloxam, *Journ. Chem. Soc.*, **13.** 338, 1861 ; **15.** 52, 281, 1862 ; L. Rosenthaler, *Apoth. Ztg.*, **19.** 186, 1904 ; F. Selmi, *Gazz. Chim. Ital.*, **10.** 40, 1880 ; F. A. Genth, *Journ. Franklin Inst.*, **66.** 261, 1858 ; *Phil. Mag.*, (4), **16.** 420, 1858 ; C. E. Schafhäutl, *ib.*, (3), **17.** 570, 1840 ; *Journ. prakt. Chem.*, (1), **21.** 151, 1840 ; T. Bosch, *Pharm. Weekbl.*, **42.** 951, 1906 ; R. Kissling, *Chem. Ind.*, **9.** 137, 1886 ; E. Bonjean, *Rev. Intern. Falsif.*, **17.** 171, 1905 ; A. Houzeau, *Bull. Soc. Chem.*, (2), **3.** 19, 1864 ; A. Gautier, *ib.*, (3), **29.** 31, 913, 1903 ; *Chem. News*, **88.** 189, 1903 ; L. Grimbert, *Journ. Pharm. Chim.*, (6), **21.** 385, 1905 ; L. Garnier, *ib.*, (5), **12.** 9, 1885 ; L. Barthe, *ib.*, (6), **16.** 52, 1902 ; J. Galimard and E. Verdier, *ib.*, (6), **23.** 183, 1906 ; J. Bougault, *ib.*, (6), **15.** 527, 1902 ; *Chem. News*, **86.** 312, 1902 ; J. Loewe, *Jahresb. Frankfurt. Phys. Ver.*, 41, 1853 ; A. Loir, *Compt. Rend.*, **47.** 126, 1858 ; W. Tod, *Arch. Pharm.*, (2), **87.** 269, 1856 ; A. S. Deléphine, *Journ. Sanit. Inst.*, **23.** 244, 1902 ; F. Springmühl, *Dingler's Journ.*, **205.** 174, 1872 ; W. F. Gintl, *ib.*, **214.** 425, 1874 ; H. Fleck, *Zeit. Biol.*, **8.** 444, 1872 ; *Dingler's Journ.*. **207.** 146, 1873 ; A. Latour de Trée and E. Lefrançois, *ib.*, **38.** 235, 1830 ; *Journ. Pharm. Chim.*, (3), **16.** 618, 1850 ; J. Wolf, *Chem. Ztg.*, **2.** 433, 1887 ; O. Krey, *ib.*, **1.** 1272, 1886 : E. Seybel and H. Wikander, *ib.*, **26.** 50, 1902 ; E. Buchner, *Liebig's Ann.*, **94.** 241, 1885 ; **130.** 249, 1863 ; *Chem. Ztg.*, **2.** 417, 1887 ; H. Fresenius, *ib.*, **3.** 1262, 1888 ; *Zeit. anal. Chem.*, **28.** 64, 1889 ; C. R. Fresenius, *ib.*, **6.** 201, 1867 ; W. Fresenius, *Chem. News*, **48.** 147, 1883 ; *Zeit. anal. Chem.*, **28.** 397, 1883 ; H. Hager, *ib.*, **22.** 556, 1883 ; E. Donath, *ib.*, **21.** 404, 1882 ; C. Kippenberger, *ib.*, **42.** 509, 1903 ; H. Vohl, *Dingler's Journ.*, **200.** 497, 1871 ; *Arch. Pharm.*, (2), **82.** 131, 1855 ; T. Husemann, *ib.*, (3), **15.** 518, 1879 ; H. Grimshaw, *Chem. News*, **44.** 177, 1881 ; *Proc. Manchester Lit. Phil. Soc.*, **20.** 122, 1881 ; T. E. Thorpe, *Journ. Chem. Soc.*, **83.** 974, 1903 ; A. Scott, *ib.*, **77.** 648, 1900 ; J. J. H. Spirgatis, *Liebig's Ann.*, **181.** 394, 1876 ; T. Poleck and C. Thümmel, *Arch. Pharm.*, (3), **22.** 1, 1884 ; H. A. Smith, *Amer. Chemist*, **3.** 413, 1873 ; *Chem. News*, **23.** 221, 1871 ; T. T. P. B. Warren, *ib.*, **58.** 206, 1888 ; A. W. Stokes, *ib.*, **58.** 189, 1888 ; J. W. Gunning, *ib.*, **17.** 260, 1868 ; A. C. Langmuir, *ib.*, **79.** 171, 1899 ; W. Thomson, *ib.*, **86.** 179, 1902 ; F. M. Lyte, *ib.*, **9.** 98, 1864 ; J. Lewkowitsch, *ib.*, **67.** 46, 1893 ; W. B. Herapath, *ib.*, **6.** 304, 1861 ; 7. 77, 1863 ; F. W. Draper, *ib.*, **26.** 29, 39, 52, 90, 102, 1872 ; G. J. Warner, *ib.*, **26.** 69, 1892 ; J. W. Young, *ib.*, **26.** 105, 1872 ; A. P. Smith, *ib.*, **39.** 161, 1879 ; J. Marshall and C. S. Potts, *Amer. Chem. Journ.*, **10.** 425, 1888 ; K. Scholvien, *Apoth. Ztg.*, **2.** 14, 1887 ; W. Foster, *Chem. News*, **41.** 3, 1880 ; M. Ritter and M. Clouet, *Ind. Blatt.*, 370, 1878 ; L. W. McCay, *Chem. Ztg.*, **13.** 725, 1889 ; O. Schweissinger, *Pharm. Centrh.*, **8.** 62, 1887 ; N. P. Hamberg, *Pharm. Journ.*, (3), **4.** 81, 1874 ; O. Gottheil, *Pharm. Ztg.*, **46.** 992, 1901 ; E. Ritsert, *Pharm. Ztg.*, **34.** 104, 1889 ; L. Riedal, *Sprech.*, **59.** 237, 1926 ; Anon., *Med. Times and Gaz.*, 467, 1876 ; C. Pedersen, *Compt. Rend. Carlsberg*, **5.** 108, 1902 ; B. H. Paul and A. J. Cownley, *Pharm. Journ.*, **53.** 685, 1894 ; J. Morland, *ib.*, (2), **1.** 356, 1860 ; G. Hattensaur, *Zeit. angew. Chem.*, **9.** 130, 1896 ; E. W. Davy, *Journ. Dublin Soc.*, **2.** 270, 1859 ; *Phil. Mag.*, (3), **18.** 108, 1859 ; F. W. Richardson, *Journ. Soc. Chem. Ind.*, **21.** 901, 1902 ; A. Andouard, *Journ. Chim. Méd.*, (3), **5.** 466, 1849 ; *Journ. Pharm. Chim.*, (4), **9.** 336, 1869 ; A. Bussy and H. Buignet, *ib.*, (3), **44.** 177, 1863 ; (3), **45.** 465, 1864 ; (3), **46.** 257, 1864 ; C. F. Bärwald, *Berlin. Jahrb. Pharm.*, **32.** 113, 1833 ; F. P. Dulk, *ib.*, **34.** 247, 1834 ; C. Wittstock, *ib.*, **32.** 125, 1833 ; *Pogg. Ann.*, **31.** 126, 1834 ; H. W. F. Wackenroder, *Journ. prakt. Chem.*, (1), **2.** 340, 1834 ; *Repert. Pharm.*, (1), **46.** 225, 1832 ; (1), **47.** 337, 1833 ; G. C. Wittstein, *ib.*, (2), **323.** 1840 ; J. von Liebig, *Liebig's Ann.*, **11.** 260, 1834 ; G. Denigès.

Journ. Pharm. Chim., (5), **25**. 237, 1892 ; A. Dupasquier, *ib.*, (2), **27**. 717, **1841** ; (3), **9**. 415, 1846 : E. Noelting and W. Feuerstein, *Ber.*, **33**. 2685, 1900 ; O. Emmerling, *ib.*, **30**. 1026, 1897 : N. J. B. G. Guibourt, *Journ. Chim. Méd.*, (1), **2**. 55, 106, 1826 ; A. Chevallier, *ib.*, (3), **2**. 334, 1846 ; M. Piron, *ib.*, (4), **5**. 44, 1859 ; G. S. Sérullas, *Journ. Phys.*, **93**. 115, 1821 ; E. Filhol and M. Lacassin, *ib.*, **4**. 222, 1862 ; G. E. Barton, *Journ. Amer. Chem. Soc.*, **17**. 883, 1895 ; J. Marshall and C. Pott, *Amer. Chem. Journ.*, **10**. 425, 1888 ; B. Gosio, *L'Orosi*, **23**. 361, 1900 ; *Riv. d'ig. e san. pubbl.*, 223, 1892 ; R. Engel and J. Bernhard, *Compt. Rend.*, **122**. 390, 1896 ; A. Barthélemy, *ib.*, **97**. 752, 1883 ; B. Galli-Valerio and C. Strzyzowsky, *Pharm. Post.*, **33**. 637, 649, 1901 ; R. Abel and P. Buttenberg, *Zeit. Hyg.*, **32**. 449, 1899 ; P. Biginelli, *Atti Accad. Lincei*, (5), **9**. ii, 210, 242, 1900 ; G. Kirchgasser, *Viertelj. ger. Med.*, (2), **9**. 96, 1868 ; M. Segale, *Zeit. physiol. Chem.*, **42**. 175, 1904 ; E. T. Allen and E. G. Zies, *Journ. Amer. Cer. Soc.*, **1**. 739, 1918 ; E. E. Hjelt, *Dingler's Journ.*, **226**. 174, 1877 ; A. Wagner, *ib.*, **218**. 32, 1875 ; W. Thorn, *ib.*, **217**. 495, 1875 ; N. Blondlot, *Compt. Rend.*, **58**. 769, 1863 ; *Journ. Pharm. Chim.*, (3), **46**. 252, 1864 ; H. Hager, *Pharm. Ztg.*, **33**. 473, 1888 ; H. Reckleben, G. Lockemann, and A. Eckardt, *Zeit. anal. Chem.*, **46**. 671, 1907 ; L. Ducher, *Monit. Scient.*, (4), **3**. 1273, 1889 ; N. Gräger, *Chem. Centr.*, (1), **2**. 224, 1860 ; W. Harding, *Lancet*, i, 525, 1892 ; G. Lockemann, *Zeit. angew. Chem.*, **35**. 357, 1922 ; C. Winkler, *Ber.*, **33**. 1693, 1900 ; P. Klason, *ib.*, **47**. 2634, 1915 ; A. Glénard, *Journ. Pharm. Chim.*, (3), **26**. 184, 1854 ; R. S. Morrell and C. I. Smyth, *Analyst*, **52**. 239, 1927.

§ 3. The Extraction of Arsenic

Elemental arsenic is used in commerce only to a small extent. Formerly, at Altenberg, Silesia, arsenic was made by reducing arsenic trioxide by charcoal in clay crucibles covered by another crucible or a conical iron cap. The method was economical, but the product was grey and pulverulent, and contaminated with arsenic trioxide. Arsenic is also formed when arsine is decomposed by heat. N. Tarugi [1] obtained arsenic by reducing arsenic oxide, an arsenite or arsenate by hydrogen, carbon, calcium carbide, or potassium cyanide ; and A. Bettendorff, by reducing a soln. of arsenic trioxide in hydrochloric acid by means of stannous chloride.

The main sources of arsenic are as a side-product in the treatment of ores from tin mines, tin-copper mines, and tin-copper-tungsten mines ; the waste heaps of exhausted copper mines ; the arsenical pyrites mined solely for the arsenic. The common method of preparing arsenic is to heat mispickel, native arsenic, or leucopyrite in the absence of air when the arsenic sublimes. With mispickel : $FeAsS=FeS+As$, about half the arsenic is recovered ; and with leucopyrite : $4FeAs_2=Fe_4As+7As$, the residue contains more arsenic than is represented by this equation. In both cases, therefore, the residues can be roasted in a reverberatory furnace so as to recover more of the arsenic in the form of arsenic trioxide (*q.v.*). The distillation is performed in retorts consisting of fireclay tubes or pots, each fitted with a piece of sheet-iron rolled so that one end fits the mouth of the retort, and the other end is luted to a fireclay receiver. The retorts are arranged in rows and tiers. With mispickel ores, arsenic sulphide collects in the receiver at the beginning of the operation. This can be prevented by mixing the ore with alkali or lime. In from 8 to 12 hrs., the receivers are removed. Crystalline arsenic collects on the iron spiral in the mouth of the retort while the pulverulent arsenic collects in the cooler part of the receivers. The object is to collect as large a proportion of the crystalline form as possible. The pulverulent form is used for the preparation of arsenical compounds. The process at Freiberg was described by O. Kast and J. Bräuning ; [2] that at Reichenstein, Silesia, by B. Kerl ; that at Ribas, Spain, by E. Lampadius ; that near Chicago, by C. H. Jones ; and that in Cornwall, by V. Thomas, and H. Dewey. J. F. Cullen proposed to feed the oxide with an incandescent mass of coke and collect the arsenic from the flue gases. A suggestion was made by G. M. Westman to heat the mispickel in an electric furnace in an atm. of nitrogen whereby arsenic is volatilized, and iron sulphide is run from the furnace as a matte. The arsenic vapour and nitrogen are conveyed by fans into condensers where the arsenic is deposited ; the nitrogen is sent back again to the furnace. The process is used at Newark, New Jersey. E. H. Robie described the process at Jardine, Mont., where the ore is roasted for arsenic trioxide and the residue sent to the smelter for recovering gold since the concentrates contain 2 ozs. of gold per ton.

M. G. Bachimont [3] suggested heating the arsenical ore with ferrous chloride in closed vessels whereby arsenic trichloride is volatilized and iron sulphide or oxide remains. The arsenic trichloride is received in a soln. of ferric chloride and arsenic precipitated from the soln. by metallic iron. J. Robinson proposed to extract the arsenic as sulphide from arsenical ores by means of a soln. of sodium poly-sulphide, and precipitating the arsenic from the liquor. A. Siemens extracted the arsenic as sulphide by means of soln. of the alkali, alkaline earth, or magnesium hydrosulphide : $As_2S_3 + 6NaHS = 3H_2S + As_2S_3.3Na_2S$, and electrolyzed the liquor. Arsenic is deposited at the cathode, and the sulphide of the basic metal at the anode : $As_2S_3.3Na_2S + 3H_2 = 2As + 6NaHS$. E. W. von Siemens and J. G. Halske tried a somewhat analogous process. The electrolytic precipitation of arsenic was discussed by A. Riche, and H. Moissan. The winning of arsenic from the arsenical residues obtained in the manufacture of aniline dyes, was discussed by C. A. Winkler,[4] M. Tabourin and M. Lemaire, Randu et Cie., C. Martins, E. A. Parnell, A. Leonhardt, and R. Brimmeyr. R. Jahn roasted the ore and passed the purified fumes through a reducing flame.

Arsenic can be purified by mixing it with charcoal powder and subliming ; the arsenic sulphide is most volatile and comes off before the arsenic. Any undecomposed pyrites, or earthy matric remains as a residue. The sublimation is conducted in two crucibles mouth to mouth, and luted with fireclay. The under crucible is fitted into a hole in an iron plate to keep as much heat as possible away from the upper crucible. As A. Bette [5] showed, some arsenic trioxide is nearly always found associated with the sublimed arsenic ; and to avoid this, the arsenic can be sublimed in a current of hydrogen. J. W. Retgers prepared arsenic free from sulphur by fractional sublimation. H. Ludwig obtained arsenic free from oxide, by mixing it with a little iodine before sublimation ; and R. Böttger, by digesting it with a soln. of potassium dichromate in dil. sulphuric acid, or with an aq. soln. of sodium hypochlorite, or with chlorine-water. According to N. A. Orloff, arsenic cannot be freed from antimony by sublimation. To obtain arsenic free from antimony, crystallized sodium arsenate is precipitated as magnesium arsenate, dissolved in hydrochloric acid, and fractionally precipitated with ammonia. The middle fraction is dried, mixed with sugar-charcoal, and sublimed.

V. Augur [6] found that when a soln. of arsenic trichloride in absolute alcohol at $-15°$ is added to a soln. of hypophosphorous acid in the same solvent and cooled to the same temp., an ochre-yellow precipitate is slowly formed, which becomes reddish-brown on drying in a vacuum. This powder, which contains 68·2 per cent. of arsenic, 0·97 per cent. of phosphorus, 2·5 per cent. of alcohol, and (by difference) 28·33 per cent. of water, is rapidly and completely dissolved by dil. alkali hydroxides. This property is retained from two days to as many months, according to the conditions of preparation, but in time the substance becomes insoluble in alkalies. The same change is effected rapidly by contact with water, more slowly by alcohol, and immediately by heating at 100°. When heated to redness in a current of carbon dioxide, it loses water, alcohol, and hydrogen phosphide. The soln. in alkali is brownish-red, quite limpid by transmitted light, but cloudy by reflection. It is unaltered by boiling, but is rapidly oxidized by the air, forming arsenite. Alcohol, or excess of alkali, precipitates brown flakes, which are soluble in water, dil. acids and all soluble salts give a similar precipitate insoluble in water or alkalies. The brown, alkaline soln. can be freed from alcohol by dialysis, but it is impossible to remove all the phosphorus or all the alkali. The liquid is considered to be a true **colloidal solution of arsenic.** E. Lecoq obtained the soln. less contaminated with impurities by electrolyzing an alkaline soln., using an anode of arsenic, or, better, by the electrolytic reduction of a soln. of 3 grms. of arsenious oxide in a litre of 0·3 per cent. sodium hydroxide. A current of 2–3 ampères and 100 volts should be employed, using a platinum cathode and a mercury anode. The soln. is cooled during electrolysis and purified by dialysis. The addition of a trace of gum renders the colloid much more stable. A soln. prepared in this way appears deep brown, and contains about 0·07 per cent. of arsenic. He found the colloid less toxic to animals than arsenic trioxide. F. Heyden found that a stable colloidal soln. of arsenic may be obtained by reducing its compounds in an alkaline medium in the presence of a protective colloid. White arsenic dissolved in aq. sodium hydroxide containing some protein material, such as white-of-egg, lysalbic acid or gelatin, is reduced by alkaline pyrogallol. The soln. is dialyzed or the colloidal arsenic precipitated by acid, washed, and again dissolved in water. The colloidal arsenic may be precipitated from soln. by acetone, alcohol, or a mixture of the latter with ether. On evaporating the soln., it is obtained in black, lustrous lamellæ, which dissolve in water to a deep brown soln. A. Gutbier and N. Kräutle examined the protective action of extracts of various plant colloids on colloidal arsenic prepared by the reducing action of sodium hyposulphite on slightly acidified soln. of arsenic trioxide, and so found it possible to obtain by evaporation solid colloids containing about 3 per cent. of arsenic which are quite soluble in water. The protected soln. of colloidal arsenic are not appreciably influenced by the addition of hydrochloric acid, sulphuric acid, sodium chloride, and barium chloride, whereas sodium hydroxide and sodium carbonate change the colour from dark brown to light yellow—*vide infra*, brown arsenic. A. Chwala obtained colloidal arsenic compounds by using salts of the metallic acids as protective colloids—*e.g.* calcium plumbate, or sodium antimonate with or without the addition of protalbinic acid. L. Dede and T. Walther prepared colloidal soln. of arsenic by bubbling purified arsine through water exposed to light of short wave lengths. According to the dilution, these soln. are yellow to bluish-violet in colour. Only the most conc. soln. show any tendency towards flocculence ; more dil. soln. gradually become colourless owing to the slow oxidation of arsenic to arsenic trioxide. They are very insensitive towards electrolytes. The particles are negatively charged. H. Plauson treated a colloidal soln. of arsenic by treating the element in the so-called colloidal mill using agar-agar as protective colloid. E. Fouard prepared colloidal arsenic by electrolyzing a soln. of a salt of the metal containing a pure organic colloid (albumin, starch, or gelatin) with a current of a few milliampères. At the cathode, the metal ions are neutralized by the repelled, negatively-charged colloid micelles. A colloidal organo-metallic complex is thus formed. The anode is separated by immersion in a collodion cell rendered semipermeable by precipitated copper ferrocyanide. The cathode should be a bad conductor so as to reduce the frequency with which formation of the complex occurs on the cathode.

REFERENCES.

¹ N. Tarugi, *Gazz. Chim. Ital.*, 29. 509, 1899 ; A. Bettendorff, *Zeit. Chem.*, (2), 5. 492, 1870.
² O. Kast and J. Bräuning, *Zeit. Berg. Hutt. Sal.*, 18. 189, 1870 ; E. H. Robie, *Eng. Min. Journ.*, 120. 765, 1925 ; B. Kerl, *Handbuch der metallurgischen Hüttenkunde*, Freiberg, 1855 ; G. M. Westman, *Electrochemist and Metallurgist*, 1. 242, 1901 ; *U.S. Pat. No.* 658412, 658536, 1900 ; E. Lampadius, *Berg. Hutt. Ztg.*, 12. 764, 1853 ; V. Thomas, *Min. Ind.*. 2. 25, 1893 ; 11. 42, 1902 ; H. Dewey, *Arsenic and Antimony Ores*, London, 1920 ; C. P. Linville, *Trans. Amer. Inst. Min. Met. Eng.*, 71. 953, 1925 ; J. F. Cullen, *U.S. Pat. No.* 1433533, 1923 ; C. H. Jones, *Chem. Met. Engg.*, 23. 957, 1920.
³ M. G. Bachimont, *German Pat., D.R.P.* 80225, 1895 ; E. W. von Siemens and J. G. Halske, *ib.*, 67973, 1892 ; J. Robinson, *Brit. Pat. No.* 497, 1885 ; A. Siemens, *ib.*, 7123, 1896 ; *Zeit. Elektrochem.*, 2. 130, 1897 ; *Zeit. angew. Chem.*, 6. 291, 1893 ; A Riche, *Ann. Chim. Phys.*, (5), 13. 523, 1878 ; H. Moissan, *Compt. Rend.*, 99. 874, 1884.
⁴ C. A. Winkler, *Deut. Ind. Ztg.*, 333, 1876 ; *Verh. Ver. Beförd.*, 211, 1876 ; C. Martins, *ib.*, 155, 1877 ; M. Tabourin and M. Lemaire, *French Pat. No.* 70183, 1866 ; *Bull. Soc. Chim.*, (2), 6. 254, 1866 ; Randu et Cie., *ib.*, (2), 6. 254, 1866 ; *French Pat. No.* 70795, 1866 ; R. Brimmeyr, *Dingler's Journ.*, 179. 388, 1866 ; E. A. Parnell, *Brit. Pat. No.* 2002, 1876 ; A. Leonhardt, *German Pat., D.R.P.* 3216, 1879 ; R. Jahn, *Austrian Pat. No.* 102293, 1925.
⁵ A. Bette, *Liebig's Ann.*, 33. 355, 1840 ; J. W. Retgers, *Zeit. anorg. Chem.*, 4. 403, 1903; R. Böttger. *Journ. prakt. Chem.*, (2), 2. 134, 1870 ; H. Ludwig, *Arch. Pharm.*, (2), 97. 23, 1899; N. A. Orloff, *Chem. Ztg.*, 26. 290, 1901.

* V. Augur, *Compt. Rend.*, **145**. 718, 1907 ; E. Fouard, *ib.*, **184**. 328, 1927 ; E. Lecoq, *ib.*, **150**. 700, 887, 1910 ; F. Heyden, *German Pat.*, *D.R.P.* 202561, 1908 ; A. Gutbier and N. Kräutle, *Koll. Zeit.*, **20**. 186, 1917 ; H. Plauson, *Brit. Pat. No.* 155834, 182696, 1921 ; L. Dede and T. Walther, *Ber.*, **58**. 99, 1925 ; A. Chwala, *U.S. Pat. No.* 1573375, 1926.

§ 4. The Allotropic Forms of Arsenic

In 1725, J. F. Henkel [1] first prepared the so-called metallic arsenic by sublimation ; and in 1843, J. J. Berzelius, in his memoir *Om allotropi*, showed that arsenic can exist in two allotropic states. One of these, *metallic* or *crystalline arsenic*, or *α-arsenic*, is produced when arsenic vapour mixed with another heated gas is deposited on a part of the vessel which is not strongly heated. It is a dark grey, crystalline mass which oxidizes in air, especially at 40°, forming what he called " black, pulverulent suboxide." The other modification, *amorphous* or *vitreous arsenic*, or *β-arsenic*, is produced when arsenic is very strongly heated, or when the vapour is condensed on a part of the vessel which is near the temp. at which arsenic volatilizes, so that the element is deposited in an atm. of its own vap. This modification of arsenic forms a light grey vitreous mass which, according to J. J. Berzelius, is denser than the α-form, and remains unaltered in air even when finely powdered, and heated to 70° or 80°. There is nothing here to show that these supposed allotropic states are not, as H. Watts suggested, due to differences in mechanical structure rather than to differences in atomic structure. The different allotropes are produced by differences in the compactness of the constituent matter. J. W. Hittorf showed that J. J. Berzelius was not correct in stating that the grey, vitreous form is denser than the metallic form, for the sp. gr. of the vitreous form is 4·72 when that of the metallic form is 5·72. A. Bettendorf showed that vitreous or β-arsenic, is always formed when the vap. of arsenic is cooled at 210°–220°, and it is deposited beside crystalline or α-arsenic when the element is sublimed in a current of hydrogen. The β-form of arsenic has a sp. gr. 4·716–4·740, and at 360° it is transformed into crystalline α-arsenic of sp. gr. 5·72. It will be observed that these sp. gr. also are not in harmony with J. J. Berzelius' statement that vitreous β-arsenic is specifically heavier than ordinary crystalline α-arsenic. A. Bettendorf also noticed that when arsenic is sublimed in a current of hydrogen, (i) the crust of vitreous arsenic, deposited in the hottest part of the zone of condensation, is succeeded by (ii) the crust of ordinary, crystalline arsenic, and beyond that is deposited (iii) a yellow powder which rapidly becomes (iv) grey pulverulent arsenic which he regarded as another allotropic form, and called *γ-arsenic*. The yellow unstable—possibly allotropic—form was not examined because it was transformed so rapidly into the grey form. Microscopically, γ-arsenic resembles flowers of sulphur ; its sp. gr. is 4·71 ; and it is readily attacked by nitric acid. The γ-variety became crystalline α-arsenic at 358°.

R. Engel showed that β-arsenic, γ-arsenic, and the brown precipitates obtained by the reduction of arsenic trioxide with stannous chloride, hypophosphorous acid, or copper, or by electrolysis, are probably the same allotropic form having a sp. gr. 4·6–4·7, and the differences observed in their chemical behaviour are due to differences in the state of subdivision. He admitted only two allotropic forms —the crystalline of sp. gr. 5·7 and the vitreous of sp. gr. 4·6–4·7 ; the crystalline form sublimes in vacuo at 360°, and the vitreous at 260°. He compared vitreous arsenic with yellow phosphorus, and crystalline arsenic with red phosphorus. A. Geuther reported another modification of amorphous arsenic of sp. gr. 3·7 at 15° to be produced when a mixture of 3 parts of phosphorus trichloride, and 2 of arsenic trichloride is treated with water. R. Engel said that the low sp. gr. of this product is due to the presence of impurities—principally arsenic trioxide. M. Berthelot and R. Engel measured the heat of transformation of the vitreous and crystalline forms of arsenic, and found it to be of the order of that of the diamond and graphite.

The existence of a yellow modification of arsenic, in addition to the crystalline and the vitreous or amorphous form was indicated by the work of A. Bettendorff, J. P. Cooke, L. Elsner, R. W. E. MacLeod, T. Petersen, J. W. Retgers, H. Rose, and A. Schuller. There was some doubt about this as a specific allotropic form because it had only an ephemeral existence, and could not be isolated; and R. Engel maintained that it was not a definite allotropic form, and suggested that the yellow colour is due to the vap. of arsenic. A. Bettendorf then showed that when stannous chloride acts on a soln. of arsenic trioxide in hydrochloric acid, a brown precipitate is obtained containing 96–99 per cent. of arsenic, and traces of tin. He also noticed that a faint yellow coloration temporarily appears when arsenic is distilled with hydrochloric acid; arsenic is then present in the hydro-chloric acid, but it was not proved that the transient yellow coloration was due to arsenic. R. G. Durrant observed that when stannous chloride acts on the hydrochloric acid soln. of arsenic trioxide, or magnesium ammonium arsenate, the appearance of the solid arsenic is always preceded by a pale buff tint, and from this, the brown precipitate is formed. The buff coloration is best observed with mixtures which yield a very slow deposit; and shaken with carbon disul-phide, a small proportion of arsenic is dissolved. The reaction was studied by F. A. Flückiger, R. Lobello, C. O. Curtman and H. Bekurts, G. Lochmann, S. H. de Jong, A. Ferraro and A. Carobrio, H. Hager, J. Mayerhofer, P. Lohmann, and K. Zwicknagl. The Farbenindustrie A.G. passed the vapour of a solvent for yellow arsenic over strongly heated arsenic, and immediately condensed the vapour. G. E. Linck obtained the yellow variety by gently heating arsenic in a current of carbon dioxide and strongly cooling the tube, which must not be exposed to light; in these circumstances, a yellow powder is deposited, which is converted into the mirror form of arsenic by heat or exposure to light. This yellow powder is readily soluble in carbon disulphide, and by evaporating the solvent is deposited in microscopic, rhombic dodecahedra which smell strongly of garlic. These change spontaneously into mirror arsenic, and the transforma-tion, which can be watched under the microscope, is complete in about 3 minutes. H. Erdmann and M. von Unruh also obtained the yellow form by distilling arsenic in an aluminium tube in a current of carbon dioxide. The aluminium tube passed directly into a side-tube of a U-tube with a bulb on the opposite limb. A rapid current of cooled carbon dioxide played on to the distilled substance just as it emerged from the hot tube. By this sudden cooling, the arsenic is deposited in the yellow modification, which was at once dissolved in carbon disulphide in the U-tube, surrounded by ice-water. The yellow modification of the arsenic can be obtained from the soln. either by evaporation of the carbon disulphide or by cooling to −70°, when most of it separates from soln. The solid, yellow arsenic is extremely sensitive to all forms of light. It can be preserved for some time by keeping it at a temperature below −60° and away from the light. Even at very low temp., it is quickly turned black by the action of light. They added that there is no tendency for the dissolved yellow arsenic to change into the metallic modification, but the soln. slowly deposits a reddish-brown modification on standing. This reddish-brown variety is not changed into the metallic form by the action of light. A. Stock and W. Siebert obtained yellow arsenic by subliming arsenic in vacuo, and cooling the vap. by liquid air in darkness. The yellow arsenic is immediately blackened in light. They also found that a soln. of yellow arsenic is most readily prepared by passing a current of about 12 amp. between a carbon anode and a cathode consisting of an alloy of equal parts of arsenic and antimony, both electrodes being immersed in carbon disulphide contained in a vessel sur-rounded and covered by water and ice, the arsenic under these conditions dissolving in the carbon disulphide in the form of the yellow modification, whilst the antimony is disintegrated but does not enter into soln. After a sufficient quantity has dissolved, the carbon disulphide is separated from the water and filtered, and may be concentrated by distillation. D. Vörländer and co-workers observed no

sign of the formation of a doubly refracting form of yellow arsenic above —190°
analogous to doubly refracting yellow phosphorus.

P. N. Laschtschenko measured the heat evolved on cooling heated arsenic and
obtained the results shown in Fig. 1. The break between 738° and 750° refers to
the transition of yellow to metallic arsenic, a change attended by the evolution of
about 7 cals. per gram. The break between 822° and 868° is due to the change
of arsenic from the liquid to the solid state of
aggregation. With amorphous arsenic, it is not
certain whether the temp. 360° or 270°–280° is the
transition point. The sp. gr. of amorphous arsenic,
heated to 360° and rapidly cooled to 15°, is the
same as that of metallic arsenic ; while that which
has been heated to 275° is the same as that of grey
arsenic. R. Engel gave 360° for the transition,
and P. Jolibois, and R. Goubau gave 270°–280°.
P. N. Laschtschenko assumed that amorphous
arsenic is a solid soln. of the yellow and metallic
forms, just as ordinary red phosphorus is assumed
to be a solid soln. of yellow and metallic phosphorus. This view is supported by the change in
the sp. gr. of amorphous phosphorus with temp.,
and R. Engel's observations on the sublimation of

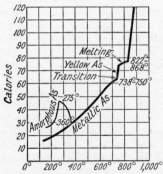

FIG. 1.—The Evolution of Heat
by Cooling Arsenic.

arsenic. The sublimation temp. of amorphous arsenic is much lower than that of
metallic arsenic. The sublimation of amorphous arsenic ceases at 360°, and transformation of amorphous into metallic arsenic can be effected by a prolonged sublimation at 310°, for the more volatile constituent of the solid soln. distils off, and metallic
arsenic, non-volatile at that temp., remains ; the irreversible, exothermal transformation is complete. H. Erdmann and co-workers gave 303° for the transition
temp. because at this temp. the amorphous form becomes electrically conducting.
P. N. Laschtschenko found that the temp. at which electrical conductivity appears
depends on the conditions of the experiment. On heating the amorphous form
in a sealed tube, he found that minute crystals of metallic arsenic appear at 270°–
280° ; while above this temp., the transformation proceeds by the distillation of
the metastable amorphous form and its condensation in the metallic state.

According to H. Erdmann and M. von Unruh, the raising of the b.p. of carbon
disulphide by dissolved yellow arsenic corresponds with the mol. formula As_4 ;
and H. Erdmann and R. Reppert suggest that when yellow arsenic passes into
metallic arsenic under the influence of violet or ultra-violet light, *grey arsenic* is
produced as an intermediate stage, and they assumed that it has the mol. formula
As_2, while metallic arsenic is assumed to be monatomic. Grey arsenic, also called
mirror-arsenic, is formed as a by-product in the preparation of the carbon disulphide
soln. of yellow arsenic ; when solid yellow arsenic is exposed to light at low temp.,
or when dissolved yellow arsenic is treated with alcohol, or cooled with carbon
dioxide and ether, or with liquid air. The sp. gr. is 4·64 at 20°. While J. J. Berzelius, A. Bettendorff, A. Geuther, J. W. Hittorf, C. Ehlers, and T. Petersen believed
that grey arsenic is amorphous, J. W. Retgers, G. E. Linck, H. Erdmann, and
R. Reppert, and E. Frank hold that the grey form is crystalline or cryptocrystalline.
Grey arsenic is stable towards atm. oxygen, and is oxidized by nitric acid more
slowly than brown, or metallic arsenic. When a soln. of yellow arsenic is treated
with oxygen, with arsenic tribromide, or with acetylene tetrabromide, or is allowed
to remain in the dark, H. Erdmann and R. Reppert found that what they call
brown arsenic is produced. Brown arsenic was obtained by A. Geuther, and
R. Engel—*vide supra ;* it was probably obtained by J. V. Janowsky in 1873 by
the action of water on sodium arsenide ; he regarded it as solid hydrogen arsenide ;
and O. Brunn, in 1889, by the action of air on arsine, and he regarded it as a
soln. of arsine in arsenic ; by A. Bettendorf, and R. G. Durrant, by the action of

stannous chloride on arsenic trichloride ; by E. Frank, by the action of phosphorus trichloride, arsenic diiodide, hypophosphorous acid, and hydrazine hydrate on arsenic trichloride ; and by O. Brunck, by reducing strongly acid soln. of arsenic trioxide with sodium hyposulphite—*vide supra*, colloidal arsenic. H. Jung found that the X-radiograms of precipitated brown arsenic ; brown, translucent arsenic derived from cubic arsenic ; and the arsenic mirror, all indicate that the arsenic is amorphous. H. Erdmann and R. Reppert said that brown arsenic has a sp. gr. of 3·67–3·69 at 20°. They assume that its mol. formula is As_8. C. Ehlers examined the gaseous and solid impurities a high proportion of which is always present in brown arsenic. H. Erdmann and co-workers thus represent the mol. structure of these different allotropes of arsenic :

As	As $\overset{...}{As}$	As : As $\overset{.\quad.}{As : As}$	As : As : As $\overset{.\quad.\quad.}{As : As : As}$
Metallic arsenic.	Grey arsenic.	Yellow arsenic.	Brown arsenic.

While H. Erdmann and co-workers attributed the differences in the four modifications of arsenic to differences in their mol. complexity, V. Kohlschütter and co-workers assumed that the different allotropic forms are due to differences in the quantity of matter distributed in a given space. Thus, the sp. vol. of yellow arsenic is 0·5, while that of metallic arsenic is 0·175. Hence, the conversion of yellow to metallic arsenic is a process of condensation. Grey arsenic is likewise assumed to be the same matter as metallic arsenic, but occupying a larger space ; while brown arsenic is more diffuse than grey arsenic, and it is always obtained under the influence of a foreign substance which acts in a certain sense as a dispersing medium, the nature and conc. of which determines the state of distribution. This hypothesis is virtually the same as that of H. Watts previously indicated. H. Erdmann and co-workers gave 180° as the transition temp. of yellow to grey arsenic. P. N. Laschtschenko could find no evidence of such a transition point— Fig. 1—and there is no proof that the mol. wt. of grey, brown, and metallic arsenic are actually those which have been assigned to them. The results of these investigations indicate the existence of four allotropic forms of arsenic with the properties indicated in Table I. According to P. N. Laschtschenko, the probable **transition**

TABLE I.—COMPARISON OF THE FOUR ALLOTROPIC FORMS OF ARSENIC.

	Metallic.	Yellow.	Grey.	Brown.
Colour	Steel-grey	Yellow	Grey to b'ack	Pale reddish brown to dark brown
Translucency	Opaque	Trans'ucent	Translucent	Opaque
Crystalline form	Trigonal	Cubic	Cryptocrystalline	Amorphous
Sp. gr.	5·72	(2 06)	4·64	3·67–4·13
Electrical	Conductor	Non-conductor	Non-conductor	Non-conductor

temperatures for metallic to yellow arsenic is between 738° and 750° ; R. Engel gave 360° for the passage of amorphous to metallic arsenic ; and P. Jolibois, and R. Goubau, gave 270°–280°. P. N. Laschtschenko found the irreversible transformation of brown or amorphous arsenic to grey arsenic occurs at 270°–280° ; and of grey to metallic arsenic, at 360°. H. Erdmann and R. Reppert gave respectively 180°–200°, and 303°.

REFERENCES.

¹ J. J. Berzelius, *Acad. Handl. Stockholm*, 1, 1843 ; *Liebig's Ann.*, **49**. 253, 1844 ; *Taylor's Scientific Memoirs*, **4**. 240, 1846 ; A. Bettendorf, *Sitzber. Niederrh. Ges. Bonn.*, 67, 1867 ; **128**, 1869 ; *Liebig's Ann.*, **144**. 110, 1867 ; A. Geuther, *ib.*, 240, 208, 1887 ; *Jena Zeit.*, **10**. 123, 1875 ; M. Berthelot and R. Engel, *Ann. Chim. Phys.*, (6), **21**. 285, 1890 ; *Compt. Rend.*, **110**. 498, 1890 ; R Engel, *Bull. Soc. Chim.*, (2), **50**. 194, 1888 ; (3), **13** 721, 1895 ; *Compt. Rend.*,

86. 497, 1314, 1883; P. Jolibois, *ib.*, 152. 1767, 1911; R. Goubau, *ib.*, 158. 121, 1914; J. W. Hittorf, *Pogg. Ann.*, 126. 218, 1865; H. Rose, *ib.*, 76. 75, 1849; H. Watts, in L. Gmelin, *Handbook of Chemistry*, London, 4. 251, 1850; A. Schuller, *Wied. Ann.*, 18. 321, 1883; *Ber. Math. Nat. Ges. Ungarn*, 6. 94, 1889; O. Brunck, *Liebig's Ann.*, 336. 281, 1904; T. Petersen, *Zeit. phys. Chem.*, 8. 601, 1891; J. W. Retgers, *Zeit. anorg. Chem.*, 4. 403, 1893; 6. 317, 1894; H. Erdmann, *ib.*, 32. 453, 1902; H. Erdmann and M. von Unruh, *ib.*, 32. 457, 1902; M. von Unruh, *Ueber gelbes Arsen*, Halle, 1901; H. Erdmann and R. Reppert, *Liebig's Ann.*, 361. 6, 1908; R. Reppert, *Ueber gelbes, braunes, und graues Arsen*, Halle, 1907; M. Thiele, *Ueber die allotropen Modifikationen des Arsens*, Berlin, 1910; E. Frank, *Zur Kenntnis des braunen und grauen Arsens*, Bern, 1912; V. Kohlschütter, E. Frank, and C. Ehlers, *Liebig's Ann.*, 400. 268, 1913; C. Ehlers, *Zur Kenntnis der Bildungsformen von Metallen*, Halle a. S., 1912; R. W. E. MacLeod, *Chem. News*, 70. 139, 1894; G. E. Linck, *Ber.*, 32. 888, 1899; 33. 2284, 1900; O. Brunn, *ib.*, 22. 3023, 1889; J. V. Janowsky, *ib.*, 6. 220, 1873; A. Stock and W. Siebert, *ib.*, 37. 4572, 1904; 38. 966, 1905; W. Siebert, *Zur Kenntnis der Modifikationen des Arsens und Antimons*, Berlin, 1905; J. F. Henkel, *Pyritologia*, Leipzig, 1725; R. G. Durrant, *Journ. Chem. Soc.*, 115. 134, 1919; P. N. Laschtschenko, *ib.*, 121. 972, 1922; L. Elsner, *Journ. prakt. Chem.*, (1), 22. 344, 1844; J. P. Cooke, *Amer. Journ. Science*, (2), 31. 91, 1861; D. Vörländer, W. Silke, and S. Kriess, *Ber.*, 58. B, 1802, 1925; K. Zwicknagl, *Zeit. anorg. Chem.*, 151. 41, 1926; E. Zettnow, *Pogg. Ann.*, 146. 318, 1872; *Zeit. gesammt. Naturw. Halle*, 40. 407, 1872; J. Mayerhofer, *Liebig's Ann.*, 158. 326, 1871; H. Hager, *Pharm. Centrh.*, 13. 52, 92, 1872; A. Ferraro and A. Carobrio, *Boll. Chim. Pharm.*, 44. 805, 1906; G. Lochmann, *Zeit. angew. Chem.*, 18. 416, 1905; J. H. de Jong, *Zeit. anal. Chem.*, 41. 596, 1902; C. O. Curtman and H. Bekurts, *Chem. Centr.*, (4), 3. 725, 1891; R. Lobello, *Boll. Chim. Pharm.*, 44. 445, 1905; P. Lohmann, *Pharm. Zeit.*, 34. 274, 1889; F. A. Flückiger, *Arch. Pharm.*, (3), 27. 1, 1889; Farbenindustrie A.G., *German Pat.*, D.R.P. 428040, 1924; H. Jung, *Centr. Min.*, 107, 1926.

§ 5. The Physical Properties of Arsenic

Arsenic in its ordinary form is a silver-grey, or tin-white substance with a metallic lustre. The colours of the different allotropes have been previously indicated. F. P. Leroux said that the vap. of arsenic is lemon-yellow, but A. Schuller and later observers found it to be colourless. Arsenic occurs in nature usually massive, but is sometimes reticulated, reniform, stalactitic, or columnar. The natural **crystals** are usually acicular. G. Rose [1] found the crystals are trigonal with the axial ratio $a : c = 1 : 1.4025$; V. R. von Zepharovich gave $1 : 1.4013$. The **cleavage** on the (111)-face is perfect; that on the (110)-face, imperfect. M. L. Huggins studied the relation between the cleavage and the electronic structure. Twinned forms are common with sublimed crystals. O. Mügge showed that the (110)-plane is a gliding plane. The crystals were also examined by A. de Schulten, and C. W. Zenger. The **X-radiogram** of metallic arsenic was studied by A. J. Bradley, M. L. Huggins, and S. von Olshausen. The structure consists of two interpenetrating trigonal lattices—Fig. 4, **8**. 52, 5. A comparison of the results of A. J. Bradley with those for antimony by R. W. James and N. Tunstall, and of bismuth by R. W. James, is shown in Table II. G. E. Linck and H. Jung esti-

TABLE II.—LATTICE CONSTANTS OF ARSENIC, ANTIMONY, AND BISMUTH.

	Arsenic.	Antimony.	Bismuth.
Edge unit rhomb, $2a$	5.6 A.	6.20 A.	6.56 A.
Parameter, $2x$	0.097	0.074	0.052
Longer at. distance	3.15 A.	3.37 A.	3.47 A.
Shorter at. distance	2.51 A.	2.87 A.	3.11 A.

mated the lattice constants of the trigonal crystals to be $a = 5.593$, and $a = 84° 38'$. The data were summarized by P. P. Ewald and C. Hermann. G. Rose believed that arsenic can be obtained in octahedral crystals belonging to the cubic system; L. Elsner, F. von Kobell, and M. L. Frankenheim came to the same conclusion; but J. P. Cooke suggested that the octahedral crystals are those of arsenic trioxide coloured with arsenic. This subject was discussed by C. F. Rammelsberg and

J. W. Retgers. The arsenolamprite of A. Breithaupt, and A. Frenzel, is probably, according to C. Hintze, a modification of arsenic belonging to the rhombic system— G. E. Linck said the monoclinic system. H. Jung showed that the X-radiogram of arsenolamprite agrees with that for metallic arsenic suggesting impure rhombohedral arsenic, or arsenic in which an allotropic form resembling black phosphorus is present. As previously indicated, the allotropic form called grey arsenic is crypto-crystalline. According to H. Erdmann and R. Reppert, grey arsenic is trigonal ; J. W. Retgers, cubic ; and G. E. Linck, monoclinic. Yellow arsenic is also crystalline and the crystals belong to the cubic system. The so-called brown arsenic, and arsenic mirrors, were shown by H. Jung to be amorphous.

G. E. Linck defined a *eutropic series* as one formed by the combination of successive elements of a sub-group by elements in the periodic system with the same radicle so that the compounds thus formed are characterized by similar crystalline form, and similar physical and chemical constants, which show a progressive change with the change in mol. wt. Red phosphorus is not eutropic with the trigonal forms of arsenic, antimony, and bismuth because the calculated ratios of the axes, at. vol., etc., do not fit the eutropic series of the other three elements. On the other hand, red phosphorus forms a eutropic series with mirror (grey) arsenic ; and yellow phosphorus corresponds eutropically with yellow arsenic. The trigonal form of arsenic corresponds eutropically with crystalline antimony and bismuth, but no corresponding form of phosphorus is known. G. E. Linck illustrated this by Table III. E. Mitscherlich supposed metallic

TABLE III.—EUTROPIC SERIES WITH TRIGONAL ARSENIC, ANTIMONY, AND BISMUTH.

	At. wt.	Colour.	$a : c$	Lattice constants.		Sp. gr.	M.p.	Sublimation temp.	Oxidiza-bility.
				a	β				
As	75·0	grey	1 : 1·4035	5·593 A.	84° 38′	5·727	—	449°–450°	easy
Sb	120·2	greyish-white	1 : 1·3236	6·20 A.	86° 58′	6·71	440°	1500°–1700°	difficult
Bi	208·0	reddish-white	1 : 1·3035	6·54 A.	87° 34′	9·76	268·3°	1700°	very difficult

arsenic to be isomorphous with tellurium and antimony. The polymorphism of phosphorus, arsenic, antimony, and bismuth is illustrated by Table IV ; the

TABLE IV.—POLYMORPHISM OF THE PHOSPHORUS-BISMUTH FAMILY.

	Phosphorus.	Arsenic.	Antimony.	Bismuth.
Form	Yellow P	Yellow As	Yellow Sb	
Crystals	Cubic	Cubic	(Cubic)	
Colour	Yellowish-white	Yellow	Yellow	Unknown
Sp. gr.	1·83	2·06	—	
Form	Red P	Grey or mirror As	Black or mirror Sb	
Crystals	Monoclinic	Arsenolamprite	Monoclinic	Unknown
Colour	Reddish-brown	Brown	Black	
Sp. gr.	2·16	3·71	—	
Form	Black P	Metallic As	Metallic Sb	Metallic Bi
Crystals	Trigonal	Trigonal	Trigonal	Trigonal
Colour	Black	Tin-white	Greyish-white	Reddish silver-white
Sp. gr.	2·699	5·727	6·71	9·76

eutropism is also illustrated by passing from left to right. The subject was also discussed by P. Möller, and R. Neumann. According to H. Erdmann and R. Reppert, although yellow phosphorus and yellow arsenic are so closely related crystallographically, they do not form mixed crystals. This is ascribed to the great difference of their solubilities in carbon disulphide. J. Nicklès discussed the isomorphism of this family of elements.

The **specific gravity** of native arsenic given by A. Breithaupt is 5·722–5·734 ; and by A. Russell and H. F. Harwood, 5·636. T. Bergman's value 8·31 was far too high for metallic arsenic. A. Bettendorf gave 5·726–5·728 at 14° ; N. J. B. G. Guibourt, 5·700–5·959 ; A. L. Lavoisier, 5·76 ; C. J. B. Karsten, 5·6281 ; W. Herapath, 5·672–5·709 ; M. J. Brisson, and F. Stromeyer, 5·7633 ; V. Kohlschütter and co-workers, 5·73 ; T. Turner, 5·8843 ; L. Playfair and J. P. Joule, 5·230 at 3·9° ; H. Ludwig, 5·395 at 12·5° ; A. Wigand, 5·87 ; P. N. Laschtschenko, 5·7301 at 15°/15° ; J. W. Mallet, for a sample which had been fused, 5·709 at 19° ; and W. Spring, for a sample which had been compressed, 4·91. The sp. gr. of **vitreous** arsenic given by A. Bettendorf is 4·710–4·716 at 14° ; A. Wigand, 4·78 ; V. Kohlschütter and co-workers, 4·60–4·72 at 18° ; R. Engel, 4·6–4·7 ; and J. W. Hittorf, 4·69 at 17° for the material in pieces, and 4·72, when in powder. H. Erdmann and R. Reppert gave 4·64 at 20° for the sp. gr. of **grey** arsenic. E. Frank found the sp. gr. of grey arsenic sublimed in a current of carbon dioxide, 4·708 at 20°, and in a current of hydrogen, 4·7065 at 20°. The form prepared by treating arsenic trichloride with phosphorus trichloride was found by E. Frank to have a sp. gr. 4·17 at 16° and if heated to 200°, 4·42 ; if obtained with arsenic diiodide, 4·185 at 15° ; if with hypophosphorous acid, 4·20 at 16°, and if heated to 200°, 4·54 ; and if with hydrazine hydrate, 4·54 at 18°. The product in these cases is probably a mixture of the brown and grey forms of arsenic. The **brown** arsenic prepared by A. Geuther had a sp. gr. 3·7 at 15° ; H. Erdmann and R. Reppert gave 3·67–4·06 for the sp. gr. at 20°. V. Kohlschütter and co-workers, 3·7–4·7 ; and P. N. Laschtschenko, 3·693 at 15°/15°. This agrees with general experience that while a crystalline individual has a definite sp. gr., amorphous substances have a variable sp. gr. V. Kohlschütter and co-workers said that the purest brown arsenic they could obtain had a sp. gr. 4·52 ; and added that the sp. gr. of the grey and brown forms of arsenic, free from all impurities, are nearly the same so that the sp. gr. is not a sufficient criterion, to distinguish these modifications. I. I. Saslowsky gave 5·701 for the sp. gr. at room temp., and 13·2 for the at. vol. C. del Fresno studied this subject. R. M. Bozorth calculated the **atomic radius** of arsenic to be 1·36 A. when that of oxygen is 0·65 A. ; W. L. Bragg gave 1·26 A. for the at. radius ; E. N. Gapon, 1·37 A. ; W. F. de Jong and H. W. V. Willems, 1·16 A. ; and M. L. Huggins, 2·32 A. H. G. Grimm made observations on the ionic radius. P. N. Laschtschenko found the sp. gr. of amorphous arsenic at 15°/15°, and after heating in sealed quartz-glass tubes at different temp. and rapidly cooling :

	15°	175°	235°	255°	275°	305°	365°	400°
Sp. gr.	3·693	3·698	3·974	4·493	4·947	5·365	5·731	5·729

The corresponding curve is continuous, becoming horizontal at 360° ; at 270°–280°, the sp. gr. becomes equal to that of grey arsenic, and at 360°, to that of metallic arsenic. H. Erdmann and R. Reppert found the sp. gr. of yellow arsenic at −50° to be 2·35 ; at −63°, 2·46 ; at −75°, 2·63 ; and at 18°, 2·026. J. J. van Laar calculated b of J. D. van der Waals' equation to be $b=0{\cdot}00195$; for a, $\sqrt{a}=0{\cdot}089$; and for the valency attraction, A, $\sqrt{A}=33$.

E. Mitscherlich, and A. Bineau found the **vapour density** to be anomalous. H. St. C. Deville and L. Troost gave 10·6 for the vap. density of arsenic at 563°, and 10·20 at 720°—the calculated value for As_4 is 10·38. J. Mensching and V. Meyer found the vap. density approximates more and more to the value for As_2 as the temp. is raised ; and H. Biltz and V. Meyer obtained 5·543 at 1714°, and 5·451 at

1736°—the calculated value for As_2 is 5·20. H. Erdmann and M. von Unruh found that the effect of yellow arsenic on the b.p. of carbon disulphide is in agreement with the tetratomic mol. As_4. S. Dushman studied the reactions $As_4 \rightleftharpoons 2As_2$; and $As_2 \rightleftharpoons 2As$. G. Preuner and J. Brockmöller's total press., P, at temp. between 300° and 1200° at constant vol., with the amounts of arsenic calculated in grams per c.c. are shown in Fig. 2. The corresponding partial press. for p_4 of As_4; p_2 of As_2; and of As are indicated in Table V. The average number of atoms, i, per mol. is as follows:

800°	P		21	48	93	107	141	242	721 mm.
	i		2·86	3·29	3·60	3·55	3·80	3·70	3·93
1000°	P		31	63	127	143	185	323	913 mm.
	i		2·30	2·57	3·10	3·18	3·42	3·23	3·69
1200°	P		45	111	181	200	266	441	1190 mm.
	i		1·74	1·95	2·36	2·58	2·76	2·70	3·15

TABLE V.—PARTIAL PRESSURES DUE TO As_4-, As_2-, AND As-MOLECULES.

Total press. P mm.	800°			1000°			1200°		
	p_4	p_2	p_1	p_4	p_2	p_1	p_4	p_2	p_1
5	1·7	2·0	1·3	0·8	2·4	1·8	0·4	2·6	2·0
10	4·6	4·0	1·4	1·8	4·9	3·3	0·8	4·0	5·2
20	12·0	6·3	1·7	4·3	9·2	6·5	1·5	8·2	10·3
40	27·6	10·2	2·2	12·2	17·9	9·9	2·4	16·8	20·8
60	44·4	13·2	2·4	23·3	24·6	12·1	7·3	26·3	26·4
80	62·1	15·3	2·6	36·5	30·4	13·1	13·4	32·7	33·9
100	82·9	17·2	2·9	50·6	34·8	14·6	20·2	43·6	37·2
200	174·3	22·3	3·4	125·8	57·4	16·8	64·4	81·9	53·7
300	265·4	30·4	4·2	207·4	73·0	19·6	126·5	112·3	61·2
600	548·6	46·5	4·9	449·1	151·9	21·4	338·1	186·2	75·7
750	696·2	47·6	5·2	529·4	198·4	22·3	452·6	216·4	81·0

The calculated thermal values of the dissociation $As_4 = 2As_2$ are 24,050 cals. between 800° and 1100°; and for $As_2 = 2As$, 28,800 cals. at 800°, and 30,000 cals. between 900° and 1100°. The effect of temp. on the equilibrium constant, K_4 for $As_4 = 2As_2$ is log $(K/760) = -(30,000+2T)/4·57T +1·75$ log $T-2·4$; and K_2 for $As_2 = 2As$ is log $(K_2/760) = -(24,050+2T)/14·57T+1·75$ log $T-2$, where the chemical constant for the As_4-mol. is $-2·4$, and for the As_2-mol., $-2·0$. The dissociation constants are:

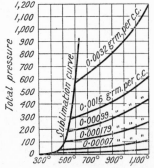

FIG. 2.—Dissociation Pressures of Arsenic Vapour at Different Temperatures.

	800°	900°	1000°	1100°	1200°
K_4	3·50	10·0	24·0	52·7	10·3
K_2	0·52	1·8	5·4	13·9	31·5

Crystalline arsenic is brittle and somewhat hard; the cast metal flattens slightly under the hammer, but is easily broken. J. R. Rydberg[2] gave 3·5 for the hardness of arsenic when that of the diamond is 10; and C. A. Edwards and A. M. Herbert gave 147·0 for Brinnell's hardness number. T. W. Richards found the average compressibility to be $4·5 \times 10^{-6}$ between 100 and 500 megabars at 20°. According to C. I. Burton and W. Marshall, a press. of 300 atm. raises the temp. 0·261°, and when the press. is released the temp. falls 0·248°. The linear coeff. of thermal expansion was found by H. Fizeau to be 0·00000559 at 40°, and 0·00000602 at 50°. A. Bettendorf and A. Wüllner found the specific heat of metallic arsenic between

21° and 66° to be 0·0830, and for amorphous arsenic 0·0758 between 21° and 65°; H. V. Regnault gave for metallic arsenic 0·0814. A. Wigand gave 0·0822 between 0° and 100° for metallic arsenic, and 0·0840 for grey arsenic. J. Dewar gave for the sp. ht. of metallic arsenic 0·0258 between —253° to —196°; T. W. Richards and F. G. Jackson, between —188° and 20°; and R. Ewald gave 0·0619 at —136°; 0·0736 at —39°; and 0·0772 at 28°. A. Bettendorf and A. Wüllner's value for the **atomic heat** is C_p=6·22 between 22° and 68°; A. Wigand, 6·17 between 0° and 100°; and R. Ewald, 5·79 between 1° and 55°. E. Jannettaz found the **heat conductivity** perpendicular to the (111)-face of a crystal of metallic arsenic to be 1½ to 2 times as great as it is parallel to the chief axis. Arsenic volatilizes at a dull red-heat without fusion; J. K. Mitchell found that it does not volatilize at 294°, or even at the m.p. of zinc, but volatilization begins at dull red-heat visible in darkness—*circa* 530°. R. Engel observed no sublimation with metallic arsenic at 360°; but C. Zenghelis showed that even at ordinary temp. arsenic has an appreciable vap. press. for a piece of silver enclosed in the same vessel as arsenic acquires a film of arsenide in a few months. F. Krafft and A. Knocke showed that arsenic in a vacuum commences to volatilize at 96°, and sublimes rapidly at the constant temp. of 325°; under 760 mm. press., it sublimes constantly at 554°. E. G. M. Conechy concluded that metallic arsenic does not volatilize below 446°, but it does so below 457°, he therefore gave 449°–450° for the **sublimation temperature**. H. Erdmann estimated 360°–365°. W. P. A. Jonker gave 616° as the sublimation temp. at 760 mm. press.; O. Ruff and S. Mugdan, 633°; and G. Preuner and J. Brockmöller, 600° at 586 mm., 580° at 430 mm., and 569° at 334°. O. Ruff and B. Bergdahl gave 568° for the **boiling point** of arsenic; W. R. Mott, 616°. J. Johnston calculated 220° at 10⁻³ mm.; 260° at 10⁻² mm.; 310° at 0·1 mm.; 360° at 1 mm.; 430° at 10 mm.; 490° at 50 mm.; 510° at 100 mm.; and 610° at 760 mm. The **vapour pressures** of arsenic, measured by G. Preuner and J. Brockmöller, and G. E. Gibson (in brackets), are :

	400°	469·4°	470°	499·9°	500°	526°	563·9°	633°
Vap. press.	6	(26·0)	28	(67·4)	61	130	(334·1)	760 mm.

The last value is by O. Ruff and co-workers, who also measured the vap. press. of arsenic. S. Horiba gave for the vap. press., p atm., curve of the solid, $T \log p = -7357 + 8·279T$; and for that of the liquid, $T \log p = -2450 + 3·80T$. The curves are shown in Fig. 3. He did not succeed in measuring the vap. press. of black arsenic. J. Johnston gave $\log p = -6670T^{-1} + 10·47$. W. Herz found that the constant c in the equation $\theta_1/\theta_2 = T_1/T_2 + c(\theta_1 - T_1)$ approximates —0·0005882, but has not a constant value—here θ_1 and θ_2 are the b.p. of two liquids at a definite press., and T_1 and T_2 the b.p. of the same liquid at another press. J. W. Retgers observed no signs of fusion in the partly sublimed crystals, but he noticed that corrosion figures were produced. F. Krafft observed that for many metals the interval between the commencement of vaporization and the b.p. in vacuo is nearly equal to the difference between the b.p. in vacuo and the b.p. at ordinary press.; and F. Krafft and A. Knocke observed the same rule applies also to the sublimation of arsenic, and thallium. In vacuo, arsenic commences to volatilize at 96°, and sublimes rapidly at 325°; and under atm. press., it sublimes rapidly at 554°. O. Ruff and B. Bergdahl gave 568° for the b.p. P. N. Laschtschenko found that amorphous arsenic begins to sublime between 270°–280°. N. W. Fischer tried to fuse it in a sealed glass tube, but the tube burst before fusion occurred; but A. N. Guntz and W. Broniewsky even stated

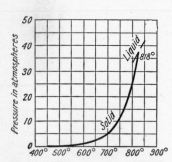

FIG. 3.—Vapour Pressure Curves of Liquid and Solid Arsenic.

that arsenic has not a true m.p. but passes through a viscous state during the transformation from a crystalline solid to a liquid when arsenic is heated in evacuated quartz glass tubes. Above 500°, the fragments of arsenic soften, stick together, and slowly assume the shape of the containing vessel. The melted portion is distinguished from the solid arsenic by its brilliant steel-grey appearance, the solid being dull black. When all the arsenic is melted, a meniscus slowly appears. The same proportion of arsenic is melted by ten minutes' heating at 700° as by twelve hours' heating at 520°. Fusion is extremely slow at 500°, but at 1200°, it is practically instantaneous. At the latter temp., the interior of the quartz tube becomes roughened. The conclusion is drawn that at 500° arsenic forms a very viscous liquid of which the viscosity diminishes with rising temp. H. H. Landolt, and J. W. Mallet were more successful, for they were able to melt it in sealed tubes and they found the **melting point** lies between that of antimony and that of silver : and this agrees with W. P. A. Jonker's statement that arsenic does not show any signs of fusion when heated in a sealed tube at 800°. S. F. Schemtschuschny gave 624° for the m.p. of arsenic ; W. Guertler and M. Pirani, and P. Jolibois, 850°±10° ; R. Goubau, 817° ; W. R. Mott, 800° ; and P. N. Laschtschenko, 822°–868°—*vide* Fig. 1. H. Rassow gave 818° ; S. Horiba, 818° to 822° ; and W. Heike obtained 830°, but his later work showed that 814·5° is nearer the mark. W. Guertler and M. Pirani gave 800° for the best representative value, but this is too low. H. Carlsohn said that the m.p. of arsenic compounds does not follow the additive rule. S. Horiba gave for the **triple point,** 36·5 atm. press. and 822°. L. Rolla estimated 929° for the m.p. of arsenic if it is melted under atm. press. The latent **heat of fusion** of arsenic is not known. S. Horiba calculated from the vap. press. curve, 22·4 cals. per mol. When sublimed in a sealed tube, arsenic melts when its b.p. does not coincide with the temp. of fusion ; in other words, at this temp. we have to deal with a triple point in the system : solid, liquid, and gaseous arsenic. R. de Forcrand calculated the **heat of vaporization** to be 5128 cals. ; J. Johnston, 30·5 cals. per mol. ; and A. Henglein, gave 0·349 cals. for the mol. heat of evaporation. S. Horiba calculated 11·2 cals. per mol. for the liquid to gas transition, and 33·6 cals. per mol. for the **heat of sublimation** for the solid to gas transition. H. Rassow estimated that the **critical temperature** is over 1400°. P. N. Laschtschenko's observations on the thermal effect with cooling arsenic are summarized in Fig. 1 ; he gave 7 cals. per gram for the **heat of transformation** of metallic to yellow arsenic. The heat effect observed by S. F. Schemtschuschny was probably due to this transformation and not to the heat of fusion. According to T. Petersen, the heat of transformation of yellow into metallic arsenic is 33·4 Cals. ; and for mirror arsenic into metallic arsenic, 10 Cals. M. Berthelot and R. Engel gave for the heat of the reaction: $2As+5Br_{2aq.}+5H_2O=As_2O_{5aq.}+10HBr+83·00$ Cals., with metallic arsenic, and 84·10 Cals. with mirror arsenic. T. Petersen found the **heat of oxidation** to be (2As,3O)=1568·3 Cals. with metallic arsenic, 1547·4 Cals. with mirror arsenic, and 1635·0 Cals. with yellow arsenic. H. Collins, and J. C. Thomlinson made some speculations on the heat of formation of some arsenic compounds.

J. H. Gladstone [3] gave 0·2050 for the **refractory power** of arsenic vapour, and A. Haagen, 0·2696 ; J. H. Gladstone found the **refraction equivalents** to be 15·8 ; and A. Haagen, 20·22 for the $H\alpha$-line, and 18·84 for the A-line. C. Cuthbertson and E. P. Metcalfe gave 1·001550 for the **refractive index** of arsenic vap. for light of wave-length $\lambda=5893$; and for $\lambda=5460$, 1·001580. J. E. Calthrop studied the relation between the at. vol. and the index of refraction. F. Gryszkiewicz-Trochimovsky and S. F. Sikorsky found that the at. refractions of arsenic in combination with aliphatic radicles are 10·8, 10·9, and 11·3 for the $H\alpha$-, D-, and $H\beta$-lines respectively. The at. refractions of the arylarsines increase with the number of aryl radicles combined with the arsenic atom.

J. Joubert [4] found that arsenic exhibits **phosphorescence** if it be heated to 200° and some oxygen is present. According to L. Bloch, the phosphorescence of arsenic at 200°, like that of sulphur and phosphorus, is accompanied by oxidation, by which arsenic trioxide is produced. As in the case of sulphur, no ionization occurs, and there is also no formation of ozone, which is produced by both sulphur and phosphorus. The product of oxidation of arsenic, either phosphorescently or with flame, always contains arsenic trioxide, just as some phosphoric oxide and sulphur trioxide are always produced in the parallel cases. The arsenic oxide, which may amount to $\frac{1}{30}$th of the whole, seems to be formed directly from arsenic, since arsenious oxide cannot be oxidized under the conditions. It is assumed conversely that arsenic oxide is the sole original product, and this is mainly decomposed into arsenious oxide by a secondary change. The synthesis of arsenic trichloride without incandescence is unaccompanied by ionization.

H. Erdmann and R. Reppert found yellow arsenic to be unstable in **violet or ultra-violet light,** and in red-light it is slowly converted into metallic arsenic ; **radium rays** have no effect on the speed of conversion. W. Thomson found that yellow arsenic is blackened almost instantly when exposed to a magnesium light. The rate of transformation in the dark is quickened by a rise of temp. ; and at the temp. of liquid air, the yellow form remains unchanged for hours. A. L. Hughes found that arsenic exhibits a **photoelectric effect** giving off electrons when illuminated by the light from a mercury lamp. The longest wave-length effective in exciting the emission of photoelectrons from arsenic was $\lambda=2360$.

J. Piccard and E. Thomas [5] discussed the colour of arsenic ions. According to R. Bunsen,[6] arsenic and its compounds tinge the upper part of the colourless gas-flame pale blue. The **flame spectrum** was examined by V. Volpicelli, W. N. Hartley, W. N. Hartley and H. Ramage, C. de Watteville, etc. J. C. McLennan and co-workers said that the flame spectrum of arsenic consists of five lines 3266, 2860, 2780, 2350, and 2288 A., and four bands with heads at 2634·5, 2570, 2503·5, and 2437·2 A. G. Kirchhoff first examined the **spark spectrum** of arsenic, and observations have since been made by T. R. Robinson, W. A. Miller, J. Herpertz, E. O. Hulburt, W. Huggins, J. Plücker and J. W. Hittorf, R. Thalén, R. Capron, A. Ditte, G. Ciamician, R. J. Lang, O. W. Huntington, W. N. Hartley and co-workers, A. de Gramont, E. Demarçay, L. and E. Bloch, F. Exner and E. Haschek, A. Hagenbach and H. Konen, H. H. Pollock, J. M. Eder and E. Valenta, etc. The more prominent lines in the visible spectrum have the wave-length 6170 A. ; 6111 and 6022 in the orange-yellow ; 5651 in the yellowish-green ; 5559, 5499, and 5332 in the green. There are also numerous lines in the ultra-violet. A. de Gramont, and W. N. Hartley and H. W. Moss investigated *les raies ultimes* of the arsenic spectrum ; E. O. Hulburt, and M. C. W. Buffam and H. J. C. Ireton, the under-water spark spectrum of the salts. The **arc spectrum** was examined by H. Kayser and C. Runge, and F. Exner and E. Haschek; the **ultra-violet spectrum,** by J. M. Eder, V. Schumann, R. J. Lang, L. and E. Bloch, W. A. Miller, and F. Exner and E. Haschek; and the **absorption spectrum** of the vapour by J. C. McLennan and A. B. McLay, J. N. Lockyer, A. Terenin, B. Rosen, A. E. Ruark and co-workers, and J. J. Dobbie and J. J. Fox. A. Terenin examined the spectrum of the light emitted by arsenic vapour at 1100°. According to J. Formanek, soln. of arsenic salts give no perceptible absorption spectrum, and there is no reaction with alkanna. The absorption arc spectrum of arsenic was found by J. C. McLennan and co-workers to have four, strong, univalent bands, the sharp edges of which were towards the red, and which occurred at wavelengths 2634·5, 2570·0, 2503·5, and 2437·31 A. The effect of *pressure* was examined by G. Ciamician, and W. J. Humphreys ; and of *self-induction,* by A. de Gramont. The **series spectrum** was studied by J. C. McLennan and A. B. McLay, B. Rosen, G. Ciamician, T. van Lohuizen, and A. Fowler, but no series have yet been identified, though H. Kayser and C. Runge, and A. E. Ruark and co-workers observed lines with a constant difference in the spectra of arsenic, antimony, and bismuth. The **X-ray spectrum** was examined by E. Wagner, etc. The K-series was found by W. Duane and H. Fuh-Hu, H. R. Robinson and A. M. Cassie, A. Leide, Y. H. Woo,

R. Thoraeus, and M. Siegbahn to have the lines 1·17749 A. for a_2a' ; 1·17345 A. for a_1a ; 1·052 A. for $\beta_1\beta$; and 1·038 A. for $\beta_2\gamma$; and the L-series, by M. Siegbahn, H. Hirata, E. Friman, D. Coster and F. P. Mulder, M. Siegbahn and E. Friman, R. Thoraeus, A. Leide, L. H. Martin, and E. Hjalmar, to have the lines 9·6503 A. for a_1a ; 9·6173 A. for a_3a'' ; and 9·3940 A. for $\beta_1\beta$. D. Coster and F. P. Mulder also studied the M- and N-series ; and A. L. Foley, the effect on the spectrum of exposing arsenic to X-rays or to ultra-violet light. J. E. P. Wagstaff gave $4·36 \times 10^{12}$ for the **vibration frequency**, and W. Herz, $4·53 \times 10^{12}$.

According to P. D. Foote and co-workers, the **ionization potential** of arsenic vapour is 11·54 volts ; and the inelastic collision potential 4·69 volts, and the **resonance potential**, 4·7 volts. K. T. Compton gave 3·49 to 4·5 volts. The subject was discussed by G. Piccardi, and B. Rosen. C. G. Barkla and co-workers [7] found that the K-series of **X-rays** of wave-length 1·172 A., from the arsenic radiator, have the ratios of the mass absorption coeff., μ, divided by the density of the absorber for carbon, 2·49 ; magnesium, 19·3 ; iron, 134 ; nickel, 166 ; copper, 176 ; tin, 131·5 ; platinum, 105·7 ; and gold, 106·1 ; while W. H. Bragg and H. L. Porter found for aluminium, 23·6, and for zinc, 186. E. A. Owen found for the absorption coeff., μ, for gases at 0° and 760 mm., with the same rays, air, 0·00592 ; carbon dioxide, 0·00988 ; sulphur dioxide, 0·0548 ; and C. G. Barkla and V. Collier, for ethyl bromide, 0·028. T. E. Aurén gave 128 for the absorption coeff. when that of hydrogen is unity. The effect of X-rays in ejecting high-speed electrons from arsenic (oxide) was examined by R. Whiddington. A. L. Foley examined the effect of X-rays on arsenic, but with no definite results.

P. E. Shaw and C. S. Jex [8] found the **tribolectricity** with glass is negative. According to H. Erdmann and R. Reppert, metallic arsenic is a conductor of electricity, but the yellow, grey, and brown forms of arsenic are non-conductors. A. Günther-Schulze, and K. F. Herzfeld studied the metallic conduction of arsenic. A. Matthiessen and M. von Bose found the **electrical conductivity** of metallic arsenic at 0° to be 0·00285 mho. E. Frank found the resistance of grey arsenic to be indefinitely large when cold, 40,000 ohms at 190° ; 30,000 ohms at 200° ; 15,000 ohms at 220° ; 7000 ohms at 240° ; and 4100 ohms at 255°. When kept for 20 minutes at 260°, the resistance was 3400 ohms ; after 70 minutes, 1000 ohms ; after 90 minutes, 250 ohms ; and after 170 minutes, 11 ohms. The data were reviewed by A. Schulze. The **overvoltage** of hydrogen in a cell consisting of a platinum anode, arsenic cathode, and N-H_2SO_4 was found by V. B. Marquis to be 0·379–0·478 volt ; and A. Thiel and W. Hammerschmidt gave 0·369 volt. G. Grube and H. Kelber found that with the arsenic cathode, hydrogen begins to come off in $2N$-H_2SO_4 at 0·284 volt ; in $0·1N$-H_2SO_4 at 0·358 volt ; N-NaOH at 1·016 volts ; and in $0·1N$-NaOH at 0·948 volt—$vide\ infra$, arsine. A. Günther-Schulze studied the cathodic spluttering of arsenic. A. Matthiessen and M. von Bose gave for the **electrical resistance** at $\theta°$ between 12° and 100°, $R = R_0(1-0·0038996\theta+0·0588790\theta^2)$. P. W. Bridgman found 0·0038 for the temp. coeff. of the electrical resistance ; A. Matthiessen and M. von Bose gave 0·00076 between 0° and 95°. The coeff. is similar to that of a number of metals both with respect to magnitude and sign. Arsenic acquires neither the abnormal sign of the coeff. of its neighbours bismuth and antimony on the one side, nor the abnormally high coeff. of black phosphorus on the other. A. Matthiessen found the **thermoelectric power of arsenic** and lead to be —13·56 microvolts. N. C. Little gave the results indicated in Table VI for the **thermomagnetic effect** and the **galvanomagnetic effect** expressed in absolute electromagnetic units.

B. Neumann gave —0·550 volt for the absolute electrode potential of arsenic in N-$AsCl_3$. N. T. M. Wilsmore gave —0·293 volt for the **electrode potential** of arsenic in contact with a normal salt soln.—when the hydrogen electrode is zero. V. B. Marquis found the normal electrode potential of arsenic, calculated from the e.m.f. of the cell Hg, HgCl | LiCl in absolute alcohol | $0·176M$-$AsCl_3$ in absolute alcohol | As=0·153 volt. This gave 0·040 volt for the arsenic-alcohol potential,

TABLE VI.—THERMOMAGNETIC AND GALVANOMAGNETIC EFFECTS IN ARSENIC, ANTIMONY, AND BISMUTH.

	Arsenic.	Antimony.	Bismuth.
Specific resistance . . .	4.60×10^4	4.05×10^4	16×10^4
Thermal conductivity . .	3.68×10^6	1.67×10^6	$.81 \times 10^6$
Peltier heat against lead . .	3.80×10^5	0.78×10^5	-21.6×10^5
Thomson heat . . .	3.33×10^3	2.34×10^3	0.94×10^3
Hall coefficient . . .	4.52×10^{-2}	21.9×10^{-2}	-633×10^{-2}
Nernst coefficient . . .	2.25×10^{-3}	17.6×10^{-3}	178×10^{-3}
Ettingshausen coefficient . .	1.75×10^{-7}	19.4×10^{-7}	350×10^{-7}
Righi-Leduci coefficient . .	4.15×10^{-7}	20.1×10^{-7}	-20.5×10^{-7}

0·111 volt for the arsenic-water potential, and 0·138 volt for the electrode potential. This places arsenic between hydrogen and copper in the **electrochemical series**. M. le Blanc found the electrochemical series to be : Pb, Sn, H, Sb, Bi, As, Cu, Ag, Hg ; and W. Ostwald, Pb, H, Sb, Bi, **As,** Cu, Hg, Ag, Pd. L. Kahlenberg and J. V. Steinle showed that the nature of the electrolyte determines the relative position of the metals in the electrochemical series—especially about the middle of the series. F. W. Bergstrom gave for the series in liquid ammonia : Pb, Bi, Sn, Sb, **As,** P, Te, Se, S, I. V. Bayerle found that the cathodic deposition of arsenic does not show reversible shifts on the polarization curves. B. Neumann gave —0·550 volt for the absolute electrode potential of arsenic against a normal chloride soln. ; J. von Zawidsky found —0·539 volt ; M. le Blanc and D. Reichenstein found the potentials of arsenic in soln. of potassium hydroxide, and sulphuric acid ; and N. A. Puschin, the potentials of alloys of arsenic with tin or lead. E. W. Washburn and E. K. Strachan gave 0·293 volt on the assumption that the potential of the normal iodine electrode is 0·256 volt, and R. Schumann, —0·2375 volt for a soln. of meta-arsenious acid : $As + 2H_2O = HAsO_2 + 3H·$. L. Kahlenberg and J. V. Steinle found the electrode potential of various forms of arsenic in a soln. of arsenic trichloride, containing a gram eq. per litre, varied from 0·544 to 0·554 volt ; in arsenic triiodide, from 0·533 to 0·544 volt ; in arsenic tribromide, intermediate between that of the chloride and iodide—viz. 0·544 volt ; in N-NaCl sat. with arsenic trioxide, 0·360–0·365 volt ; in 0·5N-HCl sat. with copper arsenate, 0·367 volt ; with copper arsenite, 0·365 ; Paris green, 0·351 ; ammonium polysulphide, —0·065 volt ; 0·5 eq. arsenic pentasulphide in ammonium polysulphide, 0·052 volt ; and in soln. with 0·5, 0·25, and 0·125 mol. wt. of arsanilic acid per litre, respectively 0·152, 0·160, and 0·167 volt ; parahydroxyarsenic acid, respectively 0·090, 0·095, and 0·100 volt ; glycerine arsanilic acid, respectively 0·141, 0·146, and 0·152 volt ; secondary arsanilic acid, respectively 0·211, 0·223, and 0·234 volt ; and with acetoarsanilic acid, respectively 0·129, 0·141, and 0·152 volt. H. von Steinwehr gave $1·6 \times 10^{-26}$ atm. for the **electrolytic solution pressure** $As \rightarrow As^{···}$. According to D. Reichinstein, arsenic dissolves from the anode in acidic and alkaline soln. ; and S. Berberich found that with a current of 40 milliampères, at room temp., a 100 per cent. yield of arsenious acid is formed in acidic or alkaline soln.—but in acidic soln., traces of arsenic acid are also formed. When the current is increased, a resistant film is formed on the anode, and this appears to increase the proportion of arsenic acid which is produced. C. Luckow found that arsenic can be **electro-deposited** as a dark brown or black mass resembling graphite, and at the cathode arsine is simultaneously evolved. A. Classen and M. A. von Reiss were unable to precipitate arsenic quantitatively by electrolysis from aq. soln., or in the presence of hydrochloric acid, ammonium oxalate, or alkali sulphides. Arsenic in every case was lost as arsine, or else a part remained in soln. undecomposed. G. Vortmann said that if the separated arsenic be collected by a mercury cathode, the loss as arsine is prevented. The electrodeposition of arsenic in the presence of other metals was examined by E. F. Smith and co-workers : P. E. Jannasch and V. Wasowicz. L. K. Frankel,

O. Piloty, B. Neumann, N. Revay, H. J. S. Sand and J. E. Hackford, S. R. Trotman, A. Hollard and L. Bertiaux, A. Classen, S. C. Schmucker, L. W. McCay, etc. V. Bayerle found that the cathodic deposition of arsenic at the dropping mercury cathode is complex in both acidic and alkaline soln., and does not show reversible shifts on the polarization curve. V. Bayerle found that in the electrolysis of soln. of arsenic trioxide in hydrochloric acid a tenfold increase in the H-ion conc. raised the potential 0·120 volts, but changes in the deposition of arsenic by changing the conc. of the arsenic in the same acid are small. The main part of the current is concerned with the evolution of hydrogen, some arsine and arsenic may be formed. In the electrolysis of soln. of arsenic trioxide in alkali-lye, the reduction to arsenic at the cathode is probably a secondary effect produced by nascent hydrogen. The complexity of the cathode processes prevented conclusions being drawn as to the ionic behaviour of arsenious acid. T. Moore proposed to determine arsenic in soln. by converting it all into arsine electrolytically. This method was also used by T. E. Thorpe, and many others. E. T. Wherry found arsenic to be a poor **radio-detector**.

K. Honda [9] found the **magnetic susceptibility** of diamagnetic arsenic to be $-0·3 \times 10^{-6}$ mass units at $18°$–$200°$; and M. Owen gave $-0·30 \times 10^{-6}$. B. H. Wilsdon examined the magnetic properties of arsenic. According to P. Pascal, in completely sat. derivatives, the diamagnetism of arsenic and of oxyarsenious groupings is considerably less than that of arsenic in higher states of oxidation, but these groupings have a constant magnetic individuality from one compound to the next, namely, $As = -209 \times 10^{-7}$; $AsO = -250 \times 10^{-7}$; $AsO_3 = -351 \times 10^{-7}$. These numbers form an arithmetical progression, which is taken as evidence that an atom of arsenic has the same degree of saturation in the arsines, oxyarsines, derivatives of arsenobenzene, organic arsenites, and minerals. The oxygen serves merely as a bond between the metalloids on the one hand and the metals, hydrogen, and organic radicals of the rest of the molecule on the other. If arsines are denoted as AsR_3, the oxyarsines are $AsR_2(OR)$, and arsenites $As(OM)_3$. In derivatives of saturated arsenic, the diamagnetism of the following radicals forms an arithmetical progression also, but arsenic is excluded from it: $As = -430 \times 10^{-7}$; $AsO = -428 \times 10^{-7}$; $AsO_2 = -474 \times 10^{-7}$; and $AsO_3 = -518 \times 10^{-7}$. In the oxides of arsines, the cacodylates, the arsonates, and arsenates, therefore, the oxygen atom is distinctly similar to the oxygen of aldehydes and ketones, since it hardly represses the diamagnetism. The corresponding formulæ are then R_3AsO, $R_2AsO(OH)$, $RAsO(OH)_2$, and $AsO(OH)_3$, which recall phosphonic and phosphoric acids. Arsenic in combination thus possesses two atomic susceptibilities according to the degree of saturation of the compounds.

REFERENCES.

[1] A. L. Lavoisier, *Traité élémentaire de chimie*, Paris, 2. 254, 1793; A. Russell and H. F. Harwood, *Min. Mag.*, 20. 299, 1925; M. J. Brisson, *Pésanteur spécifique des corps*, Paris, 1787; A. Breithaupt, *Vollständiges Charakteristik der Mineralsystem*, Dresden, 261, 1832; *Schweigger's Journ.*, 52. 167, 1828; *Journ. prakt. Chem.*, (1), 4. 249, 1835; (1), 11. 151, 1837; (1), 16. 475, 1839; L. Elsner, *ib.*, (1), 22. 344, 1841; F. von Kobell, (1), 33. 495, 1844; N. J. B. G. Guibourt, *Journ. Chim. Méd.*, (1), 2. 55, 1826; W. Herapath, *Phil. Mag.*, (1), 64. 321, 1824; W. L. Bragg, *ib.*, (6), 40. 169, 1920; C. J. B. Karsten, *Schweigger's Journ.*, 65. 394, 1832; L. Playfair and J. P. Joule, *Mem. Chem. Soc.*, 3. 72, 1848; J. W. Mallet, *Chem. News*, 26. 97, 1872; R. Engel, *Compt. Rend.*, 96. 498, 1314, 1883; *Bull. Soc. Chim.*, (2), 50. 194, 1888; W. Spring, *Bull. Acad. Belg.*, (3), 5. 229, 1883; *Ber.*, 16. 326, 1883; G. E. Linck, *ib.*, 32. 888, 1899; 33. 2284, 1900; 41. 822, 1908; *Zeit. anorg. Chem.*, 56. 400, 1908; *Grundriss der Kristallographie*, Jena, 1915; P. P. Ewald and C. Hermann, *Zeit. Kryst.*, 65. Suppl., 27, 1927; F. Stromeyer, *Comment. Soc. Gött.*, 16. 141, 1808; T. Turner, *Elements of Chemistry*, London, 455, 1842; V. R. von Zepharovich, *Sitzber. Akad. Wien*, 71. 272, 1875; C. W. Zenger, *ib.*, 44. 309, 1861; G. Rose, *Sitzber. Akad. Berlin*, 72, 1849; *Pogg. Ann.*, 77. 146, 1849; J. W. Hittorf, *ib.*, 126. 218, 1865; A. Frenzel, *Neues Jahrb. Min.*, 677, 1874; T. Bergman, *De arsenico*, Upsala, 1777; J. P. Cooke, *Amer. Journ. Science*, (2), 31. 192, 1861; M. L. Frankenheim, *System der Krystalle*, Breslau, 28, 1842; J. W. Retgers, *Zeit. anorg. Chem.*, 4. 413, 1893; G. E. Linck and H. Jung, *ib.*, 147. 288, 1925; H. Jung, *Centr. Min.*, 107, 1926; A. Wigand,

Ann. Physik, (4), **22**. 64, 1907 ; A. Bettendorf, *Liebig's Ann.*, **144**. 112, 1867 ; A. Geuther, *ib.*, **240**. 208, 1887 ; H. Erdmann and R. Reppert, *ib.*, **361**. 7, 1908 ; R. Reppert, *Ueber gelbes, braunes, und graues Arsen*, Halle, 1907 ; T. Petersen, *Zeit. phys. Chem.*, **8**. 607, 189 ; H. G. Grimm, *ib.*, **122**. 177, 1926 ; H. Ludwig, *Arch. Pharm.*, (2), **97**. 23, 1889 ; M. L. Huggins, *Amer. Journ. Science*, (5), **5**. 303, 1923 ; *Journ. Amer. Chem. Soc.*, **44**. 1841, 1922 ; *Phys. Rev.*, (2), **19**. 369, 1922 ; (2), **28**. 1086, 1926 ; V. Kohlschütter, E. Frank, and C. Ehlers, *Liebig's Ann.*, **400**. 268, 1913 ; E. Frank, *Zur Kenntnis des braunen und grauen Arsens*, Bern, 1912 ; P. N. Laschtschenko, *Journ. Chem. Soc.*, **121**. 972, 1922 ; W. F. de Jong and H. W. V. Willems, *Physica*, **7**. 74, 1927 ; E. N. Gapon, *Zeit. Physik*, **44**. 535, 1927 ; A. Stock and W. Siebert, *Ber.*, **37**. 4572, 1904 ; **38**. 966, 1905 ; W. Siebert, *Zur Kenntnis der Modifikationen des Arsens und Antimons*, Berlin, 1905 ; O. Mügge, *Neues Jahrb. Min.*, ii, **40**, 1884 ; 1, 183, 1886 ; *Tschermak's Mitt.*, (2), **19**. 105, 1900 ; A. de Schulten, *Bull. Soc. Min.*, **26**. 117, 1903 ; F. P. Leroux, *Ann. Chim. Phys.*, (3), **61**. 415, 1861 ; *Compt. Rend.*, **51**. 171, 1860 ; H. St. C. Deville and L. Troost, *ib.*, **56**. 591, 1863 ; A. Bineau, *ib.*, **49**. 799, 1859 ; R. de Forcrand, *ib.*, **133**. 513, 1901 ; A. Schuller, *Chem. Ztg.*, **13**. 271. 1888 ; J. Mensching and V. Meyer, *Ber.*, **20**. 1833, 1887 ; H. Biltz and V. Meyer, *ib.*, **22**. 726, 1889 ; H. Biltz, *Zeit. phys. Chem.*, **19**. 385, 1896 ; P. Möller, *Ueber den roten Phosphor und die eutropische Reihe Phosphor, Arsen, Antimon, Wismuth*, Langensalza, 1908 ; R. Neumann, *Beiträge zur Kenntnis der Phosphor-Arsen-Antimon-Gruppe*, Heidelberg, 1900 ; G. Preuner and J. Brockmöller, *Zeit. phys. Chem.*, **81**. 129, 1912 ; J. Brockmöller, *Dissociationsisothermen des Selens, Schwefels, Arsens, und Phosphors*, Kiel, 1912 ; E. Mitscherlich, *Ann. Chim. Phys.*, (2), **24**. 270, 1825 ; (2), **55**. 5, 1833 ; A. J. Bradley, *Phil. Mag.*, (6), **47**. 657, 1924 ; R. W. James, *ib.*, (6), **42**. 193, 1921 ; R. W. James and N. Tunstall, *ib.*, (6), **40**. 233, 1920 ; S. von Olshausen, *Zeit. Kryst.*, **61**. 463, 1925 ; J. J. van Laar, *Die Zustandsgleichung von Gasen und Flüssigkeiten*, Leipzig, 1924 ; *Proc. Acad. Amsterdam*, **18**. 1220, 1915 ; **19**. 2, 1916 ; R. M. Bozorth, *Journ. Amer. Chem. Soc.*, **45**. 1621, 1923 ; S. Dushman, *ib.*, **43**. 397, 1921 ; J. Nicklès, *Mém. Acad. Nancy*, 351, 1860 ; 126, 1861 ; *Journ. Chim. Pharm.*, (3), **37**. 436, 1860 ; (3), **39**. 116, 1861 ; (3), **40**. 191, 277, 1861 ; (3), **41**. 142, 1862 ; *Ann. Chim. Phys.*, (3), **62**. 230, 1861 ; *Compt. Rend.*, **50**. 872, 1860 ; **51**. 1097, 1860 ; **52**. 396, 1861 ; I. I. Saslowsky, *Zeit. anorg. Chem.*, **145**. 315, 1926 ; C. del Fresno, *ib.*, **152**. 25, 1926 ; H. Erdmann and M. von Unruh, *ib.*, **32**. 457, 1902 ; M. von Unruh, *Ueber gelbes Arsen*, Halle, 1901.

[2] C. I. Burton and W. Marshall, *Proc. Roy. Soc.*, **50**. 130, 1891 ; A. Bettendorf and A. Wüllner, *Pogg. Ann.*, **131**. 293, 1867 ; H. V. Regnault, *Ann. Chim. Phys.*, (2), **73**. 39, 1840 ; H. Fizeau, *Compt. Rend.*, **68**. 1125, 1869 ; A. Wigand, *Ann. Physik*, (4), **22**. 64, 91, 1907 ; R. Engel, *Compt. Rend.*, **96**. 497, 1314, 1883 ; M. Berthelot and R. Engel, *ib.*, **110**. 498, 1890 ; P. Jolibois, *ib.*, **152**. 1767, 1911 ; **158**. 121, 1914 ; R. Goulau, *ib.*, **158**. 121, 1914 ; R. de Forcrand, *ib.*, **133**. 513, 1901 ; J. W. Mallet, *Chem. News*, **26**. 97, 1872 ; E. G. M. Conechy, *ib.*, **41**. 181, 1880 ; H. F. Landolt, *Neues Jahrb. Min.*, 733, 1859 ; J. W. Retgers, *Zeit. anorg. Chem.*, **4**. 403, 1893 ; W. P. A. Jonker, *ib.*, **62**. 91, 1909 ; H. Rassow, *ib.*, **114**. 131, 1920 ; A. N. Guntz and W. Broniewsky, *Bull. Soc. Chim.*, (4), **1**. 977, 1907 ; W. Heike, *Verh. deut. phys. Ges.*, **16**. 369, 1914 ; *Zeit. anorg. Chem.*, **118**. 254, 1921 ; *Internat. Zeit. Metallog.*, **6**. 168, 1914 ; W. Heike and A. Leroux, *Zeit. anorg. Chem.*, **92**. 125, 1915 ; S. F. Schemtschuschny, *Journ. Russ. Phys. Chem. Soc.*, **39**. 1463, 1907 ; P. N. Laschtschenko, *Journ. Chem. Soc.*, **121**. 972, 1922 ; J. R. Rydberg, *Zeit. phys. Chem.*, **33**. 353, 1900 ; J. K. Mitchell, *Amer. Journ. Science*, (1), **10**. 121, 1832 ; N. W. Fischer, *Schweigger's Journ.*, **6**. 236, 1812 ; **12**. 155, 1814 ; **39**. 364, 1823 ; L. Rolla, *Atti Accad. Lincei*, (5), i, 616, 693, 1914 ; W. Heike, *Internat. Zeit. Metallog.*, **6**. 168, 1914 ; *Zeit. anorg. Chem.*, **117**. 147, 1921 ; **118**. 254, 1921 ; W. Heike and A. Leroux, *ib.*, **92**. 119, 1915 ; O. Ruff and S. Mugdan, *Zeit. anorg. Chem.*, **117**. 147, 1921 ; O. Ruff and B. Bergdahl, *ib.*, **106**. 76, 1919 ; H. Erdmann, *ib.*, **32**. 437, 1902 ; G. Preuner and J. Brockmöller, *Zeit. phys. Chem.*, **81**. 129, 1913 ; T. W. Richards and F. G. Jackson, *ib.*, **70**. 414, 1910 ; T. Petersen, *ib.*, **8**. 603, 1891 ; G. E. Gibson, *Einige Dampf-druck- und Dampfdichtebestimmungen mit einem neuen Quarzmanometer*, Breslau, 1911 ; J. Dewar, *Proc. Roy. Soc.*, **89**. A, 158, 1913 ; R. Ewald, *Ann. Physik*, (4), **44**. 1213, 1914 ; F. Krafft, *Ber.*, **38**. 262, 1905 ; F. Krafft and A. Knocke, *ib.*, **42**. 202, 1909 ; J. C. Thomlinson, *Chem. News*, **98**. 226, 1908 ; **99**. 133, 1909 ; E. Jannettaz, *Compt. Rend.*, **114**. 1352, 1892 ; *Bull. Soc. Min.*, **15**. 133, 1892 ; A. Henglein, *Zeit. Elektrochem.*, **26**. 431, 1920 ; W. Herz, *ib.*, **25**. 45, 1919 ; W. Guertler and M. Pirani, *Zeit. Metallkunde*, **11**. 1, 1919 ; C. Zenghelis, *Zeit. phys. Chem.*, **57**. 90, 1906 ; S. Horiba, *ib.*, **106**. 295, 1923 ; C. A. Edwards and A. M. Herbert, *Metal Ind.*, **18**. 221, 1921 ; *Journ. Inst. Metals*, **25**. 175, 1921 ; C. A. Edwards, *Proc. Manchester Assoc. Eng.*, 225, 1919 ; T. W. Richards, *Journ. Amer. Chem. Soc.*, **37**. 1643, 1915 ; W. R. Mott, *Trans. Amer. Electrochem. Soc.*, **34**. 255, 1918 ; H. Collins, *Chem. News*, **129**. 205, 1914 ; H. Carlsohn, *Ber.*, **59**. B, 1916, 1926 ; J. Johnston, *Journ. Ind. Eng. Chem.*, **9**. 873, 1917.

[3] A. Haagen, *Pogg. Ann.*, **131**. 117, 1867 ; J. H. Gladstone, *Proc. Roy. Soc.*, **16**. 439, 1868 ; **18**. 49, 1870 ; *Journ. Chem. Soc.*, **23**. 101, 1870 ; *Phil. Trans.*, **160**. 9, 1870 ; *Amer. Journ. Science*, (3), **29**. 57, 1885 ; C. Cuthbertson and E. P. Metcalfe, *Phil. Trans.*, **207**. A, 135, 1907 ; *Proc. Roy. Soc.*, **79**. A, 202, 1907 ; J. E. Calthrop, *Phil. Mag.*, (6), **47**. 772, 1924 ; F. Gryszkiewicz-Trochimovsky and S. F. Sikorsky, *Rocz. Chem.*, **7**. 54, 1927 ; *Bull. Soc. Chem.*, (4), **41**. 1570, 1927.

[4] J. Joubert, *Sur la phosphorescence du phosphore*, Paris, 1874 ; *Compt. Rend.*, **78**. 1853, 1874 ; L. Bloch, *ib.*, **149**. 775, 1909 ; H. Erdmann and R. Reppert, *Liebig's Ann.*, **361**. 1, 1908 ; W. Thomson, *Mem. Manchester Lit. Phil. Soc.*, **50**. 12, 1906 ; A. L. Hughes, *Phil. Trans.*, **212**. A, 205, 1912.

⁵ J. Piccard **and** E. Thomas, *Helvetica Chim. Acta*, **6**. 1040, 1923.

⁶ R. Bunsen, *Liebig's Ann.*, **138**. 257, 1861 ; T. R. Robinson, *Phil. Trans.*, **152**. 939, 1862 ; W. A. Miller, *ib.*, **152**. 861, 1862 ; W. Huggins, *ib.*. **154**. 139, 1864 : J. Plücker and J. W. Hittorf, *ib.*, **155**. 1, 1865 ; R. J. Lang, *ib.*, **224**. A, 371, 1924 ; W. N. Hartley and H. W. Moss, *Proc. Roy. Soc.*, **87**. A, 38, 1912 ; W. N. Hartley and W. E. Adeney, *ib.*, **175**. 63, 1884 ; W. N. Hartley, *ib.*, **175**. 325, 1884 ; **185**. A, 161, 1894 ; *Proc. Roy. Soc.*, **78**. 403, 1907 ; *Trans. Roy. Dublin Soc.*, (2), **1**. 231, 1882 ; W. N. Hartley and H. Ramage, *ib.*, (2), **7**. 339, 1901 ; A. de Gramont, *Analyse spectrale directe des minéraux*, Paris, 1895 ; *Compt. Rend.*, **118**. 591, 746, 1894 ; **134**. 1205, 1902 ; **146**. 1260, 1908 ; A. Leide, *ib.*, **180**. 1203, 1925 ; L. and E. Bloch, *Journ. Phys. Rad.*, **2**. 229, 1921 ; *Compt. Rend.*, **158**. 1416, 1914 ; **171**. 709, 1920 ; A. Ditte, *ib.*, **73**. 738, 1871 ; V. Volpicelli, *Atti Accad. Lincei*, (1), **16**. 91, 1862 ; E. Paterno and A. Mazzucchelli, *ib.*, (5), **17**. ii, 428, 1908 ; R. Thalén, *Om Spectralanalyse*, Upsala, 1866 ; *Nova Acta. Soc. Upsala*, (3), **6**. 9, 1868 ; *Ann. Chim. Phys.*, (4), **18**. 244, 1869 ; T. Brasack, *Abhand. Nat. Ges. Halle*, **9**. 1, 1864 ; R. Capron, *Photographed Spectra*, London, 1877 ; V. Schumann, *Phot. Runds.*, **41**. 71, 1890 ; G. Kirchhoff, *Sitzber. Akad. Berlin*, 63, 1861 ; 227, 1863 ; H. Kayser and G. Runge, *ib.*, **3**, 1893 ; *Wied. Ann.*, **52**. 93, 1894 ; O. W. Huntington, *Amer. Journ. Science*, (3), **22**. 214, 1881 ; G. Ciamician, *Sitzber. Akad. Wien*, **78**. 867, 1878 ; **82**. 425, 1880 ; F. Exner and E. Haschek, *ib.*, **110**. 964, 1901 ; *Wellenlängen-Tabellan für spectralanalytische Untersuchungen auf Grund der ultravioletten Funkenspectren der Elemente*, Leipzig, 1902 ; *Wellenlängen-Tabellan für spectralanalytischen Untersuchungen auf Grund der ultravioletten Bogenspectren der Elemente*, Leipzig, 1904 ; *Die Spektren der Elemente bei normalen Druck*, Leipzig, 1912 ; E. Demarçay, *Spectres électriques*, Paris, 1895 ; A. Hagenbach and H. Konen, *Atlas der Emissionsspectra*, Jena, 1905 ; H. Konen, *Arch. Sciences Genève*, (4), **37**. 262, 1914 ; J. Herpertz, *Die Spectren von Arsen und das Geisslerrohrspectrum von Antimon*, Bonn, 1906 ; *Zeit. wiss. Photochem.*, **4**. 175, 1906 ; C. de Watteville, *ib.*, **7**. 279, 1909 ; T. van Lohuizen, *ib.*, **11**. 388, 1913 ; W. J. Humphreys, *Astrophys. Journ.*, **6**. 169, 1897 ; J. J. Dobbie and J. J. Fox, *Proc. Roy. Soc.*, **98**. A 147, 1920 ; H. Hirata, *Proc. Roy. Soc.*, **104**. A, 40, 1924 ; L. H. Martin, *ib.*, **115**. A, 420, 1927 ; J. N. Lockyer, *ib.*, **22**. 374, 1874 ; *Phil. Mag.*, (4), **49**. 320, 1875 ; J. Evershed, *ib.*, (5), **39**. 460, 1895 ; E. Friman, *ib.*, (6), **32**. 497, 1916 ; M. Siegbahn and E. Friman, *Ann. Physik*, (4), **49**. 611, 1916 ; M. Siegbahn, *Jahrb. Rad. Elektron.*, **13**. 296, 1916 ; F. E. Baxandall, *Researches on the Chemical Origin of Various Lines in Solar and Stellar Spectra*, London, 1910 ; J. M. Eder and E. Valenta, *Atlas typischer Spektren*, Wien, 1911 ; J. M. Eder, *Sitzber. Akad. Wien*, **122**. 607, 1913 ; H. H. Pollock, *Proc. Roy. Dublin Soc.*, (2), **13**, 202, 1912 ; E. Wagner, *Phys. Zeit.*, **18**. 405, 432, 461, 488, 1917 ; F. Hjalmar, *ib.*, **21**. 262, 1920 ; W. Duane and H. Fuh-Hu, *Phys. Rev.*, (2), **14**. 576, 1920 ; P. D. Foote, B. Rognley, and F. L. Mohler, *ib.*, (2), **13**. 59, 1919 ; A. E. Ruark, F. L. Mohler, P. D. Foote, and R. L. Chenault, *Journ. Franklin Inst.*, **198**. 541, 1924 ; *Nature*, **112**. 831, 1923 ; *Phys. Rev.*, (2), **23**. 770, 1924 ; B. Rosen, *Naturwiss.*, **14**. 978, 1926 ; *Zeit. Physik*, **43**. 69, 1927 ; D. Coster and F. P. Mulder, *Zeit. Physik*, **38**. 264, 1926 ; A. Terenin, *ib.*, **31**. 26, 1925 ; **37**. 98, 1926 ; A. Leide, *ib.*, **39**. 686, 1926 ; Y. H. Woo, *Phys. Rev.*, (2), **28**. 427, 1926 ; K. T. Compton, *ib.*, (2), **8**. 412, 1916 ; E. O. Hulburt, *ib.*, (2), **25**. 888, 1925 ; A. Fowler, *Report on Series in Line Spectra*, London, 164, 1922 ; J. C. McLennan, J. F. T. Young, and H. J. C. Ireton, *Trans. Roy. Soc. Canada*, (3), **13**. 7, 1919 ; M. C. W. Buffam and H. J. C. Ireton, *ib.*, (3), **19**. 113, 1925 ; J. C. McLennan and A. B. McLay, *ib.*, (3), **19**. 89, 1925 ; *ib.*, (3), **4**. 407, 1927 ; J. Formanek, *Die qualitative Spektralanalyse anorganischer und organischer Körper*, Berlin, 151, 1905 ; H. R. Robinson and A. M. Cassie, *Proc. Roy. Soc.*, **113**. A, 282, 1926 ; H. R. Robinson, *Phil. Mag.*, (6), **50**. 241, 1925 ; J. E. P. Wagstaff, *ib.*, (6), **47**. 84, 1924 ; R. Thoraeus, *ib.*, (7), **1**. 312, 1926 ; (6), **2**. 1007, 1926 ; A. L. Foley, *Proc. Indiana Acad.*, **34**. 185, 1925 ; W. Herz, *Zeit. anorg. Chem.*, **163**. 220, 1927 ; G. Piccardi, *Atti Accad. Lincei*, (6), **6**. 428, 1927.

⁷ C. G. Barkla, *Phil. Mag.*, (6), **5**. 685, 1903 ; C. G. Barkla and V. Collier, *ib.*, (6), **23**. 987, 1912 ; C. G. Barkla and C. A. Sadler, *ib.*, (6), **17**. 739, 1909 ; T. E. Aurén, *ib.*, (6), **33**. 471, 1917 ; R. Whiddington, *ib.*, (6), **43**. 1116, 1923 ; W. H. Bragg and H. L. Porter, *Proc. Roy. Soc.*, **85**. A, 349, 1911 ; E. A. Owen, *ib.*, **86**. A, 426, 1912 ; *Proc. Cambridge Phil. Soc.*, **16**. 161, 1911.

⁸ H. Erdmann and R. Reppert, *Liebig's Ann.*, **361**. 1, 1908 ; A. Matthiessen and M. von Bose, *Phil. Trans.*, **152**. 1, 1862 ; *Proc. Roy. Soc.*, **11**. 516, 1862 ; *Pogg. Ann.*, **115**. 353, 1862 ; A. Matthiessen, *ib.*, **103**. 412, 1858 ; E. Frank, *Zur Kenntnis des brauen und grauen Arsens*, Bern, 1912 ; V. B. Marquis, *Journ. Amer. Chem. Soc.*, **42**. 1569, 1920 ; D. Reichinstein, *Das Amphoteritätsproblem und die elektromotorische Wirksamkeit*, Leipzig, 1908 ; L. Rosenthaler, *Zeit. anal. Chem.*, **45**. 596, 1906 ; C. Luckow, *ib.*, **19**. 1, 1880 ; S. Berberich, *Ueber das anodische Verhalten des Jodes, Arsens, und Antimons*, München, 1913 ; A. Classen and M. A. von Reiss, *Ber.*, **14**. 1622, 1881 ; A. Classen, *ib.*, **27**. 2074, 1894 ; G. Vortmann, *ib.*, **24**. 2764, 1891 ; T. Moore, *Chem. News*, **53**. 209, 1886 ; L. K. Frankel, *ib.*, 65, 54, 66, 1891 ; E. F. Smith and L. K. Frankel, *Amer. Chem. Journ.*, **12**. 104, 428, 1890 ; *Journ. Franklin Inst.*, **128**. 140, 154, 1889 ; **129**. 236, 1890 ; E. F. Smith and D. L. Wallace, *Ber.*, **25**. 779, 1892 ; O. Piloty, *ib.*, **27**. 280, 1894 ; P. W. Bridgman, *Proc. Amer. Acad.*, **56**. 61, 1921 ; S. R. Trotman, *Journ. Soc. Chem. Ind.*, **23**. 177, 1904 ; B. Neumann, *Zeit. phys. Chem.*, **14**. 193, 1894 ; N. T. M. Wilsmore, *ib.*, **35**. 291, 1900 ; V. Bayerle, *Rec. Trav. Chim. Pays-Bas*, **44**. 514, 1925 ; H. J. S. Sand and J. E. Hackford, *Journ. Chem. Soc.*, **85**. 1018, 1904 ; T. E. Thorpe, *ib.*, **83**. 974, 1903 ; S. C. Schmucker, *Zeit. anorg. Chem.*, **5**. 199, 1893 ; A. Thiel and W. Hammerschmidt, *ib.*, **132**. 15, 1923 ; M. le Blanc, *Lehrbuch der Elektrochemie*, Leipzig, 1914 ; W. Ostwald, *Grundlinien der anor-*

ganischen Chemie, Leipzig, 1912; L. Kahlenberg and J. V. Steinle, *Trans. Amer. Electrochem. Soc.*, **44**. 493, 1923; J. von Zawidsky, *Ber.*, **36**. 1435, 1903; M. le Blanc and D. Reichenstein, *Zeit. Elektrochem.*, **15**. 261, 1909; N. A. Puschin, *Journ. Russ. Phys. Chem. Soc.*, **39**. 528, 1908; P. E. Jannasch and V. Wasowicz, *Journ. prakt. Chem.*, (2), **45**. 94, 1892; N. C. Little, *Phys. Rev.*, (2), **28**. 418, 1926; K. F. Herzfeld, *ib.*, (2), **29**. 703, 1927; L. W. McCay, *Chem. Ztg.*, **14**. 509, 1890; *Beitrag zur Kenntnis der Kobalt-, Nickel, und Eisenkiese* Freiberg, 1884; B. Neumann, *Zeit. Elektrochem.*, **2**. 252, 269, 1895; G. Grube and H. Kelber, *ib.*, **30**. 517, 1925; N. Revay, *ib.*, **4**. 313, 1897; E. T. Wherry, *Amer. Min.*, **10**. 28, 1925; A. Hollard and L. Bertiaux, *Bull. Soc. Chim.*, (3), **31**. 900, 1904; R. Schumann, *Journ. Amer. Chem. Soc.*, **46**. 1444, 1924; E. W. Washburn and E. K. Strachen, *ib.*, **35**. 681, 1913; F. W. Bergstrom, *ib.*, **47**. 1503, 1925; V. Bayerle, *Rec. Trav. Chim. Pays-Bas*, **44**. 514, 1925; H. von Steinwehr, *Zeit. Instrk.*, **33**. 321, 1913; A. Schulze, *Zeit. Metallkunde*, **15**. 158, 1923; A. Günther-Schulze. *Zeit. Physik*, **36**. 563, 1926; *Zeit. Elektrochem.*, **33**. 360, 1927; P. E. Shaw and C. E. Jex, *Proc. Roy. Soc.*, **118**. A. 97, 1928.

[9] K. Honda, *Science Rep. Tohoku Univ.*, **1**. 1, 1912; **2**. 25, 1913; **3**. 139, 223, 1914; **4**. 215, 1915; *Ann. Physik*, (4), **32**. 1027, 1910; M. Owen, *ib.*, (4), **37**. 657, 1912; B. H. Wilsdon, *Phil. Mag.*, (6), **49**. 1145, 1925; P. Pascal, *Compt. Rend.*, **174**. 1698, 1922.

§ 6. The Chemical Properties of Arsenic

In its chemical reactions, arsenic has the characteristics of an electronegative element, although in certain of its combinations it may act as an electropositive element—*e.g.* in arsenic sulphate, $As_2(SO_4)_3$. Arsenic replaces phosphorus, and antimony in the oxides, chlorides and sulphides at 200° or 300°. On the contrary, with the triphenyl compounds this order of replacement is reversed—triphenyl stibine, $Sb(C_6H_5)_3$, is decomposed by arsine, and triphenylarsine, $As(C_6H_5)_3$, is simply decomposed by phosphorus at 300°. Yellow arsenic like yellow phosphorus is a strong reducing agent. The garlic-like odour of the fumes from burning arsenic is supposed by P. N. Laschtschenko [1] to be characteristic of yellow arsenic because when a sealed tube, containing the vap. of arsenic above the transition temp., burst, a strong odour of garlic was perceived.

W. T. Cooke [2] observed that the vap. density of arsenic in an atm. of **argon** and **helium** is quite normal, and there is no sign of chemical change. F. Fischer and F. Schrötter observed that no combination occurs when arsenic is sparked beneath liquid argon. W. Ramsay and J. N. Collie observed no reaction with **helium** at a red-heat. According to A. J. J. Vandevelde, and H. Reckleben and J. Scheiber, arsenic does not unite directly with **hydrogen**; the element can be sublimed in an atm. of that gas without change; and J. W. Retgers' statement that a solid hydride, AsH, is formed is wrong, for the product is an allotropic modification of arsenic. J. N. Lockyer observed no occlusion of hydrogen by arsenic. C. R. Fresenius and C. H. L. von Babo observed no arsine is formed by the passage of hydrogen over heated arsenic. If the gas appears to be arsenical, it is due to the mechanical transport of arsenic by the hydrogen, and this arsenic can be filtered from the hydrogen by cotton-wool. W. Ipatieff and co-workers found that when arsenic is heated with hydrogen and water under press., a little arsine and arsenious acid are formed. Hydrogen arsenides can be readily formed indirectly. Hydrogen has no action on a carbon disulphide soln. of yellow arsenic. F. H. Newman studied the adsorption of hydrogen by arsenic in discharge tubes. T. Panzer found that arsenic is not attacked in moist hydrogen.

T. Bergman found that dry **air** has no action on arsenic, and a similar observation was made by P. A. von Bonsdorff; and T. Panzer showed that arsenic is not attacked by air dried by phosphorus pentoxide. Amorphous arsenic does not appear to change on exposure to air; and crystalline arsenic retains its lustre in dry air, but in moist air it acquires a bronze colour and matte surface, and, in some cases, disintegrates into a black powder. The change takes place more quickly at 30°–40°. R. Engel also found that vitreous arsenic does not change in moist air, but the crystalline form is rapidly oxidized. According to J. J. Berzelius, J. A. Buchner, and T. Thomson, some specimens seem to retain their lustre and solidity without increasing in weight. If arsenic has been long exposed to dry

air, it may be kept longer without tarnishing in moist air than is the case with fresh arsenic. The early observers thought that arsenic suboxide is formed when arsenic is exposed to moist air, but A. Geuther did not agree with this—arsenic trioxide was always produced. T. Panzer said that the oxidation of arsenic exposed to air proceeds more quickly in light than in darkness ; an arsenic mirror suffered no perceptible change after a year's exposure in darkness, but an arsenic mirror was changed by a few days' exposure in light, forming arsenic trioxide. M. François and L. Seguin found that with fly-papers containing metallic arsenic, air and moisture oxidize the arsenic to arsenious acid—3 per cent. was so oxidized in 48 hrs. When arsenic is heated in air, it burns, emitting a reddish fume having an odour of garlic, and it forms arsenic trioxide ; at a higher temp., the arsenic burns with a pale blue flame. This occurs, for example, when arsenic is held in the flame of a candle, and when removed from the flame, the arsenic smoulders away emitting a brown smoke. Arsenic which has been sublimed in hydrogen also smoulders in a similar way. J. K. Mitchell assumed that a suboxide is formed as an intermediate stage in the oxidation, because arsenic trioxide does not emit the garlic odour, and metallic arsenic does not volatilize at the temp. at which the smouldering with the emission of brown fumes occurs. C. F. Schönbein suggested that the garlic-odour may be due to an allotropic form of arsenic trioxide. Arsenic burns vigorously in **oxygen,** and, according to H. B. Baker and H. B. Dixon, the thorough desiccation of the oxygen has no perceptible influence on this reaction. M. Thiele found that oxygen precipitates brown arsenic from a soln. of yellow arsenic in carbon disulphide. According to H. J. Emeléus, arsenic undergoes a slow luminous oxidation between 260° and 300°. This glow occurs in pure oxygen only on reducing the press. to a limiting value, which is analogous with the glow of phosphorus. The influence of temp. on the glow-pressure is largely influenced by the dimensions of the apparatus, occurring most readily when conditions favour diffusion and consequent removal of the oxidation product. In a gas-stream, arsenic glows at approximately the same temp. in air as in oxygen. The reduction of press. appears to produce the glow by accelerating the diffusion of the oxide. C. F. Schönbein found that **ozone** or ozonized turpentine or ether oxidizes arsenic to arsenic acid.

According to P. A. von Bonsdorff, at ordinary temp. and out of contact with air, arsenic undergoes no alteration when immersed in **water** freed from air by boiling ; and J. W. Mellor observed that purified water and crystallized arsenic in a sealed glass tube suffered no detectable change during ten years. P. A. von Bonsdorff found that arsenic trioxide is quickly formed. H. M. Elsey found that there is a probable reaction : $4As + 3H_2O = As_2O_3 + 2AsH_3$. Water condenses on the surface of pulverulent arsenic exposed in air ; and P. Orfila said that if arsenic covered with water be exposed to air at ordinary temp., it forms arsenic trioxide ; the water absorbs oxygen from the air, transfers it to the arsenic, and dissolves the arsenic trioxide as it forms ; if air be blown for ten minutes through the water holding powdered arsenic in suspension, the filtered liquid contains arsenic trioxide in soln. ; P. F. G. Boullay, E. Hirschsohn, and H. Schwabe reported that when a mass of powdered arsenic—say 4 kgrms.—is exposed to air, it becomes heated, and may be inflamed ; if the combustion be stopped by moistening with water, it may start again in the course of a few days. A. W. Büchner, however, said that this development of heat occurs only when the arsenic is moistened during its pulverization. W. T. Cooke found that in the absence of air, amorphous arsenic is but slightly attacked by boiling water ; and when air was aspirated through the boiling water, only 0·0010 grm. of the element was dissolved by 50 c.c. of water, thus showing that the action is very little influenced by the presence of air. When crystallized arsenic is similarly treated, only 0·0025 grm. of arsenic is dissolved in about 1½ hrs. by 50 c.c. of water. If air be present, 0·0233 grm. was dissolved in the same time. If water were concerned in the oxidation of the arsenic, the formation of arsine might be anticipated : $2As + 3H_2O = As_2O_3 + 6H$; and $2As + 6H = 2AsH_3$; but this gas was never observed. T. Panzer also said that the oxidation by moist air is due to the intervention of free oxygen, and not as a result of the decomposition of water.   P. Orfila, however, did find that with boiling water some brown arsenic hydride, AsH, is formed.   H. V. Regnault observed that very little hydrogen is produced when a mixture of the vapours of arsenic and water is passed through a red-hot tube.   The presence of alkali in the water favours the attack.   W. T. Cooke showed that in the absence of air, dil. soln. of **sodium hydroxide** have a slightly greater action on amorphous arsenic than water ; the action increases with the conc. of the alkali ; and is not influenced by the presence of air ; with crystalline arsenic, the action is very slight in the absence of air, but direct oxidation occurs in the presence of air.   P. L. Chastaing said that a dil. soln. of sodium or potassium hydroxide attacks arsenic more rapidly in red light than it does in violet light. A. F. Gehlen, and E. Soubeiran found that when a mixture of alkali hydroxide and arsenic is heated, but not to redness, the alkali arsenide and arsenite is formed and hydrogen is evolved.   According to C. F. Schönbein, **hydrogen dioxide** oxidizes arsenic to arsenic pentoxide ; and L. J. Thénard noted a vigorous action with powdered arsenic.

According to H. Moissan,[3] **fluorine** vigorously reacts with arsenic at ordinary temp. with incandescence forming a mixture of arsenic tri- and penta-fluorides ; and J. Davy, and J. B. A. Dumas found that **chlorine** also reacts with arsenic with incandescence, forming the trichloride.   Liquid chlorine was found by V. Thomas and P. Dupuis to react with incandescence near its b.p., forming a white cloud of arsenic trichloride.   M. Thiele found that chlorine first precipitates brown arsenic from a soln. of yellow arsenic in carbon disulphide, and it then converts the brown arsenic into the trichloride.   G. S. Sérullas obtained arsenic tribromide by the action of **bromine ;** and A. Plisson observed that arsenic unites with **iodine** when the powdered mixture is warmed, forming the triiodide.   G. E. Linck found that when arsenic is added to a carbon disulphide soln. of iodine or bromine, a reddish-brown powder separates out.   H. Moissan found that arsenic reacts energetically with **iodine fluoride.**   K. A. Hofmann and co-workers found the activity of **ammonium chloride** vapour on arsenic is greater than that of dry **hydrogen chloride** at 250°–350°.   R. Napoli said that neither **hydrofluoric acid** nor **hydrochloric acid** attacks arsenic in the absence of air, but if air be present, the trihalide is formed ; **hydrobromic acid,** and **hydriodic acid** act in consequence of their easy dissociation into the halogen, etc.   M. Thiele observed no reaction between hydrochloric acid and yellow arsenic dissolved in carbon disulphide. W. S. Hendrixson, and F. A. Gooch and J. C. Blake observed that finely divided arsenic is oxidized by **chloric acid** or **bromic acid,** to form arsenic.   Very dil. chloric acid has no action.   A. F. de Fourcroy and L. N. Vauquelin observed that a mixture of arsenic and **potassium chlorate** detonates by percussion ; and J. W. Slater found that a boiling soln. of the chlorate is reduced by arsenic, forming the alkali arsenate and chloride.   K. A. Hofmann found that in the presence of a trace of osmium tetroxide, neutral or slightly acid soln. of potassium chlorate oxidize arsenic to arsenic acid.

J. J. Berzelius,[4] and A. Gélis observed that arsenic unites directly with **sulphur** when a mixture of the two elements is heated.   W. Guertler studied the affinity of arsenic for sulphur.   M. Thiele found that **hydrogen sulphide** precipitates arsenic sulphide from a carbon disulphide soln. of yellow arsenic ; O. Brunn, that hydrogen sulphide at 230° slowly converts arsenic into the trisulphide—*vide infra*, arsenic disulphide ; and O. Ruff, that arsenic interacts with hydrogen sulphide in the presence of aluminium chloride, forming arsenic trisulphide and hydrogen chloride. H. Moissan and P. Lebeau found that **sulphur hexafluoride** can be distilled in the presence of arsenic without change.   C. Heumann and P. Köchlin showed that arsenic reacts with **sulphur monochloride,** forming arsenic trichloride and sulphide or sulphur ; and **sulphuryl chloride** reacts with powdered arsenic in the cold ; and when heated, sulphur dioxide and arsenic trichloride are produced.   H. Schiff said that dry **sulphur dioxide** reacts only with the vapour of arsenic, forming arsenic sulphide, and **trioxide**; while C. Geitner observed that in a sealed tube at 200°, a mixture of arsenic and an aq. soln. of sulphur dioxide produces sulphuric acid and arsenic trioxide—some sulphur separates out, but no arsenic sulphide is formed. M. Thiele found that sulphur dioxide precipitates a little brown arsenic from a carbon disulphide soln. of yellow arsenic. G. Aimé found that **sulphur trioxide** oxidizes arsenic to the trioxide. R. H. Adie found that boiling conc. **sulphuric acid** dissolves arsenic with the evolution of sulphur dioxide and the formation of arsenic trioxide. The reaction begins at about 110°, and no hydrogen sulphide or arsine is formed. M. Thiele observed no reaction between sulphuric acid and yellow arsenic dissolved in carbon disulphide. M. G. Levi and co-workers observed the formation of arsenic acid by the action of a soln. of **alkali persulphate**. C. Heumann and P. Köchlin represented the reaction with **chlorosulphonic acid** by the equation : $2As+6HSO_3Cl=2AsCl_3+3SO_2+3H_2SO_4$. J. J. Berzelius [5] found that molten **selenium** slowly dissolves arsenic, forming a selenide, and **hydrogen selenide** also readily reacts with arsenic. J. J. Berzelius [6] also found that arsenic similarly reacts with **tellurium**, and with **hydrogen telluride**. E. B. Hutchins found that hot soln. of **telluric acid** attack arsenic.

Arsenic has no perceptible action on **nitrogen** ; F. H. Newman [7] studied the adsorption of nitrogen in discharge tubes ; G. Gore, E. C. Franklin and C. A. Kraus, and C. Hugot found that arsenic is not attacked by liquid **ammonia** ; C. A. Kraus observed complex ion formation with arsenic in ammonia soln. K. A. Hofmann and co-workers observed that ammonium chloride vapour at 250°–350° acts on arsenic much like an acid. J. J. Sudborough found that arsenic is attacked by **nitrosyl chloride** in the cold. Both **nitric acid,** and **aqua regia** oxidize arsenic with great vigour, forming arsenic trioxide and arsenic acid ; if the nitric acid be dilute, added J. Personne, a part of the acid is reduced to ammonia. M. Thiele observed that yellow arsenic in carbon disulphide soln. is completely oxidized by nitric acid. According to P. Askenasy and co-workers, arsenic is not oxidized by nitric acid of a conc. up to 40 per cent., and no nitric oxide is formed by 50 per cent. HNO_3 in the cold, but with the boiling acid, there is a feeble reaction. In the absence of nitric acid, arsenic with an oxygen press. of 20 atm. and at 200° forms only arsenious acid. T. Curtius and A. Darapsky found that a 29 per cent. soln. of **hydrazoic acid** dissolves arsenic with the liberation of hydrogen, and, on evaporation, arsenic trioxide is deposited. C. C. Palit and N. R. Dhar observed but a slight action by 13 and 26 per cent. **nitric acid** at ordinary temp., and only a slight formation of nitrous acid. E. J. Maumené, and J. Personne said that some ammonia is formed when nitric acid acts on arsenic. F. W. Bergstrom found arsenic to be slightly attacked by **potassium amide,** and by **ammonium nitrate** soln. J. W. Slater found that a mixture of **potassium nitrate** and arsenic detonates vigorously when ignited ; and a boiling soln. of **barium nitrate** dissolves arsenic slowly forming arsenate and arsenic trioxide. G. Landgrebe, and J. V. Janowsky found that arsenic phosphide, or phosphorus arsenide, is formed when a mixture of arsenic and **phosphorus** is heated to dull redness. O. Ruff observed that arsenic reacts with phosphorus in the presence of aluminium trichloride, forming a red substance which is decomposed by water giving a violet black substance with the composition PAs_4O_2. According to H. Moissan, a mixture of **phosphorus trifluoride** and arsenic can be distilled without reaction. F. Krafft and R. Neumann found that **phosphorus trichloride** does not react with arsenic, but with 12 hrs.' heating at 200°, arsenic trichloride and phosphorus are quantitatively formed ; with **phosphorus pentachloride,** B. Reinitzer and H. Goldschmidt observed the formation of arsenic and phosphorus trichlorides ; while **phosphoryl chloride** dissolves arsenic, and with a prolonged heating at 250°, arsenic and phosphorus trichloride and pyrophosphoryl chloride are formed. F. Krafft and R. Neumann observed that with **phosphorus pentoxide,** arsenic trioxide and phosphorus are formed at 290° ; and **phosphorus tetritahexasulphide** reacts in an analogous manner. M. Thiele observed no reaction between a carbon disulphide soln. of yellow arsenic and **phosphoric acid.** T. Bergman, A. F. Gehlen, and A. Descamps observed that alloys of **antimony** and arsenic can be readily produced; and C. M. Marx, and A. Descamps obtained alloys with **bismuth.** A. Ditte observed that **vanadium pentoxide** is reduced by arsenic. F. E. Brown and J. E. Snyder observed no reaction between arsenic and **vanadium oxytrichloride.**

No direct chemical action between arsenic and **boron** has been observed; and similar remarks apply to **carbon,** and to **silicon.** E. Guenez [8] observed that when arsenic is heated with **cyanogen iodide,** arsenic tricyanide is formed. V. Auger observed that when a mixture of arsenic and **carbon tetrachloride** is heated in a sealed tube at 160°, arsenic trichloride and carbon hexachloride are formed. G. E. Linck found yellow arsenic to be soluble in **carbon disulphide,** and H. Erdmann and M. von Unruh found that 1C0 c.c. of carbon disulphide dissolved

	−80°	−60°	−15°	0°	12°	18°–20°	46°
As . .	0	0·8–1·0	2·0–2·5	3·8–4·0	5·5–6·0	7·5–8·0	11 grms.

H. Erdmann and R. Reppert found that yellow arsenic is precipitated when alcohol is added to soln. of yellow arsenic in carbon disulphide; and the observation was repeated by M. Thiele who also found that ether acts similarly, while with benzene, and chloroform, brown arsenic is precipitated; and with ligroïn, yellow arsenic precipitates. F. W. Bergstrom observed that arsenic showed no sign of reaction with liquid ammonia soln. of cyanide of potassium or aluminium, over a long period of time. G. E. Linck also found yellow arsenic to be soluble to a less extent in **benzene, glycerol,** and **fatty oils.**

As A. Descamps showed, most of the **metals** unite with arsenic, forming alloys or definite arsenides—*vide infra*—and W. Spring believed that a high press. could bring about the combination of an intimate mixture of powdered arsenic and powdered **copper,** silver, zinc, cadmium, tin, or lead. Sodium arsenide is one of the **primary** products of the action of **sodium hydroxide** on arsenic, and the hydrolysis of this may be the source of arsine (*q.v.*). According to H. Erdmann and R. Reppert, yellow arsenic reduces a soln. of **copper sulphate,** and M. Thiele obtained a mixed precipitate of copper and copper arsenide from a soln. of a copper salt—sulphate, nitrate, or chloride; A. Descamps noted the reduction of copper salts by arsenic. C. Strzyzowsky said that Fehling's soln. is reduced by arsenic at 50°. M. Kohn represented the reaction in ammoniacal soln. by $6CuSO_4+2As+6NH_4OH=2(NH_4)_3AsO_3+3Cu_2SO_4+3H_2SO_4$; the cuprous salt is then reduced further : $3Cu_2SO_4+2As+6NH_4OH=2(NH_4)_3AsO_3+3H_2SO_4+6Cu$, and the copper reacts with the excess of arsenic, forming arsenide. Arsenic reacts with soln. of **silver nitrate,** and silver contaminated with a little arsenic is precipitated ; likewise also with a soln. of **gold chloride.** A. Descamps also found that ordinary arsenic reduces auric chloride, forming gold arsenides. H. Erdmann and R. Reppert observed that **mercurous nitrate** is reduced by yellow arsenic to mercury contaminated with a little arsenic ; and M. Thiele obtained an analogous result with the same salt and with **mercuric chloride.** M. J. B. Orfila also obtained mercury by the action of arsenic at ordinary temp. on soln. of mercurous nitrate and sulphate. J. W. Slater found that arsenic reduces **potassium permanganate** to manganese dioxide. R. Böttger found that arsenic reduces soln. of **ferric chloride or sulphate.** M. Thiele found that yellow arsenic reduces an aq. soln. of **platinum tetrachloride** to the metal ; likewise also a soln. of **palladous chloride,** and **sodium rhodium chloride.** L. Kahlenberg and J. V. Steinle found that with an aq. soln. of silver nitrate arsenic reacts : $3AgNO_3+4As=2As_2O_3+3Ag+3NO$; but the reaction is not completed in several months ; with **silver nitrite :** $6AgNO_2+2As$ $=As_2O_3+6Ag+3NO_2+3NO$; with **silver sulphate :** $3Ag_2SO_4+2As+3H_2O=6Ag$ $+3H_2SO_4+As_2O_3$; **silver acetate,** $6CH_3COOAg+2As+3H_2O=6CH_3COOH+6Ag$ $+As_2O_3$; similarly with **silver tartrate;** with **potassium silver cyanide :** $3KAgCy_2$ $+As=K_3AsCy_6+3Ag$; and with **silver fluoride :** $6AgF+2As+3H_2O=6HF+6Ag$ $+As_2O_3$. In pyridine soln., silver nitrate reacts as in the case of aq. soln., but the reactioı is complete within a week; with silver chloride, $3AgCl+As=AsCl_3+3Ag$; and with silver sulphate, the black precipitate formed seems to be due to light. Arsenic does not replace the silver in soln. of silver palmitate or stearate in acetone and anhydrous ether. Aq. soln. of mercuric nitrate react with arsenic: $3Hg(NO_3)_2 +8As=4As_2O_3+6NO+3Hg$; mercurous nitrate: $3HgNO_3+4As=2As_2O_3+3Hg +3NO$; mercurous sulphate: $3Hg_2SO_4+2As+3H_2O=3H_2SO_4+As_2O_3+6Hg$; mercuric cyanide: $3HgCy_2+2As+3H_2O=6HCy+As_2O_3+3Hg$; mercuric acetate: $3(CH_3COO)_2Hg+2As+3H_2O=3Hg+As_2O_3+6CH_3COOH$; and mercuric chloride (or bromide): $3HgCl_2+2As+3H_2O=6HCl+As_2O_3+3Hg$. Pyridine soln. of mercuric stearate give a grey deposit of mercury; and with a soln. of mercuric palmitate in anhydrous ethyl alcohol, a white precipitate, probably of mercurous palmitate, is formed. An aq. soln. of cupric chloride reacts: $4CuCl_2 +2As+3H_2O=2Cu+2CuCl+6HCl+As_2O_3$; cupric sulphate: $3CuSO_4+2As +3H_2O=3H_2SO_4+3Cu+As_2O_3$; copper nitrate, acetate, and tannate act like the salts of mercury; copper phosphate: $Cu_3(PO_4)_2+2As+3H_2O=2H_3PO_4+As_2O_3 +3Cu$; copper arsenite: $Cu_3(AsO_3)_2+2As=3Cu+2As_2O_3$; copper arsenate: $Cu_3(AsO_4)_2+2As=3Cu+As_2O_3+As_2O_5$; and an aq. soln. of copper glycine lost all its copper. Soln. of copper abietate and oleate in xylene or toluene gave precipitates of copper without arsenic passing into soln.; copper stearate and palmitate in chloroform or ether gave small deposits of copper. Molten copper oleate alone at 120°–130° gives a precipitate of copper, but in presence of arsenic the precipitate is greater, but no arsenic passes into soln. Aq. soln. of platinum tetrachloride react: $3PtCl_4+4As+6H_2O=3Pt+2As_2O_3+12HCl$; gold chloride: $2AuCl_3+2As+3H_2O \rightleftharpoons 2Au+As_2O_3+6HCl$; ferric chloride: $6FeCl_3+2As+3H_2O=6FeCl_2+As_2O_3 +6HCl$; cadmium sulphate: $3CdSO_4+8As=3CdS+4As_2O_3$. Arsenic gave white precipitates with aq. soln. of zinc chloride, aluminium sulphate, and lead nitrate; and no perceptible effect with soln. of manganese, cobalt, and nickel sulphates. H. Lessheim and co-workers discussed the co-ordination number of arsenic in its complex salts.

Some reactions of analytical interest.—Arsenic yields two series of salt, arsenious and arsenic salts derived respectively from arsenic trioxide and pentoxide. Neither of these salts gives a precipitate with hydrochloric acid. If **hydrogen sulphide** be passed into acidic soln. of arsenic trioxide, yellow flocculent arsenic trisulphide is precipitated: $2AsCl_3+3H_2S=6HCl+As_2S_3$. The precipitate is insoluble in acids, even in boiling hydrochloric acid (1 : 1), but a protracted boiling with the conc. acid slowly forms volatile arsenic trichloride. This enables arsenic to be separated from other elements which do not form chlorides volatile under these conditions—*vide infra*. The sulphide is oxidized by conc. nitric acid to arsenic and sulphuric acids; it is also soluble in an ammoniacal soln. of hydrogen dioxide, and in a soln. of alkali hydroxide or sulphide, or in one of ammonium carbonate. The solubility is due to the formation of soluble alkali thioarsenites: $As_2S_3+6KOH =3H_2O+As(OK)_3+As(SK)_3$; or $As_2S_3+3(NH_4)_2S=2As(SNH_4)_3$—*vide infra*, the action of hydrogen sulphide on arsenic acid. The reaction may be reversed by treating the soln. with hydrochloric acid. Hydrogen sulphide gives no precipitate with normal arsenites because of the formation of the soluble thioarsenites: $As(OK)_3 +3H_2S \rightleftharpoons 3H_2O+As(SK)_3$. If enough acid be present, the soluble thioarsenite is not formed. When hydrogen sulphide is passed into a cold, acidic soln. of arsenic pentoxide, the liquid remains clear for some time, and gradually becomes turbid owing to the separation of sulphur as the arsenic pentoxide is reduced to the trioxide and the formation of arsenic trisulphide: $2H_3AsO_4+5H_2S=8H_2O+2S+As_2S_3$; this reaction proceeds much more quickly if the soln. is warm. If a great excess of hydrochloric acid be present, it is possible that arsenic pentachloride is formed since the hydrogen sulphide precipitates from the cold soln. arsenic pentasulphide; with a warm soln. a mixture of the tri- and penta-sulphides is precipitated. If the acid soln. of arsenic acid be heated with a little sulphur dioxide or ammonium iodide before passing in the hydrogen sulphide, the arsenic acid is reduced to arsenious acid, and this forming arsenic trichloride behaves as indicated above. Arsenic pentasulphide like the trisulphide is insoluble in hydrochloric acid, but is soluble in a soln. of alkali hydroxide or sulphide, or in one of ammonium carbonate. This is due to the formation of soluble sulphoarsenate : $As_2S_5+6NaOH=3H_2O+AsS(SNa)_3+AsS(ONa)_3$. Hydrochloric acid reverses these reactions. The pentasulphide is oxidized by nitric acid and by an ammoniacal soln. of hydrogen dioxide. J. F. Lassaigne [9] said that one part of arsenic trioxide in 10,000 parts of water gives a yellow coloration with hydrogen sulphide ; and if hydrochloric acid be present, the coloration is produced by one part in 80,000 parts of soln. ; H. Reinsch gave 1 in 90,000 parts ; R. Brandes and G. Ebeling, 1 in 160,000 parts ; C. H. Pfaff, 1 in 24,000 ; T. G. Wormley, 1 in 13,200 parts ; and F. Jackson, 1 in 1,024,000 parts. Some of these estimates must be rather poor shots. If **ammonium sulphide** be added to neutral, or alkaline soln. of arsenic trioxide, no precipitation of the sulphide occurs until an excess of acid has been added. Similar remarks apply to soln. of arsenic pentoxide. R. Schiff and N. Tarugi also noted that **ammonium thioacetate** gives a precipitate of arsenic trisulphide with acidified soln. of arsenic trioxide, or pentoxide. Arsenic trisulphide is precipitated by **sodium thiosulphate** completely from acidified soln. of arsenic trioxide ; and arsenic pentasulphide from acidified soln. of arsenic pentoxide.

A soln. of **iodine** is decolorized by arsenious acid, the latter being oxidized to arsenic acid. The reaction is not quantitative in acid soln., but in alkaline soln. it proceeds : $As(OH)_3+NaHCO_3+I_2=NaI+HI+CO_2+AsO(OH)_3$. When **potassium iodide** is added to a hot soln. of arsenic trioxide in conc. hydrochloric or sulphuric acid, a red precipitate of arsenic triiodide is deposited. Neutral soln. of the arsenites with **silver nitrate** give a yellow precipitate of silver orthoarsenite soluble in nitric acid and aq. ammonia ; arsenates under similar conditions give a chocolate-brown precipitate of silver arsenate. The precipitate from acidic soln. is the hydro-arsenite so that an alkali preferably ammonia should then be added to make the soln. neutral ; or better, employ ammoniacal silver nitrate. A. Marcet discussed the use of silver nitrate in detecting minute quantities of arsenic. Aq. soln. of arsenic trioxide are not precipitated by soln. of **copper sulphate,** but if the soln. be alkaline, greenish-yellow cupric hydroarsenite is precipitated. The precipitate dissolves in alkali-lye, and when the soln. is boiled, red cuprous oxide is deposited. J. F. Lassaigne said that one part of arsenic trioxide in 160,500 parts of water gives a precipitate with ammoniacal soln. of copper sulphate ; R. Brandes and G. Ebeling, 1 in 250,000 ; and P. Harting, 1 in 12,000. P. Harting found that **lime-water** gives a precipitate with up to one part of arsenic trioxide in 4000 parts of water ; and J. F. Lassaigne said 1 in 5000. **Magnesia mixture**—a soln. of ammonium and magnesium chlorides in aq. ammonia—gives no precipitate with dil. soln. of arsenites, but with arsenates, a white crystalline precipitate of magnesium ammonium arsenate is produced : $Na_2HAsO_4+MgCl_2+NH_3=2NaCl+NH_4O.AsO : O_2 : Mg$. The precipitate is insoluble in aq. ammonia, and when ignited it forms magnesium pyroarsenate, $Mg_2As_2O_7$. These reactions are utilized in the quantitative determination of arsenic. R. Brandes and G. Ebeling said that a green coloration is produced by **potassium chromate** when one part of arsenic trioxide is present in 1000 parts of water. An excess of **ammonium molybdate** with a boiling nitric acid soln. of an arsenate gives a yellow precipitate of ammonium arsenomolybdate : $H_3AsO_4+12(NH_4)_2MoO_4+21HNO_3=12H_2O+21NH_4NO_3+(NH_4)_3AsO_4.12MoO_3$. When a few drops of an arsenite soln. are added to conc. hydrochloric acid, and then a little stannous chloride, the soln. becomes brown and then black owing to the separation of metallic arsenic : $2AsCl_3+3SnCl_2=3SnCl_4+2As$. The reaction proceeds more quickly on warming, and it does not occur in dil. soln.—*vide infra*, arsenic trichloride. *A. Bettendorff's reagent* is essentially **stannous chloride** which reduces soln. of arsenious acid (*q.v.*) ; E. Deussen, and E. Rupp and E. Muschiol recommended **calcium hypophosphate** as a precipitant.

According to A. Pinkus and F. Martin, arsenious and arsenic salts give no precipitate with **cupferron** (nitrosophenylhydroxylamine).

Compounds containing arsenic may be reduced in acid soln. by means of nascent hydrogen, forming arsine, AsH_3. With sulphides, the reduction is slow : $As_2S_3 + 12H = 3H_2S + 2AsH_3$; but oxides are quickly reduced at ordinary temp. : $As_2O_3 + 12H = 3H_2O + 2AsH_3$. The hydrogen is produced by zinc and sulphuric acid, or electrolytically. The arsine which is given off enables as little as 0.007 mgrm. of arsenic to be detected with certainty. If the arsine along with hydrogen be passed through a heated glass it is decomposed into hydrogen and arsenic. The arsenic is deposited as a brownish-black mirror on the sides of the glass tube just beyond the place where it was heated. Details of the required manipulation are described in works devoted to analytical chemistry. This test—*Marsh's test*—was devised by J. Marsh about 1836. Numerous modifications have been suggested. By making a series of standard " mirrors " with known amounts of arsenic, and working under uniform conditions, the test can be made quantitative. Blank tests are made to be sure that all the reagents are free from arsenic, and antimony. Antimony also gives a mirror when antimonal compounds are treated in a similar way— *vide infra*, arsine, and stibine. The mirrors or crusts produced by the two elements are distinguished in the following manner :

(1) Arsenic is deposited a short distance from the flame, while the antimony is deposited close to the flame and on both sides of it. (2) The arsenic deposit is in two portions— glittering black, and brown ; while the antimony stain is nearly homogeneous and usually tin-white. (3) When the arsenic stain is heated, it rapidly volatilizes as crystalline arsenic trioxide ; while the antimony volatilizes slowly and does not give a crystalline sublimate. (4) If hydrogen sulphide be passed through the heated tube, yellow arsenic sulphide is formed, and if dry hydrogen chloride be now passed, the arsenic sulphide is not altered ; antimony under similar conditions gives an orange or black sulphide, and hydrogen chloride forms volatile antimony chloride. (5) A soln. of bleaching powder dissolves the arsenic stain but not the antimony stain. (6) A soln. of stannous chloride slowly dissolves the antimony stain, but not the arsenic stain. (7) The arsenic stain dissolved in aqua regia, and treated with tartaric acid, ammonia, and magnesia mixture gives a precipitate of ammonium magnesium arsenate—not so with the antimony stain.

In the so-called *Gutzeit's test*, devised by H. Gutzeit, the arsine is passed through filter-paper impregnated with silver nitrate. A yellow or orange stain of $AsAg_3.3AgNO_3$ is produced, if arsine eq. to over 0.005 mgrm. of arsenic trioxide be present. Antimony, selenium, and tellurium do not give the reaction—*vide* **3.** 22, 21. In *Reinsch's test*, devised by H. Reinsch, a strip of polished copper foil is placed in the soln. of arsenious acid ; the copper is coloured grey owing to the deposition of arsenic thereon, and the formation of copper arsenide. Conc. soln. give this result in the cold ; dil. soln. with one part of arsenious acid in 100,000 parts of water give a grey film immediately on warming ; a soln. with one part in 200,000 parts of water takes half an hour to form ; and the limit is reached with about 1 in 250,000 to 300,000. If a large proportion of arsenic be present, the arsenical film may drop off. Arsenic acid requires warming to give the deposit. If antimony be present, it too is deposited. In the so-called *biological test* the *penicillium brevicaule* is grown on sterilized bread at 37°. The garlic smell developed in about 24 hrs. enables 0.001 mgrm. of arsenic trioxide to be detected—*vide infra*. Arsenical compounds yield metallic arsenic when heated with potassium cyanide, or with a mixture of charcoal and potassium carbonate.

Some uses of arsenic.—The metal is used [10] in making a number of alloys-- *e.g.* speculum metal contains copper, tin, and a little arsenic ; white copper is an alloy of copper with about 10 per cent. of arsenic ; and lead-shot has 0.3–0.6 per cent. of arsenic. The arsenic renders the lead more fusible and harder ; in the shot towers, the drops of lead assume the spherical form during their descent. Britannia metal often contains arsenic. Brass is sometimes " bronzed," " oxidized." or " black-nickelled " with a thin film of arsenic.[11] The use of arsenic oxide in the manufacture of glass is not so common as was formerly the case. Recipes for some enamels for enamelled iron contain arsenic. Considerable quantities of arsenic are employed in the manufacture of Paris green and other insecticides for the preservation of fruit-trees in Canada, United States, Australasia, Algiers, etc. ; of the vines in France ; and of the indiarubber trees of the East Indies, and Malaya. It has been successfully used in the form of Paris green or white arsenic to kill the Colorado beetle so destructive to potatoes ; and in the form of calcium arsenate, to control the boll weevil in infested cotton fields. A sat. aq. soln. of white arsenic is used as a wood-preserver, and as a preventative of " dry rot " and other similar afflictions. It is used for preventing the decay of vegetable matter in the holds of ships ; in the wash used for walls in houses in India, etc., in order to prevent the attacks of insects. White arsenic is used in some forms of calico printing as a conveyor or fixer for certain aniline dyes ; and it is used in making some glazes, and enamels. Arsenic is a constituent of the sheep-dips—*le bain de terse ;* of arsenical soaps used in preserving the skins of animals ; of various pyrotechnic recipes ; of arsenical pastes used as rat-poisons ; of fly-water, fly-powder, and fly-papers—*papier moure*—used for killing flies ; of various quack nostrums for external use in cancer ; various veterinary preparations contain arsenic—*e.g.* worm-balls, and tonic-balls ; and it appears in a number of pharmaceutical preparations— thus, *liquor arsenicalis,* or *Fowler's solution,* is virtually a mixture of potassium arsenite and arsenious acid ; and *liquor arsenici hydrochloricus* is a dil. soln. of arsenic trioxide in dil. hydrochloric acid. *Donovan's solution* of arsenic is about a one per cent. soln. of the iodides of mercury and arsenic used sometimes in skin diseases ; *Clemen's solution* is a soln. of potassium bromide and arsenate ; the *pilula asiatica* is a pill composed of arsenious acid, gentian, and black pepper. Several organic preparations are used medicinally : *dioxydiaminoarsenobenzol dihydrochloride*—with various trade-names, *salvarsan, 606, arsenobillon,* or *kharsivan,* and *novarsenobenzol,* $C_6H_3(OH)(NH_2)As : (NH_2)(OH)C_6H_3$—with the trade-name *neosalvarsan,* or *novarsenobillon,* $C_6H_3(OH)(NH_2)As : As(NH_2)(OH)C_6H_3.CH_2O.SONa$ —are used intravenously for syphilis ; *sodium aminophenylarsenate*—also called *atoxyl,* $NH_2.C_6H_4.AsO(OH).ONa.nH_2O,$ *soamine, arsamine,* etc.—and *sodium acetarsenate*—or *arsacetin*—used subcutaneously as a remedy for trypanosomiasis, malaria, relapsing fever, and epidemic cerebro-spinal meningitis. Arsenious oxide is used by dentists to destroy the nervous pulp of decaying and painful teeth.[12]

REFERENCES.

[1] P. N. Laschtschenko, *Journ. Chem. Soc.,* **121**. 975, 1922.
[2] A. J. J. Vandevelde, *Des affinités de l'hydrogène moléculaire à chaud,* Bruxelles, 1895 ; *Bull. Acad. Belg.,* (3), **30**. 78, 1895 ; W. Spring, *ib.,* (3), **5**. 229, 1883 ; J. W. Retgers, *Zeit. anorg. Chem.,* **4**. 429, 1893 ; H. Reckleben and J. Scheiber, *ib.,* **70**. 255, 1911 ; J. W. Mellor, *Private Communication ;* F. Fischer and F. Schrötter, *Ber.,* **43**. 1442, 1454, 1910 ; J. N. Lockyer, *Chem. News,* **40**. 101, 1879 ; T. Thomson, *Ann. Phil.,* **18**. 130, 1821 ; T. Panzer, *Verh. Vers. Deut. Nat. Aerzte,* **2**. i, 79, 1902 ; M. Thiele, *Ueber die allotropen Modifikation des Arsens,* Berlin, 1910 ; R. Engel, *Compt. Rend.,* **96**. 1314, 1883 ; E. Soubeiran, *Journ. Pharm. Chim.,* (2), **16**. 353, 1830 ; A. Geuther, *Liebig's Ann.,* **240**. 217, 1887 ; C. R. Fresenius and C. H. L. von Babo, *ib.,* **49**. 305, 1844 ; W. Ramsay and J. N. Collie, *Proc. Roy. Soc.,* **60**. 57, 1896 ; P. L. Chastaing, *Ann. Chim. Phys.,* (5), **11**. 169, 1877 ; A. F. Gehlen, *ib.,* (2), **3**. 135, 1816 ; J. J. Berzelius, *ib.,* (1), **80**. 9, 1811 ; (2), **5**. 179, 1817 ; (2), **11**. 225, 1819 ; *Schweigger's Journ.,* **34**. 46, 1822 ; *Pogg. Ann.,* **7**. 1, 137. 1826 ; T. Bergman, *De arsenico,* Upsala, 1777 ; F. H. Newman, *Proc. Phys. Soc.,* **33**. 73, 1921 ; P. A. von Bonsdorff, *L'Inst.,* **3**. 99, 1835 ; J. K. Mitchell, *Amer. Journ. Med. Science,* (1), **10**. 122, 1832 ; H. B. Baker and H. B. Dixon, *Proc. Roy. Soc.,* **45**. 1, 1888 ; P. Orfila, *Journ. Chim. Méd.,* (1), **6**. 6, 1830 ; H. J. Emeléus, *Journ. Chem. Soc.,* 783, 1927 ; H. Schwabe, *Brandes' Arch.,* **11**. 262, 1825 ; A. W. Büchner, *ib.,* **19**. 258, 1826 ; *Repert. Pharm.,* **21**. 28, 1825 ; P. F. G. Boullay, *Journ. Pharm. Chim.,* (2), **13**. 433, 1827 ; M. François and L. Seguin, *ib.,* (8), **2**. 334, 1925 ; E. Hirschsohn, *Russ. Journ. Pharm.,* **32**. 612, 1892 ; W. T. Cooke, *Proc. Roy. Soc.,* **77**. A, 148, 1906 ; *Zeit. phys. Chem.,* **55**. 537, 1906 ; *Chem. News,* **88**. 290, 1903 ; *Proc. Chem. Soc.,* **19**. 243, 1903 ; H. V. Regnault, *Ann. Chim. Phys.,* (2), **62**. 364, 1836 ; C. F. Schönbein, *Pogg. Ann.,* **78**. 514, 1849 ; *Verh. Nat. Ges. Basel,* **1**. 237, 1857 ; W. Ipatieff, *Ber.,* **59**. B, 1412, 1926 ; W. Ipatieff and D. Nikolaief, *Journ. Russ. Phys. Chem. Soc.,* **58**. 664, 686, 692, 698, 1926 ; L. J. Thénard, *Traité de chimie,* Paris, **2**. 68, 1824 ; J. A. Buchner, *Repert. Pharm.,* **21**. 28, 1825 ; H. M. Elsey, *Science,* (2), **66**. 300, 1927.

[8] H. Moissan, *Compt. Rend.*, **99**. 874, 1884 ; **135**. 563, 1902 ; V. Thomas and P. Dupuis, *ib.*, **143**. 282, 1906 ; G. S. Sérullas, *Ann. Chim. Phys.*, (2), **38**. 319, 1828 ; J. B. A. Dumas, *ib.*, (2), **33**. 351, 1826 ; A. F. de Fourcroy and L. N. Vauquelin, *ib.*, (1), **21**. 237, 1797 ; A. Plisson, *ib.*, (2), **39**. 265, 1828 ; *Journ. Pharm. Chim.*, (1), **14**. 46, 592, 1828 ; J. Davy, *Phil. Trans.*, **102**. 169, 1812 ; G. E. Linck, *Ber.*, **32**. 892, 1899 ; **33**. 2284, 1900 ; K. A. Hofmann, *ib.*, **45**. 3329, 1912 ; K. A. Hofmann, F. Hartmann, and K. Nagel, *Ber.*, **58**. B, 808, 1925 ; W. S. Hendrixson, *Journ. Amer. Chem. Soc.*, **26**. 747, 1904 ; F. A. Gooch and J. C. Blake, *Amer. Journ. Science*, (4), **14**. 285, 1902 ; R. Napoli, *ib.*, (2), **18**. 190, 1854 ; *Journ. prakt. Chem.*, (1), **64**. 93, 1854 ; J. W. Slater, *ib.*, (1), **60**. 247, 1853 ; M. Thiele, *Ueber die allotropen Modifikationen des Arsens*, Berlin, 1910.

[4] A. Gélis, *Ann. Chim. Phys.*, (4), **30**. 114, 1873 ; J. J. Berzelius, *ib.*, (2), **5**. 179, 1817 ; (2), **11**. 225, 1819 ; *Schweigger's Journ.*, **34**. 46, 1823 ; *Pogg. Ann.*, **7**. 1, 137, 1826 ; M. Thiele, *Ueber die allotropen Modifikationen des Arsens*, Berlin, 1910 ; E. B. Hutchins, *Journ. Amer. Chem. Soc.*, **27**. 1157, 1905 ; O. Brunn, *Ber.*, **21**. 2546, 1888 ; **22**. 3205, 1889 ; G. Aimé, *Journ. Pharm. Chim.*, (3), **21**. 84, 1852 ; O. Ruff, *Ber.*, **34**. 1749, 1901 ; H. Schiff, *Liebig's Ann.*, **117**. 95, 1861 ; C. Geitner, *ib.*, **129**. 250, 1864 ; *Ueber das Verhalten des Schwefels und der schwefligen Säure zu Wasser bei hohen Druck und hoher Temperatur*, Göttingen, 1863 ; C. Heumann and P. Köchlin, *Ber.*, **15**. 418, 1736, 1882 ; R. H. Adie, *Proc. Chem. Soc.*, **15**. 133, 1899 ; H. Moissan and P. Lebeau, *Bull. Soc. Chim.*, (3), **27**. 230, 1902 ; W. Guertler, *Metall Erz*, **22**. 199, 1925 ; M. G. Levi, E. Migliorini, and G. Ercolini, *Gazz. Chim. Ital.*, **38**. i, 598, 1908.

[5] J. J. Berzelius, *Schweigger's Journ.*, **23**. 309, 430, 1818 ; **34**. 79, 1823 ; *Pogg. Ann.*, **7**. 242, 1826 ; **8**. 423, 1826.

[6] J. J. Berzelius, *Schweigger's Journ.*, **6**. 311, 1812 ; **34**. 78, 1823 ; E. B. Hutchins, *Journ. Amer. Chem. Soc.*, **27**. 1157, 1905.

[7] C. Hugot, *Ann. Chim. Phys.*, (7), **21**. 5, 1900 ; H. Moissan, *ib.*, (6), **6**. 456, 1885 ; A. Ditte, *ib.*, (6), **13**. 199, 1888 ; F. E. Brown and J. E. Snyder, *Journ. Amer. Chem. Soc.*, **47**. 2671, 1925 ; C. A. Kraus, *ib.*, **44**. 1216, 1922 ; M. Thiele, *Ueber die allotropen Modifikationen des Arsens*, Berlin, 1910 ; F. W. Bergstrom, *Journ. Phys. Chem.*, **29**. 165, 1925 ; F. W. Bergstrom, *Journ. Phys. Chem.*, **30**. 15, 1926 ; C. C. Palit and N. R. Dhar, *ib.*, **30**. 1125, 1926 ; F. H. Newman, *Proc. Phys. Soc.*, **33**. 73, 1921 ; C. Keumann and P. Köchlin, *Ber.*, **15**. 1736, 1882 ; B. Reinitzer and H. Goldschmidt, *ib.*, **13**. 850, 1880 ; F. Krafft and R. Neumann, *ib.*, **34**. 566, 1901 ; J. V. Janowsky, *ib.*, **6**. 216, 1873 ; G. Gore, *Proc. Roy. Soc.*, **20**. 441, 1872 ; **21**. 140, 1873 ; E. C. Franklin and C. A. Kraus, *Amer. Chem. Journ.*, **20**. 820, 1898 ; J. Personne, *Bull. Soc. Chim.*, (2), **1**. 163, 1864 ; *Chem. News*, **9**. 242, 1864 ; J. W. Slater, *Journ. prakt. Chem.*, (1), **60**. 247, 1853 ; T. Curtius and A. Darapsky, *ib.*, (2), **61**. 408, 1900 ; J. J. Sudborough, *Journ. Chem. Soc.*, **59**. 655, 1891 ; G. Landgrebe, *Schweigger's Journ.*, **60**. 184, 1830 ; C. M. Marx, *ib.*, **54**. 464, 1828 ; A. F. Gehlen, *ib.*, **15**. 501, 1815 ; T. Bergman, *De antimonialibus sulfuratis*, Upsala, 1782 ; O. Ruff, *Ber.*, **34**. 1749, 1901 ; A. Descamps, *Compt. Rend.*, **86**. 1066, 1878 ; E. J. Maumené, *Ann. Chim. Phys.*, (4), **3**. 349, 1864 ; P. Askenasy, K. Elöd, and H. Zieler, *Zeit. anorg. Chem.*, **162**. 161, 1827 ; K. A. Hofmann, F. Hartmann, and K. Nagel, *Ber.*, **58**. B, 808, 1925.

[8] E. Guenez, *Compt. Rend.*, **114**. 1186, 1892 ; V. Auger, *ib.*, **145**. 809, 1907 ; A. Descamps, *ib.*, **86**. 1022, 1065, 1878 ; C. Strzyzowsky, *Oester. Chem. Ztg.*, **7**. 77, 1904 ; G. E. Linck, *Ber.*, **32**. 892, 1899 ; **33**. 2284, 1900 ; H. Erdmann and M. von Unruh, *Zeit. anorg. Chem.*, **32**. 437, 1902 ; H. Lessheim, J. Meyer, and R. Samuel, *ib.*, **165**. 253, 1927 ; L. Kahlenberg and J. V. Steinle, *Trans. Amer. Electrochem. Soc.*, **44**. 493, 1923 ; H. Erdmann and R. Reppert, *Liebig's Ann.*, **361**. 6, 1908 ; R. Reppert, *Ueber gelbes, braunes, und graues Arsen*, Halle, 1907 ; M. Thiele, *Ueber die allotropen Modifikationen des Arsens*, Berlin, 1910 ; M. Kohn, *Monatsh.*, **42**. 83, 1921 ; W. Spring, *Bull. Acad. Belg.*, (3), **5**. 229, 1883 ; R. Böttger, *Dingler's Journ.*, **206**. 155, 1872 ; A. Ditte, *Ann. Chim. Phys.*, (6), **13**. 199, 1888 ; M. J. B. Orfila, *Journ. Chim. Méd.*, **6**. 321, 1830 ; F. W. Bergstrom, *Journ. Amer. Chem. Soc.*, **48**. 2319, 1926 ; J. W. Slater, *Journ. prakt. Chem.*, (1), **60**. 247, 1853.

[9] J. F. Lassaigne, *Journ. Chim. Méd.*, (1), **8**. 584, 1842 ; H. Reinsch, *Journ. prakt. Chem.*, (1), **13**. 133, 1838 ; (1), **21**. 244, 1840 ; (1), **24**. 244, 1841 ; P. Harting, *ib.*, (1), **22**. 49, 1841 ; *Bull. Sciences Phys. Nat. Neerl*, **2**. 164, 1841 ; R. Brandes and G. Ebeling, *Brandes' Arch. Apoth.*, **25**. 269, 1828 ; E. Deussen, *Arch. Pharm.*, **264**. 355, 1926 ; E. Rupp and E. Muschiol, *Ber. deut. phys. Ges.*, **33**. 62, 1923 ; F. Jackson, *Journ. Amer. Chem. Soc.*, **25**. 992, 1903 ; T. G. Wormley, *Microchemistry of Poisons*, New York, 1867 ; C. H. Pfaff, *Handbuch der analytischen Chemie*, Altona, **1**. 112, 1822 ; R. Schiff and N. Tarugi, *Ber.*, **27**. 3437, 1884 ; J. Marsh, *Edin. Phil. Journ.*, **21**. 229, 1836 ; H. Gutzeit, *Pharm. Ztg.*, **24**. 263, 1879 ; A. Marcet, *Trans. Med. Chim. Soc.*, **3**. 342, 1812 ; **6**. 663, 1815 ; *Phil. Mag.*, **41**. 121, 1813 ; A. Bettendorff, *Zeit. anal. Chem.*, **9**. 105, 1870 ; A. Pinkus and F. Martin, *Journ. Chim. Phys.*, **24**. 83, 137, 1927.

[10] H. W. Ambuster, *Chem. News*, **138**. 39, 1924 ; J. C. Brown, *Bull. Indian Ind. and Labour*, **6**, 1921.

[11] A. Renault, L. Fournier, and L. Guénot, *Compt. Rend.*, **161**. 685, 1915 ; R. Dalimier, *ib.*, **162**. 440, 1916 ; G. T. Morgan, *Organic Compounds of Arsenic and Antimony*, London, 1918 ; G. W. Raiziss and J. L. Gavron, *Organic Arsenical Compounds*, New York, 1923 ; A. Valeur, *Chimie et toxicologie de l'arsenic et de ses composés*, Paris, 1904.

[12] A. Eckmann, *U.S. Pat. No.* 1650333, 1927.

§ 7. The Physiological Action of Arsenic

So far as the published records go, arsenical preparations have been used for criminal purposes more than is the case with any other poison. The destruction of life by poison has been practised from very early times. It is probable that some of the accounts of the secret poisons of the ancients are highly exaggerated, like those recorded by F. Hoffmann.[1] The infamous Lucusta—mentioned by Tacitus (*Annales*, **4.** 8 ; **12.** 66 ; **13.** 15), Suetonius (*Vitæ duodecim Cæsarum*, **6.** 33), and Juvenal (*Satiræ*, **1.** 71)—was apparently a recognized adept in the early part of the Christian era ; she is said to have prepared the poison by which Agrippina removed Claudius, and by which Nero disposed of Britannicus, the son of Agrippina. J. B. Porta, in his *Magiæ naturalis* (Neapoli, 1589), introduces quite a lot of information about poisons. Assassination by poison appears to have been a tolerated if not a professed expedient among the Italian statesmen in the fifteenth and sixteenth centuries. During the latter half of the seventeenth century, the iniquitous La Spara and La Tofagna were notorious for their skill in the nefarious profession. In the art *negrós efferre maritos*, they rivalled Lucusta herself. The attention of the Roman Government was first drawn to these proceedings partly by the unaccountable mortality amongst married men, and partly by the reports of the clergy, who, though bound by their vows not to betray individuals, could not help representing to the authorities the fearful number of accounts of domestic murders to which they were compelled to listen in the confessional. The two sorceresses compounded liquids in small glass phials bearing the image of a saint, and labelled with various names : *Acquetta di Napoli, Acqua Toffana*, the *Manna of St. Nicholas, Manna of Bari*, etc. It has been shown that the mysterious liquid was mainly a soln. of arsenious acid of varying concentration. The preparation was sold ostensibly for use as a cosmetic or for some other innocent purpose ; actually over six hundred persons, including the popes Pius III, and Clement XIV, are said to have been poisoned through its instrumentality. The *acquetta di Perugia* is supposed to have been made by sprinkling pieces from the carcase of a pig, with white arsenic, and collecting the juice which ran from the meat. According to F. Hoffmann, and S. Hahnemann, arsenical poisons were used by the traditionally infamous Lucretia Borgia of Italy, and the Marchioness de Brinvilliers, and M. de St. Croix of Paris. According to one version, the two French poisoners learned the toxic art from Exili Gilles, but F. Funck-Brentano [2] supposed that they obtained their knowledge from C. Glaser, author of *Traité de chimie* (Paris, 1663).

Plants gradually wither when the root and stem are placed in a soln. of arsenious acid ; and a small proportion of arsenic will be found in all parts of the plant. E. F. von Gorup-Besanez [3] found that only infinitesimal amounts of arsenic are taken up by plants grown in arsenical soils—*vide supra*. The steeping of seed corn in arsenical preparations to prevent smut does not deleteriously affect the future growth of the plant. Arsenical fumes and smelter smoke from factories do not have a very marked injurious action on shrubs and trees in the vicinity. W. C. Ebaugh decided that the appearance of the leaves of lucerne and sugar-beet grown in smelter districts is entirely analogous to that produced when solid particles of fine dust are allowed to fall upon plants ; and the effects observed in moist weather, when a whole field may be blighted, are due to the sulphur oxides. The complaints, however, show that not only are the trees and grass injured by the sulphur oxides in the fumes, but the grass is rendered poisonous for horses and stock. J. Haubner, J. Sussdorf, M. Freytag, and others have shown that in many cases the damage is due to the deposition of arsenious oxide on the vegetation. W. D. Harkins and R. E. Swain found excessive amounts of deposited not absorbed arsenic in the soils, snow, hay and grain, and the vegetation of the region about the Anaconda smelting works. The Inspector under the Alkali Acts of Great Britain reported in 1893 :

The inspection of the arsenic works had been much called for by residents in the district where they are found, and the necessity for the adoption of remedial measures was shown by the frequent litigation brought about by the alleged destruction of cattle through eating grass said to be poisoned by the arsenic too freely distributed through the air from the chimneys up to which it had been carried by the draught. The arsenic driven off by the heat of the roasting furnace was caught and retained as far as possible, in long flues, culverts, and settling chambers, but although these were often of great extent, reaching in one place, a length of 2895 feet, or more than half a mile, and having a capacity of 60,795 cubic feet, yet arsenic was always liable to pass away. In one case, a test of the chimney gases showed the presence of as much as 7·40 grains of arsenic trioxide in a cubic foot of gases passing into the air, and small flakes of it were seen falling continually in a mild snow-shower;

and in 1906, he reported that the average escape of arsenic trioxide per cubic foot of chimney gases from furnaces provided with wash-towers was 0·080 grain in 1896, and 0·030 grain in 1906.

Infusoria, and the lower forms of animal life quickly perish in the presence of a dil. soln. of arsenious acid; although F. C. Calvert found that a 1 : 1000 soln. has no action on fungi and protoplasmic life. The effect of very dil. soln. on moulds has been indicated above. The toxic effect of arsenical preparations on insects is illustrated by the arsenical fly-papers. H. Eulenberg studied the effects on birds; H. Schulz, on rabbits and guinea-pigs; J. Lolliot, on dogs; and F. S. Hammett and co-workers, on rats. J. J. Theron and T. D. Hall discussed the toxicity of locusts poisoned by arsenic, when eaten by animals.

White arsenic has no action on the skin of man, but eczematous eruptions on the legs have been produced by wearing stockings coloured with aniline dyes prepared with arsenic. This recalls the reputed effects produced by the *poisoned shirts*, a favourite medium of the poisoners of the seventeenth century. The tail of the shirt was soaked in a conc. soln. of an arsenical preparation. When the dried garment was worn, it produced violent dermatitis with ulceration about the perineum and neighbouring parts. The Duke of Savoy is said to have succumbed to the effects of a poisoned shirt of this kind. C. M. Tidy [4] mentioned fatal effects produced by the external applications of arsenical violet powder to infants; and A. Haberda, and C. E. Mangor, cases of death criminally produced by placing white arsenic in the vagina; and G. Feinstein, a case of acute poisoning from the use of arsenic in dentistry. In the so-called *Haff sickness*, more or less prevalent about the Haff lagoon, off the Baltic Sea, F. Glaser suggested that it is a form of arsenical poisoning from arsenical chloride fumes derived from the waste discharge, containing arsenic chloride, from the sulphite pulp plants on or near the Haff. This does not agree with the observations of the Königsberger Zellstoff-Fabriken und Chemische Werke, G. Lockemann, and S. Hilpert. A. Juckenack and A. Brüning said that arsenical gases could be produced by the action of algæ on arsenical trade wastes.

When used internally arsenic is considered to be a severe gastrointestinal irritant; but in minute doses the arsenic acts as a gastric stimulant causing a dilation of the gastric vessels, and an increased flow of gastric juice. Small doses stimulate the duodenum. Larger doses produce effects within 8 to 60 minutes. The sufferer experiences faintness, nausea, sickness, epigastric pains, and vomiting. The ejected matters are at first composed of the substances eaten, then they may appear brown and streaked with blood. Diarrhœa may accompany the vomiting, and the symptoms then bear a close resemblance to those of cholera. The extremities become cold, and the pulse is feeble. The face is at first pale, and then acquires a bluish tint; the temp. falls lower and lower, and there is finally a collapse. Death follows in from 5 to 20 hrs. after taking the poison. The dangerous doses of white arsenic are 0·13 grm. for an adult; 1·9 grms. for a horse; 0·64 grm. for a cow; and 0·32 to 0·64 grm. for a dog. E. W. Schwartze said that a fatal dose of dissolved arsenic trioxide administered by the mouth is 75 mgrms. per kilogram with rats; and the fatal dose with undissolved arsenic trioxide ground to an impalpable powder—0·0125–0·0025 mm. diam.—is about 100 mgrms. per kgrm.;

for rabbits, the fatal dose of dissolved arsenic trioxide is 15–20 mgrms. per kgrm. ; and for the undissolved arsenic trioxide powdered as just indicated, about 200 mgrms. per kgrm. ; and for chickens, respectively 66·7 mgrms. per kgrm., and 75 mgrms. per kgrm.

As observed by B. C. Brodie, whether the arsenic be taken internally or externally, the stomach is intensely inflamed, showing that arsenic is excreted by the blood into the stomach. The small intestine is also inflamed. The *gelation médico-legale de l'assassinat de la Duchesse de Praslin* was discussed by A. Tardieu.[5] In chronic poisoning with small doses, arsenic is not classed as a cumulative poison. There is a loss of appetite, nausea, perhaps vomiting, slight abdominal pain, and mild diarrhœa. The eyelids become a little puffy, there is a watering of the eyes and nose—explained by the complaint of " always having a cold "— attended by an inflammation of the pharynx, air-passages, and lung-tissue ; salivation and sore gums ; and a slight headache. With the slow poisoning by repeated small doses, the illness may resemble in miniature that produced by large doses, or it may resemble very closely that state described by a general condition of ill health. There may be a slight yellowness or a brown pigmentation of the skin best marked about the neck. There may be a general increase of the epiderm scales, called keratosis. The relation between arsenic and the keratine tissue has been studied by H. G. Brooke and L. Roberts, S. Delépine, and A. Erlicki and J. Rybalkin. The exanthema sometimes produced is called *eczema arsenicale*. The nervous system is nearly always disturbed, but in a variety of ways. There may be fainting, and paralysis of the muscles of the limbs especially the extensors of the hands and feet ; ataxic gait, severe darting pains in the limbs, and rapid muscular atrophy. This subject was studied by G. Brouardel, W. H. Willcox, etc. There may be delirium, acute mania, and convulsions ; while, towards the end, a kind of hectic fever supervenes, ending in death by exhaustion. After death, there appears to have been widespread fatty degeneration of the heart, liver, kidneys, stomach, and muscles. The interference of arsenic with tissue oxidation determines the fatty degeneration. C. Binz and H. Schulz suggested that arsenic can take oxygen from and give up oxygen to the tissues. C. Binz stated that the white arsenic is excreted mostly as arsenic acid ; but this does not agree with the observations of T. Husemann, and J. D. Mann, who found the ingested arsenic is excreted as arsenious acid. T. Araki considers that both arsenic and phosphorus lessen oxidation because lactic acid appears in the urine when either of these poisons is taken ; that acid is the result of insufficient oxidation. Arsenic is excreted *viâ* the kidneys, then through the bile, and by the skin and hair. Arsenic appears in the urine 5 or 6 hrs. after it has been taken, and the elimination of one dose requires 5–8 days. According to D. Vitali, neither arsenic acid nor arsenious acid combines with albumin to form albuminates. By experiments on dogs, this author confirms the observation that arsenic anhydride is converted by the organism into arsenic trioxide, which then passes into the urine ; the arsenic acid is not found free in the urine, but rather in a state of combination ; and it probably displaces phosphoric acid in phosphoglyceric acid. This acid is a decomposition product of lecithin, and it thus seems as if the arsenic can really replace phosphorus.

It is well known to grooms, and horse-dealers that a little white arsenic given daily with the corn of a horse improves its coat, and renders it plump and fat, probably acting by increasing the assimilation of the food owing to the stimulation of the various cells and glands in the alimentary canal to superaction. When a horse has been so treated for a long time, and the practice is discontinued, the animal rapidly loses condition, presumably owing to the enfeebled secreting power of the cells and glands in the intestinal tract when the stimulus is withdrawn. According to J. Schallgruber,[6] A. Tardieu, J. J. Tschudi, C. Maclagan, B. Knapp and co-workers, G. Joachimoglu, F. Kübler, J. F. W. Johnston, E. Schäfer, C. Heisch, E. Kopp, and H. E. Roscoe, white arsenic is widely distributed in some parts of lower Austria, in Styria, and in the hilly country extending towards Austria. The white arsenic is locally known as *hidrach*—a corruption of *Huttenrauch*, smelter-house smoke—and is obtained from the flues attached to the smelting furnaces. The white arsenic is regularly eaten by some of the peasants. The doses taken are at first small, and they are progressively increased so that the arsenic-eaters can swallow with impunity 4 or 5 grains of arsenious oxide at a time. It is said that the object of the arsenic-eater is to be able to endure greater fatigue in mountain climbing by increasing the respiratory power. This recalls the medicinal use of arsenic in the cases of asthma and other chest diseases. It is also said that the arsenic-eater becomes plump and fat, and the skin greatly improved. The following is J. F. W. Johnston's romantic description of the effects:

By the use of hidrach the Styrian peasant-girl adds to the natural graces of her filling and rounding form, paints with brighter hues her blushing cheeks and tempting lips, and imparts a new and winning lustre to her sparkling eyes. Every one sees and admires the reality of her growing beauty ; the young men sound her praises, and become suppliants for her favour. She triumphs over the affections of all, and compels the chosen one to her feet. Thus, even cruel arsenic, so often the minister of crime and the parent of sorrow, bears a blessed jewel in its forehead, and, as a love-awakener, becomes at times the harbinger of happiness, the soother of ardent longings, and the bestower of contentment and peace.

It is also said that in some parts of India, particularly the Punjaub, arsenic-eating is practised as an aphrodisiac. According to C. Heisch's report, once the practice of arsenic-eating has begun, it can only be left off by very gradually diminishing the daily dose, as a sudden cessation causes sickness, burning pains in the stomach, and other symptoms of poisoning, very speedily followed by death. J. F. W. Johnston said that, as a rule, arsenic-eaters are long-lived, and are peculiarly exempt from infectious diseases, fevers, etc., but unless they gradually give up the practice invariably die suddenly. It is further stated :

In this part of the world, when a graveyard is full, it is shut up for about twelve years, when all the graves which are not private property by purchase are dug up, the bones are collected in the charnel-house, the ground is ploughed over, and burying begins again. On these occasions the bodies of arsenic-eaters are found almost unchanged, and recognizable by their friends. Many people suppose that the finding of their bodies is the origin of the story of the vampire.

The doctrine of habituation, outlined with some poetic licence by J. F. W. Johnston, was generally accepted for many years, although it now appears to be based on plausible evidence which, when critically examined, does not justify the conclusions. There have been sceptics—*e.g.* W. B. Kesteven, A. S. Taylor, and R. Christison—who called the reports a " mass of absurdity " and " a pure fable." W. B. Kesteven collected data from the arsenic-workers of Cornwall which showed that the so-called arsenic or hidrach of the Styrian peasants cannot be ordinary arsenic trioxide. Experiments on the subject have been made by G. Brouardel, L. de Busscher, M. Cloetta, A. R. Cushny, M. Danger and C. Flandin, M. Doyon and A. Morel, W. Hausmann, D. J. Healey and W. W. Dimock, A. Heffter, G. Joachimoglu, B. Knapp and E. and H. Buchner, F. Kübler, F. H. McCrudden, E. D. Mackenzie, K. Morishima, W. C. O'Kane and co-workers, D. McN. Parker, E. Schefer, T. Sollmann, J. J. von Tschudi, M. Willberg, R. A. Witthaus and T. C. Becker, etc. H. G. Wells said that the tacit assumption has frequently been made that all preparations of arsenic are equally toxic, and that they approach in toxicity very nearly to that of dissolved arsenic trioxide. The rate of soln. of arsenic trioxide depends on its grain-size, and so does its toxicity. Many vital factors have not been under the control of the experimenters. E. W. Schwartze showed that the toxicity of undissolved arsenic trioxide depends on its state of subdivision, and slight differences in the toxicity of dissolved arsenic trioxide occur with different species of animals. He concluded :

No unimpeachable evidence exists that either man or other higher animals can acquire a tolerance to this drug, owing chiefly to the erroneous assumption that all preparations of undissolved arsenic trioxide possess equal potency, and approach in degree the potency of dissolved arsenious oxide. The consumption of large amounts of undissolved arsenious oxide can be as readily explained on the basis that a relatively insoluble and coarse preparation was used as by assuming that habituation had been produced. The toleration of large doses may therefore be due not to an attribute inherent in the consumer, but to an attribute inherent in the preparation used, namely, its relative insolubility due to the relatively small extent of exposed surface of the particles and the low specific rate of solution.

In cases of poisoning the stomach should be washed out ; and the least irritating and depressing of emetics applied. Unlimited quantities of freshly precipitated ferric hydroxide or dialyzed iron should be taken ; and if neither of these be available, magnesia, or castor oil and water, may be used. Give brandy or ether subcutaneously ; and apply hot blankets to the feet and abdomen. The ferric hydroxide converts the arsenious acid into an insoluble form. This remedial measure was proposed by R. Bunsen and A. A. Berthold.[7] It is not a true antidote, for it acts only where it comes in contact with the arsenious acid ; and if the poison has been removed from the stomach by absorption with the tissues, the administration of the hydroxide is useless. Neither R. H. Brett, nor J. H. Orton obtained good results; but, according to D. Maclagan, this was owing to the incorrect application. T. and H. Smith found that hydroxide five months old has only one-fourth the power of the freshly prepared hydroxide in taking up arsenious acid—*vide infra*, chemical properties of arsenic trioxide. H. W. Fischer and co-workers tried the use of a negative hydrosol of ferric oxide, stabilized with glycerol, for intravenous injection in arsenical poisoning.

REFERENCES.

[1] L. Lewin, *Die Gifte in der Weltgeschichte*, Berlin, 1920 ; F. Hoffmann, *Dissertatio de læsionibus externis, aborbtivis venenis ac philtris*, Francofurti, 1729 ; *Medicinæ rationalis systematicæ*, Halæ, 2. 185, 1729 ; S. Hahnemann, *Ueber die Arsenikvergiftung*, Leipsiæ, 35, 1786 ; J. Beckmann, *Beyträge zur Geschichte der Erfindungen*, Leipzig, 1. 257, 1786 ; London, 1. 47, 1846 ; C. J. S. Thompson, *Poison Romance and Poison Mysteries*, London, 1899 ; A. W. and M. W. Blyth, *Poisons : Their Effects and Detection*, London, 1906 ; C. Mackay, *Memoirs of Extraordinary Delusions*, London, 1842 ; K. Petrén, *Les différentes formes de l'arsénicisme et en particulier de l'arsénicisme provenant de l'habitation ou des objets domestiques*, Paris, 1926.

[2] F. Funck-Brentano, *Princes and Poisoners : Studies of the Court of Louis XIV*, London, 1901 ; F. M. A. de Voltaire, *Siècle de Louis XIV*, Berlin, 1751 ; M. du Noyer, *Lettres historiques et galantes par Madam de C—*, Cologne, 2. 101, 1700 ; 4. 376, 1711 ; Madame de Sévigné, *Lettres de Madame Rabutin-Chantal, Marquise de Sévigné, à Madame la Comtesse de Grignan, la fille*, La Haye, 2. 44, 1726 ; B. de la Martinière, *Histoire de la vie et du regne de Louis XIV*, La Haye, 4. 229, 1740 ; C. G. Stenzel, *De veneris terminatis et temporaneis, quæ Galli les poudres de succession vocant*, Vitebergæ, 1730 ; M. de Reboulet, *Histoire du règne de Louis XIV*, Avignon, 5. 159, 1746 ; G. de Pitaval, *Causes celèbres*, La Haye, 1. 267, 1737.

[3] E. F. von Gorup-Besanez, *Liebig's Ann.*, 128. 243, 1866 ; H. Eulenberg, *Handbuch der Gewerbe-Hygiene*, Berlin, 1876 ; J. J. Theron and T. D. Hall, *Chem. News*, 130. 133, 1925 ; H. Schulz, *Arch. Exp. Pathol. Pharmakol.*, 15. 322, 1882 ; J. Lolliot, *Etude physiologique d'arsènic*, Paris, 1868 ; W. C. Ebaugh, *Journ. Amer. Chem. Soc.*, 29. 951, 1907 ; W. D. Harkins and R. E. Swain, *ib.*, 29. 970, 1909 ; 30. 915, 1908 ; J. Haubner, *Arch. wiss. prakt. Tierheilk.*, 4. 97, 241, 1878 ; J. Sussdorf, *Allgem. deut. naturhist. Ztg.*, 1. 97, 1855 ; M. Freytag, *Jahrb. Berg. Hütt.*, (3), 1873 ; E. Haselhoff and G. Lindau, *Die Beschädigung der Vegetation durch Rauch*, Leipzig, 1903 ; J. von Schröder and C. Reuss, *Die Beschädigung der Vegetation durch Rauch*, Berlin, 1883 ; R. Hasenclever, *Die Beschädigung der Vegetation durch saure Gase*, Berlin, 1879 ; G. Jäger, *Ueber die Wirkung des Arseniks auf die Pflanzen*, Stuttgart, 1864 ; F. S. Hammett, J. H. Muller, and J. E. Mowrey, *Journ. Pharm. Exp. Therapeutics*, 19. 337, 1922 ; A. Stöckhardt, *Chem. Ackermann*, 24, 111, 1872 ; F. C. Calvert, *Proc. Roy. Soc.*, 20. 197, 1872 ; *Compt. Rend.*, 75. 1015, 1872 ; *Chem. News*, 25. 151, 157, 1872.

[4] C. M. Tidy, *Lancet*, 250, 1878 ; A. Haberda, *Wien Klin. Wochenschr.*, 10. 201, 1897 ; C. E. Mangor, *Acta Reg. Soc. Med. Havniens*, 3. 178, 1792 ; B. C. Brodie, *Phil. Trans.*, 102. 205, 1812 ; E. W. Schwartze, *Journ. Pharmacol.*, 20. 181, 1922 ; G. Feinstein, *Ueber Fälle von acuter Arsenintoxikation nach zahnärztlichen Einlagen*, Königsberg, 1925 ; F. Glaser, *Chem. Ztg.*, 50. 185, 1926 ; Königsberger Zellstoff-Fabriken und Chemische Werke, *ib.*, 50. 282, 1926 ; A. Juckenack and A. Brüning, *ib.*, 50. 513, 1926 ; G. Lockemann, *ib.*, 50. 313, 1926 ; S. Hilpert, *Papierfabr.*, 162, 1926.

[5] A. Tardieu, *Ann. Hyg.*, 38. 390, 1847 ; H. G. Brooke and L. Roberts, *Brit. Journ. Dermatology*, 13. 121, 1901 ; S. Delépine, *Journ. Physiol.*, 12. 27, 1891 ; A. Erlicki and J. Rybalkin, *Arch. Psych. Nerven.*, 23. 861, 1892 ; C. Binz and H. Schulz, *Arch. Exp. Pathol.*, 11. 200, 1879 ; C. Binz, *ib.*, 38. 259, 1897 ; C. Binz and C. Laar, *ib.*, 41. 179, 1898 ; T. Husemann, *Deut. med.*

Wochenschr., **18**. 1081, 1137, 1892 ; J. D. Mann, *Forensic Medicine and Toxicology*, London, 463, 1908 ; T. Araki, *Zeit. physiol. Chem.*, **17**. 311, 1893 ; D. Vitali, *L'Orosi*, **16**. 73, 145, 1893 ; G. Brouardel, *Étude sur l'arsenicisme*, Paris, 1897 ; A. Read, *Recherches de l'arsenic dans les cas d'empoisonnement*, Paris, 1867 ; W. H. Willcox, *Brit. Med. Journ.*, ii, 118, 371, 1922 ; *Med. Press and Circular*, **173**. 7, 1926.

• C. Maclagan, *Pharm. Journ.*, (2), **6**. 615, 1865 ; *Edin. Med. Journ.*, **10**. 201, 1864 ; R. Christison, *ib.*, **2**. 709, 1856 ; *Edin. Journ. Science*, **7**. 379, 1827 ; A. Tardieu, *Étude médico-légale et clinique sur l'empoisonnement*, Paris, 449, 1857 ; M. Cloetta, *Arch. Exp. Path.*, **54**. 196, 1906 ; G. Joachimoglu, *ib.*, **79**. 419, 1916 ; F. H. McCrudden, *ib.*, **62**. 374, 1910 ; F. Kübler, *ib.*, **98**. 185, 1923 ; H. E. Roscoe, *Mem. Manchester Lit. Phil. Soc.*, **2**, 11, 208, 1862 ; *Chem. News*, **2**. 261, 1860 ; C. Heisch, *ib.*, **1**. 280, 1860 ; *Pharm. Journ.*, (2), **1**. 556, 1860 ; E. Schäfer, *Sitzber. Akad. Wien*, **25**. 495, 1857 ; **41**. 573, 1860 ; *Chem. News*, **4**. 19, 1861 ; J. F. W. Johnston, *The Chemistry of Common Life*, London, **2**. 201, 1855 ; E. W. Schwartze, *Journ. Franklin Inst.*, **195**. 121, 1923 ; *Journ. Pharmacol.*, **20**. 181, 1922 ; E. W. Schwartze and C. L. Alsberg, *ib.*, **21**. 1, 1923 ; E. W. Schwartze and J. C. Munch, *ib.*, **28**. 351, 1926 ; E. Kopp, *Monit. Scient.*, (1), **3**. 105, 1861 ; L. de Busscher, *Arch. Internat. Pharmacol.*, **10**. 415, 1902 ; K. Morishima, *ib.*, **8**. 765, 1900 ; G. Brouardel, *Étude sur l'arsenicisme*, Paris, 1897 ; M. Danger and C. Flandin, *De l'arsenic*, Paris 1841 ; C. Flandin, *Traité des poisons ou toxicologie*, Paris, **1**. 736, 1846 ; A. R. Cushny, *Pharma, cology and Therapeutics*, Philadelphia, 596, 1915 ; H. G. Wells, *Chemical Pathology*, Philadelphia, 237, 1920 ; R. A. Witthaus and T. C. Becker, *Medical Jurisprudence, Forensic Medicine and Toxicology*, New York, **4**. 379, 446, 1896 ; A. S. Taylor, *Medical Jurisprudence*, London, 1886 ; *On Poisons*, London, 1848 and 1859 ; M. Doyon and A. Morel, *Compt. Rend. Soc. Biol.*, **61**. 116, 1906 ; W. Hausmann, *Deut. Med. Woch.*, **29**. 987, 1903 ; *Arch. ges. Physiol.*, **113**. 327, 1906 ; *Arch. Internat. Pharmacol.* **11**. 483, 1903 ; *Ergeb. Physiol.*, **6**. 83, 1907 ; A. Heffter, *ib.*, ii, 115, 1903 ; B. Knapp and E. and H. Buchner, *Ergänzhft. Centr. allgem. Gesund.*, ii, 1, 1889 ; E. D. Mackenzie, *Indian Med. Gaz.*, **7**. 183, 1872 ; W. C. O'Kane, C. H. Hadley, and W. A. Osgood, *Bull. New Hampshire Agr. Exper. Stat.*, 183, 1917 ; J. Schallgruber, *Med. Jahrb. Oesterr. Staates*, (2), **1**. i, 99, 1822 : T. Sollmann, *Journ. Pharmacol.*, **18**. 43, 1921 ; J. J. von Tschudi, *Wien Med. Woch.*, **1**. 453, 1851 ; **3**. 8, 1853 ; M. Willberg, *Biochem. Zeit.*, **51**. 231, 1913 ; W. B. Kesteven, *Assoc. Med. Journ.*, 811, 1856 ; D. McN. Parker, *Edin. Med. Journ.*, **10**. 116, 1864 ; D. J. Healey and W. W. Dimock, *Science*, (2), **54**. 157, 1921.

⁷ D. Maclagan, *Edin. Med. Surg. Journ.*, **54**. 106, 1840 ; R. H. Brett, *Med. Gaz.*, 220, 1835 ; J. H. Orton, *Lancet*, 232, 1835 ; T. and H. Smith, *Pharm. Journ.*, (2), **7**. 139, 1865 ; R. Bunsen and A. A. Berthold, *Das Eisenoxydhydrat, ein Gegengift des weissen Arseniks oder der arsenigen Säure*, Göttingen, 1834 ; J. Zeller, *Schwefelsaures Eisenoxyd mit gebrannter Magnesia als Gegenmittel gegen arsenige Säure*, Tübingen, 1853 ; H. W. Fischer, *Biochem. Zeit.*, **27**. 223, 258, 1910 ; H. W. Fischer and E. Kuznitzky, *ib.*, **27**. 311, 1910.

§ 8. The Atomic Weight and Valency of Arsenic

Prior to 1826, J. J. Berzelius [1] considered the at. wt. of arsenic to be 150·52 when that of oxygen is 16, and he represented the formula of arsenious and arsenic anhydrides to be respectively AsO_3 and AsO_5, but when he found that the respective formulæ As_2O_3 and As_2O_5 better represented the facts, the at. wt. became nearer 75·26. P. T. Meissner, and O. B. Kühn took the equivalent of arsenic to be 37·5 ; and J. Dalton, 42. T. Thomson also made an estimate. The assumption that the at. wt. of arsenic is near 75 fits with Avogadro's law ; with the sp. ht. rule ; with the law of isomorphism ; and the periodic rule.

Arsenic is tervalent in arsine, as is the case with nitrogen in ammonia, and of phosphorus in phosphine. In the arsenamide, too, of C. Hugot the arsenic is terva-lent, $As(NH_2)_3$; and in the arsenic nitride, AsN, the arsenic has the same valency as nitrogen. Although W. R. Smith and J. E. Hora were unable to prepare arsenic pentachloride, $AsCl_5$, yet O. Ruff and H. Graf prepared arsenic pentafluoride, AsF_5, in which the arsenic is very probably quinquevalent. R. Bunsen, A. Cahours and A. Riche, H. H. Landolt, A. Michaelis, etc., have prepared many alkyl deriva-tives in which the arsenic is either ter- or quinquevalent. Thus, cacodyl with the empirical formula $As(CH_3)_2$ has a vap. density in agreement with the mol. formula $(CH_3)_2As.As(CH_3)_2$. Similarly with phenyl-cacodyl $As_2(C_6H_5)_4$, and A. von Baeyer's two series of chloro-alkyl derivatives—namely, $As(CH_3)_2Cl, As(CH_3)_2Cl$, and $AsCl_3$; and $As(CH_3)_3Cl_2$, $As(CH_3)_2Cl$, and $As(CH_3)Cl_4$—illustrates the same thing. Substances like realgar, AsS, and arsenic selenide, $AsSe$, have mol. wts. in agreement with more complex molecules. Thus, above 1000°, the mol. of the sulphide is probably As_2S_2, and below that temp. As_4S_4. W. Schenk and G. Racky found no evidence of bivalent arsenic, for the mol. wt. of the so-called arsenic diiodide corresponds with the formula As_2I_4. W. H. Mills and R. Raper, and A. Rosenheim and W. Plato prepared optically active compounds of arsenic. M. Padoa discussed the valency of arsenic.

In 1811, J. J. Berzelius obtained the high value 80·2 (oxygen 16, silver 107·92) for the at. wt. of arsenic when calculated from the ratio $2As : 50$; the low value 69·7–70·1 from the synthesis of lead arsenite, $Pb_3(AsO_3)_2$; and in 1818, he obtained 75·01 from the action of sulphur on arsenic trioxide, $2As_2O_3 : 3SO_2$. T. Thomson obtained 76·35 for the ratio $2As : As_2O_5$. J. Pelouze calculated 74·95 from the ratio $AsCl_3 : 3Ag$, and J. B. A. Dumas, 74·90; while from the ratio $AsBr_3 : 3Ag$, W. Wallace obtained 74·22. F. Kessler obtained 75·13 from the ratio $3As_2O_3 : 2K_2Cr_2O_7$; and 75·26 from the ratio $3As_2O_3 : 2KClO_3$. J. G. Hibbs obtained 74·98 from the ratio $Na_4As_2O_7 : 4NaCl$; W. Ebaugh, 75·07 from $Ag_3AsO_4 : 3AgCl$; 74·97 from $Ag_3AsO_4 : 3Ag$; 75·09 from $Pb_3(AsO_4)_2 : 3PbCl_2$; and 75 from $Pb_3(AsO_4)_2 : 3PbBr_2$; and G. P. Baxter and F. B. Coffin, 74·95 from the ratios $Ag_3AsO_4 : 3AgCl$, and $Ag_3AsO_4 : 3AgBr$. F. W. Clarke gave 74·957 for the general average; B. Brauner, 75; and the International Table for 1925, 74·96.

The **atomic number** of arsenic is 33. F. W. Aston [2] found no **isotopes** other than for atoms of mass 75. G. Kirsch and H. Pettersson found that arsenic does not give off long-range particles corresponding with an **atomic disintegration** when bombarded by the a-particles from radium-C. N. Bohr [3] represented the **electronic structure** of arsenic by (2)(4,4)(6,6,6)(4,1). The subject was also discussed by L. Brüninghaus, J. H. W. Booth, M. L. Huggins, H. G. Grimm and A. Sommerfeld, C. D. Niven, S. Meyer, and H. Collins. M. Padoa discussed the valencies of the crystal lattices.

REFERENCES.

[1] J. J. Berzelius, *Ann. Chim. Phys.*, (1), **80**. 9, 1811 ; (2), **2**. 179, 1817 ; (2), **11**. 237, 1819 ; *Schweigger's Journ.*, **21**. 328, 1817 ; **23**. 173, 1818 ; *Gilbert's Ann.*, **38**. 204. 1811 ; *Afhand. Fys. Kemi Min.*, **5**. 459, 464, 1818 ; *Pogg. Ann.*, **8**. 1, 1826 ; F. Kessler, *ib.*, **95**. 204, 1855 ; **113**. 134, 1861 ; P. T. Meissner, *Chemische Æquivalenten-oder Atomenlehre*, Wien, 1838 ; J. Pelouze, *Compt. Rend.*, **20**. 1047, 1845 ; O. B. Kühn, *Lehrbuch der Stöchiometrie*, Leipzig, 1837 ; J. Dalton, *A New System of Chemical Philosophy*, Manchester, **2**. 264, 1810 ; T. Thomson, *Ann. Phil.*, (2). **1**. 1, 1821 ; J. B. A. Dumas, *Ann. Chim. Phys.*, (3), **55**. 174, 1859 ; J. D. van der Plaats, *ib.*, (6), **7**. 499, 1886 ; W. Wallace, *Phil. Mag.*, (4), **18**. 279, 1859 ; *B.A. Rep.*, **88**, 1859 ; J. G. Hibbs, *Action of Hydrochloric Acid Gas upon Arsenates and Nitrates. The Atomic Weights of Nitrogen and Arsenic*, Philadelphia, 1896 ; *Journ. Amer. Chem. Soc.*, **18**. 1044, 1896 ; W. Ebaugh, *ib.*, **24**. 489, 1902 ; *The Atomic Weight of Arsenic*, Philadelphia, 1901 ; G. P. Baxter and F. B. Coffin. *Journ. Amer. Chem. Soc.*, **31**. 297, 1909 ; F. W. Clarke, *A Recalculation of the Atomic Weights*, Washington, 308, 1910 ; W. H. Mills and R. Raper, *Journ. Chem. Soc.*, **127**. 2879, 1925 ; A. Rosenheim and W. Plato, *Ber.*, **58**. 2000, 1925 ; B. Brauner in R. Abegg, *Handbuch der anorganischen Chemie*, Leipzig, **3**. iii, 490, 1907 ; *Monatsh.*, **11**. 549, 1891 ; T. Thomson, *Ann. Phil.*, **4**. 171, 1814 ; **7**. 343, 1816 ; W. Schenk and G. Racky, *Liebig's Ann.*, **394**. 178, 1912 ; A. von Baeyer, *ib.*, **107**. 257, 1858 ; R. Bunsen, *ib.*, **37**. 1, 1841 ; **42**. 14, 1842 ; **46**. 1, 1843 ; H. H. Landolt, *ib.*, **92**. 370, 1854 ; W. R. Smith and J. E. Hora, *Journ. Amer. Chem. Soc.*, **26**. 632, 1904 ; O. Ruff and H. Graf, *Ber.*, **39**. 67, 1906 ; A. Michaelis, *ib.*, **8**. 1316, 1875 ; C. Hugot, *Compt. Rend.*, **139**, 54, 1904 ; A. Cahours and A. Riche, *ib.*, **35**. 91, 1852 ; **36**. 1001, 1853 ; M. Padoa, *Gazz. Chim. Ital.*, **52**. ii, 189, 1922.

[2] F. W. Aston, *Phil. Mag.*, (6), **40**. 628, 1920 ; (6), **49**. 1191, 1925 ; *Isotopes*, London, 1922 ; *Proc. Roy. Soc.*, **115**. A, 487, 1927 ; G. Kirsch and H. Pettersson, *Nature*, **112**. 394, 1923 ; *Phil. Mag.*, (6), **47**. 500, 1924 ; *Sitzber. Akad. Wien*, **132**. 299, 1924.

[3] N. Bohr, *Nature*, **112**. Suppl., 1923 ; L. Brüninghaus, *Rev. Gén. Elect.*, **12**. 466, 1922 ; H. Collins, *Chem. News*, **129**. 205, 1924 ; J. H. W. Booth, *ib.*, **130**. 237, 1925 ; M. Padoa, *Gazz. Chim. Ital.*, **52**. ii, 189, 1922 ; H. G. Grimm and A. Sommerfeld, *Zeit. Physik*, **36**. 36, 1926 ; M. L. Huggins, *Journ. Phys. Chem.*, **26**. 601, 1922 ; C. D. Niven, *Phil. Mag.*, (7), **3**. 1314, 1927 ; S. Meyer, *Naturwiss.*, **15**. 623, 1927.

§ 9. Hydrogen Arsenide, or Arsenic Hydride

As a result of the observations of A. J. J. Vandevelde,[1] and H. Reckleben and J. Scheiber, it is not certain that arsenic and hydrogen can be made to unite directly —*vide supra*. Three hydrogen arsenides are known, AsH or As_2H_2; As_2H or

As_4H ; and AsH_3. H. Davy first reported the formation of a solid hydrogen arsenide when water is electrolyzed by means of an arsenic cathode ; G. Magnus was able to obtain only a very small quantity in this way ; and E. Soubeiran, none at all. K. Olszewsky, however, obtained the solid arsenide by electrolyzing an aq. soln. of arsenic trioxide by means of platinum electrodes. Assuming that these products are the same as the brown arsenide obtained by J. V. Janowsky, E. J. Weeks and J. G. F. Druce, and H. Reckleben and J. Scheiber, the brown product is **hydrogen monoarsenide,** AsH, often written As_2H_2 in order to make the analysis correspond with the valency hypothesis H.As : As.H. E. Soubeiran gave H_2As ; and E. Wiederhold, and J. Ogier, HAs_2. E. J. Weeks obtained the same brown hydride by the electrolysis of sodium hydroxide, using an arsenic cathode. The cathode was suspended in a porous pot, the electrolyte being a normal soln. of the alkali. A platinum anode was employed. A current of 100 milliamps. per sq. cm. was passed for about half an hour. Gaseous arsine was evolved, and a brown deposit appeared in the porous cell. J. L. Gay Lussac and L. J. Thénard, and H. Reckleben and J. Scheiber reported a solid arsenide to be formed when an alkali arsenide is decomposed by water : $2K_3As+6H_2O=As_2H_2+6KOH+2H_2$. J. V. Janowsky said that the product so prepared is only a mixture since it is not formed when a purified sodium arsenide is employed. H. Reckleben and J. Scheiber, and L. Moser and A. Brukl, obtained it by the action of water on sodium arsenide ; and H. Thoms and L. Hess, by the action of water on calcium arsenide. E. Wiederhold obtained this arsenide when hydrochloric acid acts on an alloy of zinc and arsenic, although R. Engel seems to have supposed that the solid product is arsenic itself. N. Blondlot observed the formation of a brown solid when zinc acts on a hydrochloric acid soln. of arsenic trioxide in the presence of sulphuric, nitric, or nitrous acid. L. Moser and A. Brukl obtained this arsenide of a high degree of purity, but in small yield, by the atm. oxidation of an aq. soln. of arsine. J. Ogier obtained the brown solid by passing a silent electrical discharge through arsine ; H. Reckleben and J. Scheiber obtained this arsenide together with some crystalline arsenic. J. W. Retgers said this arsenide is formed by heating that gas, or by holding a cold porcelain plate in the burning gas, but there is some doubt about this, for H. Reckleben and J. Scheiber obtained only arsenic by cooling the flame of arsine. J. L. Gay Lussac and L. J. Thénard obtained the solid by the incomplete decomposition of arsine by chlorine, but E. Wiederhold seems to have considered the product to be a mixture of arsenic and its hydride. O. Brunn obtained the solid by the action of air, nitric acid, or nitric oxide on arsine ; E. Soubeiran, by the slow action of air or chlorine on arsine ; T. Humpert, by the action of sulphuric acid on arsine ; J. V. Janowsky, by the action of phosphorus pentachloride on arsine : $AsH_3+PCl_5=PCl_3+2HCl+AsH$—no hydrogen appeared from this reaction. L. Moser and A. Brukl could not confirm this reaction in carbon tetrachloride soln. J. B. A. Dumas obtained the solid by the action of mercuric chloride on arsine ; and E. J. Weeks and J. G. F. Druce by the action of stannous chloride on arsenic trichloride : $2AsCl_3+4SnCl_2+2HCl=As_2H_2+4SnCl_4$. The reaction occurs in aq. soln. or when alcohol, benzene, or chloroform are used as solvents. The yields are small. When an ethereal soln. of stannous chloride reacts with the hydrochloric soln. of arsenic trichloride, a 93 per cent. yield is obtained. The product cannot be dried in a steam-oven because it oxidizes so easily. It is therefore washed with alcohol, and ether, and dried in vacuo over sulphuric acid. H. Reckleben and J. Scheiber obtained the solid arsenide by the action of arsine on solid potassium hydroxide : $AsH_3+3KOH=K_3As+3H_2O$; followed by $2K_3As+6H_2O=As_2H_2+6KOH+2H_2$. The solid hydride was also obtained from a mixture of oxygen, hydrogen, and arsine. Very little is known about this solid hydrogen arsenide— *vide supra,* brown arsenic. The brown pulverulent solid is said to be insoluble in water, alcohol, and ether. When the solid arsenide is heated in vacuo, it forms hydrogen and arsenic ; and, according to G. Magnus, hydrogen free from arsenic is given off when the product has been previously dried by heating it in a current

of hydrogen at 100°. H. Reckleben and J. Scheiber said that J. W. Retgers'
statements about the solubility of this arsenide—in methylene iodide, xylene, or
conc. alkali-lye—really refer to yellow arsenic. They represented the reaction with
ammoniacal silver nitrate : $As_2H_2+6Ag_2O=As_2O_5+12Ag+H_2O$. E. J. Weeks
and J. G. F. Druce said that it is stable in air at ordinary temp. but is readily
oxidized when warmed. A litre of water dissolves 0·35 grm. at 20°. Hot or cold
conc. nitric acid, or hot dil. nitric acid oxidizes the arsenide to arsenic acid :
similarly with aqua regia.

According to L. Moser and A. Brukl, **hydrogen diarsenide,** H_2As_4, is formed
during the oxidation of arsine with stannic chloride in the presence of hydrochloric
acid. The red, amorphous, insoluble diarsenide is decomposed by heat into arsenic,
arsine, and hydrogen. The compound is more stable than As_2H_2, but gradually
forms arsenic, especially if damp. It is unchanged by boiling water or hydrochloric
acid, but forms arsenic with boiling concentrated (or fused) alkali. With nitric
acid, bromine, or hydrogen dioxide, it gives arsenic acid.

In 1775, C. W. Scheele [2] discovered that a gaseous hydrogen arsenide is given
off when a soln. of arsenic acid reacts with zinc. He said that the effervescence
which first occurs soon ceases because each particle of zinc is surrounded by a
regulus which protects the zinc from the acid. He collected some of the gas by
tying a bladder to a phial containing the mixture of zinc and arsenic acid. He said
that the air had the following properties :

It would not unite with water, nor did it precipitate lime-water ; it was not absorbed
when mixed with two-thirds of common air ; and when a burning candle was brought to
the mouth of the vessel, the air in the vessel inflamed with detonation ; the flame took its
direction towards the hand, which was thereby coloured brown. The matter that produced
this colour proved to be arsenic, and it left a disagreeable smell behind. The internal
surface of the vessel too was covered with a brown pellicle. Consequently, the air which
holds the arsenic in soln. is of the inflammable kind.

J. Priestley passed steam over heated arsenic and obtained a gas whose " smell
could not be distinguished from that of phosphorus." The gas was further examined
by A. F. Gehlen, J. B. Trommsdorff, J. L. Proust, F. Stromeyer, and E. Soubeiran.
Le gas proved to be what they called *hydrogène arsenié,* or *Arsenwasserstoff,*
arseniuretted hydrogen gas ; also called **hydrogen tritarsenide,** AsH_3, or *arsenic
trihydride,* commonly called **arsine.**

Although arsenic does not unite directly with ordinary hydrogen, the case is
different with hydrogen under press. and at an elevated temp., as shown by
W. Ipatieff and co-workers, or when the hydrogen is *in statu nascendi.* F. Paneth
and co-workers have shown that when rods of arsenic are used as in the preparation
of activated hydrogen, arsine is produced. E. Soubeiran found that if arsenic
powder be present when zinc is reacting with hydrochloric acid, some arsine is
formed along with the hydrogen ; and J. Thiele likewise obtained a similar result,
and added that only traces of arsine are formed if iron be used in place of zinc, but
if a little antimony chloride be present, more arsine is formed. If the arsenic be
alloyed with the metal, more arsine is formed. Thus, H. Davy, and J. L. Gay
Lussac and L. J. Thénard obtained arsine by the action of water or dil. acids on the
alkali arsenides, and with suitable proportions of the alkali metal and arsenic—
say K_3As—J. V. Janowsky, and A. P. Saunders obtained a gas very rich in arsine.
G. S. Sérullas used an alloy of arsenic, antimony, and potassium obtained by
igniting a mixture of antimony sulphide, arsenic trioxide, and cream of tartar, and
P. Lebeau, and H. Thoms and L. Hess obtained arsine free from hydrogen by the
action of water or dil. acids on calcium arsenide, Ca_3As_2. E. Soubeiran, A. Vogel,
and J. Ogier heated an alloy of zinc and arsenic with dil. sulphuric or hydrochloric
acid, and obtained arsine almost free from hydrogen ; J. V. Janowsky treated an
alloy of arsenic with zinc, tin, or iron in a similar way ; and H. Fonzes-Diaçon
employed aluminium arsenide and water. H. M. Elsey noted that glasses contain-

ing arsenic give an odour of arsine when heated and stretched. The source of the odour is attributed to the reaction: $4As + 3H_2O = As_2O_3 + 2AsH_3$.

L. Gmelin said that when zinc is immersed in an aq. soln. of arsenic trioxide no gas is given off if no other acid be present. J. L. Proust found that arsine is produced if arsenic trioxide be present when zinc is dissolved in dil. hydrochloric or sulphuric acid. In the celebrated test for arsenic devised by J. Marsh, arsine is produced in this way. H. Beckurts said that sulphuric acid acts as well as hydrochloric acid; and N. Blondlot showed that if the sulphuric acid contains nitric or nitrous acid, some solid hydrogen arsenide is formed. D. Vitali said that the presence of mercuric chloride inhibits the production of arsine. L. A. Buchner, and A. Dupasquier added that if iron be employed in place of zinc no arsine is formed, and if tin be used, very little arsine is produced. J. Thiele, however, did obtain arsine by using iron free from sulphur, and he found that the reaction is promoted—without forming stibine—if a little antimony trichloride be present. J. C. Draper used magnesium in place of zinc. F. A. Abel and F. Field observed the formation of arsine when arsenical copper is boiled with hydrochloric acid; and A. Harding, when arsenical lead is boiled with hydrobromic acid. H. Anthes studied the production of arsine by the action of arsenical sulphuric acid on zinc, iron, and lead.

Metal salts, like the antimony trichloride just indicated, may stimulate the formation of arsine. J. Thiele seems to have found that hydrochloroplatinic acid, and platinized or silvered zinc diminish the sensitiveness of J. Marsh's test. C. Mai and H. Hurt found that copper sulphate, or hydrochloroplatinic acid accelerates the development of arsine; manganese sulphate has very little effect; ferrous sulphate hindered the production of arsine; while the addition of silver, mercury, cobalt, nickel, and other sulphates offers no advantage; Z. de Vamossy also recommended copper and platinum salts as promotors of the reaction, but, added A. Gautier, copper should not be used when a quantitative yield of arsine is desired; and D. Vitali said that mercury, by forming an alloy with arsenic, hinders the conversion of arsenic to arsine. According to E. Polenske, organic substances, and metallic salts which are reduced by zinc, interfere with the production of arsine; and conc. acids do not act so well as dil. acids. A. C. Chapman and H. D. Law found that the reducing efficiency of hydrogen obtained by the interaction of metals and acids depends on a number of chemical and physical factors. When pure zinc dissolves in sulphuric acid in the presence of arsenic trioxide, there remains in soln. a minute quantity C_{AsH_3} proportional to the product $C_{As}C_H$ which is influenced by the potential, E, of the active ions. With very dil. soln., $C_{AsH_3} = K[As_2O_3]P_H$, when $[As_2O_3]$ represents the amount of unreduced trioxide, and K, the equilibrium constant. The action of metal salts on the formation of arsine was also examined by G. Lockemann, and H. Reckleben and co-workers. D. Vitali said that a stick of zinc which has once been used for generating hydrogen in testing for arsenic in arsenical liquids, should not be used again because it may have retained some of the arsenic. On the other hand, N. Blondlot said that if stannous chloride be added to the flask containing the zinc and acid, the *whole* of the arsenic is given off as arsine; and A. C. Chapman and H. D. Law found that salts like palladium or platinum chloride, and nickel or cobalt sulphate cause much arsenic to be retained in the apparatus, and similarly with alloys of zinc with iron, nickel, cobalt, copper, silver, platinum, and sodium, but not with alloys of zinc with tin or cadmium; they also discovered that the presence of one or two grams of cadmium sulphate, lead acetate, or stannous chloride acts in a similar way and completely overcomes the " insensitiveness " due to the use of purified zinc and acid. G. Bischof, and C. L. Bloxam found that when arsenical liquids are electrolyzed, some arsenic is converted into arsine, at the anode, and C. L. Bloxam was able to detect the presence of 0·015 mgrm. of arsenic trioxide in this way. If arsenic acid is present it is first reduced to arsenious acid by sulphur dioxide or hydrogen sulphide. Observations on the electrolysis of the soln. were made by

K. Olszewsky, H. J. S. Sand and J. E. Hackford, S. R. Trotman, L. Ramberg, H. Blumenberg, C. Mai and H. Hurt, H. Frerichs and G. Rodenberg, C. H. Wolff, and F. M. L. Donny and M. Szuch. G. Grube and H. Kleber—*vide supra*, arsenic —found that the electrolytic formation and decomposition of arsine at the arsenic cathode is a reversible process. Arsine is the primary product of the electrolytic discharge of H-ions at the arsenic cathode, and hydrogen is formed by the decomposition of arsine. T. Moore attempted to determine the arsenic by electrolyzing the acidic soln., and catching the evolved arsine in a soln. of silver nitrate. T. E. Thorpe, W. Thomson, and others developed this mode of estimating arsenic in liquids of various kinds ; and T. E. Thorpe studied the effects obtained with anodes of different metals. T. Fleitmann found that alkaline liquids containing arsenic give arsine and hydrogen when treated with zinc. H. Hager said that if antimony is present, the arsenic furnishes arsine, and the antimony is precipitated. According to J. W. Gatehouse, and O. C. Johnson, arsenical alkaline liquids yield arsine when treated with aluminium ; or, according to E. W. Davy, with sodium amalgam. E. Reichardt also found that arsenates are slowly reduced to arsine by nascent hydrogen in alkaline soln. ; C. Himmelmann, that arsenical liquids also furnish arsine when heated with aq. ammonia or ammonium chloride and zinc or iron. A. C. Vournasos prepared arsine by passing the vapour of arsenic at about 460° over sodium formate just below its decomposition temp. ; or by heating a mixture of three parts of powdered arsenic and eight parts of dry sodium formate at 400° in a round-bottomed flask. A mixture of calcium oxide or sodium hydroxide with the sodium formate gives better results since it prevents the formation of sodium oxalate and of carbon monoxide if the temp. is too high. Arsenic trioxide or pentoxide, sodium arsenite, solid hydrogen arsenide, Schweinfurt's green, arsenic trisulphide, etc., all give the arsine when used in place of arsenic. According to F. Selmi, arsine is formed when certain fungi grow on arsenical liquids and compounds—*vide supra ;* and, according to H. Fleck, E. Reichardt, and J. Wolf, when tapestries coloured with arsenical pigments are exposed to moist air. M. E. Pozzi-Escott observed that arsenic is scarcely affected by the hydrogenases—*e.g.* philothion —*vide* hydrogen sulphide.

C. W. Scheele said that zinc, tin, and iron dissolve in aq. arsenic acid liberating this gas particularly when the dissolution of the metal is assisted by the presence of hydrochloric or sulphuric acid. N. W. Fischer obtained only hydrogen with zinc and aq. arsenic acid unmixed with any other oxide ; but L. Gmelin confirmed C. W. Scheele's observation with purified arsenic acid and zinc. There have been contradictory reports on the production of arsine by the reduction of arsenical sulphides of different metals. The discrepant results may be due to differences in the way the arsenic is associated with the other elements. Thus, it may be present as free arsenic, free arsenic sulphide, or the arsenic and the metal may be together combined with the sulphur. C. L. Bloxam, A. Gautier, and J. Myers observed the presence of arsine in hydrogen sulphide prepared by the action of dil. sulphuric acid on arsenical iron sulphide ; and J. Myers said that freshly precipitated arsenic trisulphide is reduced to arsine by zinc and sulphuric acid. Hence, too, arsenical sulphuric acid and zinc or iron sulphide furnish some arsine. R. Otto reported that fused and powdered arsenic trisulphide is not attacked by hydrogen *in statu nascendi.* W. Skey obtained some arsine by treating arsenical pyrites with a mixture of zinc and sulphuric acid. C. R. Fresenius and C. H. L. von Babo observed that no arsine is formed when a mixture of arsenic sulphide and sodium carbonate is heated in a current of hydrogen. If a ring of arsenic is obtained when the gas is passed through a red-hot tube, it is produced by the mechanical transport of finely divided arsenic by the gas, for if the gas is filtered by moist and dry cotton-wool, no arsenic passes along.

According to H. Reckleben and co-workers, potassium hydroxide, soda-lime, or granular calcium chloride should not be used for drying purposes because they may decompose the gas. A. Güttich found that hexahydrated calcium chloride exerts a slight catalytic action on the decomposition of arsine; likewise also when the salt has somewhat effloresced, potassium and sodium hydroxides, and soda-lime, calcium oxide, and phosphorus pentoxide, also decompose the gas. Of all the desiccating agents tried, hydrated and weathered calcium chloride exerts the least action; phosphorus pentoxide can be used when large quantities of the gas have to be dried and a small loss does not matter. P. Lebeau recommended preparing the gas by the action of water or dil. acid on normal calcium arsenide. The gas is then to be cooled to —20° to condense out most of the moisture; passed over metaphosphoric acid to remove the rest of the moisture; and then cooled by a mixture of acetone and solid carbon dioxide. The liquid so obtained is arsine of a high degree of purity.

The physical properties of arsine.—At ordinary temp. arsine is a colourless gas. The early estimates of the **vapour density** were made on the gas admixed with hydrogen; J. B. A. Dumas [3] gave 2·695 (air unity), when the theoretical value for AsH_3 is 2·692. The litre weight of the gas under standard conditions is 3·4944 grms. H. Remy discussed the structure of arsine; and H. Henstock, the electronic structure of the family of trihydrides. A. O. Rankine gave $0·985 \times 10^{-15}$ sq. cm. for the mean collision area of arsine. A. O. Rankine and C. J. Smith found the **viscosity** of the gas at 0° to be 0·0001470 at 0°; 0·0001552 at 15°; and 0·0001997 at 100°; and he gave 300 for the constant C. They also calculated the collision area of the mols. of the gas to be $0·985 \times 10^{-15}$ sq. cm. F. Stromeyer found that the gas at —40° condenses to a transparent, colourless liquid which at higher temp. again becomes gaseous. M. Faraday was unable to solidify arsine at —110°. K. Olszewksy found the liquid has a **boiling point** of —54·8°—H. Schlundt and O. C. Schaefer said about —70°. M. Faraday gave for the **vapour pressure,** p atm., of the liquid.

	—59·4°	—46·6°	—30·6°	—17·8°	—12·2°	0°	10°	15·1°
p . .	0·94	1·73	3·33	5·21	6·24	8·95	11·56	13·19

K. Olszewsky obtained a white solid at —119° which had a **melting point** of —113·5°. J. Ogier gave $(As,3H)=57·7$ Cals. for the **heat of formation.** The subject was studied by R. de Forcrand. J. C. Thomlinson found the heat of formation of the trihydrides of the phosphorus family decreases as the at. wt. of the elements increase. The reverse might have been anticipated. The discrepancy is due to the heats of formation being referred to the solid elements. L. Bleekrode found the liquid to have but a small **electrical conductivity.** According to G. Grube and H. Kleber, the potential imparted by arsine when it decomposes at an arsenic electrode in presence of sodium hydroxide soln. is also about 1·0 volt. Hence, whereas in acidic soln. formation and decomposition of arsine play a minor part, in alkaline soln. electrolysis leads primarily to arsine of which the hydrogen evolved is a decomposition product. H. Schlundt and O. C. Schaefer gave 2·58 for the **dielectric constant** at —50°, and 2·05, at 15°; H. E. Watson gave for $(\epsilon-1) \times 10^{-5}$, 2·51 at —47°; 1·916 at 16°; and 1·46 at 100°, and these values satisfy Debye's equation. The effect of press. at —47° is:

p . .	669·5	405	205·5	103·5	81	42	23
$\epsilon-1$ . .	701	420	212	106	82	40	21

Arsine has a repulsive nauseating odour. It is extremely poisonous, and when diluted with much air produces nausea, eructation, giddiness, and oppression. A. F. Gehlen [4] was one of the first victims. According to L. Gmelin, in order to detect a leak in his apparatus he smelt strongly at the joints, he found the leak, but died in 8 to 9 days from the effects of the inhalation, in spite of all remedial measures; and M. Bullacker likewise terminated his life 12 days after accidentally inhaling the gas. Arsine is formed in some industrial work when arsenical metals are treated with acids or with arsenical acids—e.g. in pickling sheet iron for tinning; and in desilvering lead by the zinc process. The effect on dogs was studied by E. Stadelmann, and on man by M. Trost, A. Tardieu, etc. J. D. Mann and J. G. Clegg said that arsine is a powerful blood poison which disintegrates the red blood corpuscles and sets free the hæmaglobin. The red blood corpuscles are thus greatly reduced in number. In the spectroscope the blood shows that the D- and C-bands have coalesced and almost vanished. H. Fühner found the minimum conc. of arsine in the atm. to cause the death of white mice from acute poisoning is 0·1 to 0·2 mgrm. per litre ; and L. O. Dubitsky found that 0·005 per cent. is fatal to cats in 60–90 minutes ; and 0·004 per cent. in 3 hrs. A. Hébert and F. Hein found 0·005 per cent. was fatal to guinea-pigs for long exposures and 0·35 per cent. for short exposures ; while for birds the corresponding quantities were 0·002 and 0·009 per cent.

According to P. Lebeau,[5] purified arsine is fairly stable ; but M. Berthelot found that when kept in a sealed tube, in light or darkness, arsine is slowly decomposed. A. Vogel observed that in sunlight the gas deposits a black film of arsenic on the walls of the glass containing vessel in a few days ; and in darkness black flecks appear in about 8 days. G. Lockemann found that the gas is perceptibly decomposed when passed through cotton-wool or glass-wool. J. L. Gay Lussac and L. J. Thénard said that the heat of a spirit-lamp is sufficient to resolve the gas into free hydrogen, and arsenic which settles on the walls of the containing vessel— one vol. of arsine, said E. Soubeiran, furnishes $1\frac{1}{2}$ vols. of hydrogen. The deposition of arsenic which occurs when arsine is passed through a heated glass tube is the foundation of J. Marsh's well-known method of detecting arsenic. O. Brunn observed that arsine is not appreciably decomposed when passed through a spiral tube at 225°, but at 230° some arsenic is deposited in the cooler part of the tube ; and J. P. Cooke detected crystals in the arsenic deposited by the thermal decomposition of arsine. The thermal decomposition of arsine proceeds something like that of phosphine observed by D. M. Kooij—vide supra, phosphine. E. Cohen found that the velocity constant K, at 310°, is not constant until the walls of the reaction vessel are covered with a film of arsenic. With the same equation as that employed for phosphine ($q.v.$), $kt=\log\{P_0/(3P_0-2p)\}$, derived from $dC/dt=kC$, using a vessel previously employed in another series of observations :

t	0	5·5	6·5	8	9·5 hrs.
p	733·32	805·78	818·11	835·34	850·15 mm.
k		0·01738	0·01757	0·01770	0·01754

E. Echeandia made a number of observations on this subject, and found the percentage decomposition at 304°, to be :

	24	48	71	99	121	146	167 hrs.
Decomposition .	56·6	82·3	94·9	98·7	99·3	99·8	99·93 per cent.

The presence of hydrogen sulphide, or of oxygen, retards the rate of decomposition by " poisoning " the catalytic film of arsenic on the walls of the containing vessel. The reaction was studied by S. Dushman, and M. Trautz. M. Berthelot said that arsine cannot be made to decompose explosively by an electric spark, but it will do so when fired by a mercury fulminate cartridge. J. Ogier, N. Klobukoff, C. H. Wolff, and H. Reckleben and J. Scheiber found that when arsine is exposed to the silent electric discharge it decomposes into arsenic, hydrogen, and some solid hydrogen arsenide—vide supra.

The chemical properties of arsine.—Arsine can be inflamed when in contact with air or oxygen, and it burns with a bluish-white flame : $2AsH_3+3O_2$ $=As_2O_3+3H_2O$. J. B. A. Dumas, and E. Soubeiran observed that one vol. of arsine consumes $1\frac{1}{2}$ vols. of oxygen ; but F. Stromeyer, and J. L. Gay Lussac and L. J. Thénard found other proportions owing to the contamination of the arsine they employed with hydrogen. If the quantity of air or oxygen in contact with the burning gas is deficient, the hydrogen is first consumed, and free arsenic is deposited on the sides of the vessel. G. Lockemann represented the reaction between oxygen and arsine : $4AsH_3+3O_2=4As+6H_2O$. In the spontaneous oxidation of arsine by oxygen at ordinary temp., H. Reckleben and G. Lockemann found that arsenic is liberated in a free state, and only the hydrogen is oxidized ;

when the mixture is exposed to β-rays or γ-rays, the reaction is accelerated, and arsenious acid is formed : $2H_3As+3O_2=2H_3AsO_3$; since the α-rays are excluded it is supposed that the oxidation cannot be due to the intermediate formation of ozone. According to E. Soubeiran, 100 vols. of **water** absorb 20 vols. of arsine, and the aq. soln. can precipitate metals from metal salt soln. ; and the aq. soln. in contact with air, deposits arsenic when allowed to stand for some time. F. Stromeyer obtained a similar result, and O. Brunn suggested the substance which separates from the soln. may be solid hydrogen arsenide. He also said that if the water is free from dissolved air or oxygen, it does not change after standing for a long time even in light. According to R. de Forcrand, **hexahydrated arsine**, $AsH_3.6H_2O$, is formed by compressing the gas in the presence of a few drops of water, followed by a sudden expansion and a second compression. The solid hydrate can be kept indefinitely between 0° and 28·2°, the dissociation press. at these two temp. being, respectively, 0·806 atm. and 17·5 atm. He calculated the heat of formation of the solid hydrate, from water and the gaseous hydride, to be $+17\cdot753$ Cals., and from ice and the gaseous hydride $+8\cdot238$ Cals., which values gave the formula of the hydrate as $AsH_3.6H_2O$. H. Reckleben and co-workers found that arsine is completely oxidized after shaking with 3–30 per cent. **hydrogen dioxide** for over 3 hrs.

J. J. Berzelius showed that when **chlorine** is bubbled into arsine, each bubble produces a flame, forming hydrochloric acid, and a brown cloud of arsenic. F. Stromeyer, J. J. Berzelius, A. Vogel, and E. Soubeiran found that when chlorine is mixed with arsine, combustion occurs, and hydrogen chloride and arsenic are formed ; if the chlorine is present in excess, arsenic trichloride is formed ; if water be present, arsenious and arsenic acids are produced—as in the case where the gas comes in contact with chlorine-water ; if hydrogen sulphide be present, arsenic sulphide is formed ; if 50 times its vol. of air or hydrogen be present, a single bubble of chlorine separates arsenic ; and if a large proportion of carbon dioxide be present, a single bubble of chlorine separates arsenic, but without inflammation. H. Reckleben and co-workers also examined the action of arsine on chlorine-water. A. Stock found that arsine reacts with liquid chlorine even at $-140°$, forming reddish products—possibly forming unstable intermediate products, arsenic dihydrochloride, AsH_2Cl, and arsenic hydrodichloride, $AsHCl_2$; even at $-100°$, chlorine reacts with arsine dissolved in liquid hydrogen chloride. According to J. E. Simon, an aq. soln. of **bromine** absorbs arsine, forming arsenic trioxide, arsenic acid, and hydrobromic acid ; and, according to J. Ogier, if the bromine is in excess, arsenic and hydrobromic acid alone. H. Reckleben and co-workers also examined the action of arsine on bromine-water. E. Soubeiran found that **iodine** decomposes arsine, slowly in the cold, rapidly when hot, forming hydrogen and arsenic iodides. O. Jacobsen observed that at ordinary temp. arsine is readily decomposed when passed over solid iodine, and all the arsenic is removed from the gas. Observations to this effect were also made by C. Husson, and O. Brunn. H. Reckleben and G. Lockemann represented the reaction with iodine and water : $AsH_3+4I_2+4H_2O$ $=H_3AsO_4+8HI$; H. Thoms and L. Hess showed that the reaction takes place in two stages, the first stage in neutral soln. being represented : $AsH_3+3I_2+3H_2O$ $=H_3AsO_3+6HI$. J. E. Simon found that an alcoholic soln. of iodine is decolorized by arsine at ordinary temp.—part of the arsenic is retained as arsenious acid ; a black precipitate is also formed. J. V. Janowsky showed that **hydrogen chloride** and arsine form a brown cloud of arsenic ; and R. Napoli, that with **hydrochloric acid,** arsenic trichloride is produced. The removal of arsine from hydrogen sulphide, contaminated with that gas, by passing through hot dil. hydrochloric acid, is not complete. The subject was discussed by R. Otto, and W. Lenz. H. B. Parsons said that **hydrobromic acid** and **hydriodic acid** do not act on arsine. A. J. Balard said that in chlorine monoxide, arsine burns to arsenic pentoxide and hydrogen chloride, and if it is not in excess, some chlorine is formed. H. Reckleben and co-workers found that arsine is completely absorbed by a soln. of **sodium**

hypochlorite or **calcium hypochlorite :** $AsH_3+4HOCl=H_3AsO_4+4HCl$; if an excess is present, side reactions occur.   H. B. Parsons said that **chloric acid** in acidic soln. has no action on arsine, but in neutral soln., arsenic and a chloride of the metal are formed.   H. Reckleben and G. Lockemann found that a neutral soln. of **potassium chlorate** acts only slowly, but if the soln. is acidified and a trace of silver nitrate is employed as a catalyst, the reaction : $AsH_3+HClO_3=As(OH)_3$ $+HCl$ occupies some hours ; they found that **bromic acid** is indifferent towards arsine, but if a trace of silver nitrate is present : $5AsH_3+8HBrO_3=5H_3AsO_4$ $+4Br_2+4H_2O$. The acidified soln. acts more rapidly and without the catalyst. H. B. Parsons said that **iodic acid** forms free iodine and arsenic trioxide, and H. Reckleben and G. Lockemann represented the reaction : $5AsH_3+8HIO_3$ $=5H_3AsO_4+4I_2+4H_2O$; and with **periodic acid :** $AsH_3+4HIO_4=H_3AsO_4+4HIO_3$.

According to J. L. Gay Lussac and L. J. Thénard, and E. Soubeiran, when **sulphur** is heated with arsine, hydrogen sulphide, arsenic, and, later, arsenic sulphide are formed.   F. Jones found that sulphur reacts slowly with arsine in sunlight at ordinary temp., but not in darkness ; it also reacts slowly at 100°.   The reaction with stibine is much faster than with arsine.   Both **selenium** and **tellurium** react with arsine in sunlight, but not in darkness or at 100°.   O. Brunn found that a mixture of equal vols. of arsine and **hydrogen sulphide** did not change in a week's time, in darkness or in sunlight ; but if a little air be present, arsenic trisulphide is quickly formed in darkness or in light.   O. Brunn said that at 230° the reaction between the two gases proceeds slowly with the separation of arsenic, which is converted by the hydrogen sulphide into arsenic trisulphide.   J. Myers observed that at 357°, arsine and hydrogen sulphide form hydrogen and arsenic trisulphide. O. von der Pfordten said that the transformation is incomplete.   If a mixture of the two gases be passed into air-free water, O. Brunn observed the clear liquid becomes turbid, by the separation of arsenic trisulphide, as oxygen is absorbed by the liquid.   O. von der Pfordten represented the reaction with **potassium poly-** **sulphide** at 350°–360° : $2AsH_3+3K_2S_3=2K_3AsS_3+3H_2S$; while a soln. of **silver** **sulphide** in potassium cyanide ; or a soln. of **molybdenum trisulphide** or **stannic** **sulphide** in potassium sulphide, does not remove arsine completely from hydrogen sulphide contaminated with that gas.   H. B. Parsons found that arsine and **sulphur** **dioxide** form arsenic and its trisulphide ; and G. Aimé, that **sulphur trioxide** produces sulphur dioxide and arsenic which is then oxidized to the trioxide. According to E. Soubeiran, conc. **sulphuric acid** decomposes arsine at ordinary temp., forming brown flakes which are dissolved on gently heating the liquid ; sulphuric acid diluted with an equal vol. of water acts with difficulty, and when diluted with 3 vols. of water, not at all.   E. Lyttkens, and W. Lenz dried arsine with sulphuric acid without loss of arsenic.   The removal of arsine from hydrogen sulphide contaminated with that gas is not completely effected by passing through hot dil. sulphuric acid.   The subject was discussed by R. Otto, and W. Lenz. M. Forbes said that when arsine is passed through sulphuric acid at 160°–180° a metal mirror is formed—as well as some sulphur dioxide, and arsenic trisulphide. According to T. Humpert, when arsine is passed into sulphuric acid of sp. gr. 1·75–1·84, it is coloured brown, brown flecks separate, and the liquid contains hydrogen sulphide and yellow arsenic sulphide.   The brown flecks were thought to be solid arsenic hydride.

H. Reckleben and co-workers found that conc. aq. **ammonia** decomposes arsine incompletely with the separation of arsenic.   F. Stromeyer said that arsine is decomposed by **nitrogen peroxide** oxidizing the hydrogen and liberating the arsenic. H. B. Parsons found that **nitrous acid,** and C. Bozenhardt, that a soln. of potassium hydroxide containing some **potassium nitrite,** readily decompose arsine, forming a grey crust of arsenic.   F. Stromeyer showed that **nitric acid** acts similarly, while fuming nitric acid reacts explosively with inflammation.   J. E. Simon said that conc. nitric acid has no action on arsine.   E. Soubeiran observed that if arsine be passed into a receiver filled with nitric acid, it disappears entirely, covering the sides of the vessel with a brown film. F. M. Bergstrom found that arsenic is slightly attacked by a soln. of **ammonium nitrate.** E. Soubeiran showed that if **phosphorus** be heated to its vaporizing temp. in arsine gas, arsenic phosphide is formed, and some phosphine. H. B. Parsons found **hypophosphorous acid** to be without action. A. Güttich examined **phosphorus pentoxide** as a desiccating agent for the gas— *vide supra.* J. V. Janowsky found that arsine reacts with **phosphorus trichloride,** forming hydrogen chloride and arsenic phosphide ; with **phosphorus penta-chloride** he represented the reaction : $PCl_5 + AsH_3 = PCl_3 + AsH + 2HCl$; and with **arsenic trichloride,** arsenic and hydrogen chloride are formed. D. Tivoli found that arsine furnishes arsenic and water in contact with a soln. of arsenic trioxide in hydrochloric acid.

A. Stock found that the addition product, **boron arsenotribromide,** $BBr_3.AsH_3$, is obtained when boron bromide is gradually dropped into liquefied hydrogen arsenide at $-80°$ to $-100°$. It is essential that all moisture and oxygen be previously removed, and the operation is best carried out while a stream of dry hydrogen is passed through the apparatus. The product is a white, amorphous substance which, when heated, decomposes, but does not melt. It may be obtained in a crystalline form by careful sublimation in a closed vessel. It is insoluble in carbon disulphide, but dissolves in boron tribromide. In contact with air or oxygen, it is readily oxidized, and in most cases is spontaneously inflammable, yielding boric and arsenious oxides, and hydrogen bromide. It is not acted on by oxygen at temp. below $-40°$. If the amount of oxygen is carefully regulated and the temp. kept moderately low, the products are boric oxide, hydrogen bromide, and free arsenic, together with arsenic tribromide. Even at $0°$, slow decomposition into its constituents occurs, and this is accelerated if a current of some indifferent gas is employed to remove the hydrogen arsenide as it is formed ; a small amount of arsenic is also deposited. When kept for several weeks at the ordinary temp. in a closed vessel protected from light, it is completely decomposed into boron bromide, arsenic, and hydrogen. In contact with water, it is decomposed into boric acid, hydrogen bromide, hydrogen arsenide, and a small amount of free arsenic. Conc. sulphuric acid has no apparent action, but conc. nitric acid produces violent oxidation. Arsenic trichloride reacts with the compound, even at $-50°$. Ammonia at $10°$ yields the compound $2BBr_3.9NH_3$. A. W. Hofmann found that triethylarsine is without action on **carbon disulphide** even at $100°$. L. Gmelin said that arsine is not perceptibly absorbed by **alcohol** or **ether ;** but is rapidly absorbed by **turpentine,** and slowly by **fixed oils.** H. Reckleben found that a 5 per cent. soln. of **lead acetate** absorbs arsine completely after many hours' shaking, and the reaction is analogous to that which occurs with silver nitrate. J. F. Simon said that lead acetate is not changed by arsine, likewise also with **tartar emetic ;** while H. B. Parsons observed no change with **oxalic acid.** W. R. Hodgkinson found that arsine gives a reddish-brown precipitate with alcoholic soln. of **mercuric cyanide.** H. Reckleben and co-workers showed that arsine reacts very slowly with a neutral soln. of **potassium ferrocyanide,** but energetically with an alkaline soln. H. B. Parsons observed no change with **hydroferrocyanic and hydro-ferricyanic acids.** W. Steinkopf and W. Mieg prepared some organic thiocyanates of the type $RAs(SCN)_2$ and $R_2As(SCN)$. Numerous **organic arsines** have been made. A. Job and R. Reich reported **magnesium dibromophenylarsine,** $C_6H_5As(MgBr)_2$. H. B. Parsons found that **thiocyanic acid** has no action on arsine. R. Meissner measured the solubility of arsine in various constituents of the **blood,** and in soln. of **sodium nitroprusside.**

J. L. Gay Lussac and L. J. Thénard observed that when arsine is passed over heated **potassium,** hydrogen is liberated, and the arsenic unites with the metal. J. V. Janowsky found that **sodium** acts in a similar manner ; P. Lebeau, **calcium ;** J. B. A. Dumas, **zinc ;** and J. L. Gay Lussac and L. J. Thénard, **tin.** E. Soubeiran observed that since arsine is decomposed, the presence of tin is not a necessary factor. J. C. Draper found that hot **platinum** removes arsenic completely from arsine. P. Lebeau found that the **metal-ammoniums** react with arsine, forming arsenides. According to E. Soubeiran, hot solid **potassium or sodium hydroxide** quickly decomposes the gas, forming arsenite which, at a higher temp., forms arsenate and arsenide—some arsenic trioxide is also formed. L. Gmelin said that an aq. soln. of the alkali hydroxide has no appreciable action on the gas ; and J. J. Berzelius, that the gas is no more soluble in alkaline soln. than in water alone. C. B. Kühn and O. Saeger, A. Güttich, M. Schenkel and T. Rickher, and G. Dragendorff found that some arsenic is retained by the alkali when arsine is passed over solid alkali hydroxide. E. Soubeiran found that **barium oxide** heated in arsine liberates hydrogen, and forms a mixture of barium arsenite and arsenide ; while heated **calcium oxide** produces no effect other than that of heat alone. For A. Güttich's observations, *vide supra*, the desiccation of the gas ; I. Guareschi found that arsine is readily absorbed by **soda-lime**. H. B. Parsons said that **chromic anhydride** in neutral or acidic soln. suffers no change, while in alkaline soln. arsenic and chromic oxide are formed.

E. Soubeiran observed no reaction with **salts of the alkalies and alkaline earths** ; he also said that soln. of many heavy **metal salts** decompose the gas, forming water and the metal arsenide. Thus, with **copper sulphate,** copper arsenide is formed : $3CuSO_4 + 2AsH_3 = Cu_3As_2 + 3H_2SO_4$. The absorption of arsine by soln. of copper sulphate was also examined by J. B. A. Dumas, and J. E. Simon. Paper soaked in a soln. of this salt was found by H. Hager to be blackened by arsine. R. J. Kane found dry copper sulphate to be decomposed by arsine ; and likewise with dry **copper chloride**—copper arsenide and hydrogen chloride are formed. J. Riban observed that arsine is absorbed by a soln. of cuprous chloride in hydrochloric acid ; E. Dowzard said that arsine is not absorbed by a 15 per cent. soln. of cuprous chloride in hydrochloric acid. The work of J. A. Wanklyn, H. Gutzeit, H. Hager, H. Strauss, A. H. Gotthelf, E. Dowzard, F. C. J. Bird, J. F. Lassaigne, A. W. Hofmann, J. F. Simon, E. Reichardt, E. Soubeiran, J. B. Senderens, L. Marchlewsky, K. Preis and B. Rayman, H. Reckleben and co-workers, D. Vitali, T. Poleck and C. Thümmel, R. Otto, and J. A. Goode and F. M. Perkin on the action of arsine on **silver nitrate** is discussed in connection with that salt—**3.** 22, 21. **Gold salts** precipitate the metal when treated with arsine, and A. Güttich made some observations on this subject. For H. Reckleben and co-workers', and A. Güttich's observations on drying the gas with **calcium chloride,** *vide supra.* E. Soubeiran found that **zinc salts** are slowly decomposed by arsine. R. Meissner examined the action of **cadmium chloride** on arsine. He also found that with arsine dry **mercurous chloride** or **mercuric chloride** forms hydrogen chloride and solid hydrogen arsenide ; and H. Rose represented the reaction with a soln. of mercuric chloride : $3HgCl_2 + AsH_3 = 3HCl + As(HgCl)_3$. D. Vitali, and J. Lohmann obtained a similar product. The brown *trischloromercuriarsine*, $As(HgCl)_3$, passes into the black arsenide Hg_3As_2 with the continued passage of the gas. M. Mayençon and M. Bergeret represented the reaction : $3HgCl_2 + AsH_3$ $= 3HgCl + As + 3HCl$. A. Partheil and E. Amort observed a sequence of changes with alcoholic soln. of mercuric chloride, whereby *chloromercuriarsine*, $AsH_2(HgCl)$; *bischloromercuriarsine*, $AsH(HgCl)_2$; and *trischloromercuriarsine*, $As(HgCl)_3$, are formed. Each of these three substances yields mercurous chloride, arsenious acid, and hydrochloric acid when treated with an excess of the mercuric chloride soln. G. Franceschi obtained bischloromercuriarsine by the action of arsine on a soln. of mercuric chloride in ether. According to W. R. Hodgkinson, a soln. of mercuric chloride used in place of silver nitrate in H. Gutzeit's test gives a lemon-yellow coloration with arsine, and it enables one part of arsenic trioxide in 120,000 parts of liquid to be detected. P. Lemoult found that a soln. of **potassium tetraiodomercuriate** in 2 to 5 litres of water yields with arsine a yellowish-brown crystalline precipitate of *trisiodomercuriarsine*, $As(HgI)_3$. E. Soubeiran found that **stannous salts** are slowly decomposed by arsine, while **stannic chloride** yields a yellowish-brown precipitate. E. Defacqz found that arsine reacts with **tungsten hexa-**

chloride at 200°–300°, forming tungsten arsenide, and with the salt dissolved in liquid ammonia, *tungsten arsenicenneachloride*, $2WCl_3.AsCl_3$, is formed. E. Schobig represented the reaction between arsine and a soln. of **potassium permanganate** by the equation: $10AsH_3+16KMnO_4=5K_3AsO_4+KMnAsO_4+2Mn_3(AsO_4)_2 +9Mn(OH)_2+6H_2O$; without giving any confirmatory evidence. H. B. Parsons represented the reaction: $6KMnO_4+4AsH_3=3Mn_2O_2(OH)_2+2As_2O_3+6KOH$; while F. Jones showed that the reaction is better represented by: $2KMnO_4+AsH_3 =Mn_2O_3+K_2HAsO_4+H_2O$; thus falling in line with the effects of ammonia, phosphine, and stibine on the permanganate soln. H. Reckleben and G. Locke-mann observed a slow change in acid and neutral soln., and added that the oxidation of arsine by neutral or acidic soln. of permanganate proceeds only slowly and incompletely. R. J. Kane studied the action of arsine on manganic alum. O. von der Pfordten found that a soln. of **bismuth salt**—nitrate or chloride—in conc. hydrochloric acid, or a soln. **of a nickel salt** mixed with acetic or citric acid did not remove arsine completely from hydrogen sulphide contaminated with that gas. E. Soubeiran found that **ferric salts** give no precipitate with arsine ; he also found that soln. of **platinum and rhodium salts** give precipitates of the metals when treated with arsine. J. F. Simon said that a soln. of hydrochloroplatinic acid removes all the arsenic from the gas and forms a black precipitate of arsenic and platinum. D. Tivoli said that a not too conc. soln. of the platinum salt gives a precipitate of *platinum oxyarsenide*, $HAsPtO$, and a conc. soln., of platinum alone.

REFERENCES.

¹ H. Davy, *Phil. Trans.*, **100.** 31, 1910 ; J. L. Gay Lussac and L. J. Thénard, *Recherches physico-chimiques*, Paris, **1.** 232, 1811 ; *Ann. Chim. Phys.*, (1), **73.** 229, 1810 ; N. Blondlot, *ib.*, (3), **64.** 486, 1862 ; L. Moser and A. Brukl, *Monatsh.*, **45.** 26, 1924 ; G. Magnus, *Pogg. Ann.*, **17.** 526, 1829 ; E. Wiederhold, *ib.*, **118.** 615, 1863 ; A. J. J. Vandevelde, *Bull. Acad. Belg.*, (3), **30.** 78, 1895 ; J. W. Retgers, *Zeit. anorg. Chem.*, **4.** 429, 1893 ; H. Reckleben and J. Scheiber, *ib.*, **70.** 255, 1911 ; J. V. Janowsky, *Ber.*. **6.** 220, 1873 ; **8.** 1638, 1875 ; O. Brunn, *ib.*, **22.** 3205, 1889 ; H. Thoms and L. Hess, *Ber. deut. Pharm. Ges.*, **30.** 483, 1920 ; E. Soubeiran, *Ann. Chim. Phys.*, (2), **43.** 407, 1830 ; J. B. A. Dumas, *ib.*, (2), **33.** 355, 1826 ; (2), **44.** 289, 1830 ; J. Ogier, *ib.*, (5), **20.** 17, 1860 ; *Compt. Rend.*, **57.** 596, 1863 ; *Journ. Pharm. Chim.*, (3), **44.** 486, 1863 ; R. Engel, *Compt. Rend.*, **77.** 1547, 1873 ; T. Humpert, *Journ. prakt. Chem.*, (1), **94.** 392, 1865 ; K. Olszewsky, *Arch. Pharm.*. (3), **13.** 563, 1878 ; E. J. Weeks and J. G. F. Druce, *Chem. News*, **129.** 31, 1924 ; E. J. Weeks, *ib.*, **128.** 54, 1924 ; J. G. F. Druce, *Chem. Listy*, **19.** 156, 1925.

² C. W. Scheele, *Svenska Vet. Akad. Handl.*, **36.** 265, 1775 ; E. Soubeiran, *Ann. Chim. Phys.*, (2), **43.** 407, 1830 ; P. Lebeau, *Sur la préparation et les propriétés des arseniures alcalino-terreux*, Paris, 13, 1899 ; *Ann. Chim. Phys.*, (7), **25.** 478, 1902 ; J. Ogier, *ib.*, (5), **20.** 17, 1880 ; J. L. Proust, *ib.*, (1), **28.** 213, 1798 ; J. B. A. Dumas, *ib.*, (2), **33.** 355, 1826 ; (2), **44.** 289, 1830 ; N. Blondlot, *ib.*, (3), **64.** 486, 1862 ; (3), **68.** 186, 1863 ; *Journ. Pharm. Chim.*, (3), **44.** 486, 1863 ; *Compt. Rend.*, **57.** 596, 1863 ; A. Dupasquier, *ib.*, **14.** 511, 1842 ; H. Fonzes-Diaçon, *ib.*, **130.** 1315, 1900 ; H. Moissan, *ib.*, **137.** 363, 1904 ; F. Stromeyer, *Comment. Soc. Gött.*, **16.** 141, 1808 ; J. V. Janowsky, *Ber.*, **6.** 220, 1873 ; **8.** 1638, 1875 ; A. Harding, *ib.*, **14.** 2092, 1881 ; A. C. Vournasos, *ib.*, **43.** 2264, 1910 ; R. Otto, *ib.*, **12.** 216, 1879 ; F. Selmi, *ib.*, **7.** 1642, 1874 ; *Ann. Chim. Applicata*, **59.** 338, 1874 ; G. Bischof, *Kastner's Arch.*, **4.** 13, 1825 ; **6.** 438, 1825 ; A. Vogel, *Journ. prakt. Chem.*, (1), **6.** 345, 1835 ; D. Vitali, *Boll. Chim. Farm.*, **44.** 49, 1905 ; L. A. Buchner, *Repert. Pharm.*, **50.** 234, 1835 ; **59.** 23, 1837 ; A. P. Saunders, *Chem. News*, **79.** 66, 1899 ; J. W. Gatehouse, *ib.*, **27.** 189, 1873 ; T. Moore, *ib.*, **53.** 209, 1886 ; O. C. Johnson, *ib.*, **38.** 301, 1878 ; E. W. Davy, *ib.*, **33.** 58, 1876 ; W. Skey, *ib.*, **34.** 147, 1876 ; W. Thomson, *ib.*, **94.** 156, 1906 ; *Mém. Manchester Lit. Phil. Soc.*, **48.** 17, 1906 ; *Proc. Roy. Soc. Edin.*, **29.** 84, 1909 ; G. S. Sérullas, *Journ. Phys.*, **98.** 136, 1820 ; *Edin. Phil. Journ.*, **4.** 389, 1821 ; J. Priestley, *Experiments and Observations on Different Kinds of Air*, Birmingham, **1.** 204, 1790 ; J. B. Trommsdorff, *Trommsdorff's Journ.*, **12.** 14, 1804 ; *Nicholson's Journ.*, **6.** 200, 1803 ; H. Bechurts, *Arch. Pharm.*, (3), **22.** 681, 1884 ; E. Reichardt, *ib.*, (3), **21.** 592, 1883 ; K. Olszewsky, *ib.*, (3), **13.** 563, 1878 ; J. Thiele, *Apoth. Ztg.*, **5.** 86, 1890 ; *Analytische Beiträge zur Kenntnis von Antimon und Arsen*, Halle, 25, 1890 ; J. C. Draper, *Amer. chemist.*, **2.** 456, 1872 ; *Dingler's Journ.*, **204.** 320, 1872 ; H. Fleck, *ib.*, **207.** 146, 1873 ; Z. de Vamossy, *Bull. Soc. Chim.*, (3), **35.** 24, 1906 ; A. Gautier, *ib.*, (3), **35.** 239, 1906 ; D. Vitali, *Boll. Chim. Farm.*, **44.** 49, 1905 ; **46.** 89, 1907 ; A. C. Chapman and H. D. Law, *Analyst*, **31.** 3, 1906 ; A. C. Chapman, *ib.*, **32.** 247, 1907 ; E. Polenske, *Pharm. Ztg.*, **34.** 299, 1889 ; *Zeit. angew. Chem.*, **2.** 318, 1889 ; G. Lockemann, *ib.*, **19.** 1362, 1906 ; H. Reckleben, G. Lockemann. and

A. Eckardt, *Zeit. anal. Chem.*, **46**. 671, 1907 ; H. Blumenberg, *U.S. Pat. No.* 1375819, 1921 : A. Eckardt, *Ueber Reaktionen und Bestimmungsmethoden von Arsenwasserstoff*, Weida i. Th., 1907 ; C. Mai and H. Hurt, *Zeit. anal. Chem.*, **43**. 557, 1904 ; *Zeit. Unters. Nachr. Genuss.*, **9**. 193, 1905 : C. Himmelmann, *ib.*, **7**. 477, 1868 ; H. Hager, *ib.*, **11**. 82, 1872 ; F. M. L. Donny and M. Szuch, *Bull. Acad. Belg.*, (2), **25**. 192, 1868 ; C. L. Bloxam, *Journ. Chem. Soc.*, **13**. 12, 338, 1860 ; T. E. Thorpe, *ib.*, **83**. 974, 1903 ; F. A. Abel and F. Field, *ib.*, **14**. 290, 1861 ; L. Gmelin, *Handbook of Chemistry*, London, **4**. 264, 1850 ; C. R. Fresenius and C. H. L. von Babo, *Liebig's Ann.*, **19**. 305, 1844 ; J. Myers, *ib.*, **159**. 127, 1871 ; T. Fleitmann, *ib.*, **77**. 127, 1850 ; C. H. Wolff, *Pharm. Centrh.*, **27**. 608, 1886 ; J. Wolf, *Chem. Ztg.*, **11**. 433, 1887 ; B. Newmann, *ib.*, **30**. 33, 1906 ; N. W. Fischer, *Pogg. Ann.*, **9**. 261, 1827 ; J. Marsh, *Edin. Phil. Journ.*, **21**. 229, 1836 ; *Phil. Mag.*, (3), **15**. 282, 1839 ; (3), **17**. 442, 1841 ; H. Davy, *Phil. Trans.*, **100**. 31, 1810 ; J. L. Gay Lussac and L. J. Thénard, *Recherches physico-chimiques*, Paris, **1**. 232, 1811 ; *Ann. Chim. Phys.*, (1), **73**. 229, 1810 ; H. Thoms and L. Hess, *Ber. deut. pharm. Ges.*, **30**. 483, 1921 ; A. F. Gehlen, *Schweigger's Journ.*, **15**. 89, 1815 ; H. Anthes, *Ueber die Bildung von Arsenwasserstoff*, Frankfurt a. M., 1909 ; A. Güttich, *Ueber Bestimmung für Arsenund Antimonwasserstoff*, Leipzig, 1909 ; H. J. S. Sand and J. E. Hackford, *Journ. Chem. Soc.*, **86**. 1018, 1904 ; S. R. Trotman, *Journ. Soc. Chem. Ind.*, **23**. 177, 1904 ; H. Frerichs and G. Rodenberg, *Arch. Pharm.*, **243**. 348, 1905 ; G. Grube and H. Kleber, *Zeit. Elektrochem.*, **30**. 517, 1924 ; L. Ramberg, *Acta Lund. Univ.*, **14**. 1, 1918 ; F. Paneth, M. Matthies, and E. Schmidt Hebbel, *Ber.*, **55**. B, 775, 1922 ; M. E. Pozzi-Escott, *Bull. Soc. Chim.*, (3), **27**. 346, 1902, W. Ipatieff, *Ber.*, **59**. B, 1412, 1926 : *Journ. Russ. Phys. Chem. Soc.*, **58**. 664, 686, 692, 698, 1926 ; H. M. Elsey, *Science*, (2), **66**. 300, 1927.

³ J. B. A. Dumas, *Ann. Chim. Phys.*, (2), **33**. 357, 1826 ; (2), **44**. 289, 1830 ; K. Olszewsky, *Monatsh.*, **5**. 127, 1884 ; *Phil. Mag.*, (5), **39**. 188, 1895 ; A. O. Rankine and C. J. Smith, *ib.*, (6), **42**. 601, 1921 ; A. O. Rankine, *Trans. Faraday Soc.*, **17**. 719, 1922 ; R. de Forcrand, *Journ. Chim. Phys.*, **15**. 516, 1917 ; H. Remy, *Zeit. anorg. Chem.*, **116**. 255, 1921 ; J. Ogier, *Compt. Rend.*, **87**. 210, 1878 ; F. Stromeyer, *Comment. Soc. Gött.*, **16**. 141, 1808 ; H. Schlundt and O. C. Schaefer, *Journ. Phys. Chem.*, **16**. 253, 1912 ; J. C. Thomlinson, *Chem. News*, **99**. 133, 1909 ; H. Henstock, *ib.*, **126**. 337, 1923 ; M. Faraday, *Phil. Trans.*, **135**. 155, 1845 ; L. Bleekrode, *Wied. Ann.*, **3**. 161, 1878 ; *Phil. Mag.*, (5), **5**. 375, 439, 1878 ; G. Grube and H. Kleber, *Zeit. Elektrochem.*, **30**. 517, 1924 ; H. E. Watson, *Proc. Roy. Soc.*, **117**. A, 43, 1927.

⁴ M. Trost, *Viertelj. ger. Med.*, (2), **18**. 269, 1873 ; E. Stadelmann, *Arch. Exp. Path. Pharm.*, **16**. 221, 1882 ; A. Tardieu, *Étude médico-légale et chimique sur l'empoisonnement*, Paris, 449, 1867 ; J. D. Mann and J. G. Clegg, *Med. Chronicle*, (2), **3**. 161, 1895 ; J. D. Mann, *Forensic Medicine and Toxicology*, London, 460, 1908 ; M. Fühner, *Arch. Exp. Path. Pharm.*, **92**. 288, 1922 ; L. O. Dubitsky, *Arch. Hyg.*, **73**. 1, 1910 ; A. Hébert and F. Heim, *Bull. Soc. Chim.*, (4), **1**. 571, 1907 ; L. Gmelin, *Handbook of Chemistry*, London, **4**. 265, 1850 ; A. F. Gehlen, *Schweigger's Journ.*, **13**. 504, 1815 ; J. S. C. Schweigger, *ib.*, **15**. 501, 1815 ; P. Driesen, *Ueber einen Fall von Arsenwasserstoffvergiftung*, München, 1904.

⁵ O. Brunn, *Ber.*, **21**. 2546, 1888 ; **22**. 3205, 1889 ; O. Jacobsen, *ib.*, **20**. 1099, 1887 ; A. Partheil and E. Amort, *ib.*, **31**. 594, 1898 ; O. von der Pfordten, *ib.*, **17**. 2897, 1884 ; C. B. Kühn and O. Saeger, *ib.*, **23**. 1798, 1890 ; J. V. Janowsky, *ib.*, **6**. 220, 1873 ; **8**. 1683, 1875 ; L. Marchlewsky *ib.*, **24**. 2269, 1891 ; A. Stock, *ib.*, **34**. 949, 1901 ; W. Steinkopf and W. Mieg, *ib.*, **53**. B, 1013, 1920 J. P. Cooke, *Amer. Journ. Science*, (2), **31**. 192, 1861 ; R. Napoli, *ib.*, (2), **18**. 190, 1854 ; *Il Giamb. Vico*, 247, 1857 ; M. Berthelot, *Sur la force de matières explosifs*, Paris, **1**. 114, 1888 ; *Compt. Rend.*, **93**. 615, 1880 ; *Ann. Chim. Phys.*, (5), **20**. 20, 1880 ; E. Soubeiran, *ib.*, (2), **43**. 407, 1830 ; P. Lebeau, *ib.*, (7), **25**. 478, 1902 ; *Sur la préparation et les propriétés des arseniures alcalinoterreux*, Paris, 1899 ; H. Thoms and L. Hess, *Ber. deut. pharm. Ges.*, **30**. 483, 1921 ; A. Vogel, *Journ. prakt. Chem.*, (1), **6**. 345, 1835 ; S. Dushman, *Journ. Amer. Chem. Soc.*, **43**. 397, 1921 ; J. Marsh, *Edin. Phil. Journ.*, **21**. 229, 1836 ; *Phil. Mag.*, (3), **15**. 282, 1839 ; (3), **17**. 442, 1841 ; J. L. Gay Lussac and L. J. Thénard, *Recherches physico-chimiques*, **1**. 232, 1811 ; *Ann. Chim. Phys.*, (1), **73**. 229, 1810 ; J. Ogier, *ib.*, (5), **20**. 17, 1880 ; J. B. A. Dumas, *ib.*, (2), **33**. 355, 1826 ; (2), **44**. 289, 1830 ; J. J. Berzelius, *ib.*, (2), **5**. 179, 1817 ; (2), **11**. 225, 1819 ; A. J. Balard, *ib.*, (2), **57**. 225, 1834 ; *Taylor's Scientific Memoirs*, **1**. 269, 1837 ; G. Lockemann, *Zeit. angew. Chem.*, **18**. 491, 1905 ; H. Reckleben and G. Lockemann, *Zeit. anorg. Chem.*, **92**. 145, 1915 ; H. Reckleben and J. Scheiber, *ib.*, **70**. 255, 1911 ; M. Trautz, *ib.*, **104**. 69, 1918 ; H. Reckleben, G. Lockemann, and A. Eckardt, *Zeit. anal. Chem.*, **46**. 671, 1907 ; N. Klobukoff, *ib.*, **29**. 129, 1890 ; C. H. Wolff, *Pharm. Centrh.*, **32**. 493, 1891 ; E. Echeandia, *Ueber den Gang des Arsen- und Antimon-wasserstoffzerfalles*, Berlin, 1909 ; A. Stock, E. Echeandia, and P. R. Voigt, *Ber.*, **41**. 1319, 1908 ; D. M. Kooij, *Zeit. phys. Chem.*, **12**. 155, 1892 ; E. Cohen, *ib.*, **20**. 303, 1896 ; F. Stromeyer, *Comment. Soc. Gött.*, **16**. 141, 1808 ; C. Husson, *Compt. Rend.*, **67**. 56, 1868 ; E. Lemoult, *ib.*, **139**. 478, 1904 ; M. Mayençon and M. Bergeret, *ib.*, **79**. 118, 1874 ; E. Defacqz, *ib.*, **132**. 138, 1901 ; J. B. Senderens, *ib.*, 104. 175, 1887 ; R. de Forcrand, *ib.*, **160**. 467, 1915 ; J. Riban, *ib.*, **88**. 581, 1879 ; J. F. Simon, *Pogg. Ann.*, **41**. 463, 1837 ; H. Rose, *ib.*, **51**. 423, 1840 ; H. B. Parsons, *Chem. News*, **35**. 235, 1877 ; F. Jones, *ib.*, **37**. 36, 1878 ; W. R. Hodgkinson, *ib.*, **34**. 167, 1876 ; M. Forbes, *ib.*, **64**. 235, 1891 ; J. A. Wanklyn, *ib.*, **85**. 181, 1902 ; G. Aimé, *Journ. Pharm. Chim.*, (3), **21**. 84, 1852 ; D. Tivoli, *Gazz. Chim. Ital.*, **14**. 487, 1884 ; **19**. 630, 1889 ; I. Guareschi, *Atti Accad. Torino*, **51**. 4, 59, 263, 1916 ; F. M. Bergstrom, *Journ. Phys. Chem.*, **29**. 168, 1925 ; E. Lyttkens, *Landw. Vers. Stat.*, **26**. 305, 1881 ; *Zeit. anal. Chem.*, **22**. 147, 1883 ; W. Lenz, *ib.*, **22**. 148, 1883 ; *Ber.*, **17**. 209, 674, 1884 ; T. Humpert, *Journ. prakt. Chem.*, (1), **94**. 392, 1865 ;

E. Schobig, *ib.*, (2), **14.** 289, 1876 ; J. Myers, *Liebig's Ann.*, **159.** 127, 1870 ; A. W. Hofmann, *ib.*, **115.** 287, 1860 ; R. Meissner, *Zeit. Exp. Path. Therap.*, **13.** 284, 1913 ; M. Schenkel and T. Rickher, *Jahrb. prakt. Pharm.*, (1), **19.** 257, 1849 ; H. Hager, *ib.*, (3), 35. 92. 1871 ; *Zeit. anal. Chem.*, **11.** 82, 478, 1872 ; G. Dragendorff, *Journ. Russ. Phys. Chem. Soc.*, 5. 159, 1866 ; G. Franceschi, *Boll. Chim. Farm.*, **29.** 317, 1890 ; *L'Orosi*, **13.** 289, 1890 ; H. Strauss, *ib.*, **29.** 51, 1905 ; D. Vitali, *ib.*, **16.** 397, 1893 ; *Boll. Chim. Farm.*, **44.** 49, 1905 ; J. F. Lassaigne, *Journ. Chim. Méd.*, (2), **6.** 685, 1840 ; E. Reichardt, *Arch. Pharm.*, (3), **17.** 1, 1880 ; (3), **21.** 590, 1883 ; A. Göpel, *ib.*, (2), **60.** 141, 1849 ; T. Poleck and C. Thümmel, *ib.*, (3), **22.** 1, 1883 ; R. Otto, *ib.*, (3), **21.** 583, 1883 ; *Ber.*, **16.** 2947, 1883 ; A. Job and R. Reich, *Compt. Rend.*, **177.** 56, 1923 ; K. Preis and B. Rayman, *Listy Chem.*, **11.** 34, 1887 ; A. Güttich, *Ueber Bestimmungsmethoden für Arsen- und Antimonwasserstoff*, Leipzig, 1909 ; R. J. Kane, *Proc. Irish Acad.*, **1.** 182, 1840 ; F. C. J. Bird, *Analyst*, **26.** 181, 1901 ; H. Gutzeit, *Pharm. Ztg.*, **24.** 263, 1879 ; J. Lohmann, *ib.*, **36.** 748, 1891 ; C. Bozenhardt, *Apoth. Ztg.*, **21.** 580, 1906 ; J. C. Draper, *Amer. Chemist*, **2.** 456, 1872 ; *Dingler's Journ.*, **204.** 385, 1872 ; A. H. Gotthelf, *Journ. Soc. Chem. Ind.*, **22.** 191, 1903 ; J. A. Goode and F. M. Perkin, *ib.*, **25.** 507, 1906 ; E. Dowzard, *Journ. Chem. Soc.*, **79.** 715, 1901 ; F. Jones, *ib.*, **29.** 641, 1876 ; **33.** 95, 1898 ; *Proc. Chem. Soc.*, **23.** 164, 1907 ; A. Stock, *Ber.*, **53.** 837, 1920 ; L. Gmelin, *Handbook of Chemistry*, London, **4.** 264, 1850 ; R. J. Kane, *Proc. Irish Acad.*, **1.** 193, 1840.

§ 10. The Arsenides

W. Guertler [1] studied the affinity of arsenic for the metals. H. Davy, J. L. Gay Lussac and L. J. Thénard, and E. Soubeiran found that potassium unites with arsenic with incandescence ; and when potassium is heated in an atm. of arsine, it forms an arsenide, and liberates the hydrogen. H. Davy also found that when potassium hydroxide is electrolyzed with an arsenic cathode, a dark grey alloy of arsenic and potassium is formed. A. F. Gehlen also obtained an impure alloy by igniting a mixture of arsenic and potassium hydroxide to dull redness. The alloy obtained by J. L. Gay Lussac and L. J. Thénard by heating potassium in an atm. of arsine ; and by E. Soubeiran by heating the correct proportions of potassium and arsenic in a glass-tube corresponded with **potassium tritarsenide**, K_3As. P. Lebeau also obtained it by heating a mixture of the elements in the correct proportions at a red-heat—washing with liquid ammonia to remove the excess of potassium, and heating in nitrogen to remove the ammonia ; but he was unable to obtain potassium arsenide by the method he used for normal calcium arsenide—*vide infra.* C. Hugot obtained it by heating the ammino-compound in vacuo at 300°. The early observers noted that when treated with water, arsine is evolved and some solid hydrogen arsenide is formed. C. Hugot prepared brick-red **potassium amminoarsenide**, $K_3As.NH_3$, by the action of an excess of a soln. of potassium in liquid ammonia on arsenic ; if the arsenic be in excess, orange-coloured **potassium amminotetrarsenide**, $K_2As_4NH_3$, is formed, which when heated in vacuo at 300° produces **potassium tetrarsenide**, K_2As_4, as a red powder. P. Lebeau prepared **lithium tritarsenide**, Li_3As, by heating a mixture of the constituent elements in the right proportions at a red-heat ; and also by heating a mixture of dried lithium arsenite and sugar charcoal in an electric arc furnace for 2–3 minutes. The molten mass when cold forms a reddish-brown crystalline mass, which at a red-heat burns in oxygen with a violet light. It is decomposed by water, giving off arsine and acetylene. The hydrocarbon is derived from the lithium carbide as an impurity formed at the same time. The impure arsenide becomes red-hot when placed in cold fluorine, chlorine, or bromine ; and it unites with iodine when a mixture is triturated in a mortar. It reacts vigorously with conc. nitric acid; and at a comparatively low temp., it reduces metal oxides. An impure sodium arsenide was obtained by J. L. Gay Lussac and L. J. Thénard, J. V. Janowsky, and H. H. Landolt by the direct union of arsenic and sodium. A. P. Saunders obtained an arsenide by heating sodium with arsenic trioxide. P. Lebeau prepared impure **sodium tritarsenide**, Na_3As, by the action of arsine on sodium, or on a soln. of sodium in liquid ammonia. He also made this compound by heating a mixture of the elements to redness. The product was digested with liquid ammonia to remove the excess of sodium, and heated in nitrogen to remove the ammonia. He was unable to make this arsenide by the method used for normal calcium arsenide—*vide infra*. C. Hugot obtained **sodium amminoarsenide**, $Na_3As.NH_3$, by the action of liquid ammonia on a mixture of arsenic and sodium. The reddish-brown substance, which is slowly formed, is washed with liquid ammonia. The brick-red, crystalline mass forms impure sodium tritarsenide when heated in vacuo at 300°. Some sodium amide is always present. G. Bredig and F. Haber obtained colloidal soln. of potassium and sodium arsenides by the submerged arc process.

As indicated in connection with copper—**3. 21, 6**—T. Bergman [2] thought that copper can be alloyed with five-sixths its weight of arsenic, but by fusion K. Friedrich could not obtain alloys with more than 44 per cent. of arsenic. P. Berthier made the same alloys. H. Weiss studied the rate of formation of homogeneous alloys from the heterogeneous state. Many more or less impure **copper arsenides** occur in nature. J. H. Stansbie, A. H. Hiorns, and C. D. Bengough and B. P. Hill prepared alloys of these elements by fusion. The f.p. curve—Fig. 18, of **3. 21, 6**—by K. Friedrich shows the existence of two arsenides, Cu_3As, and Cu_5As_2; while A. H. Hiorns said that there is an additional arsenide, Cu_2As. There are solid soln. with up to 4 per cent. of arsenic; J. H. Stansbie said 0·25 per cent. of arsenic. C. D. Bengough and B. P. Hill believed that the two arsenides Cu_3As and Cu_5As_2 form solid soln. The observations of W. C. Roberts-Austen, C. J. B. Karsten, P. Jolibois and M. Merle, P. Thomas, W. Stahl, E. A. Lewis, D. Hanson and C. B. Marryat, C. D. Bengough and B. P. Hill, F. Johnson, R. H. Greaves, L. Archbutt, P. Oberhoffer, C. Blazey, H. D. Law, H. Baucke, A. Mathiessen and C. Vogt, A. Matthiessen and M. Holzmann, A. Pinkerton and W. H. Tait, and J. H. Stansbie on the properties of these alloys were previously indicated— **3. 21, 6.** H. Weiss studied the diffusion of arsenic in copper; E. Kordes, the eutectic mixtures; E. Ruhrmann, the mechanical properties; A. Rietzsch, the thermal and electrical conductivities; J. Arnold and J. Jefferson, the effect of small traces of arsenic on copper; A. Gibb, the elimination of arsenic from copper; W. Hampe, the effect of arsenic on the metallurgy of copper; G. Lippert, the effect of arsenic on the copper in H. Reinsch's test; P. Jolibois and M. Merle, the constitution; C. A. Kraus, the electrical conductivity. The various natural and artificial arsenides with a higher mol. proportion of copper than $Cu:As=3:1$ are probably mixtures of copper with more or less arsenide or arsenic.

A variety of whitneyite called *semi-whitneyite* was found by G. A. Koenig in the Mohawk mine, Keweenaw Co., Michigan; it contained about 3·8 per cent. of free arsenic and 96·2 per cent. of copper; he found that the molar ratio of copper to arsenic in the copper arsenides from this mine reached as high as 30:1; and added that they are rather of the nature of indefinite alloys than definite mineral species. As mixtures, they have no particular interest to the chemist. The arsenide, $Cu_{30}As$, obtained by C. Lefèvre by the action of carbon monoxide on cupric arsenate at 550° is probably a mixture. The crystalline mineral **whitneyite**,—named after J. D. Whitney—was described by F. A. Genth. D. Forbes called a similar mineral from Chili, *darwinite*. Whitneyite was also described by I. Domeyko, G. J. Brush, J. D. Dana, G. A. Koenig, and A. Bertrand. It was analyzed by F. A. Genth, T. Scheerer, and D. Forbes. Its composition approximates Cu_9As; its sp. gr. is 8·3 to 8·7, and its hardness 3–4. J. Joly found that a sublimation occurs at 395°. T. W. Case observed that the resistance is less than a megohm, and darkness has no measurable influence. The Chilian ore, described by A. Bertrand, corresponded with $Cu_{15}As$, and is probably an impure whitneyite. The crystalline mineral **algodonite** was obtained by F. Field from Algodones, near Coquimbo. Its sp. gr. is 6·90–7·62, and its hardness 4. It was analyzed by F. Field, F. A. Genth, and G. A. Koenig; and its composition approximates Cu_6As. The last-named synthesized *argento-algodonite*, $(CuAg)_6As$—*vide infra*. T. W. Case observed that the resistance is less than a megohm, and that insolation has no measurable effect. H. Reinsch obtained a substance of the same composition by heating the arsenide Cu_5As_2; and A. Descamps, by heating copper tritarsenide with molten boric acid for a long time. A sample of algodonite from the Mohawk mine was found by G. A. Koenig to have the sp. gr. 8·364–8·378, and to have a composition approximating Cu_5As. J. B. Senderens obtained a substance of this composition by treating a soln. of cupric nitrate with arsenic. J. Joly said that a sublimation occurs at 350°. L. Ledoux applied the term *mohawkite* to a mineral of sp. gr. 8·07 from the Mohawk mine, and he assigned to it the formula Cu_4As. Since G. A. Koenig applied this term to a variety of domeykite, J. W. Richards suggested calling L. Ledoux's mineral *ledouxite*. C. Winkler melted copper with an excess of silicon under cryolite, and obtained a brittle, crystalline *copper silicoarsenide*, approximating $Cu_4As_4Si_9$.

As indicated above, K. Friedrich, and A. H. Hiorns found that **copper tritar-senide**, Cu_3As, appears as a maximum on the f.p. curve of mixtures of copper and arsenic. It also occurs in nature as the mineral **domeykite**—named by W. Haidinger after I. Domeyko. I. Domeyko called it *arséniure de cuivre*, and J. F. L. Hausmann, *cobre blanco* or *white-copper*. The mineral occurs in various localities, and has been described by C. F. Zincken, A. Krantz, J. D. Whitney, F. A. Genth, T. S. Hunt, A. Frenzel, C. F. de Landero, W. Phillips, R. P. Greg and W. G. Lettsom, C. F. Rammelsberg, J. Blyth, F. Field, F. Navarro, C. Winkler, J. A. Weisbach, D. Forbes, G. A. Koenig, T. Haege, etc. The analyses are in agreement with the empirical formula Cu_3As. According to G. A. Koenig, the analysis of a yellowish-grey mineral in the Mohawk mine, Keweenaw Co., Michigan, corresponds with nickeliferous domeykite, $(Cu,Ni,Co)_3As$—*nickelodomeykite*, or *mohawkite*; of an argentiferous domeykite, $(Cu,Ag)_3As$—*argento-domeykite*; and an antimoniferous domeykite, $Cu_3(As,Sb)$—*stibio-domeykite*; the last-named mineral has a sp. gr. 7·902 at 21°, a hardness under 4; and is incompletely soluble in conc. nitric acid. Domeykite occurs massive and in reniform and botryoidal forms, as well as being disseminated in other minerals and rocks. The colour ranges from tin-white to steel-grey; and it may be yellowish or brown with an iridescent tarnish. G. A. Koenig described hexagonal plates. According to S. Stevanovic, the crystals of artificial domeykite are pseudo-hexagonal, rhombic bipyramids, and have the axial ratios $a : b : c = 0·5771 : 1 : 1·0206$; on the other hand, F. E. Wright added that the crystals are holohedral hexagonal, not rhombic, and A. Descamps added that they are isomorphous with dyscrasite. E. Herlinger examined the crystals. The sp. gr. ranges from 6·7 to 7·8; F. E. Wright gave 7·0–7·5; F. Cornu and K. A. Redlich, 6·708 at 26°; A. Descamps, 7·81; G. A. Koenig, 8·05 at 21°; and S. Stevanovic, 7·92–8·10. The hardness is 3–4; F. E. Wright gave 3–3·5. T. W. Case observed that the resistance is less than a megohm in darkness, and light has no measurable effect.

The tritarsenide was prepared by W. Spring by compressing an intimate mixture of the powdered elements at 6500 atm. press.; by A. Descamps, by melting together a mixture of the components under fused boric acid; by G. Lippert, by heating the Cu_5As_2-oxide in an atm. of hydrogen; by W. Ipatieff and W. Nikolaieff, by the action of hydrogen at a high temp. and press. on copper arsenate; and by G. A. Koenig, by heating a mixture of the hemiarsenide and copper, or by the action of arsenic vapour on copper. A. Granger obtained it in preparing the dipentitarsenide at too high a temp.—*vide infra*; and A. Brukl obtained it by the action of arsine on a soln. of potassium cuprous chloride; he added that if the reaction occurs in soln., with an excess of the metal, there is a secondary reaction, $M_3As + 3M' + 3H_2O = 6M + 3H' + As(OH)_3$. According to G. A. Koenig, a glass tube containing arsenic at one end and metallic copper (filings, turnings, or wire) in the middle is heated to dull redness (about 600°) by means of an electric current passing through a platinum wire wound around the tube. As the arsenic sublimes over the heated copper, brilliant crystals grow out from the surface of the copper. The growth takes place in such a manner as to suggest that there must be a free movement of the copper mols. Using, in place of copper, an alloy of copper, nickel, and cobalt, crystals of $(Cu,Ni,Co)_3As$ (mohawkite) were obtained; with an alloy of copper and silver, crystals of $(Cu,Ag)_3As$ (argento-domeykite) and of $(Cu,Ag)_6As$ (argento-algodonite); and with an alloy of copper and antimony, crystals of $Cu(As,Sb)$ (stibio-domeykite). When arsenic vapours are passed over zinc, lead, or nickel, there is also some action, but no crystals were formed. A. Granger said that this arsenide decomposes when strongly heated. A. Sella found the sp. ht. to be 0·0919. J. Joly said that a sublimation occurs at 345°–370°. A. de Gramont examined the spark spectrum of the mineral. E. T. Wherry found domeykite to be a poor radio-detector. F. Cornu and K. A. Redlich found that the mineral can be completely reduced when heated in hydrogen; and by natural processes is transformed into cuprite. F. E. Wright examined the corrosion figures with cold nitric acid of sp. gr. 1·426; and hydrochloric acid which has only a slight attack on domeykite. Nitric acid alone acts energetically on domeykite and causes a strong evolution of gas.

K. Friedrich, and A. H. Hiorns found that copper dipentitarsenide, Cu_5As_2, appears as an unstable compound on the f.p. curve of the constituent elements— *vide supra*. A. Granger obtained it by passing arsenic vapour in a stream of carbon dioxide over finely divided copper at 444·5°, and also by the action of arsenic trichloride on copper, or of arsenic on cuprous chloride. H. Reinsch obtained it by the action of copper on arsenic dissolved in hydrochloric acid. B. H. Paul and A. J. Cownley also obtained this compound. According to A. Granger, it forms regular crystals with a metallic lustre, has a sp. gr. 7·56, and is soluble in nitric acid. It is easily attacked by chlorine and bromine and tarnishes in the air. At a higher temp., crystals of copper arsenide, Cu_3As, are formed. Both of these arsenides decompose when strongly heated.

K. Friedrich could not obtain any evidence of the formation of copper hemiarsenide, Cu_2As, on the f.p. curve of copper and arsenic; but A. H. Hiorns alleged that it is formed. G. A. Koenig also reported its formation along with the tritarsenide when the vapour of arsenic is passed over copper. A. F. Gehlen also said that it is produced when the elements are melted together; and A. Descamps, when the black precipitate obtained by adding arsenic to a soln. of a copper salt, is fused under borax. The grey crystalline mass has a sp. gr. 7·71 at 21° according to G. A. Koenig, and 7·76 according to A. Descamps. G. A. Koenig found a mineral which he called keweenawite associated with domeykite and mohawkite in the rock of the Mohawk mine, Keweenaw Co., Michigan. Its composition shows that it is a nickeliferous hemiarsenide, $(Cu,Ni,Co)_2As$. It is massive, very finely granular, and of a pale pinkish-brown colour with metallic lustre; on exposure, it tarnishes to brownish-red; sp. gr. 7·681. The mineral *orileyite* of D. Waldie, C. F. Rammelsberg, and F. R. Mallet is an impure form of the hemiarsenide, $(Cu,Fe)_2(As,Sb)$. R. J. Kane reported that he had made copper ditritarsenide, Cu_3As_2, by the action of arsine on dry copper sulphate or chloride —A. Brukl confirmed this; J. B. A. Dumas obtained it by the action of arsine on a soln. of cupric sulphate; A. Descamps, by reducing cupric arsenite with fused potassium cyanide; A. Mazzucchelli and A. Vercillo, by the action of a soln. of arsenic trichloride in hydrochloric acid on copper at 100°; and W. Spring, by compressing a mixture of the powdered elements at 6500 atm. press. A. Descamps found that the bluish-grey crystalline mass is brittle and has a sp. gr. 6·94.

A number of silver-arsenic alloys of different composition have been reported by A. F. Gehlen,[3] T. Bergman, P. Berthier, J. Percy, P. Hautefeuille and A. Perrey, and K. Friedrich and A. Leroux. The alloys were made by the action of molten silver on arsenic. S. Hilpert and F. Herrmann did not make arsenic and silver unite directly even when the vap. of the arsenic under press. is passed over heated silver. Impure silver arsenides occur in nature. A number of these have been described by S. R. I. Eques a Born, A. des Cloizeaux, J. D. Dana, I. Domeyko, L. A. Emmerling, J. D. Forbes, J. B. Hannay, J. F. L. Hausmann, R. J. Haüy, J. L. Jordan, C. A. S. Hofmann, G. A. Kenngott, M. H. Klaproth, G. A. Koenig, O. Luedecke, T. Macfarlane, A. P. J. du Mênil, A. Raimondi, C. F. Rammelsberg, and H. Wurtz. The analyses correspond roughly with silver tritarsenide, Ag_3As. E. V. Zappi and J. J. Landaburu did not produce silver arsenide by reducing the arsenate with formaldehyde.

The *pyritolamprite* of M. Adam, analyzed by M. H. Klaproth, and A. P. J. du Mênil, was considered by C. F. Rammelsberg to be a mixture of arsenical pyrites, arsenical iron, and dyscrasite. The name *macfarlanite*—after T. Macfarlane—was given to a complex arsenical silver ore from Silver Islet, Lake Superior, and it was investigated by T. Macfarlane. Another impure arsenical silver ore was named by H. Wurtz *huntilite*—after T. S. Hunt. Its sp. gr. is 6·27–7·47. The *arsenargentite* of J. B. Hannay occurs in rhombic crystals of sp. gr. 8·825, and composition Ag_3As. Little is known about it. The *chanarcillite* of J D. Dana occurring in Chanarcillo, is represented by the formula $Ag_4(Sb As)_3$. W. Spring made alloys corresponding with Ag_6As and Ag_3As by compressing intimate mixtures of the powdered constituents at 6500 atm. press.

A portion of the f.p. curve of mixtures of silver and arsenic was worked out by K. Friedrich and A. Leroux. There is evidence of the formation of the tritarsenide —*vide* Fig. 10, **3.** 22, 7. A. Brukl made the tritarsenide by the action of arsine on a dil. soln. of silver nitrate or acetate. A. Descamps said that this same compound is formed when the monoarsenide is melted at a high temp. Its sp. gr. is 9·01. H. E. McKinstry observed no effect on exposing huntilite to the electric arclight. The formation of an unstable **silver nitratoarsenide,** $Ag_3As.3AgNO_3$, was indicated in connection with the action of arsine on silver nitrate—**3.** 22, 7. The reaction has been discussed by T. Poleck and K. Thümmel, H. Reckleben and co-workers, A. Brukl, A. Eckardt, D. Vitali, R. Fanto, R. Otto, J. B. Senderens, etc.—*loc. cit.* A. Descamps reported **silver monarsenide,** AgAs, to be formed by reducing silver arsenate with molten potassium cyanide. The white, brittle alloy has a sp. gr. of 8·51. S. Hilpert and F. Herrmann reported **silver diarsenide,** $AgAs_2$, to be formed when silver arsenic chloride, $Ag_7As_2Cl_6$, is treated for 24 hrs. with a conc. soln. of potassium cyanide. More silver is lost if the digestion be continued for a longer time. It is not clear if the brown powder is a chemical individual; and similar remarks apply to the **silver tetrarsenide,** $AgAs_4$, obtained as a residue by the action of a conc. soln. of potassium cyanide on silver arsenic bromide, Ag_3AsBr_3.

The action of arsenic on gold has been indicated in **3.** 23, 6. T. Bergman [4] noticed that gold dissolves only a small proportion of arsenic; and C. Hatchett, and A. Liversidge prepared **gold-arsenic alloys.** A. P. Schleicher could prepare alloys with over 74·53 at. per cent. of gold by the ordinary methods; and his study of a portion of the equilibrium diagram is indicated in Fig. 4. A. Descamps believed that he had prepared **gold hemiarsenide,** Au_2As, by reducing gold chloride with arsenic; and **gold tritetritarsenide,** Au_4As_3, by melting the hemiarsenide and arsenic under molten potassium cyanide. The sp. gr. is 16·2. D. Tivoli reported **gold monarsenide,** AuAs, which is unstable and loses its arsenic at 120°–130°. A. Brukl obtained this compound by the action of arsine on a soln. of sodium chloroaurate. J. Arnold and J. Jefferson examined the effect of small traces of arsenic on gold.

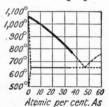

Fig. 4.—Portion of Freezing-point Curve of Gold-Arsenic Alloys.

E. Soubeiran [5] did not obtain **calcium arsenide,** Ca_3As_2, by the action of arsenic vap. on red-hot calcium oxide, but H. Moissan, and P. Lebeau did obtain it by the action of arsenic vap. on calcium at dull redness. An arsenide of the same composition was prepared by P. Lebeau by heating 100 parts of calcium arsenate and 31 parts of petroleum coke in a carbon crucible in an electric furnace for two or three minutes, using a current of 950–1000 ampères and 45 volts. It forms a crystalline mass, which is transparent and reddish-brown in small fragments, has a sp. gr.=2·5 at 15°, and in hardness lies between calcite and glass. It is not affected by dry air or oxygen at the ordinary temp., but when heated burns brilliantly, especially in oxygen, with formation of the arsenate if the oxygen is in large excess, but with sublimation of arsenic trioxide and even of arsenic if it is not. Sulphur attacks the arsenide at a dull red-heat, but boron and carbon have no action at 1000°; in the electrical furnace, however, carbon rapidly and completely decomposes it. In contact with water, the arsenide is completely converted into hydrogen arsenide and calcium hydroxide, without any liberation of hydrogen or separation of a solid brown arsenide as in the action of water on the arsenide obtained by direct synthesis. Moist air somewhat quickly decomposes the arsenide, and it is attacked at a dull red-heat by hydrogen sulphide, by the gaseous hydracids and various oxidizing agents. The arsenide reduces sulphuric acid in the cold, and fuming nitric acid on gently heating ; it also decomposes many metallic salts. J. Riedel made an alloy by heating calcium and arsenic with sand as a diluent. O. Ruff and H. Hartmann studied the velocity of absorption of nitrogen by the alloys at 400°–520°. P. Lebeau prepared **strontium arsenide,** Sr_3As_2, by reducing strontium arsenate with petroleum coke as in the case of calcium arsenide. It is a crystalline mass which is transparent and reddish-brown in thin sections, has a sp. gr. 3·6 at 15°, and closely resembles the corresponding calcium compound in its reactions. It is attacked by fluorine at the ordinary temp. with incandescence and production of arsenious fluoride, and a similar reaction takes place with chlorine at 160°, with bromine at 200°, and with iodine vap. at higher temp. Vivid combustion also occurs when the arsenide is heated to dull redness in oxygen and in sulphur vap. It is converted into strontium carbide when heated with carbon in the electric furnace. In contact with water, it is decomposed, with production of strontium hydroxide and hydrogen arsenide. Strontium arsenide reduces most metallic oxides and is violently attacked by oxidizing agents. E. Soubeiran prepared **barium arsenide,** Ba_3As_2, mixed with the arsenite by heating barium oxide in an atm. of arsine. P. Lebeau obtained barium arsenide by reducing the arsenate as in the case of the calcium and strontium arsenides. It has a darker colour, is more fusible, and is more chemically active than the arsenides of calcium and strontium. Its sp. gr. is 4·1 at 15°. It burns at ordinary temp. when placed in an atm. of fluorine, chlorine, or bromine. It burns in oxygen at 300°, and in sulphur at dull redness.

F. Wöhler [6] observed that an arsenic beryllium alloy can be made by heating the two elements together ; **beryllium arsenide** is formed with incandescence. The alloy is decomposed by water giving off arsine. J. Parkinson heated to redness a mixture of arsenic and magnesium filings in a current of hydrogen, and obtained **magnesium arsenide,** approximating Mg_3As_2. The brittle, chocolate-brown mass decomposed rapidly on exposure to air. J. Riedel made the alloy by heating arsenic and magnesium with sand as a diluent. G. Natta studied its action on alcohols and ethers.

As indicated in connection with the action of arsenic on zinc—**4.** 30, 6— T. Bergman,[7] E. Soubeiran, J. P. Cooke, F. H. Storer, A. Vogel, and A. F. Gehlen found that arsenic readily alloys with zinc ; and W. Spring observed the union of the two elements under a press. 6500 atm. E. Soubeiran, A. Vogel, and W. Spring observed that the alloys are decomposed by dil. acids. E. Kordes studied the eutectic mixtures. The f.p. diagram was worked out by K. Friedrich and A. Leroux, and W. Heike—Fig. 17, **4.** 30, 6. The diagram shows the existence of two compounds—**zinc ditritarsenide,** Zn_3As_2, which melts at 1015°, and at 672° undergoes a reversible transformation, $\alpha\text{-}Zn_3As_2 \rightleftharpoons \beta\text{-}Zn_3As_2$. A. Descamps obtained this compound by the action of arsenic vap. in a current of hydrogen on heated zinc. The second compound, **zinc diarsenide,** $ZnAs_2$, melts at 771°. Both compounds are brittle, and have an approximate hardness of 3 on Mohs' scale. They have a marked thermoelectric force towards zinc. A. Descamps fused arsenic with zinc under molten boric acid and obtained what he regarded as **zinc tritarsenide,** Zn_3As. G. A. Koenig obtained **zinc hemiarsenide,** Zn_2As, by the action of arsenic vap. on heated zinc, as in the case of copper arsenide (q.v.). W. Heike found alloys with less than the molar ratio Zn : As=1 : 2 were not very sensitive as radiodetectors ; with this proportion the results were as good as with pyrite ; a little silver improved the sensitivity of the diarsenide.

The f.p. curve of the **cadmium-arsenic alloys** was partially examined by S. F. Schemtschuschny,[8] and the result was indicated in connection with the action of arsenic on cadmium—Fig. 18, **4.** 30, 6. The required mixture was melted under alkali-chloride. W. Spring made the alloys by compressing the mixture at 6500 atm. press. The colour of alloys with 22–55 at. per cent. of arsenic is dark grey with a tinge of red ; those with more arsenic acquire a bluish tinge. The sp. gr. curve has a marked maximum with 40 at. per cent. of arsenic, and a small break with 66·6 at. per cent. C. T. Heycock and F. H. Neville examined the lowering of the f.p. of cadmium by arsenic. W. Zimmer suggested using these alloys in the preparation of bearing metals, etc. No mixed crystals were observed by S. F. Schemtschuschny. A. Descamps prepared an alloy corresponding with cadmium triarsenide, Cd_3As, by reducing cadmium arsenate under molten potassium cyanide. Its sp. gr. was 6·26. There is no evidence of its existence on the f.p. diagram. W. Spring obtained cadmium ditritarsenide, Cd_3As_2, by compressing the powdered elements; S. F. Schemtschuschny, by fusing a mixture of the components beneath a layer of fused lithium and potassium chlorides; A. Granger, by passing the vap. of arsenic in a current of hydrogen over cadmium; and A. Brukl, by slowly dropping a soln. of cadmium sulphate in dil. aq. ammonia into a globe filled with arsine. The conditions of equilibrium are shown in the diagram, Fig. 18, **4**. 30, 6. A. Granger obtained octahedra and cubes. S. F. Schemtschuschny's preparation was dark grey with a reddish tinge, and a sp. gr. of 6·25 at 4°/20°, the sp. gr. calculated by the mixture rule is 7·47. A. Granger gave 6·211 for the sp. gr. at 15°. The hardness is nearly 3·5. S. F. Schemtschuschny found the m.p. to be 721°, and the compound undergoes a transformation at 578°, $\alpha\text{-}Cd_3As_2 \rightleftharpoons \beta\text{-}Cd_3As_2$. According to W. Spring, and A. Brukl, cadmium arsenide dissolves slowly in cold dil. acids giving off arsine; and A. Granger found that it is soluble in dil. nitric acid, while chlorine, bromine, aqua regia, and oxidizing agents readily attack the arsenide, and A. Brukl said that strong oxidizing agents attack the arsenide with incandescence; some arsine is given off in the attack by conc. nitric acid. S. F. Schemtschuschny found a second compound, cadmium diarsenide, $CdAs_2$, appears on the equilibrium diagram. It furnishes greyish-black crystals. The sp. gr. is 5·86 at 20°/4° when the value calculated by the mixture rule is 6·69. The hardness is 3·5–4·0 on Mohs' scale. The m.p. is 621°.

T. Bergman [9] reported a grey arsenic amalgam to be formed by stirring arsenic into heated mercury; but W. Ramsay said that arsenic is insoluble even in boiling mercury, and that no amalgam is formed by the electrolysis of a dil. soln. of arsenic trichloride using a mercury cathode. W. J. Humphreys also said that arsenic is insoluble in mercury. G. Tammann and J. Hinnüber obtained a very dil. soln. by the electrolysis of arsenic trichloride with a mercury cathode; but the solubility of arsenic in mercury is too small for measurement. R. Böttger failed to make an amalgam by bringing sodium amalgam in contact with moist arsenic trioxide. The mass becomes heated, and brownish-black arsenic is formed. M. Dranty said that arsenic amalgam sublimes when an intimate mixture of arsenic trioxide, mercuric oxide, and charcoal is heated in a tube; but J. F. Lassaigne asserted that the sublimate is a mixture of mercury, arsenic, and arsenic trioxide. According to G. Vortmann, arsenic amalgam can be made by the electrolysis of a hydrochloric acid soln. of mercuric and arsenic chlorides after the addition of potassium iodide to prevent the precipitation of basic salts. The amalgam is brownish-black in colour and is stable in air. A. Brukl obtained mercurous arsenide, Hg_3As, by the action of arsine on a soln. of a mercurous salt. The black precipitate is soluble in nitric acid. He also obtained a black precipitate of mercuric arsenide, Hg_3As_2, from an alcoholic soln. of mercuric chloride. It is easily oxidized, and inflames spontaneously when dry and exposed to air. F. Stromeyer said that mercuric arsenide is the end-product of the action of potassium tritarsenide on a soln. of mercuric chloride. H. Rose had his doubts about this, and A. Partheil and E. Amort were able to confirm the result—vide supra, the action of arsine on mercuric chloride. E. Dumesnil recommended the following process: 10 grms. of arsenious oxide dissolved in 100 grms. of conc. hydrochloric acid are treated with 40·65 grms. of mercuric chloride in 700–800 grms. of dil. hydrochloric acid (1 : 5). After filtration, 60 grms. of sodium hypophosphite are added, the mixture is shaken from time to time, and allowed to remain for several hours. On heating to boiling, a black precipitate of microscopic, mamellated crystals appears. These approximate in composition to the formula Hg_3As_2. Mercuric arsenide is easily oxidized on exposure to air; and when heated in a tube it volatilizes without melting, forming a mixture of arsenic, mercury, and a little arsenic trioxide. The behaviour of the amalgam towards alkyl iodide was considered by A. Partheil and E. Amort to indicate that it is truly a chemical individual.

No **boron arsenide** has been reported. C. Winkler [10] said that molten aluminium does not dissolve arsenic. F. Wöhler said that when a mixture of powdered arsenic and aluminium is heated, a dark grey powder is formed with incandescence, and the resulting **aluminium arsenide** is decomposed slowly by cold water and rapidly by hot water with the evolution of arsine. Q. A. Mansuri found that the two elements unite to form a compound **aluminium tritadiarsenide,** Al_3As_2. The action commences at about 750° and a low press., where yellow arsenic is formed and acts upon the aluminium. The compound Al_3As_2 is stable at high temp., but begins to break up at lower temp. When the compound breaks up, yellow arsenic is first formed. The equilibrium diagram of the system is probably like that of the system aluminium-antimony. The compound Al_3As_2 is a brown, amorphous powder which looks like iron rust and does not melt up to the temp. of fusion of silica (about 1600°). It is very reactive and evolves arsenic trihydride freely when exposed to moisture. For this reason, the alloys were always stored in stoppered bottles, and all polishing, etc., was done in fume chambers. When heated in air, the compound oxidizes to alumina and arsenious oxide. G. Natta studied its action on alcohols and ethers. The solid compound does not seem to dissolve in molten aluminium to any appreciable extent, but separates from it almost completely at its f.p., nor does it alloy with arsenic to form a eutectic. No **gallium or indium arsenide** has been reported. E. Carstanjen found that mol. proportions of thallium and arsenic readily dissolve when melted, forming crystalline **thallium arsenide,** Tl_2As. The alloy is soft enough to be cut with a knife, and the freshly cut surface is silvery-white, but it soon acquires a yellowish film on exposure to air; it readily dissolves in dil. sulphuric acid with the evolution of arsine. The observations of Q. A. Mansuri on the f.p. curve of alloys of arsenic and thallium—Fig. 2, **5.** 36, 4—render it very probable that no definite arsenide of thallium has yet been isolated. A. Hirsch said that the reaction between arsenic and cerium appears to be exothermal. Possibly **cerium arsenide** is formed. The alloy is soft and non-pyrophoric; and does not decompose on keeping.

For *carbon arsenide, vide* arsenic carbide—**5.** 39, 19 ; for *silicon arsenide, vide* arsenic silicide—**6.** 40, 12. *Titanium* and *zirconium arsenides* have not been reported. C. Winkler prepared a series of silicoarsenides by melting the metal with silicon and an excess of arsenic under a layer of molten cryolite and sodium chloride. Thus, **copper silicoarsenide** is a grey, crystalline, brittle mass ; **zinc silicoarsenide** is soluble in hydrochloric acid, giving off arsine at the same time ; **iron silico-arsenide,** $Fe_2Si_9As_4$, is a grey, brittle, crystalline mass ; **cobalt silicoarsenide,** $Co_2Si_9As_4$, is a grey, fine-grained, brittle mass ; and **nickel silicoarsenide,** $Ni_2Si_9As_4$, is grey. The general properties of the alloys of tin and arsenic have been discussed in connection with the action of arsenic on tin—**7.** 46, 5. E. Kordes [11] studied the eutectic mixtures. The equilibrium diagram shows the existence of **tin mono-arsenide,** SnAs, and of **tin tritadiarsenide,** Sn_3As_2. The possible existence of **tin hemitriarsenide,** Sn_2As_3 ; of **tin tritatetrarsenide,** Sn_3As_4; of **tin ditritarsenide,** Sn_3As_2 ; of **tin tetritatriarsenide,** Sn_4As_3 ; and of **tin hexitarsenide,** Sn_6As, is there discussed. The general properties of the lead-arsenic alloys were indicated in connection with the action of arsenic on lead—**7.** 47, 5. Five **lead arsenides** have been reported, although K. Friedrich, working with alloys containing up to 40 per cent. of arsenic, observed no signs of the formation of a definite compound. S. Stevanovic showed that the crystals of the hexitarsenide reported by W. P. Headden to be found in the Cornish tin mines, are six-sided trigonal plates with the axial ratio $a : c = 1 \cdot 2299$; and L. J. Spencer, that the trigonal crystals of the ditritarsenide prepared by J. E. Stead have the axial ratio $a : c = 1 : 1 \cdot 2538$; while arsenic itself has the axial ratio $a : c = 1 : 1 \cdot 4013$.

G. A. Koenig obtained **lead enneatitarsenide**, Pb_9As, by the action of arsenic on molten lead for 20 hrs. The crystalline alloy was malleable; A. Descamps obtained **lead hemiarsenide**, Pb_2As, by heating lead tetratritarsenide in molten boric acid; and at a higher temp. **lead tritadiarsenide**, Pb_3As_2, was formed—the sp. gr. was 9·76. A. Brukl obtained it by the action of arsine on a soln. of lead acetate; ammonia should be added to prevent the decomposition of the arsenide by the liberated acid. A. Descamps obtained **lead monarsenide**, $PbAs$, of sp. gr. 9·55, by reducing lead arsenate under molten potassium cyanide; and **lead tritatetrarsenide**, Pb_3As_4, by melting an excess of arsenic with lead under molten boric acid at as low a temp. as possible, and also by passing arsenic vap. in a current of hydrogen over molten lead. The sp. gr. was reported to be 9·65, although in comparison with the sp. gr. of the other lead arsenides there seems to be something wrong. K. Kawai described a mineral—named **reniformite**—occurring as reniform aggregates in the Yanosawe Mine of Mutsu, Japan. Its composition approximates $5PbS.As_2S_3$, or **lead disulphorthosulpharsenate**, $2PbS.Pb_3(AsS_4)_2$. Its sp. gr. is 6·451. No **thorium arsenide** has yet been isolated.

For **nitrogen arsenide**, *vide* arsenic nitride—**8**. 49, 12; and for **phosphorus arsenide**, *vide* arsenic phosphide—**8**. 50, 12. T. Bergman,[12] and A. F. Gehlen prepared alloys of antimony and arsenic by melting the elements together; and J. von Liebig said that when these alloys are heated white-hot in a current of hydrogen or in the absence of air, the arsenic is volatilized. A. Descamps reported crystalline **antimony hemiarsenide**, Sb_2As, to be formed by heating a mixture of the constituent elements under molten boric oxide. The sp. gr. is 6·46. R. J. Haüy mentioned an *antimoine natif arsenifère*, and F. X. M. Zippe an *Arsenikspiessglanz* which was called **allemontite** by W. Haidinger. It occurs in reniform and amorphous masses, granular, and in crystals at Allemont, France; Pribram, Bohemia; Schladming,

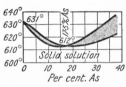

FIG. 5. — Freezing-point Curve of Arsenic-Antimony Alloys.

Styria; Andreasberg, Harz; etc. The composition corresponds with **antimony triarsenide**, $SbAs_3$; the crystals of the tin-white or reddish-grey mineral are trigonal. The hardness is 3·5; and the sp. gr. 6·203. J. Joly said that sublimation occurs at 200°–250°. There is, however, no satisfactory evidence of chemical combination. N. Parravano and P. de Cesaris found that only alloys with 0 to 40 per cent. arsenic can be prepared under ordinary atm. press. Within this range, the continuous series of solid soln. is formed, the f.p. curve, Fig. 5, has a minimum at 612°, with 17·5 per cent. of arsenic. Q. A. Mansuri obtained similar results. G. Kalb found that at a high temp. arsenic-antimony alloys have a gel-like structure which is retained when the alloys are rapidly cooled. With slower cooling, crystals of one or both metals are formed. The eutectic with allemontite (×220) is shown in Fig. 6. M. Padoa measured the electrical

FIG. 6.—Eutectic Structure with Allemontite.

conductivity of the alloys. Antimony associated with a little arsenic, and arsenic associated with a little antimony are not uncommon in nature. Varieties specially rich in arsenic were called *allemontite*—from its occurrence at Allemont, Dept. de l'Isère—by W. Haidinger.   Native arsenical antimony or antimonial arsenic was described by D. Bizzarri and G. Campani, F. Babanek, G. Benko, F. S. Beudant, P. A. Dufrénoy, F. A. Genth, W. Haidinger, R. J. Haüy, J. F. L. Hausmann, C. C. von Leonhard, A. Madelung, F. Mohs, W. Phillips, C. F. Rammelsberg, A. Raimondi, F. A. Reuss, J. B. L. Romé de l'Isle, B. G. le Sage, T. Thomson, V. R. von Zepharovich, and F. X. M. Zippe.   It resembles pyrolusite, and is a hard greyish-white mass of sp. gr. 5·55.   When exposed to air it becomes covered with a black powder.   The spark spectrum was examined by A. de Gramont.

Alloys of bismuth and arsenic were made by T. Bergman,[13] and C. M. Marx ; and by melting bismuth and an excess of arsenic at as low a temp. as possible while under molten boric oxide, A. Descamps obtained what he regarded as **bismuth tetritarsenide,** Bi_3As_4, of sp. gr. 8·45.   There is, however, no satisfactory evidence of chemical combination.   C. T. Heycock and F. H. Neville made some observations on the f.p. of the alloy.   K. Friedrich and A. Leroux found that bismuth and arsenic are only slightly miscible in the molten state, and they separate completely on solidification so that the f.p. curve has two arrests, one corresponding with the soln. of bismuth in arsenic, the other of arsenic in bismuth—Fig. 7.   W. Heike said that the two elements are perfectly miscible in sealed tubes, but not in open tubes, and that there is a eutectic close to the bismuth end of the f.p. curve.   E. Becquerel studied the thermo-electric properties.   Arsenical bismuth occurring in nature has been described by C. M. Kersten, C. Hintze, A. Frenzel, and A. Weisbach.   A. Brukl obtained **bismuth monarsenide,** BiAs, as a black precipitate, by the action of arsine on a soln. of bismuth trichloride with a minimum of hydrochloric acid.   The product is not attacked by water, dil. acids, or alkali-lye, but is decomposed by conc. hydrochloric acid with the liberation of arsine.

FIG. 7. — Freezing-point Curves of the Arsenic - Bismuth Alloys.

T. Dieckmann [14] prepared **chromium diarsenide** by heating a mixture of chromium and arsenic in a sealed tube for 10 hrs. at 700°.   The product was washed with hot dil. hydrochloric acid.   It is non-magnetic.   W. F. de Jong and H. W. V. Willems found that the X-radiogram shows that **chromium monarsenide,** CrAs, is hexagonal, but does not have the pyrrhotine structure.   E. Defacqz prepared **tungsten diarsenide,** WAs_2, by heating tungsten hexachloride in a current of hydrogen arsenide from 150° to 350°.   The product is a black, crystalline substance insoluble in water and other solvents, and having a sp. gr. 6·9 at 18°.   The compound is stable in air at the ordinary temp., but is readily oxidized at a dull red-heat to arsenious and tungstic oxides ; hydrogen reduces it completely at 400°–550°, chlorine under these conditions yields arsenious chloride and tungsten hexachloride, whilst tungsten disulphide and phosphide are produced by the action of heated sulphur and phosphorus respectively.   Hot sulphuric acid attacks the arsenide, evolving sulphur dioxide ; and hot nitric acid oxidizes the substance to tungstic acid.   Hydrofluoric and hydrochloric acids have no action on the arsenide, but a mixture of either of these with nitric acid readily dissolves the substance.   Tungsten arsenide is insoluble in aq. soln. of the alkaline hydroxides, but is readily decomposed by the fused reagents and also by potassium nitrate and carbonate, the final products being alkali arsenates and tungstates.   Fused copper reduces the arsenides, yielding metallic tungsten ; it was not found to produce a sub-arsenide corresponding with the lower phosphide.   E. Defacqz also made **tungsten enneachloroarsenide,** W_2AsCl_9, by heating a mixture of tungsten hexachloride and liquid hydrogen arsenide in a sealed tube at 60°–75°.   The product is in the form of bluish-black crystals resembling the hexachloride ; the substance is hygroscopic and decomposed by water and acids ; it is insoluble in the common anhydrous organic solvents, but readily dissolves in aq. soln. of the alkali hydroxides ; dil. nitric acid readily oxidizes the substance, yielding a colourless soln. and a yellow precipitate of tungstic acid.

R. J. Kane [15] reported a natural **manganese monarsenide,** MnAs. When arsenic is heated on platinum foil, it melts and alloys with the metal. The product burns when heated in air, and dissolves in aqua regia, and in a great excess of nitric acid. E. Wedekind reported the monarsenide to be formed by heating together manganese and arsenic, and freeing the resulting regulus from manganese by dil. hydrochloric acid, and from arsenic by heating it in chlorine or bromine. G. Arrivant could not prepare the monarsenide. S. Hilpert and T. Dieckmann found that manganese could not be satisfactorily prepared by the aluminothermic process, while the preparation from the amalgam gave good results. It forms octahedral and eight-sided columnar crystals which are strongly magnetic ; it is very sensitive towards acids, with the exception of conc. hydrochloric acid, which reacts very slowly and may be used for purification. The same compound was also obtained, but with difficulty, by the direct fusion of the components in an atm. of hydrogen. The product is a black powder of sp. gr. 6·17 at 20°/4°. W. F. de Jong and H. W. V. Willems found that the X-radiogram agreed with the hexagonal structure with $a=3·74$ A., and $c=5·75$; and sp. gr. 6·20. I. Oftedal gave $a=3·716$, and $c=5·704$ A., and $a : c=1 : 1·535$. When heated in a current of hydrogen, arsenic is volatilized. The critical temp. at which manganese arsenide changes from the ferromagnetic to the paramagnetic state is 45°. When the substance cools it regains its ferromagnetic properties. The ferromagnetic substance shows a temp. hysteresis. L. F. Bates showed that the sp. ht. of one specimen, Fig. 8, rises slowly from 0·122 at 28° to 0·14 at 36°, and then rises with increasing rapidity to a value of 0·8 in the neighbourhood of 42°, and then falls rapidly to 0·13 at 45° and to a slight minimum of 0·10 at 46·5°. Hereafter, the sp. ht. rises slowly with temp. Hence, heat is rapidly absorbed as the arsenide changes

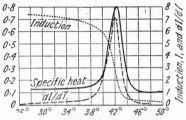

FIG. 8.—The Effect of Temperature on the Specific Heat, Magnetic Induction, and the Rate of Change of the Magnetic Induction of Manganese Arsenide.

from the ferromagnetic to the paramagnetic state. Fig. 8 represents the curve showing the effect of temp. on the magnetic induction, in arbitrary units, and also the curve showing the rate of change of magnetic induction, in arbitrary units, with temp., namely, dI/dT. This curve exhibits a maximum at 42·2°, and there is a marked resemblance between this curve and that of the sp. ht. E. Wedekind and T. Veit said that when the monarsenide is heated it forms **manganese hemi-arsenide,** Mn_2As, but this was denied by S. Hilpert and T. Dieckmann, who observed no break corresponding with the hemiphosphide or with *manganese tritadiarsenide,* Mn_3As_2. The monarsenide is strongly magnetic, but loses its magnetic property at 40°–50° by a reversible action. G. Arrivant examined the e.m.f. of the alloys, Mn_3As_2 and Mn_2As.

T. Bergman,[16] C. J. B. Karsten, and A. F. Gehlen prepared alloys of arsenic and iron by heating mixtures of the two elements in a closed vessel. The alloy was said to be white, brittle, easily pulverized, and infusible, whereas P. Berthier said that the alloy is very fusible. He also added that the alloy is non-magnetic, and is not attacked by hydrochloric and sulphuric acids, but is easily attacked by nitric acid and by aqua regia. The alloys were also described by J. Percy ; his analysis of an iron cannon-ball from Sinope had 16 per cent. arsenic corresponding with Fe_7As. P. Berthier described some Spanish bombs and cannon-balls from the arsenal at Algiers, which contained respectively 9·8 and 27·0 per cent. of arsenic, and 88·7 and 72 per cent. of iron. The effect of arsenic on iron and steel was discussed by A. Carnot and E. Goutal, M. Merle, F. Osmond, and E. Kordes. K. Friedrich examined alloys of iron with up to 56 per cent. of arsenic. The f.p. curve, Fig. 8, falls from the f.p. of iron to a eutectic point at 30 per cent. of arsenic and 835°, then rises to a maximum at 40·1 per cent. and 919°. Less distinct maxima are indicated at 51·7 per cent. of arsenic and 964° and at 57·3 per cent. and 1031°, the latter point being obtained by extrapolation of the curve of solidification times. The compounds indicated are Fe_2As, Fe_3As_2, $FeAs$, and Fe_5As_4, the existence of the last being uncertain. The microphotographs of the alloys, etched by means of a hot soln. of iodine in potassium iodide, confirm the conclusions drawn from the f.p. curve. The alloys are brittle, especially in the neighbourhood of a maximum. Alloys containing more than 40 per cent. of arsenic are not attracted by a magnet. G. Tammann and E. Schaarwächter found the reaction between iron and arsenic begins at about 420°; and P. Oberhoffer and A. Gallaschik observed that the maximum solubility of arsenic in δ-iron is 0·9 per cent. and in γ-iron 6·8 per cent. Iron alone melts at 1528°. The change point of the δ-mixed crystals with liquid to γ-mixed crystals is 1440°. No decomposition of γ-mixed crystals was found from 0 to 7 per cent. As. The magnetic change point on cooling was depressed 80° by 0·5 per cent. of As, and then remained constant. The change point on heating was not affected. Above 3 per cent. of As, no change point could be detected. Micro-examination showed homogeneous mixed crystals up to 6·67 per cent. As. Alloys richer in arsenic coloured more quickly on etching and showed a striped appearance. The alloy with 7·29 per cent. As contained traces of eutectic. The eutectic point is at 30·3 per cent. As above which a new constituent, X, appeared embedded in eutectic. For *arsenical pyrites, vide infra*, the iron arsenic sulphides.

According to J. Percy, in the dry assay of arsenical ores, a spiess is often produced consisting of iron and arsenic in the proportion required for **iron tritarsenide**, Fe_3As. It has the same composition when produced under varying conditions. It is greyish-white; hard, and brittle, and the fractured surface has a close texture, and is bright, and crystalline. It is formed at a temp. below the m.p. of wrought iron. It is very liquid when melted, and takes sharply the impression of the mould in which it solidifies. There is no sign of this as a compound on the f.p. curves, Fig. 9;

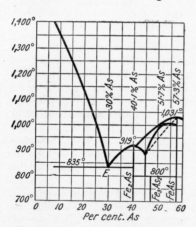

FIG. 9.—The Freezing-point Curve of the Arsenic-Iron Alloys.

rather does it correspond with the eutectic mixture E. J. Percy also described **iron hemiarsenide**, Fe_2As, obtained by fusing mixtures of iron and arsenic under fused plate-glass in a covered clay crucible. There is no sign of the existence of this compound on the f.p. curve, Fig. 9. P. Berthier heated mispickel with borax in a carbon crucible, and digested the product with hydrochloric acid—hydrogen sulphide was evolved, and the composition of the solid residue corresponded with iron hemiarsenide. K. Friedrich obtained this compound by melting a mixture of the two elements, and the conditions for its existence are indicated in Fig. 9. It melts at 919°. E. Vigouroux observed indications of this compound on the e.m.f. diagram. Alloys with 40 to 56 per cent. of arsenic react at about 800°, Fig. 9 and there is a maximum development of heat on the cooling curve corresponding with the formation of **iron ditritarsenide**, Fe_3As_2. The conditions of existence of **iron monarsenide**, $FeAs$, are indicated in K. Friedrich's diagram, Fig. 9. A. Beutell and F. Lorenz said that it is formed between 335° and 380° by heating iron in arsenic vapour. A. Brukl obtained it by dropping a soln. of a ferrous salt into an atm. of arsine. S. Hilpert and T. Dieckmann reported this compound to be formed as a non-magnetic, silver-grey powder, by heating the diarsenide in a current of hydrogen at 680°. Its sp. gr. is 7·83, and its m.p. 1020°—K. Friedrich

gave 1031° for the m.p. P. Lebeau obtained a compound of the same composition by heating a mixture of arsenic trioxide, iron, and carbon in the electric arc-
furnace for a short time; and A. Descamps, by heating iron arsenate with molten
potassium cyanide. W. F. de Jong and H. W. V. Willems found that the X-radiogram of the monarsenide agreed with the crystals having rhombic symmetry.
K. Friedrich showed that iron tetrapentitarsenide, Fe_5As_4, is probably formed
when the elements in the right proportions are fused together. J. Percy reported
a product with the composition of iron diarsenide, $FeAs_2$, by passing the vapour
of arsenic over red-hot iron for a long time. A. F. Gehlen's and T. Bergman's
alloys approximated to this composition. The diarsenide also occurs in nature—
vide infra; but it is not represented as a singular point on K. Friedrich's diagram,
Fig. 9. W. P. Headden obtained iron monarsenide associated with stannous
sulphide in masonry of a tin smelting furnace near Truro, Cornwall. G. Tammann
and H. Bredemeier studied the surface oxidation of this compound. S. Hilpert
and T. Dieckmann prepared iron diarsenide, $FeAs_2$, by heating the finely-powdered
metal and arsenic sealed up in an evacuated bomb-tube of Jena glass for
several hours at 700°–750°, a temp. much higher than the b.p. of arsenic. After
cooling, the almost chemically pure arsenide can be mechanically separated from
the arsenic which has condensed on the walls of the tube, and it can then readily
be purified by further treatment. After purification by dil. hydrochloric acid, the
diarsenide appears as a silver-grey, microcrystalline powder with a sp. gr. 7·38,
and m.p. 980°–1040°. It is non-magnetic. A. Beutell and F. Lorenz said that
the temp. of formation is 480°–618° in arsenic vapour. J. Percy also reported
what may have been iron tetrarsenide, $FeAs_4$, which he obtained by passing the
vap. of arsenic in a current of hydrogen over reduced iron at a bright red-heat.
The product is not sensibly affected by hydrochloric or dil. sulphuric acid.
E. Vigouroux observed indications of iron tetrapentitarsenide, Fe_4As, on the e.m.f.
diagram. A. Brukl obtained ferrous arsenide, Fe_3As_2, by the action of arsine
on an alcoholic soln. of ferrous ammonium sulphate. The black precipitate is
stable; is slightly attacked by conc. hydrochloric and sulphuric acids; is soluble
in nitric acid, aqua regia, and bromine-water. It could not be obtained from
acid or neutral soln., and with alkaline soln., the precipitate contains an excess of
arsenic.

The mineral called löllingite by W. Haidinger approximates to iron diarsenide,
although it passes through ferric arsenide, Fe_3As_4, towards Fe_2As_3. It occurs at
Lölling in Carinthia, and elsewhere. It was called by R. Jameson prismatic arsenical
pyrites, and later, axotomous arsenic pyrites by R. Jameson, and F. Mohs; arsenical
pyrites, or an equivalent term by C. J. B. Karsten, E. Hoffmann, J. F. L. Hausmann,
C. Hartmann, M. H. Klaproth, G. Rose, E. F. Glocker, and A. Breithaupt; leucopyrite—from λευκός, shining—by C. U. Shepard; mohsine, by E. J. Chapman;
hoffmannite, by E. F. Glocker; pharmacopyrite, by A. Weisbach; and hüttenbergite,
by A. Breithaupt. Analyses were reported by G. A. Behncke, A. Breithaupt,
L. Broz, I. Domeyko, A. Frenzel, F. A. Genth, C. Güttler, H. Hahn, W. F. Hillebrand, E. Hofmann, B. Illing, W. J. Jordan, C. J. B. Karsten, J. Loczka,
L. W. McCay, W. Marzek, J. Niedzwiedzky, A. E. Nordenskjöld, T. Petersen,
A. Raimondi, C. F. Rammelsberg, G. Rose, T. Scheerer, R. Scheibe, R. Senfter,
T. L. Walker, and V. R. von Zepharovich, etc. G. A. Kenngott called the diarsenide, sätersbergite, and Fe_2As_3 or $FeAs.FeAs_2$, löllingite; while J. D. Dana
called the diarsenide, löllingite, and Fe_2As_3, leucopyrite. V. R. von Zepharovich
likewise assumed that $FeAs_2$ and Fe_2As_3 or Fe_3As_4 represent two different mineral
species; but C. F. Rammelsberg, G. Tschermak, and P. Groth did not agree with
this, and supposed that mechanical mixtures are involved. The subject was
discussed by A. Beutell and F. Lorenz, and A. Beutell. Löllingite is also
associated with some sulphur and merges gradually into mispickel, FeSAs, and
safflorite, $CoAs_2$. A. Breithaupt called the sulphurous arsenide from Geyer,
geyerite, and that from La Paz, pazite : and F. Sandberger called the cobaltiferous

arsenides *glaucopyrite*. Some varieties also contain antimony, and bismuth. In addition to the analyses mentioned above, the mineral from different localities has been described by A. d'Achiardi, L. Bombicci, A. Breithaupt, W. C. Brögger, A. Brunlechner, J. H. Collins, J. D. Dana, A. Frenzel, E. Fugger, E. F. Glocker, B. Hare, G. P. Jervis, F. A. Kohlenati, A. Lacroix, A. Liversidge, O. Luedecke, A. Ossent, W. F. Petterd, J. Rumpf, L. H. Bauer and H. Berman, F. Sandberger, R. Scheibe, C. J. Selb, G. Sillem, F. J. Wiik, etc. A. Beutell and F. Lorenz gave $305°-514°$ as the temp. of formation of Fe_2As_3 when iron is heated in arsenic vapour.

Löllingite or arsenical pyrites is represented as a compact mineral with a granular or radiating structure ; or in rhombic crystals which, according to W. C. Brögger, have the axial angles $a : b : c = 0.66888 : 1 : 1.2331$. This sample came from Norway. L. H. Bauer and H. Berman gave for a sample from Franklin, New Jersey, $a : b : c = 0.5438 : 1 : 1.130$. Arsenopyrite from Hokenstein had the ratio $0.6773 : 1 : 1.188$; and marcasite, $0.7580 : 1 : 1.212$. The measurements by A. Schrauf were shown by P. Groth to have been made on a sample of mispickel not löllingite. The crystals were also examined by F. Mohs. W. F. de Jong examined the X-radiogram and found the lattice constants of the rhombic crystals to be $a = 6.35$ A., $b = 4.86$ A., and $c = 5.80$ A.; and the calculated density is in agreement with the observed if 4 mols. are present per unit cell. N. S. Kurnakoff and N. S. Konstantinoff regard the crystals as isomorphous with safflorite and iron diantimonide :

$$Fe{<}\substack{As \\ \cdot\cdot \\ As}$$

The colour of löllingite is greyish-black, steel-grey, or silver-white. The lustre is metallic ; the fracture uneven ; and the cleavage basal, often distinct. The twinning planes (101) cross at angles of nearly $60°$; and sometimes trillings occur. The hardness ranges from 5.0 to 5.5 ; and the sp. gr. from 7.0 to 7.4. A. Sella gave 0.0864 for the sp. ht. A. de Gramont examined the spark spectrum ; and F. Beijerinck found the mineral to conduct electricity. E. T. Wherry found the crystals to be fair radio-detectors. W. Hicks studied the magnetic properties of iron arsenides. According to J. Loczka, the arsenic is set free when löllingite is heated with sulphur : $FeAs_2 + S = FeS + 2As$; or with iron pyrites : $FeAs_2 + FeS_2 = 2FeS + 2As$. J. Lemberg found that an alkaline soln. of bromine oxidizes it to ferric oxide more slowly than is the case with mispickel ; and when allowed to stand in a cold acidified soln. of silver sulphate, the mineral acquires a crust of silver crystals. C. A. Burghardt found that löllingite is decomposed when heated with ammonium nitrate. It dissolves in nitric acid with the separation of arsenic acid. E. Thomson studied the corrosion figures of löllingite produced by nitric acid, and soln. of mercurous and ferric chlorides ; and T. L. Walker and A. L. Parsons, the oxidation of the mineral of aerated water— *vide* rammelsbergite.

Alloys of cobalt and arsenic were prepared by A. F. Gehlen,[17] P. Berthier, H. Kopp, and C. F. Rammelsberg. T. Scheerer and W. Francis observed that truncated rhombic needles, and large plates, approximating $(Co,Fe,Cu)_5As$, were formed in the furnaces of a cobalt-blue colour works at Modum. F. Ducelliez found that cobalt is transformed by the action of arsenic trichloride into a mixture of chloride and arsenide, the arsenide ranging from Co_3As_2 to $CoAs_2$, according to the temp. of the reaction. The different arsenides can be prepared by heating mixtures of arsenic trichloride and cobalt, or alloys of arsenic and cobalt, or mixtures of the two powdered elements in an inert atm.—hydrogen or carbon monoxide—or by heating powdered cobalt in an atm. of arsenic vap. A. Beutell and F. Lorenz supposed that there are five arsenides with $Co : As = 1 : 1$; $2 : 1$; $1 : 2$; $2 : 5$; and $1 : 3$. The f.p. curve was studied by K. Friedrich, and his results are summarized in Fig. 9. The alloys are particularly liable to under-cooling. The first series of crystals consists of cobalt containing not more than 1 per cent. of arsenic in solid soln. There is a eutectic point at 916° and 30 per cent. As. There is a maximum at 926° and 33·7 per cent. As, corresponding with **cobalt dipentitarsenide,** Co_5As_2. A second maximum, corresponding with **cobalt hemiarsenide,** Co_2As, occurs at 959° and 38·9 per cent. As. The existence of Co_3As_2, dissociating without melting at 1014°, is also indicated, and the curve then rises, apparently reaching a maximum near 1180°, corresponding with the monoarsenide CoAs. It was not possible to follow the curve to higher percentages of arsenic. The three compounds first mentioned exist each in an α- and a β-form, the transformation occurring on cooling with development of heat whether the compound is present in primary crystals or as a constituent of a eutectic. The respective transition temp. are : for Co_5As_2, 828° ; Co_2As, 352° ; and Co_3As_2, 915°. Alloys containing from 12 per cent. to 46 per cent. As also undergo a transformation at temp. ranging from 250° to 350°, both temp. and heat development reaching a maximum at the composition Co_2As. This change is accompanied by a considerable increase of volume on cooling, sometimes causing disruption of the alloy. Its nature is not to be discovered by a microscopic examination of the alloys. The hardness of cobalt is progressively increased by the addition of arsenic. Only alloys containing 0–38 per cent. As are attracted by a magnet. E. Kordes studied the eutectic mixtures of cobalt and arsenic.

In addition to the dipentitarsenide, and the hemiarsenide, there is **cobalt ditritarsenide,** Co_3As_2, whose conditions of existence are indicated in Fig. 10. This compound was prepared by F. Ducelliez by heating cobalt, or an alloy with 39 per cent. of arsenic in contact with arsenic trichloride between 800° and 1400°, by reducing cobalt arsenite or arsenate with hydrogen at 900°— the heat developed, volatilizing part of the arsenic, prevents the formation of cobalt monarsenide ; or by passing the vap. of arsenic in a current of hydrogen over powdered cobalt at 800°–1400°. When prepared below 1000°, it has a metallic lustre. Its sp. gr. is 7·82 at 0° ; at 1400°, it loses arsenic. Oxygen, chlorine, and sulphur react vigorously with this arsenide ; hot, conc. hydrochloric acid acts feebly ; sulphuric acid has very little action ; nitric acid, and aqua regia dissolve it easily ; and molten alkali hydroxides and carbonates attack it slowly. The conditions of formation of **cobalt monarsenide,** CoAs, are indicated in Fig. 10. F. Ducelliez made this compound by heating the ditritarsenide

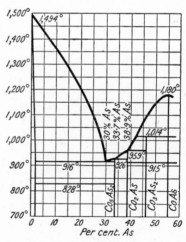

FIG. 10.—Freezing-point Curves of Cobalt-Arsenic Alloys.

between 600° and 800° ; by heating cobalt with arsenic trichloride between 600° and 800° ; and by heating a mixture of arsenic and cobalt in hydrogen, or by passing the vap. of arsenic in a current of hydrogen over powdered cobalt at 600°–800°. A. Beutell and F. Lorenz gave 275°–335° for its temp. of formation from cobalt and arsenic vap. W. F. de Jong and H. W. V. Willems said that the X-radiogram did not enable them to determine the structure of the monarsenide. According to A. Beutell and F. Lorenz, the pale grey, crystalline mass has a sp. gr. of 7·62 at 0° ; and m.p. 1180°. When exposed to air, it becomes matte ; and when heated in hydrogen above 800°, it loses arsenic. G. Tammann and H. Bredemeir studied the surface oxidation. Cobalt monarsenide reacts chemically like the ditritarsenide. When cobalt or the monarsenide is heated with arsenic trichloride between 400° and 600°, **cobalt hemitriarsenide,** Co_2As_3, is formed ; and the same compound is produced by heating at 400°-600° a mixture of powdered arsenic and cobalt, in hydrogen, or by heating at 400°-600° powdered cobalt in a current of arsenic vap. carried by hydrogen. A. Beutell and F. Lorenz gave 345°-365° for its temp. of formation from cobalt in arsenic vap. The product has a sp. gr. of 7·35 at 0°. It begins to decompose at 600°. Its chemical reactions are like those of the ditritarsenide. When the hemitriarsenide is heated below 400°, it slowly forms cobalt **diarsenide**, $CoAs_2$. It cannot be obtained directly from cobalt and arsenic trichloride below 400°. A. Beutell and F. Lorenz gave 385°-405° for its temp. of formation from cobalt in arsenic vap. It is a grey powder of sp. gr. 6·97 at 0°, and is readily oxidized by exposure to air. It behaves chemically like the other cobalt arsenides. It occurs as a mineral in two forms—cubic *smaltite*, or cobalt speiss, and rhombic *safflorite*. The cubic diarsenide was reported by J. Durocher,[18] and F. Fouqué and A. Michel-Lévy to have been made by the action of hydrogen at a high temp. on a mixture of cobalt and arsenic chlorides. The speiss of a cobalt-blue works was described by C. W. C. Fuchs.

The mineral called by G. Agricola [19] *cobaltum cineraceum* received several other names : *Koboltmalm*, *Koboltglantz*, and *cobaltum arsenico mineralisatum* from J. G. Wallerius, and A. Cronstedt. J. B. L. Romé de l'Isle called it *mine de cobalt grise* or *mine de cobalt arsenicale ;* while A. G. Werner, L. A. Emmerling, C. A. S. Hofmann, J. F. L. Hausmann and R. Kirwan called it *Speiskobalt*, or *cobalt speiss*, white or grey cobalt speiss, or equivalent terms. F. S. Beudant designated the mineral *smaltine*, and this name was altered by E. F. Glocker, and J. D. Dana to **smaltite**. J. G. Wallerius knew that the smaltite contained cobalt and arsenic, and the analyses of J. F. John, and F. Stromeyer agreed with the formula $CoAs_2$, or $(Co,Fe)As_2$. E. Hoffmann observed that the mineral also contained some nickel ; although A. Breithaupt obtained a variety from Schneeberg free from nickel. The analyses of P. Berthier, J. C. Booth, I. Domeyko, A. Frenzel, E. von Gerichten, H. Hahn, W. Harres, W. F. Hillebrand, F. von Kobell, G. A. Koenig, A. Löwe, L. W. McCay, T. Petersen, C. F. Rammelsberg, G. Rose, F. Sandberger, W. Sartorius, J. F. Vogel, and G. Vollhardt, etc., show that there are all intermediate forms. Hence, P. Groth used the generalized formula $(Co,Ni,Fe)As_2$. The varieties richest in nickel were called by C. M. Kersten, *nickel biarseniet ;* and by A. B. Breithaupt, **chloanthite**—from χλοανθής, greenish—because the colour of the metal salt obtained from it was green in contrast with the red colour of that from smaltite. C. U. Shepard called a variety from Chatham, *chathamite* ; A. Frenzel called a variety containing bismuth, *chelentite*—from χηλευτός,—and W. Haidinger, *kerstenite*—after C. M. Kersten—*cf.* lead selenite. There is only an arbitrary division between the two forms—smaltite has less nickel than cobalt, and chloanthite more nickel than cobalt.

Numerous other observations have been made as to the occurrence of these two minerals —*e.g.* by H. Baumhauer, F. Beyschlag, J. R. Blum, A. des Cloizeaux, J. H. Collins, A. Erdmann, E. Fugger, M. C. Grandjean, R. P. Greg and W. G. Lettsom, C. W. Gümbel, E. Hatle, C. von Hauer, W. Hisinger, G. C. Hoffmann, G. A. Kenngott, A. Koch, C. Koch, N. von Kokscharoff, F. A. Kolenati, A. Lacroix, C. F. de Landero, A. Laspeyres, G. Leonhard, O. Luedecke, C. F. Naumann, S. Navia, H. Oehmichen, A. Orio, A. Ossent, W. F. Petterd, A. Raimondi, G. vom Rath, J. Rumpf, A. Russell, N. von Szontagh, H. Traube, M. Websky, V. R. von Zepharovich, etc.

Observations on the crystals of smaltite and chloanthite were made by I. S. R. I. Eques a Born,[20] J. B. L. Romé de l'Isle, R. J. Haüy, F. Mohs, M. Bauer, P. Groth, and A. Breithaupt. The crystals belong to the cubic system, being usually in the form of cubes, and rarely show pyritohedral forms. The minerals also occur in compact and granular masses ; these are penetration twins ; the cleavage on the (111)-face is distinct, and that on the (100)-face in traces. H. Baumhauer reported that the crystals may have a zonal structure. A. Beutell found smaltite crystals with an outer zone of $CoAs_2$, and an inner core of $CoAs_3$ or Co_2As_3. H. Baumhauer, and G. Vollhardt studied the corrosion figures obtained with nitric acid, or chlorine-water. L. S. Ramsdall found a difficulty in interpreting the X-radiograms of smaltite and chloanthite. Assuming that the unit cell contains four mols. as in the case of pyrite, the unit cubic cell has a side of length 5·96 A. I. Oftedal regarded speiscobalt and chloanthite as impure skutterudites, for the X-radiogram corresponded with a cubic lattice having $a=8·24$ A.; the mineral is not isomorphous with pyrite. The fracture of smallite and chloanthite is granular and uneven. The colour is tin-white or steel-grey. The lustre is metallic. The surface may appear iridescent, or may be grey from tarnish. The sp. gr., given by many of those quoted in connection with the analyses of these minerals, ranges from 5·734 given by C. F. Rammelsberg, to 6·98 given by J. F. Vogl. I. I. Saslavsky studied the mol. vol. and the contraction which occurs when the diarsenide is formed from its elements. The hardness likewise ranges from 6·3 to 7·0. H. Fizeau gave $0·0_{5}919$ for the linear coeff. of thermal expansion at 40°. F. E. Neumann found the sp. ht. to be 0·0920 ; A. Sella gave for a variety rich in iron 0·0848 ; and calculated for $CoAs_2$, 0·0897, for $NiAs_2$, 0·0900, and for $FeCoNiAs_6$, 0·0902. H. Kopp also measured the sp. ht. A. de Gramont examined the spark spectrum. F. Beijerinck found these minerals to be good electrical conductors ; while P. Groth, and A. Schrauf and E. S. Dana examined the thermoelectric qualities against copper. E. T. Wherry found smaltite and safflorite to be poor radio-detectors.

The mineral may occur in nature altered to erythrite—cobalt arsenite—owing to the oxidation of the cobalt and arsenic by exposure to moisture and air. Oxidation readily occurs when the minerals are heated in air, and arsenic trioxide is formed as a sublimate. P. Groth also found that the mineral is oxidized by water. F. von Kobell showed that the minerals are dissolved by nitric acid with the separation of arsenic acid, and C. A. Burghardt, by fused ammonium nitrate. E. F. Smith showed that sulphur monochloride at 180° completely decomposes the minerals ; and J. Lemberg, that silver is rapidly precipitated when the minerals are placed in an acidified soln. of silver sulphate, and that an alkaline soln. of bromine oxidized the cobaltiferous more rapidly than the nickeliferous mineral. G. Vollhardt found that the minerals with a low proportion of arsenic readily dissolve in a mixture of hydrochloric acid and potassium chlorate, while those rich in arsenic require repeated treatments with the mixture. E. Thomson studied the etching reactions of smaltite, and chloanthite with nitric acid, and with soln. of mercurous and ferric chlorides.

The rhombic form of cobalt diarsenide was regarded by A. Breithaupt [21] as a distinct mineral species, and named **safflorite**—from the German *Safflor*, safflower, or bastard saffron in allusion to its use as a blue pigment for glass, etc. It is the *flaserigen weissen Speiskobalt* of A. G. Werner ; and it was also mentioned by F. von Kobell, F. Mohs, E. F. Glocker, G. Rose, and G. A. Kenngott. F. Sandberger called it *Quirlkies*, or *spathiopyrite*—from σπάθη, a quirl, or spatula. Analyses were made by E. Hoffmann, G. Rose, L. W. McCay, F. Sandberger, F. Varrentrapp, E. von Gerichten, T. Petersen, and H. Sjögren. These are in agreement with the formula $CoAs_2$. Up to 18·48 per cent. of iron, and 7·39 per cent. nickel, 4·76 per cent. bismuth, and 4·22 per cent. copper has been found in the mineral. Safflorite was also described by A. Frenzel, P. Poni, and J. D. Dana. Safflorite occurs massive, and with a fibrous radiated structure. It also occurs in tin-white rhombic crystals resembling those of arsenopyrite. H. Sjögren gave for the axial ratios of the rhombic crystals $a:b:c=0·5085:1:0·8944$. Twinning occurs about the (110)-plane, and there are cruciform twins crossing at an angle of nearly 120°. The cleavage on the (010)-face is distinct. W. F. de Jong found the lattice constants deduced from the X-radiogram are in agreement with those obtained for löllingite. N. S. Kurnakoff and N. S. Konstantikoff represented the compound as isomorphous with löllingite, and iron diantimonide. The hardness is 4·5–5·0, and the sp. gr. determined on most of the samples analyzed ranged from G. Rose's 6·84 to H. Sjögren's 7·41. F. Beijerinck found that safflorite is a conductor of electricity. The lustre is metallic, but the mineral soon tarnishes on exposure to air. The general properties are like those of smaltite. E. Thomson studied the etching reactions with nitric acid, and soln. of mercurous and ferric chlorides; and T. L. Walker and A. L. Parsons, the oxidizing action of aerated water—*vide* rammelsbergite.

A. Breithaupt [22] described a mineral from Skutterud, near Modum, Norway, which he called *tesseral pyrites*, or *hard cobalt pyrites*. J. F. L. Hausmann used similar names. W. Haidinger called it **skutterudite**, and J. Nicol, *modumite*. Analyses reported by C. F. Rammelsberg, T. L. Walker, T. Scheerer, F. Wöhler, and L. Staudenmaier corresponded with **cobalt triarsenide**, $CoAs_3$. The occurrence in Italy was described by L. Bombicci, and A. d'Achiardi. E. Waller and A. J. Moses, and G. Vollhardt described *nickel-skutterudite*, $(Co,Ni,Fe)As_3$, containing up to nearly 13 per cent. of nickel and 5 per cent. of cobalt, and W. Ramsay, and A. Frenzel, *bismuth-skutterudite*, $Co(As,Bi)_3$, with up to 30 per cent. of bismuth. J. D. Dana questioned the homogeneity of bismuth-skutterudite. A. Beutell and F. Lorenz gave 450°–618° as the temp. of its formation from the metal and arsenic vap. They said that at 415°–430°, cobalt hemipentarsenide, Co_2As_5, is formed. Skutterudite occurs massive and granular, and in octahedral or pyritohedral crystals belonging to the cubic system. The crystals were examined by T. Scheerer, G. vom Rath, L. Fletcher, and W. H. Miller. The cleavage on the (100)-face is distinct, and that on the (110)-face occurs in traces. A. Beutell regarded skutterudite as probably not cubic, but rather occurring as a pseudomorph after smaltite. The fracture is uneven, and the colour varies from tin-white to lead-grey with a bright metallic lustre, or there may be an iridescent film on the surface. The hardness is about 6; and the sp. gr. ranges from 6·664 to 6·934. I. Oftedal observed that the X-radiogram agreed with a cubic lattice having $a = 8·189$ A., and 8 mols. of $CoAs_3$ per unit cell. The shortest distance between the arsenic atoms is 2·46 A., and between the cobalt and arsenic atoms, 2·35 A. F. Beijerinck found the mineral to be a good conductor of electricity; and A. Schrauf and E. S. Dana showed that the thermoelectric properties may be positive or negative. E. Thomson examined the etching reactions with nitric acid, and soln. of mercurous and ferric chlorides; and T. L. Walker and A. L. Parsons, the oxidation of the mineral by aerated water—*vide* rammelsbergite.

Alloys of nickel and arsenic were made, by J. J. Berzelius,[23] and A. F. Gehlen, by the action of arsenic on nickel; by P. Berthier, by reducing nickel arsenate with carbon; and by A. Granger, by heating nickel in the vap. of arsenic chloride. The composition of these products approximated *nickel hemiarsenide*, Ni_2As; but there is nothing to show that this product is a chemical individual. K. Friedrich and F. Bennigson [24] studied the f.p. curves of alloys with up to 57·4 per cent. of arsenic. The results are illustrated by Fig. 11. The f.p. of nickel is lowered by the addition of arsenic until a eutectic point is reached at 900° and 27·8 per cent. The curve then rises to a maximum at 998° and 34·3 per cent. of arsenic, corresponding with the compound Ni_5As_2. Another eutectic point is reached at 804° and 43·3 per cent., and the curve then rises to a second maximum at 968° and 56·0 per cent., corresponding with the compound $NiAs$. Solid soln. are formed between the limits 0–5·5 per cent. and 33·5–35·7 per cent. of arsenic. The compound Ni_5As_2, holding nickel in soln., occurs in two modifications. Alloys containing

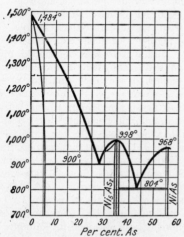

FIG. 11.—Freezing-point Curve of the Nickel-Arsenic Alloys.

from 35·7 per cent. to 56 per cent. undergo a change at a temp. which could not be determined accurately owing to supercooling; the maximum development of heat occurs at 45·5 per cent. of arsenic, thus indicating the formation of a compound Ni_3As_2. The microscopic structure of the alloys is in accordance with these conclusions. The alloys are hard, the maximum hardness corresponding with the compound Ni_5As_2. The brittleness is greatest at the points indicated by maxima on the f.p. curve. Alloys containing more than 29 per cent. of arsenic are no longer attracted by a magnet. A. Beutell reported two nickel arsenides to be formed by the action of arsenic vapour on the powdered metal. O. Hackl reported **nickel tritarsenide,** Ni_3As, to occur as a mineral, which he called **dienerite**—after C. Diener —without giving particulars.

K. Friedrich and F. Bennigson prepared **nickel dipentitarsenide,** Ni_5As_2, and the conditions of stability are indicated in Fig. 10. It melts at 998°. As indicated above, there is some evidence on the fusion curve of the existence of **nickel ditritarsenide,** Ni_3As_2. A. Descamps said that he made it by the reduction of nickel arsenate with molten potassium cyanide; E. Vigouroux obtained it by passing arsenic trichloride vap. over powdered nickel or a nickel arsenide at 800°–1400°; he also found that nickel monarsenide loses arsenic at 800° and passes into the ditritarsenide; and A. Granger and G. Didier, by heating the finely-divided metal at 600° in the vapour of arsenious chloride; the compound thus obtained forms reddish, crystalline granules having a metallic lustre and resembling the impure arsenide isolated by F. Wöhler from smalt residues. Although the arsenide differs in composition from the phosphide, Ni_2P, obtained under similar conditions, it resembles this compound in its chemical properties. A. Brukl made this arsenide by the method employed for ferrous arsenide. According to E. Vigouroux, the grey powder has a metallic lustre, it melts at 1000°, and freezes to a silver-white, hard mass of sp. gr. 7·86 at 0°. It begins to decompose near 1400°; when heated with arsenic in an atm. of hydrogen, it takes up arsenic, and this the more the lower the temp., until, at 400°, it forms the grey, pulverulent diarsenide. The arsenides are attacked by heated chlorine, oxygen, or sulphur vap. They are rapidly dissolved by nitric acid and aqua regia, are very slightly attacked by hydrochloric and sulphuric acids, are decomposed by fused potassium chlorate and nitrate, but are only slowly attacked by alkali hydroxides or carbonates. By heating nickel tridiarsenide under molten boric oxide, A. Descamps believed that he had formed *nickel tritarsenide,* Ni_3As. He also said that the same compound can be produced by reducing nickel oxide with molten potassium cyanide in the presence of a large proportion of arsenic, and at a temp. at which the excess of arsenic will volatilize. The individuality of this compound has not been established. R. Lorenz and W. Herz studied the relations between the transformation temp., 970°, and the m.p., 962°, of this and other compounds.

A substance occurring as a furnace product has been described as *nickel speise.* It was analyzed by J. W. Döbereiner, F. Wöhler, C. Schnabel, C. F. Plattner, W. Francis, C. F. Rammelsberg, G. Rose, E. F. Anthon, E. R. Schneider, and J. Braun. Its composition varies between Ni_4As_2 and Ni_3As_2. A. Breithaupt described monoclinic plates of what he called *ein neuer Kies* from Müsen near Siegen, and he named it *placodine*— from πλακώδης, flat, plate-like—in reference to the tabular form of the crystals. G. Rose assigned the crystals to the tetragonal system, and J. Braun gave for the axial ratio $a : c = 1 : 1·125$. J. Braun gave 7·6941 for the sp. gr.; and A. Breithaupt, 7·988–8·062. C. F. Plattner, C. Schnabel, G. Rose, and A. Gurlt considered placodine as a furnace product analogous with the nickel speise of F. Wöhler. C. F. Rammelsberg explained the variable composition to its forming isomorphous mixtures or solid soln. with other arsenides or sulphides.

K. Friedrich and F. Bennigson's [25] f.p. curve shows the conditions under which **nickel monarsenide,** $NiAs$, is formed. F. Fouqué and A. Michel-Lévy obtained a similar product by the action of arsenic trichloride vapour on nickelous chloride at a red-heat. E. Vigouroux prepared the monarsenide by passing the vap. of arsenic trichloride over powdered nickel or nickel arsenide at 400°–800°. It is said that the product is a pale red crystalline powder of sp. gr. 7·57 at 0°. W. F. de Jong and H. W. V. Willems found that the X-radiogram agreed with a hexagonal structure with $a=3·57$ A., and $c=5·10$ A.; and sp. gr. 7·88. K. Friedrich and F Bennigson said that the monarsenide loses arsenic above 800°, and forms the ditritarsenide. It takes up arsenic at a low temp. as in the case of the ditritarsenide and forms the diarsenide at 400°. The chemical reactions of the monarsenide and the ditritarsenide are similar. W. Herz gave $5·84 \times 10^{12}$ for the vibration frequency of NiAs.

This arsenide occurs in nature. It was called *Kupfernickel* by U. Hiärne,[26] in 1694, probably on account of its colour, and J. Woodward, through some mistake, called it *cuprum nicolai*. J. D. Denso recognized the presence of arsenic. J. G. Wallerius regarded it as *arsenicum sulphure et cupro mineralisatum;* A. Cronstedt as *niccolum ferro et cobalto arsenicatis et sulphuratis;* and B. G. Sage, and J. B. L. Romé de l'Isle, as *mine de cobalt arsenicale tenant cuivre.* F. Stromeyer analyzed the mineral in 1817, and showed that it consisted essentially of nickel and arsenic, nearly in the proportions required for NiAs. The original term *Kupfernickel*, used by L. A. Emmerling, A. Estner, C. A. S. Hofmann, etc., was gradually dropped, and the mineral came to be called *arsenical nickel* by R. J. Haüy, and C. C. von Leonhard; *nickel pyrites*, by F. Mohs, and W. Haidinger; and *red nickel pyrites* by A. Breithaupt, and E. F. Glocker. F. S. Beudant called it *nickeline*, and J. D. Dana, **niccolite** or *niccoline*. Analyses were reported by P. Berthier, A. Breithaupt, I. Domeyko, J. J. Ebelmen, F. A. Genth, A. Grunow, H. Hahn, C. Heusler, T. Petersen, C. H. Pfaff, F. Pisani, C. F. Rammelsberg, T. Scheerer, L. Sipöcz, G. Suckow, and C. Winkler. The mineral usually contains sulphur, iron, and cobalt. Sometimes part of the arsenic is replaced by antimony; in the extreme case, breithauptite, NiSb, appears. Intermediate varieties, Ni(As,Sb), were called *aarite* by M. Adam, and *arite*, by F. Pisani.

Numerous occurrences have been reported—*e.g.* by F. Babanek, M. Bäumler, A. Breithaupt, L. Brunrucker, A. des Cloizeaux, J. H. Collins, J. D. Dana, I. Domeyko, A. Frenzel, E. Fugger, P. Giebe, E. F. Glocker, R. P. Greg and W. G. Lettsom, C. W. Gümbel, E. Hatle, C. A. S. Hofmann, G. C. Hofmann, T. S. Hunt, G. P. Jervis, G. A. Kenngott, J. F. Kemp, G. A. Koenig, N. von Kokscharoff, A. Lacroix, A. von Lasaulx, H. Laspeyres, G. Leonhard, A. Liversidge, D. S. Lovisato, O. Luedecke, W. H. Miller, F. Navarro, J. S. Newberry, J. J. Nöggerath, A. Orio, W. F. Petterd, A. Raimondi, G. Rose, J. Rumpf, A. Russell, F. Sandberger, A. Sjögren, H. Traube, M. Websky, J. D. Whitney, and V. R. von Zepharovich.

Niccolite usually occurs massive with a fine texture; it also occurs in reniform masses with a columnar structure, and reticulated and arborescent. The colour is pale copper-red with a grey or black tarnish. Crystals are rare. W. Phillips said that the crystals are probably hexagonal, and A. Breithaupt, F. Mohs, and W. Haidinger, rhombic. E. F. Glocker, F. von Kobell, H. J. Brooke, and J. F. L. Hausmann showed that W. Phillips' opinion was correct; and A. Breithaupt gave for the axial ratio $a : c = 1 : 0·8194$. P. Groth gave $1 : 0·9462$. This agrees with the measurements of A. des Cloizeaux. G. Aminoff found that the X-radiogram corresponds with an hexagonal lattice with 2 mols. in each elementary parallelogram, and $a : c = 1 : 1·430$. W. F. de Jong obtained a different structure. He found that the elementary parallelopiped contains two molecules and has $a=3·57$ A., $c=5·10$ A., and the distance between the nickel and arsenic atoms is 2·42 A. W. F. de Jong concluded that the nickel and arsenic form alternate layers along the c-axis, at distances $\frac{1}{4}c=1·27$ A. The shortest distance is 2·42 A., and $a=3·57$ A.; he also found the lattice constants of the rhombic crystals closely resemble those of löllingite. W. F. de Jong and H. W. V. Willems found that the hexagonal lattice of arite, Ni(AsSb), agrees with a solid soln. having $a=3·80$ A., and $c=5·20$ A.; and a sp. gr. 7·19. I. Oftedal studied the lattices of a number of other compounds of the nickel arsenide type. The cleavage of the crystals is scarcely recognizable. The hardness is about 5·0–5·5; and the sp. gr. reported by those who have analyzed samples ranges from 7·33 to 7·72. A. de Gramont examined the spark spectrum. F. Beijerinck found the mineral to be a good electrical conductor ; though T. W. Case found it to be a non-conductor in the dark and observed no measurable effect by light. H. S. Roberts and L. H. Adams studied the rectifying action of crystals of niccolite used as radio-detectors. Arsenic trioxide sublimes when the mineral is roasted. T. L. Walker and A. L. Parsons studied the oxidation of niccolite by aerated water—vide rammelsbergite. Niccolite is soluble in aqua regia and in nitric acid with the separation of arsenic acid. J. Lemberg found that niccolite is scarcely affected by an alkali soln. of bromine ; and that when placed in an acidified soln. of silver sulphate, silver is immediately precipitated. The mineral keweenawite was shown by E. Thomson to be probably a mixture of niccolite with other related arsenides.

According to E. Vigouroux,[27] **nickel diarsenide,** NiAs$_2$, is produced when the lower arsenides are heated to 400° with arsenic in an atm. of hydrogen. This compound is dimorphic, being represented in nature by the cubic mineral chloanthite —which has been described in connection with smaltite—and the rhombic mineral **rammelsbergite.** W. Haidinger applied the term rammelsbergite—after C. F. Rammelsberg—to the cubic white nickel ore from Schneeberg, called by C. M. Kersten nickel biarseniet ; but after A. Breithaupt had established the dimorphism of the diarsenide, and applied the term chloanthite to the cubic form, J. D. Dana employed rammelsbergite for the rhombic form. Analyses were reported by T. L. Walker, F. Wöhler, E. Hoffmann, F. Sandberger, L. W. McCay, C. F. Rammelsberg, and I. Domeyko. Occurrences were also mentioned by A. Frenzel, T. L. Walker and A. L. Parsons, P. Groth, V. R. von Zepharovich, J. Haberfelner, G. A. Kenngott, and G. P. Jervis. Rammelsbergite occurs massive, and also in rhombic crystals resembling arsenopyrite. A. Breithaupt's data correspond with $a : b : c = 0·537 : 1 : —$. The cleavage is prismatic. The colour is tin-white with a tinge of red. The hardness is 5·25 to 5·75 ; and the sp. gr. 6·9 to 7·2. T. L. Walker and A. L. Parsons gave 7·0 for the sp. gr. F. Beijerinck found the mineral is a conductor of electricity ; and E. T. Wherry, a fair radio-detector. The general chemical properties resemble those of chloanthite, and niccolite. E. Thomson studied the etching reactions of rammelsbergite. E. F. Smith found that it dissolves in sulphur monochloride at 180°. T. L. Walker and A. L. Parsons found that the rate of oxidation of rammelsbergite by aerated water is four times as rapid as that of niccolite, eight times as rapid as a mixture consisting of löllingite seventy, safflorite ten, and skutterudite twenty, and seventy-five times as rapid as a mixture consisting of arsenopyrite one, löllingite eighty-five, safflorite six, and skutterudite eight. Meteoric waters might, therefore, be expected to remove rammelsbergite before attacking most of the other arsenides.

E. Waller and A. J. Moses[28] found a mineral, which they called nickel-skutterudite, in the Bullard's Peak district, New Mexico. The analysis corresponds with RAs$_3$, where R stands for Ni : Co : Fe in the proportions 4 : 2 : 1. This mineral is the nearest representative of **nickel triarsenide,** NiAs$_3$. It occurs in grey, granular masses of hardness 5. A. Gibb[29] studied the elimination of arsenic from copper nickel alloys.

The arsenides of the elements of the platinum family have not been closely examined. According to W. H. Wollaston,[30] an alloy of rhodium and arsenic is produced when the two elements are fused together, and the arsenic is given off when the alloy is heated in air. N. W. Fischer, and R. Chenevix also found that palladium and arsenic unite with the evolution of heat, forming a brittle fusible alloy. C. Winkler obtained platinum silicoarsenide as an indefinite alloy by melting together platinum, arsenic, and silicon under molten cryolite and sodium chloride. The hard, white alloy is almost insoluble in nitric acid.

A. F. Gehlen[31] found that when spongy platinum is heated with an excess of arsenic, the combination which occurs is attended by lebhafter Feuererscheinung, the alloy was also made by heating platinum mixed with arsenic trioxide and

sodium carbonate—if the alkali carbonate be omitted, A. F. Gehlen said that
neither arsenic trioxide nor arsenic acid exerts any action on the metal. The
arsenic alloys were also made by J. Murray, W. Lewis, R. W. Fox, and N. W. Fischer.
W. R. Hodgkinson and F. K. S. Lowndes found that a platinum wire immediately
fuses when heated in contact with arsenic. The binary system with up to about
28 per cent. of arsenic was studied by K. Friedrich and
A. Leroux, and the results are illustrated by Fig. 12.
The two elements form a eutectic at 598° with 13 per
cent. of arsenic, and there is a probable maximum in
the curve near 1500° corresponding with **platinum
hemitriarsenide**, Pt_2As_3. It was not found possible
to extend the curve beyond this region. E. Kordes
studied the eutectic mixtures. D. Tivoli found that
when platinum hydroxyarsenide is heated in an atm. of
carbon dioxide at a high temp., the hemitriarsenide is
formed, as a white mass with a metallic appearance.
It is decomposed by hot conc. sulphuric acid.

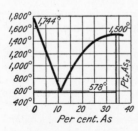

FIG. 12.—Freezing-point
Curves of the Arsenic-
Platinum Alloys.

H. L. Wells described a tin-white mineral from
Algoma, near Sudbury, Ontario, and named it
sperrylite—after F. L. Sperry, who first drew his attention to the mineral.
Analyses by H. L. Wells, and F. Rössler showed that sperrylite approximates
to **platinum diarsenide**, $PtAs_2$, with a trace of the platinum replaced by
rhodium, and of arsenic by antimony. This arsenide was obtained as an alloy
by A. F. Gehlen, and J. Murray; while H. L. Wells obtained it as a porous mass by
passing the vap. of arsenic in a current of hydrogen over red-hot platinum ; and by
fusing the washed and dried anode mud from the copper refinery with borax and
sodium carbonate. S. L. Penfield showed that the crystals belong to the cubic
system—simple cubes are common, octahedra exceptional ; the majority of the
crystals show combinations of the cube and octahedron. L. J. Spencer also
described the crystals of sperrylite from the Transvaal. L. S. Ramsdall examined
the X-radiograms of sperrylite, and regarded the structure as pyritic with arsenic
atoms occupying the same relative positions as the sulphur atoms of pyrite. The
unit cubic cell has a side of length 5·94 A. ; G. Aminoff and A. L. Parsons, 6·00 A. ;
W. F. de Jong gave 5·92 A., and said that unit cube has 4 platinum and 8 arsenic
atoms. Assuming that the 4 platinum atoms are equivalent, and also the 8 arsenic
atoms, there is a dyakisdodecahedral symmetry; and with the pyritic structure,
the smallest distance between the platinum and arsenic atoms is 2·47 A.; and
between two arsenic atoms, 2·46 A. Sperrylite was described by W. E. Hidden
and J. H. Pratt, and J. F. Donald, etc. L. J. Spencer gave 10·58 for the sp. gr.
at 19·5°.4°. According to T. L. Walker, sperrylite is dissolved by aqua regia, and
more slowly by hydrochloric acid, but it is almost insoluble in nitric, sulphuric,
and hydrofluoric acids.

D. Tivoli obtained minute, black scales of **platinum hydroxyarsenide**,
PtAs(OH), by passing a rapid current of arsine into a soln. of platinum tetrachloride :
$PtCl_4+AsH_3+H_2O=PtAs.OH+4HCl$. This substance is insoluble in water, and
is only altered to a slight extent by hydrochloric and nitric acids and potash ; it is
readily soluble in aqua regia. Conc. sulphuric acid decomposes it in accordance
with the eq. : $2PtAs.OH+2H_2SO_4=2Pt+As_2O_3+3H_2O+2SO_2$. It may be dried
at 130° without decomposition, but above that temp. is transformed into a platinum
arsenide thus : $6PtAs.OH=As_2O_3+2Pt_3As_2+3H_2O$. These two decompositions
served as a basis for the analysis of platinum hydroxyarsenide.

REFERENCES.

[1] H. Davy, *Phil. Trans.*, **100**. 31, 1810 ; J. L. Gay Lussac and L. J. Thénard, *Recherches
physico-chimiques*, Paris, **1**. 232, 1811 ; *Ann. Chim. Phys.*, (1), **73**. 229, 1810 ; W. Guertler,
Metall Erz, **22**. 199, 1925 ; A. F. Gehlen, *Schweigger's Journ.*, **15**. 501, 1815 ; E. Soubeiran,

Journ. Pharm. Chim., (2), **16.** 353, 1830 ; C. Hugot, *Compt. Rend.*, **129.** 603, 1899 ; P. Lebeau, *ib.*, **129.** 47, 1899 ; **130.** 502, 1900 ; *Bull. Soc. Chim.*, (3), **23.** 250, 1900 ; H. H. Landolt, *Liebig's Ann.*, **89.** 301, 1854 ; *Journ. prakt. Chem.*, (1), **40.** 385, 1853 ; J. V. Janowsky, *Ber.*, **6.** 220, 1873 ; A. P. Saunders, *Chem. News*, **79.** 66, 1899 ; G. Bredig and F. Haber, *Ber.*, **31.** 2741, 1898. ² K. Friedrich, *Met.*, **2.** 484, 1905 ; **5.** 530, 1908 ; J. H. Stansbie, *Journ. Soc. Chem. Ind.*, **25.** 47, 1071, 1906 ; A. H. Hiorns, *Electrochem. Met.*, **3.** 648, 1904 ; *Journ. Inst. Metals*, **3.** 54, 1910 ; *Chem. News*, **89.** 200, 1904 ; *Journ. Soc. Chem. Ind.*, **25.** 617, 1906 ; G. D. Bengough and B. P. Hill, *Journ. Inst. Metals*, **3.** 34, 1910 ; W. C. Roberts-Austen, *Report of the Alloys Research Committee*, London, **2.** 119, 1893 ; *Proc. Inst. Mech. Eng.*, 102, 1893 ; 238, 1895 ; C. J. B. Karsten, *System der Metallurgie*, Berlin, 1831 ; P. Jolibois and M. Merle, *Monit. Scient.*, (4), **9.** 35, 1895 ; P. Thomas, *Rev. Mét.*, **10.** 1204, 1913 ; W. Stahl, *Met.*, **6.** 611, 1909 ; E. A. Lewis, *Chem. News*, **83.** 3, 1901 ; *Engg.*, **76.** 733, 1903 ; *Journ. Soc. Chem. Ind.*, **20.** 254, 1901 ; **22.** 1351, 1903 ; F. Johnson, *Journ. Inst. Metals*, **4.** 163, 1910 ; **8.** 192, 1912 ; **10.** 275, 1913 ; *Met. Chem. Eng.*, **8.** 570, 1910 ; R. H. Greaves, *Journ. Inst. Metals*, **7.** 218, 1912 ; C. Blazey, *ib.*, **37.** 51, 1927 ; A. Pinkerton and W. H. Tait, *ib.*, **36.** 233, 1926 ; D. Hanson and C. B. Marryat, *ib.*, **37.** 121, 1927 ; L. Archbutt, *ib.*, **7.** 262, 1912 ; P. Oberhoffer, *Metall Erz*, **17.** 49, 345, 1920 ; H. D. Law, *Journ. Inst. Metals*, **8.** 222, 1912 ; D. Hanson and C. B. Marryat, *ib.*, **37.** 121, 1927 ; H. Baucke, *Internat. Zeit. Metallog.*, **3.** 195, 1913 ; A. Matthiessen and C. Vogt, *Pogg. Ann.*, **122.** 19, 1864 ; *Phil. Trans.*, **154.** 167, 1864 ; A. Matthiessen and M. Holzmann, *ib.*, **150.** 85, 1860 ; *Pogg. Ann.*, **110.** 222, 1860 ; T. Bergman, *De arsenico*, Stockholm, 1777 ; A. Brukl, *Zeit. anorg. Chem.*, **131.** 236, 1923 ; P. Berthier, *Ann. Chim. Phys.*, (2), **62.** 113, 1836 ; J. Arnold and J. Jefferson, *Engg.*, **61.** 176, 1896 ; A. Gibb, *ib.*, **59.** 778, 1895 ; *Proc. Inst. Mech. Eng.*, 254, 1895 ; W. Hampe, *Zeit. Berg. Hütt. Sal.*, **21.** 218, 1873 ; **22.** 93, 1874 ; **24.** 6, 1876 ; *Chem. Ztg.*, **16.** 726, 1892 ; G. Lippert, *Journ. prakt. Chem.*, (1), **81.** 168, 1860 ; A. Rietzsch, *Ueber die thermische und elektrische Leitfähigkeit von Kupferphosphor und Kupferarsen*, Leipzig, 1900 ; *Ann. Physik*, (4), **3.** 403, 1900 ; H. Weiss, *Ann. Chim. Phys.*, (9), **20.** 131, 1923 ; C. A. Kraus, *Journ. Amer. Chem. Soc.*, **44.** 1232, 1922 ; G. A. Koenig, *Proc. Amer. Phil. Soc.*, **42.** 219, 1903 ; *Zeit. Kryst.*, **34.** 67, 1901 ; **38.** 529, 1904 ; *Amer. Journ. Science*, (4), **10.** 439, 1900 ; (4), **14.** 404, 1902 ; J. W. Richards, *ib.*, (4), **11.** 457, 1901 ; J. D. Whitney, *ib.*, (2), **28.** 15, 1854 ; (2), **29.** 377, 1855 ; F. A. Genth, *ib.*, (2), **27.** 400, 1859 ; (2), **28.** 143, 1859 ; (2), **33.** 191, 1862 ; (2), **45.** 306, 1868 ; G. J. Brush, *ib.*, (2), **35.** 297, 1863 ; T. S. Hunt, *Geol. Sur. Canada*, 388, 1856 ; 506, 1863 ; L. Ledoux, *Eng. Min. Journ.*, **69.** 414, 1900 ; C. Lefèvre, *Ann. Chim. Phys.*, (6), **27.** 59, 1892 ; A. Bertrand, *Ann. Mines*, (7), **1.** 413, 1872 ; D. Waldie, *Proc. Asiatic Soc. Bengal*, 279, 1870 ; T. Scheerer, *Berg. Hütt. Ztg.*, **20.** 152, 1861 ; F. R. Mallet, *A Manual of the Geology of India*, Calcutta, **4.** 14, 1887 ; J. D. Dana, *A System of Mineralogy*, New York, 45, 1892 ; I. Domeyko, *Elementos de mineralojia*, Santiago, 246, 1879 ; *Ann. Mines*, (4), **3.** 5, 1843 ; H. Reinsch, *Journ. prakt. Chem.*, (1), **24.** 244, 1841 ; A. Descamps, *Compt. Rend.*, **86.** 1023, 1878 ; J. B. Senderens, *ib.*, **104.** 177, 1887 ; A. de Gramont, *ib.*, **108.** 747, 1894 ; *Bull. Soc. Min.*, **18.** 281, 1895 ; F. Field, *Journ. Chem. Soc.*, **10.** 289, 1857 ; J. Blyth, *ib.*, **1.** 213, 1849 ; K. A. Redlich, *Oesterr. Zeit. Berg. Hütt.*, **49.** 639, 1901 ; R. Freyn, *Mitt. Nat. Ver. Steiermark*, **42.** 311, 1925 ; W. Spring, *Bull. Acad. Belg.*, (3), **5.** 234, 1883 ; *Ber.*, **16.** 324, 1883 ; S. Stevanovic, *Zeit. Kryst.*, **37.** 245, 1903 ; **40.** 321, 1905 ; F. E. Wright, *Proc. Amer. Phil. Soc.*, **42.** 237, 1903 ; F. Cornu and K. A. Redlich, *Centr. Min.*, 277, 1908 ; J. A. Weisbach, *Neues Jahrb. Min.*, 64, 1873 ; 255, 1882 ; A. Frenzel, *ib.*, 26, 1873 ; E. Bergman, *Ber. Niederrh. Ges. Bonn*, 17, 1866 ; A. Krantz, *ib.*, 3, 1866 ; *Neues Jahrb. Min.*, **458**, 1866 ; C. Winkler, *ib.*, ii, 255, 1882 ; *Berg. Hütt. Ztg.*, **18.** 383, 1859 ; C. F. Rammelsberg, *Handbuch der Mineralchemie*, Leipzig, 24, 1875 ; *Pogg. Ann.*, **71.** 305, 1847 ; **128.** 441, 1866 ; C. F. Zincken, *ib.*, **41.** 659, 1837 ; D. Forbes, *Journ. Geol. Soc.*, **17.** 44, 1861 ; *Phil. Mag.*, (4), **20.** 423, 1860 ; W. Phillips, *ib.*, (2), **2.** 286, 1827 ; A. Sella, *Ges. Wiss. Gött.*, 311, 1891 ; J. Joly, *Phil. Mag.*, (6), **27.** 1, 1914 ; *Chem. News*, **107.** 341, 1913 ; A. Granger, *Bull. Soc. Chim.*, (3), **29.** 729, 1903 ; *Compt. Rend.*, **136.** 1397, 1903 ; B. H. Paul and A. J. Cownley, *Pharm. Journ.*, (4), **12.** 136, 1901 ; E. Herlinger, *Zeit. Kryst.*, **62.** 454, 1926 ; A. F. Gehlen, *Schweigger's Journ.*, **15.** 89, 1815 ; R. J. Kane, *Proc. Irish Acad.*, **1.** 182, 1840 ; J. B. A. Dumas, *Ann. Chim. Phys.*, (2), **33.** 355, 1826 ; (2), **44.** 289, 1830 ; C. F. de Landero, *Sinopsis mineralogica*, Mexico, 142, 1888 ; J. F. L. Hausmann, *Handbuch der Mineralogie*, Göttingen, 82, 1847 ; W. Haidinger, *Handbuch der bestimmenden Mineralogie*, Wien, 562, 1845 ; T. Haege, *Die Mineralien des Siegerlandes und der abgrenzenden Bezirke*, Siegen, 38, 1887 ; F. von Kobell, *Anz. München Gel.*, 223, 1846 ; *Journ. prakt. Chem.*, (1), **39.** 204, 1846 ; R. P. Greg and W. G. Lettsom, *Manual of the Mineralogy of Great Britain and Ireland*, London, 329, 1858 ; F. Navarro, *Acta Soc. Espan. Hist. Nat.*, **4.** 5, 1895 ; C. Winkler, *Journ. prakt. Chem.*, (1), **91.** 193, 1864 ; E. T. Wherry, *Amer. Min.*, **10.** 28, 1925 ; A. Mazzucchelli and A. Vercillo, *Atti Accad. Lincei*, (6), **1.** 233, 1925 ; E. Kordes, *Zert. anorg. Chem.*, **154.** 97, 1926 ; T. W. Case, *Phys. Rev.*, (2), **9.** 305, 1917 ; J. Ruhrmann, *Metall Erz*, **22.** 339, 1925 ; W. Ipatieff and W. Nikolaieff, *Journ. Russ. Phys. Chem. Soc.*, **58.** 664, 686, 692, 698, 1926. ³ A. F. Gehlen, *Ann. Chim. Phys.*, **3.** 135, 1816 ; T. Bergman, *De arsenico*, Stockholm, 1777 ; *Physical and Chemical Essays*, London, **2.** 287, 1788 ; P. Berthier, *Traité des essais par la voie sèche*, Paris, **2.** 671, 1834 ; W. Spring, *Bull. Acad. Belg.*, (3), **5.** 229, 1883 ; *Ber.*, **16.** 324, 1883 ; J. B. Senderens, *Compt. Rend.*, **104.** 175, 1887 ; A. Descamps, *ib.*, **86.** 1022, 1878 ; J. B. Hannay, *Min. Mag.*, **1.** 149, 1877 ; S. R. I. Eques a Born, *Catalogue méthodique et raisonné de la collection des fossiles de Mlle. Eleonore de Raab*, Wien, **2.** 418, 1790 ; M. Adam, *Tableau minéralogique*, Paris, 1669 ; C. A. S. Hofmann, *Handbuch der Mineralogie*, Freiberg,

3 b, 48, 1816; J. F. L. Hausmann, *Handbuch der Mineralogie*, Göttingen, 121, 1813; I. Domeyko, *Elementos de Mineralojia*, Santiago, 365, 411, 1870; *Phil. Mag.*, (4), 25. 106, 1863; C. F. Rammelsberg, *Handbuch der Mineralchemie*, Leipzig, 28, 1860; 27, 1875; *Pogg. Ann.*, 17. 202, 1849; R. J. Haüy, *Traité de minéralogie*, Paris, 3. 396, 1801; A. des Cloizeaux, *Manuel de minéralogie*, Paris, 326, 1893; J. D. Dana, *A System of Mineralogy*, New York, 36, 1868; 43, 1892; M. H. Klaproth, *Beiträge sur chemischen Kenntniss der Mineralkörper*, Berlin, 1. 187, 1795; 3. 176, 1802; G. A. Kenngott, *Sitzber. Akad. Wien*, 10. 180, 1853; L. A. Emmerling, *Lehrbuch der Mineralogie*, Giessen, 2. 165, 1796; A. Raimondi, *Minéraux du Perou*, Paris, 48, 60, 1878; O. Luedecke, *Die Minerale des Harzes*, Berlin, 53, 1896; H. Wurtz, *Eng. Min. Journ.*, 27. 55, 1875; T. Macfarlane, *Canadian Naturalist*, 5. 47, 159, 304, 1870; *Trans. Amer. Inst. Min. Eng.*, 8. 236, 1880; G. A. Koenig, *Proc. Acad. Philadelphia*, 276, 1877; J. D. Forbes, *Phil. Mag.*, (4), 25. 104, 1863; A. P. J. du Mênil, *Schweigger's Journ.*, 34. 357, 1822; J. L. Jordan, *Mineralogische und chemische Beobachtungen und Erfahrungen*, Göttingen, 279, 1800; S. Hilpert and F. Herrmann, *Ber.*, 46. 2220, 1913; T. Poleck and K. Thümmel, *ib.*, 16. 2435, 1883; R. Fanto, *Monatsh.*, 24. 477, 1903; D. Vitali, *L'Orosi*, 15. 397, 1893; 16. 10, 1893; R. Otto, *Arch. Pharm.*, (3), 21. 583, 1883; H. Reckleben, G. Lockemann, and A. Eckardt, *Zeit. anal. Chem.*, 46. 671, 1908; A. Eckardt, *Ueber Reaktionen und Bestimmungsmethoden von Arsenwasserstoff*, Weida i. Th., 1907; J. Percy, *Silver and Gold*, London, 1. 139, 1880; P. Hautefeuille and A. Perrey, *Compt. Rend.*, 98. 1378, 1884; K. Friedrich and A. Leroux, *Met.*, 3. 193, 1906; A. Brukl, *Zeit. anorg. Chem.*, 131. 236, 1923; E. V. Zappi and J. J. Landaburu, *Anal. Soc. Quim. Argentina*, 4. 218, 1916; H. E. Kinstry, *Econ. Geol.*, 22. 669, 1927.

4 T. Bergman, *De arsenico*, Stockholm, 1777; J. Arnold and J. Jefferson, *Engg.*, 61. 176, 1896; C. Hatchett, *Phil. Trans.*, 93. 43, 1803; A. Liversidge, *Chem. News*, 69. 152, 1894; A. P. Schleicher, *Internat. Zeit. Met.*, 6. 18, 1914; A. Descamps, *Compt. Rend.*, 86. 1022, 1065, 1878; D. Tivoli, *Rend. 1st. Bologna*, 105, 1886; A. Brukl, *Zeit. anorg. Chem.*, 131. 236, 1923.

5 P. Lebeau, *Sur la préparation et les propriétés des arseniures alcalino-terreux*, Paris, 1899; *Bull. Soc. Chim.*, (3), 21. 769, 931, 1902; *Compt. Rend.*, 128. 95, 1899; 129. 47, 1899; *Ann. Chim. Phys.*, (7), 25. 470, 1902; E. Soubeiran, *ib.*, (2), 43. 412, 1830; J. Riedel, *German Pat.*, *D.R.P.* 300152, 1916; H. Moissan, *Compt. Rend.*, 127. 584, 1898; O. Ruff and H. Hartmann, *Zeit. anorg. Chem.*, 121. 167, 1922.

6 F. Wöhler, *Pogg. Ann.*, 13. 577, 1828; J. Parkinson, *Journ. Chem. Soc.*, 20. 309, 1867; J. Riedel, *German Pat.*, *D.R.P.* 300152, 1916; G. Natta, *Giorn. Chim. Ind. Appl.*, 8. 367, 1926.

7 T. Bergman, *De arsenico*, Stockholm, 1779; A. Descamps, *Compt. Rend.*, 86. 1065, 1878; E. Soubeiran, *Ann. Chim. Phys.*, (2), 43. 407, 1830; A. F. Gehlen, *Schweigger's Journ.*, 20. 353, 1817; K. Friedrich and A. Leroux, *Met.*, 3. 477, 1906; A. Vogel, *Journ. prakt. Chem.*, (1), 6. 345, 1835; W. Heike, *Zeit. anorg. Chem.*, 118. 254, 1921; E. Kordes, *ib.*, 154. 97, 1926; J. P. Cooke, *Amer. Journ. Science*, (2), 31. 196, 1861; F. H. Storer, *Chem. News*, 2. 303, 1860; W. Spring, *Ber.*, 16. 324, 1883; *Bull. Acad. Belg.*, (3), 5. 229, 1883; G. A. Koenig, *Zeit. Kryst.*, 38. 543, 1904; *Proc. Amer. Soc.*, 42. 219, 1903.

8 S. F. Schemtschuschny, *Journ. Russ. Phys. Chem. Soc.*, 45. 1137, 1913; *Internat. Zeit. Met.*, 4. 228, 1913; W. Spring, *Bull. Acad. Belg.*, (3), 5. 235, 1883; *Ber.*, 16. 325, 1883; C. T. Heycock and F. H. Neville, *Journ. Chem. Soc.*, 61. 888, 1892; *Chem. News*, 62. 280, 1890; W. Zimmer, *German Pat.*, *D.R.P.* 306382, 1917; A. Brukl, *Zeit. anorg. Chem.*, 131. 242, 1923; A. Descamps, *Compt. Rend.*, 86. 1066, 1878; A. Granger, *ib.*, 138. 574, 1904; *Bull. Soc. Chim.*, (3), 31. 568, 1904.

9 T. Bergman, *De arsenico*, Stockholm, 1777; W. Ramsay, *Journ. Chem. Soc.*, 55. 531, 1889; W. J. Humphreys, *ib.*, 69. 1685, 1896; R. Böttger, *Journ. prakt. Chem.*, (1), 3. 283, 1834; M. Dranty, *Journ. Chim. Méd.*, (2), 2. 650, 1836; J. F. Lassaigne, *ib.*, (2), 2. 650, 1836; G. Vortmann, *Ber.*, 24. 2764, 1891; F. Stromeyer, *Comment. Soc. Gött.*, 16. 141, 1808; H. Rose, *Pogg. Ann.*, 51. 423, 1840; A. Partheil and E. Amort, *Arch. Pharm.*, 237. 126, 1899; *Ber.*, 31. 595, 1898; E. Dumesnil, *Compt. Rend.*, 152. 868, 1911; A. Brukl, *Zeit. anorg. Chem.*, 131. 236, 1923; G. Tammann and J. Hinnüber, *ib.*, 160. 256, 1927.

10 F. Wöhler, *Pogg. Ann.*, 11. 161, 1827; C. Winkler, *Journ. prakt. Chem.*, (1), 91. 193, 1864; E. Carstanjen, *ib.*, (1), 102. 82, 1867; A. Hirsch, *Trans. Amer. Electrochem. Soc.*, 24. 57, 1911; *Journ. Ind. Eng. Chem.*, 3. 880, 1911; 4. 65, 1912; Q. A. Mansuri, *Metal Ind.*, 21. 388, 1912; *Journ. Inst. Metals*, 28. 453, 1922; *Journ. Chem. Soc.*, 121. 2272, 1922; G. Natta, *Giorn. Chim. Ind. Appl.*, 8. 367, 1926.

11 K. Friedrich, *Met.*, 3. 42, 1906; A. Descamps, *Compt. Rend.*, 86. 1065, 1878; G. A. Koenig, *Proc. Amer. Phil. Soc.*, 42. 219, 1903; *Zeit. Kryst.*, 38. 544, 1904; Q. A. Mansuri, *Journ. Chem. Soc.*, 123. 214, 1923; J. E. Stead, *Journ. Inst. Metals*, 22. 127, 1919; *Engg.*, 108. 663, 1919; S. Stevanovic, *Zeit. Kryst.*, 40. 326, 1905; W. P. Headden, *Proc. Colorado Scient. Soc.*, 6. 80, 1901; *Amer. Journ. Science*, (4), 5. 95, 1898; L. J. Spencer, *Min. Mag.*, 19. 113, 1921; A. Brukl, *Zeit. anorg. Chem.*, 131. 236, 1923; E. Kordes, *ib.*, 159. 97, 1926; K. Kawai, *Journ. Geol. Soc. Tokyo*, 32. 106, 1925.

12 A. de Gramont, *Bull. Soc. Min.*, 18. 276, 1895; A. F. Gehlen, *Schweigger's Journ.*, 15. 501, 1815; 20. 353, 1817; T. Bergman, *De antimonialibus sulphuratis*, Upsala, 1782; A. Descamps, *Compt. Rend.*, 86. 1066, 1878; W. Haidinger, *Handbuch der bestimmenden Mineralogie*, Wien, 557, 1845; R. J. Haüy, *Traité de minéralogie*, Paris, 4. 263, 281, 1822; F. X. M. Zippe, *Verh. Ges. Mus. Böhmen*, 102, 1824; C. F. Rammelsberg, *Pogg. Ann.*, 62. 137, 1844; *Handbuch der Mineralchemie*, Leipzig, 984, 1860; T. Thomson, *Outlines of Mineralogy, Geology, and Mineral*

Analysis, London. 1. 84, 1836 ; **F. A.** Genth, *Amer. Journ. Science*, (2), 33. 190, 1862 ; **D.** Bizzarri and G. Campani, *Gazz. Chim. Ital.*, 15. 349, 1886 ; J. Joly, *Phil. Mag.*, (6), 27. 1, 1914 ; *Chem. News*, 107. 241, 1913 ; J. von Liebig, *Handwörterbuch der reinen und angewandter Chemie*, Braunschweig, 1. 414, 1837 ; J. F. L. Hausmann, *Handbuch der Mineralogie*, Göttingen, 13, 1847 ; B. G. le Sage, *Élémens de minéralogie docimastique*, Paris, 2. 71, 1772 ; F. S. Beudant, *Traité élémentaire de minéralogie*, Paris, 469, 1824 ; P. A. Dufrénoy, *Traité de minéralogie*, Paris, 2. 640, 1845 ; W. Phillips, *Elementary Introduction to Mineralogy*, London, 397, 1837 ; V. R. von Zepharovich, *Mineralogisches Lexikon für das Kaiserthum Oesterreich*, Wien, 5, 1859 ; F. A. Reuss, *Sitzber. Akad. Wien*, 22. 129, 1856 ; F. Babanek, *Tschermak's Mitt.*, (1), 5. 82, 1875 ; G. Benko, *Orv. Ertes.*, 14. 185, 1889 ; J. B. L. Romé de l'Isle, *Cristallographie*, Paris, 3. 47, 1783 ; F. Mohs, *Grundriss der Mineralogie*, Wien, 2. 475, 1839 ; C. C. von Leonhard, *Handbuch der Oryktogonosie*, Heidelberg, 151, 1821 ; M. Padoa, *Gazz. Chim. Ital.*, 57. 399, 1927 ; A. Madelung, *Ueber den Vorkommen des gediegenen Arsen in der Natur*, Göttingen, 1862 ; A. Raimondi, *Minéraux du Pérou*, Paris, 191, 1878 ; N. Parravano and P. de Cesaris, *Internat. Zeit. Metallog.*, 2. 70, 1912 ; G. Kalb, *Metall Erz*, 23. 113, 1926 ; *Zeit. Kryst.*, 57. 572, 1922 (I am greatly indebted to Dr. Kalb for Fig. 6) ; Q. A. Mansuri, *Journ. Chem. Soc.*, 2107, 1928.

¹³ T. Bergman, *De arsenico*, Stockholm, 1777 ; E. Becquerel, *Ann. Chim. Phys.*, (4), 8. 893, 1866 ; C. T. Heycock and F. H. Neville, *Chem. News*, 62. 280, 1890 ; *Journ. Chem. Soc.*, 61. 888, 1892 ; C. M. Marx, *Schweigger's Journ.*, 54. 464, 1828 ; C. M. Kersten, *ib.*, 53. 371, 1828 ; *Pogg. Ann.*, 26. 492, 1832 ; A. Descamps, *Compt. Rend.*, 86. 1065, 1878 ; K. Friedrich and A. Leroux, *Met.*, 5. 148, 1908 ; C. Hintze, *Zeit. Kryst.*, 11. 606, 1886 ; W. Heike, *Internat. Zeit. Metallog.*, 6. 209, 1914 ; A. Frenzel, *Neues Jahrb. Min.*, 25, 1873 ; 677, 1874 ; A. Weisbach, *Jahrb. Berg. Hütt.*, 42, 1877 ; A. Brukl, *Zeit. anorg. Chem.*, 131. 236, 1923.

¹⁴ T. Dieckmann, *Ueber einige Mono- und Bi-Arsenide des Eisens, Mangans und Chroms, über ihre chemischen und magnetischen Eigenschaften, sowie über die magnetischen Eigenschaften einiger Mangan-Wismut Legierungen*, Berlin, 1911 ; W. F. de Jong and H. W. V. Willems, *Physica*, 7. 74, 1927 ; E. Defacqz, *Compt. Rend.*, 132. 138, 1901.

¹⁵ R. J. Kane, *Quart. Journ. Science*, 6. 381, 1830 ; E. Wedekind, *Zeit. Elektrochem.*, 11. 850, 1906 ; *Ber. deut. phys. Ges.*, 4. 412, 1907 ; *Phys. Zeit.*, 7. 805, 1907 ; *Zeit. phys. Chem.*, 66. 614, 1909 ; E. Wedekind and T. Veit, *Ber.*, 44. 2663, 1911 ; T. Dieckmann, *Ueber einige Mono- und Bi-arsenide des Eisens, Mangans und Chroms, über ihre chemischen und magnetischen Eigenschaften, sowie über die magnetischen Eigenschaften einiger Mangan-Wismut Legierungen*, Berlin, 1911 ; S. Hilpert and T. Dieckmann, *Ber.*, 44. 2378, 2831, 1911 ; G. Arrivant, *Proc. Internat. Congr. Appl. Chem.*, 7. ii, 100, 1909 ; *Chim. et Ind.*, 13. 284, 1925 ; W. F. de Jong and H. W. V. Willems, *Physica*, 7. 74, 1927 ; L. F. Bates, *Proc. Roy. Soc.*, 117. A, 680, 1927 ; I. Oftedal, *Zeit. phys. Chem.*, 132. 208, 1928.

¹⁶ F. Sandberger, *Untersuchungen über Erzgänge*, Wiesbaden, 385, 1885 ; *Neues Jahrb. Min.*, 412, 1868 ; 315, 1869 ; 196, 1870 ; *Journ. prakt. Chem.*, (2), 1. 230, 1870 ; E. Vigouroux, *Chim. et Ind.*, 13. 283, 1925 ; A. Weisbach, *Synopsis Mineralogica*, Freiberg, 75, 1875 ; W. Haidinger, *Handbuch der bestimmenden Mineralogie*, Wien, 559, 1845 ; E. F. Glocker, *Handbuch der Mineralogie*, Nürnberg, 451, 1831 ; 321, 1839 ; *Generum et specierum mineralium secundum ordines naturales digestorum synopsis*, Halle, 37, 1847 ; C. U. Shepard, *Treatise on Mineralogy*, New Haven, 2. 9, 1835 ; J. D. Dana, *A System of Mineralogy*, New York, 76, 1868 ; 34, 1877 ; 92, 1892 ; E. S. Dana, *A Textbook on Mineralogy*, New York, 96. 1892 ; V. R. von Zepharovich, *Mineralogisches Lexicon für das Kaiserthum Oesterreich*, Wien, 1. 232, 351, 1859 ; 2. 187, 1873 ; *Sitzber. Akad. Wien*, 56. 46, 1867 ; N. von Kokscharoff, *Materialien zur Mineralogie Russlands*, St. Petersburg, 3. 24, 1867 ; G. Tschermak, *Lehrbuch der Mineralogie*, Wien, 343, 1897 ; P. Groth, *Tabellarische Uebersicht der Mineralien*, Braunschweig, 24, 1898 ; *Ber. Akad. München*, 384, 1885 ; J. Rumpf, *Tschermak's Mitt.*, (1), 4. 234, 1874 ; C. Güttler, *Ueber die Formel das Arsenikalkieses zu Reichenstein in Schlesiens*, Breslau, 14, 1870 ; *Berg. Hütt. Ztg.*, 29. 372, 1870 ; *Neues Jahrb. Min.*, 81, 1871 ; A. Schrauf, *ib.*, 677, 1875 ; A. Frenzel, *Mineralogisches Lexikon für das Königreich Sachsen*, Leipzig, 183, 1874 ; H. Traube, *Die Minerale Schlesiens*, Breslau, 135, 1888 ; O. Luedecke, *Die Minerale des Harzes*, Berlin, 90, 1896 ; G. Sillem, *Neues Jahrb. Min.*, 531, 1852 ; G. Roster, *ib.*, 534, 1877 ; R. Scheibe, *Centr. Min.*, 120, 1900 ; C. J. Selb, *Geognostische Beschreibung des Kinzigerthals*, Hanau, 1805 ; *Denk. Ges. Nat. Schwaben*, 1. 373, 1805 ; F. A. Kohlenati, *Die Mineralien Mährens und österreichisch Schlesiens*, Brunn, 79, 1854 ; A. Brunlechner, *Die Minerale des Herzegthuons Kärnten*, Klagenfurt, 62, 1884 ; E. Fugger, *Die Mineralien des Herzogthums Salzberg*, Salzburg, 8, 1878 ; G. P. Jervis, *I Tesori Sotterranei dell' Italia*, Turin, 1. 53, 269, 1873 ; A. d'Achiardi, *Mineralogia della Toxana*, Pisa, 2. 253, 1873 ; L. Bombicci, *Corso di Mineralogia*, Bologna, 497, 1862 ; A. Lacroix, *Minéralogie de la France et ses colonies*, Paris, 2. 662, 1897 ; F. J. Wiik, *Bedrag kann. Finlands Nat.*, 46. 12, 1887 ; G. Flink, *Medd. Grönland*, 14. 245, 1898 ; F. A. Genth, *The Minerals of North Carolina*, Washington, 26, 1891 ; *Amer. Journ. Science*, (3), 44. 384, 1892 ; C. Hoffmann, *Ann. Rep. Geol. Sur. Canada*, 6. 19, 1895 ; W. J. Jordan, *Journ. prakt. Chem.*, (1), 10. 436, 1837 ; K. Friedrich, *Met.*, 4. 129, 1907 ; T. Dieckmann, *Ueber einige Mono- und Bi-Arsenide des Eisens, Mangans und Chroms, über ihre chemischen und magnetischen Eigenschaften, sowie über die magnetischen Eigenschaften einiger Mangan-Wismut Legierungen*, Berlin, 1911 ; S. Hilpert and T. Dieckmann, *Ber.*, 44. 2378, 2831, 1911 ; A. F. Gehlen, *Schweigger's Ann.*, 15. 501, 1815 ; 20. 353, 1817 ; T. Bergman, *De arsenico*, Stockholm, 1777 ; P. Lebeau, *Compt. Rend.*, 129. 47, 1899 ; A. Descamps, *ib.*, 86. 1066, 1878 ; F. Osmond, *ib.*, 110. 242, 346, 1890 ; A. Carnot and E. Goutai, *ib.*,

125. 148, 213, 1897; 131. 92, 1900; Ann. Mines, (9), 18. 263, 1900; Contributions à l'étude des alliages, Paris, 493, 1901; P. Berthier, Ann. Chim. Phys., (2), 62. 113, 1836; Ann. Mines, (3), 11. 501, 1837; Traité des essais par la voie seche, Paris, 2. 203, 1834; C. F. Rammelsberg, Pogg. Ann., 128. 441, 1866; Handbuch der Mineralchemie, Leipzig, ii, 15, 1895; Zeit. deut. geol. Ges., 25. 270, 1873; J. Lemberg, ib., 46. 796, 1894; A. Sella, Ges. Wiss. Gött., 311, 1891; W. C. Brögger, Zeit. Kryst., 16. 9, 1890; J. Loczka, ib., 11. 261, 1886; 15. 42, 1889; A. Ossent, ib., 9. 564, 1884; B. Hare, ib., 4. 296, 1880; Ber., 12. 1895, 1879; J. Percy, The Metallurgy of Iron and Steel, London, 74, 1864; A. de Gramont, Bull. Soc. Min., 18. 283, 1895; F. Beijerinck, Neues Jahrb. Min. B.B., 11. 433, 1897; C. A. Burghardt, Min. Mag., 9. 227, 1891; R. Jameson, A System of Mineralogy, Edinburgh, 3. 272, 1820; Manual of Mineralogy, Edinburgh, 268, 1821; F. Mohs, Grundriss der Mineralogy, Dresden, 2. 525, 1824; C. J. B. Karsten, System der Metallurgie, Berlin, 4. 579, 1832; E. Hofmann, Pogg. Ann., 25. 485, 1832; C. Hartmann, Handwörterbuch der Mineralogie und Geologie, Leipzig, 2. 571, 1843; P. Oberhoffer and A. Galla-schik, Stahl Eisen, 43. 398, 1923; J. F. L. Hausmann, Handbuch der Mineralogie, Göttingen, 152, 1813; E. J. Chapman, Practical Mineralogy, London, 138, 1843; M. H. Klaproth, Abhand. Akad. Berlin, 27, 1815; G. Rose, Das krystallochemischen Mineralsystem, Leipzig, 54, 1852; Pogg. Ann., 13. 169, 1828; T. Scheerer, ib., 49. 536, 1840; 50. 155, 1840; A. Breithaupt, ib., 54. 265, 1841; Journ. prakt. Chem., (1), 4. 260, 1835; Berg. Hütt. Ztg., 25. 167, 1866; Die Paragenesis der Mineralien, Freiberg, 217, 1849; Mineralogische Studien, Leipzig, 95, 1866; M. Merle, Monit. Scient., (4), 9. 35, 1895; J. H. Collins, A Handbook to the Mineralogy of Cornwall and Devon, London, 62, 1876; W. F. Hillebrand, Amer. Journ. Science, (3), 27. 349, 1884; W. P. Headden, ib., (4), 5. 94, 1898; W. Hicks, Nature, 65. 558, 1902; A. Raimondi, Minéraux du Pérou, Paris, 209, 1878; C. F. de Landero, Sinopsis Mineralogica, Mexico, 285, 1888; I. Domeyko, Elementos de Mineralojia, Santiago, 162, 1879; A. Liversidge, The Minerals of New South Wales, Sydney, 37, 1882; W. F. Petterd, Catalogue of the Minerals of Tasmania, Launceston, 56, 1896; G. A. Behncke, Pogg. Ann., 98. 187, 1856; T. Petersen, ib., 137. 393, 1869; L. W. McCay, Beitrag zur Kenntniss der Kobalt-, Nickel- und Eisenkiese, Freiberg, 45, 1883; Neues Jahrb. Min., ii, 161, 1884; L. H. Bauer and H. Berman, Amer. Min., 11. 39, 1927; J. L. Jordan, Journ. prakt. Chem., (1), 10. 436, 1837; R. Senfter, ib., (2), 1. 230, 1870; B. Illing, Neues Jahrb. Min., 818, 1853; Zeit. Ges. Nat. Halle, 3. 339, 1854; Berg. Hütt. Ztg., 13. 56, 1854; H. Hahn, ib., 20. 281, 1861; L. Broz, Berg. Hütt. Jahrb., 18. 358, 1869; W. Mrazek, ib., 13. 372, 1864; Sitzber. Akad. Wien, 56. 46, 1867; A. E. Nordenskjöld, Geol. För. Förh., Stockholm, 2. 242, 1875; J. Niedzwiedzky, Tschermak's Mitt., (1), 2. 161, 1872; E. T. Wherry, Amer. Min., 10. 28, 1925; N. S. Kurnakoff and N. S. Konstantinoff, Journ. Russ. Phys. Soc., 40. 227, 1908; Zeit. anorg. Chem., 58. 1, 1908; E. Kordes, ib., 154. 97, 1926; A. Brukl, ib., 131. 236, 1923; G. Tammann and H. Bredemeier, ib., 136. 337, 1924; G. Tammann and E. Schaarwächter, ib., 167. 403, 1927; T. L. Walker, Univ. Toronto Geol. Studies, 20. 49, 1925; T. L. Walker and A. L. Parsons, ib., 17. 9, 1924; 20. 41, 1925; E. Thomson, ib., 20. 54, 1925; A. Beutell and F. Lorenz, Centr. Min., 367, 1915; 10, 49, 1916; A. Beutell, ib., 234, 300, 1912; W. F. de Jong, Physica, 6. 325, 1926; W. F. de Jong and H. W. V. Willems, ib., 7. 74, 1927; G. A. Kenngott, Uebersicht der Resultate mineralogischer Forschungen, Wien, 97, 1852; C. J. B. Karsten, System der mineralogie, Berlin, 4. 34, 1831.

¹⁷ A. F. Gehlen, Schweigger's Journ., 15. 501, 1815; 20. 353, 1817; P. Berthier, Ann. Chim. Phys., (2), 62. 113, 1836; H. Kopp, Liebig's Ann. Suppl., 3. 289, 1864; W. F. de Jong and H. W. V. Willems, Physica, 7. 74, 1927; C. F. Rammelsberg, Pogg. Ann., 128. 441, 1866; Neues Jahrb. Min., ii. 45, 1897; F. Ducelliez, Compt. Rend., 147. 424, 1908; K. Friedrich, Met., 5. 150, 1908; T. Scheerer and W. Francis, Pogg. Ann., 50. 513, 1840; Phil. Mag., (3), 17. 331, 1840; A. Brukl, Zeit. anorg. Chem., 131. 236, 1923; G. Tammann and H. Bredemeier, ib., 136. 337, 1924; A. Beutell and F. Lorenz, Centr. Min., 10, 49, 1916; E. Kordes, Zeit. anorg. Chem., 154. 97, 1926.

¹⁸ J. Durocher, Compt. Rend., 32. 823, 1851; F. Fouqué and A. Michel-Lévy, Synthèse des minéraux et des roches, Paris, 276, 1882; C. W. C. Fuchs, Die künstliche dargestellten Mineralien nach Roses System geordnet, Haarlem, 54, 1872.

¹⁹ G. Agricola, Bermannus sive de re metallica, Basilæ, 459, 1529; J. G. Wallerius, Mineralogia, Stockholm, 231, 1747; A. G. Werner, Letztes Mineralsystem, Freiberg, 25, 1817; J. B. L. Romé de l'Isle, Essai de cristallographie, Paris, 333, 1772; Cristallographie, Paris, 3. 123, 1783; C. A. S. Hofmann, Handbuch der Mineralogie, Freiberg, 4. a, 173, 1817; L. A. Emmerling, Lehrbuch der Mineralogie, Giessen, 2. 493, 1796; J. F. L. Hausmann, Handbuch der Mineralogie, Göttingen, 153, 1813; E. F. Glocker, Generum et specierum mineralium secundum ordines naturales digestorum synopsis, Halle, 35, 1847; R. Kirwan, Elements of Mineralogy, London, 1796; F. S. Beudant, Traité élémentaire de minéralogie, Paris, 2. 584, 1832; C. Cronstedt, Mineralogie, Stockholm, 212, 1758; J. D. Dana, A System of Mineralogy, New York, 61, 1854; A. Breithaupt, Vollständiges Charakteristik des Mineralsystems, Dresden, 252, 1832; Die Paragenesis der Mineralien, Freiberg, 207, 1849; Pogg. Ann., 64. 184, 1845; J. C. Booth, Amer. Journ. Science, (1), 29. 241, 1836; Pogg. Ann., 32. 395, 1834; W. Haidinger, Handbuch der bestimmenden Mineralogie, Wien, 560, 1845; J. F. John, Chemische Untersuchungen mineralischer, vegetabilischer, und animalischer Substanzen, Berlin, 2. 236, 1810; F. Stromeyer, Gött. gel. Anz., 715, 1817; E. Hoffmann, Pogg. Ann., 25. 485, 1832; C. F. Rammelsberg, ib., 128. 444, 1866; 160. 131, 1877, Zeit. deut. geol. Ges., 25. 275, 1873; Neues Jahrb. Min., ii, 57, 1897; Handbuch, der Mineralchemie, Leipzig, 15, 1843; 226. 1853; 24, 1860; 20, 1895; W. H. Miller, Introduction

to *Mineralogy*, London, 145, 1852 ; H. Baumhauer, *Zeit. Kryst.*, 12. 18, 1887 ; G. Vollhardt, *ib.*, 14. 407, 1888 ; *Versuch über Speiskobalt*, München, 1886 ; G. A. Kenngott, *Neues Jahrb. Min.*, 754, 1869; *Sitzber. Akad. Wien*, 13. 462, 1854 ; *Mineralogische Untersuchungen*, Breslau, 22, 1849 ; P. Groth, *Tabellarische Uebersicht der Mineralien*, Braunschweig, 18, 1882 ; *Pogg. Ann.*, 152. 251, 1874 ; *Die Mineraliensammlung der Universität Strassburg*, Strassburg, 261, 1878 ; G. Leonhard, *Handwörterbuch der topographischen Mineralien*, Heidelberg, 477, 1843 ; K. Laspeyres, *Ver. Nat. Hist. Rheinl.*, 50. 234, 1893 ; A. Koch, *Jahrb. Ver. Nat. Nassau*, 12. 401, 1857 ; M. C. Grandjean, *ib.*, 19. 90, 1866 ; A. Lacroix, *Minéralogie de la France et de ses colonies*, Paris, 2. 631, 1897 ; T. Haege, *Die Mineralien des Siegerlandes und der abgrenzenden Bezirke*, Siegen, 27, 1887 ; F. Sandberger, *Untersuchungen über Erzgänge*, Wiesbaden, 374, 1885 ; *Neues Jahrb. Min.*, 201, 1866 ; 403, 1868 ; *Sitzber. Akad. München*, 135, 1873 ; *Uebersicht der Mineralien Unterfrankens und Aschaffenburgs*, Würzburg, 3, 1892 ; O. Luedecke, *Die Minerale des Harzes*, Berlin, 81, 1896 ; W. Harres, *Ver. Erdkunke Darmstadt*, 13, 1881 ; *Neues Jahrb. Min.*, i, 190, 1882 ; *Zeit. Kryst.*, 11. 112, 1886 ; C. W. Gümbel, *Geognostische Beschreibung des königreichs Bayern*, Gotha, 3. 303, 1879 ; C. F. Naumann, *Pogg. Ann.*, 7. 337, 1826 ; 31. 537, 1834 ; G. vom Rath, *Ber. Niederrh. Ges. Bonn.*, 6, 1877 ; *Zeit. Kryst.*, 1. 8, 1877 ; F. Beyschlag, *Zeit. prakt. Geol.*, 6. 3, 1898 ; J. R. Blum, *Die Pseudomorphosen des Mineralreichs*, Stuttgart, 212, 1843 ; A. Frenzel, *Tschermak's Mitt.*, (2), 16. 525, 1897 ; *Mineralogisches Lexikon für das Königreich Sachsen*, Leipzig, 66, 1874 ; F. von Kobell, *Ber. Akad. München*, 402, 1868 ; E. von Gerichten, *ib.*, 137, 1873 ; H. Traube, *Die Minerale Schlesiens*, Breslau, 218, 1888 ; C. U. Shepard, *A Treatise on Mineralogy*, New Haven, 158, 1844 ; *Amer. Journ. Science*, (1), 47. 351, 1844 ; M. W. Iles, *ib.*, (2), 23. 380, 1882 ; R. P. Greg and W. G. Lettsom, *Manual of the Mineralogy of Great Britain and Ireland*, London, 302, 1858 ; J. H. Collins, *A Handbook to the Mineralogy of Cornwall and Devon*, London, 94, 1876 ; N. von Kokscharoff, *Materialen zur Mineralogie Russlands*, St. Petersburg, 7. 158, 1877 ; V. R. von Zepharovich, *Mineralogisches Lexikon für das Kaiserthum Oesterreich*, Wien, 110, 225, 415, 1859 ; 98, 300, 1873 ; *Sitzber. Akad. Wien*, 50. 122, 1865 ; C. M. Kersten, *Schweigger's Journ.*, 47. 265, 1826 ; *Kastner's Arch.*, 9. 49, 1826 ; L. W. McCay, *Beitrag zur Kenntnis der Kobalt-, Nickel-, und Eisenkiese*, Freiberg, 25, 1883 ; *Zeit. Kryst.*, 9. 607, 1884 ; G. C. Hoffmann, *The Minerals of Canada*, Ottawa, 99, 1890 ; M. Websky, *Zeit. deut. geol. Ges.*, 5. 414, 1853 ; E. Hatle, *Die Minerale Steiermarks*, Graz, 6, 1885 ; F. A. Kolenati, *Die Mineralien Mährens und österreichisch Schlesiens*, Brünn, 1854 ; E. Fugger, *Die Mineralien des Herzogthums Salzburg*, Salzburg, 9, 1878 ; C. von Hauer, *Jahrb. Geol. Reichsanst. Wien*, 4. 400, 1853 ; A. Ossent, *Zeit. Kryst.*, 9. 563, 1884 ; G. P. Jervis, *I. Tesori Sotterranei dell' Italia*, Turin, 1. 53, 1873 ; 3. 99, 346, 1881 ; A. Orio, *Elementos de mineralogia*, Madrid, 399, 1882 ; A. Erdmann, *Lärobok i Mineralogien*, Stockholm, 185, 1853 ; W. F. Petterd, *Catalogue of the Minerals of Tasmania*, Launceston, 82, 1896 ; A. Raimondi, *Minéraux du Pérou*, Paris, 208, 1878 ; A. des Cloizeaux, *Manuel de minéralogie*, Paris, 357, 1893 ; G. A. Koenig, *Zeit. Kryst.*, 17. 92, 1890 ; *Proc. Acad. Philadelphia*, 184, 1889 ; H. Oehmichen, *Zeit. prakt. Geol.*, 7. 271, 1899 ; S. Navia, *Naturaleza*, 4. 41, 1877 ; C. F. de Landero, *Sinopsis mineralogica*, Mexico, 161, 1888 ; G. Rose, *Das krystallochemischen Mineralsystem*, Leipzig, 52, 1852 ; I. Domeyko, *Elementos de mineraljia*, Santiago, 177, 1879 ; T. Petersen, *Pogg. Ann.*, 134. 70, 1868 ; W. Sartorius, *Liebig's Ann.*, 66. 278, 1848 ; G. Wertheim, *Ann. Chim. Phys.*, (3), 12. 610, 1844 ; (3), 13. 385, 1844 ; W. F. Hillebrand, *Proc. Acad. Philadelphia*, 3. 46, 1888 ; P. Berthier, *Ann. Mines*, (3), 11. 504, 1837 ; J. F. Vogl, *Gangverhältnisse und Mineralreichthum Joachimsthals*, Teplitz, 142, 1856 ; A. Löwe, *Jahrb. Geol. Reichsanst. Wien*, 1. 363, 1850 ; *Berg. Hütt. Jahrb.*, 13. 25, 1862 ; H. Hahn, *Berg. Hütt. Ztg.*, 20. 281, 1861 ; N. von Szontagh, *Neues Jahrb. Min.*, 351, 1860 ; W. Hisinger, *Versuch einer mineralogischen Geographie von Schweden*, Leipzig, 230, 1826 ; J. Rumpf, *Tschermak's Mitt.*, (1), 4. 235, 1874 ; E. Thomson, *Univ. Toronto Geol. Studies*, 20. 54, 1925 ; A. Russell, *Min. Mag.*, 20. 299, 1924.

²⁰ J. B. L. Romé de l'Isle, *Essai de cristallographie*, Paris, 333, 1772 ; *Cristallographie*, Paris, 3. 123, 1783 ; R. J. Haüy, *Traité de minéralogie*, Paris, 4. 202, 1801 ; F. Mohs, *Grundriss der Mineralogie*, Dresden, 2. 530, 1824 ; H. Kopp, *Liebig's Ann. Suppl.*, 3. 289, 1864 ; P. Groth, *Tabellarisch Uebersicht der Mineralien*, Braunschweig, 77, 1874 ; *Die Mineraliensammlung der Universität Strassburg*, Strassburg, 43, 1878 ; *Pogg. Ann.*, 152. 249, 1874 ; F. E. Neumann, *ib.*, 23. 1, 1831 ; M. Bauer, *Zeit. deut. geol. Ges.*, 27. 246, 1875 ; A. Breithaupt, *Pogg. Ann.*, 64. 184, 1845 ; *Journ. prakt. Chem.*, (1), 4. 265, 1835 ; A. Beutell, *Centr. Min.*, 206, 1916 ; L. S. Ramsdall, *Amer. Min.*, 10. 281. 1925 ; H. Fizeau, *Compt. Rend.*, 135. 372, 1868 ; H. Baumhauer, *Zeit. Kryst.*, 12. 15, 1887 ; A. Sella, *Ges. Wiss. Gött.*, 311, 1891 ; I. S. R. I. Eques a Born, *Lythophylacium Bornianum*, Prague, 1. 144, 1772 ; E. F. Smith, *Journ. Amer. Chem. Soc.*, 20. 289, 1898 ; I. I. Saslavsky, *Proc. Russ. Polyt. Inst.*, 1. 61, 1919 ; F. Beijerinck, *Neues Jahrb. Min. B.B.*, 11. 436, 1897 ; A. de Gramont, *Bull. Soc. Min.*, 18. 279, 1895 ; F. von Kobell, *Tafeln zur Bestimmung der Mineralien*, München, 5, 1873 ; J. Lemberg, *Zeit. deut. geol. Ges.*, 46. 797, 1894 ; C. F. Rammelsberg, *ib.*, 25. 283, 1873 ; C. A. Burghardt, *Min. Mag.*, 9. 233, 1891 ; G. Vollhardt, *Versuch über Speiskobalt*, München, 1886 ; *Zeit. Kryst.*, 14. 407, 1888 ; J. F. Vogt, *Gangverhältnisse und Mineralreichthum Joachimsthals*, Teplitz, 1856 ; A. Schrauf and E. S. Dana, *Sitzber. Akad. Wien*, 69. 149, 1874 ; E. T. Wherry, *Amer. Min.*, 10. 28, 1925 ; I. Oftedal, *Zeit. Kryst.*, 66. 517, 1928.

²¹ T. L. Walker and A. L. Parsons, *Univ. Toronto Geol. Studies*, 20. 41, 1925 ; E. Thomson, *ib.*, 20. 54, 1925 ; F. Varrentrapp, *Pogg. Ann.*, 48. 505, 1839 ; E. Hoffmann, *ib.*, 25. 485, 1832 ; A. G. Werner, *Letztes Mineralsystem*, Freiberg, 25, 1817 ; L. M. McCay, *Beitrag zur Kenntniss*

der Kobalt-, Nickel- und Eisenkiese, Freiberg, 20, 1883; *Zeit. Kryst.,* **9**. 607, 1884; **11**. 297, 1886; *Amer. Journ. Science,* (3), **29**. 373, 1885; F. von Kobell, *Grundzüge der Mineralogie,* Nürnberg, 300, 1838; A. Frenzel, *Mineralogisches Lexikon für das Königreich Sachsen,* Leipzig, 282, 1874; W. F. de Jong, *Physica,* **6**. 325, 1926; F. Mohs, *Grundriss der Mineralogie,* Dresden, 2. 534, 1824; E. von Gerichten, *Sitzber. Akad. München,* 138, 1873; J. D. Dana, *A System of Mineralogy,* New York, 101, 1892 · F. Sandberger, *ib.,* 135, 1873; *Untersuchungen über Erzgänge,* Wiesbaden, 383, 1885; *Neues Jahrb. Min.,* 410, 1868; 59, 1873; 82, 1874; i, 70, 1884; T. Petersen, *ib.,* 410, 1868; G. A. Kenngott, *ib.,* 754, 1869; *Uebersicht der Resultate mineralogischer Forschungen,* Wien, 97, 1852; E. F. Glocker, *Handbuch der Mineralogie,* Nürnberg, 318, 1839; *Generum et specierum mineralium secundum ordines naturales digestorum synopsis,* Halle, 36, 1847; G. Rose, *Das krystallochemischen Mineralsystem,* Leipzig, 53, 1852; A. Breithaupt, *Vollständiges Charakteristik des Mineralsystems,* Dresden, 245, 1832; *Journ. prakt. Chem.,* (1), **4**. 265, 1835; H. Sjögren, *Bull. Geol. Inst. Upsala,* **2**. 95, 1894; N. S. Kurnakoff and N. S. Konstantinoff, *Journ. Russ. Phys. Chem. Soc.,* **40**. 227, 1908; *Zeit. anorg. Chem.,* **58**. 1, 1908; P. Poni, *Études sur les minéraux de la Roumanie,* Jassy, 17, 1900; F. Beijerinck, *Neues Jahrb. Min. B.B.,* **11**. 436, 1897.

²² T. L. Walker and A. L. Parsons, *Univ. Toronto Geol. Studies,* **17**. 9, 1924; **20**. 41, 1925; E. Thomson, *ib.,* **20**. 54, 1925; T. L. Walker, *ib.,* **20**. 49, 1925; W. Haidinger, *Handbuch der bestimmenden Mineralogie,* Wien, 560, 1845; J. F. L. Hausmann, *Handbuch der Mineralogie,* Göttingen, 69, 1847; L. Staudenmaier, *Zeit. Kryst.,* **20**. 468, 1890; A. Schrauf and E. S. Dana, *Sitzber. Akad. Wien,* **69**. 153, 1874; J. D. Dana, *A System of Mineralogy,* New York, 93, 1892; A. Breithaupt, *Vollständiges Charakteristik des Mineralsystems,* Dresden, 250, 1832; *Journ. prakt. Chem.,* (1), **4**. 263, 1835; *Pogg. Ann.,* **9**. 115, 1827; T. Scheerer, *ib.,* **42**. 553, 1837; F. Wöhler, *ib.,* **43**. 591, 1838; G. vom Rath, *ib.,* **15**. 48, 1862; *Zeit. Kryst.,* **14**. 258, 1888; J. Nicol, *Manual of Mineralogy,* Edinburgh, 457, 1849; W. H. Miller, *An Elementary Introduction to Mineralogy,* London, 147, 1852; L. Fletcher, *Phil. Mag.,* (5), **13**. 474, 1882; L. Bombicci, *Corso di Mineralogia,* Bologna, 497, 1862; A. d'Achiardi, *Mineralogia della Toscana,* Pisa, 2. 354, 1873; E. Waller and A. J. Moses, *School Mines Quart.,* **14**. 49, 1892; G. Vollhardt, *Versuch über Speiskobalt,* München, 1886; *Zeit. Kryst.,* **14**. 408, 1888; A. Frenzel, *Tschermak's Mitt.* (2), **16**. 524, 1897; W. Ramsay, *Journ. Chem. Soc.,* **29**. 153, 1874; C. F. Rammelsberg, *Handbuch der Mineralchemie,* Leipzig, 12, 1895; *Zeit. deut. Geol. Ges.,* **25**. 266, 1873; *Neues. Jahrb Min.,* ii, 45, 1897; F. Beijerinck, *Neues Jahrb. Min. B.B.,* **11**. 436, 1897; A. Beutell, *Centr. Min.,* 206, 1916; A. Beutell and F. Lorenz, *ib.,* **16**. 40, 1916; I. Oftedal, *Zeit. Kryst.,* **66**. 517, 1928.

²³ A. F. Gehlen, *Schweigger's Journ.,* **15**. 501, 1815; **20**. 353, 1817; P. Berthier, *Ann. Chim. Phys.,* (2), **62**. 113, 1836; J. J. Berzelius, *ib.,* (2), **5**. 179, 1817; (2), **11**. 225, 1819; A. Granger, *Arch. Sciences Genève,* (4), **6**. 391, 1898.

²⁴ K. Friedrich and F. Bennigson, *Met.,* **4**. 200, 1907; E. Vigouroux, *Compt. Rend.,* **147**. 426, 1908; A. Descamps, *ib.,* **86**. 1065, 1878; A. Granger and G. Didier, *ib.,* **130**. 914, 1900; *Bull. Soc. Chim.,* (3), **23**. 506, 1900; J. W. Döbereiner, *Gilbert's Ann.,* **73**. 226, 1823; F. Wöhler, *Pogg. Ann.,* **25**. 302, 1832; A. Breithaupt, *ib.,* **53**. 434, 631, 1841; C. F. Plattner, *ib.,* **58**. 283, 1843; G. Rose, *Das krystallochemischen Mineralsystem,* Leipzig, 47, 1852; *Pogg. Ann.,* **84**. 589, 1851; W. Francis, *ib.,* **50**. 519, 1840; C. F. Rammelsberg, *Handbuch der Mineralchemie,* Leipzig, 19, 1895; *Neues Jahrb. Min.,* ii, 57, 1897; *Zeit. deut. geol. Ges.,* **25**. 275, 1873; *Pogg. Ann.,* **120**. 54, 1863; **128**. 442, 1866; C. Schnabel, *ib.,* **84**. 585, 1851; *Ber. Nat. Hist. Ver. Rheinl.,* **8**. 573, 1851; J. Braun, *Zeit. Kryst.,* **3**. 421, 1879; A. Gurlt, *Uebersicht der pyrogenneten künstlichen Mineralien,* Freiberg, 35, 1857; O. Hackl, *Verh. Geol. Reichsanst. Wien,* 107, 1921; E. F. Anthon, *Journ. prakt. Chem.,* (1), **9**. 12, 1836; E. R. Schneider, *ib.,* (1), **43**. 317, 1848; A. Brukl, *Zeit. anorg. Chem.,* **131**. 236, 1923; R. Lorenz and W. Herz, *ib.,* **135**. 374, 1924; W. Herz, *ib.,* **163**. 220, 1927; A. Beutell, *Centr. Min.,* 49, 1916.

²⁵ K. Friedrich and F. Bennigson, *Met.,* **4**. 200, 1907; F. Fouqué and A. Michel-Lévy, *Synthèse des minéraux et des roches,* Paris, 277, 1882; E. Vigouroux, *Compt. Rend.,* **147**. 426, 1908; W. F. de Jong and H. W. V. Willems, *Physica,* **7**. 74, 1927; W. F. de Jong, *ib.,* **5**. 194, 1925; W. Herz, *Zeit. anorg. Chem.,* **163**. 220, 1927.

²⁶ J. G. Wallerius, *Mineralogia,* Stockholm, 228, 1747; A. Cronstedt, *Mineralogie,* Stockholm, 218, 1758; *Abad. Handl. Stockholm,* 293, 1751; 38, 1754; R. J. Haüy, *Traité de minéralogie,* Paris, 3. 513, 1801; C. C. von Leonhard, *Handbuch der Oryktognosie,* Heidelberg, 292, 1821; G. Leonhard, *Handwörterbuch der topographischen Mineralogie,* Heidelberg, 42, 1843; F. S. Beudant, *Traité élémentaire de minéralogie,* Paris, 2. 586, 1832; J. D. Dana, *A System of Mineralogy,* New York, 60, 1868; 71, 1892; F. Sandberger, *Untersuchungen über Erzgänge,* Wiesbaden, 305, 1885; *Uebersicht der Mineralien Unterfrankens und Aschaffenburgs,* Würzburg, 1892; J. F. L. Hausmann, *Handbuch der Mineralogie,* Göttingen, 63, 1847; *Stud. Gött. Ver. Berg.,* **4**. 347, 1818; L. A. Emmerling, *Lehrbuch der Mineralogie,* Giessen, 2. 513, 1796; A. Estner, *Versuch einer Mineralogie,* Wien, 3. b, 144, 1804; E. F. Glocker, *Handbuch der Mineralogie,* Nürnberg, 329, 1839; *Generum et specierum mineralium secundum ordines naturales digestorum synopsis,* Halle, 43, 1847; *Journ. prakt. Chem.,* (1), **12**. 183, 1837; W. Phillips, *Elementary Introduction to Mineralogy,* London, 283, 1823; C. A. S. Hofmann, *Handbuch der Mineralogie,* Freiberg, 4. a, 164, 1817; F. Mohs, *Grundriss der Mineralogie,* Dresden, 2. 523, 1824; W. Haidinger, *Treatise on Mineralogy,* Edinburgh, 2. 447, 1825; H. Laspeyres, *Ber. Nat. Hist. Ver. Rheinl.,* **50**. 173, 1893; F. von Kobell, *Geschicht der Mineralogie,* München, 630, 1864; H. J. Brooke *Phil. Mag.,* (2), **10**. 110, 1831; G. A. Kenngott, *Mineralogische Untersuchungen,*

Breslau, 209, 1858; *Sitzber. Akad. Wien*, 13. 464, 1854; *Die Minerale der Schweiz nach ihren Eigenschaften und Fundorten*, Leipzig, 395, 1866; J. Woodward, *Fossils of all kinds digested into a method suitable to their Mutual Relation*, London, 1728; U. Hiärne, *Een Kort Anledning till ätskillige Malm-och Bergarters, Mineraliers Wäxters, och Jordeslags, sampt flere sällsamme Tings effterspöriande och angifwande*, Stockholm, 76, 1694; J. B. L. Romé de l'Isle, *Cristallographie*, Paris, 3. 135, 1783; P. Groth, *Tabellarische Uebersicht der Mineralien*, Braunschweig, 20, 1898; V. R. von Zepharovich, *Mineralogisches Lexikon für das Kaiserthum Oesterreich*, Wien, 289, 1859; 218, 1873; 174, 1893; A. des Cloizeaux, *Manuel de minéralogie*, Paris, 2. 351, 1898; R. P. Greg and W. G. Lettsom, *Manual of the Mineralogy of Great Britain and Ireland*, London, 298, 1858; A. Frenzel, *Mineralogisches Lexikon fur das Königreich Sachsen*, Leipzig, 216, 1874; O. Luedecke, *Die Minerale des Harzes*, Berlin, 70, 1896; C. W. Gümbel, *Geognostische Beschreibung des Königreichs Bayern*, Gotha, 3. 404, 1879; E. Hatle, *Die Minerale Steiermarks*, Graz, 7, 1885; H. Traube, *Die Minerale Schlesiens*, Breslau, 148, 1888; E. Fugger, *Die Mineralien des Herzogthums Salzburg*, Salzburg, 12, 1878; J. D. Denso, *Physikalische Briefe*, Stettin, 297, 1750; B. G. Sage, *Élémens de minéralogie docimastique*, Paris, 58, 1772; A. Breithaupt, *Vollständiges Charakteristik das Mineralsystems*, Dresden, 245, 1832; *Schweigger's Journ.*, 68. 444, 1833; *Journ. prakt. Chem.*, (1), 4. 266, 1835; *Neues Jahrb. Min.*, 818, 1872; *Pogg. Ann.*, 51. 515, 1840; T. Petersen, *ib.*, 134. 82, 1868; 137. 396, 1869; C. Winkler, *Neues Jahrb. Min.*, 818, 1872; M. Bäumler, *Zeit. anal. geol. Ges.*, 9. 33, 1857; G. Rose, *ib.*, 10. 91, 1858; M. Websky, *ib.*, 5. 414, 1853; C. Heusler, *ib.*, 28. 245, 1876; A. Grunow, *ib.*, 9. 40, 1857; G. Suckow, *ib.*, 9. 33, 1857; *Der Verwitterung im Mineralreiche*, Leipzig, 58, 1848; A. von Lasaulx, *Ber. Niederrh. Ges. Bonn*, 10, 1886; A. Hofmann, *Jahrb. Geol. Reichsanst. Wien*, 45. 33, 1895; F. Babanek, *Tschermak's Mitt.*, (1), 2. 29, 1872; J. Rumpf, *ib.*, (1), 4. 235, 1874; J. D. Whitney, *The Metallic Wealth of the United States*, Philadelphia, 1854; G. C. Hoffmann, *Ann. Rep. Geol. Sur. Canada*, 45, 1892; T. S. Hunt, *ib.*, 506, 1863; G. P. Jervis, *I Tesori Sotterranei dell'Italia*, Turin, 3. 375, 1881; L. Brunrucker, *Zeit. Kryst.*, 19. 133, 1891; L. Sipöcz, *ib.*, 11. 215, 1885; *Ber.*, 19. 101, 1886; W. F. Petterd, *Catalogue of the Minerals of Tasmania*, Launceston, 64, 1896; A. Raimondi, *Les minéraux du Pérou*, Paris, 204, 1878; I. Domeyko, *Elementos de mineralogia*, Santiago, 185, 1879; A. Orio, *Elementos de mineralogia*, Madrid, 426, 1882; A. Lacroix, *Minéralogie de la France et de ses colonies*, Paris, 2. 557, 1897; F. Navarro, *Anales Soc. Esp. Hist. Nat.*, 23. 40, 1894; A. Liversidge, *The Minerals of New South Wales*, Sydney, 57, 1882; A. Sjögren, *Geol. För. Förh. Stockholm*, 7. 177, 1884; N. von Kokscharoff, *Materialen zur Mineralogie Russlands*, St. Petersburg, 5. 156, 1869; W. H. Miller, *Introduction to Mineralogy*, London, 144, 1852; J. H. Collins, *A Handbook to the Mineralogy of Cornwall and Devon*, London, 72, 1876; J. J. Nöggerath, *Ber. Niederrh. Ges. Bonn*, 15, 1857; P. Giebe, *Uebersicht der Mineralien des Fichtelgebirgs und des angrenzenden fränkischen Gebietes*, Cassel, 7, 1895; C. F. Rammelsberg, *Handbuch der Mineralchemie*, Leipzig, 122, 1849; F. Stromeyer, *Gött. Gel. Anz.*, 2034, 1817; C. H. Pfaff, *Schweigger's Journ.*, 22. 256, 1818; H. Hahn, *Berg. Hütt. Ztg.*, 20. 281, 1861; J. J. Ebelmen, *Ann. Mines*, (4), 11. 55, 1847; P. Berthier, *ib.*, (1), 4. 467, 1819; (3), 7. 538, 1835; *Ann. Chim. Phys.*, (2), 13. 52, 1820; F. A. Genth, *Proc. Amer. Phil. Soc.*, 20. 403, 1882; T. Scheerer, *Pogg. Ann.*, 65. 292, 1845; M. Adam, *Tableau minéralogique*, Paris, 40, 1869; F. Pisani, *Compt. Rend.*, 76. 239, 1873; A. de Gramont, *Bull. Soc. Min.*, 18. 278, 1895; G. A. Koenig, *Zeit. Kryst.*, 17. 92, 1890; J. F. Kemp, *ib.*, 25. 286, 1896; *Trans. New York Acad. Sciences*, 13. 76, 1893; F. Beijerinck, *Neues Jahrb. Min. B.B.*, 11. 431, 1897; J. Lemberg, *Zeit. deut. geol. Ges.*, 46. 797, 1894; D. S. Lovisato, *Atti Accad. Lincei*, (5), 3. 82, 1894; H. S. Roberts and L. H. Adams, *Amer. Min.*, 7. 131, 1922; E. T. Wherry, *ib.*, 10. 28, 1925; T. W. Case, *Phys. Rev.*, (2), 9. 305, 1917; G. Aminoff, *Zeit. Kryst.*, 58. 108, 1923; T. L. Walker and A. L. Parsons, *Univ. Toronto Geol. Studies*, 20. 41, 1925; E. Thomson, *ib.*, 20. 35, 1925; A. Russell, *Min. Mag.*, 20. 299, 1924; 21. 383, 1927; W. F. de Jong, *Physica*, 5. 194, 1925; 6. 325, 1926; W. F. de Jong and H. W. V. Willems, *ib.*, 7. 74, 1927; J. S. Newberry, *Amer. Journ. Science*, (3), 28. 122, 1884; I. Oftedal, *Zeit. phys. Chem.*, 128. 135, 1927.

27 W. Haidinger, *Handbuch der bestimmenden Mineralogie*, Wien, 560, 1845; A. Breithaupt, *Pogg. Ann.*, 64. 184, 1845; T. L. Walker and A. L. Parsons, *Univ. Toronto Geol. Studies*, 12, 1921; 20, 1925; E. Thomson, *ib.*, 20, 1925; T. L. Walker, *ib.*, 20, 1925; C. M. Kersten, *Schweigger's Journ.*, 47. 265, 1826; *Kastner's Arch.*, 9. 49, 1826; J. D. Dana, *A System of Mineralogy*, New York, 61, 1854; I. Domeyko, *Elementos de mineralojia*, Santiago, 186, 1879; E. Hoffmann, *Pogg. Ann.*, 25. 492, 1832; H. Baumhauer, *Zeit. Kryst.*, 12. 32, 1887; F. Sandberger, *Sitzber. Akad. München*, 202, 1871; 199, 1893; *Neues Jahrb. Min.*, 935, 1871; G. A. Kenngott, *Die Minerale der Schweiz nach ihren Eigenschaften und Fundorten*, Leipzig, 395, 1866; G. P. Jervis, *I Tessori Sotterranei dell'Italia*, 1. 53, 1873; F. Wöhler, *Liebig's Ann.*, 25. 302, 1832; V. R. von Zepharovich, *Mineralogisches Lexikon für das Kaiserthum Oesterreich*, Wien, 270, 1873; *Proc. Russ. Min. Soc.*, 3. 24, 1867; A. Frenzel, *Mineralogisches Lexikon für das Königreich Sachsen*, Leipzig, 278, 1874; P. Groth, *Die Mineraliensammlung der Universität Strassburg*, Strassburg, 45, 1878; G. Aminoff, *Zeit. Kryst.*, 58. 203, 1923; F. Beijerinck, *Neues Jahrb. Min. B.B.*, 11. 436, 1897; E. F. Smith, *Journ. Amer. Chem. Soc.*, 20. 289, 1898; L. W. McCay, *Beitrag zur Kenntnis der Kobalt-, Nickel-, und Eisenkiese*, Freiberg, 8, 1884; *Zeit. Kryst.*, 9. 606, 1884; J. Haberfelner, *Zeit. prakt. Chem.*, 1. 309, 1893; E. Vigouroux, *Compt. Rend.*, 147. 426, 1908; E. T. Wherry, *Amer. Min.*, 10. 28, 1925.

28 E. Waller and A. J. Moses, *School Mines Quart.*, 14. 49, 1892.

29 A. Gibb, *Proc. Inst. Mech. Eng.*, 254, 1895; *Engg.*, 59. 778, 1895.

¹⁰ W. H. Wollaston, *Phil. Trans.*, **94.** 419, 1804; R. Chenevix, *ib.*, **93.** 4, 1803; C. Winkler, *Journ. prakt. Chem.*, (1), **91.** 193, 1864; N. W. Fischer, *Schweigger's Journ.*, **51.** 192, 1827; *Pogg. Ann.*, **71.** 431, 1847 ; *Phil. Mag.*, (2), **4.** 230, 1828.

³¹ A. F. Gehlen, *Schweigger's Journ.*, **20.** 353, 1817; R. W. Fox, *Ann. Phil.*, **13.** 467, 1819; J. Murray, *Edin. Phil. Journ.*, **4.** 202, 1821; N. W. Fischer, *Kastner's Arch.*, **11.** 224, 1827; K. Friedrich and A. Leroux, *Met.*, **5.** 148, 1908; D. Tivoli, *Gazz. Chim. Ital.*, **14.** 488, 1884 ; S. L. Penfield, *Amer. Journ. Science*, (3), **37.** 71, 1889; H. L. Wells, *ib.*, (3), **37.** 67, 1889 ; (4), **35.** 171, 1913 ; T. L. Walker, *ib.*, (4), **1.** 110, 1896; W. E. Hidden and J. H. Pratt, *ib.*, (4), **6.** 382, 1898 ; W. Lewis, *Commercium Philosophico-Technicum*, London, 515, 1763 ; W. F. de Jong, *Physica*, **5.** 292, 1925 ; L. J. Spencer, *Min. Mag.*, **21.** 94, 1926 ; J. F. Donald, *Eng. Min. Journ.*, **55.** 81, 1893 ; *Berg. Hütt. Ztg.*, **52.** 209, 1893 ; F. Rössler, *Synthese einiger Erzmineralien und analoger Metallverbindungen durch Auflösen und Kristallisierenlassen derselben in geschmolzenen Metallen*, Berlin, 48, 1895 ; *Zeit. anorg. Chem.*, **9.** 64, 1895; *Chem. Ztg.*, **24.** 733, 1900; W. R. Hodgkinson and F. K. S. Lowndes, *Chem. News*, **58.** 223, 1888 ; L. S. Ramsdall, *Amer. Min.*, **10.** 281, 1925 ; **12.** 79, 1927 ; E. Kordes, *Zeit. anorg. Chem.*, **154.** 97, 1926 ; G. Aminoff and A. L. Parsons, *Amer. Min.*, **13.** 110, 1928.

§ 11. Arsenic Suboxide, and Trioxide

J. J. Berzelius [1] regarded the black film which forms on the surface of arsenic as *arsenic suboxide*, and P. A. von Bonsdorff represented it as **arsenic hemioxide**, As_2O. J .J. Berzelius also said that the suboxide is produced as a dark brown sublimate which first appears during the preparation of arsenic ; and J. W. Retgers observed the brown film as produced along with the arsenic mirror during the sublimation of commercial arsenic. E. Mitchell believed that the suboxide is an intermediate product in the oxidation of arsenic (*q.v.*), and is the cause of the garlic odour. He also said that the suboxide is more volatile than arsenic trioxide. It is not unlikely that E. Mitchell mistook the amorphous arsenic for arsenic hemioxide. J. W. Retgers supposed that the alleged suboxide is truly a chemical individual, but A. Geuther, and G. Suckow showed that the suboxide is probably a mixture of arsenic and arsenic trioxide.

As indicated in connection with the history of arsenic, the twelfth-century Arabian chemists alluded to white arsenic, and G. Brandt [2] showed that *arsenicum album* is the oxide or calx of arsenic. In 1747, J. G. Wallerius spoke of *arsenicum nativum*, *arsenicum faricaceum* or *farina arsenicalis*, and *arsenicum cristallinum*. The *arsenic-meal*, furnace fume, or white arsenic was the *arsenicum calciforme* of A. Cronstedt, and the *arsenicum cubicum* of C. Linnæus. This oxide received various names in the Middle Ages—*white arsenic, arsenic, flowers of arsenic, rat-poison, poison meal, furnace fume, arsenious acid*, etc. The modern designation is **arsenic trioxide**, As_2O_3, or As_4O_6. The formation of arsenic trioxide during the oxidation of arsenic has already been discussed. It is also produced when arsenic, mispickel, or arsenical pyrites alone or mixed with other ores, is roasted in air. With löllingite, arsenic vapour is given off at a dull red-heat, and at a higher temp., arsenic trioxide is produced ; the iron is nearly all converted into ferric oxide, and but a small proportion of ferric arsenate is formed. When mispickel is heated in air, arsenic sulphide vapour is evolved below a red-heat ; but at a higher temp., ferric oxide, sulphate, and arsenate are formed, while sulphur dioxide and arsenic trioxide are given off.

Arseniferous ores are a by-product from the tin-mines of Cornwall, and their treatment is accordingly connected with the production of tin, and tungsten. The ore is hand-picked, broken first with hammers, then in jaw-crushers, and finally in stamp-mills. The stamp pulp is then screened and passed through hydraulic classifiers. The ore is then calcined. There are different types of calciner ; these were illustrated in connection with the extraction of tin—Figs. 2 and 3, **7.** 46, 3. In Cornwall, the calciner is a kind of reverberatory furnace with a revolving floor of cast-iron and firebrick sloping from the centre to the periphery, and revolving 4–6 times per hour. Three sets of scrapers are arranged over the floor. The ore is fed on the revolving floor by means of a hopper, and heated to dull redness for about 10 hours, it is at the same time raked into a central trough and thence into a chamber beneath.   The oxidized sulphur and arsenic vapours pass zig-zag over a large condensing surface.   The sulphur vapours escape, and dark grey, crude arsenic or *arsenic soot* is collected.   It contains 4–10 per cent. of carbon and sulphur. The arsenic soot is refined by recalcination in a flat-bottomed reverberatory furnace using a smokeless fuel—say a mixture of coke and anthracite—and connected with a series of zig-zag condensing chambers.   The charge is fed from the top, and paddled down to the side-doors while being roasted.   The first condensing chamber collects the *slag arsenic*, which is re-ground and calcined ; in the other chambers, snow-white, crystalline arsenic trioxide collects on the walls, often in stalactitic forms.   This is raked out, ground in stone-mills, and passed through leather pipes into 4 cwt. casks.   Great care is taken to prevent the leakage of the poisonous dust during these operations.   About 60 per cent. of arsenic is recovered from the ores, while 40 per cent. is lost in the slimes.   The mispickel ores employed contain from 10 to 30 per cent. of arsenic.   There are several types of chamber—*poison tower*— for condensing the white arsenic—*poison flour*, or *arsenical soot*.   Modifications of the process were described by C. Doremus,[3] G. J. Young, E. C. Williams, H. P. Bassett and S. S. Sadtler.   C. L. Read discussed the purification from the less volatile antimony trioxide.

V. Kohlschütter and J. L. Tüscher [4] prepared highly dispersed, or **colloidal arsenic trioxide** by vaporization in the electric arc.   F. Schoucroum showed that it is a colloid with a negative charge which does not reverse with increasing conc. of H-ions.   In addition to the white, glistening, minutely crystalline flowers of arsenic, white *arsenic-glass*, or *vitreous arsenic* is prepared by collecting the vaporized arsenic trioxide at so high a temp. that the sublimate fuses into a white glassy mass. **Vitreous arsenic trioxide** may be prepared by heating the trioxide—preferably under slight press.—in a cast-iron pan surmounted by wrought or cast-iron bell. The pans containing the arsenic are heated to redness, and a layer of vitreous arsenic collects in the bell.   More white arsenic is introduced into the pan ; and the operation is repeated until the glass has a thickness of about an inch.   There are several different modifications of the process for converting ordinary white arsenic into the glassy form.[5]   As shown by H. A. L. Wiggers, and A. Streng, antimony oxide is one of the most likely impurities.   L. Kessler tried to eliminate it by dissolving the oxide in warm aq. ammonia, evaporating the filtrate, and subliming the residue ; but F. Wöhler did not succeed by this process.   R. Suchy and J. Michel dissolved the crude trioxide in a soln. of sodium carbonate, and precipitated the trioxide from the filtered soln. by carbon dioxide.   R. M. Chapin recommended the following mode of purification :

Ordinary arsenic trioxide is boiled for about one hour with a quantity of water insufficient to dissolve the whole of it, the soln. filtered while hot, the filtrate conc. until arsenic trioxide begins to precipitate, and the soln. again filtered.   The separated oxide is tested for antimony by dissolving a portion in ammonia adding hydrogen sulphide, boiling the mixture, and then cooling in ice-water ; a turbidity is obtained if more than 0·15 per cent. of antimony trioxide is present, and in such case the arsenic trioxide must be treated further as described.   The purification depends on the fact that antimony, if present, is absorbed almost completely by the solid arsenic trioxide which remains undissolved in the aq. soln. The final crystallization of the pure arsenic trioxide is best made from a slightly hydrochloric acid soln., and the product is then sublimed.

The general methods employed for the preparation of the flowers of arsenic, and arsenic glass, are described by G. Vié, and by C. Schnabel, *Handbuch der Metall-hüttenkunde*, (Berlin, 1904) ;   T. E. Thorpe, *A Dictionary of Applied Chemistry*, (London, 1. 380, 1921) ; etc.   C. P. Linville removed selenium by the addition of a reagent capable of forming a non-volatile selenide and volatilizing the arsenic trioxide.

The analyses of L. J. Thénard,[6] H. Davy, J. L. Proust, J. J. Berzelius, E. Mitscherlich, T. Thomson, and C. F. Richter have shown that the composition can be represented by the empirical formula As_2O_3.   The impurities in commercial arsenic trioxide were discussed by W. D. Collins and co-workers.   E. Mitscherlich found that the vapour density at 563° is 13·85 when the value calculated for As_4O_6 is 13·68; V. and C. Meyer obtained analogous results at much higher temp.; and A. Scott, at 1050°. On the other hand, H. Biltz found that the dissociation of the complex mol. into a simpler form $As_4O_6 \rightleftharpoons 2As_2O_3$ is appreciable at 800°; and he found for the vap. density, D,

	518°	769°	851°	1059°	1256°	1450°	1584°	1732°
D	13·92	13·62	13·15	12·76	12·36	9·41	8·81	7·32

The mol. wt. of the octahedral crystals in nitrobenzene soln. was found by H. Biltz to be 396 in agreement with the value required for As_4O_6. R. M. Bozorth's examination of the X-radiograms of arsenic trioxide show that the molecules of the solid consist of As_4O_6—*vide infra*. No suitable solvent was found for the vitreous arsenic trioxide, and its mol. wt. is unknown. E. Beckmann found the mol. wt. of arsenic trioxide from its effect on the f.p. of antimony trichloride to be about half the normal value—probably an effect of a chemical reaction—*vide* arsenic triiodide. H. Erdmann argued that since a certain amount of yellow arsenic is produced when arsenic trioxide is reduced with zinc dust in the presence of carbon disulphide, yellow arsenic and arsenic trioxide have a similar constitution.

$$
\begin{array}{cc}
O & \\
/ \backslash & \\
O{=}As - As{=}O & As{=}As \\
O{=}\dot{A}s - \dot{A}s{=}O & \dot{A}s{=}\dot{A}s \\
\backslash / & \\
O & \\
\text{Arsenic trioxide.} & \text{Yellow arsenic.}
\end{array}
$$

V. Meyer, however, preferred one of the following formulæ :

$$
\begin{array}{cc}
As{<}{}^{O}_{O}{>}As & As.O.As : O \\
\dot{O} \quad \dot{O} & \wedge \\
\dot{A}s{<}{}^{O}_{O}{>}\dot{A}s & OO \\
& \vee \\
& As.O.As : O
\end{array}
$$

The octahedral form of the crystals was noted by T. Bergman,[7] and by J. B. L. Romé de l'Isle. The crystals belong to the cubic systems, and they were described in detail by A. des Cloizeaux, whilst A. Grosse-Bohle compared the crystals with the cubic form of antimony trioxide. R. M. Bozorth examined the X-radiogram of the octahedral crystals of arsenic trioxide and found that the corresponding space-lattice is of the diamond form, Fig. 13, with one mol of As_4O_6 corresponding with one carbon atom. The mol. is a regular tetrahedron, and there are two orienta-

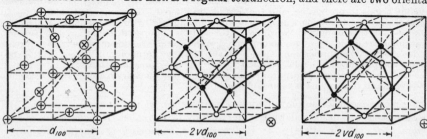

FIG. 13.—Arrangement of the Molecules of Arsenic Trioxide, As_4O_6, in the Space-lattice.

FIGS. 14 and 15.—Arrangements of the Atoms in the Molecules of Arsenic Trioxide.

tions of the atoms, one being a reflection of the other in any plane parallel to a cube face. The four arsenic atoms lie on the four lines joining the centre of the tetrahedron to its corners, and the six oxygen atoms on the six perpendiculars from the centre on the six sides. The unit cube with 8 mols. of As_4O_6 has a side 11·06 A. ; and the shortest shows the arrangement of the atoms of arsenic, ●, and of oxygen, ◯, in the ⊗ molecules of Fig. 14 ; and Fig. 15, the arrangement of these atoms in the ⊕ molecules. R. Brauns observed no optical anomalies. The cleavage of the crystals is octahedral. The octahedral crystals are produced during the sublimation of arsenic trioxide when the vap. is rapdily cooled without passing though a state of fusion ; by cooling a hot sat. aq. soln. of arsenic trioxide ; and, according to J. N. von Fuchs, when white arsenic glass is kept for a long time it becomes opaque, owing to devitrification. The crystallization was observed by J. F. L. Hausmann. H. V. Regnault said that the devitrification proceeds rapidly at 100°. H. Rose showed that if air be excluded, arsenic-glass can be kept over a year without devitrification ; and C. Winkler found that the glass remains clear if kept in thoroughly dried hydrogen, air, or carbon dioxide. W. Krüger also found that moisture is necessary to develop the turbidity in air ; and that the change is accompanied by an increase of 0·625 per cent. in weight. R. Christison said that the glass remains transparent for years if kept under water ; and H. Rose obtained a similar result under alcohol. On the contrary, according to C. Winkler, the transformation of arsenic-glass into octahedral crystals proceeds quickly under water, under a cold aq. soln. of arsenic trioxide, or under ether or alcohol ; and, according to H. A. L. Wiggers, under hydrochloric acid. C. Winkler said that if a stick of arsenic-glass be dipped in boiling water, octahedral crystals quickly form on the surface of the glass. A. Bussy found that if opaque arsenic-glass be treated with boiling water, it becomes transparent again, not, as A. Bussy supposed, on account of the greater solubility of the arsenic-glass, but, according to C. Winkler, because of the conversion of the amorphous mass into a crystalline solid. C. Winkler explained the action of water by assuming that the film of water condensing on the surface of the glassy oxide forms a soln. which deposits crystals of the less soluble cubic form ; the water then dissolves more vitreous oxide, and so there is a continuous cycle of changes involving the transformation of the vitreous oxide into octahedral crystals from the exterior towards the interior.

A. Scheurer-Kestner found that when arsenic trioxide is crystallized from a soln. containing colouring agents—say, sulphindigotic acid, brazil-wood, or curcuma— the crystals retain the dye, leaving the mother-liquor colourless. According to H. Rose, the crystallization of arsenic trioxide from soln. is attended by crystalloluminescence. He said :

When from one to one and a half parts of transparent arsenic trioxide are dissolved by half an hour's boiling, in a mixture of six parts of fuming hydrochloric acid with two parts of water, and the soln. left to cool as slowly as possible, the arsenic trioxide crystallizes in transparent octahedra and the formation of each crystal is accompanied by a flash of light ; on agitation, many new crystals are formed, and a corresponding number of sparks is produced. If from four to six parts of arsenic-glass are dissolved in the acid, the light produced by the crystallization is sufficient to illuminate a dark room. As long as the deposition of crystals goes on, so long is light perceived on agitating the liquid ; and this appearance may be visible on the second, and even, though very faintly, on the third evening. If the liquid be then boiled, so as to dissolve the remaining portion of the glassy oxide, crystallization again takes place, accompanied by emission of light, though not so bright as before. If the liquid be rapidly cooled, the acid separates in the pulverulent state, and little or no light is emitted. A soln. of arsenic trioxide in a hot mixture of hydrochloric with sufficient nitric acid to convert the whole of the arsenic trioxide into the pentoxide, likewise emits a strong light as the acid crystallizes. Boiling dil. sulphuric acid dissolves arsenic trioxide in smaller quantity, and exhibits only occasional luminosity. Nitric and acetic acids, which dissolve still less of the arsenic trioxide, exhibit no luminosity whatever. Arsenic trioxide which has acquired the porcelainic texture, and also arsenic-meal, likewise exhibits, when dissolved in hydrochloric acid, a very feeble luminosity on agitation.

E. von Bandrowsky found that the faculty is not lost if the arsenic trioxide has been recrystallized from acidic soln. J. Guinchant, and D. Gernez attribute the phenomenon to triboluminescence ; and it is exhibited when the crystals are compressed ; or when the crystals are stirred with a steel, iron, or platinum rod.

M. Trautz discussed the phenomenon. J. Guinchant found the spectrum of the light is continuous ; and that an adjacent electroscope is not affected during the phenomenon.

L. A. Emmerling referred to the natural occurrence of white arsenic—*naturlichen Arsenikkalk.* D. L. G. Karsten called the mineral *Arsenikblüthe ;* W. Haidinger, *arsenite ;* and J. D. Dana, *arsenolite.* The occurrence of arsenolite in nature is a result of the weathering, or oxidation of arsenical ores ; and it is found accompanying arsenical ores—*e.g.* mispickel, smaltite, etc. Arsenolite may appear earthy, stalactitic, or botryoidal ; but it usually occurs in minute capillary crystals, in stellar aggregates or crusts. The dark grey, or greyish-black crust or powder found on native arsenic, sometimes regarded as a suboxide (*q.v.*), is, according to G. Suckow, a mixture of arsenic and arsenic trioxide. C. Hintze [8] has described numerous occurrences of arsenolite.

In addition to the octahedral form crystallizing in the cubic system, F. Wöhler,[9] in his paper *Ueber die Dimorphie der arsenigen Säure,* observed that the arsenical sublimate from a Hessian furnace roasting cobalt ores contained some monoclinic crystals. This was verified by L. Pasteur, F. Ulrich, M. Bauer, A. Scheurer-Kestner, P. Groth, and F. Claudet. According to N. Zenzen and co-workers, the reported occurrence of arsenophyllite at Dalarne, Sweden, is a decomposition product of arsenopyrite caused by fire in the mines. The prismatic crystals were at first thought to be rhombic, and isomorphous with valentinite, the rhombic form of antimony trioxide, but the measurements made by A. des Cloizeaux, and A. Schmidt, showed that the crystals of the prismatic form of antimony trioxide are monoclinic. A. Schmidt showed that the crystals of the prismatic form of arsenic trioxide are monoclinic. A. Schmidt gave for the axial ratios $a : b : c = 0.4040 : 1 : 0.3445$, and $\beta = 86° 3'$. The crystals may appear in thin plates resembling selenite, and there may be penetration twins, and P. Groth said that the pseudo-rhombic form of the crystals is due to twinning about the (100)-plane. The cleavage on the (010)-face is perfect. A. Schmidt found that the optical character is negative, and the optical axial angle $2H = 66° 14'$ for red-light, and $2H = 65° 21'$ for yellow-light. The natural, monoclinic, prismatic form of arsenic trioxide was designated *rhombarsenite* by M. Adam, and **claudetite,** by J. D. Dana. It is assumed by A. Schmidt that the discovery of a rhombic modification of arsenic trioxide, and of a monoclinic form of antimony trioxide, will make these two trioxides iso-trimorphous. J. D. Dana called the hypothetical rhombic form of arsenic trioxide *arsenophyllite* isomorphous with valentinite. This term was first employed by A. Breithaupt for a mineral which he considered to be the rhombic form isomorphous with valentinite, but he later said that the statement was based on *eine ganz falsche Annahme.* The facts permit only the statement that arsenic trioxide is dimorphous.

H. Debray [10] prepared the monoclinic form of arsenic trioxide by heating the octahedral crystals or the vitreous form in a sealed glass tube so that the temp. near one end is about 400°, and at the other end, 200°. In a few hours, octahedral crystals collect at the cooler end, the vitreous oxide at the hotter end, and the monoclinic form in the middle. C. Gänge used a similar process. According to H. V. Welch and L. H. Duschak, when the cubic crystals are fused in an evacuated capillary tube, and kept at a temp. between 251° and 300°, star-like masses of crystals of the monoclinic form appear in half an hour, but the transformation proceeds very slowly, requiring days for its completion. The change is very sluggish at 218°. The rate of transformation at this temp. is greatly increased if a trace of water be present. The change from the octahedral to the monoclinic crystals was observed after several hours' heating at 100° in the presence of water, or dil. or conc. sulphuric acid ; but no perceptible change occurred during several months at room temp. Hence, the monoclinic oxide is the stable form at temp. above 100° and possibly even at room temp. There is indeed no evidence to show that the transformation from the cubic to the monoclinic form is not monotropic, *i.e.* irreversible.

H. Debray also found that when the octahedral crystals and a little water are heated in a sealed tube at 250° for some time, both octahedral and monoclinic crystals appear in the cold tube. L. Pasteur, and A. E. Nordenskjöld obtained monoclinic crystals from a boiling sat. soln. of arsenic trioxide in potash-lye ; A. Scheurer-Kestner, from a hot sat. soln. of arsenic trioxide in one of arsenic pentoxide ; O. B. Kühn, from a soln. of silver arsenite in nitric acid : and C. H. Hirzel, by adding ammonia to a boiling sat. soln. of arsenic trioxide in aq. ammonia, and cooling the mixture rapidly—if slowly cooled, the octahedral crystals are formed. F. Wöhler also seems to have obtained what he called *ungewöhnlich* crystals of arsenic trioxide by heating a soln. of the trioxide in aq. ammonia. F. Ulrich observed octahedral crystals of this form of arsenic which were paramorphs after the cubic form. F. Ulrich's, and F. Claudet's observations on the sp. gr. indicate that the monoclinic crystals are slowly transformed into the cubic form. According to F. Wöhler, and F. Claudet, the monoclinic trioxide is converted into the octahedral form when it is sublimed, or when it is crystallized from an aq. soln. The prismatic form of arsenic trioxide was found by F. Claudet in the arsenical pyrites of a mine near San Domingo, Portugal. The mineral also appears to have been formed as a result of fires in mines containing arsenical ores ; and as a furnace product. C. Hintze [11] has indicated a number of these occurrences.

The **vapour density** of arsenic trioxide has been previously discussed. The **specific gravity** of the cubic trioxide as it occurs in nature—arsenolite—ranges from 3·69 to 3·72 ; and for the artificially prepared oxide, N. J. B. G. Guibourt [12] gave 3·695 ; W. Herapath, 3·729 at 17·2° ; E. Filhol, 3·884 ; C. F. Rammelsberg, 3·80 ; L. Troost and P. Hautefeuille, 3·689 ; C. J. B. Karsten, 3·703–3·720 ; and C. Winkler, 3·6461 at 12·5° when weighed under petroleum, and 3·6283 when weighed under water. In the latter case, the results are affected by the slight solubility of the trioxide in water. A. S. Taylor gave 3·529 for the sp. gr. of devitrified arsenic-glass. G. P. Baxter and C. F. Hawkins found for the sp. gr. of cubic arsenic, 3·874 at 0° ; 3·865 at 25° ; and 3·851 at 50°. F. Claudet found the sp. gr. of claudetite to be 3·85 ; P. Groth gave 4·15. For arsenic-glass, A. le Royer and J. B. A. Dumas gave 3·698 at 4° ; C. J. B. Karsten, 3·7026 ; N. J. B. G. Guibourt, 3·7385 ; C. F. Rammelsberg, 4·00 ; L. Troost and P. Hautefeuille, 3·738 ; A. S. Taylor, 3·798 ; and C. Winkler, 3·7165 at 12·5° when weighed under water, and 3·6815 when weighed under petroleum. For E. Anderson and L. G. Story's measurements of the sp. gr. of aq. soln. of arsenic trioxide, *vide infra*; the refractive index of aq. soln. of the trioxide. The **hardness** of arsenolite is 1·5 ; and that of claudetite, 2·5. P. Groth said that claudetite is softer and tougher than gypsum. The glass is very brittle, and, according to C. Winkler, it is as hard as calcite. R. Schaefer studied the **diffusion** of arsenic trioxide dissolved in gelatin—the mixture was also made into a paste with water, and laid on a sheet of gelatin. In the case of arsenic gel, it was found that the amount of arsenic diffused quite regularly as the distance travelled increases, but with the paste there is no apparent diffusion beyond the surface of the gelatin, although this has undoubtedly taken place. R. Schaefer suggested that in the paste simple mols. are present, but in the gel more complicated mols. are present, and these move more slowly, but the total amount of arsenic diffused is greater in the latter case than in the former. H. Fizeau gave 0·00012378 at 40° for the linear coeff. of **thermal expansion** of the cubic crystals. G. P. Baxter and C. F. Hawkins found the coeff. of cubical expansion between 0° and 25° to be 0·00011 ; and between 25° and 50°, 0·00012. H. V. Regnault gave 0·1279 for the **specific heat** of the cubic crystals. A. de la Rive and F. Marcet gave 0·1309 for the crystalline oxide, and 0·1320 for the glassy oxide. A. S. Russell obtained $C_p=28\cdot83$ for the mol. ht. of the octahedral crystals between 3° and 41° ; and R. Schuhmann, $C_p=1\cdot64+0\cdot0015T$. G. Nonhebel and co workers studied the coagulation of the aerosol. According to F. Wöhler, glassy arsenic trioxide melts before **volatilization** begins, while the crystals, as M. Faraday observed, sublime without melting ; if the vap. condenses on a hot enough part of the tube in which the trioxide is volatilized, H. Ludwig found that the oxide may fuse. H. V. Welch and L. H. Duschak gave 251° for the **melting point** of the cubic form of arsenic trioxide, and 313° for that of the monoclinic form; E. R. Rushton and F. Daniels gave respectively 275°, and approximately 315°. J. K. Mitchell found that the trioxide volatilizes more easily than the metal at 218°; and F. Selmi showed that some trioxide volatilizes even at 100°–125°. H. Saito found that with a rising temp., sublimation occurs rapidly at 190° and is completed at 300°. P. Smellie found the **vapour pressure** of the trioxide to be $2\cdot4\times10^{-7}$ at 60°–61°; $2\cdot5\times10^{-5}$ at 81°–86°; $4\cdot6\times10^{-4}$ at 101°–105°; $1\cdot9\times10^{-3}$ at 117°–124°; $2\cdot2\times10^{-3}$ at 119°–126°; and $2\cdot6\times10^{-2}$ mm. at 149°–152°. G. Niederschulte measured the vap. press. of arsenic trioxide below 165°, and K. Stelzner, above that temp.

	129°	153·5°	165°	240·8°	253·1°	268·6°	290·9°	306·8°
p mm.	0·00	0·01	0·027	6·3	12·2	24·4	65·4	100·6

K. Stelzner represented his data by the formula $\log p=482\cdot72051-46645\cdot204132T^{-1}-62\cdot50645\log T$; and H. V. Welch and L. H. Duschak believe that these results refer to the vap. press. of the glassy oxide; and that the following determinations, p mm., apply to the unstable cubic form between 100° and 251°, while above that temp. apply to the glassy form:

	100°	120°	140°	160°	180°	200°	220°	240°	260°	280°	300°
p	$0\cdot0_3266$	0·00180	0·01035	0·0473	0·186	0·653	2·065	5·96	15·7	38·5	89·1

E. R. Rushton and F. Daniels measured the vap. press. of arsenic from about 220° to 520°. The curves are shown in Fig. 16. The curve for liquid arsenic trioxide,

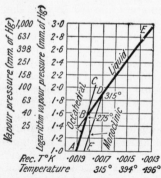

FIG. 16.—Vapour Pressure of Arsenic Trioxide.

upwards of 275°, can be represented by $\log p =2722T^{-1}+6\cdot513$, and that for octahedral arsenic trioxide, by $\log p=-6670T^{-1}+13\cdot728$ for temp. up to 250°. ABC, Fig. 16, is the curve for the octahedral trioxide; and BDE, the curve for liquid arsenic trioxide; the intersection at B, 275°, represents the m.p. of octahedral arsenic trioxide. The line FD represents the estimated vap. press. curve of monoclinic arsenic trioxide, and the point of intersection, D, 315°, represents the m.p. of the monoclinic trioxide. W. M. Mott calculated 500° for the b.p. H. V. Welch and L. H. Duschak found the total and inner **heats of vaporization**—respectively Q cals. and E cals. —increase with rising temp.; the latter so rapidly that the sp. ht. of the solid and undercooled liquid is greater than that of the vapour:

	110°	150°	170°	190°	210°	230°	270°	290°
Q	27,930	27,210	26,710	26,750	26,610	26,656	26,240	26,500
E	27,170	26,370	25,830	25,830	25,650	25,650	25,160	25,380

E. R. Rushton and F. Daniels gave for the heat of vaporizing a gram of the trioxide as liquid, 31·5 cals., as octahedral crystals, 77·1 cals.; and as monoclinic crystals, 71 cals.; for the **heat of fusion** of octahedral trioxide, 45·6 cals.; and monoclinic trioxide, 39 cals.; and for the **heat of transition** of octahedral to monoclinic arsenic trioxide, 6 cals.

J. Thomsen [13] gave for the **heat of formation** $(2As_{cryst}.3O)=As_2O_{3cubic}+156\cdot4$ Cals.; and M. Berthelot gave 148·9 Cals. R. Schuhmann calculated the **free energy**, E, of formation of the cubic trioxide from arsenic and oxygen at 25° to be $-137\cdot3$ Cals., and the heat content, Q, to be $-153\cdot8$ Cals. He also gave for the effect of temp. between 0° and 100° on the free energy change accompanying the formation of the octahedral crystals, $E=-154200-164T\log T+0\cdot00075T^2+65\cdot8T$

cals.; and $Q=-154200-1\cdot64T-0\cdot00075T^2$. P. A. Favre gave for the **heat of transformation** of the glassy trioxide into cubic crystals, 2·70 Cals., and M. Berthelot, 2·40 Cals.; L. Troost and P. Hautefeuille found the heat of transformation of the monoclinic into the glassy form, 1·30 Cals., and M. Berthelot, 1·20 Cals. J. Thomsen found the **heat of solution** of the cubic crystals to be 7·55 Cals. at 18°. L. Bruner and S. Tolloczko hence calculated that the mol. wt. of the trioxide in aq. soln. is represented $\frac{1}{2}As_2O_3.yH_2O$, not $As_2O_3.xH_2O$. J. Thomsen found the **heat of neutralization** of a mol of the trioxide, As_2O_3, to be 73·0 Cals. per mol NaOH; 137·8 Cals. for 2 mols; 150·7 Cals. for 4 mols; and 155·8 Cals. for 6 mols.

According to A. des Cloizeaux,[14] the **index of refraction** of the cubic trioxide for red-light is 1·748, and for yellow-light, F. Klocke found that the sublimed crystals exhibited a double refraction without regular interference figures, although R. Brauns observed the crystals are isotropic without showing any optical anomaly. E. Anderson and L. G. Story found the sp. gr., D, of aq. soln. with w grms. of arsenic trioxide per litre at 25°, and the refractive indices, μ, at 22°, to be :

w	.	1·796	3·212	5·060	7·184	10·13	12·85	14·368
D	.	1·0014	1·0025	1·0039	1·0057	1·0080	1·0102	1·0113
μ	.	1·33309	1·33326	1·3334	1·33376	1·33417	1·33450	1·33469

Each increase of 1° between 21° and 27° caused the refractive index of the soln. to decrease 0·000097. A. des Cloizeaux found the **birefringence** of the monoclinic crystals is strong. J. C. Ghosh and S. C. Bisvas measured the extinction coeff. of aq. soln. of arsenic trioxide; and R. Wright found that while the absorption spectrum of the strong acids is the same as that of the sodium salts, the reverse is the case with weak acids like aq. soln. of arsenic trioxide. It is assumed that a non-ionized molecule capable of ionization exists in a state of stress, and is more capable of absorbing light than a similar free ion, or a molecule incapable of ionization. H. R. Robinson studied the **X-ray spectrum** of arsenic trioxide. R. Whiddington measured the velocity of the electrons liberated by X-rays impinging on arsenic trioxide. H. R. Robinson and A. M. Cassie studied the line spectra of secondary and tertiary radiations from arsenious oxide—using the primary K-rays.

L. Bleekrode showed that the **electrical conductivity** of the cubic trioxide is feeble ; and F. Beijerinck said that both the crystalline forms are non-conductors. Observations on the electrical conductivity of aq. soln. of arsenic trioxide were made by L. Bleekrode, and E. Bouty. P. Walden measured the mol. conductivity of aq. soln. of sodium meta- and ortho-arsenites ($q.v.$) ; and J. von Zawidzky gave for the mol. conductivity μ of a soln. of a mol of H_3AsO_4 in v litres of water at 25°:

	16	**32**	**64**	**128**	**256**	**512**	**1024**
μ .	0·22	0·30	0·40	0·60	0·96	1·45	2·11
$K \times 10^9$	22	21	19	21	(27)	(30)	(32)

The acid **ionization constant**, K, has an average value of 21×10^{-9}—*vide infra*. E. W. Washburn found the basic ionization constant for $[AsO'_2][OH']/[H_3AsO_3]$ $=0\cdot15 \times 10^{-14}$ in a soln. with an ion conc. of 0·1 eq. per litre at 25°. J. K. Wood also measured the electrical conductivity of these soln., and he found for metarsenious acid the ionization constant $K=16\cdot9 \times 10^{-10}$ for 0·1385N-acid ; $20\cdot1 \times 10^{-10}$ for 0·0542N-acid ; $23\cdot9 \times 10^{-10}$ for 0·086N-acid ; and $38\cdot6 \times 10^{-10}$ for 0·195N-acid. The mean value is $26\cdot5 \times 10^{-10}$, which is smaller than J. von Zawidzky's value. N. R. Dhar calculated values for the ionization constants from the solubility data. E. Anderson and L. G. Story found the **hydrogen-ion** conc. of arsenious acid to be $p^H=6\cdot60$, or $[H']=0\cdot25 \times 10^{-6}$, using phenol-red, or bromothymol-blue as indicators—the hydrogen electrode process was unsatisfactory. E. Blanc found that when the neutralization of a soln. of 0·0104N-arsenious acid with 0·588N-NaOH has proceeded to NaH_2AsO_3, $C_H=2 \times 10^{-10}$, and $C_{OH}=4\cdot1 \times 10^{-5}$. G. Bischof, and J. F. Simon found that an aq. soln. of arsenic trioxide is electrolyzed more slowly than one of the pentoxide ; oxygen is given off at the anode, and arsenic and arsine appear at the cathode. B. Neumann said that a part of the arsenic trioxide is oxidized to the pentoxide at the anode. L. Ramberg compared the nature of the cathode surface with different metals on the reduction of arsenic acid to arsine. The nature of the surface has less influence in the case of arsenic trioxide than is the case with arsenic acid (q.v.). When the metals are arranged in the order of their reducing power, a different series is obtained with arsenious and arsenic acids. A mercury cathode is unsuited for the reduction of considerable quantities of arsenic trioxide since the arsenic is not hydrogenated as rapidly as it is formed, and a solid phase of arsenic and arsenic amalgam is formed which is but slowly transformed into arsine. N. Isgarischeff and E. Koldaewa found that arsenic trioxide reduced the potential of the hydrogen electrode which rises to its normal value in a few hours ; but the oxygen electrode is " poisoned " and does not return to its normal value. It is supposed that the effects are not due to depolarization, but rather to a combination of platinum and the arsenic forming compounds with a lower potential. The compound is unstable in the acidic soln., and the arsenic is carried off in a few hours by the stream of hydrogen. The subject was discussed by A. H. W. Aten, P. Bruin and W. de Lange. For the electrolytic oxidation of arsenic trioxide. vide infra, calcium arsenate. R. Schuhmann found the e.m.f. of the cell As | As$_2$O$_3$ and HClO$_4$ | 0·22–0·94N-H at 25° and 45° was respectively −0·2340 volt and −0·2250 volt. R. J. Clark estimated the electrostatic moment of the molecule to be rather greater than 10^{-18} electrostatic unit.

Chemical reactions of arsenic trioxide.—Arsenic trioxide is reduced by **hydrogen** at a temp. below redness ; possibly the reduction occurs only with the vap. of the trioxide. P. Hautefeuille [15] said that if arsenic trioxide be heated in a sealed tube filled with hydrogen, it passes into the pentoxide, but this statement needs verification. It is, however, in agreement with J. F. Simon's observation that the action of heat on many arsenites involves a kind of autoxidation : 5As$_2$O$_3$=3As$_2$O$_5$+4As. Nascent hydrogen reduces arsenic trioxide in aq. soln., forming arsine (q.v.). W. Thomson found the velocity of the electrolytic reduction followed the unimolecular law $dx/dt=k(a-x)$, where a denotes the original conc. of the soln. ; x, the conc. at the time t ; and k, the velocity constant. He tried to correlate the overvoltage with different metals with the power of the metal cathode to reduce arsenic trioxide, but concluded that this power is a peculiarity of the individual metal, and is independent of its overvoltage. J. H. Gladstone and A. Tribe found that an aq. soln. of arsenic trioxide is reduced to arsenic by the occluded hydrogen in palladium, and the occluded hydrogen in platinum at 100° ; and to arsine, by the copper-zinc couple. L. Vallery examined the effect of traces of arsine in hydrogen on the catalytic activity of palladinized asbestos in burning the hydrogen. According to M. Berthelot, **oxygen** does not oxidize the trioxide either at ordinary temp. or at 100° ; but T. E. Thorpe found that the trioxide is thermoluminescent in oxygen. According to C. Matignon and J. A. Lecanu, it should be possible directly to oxidize arsenic trioxide to the pentoxide, and experiments were carried out at temp. between 400° and 450°, the press. of the oxygen being 130, 127, and 138 atm. The production of the pentoxide was proved, but the oxidation of the arsenic trioxide was not complete : As$_2$O$_3$+O$_2$=As$_2$O$_5$+62·2 Cals. A conc. soln. of the trioxide in sodium hydroxide at 80° and with oxygen at 50 atm. press. suffered 10·9 per cent. oxidation in 5 hrs. When an aq. soln. of arsenic trioxide is treated with an excess of sodium carbonate, it is readily oxidized by the oxygen of the air. The reaction was examined by H. Croft, H. Ludwig, J. M'Donnell, and A. Vogel. C. C. Palit and N. R. Dhar observed that copper, lead, manganese, cobalt, and nickel nitrates, cuprous, mercuric, uranium and ferric chlorides, and ferrous sulphate act as catalytic agents. F. Mohr said that a soln. containing sodium dihydroarsenite and hydrocarbonate is not oxidized when warmed in air, but F. Reinthaler said that a slow oxidation does occur ; both observers, however, agree that at ordinary temp. no oxidation occurs after 4 months' exposure to air. J. B. Tingle said that arsenic trioxide, dissolved in a mixture of 95 per cent. alcohol and 60 per cent. of water, is oxidized to arsenic pentoxide when boiled for 26 hrs., but P. Edgerton could not verify this statement. I. M. Kolthoff found that neutral or weakly acidic soln. of arsenic trioxide are stable, and may be kept indefinitely without change, but in alkaline soln., the trioxide is oxidized to the pentoxide. According to G. Gire, the absorption of oxygen by a soln. of arsenic trioxide and ferrous sulphate in the presence of sodium hydroxide varies with the amount of alkali present. The vol. of oxygen absorbed at first diminishes as the amount of alkali increases, reaching a minimum when the alkali is slightly in excess of that required to form the metarsenite. It then increases to a constant maximum, when the amount of alkali present is slightly in excess of that required to form the pyroarsenite. If the amount of alkali present is kept constant, the oxygen absorbed is proportional to the amount of iron present, but is always in excess of that required to oxidize the ferrous salt to the ferric state. F. Kessler found that when sodium arsenite is undergoing oxidation by chromic acid, it is simultaneously oxidized by air ; F. Mohr observed a similar phenomenon in the presence of an oxidizing soln. of sodium sulphite. The reaction was studied by W. P. Jorissen. A. K. Goard and E. K. Rideal measured the oxidation potential of soln. of arsenic tri- and penta-oxides, and found for soln. containing different molar percentages of ter- and quinquevalent arsenic: 97·5 As'''+2·5 As'', 0·2075 volt., and 2·5 As'''+97·5 As'', 0·1536 volt. The oxidizing powers of the soln. can be inferred from these values, and the results applied to the oxidation of arsenite (acceptor) with a cerous salt (acceptor) as catalyst. W. D. Bancroft and H. B. Weiser obtained the familiar arsenic mirror when a cold surface is placed in a flame to which a little arsenic trioxide has been added. N. N. Mittra and N. R. Dhar found that the reaction with mercuric chloride and sodium sulphite, or phosphite or formic acid, as primary reaction, is accelerated by the simultaneous secondary reaction of mercuric chloride with arsenious acid or sodium arsenite. C. F. Schönbein found that ozone and **hydrogen dioxide** oxidize the trioxide to the pentoxide ; and C. F. Schönbein, P. Thénard, J. L. Soret, and A. Ladenburg found that **ozone** incompletely oxidizes an alkaline soln. of arsenic trioxide.

C. Winkler [16] was unable to prepare a hydrated form of arsenic trioxide ; the turbidity produced when arsenic-glass is exposed to moist air is attended by the absorption of up to 0·33 per cent. moisture which cannot be completely expelled in a desiccator with phosphorus pentoxide, or by heating at 110°. Cubic arsenic trioxide dissolves slowly in cold **water,** the glassy form dissolves more quickly ; both forms dissolve more rapidly in boiling water. For the effect of moisture in the transformation of the glassy trioxide into octahedral crystals, *vide supra.* The aq. soln. of arsenic trioxide is colourless, and tastes feebly acid. A. Bussy found that aq. soln. of the octahedral crystals, and of the glassy oxide redden litmus very feebly ; while G. Favrel said that the aq. soln. has no action on cochineal-red ; and A. L. Cohn, that arsenious acid is neutral towards lacmoid ; it behaves like a monobasic acid towards methyl orange ; and shows only about 90 per cent. of combined sodium or potassium when the acid is treated with standard alkali-lye with phenolphthalein as an indicator. The action of indicators was examined by R. T. Thomson, G. Favrel, and F. A. Flückiger. According to the first-named, arsenious acid behaves like a monobasic acid when titrated with soda-lye, and litmus, methyl orange, rosolic acid, and phenacetolin as indicators.

Numerous observations have been reported on the solubility of arsenic trioxide in water—*e.g.* E. Bacaloglo, A. Baumé, T. Bergman, G. Brandt, L. A. Buchner, C. F. Bucholz, J. Dalton, J. C. Delamétherie, N. W. Fischer, N. J. B. G. Guibourt, J. F. Hagen, J. H. G. Justi, C. F. S. Hahnemann, M. H. Klaproth, W. Nasse, P. T. Navier, P. von Musschenbroek, K. W. Pörner, H. Rose, J. R. Spielmann, A. S. Taylor, A. Vogel, and C. F. Wenzel. The reported values here range from N. W. Fischer's 16·6 parts of the trioxide per 100 parts of water to W. Nasse's 0·312 part of the trioxide at ordinary temp. The extraordinary diversity of the early observations is attributed by C. Winkler to the difference in the solubility of the cubic and glassy forms ; to the length of time necessary to obtain a sat. soln. with these two modifications ; and to the tendency of the glassy form to pass into the octahedral crystals. He also added that while the glassy form is easily wetted with water, the crystalline oxide is not easily moistened. According to N. J. B. G. Guibourt, the glassy form is less soluble in water than the cubic form ; on the contrary, A. S. Taylor, C. Winkler, and A. Bussy attribute the greater solubility to the glassy form. A. Bussy said that when the aq. soln. is boiled for a long time, the cubic form is converted into the glassy variety and acquires the solubility of the latter, viz., 11 parts of the trioxide in 100 parts of boiling water ; but at low temp., the glassy form is converted into the cubic form and hence the soln. becomes more dil. on standing, retaining for equilibrium only the proportion of trioxide corresponding with the cubic form. Comminution hastens the speed of dissolution of the cubic form without increasing the amount dissolved, but it lowers the speed of dissolution of the glassy form because of its conversion into the cubic form by the friction or contact with water. According to C. Winkler, 100 parts of water at ordinary temp. dissolve the following proportion of the cubic, A, and glassy, B, forms of arsenic trioxide in the stated time (in hours) :

Hrs.	1	3	6	12	24	48	96	168	504	19710
A .	0·023	0·088	0·353	0·364	0·956	1·627	1·814	1·673	1·776	1·712
B .	1·589	2·356	3·666	3·361	3·306	2·629	2·429	1·763	1·713	1·707

When the glassy form was dissolving, octahedral crystals were deposited on the sides of the vessel after 12 hrs., and these continued to increase ; there was no such deposit in the case of the glassy form. The maximum values in the above table are taken to represent the solubilities of the two forms of arsenic trioxide at ordinary temp., namely, 1·70 parts of the cubic form and 3·7 parts of the glassy form at ordinary temp. He also found that 100 parts of boiling water dissolve 10·140 parts of the cubic crystals in 3 hrs., and 10·176 parts in 12 hrs., and 11·46 parts of the glassy oxide in 3 hrs., and 11·86 parts in 12 hrs. The following results, expressed in grams of trioxide per 100 c.c. of sat. soln., for the cubic modification were found by L. Bruner and S. Tolloczko : 1·201 at 2° ; 1·657 at 15° ; 2·038 at 25° ; 2·930 at 39·8° ; and 6·000 at 100°. K. Chodounsky gave 0·8507 grm. per 100 c.c. for the solubility of glassy arsenic trioxide in water at 18·5°. For the octahedral crystals, J. K. Wood gave 1·495 to 1·55 grm. per 100 c.c. at 15° ; F. A. H. Schreinemakers and W. C. de Baat, 2·26 per cent. at 30° ; and F. Claudet, 100 parts of water at ordinary temp. dissolve 1·75 parts of the monoclinic form, and at 100°, 2·75 parts. E. Anderson and L. G. Story found the following amounts, S, of the octahedral trioxide in grams were dissolved by 100 grms. of water :

	0°	15°	25°	39·8°	48·2°	62°	75°	98·5°
S .	1·21	1·66	2·05	2·93	3·43	4·45	5·62	8·18

They represented the results at $\theta°$ by $S=1·21+0·021\theta+0·000505\theta^2$.

According to K. Drucker, hydrogen ions—i.e. acidic soln.—accelerate the rate of dissolution of arsenic trioxide ; and the hydroxyl ion acts more strongly than the hydrogen ion. In both cases, the action is proportional to the sq. root of the conc. of the respective ions. Excepting with soln. approaching saturation, the rate of dissolution is not dependent on the conc. of the arsenic trioxide in soln., but only on that of the catalyzing acid or alkali. Non-ionized sodium acetate accelerates the action, while amyl alcohol retards the speed. E. Brunner said that the rate of dissolution is governed both by the rate of diffusion ; by the rate of hydration of the trioxide in soln. ; by the conc. of the dissolved trioxide, and by the conc. of the hydrogen or hydroxyl ions ; but it is independent of the speed of agitation of the liquid. While C. S. Hudson did not consider the dissolution of arsenic trioxide as a chemical process, E. Brunner showed that some hydration probably takes place. P. Walden inferred from their observations on the electrical conductivity of the sodium arsenites (q.v.), that tribasic orthoarsenious acid, H_3AsO_3, does not exist, and that in soln., arsenious acid behaves like *dimetarsenious acid*, $(HO)OAs.AsO(OH)$. J. von Zawidzky, H. Biltz, and F. M. Raoult showed that the mol. wt. of arsenic trioxide in aq. soln. is in agreement with the assumption that the mol. of arsenious acid contains one atom of arsenic. H. Remy discussed the structure of arsenious acid. The acid is a poor conductor, and is only slightly ionized ; the conductivity of sodium dihydroarsenite, NaH_2AsO_3, determined in the presence of arsenious acid to prevent hydrolysis, resembles that of a monobasic acid. The increased conductivity at high dilutions is attributed to hydrolysis, and not to further ionization of the H_2AsO_3-ion. This is taken to be in agreement with J. Thomsen's observation that 137·8 Cals. are liberated when arsenic trioxide is neutralized with 2 mols of sodium hydroxide, and only 12·9 Cals. more when another 2 mols of sodium hydroxide are added. E. Cornec's observations on the effect of alkalies on the f.p. of soln. of arsenic trioxide, A. Miolati and E. Masceti's observations on the electrical conductivity, W. Böttger's on the e.m.f., and J. Thomsen's, on the heats of neutralization agree that in aq. soln. arsenic trioxide behaves like a feeble mono-basic acid : arsenious acid, $HO(H_2AsO_2)$, is also an extremely feeble base, but the basic properties were too small for accurate measurement. J. K. Wood, however, found the ionization constant of arsenious hydroxide as a base to be of the order 10^{-14} ; and for arsenious acid, $6·3\times10^{-11}$—*vide supra*. He symbolized the reaction with water : $HO'+As(OH)_2 \rightleftharpoons As(OH)_3 \rightleftharpoons AsO(OH)_2'+H^{\cdot}$. W. A. Roth and O. Schwartz found that in the most dil. soln. which can be cryoscopically examined the arsenic trioxide is weakly associated, and almost completely converted into $HAsO_2$, or H_3AsO_3.

Some derivatives of ortho- (more accurately meso-) arsenic acid, $AsO(OH)_3$, have been prepared. Thus by replacing one hydroxyl group by a univalent hydrocarbon radicle, R, the so-called **arsonic acid**, $RAsO(OH)_2$, is obtained ; and by replacing two hydroxyl radicles in a similar way, the **arsinic acids**, $R_2AsO.OH$, result graphically :

$$O=As{<}^{OH}_{OH}\ ^{OH} \qquad O=As{<}^{OH}_{R}\ ^{OH} \qquad O=As{<}^{OH}_{R}\ ^{R}$$

Ortho-arsenic acid.   Arsonic acid.   Arsinic acid.

The first member of the arsinic acids has the methyl radicle, CH_3, and is hence called **methylarsinic acid**, $(CH_3)_2AsO.OH$. The derivatives of the univalent radicle, $(CH_3)_2As$—discovered by R. Bunsen, 1837–1843—were called cacodyl compounds, by J. J. Berzelius from κακώδος (*cacodos*, stinking), in allusion to their disgusting odour. Hence, methylarsinic acid is called cacodylic acid, and the series of arsinic acids are also called the *cacodylic acids*. A series of over thirty arsonic acids has been prepared, all dibasic, and over a dozen monobasic arsinic acids have been prepared by organic chemists. There is evidence of a polymerization of methyl-arsonic acid to a tribasic acid in the presence of an excess of a soln. of potassium hydroxide over $\frac{1}{48}$th normality. The quinquevalency of the arsenic is evidenced by their indifference towards nitric acid and bromine water, for all known soluble tervalent arsenic compounds reduce the former and decolorize the latter. This subject is discussed in the works on the organic derivatives of arsenic cited below.

According to H. Moissan,[17] **fluorine** reacts violently with arsenic trioxide, forming a colourless ˌquid containing arsenic trifluoride, and oxyfluoride ; he also found that **hydrogen fluoride** reacts with incandescence. When distilled with a mixture of sulphuric acid and calcium fluoride, arsenic trifluoride is formed (*q.v.*). R. Weber showed that when heated at a suitable temp., **chlorine** forms arsenic trichloride and pentoxide, and C. L. Bloxam represented the reaction : $11As_2O_3+6Cl_2=4AsCl_3+3(As_4O_6.As_2O_5)$. L. Cambi represented the reaction with dil. soln. : $AsCl_3+Cl_2+(2·5+nH_2O) \rightleftharpoons 0·5As_2O_5.nH_2O+5HCl$; with conc. soln., $0·5As_2O_3+3HCl \rightleftharpoons AsCl_3+1·5H_2O$. L. Cambi found that when chlorine is passed into an aq. suspension of 70–80 per cent. of arsenic trioxide, with agitation, at

60°–70°, about 70 per cent. of arsenic trioxide is changed to the pentoxide, and the remainder to trichloride. E. Anderson and L. G. Story found the mol. wt. of arsenic trioxide in aq. soln. by the b.p. method is 92·5 ; and 99·17 by the f.p. process. This seems to indicate that at 0° the trioxide is present in the hydrated form— probably **metarsenious acid,** $HAsO_2$. A soln. of arsenic trioxide in hydrochloric acid is completely oxidized by chlorine, and in the presence of alkali hydroxide, an arsenate is formed. The action of **bromine** is analogous to that of chlorine. W. Manchot and F. Oberhauser found that the oxidation of arsenic trioxide by bromine, and the reduction of sodium hydroarsenate by hydrobromic acid can be represented by the equation $As_2O_5+4HBr\rightleftharpoons As_2O_3+4Br+2H_2O$. If the conc. of the hydrobromic acid is less than 24 per cent., the reaction proceeds entirely from right to left ; under these conditions, arsenious acid may be accurately titrated with bromine, the end-point of the titration being unaffected by the exact conc. of hydrochloric acid. The reverse reaction, however, may take place if the conc. of hydrochloric acid exceeds 24 per cent. ; the equilibrium conditions depend on the conc. of arsenate, bromide, and hydrochloric acid. A. W. Francis also studied the speed of oxidation of sodium arsenite by bromine-water. J. Guinchant said that in the presence of **hydrochloric acid,** some arsenic trioxide is converted into arsenic trichloride—*vide supra*, the crystalloluminescence of the trioxide—and H. Davy said that when distilled with a mixture of sulphuric and hydrochloric acids, and L. Gmelin, with a mixture of sodium chloride and sulphuric acid, arsenic trichloride is formed. According to B. J. Smart and J. T. Philpot, when soln. of arsenic trioxide in hydrochloric acid are distilled, those which contain the greatest conc. of hydrochloric acid give off the arsenic most rapidly. When the hydrochloric acid is present to the extent of about 190 grms. per litre or more, the conc. of arsenic in the soln. remaining undistilled rapidly falls as the soln. is fractionated. With soln. containing less than 180 grms. of hydrochloric acid per litre, the conc. of arsenic in the soln. remaining undistilled rises, although some of the arsenic passes over, the ratio between acid and arsenic remaining practically constant until the soln. contains about 185 grms. of hydrochloric acid per litre. This point corresponds approximately with a hydrate of the formula $HCl.10H_2O$. According to E. Oeman, arsenic trichloride accumulates in the distillate although its b.p., 130·2°, exceeds the maximum b.p. of aq. hydrochloric acid, 110°. Hydrochloric acid may be freed from arsenic trichloride by the passage of hydrogen chloride. Vaporization occurs only at the surface of the liquid which becomes relatively poorer in hydrochloric acid, and a greater quantity of distillate is required to remove the arsenic trichloride. When the acid becomes more conc. the proportion of arsenic volatilized increases rapidly. J. T. D. Hinds also studied this reaction. The effect of hydrochloric acid is to raise the solubility of arsenic trioxide ; thus, K. Chodounsky, and C. Schultz-Sellac found that arsenic trioxide is more soluble in hydrochloric acid than in water, and that the glassy form dissolves more rapidly than the octahedral crystals. K. Chodounsky found that while 100 c.c. of water dissolve 0·8507 grm. of glassy arsenic trioxide at 18·5°, if the water contained 1·3196 grms. of HCl, 1·1513 grms. of the trioxide are dissolved, and if 6·09 grms. of HCl are present, 1·2724 grms. of the trioxide are dissolved. Expressing the solubility, S, of arsenic trioxide in grams per 100 c.c of soln., J. K. Wood found with hydrochloric acid of different conc. at 15° :

HCl .	0	0·46N-	0·98N-	2·03N-	3·13N-	3·81N-	5·32N-	6·50N-	7·85N-	9·17N-
S .	1·55	1·52	1·41	1·17	1·11	1·13	2·20	5·11	12·28	18·16

As the conc. of the acid increases, the solubility of the trioxide decreases, and a minimum is reached when the conc. of the acid is about 3·2N-HCl ; beyond this point an increase in the conc. of the solvent leads to a corresponding increase in solubility. This agrees with K. Drucker's observation that the presence of hydrogen ions augments the solubility of the trioxide. The decreased solubility is assumed to show that in aq. soln. the arsenic trioxide is acting as an acid so that in the presence of another acid, the H$^\cdot$-ion conc. of the arsenious acid is diminished ; on the other hand, when arsenic trioxide acts as a base, the solubility is augmented by the acid.

C. Brame found that whilst **iodine** vapour does not act on the octahedral crystals of arsenic trioxide, the vitreous form is coloured brown. J. R. Roebuck studied the oxidizing action of iodine on arsenic trioxide in alkaline soln., and he represented the reaction : $AsO_3'''+I'_3+H_2O \rightleftharpoons AsO_4'''+3I'+2H^\cdot$. The velocity of the direct reaction was directly proportional to the first power of the conc. of the arsenious acid and the I$'_3$-ion ; and inversely proportional both to the square of the conc. of the iodine-ions and to the conc. of the hydriodic or sulphuric acid—when this conc. is not too high. The velocity of the reverse reaction was found to be proportional to the first power of the conc. of the arsenic acid, the iodine-ion, and the acid-ion provided the conc. of the acid is sufficiently low, but if the acid be more conc., the velocity is proportional to higher powers of the iodine-ion and acid conc. values as high as 2·4 and 3·7 being obtained. He explained his results by assuming that the reverse reaction proceeds in two stages : $H^\cdot+I'+H_3AsO_4=H_3AsO_4.HI$; and $H_3AsO_4.HI=HIO+H_3AsO_3$. He found the equilibrium constant $[AsO_3'''][I_3']$ $=K[AsO_4][I']^3[H^\cdot]^2$ to be 1·5×10^5 ; and the temp. coeff. between 0° and 10° is 1·41. E. W. Washburn and E. K. Strachan showed that the equilibrium $H_3AsO_3+I'_3+H_2O \rightleftharpoons H_3AsO_4+2H^\cdot+3I'$ obeys the mass law over a fairly wide range of conc., and that $[H_3AsO_4][H^\cdot]^2[I]^3=K[H_3AsO_3][I_3]$, where $K=0.55$. The effect of temp. is represented by $\log_{10} K=-1.3495+0.003720$. The heat of the reaction between arsenious acid and iodine is 1360 cals., and the free energy $RT \log_e K=5690×5.42T$ joules in an aq. soln. with a constant ion conc. of 0·1 eq. per litre. The reaction was also studied by W. C. Bray, K. P. Bjergaard, and P. Fleury. I. M. Kolthoff examined the reaction $As_2O_3+2I_2+2H_2O \rightleftharpoons As_2O_5+4HI$ with reference to the limits of the acid conc., within which a definite end-point is obtained. He found that in titrating 0·1N-As$_2$O$_3$ and 0·01N-As$_2$O$_3$ soln. with iodine, the final acidity must be between 10^{-11} and 10^{-15} mol. hydrogen-ion per litre ; and in titrating 0·1N-, or 0·01N-iodine soln. with soln. of arsenious acid, the initial limits are 10$^{-9.0}$ and 10$^{-5.5}$, and the final limits 10^{-8} and 10^{-5}. D. A. MacInnes discussed the electrometric titration of arsenic trioxide with iodine soln. F. C. Bowman inquired whether the oxidation of arsenic trioxide in soln. containing **bromic acid** and hydriodic acid is effected by the hydriodic acid, or by the iodine which is the end-product of the oxidation of the hydriodic acid. He found that the rate of reduction of bromic acid by hydriodic acid is not affected by the presence of arsenious acid except in so far as the oxidation of the latter affects the conc. of acid and iodide in the soln. The arsenious acid oxidized corresponds with the iodine liberated during the reaction, and is very much smaller than the amount which would be oxidized if the oxidation were affected by hypobromous and bromous acids formed as intermediate products. The reduction of bromic acid by hydriodic acid does not therefore " induce " the oxidation of arsenious acid. I. N. Schiloff suggested that the oxidation of arsenious acid by bromic acid is too slow for measurement unless in the presence of sulphurous acid. J. S. Chodkowsky showed that at 40° in the presence of an excess of hydrogen-ions, the reaction proceeds spontaneously and at a measurable rate. The reaction is autocatalytic, and of the second order $dx/dt=kax(1-x)$, where the velocity constant $k=9.7$ at 30·7°, and in the presence of 0·1M-H$_2$SO$_4$. The arsenious acid does not appear to exert any influence on the reaction and merely acts as an inductor of the reaction between bromic and hydrobromic acid. The initial production of hydrobromic acid must, however, be due to the interaction of arsenious acid with bromic acid. The action of sulphuric acid is proportional to the square of the conc. of hydrogen-ions ; the addition of neutral sulphates which reduce this conc. retards the reaction. The addition of hydrogen bromide causes the reaction to proceed in accordance with $dx/dt=ka(b-x)(1-x)$, where b is the conc. of the hydrobromic acid ; k is the same as before. Hydriodic acid acts like hydrobromic acid, but the effect is greater ; and hydrochloric acid acts more vigorously than sulphuric acid on account of the simultaneous effect of both hydrogen and chlorine ions. The relative accelerating effects of potassium chloride, bromide, and iodide are as $1:15:3000$. Arsenic acid acts as a positive catalyst, but its effect is 9 times weaker than sulphuric acid. The thermal coeff. of the reaction is $2\cdot14$. According to R. P. Sanyal and N. R. Dhar, the period of induction between **iodic acid** and a soln. of arsenic trioxide is curtailed by (1) excess of iodic acid, (2) increase in the conc. of the reactants, (3) addition of a trace of arsenic acid, (4) addition of many mineral acids, and (5) exposure to sunlight ; it is prolonged by addition of mercuric chloride or by violent shaking. The fraction of the iodine liberated increases with the arsenious acid conc. and passes through a maximum. The iodine appears on the surface of the soln. even if the latter is covered with benzene or hydrogen ; occasionally it appears at a nucleus on the glass. H. Kubina showed that the reduction of **chlorates** by arsenic trioxide is a coupled reaction being independent of the conc. of the arsenious acid— there is a slow reduction of the chlorate by the halide followed by the rapid oxidation of the arsenite. The mechanism of the reaction is considered to involve : (a) A measurable reaction : $ClO'_3+Cl'+2H\rightarrow H_2ClO_3+Cl$, followed by the rapid reactions, (b) $H_2ClO_3+4Cl'+4H^{\cdot}\rightarrow5Cl+3H_2O$, and $3Cl_2+3AsO_3'''+3H_2O\rightarrow3AsO_4'''+6Cl'+6H^{\cdot}$. The initial velocity of interaction of chloric acid and arsenite does not increase rapidly ; catalytic acceleration by chloride-ion is not observed, owing to the high initial conc. of this ion. Were the latter present, initially, in small quantities, such catalytic accelerative influence should be in evidence. On this supposition, the velocity of chlorate reduction by arsenite would be expressed by the equation : $dx/dt=[K_1+K_2(S)x(Cl')](ClO'_3)$. The reduction of **iodates** is also an induced reaction in which there is an initial acceleration owing to the catalytic effect of the chloride ion. The mechanism is assumed to involve (a) A measurable reaction : $IO'_3+2I'+H^{\cdot}\rightarrow HIO+2IO'$, followed by the rapid reactions (b) $2IO+2AsO_3'''\rightarrow2AsO_4'''+2I'$, and $HIO+AsO_3'''\rightarrow AsO_4'''+H+I'$, giving the velocity equation : $dx/dt=[K_1+K_2(I')_2](IO_3)(H^{\cdot})$. E. Abel and A. Fürth studied the reduction of **periodates** to iodates by arsenites, and found the reaction to be bimolecular. The speed of the reaction is independent of the conc. of acids between $1\cdot3\times10^{-3}$ and $3\cdot4\times10^{-7}[H^{\cdot}]$.

According to J. J. Berzelius,[18] when a mixture of arsenic trioxide and **sulphur** is heated, arsenic disulphide is formed ; and L. F. Nilson represented the reaction : $2As_2O_3+7S=2As_2S_2+3SO_2$; with an excess of sulphur, the reaction was symbolized : $2As_2O_3+9S=2As_2S_3+3SO_2$, but W. Marckwald and A. Foizik showed that some sulphur trioxide is at the same time probably formed. G. Vortmann and C. Padberg found that an acid soln. of arsenic trioxide does not react with sulphur. The action of **hydrogen sulphide** on acidified soln. of arsenic trioxide has been studied by J. F. Lassaigne, H. Reinsch, R. Brandes, E. Becker, J. Lefort and P Thibault, etc.—*vide supra*, reactions of arsenic. Aq. soln. of arsenites give a yellow coloration with hydrogen sulphide, and a yellow precipitate if an acid be added. The action of metal sulphides was discussed by E. Schürmann. H. Prinz, and G. Oddo and E. Serra found that in a sealed tube at 120° arsenic trioxide and **sulphur monochloride** react : $2As_2O_3+6S_2Cl_2=4AsCl_3+3SO_2+9S$. K. Chodounsky found that the solubility of arsenic trioxide in dil. **sulphuric acid** depends on the conc. of the acid and is not so great as in hydrochloric acid ; it is of the order $0\cdot5422-0\cdot7203$ at $18\cdot5°$, and, nearly twice this value at 80°. C. Schultz-Sellac found that the trioxide is readily soluble in fuming sulphuric acid, forming a sulphate (q.v.). F. Schwers found that when air is bubbled through sulphuric acid containing $0\cdot001-0\cdot015$ per cent. of arsenic trioxide, small but appreciable quantities of arsenic are carried forward, in amounts proportional to the conc. of the trioxide dissolved in the acid. P. Smellie found the vap. press. of the trioxide in sulphuric acid at 60°–64° to be $2\cdot7\times10^{-7}$ to $9\cdot0\times10^{-7}$ mm. According to F. Faktor, when the trioxide is fused with **sodium thiosulphate** a mixture of arsenic di- and trisulphides is formed. G. Vortmann found the trisulphide is precipitated when aq. soln. of arsenic trioxide, or acidified soln. of the arsenites, are treated with sodium thiosulphate. R. F. Weinland and A. Gutmann represent the reaction with normal arsenites : $Na_3AsO_3+Na_2S_2O_3=Na_3AsO_3S+Na_2SO_3$; with hydroarsenites : $Na_2HAsO_3+Na_2S_2O_3=Na_3AsO_3S+NaHSO_3$; and with dihydro-arsenites, the reaction is more complex—thioxides are formed (q.v.). The reaction was also examined by J. von Szilagyi, and J. E. Mackenzie and H. Marshall. G. S. Forbes and co-workers found that the precipitation of arsenic trisulphide is preceded by a well-defined period of induction when a soln. containing sodium thiosulphate and an arsenite is acidified with acetic acid—thus furnishing a so-called *clock-reaction* analogous with the reduction of an iodate by sulphurous acid (2. 19, 12). The duration of the period of induction is inversely proportional to the conc. of the thiosulphate, but independent of the conc. of the arsenite or acetic acid. Hydrochloric acid prolongs the period of induction. O. Brunck observed that brown arsenic is precipitated by **sodium hyposulphite** from an aq. soln. of arsenic trioxide. A. Gutmann said that **sodium dithionate** is not changed in soln. of sodium arsenite ; **sodium trithionate** reacts : $Na_2S_3O_6+2Na_3AsO_3+2NaOH=2Na_2SO_3+Na_3AsO_3S+Na_3AsO_4+H_2O$; and **sodium tetrathionate** reacts : $Na_2S_4O_6+3Na_3AsO_3+2NaOH=2Na_2SO_3 +2Na_3AsO_3S+Na_3AsO_4+H_2O$. B. Grützner represented the reaction with **potassium persulphate** : $As_2O_3+2H_2O+2K_2S_2O_8=As_2O_5+2K_2SO_4+2H_2SO_4$, and G. Newbery utilized the reaction for oxidizing the combined arsenic in organic substances to arsenic acid.

I. A. Bachman [19] observed no evidence of the formation of arsenic nitride when the trioxide is heated in **ammonia** gas—*vide infra*, ammonium arsenites. G. Gore, and E. C. Franklin and C. A. Kraus found that liquid ammonia does not dissolve arsenic trioxide. V. de Luynes observed that with **ammonium chloride**, much ammonia is evolved and some arsenic trichloride is formed. L. Möser and W. Eidmann found that **boron nitride** reduces arsenic trioxide to the metal ; and F. D. Chattaway and H. P. Stevens represented the reaction with **nitrogen iodide**: $3As_2O_3+2N_2H_3I_3+6H_2O=3As_2O_5+6HI+4NH_3$. The oxidation of arsenious acid by **nitric oxide** (q.v.) was studied by A. Gutmann. A. Klemenc regarded the reaction as termolecular : $H_3AsO_3+2NO=H_3AsO_4+N_2O$. The speed of the reaction increases with increasing concentration of the alkali hydroxide. T. L. Bailey found that arsenious acid is oxidized by **nitrous acid** in the presence of sulphuric acid ; the maximum rate occurs when the acid has a sp. gr. 1·39 to 1·47. Arsenic trioxide is oxidized to the pentoxide by **nitric acid** ; and, as shown by A. Geuther, G. Lunge, etc., with the conc. acid, nitrogen oxides are formed (q.v.). P. Askenasy and co-workers found that arsenic trioxide is oxidized to arsenic acid by nitric acid over 50 per cent. conc., but under an oxygen press. of 20 atm., the nitrous acid so formed is regenerated, and the nitric acid acts merely as a catalyst. A. Klemenc and F. Pollak showed that mercuric salts inhibit the oxidation of arsenic trioxide by nitric acid. The effect is dependent on the conc. At a conc. of 7×10^{-6} mol per litre, the oxidation is prevented ; with a conc. between $7·7 \times 10^{-8}$ and $7·7 \times 10^{-9}$ the effect passes through zero ; and at a conc. of $7·7 \times 10^{-11}$ mol per litre mercuric salts act as a strong positive catalyst—*vide* nitric acid. The reaction was also studied by A. Klemenc and R. Schöller. The effect of mercury and other salts on the oxidation of the trioxide by nitric acid was studied by C. M. Smith and G. E. Miller. J. A. Buchner examined the solubility of arsenic trioxide in nitric acid. According to J. J. Berzelius, **phosphorus** reduces arsenic trioxide, forming arsenic phosphide, and phosphorus pentoxide. R. Engel, N. W. Fischer, J. Thiele, J. V. Janowsky, etc., found that arsenic trioxide is reduced to brown arsenic (q.v.) by aq. soln. of **hypophosphorous acid**, or by **phosphorous acid**. T. Bergman found that arsenic trioxide is soluble in a hot soln. of **phosphoric acid**, and it does not separate out again on cooling. According to A. Oppenheim, phosphorus forms a phosphide with an aq. soln. of the trioxide at 200°. A. Michaelis represented the reaction of arsenic trioxide on **phosphorus trichloride** in a sealed tube at 110°–130° : $5As_2O_3+6PCl_3=4As+3P_2O_5+6AsCl_3$. N. N. Sen found that when **phosphorus**

trichloride is added to an aq. soln. of arsenic trioxide, the soln. turns yellow, then opaque brown, and finally deposits amorphous arsenic insoluble in carbon disulphide : $As_2O_3 + 3PCl_3 + 9H_2O = 2As + 3H_3PO_4 + 9HCl$. The reaction is visible with 0·000075 grm. of arsenic per c.c. It also occurs with arsenates. The reaction does not occur with hypophosphorous acid, or with an aq. soln. of the trichloride ; the reaction is slower with **phosphorus tribromide and triiodide,** and it also occurs with aq. soln. of these compounds. E. Deussen, and E. Rupp and E. Muschiol found that **calcium hypophosphite** gives a brown coloration or precipitation with soln. containing arsenious acid. L. Hurtzig and A. Geuther represented the reaction of arsenic trioxide with **phosphorus pentachloride** by $As_2O_3 + 3PCl_5 = 2AsCl_3 + 3POCl_3$; and B. Reinitzer and H. Goldschmidt, on **phosphoryl chloride** : $As_2O_3 + 2POCl_3 = 2AsCl_3 + P_2O_5$, at 250°, but at 160°, A. Michaelis observed no reaction. J. J. Berzelius found that arsenic trioxide dissolves in a soln. of **ammonium arsenite** at 70°–80°, and it crystallizes out from the soln. on cooling. W. Wallace and F. Penny, and L. Hurtzig and A. Geuther found that **arsenic trichloride** dissolves the trioxide, forming an oxychloride.

According to J. J. Berzelius,[20] **carbon,** and **carbon monoxide,** below a red-heat, reduce arsenic trioxide to arsenic. Thus when a mixture of arsenic trioxide and carbon is heated in a narrow glass tube, arsenic sublimes on to the cooler part of the tube. A. C. Pereira modified the experiment. A. Vogel ignited a mixture of the trioxide and charcoal moistened with alcohol, and observed the garlic odour of arsenic. J. Marshall and L. A. Ryan found that when an aq. soln. of arsenic trioxide is filtered through animal charcoal, a part is retained by that solid. M. Dubinin studied this subject. I. W. Fay and co-workers found 60° to be the lowest temp. at which the reduction of arsenic trioxide occurs in an atm. of carbon monoxide. E. H. Büchner found the trioxide to be insoluble in liquid **carbon dioxide.** C. Winkler[21] found that 100 parts of **carbon disulphide** dissolved 0·001 part of glassy arsenic trioxide in 2½ years at ordinary temp. Glassy arsenic trioxide under carbon disulphide is coloured reddish, but remains transparent until it begins to crystallize. F. Ephraim prepared complexes with **potassium thiocyanate.** C. Winkler also found that 100 parts of absolute **ethyl alcohol,** at ordinary temp., dissolved 0·446 part of the trioxide in 2½ years ; and J. Girardin showed that, expressing the solubility, S, grams of the trioxide per 100 parts of solvent :

Alcohol		56	79	84	86	88	100 vol. per cent.
S at 15°	Cubic	1·680	1·430	—	0·715	—	0·025
	Glassy	0·504	0·540	0·565	—	0·717	1·060
S at b.p.	Cubic	4·895	4·551	—	3·197	—	3·402

Isolated observations were also made by C. F. Wenzel, L. Thompson, A. Vogel, F. Selmi, and N. W. Fischer. H. Meerwein studied the alcoholates of arsenic trioxide. The trioxide was also found by F. Selmi to be soluble in **methyl alcohol ;** and F. Auerbach found the solubility in **amyl alcohol** and the partition coeff. between water and amyl alcohol is 5·47. A. Naumann, and W. Eidmann showed that the trioxide is insoluble in **acetone ;** and 100 parts of **ether** were found by C. Winkler to dissolve 0·454 part of the glassy trioxide in 2½ years. F. Selmi showed that every 15 c.c. of ether extracts a milligram of the trioxide from a sat. aq. soln.—less is extracted if the soln. be acidified with hydrochloric acid, and none if acidified with sulphuric or acetic acid. P. A. Cap observed that a little arsenic trioxide dissolves in **glycerol.** F. Selmi found that the cubic trioxide is soluble in **chloroform,** and very slightly soluble in **petroleum ether,** and in **benzene.** F. Auerbach showed that the octahedral crystals dissolve in boiling **nitrobenzene,** but not so with the glassy trioxide. F. Selmi observed that while the glassy form dissolves in **turpentine,** the octahedral crystals are insoluble. J. J. Berzelius, J. J. Heimpel, and K. von Grundner stated that the trioxide is slightly soluble in **fatty oils,** 1000 parts dissolving 0·6–0·8 part of the trioxide in the cold, and about 1·7 parts on boiling ; 1000 parts of **castor oil** also dissolve 1·33 parts of the trioxide at ordinary temp., and 9 parts when boiling. E. Beckmann and W. Gabel said that the trioxide is moderately soluble in **quinoline**, while A. W. Hofmann found it to be insoluble in that menstruum, and also in **aniline**. O. Aschan said that 100 grms. of 95 per cent. **formic acid** dissolve 0·02 grm. of the trioxide at 19·8°. The trioxide is less soluble in **acetic acid** than in sulphuric acid. The reaction with this acid was studied by A. Pictet and A. Bon, A. Rack, P. Schützenberger, T. Bergman, and A. Souchay; and E. Lenssen said that the trioxide is easily soluble in a cold soln. of **oxalic acid**, and the trioxide crystallizes out on cooling a hot sat. soln. of the trioxide in oxalic acid ; the trioxide is also easily soluble in a soln. of **tartaric acid**, and of **benzoic acid**. The action of tartaric acid was examined by T. Bergman, J. Pelouze, G. Baudran, and G. G. Henderson and A. R. Ewing. G. Lockemann and M. Paucke found that arsenic trioxide is adsorbed from soln. by coagulating **egg-albumen** and by **blood-serum**. The organic compounds of arsenic are discussed by G. T. Morgan, *Organic Compounds of Arsenic and Antimony* (London, 1918) ; G. W. Raiziss and L. J. Gavron, *Organic Arsenical Compounds* (New York, 1923) ; and A. Bertheim, *Handbuch der organischen Arsenverbindungen* (Stuttgart, 1913).

L. Kahlenberg and W. J. Trautmann [22] observed that when heated with **silicon**, the arsenic oxide volatilizes. W. Biltz found the amount of arsenic trioxide absorbed from soln. by **silicic acid** is very small, and practically independent of the conc. of the soln. Arsenic trioxide is used in the manufacture of **glass** on account of its decolorizing qualities ; and its influence in accelerating the corrosive action of glass has been discussed by D. J. McSwiney and W. E. S. Turner, S. English and co-workers, and K. Fuwa. E. Vigouroux found that arsenic trioxide is reduced to arsenic by **silicon;** and E. Berger, by **calcium silicide**. O. Ruff and K. Albert represented the reaction with **silicochloroform** by : $As_2O_3 + 9NaOH + 3SiHCl_3 = 9NaCl + 2As + 3Si(OH)_4$; and G. Rauter, the reaction with **silicon tetrachloride** by $2As_2O_3 + 3SiCl_4 = 3SiO_2 + 4AsCl_3$.

F. Auerbach found that with a mixture of **boric acid,** and an aq. soln. of arsenic trioxide—arsenious acid—containing an insufficiency of sodium hydroxide for complete neutralization, a complicated condition of equilibrium is established between the two simple acids, several complex acids, and their salts. The relationship in amount of the total borate to the total arsenite in such a soln. is accordingly dependent on the extent to which both acids form complex compounds. According to E. Wedekind and H. Wilke, the adsorption of arsenious acid by **zirconium dioxide** gels is normal and reversible, equilibrium being attained in a few hours ; the amount of arsenious acid removed from soln. continues to increase for some days, and only part of the acid can be recovered from the gel by washing. It is supposed that slow chemical combination occurs, forming $Zr(HAsO_4)_2$.

J. L. Gay Lussac and L. J. Thénard,[23] and A. F. Gehlen found that **potassium, sodium, zinc,** and other **metals** reduce arsenic trioxide at a red-heat, and the reaction in many cases is accompanied by *une lumière vive*. E. Berger observed its reduction by **aluminium**. The action of various metals—copper, zinc, cadmium, aluminium, tin, lead, antimony, and bismuth—on aq. soln. of arsenic trioxide in the production of hydrogen arsenides has been discussed in connection with those gases ; and the action of copper, in connection with the analytical reactions of arsenic. The reducing action of sodium-amalgam on aq. soln. of arsenic trioxide was examined by E. Frémy—*vide supra*, solid hydrogen arsenides. For the poisoning of the platinum catalyst in the oxidation of sulphur dioxide, *vide* the contact process for sulphuric acid. W. Biltz examined the absorptive power of **iron hydrosol** for arsenic trioxide in aq. soln.; and K. C. Sen, the adsorptive power of the hydrated oxides of aluminium, chromium, and iron.

Aq. soln. of the **alkali hydroxides** and aq. ammonia react with arsenic trioxide, forming arsenites (*q.v.*). The arsenites give a white precipitate when treated with **calcium hydroxide** soln., or a soln. of a calcium salt, forming the arsenite. W. H. Wollaston [24] also found that **calcium oxide** when heated with arsenic trioxide calcium arsenate and arsenic are formed, and, added J. F. Simon, some arsenite is produced—the proportion of arsenite is greater the lower the temp. C. Brame found that **barium oxide**, and J. L. Gay Lussac that the alkali **carbonates**, react similarly. B. L. Vanzetti found that on heating a mixture of arsenic trioxide and alkali carbonate, carbon dioxide is eliminated slowly and incompletely ; the reaction can be represented by the equation : $3Na_2CO_3 + As_2O_3 \rightarrow 2Na_3AsO_3 + 3CO_2$, but the reaction is completed only by removing the carbon dioxide as it is formed. The orthoarsenate may be hydrolyzed. L. G. Story and E. Anderson examined the absorption of arsenic trioxide from aq. soln. by **calcium, barium, lead and magnesium hydroxides.** Equilibrium was attained in 3 days at 99°, but several more days are required at a lower temp.—*vide infra*, the arsenites. A. Stavenhagen, and C. Reichard investigated the action of soln. of arsenic trioxide in water, soda-lye, and aq. ammonia, of an aq. soln. of potassium arsenite, and of sodium pyroarsenite on a number of metal salt soln.—*vide infra*, the arsenites. C. Reichard found that a soln. of arsenic trioxide in soda-lye does not act on **copper oxide,** but on **copper hydroxide,** a pale blue, fluorescent soln. is produced which in about 12 hrs. reacts : $4Cu(OH)_2 + As_2O_3 = 2Cu_2O + As_2O_5 + 4H_2O$, while with the trioxide ammoniacal soln., copper hydroxide forms a blue soln. which gives no precipitate with potash-lye, but when heated, loses ammonia, and deposits copper arsenite. An aq. soln. of arsenic trioxide does not react with copper oxychloride ; the ammoniacal soln. reacts as with copper hydroxide ; and the soln. in soda-lye reacts : $2Cu_2OCl_2 + 4NaOH + As_2O_3 = As_2O_5 + 4NaCl + 2Cu_2O + 2H_2O$. A warm soln. of the trioxide in soda-lye reduces **silver oxide** to a silver mirror ; and with a boiling, ammoniacal soln. the reduction is feeble ; this soln. deposits normal silver arsenite when treated with acid. When the soln. of the trioxide in soda-lye acts on **mercuric oxide,** it becomes grey, and forms an arsenite and some arsenate ; with an ammoniacal soln., the product is very unstable, but does not give a precipitate of mercurous chloride with hydrochloric acid. When **mercurous oxide** is treated with the alkaline soln. of the trioxide, the oxide becomes grey, mercury is deposited when the soln. is warmed, and a soluble arsenate is formed. The ammoniacal soln. of the trioxide reduces **mercuric amidochloride,** and partially reduces **mercurous amidochloride.** J. H. Yoe studied the adsorption of arsenic trioxide by hydrated **alumina.** The alkaline soln. of arsenic trioxide does not act on **stannic hydroxide,** but with stannous hydroxide the reaction : $3Sn(OH)_2 + As_2O_3 + 6KOH = 3K_2SnO_3 + 2As + 6H_2O$ occurs, and some arsine is formed. The deposited arsenic contains some tin. **Lead monoxide** is not attacked by these soln. of arsenic trioxide ; nor is **lead dioxide** attacked by the aq. or ammoniacal soln., but with the alkaline soln., $2PbO_2 + As_2O_3 = 2PbO + As_2O_5$. F. Feigl and F. Weiner pointed out that when the reaction is employed quantitatively for the volumetric determination of lead or manganese dioxide, the consumption of arsenite is too high owing to the catalytic action of lead and manganese hydroxides in promoting the oxidation of the arsenite by air. C. Reichard found that there is no reaction with **bismuth trioxide,** but with the soda-soln., alone, **bismuth pentoxide** reacts : $Bi_2O_5 + As_2O_3 = Bi_2O_3 + As_2O_5$. Aq. and ammoniacal soln. of the trioxide reduce **cobaltic hydroxide ;** but with the boiling alkaline soln., a deep blue soln. of cobaltic acid is formed ; **cobaltous hydroxide** is not changed ; **nickelic hydroxide** is reduced to **nickelous hydroxide ;** and the latter remains unchanged in the alkaline soln., but with the ammoniacal soln., it dissolves. When the soln. is boiled or treated with acids, $Ni_3As_4O_9$ is deposited. An alkaline soln. of the trioxide quickly reduces **manganese dioxide,** and an aq. soln. begins the reduction at 50°—*vide supra*. K. C. Sen studied the adsorption of arsenious acid by **chromic oxide.** According to F. Feigl and F. Weiner, the cold alkaline soln. slowly reduces **chromic acid.** An aq. soln. of arsenic trioxide slowly reduces **potassium dichromate,** but in the presence of acids, the reaction is much faster, and the reaction was employed by F. Kessler, and L. P. de St. Gilles for the volumetric determination of arsenic trioxide. The rate of oxidation of arsenic trioxide by a mixture of potassium dichromate and sulphuric acid was found by R. E. de Lury to be nearly proportional to the first power of the conc. of the dichromate, the inexactness being probably ascribable to incomplete dissociation. It was proportional to the first power of the conc. of the arsenic trioxide, and to the $\frac{1}{4}$th power of that of the sulphuric acid. The deviation from the second power is considered to be probably due to the influence of the hydrogen ion on the dissociation of the arsenic trioxide. The temp. coeff. is low ; the rise from 0° to 10° only increased the rate of oxidation by 26 per cent. The induced reaction in which arsenic trioxide and potassium iodide are oxidized by acid soln. of potassium dichromate was studied by R. E. de Lury. The arsenic trioxide acts as the inductor and the potassium iodide as the acceptor of the oxidation. It was found that the rate of reduction of the chromic acid in soln. of arsenic trioxide and iodide is equal to the sum of the rates of reduction of the arsenic trioxide and iodide separately, the retardation of the former being equal to the acceleration of the latter. The temp. coeff. of the single actions and the joint action are equal. The ratio also of the rate of oxidation of the iodide alone and in presence of arsenic trioxide is independent of the conc. of dichromate and sulphuric acid. The results may be accounted for by the assumption of the formation of a higher oxide (most probably a complex oxide of chromium and arsenic), which is reduced instantaneously by arsenic trioxide or iodide, the quantity reduced by each in mixtures being dependent on their relative conc. An aq. soln. of arsenic trioxide slowly reduces **potassium permanganate**; the reaction is rapid in the presence of acids. M. Geloso obtained colloidal manganese dioxide by reducing permanganate soln. with one of arsenic trioxide. In alkaline soln., F. Feigl and F. Weiner found that the reaction : $3As_2O_3 + 4KMnO_4 = 3As_2O_5 + 2K_2O + 4MnO_2$ proceeds to a definite end-point only when there is a constant excess of permanganate. If the arsenite is in excess, the permanganate is reduced to manganous hydroxide in the complete absence of air ; in the presence of air, oxidation of the manganous hydroxide takes place with the formation of an indefinite mixture of oxides intermediate between MnO and MnO_2. An excess of arsenite also results in a considerable adsorption of arsenious and arsenic acids by the precipitated manganese hydroxide, and the amount of arsenic acid formed does not correspond with the oxygen consumed by reduction of the permanganate. According to A. Travers, permanganic acid is reduced by arsenic trioxide in presence of sulphuric or nitric acid to a manganic salt and manganese dioxide. In presence of hydrofluoric, phosphoric, or arsenic acid the whole of the manganese may be converted into the corresponding manganic salt. Reduction to manganous salts occurs in presence of a considerable excess of arsenic trioxide. W. Trautmann showed that arsenic trioxide is quantitatively oxidized by permanganate in the presence of an excess of sulphuric acid at a boiling heat. The reaction was studied by B. Brauner, A. Bose, A. Bussy, E. Deiss, F. Feigl and F. Weiner, M. Geloso, T. Oryng, W. T. Hall and C. E. Carlson, J. Holluta, F. Kessler, A. Klemenc, A. Travers, K. Swoboda, O. Kühling, R. Lang, E. Lenssen, L. Moser and F. Perjatel, L. P. de St. Gilles, L. Vanino, and E. Waitz. O. Cantoni showed that the reaction is considerably accelerated if a little potassium iodide be present. R. Lang studied the electrometric titration of arsenious acid with potassium permanganate soln. Arsenic trioxide forms complexes with **tungstic, molybdic, and vanadic acids** (q.v.).

According to W. Biltz,[25] the amount of arsenic trioxide absorbed from aq. soln. by **aluminium hydroxide** is very small, and is practically independent of the conc. The adsorption was also studied by G. Lockemann and M. Paucke, and K. C. Sen. The effect of **ferric hydroxide** in fixing arsenic trioxide so that it is no longer in a condition to dissolve was utilized by R. Bunsen and A. A. Berthold as an antidote for arsenic poisoning—vide supra. A. Stavenhagen was unable to prepare a definite compound by the action of ferric hydroxide on soln. of arsenic trioxide. According to G. Lockemann, the quantity of ferric hydroxide necessary for the complete adsorption of arsenic present in a soln. as arsenite or arsenate is in accordance with the formula $E = kA^p$, where E is the number of mgrms. of ferric hydroxide in 100 c.c. ; A, the number of mgrms. of arsenic in 100 c.c.; k, a constant which varies with the temp.; and p has the value 0·57 for all temp. The value of A varied from 0·1 to 500, and the values of k were respectively 70, 90, and 130 at 0°, 25°, and 80°. With a rise of temp., the adsorption decreases considerably. At all temp., very small quantities of arsenic require relatively much more ferric hydroxide for complete adsorption than do larger quantities of arsenic. In preparing the ferric hydroxide, twice the theoretical quantity of ammonium hydroxide necessary for the precipitation of the iron was added ; if only the theoretical quantity is added, the adsorption of arsenic is considerably increased. R. Bunsen, N. J. B. G. Guibourt, T. Oryng, and A. Reychler attributed the action to the formation of a hydrolyzed ferric arsenite ; but W. Biltz showed that the antidotal action of ferric hydroxide is not due to the formation of a basic arsenate, or of a solid soln., but to reversible adsorption. The amount of arsenic trioxide adsorbed from soln. is diminished with the ageing of the ferric hydroxide. W. Biltz measured the distribution of arsenic trioxide between water and ferric hydroxide at different temp., and represented the results by the relation $C_1 = kC_2{}^n$, where k and n are constants ; C_1, the conc. of the arsenic trioxide in the ferric hydroxide ; and C_2, the conc. of the arsenic trioxide in soln. at equilibrium—vide 5. 39, 9. M. C. Boswell and J. V. Dickson found that the observed results deviate a little from this relation. W. Mecklenberg stated that the adsorption curves for different preparations of ferric hydroxide are each related by a particular factor to a unit curve, so that the ordinate corresponding to a given abscissa on one curve may be obtained by multiplying by the factor the ordinate for that abscissa on the unit curve. This means that if the adsorption follows the law $C_1 = kC_2{}^n$, n will be constant for the same adsorbent, and an absorbent prepared under different conditions, or of different ages will vary only in the values of k. M. C. Boswell and J. V. Dickson found that while n varied only from 0·183 to 0·284 with differently prepared samples of ferric hydroxide, k varied from 33·3 to 200. G. Lockemann and coworkers, and M. C. Boswell and J. V. Dickson showed that the adsorption of arsenic trioxide by ferric hydroxide is diminished when sodium hydroxide is present ; and conversely, the adsorption of sodium hydroxide by ferric hydroxide is increased in the presence of arsenic trioxide. K. C. Sen studied the effect with different modes of preparation and of the ageing of the colloid, the effect of neutral salts and of variations in the conc. of the soln. on the adsorption of arsenious acid by ferric hydroxide ; L. Herboth, the adsorption of arsenic trioxide by saccharated iron ; and J. M. Clavera, by ferric hydroxide, and by ferric magnesium hydroxide.

The action of arsenic trioxide on the halides of the alkalies and alkaline earths is discussed in a special section below. The action on copper, silver, mercury, and lead salts is indicated in connection with the arsenites. It may be observed, however, that M. Kohn [26] found that when copper sulphate is heated with aq. ammonia and arsenic trioxide, in a sealed tube at 100°, it undergoes reduction to cuprous salt with formation of arsenic acid. After the resulting cuprous soln. has been oxidized to the cupric condition by atm. oxygen, estimation of the arsenic acid reveals more of the latter than corresponds with the eq., $2Cu^{··} + AsO_3''' + 2OH' = H_2O + 2Cu^· + AsO_4'''$. Evidently oxidation of the ammoniacal cuprous soln. to the cupric stage activates the atm. oxygen for the oxidation of the residual unchanged arsenious acid. Depression of the conc. of hydroxyl ions by addition of ammonium salts retards the reduction of cupric to cuprous salt. Again, he found that **silver nitrate** is completely reduced to metallic silver in ammoniacal soln. by arsenious acid, which is oxidized to arsenic acid. The reduction is not affected by the addition of neutral salts such as sodium nitrate or sulphate, but is hindered by ammonium sulphate, which causes a decrease in the conc. of hydroxyl-ions. The reduction of **cupric sulphate** by arsenious acid in presence of aq. ammonia is not influenced by neutral salts such as potassium chloride or nitrate. H. Rose found that soln. of **gold chloride** are reduced to the metal by soln. of arsenic trioxide or the arsenites. P. Woulfe

found that when a soln. of **stannous chloride** is digested for a long time with
arsenic trioxide, tin is deposited ; and if conc. hydrochloric acid be present,
F. Kessler said that some arsine is formed. According to A. Bettendorff, aq.
soln. of arsenic trioxide or pentoxide give no precipitate with stannous chloride
unless conc. hydrochloric acid be present—*Bettendorf's reaction.* With an acid
of sp. gr. between 1·135 and 1·185, a precipitate forms immediately ; with an acid
of sp. gr. 1·123, complete precipitation occurs in a few minutes ; with an acid of
sp. gr. 1·115, the precipitation is incomplete ; and with an acid of sp. gr. less than
1·100, no precipitation occurs. The reaction was studied by C. O. Curtman,
G. Frerichs, A. Ferraro and A. Carobbio, and O. Schlickum. K. Zwicknagl
observed that the reaction is exothermic, giving off about 20 Cals. per gram-atom of
arsenic, depending on the conditions. The precipitate from a soln. in pure hydrochloric acid contained 98·18 per cent. of arsenic, and 1·82 per cent. of tin. R. Lang
and J. Zwerina observed that arsenious acid induces the reaction between **chromic
acid** and manganous salts. The reaction of an aq. soln. of arsenic trioxide and
ferric chloride in 1·5N- to 4N-HCl in sealed tubes at 107° and 127° was studied
by K. Jellinek and L. Winogradoff. They found the equilibrium constant
of the reaction : $2FeCl_3 + H_3AsO_3 + H_2O \rightleftharpoons 2FeCl_2 + H_3AsO_4 + 2HCl$, namely,
$k=[H_3AsO_3][FeCl_3]^2/[H_3AsO_4][FeCl_2]^2[HCl]^2$, is 0·0354 at 107°, and 0·117 at 127°.
The thermal value of the reaction represented in the above equation from left
to right is 18 Cals. ; both reactions are termolecular, and are accelerated by
hydrochloric acid. W. Manchot and F. Glaser found that a mixture of equimolar
parts of arsenic trioxide, ferrous sulphate, and potassium hydroxide absorbed nearly
twice as much oxygen as was required to produce ferric oxide, and assumed that
a dioxide, FeO_2, was formed. For G. Gire's observations on this subject, *vide
supra.*

REFERENCES.

¹ J. J. Berzelius, *Ann. Chim. Phys.*, (1), **80**. 9, 1811 ; (2), **5**. 179, 1817 ; (2), **11**. 225, 1819 ;
P. A. von Bonsdorff, *L'Insc.*, **3**. 99, 1835 ; J. W. Retgers, *Zeit. anorg. Chem.*, **4**. 403, 1893 ;
A. Geuther, *Liebig's Ann.*, **240**. 217, 1887 ; E. Mitchell, *Amer. Journ. Science*, (1), **19**. 122,
1831 ; G. Suckow, *Der Verwitterung im mineralreiche*, Leipzig, 1848.
² G. Brandt, *Arch. Akad. Upsala*, **3**. 39, 1733 ; J. G. Wallerius, *Mineralogia*, Stockholm,
224, 1747 ; A. Cronstedt, *Mineralogie*, Stockholm, 207, 1758 ; D. L. G. Karsten, *Mineralogische
Tabellen*, Berlin, 79, 1800 ; W. Haidinger, *Handbuch der bestimmenden Mineralogie*, Wien, 487,
1845 ; J. D. Dana, *A System of Mineralogy*, New York, 139, 1854 ; C. Linnæus, *System naturæ*,
Lugduni Batavorum, 1735.
³ C. Doremus, *Trans. Amer. Electrochem. Soc.*, **35**. 187, 1919 ; G. J. Young, *Eng. Min. Journ.*,
117. 757, 1924 ; E. C. Williams, **110**. 671, 1920 ; H. P. Bassett and S. S. Sadtler, *U.S. Pat. No.*
1528004, 1925 ; C. L. Read, *Journ. Ind. Eng. Chem.*, **20**. 97, 1927.
⁴ V. Kohlschütter and J. L. Tüscher, *Zeit. Elektrochem.*, **27**. 225, 1921 ; F. Schoucroum,
Journ. Phys. Rad., **1**. 65, 1920.
⁵ L. Souheur, *German Pat.*, *D.R.P.* 159541, 1903 ; R. M. Chapin, *Journ. Ind. Eng. Chem.*,
10. 522, 1918 ; R. Suchy and J. Michel, *U.S. Pat. No.* 1532454, 1925 ; C. P. Linville, *ib.*,
1372332, 1921 ; T. P. Sims and W. Terrill, *Brit. Pat. No.* 9076, 1896 ; A. Streng, *Berg. Hütt. Ztg.*,
19. 128, 1860 ; L. Kessler, *Pogg. Ann.*, **95**. 207, 1855 ; F. Wöhler, *Liebig's Ann.*, **101**. 364, 1857 ;
H. A. L. Wiggers, *ib.*, **41**. 347, 1842 ; G. Vié, *Chem. Trade Journ.*, **68**. 35, 1921 ; *L'Ind. Chim.*, **7**.
426, 1920 ; *Chem. Met. Engg.*, **24**. 527, 1921.
⁶ H. Davy, *Elements of Chemical Philosophy*, London, 1912 ; E. Mitscherlich, *Liebig's Ann.*,
12. 165, 1834 ; *Sitzber. Akad. Berlin*, 425, 1833 ; *Pogg Ann.*, **29**. 133, 1833 ; V. Meyer, *Ber.*, **12**.
12, 1879 ; V. and C. Meyer, *ib.*, **12**. 1116, 1879 ; H. Erdmann, *Zeit. anorg. Chem.*, **32**. 453, 1902 ;
E. Beckmann, *ib.*, **51**. 111, 1906 ; H. Biltz, *Zeit. phys. Chem.*, **19**. 417, 1896 ; *Sitzber. Akad. Berlin*,
67, 1896 ; A. Scott, *Proc. Roy. Soc. Edin.*, **14**. 410, 1887 ; T. Thomson, *Ann. Phil.*, **4**. 171, 1814 ;
C. F. Richter. *Zeit. Phys. Math.*, **5**. 129, 481, 1837 ; J. J. Berzelius, *Gilbert's Ann.*, **38**. 207, 1811 ;
Ann. Chim. Phys., (1), **80**. 9, 1811 ; (2), **5**. 179, 1817 ; (2), **11**. 225, 1819 ; L. J. Thénard, *Traité
de chimie élémentaire*, Paris, **2**. 33, 1814 ; J. L. Proust, *Journ. Phys.*, **49**. 151, 1799 ; **59**. 321, 1804 ;
R. M. Bozorth, *Journ. Amer. Chem. Soc.*, **45**. 1621, 1923 ; W. D. Collins, H. V. Farr, J. Rosin,
G. C. Spencer, and E. Wichers, *Journ Ind. Eng. Chem.*, **19**. 1370. 1927.
⁷ J. B. L. Romé de l'Isle, *Cristallographie*, Paris, **1**. 252, 1783 ; **3**. 40, 1783 ; T. Bergman,
De arsenico, Upsala, 1777 ; G. Suckow, *Der Verwitterung im Mineralreiche*, Leipzig, 1848 ;
A. Geuther, *Liebig's Ann.*, **240**. 27, 1887 ; J. F. L. Hausmann, *ib.*, **74**. 188, 1850 ; A. des Cloizeaux,
Manuel de minéralogie, Paris, **2**. 363, 1893 ; *Compt. Rend.*, **105**. 96, 1887 ; *Bull. Soc. Min.*, **10**.

306, 1837 ; A. Grosse-Bohle, *Zeit. Kryst.*, 5. 233, 1881 ; R. Brauns, *Die optischen Anomalien der Krystalle*, Leipzig, 191, 1891 ; C. Winkler, *Journ. prakt. Chem.*, (2), 31. 247, 1885 ; H. Rose, quotation from L. Gmelin, *Handbook of Chemistry*, London, 4. 255, 1850 ; *Pogg. Ann.*, 35. 481, 1835 ; 52. 454, 1841 ; R. Christison, *ib.*, 36. 494, 1835 ; H. A. L. Wiggers, *Liebig's Ann.*, 41. 347, 1842 ; H. V. Regnault, *Ann. Chim. Phys.*, (3), 1. 144, 1841 ; W. Krüger, *Kastner's Arch.*, 2. 473, 1824 ; J. N. von Fuchs, *Schweigger's Journ.*, 67. 429, 1833 ; A. Bussy, *Journ. Pharm. Chim.*, (3), 12. 321, 1847 ; *Compt. Rend.*, 24. 774, 1847 ; *Phil. Mag.*, (3), 31. 151, 1847 ; E. von Bandrowsky, *Zeit. phys. Chem.*, 17. 234, 1895 ; M. Trautz, *ib.*, 53. 1, 1905 ; J. Guinchant, *Compt. Rend.*, 140. 1101, 1170, 1905 ; D. Gernez, *ib.*, 140. 1134, 1905 ; A. Scheurer-Kestner, *Repért. Chim. Appl.*, 4. 406, 1862 ; R. M. Bozorth, *Journ. Amer. Chem. Soc.*, 45. 1621, 1925 ; L. A. Emmerling, *Lehrbuch der Mineralogie*, Giessen, 2. 566, 1796 ; D. L. G. Karsten, *Mineralogische Tabellen*, Berlin, 79, 1800 ; J. D. Dana, *A System of Mineralogy*, New York, 198, 1892 ; W. Haidinger, *Handbuch der bestimmenden Mineralogie*, Wien, 487, 1845.

    [8] G. Werner, *Jahresb. Nat. Württemberg*, 135, 1869 ; G. Leonhard, *Handwörterbuch der topographischen Mineralogie*, Heidelberg, 38, 1843 ; R. M. Bozorth, *Journ. Amer. Chem. Soc.*, 45. 1621, 1925 ; F. Sandberger, *Untersuchungen über Erzgänge*, Wiesbaden, 380, 1885 ; C. Hintze, *Handbuch der Mineralogie*, Leipzig, 1. 1227, 1904 ; R. P. Greg and W. G. Lettsom, *Manual of the Mineralogy of Great Britain and Ireland*, London, 370, 1858 ; G. C. Hoffmann, *Ann. Rep. Geol. Sur. Canada*, 6. 30, 1893 ; A. Raimondi, *Minéraux du Pérou*, Paris, 184, 1878 ; A. Frenzel, *Mineralogisches Lexikon für das Königreich Sachsen*, Leipzig, 26, 1874 ; H. Traube, *Die Minerale Schlesiens*, Breslau, 19, 1888 ; V. R. von Zepharovich, *Mineralogisches Lexikon für das Kaiserthum Oesterreich*, Wien, 35, 1859 ; 37, 1873 ; W. F. Petterd, *Catalogue of the Minerals of Tasmania*, Launceston, 5, 1896 ; O. Leudecke, *Die Minerale des Harzes*, Berlin, 177, 1896 ; J. F. L. Hausmann, *Ges. Wiss. Gött.*, 1, 1850 ; *Neues Jahrb. Min.*, 695, 1850 ; G. C. Laube, *Jahrb. Geol. Reichsanst. Wien*, 15. 250, 1865 ; J. Szabo, *Földt. Közl.*, 18. 49, 1888 ; A. des Cloizeaux, *Bull. Soc. Min.*, 10. 307, 1887 ; G. A. Kenngott, *Sitzber. Akad. Wien*, 9. 593, 1892 ; *Uebersicht der Resultate mineralogischer Forschungen*, Wien, 36, 1855 ; A. Breithaupt, *Vollständiges Handbuch der Mineralogie*, Dresden, 2. 126, 1841 ; C. A. Tenne and S. Calderon, *Mineralfundstätten der iberischen Halbinsel*, Berlin, 94, 1902 ; A. Lacroix, *Minéralogie de la France et de ses colonies*, Paris, 3. 12, 1901 ; J. H. Collins, *A Handbook to the Mineralogy of Cornwall and Devon*, London, 10, 1876 ; P. W. Jeremejeff, *Proc. Russ. Min. Soc.*, 20. 204, 1902 ; J. S. Berge, J. H. Brownlee, and R. C. Ringrose, *Proc. Roy. Soc. Queensland*, 15. 47, 1900 ; F. A. Genth, *Amer. Journ. Science*, (2), 33. 190, 1862 ; (2), 34. 205, 1862 ; J. D. Dana, *A System of Mineralogy*, New York, 198, 1892 ; P. Groth, *Die Mineraliensammlung der Universität Strassburg*, Strassburg, 78, 1878 ; P. Sigismund, *I minerali del comune di Sondalo*, Milano, 9, 1901 ; E. Fugger, *Die Mineralien des Herzogthums Salzburg*, Salzburg, 31, 1878 ; E. Federoff, *Neues Jahrb. Min.*, ii, 227, 1903.

    [9] F. Wöhler, *Pogg. Ann.*, 26. 177, 1832 ; P. Groth, *ib.*, 137. 416, 1869 ; *Tabellarisch Uebersicht der Mineralien*, Braunschweig, 41, 1898 ; A. des Cloizeaux, *Manuel de minéralogie*, Paris, 2. 364, 1893 ; *Bull. Soc. Min.*, 10. 303, 1887 ; J. D. Dana, *A System of Mineralogy*, New York, 796, 1868 ; M. Adam, *Tableau minéralogique*, Paris, 41, 1869 ; M. Bauer, *Lehrbuch der Mineralogie*, Berlin, 372, 509, 1904 ; A. Schmidt, *Zeit. Kryst.*, 14. 575, 1888 ; 17. 515, 1890 ; L. Pasteur, *Journ. Pharm. Chim.*, (3), 13. 399, 1848 ; F. Claudet, *Journ. Chem. Soc.*, 21. 179, 1868 ; *Chem. News*, 22. 128, 1868 ; G. A. Kenngott, *Uebersicht der Resultate mineralogischer Forschungen*, Wien, 16, 1854 ; A. Breithaupt, *Vollständiges Charakteristik der Mineralsystems*, Dresden, 38, 1832 ; *Vollständiges Handbuch der Mineralogie*, Dresden, 2. 126, 1841 ; A. Scheurer-Kestner, *Bull. Soc. Chim.*, (2), 10. 344, 1868 ; F. Ulrich, *Zeit. Ges. Nat. Halle*, 11. 261, 1838 ; N. Zenzen, H. G. Söderbaum, and H. J. Sjögren, *Arkiv Kemi Min. Geol.*, 8. 20, 1922.

    [10] H. Debray, *Compt. Rend.*, 58. 1209, 1864 ; *Bull. Soc. Chim.*, (2), 2. 9, 1864 ; A. Scheurer, Kestner, *ib.*, (2), 10. 344, 1868 ; L. Pasteur, *Compt. Rend.*, 24. 774, 1847 ; *Journ. Pharm. Chim.* (3), 13. 399, 1847 ; O. B. Kühn, *ib.*, (3), 22, 75, 1852 ; *Arch. Pharm.*, (2), 69. 267, 1852 ; F. Ulrich, *Zeit. Ges. Nat. Halle*, 11. 261, 1858 ; A. E. Nordenskjöld, *Pogg. Ann.*, 114. 612, 1861 ; F. Wöhler, *ib.*, 26. 177, 1832 ; 137. 414, 1869 ; *Liebig's Ann.*, 101. 364, 1857 ; C. H. Hirzel, *Zeit. Pharm.*, 4. 81, 1852 ; C. Gänge, *Sitzber. Ges. Med. Nat. Jena*, 2, 1879 ; F. Claudet, *Journ. Chem. Soc.*, 21. 179, 1868 ; *Chem. News*, 22, 128, 1868 ; H. V. Welch and L. H. Duschak, *The Vapour Pressure of Arsenic Trioxide*, Washington, 1915.

    [11] C. Hintze, *Handbuch der Mineralogie*, Leipzig, 1. 1230, 1904 ; A. Lacroix, *Minéralogie de la France et ses colonies*, Paris, 3. 18, 1901 ; C. A. Tenne and S. Calderon, *Mineralfundstätten der iberischen Halbinsel*, Berlin, 95, 1902 ; G. A. Kenngott, *Sitzber. Akad. Wien*, 9. 589, 1852 ; A. des Cloizeaux, *Bull. Soc. Min.*, 10. 304, 1887 ; J. Loczka, *Zeit. Kryst.*, 39. 525, 1904 ; A. Schmidt, *ib.*, 14. 579, 1888 ; 17. 515, 1890 ; P. Groth, *Pogg. Ann.*, 137. 421, 1869 ; J. Szabo, *Földt. Közl.*, 18. 332, 1888 ; F. Claudet, *Journ. Chem. Soc.*, 21. 179, 1868 ; *Chem. News*, 22. 128, 1868.

    [12] E. R. Rushton and F. Daniels, *Journ. Amer. Chem. Soc.*, 48. 384, 1926 ; A. le Royer and J. B. A. Dumas, *Ann. Pharm. Chim.*, (1), 8. 408, 1821 ; E. Filhol, *Ann. Chim. Phys.*, (3), 21. 415, 1847 ; C. J. B. Karsten, *Schweigger's Journ.*, 65. 394, 1832 ; A. S. Taylor, *Phil. Mag.*, (3), 11. 482, 1837 ; W. Herapath, *ib.*, (1), 64. 321, 1829 ; N. J. B. G. Guibourt, *Journ. Chim. Méd.*, (1), 2. 55, 106, 1826 ; F. Claudet, *Journ. Chem. Soc.*, 21. 179, 1868 ; *Chem. News*, 22. 128, 1868 ; W. M. Mott, *Trans. Amer. Electrochem. Soc.*, 34. 255, 1918 ; G. P. Baxter and C. F. Hawkins, *Journ. Amer. Chem. Soc.*, 38. 266, 1916 ; E. Anderson and L. G. Story, *ib.*, 45. 1102, 1923 ; R. Schuhmann, *ib.*, 46. 1444, 1924 ; C. Winkler, *Journ. prakt. Chem.*, (2), 31. 247, 1885 ; C. F. Rammelsberg, *Handbuch der krystallographisch-physikalischen Chemie*, Leipzig, 1. 107.

1881 ; P. Groth, *Pogg. Ann.*, **137**. 416, 1869 ; H. Saito, *Science Rep. Tohoku Univ.*, **16**. 37, 1927 ; P. Smellie, *Journ. Soc. Chem. Ind.*, **42**. 466, T, 1923 ; F. Wöhler, *Liebig's Ann.*, **41**. 155, 1842 ; R. Schaefer, *Koll. Zeit.*, **33**. 286, 1923 ; H. Ludwig, *Arch. Pharm.*, (2), **97**. 23, 1859 ; A. de la Rive and F. Marcet. *Bibl. Univ. Genève*, **28**. 381, 1840 ; M. Faraday, *Journ. Roy. Inst.*, **1**. 70, 1830 ; *Phil. Trans.*, **116**. 484, 1826 ; J. K. Mitchell, *Amer. Journ. Science*, (1), **10**. 122, 1832 ; A. S. Russell, *Phys. Zeit.*, **13**. 60, 1912 ; F. Selmi, *Mem. Accad. Bologna*, **9**. 133, 1878 ; *Gazz. Chim. Ital.*, **9**. 154, 1879 ; *Monit. Scient.*, (3), **8**. 1012, 1878 ; G. Niederschulte, *Ueber den Dampfdruck fester Körper*, Er angen, 1903 ; K. Stelzner, *Ueber den Dampfdruck fester Körper*, Braunschweig, 1901 ; H. V. Welch and L. H. Duschak, *The Vapour Pressure of Arsenic Trioxide*, Washington, 1915 ; L. Troost and P. Hautefeuille, *Compt. Rend.*, **69**. 84, 1869 ; G. Tammann and G. Bätz, *Zeit. anorg. Chem.*, **156**. 96, 1926 ; H. Fizeau, *Compt. Rend.*, **60**. 1161, 1865 ; G. Nonhebel, J. Colvin, H. S. Pattersen, and R. Whytlaw-Gray, *Proc. Roy. Soc.*, **116**. A, 540, 1927 ; H. V. Regnault, *Ann. Chim. Phys.*, (3), **1**. 129, 1841.

13 J. Thomsen, *Thermochemische Untersuchungen*, Leipzig, **1**. 199, 1882 ; **2**. 234, 236, 1882 ; *Ber.*, **7**. 935, 1002, 1874 ; M. Berthelot, *Thermochimie*, Paris, **2**. 117, 1897 ; R. Schuhmann, *Journ. Amer. Chem. Soc.*, **46**. 1444, 1924 ; P. A. Favre, *Journ. Pharm. Chim.*, (3), **24**. 241, 311, 412, 1853 ; L. Troost and P. Hautefeuille, *Compt. Rend.*, **69**. 48, 1869 ; L. Bruner and S. Tolloczko, *Zeit. anorg. Chem.*, **37**. 455, 1903.

14 A. des Cloizeaux, *Manuel de minéralogie*, Paris, **2**. 364, 1893 ; *Bull. Soc. Min.*, **10**. 306, 1887 ; *Nouvelles recherches sur les propriétés optiques des cristaux*, Paris, 513, 1867 ; E. W. Washburn and E. K. Strachan. *Journ. Amer. Chem. Soc.*, **35**. 681, 1913 ; F. Klocke, *Neues Jahrb. Min.*, i, 82, 1880 ; F. Beijerinck, *Neues Jahrb. Min. B.B.*, **11**. 442, 1897 ; L. Bleekrode, *Proc. Roy. Soc.*, **25**. 322, 1877 ; *Phil. Mag.*, (5), **5**. 375, 439, 1878 ; J. C. Ghosh and S. C. Bisvas, *Zeit. Elektrochem.*, **30**. 97, 1924 ; R. Brauns, *Die optischen Anomalien der Krystalle*, Leipzig, 191, 1891 ; P. Walden, *Zeit. phys. Chem.*, **2**. 56, 1888 ; J. von Zawidzky, *Ber.*, **36**. 1429, 1903 ; E. Bouty, *Ann. Chim. Phys.*, (6), **3**. 478, 1884 ; G. Bischof, *Kastner's Arch.*, **4**. 13, 1825 ; **6**. 438, 1825 ; B. Neumann, *Chem. Ztg.*, **30**. 33, 1906 ; *Zeit. phys. Chem.*, **14**. 193, 1894 ; R. J. Clark, *Nature*, **118**. 555, 1926 ; E. Blanc, *Journ. Chim. Phys.*, **18**. 28, 1920 ; J. K. Wood, *Journ. Chem. Soc.*, **93**. 415, 1908 ; R. Wright, *ib.*, **105**. 669, 1914 ; J. F. Simon, *Trommsdorff's Journ.*, **22**. 14, 1813 ; L. Ramberg, *Arsskr. Lunds Univ.*, **14**. 21, 1918 ; R. Schuhmann, *Journ. Amer. Chem. Soc.*, **46**. 1444, 1924 ; E. Anderson and L. G. Story, *ib.*, **45**. 1102, 1923 ; H. R. Robinson, *Phil. Mag.*, (6), **50**. 241, 1925 ; R. Whiddington, *ib.*, (6), **43**. 1116, 1922 ; N. Isgarischeff and E. Koldaewa, *Zeit. Elektrochem.*, **30**. 83, 1924 ; N. R. Dhar, *Zeit. anorg. Chem.*, **153**. 323, 1926 ; H. R. Robinson and A. M. Cassie, *Proc. Roy. Soc.*, **113**. A, 282, 1926 ; A. H. W. Aten, P. Bruin, and W. de Lange, *Rec. Trav. Chim. Pays-Bas*, **46**. 417, 1927.

15 P. Hautefeuille, *Bull. Soc. Chim.*, (2), **7**. 206, 1867 ; M. Berthelot, *Compt. Rend.*, **84**. 408, 1877 ; G. Gire, *ib.*, **171**. 174, 1920 ; P. Thénard, *ib.*, **75**. 174, 458, 1872 ; J. L. Soret, *ib.*, **38**. 445, 1854 ; C. Matignon and J. A. Lecanu, *ib.*, **170**. 941, 1920 ; T. E. Thorpe, *Pharm. Journ.*, (3), **20**. 845, 1890 ; *Chem. News*, **61**. 140, 1890 ; C. R. Fresenius, *Liebig's Ann.*, **93**. 384, 1855 ; F. Mohr, *ib.*, **94**. 222, 1855 ; *Lehrbuch der chemisch-analytischen Titrirmethode*, Braunschweig, 291, 1855 ; H. Croft, *Canadian Journ. Ind.*, **3**. 126, 1858 ; *Chem. Gaz.*, **16**. 121, 1858 ; J. M'Donnell, *ib.*, **17**. 414, 1859 ; *Journ. prakt. Chem.*, (1), **79**. 502, 1860 ; H. Ludwig, *Arch. Pharm.*, (2), **97**. 27, 1859 ; A. Ladenburg, *Ber.*, **36**. 115, 1903 ; W. D. Bancroft and H. B. Weiser, *Journ. Phys. Chem.*, **18**. 256, 1914 ; F. Kessler, *Pogg. Ann.*, **113**. 145, 1861 ; C. F. Schönbein, *ib.*, **75**. 361, 1848 ; J. F. Simon, *ib.*, **40**. 435, 1837 ; A. Vogel, *Repert. Pharm.*, **22**. 577, 1873 ; P. Edgerton, *Journ. Amer. Chem. Soc.*, **35**. 1769, 1913 ; J. B. Tingle, *ib.*, **33**. 1762, 1911 ; F. Reinthaler, *Chem. Ztg.*, **36**. 713, 1912 ; W. Thomson, *Proc. Roy. Soc. Edin.*, **29**. 84, 1909 ; I. M. Kolthoff, *Pharm. weekbl.*, **56**. 621, 1919 ; J. H. Gladstone and A. Tribe, *Journ. Chem. Soc.*, **33**. 306, 1878 ; A. K. Goard and E. K. Rideal, *Proc. Roy. Soc.*, **105**. A, 135, 1924 ; W. P. Jorissen, *Rec. Trav. Chim. Pays-Bas*, **42**. 855, 1923 ; N. N. Mittra and N. R. Dhar, *Zeit. anorg. Chem.*, **122**. 146, 1922 ; C. C. Palit and N. R. Dhar, *Journ. Phys. Chem.*, **30**. 939, 1926 ; L. Vallery, *Compt. Rend.*, **185**. 538, 1927.

16 N. J. B. G. Guibourt, *Journ. Chem. Med.*, (1), **2**. 55, 106, 1826 ; N. W. Fischer, *Schweigger's Journ.*, **12**. 155, 1814 ; **39**. 364, 1823 ; M. H. Klaproth, *ib.*, **6**. 231, 1812 ; *Ann. Phil.*, **4**. 132, 1814 ; C. F. Bucholz, *Schweigger's Journ.*, **7**. 387, 1813 ; W. Nasse, *ib.*, **5**. 217, 1812 ; A. Vogel, *München Gel. Anz.*, **40**. 33, 1855 ; *Kastner's Arch.*, **9**. 319, 1826 ; A. S. Taylor, *Phil. Mag.*, (3), **14**. 482, 1837 ; J. C. Delamétherie, *Leçons de minéralogie*, Paris, **1**. 269, 1811 ; C. F. S. Hahnemann, *Ueber Arsenik vergiftungen ihre Hülft und gerichtliche Ausmittelung*, Leipzig, 10, 1786 ; J. R. Spielmann, *Institutiones materiæ mdeicæ*, Argentorati, 498, 1784 ; C. F. Wenzel, *Lehre von der Verwandschaft der Korper*, Dresden, 444, 1777 ; G. Brandt, *Arch. Akad. Upsala*, **3**. 39, 1733 ; J. H. G. Justi, *Gesammelte chymische Schriften worinnen das Weren der Me alle und die wichtigen chymischen Schriften vor dem Nahrungsstand und das Bergwesen ausführlich abgehandelt werden*, Berlin, **2**. 6, 1761 ; T. Bergman, *De arsenico*, Upsala, 1777 ; A. Baumé, *Chymie éxperimentale et raisonnée*, Paris, **2**. 231, 1773 : P. T. Navier, *Contrepoisons de l'arsenic*, Paris, 1777 ; J. F. Hagen, *Grundsätze der Chemie*, Königsberg, 456, 1796 ; A. L. Cohn, *Indicators and Test-papers*, New York, 1899 ; P. von Musschenbroek, *Introductio ad philosophiam naturam*, Lugduni Batavorum, **2**. 589, 1762 ; L. Gmelin, *Handbook of Chemistry*, London, **4**. 257, 1850 ; H. Rose, *Pogg. Ann.* **36**. 494, 1835 ; F. Claudet, *Chem. News*, **22**. 128, 1868 ; *Journ. Chem. Soc.*, **28**. 179, 1868 ; J. K. Wood, *ib.*, **93**. 412, 1908 ; C. Schultze-Sellac, *Ber*, **4**. 109, 1871 ; J. Girardin, *Bull. Soc. Chim*, (2), **10**. 230, 1868 ; *Journ. Chim. Pharm.*, (3), **46**. 269, 1864 ; G. Favrel, *ib.*, (5), **28**. 301, 1893 ; *Bull. Soc.*

Chim., (3). **9**. 448, 1893 ; J. Dalton, *A New System of Chemical Philosophy*, Manchester, **2**. 63, 1827 ; J.Thomsen, *Ber.*, 7. 935, 1002, 1874 ; *Thermochemische Untersuchungen,* Leipzig, 1. 199, 1882 ; F. A. Flückiger, *Arch. Pharm.*, (3), **22**. 605, 1884 ; L. A. Buchner, *Bull. Soc. Chim.*, (2), **20**. 10, 1873 ; *Repert. Pharm.*, **22**. 265, 1873 ; F. A. H. Schreinmakers and W. C. de Baat, *Proc. Acad. Amsterdam*, **17**. 1111, 1916 ; J. T. D. Hinds, *Proc. Internat. Cong. App. Chem.*, **8**. i, 227, 1912 ; E. Anderson and L. G. Story, *Journ. Amer. Chem. Soc.*, **45**. 1102, 1923 ; A. Miolati and F. Masceti, *Gazz. Chim. Ital.*, **31**. i, 93, 1901 ; E. Cornec, *Contribution à l'étude de la neutralisation*, Paris, 1912 ; *Compt. Rend.*, **149**. 676, 1909 ; *Ann. Chim. Phys.*, (8), **29**. 490, 1913 ; (8), **30**. 63, 1913 ; E. G. Clayton, *Chem. News*, **64**. 27, 1891 ; R. T. Thomson, *ib.*, **49**. 119, 1884 ; **52**. 18, 29, 1885 ; L. Bruner and S. Tolloczko, *Zeit. anorg. Chem.*, **37**. 455, 1903 ; H. Remy, *ib.*, **116**. 255, 1921 ; C. Winkler, *Journ. prakt. Chem.*, (2), **31**. 247, 1885 ; E. Bacaloglo, *ib.*, (1), **83**. 111, 1861 ; A. Bussy, *Phil. Mag.*, (3), **31**. 151, 1847 ; *Journ. Pharm. Chim.*, (3), **12**. 321, 1847 ; *Compt. Rend.*, **24**. 774, 1847 ; F. M. Raoult, *Ann. Chim. Phys.*, (6), **2**. 84, 1884 ; K. Chodounsky, *Listy Chem.*, **13**. 114, 1889 ; K. Drucker, *Zeit. phys. Chem.*, **36**. 173, 693, 1901 ; C. S. Hudson, *ib.*, **50**. 273, 1904 ; E. Brunner, *ib.*, **51**. 494, 1905 ; P. Walden, *ib.*, **2**. 56, 1888 ; W. Böttger, *ib.*, **24**. 293, 1897 ; H. Biltz, *ib.*, **19**. 422, 1896 ; J. von Zawidzky, *Ber.*, **36**. 1429, 1903 ; W. A. Roth and O. Schwartz, *ib.*, **59**. B, 238, 1926 ; K. W. Pörner, *Chymische Versuche zum Nutzen der Färbekunst*, Leipzig, 1773.

¹⁷ H. Moissan, *Le fluor et ses composés*, Paris, 136, 1900 ; *Ann. Chim. Phys.*, (6), **24**. 224, 1891 ; R. Weber, *Pogg. Ann.*, **112**. 619, 1861 ; C. L. Bloxam, *Journ. Chem. Soc.*, **18**. 3, 1865 ; W. Manchot and F. Oberhauser, *Zeit. anorg. Chem.*, **130**. 163, 1923 ; **138**. 357, 1924 ; R. P. Sanyal and N. R. Dhar, *ib.*, **139**. 161, 1924 ; H. Davy, *Phil. Trans.*, **101**. 1, 1811 ; L. Gmelin, *Handbook of Chemistry*, London, 4. 256, 1850 ; C. Brame, *Ann. Chim. Phys.*, (3), **37**. 221, 1853 ; *Compt. Rend.*, **19**. 1107, 1844 ; **33**. 579, 1851 ; **37**. 90, 1853 ; J. Guinchant, *ib.*, **140**. 1101, 1170, 1905 ; P. Fleury, *Bull. Soc. Chim.*, (4), **29**. 490, 1920 ; H. Kubina, *Monatsh.*, **43**. 439, 1923 ; J. S. Chodkowsky, *Roozniki Chemji*, **2**. 183, 1923 ; K. Chodounsky, *Listy Chem.*, **13**. 114, 1889 ; J. K. Wood, *Journ. Chem. Soc.*, **93**. 412, 1908 ; L. Cambi, *Giorn. Chim. Ind. Appl.*, **6**. 527, 1924 ; C. Schultz-Sellac, *Ber.*, **4**. 109, 1871 ; K. Drucker, *Zeit. phys. Chem.*, **36**. 173, 693, 1901 ; I. N. Schiloff, *ib.*, **42**. 641, 1903 ; E. Abel and A. Fürth, *ib.*, **107**. 305, 1923 ; J. R. Roebuck, *Journ. Phys. Chem.*, **6**. 365, 1902 ; **9**. 727, 1905 ; W. C. Bray, *ib.*, **9**. 573, 1905 ; F. C. Bowman, *ib.*, **11**. 292, 1907 ; I. M. Kolthoff, *Pharm. Weekbl.*, **56**. 621, 1919 ; E. Oeman, *Svenska Kem. Tids.*, **36**. 322, 1924 ; **37**. 37, 1925 ; L. Ramberg, *ib.*, **37**. 31, 1925 ; B. J. Smart and J. T. Philpot, *Journ. Soc. Chem. Ind.*, **33**. 900, 1914 ; E. W. Washburn and E. K. Strachan, *Journ. Amer. Chem. Soc.*, **35**. 681, 1913 ; A. W. Francis, *ib.*, **48**. 655, 1926 ; L. Cambi, *Giorn. Chim. Ind. Appl.*, **6**. 527, 1924 ; D. A. MacInnes, *Zeit. phys. Chem.*, **130**. 217, 1927 ; E Anderson and L. G. Story, *Journ. Amer. Chem. Soc.*, **45**. 1102, 1923 ; J. T. D. Hinds, *Proc. Internat. Congress Appl. Chem.*, **8**. i, 227, 1912 ; K. P. Bjergaard, *Danske Tidsskr. Farm.*, **2**. 1, 1928.

¹⁸ H. Prinz, *Liebig's Ann.*, **223**. 357, 1884 ; E. Schürmann. *ib.*, **249**. 326, 1888 ; O. Brunck, *ib.*, **336**. 281, 1905 ; J. E. Mackenzie and H. Marshall, *Journ. Chem. Soc.*, **93**. 1726, 1908 ; G. Oddo and E. Serra, *Gazz. Chim. Ital.*, **29**. ii, 355, 1899 ; F. Schwers, *Journ. Soc. Chem. Ind.*, **39**. 33, T, 1920 ; P. Smellie, *ib.*, **42**. 466, T, 1923 ; J. J. Berzelius, *Schweigger's Journ.*, **34**. 46, 1822 ; *Pogg. Ann.*, **7**. 1, 137, 1826 ; L. F. Nilson, *Akad. Handl. Stockholm*, **10**. 2, 1871 ; *Oefvers. Akad. Stockholm*, **28**. 303, 1871 ; *Journ. prakt. Chem.*, (2), **14**. 159, 1876 ; H. Reinsch, *ib.*, (1), **13**. 133, 1838 ; F. Faktor, *Pharm. Post*, **38**. 527, 1905 ; G. Vortmann and C. Padberg, *Ber.*, **22**. 2642, 1888 ; G. Vortmann, *ib.*, **22**. 2307, 1889 ; J. F. Lassaigne, *Journ. Chim. Méd.*, (2), **8**. 584, 1842 ; G. Newbery, *Journ. Chem. Soc.*, **127**. 1751, 1925 ; R. Brandes, *Brandes' Arch.*, **25**. 200. 1828 ; E. Becker, *Arch. Pharm.*, **156**. 287, 1847 ; B. Grützner, *ib.*, **237**. 507, 1899 ; J. Lefort and P. Thibault, *Pharm. Journ.*, (3), **13**. 301, 1882 ; V. Auger and L. Odinot, *Compt. Rend.*, 178. 213, 1924 ; R. F. Weinland and A. Gutmann, *Zeit. anorg. Chem.*, **17**. 409, 1898 ; A. Gutmann, *Ber.*, **38**. 1728, 3277, 1905 ; **40**. 2818, 1907 ; **41**. 1650, 1908 ; W. Marckwald and A. Foizik, *ib.*, **43**. 1710, 1910 ; J. von Szilagyi, *Zeit. anorg. Chem.*, **113**. 75, 1920 ; K. Chodounsky, *Listy Chem.*, **13**. 114. 1889 ; G. S. Forbes, H. W. Estill, and O. J. Walker, *Journ. Amer. Chem. Soc.*, **44**. 97, 1922 ; W. Trautmann, *Zeit. anal. Chem.*, **50**. 371, 1911 ; C. Schultz-Sellac, *Ber.*, **4**. 109, 1871.

¹⁹ I. A. Bachman, *Amer. Chem. Journ.*, **10**. 42, 1888 ; F. D. Chattaway and H. P. Stevens, *ib.*, **23**. 369, 1900 ; T. L. Bailey, *Ann. Rept. Alkali*, **62**. 12, 1926 ; E. Deussen, *Arch. Pharm.*, **264**. 355, 1926 ; E. Rupp and E. Muschiol, *Ber. deut. pharm. Ges.*, **33**. 62, 1923 ; L. Möser and W. Eidmann, *Ber.*, **35**. 535, 1902 ; G. Lunge, *ib.*, **11**. 1229, 1878 ; J. V. Janowsky, *ib.*, **8**. 1636, 1875 ; J. A. Buchner, *Journ. Pharm. Chim.*, (3), **2**. 421, 1842 ; A. Klemenc and F. Pollak, *Zeit. anorg. Chem.*, **115**. 131, 1921 ; V. de Luynes, *Compt. Rend.*, **44**. 1354, 1857 ; R. Engel, *ib.*, **96**. 498, 1883 ; T. Bergman, *De arsenico*, Upsala, 1777 ; A. Klemenc and R. Schöller, *Zeit. anorg. Chem.*, **141**. 231, 1924 ; A. Geuther, *Liebig's Ann.*, **245**. 96, 1888 ; L. Hurtzig and A. Geuther, *ib.*, **111**. 172, 1859 ; L. Hurtzig, *Einige Beiträge zur näheren Kenntniss der Säuren des Phosphors und Arseniks*, Göttingen, 1859 ; A. Oppenheim, *Bull. Soc. Chim.*, (2), **1**. 165, 1864 ; W. Wallace and F. Penny, *Phil. Mag.*, (4), **4**. 361, 1852 ; N. W. Fischer, *Pogg. Ann.*, **9**. 260, 1827 ; J. J. Berzelius, *Ann. Chim. Phys.*, (2), **5**. 179, 1817 ; (2), **11**. 225, 1819 ; A. Michaelis, *Jena. Zeit.*, (1), **6**. 239, 1870 ; B. Reinitzer and H. Goldschmidt, *Monatsh.*, **1**. 427, 1881 ; G. Gore, *Proc. Roy. Soc.*, **20**. 441, 1872 ; **21**. 140, 1873 ; E. C. Franklin and C. A. Kraus, *Amer. Chem. Journ.*, **20**. 820, 1898 ; N. N. Sen, *Proc. Asiatic Soc. Bengal*, **15**. 263, 1919 ; C. M. Smith and G. E. Miller, *Journ. Ind. Eng. Chem.*, **16**. 1168, 1924 ; J. Thiele, *Apoth. Ztg.*, **5**. 86, 1890 ; A. Gutmann, *Ber.*,

55. B, 3007, 1922 ; A. Klemenc, *ib.*, 58. B, 492, 1925; P. Askenasy, E. Elöd, and H Zieler, *Zeit. anorg Chem.*, 162. 161, 1927.
²⁰ J. J. Berzelius, *Ann. Chim. Phys.*, (2), 5. 179, 1817 ; (2), 11. 225, 1819 ; I. W. Fay, A. F. Seeker, F. H. Lane, and G. E. Ferguson, *Polyt. Eng.*, 10. 72, 1910 ; A. Vogel, *Dingler's Journ.*, 144. 159, 1857 ; A. C. Pereira, *Riv. Chim. Appl.*, 4. 174, 1919 ; E. H. Büchner, *Zeit. phys. Chem.*, 54. 674, 1906 ; M. Dubinin, *ib.*, 123. 86, 1926 ; *Journ. Russ. Phys. Chem. Soc.*, 58. 1187, 1926 ; J. Marshall and L. A. Ryan, *Amer. Journ. Pharmacy*, 75. 251, 1903.
²¹ H. Rose, *Pogg. Ann.*, 52. 455, 1841 ; G. Lockemann and M. Paucke, *Zeit. Koll.*, 8. 273, 1911 ; C. Winkler, *Journ. prakt. Chem.*, (2), 31. 347, 1885 ; G. G. Henderson and A. R. Ewing, *Journ. Chem. Soc.*, 67. 105, 1895 ; A. W. Hofmann, *Phil. Mag.*, (3), 24. 115, 193, 261, 1844 ; *Ann. Chim. Phys.*, (3), 9. 143, 169, 1843 ; G. Baudran, *ib.*, (7), 19. 549, 1900 ; J. Pelouze, *ib.*, (2), 6. 63, 1817 ; J. J. Berzelius, *ib.*, (2), 5. 179, 1817 ; (2), 11. 225, 1819 ; E. Beckmann and W. Gabel, *Zeit. anorg. Chem.*, 51. 236, 1906 ; F. Auerbach, *ib.*, 37. 376, 1903 ; T. Bergman, *De arsenico*, Upsala, 1777 ; A. Naumann, *Ber.*, 37. 4329, 1904 ; F. Selmi, *ib.*, 13. 206, 1880 ; W. Eidmann, *Ein Beitrag zur Erkenntnis des Verhaltens chemischer Verbindungen in nichtwässrigen Lösungen*, Giessen, 1899 ; A. Pictet and A. Bon, *Bull. Soc. Chim.*, (3), 33. 1139, 1905 ; A. Rack, *Compt. Rend.*, 57. 203, 1863 ; P. Schützenberger, *ib.*, 53. 538, 1861 ; A. Souchay and E. Lenssen, *Liebig's Ann.*, 105. 255, 1858 ; P. A. Cap, *Répert. Chim. Appl.*, 3. 356, 1861 ; J. J. Heimpel, *Repert. Pharm.*, 62. 1, 1838 ; K. von Grundner, *ib.*, 61. 289, 1837 ; F. Ephraim, *Helvetica Chim. Acta*, 3. 800, 1920 ; H. Meerwein, *Liebig's Ann.*, 455. 227, 1927 ; J. Giradin, *Journ. Pharm. Chim.*, (3), 46. 269, 1864 ; *Bull. Soc. Chim.*, (2), 10. 230, 1868 ; N. W. Fischer, *Schweigger's Journ.*, 12. 155, 1814 ; 39. 364, 1823 ; A. Vogel, *München Gel. Anz.*, 40. 33, 1855 ; *Kastner's Arch.*, 9. 319, 1826; C. F. Wenzel, *Lehre von der Verwandschaft der Korper*, Dresden, 444, 1777 ; L. Thompson, *Phil. Mag.*, (3), 10. 353, 1837 ; O. Aschau, *Chem. Ztg.*, 37. 1117, 1913.
²² E. Vigouroux, *Ann. Chim. Phys.*, (7), 12. 153, 1897 ; E. Berger, *Compt. Rend.*, 170. 1492, 1920 ; O. Ruff and K. Albert, *Ber.*, 38. 2234, 1905 ; W. Biltz, *ib.*, 37. 3138, 1904 ; F. Auerbach, *Zeit. anorg. Chem.*, 37. 353, 1903 ; G. Rauter, *Liebig's Ann.*, 270. 236, 1892 ; E. Wedekind and H. Wilke, *Koll. Zeit.*, 34. 83, 1924 ; K. Fuwa, *Journ. Japan. Cer. Assoc.*, 32. 469, 1924 ; D. J. McSwiney, *Journ. Amer. Cer. Soc.*, 8. 507, 1925 ; W. E. S. Turner, *ib.*, 9. 412, 1926 ; S. English, E. M. Firth, and W. E. S. Turner, *Journ. Soc. Glass Tech.*, 11. 65, 1927 ; E. M. Firth, F. W. Hodkin, and W. E. S. Turner, *ib.*, 11. 190, 1927 ; E. M. Firth, F. W. Hodkin, W. E. S. Turner, and F. Winks, *ib.*, 11. 205, 1927 ; L. Kahlenberg and W. J. Trautmann, *Trans. Amer. Electrochem. Soc.*, 39. 377, 1921.
²³ J. L. Gay Lussac and L. J. Thénard, *Recherches physico-chimiques*, Paris, 1. 516, 1811 ; A. F. Gehlen, *Schweigger's Journ.*, 15. 501, 1815 ; 20. 353, 1817 ; E. Frémy, *Compt. Rend.*, 70. 66, 1870 ; E. Berger, *ib.*, 170. 1492, 1920 ; W. Biltz, *Ber.*, 37. 3138, 1904 ; K. C. Sen, *Journ. Phys. Chem.*, 31. 1840, 1927.
²⁴ J. F. Simon, *Pogg. Ann.*, 40. 417, 1837 ; W. H. Wollaston, *Phil. Trans.*, 98. 96, 1808 ; J. L. Gay Lussac, *Ann. Chim. Phys.*, (2), 3. 136, 1816 ; *Phil. Mag.*, 49. 280, 1817 ; C. Brame, *Compt. Rend.*, 92. 188, 1881 ; L. P. de St. Gilles, *ib.*, 46. 424, 1858 ; *Ann. Chim. Phys.*, (3), 55. 385, 1859 ; C. Reichard, *Ber.*, 27. 1019, 1894 ; 30. 1913, 1897 ; 31. 2163, 1898 ; B. L. Vanzetti, *Gazz. Chim. Ital.*, 55. 110, 1925 ; F. Kessler, *Pogg. Ann.*, 95. 204, 1853 ; 118. 17, 1863 ; W. L. Miller, *Journ. Phys. Chem.*, 11. 9, 1907 ; R. E. de Lury, *ib.*, 11. 47, 54, 1907 ; W. Trautmann, *Zeit. anal. Chem.*, 50. 371, 1910 ; L. G. Story and E. Anderson, *Journ. Amer. Chem. Soc.*, 46. 533, 1924 ; F. Feigl and F. Weiner, *Zeit. anal. Chem.*, 64. 302, 1924 ; K. C. Sen, *Journ. Phys. Chem.*, 31. 922, 1927 ; O. Cantoni, *Annali Chim. Appl.*, 16. 153, 1926 ; R. Lang, *Zeit. Elektrochem.*, 32. 454, 1926 ; L. Moser and F. Perjatel, *Monatsh.*, 33. 751, 1912 ; F. Feigl and F. Weiner, *Zeit. anal. Chem.*, 64. 302, 1924 ; I. M. Kolthoff, *Pharm. Weekbl.*, 61. 738, 1924 ; A. Stavenhagen, *Journ. prakt. Chem.*, (2), 51. 1, 1895 ; A. Travers, *Bull. Soc. Chim.*, (4), 37. 456, 1925 ; M. Geloso, *ib.*, (4), 37. 641, 1925 ; *Compt. Rend.*, 171. 1145, 1920 ; A. Bussy, *ib.*, 24. 774, 1847 ; L. Moser and F. Perjatel, *Monatsh.*, 33. 751, 1912 ; L. Vanino, *Zeit. anal. Chem.*, 34. 426, 1895 ; A. Klemenc, *ib.*, 61. 448, 1922 ; B. Brauner, *ib.*, 55. 242, 1916 ; E. Waitz, *ib.*, 10. 174, 1871 ; K. Swoboda, *ib.*, 64. 156, 1924 ; O. Kühling, *Ber.*, 34. 404, 1901 ; E. Lenssen, *Journ. prakt. Chem.*, (1), 78. 197, 1859 ; W. T. Hall and C. E. Carlson, *Journ. Amer. Chem. Soc.*, 45. 1615, 1923 ; J. H. Yoe, *ib.*, 46. 2390, 1924 ; E. Deiss, *Chem. Ztg.*, 34. 237, 1910 ; A. Bose, *Chem. News*, 117. 369, 1918 ; R. Lang, *Sitzber. böhm. Ges. Wiss.*, 20, 1904 ; *Zeit. anorg. Chem.*, 152. 197, 1926 ; T. Oryng, *ib.*, 163. 195, 1927 ; J. Holluta, *ib.*, 168. 361, 1927.
²⁵ W. Biltz, *Ber.*, 37. 1766, 3138, 1904 ; *Journ. Chim. Phys.*, 7. 370, 1909 ; A. Reychler, *ib.*, 7. 362, 1909 ; 8. 10, 1910 ; R. Bunsen and A. A. Berthold, *Das Eisenoxydhydrat, ein Gegengift des weissen Arseniks oder der arsenigen Säure*, Göttingen, 1834 ; R. Bunsen, *Pogg. Ann.*, 32. 124, 1834 ; G. Lockemann, *Verh. Ges. deut. Naturforsh. Aertze*, 11. 25, 1911 ; G. Lockemann and M. Paucke, *Zeit. Koll.*, 8. 273, 1911 ; G. Lockemann and F. Lucius, *Zeit. phys. Chem.*, 83. 735, 1913 ; W. Mecklenberg, *ib.*, 83. 609, 1913 ; J. M. Clavera, *Anal. Fis. Quim.*, 24. 168, 1926 ; K. C. Sen, *Journ. Phys. Chem.*, 31. 419, 687, 1840, 1927 ; M. R. Mehrotra and K. C. Sen, *Koll. Zeit.*, 42. 35, 1927 ; T. Oryng, *ib.*, 22. 149, 1918 ; A. Stavenhagen, *Journ. prakt. Chem.*, (2), 51. 1, 1895 ; A. Reynoso, *Compt. Rend.*, 31. 68, 1850 ; N. J. B. G. Guibourt, *Journ. Chim. Méd.*, 15. 306, 1839 ; M. C. Boswell and J. V. Dickson, *Journ. Amer. Chem. Soc.*, 40. 1793, 1918 ; L. Herboth, *Arch. Pharm.*, (2), 264. 181, 1926 ; C. Mannich and C. A. Rojahn, *ib.*, 262. 293, 1924.
²⁶ P. Woulfe, *Phil. Trans.*, 61. 127, 1771 ; *Crell's Chem. Journ.*, 1. 155, 1778 ; F. Kessler,

Pogg. Ann., **113**. 150, 1861; M. Kohn, *Monatsh.*, **43**. 367, 1923; A. Bettendorff, *Zeit. anal. Chem.*, **9**. 105, 1870; A. Ferraro and A. Carobbio, *Boll. Chim. Farm.*, **44**. 805, 1905; O. Schlickum, *Arch. Pharm.*, (3), **23**. 710, 1885; K. Jellinek and L. Winogradoff, *Zeit. Elektrochem.*, **30**. 477, 1924; L. Winogradoff, *Ueber die Statik und Kinetik der Reaktion zwischen Ferrichlorid und arseniger Säure*, Danzig, 1924; C. O. Curtman, *Journ. Amer. Chem. Soc.*, **16**. 581, 1894; G. Frerichs, *Apoth. Ztg.*, **12**. 176, 1897; H. Rose, *Pogg. Ann.*, **76**. 534, 1849; W. Manchot and F. Glaser, *Zeit. anorg. Chem.*, **27**. 240, 1901; K. Zwicknagl, *ib.*, **151**. 41, 1926; R. Lang and J. Zwerina, *ib.*, **170**. 389, 1928; J. Zwerina, *Ueber einige Arsenit methoden, insbesondere unter Anwendung der Manganosalz- und Jodkatalyse*, Brunn, 1927; G. Gire, *Compt. Rend.*, **171**. 174, 1920.

§ 12. The Arsenites

There are several reported [1] occurrences of sodium arsenite in natural waters. Thus, C. Morelli observed 6·2 mgrms. per litre in the water of Ceresole Reale of Piedemont; O. Henry and C. L. Lhéritier, traces in the waters of Plombières; and R. Pribram, 3·43 mgrms. per litre in the waters of Donna Sara, Roumania. In 1746, P. J. Macquer [2] prepared an impure alkali arsenite by treating white arsenic with alkali-lye; he called the product *foie d'arsenic—liver of arsenic—* apparently regarding arsenic as a compound of sulphur. In 1855, C. R. Fresenius [3] said that no definite alkali arsenite had been prepared other than syrups and evaporation residues of variable composition. J. Thomsen's results for the heat of neutralization of an aq. soln. of arsenic trioxide with soda-lye, are indicated above. The action of indicators in the neutralization of alkali arsenites with acids was discussed by G. Favrel, R. T. Thomson, F. A. Flückiger, etc.—*vide supra*.

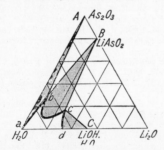

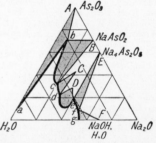

Fig. 17.—Equilibrium in the Ternary System : As_2O_3-Li_2O-H_2O at 25°.

Fig. 18.—Equilibrium in the Ternary System : Na_2O-As_2O_3-H_2O at 30°.

F. A. H. Schreinemaker and W. C. de Baat studied the ternary system : As_2O_3-Li_2O-H_2O at 25°. The results are summarized in Fig. 17. The curve *ab* represents the solubility of arsenic trioxide in lithia-lye; *bc*, the solubility of lithium metarsenite, $LiAsO_2$; and *cd*, the solubility of hydrated lithium hydroxide, $LiOH.H_2O$. The shaded areas represent supersaturated soln. The conditions of stability of lithium metarsenite are shown in the diagram. The results of F. A. H. Schreinemaker and W. C. de Baat's study of the system Na_2O-As_2O_3-H_2O at 30° are illustrated by Fig. 18. Here *A* denotes the solubility of arsenic trioxide in water ; the region *abA*, the supersaturated soln. with arsenic trioxide as solid phase ; *bcB*, of the solid phase $NaAsO_2$; *cdC*, of the solid $Na_4As_2O_5.9H_2O$; *deD*, of the solid $Na_{10}As_4O_{11}.26H_2O$; *efE*, of the solid $Na_4As_2O_5$; and *fgF*, of the hydrate $NaOH.H_2O$. The solubility curve *ab* shows the rapid increase in the solubility of arsenic trioxide as the proportion of alkali in the soln. increases. The results of F. A. H. Schreinemaker and W. C. de Baat's study of the ternary

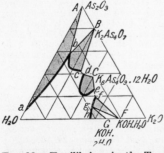

Fig. 19.—Equilibrium in the Ternary System : As_2O_3-K_2O-H_2O at 25°.

system As_2O_3-K_2O-H_2O at 25° are shown in Fig. 19. *ab* represents the solubility curve of arsenic trioxide ; *bc*, that of potassium paratetrarsenite, $K_2As_4O_7$; *de*, that of potassium metatetrarsenite, $K_6As_4O_9.12H_2O$; *fg*, that of KOH.H_2O ; and *gh*, that of KOH.$2H_2O$. The dotted lines *cd* and *ef* represent unstable phases not yet recognized. The shaded areas represent supersaturated soln. The constitution of the tetrarsenites may be referred to that of the arsenic trioxide, As_4O_6, which, with the *orthotetrarsenious acid*, $H_8As_4O_{10}$, can be represented graphically :

$$O\!\!>\!\!\underset{O}{\overset{O}{\text{As}:\text{As}}}\!\!<\!\!{}^{O}_{O}$$

Arsenic trioxide, As_4O_6.

$$(HO)_2\!\!>\!\!\underset{(HO)_2}{\overset{O}{\text{As}:\text{As}}}\!\!<\!\!{}^{(OH)_2}_{(OH)_2}$$

Orthotetrarsenious acid, $H_8As_4O_{10}$.

The derivatives of the ortho-acid are therefore :

Orthotetrarsenious acid	$H_8As_4O_{10}$ (or $H_4As_2O_5$)
Metatetrarsenious acid	$H_6As_4O_9$
Mesotetrarsenious acid	$H_4As_4O_8$ (or H_2AsO_2)
Paratetrarsenious acid	$H_2As_4O_7$

A. Stavenhagen heated finely-powdered arsenic trioxide with an excess of an alcoholic soln. of sodium hydroxide in a reflux condenser, and after repeated extraction with alcohol, allowed the product to dry at 100°. The white powder has a composition approximating that of **sodium orthoarsenite**, Na_3AsO_3. There is some doubt about the existence of the alkali orthoarsenites, and B. L. Vanzetti made sodium orthoarsenite by reacting on arsenic trioxide with sodium methoxide : $As_2O_3+6NaOCH_3 \rightarrow 2Na_3AsO_3+3(CH_3)_2O$. The arsenic trioxide easily dissolves in sodium methoxide, but not in sodium ethoxide, even after long boiling. The excess of methyl alcohol was distilled off on the water-bath. The remaining soln., when evaporated in vacuo, gives a white crystalline crust. The first fractions were nearly 80 per cent. Na_3AsO_3, and the last fractions 20 per cent. The salt gives yellow silver orthoarsenite when treated with silver nitrate. The reaction with arsenic trioxide and sodium methoxide was not completed even after long boiling. B. L. Vanzetti prepared **potassium orthoarsenite**, K_3AsO_3, in a similar manner, but the syrup could not be crystallized. A. Stavenhagen obtained a crystalline mass of potassium orthoarsenite by treating arsenic trioxide with an alcoholic soln. of potassium hydroxide. The potassium salt was also obtained by H. O. Schulze by exposing a soln. of arsenic trioxide and potassium iodide to air ; and by A. Stavenhagen by treating the barium salt with potassium sulphate, and drying the clear liquid over conc. sulphuric acid at 100° in an atm. of hydrogen. The potassium salt forms a group of clear, transparent needles which become turbid when exposed to air ; the sodium salt is a white powder. Both sodium and potassium arsenites dissolve freely in water. R. Robl observed no fluorescence with sodium arsenite in ultra-violet light. P. Walden gave for the eq. electrical conductivity of one-third of a mol of sodium orthoarsenite in *v* litres of water :

v . .	32	64	128	256	512	1024
λ . .	158·3	160·1	161·1	160·6	156·7	154·3

J. von Zawidzky discussed this subject, and concluded from his observations that the soln. contains $Na(H_2AsO_3)$, not Na_3AsO_3—*vide supra*, aq. soln. of arsenic trioxide. E. Blanc estimated that in 0·0104N-aq. soln., sodium dihydrarsenite is 0·394 per cent. hydrolyzed. A. Miolati and E. Mascetti studied the sp. conductivity of arsenious acid during the progressive addition of a soln. of sodium hydroxide ; and E. Cornec, the lowering of the f.p. According to R. Suchy and J. Michel, arsenic trioxide dissolved in a soln. of sodium carbonate is precipitated by carbon dioxide. A. W. Francis studied the speed of oxidation by bromine, and found the velocity constant of the reaction to be 4. K. H. Butler and D. McIntosh found sodium arsenite to be insoluble in liquid chlorine. According to A. Gutmann, sodium thiosulphate reacts with a soln. of the tertiary sodium or potassium orthoarsenites : $Na_3AsO_3+Na_2S_2O_3=Na_3AsSO_3+Na_2SO_3$, and with the secondary salt, sodium hydroarsenite, $Na_2HAsO_3+Na_2S_2O_3=NaHSO_3+Na_3AsSO_3$; and with the primary salt, a complex salt is formed, $Na_8As_{18}O_7S_{24}.3H_2O$; sodium tetrathionate reacts only slowly at ordinary temp., but when warmed, brown arsenic separates, and a soln. of sulphite, arsenate, and trioxysulpharsenate is produced; similar products are formed by the action of a warm soln. of sodium trithionate ; while a cold or boiling soln. of sodium dithionate has no action on sodium ortho-arsenite. According to A. Gutmann, the azides of sodium, barium, and lead do not react with normal sodium arsenite, which gives a silver mirror with ammoniacal soln. of silver azide, due solely to the reducing action of the arsenite on the silver salt. Chloroazoimide and sodium arsenite yield sodium azide, arsenate, and chloride ; iodoazoimide behaves similarly. The permanence of the azido-groups in inorganic compounds appears most readily explicable on the basis of T. Curtius' formula. A. Gutmann found that sodium orthoarsenite reacts with quadrivalent oxygen in dioxides ; with sulphur in polysulphides and disulphides ; and with quinquevalent and tervalent nitrogen in organic compounds. The aq. soln. reacts alkaline, and slowly oxidizes to arsenate on exposure to air ; W. Reinders and S. I. Vles said that the oxidation of alkali arsenite with free oxygen occurs only in the presence of a catalytic agent, and with silver nitrate furnishes a precipitate of normal silver arsenite. W. Clark studied the reversal of photographic plates by sodium arsenite. A. W. Francis measured the speed of oxidation of sodium arsenite ; and J. D. Jenkins and E. F. Berger found that copper and copper salts act as catalysts. N. R. Dhar and co-workers, and W. P. Jorissen and co-workers found that the oxidation of phosphorus, sulphites, stannous salts, chloroform, benzaldehyde, and acrolein is retarded in presence of sodium arsenite ; and A. N. Dey and N. R. Dhar showed that the oxidation of sodium arsenite at ordinary temp. is effected by passing air through a soln. in which finely divided copper, cuprous chloride or oxide, zinc, or yellow phosphorus is suspended ; finely divided copper dissolves in cold soln. of sodium arsenite only in the presence of oxygen. The oxidation of sodium arsenite can be induced by the simultaneous oxidation of sodium sulphite, stannous chloride, manganous or cobaltous hydroxide, and various aldehydes. A. Gutmann found nitric oxide oxidizes sodium arsenite : $2NO+Na_3AsO_3=N_2O+Na_3AsO_4$; and with hydroxylamine, there are concurrent reactions, $NH_2OH+Na_3AsO_3=Na_3AsO_4+NH_3$; and $3NH_2OH=NH_3+N_2+3H_2O$. C. P. Jorissen and C. van den Pol said that sodium sulphite does not induce the oxidation of sodium arsenite soln. when the alkalinity is too great. F. E. Brown and J. E. Snyder found that sodium arsenite does not react with boiling vanadium oxytrichloride ; J. H. C. Smith and H. A. Spoehr observed that sodium ferropyro-phosphate acts as a catalyst in the oxidation of potassium arsenite soln., and that an intermediate compound is formed with oxygen and the catalyst. A. Gutmann also studied the oxidation of the salt by organic compounds—sodium benzen-diazoxide, azoxybenzene, etc. Sodium benzene-iso-diazoxide does not act ; neither does sodium nitroprusside. M. C. Boswell and J. V. Dickson found that sodium arsenite is oxidized by fusion with the hydroxide.

A. Stavenhagen treated barium pyroarsenite with a soln. of potassium sulphate and evaporated the soln. The white powder so obtained was **hexahydrated potassium pyroarsenite**, $K_4As_2O_5.6H_2O$. L. Pasteur reported it to be formed by adding alcohol to a mixed soln. of potassium hydroxide and hexarsenite, but A. Stavenhagen said that the product so obtained is a mixture of variable composition. P. Walden gave for the eq. electrical conductivity of one-third of a mol of sodium metarsenite in v litres of water :

v	32	64	128	256	512	1024
λ	73·2	77·3	80·9	84·4	87·6	9·6

J. K. Wood found the ionization constant to be 0·000214 ; and calculated that in a decinormal soln., 1·4 per cent. of the salt is hydrolyzed at 25°. The salt is readily soluble in water, less so in alcohol ; it is decomposed by carbon dioxide ; and forms with silver nitrate the corresponding silver pyroarsenite. L. Pasteur could not prepare the corresponding **sodium pyroarsenite,** $Na_4As_2O_5$, in crystals, and A. Stavenhagen was not satisfied about the individuality of the product ; but F. A. H. Schreinemaker and W. C. de Baat's diagram, Fig. 18, shows the condition of stability and also that of **enneahydrated sodium pyroarsenite,** $Na_4As_2O_5.9H_2O$.

According to C. L. Bloxam, if a soln. of sodium carbonate be boiled with an excess of arsenic trioxide, and the clear soln. evaporated to dryness, **sodium metarsenite,** $NaAsO_2$, is formed ; but if a mixture of dry sodium carbonate and arsenic trioxide be heated to redness, a mixture of arsenite and arsenate is formed. The conditions of stability are illustrated by Fig. 19. A. Stavenhagen found that if alcohol be poured over a soln. of arsenic trioxide in soda-lye, a yellow syrupy liquid is obtained, which, on evaporation, yields a white powder of variable composition and containing some crystals of arsenic trioxide. According to C. Reichard, salts of the type $M_3(AsO_3)_2$ are precipitated when sodium metarsenite is added to a soln. of stannous chloride, zinc sulphate, or lead or nickel nitrate ; $M_2As_2O_5$, with soln. of cadmium sulphate, or cobalt nitrate ; $Cu_4As_2O_7$, copper sulphate ; $Fe_4As_2O_9$, with ferrous sulphate ; $M_5(AsO_4)_2$, with manganese sulphate or mercuric chloride ; $Sn_7As_2O_{17}$, with stannic chloride ; and $Ag_6As_4O_9$, with silver nitrate. F. E. Brown and J. E. Snyder observed no reaction with vanadium oxytrichloride and anhydrous sodium arsenite. If potassium hexarsenite be boiled for some hours with a soln. of potassium carbonate, and the product washed with alcohol, L. Pasteur said that the syrupy mass is **potassium metarsenite,** $KAsO_2$, but A. Stavenhagen could obtain only an impure salt in this way. E. Cornec showed that the measuring of the effect of the progressive neutralization of arsenious acid by potash-lye on the f.p. of aq. soln. shows the existence of the metarsenite. J. C. Ghosh and S. C. Bisvas measured the extinction coeff. of potassium arsenite in ultra-violet light. A. Bouchonnet prepared **rubidium metarsenite,** $RbAsO_2$, by the action of arsenic trioxide on an aq. soln. of rubidium carbonate. The amorphous white powder, and the aq. soln. furnish the arsenate when heated. The aq. soln. is alkaline towards litmus, methyl-orange, and phenolphthalein. C. C. Palit and N. R. Dhar observed that metal salt soln. accelerate the oxidation of soln. of sodium arsenite by air—*vide* arsenic trioxide.

L. Pasteur, and A. Stavenhagen reported **potassium paratetrarsenite,** $K_2As_4O_7.2H_2O$, to be formed as a syrupy liquid when an excess of arsenic trioxide is treated with a cold soln. of potassium hydroxide, and mixed with alcohol. The liquid crystallizes on standing some time. C. L. Bloxam also found it to be deposited on cooling a boiling conc. soln. of potassium carbonate and arsenic trioxide. The conditions of stability of the anhydrous salt are indicated in F. A. H. Schreinemakers and W. C. de Baat's diagram, Fig. 20. The prismatic crystals of the hydrated salt lose a mol. of water at 100° ; and some water is lost at ordinary temp. over sulphuric acid. The salt melts a little over 100° in dry air, forming a yellow liquid which congeals to a glassy mass. Some arsenate, arsine, and arsenic are formed at the same time. Acids precipitate arsenic trioxide from conc. soln., but not from dil. soln. ; and silver nitrate precipitates normal silver arsenite from the aq. soln. The conditions of stability of **potassium metatetrarsenite,** $K_6As_4O_9.12H_2O$, are indicated in F. A. H. Schreine-

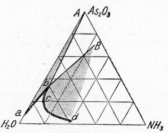

FIG. 20.—Equilibrium in the Ternary System : As_2O_3–NH_3–H_2O.

makers and W. C. de Baat's diagram, Fig. 20 ; and those of **hexacosihydrated sodium tetrarsenite,** $Na_{10}As_4O_{11}.26H_2O$, are illustrated by Fig. 20. According to

C. L. Bloxam, if arsenic trioxide be boiled with an excess of a soln. of potassium carbonate, the filtrate, on evaporation, furnishes a crystaline mass approximating potassium hexarsenite, $K_4As_6O_{11}.3H_2O$; A. Stavenhagen could not verify this.

According to J. J. Berzelius,[4] arsenic trioxide dissolves freely in hot aq. ammonia, and on cooling, or, according to J. M. F. de Lassone, on evaporating the soln., the original salt is deposited in octahedral crystals. Similar results were obtained by N. J. B. G. Guibourt, and N. W. Fischer. The results of F. A. H. Schreinemakers and W. C. de Baat's study of the ternary system $As_2O_3-NH_3-H_2O$ at 30° are summarized in Fig. 20. The point a represents the solubility of arsenic trioxide in water ; the curve ab, the solubility of the trioxide in ammoniacal soln. The area abA represents supersaturated soln. with the trioxide as the solid phase ; and the area SdB, unsaturated soln. with NH_4AsO_2 as the solid phase. Evidence of the formation of $NH_4(H_2AsO_3)$ was also obtained, but this region was not explored. E. Cornec observed no evidence of the formation of an ammonium arsenite by measuring the f.p. of soln. of arsenic trioxide progressively neutralized with aq. ammonia. A. Stavenhagen found that if arsenic trioxide be treated with an alcoholic soln. of ammonia, a pale yellow viscid mass is formed which does not become solid, and when dried in hydrogen at 40°, loses all its ammonia. A. Miolati and E. Mascetti studied the sp. conductivity of arsenious acid when progressively treated with additions of ammonia ; and E. Cornec likewise measured the lowering of the f.p. of the soln. According to L. Pasteur, the crystalline mass, obtained by pouring conc. aq. ammonia on arsenic trioxide, consists of ammonium pyroarsenite, $(NH_4)_4As_2O_5$. A. Stavenhagen could not obtain L. Pasteur's salt, but W. Stein obtained the crystals which he washed with alcohol, then with ether, and finally pressed between bibulous paper. The salt furnishes oblique, rectangular, prismatic crystals, which look like hexagonal plates. They are permanent only in contact with the ammoniacal soln., for when taken out of the liquid or dissolved in water, ammonia is given off. The ammonia is rapidly given off when the salt is confined over sulphuric acid. According to N. W. Fischer, when conc. aq. ammonia is poured over pulverized arsenic trioxide, and the mixture is warmed so as to dissolve the viscid mass which is deposited, crystals of an acid salt— ammonium metarsenite, NH_4AsO_2, separate out in rhombic prisms. C. L. Bloxam washed the crystals with alcohol, and dried them between folds of bibulous paper. V. de Luynes heated to 70° or 80° a mixture of arsenic trioxide and conc. aq. ammonia in a closed vessel, and, after the mixture has stood for some time, poured off the clear liquid, allowed the crystals to drain on porous tiles, and dried them between folds of bibulous paper. The analyses of C. L. Bloxam, F. A. H. Schreine-makers and W. C. de Baat, and V. de Luynes agreed with the formula NH_4AsO_2, but A. Stavenhagen could not confirm this. The conditions of stability are indicated in Fig. 20. The salt rapidly loses ammonia when exposed to air ; it is freely soluble in water, but sparingly soluble in aq. ammonia. If the aq. soln. be evaporated, arsenic trioxide is deposited. The aq. soln. gives precipitates with silver and copper salts. A little alcohol precipitates arsenic trioxide from the aq. soln., but much alcohol leaves the soln. transparent. The existence of ammonium dihydroarsenite, $NH_3(H_2AsO_3)$, was indicated by F. A. H. Schreine-makers and W. C. de Baat. H. Stamm measured the solubility of ammonium arsenite in aq. ammonia.

According to L. Gmelin,[5] red-hot copper oxide does not absorb the vapour of arsenic trioxide. G. Tammann found that when a mixture of cupric oxide and arsenic trioxide is heated, there is an exothermal reaction at 400°, and the grey colour of the mass becomes reddish-violet. There is a terrace in the heating curve at 468°. The reaction $4CuO+As_2O_3=2Cu_2O+As_2O_5-12.5$ cals. is endo-thermal, but if a compound is formed, its heat of formation may make the reaction exothermal. J. L. Proust, H. Braconnot, C. L. Bloxam, and R. Fittig showed that when a soln. of a copper salt is treated with a soln. of arsenic trioxide and potassium hydroxide, a greenish precipitate containing copper arsenite is formed.

Owing to the hydrolysis of the salt, the product is more or less impure. J. J. Berzelius found that a soln. of copper carbonate in an excess of arsenious acid is not precipitated by acids or alkalies; and on evaporation it furnishes a yellowish-green mass which, according to A. Stavenhagen, does not have a constant composition. Analogous observations were made by S. P. Sharples, W. Hampe, and C. Reichard. A bluish-green mineral, found by A. Damour and G. vom Rath in druses in the massive cuprite of Copiapo, Chili, was named *trippkeite*—after P. Trippke. The qualitative analysis shows that it is a copper arsenite, $nCuO.As_2O_3$. The tetragonal crystals have the axial ratio $a:c=1:0.9160$; the habit is octahedral; and the cleavage on the (100)-face is perfect, while that on the (110)-face is imperfect. J. A. Krenner supposes the mineral to be isomorphous with ferrous phosphite, $nFeO.P_2O_3$, represented by the mineral schafarzikite (*q.v.*). E. S. Larsen gave for the refractive indices $\omega=1.900$, and $\epsilon=2.12$. The optical character is positive. The mineral is readily soluble in acids.

A. Stavenhagen made **copper orthoarsenite,** $Cu_3(AsO_3)_2$, by adding a soln. of normal potassium arsenite in 50 per cent. alcohol to an alcoholic soln. of cupric chloride, and drying the product at 100°. The dirty yellowish-green mass is decomposed by water. S. P. Sharples obtained **dihydrated copper orthoarsenite,** $Cu_3(AsO_3)_2.2H_2O$, by mixing a boiling soln. of arsenic trioxide (2 parts) and decahydrated sodium carbonate (8 parts) in water (10 parts) with one of pentahydrated copper sulphate (6 parts) in water (40 parts). After boiling a few minutes, the precipitate is allowed to settle, washed with hot water, and dried at 100°. The salt is not freed from water at 150°; it is not blackened by boiling water; it is soluble in dil. acids and alkalies. The soln. in alkali-lye is decomposed by an excess of the alkali hydroxide or carbonate. The boiling ammoniacal soln. is not decomposed, while the addition of potassium hydroxide decolorizes the soln. in consequence of the formation of cuprous salts. The reports of A. Stavenhagen, and S. P. Sharples of the behaviour of copper orthoarsenite towards water need revision. C. Reichard prepared a basic salt, **copper dioxyarsenite,** $5CuO.As_2O_3$, or $2CuO.Cu_3(AsO_3)_2$, by treating an excess of copper sulphate with a dil. soln. of arsenic trioxide. The pale green precipitate was washed by decantation, and dried at ordinary temp. The salt retains its colour at 100°; at 120°–130°, it loses 10 per cent. of water and becomes dark green. It is insoluble in water, but soluble in acids, and it forms a deep blue soln. with aq. ammonia. The ammoniacal soln. is not changed by boiling, and when neutralized or when the ammonia is volatilized, the dioxyarsenite is again precipitated. The salt is soluble in conc. potash-lye, forming a blue soln. which deposits cuprous hydroxide at 20°–30°, and cuprous oxide at higher temp. Barium dioxide reacts with the salt at ordinary temp., giving off oxygen. When warmed with a soln. of arsenic trioxide in soda-lye, cuprous oxide is precipitated. L. Kahlenberg and J. V. Steinle observed that arsenic reacts with an aq. soln. of copper arsenite: $Cu_3(AsO_3)_2+2As =3Cu+2As_2O_3$.

C. W. Scheele gradually mixed, while constantly stirring, a hot filtered soln. of potassium carbonate (32 parts) and arsenic trioxide (11 parts) with an aq. soln. of copper sulphate (32 parts), and obtained a siskin-green precipitate which when washed and dried was used as a green pigment—*Scheele's green*—before the use of arsenical colours was prohibited. J. L. Proust, H. Braconnot, C. Reichard, C. L. Bloxam, W. Sattler, etc., obtained similar products by mixing potassium arsenite or the aq. acid with an aq. or ammoniacal soln. of copper salt. The Farbenindustrie A.G. treated basic cupric chloride with arsenites or arsenious acid. C. L. Bloxam represented the composition of the air-dried salt as that of **copper pyroarsenite,** $2CuO.As_2O_3$, or $Cu_2As_2O_5$, with $2.89H_2O$; when dried at 100°, the composition is $CuHAsO_3$, **copper hydroarsenite.** S. P. Sharples gave $Cu_3(AsO_3)_2.H_2O$. G. Bornemann said that Scheele's green is not really copper hydroarsenite, but approximates more closely to the normal arsenite, $Cu_3(AsO_3)_2.nH_2O$. Actually, the composition varies with the mode of preparation, and is richer in cupric oxide, the greater the excess of alkali hydroxide or carbonate used in its preparation. A. Stavenhagen also said that the precipitate has a variable composition. J. L. Proust found that when the pale green, amorphous copper pyroarsenite is heated, it gives off water and arsenic trioxide, and leaves a residue of cupric oxide, which, according to J. F. Simon, is a mixture of copper arsenide and arsenate—the latter can be extracted by dil. nitric acid. L. N. Vauquelin, G. Bonnet, and C. Reichard found that the salt is soluble in cold potash-lye, and the deep blue soln. slowly decomposes into cuprous oxide on standing, rapidly when heated. J. J. Berzelius, and S. P. Sharples said that the soln. in aq. ammonia is colourless, and is not oxidized on standing or when boiled, and when the ammonia is evaporated, the original salt remains, provided, added A. Girard, the evaporation is conducted in an atm. of ammonia ; if evaporated in air, an amminoarsenate is formed. Soln. of ammonium salts were found by C. Reichard to act like aq. ammonia. S. P. Sharples showed that when potassium hydroxide is added to the ammoniacal soln., cuprous hydroxide is precipitated. E. C. Franklin and C. A. Kraus said that the pyroarsenite is insoluble in liquid ammonia, and J. Schröder, that it is insoluble in pyridine. W. Sattler showed that the fresh precipitate dissolves freely in acetic acid, but if the precipitate has stood a long time it dissolves less readily in acetic acid, and crystals of arsenic trioxide are formed. He added that if acetic acid be present when the precipitate is formed, the so-called *Schweinfurt-green, Paris-green, mitis-green,* or *Vienna-green* is produced. According to E. Ehrmann, the composition is $Cu(C_2H_3O_2)_2.3Cu(AsO_2)_2$; and, according to H. Schiff and R. Sestini, $Cu(C_2H_3O_2)_2.3Cu_2As_2O_5$. S. Avery and H. T. Beans, T. B. Stillman, and E. W. Hilgard also found some free arsenic trioxide to be present. A. Vogel found that when copper pyroarsenite is heated with sulphurous acid, cuprous oxide is precipitated ; while H. Baubigny and P. Rivals observed that iodine oxidizes it to copper hydroarsenate.

Various commercial preparations of Scheele's green, or Schweinfurt-green have been marketed—e.g. *parrot-green* is a mixture of copper arsenite and gelatinous starch ; *Brunswick-green, Neuwied-green, mountain-green, pickle-green,* and *mineral-green* are varieties prepared in different ways described by J. G. Gentele and others.

According to S. Avery, when Schweinfurt-green is repeatedly boiled with an excess of an aq. soln. of arsenic trioxide, **copper metarsenite,** $Cu(AsO_2)_2$, is formed as a grey, crystalline powder. The crystals are pseudomorphs after those of Schweinfurt-green. A. Stavenhagen treated a feebly acidic soln. of cupric chloride in alcohol with a soln. of arsenic trioxide in 50 per cent. alcohol. The pale green, amorphous precipitate when dried over sulphuric acid corresponded with **dihydrated copper metarsenite,** $Cu(AsO_2)_2.2H_2O$. It loses one mol. of water at 100°, and the second at 200°—some arsenic trioxide is simultaneously sublimed.

When potassium or ammonium arsenite is added to an aq. soln. of silver nitrate, yellow **silver orthoarsenite,** Ag_3AsO_3, or *normal silver arsenite,* is precipitated. Aq. soln. of arsenic trioxide were found by J. F. Simon [6] to give a white turbidity which becomes yellow only in the presence of some alkali. The yellow product, said O. B. Kühn, is the normal arsenite ; and if ammonia be the alkali used for the precipitation, some arsenite remains in soln. E. Filhol said that the normal arsenite is produced when an aq. soln. of arsenic trioxide is added to ammoniacal silver nitrate. J. R. Santos obtained this salt by mixing one mol of normal sodium arsenite with 3 mols of silver nitrate, and if one mol or two mols of silver nitrate be used, he said that *silver hydroarsenite* is formed. C. L. Bloxam found normal silver arsenite is precipitated by potassium metarsenite ; and C. Reichard, by acidic potassium arsenite. J. A. Wanklyn obtained normal silver arsenite by the action of arsine (q.v.) on a soln. of silver nitrate. The preparation of this salt was also described by F. Wöhler, J. A. Wanklyn, and A. Stavenhagen. L. Meyer discussed the use of the reaction in quantitative analysis. A. Dexheimer prepared **colloidal silver arsenite** by mixing a soln. of a gram of sodium lysalbinate in 10 grms. of water with a silver nitrate soln. until no more precipitate was formed. The precipitate is washed with water until the filtrate is free from silver. The pale yellowish-brown mass loses 6·71 per cent. of water at 100° in vacuo. It dissolves in water, forming a deep brownish-red soln. which has the usual characters of colloidal soln.

J. F. Simon said that silver arsenite is yellow or greenish-yellow, and that it becomes brown when exposed to light ; and when dried at a gentle heat the colour remains yellow, but when heated more strongly it darkens, forming, according to A. Marcet, a brown basic salt with the evolution of a little arsenic trioxide. E. Filhol found that the salt melts at 140°–150° without loss of weight. When heated in air to redness, J. F. Simon, and A. Stavenhagen noted that arsenic trioxide sublimes, and the residue contains silver free from arsenic, and silver arsenate. According to A. Marcet, and J. Hume, silver arsenite is insoluble in water, but dissolves in acids ; and when recently precipitated, it dissolves in aq. ammonia. J. R. Santos thought that silver arsenite is insoluble in aq. ammonia, but readily soluble in the presence of alkali nitrates. According to O. B. Kühn, if the ammoniacal soln. be boiled for a long time, replacing ammonia as it boils off, silver is deposited and an arsenate is formed. H. Reckleben and co-workers, and R. S. Bosworth said that the reaction : $(NH_4)_3AsO_3+2AgNO_3.NH_3+H_2O$ $=(NH_4)_3AsO_4+2Ag+2NH_4NO_3$, is quantitative. O. B. Kühn found that silver arsenite is soluble in an excess of alkali or ammonium arsenite, and when the soln. is heated, silver is deposited. G. S. Whitby found that a litre of water at 20° dissolves 0·0115 grm. of the salt. G. C. Wittstein said that the salt is soluble in ammonium chloride soln. F. Bezold said that the arsenite is sparingly soluble in methyl acetate ; and M. Hamers, insoluble in ethyl acetate, or in ethyl acetate sat. with water at 18°. A. Reynoso reported that silver arsenite is soluble in potash-lye, but F. Wöhler, O. B. Kühn, and A. Stavenhagen found that the salt is decomposed by this menstruum, forming soluble alkali arsenite and arsenate, and insoluble silver and silver arsenide. F. Wöhler said that some silver tetritoxide is also formed. J. R. Santos found that silver arsenite is slightly soluble in acetic acid. O. B. Kühn, and A. Laugier and J. Pelletier observed that silver arsenite is oxidized to the arsenate by nitric acid.

According to L. Pasteur, and A. Girard, when a soln. of alkali pyroarsenite is added to one of silver nitrate, yellow **silver pyroarsenite,** $Ag_4As_2O_5$, is precipitated. L. Pasteur said that acid ammonium arsenite gives the same precipitate. Neither C. L. Bloxam, nor A. Stavenhagen could prepare this salt. According to C. Reichard, if alcohol be added to an ammoniacal soln. of silver arsenite, prismatic crystals of **silver tetramminopyroarsenite,** $Ag_4As_2O_5.4NH_3$, are deposited. A. Girard reported **silver metatetrarsenite,** $Ag_6As_4O_9$, to be formed as a white precipitate by dropping a soln. of potassium pyroarsenite into one of silver nitrate containing much ammonium nitrate. The precipitate blackens in light ; and dissolves in aq. ammonia, and potassium arsenite. A. Stavenhagen obtained only the normal arsenite when working under these conditions.

As indicated above, gold is precipitated when an aq. soln. of arsenic trioxide is added to a soln. of auric chloride. A. Stavenhagen reported **gold arsenite,** $AuAsO_3.H_2O$, to be formed when a soln. of auric chloride in 50 per cent. alcohol is treated with normal potassium arsenite. The pale brown solid slowly decomposes at 20°, rapidly at a higher temp., forming gold arsenide and gold. The arsenite is freely soluble in water, in an excess of the precipitating agents, in aq. ammonia, and in dil. acids.

A number of calcium arsenites have been reported. G. Tammann [7] heated mixtures of calcium oxide and arsenic trioxide, and observed that a chemical reaction occurs near the m.p. of the trioxide. Some calcium orthoarsenite is formed at 465°, and there is then a strong exothermal reaction. L. G. Story and E. Anderson investigated the ternary system : As_2O_3–CaO–H_2O, at 0°, 25°, and 99°, by the method indicated in connection with the basic mercurous sulphates—

4. 31, 29. The results at 0° are illustrated by Fig. 21. Only two salts appear to be formed under these conditions—calcium hydroarsenite, $Ca(OH)AsO_2$, or

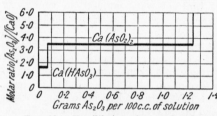

FIG. 21.—Equilibrium Curves for the System : As_2O_3–CaO–H_2O at 0°.

$Ca(HAsO_3)$, and calcium metarsenite, $Ca(AsO_2)_2$. A. Stavenhagen, and O. B. Kühn reported normal calcium arsenite, or **calcium orthoarsenite**, $Ca_3(AsO_3)_2$, to be formed by treating a boiling soln. of arsenic trioxide with an excess of lime-water; and, added O. B. Kühn, if the arsenic trioxide be in excess, no precipitate appears. A. Stavenhagen also obtained it by treating a one per cent. soln. of calcium chloride with potassium orthoarsenite. The white powder is sparingly soluble in water, and freely soluble in acids. At a red-heat, it passes into calcium arsenate. J. Altwegg converted the arsenite to arsenate by heating it in a current of oxygen. G. F. Wach mentioned the formation of acid calcium arsenites by dissolving one of the other calcium arsenites in a conc. soln. of ammonium chloride, and then evaporating the filtrate ; but the products were not further examined. Both the primary and secondary derivatives are known. The existence of **calcium hydroarsenite**, $Ca(OH)AsO_2$, or $CaHAsO_3$, was established by the observations of L. G. Story and E. Anderson, illustrated by Fig. 21. J. Perper reported **calcium dihydroarsenite**, $Ca(H_2AsO_3)_2$.5 to $11H_2O$, to be produced when an ammoniacal soln. of arsenic trioxide is mixed with an excess of lime-water ; or when an excess of ammonium metarsenite is mixed with lime-water. A soln. of calcium chloride can be used in place of lime-water. The proportion of water varied from 5 to $11H_2O$. The white powder, or gelatinous mass is fairly soluble in water, and insoluble in absolute alcohol. The aq. soln. has an alkaline reaction, and is decomposed by carbon dioxide.

J. F. Simon prepared **calcium pyroarsenite**, $Ca_2As_2O_5$, by mixing a soln. of arsenic trioxide with an excess of lime-water, or ammonium arsenite with a soln. of calcium sulphate or chloride. J. Stein regarded the product obtained by the former process as impure normal arsenite. A. Stavenhagen used this process, and added that when dried in hydrogen at 105°, the salt is anhydrous ; J. F. Simon found that the air-dried product contained a mol. of water. The salt attracts carbon dioxide from the air. The white, heavy, coherent powder is decomposed at a red-heat, forming, according to J. F. Simon, calcium arsenate. The salt is sparingly soluble in water—100 parts of water dissolving 0·025–0·030 part of salt ; if alkali chlorides be present, more pyroarsenite dissolves. The salt is readily soluble in dil. acids. According to C. Giesecke, G. C. Wittstein, and G. F. Wach, the salt is soluble in soln. of ammonium salts—chloride, sulphate, nitrate, arsenite, acetate, and succinate ; according to G. C. Wittstein, the soln. in ammonium carbonate soon becomes turbid ; and C. Giesecke found that alkali carbonates and phosphates precipitate the corresponding calcium salt. G. F. Wach said that the soln. of the salt in ammonium arsenite does not give a precipitate with alcohol, but yields an acid salt on evaporation. L. G. Story and E. Anderson established the existence of **calcium metarsenite**, $Ca(AsO_2)_2$. It was prepared by J. F. Simon, and A. Stavenhagen by mixing a boiling soln. of calcium chloride with a hot, sat. soln. of arsenic trioxide in aq. ammonia. The precipitate is washed with aq. ammonia. The white, amorphous powder contains half a mol. of water when dried in air, but it is anhydrous after being dried at 100°. It is readily dissolved by water. According to J. Stein, **calcium metatetrarsenite**, $Ca_3As_4O_9.nH_2O$, remains when the pyroarsenite is digested with a smaller quantity of a soln. of arsenic trioxide than is necessary to dissolve it ; and, according to C. Reichard, it is formed by mixing conc. soln. of calcium chloride and potassium tetrarsenite, and washing the precipitate with alcohol. The white, air-dried powder loses a mol. of water at 100° ; it is fairly soluble in water.

A. Stavenhagen obtained what was regarded as impure **strontium orthoarsenite,** $Sr_3(AsO_3)_2$, as a white precipitate on mixing a soln. of strontium chloride with potassium orthoarsenite; the composition varied a little, and had rather more strontium than was required for the normal salt. He also made **strontium pyroarsenite,** $Sr_2As_2O_5.2H_2O$, by adding an aq. soln. of arsenic trioxide to an alcoholic soln. of strontium chloride, and washing the precipitate with alcohol. If ammonia be present, the precipitate has a variable composition. It retains 2 mols. of water when dried at 100°. The salt is readily soluble in water, and acids. J. Stein reported **strontium metarsenite,** $Sr(AsO_2)_2.4H_2O$, to be precipitated when ammonium arsenite is added to a soln. of a strontium salt ; more of the precipitate is formed if alcohol be added to the soln. The evaporation of the aq. soln. yields a crystalline powder which retains 4 mols. of water when dried over sulphuric acid. It loses a mol. of water at 100°, and at a higher temp. it is decomposed into arsenate and arsenic. A. Stavenhagen could not prepare the salt. C. Reichard reported **strontium tetrarsenite,** $Sr_3As_4O_9$, to be formed when potassium tetrarsenite is added to a conc. soln. of strontium nitrate. The salt is washed with alcohol. The white powder is fairly soluble in water ; it is only slightly affected by potash-lye, and aq. ammonia ; and it is decomposed when heated, forming an arsenate and arsenic.

L. G. Story and E. Anderson found, in their study of the ternary system : $As_2O_3-BaO-H_2O$ at 25° and 50°, that only two salts are formed, barium metarsenite, and barium hexarsenite, Fig. 22. A. Stavenhagen prepared **barium orthoarsenite,** $Ba_3(AsO_3)_2$, by the method employed for the strontium salt. The white precipitate was washed with cold water. The salt is sparingly soluble in cold water, but freely soluble in hot water and in dil. acids. When digested with a soln. of potassium sulphate, it forms potassium orthoarsenite. As just indicated, L. G. Story and E. Anderson obtained **barium hydroarsenite,** $Ba(OH)AsO_2.2H_2O$, or $Ba(HAsO_3).2H_2O$. The conditions of equilibrium are indicated in Fig. 22.

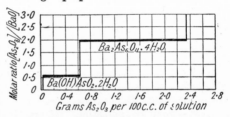

FIG. 22.—Equilibrium Curves for the System : $As_2O_3-BaO-H_2O$ at 25°.

J. Perper reported **barium dihydroarsenite,** $Ba(H_2AsO_3)_2.34H_2O$, to be formed by adding an excess of baryta-water to an aq. soln. of arsenic trioxide ; and by treating an ammoniacal soln. of arsenic trioxide with barium chloride in excess. The white powder is fairly soluble in cold water, and more so in hot water. It is insoluble in alcohol. It loses water when exposed to air, and is decomposed by the carbon dioxide in the air. The aq. soln. reacts feebly alkaline. When dried at 100°, the white powder is insoluble in water; when dried at 150°, it is yellow; and at a higher temp., the colour is darker.

J. Stein, and A. Stavenhagen obtained **barium pyroarsenite,** $Ba_2As_2O_5.nH_2O$, by the action of an excess of conc. baryta-water on a sat aq. soln. of arsenic trioxide; and E. Filhol, by treating a soln. of barium chloride with potassium pyroarsenite. J. Perper obtained the dihydroarsenite by both these processes. J. Stein said that when the white product is dried over sulphuric acid it retains 4 mols. of water ; and A. Stavenhagen, 8 mols. ; when dried at 100°, it retains 2 mols. of water. At a higher temp., it forms arsenate and arsenic. It is slightly soluble in water, and in dil. alcohol, C. L. Bloxam reported **barium metarsenite,** $Ba(AsO_2)_2.2H_2O$, to be formed by precipitation from a soln. of barium chloride and ammonium arsenite— A. Stavenhagen could not prepare the salt in this way, and J. Perper obtained the dihydroarsenite by this process. A. Stavenhagen precipitated barium metarsenite, $Ba(AsO_2)_2$, from a warm soln. of barium chloride by an ammoniacal soln. of arsenic trioxide, washed the product with water, and dried it at 100°. E. Filhol mixed soln. of potassium metarsenite and barium chloride and obtained this salt as a gelatinous precipitate, which became pulverulent when boiled with its mother-liquid.

C. Reichard obtained **barium tetrarsenite,** $BaAs_4O_7$, by the method employed for the strontium salt; and L. G. Story and E. Anderson's diagram, Fig. 22, shows the conditions of equilibrium of **barium hexarsenite,** $Ba_2As_6O_{11}.4H_2O$.

B. Bleyer and B. Müller found it impossible to prepare definite **beryllium arsenites.** What were obtained can be regarded only as adsorption products. They examined the behaviour of the hydrogel of beryllium hydroxide. with aq. soln. of arsenic trioxide, and found that only very small amounts of the arsenic trioxide were adsorbed, due probably to the rapidity with which the precipitated hydroxide loses its colloidal character. With beryllium hydroxide precipitated by ammonia and ammonium chloride in the arsenic soln., larger quantities of the trioxide were adsorbed at the ordinary temp., and these were adsorbed in accordance with the adsorption law. At the temp. of boiling water the quantities adsorbed were less than at the ordinary temp., and followed Henry's law, that is, the ratio between the quantity of arsenic trioxide absorbed and that remaining in the soln. was constant.

G. Tammann observed that when a mixture of magnesium oxide and arsenic trioxide is heated, some magnesium metarsenite is formed at the m.p. of the trioxide, and at a higher temp., a basic arsenite is formed, **magnesium trioxyorthoarsenite,** $3MgO.Mg_3(AsO_3)_3$. L. G. Story and E. Anderson observed no sign of the formation of a magnesium arsenite in their study of the ternary system : As_2O_3–MgO–H_2O at 25°. The magnesium hydroxide adsorbs the arsenic trioxide; a similar phenomenon was observed by E. Filhol, and on this property magnesia, like ferric hydroxide, has been recommended as an antidote for poisoning. J. F. Simon said an arsenite is formed when the vap. of arsenic trioxide is passed over red-hot magnesia. According to A. Stavenhagen, when a soln. of magnesium chloride in 50 per cent. alcohol is treated with a soln. of potassium orthoarsenite just neutralized with acetic acid, white pulverulent **magnesium orthoarsenite,** $Mg_3(AsO_3)_2.nH_2O$, is precipitated. If the alkali arsenite be not neutral, the precipitate will be contaminated with magnesium hydroxide. C. Reichard added a soln. of potassium tetrarsenite gradually to a soln. of magnesium sulphate, and obtained the same product; and, added E. Filhol, if the soln. be boiled, the precipitate will not have a constant composition. J. Stein reported the formation of this salt by adding a soln. of ammonium arsenite in aq. ammonia to a soln. of magnesium sulphate mixed with so much ammonium chloride that it gives no precipitate with aq. ammonia. A. Stavenhagen found that the precipitate is always contaminated with magnesium hydroxide, and J. Perper used this process for making the tetrarsenite—*vide infra.* C. L. Bloxam said that J. Stein's salt has the composition $Mg_2As_2O_5.2H_2O$ when dried at 100°; $Mg_2As_2O_5.H_2O$, *i.e.* $MgHAsO_3$, when dried at 205°; and at a higher temp., $Mg_2As_2O_5$. J. F. Simon found that at a red-heat, arsenate and arsenic are formed. C. Reichard showed that the salt is freely soluble in boiling water and in dil. acid; while potash-lye, and aq. ammonia have very little action. J. Stein observed that the salt is soluble in a soln. of ammonium chloride. A. Stavenhagen could not make **magnesium pyroarsenite,** $Mg_2As_2O_5.4H_2O$, by C. L. Bloxam's method just indicated; but he obtained it as a white, hygroscopic, amorphous powder from the calculated quantities of magnesium sulphate and barium pyroarsenite. The salt is freely soluble in water and acids. J. Perper reported **magnesium metatetrarsenite,** $Mg_3As_4O_9.nH_2O$, to be formed by treating an aq. soln. of arsenic trioxide with magnesia mixture ; or by using a soln. of magnesium sulphate in place of magnesia mixture.

C. L. Bloxam prepared a salt regarded as **zinc orthoarsenite,** $Zn_3(AsO_3)_2$, by mixing a soln. of zinc sulphate with much ammonium chloride and ammonia, and adding it to an aq. soln. of arsenic trioxide; C. Reichard obtained the same salt by adding sodium metarsenite or acid potassium arsenite to an excess of a soln. of zinc sulphate; and by A. Stavenhagen, by adding potassium orthoarsenite to a soln. of zinc chloride in 50 per cent. alcohol. S. Avery obtained an impure product by adding a butyric acid soln. of zinc butyrate to an aq. soln. of arsenic trioxide. The white, crystalline powder is decomposed by heat. G. Tammann found that when a mixture of zinc oxide and arsenic trioxide is heated to 250°, some zinc metarsenite is formed ; and at about 420°, zinc orthoarsenite, $Zn_3(AsO_3)_3$, is formed ; and at 535°, the basic arsenite, possibly zinc **trioxyorthoarsenite,** $3ZnO.Zn_2(AsO_3)_3$, is formed ; and at 535°, the basic arsenite, possibly zinc trioxy-orthoarsenite, $3ZnO.Zn_2(AsO_3)_3$, is formed. A. Stavenhagen prepared **cadmium orthoarsenite,** $Cd_3(AsO_3)_2$, in a similar manner. S. Avery prepared **zinc metar-senite,** $Zn(AsO_2)_2$, by neutralizing with sulphuric acid and phenolphthalein a soln. of arsenic trioxide in soda-lye, and added the liquid to a hot soln. of zinc sulphate. A similar product was obtained by mixing a soln. of zinc acetate in dil. acetic acid with an aq. soln. of arsenic trioxide. The product is a white crystalline powder. C. Reichard reported **cadmium pyroarsenite,** $Cd_2As_2O_5$, to be formed by adding acid potassium arsenite to a soln. of cadmium sulphate ; dissolving the precipitate, dried at 120°, in hydrochloric acid, and reprecipitating with sodium metarsenite. The white powder is decomposed by heat ; it is soluble in acids ; and not changed by alkali-lye. If sodium orthoarsenite is added to a soln. of a cadmium salt, **cadmium diarsenite,** $3CdO.Cd_2As_2O_5.2H_2O$, is precipitated as a gelatinous mass which dries at ordinary temp. to a hard mass. The water can be expelled by heat ; and at a higher temp., the compound is decomposed. It absorbs carbon dioxide from air ; it is freely soluble in dil. or conc. sulphuric acid ; it is not attacked by potassium hydroxide, barium hydroxide or dioxide, or alkali carbonates ; and it is insoluble in a soln. of potassium cyanide. M. Henglein and W. Meigen described a grass-green, crystalline mineral from Guchab, Otavi Valley, which they named **barthite.** The analysis corresponds with **copper zinc dihydroxyhexametarsenite,** $3Zn(AsO_3)_2.Cu(OH)_2.H_2O$. The crystals are optically biaxial, and probably monoclinic. E. S. Larsen found that the optic axial angle $2V=c. 90°$; the optical character is positive. The core has the indices of refraction $a=1.770$, $\gamma=1.783$; and the outer portion, $a=1.780$, $\beta=1.795$, and $\gamma=1.815$. The outer zone is feebly pleochroic. The sp. gr. is 4·19 at 14° ; and the hardness 3.

J. J. Berzelius observed that a mercurous arsenite is formed by digesting mercury with an aq. soln. of arsenic trioxide ; and J. F. Simon obtained a white precipitate of mercury arsenite by treating mercurous nitrate with a soln. of arsenic trioxide or potassium arsenite. These salts were not analyzed. A. Stavenhagen obtained a white precipitate of **mercurous orthoarsenite,** Hg_3AsO_3, by adding a soln. of arsenic trioxide in 50 per cent. alcohol to an aq. soln. of mercurous nitrate, acidified with a few drops of nitric acid, and mixed with alcohol until it just begins to appear turbid. The product is dried at 100°. C. Reichard obtained a pale yellow precipitate of this salt by adding a soln. of sodium orthoarsenite to one of mercurous nitrate. This salt becomes reddish-brown when exposed to light and air ; it is sparingly soluble in water ; and is not blackened by boiling water ; although it is gradually decomposed by water with the separation of mercury. The salt is slowly reduced by ammonia. The salt is decomposed by potassium and barium oxides, barium dioxide, and by sodium carbonate and hydrocarbonate. It is easily soluble in acids—dil. sulphuric acid slowly forms a basic sulphate ; and hydrochloric acid, a brown precipitate. C. Reichard obtained a yellowish precipitate of **mercurous metarsenite,** $HgAsO_2$, by gradually adding a soln. of acid potassium arsenite to mercurous nitrate, and drying the product at 125°. An excess of the alkali arsenite decomposes the salt with the separation of mercurous oxide and mercury. The salt is also decomposed by potash-lye and aq. ammonia.

According to J. J. Berzelius, a mercuric arsenite is formed when an aq. soln. of arsenic trioxide is added to one of mercuric nitrate. A. Dexheimer could not prepare *colloidal mercuric arsenite* on account of its ready decomposition into mercury, etc. J. F. Simon obtained a white unstable precipitate by adding potassium arsenite to a soln. of mercurous nitrate. A. Stavenhagen reported white **mercuric ortho-arsenite,** $Hg_3(AsO_3)_2$, by using a soln. of mercuric chloride in place of mercurous nitrate as described in his process for preparing mercurous orthoarsenite. C. Reichard obtained the salt by a similar modification of his mode of preparing the mercurous salt. The colour darkens when the salt is exposed to light, or heat; and at 150°, the arsenic trioxide sublimes. The salt is sparingly soluble in water, and it is slowly reduced to mercurous hydroxide and mercury in the cold, rapidly when boiled. The salt is also reduced by aq. ammonia, potassium hydroxide, and by barium hydroxide, and dioxide. It is easily soluble in acids—with sulphuric acid, a basic sulphate is formed. An excess of a soln. of sodium arsenite reduces it to mercury. G. Dessner obtained complex salts, **mercurous nitratoarsenite,** $2Hg_3AsO_3.HgNO_3$; and **mercurous sulphatoarsenite,** $2Hg_3AsO_3.Hg_2SO_4$. C. Reichard obtained **mercuric pyroarsenite,** $HgAs_2O_5$, by treating a mercuric salt with a soln. of acid potassium arsenite, and drying the product at 125°. G. Dessner could not verify this, he obtained a mixture of arsenite and arsenate. C. Reichard said that the yellowish-white pyroarsenite is darkened by exposing the salt to light. It is not decomposed by water, but is so by aq. ammonia, potassium hydroxide or carbonate, and with an excess of a soln. of alkali arsenite. It is decomposed when heated. The salt dissolves in acids without decomposition. According to C. Reichard, **mercuric diarsenite,** $Hg_5As_2O_8$, is formed by treating sodium metarsenite with an excess of a conc. soln. of mercuric chloride. The white precipitate is partly decomposed by light, and by heat. The salt is decomposed by water, aq. ammonia, alkali hydroxide and carbonate, and by a soln. of sodium metarsenite. It is sparingly soluble in sulphuric and hydrochloric acids.

C. Reichard prepared **aluminium arsenite,** $AlAsO_3$, by adding potassium tetrarsenite to a cold sat. soln. of aluminium sulphate. The gelatinous precipitate is dried. It decomposes when heated; is slightly soluble in boiling water; and easily soluble in acids, and soda-lye. E. Thorey evaporated at a gentle heat the filtered soln. from a mixture of barium arsenite and aluminium sulphate, and finally over sulphuric acid. Rhombic pyramids of aluminium arsenite were formed. A. Stavenhagen prepared **thallous orthoarsenite,** Tl_3AsO_3, as a yellowish-red precipitate by adding an aq. soln. of arsenic trioxide to the liquid prepared by boiling thallous sulphate with alkali-lye, diluting with water, and again boiling with water until all dissolves. It is also formed when a soln. of thallous sulphate is boiled with one of potassium orthoarsenite, and potash-lye gradually added; or when a soln. of thallous chloride in alkali-lye is treated with potassium orthoarsenite. The crystals resemble those of potassium dichromate; they are sparingly soluble in water, and alcohol; but freely soluble in acids—particularly sulphuric acid.

F. Frerichs and F. Smith prepared **didymium hydroarsenite,** $Di(HAsO_3)_3$, by boiling didymium hydroxide with an aq. soln. of arsenic trioxide. It is a white, granular powder which is insoluble in water. They prepared **lanthanum hydroarsenite,** $La(HAsO_3)_3$, in an analogous manner. P. T. Cleve doubted the existence of these salts. G. Tammann heated mixtures of cerium dioxide and arsenic trioxide and found that oxidation occurs; and at 600° the mixture contains CeO_2, Ce_2O_3, As_2O_3, and As_2O_5.

S. J. Thugutt reported **arsenito-sodalite,** $6Na_2Al_2Si_2O_4.12NaAlSiO_4.Na_2As_2O_6.6H_2O$, by boiling in a sealed tube, at 207°–208°, for 54 hrs., a mixture of 6 grms. china-clay, 6·5 grms. of arsenic trioxide, 12 grms. of sodium hydroxide, and 45 c.c. of water—vide the arsenitosilicates, **6**. 40, 47. C. Reichard mixed a nearly neutral soln. of titanyl sulphate with an excess of potassium tetrarsenite and obtained a gelatinous precipitate of **titanyl tetrarsenite,** $(TiO)_5As_4O_{11}$, which gradually crystallized. It is decomposed by heat; acids dissolve it without decomposition; and it is scarcely attacked by aq. ammonia or potassium hydroxide. E. Wedekind and H. Wilke observed that the hydrogel of zirconium dioxide forms true adsorption complexes with arsenic trioxide, but there is no evidence of the formation of a zirconium arsenite.

According to C. Reichard, **stannous orthoarsenite,** $Sn_3(AsO_3)_2.2H_2O$, is formed as a white precipitate when acid potassium arsenite is poured into a soln. of stannous chloride ; by the action of a warm soln. of sodium arsenite on stannous hydroxide— some arsenical tin, arsine, and sodium stannate are formed at the same time ; and by the action of sodium metarsenite on a soln. of stannous chloride. A. Stavenhagen obtained it by adding a soln. of arsenic trioxide to a soln. of potassium chlorostannite and potassium chloride. J. J. Berzelius first obtained this salt, but did not analyze it. The white, amorphous powder is decomposed by heat; it is sparingly soluble in water, but soluble in dil. acids and alkali-lye, and in an excess of arsenious acid. A. Stavenhagen obtained **stannic orthoarsenite,** $Sn_3(AsO_3)_4.5\frac{1}{2}H_2O$, by adding an aq. soln. of arsenic trioxide to an aq. soln. of stannic and sodium chlorides. According to C. Reichard, stannic hydroxide is not changed by treatment with a warm soln. of arsenic trioxide in soda-lye. He also obtained **stannic tetroxy-orthoarsenite,** $2SnO_2.Sn_3(AsO_3)_4$, by mixing aq. soln. of stannic chloride and potassium arsenite. He also made **stannic diarsenite,** $Sn_7As_2O_{17}$, by treating an excess of a soln. of stannic chloride with sodium arsenite. The white precipitate has a yellow colour when dried. It is decomposed by heat.

G. Tammann heated mixtures of lead oxide and arsenic trioxide, and found that at the m.p., a yellow glass is produced ; the heating curve shows an acceleration at 590°. J. J. Berzelius, and A. Reynoso examined the white precipitates produced when lead salt soln. are treated with an aq. soln. of arsenic trioxide, or of a soluble arsenite. Plumbiferous iron pyrites was found by E. Masing to yield crystals of **lead arsenite** when immersed in a soln. of arsenic trichloride. L. G. Story and E. Anderson studied the conditions of equilibrium in the ternary system : As_2O_3–PbO–H_2O at 25°. The results are summarized in Fig. 23. Only one compound was produced, namely, lead metaarsenite. B. Ormont prepared lead arsenate by an electrolytic process, using as catholyte a 15 per cent. soln. of sodium hydroxide or other sodium salt, or 30 per cent. potassium hydroxide soln., and a cathode of nickel, and as the anolyte,

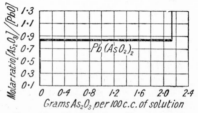

FIG. 23.—Equilibrium Curves of the System : As_2O_3–PbO–H_2O at 25°.

a soln. of an alkali arsenite neutralized towards phenolphthalein by means of acetic acid, and an anode of lead. The cathode space was separated by a diaphragm of vegetable parchment. A current yield of 97 per cent. was obtained and the energy yield amounted on the average to 1 kg. per kilowatt-hour. F. Herrmann recommended a 2 per cent. soln. of lead arsenite for killing insects, since, at this concentration, the liquid is harmless to man and domestic animals. A. Dexheimer made **colloidal lead arsenite,** by the following process :

A soln. of 2 grms. of sodium lysalbinate in 20 c.c. of water is mixed with a soln. of lead acetate so long as a precipitate forms. The precipitate is washed with hot water. It dissolves in dil. sodium hydroxide, mixed with sodium dihydroarsenite. The turbid liquid is allowed to stand for some hours, filtered, and dialyzed until the exterior liquid is free from arsenic. The filtrate is concentrated on a water-bath, mixed with absolute alcohol and ether, filtered, and the yellow, horny mass dried over sulphuric acid in vacuo. The pale yellow colloid is readily soluble in water ; and the soln. exhibits the characteristic reactions of sol colloids.

O. B. Kühn prepared **lead orthoarsenite,** $Pb_3(AsO_3)_2$, by mixing a soln. of basic lead acetate with a boiling aq. soln. of arsenic trioxide ; C. Reichard, and E. Filhol used acid potassium arsenite and basic lead acetate ; C. Reichard, soln. of lead nitrate and sodium metarsenite ; and A. Streng, soln. of an alkali plumbite, and alkali arsenite. G. Dessner also prepared this salt. A. Stavenhagen added that the alkali cannot be all removed by washing. The white powder slowly darkens when exposed to light. When heated, its colour darkens, and when incipient fusion occurs the colour is reddish-brown ; and when cold, greenish-yellow ; the salt decomposes at a red-heat. It is only slightly soluble in water; boiling water extracts some arsenic trioxide from the salt; it dissolves very sparingly in potash-lye, but is more soluble in soda-lye; and it is readily soluble in nitric and acetic acids. G. C. Wittstein said lead arsenite is insoluble in aq. ammonia and ammonium salts, but the orthoarsenite was found by C. Reichard to expel ammonia from ammonium salts even in the cold. A. Stavenhagen reported **monohydrated lead orthoarsenite**, $Pb_3(AsO_3)_2.H_2O$, to be formed by drying in air the precipitate from a mixture of potassium orthoarsenite and a dil. soln. of lead nitrate. According to J. J. Berzelius, **lead pyroarsenite**, $Pb_2As_2O_5$, is formed when basic lead acetate is mixed with an ammoniacal soln. of arsenic trioxide; C. Reichard used lead acetate and potassium tetrarsenite; E. Filhol, and A. Stavenhagen, a normal lead salt and potassium pyroarsenite; and C. L. Bloxam, normal lead acetate and an ammoniacal soln. of arsenic trioxide. The precipitate was dried at 100°.

J. F. Simon said that the vapour of arsenic trioxide is rapidly absorbed when it is passed over heated lead oxide; the oxide fuses, and becomes red-hot; the mass solidifies to a yellow enamel or glass on cooling. It is not decomposed at a bright red-heat. No reduction to arsenic or lead occurs unless one of the oxides is in excess; when the proper proportions are used, J. F. Simon said that lead pyroarsenite is formed, but A. Stavenhagen said that the product is really a mixture of lead oxide, and arsenic tri- and penta-oxides.

When the white, pulverulent lead pyroarsenite is heated it loses water, and melts to a yellow glass. It drives ammonia from ammonium salts even in the cold, and forms a basic lead salt. A. Reynoso found the salt is soluble in soda-lye, and insoluble in potash-lye. A. Stavenhagen obtained **lead metarsenite**, $Pb(AsO_2)_2$, by mixing normal lead acetate with a boiling ammoniacal soln. of arsenic trioxide. A. Schafarik recommended using dil. soln.; E. Filhol worked with potassium metarsenite and a normal lead salt; and O. B. Kühn, normal lead acetate and a boiling, sat., aq. soln. of arsenic trioxide. The white crystalline powder, said A. Schafarik, has a sp. gr. of 5·85 at 23°. J. J. Berzelius said that it melts when heated, and decomposes; it is more triboelectric than sulphur. The salt is sparingly soluble in water. G. Dessner obtained a mixture of lead meta-arsenite with basic lead nitrate from a mixture of an excess of an aq. soln. of arsenic trioxide and lead nitrate—$Pb(AsO_2)_2+3PbO.Pb(NO_3)_2$. The precipitates with lead chloride, bromide, or iodide were likewise contaminated with basic salts. C. L. Bloxam reported **lead metatetrarsenite**, $Pb_3As_4O_9.3H_2O$, or $Pb_3(AsO_3)_2.2H_3AsO_3$, to be formed by mixing soln. of lead nitrate and potassium tetrarsenite, or sodium hexarsenite; but A. Stavenhagen could not verify this. G. Aminoff described a **lead chloroarsenite**, $Pb_5Cl(AsO_3)_3$, or $3Pb_3(AsO_3)_2.PbCl_2$, occurring as a dark grey or black mineral which he named *finnemanite*—after K. J. Finneman. The prismatic crystals belong to the hexagonal system, and have the axial ratio: $a:c=1:0.6880$. The sp. gr. is 7·08–7·265; the hardness 2–3; and the indices of refraction for light of wave-length λ:

λ	486	527	540	589	656	687
ω	2·3634	2·3333	2·3242	2·2949	2·2725	2·2651
ϵ	2·3449	2·3170	2·3077	2·2847	2·2634	2·2594

J. J. Berzelius [8] reported the formation of a soln. of *antimony arsenite* to be formed when an aq. soln. of arsenic acid is digested with antimony; and the soln. diluted with water. It is also obtained as a vitreous mass on heating a mixture of arsenic and antimonic acid. A. Stavenhagen reported **bismuth arsenite**, possibly $BiAsO_3.5H_2O$, to be precipitated when an aq. soln. of arsenic trioxide is added to one of bismuth and sodium chlorides. C. Reichard found that an alkaline soln. of sodium arsenite does not change bismuth trioxide, or bismuthyl chloride, and it reduces bismuth pentoxide to bismuthyl hydroxide. L. Vanino and F. Hartl reported bismuth arsenite to be formed by the action of an aq. soln. of arsenic trioxide on a soln. of bismuth nitrate and mannite. R. Schneider said that the salt is soluble in nitric acid; and L. Jassoy, that it is not decomposed when boiled for a short time with a soln. of sodium hydroxide or carbonate.

According to G. Bonnet,[9] a soln. of chromic chloride does not give a precipitate with an aq. or an ammoniacal soln. of ammonium arsenite. R. H. C. Neville reported that **chromic arsenite**, $CrAsO_3$, is formed when a conc. soln. of chromic acid and arsenic trioxide is heated for a long time; but A. Stavenhagen could not verify this. C. Reichard found that dil. soln. of chromic sulphate and potassium tetrarsenite can be mixed and warmed without perceptible change, but when conc. soln. are heated to 100° for some time a dark green mixture of chromic arsenite and arsenic trioxide is precipitated; to remove the arsenic trioxide, the mixture is dissolved in hydrochloric acid, and reprecipitated by ammonia. The dark green arsenite decomposes when heated. It dissolves in dil. acids and in alkali-lye; it is insoluble in aq. ammonia. E. Weidenbach added hydrochloric acid of sp. gr. 1·12 to a soln. of a molybdate and alkali arsenite, and obtained white microscopic needles of **hydrodiarsenitodimolybdic acid**, $H_6[As_2O_4(MoO_4)_2].3H_2O$. The neutralization curve shows that the acid is tribasic; and the equivalent conductivity of one-sixth of a mol in v litres of water :

v . .	32	64	128	256	512	1024
λ . .	51·7	55·8	59·3	65·1	71·2	83·9 mhos

shows that the acid is but feebly ionized, and that it is rather stronger than arsenic acid. F. Ephraim and H. Feidel obtained **sodium diarsenito-dimolybdate**, $Na_2H_4[As_2O_4(MoO_4)_2].4H_2O$, in rectangular crystals of sp. gr. 3·43 at 16°, crystallized ammonium salts could not be made, but they prepared octahedral crystals of **copper ammonium octohydrobisdiarsenitodi-molybdate**, $Cu(NH_4)_2H_8[As_2O_4(MoO_4)_2]_2$, of sp. gr. 2·50 at 16°; and **copper ammonium hexahydrotrisdiarsenitodimolybdate**, $Cu(NH_4)_4H_6[As_2O_4(MoO_4)_2]_3.10H_2O$, in hexagonal prisms of sp. gr. 3·17 at 16°; and **ammonium barium icosi-hydroquiniusdiarsenitodimolybdate**, $Ba_2(NH_4)_6H_{20}[As_2O_4(MoO_4)_2]_5.40H_2O$.

O. W. Gibbs found that **arsenitomolybdates** are obtained by boiling arsenic trioxide with a conc. soln. of an acid molybdate. The general formula is $xR_2O.yAs_2O_3.zMoO_3$, where y is generally greater than unity. He thus prepared **ammonium arsenitomolybdate**, $3(NH_4)_2O.5As_2O_3.12MoO_3.24H_2O$, in colourless crystals ; **copper arsenitomolybdate**, $2CuO.3As_2O_3.6MoO_3.6H_2O$, in green octahedral crystals ; **zinc arsenitomolybdate**, $2ZnO.3As_2O_3.6MoO_3.6H_2O$, in colourless octahedral crystals ; and **manganous arsenitomolybdate**, $2MnO.3As_2O_3.6MoO_3.6H_2O$, in pale, orange octahedral crystals ; and **nickel arsenitomolybdate**, $2NiO.3As_2O_3.6MoO_3.6H_2O$. F. Ephraim and H. Feidel prepared **sodium hexahydrodiarsenitotetramolybdate**, $Na_4H_6[As_2O_4(MoO_4)_4].10H_2O$; and O. W. Gibbs obtained **barium arsenitomolybdate**, $3BaO.2As_2O_3.8MoO_3.13H_2O$, in very pale green crystals. F. Ephraim and H. Feidel mixed a soln. of 3 mols of potassium carbonate, 6 mols of molybdic acid, and one mol of arsenic trioxide ; a crop of crystals of potassium molybdate was followed by a crop of white crystals of **potassium diarsenitopentamolybdate**, $3K_2O.As_2O_3.5MoO_3.3H_2O$. E. Weidenbach prepared **potassium dihydroarsenitopentamolybdate**, $K_4H_2[AsO(MoO_4)_5].7H_2O$; and F. Ephraim and H. Feidel made white crystals of **potassium diarsenitocto-molybdate**, $3K_2O.As_2O_3.8MoO_3.18H_2O$, of sp. gr. 3·15 at 16°. E. Weidenbach reported the formation of **silver tetrahydrodiarsenitoctodecamolybdate**, $Ag_{12}H_4[As_2O_2(Mo_2O_7)_9].36H_2O$; of **barium hexahydrotetrarsenitotetratriconti-molybdate**, $Ba_{12}H_6[As_4O_4(Mo_2O_7)_{17}].58H_2O$; as well as of some *guanidine arseni-tomolybdates*. A series of **alkyl molybdatoarsenites** has been prepared by A. Miolati, and A. Rosenheim and R. Bilecki—*e.g.* $R_2[As(CH_3)(Mo_2O_7)_3]$; $R_2[HAs(C_6H_5)_2(Mo_2O_7)_2]$; etc. O. W. Gibbs reported **platinous tetrammino-arsenitomolybdate**, $2Pt(NH_3)_4O.2(PtO.As_2O_3).12MoO_3.As_2O_3.27H_2O$, by digesting platinous tetramminochloride with an arsenitomolybdate or an acid and molybdate. O. W. Gibbs also obtained a **platinum arsenitophosphatomolybdate** by the action of a phosphatoarsenitomolybdate on platinous tetramminochloride, or ammonium platinous arsenite with platinous chloride.

O. W. Gibbs also prepared a series of **arsenitotungstates** by a process similar to that employed for the arsenitomolybdates. The general formula is $xR_2O.yAs_2O_3.zWO_3$, where y is usually greater than unity. He thus prepared **ammonium arsenitotungstate**, $7(NH_4)_2O.2As_2O_3.18WO_3.18H_2O$, in pale yellow, almost colourless, crystals; **sodium arsenitotungstate**, $9Na_2O.8As_2O_3.$ $16WO_3.55H_2O$, in colourless, prismatic crystals; **barium arsenitotungstate,** $4BaO.As_2O_3.9WO_3.2H_2O$, as a white, crystalline powder. O. W. Gibbs also made pale yellow **mercurous arsenitotungstate** by adding mercurous nitrate to a soln. of the sodium salt. O. W. Gibbs reported **platinous tetramminoarsenito-tungstate**, $6Pt(NH_3)_4O.3(2PtO.As_2O_3).22WO_3.3As_2O_3.40H_2O$, by digesting ammonium platinous arsenite with an acid molybdate or platinous tetrammino-chloride with an arsenitotungstate. Likewise, by boiling a soln. of potassium platinous chloroarsenite with an acid tungstate, he obtained **platinous tetrammino-hexachloroarsenitotungstate,** $12Pt(NH_3)_4O.3(2PtCl_2As_2O_3).24WO_3.As_2O_3.6H_2O$. He also reported a series of **arsenitophosphatotungstates** to be formed by boiling arsenic trioxide with a phosphatotungstate, or by adding an orthophosphate to an arsenitotungstate. He thus obtained **potassium arsenitotetraphosphato-tungstate**, $7K_2O.As_2O_3.4P_2O_5.60WO_3.55H_2O$, in pale yellow crystals; **potassium tetradecarsenitotriphosphatotungstate**, $10K_2O.14As_2O_3.3P_2O_5.32WO_3.28H_2O$, in minute greenish-yellow crystals; **sodium potassium arsenitophosphatotungstate,** $5K_2O.Na_2O.2As_2O_3.2P_2O_5.12WO_3.15H_2O$, as a yellow oil, which dries to a pale yellow, gummy, transparent mass; and **platinum arsenitophosphatotungstate**, as in the case of the molybdate. A. Rogers obtained **ammonium arsenitovanadito-tungstate**, $16(NH_4)_2O.15V_2O_3.5As_2O_3.20WO_3.101H_2O$, by boiling a mixture of arsenic and vanadium trioxides, ammonium tungstate, and aq. ammonia. Black, octahedral crystals are obtained on evaporating the soln. The salt is sparingly soluble in cold water, and freely soluble in hot water. Dil. nitric acid changes the colour of the soln.; conc. nitric acid and conc. hydrochloric acid give yellow precipitates; silver nitrate, a greenish-black precipitate; and barium chloride, a grey precipitate.

C. Reichard reported **uranyl metarsenite**, $UO_2(AsO_2)_2$, to be precipitated when uranyl nitrate is treated with potassium tetrarsenite. It dries at $110°$ to a pale yellow powder. It first darkens in colour, and then decomposes when heated. It does not dissolve in aq. ammonia; is only slightly soluble in potash-lye; and is readily dissolved by acids.

C. Reichard reported what may not be a chemical individual, or may be a basic manganese arsenite, **manganese dioxyarsenite**, $2MnO.Mn_3(AsO_3)_2$, or *manganese diarsenite*, $Mn_5As_2O_8$, which he prepared by adding sodium metarsenite to a soln. of manganese sulphate in slight excess. The white gummy precipitate soon becomes rose-red, and brown. It is decomposed by heat. A. Stavenhagen obtained **manganese orthoarsenite**, $Mn_3(AsO_3)_2.3H_2O$, by treating manganese acetate with a soln. of potassium orthoarsenite almost neutralized with acetic acid. The pale reddish-brown precipitate was washed with 50 per cent. alcohol, dried over sulphuric acid in an atm. of hydrogen. It oxidizes at $50°$, and in a moist atm. at ordinary temp. The black mineral *armangite* described by G. Aminoff and R. Mauzelius is an orthoarsenite, $Mn_3(AsO_3)_2$, and the name is supposed to be compounded from arsenic and manganese. The trigonal crystals have the axial ratio $a : c=1 : 1.3116$; the hardness is 4. J. Stein mixed soln. of ammonium arsenite and a manganese salt, and obtained a pale red precipitate of **manganese metatetrarsenite**, $Mn_3As_4O_9.5H_2O$; C. Reichard also obtained it by mixing soln. of potassium tetrarsenite and manganese sulphate, washing the precipitate with air-free water, and drying in an atm. of an inert gas. The compound is white, but quickly turns rose-red, brown, and black on exposure to air. It loses a mol. of water at $100°$, and the rest at $130°$. It is decomposed at a higher temp. Aq. ammonia, potash-lye, and a soln. of potassium cyanide are without action. The mineral *trigonite* named from τρίμηρος, triangular, in allusion to the shape of the crystals, was described by

G. Flink. It appears to be a **manganese lead arsenite**, $6PbO.2MnO.3As_2O_3.H_2O$, or $HMnPb_3(AsO_3)_3$; and it occurs in pale sulphur-yellow or brownish, monoclinic crystals with the axial ratios $a : b : c = 1·07395 : 1 : 1·65897$, and $\beta = 91° 31'$. The sp. gr. is 8·28, the hardness 2–3 ; and the indices of refraction $a = 2·08$, and $\gamma = 2·16$.

According to G. C. Wittstein,[10] a greenish-white precipitate is produced when ammonium arsenite is added to a soln. of ferrous sulphate. The precipitate then changes to a yellow colour ; it is supposed to be **ferrous arsenite** ; and is soluble in aq. ammonia, but not in ammonium arsenite or other ammoniacal salts. N. J. B. G. Guibourt also reported that he had formed the same salt in soln. by digesting freshly precipitated ferrous hydroxide with an aq. soln. of arsenic trioxide. Some of the hydroxide dissolves. C. Reichard found that potassium tetrarsenite precipitates **ferrous metarsenite**, $Fe(AsO_3)_2$, from a soln. of ferrous sulphate. The salt is decomposed when heated.

According to R. Bunsen and A. A. Berthold, when ferric acetate is treated with a soln. of arsenic trioxide, or an alkali arsenite, a basic salt, **ferric enneaoxyarsenite**, $Fe_8As_2O_{15}.5H_2O$, or $3Fe_2O_3.Fe_2(AsO_3)_2.5H_2O$, is precipitated. If ferric sulphate, chloride, or nitrate be employed, all the ferric salt will not be precipitated. J. F. Simon added that it is difficult to wash the precipitate free from ammonium acetate. R. Bunsen and A. A. Berthold said that the same salt is formed when freshly precipitated ferric hydroxide is agitated with an aq. soln. of arsenic trioxide. N. J. B. G. Guibourt said that 6·67 parts of dry ferric oxide are not quite enough to precipitate one part of arsenic trioxide from soln., and 10 parts are not quite enough. R. Bunsen and A. A. Berthold obtained an analogous result with the moist hydroxide. The product decomposes when heated, and N. J. B. G. Guibourt said that the arsenic trioxide is not all expelled by ignition, while J. F. Simon removed all the arsenic in this way. Acetic acid has no action on the product, but the mineral acids dissolve it with the separation of arsenic trioxide. As indicated in connection with the action of ferric hydroxide on arsenic trioxide—*vide supra*—there are reasons for supposing that the product obtained by the action of ferric oxide on the soln. of arsenic trioxide is not a chemical individual, but rather an adsorption product. N. J. B. G. Guibourt found that when ferric hydroxide is mixed with a sat. soln. of arsenic trioxide, in soda-lye, freed from excess of the trioxide, by cooling, and allowed to stand 24 hrs., a yellow substance is obtained with the composition of **ferric pyroarsenite**, $Fe_4(As_2O_5)_3.7H_2O$, when dried in air ; 11·6 per cent. of water is lost at 100°. The product forms a deep red soln. with soda-lye. A. Reychler, and T. Oryng also believed that hydrated ferric oxides adsorb arsenious acid from soln. to form complex arsenites, but *vide supra*, arsenic trioxide. A. Arzruni and E. Schütz obtained three crystalline substances from a factory making chlorine by Deacon's process. The arsenical hydrogen chloride acts on the porous bricks soaked in a copper salt. Monoclinic prisms of ferric orthoarsenite, $FeAsO_3$, with the axial ratios $a : b : c = 0·9405 : 1 : 0·6234$, and $\beta = 105° 10\frac{1}{2}'$; and rhombic crystals of the *pentahydrate* were found. V. Ipatieff observed that ferric arsenite is reduced by hydrogen under press., forming colloidal iron oxide, iron arsenide, and arsenic trioxide.

A. Stavenhagen reported **cobalt orthoarsenite**, $Co_3(AsO_3)_2.4H_2O$, to be formed by adding a soln. of potassium orthoarsenite, neutralized with acetic acid, to a soln. of cobaltous chloride in 50 per cent. alcohol. The pale red precipitate blackens when heated ; it is sparingly soluble in water, readily soluble in acids. According to C. Reichard, when an excess of a soln. of cobalt nitrate is treated with sodium orthoarsenite, a voluminous, amethyst coloured mass is formed which, when dried in air, retains 20 per cent. of water which it loses at 150°, and has then the empirical composition $Co_3(AsO_3)_2.4CoO$, or **cobalt tetroxyorthoarsenite**. It is easily soluble in dil. sulphuric acid, and less soluble in the conc. acid ; it is soluble in soda-lye, and aq. ammonia ; it is oxidized by barium dioxide when suspended in water, and cobaltic oxide is formed. It is soluble in a soln. of potassium cyanide. J. L. Proust mixed a soln. of a cobalt salt with potassium arsenite and obtained a

rose-red precipitate which darkened in colour when dried. A. Girard, and
A. Stavenhagen said that if potassium pyroarsenite be used, cobalt pyroarsenite,
$Co_2As_2O_5$, is produced; and this salt was obtained by C. Reichard by adding
sodium metarsenite to a soln. of cobalt nitrate. J. L. Proust said that the inner
portion of cobalt-bloom or erythrite contains this salt. When heated in a glass
vessel, the salt gives off arsenic trioxide and colours the glass blue; when heated
with potassium hydroxide, it forms cobalt oxide and a blue liquid which deposits
the oxide when diluted with water. It dissolves in nitric and hydrochloric acids;
and forms a red soln. with aq. ammonia. A. Reynoso found that the pyroarsenite
dissolves in alkali-lye only when it is produced in that menstruum. A. Girard
obtained cobalt metatetrarsenite, $Co_3As_4O_9.4H_2O$, by adding potassium arsenite
to a soln. of cobalt chloride mixed with an excess of ammonium chloride.
C. Reichard obtained it by treating a dil. soln. of a cobalt salt with potassium
tetrarsenite. A. Stavenhagen could not prepare this salt by the action of potassium
diarsenite on a soln. of cobaltous chloride. According to A. Girard, the rose-red
precipitate loses its water at 100°, and at a higher temp. it darkens in colour, then
loses water, arsenic trioxide, and melts to a blue mass. The metatetrarsenite
is decomposed when heated with potassium hydroxide; it is also dissolved by
hydrochloric and nitric acids; with aq. ammonia it gives a reddish-brown soln.,
and with aq. potassium cyanide, a yellowish-red soln.

G. Tammann observed that when mixtures of nickel oxide and arsenic trioxide
are heated, some nickel orthoarsenite, $Ni_3(AsO_3)_3$, is formed at about 465°.
J. L. Proust, and A. Girard obtained an apple-green precipitate by adding potassium
arsenite to a soln. of a nickel salt; and C. Reichard showed that the precipitate
obtained by the action of sodium metarsenite on a soln. of nickel nitrate in excess,
is nickel orthoarsenite. As shown by J. J. Berzelius, and A. Reynoso, the compound
is decomposed when heated, and arsenic trioxide is given off. J. L. Proust said
that the salt is insoluble in water, but easily soluble in aq. ammonia. A. Reynoso
found that it dissolves in alkali-lye at the moment of its formation. A. Girard
also reported nickel metatetrarsenite, $Ni_3As_4O_9$, to be formed as in the case of the
analogous cobalt salt. The greenish-white product is decomposed by heat, forming
the arsenate, and arsenic trioxide. It is transformed by nitric acid into an
arsenate; by hydrochloric acid into a chloride; and with aq. ammonia, it forms a
yellow soln.

A. Stavenhagen reported platinic orthoarsenite, $3PtO_2.2As_2O_3$, or $Pt_3(AsO_3)_4$,
to be formed by adding alcohol to a mixture of an aq. soln. of arsenic trioxide and
an alcoholic soln. of platinum tetrachloride. The pale yellow precipitate decomposes
even at ordinary temp. into arsenical platinum and arsenic pentoxide. C. Reichard
reported platinic pyroarsenite, $PtO_2.As_2O_3$, or $PtAs_2O_5$, to be formed as a pale
yellow precipitate on mixing eq. soln. of potassium tetrarsenite and platinic chloride.
The product is dried at 100°. It decomposes when heated; it is not attacked by
potash-lye; and it forms a colourless soln. with potassium cyanide. This salt
was also prepared by J. F. Simon. O. W. Gibbs mentioned ammonium platinous
arsenite, $5(NH_4)_2O.As_2O_3.3(2PtO.As_2O_3).7H_2O$; and J. F. Simon obtained
ammonium platinic arsenite by the action of hydrochloroplatinic acid on an
ammoniacal soln. of arsenic trioxide, but A. Stavenhagen could not obtain a salt
of constant composition by this procedure. Both J. F. Simon, and C. Reichard
obtained palladium pyroarsenite, $PdAs_2O_5$, by treating a soln. of palladic chloride
with potassium tetrarsenite in a manner similar to that employed for the platinum
salt.

REFERENCES.

[1] C. Morelli, *Chem. Ztg.*, 5. 815, 1881; R. Pribram, *ib.*, 10. 145, 1886; O. Henry and
C. L. Lhéritier, *Journ. Pharm. Chim.*, (3), 28. 233, 1855.
[2] P. J. Macquer, *Mém. Acad.*, 9, 1745; 223, 1746; 35, 1748.
[3] A. Stavenhagen, *Journ. prakt. Chem.*, (2), 51. 6, 1895; H. O. Schulze, *ib.*, (2), 21. 407,
1885: E. Blanc, *Journ. Chim. Phys.*, 18. 28, 1920; E. Cornec, *Compt. Rend.*, 149. 676, 1909:

Ann. Chim. Phys., (8), **29**. 490, 1913 ; (8), **30**. 63, 1913 ; *Contribution à l'étude physicochimique de la neutralisation*, Paris, 1912 ; B. L. Vanzetti, *Gazz. Chim. Ital.*, **55**. 106, 110, 1925 ; F. Henkel and C. Meyer, *German Pat.*, *D.R.P.* 386596, 1921 ; A. Miolati and E. Mascetti, *Gazz. Chim. Ital.*, **31**. i, 93, 1901 ; J. D. Jenkins and E. F. Berger, *U.S. Pat. No.* 159662, 1926 ; F. E. Brown and J. E. Snyder, *Journ. Amer. Chem. Soc.*, **47**. 2671, 1925 ; A. W. Francis, *ib.*, **48**. 655, 1926 ; L. Pasteur, *Journ. Pharm. Chim.*, (3), **13**. 395, 1848 ; C. L. Bloxam, *Journ. Chem. Soc.*, **15**. 281, 1862 ; J. K. Wood, *ib.*, **93**. 411, 1908 ; C. Reichard, *Ber.*, **31**. 2163, 1898 ; J. Thomsen, *ib.*, **7**. 935, 1874 ; J. von Zawidzky, *ib.*, **36**. 1427, 1903 ; A. Gutmann, *ib.*, **55**. B, 3007, 1922 ; **57**. B, 1956, 1924 ; *Ueber den Abbau der Thiosulfate und einiger Polythionate zu Sulfiten durch reducierende Salze in alkalischer Lösung und über einige Monosulfoxyarsenate*, München, 1897 ; *Zeit. anal. Chem.*, **66**. 224, 1925 ; P. Walden, *Zeit. phys. Chem.*, **2**. 51, 1888 ; C. R. Fresenius, *Liebig's Ann.*, **93**. 384, 1855 ; N. R. Dhar, *Zeit. anorg. Chem.*, **144**. 289, 1925 ; *Proc. Acad. Amsterdam*, **23**. 1074, 1921 ; *Versl. Akad. Amsterdam*, **29**. 1023, 1921 ; A. N. Dey and N. R. Dhar, *ib.*, **144**. 307, 1925 ; *Proc. Asiatic Soc. Bengal*, **8**. 130, 1921 ; N. N. Mittra and N. R. Dhar, *Journ. Phys. Chem.*, **29**. 376, 1925 ; J. C. Ghosh and S. C. Bisvas, *Zeit. Elektrochem.*, **30**. 97, 1924 ; W. P. Jorissen, *Rec. Trav. Chim. Pays-Bas*, **42**. 855, 1923 ; W. Reinders and S. I. Vles, *ib.*, **44**. 29, 1925 ; S. I. Vles, *ib.*, **46**. 743, 1927 ; W. P. Jorissen and C. van den Pol, *ib.*, **23**. 667, 1924 ; M. C. Boswell and J. V. Dickson, *Journ. Amer. Chem. Soc.*, **40**. 1773, 1918 ; R. T. Thomson, *Chem. News*, **49**. 119, 1884 ; **52**. 18, 29, 1885 ; F. A. Flückiger, *Arch. Pharm.*, (3), **22**. 605, 1884 ; R. Suchy and J. Michel, *U.S. Pat. No.* 1532454, 1925 ; G. Favrel, *Zeit. anorg. Chem.*, **5**. 101, 1894 ; F. A. H. Schreinemakers and W. C. de Baat, *Chem. Weekbl.*, **14**. 262, 288, 1917 ; *Rec. Trav. Chim. Pays-Bas*, **39**. 423, 1920 ; K. H. Butler and D. McIntosh, *Trans. Roy. Soc. Canada*, (3), **21**. 19, 1927 ; J. C. G. de Marignac, *Bibl. Univ.*, **55**. 113, 1876 ; N. de Kolossowsky, *Journ. Chim. Phys.*, **22**. 225, 1925 ; A. Bouchonnet, *Compt. Rend.*, **144**. 641, 1907 ; C. C. Palit and N. R. Dhar, *Journ. Phys. Chem.*, **30**. 939, 1926 ; R. Robl, *Zeit. angew. Chem.*, **39**. 608, 1926 ; W. Clark, *Phot. Journ.*, **64**. 363, 1924 ; **73**. 155, 1925 ; J. H. Smith and H. A. Spoehr, *Journ. Amer. Chem. Soc.*, **48**. 107, 1925.

[4] J. J. Berzelius, *Ann. Chim. Phys.*, (2), **5**. 179, 1817 ; (2), **11**. 225, 1819 ; L. Pasteur, *Journ. Pharm. Chim.*, (3), **13**. 395, 1847 ; *Compt. Rend.*, **24**. 774, 1847 ; E. Cornec, *ib.*, **149**. 676, 1909 ; *Ann. Chim. Phys.*, (8), **29**. 490, 1913 ; (8), **30**. 63, 1913 ; *Contribution à l'étude physico-chimique de la neutralisation*, Paris, 1912 ; N. W. Fischer, *Kastner's Arch.*, **11**. 236, 1827 ; N. J. B. G. Guibourt, *Journ. Chim. Méd.*, (1), **2**. 55, 1826 ; A. Stavenhagen, *Journ. prakt. Chem.*, (2), **51**. 13, 1895 ; V. de Luynes, *Compt. Rend.*, **44**. 1354, 1857 ; C. L. Bloxam, *Journ. Chem. Soc.*, **15**. 281, 1863 ; F. A. H. Schreinemakers and W. C. de Baat, *Proc. Acad. Amsterdam*, **17**. 111, 1915 ; H. Stamm, *Ueber die Löslichkeit von Ammonsalzen und Alkalisalzen in wässerigem Ammoniak*, Halle, 1926 ; J. M. F. de Lassone, *Mém. Acad.*, **40**, 1775 ; A. Miolati and E. Mascetti, *Gazz. Chim. Ital.*, **31**. i. 93, 1901.

[5] C. W. Scheele, *Svenska Akad. Handl.*, **40**. 316, 1778 ; S. P. Sharples, *Proc. Amer. Acad.*, **12**. 11, 1877 ; *Chem. News*, **35**. 89, 108, 1877 ; T. B. Stillman, *ib.*, **80**. 250, 1899 ; R. Fittig, *Zeit. Chem.*, (2), **6**. 416, 1870 ; C. L. Bloxam, *Journ. Chem. Soc.*, **15**. 281, 1862 ; C. Reichard, *Chem. Ztg.*, **26**. 1142, 1902 ; *Ber.*, **27**. 1020, 1894 ; **30**. 1914, 1897 ; A. Damour and G. vom Rath, *Zeit. Kryst.*, **5**. 245, 1880 ; *Bull. Soc. Min.*, **3**. 175, 1880 ; A. Stavenhagen, *Journ. prakt. Chem.*, (2), **51**. 25, 1895 ; A. Vogel, *ib.*, (1), **6**. 347, 1835 ; W. Hampe, *Zeit. Berg. Hütt. Sal.*, **22**. 100, 1874 ; J. Schröder, *Chemisches und physikalische-chemisches Verhalten des Pyridins und von Metallsalzen zu und in Pyridin*, Giessen, 20, 1904 ; L. Gmelin, *Handbook of Chemistry*, London, **5**. 470, 1851 ; J. L. Proust, *Ann. Chim. Phys.*, (1), **60**. 260, 1806 ; *Nicholson's Journ.*, **17**. 46, 1807 ; *Phil. Mag.*, **30**. 337, 1808 ; H. Braconnot, *Ann. Chim. Phys.*, (2), **53**. 21, 53, 1822 ; J. J. Berzelius, *ib.*, (2), **5**. 179, 1817 ; (2), **11**. 225, 1819 ; J. A. Krenner, *Zeit. Kryst.*, **56**. 198, 1921 ; E. S. Larsen, *Bull. U.S. Geol. Sur.*, 679, 1921 ; W. Sattler, *Zeit. angew. Chem.*, **1**. 40, 1888 ; G. Tammann, *Zeit. anorg. Chem.*, **149**. 68, 1925 ; J. F. Simon, *Pogg. Ann.*, **40**. 440, 1837 ; **41**. 424, 1837 ; G. Bonnet, *ib.*, **37**. 300, 1836 ; A. Girard, *Compt. Rend.*, **36**. 794, 1853 ; L. N. Vauquelin, *Journ. Pharm. Chim.*, (1), **9**. 230, 1823 ; S. Avery, *Journ. Amer. Chem. Soc.*, **28**. 1159, 1906 ; S. Avery and H. T. Beans, *ib.*, **23**. 485, 1901 ; E. W. Hilgard, *ib.*, **22**. 690, 1900 ; E. Ehrmann, *Bull. Soc. Ind. Mulhausen*, **7**. 68, 1834 ; *Liebig's Ann.*, **12**. 92, 1834 ; H. Schiff and R. Sestini, *ib.*, **228**. 91, 1885 ; J. G. Gentele, *Dingler's Journ.*, **61**. 452, 1836 ; **121**. 363, 1851 ; G. Bornemann, *Zeit. anorg. Chem.*, **124**. 36, 1922 ; L. Kahlenberg and J. V. Steinle, *Trans. Amer. Electrochem. Soc.*, **44**. 493, 1923 ; A. Miolati and E. Mascetti, *Gazz. Chim. Ital.*, **31**. i, 93, 1901 ; E. Cornec, *Contribution à l'étude physicochimique de la neutralisation*, Paris, 1912 ; *Ann. Chim. Phys.*, (8), **29**. 490, 1913 ; (8), **30**. 63, 1913 ; Farbenindustrie A.G., *German Pat.*, *D.R.P.* 428239, 1924 ; E. C. Franklin and C. A. Kraus, *Amer. Chem. Journ.*, **20**. 820, 1898 ; H. Baubigny and P. Rivals, *Compt. Rend.*, **137**. 753, 1903.

[6] J. Hume, *Phil. Mag.*, **40**. 105, 294, 431, 1812 ; E. Filhol, *Journ. Pharm. Chim.*, (3), **14**. 331, 1848 ; A. Laugier and J. Pelletier, *ib.*, (1), **11**. 487, 1824 ; L. Pasteur, *ib.*, (3), **13**. 395, 1847 ; O. B. Kühn, *Arch. Pharm.*, (2), **69**. 267, 1852 ; J. R. Santos, *Chem. News*, **38**. 94, 1878 ; J. A. Wanklyn, *ib.*, **85**. 181, 1902 ; R. S. Bosworth, *Amer. Journ. Science*, (4), **38**. 287, 1909 ; *Zeit. anorg. Chem.*, **64**. 189, 1909 ; C. L. Bloxam, *Journ. Chem. Soc.*, **15**. 281, 1862 ; A. Stavenhagen, *Journ. prakt. Chem.*, (2), **51**. 26, 1895 ; L. Meyer, *ib.*, (2), **22**. 103, 1881 ; F. Wöhler, *Liebig's Ann.*, **101**. 363, 1857 ; C. Reichard, *Ber.*, **27**. 1022, 1894 ; J. F. Simon, *Pogg. Ann.* **40**. 419, 1837 ; **41**. 424, 1837 ; H. Reckleben, G. Lockemann, and A. Eckardt, *Zeit. anal. Chem.* **46**. 671, 1907 ; A. Eckardt, *Ueber Reaktionen und Bestimmungsmethoden von Arsenwasserstoff*.

Leipzig, 1907; A. Reynoso, *Ann. Chim. Phys.*, (3), **33**. 244, 1851; *Compt. Rend.*, **31**. 68, 1850; A. Girard, *ib.*, **34**. 918, 1852; G. C. Wittstein, *Repert. Pharm.*, (3), **1**. 41, 1848; *Zeit. anal. Chem.*, **2**. 19, 1863; A. Marcet, *Trans. Med. Chir. Soc.*, **3**. 342, 1812; *Nicholson's Journ.*, **34**. 174, 1813; *Ann. Phil.*, **3**. 236, 1814; G. S. Whitby, *Zeit. anorg. Chem.*, **67**. 107, 1910; A. Dexheimer, *Ueber die Darstellung anorganische Kolloide in kolloidalen organischen Medien*, Erlangen, 53, 1910; F. Bezold, *Das Verhalten chemischer Verbindungen in Methylacetat*, Giessen, 8, 1906; M. Hamers, *Verhalten der Halogenverbindungen des Quecksilbers in reinem und in bei 18° mit Wasser gesättigtem Aethylacetat*, Giessen, 1906.

⁷ A. Schafarik, *Sitzber. Akad. Wien*, **47**. 256, 1863; J. Perper, *Beiträge zur Kenntnis der arsenigsauren Salze*, Berlin, 1890; F. Herrmann, *Landw. Jahrb.*, **56**. i, 99, 1921; J. Stein, *Liebig's Ann.*, **74**. 220, 1850; F. Frerichs and F. Smith, *ib.*, **191**. 331, 1878; A. Streng, *ib.*, **129**. 241, 1864; O. B. Kühn, *Arch. Pharm.*, (2), **69**. 267, 1852; J. F. Simon, *Pogg. Ann.*, **40**. 417, 1837; J. J. Berzelius, *ib.*, **7**. 28, 1826; *Ann. Chim. Phys.*, (2), **11**. 233, 1819; E. Thorey, *Russ. Journ. Pharm.*, **10**. 331, 1871; E. Masing, *ib.*, **28**. 753, 1889; A. Stavenhagen, *Journ. prakt. Chem.*, (2), **51**. 1, 1895; S. J. Thugutt, *Zeit. anorg. Chem.*, **2**. 88, 1892; *Mineralchemische Studien*, Dorpat, 1891; G. F. Wach, *Schweigger's Journ.*, **59**. 272, 1830; C. Giesecke, *ib.*, **43**. 359, 1825; B. Ormont, *Ukraine Chem. Journ.*, **2**. 20, 1926; G. C. Wittstein, *Repert. Pharm.*, (3), i, 41, 1848; *Zeit. anal. Chem.*, **2**. 19, 1863; G. Aminoff, *Geol. För. Förh. Stockholm*, **45**. 160, 1923; C. L. Bloxam, *Journ. Chem. Soc.*, **15**. 281, 1862; P. T. Cleve, *Ber.*, **11**. 912, 1878; C. Reichard, *ib.*, **27**. 1024. 1894; **31**. 2166, 1898; *Zeit. anal. Chem.*, **37**. 749, 1898; *Chem. Ztg.*, **26**. 1143, 1902; E. Filhol, *Journ. Pharm. Chim.*, (3), **14**. 331, 401, 1848; L. G. Story and E. Anderson, *Journ. Amer. Chem. Soc.*, **46**. 533, 1924; S. Avery, *ib.*, **28**. 1163, 1906; A. Dexheimer, *Ueber die Darstellung anorganische Kolloide in kolloidalen organischen Medien*, Erlangen, 56, 1919; A. Reynoso, *Compt. Rend.*, **31**. 68, 1850; G. Dessner, *Beiträge zur Kenntnis der Arsenite des Bleis und Quecksilberoxyduls*, Proskoroff, 1897; G. Tammann, *Zeit. anorg. Chem.*, **149**. 68, 1925; B. Bleyer and B. Müller, *ib.*, **75**. 285, 1912; *Arch. Pharm.*, **251**. 304, 1913; M. Henglein and W. Meigen, *Centr. Min.*, 353, 1914; J. Altwegg, *U.S. Pat. No.* 1545873, 1925; E. Wedekind and H. Wilke, *Koll. Zeit.*, **34**. 83, 1924.

⁸ J. J. Berzelius, *Pogg. Ann.*, **7**. 28, 1826; *Schweigger's Journ.*, **32**. 162, 1821; A. Stavenhagen, *Journ. prakt. Chem.*, (2), **51**. 35, 1895; R. Schneider, *ib.*, (2), **20**. 419, 1879; L. Vanino and F. Hartl, *ib.*, (2), **74**. 142, 1906; L. Jassoy, *Arch. Pharm.*, (3), **21**. 745, 1883; C. Reichard, *Ber.*, **30**. 1913, 1897.

⁹ A. Miolati, *Journ. prakt. Chem.*, (2), **77**. 431, 1908; A. Rosenheim and R. Bilecki, *Ber.*, **46**. 539, 1913; R. Bilecki, *Zur Kenntnis der Heteropolysäuren die Molybdänarsinsauren*, Berlin, 1913; G. Bonnet, *Pogg. Ann.*, **37**. 303, 1836; H. Feidel, *Ueber Alkaliarsenigmolybdate*, Wurzburg, 1907; F. Ephraim and H. Feidel, *Zeit. anorg. Chem.*, **66**. 53, 1910; A. Rosenheim, W. Weinberg, and J. Pinsker, *ib.*, **84**. 221, 1913; R. H. C. Neville, *Chem. News*, **34**. 220, 1876; A. Rogers, *Journ. Amer. Chem. Soc.*, **25**. 298, 1903; C. Reichard, *Ber.*, **27**. 1028, 1894; A. Stavenhagen, *Journ. prakt. Chem.*, (2), **51**. 34, 1895; O. W. Gibbs, *Amer. Chem. Journ.*, **7**. 313, 1885; G. Aminoff and R. Mauzelius, *Geol. För. Förh. Stockholm*, **42**. 301, 1920; G. Flink, *ib.*, **42**. 436, 1920; G. Aminoff, *ib.*, **45**. 160, 1923; J. Stein, *Liebig's Ann.*, **74**. 220, 1850; E. Weidenbach, *Untersuchungen über die Komplexbildung beim dreiwertigen Arsen*, Berlin, 1915.

¹⁰ C. Reichard, *Zeit. anal. Chem.*, **42**. 10, 1902; *Chem. Ztg.*, **26**. 1145, 1903; *Ber.*, **27**. 1019, 1037, 1894; **31**. 2163, 1898; *Bull. Soc. Chim.*, (3), **12**. 1063, 1894; A. Stavenhagen, *Journ. prakt. Chem.*, (2), **51**. 13, 1895; *Zeit. anorg. Chem.*, **8**. 404, 1895; A. Girard, *Compt. Rend.*, **34**. 918, 1852; A. Reynoso, *ib.*, **31**. 68, 1850; O. W. Gibbs, *Amer. Chem. Journ.*, **8**. 290, 1886; J. L. Proust, *Ann. Chim. Phys.*, (1), **60**. 260, 1806; *Nicholson's Journ.*, **17**. 46, 1807; *Phil. Mag.*, **30**. 337, 1808; J. J. Berzelius, *Pogg. Ann.*, **7**. 28, 1826; *Schweigger's Journ.*, **32**. 162, 1821; G. C. Wittstein, *Repert. Pharm.*, (3), **1**. 41, 1848; *Zeit. anal. Chem.*, **2**. 19, 1863; *Viertelj. Pharm.*, **15**. 185, 1866; N. J. B. G. Guibourt, *Journ. Chim. Méd.*, **15**. 306, 1839; R. Bunsen, *Pogg. Ann.*, **32**. 124, 1834; R. Bunsen and A. A. Berthold, *Das Eisenoxydhydrat, ein Gegengift des weissen Arseniks oder der arsenigen Säure*, Göttingen, 1834; J. F. Simon, *Pogg. Ann.*, **40**. 442, 1837; H. von Fehling, *Liebig's Ann.*, **74**. 87, 1850; A. Arzruni and E. Schütz, *Zeit. Kryst.*, **23**. 529, 1894; V. Ipatieff, *Ber.*, **59**. B, 1412, 1926; T. Oryng, *Koll. Zeit.*, **22**. 149, 1918; A. Reychler *Journ. Chim. Phys.*, **7**. 362, 1909; **8**. 10, 1910; G. Tammann, *Zeit. anorg. Chem.*, **149**. 68, 1925.

§ 13. Arsenic Tetroxide ; Arsenosic Oxide

According to C. L. Bloxam,[1] if chlorine be passed over arsenic trioxide as long as arsenic trichloride is formed, and the residue melted to a clear glass, the product has a composition corresponding with *arsenosic oxide*, or *arsenoarsenic oxide*, $2As_2O_3.As_2O_5$. He also obtained the same product by fusing together a mixture of arsenic acid with two molar proportions of arsenic trioxide. The clear glass becomes turbid in a few days, and when in contact with water, a soln. containing arsenic trioxide, arsenic acid, and about 0·5 per cent. of chlorine appears. There is here no evidence of chemical combination. C. Matignon and J. A. Lecanu obtained the tetroxide as an intermediate stage in the oxidation of arsenic trioxide. E. Bacalogio said that a boiling aq. soln. of arsenic acid dissolves arsenic trioxide, and rejects it as the soln. cools ; only 1·8–1·9 parts of the trioxide remain in soln. A. Joly reported a hydrated complex of arsenic tri- and penta-oxides by allowing a mixture of 100 grms. of powdered arsenic trioxide and 25–30 c.c. of conc. nitric acid to stand for some time. Red vapours are evolved and a solid mass of needle-like crystals remains. The composition is $3As_2O_3.2As_2O_5.3H_2O$. If an excess of arsenic acid be present, tabular crystals of $As_2O_3.As_2O_5.nH_2O$ are formed ; and if arsenic trioxide be in excess, $2As_2O_3.As_2O_5.nH_2O$ is formed. These complexes are decomposed by water with the separation of the trioxide. O. W. Gibbs prepared *potassium arsenitoarsenatotungstate*, $10K_2O.As_2O_3.4As_2O_5.21WO_3.26H_2O$, in white crystals.

The so-called **arsenic tetroxide, or arsenosic oxide,** As_2O_4, can be regarded as a combination of a mol. each of arsenic trioxide and pentoxide ; H. Herbst supposed it to be a mixed anhydride of metasenious acid, $HAsO_2$, or $HO.AsO$, and metarsenic acid, $HAsO_3$, or $HO.AsO_2$:

$$O=As-O-As{<}{\begin{matrix}O\\O\end{matrix}}$$

H. Herbst said that when a mixture of equimolar parts of arsenic tri- and penta-oxides is heated to 350° no trioxide volatilized, although that oxide alone sublimes at 200° ; if an excess of the trioxide be present, the excess over the molar ratio 1 : 1 sublimes ; and if an excess of the pentoxide be present, that excess loses oxygen until the 1 : 1 ratio is formed. When arsenic pentoxide alone is heated, oxygen is given off and arsenic tetroxide is formed. E. Weidenbach showed that between 800° and 1200° the product has the composition As_6O_{11} corresponding with the compound $As_4O_6.As_2O_5$. He obtained no evidence of the formation of the compound $As_4O_6.2As_2O_5=4As_2O_4$. The fused mass freezes to a transparent glass which becomes opaque when it has stood some hours in a desiccator—*vide infra*, arsenic pentoxide. The tetroxide is slightly soluble in water, and is precipitated from the aq. soln. by alcohol ; it is easily soluble in a soln. of an alkali carbonate or hydroxide, or in hydrochloric acid.

REFERENCES.

[1] C. L. Bloxam, *Journ. Chem. Soc.*, 18. 62, 1865 ; E. Bacalogio, *Journ. prakt. Chem.*, (1), 83. 111, 1861 ; O. W. Gibbs, *Amer. Chem. Journ.*, 7. 313, 1885 ; A. Joly, *Compt. Rend.*, 100. 1223, 1886 ; C. Matignon and J. A. Lecanu, *ib.*, 170. 941, 1920 ; H. Herbst, *Ueber Arsentetroxyd*, München, 1894 ; E. Weidenbach, *Untersuchungen über die Komplexbildung beim dreiwertigen Arsen*, Berlin, 44, 1915.

§ 14. Arsenic Pentoxide ; Arsenic Acid

A manuscript entitled : *Experiments on arsenic* by H. Cavendish, written in 1765, shows that he anticipated by sixteen years the discovery of the acid of arsenic, its relation to the oxide and regulus, and the complete examination of its salts.[1] It is also true that a number of early workers investigated the action of nitric acid on arsenic trioxide. J. R. Glauber confined his attention to the red fumes which are evolved during the reaction ; but T. Paracelsus obtained a solid product which he called *arsenicum fixum ;* A. Libavius called it *butyrum arsenici ;* J. B. van Helmont said that a fiery salt is produced ; N. Lemery called the product *arsenic caustique ;* and P. J. Macquer, *sel neutre arsenical.* But so far as the development of chemistry is concerned, the discovery of this compound must be attributed to C. W. Scheele in 1775. Analyses and the composition of the product, **arsenic pentoxide**, As_2O_5, were worked out by J. L. Proust,[2] C. F. Bucholz, J. J. Berzelius, L. J. Thénard, T. Thomson, and E. Mitscherlich.

M. Berthelot found that the pentoxide can be formed by the direct action of oxygen on arsenic, or arsenic trioxide. In the oxidation of arsenic trioxide, suspended in nitric acid of sp. gr. 1·4 at 90°, by oxygen: $As_2O_{3aq.}+O_2=As_2O_{5aq.}$, H. Zieler showed that the finer the particles the faster the reaction; the more vigorously the soln. is agitated, the faster the oxidation; the more conc. the acid the faster the oxidation, thus:

Conc. of HNO_3 .	. 47·7	55·9	59·0	65·4	73·3 per cent.
As_2O_3 oxidized .	. 1·6	72·0	75·7	82·3	100 „
HNO_3 reduced .	. 26	34	36	40	60 „

The higher the temp. the faster the oxidation, thus:

	60°	70	80°	90°	100°
As_2O_3 oxidized .	. 9·0	16·2	33·1	82·3	100 per cent.
HNO_3 reduced .	. 120	89	73	40	23·5 „

and the greater the press. of the oxygen, the faster the oxidation, thus:

Press. of oxygen .	. 0	5	10	20	25 atm.
As_2O_3 oxidized .	. 12·4	30·0	49·5	80·2	88·8
HNO_3 reduced .	. —	99	68	36	33

No oxidation occurs in neutral soln., but the reaction is quantitative in the presence of nitric acid if the arsenic trioxide is finely divided. R. Weber obtained it by the action of dry chlorine on arsenic trioxide. C. Ellis and V. T. Stewart also oxidized the trioxide with chlorine. P. Askenasy and E. Elöd heated 150 parts of arsenious oxide (or sulphide) and 150 parts of 60 per cent. nitric acid in a closed vessel with a stirrer. A little arsenic pentoxide or other catalyst is added; and oxygen at 20 atm. press. is forced in and the mixture stirred for 12–18 hrs. at 70°–80°. The nitric acid is nearly always unchanged and can be distilled off. Arsenic pentoxide is obtained by heating the hydrated oxide or arsenic acid—vide infra. V. Augur showed that the water can be all driven off at 180°, and the pentoxide is stable below 400°; hence, 180°–200° is a convenient temp. for the dehydration of arsenic acid. According to A. W. C. Menzies and P. D. Potter, arsenic pentoxide retains a small quantity of water at a high temp., and its removal can be best and most rapidly effected by heating it in air containing water vapour.

Arsenic pentoxide is a white pulverulent solid, or when it has been fused it may form a transparent or opaque glass. T. Bergman gave for the sp. gr. 3·391; L. Playfair and J. P. Joule, 3·985–4·023; W. Herapath, 3·729; E. Filhol, 4·25; and V. Auger, 4·3. C. J. B. Karsten gave 3·7342 for the oxide which had been heated to dull redness. D. Balareff, and C. del Fresno studied the mol. vol. According to C. F. Bucholz, when arsenic pentoxide is heated somewhat above its m.p., it is resolved into oxygen and volatile arsenic trioxide. The residue is a mixture of arsenic tri- and penta-oxides. V. Auger, H. Kopp, and E. C. Szarvasy and C. Messinger found that the decomposition occurs at a red-heat before the pentoxide melts; and H. Kopp added that partial sintering may occur if the temp. be rapidly raised. C. F. Bucholz's product may have contained a little alkali. V. Auger said that the pentoxide begins to decompose above 400°: $2As_2O_5=As_4O_6+2O_2$. E. Weidenbach showed that between 800° and 1000°, the product has the composition As_6O_{11}, a substance also obtained by C. L. Bloxam. This is considered by E. Weidenbach to be a compound $As_4O_6.As_2O_5$, and not $As_4O_6.2As_2O_5=4As_2O_4$. A. W. C. Menzies and P. D. Potter measured the amount of water lost when the hydrated pentoxide is heated for different lengths of time at different temp. J. Thomsen found the heat of formation $(2As,5O)=219·38$ Cals., and (As_2O_3,O_2) $=32·355$ Cals., while M. Berthelot gave 32·4 Cals.; and C. Matignon and J. A. Lecanu, $As_2O_3+O_2=As_2O_5+62·2$ Cals.

Arsenic pentoxide appears at first to be tasteless, but it quickly appears to have a sharp, acidic taste; and, according to E. Filhol, it is more poisonous than arsenic trioxide towards plants. On the other hand, G. Joachimoglu said that with intravenous injections in rabbits the relative toxicity of sodium arsenites and arsenates is as 6 : 10, but arsenious acid is more toxic towards an isolated frog's heart ; and an isolated small intestine of a rabbit. He added : " Arsenic acid acts toxically only after reduction to arsenious acid." When arsenic pentoxide is heated in an atm. of **hydrogen** it is reduced to the trioxide, and finally to arsenic ; **oxygen** has no action ; **water** converts it into the hydrate or into arsenic acid, H_3AsO_4 —*vide infra.* Arsenic pentoxide attracts moisture from the air and is transformed into arsenic acid. Many of the reactions furnish products like those obtained with arsenic trioxide (*q.v.*), or with arsenic acid (*q.v.*). Thus, the pentoxide is reduced by **sulphur**, and this forms arsenic sulphide. H. A. von Vogel found that the pentoxide absorbs **hydrogen sulphide,** forming arsenic pentasulphide and water. J. Mayrhofer found that **hydrogen chloride** is vigorously absorbed by the pentoxide forming water and arsenic trichloride. No arsenic trichloride is formed at —20°. C. F. Schönbein observed that when triturated with **potassium iodide,** the mixture becomes brown, and when the mixture is heated, the reaction is symbolized : $3As_2O_5 + 4KI = 4KAsO_3 + As_2O_3 + 2I_2$; **potassium bromide** acts similarly, likewise also **alkaline earth chlorides** but not the **alkali chlorides.** H. O. Schulze found that a mixture of alkali chloride and the pentoxide is rapidly decomposed when heated in oxygen gas. E. Berl studied the oxidation of **sulphur dioxide** in the presence of the pentoxide. F. Faktor found that when the trioxide is melted with **sodium thiosulphate** arsenic di- and tri-sulphides are formed. The reaction between alkali arsenate and sodium thiosulphate in acid soln. results in the precipitation of arsenic trisulphide as indicated by G. Vortmann. G. S. Forbes and co-workers showed that there is a definite period of induction so that the appearance of the trisulphide furnishes a so-called clock reaction—*vide* arsenic trioxide. According to A. Rosenheim and F. Jacobsohn, when arsenic pentoxide is treated with liquid **ammonia** in a sealed tube at ordinary temp., **arsenic triamminopentoxide,** $As_2O_5.3NH_3$, is formed. Its constitution has not been determined. It may be **ammonium imidodimetarsenate,** $(NH_4)_2As_2O_5(NH)$, because when treated with lead iodide, in ammoniacal soln., a heavy white precipitate with the composition **lead imidodimetarsenate,** $Pb\{(NH_4)As_2O_4(NH)\}_2$, is formed. Arsenic pentoxide is reduced by **phosphorus** to the trioxide, etc. A. Michaelis said that **phosphorus trichloride** does not act on the pentoxide at 200°, but, according to L. Hurtzig and A. Geuther, **phosphorus pentachloride** reacts : $As_2O_5 + 5PCl_5 = 2AsCl_3 + 5POCl_3$ $+2Cl_2$. The pentoxide is reduced by **carbon,** as in the case of the trioxide. J. J. Berzelius said that the pentoxide is more soluble than the trioxide in **alcohol ;** that it is very slightly soluble in **fatty oils,** for 100 parts of oil dissolve only 0·2 part of the trioxide in the cold, and one part, with partial decomposition, on boiling. J. J. Heimpel, and K. von Grundner found that 100 parts of boiling **poppy oil** dissolve 2·7 parts of arsenic pentoxide ; and 100 parts of **castor oil,** 3·4 parts of the pentoxide. O. Aschan found that 100 grms. of 95 per cent. **formic acid** dissolve 7·6 grms. of the pentoxide at 19°. Arsenic pentoxide is reduced by **arsenic** to the trioxide ; **antimony,** and **bismuth** act similarly. L. Kahlenberg and W. J. Trautmann said that when heated with **silicon,** arsenic oxide is volatilized. According to J. L. Gay Lussac and L. J. Thénard, the pentoxide is vigorously reduced by heated **potassium** or **sodium ;** J. J. Berzelius found that it is reduced when heated with **zinc ;** and C. W. Scheele, when heated with **iron.** Similar results have been obtained with other metals—*e.g.* **copper, tin, lead, manganese, and cobalt—silver,** and **mercury** act only at a high temp., **gold** and **platinum** not at all.

Arsenic pentoxide is slowly dissolved by cold water and rapidly by hot water. The aq. soln. is usually designated *arsenic acid.* When the aq. soln. is evaporated C. F. Bucholz said that a syrupy liquid is obtained which ultimately furnishes crystals of arsenic acid, presumably $H_3AsO_4.nH_2O$. H. A. von Vogel found that 100 parts of water at 12·5 dissolve 244·8 parts of As_2O_5 or 302·3 parts of H_3AsO_4. E. Mitscherlich reported that at 15°, crystals of the hydrate, $2HAsO_4.H_2O$, are formed ; and T. Graham found that the products obtained by the successive loss of water are analogous in composition to those obtained with phosphorus pentoxide, namely :

$$\begin{array}{ccc}
\begin{array}{c}
\text{HO} \\
\text{HO} \!\!-\!\! \text{As} \!=\! \text{O} \\
\text{HO}
\end{array}
&
\begin{array}{c}
\quad\ \ \text{O O} \\
\quad\ \ /\ \backslash \\
\text{HO} \quad\!\!\!\!\! \text{As} \quad \text{As} \!\!<\!\! \text{OH} \\
\text{HO} \!\!>\!\! \qquad\qquad \text{OH} \\
\quad\ \ \backslash\ / \\
\quad\ \ \text{O}
\end{array}
&
\text{HO} \!-\! \text{As} \!\!<\!\! {}^{\text{O}}_{\text{O}}
\\[2mm]
\text{Arsenic acid,} & \text{Pyroarsenic acid,} & \text{Metarsenic acid,} \\
\text{H}_3\text{AsO}_4 & \text{H}_4\text{As}_2\text{O}_7 & \text{HAsO}_3
\end{array}$$

but he said that the products of the dehydration do not furnish distinctive salts as in the case of the condensation products of phosphoric acid, and accordingly should not be designated pyro- and meta-arsenic acids. J. J. Berzelius and E. Mitscherlich emphasized the similarity of the arsenates to the phosphates in their constitution, properties, and crystalline form. After T. Clark had converted sodium orthophosphate into the pyrophosphate by driving off one-third of the constitutional water, he investigated whether sodium arsenate would exhibit a similar change, and found that " the appearances were the same, but the effects were different." Both phosphates and arsenates when heated to redness lose one proportion of water, but aq. soln. of the arsenate alone gave the same precipitates with other salts as it did before the thermal change, and the soln. of the arsenate alone on crystallization gave the old salt back again. Hence, said T. Clark, " this looks as though the phosphate and the arsenate alike lose a mol. of water, but with the phosphate an additional change occurs not produced with the arsenate."

H. E. Armstrong and F. P. Worley made some observations on the constitution of arsenic acid—vide sulphuric acid. A. Joly reported the hemitrihydrate, $2\text{As}_2\text{O}_5.3\text{H}_2\text{O}$, to be formed by drying arsenic acid, i.e. the trihydrate, or the tetrahydrate at 110°, or in vacuo. D. Balareff, A. W. C. Menzies and P. D. Potter could not make this hydrate. H. Kopp prepared the monohydrate, $\text{As}_2\text{O}_5.\text{H}_2\text{O}$, or metarsenic acid, HAsO_3, by heating a very conc. soln. of arsenic acid at 200° and then raising the temp. slowly to 206°. The product dissolves slowly in cold water, with the evolution of heat, and it dissolves rapidly in hot water. V. Auger, D. Balareff, and A. W. C. Menzies and P. D. Potter could not make this hydrate. The last-named observed that when the tetrahydrate is left to stand in a superfused state, a hard, white crystalline scale is produced of the pentatritahydrate, $3\text{As}_2\text{O}_5.5\text{H}_2\text{O}$, which can be satisfactorily obtained by evaporating a soln. of arsenic acid to dryness at 100°. A supersaturated soln. of this hydrate at 9·2° was well inoculated with crystals and stirred continuously. Supersaturation was not entirely removed until after 27 days. D. Balareff said that crystals of this hydrate are always formed when a soln. of arsenic acid is evaporated in an open vessel at 50°, or under increased press. at 150°. H. Kopp evaporated an aq. soln. between 140° and 180°, and obtained a hard mass with the composition of the dihydrate, $\text{As}_2\text{O}_5.2\text{H}_2\text{O}$, or pyroarsenic acid, $\text{H}_4\text{As}_2\text{O}_7$. D. Balareff, V. Auger, A. W. C. Menzies and P. D. Potter could not make this hydrate, and similar remarks apply to the trihydrate, $\text{As}_2\text{O}_5.3\text{H}_2\text{O}$, or orthoarsenic acid, H_3AsO_4, reported by H. Kopp to be formed by heating the tetrahydrate at 100°, and allowing the fused mass to cool ; and by heating the aq. soln. for a long time on a water-bath. The needle-like crystals lost half their water at 110° ; and were said to be readily soluble in water without a perceptible rise of temp. D. Balareff, V. Auger, and A. W. C. Menzies and P. D. Potter could not make this hydrate. H. Kopp obtained the tetrahydrate, $\text{As}_2\text{O}_5.4\text{H}_2\text{O}$, or hemihydrated arsenic acid, $\text{H}_3\text{AsO}_4.\text{H}_2\text{O}$, by crystallizing the conc. aq. soln. at 15°. According to A. W. C. Menzies and P. D. Potter, the tetrahydrate can be prepared by concentrating an aq. soln. of arsenic acid until it has a b.p. of 150° ; and, after cooling, inoculating a small portion of the soln. with crystals of the corresponding hydrate of phosphoric acid, $\text{P}_2\text{O}_5.4\text{H}_2\text{O}$, and using the crystals so obtained to inoculate the remainder of the liquid. A. Joly said that the crystals of the tetrahydrates of arsenic and phosphorus pentoxides must be isomorphous because crystals of the one can be used for inducing the crystallization of sat. soln. of the other. The crystals, said H. Kopp are rhombic prisms or plates, which are deliquescent, and dissolve freely in water with the development of heat. The crystals melt and freeze between 35·5° and 36°. A. W. C. Menzies and P. D. Potter gave 36·14° for the m.p. A. Joly found the crystals lose water in vacuo, forming the hemitrihydrate; and V. Auger said that complete dehydration occurs at 180°–200°. D. Balareff said that when fused the tetrahydrate forms the pentatritahydrate. J. Kendall and co-workers, and D. I. Mendeléeff discussed the hydrate formation with this and related acids; and H. Remy, the structure of arsenic acid. A. W. C. Menzies and P. D. Potter's solubility curve of the pentoxide, expressed in percentage amounts of arsenic acid, H_3AsO_4, between 0° and 60°, the so-called ice-line, where ice is the solid phase:

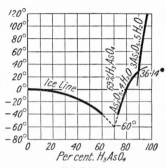

FIG. 24.—Solubility Curves of Arsenic Pentoxide in Water.

	0°	−10°	−20°	−30°	−40°	−50°	(−60°)
H_3AsO_4	0·0	23·0	46·2	54·5	60·5	65·1	(69·0) per cent.

After passing the eutectic region extrapolated in Fig. 24, the solid phase is the tetrahydrate, $As_2O_5.4H_2O$, or $H_3AsO_4.H_2O$, for which the solubility is:

	−55°	−50°	−30°	−10°	0°	20°	30°
H_3AsO_4	−69·9	70·9	74·9	78·9	81·0	86·3	90 per cent.

The unstable tetrahydrate phase at 35° has a 92·8 per cent. solubility. There is a transition point near 36·1°, and the solid phase at higher temp. is the pentatritahydrate, $3As_2O_5.5H_2O$, unstable at 10° and 20° with 88·4 and 89·1 per cent. respectively of H_3AsO_4, and the stable at

	40°	50°	60°	80°	100°	120°	140°
H_3AsO_4	90·5	91·2	91·9	93·2	94·4	95·6	96·8 per cent.

A. Simon and E. Thaler cooled to −20° to −30° a soln. of arsenic acid which had been evaporated at 130°, and obtained the *heptahydrate*, $As_2O_5.7H_2O$. The time-composition curve of the decomposition of the tetrahydrate, $As_2O_5.4H_2O$, shows no indication of any hydrate other than $3As_2O_5.5H_2O$; and no signs of solid soln. were observed. The three hydrates are represented:

$$H_7\begin{bmatrix} O & O \\ O & As & O \\ & O \end{bmatrix} \quad H_3\begin{bmatrix} O \\ OAsO \\ O \end{bmatrix}\tfrac{1}{2}H_2O \quad H_5\begin{bmatrix} O & AsO_4 \\ \cdot & As \\ O_4As & O \end{bmatrix}$$

$$As_2O_5.7H_2O \qquad As_2O_5.4H_2O \qquad 3As_2O_5.5H_2O$$

According to M. Berthelot,[3] arsenic acid is not formed when dry arsenic trioxide is heated in an atm. of oxygen in a sealed tube for 48 hrs.; nor does an aq. soln. of arsenic trioxide absorb any oxygen in the presence of hydrochloric acid when exposed in air for 2 months; but at 100°, oxygen is slowly absorbed, and arsenic acid is formed. The reaction is accelerated in the presence of platinum foil. For oxidation of arsenic trioxide by hydrogen dioxide, and by ozone, *vide supra*. Arsenic acid is formed when arsenic or arsenic trioxide is treated with oxidizing agents. T. Thomson used hot nitric acid with arsenic or arsenic trioxide (*q.v.*). L. Gmelin added that if boiling dil. nitric acid is used, a mixture of arsenic acid and arsenic trioxide is formed. Nitric acid is employed on a large scale when about 4 parts of arsenic trioxide are gradually added to 3 parts of nitric acid of sp. gr. not less than 1·35. About 65·70 kilogrms. of the trioxide are treated at a time.

Much heat is evolved, and the nitrous fumes evolved are passed over coke moistened with water, whereby up to two-thirds of the nitric acid can be recovered. In 24 hrs. a syrupy liquid is formed ; this is treated with a little more nitric acid to ensure the oxidation of all the trioxide. The liquid is evaporated to a syrup which deposits crystals of the tetrahydrate when cooled. O. C. Behse used hydrochloric acid as catalyst. The arsenic acid was formerly made in earthenware pots ; but it is now made in nitrating kettles made of a ferrosilicon alloy—duriron. C. M. Smith and G. E. Miller showed that in the oxidation of arsenic trioxide by nitric acid in the manufacture of calcium arsenate, the rate of oxidation progresses very differently with different raw materials. The sluggish action is due to the presence of small quantities of mercury in the arsenic trioxide, 0·1 per cent. being a powerful negative catalyst. Reactivity may be restored in such cases by the addition of small quantities of hydrochloric, hydrobromic, or hydriodic acids. These compounds, even in the low concentrations necessary, may, however, be corrosive to the metallic vessels in which the oxidation is frequently accomplished. The acceleration of the reaction by the haloid acids is the subject of a patent by O. C. Behse. The manufacture was discussed by C. W. Drury and C. W. Simmons, W. C. Piver, and E. A. Suverkrop. C. G. Richardson treated a soluble arsenate with ferric sulphate. forming an insoluble arsenate which was then converted to arsenic acid by sulphuric acid. C. W. Scheele, and C. F. Bucholz employed aqua regia as the oxidizing agent ; N. A. E. Millon said that if the acid is so dil. that no chlorine is evolved, it does not attack arsenic until heat is applied, or nitrous acid added. The oxidation was found by T. Bergman, C. Ellis and V. T. Stewart, and J. Girardin, to occur with chlorine or chlorine-water ; by A. J. Balard, and R. Wagner, with bromine ; by J. F. Simon, with iodine ; by A. J. Balard, with hypochlorous acid ; by H. Rose, with a mixture of potassium chlorate and hydrochloric acid ; by F. C. Schneider, with gold trichloride, or sodium chloroaurate ; and by F. Kessler, with chromic acid, or permanganic acid. J. A. Kaiser found that arsenic acid is formed when arsenic trichloride is decomposed by chlorine-water ; and W. Wallace, by chromic acid. L. L. de Koninck said that bromine-water converts arsenic trisulphide into arsenic acid ; and L. N. Vauquelin, that some metal oxides—e.g. cupric oxide—convert the trioxide into arsenic acid when in the presence of alkali-lye. The oxidation of arsenic trioxide in the presence of alkalies or alkaline earths was observed by J. L. Gay Lussac, W. H. Wollaston, A. F. Gehlen, E. Soubeiran, etc.—vide supra, the arsenites.

H. A. von Vogel[4] said that the **specific gravity** of a sat. aq. soln. of arsenic pentoxide is 2·550 ; the soln. remains liquid at −26° ; and it attracts moisture from the air until its sp. gr. is 1·935. G. T. Gerlach calculated the results indicated in Table VIII, from H. Kopp's data. H. Schiff also obtained a short table of

TABLE VIII.—SPECIFIC GRAVITIES OF AQUEOUS SOLUTIONS OF ARSENIC ACID AT 15.

Per cent. H_3AsO_4	0	2	4	6	8
0	1·000	1·013	1·026	1·039	1·052
1	1·066	1·081	1·096	1·111	1·126
2	1·142	1·158	1·175	1·192	1·210
3	1·228	1·248	1·267	1·288	1·309
4	1·331	1·353	1·376	1·400	1·425
5	1·450	1·478	1·505	1·534	1·564
6	1·594	1·626	1·659	1·693	1·730
7	1·767	1·809	1·851	1·897	1·946
8	1·995	2·045	2·095	2·149	2·207
9	2·265	2·295	—	—	—

results—for soln. with 7·5, 30, and 67·4 per cent. of arsenic acid, the sp. gr. were respectively 1·0495, 1·2350, and 1·7346. H. A. von Vogel's result does not agree with those indicated in **Table VIII**. **D. I.** Mendeléeff represented the sp. gr. of the aq. soln. containing p per cent. H_3AsO_4 at $15°/4°$ by $S=0.9992+0.0060p+0.0000576p^2$. R. Reyher found the **viscosity** of N-H_3AsO_4 to be 1.2707 (water unity), and for $\frac{1}{2}N$-soln., 1.1291; $\frac{1}{4}N$-, 1.0595; and $\frac{1}{8}N$-, 1.0309 at $25°$. L. J. Simon made some measurements of the viscosity during the progressive neutralization of the soln. with sodium hydroxide. G. Tammann found that the lowering of the **vapour pressure** of water by arsenic acid to be about half as great as is the case with sulphuric acid, being 13.1 mm. for 12.68 grms. of H_3AsO_3 in 100 grms. of water, 36.7 mm. for 34.07 grms. of acid, and 62.88 mm. for 72.5 grms. of acid. J. Thomsen gave for the **heat of neutralization** of H_3AsO_4aq. with an aq. soln. of 1, 2, and 3 mols of NaOH to be respectively 14.994, 27.580, and 35.916 Cals. This agrees with the assumption that arsenic acid in aq. soln. is tribasic. E. Baud and A. Astruc calculated for the three heats of neutralization $H_4AsO_{4 \text{solid}}+Na_{\text{solid}}$ $=H_{\text{gas}}+NaH_2AsO_{4 \text{solid}}+57.15$ Cals.; similarly, for (NaH_2AsO_4,Na), 45.87 Cals.; and for (Na_2HAsO_4,Na), 60.76 Cals. T. Graham made some observations on this subject.

J. C. Ghosh and S. C. Bisvas measured the extinction coeff. of arsenic acid for light. W. J. Pope gave 27.72 for the refraction equivalent of the H_2AsO_4-radicle. J. B. Richter, and C. F. Bucholz found that arsenic is deposited and arsine evolved at the negative pole during the electrolysis of the aq. soln. of arsenic acid. P. Walden found the **electrical conductivity**, μ, of aq. soln. of a mol of arsenic acid in v litres of water, at $25°$, to be:

v	8	16	32	64	128	256	512	1024
μ	68.4	89.4	117.4	150.2	188.4	228.0	264.2	290.3

He also gave for potassium dihydroarsenate, and for the three sodium arsenates:

v	32	64	128	256	512	1024
KN_2AsO_4	87.8	91.3	93.8	96.0	97.9	99.4
NaH_2AsO_4	67.6	70.6	73.2	75.4	77.4	78.6
Na_2HAsO_4	79.0	84.7	88.8	92.0	94.4	95.6
Na_3AsO_4	94.7	105.5	113.7	118.5	119.3	118.4

He added that the dihydroarsenates behave like salts of a monobasic acid, $H(H_2AsO)_4$; that sodium hydroarsenate behaves like a salt of a dibasic acid, $H_2(HAsO_4)$; while normal sodium arsenate is quickly decomposed with progressive dilution. The three salts behave like the corresponding salts of phosphoric acid. It is inferred that two of the three replaceable hydrogen atoms are similarly oriented in the molecule of arsenic acid, but the third hydrogen atom is not similarly disposed, for it is not so readily displaced by a metal. This is taken to be in agreement with J. Thomsen's thermochemical data; and with the behaviour of arsenic acid towards alkalies in the presence of different indicators. Arsenic acid in aq. soln. strongly reddens blue litmus. A. Joly, C. Blarez, and A. Astruc and J. Tarbouriech found that with lacmoid, and methyl-orange as indicators, arsenic acid behaves as if it were monobasic towards potassium or barium hydroxide; and with phenol-phthalein, as a dibasic acid. R. Engel showed that with Porrier's blue as indicator, arsenic acid behaves as if it were tribasic. R. T. Thomson made observations on this subject—*vide infra*. The conductivity of aq. soln. of the potassium metarsenate, obtained by calcining the dihydroarsenate; and for sodium pyro-arsenate obtained by calcining the hydroarsenate, were found by P. Walden to be:

v	32	64	128	256	512	1024
$KAsO_3$	87.8	91.3	93.8	96.0	97.6	99.4
$Na_4As_2O_7$	79.0	84.6	88.8	92.0	94.4	95.5

The values for the metarsenate agree with those of the dihydroarsenate, and it is therefore inferred that the salt is hydrated in aq. soln.: $KAsO_3+H_2O=KH_2AsO_4$. Similarly, the numbers for the pyroarsenate agree with those for the hydroarsenate, hence, in aq. soln., $Na_4As_2O_7 + H_2O = 2Na_2HAsO_4$. This means that neither the metarsenate nor the pyroarsenate can exist in aq. soln. R. Luther found the first **ionization constant** of arsenic acid : $H_3AsO_4 \rightleftharpoons H^{\cdot} + H_2AsO_4'$, that is, $K = [H_2AsO_4'][H^{\cdot}]/[H_3AsO_4]$, to be 0·005. E. W. Washburn calculated the ionization constant of the first hydrogen-ion of arsenic acid to be 0·0048 ; and added that the constants for the second and third hydrogen-ions are probably lower than $2 \cdot 1 \times 10^{-7}$ and $5 \cdot 6 \times 10^{-13}$, the respective values for those of phosphoric acid. E. Blanc calculated $K_2 = 4 \times 10^{-5}$, and $K_3 = 6 \times 10^{-10}$; and he found that in the neutralization of 0·0G2N-arsenic and with 0·595N-NaOH, there is a break corresponding with NaH_2AsO_4 when $C_4 = 0 \cdot 9 \times 10^{-4}$; and with Na_2HAsO_4, when $C_4 = 5 \times 10^{-11}$. For the affinity constant, *vide* sulphuric acid. According to G. Bischof, when an aq. soln. of arsenic acid is electrolyzed, arsenic is deposited at the cathode, and hydrogen or arsine is evolved while oxygen is given off at the anode.

A. C. Chapman and H. D. Law, and W. Thomson studied the **electrolytic reduction** of arsenic acid. L. Ramberg found that the nature of the cathode as well as of the cathodic surface has a great influence on the reduction of arsenic to arsine. The process generally occurs far more rapidly at spongy surfaces than at polished ones. The reduction is rapid and complete only at mercury cathodes. F. Förster and H. Pressprich found the reduction potential in soln. at least 0·1N-HCl to be $E = E_0 + 0 \cdot 029 \log [H_2AsO_4]/[H_2AsO_3]$, when E_0 at 18° is 0·574 volt, in agreement with R. Luther's value 0·575 volt for $H_3AsO_4 + 2H^{\cdot} + 3I' \rightleftharpoons H_3AsO_3 + I'_3 + H_2O$. Increasing the acidity of the soln. raises the potential. The subject was studied by L. Loimaranta, J. R. Roebuck, and K. Jellinek and L. Winogradoff. A. Brochet and J. Petit found that alternating currents exert a specific action on the reduction of arsenic acid by lead electrodes ; the evolution of gas varies with the current density but not the temp. L. Ramberg studied the effect of different cathodes on the reduction of arsenic acid.

The chemical properties of arsenic acid.—Arsenic acid is reduced by nascent **hydrogen** in acid soln. as in the case of aq. soln. of arsenic trioxide ; but E. Covelli [5] said that in alkaline soln. it resists reduction under conditions where arsenious acid forms arsine. Hence it is possible to detect arsenites in the presence of an arsenate. For the effect of **water,** *vide supra*, Fig. 24. According to S. Aschkenasy, if **alkaline earth peroxides** be dissolved in arsenic acid, and the soln. be evaporated under reduced press., at a low temp., a **perarsenate** of the alkaline earth is produced. The liquid before evaporation can be converted into a soln. of the alkali perarsenate by treatment with alkali sulphate. An alkali perarsenate is produced by evaporating, under reduced press., a soln. of the arsenate in dil. **hydrogen dioxide.**

According to H. Rose, when a soln. of arsenic acid and fuming **hydrochloric acid** is heated in the presence of conc. sulphuric acid, no arsenic trichloride is at first formed, but after a prolonged boiling a small quantity along with free chlorine appears in the distillate. C. R. Fresenius and A. Souchay found that on distilling a mixture of arsenic acid with hydrochloric acid of sp. gr. 1·12 mixed with more than its own vol. of water, no arsenic appears in the distillate, but if a more conc. acid be used some arsenic passes over as volatile chloride ; J. Mayrhofer found that with fuming acid much arsenic trichloride is formed in the receiver, while with an acid of sp. gr. 1·10, only traces pass over. O. Hehner found that the presence of organic matter favours the reduction of the pentoxide and the formation of the volatile trichloride. The presence of other reducing agents also results in the production of the volatile chloride. F. L. Usher and M. W. Travers represent the reaction $As_2O_5 + 10HCl \rightleftharpoons 2AsCl_3 + 2Cl_2 + 5H_2O$; they added that increasing the conc. of the hydrochloric acid, favours the production of the volatile chloride. J. Clark found that in the presence of cuprous chloride—H. Hagen used ferrous sulphate ; and E. Fischer ferrous chloride—arsenic acid is readily converted into the volatile chloride, and this reaction has been employed in analytical work—by C. W. Zenger, F. Hufschmidt, F. A. Gooch and E. W. Danner, C. Field and E. F. Smith, J. B. Moyer, M. Rohmer, C. R. Fresenius and E. Hintze—for separating arsenic from elements which do not form volatile chlorides under these conditions—*vide infra*, arsenic trichloride. W. Manchot and F. Oberhauser studied the reducing action of **hydrobromic acid** : $As_2O_5+4HBr\rightleftharpoons As_2O_3+4Br+2H_2O$—*vide supra*, arsenic trioxide. J. R. Roebuck, and W. C. Bray studied the rate of reduction of arsenic acid by **hydriodic acid,** a reaction previously considered in connection with the reverse change, namely, the oxidation of arsenic trioxide by iodine : $As_2O_3+2I_2+5H_2O\rightleftharpoons 2H_3AsO_4+4HI$. W. A. H. Naylor applied the reducing action of hydriodic acid on arsenic acid to the volumetric determination of arsenates. C. F. Schönbein found that when arsenic acid is warmed with **potassium iodide,** iodine is set free ; but R. Bunsen said that the reduction of arsenic acid to the trioxide, by warming with potassium iodide and hydrochloric acid, is not complete. F. A. Gooch and P. E. Browning based a method for the determination of iodine in the halide salts upon the action of arsenic acid in the presence of dil. sulphuric acid : $H_3AsO_4+2HI=H_3AsO_3+H_2O+I_2$. The iodine is completely volatilized, leaving behind in the amount of arsenic trioxide present, the record of the amount of iodine originally present. The reduction of arsenates by means of ammonium iodide is a common laboratory process. If **potassium bromide** be present, there is a trifling reduction of the arsenic acid, but no arsenic is lost by volatilization ; and if **potassium chloride** be present, no reduction occurs, but a proportional amount of arsenic is volatilized as trichloride.

G. Vortmann and C. Padberg found that the aq. soln. of arsenic acid is not affected by **sulphur.** J. J. Berzelius showed qualitatively that when **hydrogen sulphide** acts on a moderately conc. soln. of arsenic acid, arsenic pentasulphide is precipitated : $As_2O_5+5H_2S=As_2S_5+5H_2O$; on the other hand, H. W. F. Wackenroder said that the arsenic is first reduced by hydrogen sulphide to the trioxide even in the presence of hydrochloric acid, and that a mixture of sulphur and arsenic trisulphide is precipitated ; and H. Ludwig represented the reaction : $As_2O_5+5H_2S$ $=As_2S_3+5H_2O+2S$. E. W. Parnell also supposed the arsenic to be precipitated as trisulphide. H. Rose found that after the hydrogen sulphide has been passed through the liquid, both arsenic and arsenious acids are present, showing that a partial reduction of the arsenic acid occurs. R. Bunsen, and L. M. McCay confirmed the observation of J. J. Berzelius, for they proved that when a rapid current of hydrogen sulphide is passed into a soln. of an alkali arsenate, acidified with hydrochloric acid, and heated by a water-bath, arsenic pentasulphide is formed, and this reaction may be employed to determine arsenic quantitatively. These facts stimulated B. Brauner and F. Tomicek to examine the conditions under which the two arsenic sulphides are produced. The conditions which favour the formation of arsenic pentasulphide are (i) a high conc. of the hydrochloric acid ; (ii) a rapid passage of gas through the soln. ; and (iii) a temp. between 0° and 100°. The conditions which favour the production of a mixture of arsenic trisulphide and sulphur are (i) a low conc. of hydrochloric acid ; (ii) a slow passage of gas through the liquid ; and (iii) a high temp. in the range 0°–100°. It was also found that arsenic acid, especially in presence of ammonium chloride, is reduced more easily than an acidified soln. of an arsenate. The second limit, namely, complete formation of trisulphide, is reached, if at all, with greater difficulty than the first limit, that is, formation of pure pentasulphide. F. L. Usher and M. W. Travers added the observations that working at 15° under constant conditions with an aq. soln. of arsenic pentoxide, and varying proportions of hydrochloric acid :

HCl	.	1·8	7·9–14·34	25·10	32·27 per cent.
As_2S_5	.	91	100	58	0 ,,
As_2S_3	.	7	0	42	100 ,,

According to F. Neher, if hydrogen sulphide be passed into a soln. of an arsenate, mixed with sufficient conc. hydrochloric acid, the pentasulphide is alone precipitated in the cold. He said that the liquid should not contain less than 29 per cent. hydrogen chloride. The reaction was also examined by J. Thiele. According to

L. W. McCay, when a soln. of an alkali arsenate, strongly acidified with hydrochloric acid, and sat. with hydrogen sulphide, is heated in a closed vessel at 100° for one hour, the arsenic is completely converted into pentasulphide ; no trisulphide and no free sulphur are formed if air be excluded. He also found that when a slow stream of hydrogen sulphide is passed through an acidified soln. of an arsenate at 70°, besides arsenic pentasulphide there is also formed some free thioxyarsenic acid, H_3AsO_3S. This, under the influence of mineral acids and heat, decomposes into free sulphur and arsenious acid, the latter of which then yields arsenic trisulphide with the hydrogen sulphide. Like L. W. McCay, and unlike F. L. Usher and M. W. Travers, W. Foster found that the reduction of arsenic acid to arsenic trioxide and sulphur by hydrogen sulphide is never direct ; monosulphoxyarsenic acid, H_3AsO_3S, is first formed. This is quickly decomposed by acids, and this the more rapidly, the greater the conc. of the acid. A low conc. of hydrogen sulphide also favours the decomposition. When soln. of arsenic acid are treated with a rapid stream of hydrogen sulphide no reduction occurs even if no mineral acid be present, and arsenic pentasulphide is formed. No reduction occurs at 15° when a rapid stream of hydrogen sulphide is passed through a soln. of arsenic acid containing 0·9–32·0 per cent. of hydrochloric acid.

According to F. Wöhler, **sulphur dioxide** reduces arsenic acid in the cold, and more rapidly when heated, and the resulting arsenic trioxide separates from the sat. soln. in octahedral crystals. R. Bunsen said that the reduction of a conc. hydrochloric acid soln. of arsenic acid is complete only with a prolonged boiling, and this results in the loss of much arsenic as volatile chloride. B. Brauner and F. Tomicek found that in the absence of hydrochloric acid, the aq. soln. of arsenic acid is completely reduced to the trioxide when kept for 20 hrs. at 60° ; and with a soln. of arsenic acid acidified with sulphuric acid, and sat. with sulphur dioxide, L. W. McCay found that the reduction is completed in an hour when heated in a closed vessel on a water-bath. F. L. Usher and M. W. Travers showed that the progress of the reduction depends on the acidity of the soln. P. E. Browning, P. E. Browning and R. J. Goodman, W. Trautmann, G. Edgar, and V. Auger and L. Odinot observed that when sulphur dioxide is passed into a boiling soln. of arsenic and vanadic acids in 10 per cent. aq. sulphuric acid, very little reduction of arsenic occurs, the result being scarcely affected by the presence or absence of vanadium. If, as recommended by F. A. Gooch, the soln. sat. in the cold with sulphur dioxide, is heated in a closed vessel for an hour on the water-bath, complete reduction to arsenious acid and vanadyl salt takes place. If a trace of potassium iodide is added to a warm soln. containing arsenic, vanadic, and sulphuric acids, reduction by sulphur dioxide may be effected in fifteen minutes in an open vessel. According to C. Himly, **sodium thiosulphate** precipitates arsenic pentasulphide from an aq. soln. of arsenic acid—slowly in the cold, rapidly when heated. Arsenates acidified with hydrochloric acid and boiled with sodium thiosulphate also form the pentasulphide. G. Vortmann said that the precipitation is complete, and that pentathionic acid is formed and little or no sulphuric acid. R. M. Chapin found that the speed of the reaction depends largely on the conc. of the acid, and the course of the reduction by the conc. of the reagents and by the order in which they are mixed—*vide supra*, action of sodium thiosulphate on arsenic trioxide.

G. Gore found that crystals of arsenic acid are very slightly soluble in liquid **ammonia ;** and E. Knövenagel and E. Ebler showed that arsenic acid is only slightly reduced to the trioxide after many hours' boiling with **hydrazine salts.** L. Rosenstein said that red **phosphorus** does not reduce arsenic salts. J. Thiele found that **hypophosphorous acid** readily reduces arsenic acid to brown arsenic ; and T. Graham observed that with **phosphine,** a soln. of arsenic acid yields a copper-coloured product, possibly arsenic phosphide. For the action of **phosphorus tri-halides,** *vide* N. N. Sen's observations with arsenic trioxide. According to H. Hager, **formic acid,** and **oxalic acid** reduce arsenic acid in the presence of sulphuric acid ; and C. Patrouillard found that in a boiling soln. arsenic acid and the arsenates are reduced by oxalic acid. W. A. H. Naylor and J. O. Braithwaite hold that oxalic acid alone exerts no reducing action on arsenates; and any reduction which occurs when oxalic acid and hydrogen sulphide act simultaneously on sodium arsenate is due to the formation of a powerful reducing agent, probably formic acid, when hydrogen sulphide acts on oxalic acid. E. Wedekind and H. Wilke studied the adsorption of arsenic acid by **zirconium hydroxide.** The adsorption of arsenic acid by metal oxides was studied by P. P. Kozakevitsch.

The development of arsine by the reducing action of **metals** on soln. of arsenic acid has been indicated in connection with that gas. The deposition of arsenic on **copper** immersed in acidified soln. of arsenic acid is used as a test for the qualitative detection of arsenic. This reaction was discussed by G. Werther, H. Reinsch, C. R. Fresenius and C. H. L. von Babo, J. L. Howe and P. S. Mertins, and E. B. Kenrick. According to A. Colorianu, when an aq. soln. of arsenic acid is heated with copper in a sealed tube for 18 hrs. at 180°–200°, arsenic trioxide and copper arsenate are formed. According to C. A. Maack, **magnesium** immediately precipitates arsenic from aq. soln. of arsenic acid, gas is evolved at the same time. N. W. Fischer, and F. Mohr found that **zinc, tin,** and **iron** precipitate metal arsenates, arsine, and arsenic from soln. of arsenic acid. C. A. Maach observed that **aluminium** acts like magnesium, but more slowly. O. C. Johnson found that an alkaline soln. of arsenic acid, and aluminium react : $3As_2O_5+16Al+48KOH=6AsH_3+15H_2O +16Al(OK)_3$. O. Schlickum found that **stannous chloride** behaves towards arsenic acid much as it does with arsenic trioxide. Arsenic acid forms complexes with **molybdic, tungstic, and vanadic acids** (q.v.). The reaction with magnesia mixture was studied by F. L. Sonnenschein, and H. Struve, and is indicated in connection with some analytical reactions of arsenic. K. Jellinek and W. Kühn studied the reaction between sodium arsenate and **lead nitrate :** $2Na_3AsO_4+3Pb(NO_3)_2=Pb_3(AsO_4)_2+6NaNO_3$; and K. Jellinek and J. Czerwinsky, $Pb(NO_3)_2+Na_2HAsO_4=Pb(HAsO_4)+2NaNO_3$ in their application to analytical work.

S. Aschkenásy [6] prepared **alkali perarsenates,** analogous to the perphosphates and perborates, by the addition of the necessary quantity of alkali to a soln. of barium dioxide in aq. arsenic acid, barium arsenate is precipitated, and the filtrate containing the per-salt is then evaporated with slight warming and under reduced pressure ; an aq. soln. of a mixture of sodium dioxide with the primary or secondary alkali salts can also be submitted to evaporation. If a soln. of an arsenate, in dil. hydrogen dioxide, is evaporated to dryness with gentle warming and under reduced press., the corresponding per-salt, for example, sodium perarsenate, can be obtained with scarcely any loss of oxygen.

REFERENCES.

[1] W. V. Harcourt, *B.A. Rep.*, 50, 1840 ; H. Cavendish, *Scientific Papers*, Cambridge, 2. 298, 1921 ; C. W. Scheele, *Svenska Akad. Handl.*, 36. 265, 1775 ; J. R. Glauber, *Novis jurnis philosophicis*, Amstelodami, 1648 ; N. Lemery, *Cours de chimie*, Paris, 1675 ; P. J. Macquer, *Mém. Acad.*, 9, 1745 ; 223, 1746 ; 35, 1748 ; *Dictionnaire de chymie*, Paris, 1. 216, 1778 ; A. Libavius, *Alchemia*, Francofurti, 1595 ; T. Paracelsus, *The Hermetic and Alchemical Writings*, London, 2. 210, 1895 ; J. B. van Helmont, *Ortus medicinæ*, Lugduni, 1656.

[2] H. Kopp, *Ann. Chim. Phys.*, (3), 48. 106, 1856 ; E. Filhol, *ib.*, (3), 21. 415, 1847 ; *Journ. Pharm. Chim.*, (3), 14. 401, 1847 ; J. B. Richter, *Ueber die neuerer Gegenstände der Chemie*, Breslau, 1. 35, 1791 ; C. F. Bucholz, *Schweigger's Journ.*, 7. 387, 1813 ; *Scherer's Journ.*, 9. 397, 1802 ; E. C. Szarvasy and C. Messinger, *Ber.*, 30. 1344, 1897 ; G. Joachimoglu, *Biochem. Zeit.*, 70. 144, 1915 ; H. A. von Vogel, *Kastner's Arch.*, 9. 319, 1826 ; G. Vortmann, *Ber.*, 22. 2308, 1889 ; J. J. Berzelius, *Ann. Chim. Phys.*, (1), 80. 9, 1811 ; (2), 5. 179, 1817 ; (2), 11. 225, 1819 ; A. Michaelis, *Jena. Zeit.*, (1), 6. 239, 1871 ; L. Hurtzig and A. Geuther, *Liebig's Ann.*, 111. 172, 1859 ; H. E. Armstrong and F. P. Worley, *Proc. Roy. Soc.*, 90. A, 96, 1914 ; D. I. Mendeléeff, *Ber.*, 16. 379, 1886 ; *Élude des dissolutions aqueuses*, St. Petersburg, 365, 1887 ; D. Balareff, *Journ. prakt. Chem.*, (2), 102. 283, 1921 ; L. Hurtzig, *Einige Beiträge zur näheren Kenntniss der Säuren des Phosphors und Arseniks*, Göttingen, 1859 ; F. Faktor, *Pharm. Post*, 38. 527, 1905 ; J. Mayrhofer, *Liebig's Ann.*, 158. 326, 1871 ; H. O. Schulze, *Journ. prakt. Chem.*, (2), 21. 437, 1880 ; C. F. Schönbein, *Pogg. Ann.*, 78. 514, 1849 ; R. Weber, *ib.*, 112. 619, 1861 : E. Berl,

Zeit. angew. Chem., **18**. 252, 1905 ; *Zeit. anorg. Chem.*, **44**. 267, 1905 ; A. Simon and E. Thaler, *ib.*, **161**. 143, 1927 ; C. W. Scheele, *Svenska Vet. Akad. Handl.*, **36**. 265, 1775 ; E. Mitscherlich, *Liebig's Ann.*, **12**. 165, 1834 ; T. Thomson, *Ann. Phil.*, **4**. 171, 1814 ; **15**. 81, 1820 ; J. L. Proust, *Journ. Phys.*, **49**. 151, 1799 ; L. J. Thénard, *Ann. Chim. Phys.*, (1), **50**. 123, 1804 ; J. L. Gay Lussac and L. J. Thénard, *Recherches physico-chimiques*, Paris, **1**. 232, 1811 ; *Ann. Chim. Phys.*, (1), **73**. 229, 1810 ; T. Graham, *Phil. Trans.*, **123**. 253, 1833 ; J. Thomsen, *Thermochemische Untersuchungen*, Leipzig, **2**. 236, 1882 ; M. Berthelot, *Bull. Soc. Chim.*, (2), **28**. 496, 1877 ; *Compt. Rend.*, **84**. 1408, 1877 ; V. Auger, *ib.*, **134**. 1059, 1902 ; C. Matignon and J. A. Lecanu, *ib.*, **170**. 941, 1920 ; T. Bergman, *De arsenico*, Upsala, 1777 ; C. Ellis and V. T. Stewart, *U.S. Pat. No.* 1415323, 1922 ; C. del Fresno, *Anal. Fis. Quim.*, **24**. 707, 1926 ; P. Askenasy and E. Elöd, *Brit. Pat. No.* 255522, 1925 ; W. Herapath, *Phil. Mag.*, (1), **64**. 321, 1824 ; C. J. B. Karsten, *Schweigger's Journ.*, **65**. 394, 1832 ; L. Playfair and J. P. Joule, *Mem. Chem. Soc.*, **3**. 83, 1848 ; A. W. C. Menzies and P. D. Potter, *Internat. Cong. Appl. Chem.*, **8**. ii, 179, 1912 ; *Journ. Amer. Chem. Soc.*, **34**. 1452, 1912 ; J. Kendall, J. E. Booge, and J. C. Andrews, *ib.*, **39**. 2303, 1917 ; G. S. Forbes, H. W. Estell, and O. J. Walker, *ib.*, **44**. 97, 1922 ; L. Kahlenberg and W. J. Trautmann, *Trans. Amer. Electrochem. Soc.*, **39**. 327, 1921 ; T. Clark, *Edin. Journ. Science*, **7**. 298, 309, 311, 314, 1827 ; D. Balareff, *Zeit. anorg. Chem.*, **71**. 73, 1911 ; A. Rosenheim and F. Jacobsohn, *ib.*, **50**. 297, 1906 ; H. Remy, *ib.*, **116**. 255, 1921 ; H. Zieler, *ib.*, **162**. 161, 1927 ; O. Aschan, *Chem. Ztg.*, **37**. 1117, 1913 ; J. J. Heimpel, *Repert. Pharm.*, **62**. 1, 1838 ; K. von Grundner, *ib.*, **61**. 289, 1837 ; E. Weidenbach, *Untersuchungen über die Komplexbildung beim dreiwertigen Arsen*, Berlin, 44, 1915 ; A. Joly, *Compt. Rend.*, **100**. 1221, 1885 ; **101**. 1262, 1885.

[3] M. Berthelot, *Compt. Rend.*, **84**. 408, 1877 ; L. J. Simon, *ib.*, **176**. 437, 1923 ; J. F. Simon, *Repert. Pharm.*, **65**. 198, 1859 ; C. W. Scheele, *Svenska Vet. Akad. Handl.*, **36**. 265, 1775 ; N. A. E. Millon, *Ann. Chim. Phys.*, (3), **6**. 73, 1842 ; T. Thomson, *Ann. Phil.*, **4**. 171, 1814 ; **15**. 81, 1820 ; A. J. Balard, *Ann. Chim. Phys.*, (2), **57**. 265, 1834 ; E. Soubeiran, *ib.*, (2), **43**. 407, 1830 ; J. L. Gay Lussac, *Ann. Chim. Phys.*, (2), **3**. 136, 1816 ; *Phil. Mag.*, **49**. 280, 1817 ; W. H. Wollaston, *Phil. Trans.*, **98**. 96, 1808 ; A. F. Gehlen, *Schweigger's Journ.*, **15**. 89, 1815 ; **20**. 353, 1817 ; L. Gmelin, *Handbook of Chemistry*, London, **4**. 260, 1850 ; L. N. Vauquelin, *Journ. Pharm. Chim.*, (2), **9**. 230, 1823 ; H. A. von Vogel, *Kastner's Arch.*, **9**. 319, 1826 ; F. Kessler, *Pogg. Ann.*, **95**. 205, 1855 ; H. Rose, *ib.*, **105**. 572, 1858 ; F. C. Schneider, *ib.*, **85**. 433, 1852 ; *Sitzber. Akad. Wien*, **6**. 409, 1851 ; W. Wallace and F. Penny, *Phil. Mag.*, (4), **4**. 361, 1852 ; W. Wallace, *ib.*, (4), **18**. 279, 1859 ; *B.A. Rep.*, **69**, 88, 1859 ; J. A. Kaiser, *Zeit. anal. Chem.*, **14**. 255, 1875 ; L. L. de Koninck, *ib.*, **19**. 468, 1880 ; C. F. Bucholz, *Scherer's Journ.*, **9**. 397, 1802 ; *Schweigger's Journ.*, **7**. 387, 1813 ; J. Girardin, *Journ. Pharm. Chim.*, (3), **46**. 269, 1864 ; R. Wagner, *Wagner's Jahresb.*, 569, 1876 ; O. Schairer, *Chem. Ztg.*, **28**. 15, 1904 ; C. M. Smith and G. E. Miller, *Journ. Ind. Eng. Chem.*, **16**. 1168, 1924 ; *Journ. Franklin Inst.*, **199**. 556, 1925 ; E. A. Suverkrop, *Chem. Met. Engg.*, **34**. 96, 1927 ; O. Behse, *U.S. Pat. No.* 1493798, 1924 ; C. G. Richardson, *ib.*, 1554371, 1921 ; C. W. Drury and C. W. Simmons, *Canadian Chem. Met.*, **9**. 179, 1925 ; C. Ellis and V. T. Stewart, *U.S. Pat. No.* 1415323, 1922 ; 1515079, 1924 ; W. C. Piver, *ib.*, 1615193, 1927 ; D. I. Mendeléeff, *Ber.*, **16**. 379, 1886 ; *Étude des dissolutions aqueuses*, St. Petersburg, 365, 1887 ; T. Bergman, *De arsenico*, Upsala, 1777.

[4] R. Engel, *Ann. Chim. Phys.*, (6), **8**. 572, 1886 ; H. Kopp, *ib.*, (3), **48**. 106, 1856 ; A. Brochet and J. Petit, *ib.*, (8), **5**. 307, 1905 ; G. T. Gerlach, *Zeit. anal. Chem.*, **8**. 267, 1869 ; **27**. 316, 1888 ; H. Schiff, *Liebig's Ann.*, **113**. 193, 1860 ; E. W. Washburn, *Journ. Amer. Chem. Soc.*, **30**. 31, 1908 ; **35**. 681, 1913 ; A. Joly, *Compt. Rend.*, **100**. 1221, 1885 ; **101**. 1262, 1885 ; C. Blarez. *ib.*, **103**. 639, 1133, 1886 ; A. Astruc and J. Tarbouriech, *ib.*, **133**. 36, 1901 ; E. Baud and A. Astruc, *ib.*, **139**. 202, 1904 ; **144**. 1345, 1907 ; J. Thomsen, *Thermochemische Untersuchungen*, Leipzig, **1**. 305, 1882 ; R. T. Thomson, *Chem. News*, **49**, 119, 1884 ; **52**. 29, 1885 ; L. Ramberg, *Arsskr. Lunds Univ.*, **14**. 21, 1918 ; R. Reyher, *Zeit. phys. Chem.*, **2**. 744, 1888 ; P. Walden, *ib.*, **2**. 56, 1888 ; T. Graham, *Mem. Chem. Soc.*, **2**. 51, 1845 ; *Phil. Mag.*, (3), **24**. 401, 1844 ; G. Tammann, *Mém. Acad. St. Petersburg*, (7), **35**. 9, 1887 ; R. Luther, *Zeit. Elektrochem.*, **13**. 294, 1907 ; J. C. Ghosh and S. C. Bisvas, *ib.*, **30**. 97, 1924 ; H. A. von Vogel, *Kastner's Arch.*, **9**. 319, 1826 ; G. Bischof, *ib.*, **4**. 13, 1925 ; **6**. 438, 1925 ; A. C. Chapman and H. D. Law, *Analyst*, **31**. 3, 1906 ; W. Thomson, *Proc. Roy. Soc. Edin.*, **29**. 84, 1909 ; C. F. Bucholz, *Scherer's Journ.*, **9**. 397, 1802 ; *Schweigger's Journ.*, **7**. 387, 1813 ; J. B. Richter, *Ueber die neuerer Gegenstände der Chemie*, Breslau, **1**. 35, 1791 ; E. Blanc, *Journ. Chim. Phys.*, **18**. 28, 1920 ; W. J. Pope, *Journ. Chem. Soc.*, **69**. 1530, 1896 ; F. Förster and H. Pressprich, *Zeit. Elektrochem.*, **33**. 176, 1927 ; L. Loimaranta, *ib.*, **13**. 33, 1907 ; R. Luther, *ib.*, **13**. 289, 1907 ; K. Jellinek and L. Winogradoff, *ib.*, **30**. 483, 1924 ; J. R. Roebuck, *Journ. Phys. Chem.*, **9**. 127. 1905 ; D. I. Mendeléef, *Ber.*, **16**. 379, 1886 ; *Étude des dissolutions aqueuses*, St. Petersburg, 365, 1887 ; L. J. Simon, *Compt. Rend.*, **176**. 437, 1923.

[5] C. Field and E. F. Smith, *Journ. Amer. Chem. Soc.*, **18**. 1051, 1896 ; J. B. Moyer, *ib.*, **21**. 1029, 1899 ; T. Graham, *Phil. Trans.*, **123**. 253, 1833 ; J. Thiele, *Apoth. Ztg.*, **5**. 86, 1890 ; *Liebig's Ann.*, **265**. 55, 1891 ; J. Mayrhofer, *ib.*, **158**. 329, 1871 ; F. Mohr, *ib.*, **23**. 219, 1837 ; H. W. F. Wackenroder, *ib.*, **13**. 241, 1835 ; *Journ. prakt. Chem.*, (1), **2**. 340, 1834 ; *Pharm. Centrb.*, (1), **5**. 501, 1834 ; (1), **13**. 447, 1842 ; *Kleine analytisch-chemische Tabellen*, Jena, 1847 ; R. Bunsen, *Liebig's Ann.*, **192**. 305, 1878 ; F. Wöhler, *ib.*, **30**. 224, 1839 ; C. Himly, *ib.*, **43**. 150, 1842 ; G. Vortmann and C. Padberg, *Ber.*, **22**. 2642, 1889 ; G. Vortmann, *ib.*, **22**. 1520, 1889 ; M. Rohmer, *ib.*, **34**. 33, 1901 ; E. Knövenagel and E. Ebler, *ib.*, **35**. 3055, 1902 ; E. Fischer, *ib.*, **13**. 1778, 1881 ; F. Hufschmidt, *ib.*, **17**. 2245, 1884 ; J. Clark, *Journ Soc. Chem. Ind.*, **6**.

352, 1887 ; C. W. Zenger, *Répert. Chim. Appl.*, **5**. 203, 1862 ; H. Hagen, *Pharm. Centr.*, (3),
22. 169, 1882 ; H. Hager, (3), **25**. 443, 1884 ; H. Ludwig, *Arch. Pharm.*, (2), **97**. 32, 1859 ;
O. Schlickum, *ib.*, (3), **23**. 710, 1885 ; B. Brauner and F. Tomicek, *Monatsh.*, **8**. 627, 1887 ;
Journ. Chem. Soc., **53**. 145, 1888 ; B. Brauner, *ib.*, **67**. 532, 1895 ; A. Fuchs, *Zeit. anal. Chem.*,
1. 189, 1862 ; C. R. Fresenius and A. Souchay, *ib.*, **1**. 449, 1862 ; C. R. Fresenius and C. H. L. von
Babo, *Liebig's Ann.*, **49**. 291, 1844 ; C. R. Fresenius and E. Hintze, *Zeit. anal. Chem.*, **27**. 179,
1888 ; F. Neher, *ib.*, **32**. 45, 1893 ; H. Rose, *Pogg. Ann.*, **105**. 573, 1858 ; **107**. 186, 1859 ;
N. W. Fischer, *ib.*, **9**. 255, 1826 ; J. J. Berzelius, *ib.*, **7**. 2, 1826 ; C. F. Schönbein, *ib.*, **78**. 514,
1849 ; F. A. Gooch, *Methods of Chemical Analysis*, New York, 350, 1912 ; F. A. Gooch and
P. E. Browning, *Amer. Journ. Science*, (3), **39**. 188, 1890 ; (3), **40**. 66, 1890 ; F. A. Gooch and
E. W. Danner, *ib.*, (3), **42**. 308, 1891 ; *Chem. News*, **64**. 203, 1891 ; P. E. Browning, *Zeit. anorg.
Chem.*, **7**. 158, 1894 ; P. E. Browning and R. J. Goodman, *Amer. Journ. Science*, (4). **2**. 355,
1896 ; G. Edgar, *ib.*, (4), **27**. 299, 1909 ; O. Hehner, *Analyst*, **27**. 268, 1892 ; F. L. Usher and
M. W. Travers, *Journ. Chem. Soc.*, **87**. 1370, 1905 ; T. Graham, *Trans. Roy. Soc. Edin.*, **13**. 88,
1835 ; *Phil. Mag.*, (3), **5**. 401, 1834 ; G. A. Maack, *Untersuchungen über das Verhalten des Mag-
nesiums und Aluminiums zu den Salzlosungen verschiedener Metalle.* Göttingen, 35, 1862 ;
O. C. Johnson, *Chem. News*, **38**. 30, 1878 ; E. W. Parnell, *ib.*, (1), **53**. 339, 1851 ; H. Struve, *ib.*,
(1), **54**. 288, 1851 ; *Proc. Russ. Min. Soc.*, 111, 1851 ; H. Reinsch, *Neues Jahrb. Pharm.*, **16**.
135, 1861 ; A. Colorianu, *Bull. Soc. Chim.*, (2), **45**. 707, 1886 ; W. Manchot and F. Oberhauser.
Zeit. anorg. Chem., **130**. 163, 1923 ; **138**. 357, 1924 ; K. Jellinek and J. Czerwinsky, *ib.*, **149**.
359, 1925 ; K. Jellinek and W. Kühn, *ib.*, **138**. 128, 1924 ; E. B. Kenrick, *Journ. Amer. Chem.
Soc.*, **24**. 276, 1902 ; J. L. Howe and P. S. Mertins, *ib.*, **18**. 953, 1896 ; C. Patrouillard, *Pharm.
Trans.*, (3), **6**. 428, 1875 ; (3), **13**. 362, 1882 ; W. A. H. Naylor and J. O. Braithwaite, *ib.*, (3),
13. 228, 464, 478, 1882 ; W. A. H. Naylor, *ib.*, (3), 10. 441, 1879 ; L. W. McCay, *Amer. Chem.
Journ.*, **7**. 375, 1887 ; **9**. 174, 1888 ; **10**. 459, 1889 ; **12**. 547, 1891 ; *Chem. News*, **54**. 287, 1886 ;
Zeit. anal. Chem., **26**. 635, 1887 ; **27**. 632, 1888 ; *Zeit. anorg. Chem.*, **26**. 329, 1901 ; **29**. 46,
1902 ; *Journ. Amer. Chem. Soc.*, **24**. 661, 1902 ; L. Rosenstein, *ib.*, **42**. 883, 1920 ; W. Foster,
ib., **38**. 52, 1916 ; W. C. Bray, *Journ. Phys. Chem.*, **9**. 573, 1905 ; J. R. Roebuck, *ib.*, **6**. 363, 1902 ;
R. M. Chapin, *Journ. Agric. Research*, **1**. 515, 1914 ; E. Covelli, *Boll. Chim. Pharm.*, **48**. 623,
1909 ; G. Gore, *Proc. Roy. Soc.*, **20**. 441, 1872 ; **21**. 140, 1873 ; E. Wedekind and H. Wilke,
Koll. Zeit., **34**. 83, 1924 ; S. Aschkenasy, *German Pat.*, *D.R.P.* 296796, 296888, 299300, 1914 ;
W. Trautmann, *Zeit. anal. Chem.*, **50**. 371, 1916 ; V. Auger and L. Odinot, *Compt. Rend.*,
178. 213, 1924 ; P. P. Kozakevitsch, *Journ. Russ. Phys. Chem. Soc.*, **55**. 477, 1924 ; N. N. Sen,
Proc. Asiatic Soc. Bengal, **15**. 263, 1919.

* S. Aschkenasy, *German Pat.*, *D.R.P.* 299300, 1914.

§ 15. The Ammonium and Alkali Arsenates

P. J. Macquer [1] found that the residue obtained after distilling nitric acid from
a mixture of potassium nitrate and arsenic trioxide furnished a crystallizable
salt which he called *sel neutre arsenical*. Paracelsus had previously applied the
term *arsenicum fixum* to the product obtained by heating a mixture of arsenic
trioxide and potassium nitrate ; and A. Libavius called it *butyrum arsenici—
butter of arsenic*—although this term was used for arsenic trichloride (*q.v.*). These
preparations were all impure **alkali arsenates.** C. W. Scheele then prepared a
number of arsenates by the action of arsenic acid on the alkalies, etc. C. P. Linville
prepared alkali arsenates by roasting speiss with sodium carbonate ; and extracting the soluble arsenate from the cold mass.

According to C. F. Rammelsberg,[2] when arsenic acid is sat. with lithium carbonate, and the clear soln. evaporated for crystals, or treated with ammonia,
lithium orthoarsenate, Li_3AsO_4, or $Li_3AsO_4.\frac{1}{2}H_2O$, is formed. A. de Schulten
obtained the salt in crystals by fusing the precipitated arsenate in molten lithium
chloride, and dissolving out the alkali chloride. The crystals resemble those of
lithium orthophosphate, being tabular and rhombic. The sp. gr. is 3·07 at 15° ;
and they do not fuse at a white heat. The salt is soluble in dil. acids—*e.g.* acetic
acid. If a soln. of lithium orthophosphate be mixed with arsenic acid, rhombic
prisms of **lithium dihydroarsenate,** $LiH_2AsO_4.1\frac{1}{2}H_2O$ can be obtained. The salt
is deliquescent, and is decomposed by water into the orthoarsenate and arsenic
acids.

The occurrence of sodium arsenate in natural water has been reported by many.

Thus, J. Bouquet [3] found traces in the water of Château-neuf, 3 mgrms. per litre in the water of Lusset, 3 mgrms. per litre in the water of Saint Yorre ; and also in the water of Vaisse, and of Vichy ; E. Willm, 17·2 mgrms. per litre in the water of La Bourboule ; A. Moitessier, 0·4 mgrm. per litre in the waters of Montpellier ; A. Terreil, 0·4 mgrm. per litre in the waters of Montrond ; and T. Husemann, 1·71–1·99 mgrms. per litre in the waters of Val Sinistra.

Many observers have noted the formation of alkali arsenates during the oxidation of arsenical compounds in the presence of potassium salts. Thus, J. W. Slater [4] oxidized arsenic with potassium permanganate ; and F. Jones similarly oxidized arsine. H. O. Schulze oxidized arsenic trioxide by heating it with potassium chlorate, or with an alkali halide in the presence of air or oxygen. D. Tommasi observed the oxidation of the alkali arsenite by electrolytic gas. C. Brame heated arsenic trioxide with alkali hydroxide—arsenic is separated at the same time. H. O. Schulze observed the formation of alkali arsenate by heating the alkali iodide with arsenic pentoxide—some trioxide is formed at the same time ; J. Brode and K. Klein oxidized a boiling soln. of arsenic trioxide or an arsenite by air or oxygen under press.

Anhydrous **sodium orthoarsenate**, Na_3AsO_4, was obtained by E. Mitscherlich by calcining a mixture of the hydroarsenate with an excess of sodium carbonate. An eq. amount of carbon dioxide is given off. S. J. Lloyd and A. M. Kennedy have discussed the electrolytic preparation of sodium arsenate—*vide infra*, calcium arsenate. F. W. Clarke, and H. Stallo gave 2·8128 to 2·8577 for the sp. gr. at 21°. The following are the sp. gr. of the aq. soln. containing the following proportions of the orthoarsenate per 100 parts of soln. :

Na_3AsO_4 .	0·981	1·962	2·944	4·906	6·868	8·831	9·812
Sp. gr. .	1·0167	1·0215	1·0325	1·0547	1·0773	1·1003	1·1120

L. J. Simon studied the viscosity of soln. of arsenic acid progressively treated with soda-lye ; and A. Miolati and E. Mascetti, the sp. conductivity. J. Thomsen's, T. Graham's, and E. Baud and A. Astruc's observations on the heats of formation, and P. Walden's experiments on the electrical conductivities of these soln. were discussed in connection with arsenic acid. E. Blanc estimated that of a $0·002N$-Na_3AsO_4 soln., 8 per cent. is hydrolyzed. W. G. Mixter gave $3Na_2O+As_2O_5=2Na_3AsO_4+202·8$ Cals. J. C. Ghosh and S. C. Bisvas measured the extinction coeff. of soln. of sodium arsenate. L. W. McCay, and E. F. Smith and L. K. Frankel were able to deposit copper electrolytically from a soln. containing alkali arsenates without contamination with arsenic ; and T. Graham showed that the aq. soln. reacts alkaline ; that it attracts carbon dioxide from the air and thereby forms the hydroarsenate ; and that other dil. acids, as well as chlorine, iodine, and ammonium nitrate produce a similar result. Ammonia is liberated from ammonium nitrate by the aq. soln. W. Farmer and J. B. Firth found that in the reduction of sodium arsenate by sodium hyposulphite in cold, aq. soln., **sodium arsenohyposulphite**, $Na_3As(S_2O_4)_3$, is formed ; and as this decomposes to form arsenic trisulphide, **sodium arsenothiosulphate** is formed as an intermediate product.

According to G. I. Petrenko, the interaction of hydrogen dioxide and sodium orthoarsenate furnishes a salt with the composition $3Na_3AsO_4.5H_2O_2.16H_2O$, possibly *decahexahydrate sodium pentahydroperoxytriorthoarsenate*, in which part of the water of crystallization is replaced by hydrogen dioxide. E. P. Alvarez reported **sodium perarsenate**, $NaAsO_4$, to be formed by dissolving 100 grms. of sodium hydroarsenate in a mixture of 2000 grms. of water and 2000 grms. of alcohol at 98°, then cooling the vessel containing soln. with ice and salt ; finally, 100 grms. sodium dioxide are added by degrees, part of the salt produced is precipitated by the action of 2000 grms. absolute alcohol, the liquid is rapidly filtered on the pump, carefully washed with anhydrous alcohol, the product recovered from the filter, and finally dried in a vacuum and in presence of phosphorus anhydride.

E. P. Alvarez found that the perarsenates react with soln. of lead acetate (white precipitate), silver nitrate (white precipitate), mercurous nitrate (white precipitate with rapid decomposition), mercuric chloride (red precipitate), copper sulphate (blue precipitate), zinc and cadmium sulphates (white precipitate), bismuth nitrate (white precipitate), gold chloride (slight effervescence and escape of oxygen), manganous chloride (pink precipitate), nickelous chloride or sulphate (greenish-white precipitate), cobaltous nitrate and chloride (pink precipitate), ferrous sulphate (green or bluish-green precipitate), ferric chloride (red ferric hydroxide), and alkaline earth chlorides (white precipitates). The precipitates are all per-salts of the bases in question.

J. A. Hall said that an aq. soln. of 25 grms. of sodium hydroarsenate in 10 c.c. of 50 per cent. sodium hydroxide at 80° deposits crystals of the *hemienneahydrate*, $Na_3AsO_4.4\frac{1}{2}H_2O$; and that a soln. of 100 grms. of the hydroarsenate in 150 c.c. of 50 per cent. soda-lye deposits crystals of the *decahydrate*, $Na_3AsO_4.10H_2O$, when kept a long time at 77°. O. Schairer treated a sat. soln. of arsenic trioxide—cooled by ice—with an excess of sodium dioxide ; evaporated the filtered soln. to about half its bulk on a water-bath, and crystallized by cooling the soln. The cubic crystals resemble those of the corresponding vanadate. J. A. Hall said that they effloresce in dry air ; and melt at 85°. T. Graham prepared the *dodecahydrate*, $Na_3AsO_4.12H_2O$, by evaporating a conc. soln. of sodium hydroarsenate, mixed with one and a half times as much sodium hydroxide as it already contains, and recrystallizing the product from hot water. K. Preis observed its formation when a soln. of arsenic trioxide acts on calcium sulphide. The prismatic crystals were shown by H. Dufet, and H. B. Baker to belong to the hexagonal system, and they are isomorphous with the corresponding phosphate. H. Schiff gave 1·762 for the sp. gr. ; L. Playfair and J. P. Joule, 1·804 at 3·9° ; and H. Dufet, 1·7593. H. Schiff found that the aq. soln. sat. at 17° has a sp. gr. 1·1186. T. Graham gave 85·5° for the m.p. H. Dufet found the refractive indices for sodium light to be $\omega=1·4567$, and $\epsilon=1·4662$; and for Li-, Na-, and Tl-light, H. B. Baker gave respectively $\omega=1·4553$, 1·4589, and 1·4624 ; and $\epsilon=1·4630$, 1·4669, and 1·4704. E. Doumer gave for the mol. refraction 61·4. T. Graham said that the crystals are stable in dry air, and at 15·5°, 100 grms. of water dissolve 38·9 grms. of the salt. H. Schiff said that 100 parts of water at 17° dissolve 16·7 parts of salt ; and C. F. Wenzel, that 100 parts of alcohol dissolve 1·67 parts of sodium arsenate. For the action of many reagents—permanganates, etc.—*vide* arsenic trioxide. L. Kahlenberg and W. J. Trautmann observed no reaction with silicon at comparatively low temp., but in the arc, a black slag is formed.

According to E. Mitscherlich, C. R. Fresenius, and R. Wagner, hydrated sodium hydroarsenate, Na_2HAsO_4, is produced when a soln. of arsenic acid is mixed with a large excess of sodium carbonate, and allowed to crystallize. C. de Freycinet, J. Higgin, and A. Streng made the salt on a manufacturing scale by mixing a soln. of arsenic trioxide in soda-lye with sodium nitrate, evaporating to dryness, and calcining in a reverberatory furnace. The residue was extracted with dil. soda-lye, and allowed to crystallize. H. Lescoeur found that at temp. above 23° the soln. deposits crystals of the *heptahydrate*, $Na_2HAsO_4.7H_2O$. L. Gmelin found the heptahydrate is produced by exposing the dodecahydrate in air ; and G. C. Fleury, by leaving the commercial salt exposed to moist air. This salt was also made by H. Salkowsky, F. C. B. Schiefer, O. Hörmann, and T. Clark. G. P. Baxter and F. B. Coffin prepared the alkali hydroarsenate of a high degree of purity for their determination of the at. wt. of arsenic. According to A. Rosenheim and S. Thon, in the ternary system: $As_2O_5-Na_2O-H_2O$ at 0°, there is no evidence of the existence of polyarsenates. The solid phase with the percentage proportions $As_2O_5 : Na_2O$ above 54·16 : 5·36 is the hemihydrate, $2H_3AsO_4.H_2O$; from this to the proportions 38·03 : 10·25, the monohydrate, $NaH_2AsO_4.H_2O$, is the solid phase ; and from this stage to 3·35 : 1·81, the solid phase is the *dodecahydrate*, $Na_2HAsO_4.12H_2O$. The solubility curves show that the dodecahydrate has a transition temp. at 22° above which the heptahydrate is formed. The percentage solubility, S, of sodium hydroarsenate, is :

	0°	8·6°	11·8°	16·0°	21·0°	22·5°	28°	30·1°	34·0°	
S	5·46	9·66	12·53	17·30	25·75	26·75	30·48	32·34	35·09	per cent.
		$Na_2HAsO_4.12H_2O$					$Na_2HAsO_4.7H_2O$			

The prismatic or tabular crystals, said W. Haidinger, J. J. Bernhardi, C. M. Marx, E. Mitscherlich, and C. F. Rammelsberg, belong to the monoclinic system, and H. Dufet gave for the axial ratios : $a : b : c = 1·2294 : 1 : 1·3526$, and $\beta = 97°\ 14'$; the cleavage on the (100)-face is well-developed. The optic axial angles for Li-, Na-, and Tl-light were found by H. Dufet to be respectively $2V = 57°\ 32'$, $57°\ 7'$, and $56°\ 43'$; and $2E = 89°\ 28'$, $88°\ 59'$, and $88°\ 29'$. These angles are greater at higher temp. The sp. gr. is 1·8825—H. Schiff gave 1·87. According to O. Hörmann, the crystals melt at 120°–130°, they lose their combined water at 180°, and form a colourless liquid which solidifies to a radiating mass of crystals. H. Lescoeur gave for the dissociation press., p mm. :

	0°	5°	10°	20°	30°	40°	60°	80°	100°
p	1	1·2	2·1	4·6	15	29	77	188	424

and if the hydroarsenate has more than 7 mols. of water, the dissociation press. at 20° is greater, being 16 mm. with 7·07 mols. of water ; 15·8 mm. with 7·26 mols. ; and 16 mm. with 12 mols. H. Dufet found the double refraction to be positive ; and the indices of refraction for Li-, Na-, and Tl-light to be respectively $a = 1·4587$, 1·4622, and 1·4654 ; $\beta = 1·4623$, 1·4658, and 1·4689 ; and $\gamma = 1·4746$, 1·4782, and 1·4814. The dispersion is small. P. Walden gave for the eq. conductivity of soln. with $\frac{1}{2}Na_2HAsO_4$ mols. per v litres :

v	32	64	128	256	512	1024	∞
μ	79·0	84·7	88·8	92·0	94·4	95·9	103·8

T. Clark said that the salt does not effloresce in warm air ; and H. Lescoeur, that it absorbs water vapour at a low temp. without becoming moist. F. E. Brown and J. E. Snyder observed a reaction with the hydroarsenate and vanadium oxytrichloride.

According to E. Mitscherlich, R. F. Marchand, and C. R. Fresenius, the aq. soln. of sodium hydroarsenate in the cold deposits crystals of the *dodecahydrate*, $Na_2HAsO_4.12H_2O$—while J. Setterberg, and P. von Kotschoubey said 13 mols. C. Tomlinson found that the aq. soln. is easily obtained supersaturated. E. Mitscherlich found the monoclinic prismatic crystals to be isomorphous with those of the corresponding phosphate, and H. Dufet gave for the axial ratios $a : b : c = 1·7499 : 1 : 1·4121$, and $\beta = 121°\ 49'$. H. Dufet found the optic axial angle $2V = 65°\ 13'$, $65°\ 13'$, and $65°\ 12'$ respectively for Li-, Na-, and Tl-light. T. Thomson gave 1·759 for the sp. gr. ; L. Playfair and J. P. Joule, 1·736 at 3·9° ; H. Schiff, 1·670 ; and H. Dufet, 1·6675. H. Schiff found the sp. gr. of soln. containing the following number of grams per 100 c.c. at 14° :

Na_2HAsO_4	5	10	15	20	25	30	35	40
Sp. gr.	1·0212	1·0434	1·0665	1·0904	1·1153	1·1410	1·1677	1·1952

As indicated above, H. Lescoeur measured the dissociation press. W. A. Tilden gave 28° for the m.p. H. Dufet found that the bi-refringence is negative and the indices of refraction for Li-, Na-, and Tl-light to be respectively $a = 1·4420$, 1·4453, and 1·4482 ; $\beta = 1·4462$, 1·4496, and 1·4513 ; and $\gamma = 1·4480$, 1·4513, and 1·4545. H. de Sénarmont made some observations on this subject. R. Robl observed no fluorescence occurs when the salt is exposed to ultra-violet light. The observations of P. Walden on the electrical conductivity of the soln. have been discussed in connection with arsenic acid. E. Blanc estimated that in $0·002N\text{-}Na_2HAsO_4$ soln., 0·0455 per cent. is hydrolyzed. A. Borel gave for the dielectric constants k, 7·26; k_2, 5·91; and k_3, 5·28. T. Clark found that the crystals effloresce in dry air and form the heptahydrate. W. A. Tilden said that 100 parts of water at 0° dissolve 17·2 parts of the dodecahydrate, and at 30°, 140·7 parts. H. Schiff gave 56 parts at 14°; and T. Thomson, 22·268 parts at 7·2°. B. E. Curry and T. O. Smith studied the solubility of the salt in soln. of lead nitrate—*vide infra*, lead hydroarsenate. P. von Kotschoubey said that the conc. aq. soln. becomes turbid when warmed, and deposits the heptahydrate. K. H. Butler and D. McIntosh found sodium arsenate to be insoluble in liquid chlorine. When the hydroarsenate is calcined it forms what has been regarded as **sodium pyroarsenate**, $Na_4As_2O_7$. O. Hörmann said that this change occurs at 250°. C. M. Marx described this product as a fibrous mass with a silky lustre. T. Clark, F. C. B. Schiefer, and P. Walden said that when the pyroarsenate is dissolved in water it behaves like the orthophosphate; and they questioned the existence of the pyroarsenate. E. Soubeiran said that when heated in hydrogen gas, arsenic is given off and sodium hydroxide formed.

According to E. Mitscherlich, hydrated **sodium dihydroarsenate**, NaH_2AsO_4, is formed by adding arsenic acid to an aq. soln. of sodium carbonate until the liquid no longer gives a precipitate with barium chloride, evaporating, and leaving the soln. to stand for some time in a cold place. O. Hörmann made this salt by fusing arsenic trioxide with sodium nitrate, in eq. proportions, and crystallizing the salt from the aq. soln. P. Walden's values for the electrical conductivity of the aq. soln. have been discussed in connection with arsenic acid. The *mono-hydrate*, NaH_2AsO_4, crystallizes normally from the cold aq. soln. E. Mitscherlich said that the well-defined, rhombic crystals are isomorphous with those of the corresponding phosphate. A. Joly and H. Dufet said that the rhombic, bisphenoidal crystals have the axial ratios $a:b:c=0·9177:1:1·6039$. The optic axial angles for Li-, Na-, and Tl-light are respectively $2V=67°\ 15'$, $67°\ 57'$, and $68°\ 33'$, and $2E=118°\ 11'$, $120°\ 28'$, and $122°\ 33'$. The monohydrate is dimorphous. H. Dufet said that if the crystals are deposited from warm soln., monoclinic crystals are formed with the axial ratios $a:b:c=1·087:1:1·1588$, and $\beta=92°\ 22'$. The monoclinic crystals rapidly become turbid, without change in weight, forming the rhombic crystals. H. Dufet gave 2·6700 for the sp. gr. of the monoclinic form; and for the ordinary, rhombic, monohydrated crystals 2·6700; and H. Schiff gave 2·535. H. Dufet found the indices of refraction for Li-, Na-, and Tl-light are respectively $\alpha=1·5341$, 1·5382, and 1·5418; $\beta=1·5494$, 1·5535, and 1·5573; and $\gamma=1·5563$, 1·5607, and 1·5647. O. Hörmann said that the salt loses its water of crystallization at 100°–130°; and at 200°–280°, passes into **sodium metarsenate**, $NaAsO_3$. The product obtained by J. Higgin, and A. Streng —*vide supra*—was supposed to have been the metarsenate. According to C. Lefèvre, if the salt be heated to redness in a stream of hydrogen or carbon monoxide, nearly all the arsenic is expelled. T. Graham, and P. Walden said that the metarsenate forms the dihydroarsenate when dissolved in water. According to A. Joly and H. Dufet, if the aq. soln. of the dihydroarsenate be conc. to a sp. gr. 1·7, crystals of the *dihydrate*, $NaH_2AsO_4.2H_2O$, are formed in rhombic octahedra, isomorphous with those of the corresponding phosphate. The rhombic crystals have the axial ratios $a:b:c=0·9177:1:1·6039$; the optic axial angles are for Na-light $2V=89°\ 11'$; for Li-light, $88°\ 40'$; and for Tl-light, $88°\ 57'$. The sp. gr. is 2·309; the indices of refraction for Na-light, $\alpha=1·4794$, $\beta=1·5021$, and $\gamma=1·5265$. The crystals effloresce in air.

E. Filhol and J. B. Senderens reported that when a soln. of arsenic acid is neutralized by sodium hydroxide, with litmus as indicator, and evaporated to a syrupy liquid, it furnishes monoclinic crystals of a complex acid salt, $Na_3AsO_4.H_3AsO_4.3H_2O$, sodium trihydrodiorthoarsenate, $Na_3H_3(AsO_4)_2.3H_2O$. When heated, the salt loses its water of crystallization, without melting; it melts at a higher temp. They also obtained mono-clinic pyramids of sodium potassium trihydrodiorthoarsenate, $K_3Na_3H_6(AsO_4)_4.9H_2O$; and of sodium ammonium trihydrodiorthoarsenate, $Na_3(NH_4)_3H_6(AsO_4)_4.6H_2O$.

E. Mitscherlich prepared anhydrous **potassium orthoarsenate,** K_3AsO_4, by heating a mixture of the hydroarsenate with potassium carbonate as in the case of the sodium salt. T. Graham also found that this salt crystallizes in deliquescent needles from a soln. of arsenic acid in an excess of potash-lye. L. J. Simon studied the viscosity of soln. of arsenic acid progressively treated with potash-lye. According to A. Naumann, the salt is insoluble in ethyl acetate. C. W. Scheele obtained **potassium hydroarsenate,** $K_2HAsO_4.H_2O$, by adding potassium carbonate to a soln. of arsenic acid so long as effervescence continues. He was unable to make the soln. crystallize, and obtained the solid by evaporating the soln. to dryness, and fusing the product to form a white glass. O. Hörmann obtained the salt in triclinic prisms with the composition just indicated. The crystals lose their water of crystallization at 110°–125°, and, at a higher temp., form a white glass alleged to be *potassium pyroarsenate*, $K_4As_2O_7$—*vide supra*, sodium pyroarsenate. C. W. Scheele said that the aq. soln. of this salt colours the juice of violets green ; R. T. Thomson found that the salt is neutral towards litmus, rosolic acid, methyl-orange, and phenacetolin ; and alkaline towards phenolphthalein, and lacmoid —*vide supra*, arsenic acid. E. Mitscherlich prepared **potassium sodium hydro-arsenate,** $KNaHAsO_4.7H_2O$, by neutralizing potassium dihydroarsenate with sodium carbonate. The crystals were said to be isomorphous with the corresponding sodium salt. P. von Kotschoubey considered the salt had 9 mols. of water of crystallization ; E. Mitscherlich, 8 mols. ; and H. Schiff, 7 mols. H. Schiff gave 1·884 for the sp. gr., and he found the crystals do not effloresce in air.

P. J. Macquer, L. Glaser, and O. Hörmann melted together equal parts of arsenic trioxide and potassium nitrate, and found that **potassium dihydroarsenate,** KH_2AsO_4, crystallized from the aq. soln. E. Mitscherlich obtained it by crystal-lization from a mixture of arsenic acid with an aq. soln. of potassium carbonate so long as the soln. reddens litmus ; and from a soln. of potash-lye and arsenic acid, neutral to vegetable colours. The crystals are stable in air, and they are isomorphous with the corresponding potassium and ammonium dihydrophosphates, and with ammonium dihydroarsenate. W. Muthmann said that the potassium dihydrophosphate and dihydroarsenate form mixed crystals in all proportions. H. Töpsöe gave for the axial ratio of the tetragonal crystals $a : c = 1 : 0.9380$; H. Braumhauer found the corrosion figures to correspond with those of the corre-sponding phosphate. O. Hassel found the tetragonal crystals isomorphous with those of the ammonium salt, and with those of the corresponding phosphates. T. Thomson gave 2·638 for the sp. gr. ; H. Schiff, 2·832 ; H. Töpsöe, 2·862 ; H. G. F. Schröder, 2·851 at 4° ; W. Muthmann, 2·868 ; and B. Gossner, 2·879. T. Thomson found that the sat. aq. soln. at 6° has a sp. gr. 1·1134. V. von Lang observed that the ratio of the thermal conductivities $a : c = 1 : 0.88$. H. Kopp gave 0·175 for the sp. ht., and H. V. Regnault for the fused salt, $KAsO_3$, 0·156. J. C. G. de Marignac found the sp. ht. of soln. of sodium dihydroarsenate, NaH_2AsO_4, with 200, 100, and 50 mols. of water to be respectively 0·9595, 0·9264, and 0·8107 ; and sodium hydroarsenate, Na_2HAsO_4, with 200, 100, and 50 mols. of water 0·9500, 0·9112, and 0·8550 respectively. N. de Kolossowsky discussed this subject. F. M. Raoult measured the lowering of the f.p. of water and found for the sp. lowering of the f.p. 0·168, and for the mol. lowering of the f.p., 30·2. T. Graham gave –4·9 Cals. for the heat of dissolution in water. H. Töpsöe and C. Christiansen gave for the indices of refraction with the C-, and F-, and D-lines respectively $\omega = 1.5632$, 1·5674, and 1·5762 ; and $\epsilon = 1.5146$, 1·5179, and 1·5252. P. Walden's observation on the electrical conductivity of aq. soln. of this salt were discussed in connection with arsenic acid. V. von Lang found the ratio of the diamagnetic induction for $a : c$ to be $1 : 0.715$. T. Thomson said that the salt loses only a little water at 288° ; and O. Hörmann showed that no water is lost at 140°, and one mol. at 240°–290°. T. Thomson stated that the salt passes into *potassium metarsenate* at a dull red-heat ; and at a higher temp. C. Friedheim found that oxygen is given off. The fused masses obtained by P. J. Macquer, T. Thomson.

L. Glaser, and O. Hörmann are sometimes supposed to be the metarsenate ; but F. C. B. Schiefer, O. Hörmann, and P. Walden showed that when dissolved in water, the dihydroarsenate is formed. T. Thomson found that 100 parts of water at 6° dissolve 18·87 parts of the dihydroarsenate ; that the salt is freely soluble in hot water, and insoluble in alcohol. C. F. Wenzel said that 100 parts of boiling alcohol dissolve 0·0037 part of the salt. The aq. soln. tastes like nitre. E. Mitscherlich found that the alkaline earth salts do not give precipitates with aq. soln. of this salt. The aq. soln. of the dihydroarsenate reddens blue litmus ; and, according to R. T. Thomson, it is neutral towards lacmoid and phenolphthalein —vide supra, arsenic acid. C. Friedheim reported that fine, feathery crystals of the monohydrate, $KH_2AsO_4.H_2O$, can be formed by crystallizing a soln. of a mol of the dihydrophosphate and a mol of arsenic acid, over conc. sulphuric acid. C. Neuberg and M. Kobel said that potassium arsenate inhibits the combination of sucrose and phosphoric acid.

According to A. Bouchonnet, **rubidium orthoarsenate**, Rb_3AsO_4, is obtained by neutralizing a soln. of rubidium hydroxide with arsenic acid using Porrier's blue as an indicator. The soln. deposits hygroscopic lamellæ of the dihydrate, $Rb_3AsO_4.2H_2O$, which become anhydrous at 100°. The salt absorbs carbon dioxide from the air, and the soln. is alkaline to litmus, methyl-orange, and phenolphthalein. He also made **rubidium hydroarsenate**, Rb_2HAsO_4, by mixing aq. soln. of rubidium hydroxide and the dihydroarsenate in molar proportions. It deposits hygroscopic lamellæ of the monohydrate, $Rb_2HAsO_4.H_2O$, which become anhydrous at 100°. At 150°, **rubidium pyroarsenate**, $Rb_4As_2O_7$, is formed. Rubidium hydroarsenate absorbs carbon dioxide from the air, and more rapidly when in aq. soln. The soln. is neutral to litmus, and methyl-orange, and alkaline to phenolphthalein. A. Bouchonnet also obtained **rubidium dihydroarsenate**, RbH_2AsO_4, by melting together equal parts of arsenic trioxide and rubidium nitrate. It forms tabular crystals, or, when prepared by neutralizing rubidium carbonate soln. with arsenic acid, using methyl-orange as indicator, it forms silky needles. Both forms are anhydrous, and the aq. soln. is acid to litmus, neutral to methyl-orange, and phenolphthalein. The arsenate, when heated to dull redness, loses water and forms **rubidium metarsenate**, $RbAsO_3$, a milky-white, crystalline mass which decomposes at a bright red-heat. F. Ephraim and H. Herschfinkel reported white, well-developed crystals of **cæsium paratetrarsenate**, $Cs_2As_4O_{11}.5H_2O$, by the action of an excess of arsenic on a nitric acid soln. of cæsium hydroxide in the presence of molybdic acid.

E. Mitscherlich, and H. Uelsmann found that if a conc. soln. of ammonium hydroarsenate is mixed with aq. ammonia, it solidifies to a magma of crystals of **ammonium orthoarsenate**, $(NH_4)_3AsO_4.3H_2O$, which can be washed with aq. ammonia, and dried by press. between bibulous paper. E. Mitscherlich, and H. Salkowsky obtained the same salt by cooling a conc. soln. of arsenic acid in warm aq. ammonia, and he found that the crystals belong to the rhombic system. They can be recrystallized from hot, aq. ammonia. E. Mitscherlich said that on exposure to air ammonia is given off, and the hydroarsenate remains ; and H. Uelsmann, that when the ammoniacal soln. is boiled ammonia is lost and the dihydroarsenate is formed. H. Stamm measured the solubility of the salt in aq. ammonia. H. Uelsmann also reported **diammonium sodium orthoarsenate**, $(NH_4)_2NaAsO_4.4H_2O$, to be formed from a sat. soln. of ammonium sodium hydroarsenate in conc. ammonia. The tabular crystals lose half their ammonia when confined over 5 per cent. sulphuric acid. A. Miolati and E. Mascetti studied the sp. electrical conductivity when arsenic acid is progressively neutralized with ammonia.

C. W. Scheele, E. Mitscherlich, and H. Salkowsky prepared **ammonium hydroarsenate**, $(NH_4)_2HAsO_4$, by adding ammonia to a conc. aq. soln. of arsenic acid until a precipitate is formed, warming the liquid until the precipitate dissolves, and allowing the soln. to crystallize. A crop of the normal salt may be first deposited, but this soon forms the hydroarsenate on exposure to air. From time to time, ammonia should be added to the exposed liquid or crystals of the dihydroarsenate will be formed. The monoclinic, prismatic crystals are isomorphous with those of the corresponding phosphate. E. Mitscherlich, and C. F. Rammelsberg gave for the axial ratios $a : b : c = 0.918 : 1 : 1.1715$, and $\beta = 91° 13'$. H. Schiff found the sp. gr. to be 1.99. C. W. Scheele observed that when the salt is heated it decomposes into ammonia, water, arsenic, and nitrogen; and E. Mitscherlich, that on exposure to air it yields the dihydroarsenate. C. W. Scheele said that the aq. soln. colours violet-juice green. E. Mitscherlich obtained **ammonium sodium hydroarsenate**, $(NH_4)NaHAsO_4.4H_2O$, by crystallization from equal parts of sodium and ammonium hydroarsenates; and H. Uelsmann, by evaporating a soln. of six parts of sodium dihydroarsenate, and one part of ammonium chloride in aq. ammonia. The monoclinic crystals are like those of the corresponding phosphate. J. M. Thomson and W. P. Bloxam found that neither of the component salts will induce the crystallization of the complex salt. H. Schiff gave 1.838 for the sp. gr. when the salt is calcined, E. Mitscherlich said that sodium metarsenate remains.

The salt prepared by P. J. Macquer by heating a mixture of arsenic trioxide and ammonium nitrate, and crystallizing the aq. soln. of the product, was probably **ammonium dihydroarsenate**, $NH_4H_2AsO_4$. This salt was obtained by E. Mitscherlich by evaporating a soln. of arsenic acid saturated with ammonia; and by exposing the hydroarsenate to air. The tetragonal crystals are isomorphous with the corresponding phosphate. H. Töpsöe gave for the axial ratio $a : c = 1 : 1.0035$. No marked cleavage was observed; and H. Baunhauer found the corrosion figures resembled those of the corresponding phosphate. O. Hassel found the tetragonal crystals isomorphous with those of the corresponding potassium salt, and with those of the corresponding phosphates. H. Schiff gave 2.259 for the sp. gr.; H. Töpsöe, 2.308; H. G. F. Schröder, 2.307; W. Muthmann, 2.311; and B. Gossner, 2.317. V. von Lang found the ratio of the thermal conductivities $a : c = 1 : 0.84$; H. de Sénarmont, and H. Töpsöe and C. Christiansen found the indices of refraction for the C-, D-, and F-lines to be respectively $\omega = 1.5721$, 1.5766, and 1.5859; and $\epsilon = 1.5186$, 1.5217, and 1.5296. V. von Lang found the ratio of the diamagnetic induction to be $a : c = 1 : 0.715$. The salt deliquesces in air; and it is sparingly soluble in water—the aq. soln. has an acid reaction. When the salt is decomposed by heat, H. Salkowsky observed the formation of arsenic, arsenic trioxide, and nitrogen, but no ammonia.

V. Kohlschütter and K. A. Hofmann obtained **hydroxylamine orthoarsenate**, $(NH_3OH)_3AsO_4$, by mixing an aq. soln. of arsenic acid with an excess of sodium carbonate, and adding hydroxylamine monochloride until the soln. is feebly acid. In a short time feather crystals, resembling the corresponding phosphate, are deposited. The salt is sparingly soluble in cold water, and it can be recrystallized from hot water. It forms microscopic, rhombic prisms; the hot aq. soln. has an acidic reaction; it reduces Fehling's soln., and an ammoniacal soln. of silver nitrate.

REFERENCES.

[1] P. J. Macquer, Mém. Acad., 9, 1745; 223, 1746; 35, 1748; A. Libavius, Alchemia, Francofurti, 1595; Paracelsus, Ouvres Das Bucher und Schriften des Edlen Hochgelehrten und Bewehsten Philosophi und Medici Philippi Theophrasti Bombast von Hohenheim Paracelsi genannt, Bâle, vii, 109, 1589; C. W. Scheele, Svenska Akad. Handl., 36. 265, 1775; C. P. Linville, U.S. Pat. No. 1505718, 1924.

[2] C. F. Rammelsberg, Pogg. Ann., 128. 325, 1868; A. de Schulten, Bull. Soc. Chim., (3), 1. 479, 1889.

[3] J. Bouquet, Ann. Chim. Phys., (3), 42. 278, 1854; Repert. Chim. Appl., 3. 199, 1861; E. Willm, Bull. Soc. Chim., (2), 33. 292, 1880; A. Moitessier, Compt. Rend., 51. 636, 1860; A. Terreil, ib., 96. 1581, 1883; T. Husemann, Arch. Pharm., (3), 6. 97, 395, 1875.

[4] J. A. Hall, Journ. Chem. Soc., 51. 94, 1887; W. A. Tilden, ib., 45. 409, 1884; F. Jones, ib., 33. 95, 1878; H. B. Baker, ib., 47. 353, 1885; L. Playfair and J. P. Joule, Mem. Chem. Soc., 2. 401, 1845; E. Mitscherlich, Ann. Chim. Phys., (2), 19. 350, 407, 1821; C. Lefèvre, Sur les

arsénates cristallisés, Paris, 1891 ; *Ann. Chim. Phys.,* (6), **27**. 19, 1889 ; H. V. Regnault, *ib.,* (3), **1**. 129, 1841 ; E. Soubeiran, *ib.,* (2), **43**. 407, 1830 ; H. de Sénarmont, *ib.,* (3), **33**. 391, 1851 ; T. Graham, *Phil. Trans.,* **123**. 253, 1833 ; *Mem. Chem. Soc.,* **2**. 51, 1845 ; *Phil. Mag.,* (3), **24**. 401, 1844 ; H. G. F. Schröder, *Dichtigkeitsmessungen,* Heidelberg, 1873 ; T. Clark, *Edin. Journ. Science,* **7**. 298, 309, 311, 314, 1827 ; W. Haidinger, *ib.,* **7**. 314, 1827 ; F. W. Clarke, *A Table of Specific Gravity for Solids and Liquids,* London, 121, 1888 ; H. Stallo, *Amer. Journ. Science,* (3), **14**. 285, 1877 ; W. Muthmann, *Zeit. Kryst.,* **22**. 523, 1894 ; **23**. 368, 1894 ; B. Gossner, *ib.,* **44**. 484, 1908 ; L. Gmelin, *Pogg. Ann.,* **4**. 157, 1821 ; V. von Lang, *ib.,* **135**. 39, 1868 ; *Sitzber. Akad. Wien,* **54**. 168, 1866 ; **108**. 561, 1899 ; H. Töpsöe and C. Christiansen, *Danske Vid. Selsk. Forh.,* (5), **9**. 661, 1873 ; *Ann. Chim. Phys.,* (4), **31**. 1, 1873 ; (5), **1**. 21, 1874 ; H. Töpsöe, *Sitzber. Akad. Wien,* **66**. 32, 1872 ; *Bull. Soc. Chim.,* (2), **19**. 246, 1873 ; H. Jay and J. Dupasquier, *ib.,* (3), **13**. 441, 1895 ; C. R. Fresenius, *Journ. prakt. Chem.,* (1), **56**. 30, 1852 ; H. Salkowsky, *ib.,* (1), **104**. 129, 1868 ; H. O. Schulze, *ib.,* (2), **21**. 432, 1880 ; J. W. Slater, *ib.,* (1), **60**. 247, 1853 ; P. von Kotschoubey, *ib.,* **49**. 182, 1850 ; *Bull. Acad. St. Petersburg,* (2), **8**. 129, 1850 ; H. Lescoeur, *Ann. Chim. Phys.,* (6), **21**. 553, 1890 ; *Sur la dissociation des hydrates salins et des composés analogues,* Lille, 1888 ; *Compt. Rend.,* **104**. 1174, 1887 ; E. Filhol and J. B. Senderens, *ib.,* **93**. 388, 1881 ; **95**. 343, 1882 ; **96**. 1051, 1883 ; F. M. Raoult, *ib.,* **98**. 509, 1884 ; C. Brame, *ib.,* **92**. 188, 1881 ; A. Joly, *ib.,* **102**. 316, 1886 ; E. Doumer, *ib.,* **110**. 41, 1890 ; A. Joly and H. Dufet, *ib.,* **102**. 259, 1391, 1886 ; *Bull. Soc. Min.,* **9**. 194, 1886 ; H. Dufet, *ib.,* **10**. 77, 1887 ; A. Bouchonnet, *ib.,* **144**. 461, 1907 ; E. Baud and A. Astruc, *ib.,* **144**. 1345, 1907 ; E. Blanc, *Journ. Chim. Phys.,* **18**. 28, 1920 ; R. Robl, *Zeit. angew. Chem.,* **39**. 608, 1926 ; H. Schiff, *Liebig's Ann.,* **112**. 92, 1859 ; **113**. 196, 1860 ; K. Preis, *ib.,* **257**. 178, 1890 ; V. Kohlschütter and K. A. Hofmann, *ib.,* **307**. 330, 1899 ; H. Kopp, *Liebig's Ann. Suppl.,* **3**. 289, 1865 ; *Phil. Trans.,* **155**. 71, 1865 ; G. T. Gerlach, *Zeit. anal. Chem.,* **8**. 286, 1869 ; W. G. Mixter, *Amer. Journ. Science,* (4), **28**. 103, 1909 ; F. C. B. Schiefer, *Zeit. Ges. Naturw. Halle,* **23**. 350, 1864 ; J. Higgin, *Brit. Pat. No.* 2815, 1856 ; C. de Freycinet, *Ann. Mines,* (6), **5**. 22, 1864 ; *Dingler's Journ.,* **174**. 323, 1864 ; R. Wagner, *ib.,* **176**. 134, 1865 ; O. Schairer, *Chem. Ztg.,* **28**. 15, 1904 ; J. C. Ghosh and S. C. Bisvas, *Zeit. Elektrochem.,* **30**. 97, 1924 ; S. J. Lloyd and A. M. Kennedy, *Chem. Met. Engg.,* **32**. 624, 1925 ; O. Hörmann, *Beitrag zur Kenntniss der Pyro- und Meta-Arsensäure sowie einiger Salze derselben,* Erlangen, 1879 ; C. M. Marx, *Kastner's Arch.,* **2**. 18, 1824 ; P. Walden, *Zeit. phys. Chem.,* **2**. 53, 1888 ; G. I. Petrenko, *Journ. Russ. Phys. Chem. Soc.,* **34**. 391, 1902 ; J. Thomsen, *Thermochemische Untersuchungen,* Leipzig, **1**. 305, 1882 ; T. Thomson, *Ann. Phil.,* **15**. 85, 1820 ; R. T. Thomson, *Chem. News,* **49**. 119, 1884 ; **52**. 18, 29, 1885 ; C. Tomlinson, *ib.,* **18**. 2, 1868 ; J. M. Thomson and W. P. Bloxam, *Journ. Chem. Soc.,* **41**. 379, 1882 ; J. J. Bernhardi, *Trommsdorff's Journ.,* **11**. 10, 1825 ; C. Friedheim, *Zeit. anorg. Chem.,* **2**. 371, 1892 ; F. Ephraim and H. Herschfinkel, *ib.,* **65**. 237, 1910 ; H. Braunhauer, *Die Resultate der Aetzmethode,* Leipzig, 43, 1894 ; D. Tommasi, *Les Mondes,* **56**. 86, 123, 1881 ; C. F. Rammelsberg, *Handbuch der krystallographischen Chemie,* Berlin, 181, 1855 ; *Handbuch der krystallographische physikalischen Chemie,* Leipzig, **1**. 535, 1881 ; L. W. McCay, *Chem. Ztg.,* **14**. 509, 1890 ; E. F. Smith and L. K. Frankel, *Amer. Chem. Journ.,* **12**. 428, 1890 ; C. W. Scheele, *Svenska Akad. Handl.,* **40**. 316, 1778 ; P. J. Macquer, *Mém. Acad.,* **9**, 1745 ; 223, 1746 ; 35, 1748 ; L. Glaser, *Mag. Pharm.,* **15**. 132, 1826 ; J. Setterberg, *Oefvers. Akad. Förh. Stockholm,* **3**. 25, 1846 ; *Journ. Pharm. Chim.,* (3), **12**. 142, 1847 ; R. F. Marchand, *Ber. Sachs Ges. Leipzig,* 86, 1849 ; G. C. Fleury, *Journ. Pharm. Chim.,* (5), **2**. 367, 1880 ; A. Streng, *Berg. Hütt. Ztg.,* **19**. 128, 1860 ; *Liebig's Ann.,* **129**. 241, 1864 ; B. E. Curry and T. O. Smith, *Journ. Amer. Chem. Soc.,* **37**. 1685, 1915 ; A. Borel, *Compt. Rend.,* **116**. 1509, 1893 ; *Arch. Sciences Genève,* (3), **30**. 422, 1893 ; H. Uelsmann, *Arch. Pharm.,* (2), **99**. 145, 1859 ; E. P. Alvarez, *Ann. Chim. Anal. Appl.,* **11**. 401, 1906 ; *Chem. News,* **94**. 269, 1906 ; A. Naumann, *Ber.,* **37**. 2601, 1904 ; C. F. Wenzel, *Lehre von der Verwandschaft der Korper,* Dresden, 444, 1777 ; A. Miolati and E. Mascetti, *Gazz. Chim. Ital.,* **31**. i, 93, 1901 ; H. Stamm, *Ueber die Löslichkeit von Ammonsalzen und Alkalisalzen in wässerigem Ammoniak,* Halle, 1926 ; G. P. Baxter and F. B. Coffin, *Journ. Amer. Chem. Soc.,* **31**. 297, 1909 ; *Zeit. anorg. Chem.,* **62**. 52, 1909 ; C. Neuberg and M. Kobel, *Biochem. Zeit.,* **174**. 493, 1926 ; L. J. Simon, *Compt. Rend.,* **176**. 437, 1923 ; O. Hassel, *Zeit. Elektrochem.,* **31**. 523, 1925 ; F. E. Brown and J. E. Snyder, *Journ. Amer. Chem. Soc.,* **47**. 2671, 1925 ; L. Kahlenberg and W. J. Trautmann, *Trans. Amer. Electrochem. Soc.,* **39**. 377, 1921 ; J. Brode and K. Klein, *German Pat., D.R.P.* 423276, 1925 ; A. Rosenheim and S. Thon, *Zeit. anorg. Chem.,* **167**. 1, 1927 ; J. C. G. Marignac, *Bibl. Univ.,* **55**. 113, 1876 ; N. de Klossowsky, *Journ. Chim. Phys.,* **22**. 225, 1925 ; K. H. Butler and D. McIntosh, *Trans. Roy. Soc. Canada,* (3), **21**. 19, 1927 ; W. Farmer and J. B. Firth, *Journ. Chem. Soc.,* 2019, 1927 ; E. Mitscherlich, *Ann. Chim. Phys.,* (2), **19**. 350, 1821 ; *Akad. Handl. Stockholm,* **4**, 1821 ; *Quart. Journ. Science,* **14**. 198, 415, 1823.

§ 16. Arsenates of the Copper-Gold Family

W. Hampe [1] reported the formation of **cuprous pyroarsenate,** $Cu_4As_2O_7$, by fusing a mixture of equal parts of cupric oxide and arsenic pentoxide in an atm. of carbon dioxide. At a white-heat, this substance gives off arsenic trioxide, forming red **cuprous diarsenate,** $Cu_3As_2O_9$, or $4Cu_2O.As_2O_5$. The pyroarsenate furnishes potassium arsenate when boiled with potash-lye. Evidence for the chemcial individuality of W. Hampe's product is wanting. C. Reichard also prepared cuprous pyroarsenate by adding sodium arsenate to an excess of a soln. of cuprous sulphate. This substance is decomposed by heat ; it is soluble in aq. ammonia, and in potash-lye. The ammoniacal soln. gives the original salt on evaporation ; and the alkaline soln. deposits cuprous oxide on standing.

J. J. Berzelius,[2] J. L. Proust, J. F. Simon, A. Vogel, E. Mitscherlich, and A. Hirsch reported that when cupric salt soln. are treated with sodium hydroarsenate, a pale blue precipitate is formed. H. Salkowsky said that the filtrate reacts acid when ammonium hydroarsenate is the precipitating agent. The Farbenindustrie A.G. treated basic cupric chloride with an arsenate or arsenic acid. R. Chenevix obtained blue rhombohedral crystals from the acid liquid left after mixing a soln. of copper nitrate with ammonium arsenate. W. Skey did not succeed in producing crystallized copper arsenate by adding a soluble arsenate to a soln. of a copper salt a green precipitate was produced by dissolving copper arsenide in nitric acid, and adding enough sodium hydroxide to give a ratio Na : As=2 : 1 by weight. These arsenates were not analyzed so that their empirical composition is unknown. A similar remark applies to the arsenate obtained by A. C. Becquerel, by dipping a strip of copper in silver arsenate immersed under water. The green crystals deposited on the copper are thought to be **cupric orthoarsenate,** $Cu_3(AsO_4)_2$. This compound was made by A. Coloriano, and C. Friedel and E. Sarasin by heating to 180°–200° for 18 hrs. in a sealed tube a mixture of 2 grms. of copper, and 32 c.c. of a soln. containing 4·5 grms. of arsenic acid, and separating the copper and arsenic trioxide from the crust of crystals. The green triclinic prisms or plates become dark green when heated ; they are insoluble in water, soluble in hydrochloric acid, and are attacked with difficulty by other acids. W. Ipatieff and coworkers observed that copper arsenate, when heated with hydrogen, under press., furnishes copper, copper arsenite and arsenide, arsine, and arsenious acid. H. Debray said that the *monohydrate,* $Cu_3(AsO_4)_2.H_2O$, is obtained as a blue powder when a mixture of cupric orthoarsenate and nitrate is heated to 50° or 60°. When heated with water or an aq. soln. of cupric nitrate, the basic salt, $CuO.Cu_3(AsO_4)_2.H_2O$, or copper hydroxyorthoarsenate, $Cu(AsO_4)CuOH$, is formed. A. Hirsch obtained a higher hydrate, $Cu_3(AsO_4)_2.4$ to $7H_2O$, by drying in air the precipitates obtained by treating silver orthoarsenate with a cold soln. of cupric chloride, or by mixing sodium hydroarsenate with an excess of cupric sulphate. P. P. Kosakewitsch obtained the *tetrahydrate,* $Cu_3(AsO_4)_2.4H_2O$, by the action of arsenic acid on copper oxide. T. Shiomi and K. Otsu converted the copper orthoarsenate, produced in the electrodeposition, into calcium arsenate for use as an insecticide.

According to A. Naumann, copper arsenate is insoluble in methyl acetate ; J. Schröder, insoluble in pyridine ; and E. C. Franklin and C. A. Kraus, insoluble in liquid ammonia. L. Kahlenberg and J. V. Steinle found that arsenic, immersed in a sat. soln. of copper arsenate, reacts : $Cu_3(AsO_4)_2+2As =3Cu+As_2O_3+As_2O_5$. L. Gmelin found that if a soln. of basic cupric arsenate in aq. ammonia be allowed to crystallize ; and A. Girard, C. Reichard, and A. Damour, that if a soln. of the diarsenate in aq. ammonia mixed with alcohol be spontaneously evaporated, sky-blue prismatic crystals are formed—triclinic, according to A. Damour ; rhombic, according to C. Reichard. The salt is **cupric triamminorthoarsenate,** $Cu_3(AsO_4)_2(NH_3)_3.4H_2O$. The salt loses water and ammonia at 300° ; and at dull redness it gives off arsenic oxide, and the brick-red residue melts at a higher temp. The salt is soluble in hot and cold water ; soluble in hydrochloric acid ; and it does not decolorize potassium permanganate.

A. Frenzel obtained from Schneeberg, and Zinnwald, rhombic prisms of an emerald-green mineral which he called **chlorotile.** Its composition approximates the *hexahydrate,* $Cu_3(AsO_4)_2.6H_2O$. S. G. Gordon suggested that chlorotile and mixite are the same mineral species. P. Groth represents the hexahydrate as a basic salt : $(CuOH)_3AsO_4.Cu(OH)_2$. A mineral obtained by R. Hermann as an incrustation on the tetrahedrite in the Turginsk copper mine was called **trichalcite**, and the analysis was supposed to agree with the *penta-hydrated*, normal arsenate, $Cu_3(AsO_4)_2.5H_2O$; according to C. F. Rammelsberg, the analysis agrees better with the formula of the basic salt $10CuO.3As_2O_5.16H_2O$, or $Cu_{10}O(AsO_4)_6$. Trichalcite occurs in verdigris-green radiating groups or columns, and in dendritic forms. Its hardness is 2·5. E. S. Larsen found the optic axial angle large ; the optical character negative ; and the indices of refraction $a = 1·67$, $\beta = 1·686$, and $\gamma = 1·698$. A lavender-blue mineral found at Annaberg, Saxony, was named by A. Breithaupt, **lavendulanite**, or rather *lavendulan*. E. Goldsmith's analysis of very impure sample from Chili corresponds with the *trihydrate*, $Cu_3(AsO_4)_2.3H_2O$. E. Goldsmith found up to 1·35 per cent. of nickel oxide, and 2·51 per cent. of cobalt oxide ; he therefore wrote the formula $(Cu,Co,Ni)_3(AsO_4)_2.3H_2O$. P. Groth used the formula $Cu_3(AsO_4)_2.2H_2O$ for the idealized mineral. W. F. Foshag regarded it as a cupriferous erythrite, and gave for the indices of refraction $\beta = 1·715$, and $\gamma = 1·725$.

A. Coloriano prepared **cupric hydroarsenate**, $CuHAsO_4.H_2O$, by the spontaneous evaporation of an acid soln. of copper carbonate in arsenic acid ; H. Debray obtained the same salt by evaporating the soln. at 70°. According to H. Goguel, the pale blue, monoclinic plates are pleochroic. R. Robl observed no fluorescence when the salt is exposed to ultra-violet light. A. Coloriano said that when the salt is boiled with water, a basic salt, $CuO.Cu_3(AsO_4)_2.H_2O$, is formed. According to H. Schiff, if a soln. of the freshly precipitated hydroarsenate in aq. ammonia be evaporated over quicklime, a pale blue powder is formed which is free from water, and is stable in air. Its composition corresponds with **cupric diamminohydroarsenate**, $CuHAsO_4.2NH_3$; and if in contact with water it swells up, forming the *monohydrate*, $CuHAsO_4.2NH_3.H_2O$. When heated, both water and ammonia are given off ; and it loses its water of crystallization at 30° over sulphuric acid.

A. Hirsch and others have reported a series of acid salts. Thus, A. Hirsch said that a salt, $8CuO.3As_2O_5.12H_2O$, corresponding with $Cu_3(AsO_4)_2.CuHAsO_4.5\frac{1}{2}H_2O$, **cupric hydrotriorthoarsenate**, $Cu_4H(AsO_4)_3.5\frac{1}{2}H_2O$, is obtained as a blue precipitate by treating a soln. of 2 mols of sodium hydroarsenate with 5 mols of copper nitrate, and washing the product for many days. H. Salkowsky mixed a soln. of cupric sulphate with an excess of ammonium hydroarsenate and obtained a blue precipitate almost free from ammonia. E. Mitscherlich remarked on the acid character of the liquid obtained in this reaction. A. Hirsch said that if the pale blue product be dried in air, it retains $9\frac{1}{2}$ mols. of water, forming the *hemienneadecahydrate*, $Cu_5H_2(AsO_4)_4.9\frac{1}{2}H_2O$; and H. Salkowsky found that when dried at 130°, it had the composition $5CuO.2As_2O_5.3H_2O$, that is, the *dihydrate*, $Cu_3(AsO_4)_2.2CuHAsO_4.2H_2O$, **cupric dihydrotetraorthoarsenate**, $Cu_5H_2(AsO_4)_4.2H_2O$. This salt seems to have been made by J. L. Proust, and J. F. Simon. A. Vogel observed that it dissolves in sulphurous acid without forming a cuprous salt. A. Hirsch said that if in preparing the hydrotriorthoarsenate, the precipitate be washed until only a trace of copper escapes in the filtrate, the *heptahydrate*, $Cu_5H_2(AsO_4)_4.7H_2O$, is formed ; and if a soln. of sodium hydroarsenate be added to a large excess of cupric sulphate, the air-dried product retains $11\frac{1}{2}$ mols. of water, forming the *hemitricosihydrate*, $Cu_5H_2(AsO_4)_4.11\frac{1}{2}H_2O$.

A number of basic cupric arsenates have been reported. Most of these occur in nature where they have been formed by the oxidation of the thioarsenides. The most important of these is represented by the mineral now known as olivenite. This was analyzed by M. H. Klaproth[3] in 1786, and shortly afterwards was called by A. G. Werner *Olivenerz;* by R. Kirwan, *olive copper ore;* and by P. Rashleigh, *olive-green copper ore.* J. L. Bournon referred to it as *cuivre arsénate en octaèdre aigus;* J. F. L. Hausmann, as *pharmacochalzite,* and *pharmacolzite;* and R. Jameson, and C. C. von Leonhard gave it its present name **olivenite**, in allusion to its olive-green colour. The mineral was analyzed by M. H. Klaproth, F. von Kobell, A. Damour, K. Biehl, T. Thomson, R. Hermann, and W. F. Hillebrand. The empirical formula is $4CuO.As_2O_5.H_2O$, or $Cu_4As_2O_9.H_2O$, **copper hydroxyorthoarsenate**, in agreement with C. F. Rammelsberg's view of the constitution : $Cu_3(AsO_4)_2Cu(HO)_2$. P. Groth represented it by $HO.Cu(AsO_4)Cu$. The artificial salt was analyzed by

A. Coloriano, H. Debray, and A. Hirsch. A. Coloriano made it by boiling for half
an hour an aq. soln. of copper hydroarsenate ; H. Debray, by heating the normal
arsenate with a little water or aq. copper nitrate in a sealed tube at 200° ; C. Friedel
and E. Sarasin, by similarly heating a mixture of copper carbonate, arsenic acid,
and water at 150° ; and A. Hirsch, by dropping a conc. soln. of 2 mols of heptahydrated hydroarsenate into a conc. soln. of 4 mols of cupric chloride, washing the
blue precipitate first with cold water, and then with hot water ; and drying at 260°.
C. Friedel and E. Sarasin added that when sodium arsenate acts on copper sulphate,
products other than olivenite may be obtained—*e.g.* sodium cupric arsenates.
Olivenite may be olive-green, passing into various other shades of green, blackish-
green, brown, yellow, grey, and white. It may be nodular or massive, or fibrous,
when it may be called *wood-copper*, or *wood-arsenate*. The crystals may be prismatic or acicular. The crystals are rhombic, and, according to H. S. Washington,
have the axial ratios $a : b : c = 0.9396 : 1 : 0.6726$; K. Biehl gave $0.93934 : 1 : 0.67239$.
H. Debray said that the olive-green octahedral crystals are isomorphous with the
corresponding salt of zinc ; and P. Groth, isomorphous with libethenite,
$CuPO_4(CuOH)$, and with adamite, $ZnAsO_4(ZnOH)$. The cleavage on the (010)-,
(110)-, and (011)-faces is faint. A. des Cloizeaux gave for the optic axial angle
with red-, yellow-, and blue-light, $2H_a = 105.5°$, $106.6°$, and $109.47°$ respectively ;
the optical character is negative. E. S. Larsen said it is positive, and he gave
$2V = 82°$, and the indices of refraction $\alpha = 1.772$, $\beta = 1.810$, and $\gamma = 1.863$. For
a Cornish mineral he gave $\alpha = 1.747$, $\beta = 1.788$, and $\gamma = 1.829$. The mineral is not
pleochroic. R. Hermann gave 3.913–4.135 for the sp. gr., and A. Damour, 4.378.
The hardness is 3. T. W. Case observed that the mineral is a non-conductor of
electricity, and that insolation has no measurable effect. A. Hirsch said that
water, aq. ammonia, and baryta-water attack this compound with greater difficulty
than is the case with the other copper arsenates ; and an aq. soln. of silver nitrate
does not attack this arsenate at all. The mineral is soluble in nitric acid.

A. Hirsch said that the *hemienneahydrate*, $4CuO.As_2O_5.4\frac{1}{2}H_2O$, is formed as in
the case of the monohydrate, by mixing soln. of sodium hydroarsenate, and cupric
chloride, washing only with cold water, and drying in air. The mineral **leucochalcite**, described imperfectly by F. Sandberger, and T. Petersen approximates
in composition to the *trihydrate*, $4CuO.As_2O_5.3H_2O$. It occurs in white, slender
needles, with a tinge of green, as a coating on the malachite and calcite of the
Wilhelmine mine, Spessart, Germany. Little more is known about this rare mineral.
E. S. Larsen said that the optical character is positive, the optic axial angle large,
and the indices of refraction $\alpha = 1.79$, $\beta = 1.807$, and $\gamma = 1.84$. A. Breithaupt
described another mineral occurring at Libethen, Hungary. Its composition
resembles that of a hydrated olivenite, being a *heptahydrate*, $4CuO.As_2O_5.7H_2O$.
He called the mineral **euchroite**—from $\epsilon\ddot{v}\chi\rho oa$, beautiful colour. G. Tschermak
said that olivenite may be euchroite altered by the loss of water. Analyses were
made by F. Wöhler, E. Turner, H. Kühn, and A. H. Church. C. F. Rammelsberg
wrote the formula $Cu_3(AsO_4)_2.Cu(OH)_2.6H_2O$; and P. Groth, $CuAsO_4(CuOH).3H_2O$.
The prismatic crystals have a bright emerald-green or leek-green colour. W. Haidinger gave for the axial ratios of the rhombic crystals $a : b : c = 0.6088 : 1 : 1.0379$.
R. H. Solly made some observations on the crystals. Traces of cleavage occur
on the (110)- and the (011)-faces. A. des Cloizeaux gave for the optic axial
angle $2E = 61° 11'$ at 17°, and 56° 8′ at 86°. The optical character is negative.
E. S. Larsen said the optical character is positive and the optic axial angle of a
Libenthen specimen, 29°, and a doubtful Utah specimen, 62°. The indices of refrac-
tion of the former are $\alpha = 1.695$, $\beta = 1.698$, and $\gamma = 1.733$, and of the latter $\alpha = 1.723$,
$\beta = 1.738$, and $\gamma = 1.781$. The sp. gr. is 3.389, and the hardness 3.5–4.0. The
reactions are similar to those with olivenite. A. H. Church found that the mineral
loses 1.22 per cent. of water in vacuo ; 1.90 per cent, at 100° ; and 16.16 per cent.
at dull redness.

W. Haidinger [4] described an emerald-green or grass-green mineral which was named **erinite** because it was supposed to come from Ireland; but A. H. Church showed that it came from Cornwall. It also occurs in Utah. Analyses have been reported by E. Turner, R. Pearce, and W. F. Hillebrand and H. S. Washington. These correspond with the empirical formula $5CuO.As_2O_5.2H_2O$; that is, **copper tetrahydroxyorthoarsenate**, which C. F. Rammelsberg represents by $Cu_3As_2O_8.2Cu(OH)_2$; and P. Groth by $(CuOH)_4Cu(AsO_4)_2$. It occurs in mammillated crystalline masses, with a concentric and fibrous structure, and a rough surface from the terminations of minute crystals. The hardness is 4·5–5·0; and the sp. gr. 4·043. E. S. Larsen said that the optical character is negative, and the indices of refraction $a=1·82°$, $\beta=1·820$, and $\gamma=1·88$. The erinite of F. S. Beudant, A. des Cloizeaux, and A. Schrauf is considered to be chalcophyllite. A related mineral with $R_3(AsO_4)_2.2R(OH)_2$, with $R=Ca:Cu:Zn=4:3·5:1$ for the bases was called **staszicite** by J. Morozewicz. He found it at Miedzianka, Poland. It occurs in yellowish-green masses with a fibrous structure, and is presumably rhombic. The sp. gr. is 4·227, and the hardness 5·5–6·0. It loses $1·5H_2O$ at 500° to 600°; and $0·5H_2O$ at 800° to 880°. The m.p. is 880°. It may be an oxidation product of miedziankite. The mineral **cornwallite** found in small botryoidal masses on olivenite in Cornwall was described by F. X. M. Zippe.[5] The colour is emerald-green or verdigris-green. The analyses by J. U. Lerch corresponded with the *pentahydrate*, $5CuO.As_2O_5.5H_2O$, or, as P. Groth wrote it, $(CuOH)_4Cu(AsO_4)_2.3H_2O$; but the analyses by A. H. Church, and W. F. Hillebrand and H. S. Washington agree better with the *trihydrate*, $5CuO.As_2O_5.3H_2O$, or, as P. Groth wrote, $(CuOH)_4Cu(AsO_4)_2.H_2O$. The hardness of the amorphous mineral is 4·5, and the sp. gr. 4·16. E. S. Larsen said that the optical character is positive; the optical axial angle small; and the indices of refraction $a=1·81$, $\beta=1·815$, and $\gamma=1·85$. A. H. Church said that cornwallite loses no water at 100°. Another mineral, occurring along with copper ores at Schneeberg, and other places, was called by A. G. Werner[6] *Kupferschaum*, by C. U. Shepard, *kupaphrite;* and by W. Haidinger, *tirolit*, or **tyrolite**. Analyses by F. von Kobell, W. F. Hillebrand and H. S. Washington, R. Pearce, and A. H. Church agree with the *enneahydrate*, $5CuO.As_2O_5.9H_2O$, or, as C. F. Rammelsberg writes it, $CaCO_3.Cu_5As_2O_{10}.9H_2O$, on the assumption that some calcium carbonate is an essential and not an accidental constituent. Some calcium sulphate is also present. P. Groth represents it by the formula, $(CuOH)_4Cu(AsO_4)_2.7H_2O$. Tyrolite is pale apple-green, verdigris-green, or sky-blue. It may occur massive, reniform, in foliated aggregates, and rarely in isolated crystals. E. S. Dana gave for the axial ratios of the tabular rhombic crystals $a:b:c=0·9325:1:—$; the (011)-cleavage is micaceous. The hardness is 1·0 to 1·5; and the sp. gr. 3·02 to 3·098. F. W. Clarke reported 3·27 at 20·5°. The optic axial angle is large, and the optical character negative. E. S. Larsen gave for the optical axial angle $2V=36°$, and for the indices of refraction $a=1·694$, $\beta=1·726$, and $\gamma=1·730$. The pleochroism is $a=\gamma=$pale grass-green, and $\beta=$pale yellowish-green.

A Cornish mineral arsenate was called *strahliges Olivenerz* by M. H. Klaproth[7] in 1801, *cupreous arsenate of iron* by J. L. Bournon, and analogous terms were used by D. L. G. Karsten, R. J. Häuy, J. F. L. Hausmann, and A. Breithaupt. E. F. Glocker called it *siderochalcite;* F. S. Beudant, *aphanèse*—from ἀφανής, not manifest, in allusion to the fact that the crystals are rarely recognizable; C. U. Shepard, *aphanesite*, and J. J. Bernhardi, *abichite*. J. D. Dana called it **clinoclasite** in allusion to the basal cleavage being oblique to the sides of the prism. The mineral also occurs in a few other localities. Analyses have been reported by C. F. Rammelsberg, A. Damour and A. des Cloizeaux, R. Pearce, W. F. Hillebrand and H. S. Washington, and A. H. Church. The results agree with the empirical formula $6CuO.As_2O_5.3H_2O$, or **copper hexahydroxyorthoarsenate**, $Cu_3(AsO_4)_2.3Cu(OH)_2$. P. Groth wrote the formula $(CuOH)_3AsO_4$. The colour of the mineral is dark green, or a blackish blue-green. It occurs massive, or in hemispherical or reniform masses with a radiating fibrous structure. It also occurs in prismatic crystals with rounded uneven faces; and also in crystal aggregates. The monoclinic crystals were found by W. Phillips to have the axial ratios $a : b : c = 1.9069 : 1 : 3.8507$, and $\beta = 80° 50'$. The cleavage on the (110)-face is prismatic. A. Damour and A. des Cloizeaux gave for the optic angles, $2E = 134° 36'$ and $141° 14'$ for green light; and for blue light, $160° 52'$; $2H = 83° 42'$ and $86° 42'$ for blue light, and $81° 56'$ and $84° 12'$ for green light; E. S. Larsen said that the optical axial angle is medium, the optical character is negative; the hardness is $2.5–3.0$; and the sp. gr. $4.19–4.38$—R. Pearce gave 4.36; and W. F. Hillebrand and H. S. Washington, 4.38 at $19°$. A. Coloriano said that water begins to come off at $290°$, and is all expelled at $445°$. E. S. Larsen gave for the indices of refraction $\alpha = 1.73$, $\beta = 1.870$, and $\gamma = 1.91$; and he found the mineral to be pleochroic. The mineral is soluble in nitric acid. O. Pufahl described pale green crusts of indistinct crystals of a mineral, which he called **duftite**, occurring on azurite at Tsumeb, South Africa. The analyses correspond with **copper octohydroxyorthoarsenate**, $Cu_3(AsO_4)_2.4Cu(OH)_2$. Its sp. gr. is 6.19 and its hardness 3. It is soluble in hot dil. hydrochloric acid.

R. J. Haüy,[8] and L. N. Vauquelin described a mineral from Cornwall which they called *cuivre arsénate lamelliforme*. D. L. G. Karsten called it *Kupferglimmer* ; R. Jameson, *copper mica ;* A. Breithaupt, *Kupferphyllit*, and **chalcophyllite**; F. S. Beudant, and A. Damour and A. des Cloizeaux, *erinite (vide supra)* ; and H. J. Brooke and W. H. Miller, *tamarite*. It occurs in Cornwall, and a few other localities. Analyses were reported by R. Chenevix, L. N. Vauquelin, R. Hermann, A. Damour, A. des Cloizeaux, A. H. Church, and E. G. J. Hartley. R. Hermann represented his results by $8CuO.As_2O_5.24H_2O$. This can be written as **copper decahydroxyorthoarsenate**, $Cu_3(AsO_4)_2.5Cu(OH)_2.nH_2O$. C. F. Rammelsberg was unable to satisfy himself about the formula, P. Groth gave $(CuOH)_3AsO_4.Cu(OH)_2.3\frac{1}{2}H_2O$. A. H. Church did not regard as an accidental constituent the $1.8–5.97$ per cent. of alumina reported in the analyses, and represented chalcophyllite as *copper aluminium decahydroxyorthoarsenate :* $Cu_3Al_2As_2O_{16}.24$ or $25H_2O$. The composition of idealized chalcophyllite is still *sub judice*. E. V. Shannon described a complex variety of chalcophyllite, **copper aluminoarsenatosulphate**, $4CuO.(\frac{1}{5}Al_2O_3.\frac{-}{5}As_2O_5.\frac{3}{5}SO_3).10H_2O$, which he obtained from Rancagua, Chile. It loses half its water at $110°$. The indices of refraction of the fresh mineral are $\omega = 1.618$, and $\epsilon = 1.552$, or $\omega = \epsilon - 0.066$; the numbers for the mineral dried in air are $1.620, 1.560$, and 0.060 respectively; and for the mineral dried to constant weight at $110°$, $1.680, 1.618$, and 0.062 respectively. The colour of chalcophyllite is emerald-green, grass-green, and verdigris-green. It occurs foliated and massive; but usually in six-sided tabular crystals with the (0001)-face striated. The axial ratio of the trigonal crystals given by A. Damour and A. des Cloizeaux is $a : c = 1 : 2.5538$; C. Palache and H. E. Merwin gave $1 : 2.671$. The cleavage on the (0001)-face is perfect; that on the (1011)-face occurs only in traces. The hardness is 2; the sp. gr. $2.40–2.66$—R. Hermann gave 2.435, and A. Damour and A. des Cloizeaux, 2.659. P. Gaubert said that 14 per cent. of water is given off above $100°$, and the remainder at a much higher temp. A. Damour and A. des Cloizeaux found that the optical character is negative; and P. Gaubert gave for the indices of refraction $\omega = 1.6323$, $\epsilon = 1.5745$, and $\omega - \epsilon = 0.578$. The mineral is easily soluble in hydrochloric and nitric acids, and in aq. ammonia.

W. F. Foshag[9] described a greenish-blue mineral from Freirini, Chile, and he called it **freirinite**. Its composition approximates $6(Cu,Ca)O.3Na_2O.2As_2O_5.6H_2O.Cu_3Na_3(AsO_4)_2$, **sodium copper orthoarsenate**. It is composed of microscopic uniaxial plates or columns. The mineral is either tetragonal or rhombic with a small optic axial angle. The optical character is negative. The basal cleavage is perfect, the prismatic cleavage is imperfect. The indices of refraction are $\epsilon = 1.645$—light greenish-blue; and $\omega = 1.748$—dark greenish-blue. A. Hirsch reported a number of complex salts of copper and sodium arsenates with different values for the ratios $Na_2O : CuO : As_2O_5 : H_2O$. Thus, the ratios $2:24:9:23$, or sodium copper hydroennearsenate, Na_2HAsO_4. $4Cu_3(AsO_4)_2.11H_2O$, is obtained by mixing a soln. of 4 mols of cupric nitrate with 7 mols of sodium hydroarsenate, and washing the precipitate during 10 days. The ratios $1:12:5:12$, or sodium copper dihydropentarsenate, $NaH_2AsO_4.2Cu_3(AsO_4)_2.5H_2O$, were obtained by mixing a dil. soln. of 2 mols of sodium hydroarsenate with 4 mols of cupric sulphate, and washing the precipitate many days. H. Salkowsky also made this salt. If in preparing the first of the salts, the precipitate be washed a shorter time, the product has the ratios $2:18:7:20$, or sodium copper bishydrodecatetrarsenate, $2Na_2HAsO_4.6Cu_3(AsO_4)_2.19H_2O$; and this salt is made by treating a soln. of copper nitrate with an excess of sodium hydroarsenate. The ratios $4:36:15:16$, or sodium copper hydrobisdihydrodecapentarsenate, $Na_2HAsO_4.2NaH_2AsO_4$. $6Cu_3(AsO_4)_2.16H_2O$, was obtained by mixing soln. of 3 mols of cupric sulphate, and 3 mols of sodium hydroarsenate, and washing the precipitate for three days ; if the precipitate be washed until the runnings are free from sulphuric acid, a higher hydrate is produced, viz., $33\frac{1}{2}H_2O$. There is nothing here to show that these products do not represent arbitrary stages in a process of hydrolysis. C. Lefèvre dissolved 7–8 per cent. of cupric oxide in sodium metasenite melted at a low temp. The green, crystalline mass has the composition sodium copper arsenate, $CuNaAsO_4$. It is easily fusible, and is decomposed at a red-heat ; it is freely soluble in aq. ammonia and dil. acids. The corresponding potassium copper arsenate, $KCuAsO_4$, was obtained in an analogous manner. By saturating a fused mixture of sodium metasenite and chloride with copper oxide, C. Lefèvre obtained sodium copper tetraorthoarsenate, $2Na_3AsO_4.Cu_3(AsO_4)_2$. This product is easily fused ; it decomposes at a red-heat ; and is easily soluble in acids. He also made potassium copper triorthoarsenate, $KCu_4(AsO_4)_3$, or $KCuAsO_4.Cu_3(AsO_4)_2$, by dissolving 10 per cent. of cupric oxide in molten potassium metasenite, and heating the fused mass near its m.p. for a long time.

When a soln. of silver nitrate is treated with the primary, secondary, or tertiary arsenate of ammonium, potassium, or sodium, or with arsenic acid, brownish-red silver orthoarsenate, Ag_3AsO_4, is precipitated ; and, according to O. B. Kühn,[10] the precipitate is dark purple if the soln. of silver nitrate be boiling, and a conc. soln. of arsenic acid be the precipitant. C. W. Scheele said that the precipitation with arsenic acid, and potassium dihydroarsenate is incomplete because the precipitate is partly soluble in the nitric acid formed in the reaction. E. Mitscherlich also showed that the acid is formed if alkali hydroarsenate be used, but T. Graham said that the liquid remains neutral if normal alkali arsenate be used. T. Graham added that the silver nitrate adsorbed by the precipitate cannot be completely removed by washing ; but if ammonium nitrate be present no adsorption of silver nitrate occurs. H. Goguel obtained the arsenate by adding silver nitrate to a hot conc. soln. of arsenic acid. G. P. Baxter and F. B. Coffin found that in preparing normal silver arsenate perceptible hydrolysis occurs in soln. of the salts of the acid even when the base is a strong one. The hydrolysis is greatest with the tertiary salts. Silver orthoarsenate made by precipitation with the normal sodium salt always contains an occluded basic impurity. Silver orthoarsenate cannot be completely dried without fusion owing to the retention of liquid in pockets within the solid. A. Dexheimer prepared colloidal silver orthoarsenate by mixing a 5 per cent. soln. of silver nitrate with 2 grms. of protalbinate dissolved in 20 c.c. of water. The precipitate was dissolved in dil. sodium hydroxide and mixed with a soln. of sodium hydroarsenate. The product was dialyzed in darkness until the washings were free from water in vacuo over sulphuric acid. The powder with water yields a hydrosol which is dark green in reflected light and reddish-brown in transmitted light. In thin layers, G. P. Baxter and F. B. Coffin found the colour is ruby-red in transmitted light. The dark reddish-brown silver orthoarsenate obtained by G. P. Baxter and F. B. Coffin, H. Goguel, and H. Dufet was in the form of tetrahedral, hexahedral, or dodecahedral cubic crystals. From the X-radiogram,

R. W. G. Wyckoff calculated that the unit cell of the cubic crystals contains two Ag_3AsO_4-mols, and has a side 6·12 A. G. P. Baxter and F. B. Coffin gave 6·657 for the sp. gr. at 25°/4°. C. W. Scheele found that when heated to the softening temp. of glass, the orthoarsenate begins to fuse; and at a higher temp., it decomposes into silver, etc. J. F. Simon also found that it furnishes silver when heated in the presence of charcoal. G. S. Whitby found that a litre of water dissolved 0·0085 grm. of the salt at 20°. E. C. Franklin and C. A. Kraus said that silver orthoarsenate is insoluble in liquid ammonia, and O. Widman obtained **silver tetramminortho-arsenate**, $Ag_3AsO_4.4NH_3$, in colourless needles which lose ammonia in air, and which are freely soluble in water. C. W. Scheele said that silver orthoarsenate is soluble in aq. ammonia ; and F. Wöhler found that the ammoniacal soln. becomes brown when treated with hydrogen, and with the long-continued action of hydrogen, a black powder is deposited. G. C. Wittstein found that the normal arsenate dissolves readily in soln. of ammonium carbonate, but not ammonium sulphate, nitrate, or succinate—even when heated. T. Graham said that the salt dissolves sparingly in a soln. of ammonium nitrate, and more freely in acetic acid. C. W. Scheele said that hydrochloric acid converts the arsenate into chloride. J. Setterberg, indeed, said that on evaporating a soln. of silver orthoarsenate in nitric acid, the first crop of crystals is silver orthoarsenate, and this is followed by a crop of crystals of *silver nitratoarsenate*, which in contact with water decompose into the orthoarsenate and nitrate. A. Joly found the arsenate to be less soluble than the phosphate in arsenic acid. The silver arsenate dissolved to saturation in a soln. of less than 70 parts of arsenic acid in 100 parts of water at 80° furnishes black dodecahedral crystals of silver orthoarsenate on cooling. F. Wöhler found that if silver arsenate be treated with a soln. of ferrous sulphate it forms a dark grey powder of silver suboxide (*q.v.*). E. V. Zappi and J. J. Landaburu obtained a mixture approximating $2Ag_3AsO_4+Ag$, and not silver arsenide by reducing silver arsenate with formaldehyde.

J. Setterberg melted together a mol of arsenic acid and 2 mols of silver nitrate until the nitric acid was completely expelled and obtained a mass thought to be **silver hydroarsenate**, Ag_2HAsO_4 ; and A. Joly rapidly heated to 100° crystals of silver dihydroarsenate and obtained **silver metarsenate**, $AgAsO_3$, as a white powder ; before losing water, the crystals become red owing to the formation of arsenic acid and silver hydroarsenate. If the soln. from which silver dihydro-arsenate will crystallize is sat. with silver arsenate at a temp. a little below 100°, it deposits orange-red hexagonal prisms with rhombohedral terminations. The crystalline form resembles that of silver hydrophosphate, but the hydroarsenate could not be purified. J. Setterberg found that the salt is decomposed by water, forming the normal arsenate. H. Dufet said that the crystals of the hydroarsenate are trigonal with axial ratios $a : c = 1 : 0.7297$, and $\alpha = 105°$ 54'. According to J. Setterberg, if a soln. of the normal arsenate in arsenic acid be evaporated, colourless, monoclinic crystals of **silver dihydroarsenate**, AgH_2AsO_4, are formed. L. Hurtzig and A. Geuther could not make this salt. A. Joly found that this salt is best obtained by crystallization from a soln. of precipitated silver orthoarsenate in an acid of the composition $H_3AsO_4.H_2O$; it is decomposed by a trace of water, into the normal arsenate and arsenic acid. If the soln. of silver arsenate in arsenic acid be heated above 100°, it yields a white granular powder, **silver paratetrarsenate**, $Ag_2As_4O_{11}$, which is analogous to the product obtained by L. Hurtzig and A. Geuther. H. Dufet found the monoclinic prismatic crystals have the axial ratios $a : b : c = 0.8145 : 1 : 1.1117$, and $\beta = 90°$ 5'.

T. Thomson found sodium orthoarsenate gives a yellowish-white precipitate of **gold arsenate** when added to a warm soln. of auric chloride.

REFERENCES.

[1] W. Hampe, *Zeit. Berg. Hütt. Sal.*, 22. 102, 1874 ; C. Reichard, *Ber.*, 31. 2166, 1898.
[2] H. Goguel, *Mém. Soc. Phys. Nat. Bordeaux*, (5), 1. 135, 1896 ; *Contribution à l'étude des*

arsénates et des antimonates cristallisés préparés par voie humide, Paris, 1896; A. Coloriano, Recherches sur quelques arsénates cristallisés, Paris, 1886; Compt. Rend., 103. 274, 1886; Bull. Soc. Chim., (2), 45. 707, 1886; C. Friedel and E. Sarasin, ib., (2), 25. 482, 1876; Bull. Soc. Min., 2. 157, 1879; Arch. Sciences Genéve, (3), 27. 11, 1892; A. Hirsch, Ein Beitrag zur Kenntnis der Arsenate des Kupfers, Halle a. S., 10, 1890; J. J. Berzelius, Pogg. Ann., 7. 137, 1826; E. Mitscherlich, Ann. Chim. Phys., (2), 19. 350, 407, 1821; H. Salkowsky, Journ. prakt. Chem., (1), 104. 166, 1868; A. Vogel, ib., (1), 6. 347, 1835; A. Breithaupt, ib., (1), 10. 505, 1837; R. Hermann, ib., (1), 33. 87, 1844; A. Frenzel, Tschermak's Mitt., (1), 5. 42, 1875; Neues Jahrb. Min., 517, 1875; C. F. Rammelsberg, Handbuch der Mineralchemie, Leipzig, 348, 1875; ii. 152, 1895; R. Robl, Zeit. angew. Chem., 39. 608, 1926; P. Groth, Tabellarische Uebersicht der Mineralien, Braunschweig, 92, 1898; E. Goldsmith, Proc. Acad. Philadelphia, 192, 1877; R. Chenevix, Phil. Trans., 91. 201, 1801; E. S. Larsen, Bull. U.S. Geol. Sur., 679, 1921; W. F. Foshag, Amer. Min., 9. 29, 1924; S. G. Gordon, ib., 10. 38, 1925; P. P. Kosakewitsch, Zeit. phys. Chem., 108. 281, 1924; T. Shiomi and K. Otsu, Japanese Pat. No. 41739, 1922; L. Kahlenberg and J. V. Steinle, Trans. Amer. Electrochem. Soc., 44. 493, 1923; W. Skey, Chem. News, 22. 61, 1870; J. Pattinson, ib., 45. 136, 1882; J. L. Proust, Ann. Chim. Phys., (1), 32. 26, 1799; (1), 60. 260, 1806; Journ. Phys., 51. 173, 1800; 53. 89, 1801; 59. 393, 1804; J. F. Simon, Pogg. Ann., 40. 117, 1837; A. C. Becquerel, Compt. Rend., 4. 830, 1837; H. Debray, Ann. Chim. Phys., (3), 61. 439, 1860; Compt. Rend., 102. 44, 1861; A. Damour, ib., 21. 1422, 1845; A. Girard, ib., 36. 794, 1853; C. Reichard, Ber., 27. 1021, 1894; A. Naumann, ib., 42. 3790, 1909; L. Gmelin, Pogg. Ann., 4. 157, 1825; Handbook of Chemistry, London, 5. 473, 1851; H. Schiff, Liebig's Ann., 123. 42, 1862; Farbenindustrie A.G., German Pat., D.R.P. 428239, 1924; W. Ipatieff, Ber., 59. B, 1412, 1926; W. Ipatieff and W. Nikolaieff, Journ. Russ. Phys. Chem. Soc., 58. 664, 686, 692, 698, 1926; J. Schröder, Chemisches und physikalisch-chemisches Verhalten des Pyridins und von Metallsalzen zu und in Pyridin, Giessen, 1904; E. C. Franklin and C. A. Kraus, Amer. Chem. Journ., 20. 827, 1898.

³ M. H. Klaproth, Schrift. Ges. Nat. Berlin, 7. 160, 1786; A. G. Werner, Berg. Journ., 382, 385, 1789; R. Kirwan, Elements of Mineralogy, London, 2. 151, 1796; R. Jameson, A System of Mineralogy, Edinburgh, 2. 335, 1820; C. C. von Leonhard, Handbuch der Oryktogonosie, Heidelberg, 283, 1821; J. F. L. Hausmann, Handbuch der Mineralogie, Göttingen, 3. 1042, 1813; P. Rashleigh, Specimens of British Minerals, London, 1. 11, 1797; W. Phillips, Elementary Introduction to Mineralogy, London, 319, 1823; K. Biehl, Beiträge zur Kenntnis der Mineralien der Erzlagerstätten von Tsumeb, Münster, 1919; E. S. Larsen, Bull. U.S. Geol. Sur., 679, 1921; A. des Cloizeaux, Nouvelles recherches sur les propriétés optiques des cristaux, Paris, 81, 1867; De l'emploi des propriétés optiques biréfringentes en minéralogie, Paris, 2. 43, 1859; Ann. Mines, (5), 11. 261, 1857; Ann. Chim. Phys., (3), 13. 417, 1845; A. Damour, ib., (3), 13. 412, 1845; G. Tschermak, Sitzber. Akad. Wien, 51. 129, 1865; H. S. Washington, Amer. Journ. Science, (3), 35. 298, 1888; W. F. Hillebrand, Proc. Colorado Scient. Soc., 1. 113, 1884; F. von Kobell, Pogg. Ann., 188. 249, 1830; T. Thomson, Outlines of Mineralogy, Geology, and Mineral Analysis, London, 1. 614, 1836; R. Hermann, Journ. prakt. Chem., (1), 33. 291, 1844; J. L. Bournon, Phil. Trans., 91. 177, 1801; C. F. Rammelsberg, Handbuch der Mineralchemie, Leipzig, 349, 1875; P. Groth, Tabellarische Uebersicht der Mineralien, Braunschweig, 96, 1898; F. Wöhler, Liebig's Ann., 51. 285, 1844; H. Kühn, ib., 51. 128, 1844; A. H. Church, Min. Mag., 11. 2, 1895; W. Haidinger, Pogg. Ann., 5. 165, 1825; Edin. Journ. Science, 2. 133, 1825; E. Turner, ib., 4. 301, 1820; R. H. Solly, Proc. Cambridge Phil. Soc., 4. 6, 1883; A. Coloriano, Recherches sur quelques arsénates cristallisés, Paris, 1886; Compt. Rend., 103. 274, 1886; Bull. Soc. Chim., (2), 45. 707, 1886; C. Friedel and E. Sarasin, ib., (2), 25. 482, 1876; Bull. Soc. Min., 2. 157, 1879; Arch. Sciences Genéve, (3), 27. 11, 1892; A. Hirsch, Ein Beitrag zur Kenntnis der Arsenate des Kupfers, Halle a. S., 10, 1890; H. Debray, Ann. Chim. Phys., (3), 61. 439, 1860; Compt. Rend., 102. 44, 1861; A. Damour, ib., 21. 1422, 1845; T. Petersen, Neues Jahrb. Min., i, 263, 1881; F. Sandberger, Untersuchungen über Erzgänge, Wiesbaden, 1885; T. W. Case, Phys. Rev., (2), 9. 305, 1917; A. Breithaupt, Vollständige Charakteristik der Mineralsystems, Dresden, 172, 266, 1823.

⁴ E. Turner, Ann. Phil., (2), 4. 154, 1822; W. Haidinger, ib., 4. 154, 1828; W. F. Hillebrand and H. S. Washington, Amer. Journ. Science, (3), 35. 300, 1888; R. Pearce, Proc. Colorado Scient. Soc., 2. 150, 1886; C. F. Rammelsberg, Handbuch der Mineralchemie, Leipzig, 2. 350, 1875; P. Groth, Tabellarische Uebersicht der Mineralien, Braunschweig, 90, 1898; F. S. Beudant, Traité élémentaire de minéralogie, Paris, 2. 598, 1832; A. des Cloizeaux, Ann. Chim. Phys., (3), 13. 420, 1845; A. Schrauf, Sitzber. Akad. Wien, 41. 769, 1860; 42. 107, 1860; J. Morozewicz, Bull. Acad. Cracovie, 4, 1918; A. H. Church, Min. Mag., 11. 2, 1895; E. S. Larsen, Bull. U.S. Geol. Sur., 679, 1921.

⁵ F. X. M. Zippe, Abh. Böhm. Ges. Wiss., 4. 647, 1846; J. U. Lerch, ib., 4. 647, 1846; A. H. Church, Journ. Chem. Soc., 21. 276, 1868; P. Groth, Tabellarische Uebersicht der Mineralien, Braunschweig, 96, 1898; W. F. Hillebrand and H. S. Washington, Amer. Journ. Science, (3), 35. 300, 1888; (3), 39. 271, 1890; E. S. Larsen, Bull. U.S. Geol. Sur., 679, 1921.

⁶ A. G. Werner, Letztes Mineralsystem, Freiberg, 50, 1817; C. U. Shepard, A Treatise on Mineralogy, New Haven, 1. 294, 1835; W. Haidinger, Handbuch der bestimmenden Mineralogie, Wien, 509, 1845; C. F. Rammelsberg, Handbuch der Mineralchemie, Leipzig, 351, 1875; W. F. Hillebrand and H. S. Washington, Amer. Journ. Science, (3), 35. 300, 1888; E. S. Dana, ib., (3), 39. 273, 1890; R. Pearce, Proc. Colorado Scient. Soc., 2. 135, 150, 1886; F. von Kobell, Pogg. Ann., 18. 253, 1830; A. H. Church, Journ. Chem. Soc., 26. 108, 1873; Min. Mag., 11. 6,

1895 ; F. W. Clarke, *A Table of Specific Gravity for Liquids and Solids*, London, 123, 1888 ;
E. S. Larsen, *Bull. U.S. Geol. Sur.*, 679, 1921 ; P. Groth, *Tabellarische Uebersicht der Mineralien*,
Braunschweig, 96, 1898.
    ⁷ M. H. Klaproth, *Schrift. Ges. Nat. Berlin*, 3. 298, 1801 ; J. L. Bournon, *Phil. Trans.*, 91.
177, 1801 ; D. L. G. Karsten, *Mineralogische Tabellen*, Berlin, 64, 97, 1808 ; R. J. Häuy, *Tableau
comparatif des résultats de la cristallographie et de l'analyse chimique*, Paris, 91, 1908 ; J. F. L. Haus-
mann, *Handbuch der Mineralogie*, Göttingen, 1050, 1813 ; E. F. Glocker, *Grundriss der Mineralogie*, Nürnberg, 840, 1831 ; J. J. Bernhardi, *ib.*, 579, 1839 ; C. U. Shepard, *A Treatise on
Mineralogy*, New Haven, 1835 ; W. Phillips, *Introduction to Mineralogy*, London, 331, 1837 ;
J. D. Dana, *A System of Mineralogy*, New York, 795, 1892 ; A. Damour and A. des Cloizeaux,
Ann. Chim. Phys., (3), 13. 419, 1845 ; A. Schrauf, *Atlas der Krystallformen des Mineralreiches*,
Wien, 1871 ; F. W. Clarke, *A Table of Specific Gravity for Solids and Liquids*, London, 122,
1888 ; C. F. Rammelsberg, *Handbuch der Mineralchemie*, Leipzig, 352, 378, 1860 ; R. Pearce,
Proc. Colorado Scient. Soc., 2. 134, 1886 ; W. F. Hillebrand and H. S. Washington, *Amer. Journ.
Science*, (3), 35. 305, 1888 ; A. H. Church, *Min. Mag.*, 11. 4, 1895 ; E. S. Larsen, *Bull. U.S. Geol.
Sur.*, 679, 1921 ; P. Groth, *Tabellarische Uebersicht der Mineralien*, Braunschweig, 96, 1898 ;
A. Breithaupt, *Uebersicht des Mineralsystems*, Freiberg, 1830 ; A. Coloriano, *Bull. Soc. Chim.*,
(2), 45. 708, 1886 ; *Recherches sur quelques arsénates cristallisés*, Paris, 1886 ; *Compt. Rend.*,
103. 274, 1886 ; O. Pufahl, *Centr. Min.*, 289, 1920 ; F. S. Beudant, *Traité élémentaire de
minéralogie*, Paris, 2. 602, 1832.
    ⁸ R. J. Haüy, *Traité de minéralogie*, Paris, 3. 577, 1801 ; D. L. G. Karsten, *Hoff's Mag.*, 1.
543, 1801 ; L. N. Vauquelin, *Journ. Mines*, 10. 562, 1801 ; C. F. Ludwig, *Handbuch der Mineralogie*, Leipzig, 180, 1803 ; H. J. Brooke and W. H. Miller, *Introduction to Mineralogy*, London,
1852 ; A. Breithaupt, *Vollständiges Charakteristik des Mineralsystems*, Dresden, 42, 1832 ;
Vollständiges Handbuch der Mineralogie, Dresden, 149, 1847 ; R. Jameson, *A System of Mineralogy*, Edinburgh, 1820 ; F. S. Beudant, *Traité élémentaire de mineralogie*, Paris, 2. 598, 1832 ;
A. Damour and A. des Cloizeaux, *Ann. Chim. Phys.*, (3), 13. 413, 1845 ; R. Hermann, *Journ.
prakt. Chem.*, (1), 33. 294, 1844 ; A. H. Church, *Journ. Chem. Soc.*, 23. 168, 1870 ; E. G. J. Hartley,
Min. Mag., 12. 120, 1898 ; C. F. Rammelsberg, *Handbuch der Mineralchemie*, Leipzig, 352,
1875 ; P. Groth, *Tabellarische Uebersicht der Mineralien*, Braunschweig, 96, 1898 ; P. Gaubert,
Bull. Soc. Min., 27. 223, 1904 ; C. Palache and H. E. Merwin, *Amer. Journ. Science*, (4), 28. 537,
1909 ; H. S. Washington, *ib.*, (3), 35. 303, 1888 ; E. V. Shannon, *ib.*, (5), 7. 31, 1924 ; R. Chenevix,
Phil. Trans., 91. 201, 1801.
    ⁹ A. Hirsch, *Ein Beitrag zur Kenntnis der Arsenate des Kupfers*, Halle a. S., 1890 ; H. Sal-
kowsky, *Journ. prakt. Chem.*, (1), 104. 166, 1868 ; C. Lefèvre, *Sur les arsénates cristallisés*,
Paris, 1891 ; *Ann. Chim. Phys.*, (6), 27. 22, 1892 ; W. F. Foshag, *Amer. Min.*, 9. 30, 1924.
    ¹⁰ E. Mitscherlich, *Ann. Chim. Phys.*, (2), 19. 350, 407, 1821 ; T. Graham, *Phil. Trans.*, 123.
253, 1833 ; *Mem. Chem. Soc.*, 2. 51, 1845 ; O. B. Kühn, *Zeit. Pharm.*, 9. 24, 1857 ; R. W. G. Wyckoff, *Amer. Journ. Science*, (5), 10, 107, 1925 ; *Zeit. Kryst.*, 62. 529, 1926 ; J. Setterberg, *Oefvers.
Akad. Förh. Stockholm*, 3. 25, 1846 ; *Journ. Pharm. Chim.*, (3), 12. 142, 1847 ; O. Widman,
Bull. Soc. Chim., (2), 20. 64, 1873 ; L. Hurtzig, *Einige Beiträge zur näheren Kenntniss der Sauren
des Phosphors und Arseniks*, Göttingen, 1859 ; L. Hurtzig and A. Geuther, *Liebig's Ann.*, 111.
168, 1859 ; F. Wöhler, *ib.*, 30. 1, 1839 ; 114. 119, 1860 ; *Gött. Nachr.*, 97, 1860 ; A. Joly, *Compt.
Rend.*, 103. 1071, 1886 ; H. Dufet, *Bull. Soc. Min.*, 9. 36, 1886 ; G. C. Wittstein, *Repert. Pharm.*,
(3), 1. 41, 1848 ; *Zeit. anal. Chem.*, 2. 19, 1863 ; J. F. Simon, *Pogg. Ann.*, 40. 417, 1837 ; 41.
424, 1837 ; H. Goguel, *Contribution à l'étude des arsénates et des antimonates cristallisés préparés
par voie humide*, Paris, 1896 ; C. W. Scheele, *Svenska Akad. Handl.*, 40. 316, 1778 ; G. P. Baxter
and F. B. Coffin, *Journ. Amer. Chem. Soc.*, 31. 297, 1909 ; *Zeit. anorg. Chem.*, 62. 52, 1909 ;
G. S. Whitby, *ib.*, 67. 107, 1910 ; A. Dexheimer, *Ueber die Darstellung anorganisch Kolloide in
kolloidalen organischen Medien*, Erlangen, 53, 1910 ; E. V. Zappi and J. J. Landaburu, *Anal.
Soc. Quim. Argentine*, 4. 218, 1916 ; *Bull. Soc. Chim.*, (4), 23. 318, 1918 ; E. C Franklin and
C. A. Kraus, *Amer. Chem. Journ.*, 20. 829, 1898 ; T. Thomson, *Ann. Phil.*, 4. 171, 1814 ; 15. 81,
1820.

§ 17. The Arsenates of the Calcium Family

According to R. Bunsen,¹ and many others, calcium arsenate occurs in some
natural spring-waters. Thus, R. Bunsen found 0·7 mgrm. per litre in the waters
of Baden-Baden ; L. R. von Fellenberg, 0·00015 grm. per litre in the water of
Gurnigel ; J. Lefort, traces in the water of Jenzat ; J. Löwe, in the waters of
Kronthal ; and C. R. Fresenius, traces in the waters of Weisbaden. Calcium
arsenate occurs as the minerals haidingerite, and pharmacolite—*vide infra*. The
use of calcium arsenate as an insecticide—*e.g* the cotton boll weevil—has been
discussed by B. R. Coad,² H. W. Ambruster, etc. C. Brame made calcium arsenate
in the dry way by heating to redness a mixture of arsenic trioxide and lime—some
arsenic is at the same time volatilized. If arsenic acid be neutralized with calcium

hydroxide, C. Blarez found that the following amounts of heat, Q, are evolved for each eq. of base :

	1 Eq	2 Eq.	3 Eq.	4 Eq.	5 Eq.
$Ca(OH)_2$.	14·50	12·50	2·25	0·28	0·25 cals.
Q $Sr(OH)_2$.	14·17	12·33	3·88	1·03	1·03 „
$Ba(OH)_2$	14·00	13·50	15·50	0·25	0·50 „

Cochineal reacts alkaline when one eq. of base is added, and phenolphthalein with two eq. H. V. Tartar and co-workers prepared calcium hydroxytriorthoarsenate, $Ca(OH)_2.3Ca_3(PO_4)_2$, by the hydrolysis of calcium orthoarsenate.

Eight grams of the undried material were digested in a 2-litre flask with 1·75 litres of freshly distilled water. The flask was then connected to a reflux condenser and the contents heated to gentle boiling. The boiling was continued for days, the water being siphoned off from the solid material each morning and replaced with fresh distilled water. Qualitative tests on the liquid removed showed from day to day a steadily decreasing content of arsenate ion until about the twelfth day, when it apparently became constant. The solid material was white, amorphous, and almost gelatinous. After being filtered off by suction, it was dried to constant weight at 100°.

They found that 100 grms. of water at 25° dissolve 0·0048 grm. of the salt. If an excess of a dil. soln. of calcium chloride be allowed to stand for a long time in contact with sodium hydroarsenate, P. von Kotschoubey said that a basic salt is formed, namely, calcium trioxyorthoarsenate, $3CaO.Ca_3(AsO_4)_2.6H_2O$; he also found that if calcium chloride be added to an ammoniacal soln. of alkali arsenate, normal calcium orthoarsenate, $Ca_3(AsO_4)_2.3H_2O$, is precipitated ; when F. Field used an ammoniacal soln. of ammonium arsenate, he said that the precipitate is a mixture of the normal salt and ammonium calcium arsenate. T. Graham mixed an aq. soln. of calcium chloride and sodium orthoarsenate. If the calcium salt be added to an excess of the alkali arsenate, the precipitate entangles more of the alkali arsenate than when the procedure is reversed. H. V. Tartar and co-workers, and R. H. Robinson prepared this salt by adding a soln. of sodium hydroarsenate in slight excess to a soln. of calcium chloride. The resulting mixture was then made distinctly alkaline with sodium hydroxide. After some hours the amorphous, flocculent precipitate was washed, first by decantation and then by suction on a Büchner funnel. C. Blarez prepared this salt by treating an aq. soln. of arsenic acid with an excess of lime-water. The precipitate was washed until the washwater was neutral. C. L. Bloxam treated a mixture of the required proportions of arsenic trioxide and calcium carbonate with an excess of nitric acid, and calcined the residue. In preparing calcium arsenate, L. Cambi advocated oxidizing the arsenic trioxide with chlorine rather than with nitric acid—the apparatus is simpler, the reaction proceeds spontaneously, and the absorption of chlorine is quantitative —vide supra, action of chlorine on arsenic trioxide. M. N. and P. N. Dvornikoff studied the reaction. D. Lopez passed chlorine into a mixture of arsenic trioxide, lime, and luke-warm water, and boiled the product to lessen the production of soluble arsenates. A light, fluffy calcium arsenate was formed. The manufacture was discussed by C. W. Drury and C. W. Simmons, S. S. Sadtler, W. H. Simpson, H. W. Ambruster, J. Altwegg, C. Ellis and V. T. Stewart, the Société Chimique des Usines du Rhône, F. C. Cook and N. E. McIndoo, J. G. Lamb, E. R. Rushton, U.S. Smelting, Mining and Refining Co., L. C. Drefahl and C. H. Sakryd, C. B. Dickey, H. Howard and E. A. Taylor, and T. Shiomi and K. Otsu. J. F. Simon said that calcium orthoarsenate is not decomposed at a red-heat ; and C. L. Bloxam found that the orthoarsenate is sparingly soluble in water ; readily soluble in hydrochloric acid ; and the aq. soln. has an alkaline reaction. G. Kemp and J. von Gyulay obtained colloidal calcium arsenate by the successive addition of an ammonium salt, acetic acid, and an excess of sodium arsenate to a soln. of a calcium salt. The opalescent jelly crystallizes after some time. L. Cambi and G. Bozza studied the electrometric titration of calcium nitrate or chloride with sodium orthoarsenate or sodium hydroarsenate.

In the manufacture of calcium arsenate as an insecticide for the cotton-plant as an alternative to oxidation of arsenic trioxide or white arsenic by nitric acid, the oxidation can be effected electrolytically. The process has been examined by S. J. Lloyd and A. M. Kennedy. The white arsenic is dissolved in soda-lye so as to produce a soln. of basic sodium arsenite with $As_2O_3 : NaOH$ in the proportion 198 : 250. The reaction is symbolized : $As_2O_3 + 6NaOH = 2NaAsO_2 + 4NaOH + H_2O$. When this soln. is electrolyzed between iron electrodes, hydrogen and arsenic, corresponding to about one per cent. of the arsenic trioxide employed, are produced at the cathode. Only a small amount of oxygen is evolved at the anode, the remainder serving to convert sodium arsenite to arsenate : $2NaAsO_2 + 4NaOH = 2Na_3AsO_4 + 2H_2$. When the oxidation is complete, the soln. is filtered to remove the arsenic. Milk of lime is added : $2Na_3AsO_4 + 4Ca(OH)_2 = Ca_4As_2O_9 + 6NaOH + H_2O$; and the sludge is filtered. The calcium arsenate is washed and dried. The filtrate of soda-lye is used to dissolve more white arsenic. The raw materials employed are white arsenic, slaked lime, and sufficient sodium hydroxide to replace the inevitable losses of the operating cycle. Ordinary grey arsenic can be used and the cost of re-roasting to white arsenic avoided. The extra lime beyond that required for the normal orthoarsenate is used so that the solubility of the product in water is sufficiently low to avoid any danger of burning or injuring the foliage of the cotton plant. The current efficiency of the oxidation is very high, being practically 100 per cent. for the oxidation of the first 85 per cent. of the trioxide, Fig. 25, and is about 85 per cent. efficiency over the whole range oxidation. The relative toxicity of the different calcium arsenates to locusts and boll weevils was found by S. B. Hendricks, A. M. Bacot, and H. C. Young to be greater with the acid than with the basic arsenates.

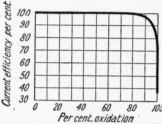

FIG. 25.—Current Efficiency of the Oxidation for Electrolytic Calcium Arsenate.

P. von Kotschoubey obtained **strontium orthoarsenate,** $Sr_3(AsO_4)_2$, by adding ammonia to a soln. of the hydroarsenate in acids ; C. Blarez, by treating arsenic acid with strontia-water, and washing the precipitate until free from acids ; and C. Lefèvre, by adding the necessary amount of strontia to a fused mixture of equal parts of sodium orthoarsenate and sodium chloride. The sodium salts are washed from the cold mass by water. The colourless rhombic crystals are not decomposed by hot water ; and they are freely soluble in dil. acids.

J. J. Berzelius obtained **barium orthoarsenate,** $Ba_3(AsO_4)_2$, by treating a soln. of hydroarsenate with ammonia, and H. Salkowsky showed that the composition of the precipitate depends on the conc. of the ammonia since both the hydroarsenate, and the orthoarsenate may be deposited. P. von Kotschoubey used a similar mode of preparation using a soln. of the hydroarsenate in as little acid as possible. H. Salkowsky said that in this case the precipitate is liable to be contaminated with barium chloride ; and if much ammonium salt is present, a complex salt is formed ; and, according to E. Mitscherlich, some hydroarsenate. T. Graham found that if a soln. of sodium orthoarsenate be gradually added to a soln. of barium chloride, the white pulverulent calcium orthoarsenate which is precipitated should be washed quickly so that it may not absorb carbon dioxide from the air ; if the barium chloride be gradually added to the sodium orthoarsenate, a gelatinous precipitate is formed ; this becomes flocculent when boiled, but the liquid is alkaline, showing that some hydroarsenate has been precipitated. The precipitate also adsorbs some sodium arsenate which cannot be all removed by washing. A. Laugier obtained the ortho-arsenate by the action of arsenic acid on an excess of baryta-water ; and F. Field by the action of barium chloride on an ammoniacal soln. of arsenic acid. C. Lefèvre obtained the normal salt in tabular crystals by fusing baryta with a mixture of sodium hydroarsenate and alkali chloride, and washing the cold mass with water ;

and O. Schairer made it by melting a mixture of arsenic trioxide and barium dioxide, and washing the product with cold water—in this case some pyroarsenate is formed. F. Field said that the white powder dried at 100° is almost free from water, and all is lost at 150° ; H. Salkowsky said that the salt dried at 130° retains 3·44–4·26 per cent. of water. O. Schairer found that the salt does not fuse in the blast-flame. T. Graham observed that about 0·8 per cent. of carbonate may be formed when the orthoarsenate is ignited in air. F. Field stated that 100 parts of cold water dissolve 0·055 part of the salt ; 100 parts of a 5 per cent. soln. of ammonium chloride, 0·193 part ; and 100 parts of a 10 per cent. soln. of aq. ammonia, 0·003 part. E. F. Anthon found the salt dissolves readily in cold hydrochloric, nitric, tartaric, and acetic acids ; and A. Laugier, that its solubility in water is not increased by ammonia or alkali salts.

The acid salt, **calcium hydroarsenate,** $CaHAsO_4$, is represented in nature by the hydrated minerals pharmacolite, and haidingerite. C. J. Selb referred to an *arseniksauer Kalk*, which D. L. G. Karsten called **pharmacolite**—from φάρμακον, poison ; and F. S. Beudant, *arsenicite*. It occurs along with arsenical ores at Wittichen, Baden ; at St. Marie-aux-Mines, Vosges ; Völlegg, Styria ; Andreasberg, Harz ; Joachimsthal, Bohemia ; Glücksbrunn, Thuringia ; Riechelsdorff and Bieber, Hesse ; etc. Analyses by M. H. Klaproth, C. F. Rammelsberg, F. Petersen, E. Jannettaz, and E. Hatle and H. Tauss correspond with the *dihydrate*, $CaHAsO_4.2H_2O$, though C. F. Rammelsberg gave $CaHAsO_4.2\frac{1}{2}H_2O$. The other mineral was described by E. Turner, and called **haidingerite**—after W. Haidinger. The mineral occurs at Joachimsthal, Bohemia ; and at Wittichen and Alpirsbach, Baden. Analyses reported by E. Turner, and C. F. Rammelsberg correspond with the *monohydrate*, $CaHAsO_4.H_2O$.

Calcium hydroarsenate is precipitated on mixing an excess of arsenic acid with lime-water. E. Mitscherlich said that if sodium hydroarsenate be added to a soln. of calcium chloride so long as a precipitate is formed, the normal arsenate is formed, but H. Salkowsky, and P. von Kotschoubey found the composition approximates $CaHAsO_4.1\frac{1}{2}H_2O$, contaminated with some sodium salt. If the acidic filtrate from sodium hydroarsenate and calcium chloride soln. be boiled, it becomes turbid, the soln. clears up again on cooling. The precipitate deposited from the boiling soln. was found by H. Salkowsky to be the monohydrate, $CaHAsO_4.H_2O$, contaminated with a little soda. According to H. Dufet, if soln. of calcium nitrate and sodium hydroarsenate be allowed to mix slowly by diffusion, crystals resembling pharmacolite are produced. H. Debray digested calcium carbonate with arsenic acid and found that the product obtained at ordinary temp. was hemitrihydrated ; that at 70° was monohydrated ; and that at 100° was anhydrous. O. Hörmann found the anhydrous salt is produced when the dihydroarsenate is boiled with water. According to A. de Schulten, if a neutral soln. of 10 grms. of calcium carbonate in hydrochloric acid be diluted to 200 c.c., mixed with 25 c.c. of hydrochloric acid of sp. gr. 1·04, and mixed with a soln. of 30 grms. of heptahydrated sodium hydroarsenate in 20 c.c. of water, in 24 hrs., crystals of the *dihydrate*, pharmacolite, are formed ; again, if 70 grms. of calcium carbonate be dissolved in hydrochloric acid, and treated with a conc. soln. of 218 grms. of heptahydrated sodium hydroarsenate, and diluted to a litre, heated to 70° on a water-bath, and treated with conc. ammonia until the precipitate is almost dissolved, the filtered soln. yields crystals of the monohydrate, haidingerite, when kept for 10 days at 50°–70°. The equilibrium conditions are indicated in Fig. 26.

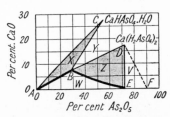

FIG. 26.—Equilibrium in the System : $CaO–As_2O_5–H_2O$ at 35°.

C. M. Smith studied the equilibrium conditions in the system $CaO–As_2O_5–H_2O$ at 35°. The composition of the soln. with different proportions of lime and arsenic acid is indicated in Fig. 26. AB and BE are solubility curves with the solid phase respectively $CaHAsO_4.H_2O$, and $Ca(H_2AsO_4)_2$; and these are the only calcium arsenates stable under these conditions. The area X refers to a soln. plus $CaHAsO_4.H_2O$; Z, soln. plus $Ca(H_2AsO_4)_2$; Y, constant soln. with 6·8 per cent. CaO and 27·5 per cent. As_2O_5 plus $CaHAsO_4.H_2O$ plus $Ca(H_2AsO_4)_2$; V, to a constant soln. plus $Ca(H_2AsO_4)_2$ plus $3As_2O_5.5H_2O$; and W, to soln. with no solid phase. F refers to the hydrate $3As_2O_5.5H_2O$.

According to W. Haidinger, the white, rhombic crystals of haidingerite have the axial ratios $a : b : c = 0·83910$; $1 : 0·49895$; A. de Schulten gave $0·4273 : 1 : 0·4923$ for the artificial crystals. The minute crystals are usually aggregated into botryoidal forms and drusy crusts. The cleavage on the (010)-face is perfect. The thin plates are slightly flexible. The hardness is 1·5–2·5; and the sp. gr. 2·858. The optical character is positive; and A. des Cloizeaux gave for the index of refraction $\gamma = 1·67$. Pharmacolite commonly occurs in delicate silky fibres, or acicular crystals which may occur in stellated groups. The mineral may also occur massive, and in botryoidal and stalactitic forms. A. Schrauf gave for the axial ratios of the grey or white, monoclinic, prismatic crystals of pharmacolite, $a : b : c = 0·61373 : 1 : 0·36223$, and $\beta = 83° 13\frac{1}{4}'$; while for the artificial crystals, H. Dufet gave $0·6236 : 1 : 0·3548$, and $\beta = 83° 13'$. The crystals are said to be isomorphous with those of gypsum; and to be closely related to those of brushite, $CaHPO_4.2H_2O$. The optic axial angle $2V = 79° 24'$. The cleavage on the (010)-face is perfect. A. des Cloizeaux said that the optic axial angle $2H_0$ for red-light is 113° 24'; for yellow-light, 112° 30'; and for blue-light, 111° 47'; the optical character is negative. The hardness is 2·0–2·5; the sp. gr., 2·64–2·73. A. de Schulten gave 2·730 at 15° for the natural crystals, and 2·754 at 15° for the artificial ones. The indices of refraction found by H. Dufet are $\alpha = 1·5825$, $\beta = 1·5891$, and $\gamma = 1·5937$ for Na-light. F. C. B. Schiefer said that calcium hydroarsenate is slightly soluble in acetic acid; and, according to C. H. Pfaff, it is insoluble in water, but dissolves freely in hydrochloric and nitric acids, as well as in an aq. soln. of ammonium chloride, sulphate, nitrate, or acetate. C. F. Wach added that the amount dissolved by soln. of ammonium salts at ordinary temp. is but slight, and that the soln. on standing deposits crystals of a complex salt. When boiled with an ammonium salt, the arsenate is dissolved with the evolution of ammonia. A. Laugier said that with ammonium oxalate, calcium oxalate is formed. According to H. Salkowsky, when hydrated calcium hydroarsenate is heated to 125°, a little water is given off; all the water of crystallization is lost at 160°; and most of the constitutional water is given off at 240°, and the remainder at a red-heat. A. H. Church found that pharmacolite lost one and retained one mol. of water at 100°–200°. The dehydrated product has been regarded as **calcium pyroarsenate**, $Ca_2As_2O_7$. C. Lefèvre made crystals of a similar substance by fusing calcium oxide or carbonate with potassium hydroarsenate; or with a mixture of the arsenate with less than 40 per cent. of calcium chloride. It forms colourless rhombic plates which when treated with cold water form calcium hydroarsenate. The pyrophosphate is decomposed at a higher temp.

H. Salkowsky prepared **strontium hydroarsenate**, $SrHAsO_4$, by mixing soln. of strontium chloride and sodium hydroarsenate, and warming the acid filtrate from the sodium strontium arsenate to 75°, or, according to A. Joly, to 60°. Crystals of the required salt are deposited. O. Hörmann obtained this salt by the action of hot water on the dihydroarsenate. C. Lefèvre obtained this salt by treating the pyroarsenate with water. A. de Schulten mixed 10 grms. of hexahydrated strontium chloride in 150 c.c. of water, with 177 grms. of heptahydrated sodium hydroarsenate dissolved in 350 c.c. of water. The resulting precipitate was dissolved in conc. hydrochloric acid, and ammonia gradually added until the precipitate produced no longer redissolved. The filtered liquid was heated to 90°, treated with 0·3 per cent. of ammonia, and allowed to stand for a few days, when the anhydrous hydroarsenate crystallized out. If the mother-liquor be allowed to stand at ordinary temp. in an atm. of ammonia, the *monohydrate*, $SrAsO_4.H_2O$—*strontium haidingerite*—separates out in crystals. The prismatic crystals belong to the triclinic system and have the axial ratios $a : b : c = 0.6466 : 1 : 0.8346$, and $a = 92° 4'$, $\beta = 86° 32'$, and $\gamma = 90° 46'$. The sp. gr. of the anhydrous salt is $4.035°$ at $15°$, and that of the monohydrate is 3.306 at $15°$. H. Salkowsky found that the water of crystallization is expelled at $130°$, and O. Hörmann, that at $360°$ **strontium pyroarsenate**, $Sr_2As_2O_7$, is formed. C. Lefèvre prepared the pyroarsenate by a method analogous to that employed for the calcium salt. The salt is sparingly soluble in mineral acids.

Several of the phosphate and arsenate minerals occur in isomorphous associations, and the so-called phosphatoarsenates may be isomorphous mixtures. Hexagonal, pyramidal crystals of a **calcium strontium phosphatoarsenate**, $3(Ca,Sr)_3(P,As)_2O_8.Ca(OH,F)_2$, occur native at Sitapar, India; and G. F. H. Smith and G. T. Prior called it **fermorite**— after L. L. Fermor. The mineral is supposed to be a member of the apatite family. It is white with possibly a pink tinge. It is uniaxial; and optically negative. Its hardness is 5; its sp. gr., 3.518; and its refractive index, about 1.660.

According to J. J. Berzelius, and E. Mitscherlich, when sodium hydroarsenate is mixed with an excess of barium chloride, **barium hydroarsenate**, $BaHAsO_4$, is precipitated in small scaly crystals. The barium chloride should be in excess, and the sodium arsenate added slowly, drop by drop. The precipitate first formed disappears; if the barium chloride be gradually added to the alkali arsenate, the precipitate is a mixture of orthoarsenate and hydroarsenate, while barium dihydroarsenate remains in soln. According to C. W. Scheele, arsenic acid does not give a precipitate with soln. of barium chloride, nitrate, or acetate. L. Gmelin, and P. von Kotschoubey said that it does give a precipitate with the acetate; and G. Moretti, that it gives a precipitate even with acid barium sulphate. A. Joly obtained the hydroarsenate by adding baryta-water drop by drop to a soln. of arsenic acid until a soln. of phenolphthalein is reddened. The gelatinous precipitate can be crystallized by shaking. O. Hörmann obtained this salt by treating the dihydroarsenate with hot water; A. de Schulten, by a method analogous to that used for the strontium salt; and C. Lefèvre, by the action of water on the pyroarsenate. S. B. Hendricks studied the equilibrium conditions in the system $BaO-As_2O_5-H_2O$ at $30°$, and the results are summarized in Fig. 27. The

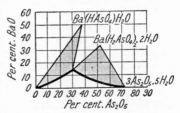

FIG. 27.—Equilibrium in the System: $BaO-As_2O_5-H_2O$ at $30°$.

solid phases are barium hydroarsenate, $BaHAsO_4.H_2O$; barium dihydroarsenate, $Ba(H_2AsO_4)_2.2H_2O$; and $3As_2O_5.5H_2O$. Alkaline hydrolysis of the former salt gave the orthoarsenate, $Ba_3(AsO_4)_2.nH_2O$. F. C. B. Schiefer recrystallized the salt from acetic acid. K. von Haushofer described this salt as forming rhombic or monoclinic plates isomorphous with the phosphate. A. de Schulten gave for the axial ratios of the rhombic crystals $a : b : c = 0.4171 : 1 : 0.4430$. J. J. Berzelius, and E. Mitscherlich said that the salt is a hemitrihydrate, $BaHAsO_4.1\frac{1}{2}H_2O$; while P. von Kotschoubey, J. Setterberg, E. J. Maumené, H. Salkowsky, O. Hörmann, and F. C. B. Schiefer found it to be a monohydrate, $BaHAsO_4.H_2O$, when dried over sulphuric acid, or at $100°$; at $120°-130°$ it loses its water of crystallization, and at $320°$ its constitutional water, forming, according to O. Hörmann, **barium pyroarsenate**, $Ba_2As_2O_7$. This same substance was prepared by C. Lefèvre by the method employed for the strontium salt. A. de Schulten gave 3.926 at $15°$ for the sp. gr. of the hydroarsenate. It is sparingly soluble in water, and in soln. of barium chloride and sodium hydroarsenate. It is soluble in dil. mineral acids. L. Gmelin found it to be decomposed by dil. sulphuric acid, and E. Duvillier, by dil. nitric acid. J. J. Berzelius, and C. Lefèvre said that water transformed it into a mixture of the orthoarsenate, and hydroarsenate, but H. Salkowsky could not confirm this.

Aq. ammonia was found by E. Mitscherlich to transform more or less of this salt into the normal arsenate.

C. L. Bloxam prepared **calcium dihydroarsenate**, $Ca(H_2AsO_4)_2.H_2O$, by the action of nitric acid on eq. proportions of calcium carbonate and arsenic trioxide ; and O. Hörmann, by treating calcium carbonate, or one of the preceding calcium arsenates, with an excess of arsenic acid, and evaporating the soln. The equilibrium conditions are indicated in Fig. 27. The colourless plates lose their water of crystal lization at 180°, and at 360° form a crystalline mass of **calcium metarsenate**, $Ca(AsO_3)_2$, which is insoluble in hydrochloric acid. The dihydroarsenate is sparingly soluble in cold water, and is decomposed by hot water into arsenic acid and the hydroarsenate. O. Hörmann obtained **strontium dihydroarsenate**, $Sr(H_2AsO_4)_2.2H_2O$, from an excess of arsenic acid and strontium carbonate. The crystals lose their water of crystallization at 240°–250°, and at a red-heat furnish **strontium metarsenate**, $Sr(AsO_4)_2$. J. J. Berzelius, and E. Mitscherlich obtained **barium dihydroarsenate**, $Ba(H_2AsO_4)_2.2H_2O$, by adding baryta-water to an aq. soln. of arsenic acid so long as a precipitate continues to form ; and by crystalliza tion from a soln. of the hydroarsenate in arsenic acid. O. Hörmann obtained it from a soln. of barium carbonate in an excess of arsenic acid. C. F. Rammelsberg reported the monoclinic crystals to have the axial ratios $a : b : c = 1.160 : 1 : 0.625$, and $\beta = 108° 34'$. E. Mitscherlich said that one mol. of water is lost at 120°–140°, and the other mol. at 180°–230° ; at a higher temp. **barium metarsenate**, $Ba(AsO_3)_2$, is formed. O. Hörmann found that the dihydroarsenate is sparingly soluble in water, and that an excess of water converts it into the hydroarsenate. The salt is freely soluble in hydrochloric acid, and less soluble in acetic acid.

C. F. Wach found that when lime-water is mixed with a dil. soln. of potassium, sodium, or ammonium arsenate and ammonium chloride, nitrate, or acetate, no precipitate is formed at first, but after a while, **ammonium calcium arsenate**, $Ca(NH_4)AsO_4.H_2O$, separates in needle-like crystals ; with more conc. soln., the lime-water produces a copious precipitate at once, and when this is digested with an excess of the ammonium salt, it does not dissolve but becomes crystalline. If arsenic acid be added to lime-water until a strong turbidity is produced, and an ammoniacal salt be then added, the liquid first becomes clear and afterwards deposits crystals of the complex salt. If calcium hydroarsenate be immersed in a soln. of ammonium chloride, it takes up a mol. of ammonia, forming this same complex salt. C. F. Wach thus described the preparation of this salt :

One part each of ammonium arsenate and chloride are dissolved in 4 parts of water, and lime-water is added so long as crystals begin to form. The crystals increase in quantity when the liquid is set aside in a cool place for 24 hrs. The salt is washed with water and dried between bibulous paper. The salt resembled ammonium magnesium arsenate.

F. Field made this salt by adding an excess of an ammoniacal soln. of ammonium arsenate to a soln. of calcium chloride ; C. L. Bloxam, by adding arsenic acid to an ammoniacal soln. of calcium chloride ; C. Lefèvre, by adding ammonia to a soln. of calcium arsenate in dil. hydrochloric acid ; and E. Baumann, by mixing soln. of calcium nitrate and arsenic acid in aq. ammonia. The salt may appear as a white crystalline powder, in needle-like crystals, or rhombic plates. The crystals effloresce in air, and, according to C. L. Bloxam, they lose all their combined water in 36 days. C. Lefèvre said that half the water is lost at 100°, and F. Field, that all is expelled at 140°. P. von Kotschoubey said that the salt dried at 125° is monohydrated. C. L. Bloxam regarded the salt as hexahydrated and said that when dried in vacuo over sulphuric acid, the composition is $(NH_4)Ca_3H_2(AsO_4)_3.3H_2O$; and when dried at 100°, $(NH_4)Ca_6H_5(AsO_4)_6.3H_2O$. When heated to a higher temp., calcium arsenate is formed. F. Field said that 100 parts of water dissolve 0.02 part of salt ; and C. Lefèvre, 0.046 part of the hemihydrate at 15°. F. Field said that 100 parts of a 5 per cent. soln. of ammonium chloride dissolve 0.42 part ; and 100 parts of a 3.5 per cent. ammonia, 0.001 part of salt ; while C. Lefèvre said that 100 parts of a soln. of one part of ammonium chloride in 7 parts of water dissolve 0.0023 part of salt, and 100 parts of a $1:3$ soln. of ammonia in water, 0·0095 part of salt. C. F. Wach added that the salt is soluble in hydrochloric and nitric acids, and that ammonia precipitates the salt from these soln. C. F. Wach found that strontium and barium hydroxides, treated in the same manner as calcium hydroxide, do not give the analogous arsenates—$NH_4SrAsO_4.6H_2O$, and $NH_4BaAsO_4.6H_2O$— since the precipitates contain no ammonia, and the equivalent of but one mol. of water, viz. $HSrAsO_4.H_2O$ and $HBaAsO_4.H_2O$. These presumably have the constitution :

$$H_2O=OH-Ca-O \atop NH_4-O \Big\rangle As \Big\langle {HO=OH_2 \atop HO=OH_2 \atop HO=OH_2} \qquad\qquad {HO \atop HO}\Big\rangle As \Big\langle{O \atop O}\Big\rangle Sr \atop OH$$

In harmony therewith, the strontium and barium arsenates lose a molecule of water below 125° and 150° respectively, and all the water at 225°. C. Lefèvre, and E. Baumann also prepared **ammonium strontium arsenate**, $(NH_4)SrAsO_4.\frac{1}{2}H_2O$, as a white crystalline powder, when dried at 100° ; and **ammonium barium arsenate**, $(NH_4)BaAsO_4.\frac{1}{2}H_2O$, when dried at 100°. H. Salkowsky said that the product is contaminated with the normal arsenate. According to C. Lefèvre, 100 parts of water dissolve 0·031 part of the strontium salt, and 0·072 part of the barium salt ; 100 parts of a mixture of ammonia and water in the proportion $1:3$, dissolve 0·0053 part of the barium salt ; 100 parts of a soln. of one part of ammonium chloride in seven parts of water, 0·5 part of the strontium salt ; and 100 parts of a soln. of one part of ammonium chloride in ten parts of water, 0·44 part of the barium salt.

C. Lefévre obtained crystals of **sodium calcium arsenate**, $NaCaAsO_4$, by fusing calcium carbonate with sodium chloride and the orthoarsenate or hydroarsenate ; and by using different proportions he obtained **sodium calcium hexarsenate**, $Na_4Ca_4As_6O_{21}$. He likewise made crystals of **sodium strontium arsenate**, $NaSrAsO_4$. H. Salkowsky, and A. Joly reported the monohydrate, $NaSrAsO_4.H_2O$, to be formed by mixing soln. of strontium chloride and sodium hydroarsenate : $3Na_2HAsO_4+2SrCl_2=2NaSrAsO_4+NaH_2AsO_4+3NaCl+HCl$. A. Joly obtained the enneahydrate, $NaSrAsO_4.9H_2O$, by allowing a mixed soln. of a mol of sodium hydro-arsenate in six litres of water and of a mol of strontium chloride in two litres, to stand for some time. H. Dufet said that the crystals obtained by A. Joly are tetratohedral. The monohydrate of H. Salkowsky lost only a little water at 100°–130° ; it is partially decomposed by treatment with hot water. A. Joly also prepared **sodium barium arsenate**, $NaBaAsO_4.9H_2O$, analogous to the strontium salt. C. Lefèvre reported **potassium calcium arsenate**, $KCaAsO_4$, to be prepared as in the case of the sodium salt ; likewise also the isomorphous **potassium strontium arsenate**, $KSrAsO_4$; and the **potassium barium arsenate**, $KBaAsO_4$.

As indicated above, tyrolite may be regarded as a calcium copper carbonato-arsenate, when the calcium carbonate found in some samples is regarded as an essential constituent ; and calciferous olivenites may be regarded as **calcium copper arsenate**. The mineral conichalcite—from κονία, powder ; and χαλκός, lime—was so named by A. Breithaupt and F. W. Fritzsche.[3] It is a bright mineral found in Andalusia, Spain ; in the Tintic district, Utah ; etc. Analyses were reported by A. Breithaupt and F. W. Fritzsche, G. S. Mackenzie, W. F. Hillebrand, and L. Michel. Samples contain up to 9·5 per cent. of phosphoric oxide, and 1·78 per cent. of vanadic oxide. The earlier analyses were represented by C. F. Rammelsberg, $2R_4(As,P,V)_2O_9.3H_2O$. W. F. Hillebrand supposed the mineral to be a **calcium copper hydroxyorthoarsenate**, $(Ca,Cu)_3(AsO_4)_2.Cu(OH)_2.\frac{1}{4}H_2O$; and P. Groth represented it by the formula $(CuOH)(Cu,Ca)(As,P,V)O_4.\frac{1}{4}H_2O$. It occurs in reniform masses, and in fibrous masses. L. Michel said that the crystals are probably rhombic ; with the optical angle $2E=c$. 88° ; the optical character is negative ; E. S. Larsen said positive, and added that the optic axial angle is small, and the indices of refraction $a=1·765$, $\beta=1·77$, and $\gamma=1·790$—for the Utah mineral he gave $\omega=1.778$, and $\epsilon=1.801$. L. Michel found the hardness to be 5·5; and the sp. gr. given by A. Breithaupt and F. W. Fritzsche, is 4·123, and by L. Michel, 4·15. It dissolves in acids. C. Palache and E. V. Shannon [4] described a mineral, which they called higginsite, from the Higgins mine, Bisbee, Arizona. The analysis corresponds with calcium copper hydroxyarsenate, $CuCa(OH)(AsO_4)$, say $Cu=AsO_4-Ca(OH)$. The bright green rhombic crystals have the axial ratio $a:b:c=0.6242:1:0.7940$. Its sp. gr. is 4·33; its hardness, 4·5; the birefringence is 0·030; the index of refraction a is greater than 1·745; E. S. Larsen found the optical character is negative, the optic axial angle about 90°, and the indices of refraction, $a=1.800$, $\beta=1.831$, and $\gamma=1.846$. C. Palache and E. V. Shannon found that the pleochroism $a=$green, $\beta=$yellowish-green, and $\gamma=$bluish-green. The mineral is readily soluble in hydrochloric or nitric acid, partly soluble in sulphuric acid, and insoluble in εq. ammonia. W. F. Foshag found a greenish-blue mineral at San Juan, Freirini Dept., Chile, and he called it freirinite. The analysis corresponds with sodium calcium copper arsenate, $6(Cu,Ca)O.3Na_2O.2As_2O_5.6H_2O$. It is uniaxial and negative; the refractive index $\epsilon=1.645$ and $\omega=1.748$; it is pleochroic, ϵ being light greenish-blue, and ω, dark greenish-blue; the optic axial angle $2V$ is small; and the basal cleavage, good.

REFERENCES.

[1] R. Bunsen, in F. Sandberger, *Geologische Beschreibung der Renchbader*, Heidelberg, 16, 1863; L. R. von Fellenberg, *Untersuchungen des Schwefelwassers des Gurnigelbades*, Bern, 1849; J. Lefort, *Journ. Pharm. Chim.*, (3), 21. 340, 1852; J. Löwe, *Jahresb. Phys. Ver. Frankfurt a. M.*, 58, 1855; C. R. Fresenius, *Untersuchungen des Mineralwassers des Herzogthums Nassau*, Wiesbaden, 1850.

[2] G. Moretti, *Sulla scoperta dell' ossisolfata di stronziana sei corpi maimi petrificati*, Pavia, 1812; *Ann. Chim. Phys.*, (1), 86. 262, 1813; C. Lefèvre, *Sur les arsénates cristallisés*, Paris, 1891; *Compt. Rend.*, 108. 1058, 1889; *Ann. Chim. Phys.*, (6), 27. 22, 1892; J. H. Debray, *ib.*, (3), 61. 419, 1860; A. Laugier, *ib.*, (1), 85. 26, 1813; E. Mitscherlich, *ib.*, (2), 19. 350, 407, 1821; C. W. Drury and C. W. Simmons, *Canadian Chem. Met.*, 9. 179, 1925; O. Hörmann, *Beitrag zur Kenntniss der Pyro- und Meta-Arsensäure sowie einiger Salze derselben*, Erlangen, 1897; T. Graham, *Phil. Trans.*, 123. 253, 1833; L. Cambi, *Giorn. Chim. Ind. Appl.*, 6. 527, 1924; P. von Kotschoubey, *Bull. Acad. St. Petersburg*, (2), 8. 129, 1850; *Journ. prakt. Chem.*, (1), 49. 189, 1850; H. Salkowsky, *ib.*, (1), 104. 143, 1868; G. Klemp and J. von Gyulay, *Koll. Zeit.*, 15. 202, 1914; 22. 57, 1918; L. Cambi and G. Bozza, *Giorn. Chim. Ind. Appl.*, 7. 687, 1925; F. Field, *Journ. Chem. Soc.*, 11. 6, 1858; T. H. Behrens, *Rec. Trav. Chim. Pays-Bas*, 10. 57, 1891; *Zeit. anal. Chem.*, 30. 164, 1891; C. L. Bloxam, *Chem. News*, 54. 193, 1886; D. Lopez, *U.S. Pat. No.* 1544250, 1925; 1578677, 1926; C. Ellis and T. V. Stewart, *ib.*, 1447203, 1447938, 1923; W. H. Simpson, *ib.*, 1507609, 1924; C. Brame, *Compt. Rend.*, 92. 180, 1881; C. Blarez, *ib.*, 103. 639, 1886; H. Dufet, *ib.*, 106. 1238, 1888; *Bull. Soc. Min.*, 11. 187, 1888; A. des Cloizeaux, *ib.*, 11. 192, 1888; *Ann. Chim. Phys.*, (3), 61. 419, 1861; *Compt. Rend.*, 52. 44, 1861; 106. 1218, 1888; A. Joly, *ib.*, 103. 746, 1197, 1886; 104. 1702, 1887; E. J. Maumené, *ib.*, 58. 250, 1864; E. Duvillier, *ib.*, 81. 1251, 1875; H. Debray, *ib.*, 52. 44, 1861; *Ann. Chim. Phys.*, (3), 61. 419, 1861; A. de Schulten, *Bull. Soc. Min.*, 26. 18, 1903; 27. 104, 1904; E. Jannettaz, *ib.*, 11. 214, 1888; E. Turner, *Edin. Journ. Science*, 3. 308, 1825; 6. 317, 1827; W. Haidinger, *ib.*, 3. 303, 1825; *Tschermak's Mitt.*, (1), 3. 138, 1873; *Pogg. Ann.*, 5. 181, 1825; J. F. Simon, *ib.*, 40. 117, 1837; *ib.*, 62. 150, 1844; F. Petersen, *ib.*, 134. 86, 1868; *Neues Jahrb. Min.*, 413, 1868; C. F. Rammelsberg, *Handbuch der krystallographisch-physikalischen Chemie*, Leipzic, 339, 1875; *Pogg. Ann.*, 62. 150, 1844; *Chemie*, Berlin, 1. 537, 1881; A. Schrauf, *Zeit. Kryst.*, 4. 284, 1880; K. von Haushofer, *ib.*, 4. 56, 1880; L. Buchrucker, *ib.*, 19. 164, 1891; C. H. Pfaff, *Schweigger's Journ.*, 45. 100, 1825; C. F. Wach, *ib.*, 59. 285, 1830; F. C. B. Schiefer, *Zeit. Ges. Naturw. Halle*, 23. 363, 1864; E. Baumann, *Arch. Pharm.*, (1), 36. 299, 1844; (1), 39. 10, 1844; P. von Kotschoubey and E. Baumann, *ib.*, (1), 36. 299, 1844; S. J. Lloyd and A. M. Kennedy, *Chem. Met. Engg.*, 32. 624, 1925; M. N. and P. N. Dvornikoff, *ib.*, 29. 1058, 1923; O. Schairer, *Chem. Ztg.*, 28. 15, 1904; J. Setterberg, *Oefvers. Akad. Förh. Stockholm*, 3. 25, 1846; *Journ. Pharm. Chim.*, (3), 12. 142, 1847; C. W. Scheele, *Svenska Akad. Handl.*, 40. 316, 1778; J. J. Berzelius, *Pogg. Ann.*, 7. 137, 1826; L. Gmelin, *ib.*, 4. 157, 1825; *Handbook of Chemistry*, London, 4. 301, 1850; E. F. Anthon, *Repert. Pharm.*, 59. 326, 1837; 76. 125, 1839; C. J. Selb, *Scherer's Journ.*, 4. 537, 1800; D. L. G. Karsten, *Mineralogische Tabellen*, Berlin, 75, 1800; F. S. Beudant, *Traité élémentaire de minéralogie*, Paris, 2. 595, 1832; H. Goguel, *Contribution à l'étude des arsénates et des antimonates cristallisés préparés par voie humide*, Paris, 1896; F. Sandberger, *Untersuchungen über Erzgänge*, Wiesbaden, 1885; A. Frenzel, *Neues Jahrb. Min.*, 684, 1874; E. Hatle and H. Tauss, *Verh. geol. Reichsanst. Wien*, 226, 1887; M. H. Klaproth, *Beiträge zur chemischen Kenntniss der Mineralkörper*, Berlin, 3. 281, 1802; A. H. Church, *Min. Mag.*, 11.

1, 1895; Société Chimique des Usines du Rhône, *U.S. Pat. No.* 1591958, 1926; *Brit. Pat. No* 214951, 1923; 216098, 1924; S. B. Hendricks, A. M. Bacot, and H. C. Young, *Journ. Ind. Eng. Chem.,* 18. 50, 1926; S. B. Hendricks, *Journ. Phys. Chem.,* 30. 248, 1926; C. M. Smith, *Journ. Amer. Chem. Soc.,* 42. 259, 1920; H. V. Tartar, L. Wood, and E. Hiner, *ib.,* 46. 809, 1924; G. F. H. Smith and G. T. Prior, *Min. Mag.,* 16. 84, 1911; B. R. Coad, *Bull. U.S. Dept. Agric.,* 875, 1920; F. C. Cook and N. E. McIndoo, *ib.,* 1147, 1923; *Chem. News,* 127. 35, 1923; H. W. Ambruster, *Chem. Met. Engg.,* 26. 1155, 1922; 27. 159, 1922; *Chem. News,* 128. 159, 217, 1924; R. H. Robinson, *Journ. Agric. Research,* 13. 281, 1918; *Bull. Oregon Agric. Exp., Stat.,* 131, 1918: C. B. Dickey, *U.S. Pat. No.* 1434650, 1922; H. M. Schleicher, *ib.,* 1588499, 1926; U.S. Smelting, Mining and Refining Co., *ib.,* 1532577, 1925; H. Howard and E. A. Taylor, *Canadian Pat. No.* 234984, 1923; J. Altwegg, *ib.,* 243033, 1924; *U.S. Pat. No.* 1608288, 1926; T. Shiomi and K. Otsu, *Japanese Pat. No.,* 41739, 1922; S. J. Lloyd and A. M. Kennedy, *Trans. Amer. Inst. Chem. Eng.,* 16. ii, 29, 1924; *Chem. Met. Engg.,* 32. 624, 1925; *Canadian Pat. No.* 253583, 1925; *Brit. Pat. No.* 239363, 1924; J. G. Lamb, *U.S. Pat. No.* 1505648, 1924; L. C. Drefahl and C. H. Sakryd, *ib.,* 1475545, 1924; S. S. Sadtler, *ib.,* 1513934, 1924; H. P. Bassett, *ib.,* 1588691, 1926; E. R. Rushton, *ib.,* 1624281, 1927.

³ P. Groth, *Tabellarische Uebersicht der Mineralien,* Braunschweig, 1898; C. F. Rammelsberg, *Handbuch der Mineralchemie,* Leipzig, 349, 1875; L. Michel, *Bull. Soc. Min.,* 31. 51, 1909; G. S. Mackenzie, *Min. Mag.,* 6. 181, 1885; W. F. Hillebrand, *Proc. Colorado Scient. Soc.,* 1. 112, 1884; A. Breithaupt and F. W. Fritzsche, *Pogg. Ann.,* 77. 150, 1849; E. S. Larsen, *Bull. U.S. Geol. Sur.,* 679, 1921.

⁴ C. Palache and E. V. Shannon, *Amer. Min.,* 5. 155, 1920; C. Palache, *ib.,* 5. 159, 1920; E. S. Larsen, *Bull. U.S. Geol. Sur.,* 679, 1921; W. F. Foshag, *Amer. Min.,* 9. 30, 1921.

§ 18. The Arsenates of the Beryllium-Mercury Family

While the magnesium arsenates are stable, those of aluminium can be obtained in aq. soln. only in a highly basic form, and those of beryllium are intermediate between the two. A. Atterberg [1] made **beryllium orthoarsenate**, $Be_3(AsO_4)_2.6H_2O$, as a flocculent precipitate, by adding sodium orthoarsenate to a soln. of a beryllium salt. J. J. Berzelius also made this salt, and said that it is insoluble in water but soluble in an excess of arsenic acid. B. Bleyer and B. Müller made this salt by mixing sodium hydroarsenate and beryllium sulphate in the proportions required for $BeSO_4+Na_2HAsO_4=BeHAsO_4+Na_2SO_4$; the product is hydrolyzed and these products furnish a voluminous white powder. The air-dried product is the *penta-decahydrate,* $Be_3(AsO_4)_2.15H_2O$. If this salt remains for a long time in contact with the mother-liquor it is hydrolyzed into a basic salt. If an attempt is made to prepare the orthoarsenate by the reaction: $2Na_3AsO_4+3BeSO_4=Be_3(AsO_4)_2$ $+3Na_2SO_4$, the basic salt, **beryllium oxyorthoarsenate,** $BeO.Be_3(AsO_4)_2.8H_2O$, is deposited as a white amorphous powder. A. Atterberg obtained **beryllium hydro-arsenate,** $BeHAsO_4.2H_2O$, by dissolving the hydroxide in arsenic acid, and precipitating with alcohol. It is viscous solid. B. Bleyer and B. Müller obtained the anhydrous salt by heating arsenic pentoxide and beryllium hydroxide in a sealed tube at about 220°. The product is impure. It was not possible to obtain it in soln. They also prepared beryllium dihydroarsenate, $Be(H_2AsO_4)_2$, by the action of a hot sat. soln. of arsenic acid on beryllium hydroxide. The conc. soln. over sulphuric acid yields colourless hygroscopic crystals which can be dried on porous tiles. They prepared **ammonium beryllium orthoarsenate,** $NH_4BeAsO_4.4\frac{1}{2}H_2O$, from a mixture of ammonium sulphate, sodium hydroarsenate, and arsenic acid. This salt readily undergoes hydrolysis, and the basic products $2(NH_4)_2O.3As_2O_5.7BeO.11H_2O$, and $(NH_4)_2O.2As_2O_5.5BeO.7H_2O$—respectively **ammonium beryllium hexaorthoarsenate,** $2(NH_4)_2Be_2(AsO_4)_2.Be_3(AsO_4)_2$, and **ammonium beryllium tetraorthoarsenate,** $(NH_4)_2Be_2(AsO_4)_2.Be_3(AsO_4)_2$, result. The potassium and sodium salts are even more easily hydrolyzed, so that B. Bleyer and B. Müller could prepare only the basic salts **sodium beryllium oxydiortho-arsenate,** $2NaBeAsO_4.BeO.12H_2O$; and **potassium beryllium oxydiorthoarsenate,** $2KBeAsO_4.BeO.10H_2O$, from the alkali hydroarsenate, and beryllium sulphate.

When a soln. of magnesium sulphate is treated with the eq. amount of sodium orthoarsenate, and the amorphous precipitate is allowed to stand in contact with the mother-liquid for some days, F. Kinkelin [2] observed that crystals of the *docosihydrate* of normal magnesium arsenate, or **magnesium orthoarsenate,**

$Mg_3(AsO_4)_2.22H_2O$, are produced; and if ammonium or potassium magnesium orthoarsenate be digested with water for a long time, crystals of the *decahydrate*, $Mg_3(AsO_4)_2.10H_2O$, appear. A. de Schulten mixed a soln. of 20 grms. of heptahydrated magnesium sulphate in a litre of water with a mixture of 16·9 grms. of heptahydrated sodium hydroarsenate and 4·5 grms. of sodium hydrocarbonate in 800 c.c. of water, and allowed the amorphous precipitate to stand for 24 hrs. at 20°. Crystals of the *octohydrate*, $Mg_3(AsO_4)_2.8H_2O$, were formed. Again, L. Chevron and A. Droixhe mixed soln. of sodium dihydroarsenate, magnesium sulphate, and sodium hydrocarbonate, and obtained the *heptahydrate*, $Mg_3(AsO_4)_2.7H_2O$. The octohydrate also occurs in nature as the mineral **hoernesite**—named after R. Hoernes—which was described by W. Haidinger. It was first recognized by A. Kenngott in a collection of minerals from Barnat, Hungary. The analysis agrees closely with $Mg_3(AsO_4)_2.8H_2O$. E. Bertrand found the hoernesite from Nagyag, Hungary, contained a little calcium and manganese. W. Haidinger said that the crystals of hoernesite are monoclinic and probably isomorphous with those of vivianite, bobierrite, and erythrite. The snow-white crystals have the gypsum habit. The crystals are also columnar and stellar foliated. The clinodiagonal cleavage is perfect. F. Zambonini, and A. de Schulten made a few measurements of the crystal angles. W. Haidinger gave for the hardness of hoernesite 1, and for the sp. gr. 2·474; A. de Schulten found the artificially prepared octohydrate to have a sp. gr. of 2·609 at 15°. W. Haushofer found the tabular crystals of the docosihydrate to be monoclinic and isomorphous with the corresponding phosphate. E. S. Larsen found the optic axial angle to be 60°; the optical character positive; and the indices of refraction of the monoclinic crystals to be $a=1·548-1·563$, $\beta=1·556-1·571$, and $\gamma=1·574-1·596$. The sp. gr. is 1·788 at 15°. The optical properties were also studied by F. Ulrich, A. de Schulten, and F. Zambonini. Hoernesite is easily soluble in acids. F. Kinkelin found that when the docosihydrate is dried over conc. sulphuric acid it contains 6 mols. of water; when dried at 100°, 5 mols.; and when dried at 200°, one mol. The docosihydrate effloresces slowly in air, and when kept under water it forms the decahydrate which does not change in air. According to C. Blarez, the neutralization of arsenic acid furnishes 14·87 cals. for the first eq. of base; 11·46 cals. for the second; and 2·03 cals. for the third. In the coagulation of magnesium arsenate, gel formation was found by E. O. Kraemer to occur comparatively suddenly following an initial induction period.

T. Graham obtained **magnesium hydroarsenate**, $MgHAsO_4.nH_2O$, by the action of sodium hydroarsenate on magnesium sulphate in aq. soln.; and, added F. Kinkelin, some of the normal arsenate is precipitated at the same time. F. Kinkelin neutralized a soln. of sodium hydroarsenate with acetic acid, added the calculated amount of magnesium sulphate, allowed the amorphous precipitate to stand for some days, and thus obtained crystals of the *heptahydrate*, $MgHAsO_4.7H_2O$. P. von Kotschoubey said both T. Graham's and F. Kinkelin's products are heptahydrates. F. C. B. Schiefer said that the salt which crystallizes from a soln. of the calcined residue of ammonium magnesium arsenate in acetic acid is the *pentahydrate*, $MgHAsO_4.5H_2O$, but F. Kinkelin said that it is the heptahydrate. A. de Schulten heated magnesium carbonate with an excess of arsenic acid in a sealed tube at 225°, and obtained monoclinic prisms of the *hemihydrate*, $MgHAsO_4.\frac{1}{2}H_2O$. Heptahydrated magnesium hydroarsenate occurs in nature as the mineral **roesslerite**—named after K. Roessler—described by J. R. Blum as occurring in thin plates with a columnar or fibrous structure at Bieber, Hasse. The monoclinic crystals of roesslerite were found by K. von Haushofer to have the axial ratios $a:b:c=0·4473:1:0·2598$, and $\beta=94°26'$. The cleavage on the (111)-face is incomplete. A. de Schulten gave 3·155 for the sp. gr. at 15° of the salt he prepared. The heptahydrate is stable in air; and F. Kinkelin found that it is decomposed by much water into the normal orthoarsenate and soluble acidic salt. C. Reischauer said that the heptahydrate loses 4·5 mols. of water when dried over sulphuric acid:

F. Kinkelin said 5·5 mols. are so lost; and 5 mols. at 100°—T. Graham said 6 mols.— and 6 mols at 200°. T. Graham, and F. Kinkelin found that when the hydro-arsenate is calcined, the so-called **magnesium pyroarsenate**, $Mg_2As_2O_7$, is formed. The same product was obtained by G. C. Wittstein, A. Levol, and C. R. Fresenius, by calcining ammonium magnesium arsenate—*vide infra*. The pyroarsenate is a white powder which H. Stallo found to have a sp. gr. of 3·7305–3·7649 at 15°–18°; and, added T. Graham, it melts at a high temp., and by a strong calcination becomes insoluble in acids. T. Graham regarded **magnesium dihydroarsenate**, $Mg(H_2AsO_4)_2$, as a gummy mass soluble in water; and F. C. B. Schiefer said that very deliquescent crystals of what was assumed to be this salt, are formed from a soln. of magnesium oxide in arsenic acid.

C. F. Wach found that **ammonium magnesium arsenate**, $(NH_4)MgAsO_4.6H_2O$, is produced by adding ammonium orthoarsenate to a soln. of magnesium chloride, sulphate, or nitrate so long as a translucent, crystalline precipitate is formed, and washing and drying the precipitate. A. Levol found that this salt is deposited when an ammoniacal soln. of an arsenate is treated with a soln. of a magnesium salt containing ammonium chloride—*vide supra*, analytical reactions of arsenic. If an excess of magnesium sulphate be used, R. E. O. Puller, and C. Freidheim and P. Michaelis observed that the precipitate may be contaminated with basic magnesium sulphate. L. F. Wood, and C. Freidheim and P. Michaelis precipitated the complex salt from alcoholic soln. A. de Schulten reported that measurable crystals of the complex salt are produced by allowing a mixture of 20 grms. of heptahydrated sodium hydroarsenate, 20 grms. of ammonium sulphate, 6 grms. of arsenic acid of sp. gr. 1·350, in 80 c.c. of water with a soln. of 16 grms. of hepta-hydrated magnesium sulphate in 120 c.c. of water, to stand for 24 hrs. Analyses in agreement with the above formula were made by C. F. Wach, R. E. O. Puller, and M. Austin. The white powder, said J. A. Streng, consists of minute crystals. According to A. de Schulten, the rhombic crystals have the axial ratios $a:b:c$ $=0.5675:1:0.9122$; and the sp. gr. is 1·932 at 15°. C. F. Wach found the crystals slowly effloresce in dry air. C. F. Wach, H. Rose, and R. E. O. Puller said that when dried over sulphuric acid, the salt is the *hexahydrate*; H. Rose, F. Field, R. E. O. Puller, and C. Lefèvre, that when dried at approximately 100°, the salt is the *hemihydrate*, and, at 102·5°–104·5°, R. Bunsen said that the water is all expelled, though R. E. O. Puller found that a little water is retained at that temp.; and E. W. Parnell, C. F. Rammelsberg, and L. Chevron and A. Droixhe, that some ammonia is lost at 100°–110°. As indicated in connection with magnesium hydroarsenate, when this salt is heated, it yields the pyroarsenate. In order to avoid a slight reduction of arsenate to arsenite, C. R. Fresenius heated the salt in an atm. of oxygen, and F. G. Reichel moistened it with nitric acid. The reaction was examined by B. Brauner, A. Levol, R. E. O. Puller, C. F. Rammels-berg, H. Rose, G. C. Wittstein, and L. F. Wood. H. Rose, and R. E. O. Puller said that if ammonium magnesium arsenate be rapidly heated, a little arsenic pentoxide is reduced to volatile arsenic trioxide, and C. Lefèvre found that this occurs even in an atm. of oxygen. O. Popp observed no luminescence during the formation of the pyroarsenate such as occurs with the pyrophosphate. C. Blarez gave for the heats of formation: $(Mg(OH)_2,H_3AsO_4)=26.50$ Cals., and $(MgHAsO_4,NH_3)=11.44$ Cals. On account of the part played by this salt in analytical work, a few special observations have been made on its solubility in various menstrua. The salt is but sparingly soluble in water, and freely soluble in acids. F. Field said that 100 parts of *water* dissolve 0·014 part of the salt. C. R. Fresenius gave for the solubility in 100 parts of water at 15°, 0·0377 part of the hemihydrate and 0·0359 part of the anhydrous salt, while R. E. O. Puller gave 0·0377 part of the hemi-hydrate, and 0·0359 part of the anhydrous salt. P. Wenger gave for the solubility of the hexahydrate in water expressed in grms. of salt per 100 grms. of soln. :

	0°	20°	40°	50°	60°	70°	80°
$NH_4MgAsO_4.6H_2O$	0·03388	0·02066	0·02746	0·02261	0·02103	0·01564	0·02364

from which it appears that the character of the solid phase undergoes changes. This has not been worked out. F. Kinkelin showed that water slowly transforms ammonium magnesium arsenate into normal magnesium arsenate; and C. Freidheim and P. Michaelis represented the reaction with water, $(NH_4)MgAsO_4 + 2H_2O = Mg(OH)_2 + (NH_4)H_2AsO_4$. C. R. Fresenius said that at 15°, 100 parts of soln. of 1·14, and 12·5 per cent. of ammonium chloride dissolve respectively 0·076 and 0·118 part of the hemihydrate, and 0·0725 and 0·113 part of the anhydrous salt; while R. E. O. Puller gave for 1·64 and 12·5 per cent. soln. of ammonium chloride respectively 0·0757 and 0·118 part of the hemihydrate, and 0·0722 and 0·113 part of the anhydrous salt. F. Field said that 100 parts of an aq. soln. of 10 parts of ammonium chloride dissolve 0·095 part of the anhydrous salt. R. E. O. Puller found that 100 parts of a 2 per cent. soln. of *ammonium nitrate*, containing a few drops of aq. ammonia, dissolve 0·0239 part of the hemihydrate, and 0·0233 part of the anhydrous salt. P. Wenger gave for the solubility of the hexahydrate in grams per 100 grms. of 5 per cent. soln. of ammonium nitrate and chloride :

	0°	20°	30°	40°	50°	60°	70°	80°
NH_4NO_3 .	0·09216	0·11358	0·11758	0·13936	0·18945	0·21115	0·18880	0·18945
NH_4Cl .	0·08397	0·12284	0·11264	0·19016	0·18889	0·21952	0·22092	0·23144

The solubility is reduced in ammoniacal soln. Thus, R. E. O. Puller found that 100 parts of a 2·6 per cent. soln. of *ammonia* dissolve 0·00660 part of the hemihydrate, and 0·00630 part of the anhydrous salt; C. R. Fresenius said 0·00664 part and 0·00633 part respectively at 15°; and F. Field found that 90 parts of water and 10 parts of aq. ammonia of sp. gr. 0·880 dissolve 0·007 part of ammonium magnesium arsenate, while P. Wenger gave for the solubility in grams of the hexahydrate in 100 grms. of aq. ammonia containing 4 parts of water and one part of ammonia of sp. gr. 0·96 :

	0°	20°	40°	50°	60°	70°	80°
NH_4OH .	0·00874	0·00958	0·01173	0·01005	0·00902	0·00949	0·00912

P. Wenger added that 100 grms. of a soln. containing 4 per cent. of ammonia and 5 per cent. ammonium chloride at 20° and 60°, dissolved respectively 0·01331 and 0·04691 grm. of the hexahydrate; and with 100 grms. of a similar soln. but with twice as much ammonium chloride, the data were respectively 0·03165 and 0·05353 grm. R. E. O. Puller also found that 100 parts of a soln. of *magnesium sulphate*, 100 c.c. of which was eq. to 0·0286 grm. $Mg_2As_2O_7$, dissolved 0·0374 part of the hemihydrate, and 0·0345 part of the anhydrous salt; 100 parts of *magnesia mixture*—10 c.c. of a soln. of one part each of ammonium chloride and magnesium sulphate in 4 parts of aq. ammonia, of sp. gr. 0·96, and 8 parts of water, mixed with 200 c.c. of water—dissolved 0·0032 part of the hemihydrate and 0·0031 part of the anhydrous salt ; 100 parts of a 5 per cent. soln. of *sodium arsenate* dissolved 0·0228 part of the hemihydrate and 0·0217 part of the anhydrous salt ; 100 parts of a 1·5 per cent. soln. of *potassium chloride* dissolved 0·0410 part of the hemihydrate, and 0·0390 part of the anhydrous salt ; 100 parts of a soln. of *ammonium tartrate*—containing 3·5 grms. of tartaric acid made feebly alkaline with ammonia and diluted to 250 c.c.—dissolved 0·0709 part of the hemihydrate, and 0·0703 part of the anhydrous salt ; while 100 parts of a soln. of *ammonium citrate*—containing 2·5 grms. of citric acid made feebly alkaline with ammonia and diluted to 250 c.c.—dissolved 0·112 part of the hemihydrate, and 0·107 part of the anhydrous salt.

According to H. Rose, and R. E. O. Puller, when ammonium magnesium **arsenate** is heated in hydrogen, reduction occurs and arsenic is lost by volatilization ; similarly also with sulphur, and with ammonium chloride. It is not possible to free the resulting magnesia from arsenic oxide by repeated ignition with ammonium chloride, but it is possible to do so by means of ammonium hydrosulphate, and, according to C. W. Zenger, by means of ammonium oxalate.

H. Rose reported white, pulverulent, **sodium magnesium arsenate**, $NaMgAsO_4$, to be formed by melting eq. proportions of sodium carbonate and magnesium pyroarsenate ; and C. Lefèvre, colourless prisms, by saturating with magnesia molten sodium dihydroarsenate or a mixture of the salt and sodium chloride, and removing the by-products with very dil. nitric acid. F. Kinkelin obtained the *enneahydrate*, $NaMgAsO_4.9H_2O$, by allowing a soln. of sodium orthoarsenate to react with less than the calculated amount of magnesium sulphate. The amorphous precipitate slowly crystallizes, forming, according to K. von Haushofer, triclinic crystals with the axial ratios $a:b:c=1.2401:1:1.4796$, and $a=87°22'$; $\beta=84°40'$; and $\gamma=87°24'$. The crystals are isomorphous with the corresponding phosphate. F. Kinkelin said that the enneahydrate is stable in air, and at 110°, passes into the *octohydrate*, $NaMgAsO_4.8H_2O$. The salt is decomposed by water into normal magnesium arsenate. The anhydrous salt, said C. Lefèvre, is very slowly soluble in acids. C. Lefèvre obtained colourless, transparent plates of $Na_4Mg_4As_3O_{21}$, **sodium magnesium hexarsenate**, from a soln. of 5 per cent. magnesia in molten dihydroarsenate; and he obtained the corresponding **potassium magnesium hexarsenate**, $K_4Mg_4As_6O_{21}$, in an analogous way.

H. Rose and C. Lefèvre prepared **potassium magnesium arsenate**, $KMgAsO_4$, by methods analogous to those they employed for the complex salt; and F. Kinkelin obtained needle-like crystals of the *heptahydrate*, $KMgAsO_4.7H_2O$, by the method employed for the analogous enneahydrated sodium complex salt. The crystals are stable in air; and at 100°, form the *monohydrate*, $KMgAsO_4.H_2O$, which is decomposed by water into magnesium and potassium orthoarsenates. F. Kinkelin mixed soln. of equimolar parts of potassium orthoarsenate and hydroarsenate with 2 mols of magnesium sulphate, and observed that the amorphous precipitate rapidly crystallized, forming monoclinic prisms of **potassium magnesium hydrodiorthoarsenate**, $Mg_2K(AsO_4)_2.15H_2O$, isomorphous with the corresponding phosphate. The *pentadecahydrate* is stable in air, but forms the *dihydrate*, $Mg_2KH(AsO_4)_2.2H_2O$, at 110°. It is decomposed by water into magnesium orthoarsenate, and potassium hydroarsenate. L. Chevron and A. Droixhe reported the *pentahydrate*, $Mg_2KH(AsO_4)_2.5H_2O$, to crystallize from a dil. soln. of potassium dihydroarsenate and hydrocarbonate, and magnesium sulphate; and crystals of the *tetrahydrate*, $Mg_2KH(AsO_4)_2.4H_2O$, from a filtered soln. of magnesia in aq. potassium dihydroarsenate. They obtained crystals of **potassium magnesium dihydrotriorthoarsenate**, $Mg_3KH_2(AsO_4)_3.5H_2O$, from a conc. soln. of magnesium sulphate and potassium dihydroarsenate and hydrocarbonate. F. Kinkelin reported crystals of **sodium potassium magnesium diorthoarsenate**, $Mg_2KNa(AsO_4)_2.14H_2O$, to separate from a mixed soln. of potassium and sodium orthoarsenates, and magnesium sulphate.

H. Behrens found that *magnesium orthoarsenate and ammonium cupric arsenate* form a series of mixed crystals. F. Stromeyer [3] described crystals of a **calcium magnesium arsenate**, which occurred as a mineral at Riechelsdorf, and which was named **picropharmacolite**—πικρός, bitter—in allusion to the contained magnesia —*magnesium pharmacolite*. Specimens have been also obtained at Freiberg, and Joplin, Mo. Analyses were reported by F. Stromeyer, A. Frenzel, and F. A. Genth. C. F. Rammelsberg represented it by the formula $5Ca_3(AsO_4)_2.6H_2O.Mg_3(AsO_4)_2.6H_2O$; A. Frenzel used $Ca_5As_4O_{15}.12H_2O$, without reference to the contained magnesia; F. A. Genth gave $(H_2,Ca,Mg)_3(AsO_4)_2.6H_2O$; and P. Groth, $(Ca,Mg)_3(AsO_4)_2.6H_2O$. It occurs in white or grey aggregates of small spherical or botryoidal forms with a radiating foliated structure; and rarely in slender acicular crystals. E. S. Larsen found the optic axial angle of the monoclinic crystals is 40°; the optical character, positive; and the indices of refraction, $a=1.631$, $\beta=1.632$, and $\gamma=1.640$. F. A. Genth gave 2.583 for the sp. gr., and found that when dried for a month over sulphuric acid, it loses a mol. of water, forming the pentahydrate, $(H_2Ca,Mg)_3(AsO_4)_2.5H_2O$.

Another calcium magnesium arsenate occurring at Schneeberg, and Joachimsthal was named by A. Frenzel [4] **wapplerite**—after H. W. Wappler. The analysis corresponds with $(Ca,Mg)HAsO_4.3\frac{1}{2}H_2O$. The mineral loses 19 of its 29.5 per cent. of water at 100°, and the remainder at 360°. According to A. Schrauf, the crystals are monoclinic with the axial ratios $a:b:c=0.9125:1:0.2660$, and $\beta=84°35'$; while P. Groth regards them as triclinic with the axial ratios $a:b:c$

$=0.9007 : 1 :$ 0.2616, and $\alpha=90°$ 14′, $\beta=95°$ 20′, and $\gamma=90°$ 11′. The optical axial angle is $2E=55°$; the hardness, 2·0–2·5; and the sp. gr., 2·48. A. de Schulten said that wapplerite is not a definite mineral species, but rather a mixture of magnesium and calcium arsenates which are not isomorphous and do not form solid soln.

The mineral **adelite** reported by H. Sjögren [5] to occur at Nordmarken and Langban, Wermland, has the composition of a basic salt, **calcium magnesium hydroxyarsenate**, $Ca(MgOH)AsO_4$, and he represents it by the formula $Ca=O_2$ $=AsO-O-MgOH$. It is supposed to be related to the wagnerite family of minerals, having magnesium phosphate replaced by calcium arsenate, and fluorine by hydroxyl—*vide infra*, tilasite. A related mineral from Nordmark was described by L. J. Igelström, and C. H. Lundström as a calcium magnesium arsenate related to berzeliite. It occurs in white or grey masses, and in monoclinic prisms with the axial ratios $a : b : c=1.0989 : 1 : 1.5642$, and $\beta=73°$ 15′. The optic axial angle is 58·47° for Na-light, and the optical character is negative. E. S. Larsen said positive, and he gave $2V=90°$, and the indices of refraction $\alpha=1.712$, $\beta=1.721$, and $\gamma=1.731$. The sp. gr. is 3·71–3·76, and the hardness nearly 5. The water is expelled only at a high temp. The mineral fuses easily, and is easily soluble in dil. acids.

A. de Schulten [6] reported **zinc orthoarsenate**, $Zn_3(AsO_4)_2$, to be formed by evaporating a mixed soln. of arsenic acid and zinc chloride to dryness, and heating the residue to about 730°. The mass is washed with water, and then rapidly with dil. acetic acid and triturated in a mortar to remove basic zinc chloride. The rhombic prisms are probably isomorphous with those of zinc orthophosphate. The sp. gr. is 4·913 at 15°. T. A. Mitchell obtained a hydrated zinc orthoarsenate by treating arsenic trioxide and zinc with nitric acid. H. Salkowsky, and W. Demel obtained the *trihydrate*, $Zn_3(AsO_4)_2.3H_2O$, as a white voluminous precipitate, by treating a soln. of zinc sulphate with sodium orthoarsenate; and by adding alkali-lye to a soln. of the hydroarsenate in hydrochloric acid. A. Bette prepared tri-hydrated **zinc diamminorthoarsenate**, $Zn_3(AsO_4)_2.2NH_3.3H_2O$, by mixing a soln. of zinc chloride with enough ammonium chloride to prevent it giving a precipitate with ammonia, and digesting the liquid with a mixture of ammonia and potassium arsenate. The flocculent precipitate soon becomes crystalline. The white powder loses almost all its water and a little ammonia at 100°; it is insoluble in water; and soluble in acids, ammonia, and potash-lye. H. B. Weiser and A. P. Bloxsom prepared a **hydrogel of zinc arsenate** by mixing soln. of a salt of a strong acid with potassium dihydroarsenate in the cold.

The *octohydrate*, $Zn_3(AsO_4)_2.8H_2O$, was prepared by W. Skey, by adding a soluble arsenate to a soln. of a zinc salt so long as the liquor remains acidic. A. de Schulten mixed soln. of 18 grms. of heptahydrated zinc sulphate in 2 litres of water with 12 grms. of heptahydrated zinc hydroarsenate in a litre of water; or similarly with soln. one-fourth this conc. In each case, the amorphous precipitate was allowed to stand in contact with the mother-liquor a few days in which crystals of the octohydrate were formed. O. Köttig, and C. F. Naumann described a zinc arsenate occurring with smaltite in a cobalt mine near Schneeberg. J. D. Dana called it **köttigite**—after O. Köttig. The mineral is coloured red owing to the presence of about 2 per cent. of nickel oxide and 6·9 per cent. of cobalt oxide, so that the formula can be written $(Zn,Co,Ni)_3(AsO_4)_2.8H_2O$. The mineral occurs massive, or in crystalline crusts with a fibrous structure. According to P. Groth, the crystals are monoclinic and isomorphous with vivianite; A. de Schulten found that artificial köttigite occurs in colourless, monoclinic prisms which are optically positive. E. S. Larsen found the optic axial angle to be 77°; and the indices of refraction $\alpha=1.662$, $\beta=1.683$, and $\gamma=1.717$. The optical properties of the mineral were studied by F. Ulrich. The hardness of the mineral is 2·5–3·0, and the sp. gr. 3·1; A. de Schulten gave for the sp. gr. of the artificial crystals 3·309 at 15°. The salt oses about 2 mols. of water at 100°. It is easily soluble in dil. acids.

The basic salt, **zinc hydroxyorthoarsenate,** $Zn(AsO_4)Zn(OH)$, $Zn_3(AsO_4)_2 \cdot Zn(OH)_2$, or $4ZnO.As_2O_5.H_2O$—*vide* sarkinite—is represented by the mineral **adamite,** discovered by C. Friedel, and named by him *adamine*—after M. Adam. It occurs at Chanarcillo, Chili ; at Mte. Valerio, Campiglia Maritima ; at Cap Garonne, Hyères, France ; and in the ancient zinc mines of Laurium, Greece, where it fills some drusy cavities in the cellular smithsonite. The colour may be white, yellow, green, rose-red, or violet. Analyses were reported by C. Friedel, A. des Cloizeaux, A. Damour, F. Pisani, V. Rosicky, V. Dürrfeld, and P. Aloisi. C. F. Rammelsberg, and V. Dürrfeld represented the analyses by the formula $Zn_3(AsO_4)_2.Zn(OH)_2$; and A. de Schulten, and P. Groth, by $Zn(ZnOH)AsO_4$, when part of the zinc is replaced mainly by copper. A. Lacroix called the mineral *cupro-adamite,* and when by cobalt, *cobaltoadamite.* A. de Schulten synthesized the mineral by keeping artificial *köttigite* in its mother-liquor for some time ; and also by adding gradually 3 grms. of heptahydrated sodium hydroarsenate dissolved in a litre of water, and made acid with a few drops of sulphuric acid, to a soln. of 4·5 grms. of heptahydrated zinc sulphate dissolved in 2 litres of water, and heated on a water-bath. After standing 3 weeks, crystals of adamite appear covering the bottom of the containing vessel. The mineral was also synthesized by C. Friedel and E. Sarasin by heating zinc phosphate with arsenic acid and water in a sealed tube at 130°–140°—*vide infra,* action of boiling water on zinc hydroarsenate. The crystals may be grouped in crusts, or fine granular aggregates. The prismatic crystals are rhombic, and A. des Cloizeaux gave for the axial ratios $a : b : c = 0.9733 : 1 : 0.7158$; P. Aloisi, $0.97359 : 1 : 0.701315$; and V. Rosicky, $0.704869 : 1 : 0.976427$. Adamite is isomorphous with libethenite, and olivenite. A. des Cloizeaux found the optic axial angles to be $2H_a = 108°\ 34'$ for red light, and $111°\ 39'$ for blue light; $2H_0 = 115°\ 51'$ for red light, and $113°\ 52'$ for blue light ; while V. Rosicky gave $2V = 82°\ 57\frac{3}{4}'$. The optical character is positive—perhaps also negative. The mean index of refraction for Na-light is 1·728. E. S. Larsen gave $a = 1.708$, $\beta = 1.734$, and $\gamma = 1.758$. The dispersion is large. The crystals were examined by L. J. Spencer, H. Ungenmach, and A. H. Means. The hardness of adamite is 3·5 ; and the sp. gr. given by C. Friedel is 4·338 ; and A. Damour gave 4·352 ; while A. de Schulten gave 4·475 for the sp. gr. of artificial adamite. C. Friedel said that the mineral is easily fused ; and is readily soluble in dil. hydrochloric acid, and is attacked by acetic acid.

J. J. Berzelius referred to the formation of cubic crystals of acidic zinc arsenate by evaporating the soln. obtained by treating zinc, zinc oxide, or zinc pyroarsenate with arsenic acid ; N. W. Fischer obtained a gelatinous mass by the action of zinc on arsenic acid ; and H. Goguel said that if the gelatinous substance be heated it forms monoclinic plates. According to G. Kemp and J. von Gyulay, when a soln. of zinc salt is treated with alkali orthoarsenate or hydroarsenate neutralized with hydrochloric acid, a gelatinous mass of **zinc hydroarsenate,** $ZnHAsO_4$, is formed which crystallizes on standing for 2 or 3 months, when dried in a water-oven. J. H. Debray reported crystals of the *monohydrate,* $ZnHAsO_4.H_2O$, to be formed when ammonium arsenate is treated with zinc sulphate, and digested for 8–14 days at 100°. W. Demel, and H. Salkowsky obtained it as a crystalline crust by evaporating a soln. of zinc oxide in arsenic acid ; H. Salkowsky, by allowing zinc orthoarsenate to stand for a long time in contact with a soln. of arsenic acid ; and A. Coloriano, by the action of arsenic acid on zinc. The rhombic prismatic crystals are decomposed by prolonged boiling with water, forming the basic arsenate ; and the hydrochloric acid soln., when treated with alkali, yields the trihydrated ortho-arsenate. H. Goguel found that when the hydroarsenate is heated in a sealed tube at 200°, rhombic, probably triclinic, plates of **zinc dihydrotetrarsenate,** $Zn_3(AsO_4)_2.2ZnHAsO_4.nH_2O$, or $Zn_5H_2(AsO_4)_4.nH_2O$, are formed.

C. Lefèvre reported **zinc pyroarsenate,** $Zn_2As_2O_7$, to be formed by dissolving zinc oxide in fused potassium metarsenate. The tabular crystals are isomorphous with manganese pyroarsenate. H. Stallo gave 4·6989–4·7034 for the sp. gr. at 21°.

The salt is decomposed by water. A. Coloriano treated zinc with an excess of arsenic acid, and boiled the filtered soln.—replacing the water lost by evaporation from time to time—until crystals appear. The rhombic or monoclinic prisms of the *trihydrate*, $Zn_2As_2O_7.3H_2O$, are attacked by cold water, and transformed by boiling water into the dihydroxyorthoarsenate. H. Goguel prepared a basic salt, **zinc dihydroxypyroarsenate**, $Zn(OH)_2.Zn_2As_2O_7.7H_2O$, by treating 100 c.c. of a 10 per cent. soln. of zinc acetate with 10 c.c. of a 25 per cent. soln. of zinc arsenate, and digesting the product for a few weeks. The fine, silky needles lose all their water at 300°. H. Salkowsky prepared **zinc metarsenate**, $Zn(AsO_3)_2$, adding water to the product obtained by heating zinc oxide with arsenic acid at 200°.

A. Schrauf described a **copper zinc phosphatoarsenate**, $9CuO.6ZnO.P_2O_5.As_2O_5.18H_2O$, which occurs as a mineral at Morawitza, Hungary. It is thought to be an isomorphous mixture of $Zn_3(AsO_4)_2.3Zn(OH)_2.3H_2O$, $Cu_3(PO_4)_2.3Cu(OH)_2.3H_2O$, and $Cu(OH)_2.H_2O$; or $(Zn,Cu)_3\{(P,As)O_4\}_2.4(Zn,Cu)(OH)_2.5H_2O$. It was called **veszelyite**—after M. Veszelyi. The crystals are thought to be triclinic with the axial ratios $a:b:c = 0.7101:1:0.9134$, and $a = 89°\ 31'$, $\beta = 103°\ 51'$, and $\gamma = 89°\ 34'$. E. S. Larsen said that the optical character is negative, the optic axial angle negative, and the indices of refraction $a = 1.640$, $\beta = 1.658$, and $\gamma = 1.695$. A. Schrauf said that the mineral loses 2.30 per cent. of water at 150°; 4.39 per cent. at 200°; and 17.05 per cent. at a red-heat. The hardness is 3.5–4.0.

H. Salkowsky obtained a gelatinous precipitate by the action of sodium ortho-arsenate on a soln. of cadmium sulphate; and the washed product, dried at 100°, had the composition of **cadmium orthoarsenate**, $Cd_3(AsO_4)_2$. W. Demel obtained it by treating a hydrochloric acid soln. of the hydroarsenate with alkali-lye. W. Demel, and H. Salkowsky made cadmium hydroarsenate, $CdHAsO_4.H_2O$, by evaporating on a water-bath a soln. of 16 grms. of cadmium carbonate in a soln. of 100 grms. of arsenic acid; A. de Schulten, by evaporating on a water-bath a sat. soln. of cadmium dihydrotetrorthoarsenate in arsenic acid; and A. Coloriano, by treating with water the product of the action of arsenic acid on cadmium at 200°. The white, needle-like crystals have a sp. gr. 4.164 at 150°. The salt is easily soluble in dil. hydrochloric acid. When treated with water, this salt furnishes **cadmium dihydrotetraorthoarsenate**, $5CdO.2As_2O_5.5H_2O$, or $Cd_3(AsO_4)_2.2CdHAsO_4.4H_2O$. H. Salkowsky made the same salt as a gelatinous precipitate by adding sodium hydroarsenate to a soln. of cadmium sulphate. The precipitate soon forms a white crystalline mass easily soluble in dil. hydrochloric acid. G. Klemp and J. von Gyulay found that by the successive addition of ammonium sulphate, acetic acid, and an excess of sodium arsenate to a soln. of a cadmium salt, an opalescent, yellow, colloidal arsenate is deposited which quickly crystallizes into $Cd_3(AsO_4)_2.2CdHAsO_4.4\frac{1}{3}H_2O$. A. de Schulten evaporated a soln. of the dihydrotetraorthoarsenate in dil. arsenic acid at ordinary temp., and obtained triclinic crystals of **cadmium dihydroarsenate**, $Cd(H_2AsO_4)_2.2H_2O$, isomorphous with the corresponding phosphate. The sp. gr. is 3.241 at 15°. At 70°–80°, this salt loses all its water of crystallization and some of its constitutional water, and forms with an excess of water, the dihydrotetraorthoarsenate. A. de Schulten made **cadmium pyroarsenate**, $Cd_2As_2O_7$, by melting 22 parts of cadmium bromide, 2 parts of potassium bromide, and 9 parts of ammonium arsenate. After washing with dil. hydrochloric acid to remove the yellow crystals of the analogue of apatite which are formed, C. Lefèvre made the salt in colourless crystals by fusing potassium metarsenate with cadmium oxide or carbonate. H. Salkowsky treated a soln. of cadmium chloride in arsenic acid at 200°, washed the residue with water, and dried it at 100°. The product corresponded with **cadmium metarsenate**, $Cd(AsO_3)_2$. H. B. Weiser and A. P. Bloxsom prepared **hydrogel of cadmium arsenate** as in the case of the zinc salt.

C. Lefèvre obtained prismatic or lamellar crystals of **sodium zinc arsenate**, $NaZnAsO_4$, by dissolving zinc oxide in fused sodium meta-, pyro-, or orthoarsenate; if an excess of zinc oxide be avoided, **sodium zinc pyroarsenate** is formed, $Na_2ZnAs_2O_7$. He also obtained **potassium zinc arsenate**, $KZnAsO_4$, by a process like that used for the analogous sodium salt. C. Lefèvre obtained isomorphous **potassium cadmium arsenate,** $KCdAsO_4$, in an analogous way; and likewise **sodium cadmium diorthoarsenate,** $Na_4Cd(AsO_4)_2$, from a soln. of cadmium oxide in molten sodium metarsenate; and **sodium cadmium trispyroarsenate,** $Na_8Cd_2(As_2O_7)_3$, from a soln. of cadmium oxide in molten sodium ortho- or pyro-arsenate.

A. Coloriano,[7] and H. Goguel obtained **mercurous orthoarsenate,** Hg_3AsO_4, by heating 35 c.c. of a soln. of 5 grms. of arsenic pentoxide and 5 grms. of mercury in a sealed tube at 230° for about 60 hrs. The reaction is very slow. K. Haack obtained this compound by dropping a cold soln. of a mol of mercurous nitrate into a cold soln. of sodium hydroarsenate, washing the yellow product with cold water, and drying in air. If the soln. of hydroarsenate be dropped into the soln. of mercurous nitrate, a basic nitratoarsenate is formed which is converted into the normal arsenate by treatment with a soln. of sodium hydroarsenate. H. Goguel prepared this compound by adding a soln. of 5 grms. of mercurous nitrate acidified with nitric acid to a soln. of 5 grms. of arsenic acid. The orange, rhombic, prismatic crystals are pleochroic—*a*, pale brown; *b*, brown; and *c*, brownish-green. The birefringence is strong and negative. The salt is insoluble in water, and is attacked slowly by acids; with hydrochloric acid, it forms mercurous chloride and arsenic acid; and with a soln. of mercurous nitrate, it forms a double salt.

According to J. F. Simon, when a soln. of mercurous nitrate is dropped into a conc. soln. of arsenic acid, the white precipitate which is first formed redissolves in the excess of acid, and becomes permanent when more of the soln. of the mercurous salt is added. The salt remains white during the washing, but becomes red when dried. The analysis corresponds with **mercurous hydroarsenate,** $HgHAsO_4.\frac{1}{2}H_2O$. The same salt was obtained by adding arsenic acid or sodium arsenate to a soln. of a mercurous salt; the white complex of mercurous arsenate and nitrate first precipitated soon turns yellow, then red, and finally assumes the purple-red colour of mercurous arsenate—particularly if warmed. The brownish-red or purple-red salt is composed of fine needles. When dried at 100°, and afterwards heated, it loses its water of crystallization, then gives off mercury to form yellow mercuric arsenate, which, at a higher temp., yields mercury, arsenic trioxide, and oxygen. Cold conc. hydrochloric acid converts it into a soln. of arsenic trioxide, and insoluble mercurous chloride; cold nitric acid dissolves the salt and it is reprecipitated by ammonia, the boiling acid converts it into mercuric nitrate. Mercurous hydroarsenate dissolves very sparingly in a soln. of ammonium nitrate from which it separates on evaporation as a red, crystalline mass. It is insoluble in water, aq. ammonia, and acetic acid.

J. J. Berzelius described a **mercurous pyroarsenate,** $Hg_4As_2O_7$, which K. Haack said was probably a complex salt with the nitrate. J. F. Simon stated that when the hydroarsenate is heated, the pyroarsenate is formed. He also reported **mercurous metarsenate,** $HgAsO_3$, to be produced as a white non-crystalline mass when mercuric oxide, or mercurous hydroarsenate, is mixed with an aq. soln. of arsenic acid and boiled to dryness; the dry mass is triturated with cold water, washed, and dried on a water-bath. H. Goguel obtained it by heating mercury with a 50–75 per cent. soln. of arsenic acid in a sealed tube at 150° for a long time. The pale yellow hexagonal plates so obtained have the axial ratio $a : c = 1 : 1 \cdot 5096$. The crystals have a strong positive birefringence. They are blackened superficially by exposure to light, and when heated in a closed tube they become yellow, red, and brown with the loss of mercury. J. F. Simon noted that the salt is converted into mercuric arsenate by heat. The salt is insoluble in water, alcohol, and acetic acid. When treated with a soln. of potassium hydroxide it forms hydroarsenate; it behaves like the hydroarsenate towards cold nitric acid; and when the nitric acid soln. is heated, and ammonia added, the hydroarsenate is precipitated. For *mercurous amidoarsenate,* see **8.** 49, 21.

P. P. Kosakewitsch found that when mercuric oxide and arsenic acid are in contact, the solid phase consisted of two layers, one of which was mercuric oxide, and the other, **mercuric trioxyarsenate,** $6HgO.As_2O_5$, or $3HgO.Hg_3(AsO_4)_2$. According to T. Bergman, when sodium arsenate is treated with mercuric chloride, a yellow precipitate is produced ; but C. J. Pretzfeld did not confirm this, and K. Haack did not obtain the precipitate by adding an aq. soln. of arsenic acid to one of mercuric chloride. T. Bergman, however, did obtain **mercuric orthoarsenate,** $Hg_3(AsO_4)_2$, by heating mercury with arsenic pentoxide whereby arsenic trioxide is also formed. He obtained the same salt by the action of arsenic acid on mercuric nitrate, and K. Haack, by dropping a soln. of arsenic acid into an excess of a soln. of mercuric nitrate ; and similarly, by the action of mercuric nitrate on sodium dihydroarsenate. The soln. of mercuric nitrate should be acidified with nitric acid, or the precipitate will be contaminated with mercuric and sodium nitrates. H. Goguel obtained crystals of mercuric orthoarsenate by the action of 25 c.c. of an acidified soln. of 5 grms. of mercuric nitrate on 5 c.c. of a 50 per cent. soln. of arsenic acid heated in a sealed tube for some hours at 180°. According to K. Haack, if the basic sulphate $2HgO.HgSO_4$ is boiled with an excess of a soln. of sodium hydroarsenate, frequently renewed, sulphur trioxide is eliminated, and a mixture of mercuric oxide and orthoarsenate is formed—not the basic arsenate. He also found that a soln. of mercuric chloride transforms silver orthoarsenate into mercuric orthoarsenate. A. Dexheimer prepared **colloidal mercuric orthoarsenate** as follows :

A soln. of one gram of sodium protalbinate in 10 c.c. of water, is mixed with mercuric chloride until a precipitate is no longer produced. The precipitate is washed free from chlorides, dissolved in sodium hydroxide, and treated with a soln. of sodium hydroarsenate. The product is dialyzed until the outflowing water is free from arsenic, evaporated on a water-bath, and then in vacuo over sulphuric acid until quite dry. The olive-green mass is very soluble in water, forming a soln. which is grey in reflected light, and olive-green in transmitted light.

Normal mercuric orthoarsenate forms a yellow powder, and prismatic or acicular crystals. H. Goguel said that the crystals belong to the monoclinic system, and have a positive birefringence. They melt at a red-heat and decompose. They are not affected by hot or cold water; K. Haack said that they are very sparingly soluble in hot water. T. Bergman, K. Haack, and H. Goguel found that mercuric orthoarsenate is soluble in nitric acid, arsenic acid, and hydrochloric acid. K. Haack said that it is soluble in arsenic acid ; it is transformed by a soln. of sodium chloride into reddish-brown mercuric oxychloride ; it is coloured brown by a soln. of potassium bromide ; and forms mercuric iodide with a soln. of potassium iodide. It undergoes double decomposition with silver nitrate. According to P. Ray and P. C. Bandopadhyay, when mercuric arsenate is digested with ammonia, washed with dil. ammonia, and then with alcohol, and dried in vacuo over sulphuric acid, there is produced a yellowish-white arsenate of Millon's base—**mercuric oxyamido-arsenate,** $[O{=}Hg_3{=}NH_3]_3AsO_4.3H_2O$, presumably by the reactions $Hg_3(AsO_4)_2 +6NH_3 \rightleftharpoons (NH_2Hg)_3AsO_4+(NH_4)_3AsO_4$; and $2(NH_2Hg)_3AsO_4+6H_2O=(NH_4)_3AsO_4 +(HO.Hg.NH_2.HgOH)_3AsO_4$.

REFERENCES.

¹ J. J. Berzelius, Ann. Chim. Phys., (2), 5. 179, 1817 ; (2), 11. 225, 1819 ; Pogg. Ann., 7. 137, 1826 ; A. Atterberg, Œfvers Akad. Förh., 7. 1875 ; Bull. Soc. Chim., (2), 24. 358, 1875 ; B. Bleyer and B. Müller, Zeit. anorg. Chem., 75. 291, 1912.
² L. Chevron and A. Droixhe, Bull. Acad. Belg., (3), 16. 488, 1888 ; A. de Schulten, Compt. Rend., 100. 877, 1885 ; Bull. Soc. Min., 26. 28, 81, 1903 ; E. Bertrand, ib., 5. 307, 1882 ; K. von Haushofer, Zeit. Kryst., 4. 49, 1880 ; 6. 137, 1882 ; 7. 258, 1883 ; F. Ulrich, ib., 64. 143, 1926 ; A. Schrauf, ib., 4. 281, 1880 ; T. Graham, Phil. Trans., 127. 47, 1837 ; F. Field, Journ. Chem. Soc., 11. 6, 1858 ; R. E. O. Puller, ib., 24. 586, 1871 ; Zeit. anal. Chem., 10. 68, 1871 ; F. Kinkelin, Ueber Magnesiumsalze der Arsen- und Phosphorsäure und ihre Zersetzungsproducte, Erlangen. 1883 ; P. von Kotschoubey, Journ. prakt. Chem., (1), 49. 182, 1850 ; C. R. Fresenius, ib., (1), 56. 33, 1852 ; F. C. B. Schiefer, Zeit. Ges. Naturw. Halle, 23. 363, 1864 ; C. Blarez, Compt. Rend., 103. 1134, 1886 ; C. Reischauer, Repert. Pharm., 14. 65, 1857 ; C. F. Wach, Schweigger's Journ., 59. 288, 1830 ; A. Levol, Ann. Chim. Phys., (3), 17. 501, 1846 ; C. Lefèvre, ib., (6), 27. 55, 1892 ;

J. A. Streng, *Ber. Oberhess. Ges. Naturkunde*, 54, 1885; H. Rose, *Pogg. Ann.*, **116**. 453, 1862; 77. 288, 1849; *Chem. News*, 7. 219, 1863; B. Brauner, *Zeit. anal. Chem.*, **16**. 57, 1877; F. G. Reichel, *ib.*, **20**. 89, 1881; G. C. Wittstein, *ib.*, **2**. 19, 1863; L. Gmelin, *Handbook of Chemistry*, London, 4. 307. 1850; C. F. Rammelsberg, *Ber.*, 7. 544, 1874; R. Bunsen, *Liebig's Ann.*, **192**. 311, 1878; E. W. Parnell, *Chem. News*, **21**. 133, 1870; A. Frenzel, *Tschermak's Mitt.*, (1), 4. 279, 1874; *Neues Jahrb. Min.*, 786, 1873; F. Stromeyer, *Gilbert's Ann.*, **61**. 185, 1819; C. Freidheim and P. Michaelis, *Ber.*, **28**. 1414, 1895; M. Austin, *Amer. Journ. Science*, (4), **9**. 55, 1900; L. F. Wood, *ib.*, (3), 6. 368, 1873; H. Stallo, *ib.*, (3), **14**. 285, 1877; C. W. Zenger, *Zeit. Chem.*, (1), **5**. 38, 1862; O. Popp, *ib.*, (2), 6. 305, 1870; C. F. Rammelsberg, *Handbuch der Mineralchemie*, Leipzig, 341, 1875; A. Kenngott, *Jahrb. geol. Reichsanst. Wien*, **11**. 10, 1860; W. Haidinger, *Sitzber. Akad. Wien*, **40**. 18, 1860; J. R. Blum, *Jahresb. Wetterauer Ges. Hanau*, 32, 1861; *Neues Jahrb. Min.*, 334, 1861; P. Wenger, *Étude sur la solubilité des phosphates et des arsénates ammoniacomagnésiens et du phosphate ammoniacomanganeux*, Genève, 1911; H. Behrens, *Rec. Trav. Chim. Pays-Bas*, **10**. 57, 1891; F. Zambonini, *Mem. Carta Geol. Ital.*, 7. 127, 1919; E. S. Larsen, *Bull. U.S. Geol. Sur.*, 679, 1921; E. O. Kraemer, *Amer. Colloid Symposium*, 2. 57, 1925.

[3] F. Stromeyer, *Gilbert's Ann.*, **61**. 185, 1819; A. Frenzel, *Neues Jahrb. Min.*, 786, 1873; C. F. Rammelsberg, *Handbuch der Mineralchemie*, Leipzig, 340, 1873; P. Groth, *Tabellarische Uebersicht der Mineralien*, Braunschweig, 94, 1898; F. A. Genth, *Amer. Journ. Science*, (3), 40. 204, 1890; E. S. Larsen, *Bull. U.S. Geol. Sur.*, 679, 1921.

[4] A. Frenzel, *Tschermak's Mitt.*, (2), 4. 279, 1874; P. Groth, *Tabellarische Uebersicht der Mineralien*, Braunschweig, 95, 1875; A. Schrauf, *Neues Jahrb. Min.*, 290, 1875; *Zeit. Kryst.*, 4. 281, 1880; A. de Schulten, *Bull. Soc. Min.*, 26. 99, 1903.

[5] E. S. Larsen, *Bull. U.S. Geol. Sur.*, 679, 1921; H. Sjögren, *Bull. Geol. Inst. Upsala*, 1. 1, 1893; *Zeit. Kryst.*, 24. 146, 1895; *Neues Jahrb. Min.*, ii, 37, 1893; *Geol. För. Förh. Stockholm*, 13. 781, 1892; C. H. Lundström, *ib.*, 7. 407, 1884; L. J. Igelström, *ib.*, 7. 101, 1884.

[6] A. de Schulten, *Bull. Soc. Min.*, 26. 93, 1903; *Bull. Soc. Chim.*, (3), 2. 300, 1889; J. H. Debray, *ib.*, (2), 2. 14, 1864; C. Friedel and E. Sarasin, *ib.*, (2), 25. 482, 1876; A. des Cloizeaux, *ib.*, (2), 5. 438, 1866; *Nouvelles recherches sur les propriétés optiques des cristaux*, Paris, 26, 1867; H. Salkowsky, *Journ. prakt. Chem.*, (1), 104. 162, 1868; *Ber.*, 12. 1447, 1879; W. Demel, *ib.*, 12. 1279, 1446, 1879; G. Klemp and J. von Gyulay, *Zeit. Koll.*, 15. 202, 1914; 22. 57, 1918; 28. 262, 1921; A. Lacroix, *Minéralogie de la France et de ses colonies*, Paris, 4. 425, 1910; C. F. Rammelsberg, *Handbuch der Mineralchemie*, Leipzig, 342, 1875; J. D. Dana, *A System of Mineralogy*, New York, 487, 1850; M. Henglein and W. Meigen, *Centr. Min.*, 353, 1914; O. Köttig, *Journ. prakt. Chem.*, (1), **48**. 183, 1849; C. F. Naumann, *ib.*, (1), **48**. 257, 1849; E. Mitscherlich, *Ann. Chim. Phys.*, (2), **19**. 350, 1821; E. Soubeiran, *ib.*, (2), **43**. 409, 1830; V. Rosicky, *Bull. Acad. Bohême*, 13. 30, 1908; *Zeit. Kryst.*, **48**. 656, 1911; V. Dürrfeld, *ib.*, **51**. 279, 1913; P. Aloisi, *Proc. Verb. Soc. Toscani*, 17. 4, 1907; N. W. Fischer, *Pogg. Ann.*, 9. 261, 1827; A. Bette, *Liebig's Ann.*, **15**. 141, 1835; J. J. Berzelius, *Lehrbuch der Chemie*, Dresden, 4. 487, 1835; E. S. Larsen, *Bull. U.S. Geol. Sur.*, 679, 1921; H. B. Weiser, *Colloid Symposium Wisconsin Univ.*, 38, 1923; H. B. Weiser and A. P. Bloxsom, *Journ. Phys. Chem.*, 28. 26, 1924; P. Groth, *Die Mineraliensammlung der Universität Strassburg*, Strassburg, 166, 1878; T. A. Mitchell, *U.S. Pat. No.* 1183315, 1183316, 1916; A. Coloriano, *Recherches sur quelques arsénates cristallisés*, Paris, 1886; *Compt. Rend.*, 103. 274, 1886; *Bull. Soc. Chim.*, (2), **45**. 707, 1886; H. Goguel, *Contribution à l'étude des arsénates et des antimonates cristallisés préparés par voie humide*, Bordeaux, 1896; *Mem. Soc. Phys. Nat. Bordeaux*, (5), **1**. 135, 1896; W. Skey, *Chem. News*, 22. 61, 1870; H. Stallo, *Amer. Journ. Science*, (3), 14. 285, 1877; A. H. Means, *ib.*, (4), **41**. 125, 1916; H. Ungenmach, *Bull. Soc. Min.*, **44**. 122, 1921; C. Friedel, *ib.*, 1. 31, 1878; *Compt. Rend.*, 62. 692, 1866; F. Pisani, *ib.*, **70**. 1001, 1870; A. Damour, *ib.*, 67. 1124, 1868; C. Lefèvre, *ib.*, **110**. 405, 1890; *Sur les arsénates cristallisés*, Paris, 1891; *Ann. Chim. Phys.*, (6), **27**. 22, 1892; L. J. Spencer, *Min. Mag.*, 17. 114, 1914; F. Ulrich, *Zeit. Kryst.*, 64. 143, 1926; A. Schrauf, *Neues Jahrb. Min.*, 290, 1875; *Zeit. Kryst.*, 4. 281, 1880.

[7] K. Haack, *Ueber Arsenate und Phosphate des Quecksilbers*, Halle, 35, 1890; *Liebig's Ann.*, 262. 190, 1891; A. Coloriano, *Sur les arsénates cristallisés*, Paris, 49, 1886; *Bull. Soc. Chim.*, (2), **45**. 707, 1886; *Compt. Rend.*, 103. 275, 1886; H. Goguel, *Contribution à l'étude des arsénates et des antimonates cristallisés préparés par voie humide*, Paris, 1896; J. F. Simon, *Pogg. Ann.*, 40. 442, 1837; 41. 424, 1837; T. Bergman, *De arsenico*, Upsala, 1777; J. J. Berzelius, *Lehrbuch der Chemie*, Dresden, 4. 611, 1835; A Dexheimer, *Ueber die Darstellung anorganische Kolloide in kolloidalen organischen Medien*, Erlangen, 51, 1910; C. J. Pretzfeld, *Journ. Amer. Chem. Soc.*, 25. 203, 1903; P. Ray and P. C. Bandopadhyay, *Journ. Indian Chem Soc.*, 1. 235, 1925; P. P. Kosakewitsch, *Zeit. phys. Chem.*, 108. 281, 1924.

§ 19. The Arsenates of the Aluminium Family of Elements

E. Berger [1] obtained **boron arsenate**, $BAsO_4$, by evaporating an aq. soln. of boric and arsenic acids, and calcining the product. It is reduced when heated with aluminium or calcium silicide. C. Palache and L. H. Bauer described a mineral, which was named **cahnite**—after L. Cahn—and obtained from Franklin, New Jersey. The composition approximates **calcium boroarsenate**, $4CaO.B_2O_3.As_2O_5.4H_2O$. It is white and glassy occurring in tetragonal sphenoids characteristically occurring in interpenetrating twins. The axial ratio $a : c = 1 : 0.615$. The prismatic cleavage is well defined. The sp. gr. is 3.15; the hardness, about 3; and the refractive index, about 1.662, or $\omega=1.662$ and $\epsilon=1.663$. The optical character is positive.

According to A. Coloriano, if a soln. of sodium orthoarsenate and an excess of aluminium sulphate be heated to 220° in a sealed tube, lentiform crystals of **aluminium orthoarsenate**, $AlAsO_4$, are produced. N. S. Maskelyne reported a white, pale blue, or greenish-blue incrustation on quartz or other minerals at Liskeard, Cornwall. The mineral was called **liskeardite**. The analysis by W. Flight corresponds in the idealized case with the *octohydrate*, $AlAsO_4.8H_2O$; actually, about 7.64 per cent. of ferric oxide is present so that the formula becomes $(Fe,Al)AsO_4.8H_2O$. The mineral lost 4.35 per cent. of water at ordinary temp.; 10.96 per cent. more at 100°; 5.55 per cent. more at 120°, and 8.22 per cent. more at 140°–190°; and 4.97 per cent. more at a red-heat. A. Lacroix has described a similar mineral from Hyères. It had an optic axial angle $2E_a=115°$; and a sp. gr. 3.011.

P. Berthier obtained a white powder, possibly **aluminium hydroarsenate**, $Al_2(HAsO_4)_3$, by treating a soln. of aluminium sulphate with sodium hydroarsenate. The powder is readily soluble in acids, and when the soln. in hydrochloric acid is boiled with ammonium sulphite, alumina is precipitated while all the arsenic remains in soln. H. Rose said that when heated alone or mixed with sulphur in a current of hydrogen, the arsenic is incompletely volatilized—C. Lefèvre said that the arsenic is completely volatilized. P. Berthier obtained a soln. of an acid arsenate which he could not crystallize. C. Lefèvre melted together 15.5–15.7 parts of potassium or sodium dihydroarsenate with one part of alumina, at as low a temp. as possible, and obtained colourless, transparent prisms of **aluminium pyroarsenate**, $Al_4(As_2O_7)_3$, which are only slightly attacked by hot water, but are easily soluble in dil. acids.

C. Lefèvre prepared transparent plates of **sodium aluminium triorthoarsenate**, $Na_3Al_2(AsO_4)_3$, by dissolving alumina in a molten mixture of sodium dihydroarsenate and chloride. The corresponding **potassium aluminium triorthoarsenate**, $K_3Al_2(AsO_4)_3$, was made in an analogous way. A. Rosenheim and S. Thon prepared **sodium dihydroaluminoarsenate**, $NaH_2[Al(AsO_4)_2].\frac{1}{2}H_2O$; and **barium hydroaluminoarsenate**, $BaH_4[Al(AsO_4)_3].H_2O$.

H. Dufet[2] reported massive clay-like material made up of very minute turquoise-blue crystals from a mine at Huanaco, Chile. It was called **coeruleite**, or ceruleite, and its analysis corresponds with $CuO.2Al_2O_3.As_2O_5.8H_2O$—**copper aluminium tetroxydiarsenate**. The water is expelled only at a high temp., for at 180° only 1.4 per cent. is given off. The mineral has a sp. gr. 2.803. It dissolves in acids leaving only a slight residue of a white clay. In 1801, J. L. Bournon,[3] and in 1802, P. Rashleigh, described what was called octahedral arsenate of copper as a mineral occurring with various ores of copper, pyrite, and quartz in Cornwall; and specimens have since been reported from Herrengrund, Hungary; and from Voigtland. The mineral was called *Linzenerz* by A. G. Werner, C. F. Ludwig, and D. L. G. Karsten; *Linzenkupfer*, by J. F. L. Hausmann; *Lirokonmalachite*, by F. Mohs; *Chalcophacite*, by E. F. Glocker; and **liroconite**—from λειρός, pale; κονία, powder—by J. D. Dana. Analyses were reported by R. Hermann, A. Damour, and A. H. Church. C. F. Rammelsberg represented the composition by the formula $Cu_{18}Al_8As_{10}O_{55}.60H_2O$; and P. Groth, by $Al_4Cu_9(AsO_4)_5(OH)_{15}.20H_2O$, that is, **copper aluminium pentadecahydroxypentarsenate**, but the available information is too meagre to enable satisfactory inferences to be made. The sky-blue or verdigris-green mineral usually occurs in crystals, rarely granular. The crystals were found by A. des Cloizeaux to be monoclinic, and to have the axial ratios $a:b:c=1.3191:1:1.6808$, and $\beta=88° 32\frac{5}{6}'$.

The thin crystals appear octahedral with the (110)- and (011)-faces faintly striated ; the cleavage on these two faces is indistinct. A. des Cloizeaux found the optical axial angles for red-, yellow-, and blue-light to be respectively $2E=132°54', 132°57'$, and $133°46'$; $2H_a=77°24\frac{2}{3}'$, $77°18'$, and $76°57\frac{2}{3}'$. The optical character is negative. J. L. Bournon gave 2·882 for the sp. gr. ; R. Hermann, 2·985 ; and A. Damour, 2·964. The hardness is 2·0–2·5. The mineral is easily soluble in aq. ammonia and in acids. F. W. Clarke [4] described an amorphous mineral from the mercury district of Utah. The analysis corresponds with $4CaO.5Al_2O_3.3As_2O_5.20H_2O$, or $Ca_2\{Al(OH)_2\}_5(AsO_4)_3.10H_2O$, **calcium aluminium decahydroxytriarsenate.**

The *arsenates of gallium and indium* have not been described. J. E. Willm [5] treated thallous dihydroarsenate with ammonia and obtained white silky needles of **thallous orthoarsenate,** Tl_3AsO_4. E. Franke gave for the conductivity of soln. with an eq. of the normal salt in v litres of water at 25°, $\lambda=107·0$, 114·3, and 119·3 for $v=170$, 340, and 680 respectively. A. Lamy saturated a boiling soln. of arsenic acid with thallous carbonate, and obtained **thallous hydroarsenate,** Tl_2HAsO_4, in needle-like crystals ; and P. S. Oettinger obtained the same salt from a filtered soln. of thallium in arsenic acid. E. Franke found the conductivity of soln. with an eq. of the salt in v litres of water at 25° to be :

v	16	32	64	128	256	512	1024
λ	70·4	74·3	78·3	81·2	82·8	84·2	85·4 mhos.

P. S. Oettinger found the salt to be sparingly soluble in water, and to melt to a glassy mass at 120°. At an elevated temp., it gives off white fumes of arsenic trioxide, and leaves behind black thallous oxide. J. E. Willm prepared **thallous dihydroarsenate,** TlH_2AsO_4, by boiling thallic oxide with a soln. of arsenic trioxide ; if the soln. be not too dil., it furnishes needle-like crystals which are not changed at 150°. J. E. Willm found that when a soln. of thallic nitrate is treated with arsenic acid, a lemon-yellow, gelatinous mass is produced, **thallic arsenate,** $TlAsO_4.2H_2O$. It is not dissolved or changed by boiling water ; but it dissolves in hydrochloric acid ; it is decomposed by aq. ammonia or potash-lye with the separation of thallic hydroxide or a basic salt. A. Rosenheim and S. Thon could not prepare **thalli-arsenates** like the aluminoarsenates.

W. Hisinger and J. J. Berzelius [6] treated cerous oxide with soln. of arsenic acid and obtained **cerous hydroarsenate,** $Ce_4(HAsO_4)_3$, as a white, insoluble powder ; and by evaporating a soln. of this salt in arsenic acid, the gelatinous mass obtained was said to be **cerous dihydroarsenate,** $Ce(H_2AsO_4)_3$. These statements have not yet been confirmed. G. A. Barbieri and J. Calzolari found that when a mixture of a mol of cerous nitrate, 4 mols of arsenic acid, and conc. nitric acid is heated for some hours, and the excess of nitric acid is distilled off, the resulting pale yellow soln. deposits white needles of **ceric dihydroarsenate,** $Ce(H_2AsO_4)_4.4H_2O$. When this salt is dissolved in the minimum quantity of nitric acid, and the cold soln. diluted with water, a white crystalline deposit of **ceric hydroarsenate,** $Ce(HAsO_4)_2.6H_2O$, appears, while arsenic acid remains in soln. A few qualitative observations have been made on the arsenates of the rare earths. F. Frerichs and F. Smith described gelatinous precipitates of **lanthanum hydroarsenate,** $La_2(HAsO_4)_3.nH_2O$, and of pale-red **didymium hydroarsenate,** $Di(HAsO_4)_3.nH_2O$, obtained by adding sodium hydroarsenate to a soln. of the corresponding sulphate. A. Rosenheim and S. Thon could not prepare lanthanoarsenates like the alumino-arsenates. J. J. Berzelius, O. Popp, and N. J. Berlin treated yttrium hydroarsenate with ammonia and obtained what he regarded as **yttrium orthoarsenate,** presumably $YAsO_4.nH_2O$; and also by treating an yttrium salt with sodium hydroarsenate. The white gelatinous precipitate dries to a yellow horny mass which when treated with nitric acid becomes gelatinous and then dissolves. N. J. Berlin obtained **yttrium dihydroarsenate,** $Y(H_2AsO_4)_3.nH_2O$, by adding a salt of yttrium to a soln. of sodium hydroarsenate in excess. The white precipitate is soluble in nitric acid, and the soln. yields a crystalline crust as the acid evaporates. A. G. Ekeberg found that arsenic acid dissolves yttria, forming a soln. of **yttrium hydroarsenate,** presumably $Y_2(HAsO_4)_3.nH_2O$, and when the soln. is warmed arsenic acid is precipitated.

REFERENCES.

[1] C. Palache and L. H. Bauer, *Amer. Min.*, **12**. 77, 149, 1927 ; A. Coloriano, *Compt. Rend.*, **103**. 273, 1886 ; *Bull. Soc. Chim.*, (2), **45**. 707, 1886 ; *Recherches sur quelques arsénates cristallisés*, Paris, 1886 ; P. Berthier, *Ann. Chim. Phys.*, (3), **7**. 76, 1843 ; C. Lefèvre, *ib.*, (6), **27**. 42, 1892 ; *Sur les arsénates cristallisés*, Paris, 1891 ; *Compt. Rend.*, **111**. 36, 1890 ; E. Berger, *ib.*, **170**. 1492, 1920 ; H. Rose, *Zeit. anal. Chem.*, **1**. 416, 1862 ; N. S. Maskelyne, *Nature*, **18**. 426, 1878 ; W. Flight, *Journ. Chem. Soc.*, **43**. 140, 1883 ; A. Lacroix, *Bull. Soc. Min.*, **24**. 27, 1901 ; A. Rosenheim and S. Thon, *Zeit. anorg. Chem.*, **167**. 1, 1927.

[2] H. Dufet, *Bull. Soc. Min.*, **23**. 147, 1900 ; W. Möricke, *Zeit. prakt. Geol.*, **1**. 143, 1893.

[3] J. L. Bournon, *Phil. Trans.*, **91**. 174, 1801 ; P. Rashleigh, *Specimens of British Minerals*, London, 2. 2, 1802 : A. G. Werner, *Letztes Mineralsystem*, Freiberg, 1803 ; C. F. Ludwig, *Handbuch der Mineralogie*, Leipzig, **2**. 215, 1804 ; D. L. G. Karsten, *Mineralogische Tabellen*, Berlin, 64, 1808 ; F. Mohs, *Grundriss der Mineralogie*, Dresden, 187, 1822 ; J. F. L. Hausmann, *Handbuch der Mineralogie*, Göttingen, 1051, 1813 ; E. F. Glocker, *Handbuch der Mineralogie*, Nürnberg, 859, 1831 ; J. D. Dana, *A System of Mineralogy*, New York, 567, 1868 ; R. Hermann, *Journ. prakt. Chem.*, (1), **33**. 296, 1844 ; A. Damour, *Ann. Chim. Phys.*, (3), **13**. 414, 1845 ; A. des Cloizeaux, *De l'emploi des propriétés optiques biréfringentes en minéralogie*, Paris, **2**. 71, 1859 ; *Nouvelles recherches sur les propriétés optiques des cristaux*, Paris, 144, 1867 ; C. F. Rammelsberg, *Handbuch der Mineralchemie*, Leipzig, 352, 1875 ; P. Groth, *Tabellarische Uebersicht der Mineralien*, Braunschweig, 98, 1898 ; A. H. Church, *Min. Mag.*, **11**. 3, 1895.

[4] F. W. Clarke, *Journ. Washington Acad.*, **2**. 516, 1912.

[5] J. E. Willm, *Ann. Chim. Phys.*, (4), **5**. 5, 1865 ; E. Franke, *Zeit. phys. Chem.*, **16**. 463, 1895 ; A. Lamy, *ib.*, (4), **5**. 410, 421, 1865 ; *Leçon sur le thallium*, Paris, 1863 ; P. S. Oettinger, *On the Combinations of Thallium*, Berlin, **64**, 1864 ; A. Rosenheim and S. Thon, *Zeit. anorg. Chem.*, **167**. 1, 1927.

[6] G. A. Barbieri and J. Calzolari, *Ber.*, **43**. 2214, 1910 ; W. Hisinger and J. J. Berzelius, *Gehlen's Journ.*, **2**. 397, 1804 ; *Schweigger's Journ.*, **17**. 424, 1816 ; J. J. Berzelius, *ib.*, **16**. 250, 404, 1816 ; A. G. Ekeberg, *Scherer's Journ.*, **3**. 189, 1800 ; **9**. 597, 1803 ; N. J. Berlin, *Pogg. Ann.*, **43**. 105, 1838 ; F. Frerichs and F. Smith, *Liebig's Ann.*, **191**. 331, 1878 ; J. C. G. de Marignac, *Ann. Chim. Phys.*, (3), **38**. 148, 1853 ; *Liebig's Ann.*, **88**. 240, 1853 ; O. Popp, *ib.*, **131**. 195, 1864 ; A. Rosenheim and S. Thon, *Zeit. anorg. Chem.*, **167**. 1, 1927.

§ 20. The Arsenates of the Titanium and Tin Families

S. J. Thugutt's [1] observations on the **arsenatosodalite** have been previously mentioned—**6**. 40, 40 and 46. H. Rose obtained what may have been **titanyl-arsenate,** by adding arsenic acid to a soln. of titanic acid in hydrochloric acid made as nearly neutral as possible. The flocculent precipitate is insoluble in an excess of either reagent.

O. Kulka,[2] and S. R. Paykull reported zirconium arsenate, or **zirconyl pyro-arsenate,** $Zr_2As_2O_9.H_2O$, or $(ZrO)_2As_2O_7.H_2O$, to be precipitated as a white powder when a soln. of zirconium sulphate is treated with sodium hydroarsenate. The former regarded the product dried at 100°–110° as a *monohydrate ;* the latter, the product dried at 100° as a hemipentahydrate. The product is insoluble in water, but soluble in hydrochloric acid. M. Weibull obtained a voluminous white precipitate by treating an hydrochloric acid soln. of zirconyl fluoride with sodium hydroarsenate. He represented the analysis by the formula $3ZrO_2.2As_2O_5.5H_2O$, or **zirconium orthoarsenate,** $Zr_3As_4O_{16}.5H_2O$, *i.e.* $Zr_3(AsO_4)_4.5H_2O$. E. Wedekind and H. Wilke studied the adsorption of arsenic acid by zirconium dioxide, and it was assumed that there is a slow chemical reaction whereby **zirconium hydroarsenate,** $Zr(HAsO_4)_2$, *i.e.* $HO.AsO : O_2 : Zr : O_2 : AsO.OH$, is formed.

J. J. Berzelius [3] treated a neutral or acid thorium salt with arsenic acid or sodium hydroarsenate, and obtained a white flocculent precipitate insoluble in water and arsenic acid. G. A. Barbieri obtained basic salts of variable composition by adding to a thorium salt soln. insufficient arsenic acid for complete precipitation. He found crystalline **thorium hydroarsenate,** $Th(HAsO_4)_2.6H_2O$, is precipitated when a 40 per cent. aq. soln. of 4 mols of arsenic acid is added to a boiling soln. of thorium nitrate holding the eq. of 2 per cent. thoria in soln. **If cold dil. soln. be used** no precipitate is formed, but a gelatinous mass is produced which eventually passes into the crystalline hydroarsenate. If less arsenic acid be used, an amorphous precipitate of variable composition is produced. The salt loses some water of crystallization when dried in air. It is insoluble in water; but is slowly hydrolyzed by that menstruum. It is insoluble in dil. nitric and arsenic acids. Colourless crystals of **thorium dihydroarsenate,** $Th(H_2AsO_4)_4.4H_2O$, are precipitated when a 50 per cent. soln. of arsenic acid is added to a soln. of thorium nitrate containing 5 per cent. thoria. Eight mols of arsenic acid per mol of thoria are used. The salt is decomposed by water, forming the hydroarsenate.

According to C. W. Scheele,[4] tin dissolves in an aq. soln. of arsenic acid with the evolution of arsine, and the formation of tin arsenate; and arsenic acid reacts with stannous acetate, or potassium arsenate with stannous chloride, forming a white insoluble precipitate. E. Lenssen showed that the voluminous precipitate formed when a conc. acetic acid soln. of potassium arsenate is mixed in small quantities at a time with stannous chloride, is **stannous hydroarsenate,** $SnHAsO_4.\frac{1}{2}H_2O$. It decomposes when heated, forming arsenic trioxide and stannic oxide, as well as a trace of arsenic. W. C. Williams found that a mixture of moderately conc. aq. soln. of arsenic acid and stannic chloride thickens on standing, and in a few weeks forms a transparent, colourless, non-crystalline mass. After dialysis, the jelly has a sp. gr. 1·135. A great deal of water is given off at 100°, but a little is retained tenaciously even at 200°. Below dull redness, decomposition occurs with the evolution of arsenic trioxide. An analysis agrees with **stannic orthoarsenate,** $Sn_3(AsO_4)_4.6H_2O$. Conc. acids, and alkali-lye dissolve it readily; water dissolves it slowly—possibly by peptization. The aq. soln. gives a gelatinous precipitate of the arsenate when treated with sulphuric, nitric, or hydrochloric acid, ammonium, calcium, barium, or iron chloride, silver nitrate, and potassium iodide; but not by acetic acid, alcohol, mercuric chloride, sodium phosphate, or the carbonate of sodium, potassium, or ammonium. E. Haeffely obtained **stannic pyroarsenate,** $Sn_2As_2O_9,10H_2O$, by boiling a soln. of sodium stannate with an excess of sodium arsenate and nitric acid. The white gelatinous precipitate dried at ordinary temp. retains 10 mols. of water which it loses at 120°. He also obtained **sodium tetrarsenatostannate,** $6Na_2O.SnO_2.2As_2O_5.50H_2O$, in needle-like crystals by boiling normal sodium arsenate with stannic hydroxide; or by treating stannic arsenate with sodium hydroxide. W. Prandtl and O. Rosenthal also reported colourless needles of **sodium pentarsenatostannate,** $Na_2SnO_3.5Na_3AsO_4.60H_2O$, to be formed by mixing 50 grms. of pentahydrated stannic chloride in aq. soln. with a soln. of 33 grms. of arsenic pentoxide in soda-lye, and neutralizing the soln.

The **lead arsenates** attracted no special attention until 1893, when F. C. Moulton [5] recommended their use for the destruction of leaf-eating insects. Since then, lead arsenate in different forms has been extensively employed as an insecticide in place of Paris green; and several thousand tons are used annually in the United States. This subject has been discussed by H. Astruc and co-workers, C. E. Bradley and H. V. Tartar, H. V. Tartar and R. H. Robinson, A. Cutolo, C. H. Hall, A. L. Lovett and R. H. Robinson, L. Moreau and E. Vinet, W. E. Ruth, C. B. Sprague, F. T. Shutt, etc. Products derived from the reaction between lead acetate or nitrate, and sodium hydroarsenate are the active constituents in various spraying mixtures employed as insecticides. These prophylactics usually contain mixtures of normal lead arsenate, and hydroarsenate. They have been described or patented by A. O. Allen, B. T. Barreto, E. O. Barstow, M. W. Butler, L. Cambi, F. C. Cook and N. E. McIndoo, J. F. Cullen and T. E. Harper, B. E. Curry and T. O. Smith, P. Denniston and J. McMillan, C. W. Drury and C. W. Simmons, Grasselli Chemical Co., G. P. Gray and A. W. Christie, A. Hamilton, J. K. Haywood and C. C. McDonnell, W. P. Headden, O. F. Hedenburg and D. S. Pratt, F. Herrmann, M. S. Hopkins, and N. Underwood, H. Howard, J. Kirby and co-workers, I. P. Lihme, J. Lytle, C. C. McDonnell and J. J. T. Graham, B. E. A. McGill, Merrimac Chemical

Co., W. Middleton, T. A. Mitchell and K. Toabe, G. R. Riches and W. C. Piver R. H. Robinson, C. H. Sakryd and H. M. Rosencrans, F. T. Shutt, H. V. Tartar and G. G. Grant, M. L. Tower and co-workers, and R. E. Wilson. The preparation of lead arsenate by the electrolytic process indicated in connection with calcium arsenate has been discussed by S. J. Lloyd and A. M. Kennedy, J. F. Cullen and T. E. Harper, and H. V. Tartar and G. G. Grant.

The early work on the lead arsenates by J. J. Berzelius, E. Mitscherlich, G. C. Wittstein, T. Graham, H. Rose, and H. Salkowsky embodies several contradictions. The term neutral lead arsenate was applied indiscriminately to both the hydroarsenate and pyroarsenate, and the mineral mimetite was regarded as a subarsenate until V. Rose, and F. Wöhler had shown

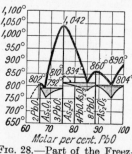

FIG. 28.—Part of the Freezing-point Curve of the Binary Mixtures: PbO–As$_2$O$_5$.

it to be a chloroarsenate. M. Amadori studied the thermal diagram of the system PbO–As$_2$O$_5$, Fig. 28. He found that there is a maximum for the pyroarsenate at 802°, and a eutectic at 792°; a second maximum for the orthoarsenate at 1042°, and a eutectic at 810°; and a third maximum for the pentoxyorthoarsenate, 8PbO.As$_2$O$_5$, at 862°, and a eutectic at 804°. L. Cambi and G. Bozza studied the electrometric titration of soln. of lead nitrate or chloride with sodium orthoarsenate, or hydroarsenate. They found that precipitates formed by the action of calcium hydroxide on soln. of arsenic acid and lead nitrate contain a negligible proportion of calcium oxide, while those produced in the presence of the chloride contain lead arsenate as well as chloroarsenate. They also studied the equilibrium conditions in the reaction Ca$_3$(AsO$_4$)$_2$+3Pb(NO$_3$)$_2$$\rightleftharpoons$Pb$_3$(AsO$_4$)$_2$+3Ca(NO$_3$)$_2$. There is a thermal change at 834° corresponding with the formation of an unstable **lead oxyorthoarsenate,** 4PbO.As$_2$O$_5$.

C. Schairer prepared **lead orthoarsenate,** Pb$_3$(AsO$_4$)$_2$, by gradually heating lead dioxide and arsenic trioxide in a covered crucible, and boiling the product with water. Some pyrophosphate was formed at the same time. O. W. Brown and co-workers roasted a mixture of lead oxide with 22·81 per cent. of arsenic trioxide at about 450°. The oxidation proceeds rapidly at first, and the speed of the reaction then slows down. M. Amadori's observations on the conditions of equilibrium of this compound, with respect to arsenic pentoxide and lead oxide, are indicated in Fig. 28. C. C. McDonnell and C. M. Smith obtained it by fusing a mixture of lead oxide and lead pyroarsenate or hydroarsenate in theoretical proportions. I. McDougall and F. Holwes mixed colloidal lead oxide with arsenic acid at 80°, and obtained a precipitate of lead arsenate in a few minutes. The normal arsenate is not an easy salt to prepare by wet processes. J. J. Berzelius reported it to be formed by the action of ammonia on lead hydroarsenate, and when a neutral hydroarsenate is mixed with neutral lead acetate. W. H. Volck said that the product has less than the theoretical quantity of arsenic pentoxide. H. V. Tartar and R. H. Robinson said that when aq. ammonia acts on lead hydroarsenate, a basic arsenate, and not the normal arsenate is produced. E. Mitscherlich obtained the same salt by adding a neutral lead salt to an excess of a soln. of an arsenate. S. U. Pickering, and G. C. Wittstein used this process; H. Salkowsky said that the product is a pyroarsenate; and E. Mitscherlich obtained the normal arsenate by adding lead acetate to the dihydroarsenate, and boiling the mixture. W. H. Volck observed the formation of the normal arsenate by the protracted treatment of the hydroarsenate with water, but H. V. Tartar and R. H. Robinson could not confirm this by using either hot or cold water. T. Graham said that the normal arsenate is produced by adding lead acetate to a soln. of sodium orthoarsenate. R. D. Holland and B. B. Reed treated sodium hydroarsenate with lead acetate in certain proportions and obtained a product with the normal ratio

PbO : As_2O_5 as 3 : 1, but H. V. Tartar and R. H. Robinson said that the ortho-arsenate cannot be obtained by a reaction between these two substances. C. C. McDonnell and C. M. Smith studied the action of lead nitrate and acetate on sodium orthoarsenate and hydroarsenate in different proportions, and found that the product is close to the 3 : 1 ratio only when lead acetate is mixed with an excess of sodium hydroarsenate. The facts thus indicate that lead orthoarsenate is relatively unstable and can exist within only very limited conditions. C. C. McDonnell and C. M. Smith agitated for seven hours on two successive days mixtures of lead hydroarsenate and water containing a constant proportion of ammonia in order to keep lead hydroxide in soln., otherwise the low solubility of lead hydroxide prevents the system being followed beyond lead hydroarsenate. Working at 32°, the dil. aq. ammonia is assumed to have no solvent action on the lead arsenates, and to form no complex salts under the conditions of the experiment, so that the system is assumed to behave like one of three components. The results are summarized in Fig. 29. The first additions of ammonia furnish the curve AB, indicating the existence of two solid phases—one being lead hydroarsenate, and the other the normal arsenate. Hence AB indicates that the lead hydroarsenate is being changed to the normal arsenate ; and at B, the change is complete. Along BC, a series of solid soln. between lead orthoarsenate, B. and a basic arsenate, C, are produced. The basic arsenate—*vide infra*, lead hydroxytriarsenate—changes very little in composition as the curve progresses from C to D. B. Ormont obtained lead arsenate by the electrolytic oxidation of a soln. of lead arsenite.

C. C. McDonnell and C. M. Smith reported a *hemihydrate*, $Pb_3(AsO_4)_2.\frac{1}{2}H_2O$, to be formed by treating lead hydroarsenate with the theoretical proportion of $0.1N$-ammonia. The water is not expelled at 110°. The amorphous powder has a sp. gr. of 7·00, at 15°/4°. A. Dexheimer did not succeed in making a **colloidal solution of lead arsenate,** by the method analogous to those employed with the other metal arsenates—*vide supra*. F. J. Brinley prepared colloidal lead arsenate, stable for a few days, by dissolving a mixture of 311·96 g. of sodium hydroarsenate, and 17·35 g. of gelatin in a small quantity of hot water diluted to 10 litres, and slowly adding a soln. of 331·4 g. of lead nitrate in 10 litres of water, with constant stirring, avoiding an excess of lead. More conc. soln. than $0.1M$-soln. give a curdy precipitate, and in $0.01M$-soln. there is tendency for needle-shaped crystals to form.

Anhydrous lead orthoarsenate prepared by the fusion processes is described as a yellowish-white crystalline mass which, according to C. C. McDonnell and C. M. Smith, has a sp. gr. 7·30 at 15°/4°. That prepared by the wet process is described as an amorphous mass with a sp. gr. 7·00 at 15°/4°. S. Motylewsky found the drop-weight of lead arsenate to be 262 when that of water at 0° is 100. M. Amadori gave 1042° for the m.p. ; H. V. Regnault, 0·0728 for the sp. ht., and 65·4 for the mol. ht. ; and C. C. McDonnell and C. M. Smith, 2·14 for the index of refraction. E. F. Smith and J. G. Hibbs said that the arsenate is decomposed completely when heated with hydrogen chloride, forming lead chloride and volatile arsenic chloride. G. C. Wittstein found that the arsenate is insoluble in water, aq. ammonia, and soln. of ammonium salts ; and C. E. Bradley and H. V. Tartar, less soluble than the hydroarsenate in dil. alkali-lye, soln. of sodium chloride, and of calcium polysulphide. E. Duvillier found that hot nitric acid liberates arsenic acid ; and decomposition is complete if the conc. of the acid is so great that the lead nitrate does not dissolve. H. V. Tartar and L. A. Bundy said that unlike the hydroarsenate, the normal arsenate is only sparingly soluble in soap soln. M. Amadori gave for mixtures of lead phosphate with 0, 25, 50, 75, 100 per cent. of lead arsenate the respective f.p. 1014°, 1020°, 1028°, 1035°, and 1042°. V. Zotier studied the decomposition of hydrogen dioxide in the presence of lead arsenate.

A number of basic salts have been reported with the ratio PbO : As_2O_5 ranging from 8 : 1 to 5 : 21. M. Amadori's diagram, Fig. 29, shows the conditions of stability of **lead pentoxyorthoarsenate**, $8PbO.As_2O_5$, or $PbO.Pb_3(AsO_4)_2$, with a m.p. of 860°. A. V. M. Kroll has reported an analogous phosphate—**7**. 47, 1. C. C. McDonnell and C. M. Smith obtained the hemihydrate, $5PbO.Pb_3(AsO_4)_2.\frac{1}{2}H_2O$. The same salt appears to have been formed by D. Strömholm by shaking freshly precipitated lead hydroxide with $0.05N$-sodium hydroarsenate until the soln. has the calculated alkalinity owing to the formation of sodium hydroxide. He assigned a formula between $9PbO.As_2O_5$ and $5PbO.As_2O_5$ to the product—preferring $15PbO.2As_2O_5$—but C. C. McDonnell and C. M. Smith showed that the composition is $8PbO.As_2O_5.\frac{1}{2}H_2O$. They also made it by pouring a filtered sat. soln. of lead hydroarsenate in cold 10 per cent. potash-lye into 5–8 vols. of boiling water, and drying the product at 110°; and by adding 100 c.c. of a 25 per cent. soln. of lead nitrate to 600 c.c. of a soln. of 50 grms. of dodecahydrated sodium orthoarsenate; treating the filtrate with 100 c.c. more of the lead nitrate soln.; repeating the operation twice more; and finally washing and drying the product at 105°. The first three precipitates are mixtures of lead hydroxide and basic lead acetate; the fourth precipitate is the required one. The product may be crystalline or amorphous. The white plates have a sp. gr. of 8·04 at 15°/15°; an index of refraction 2·22 for Na-light at 20°; and a feeble, positive birefringence. The compound is not completely dehydrated at 200°; it melts without decomposition, and solidifies to a crystalline mass. The basic salt prepared from commercial lead salts becomes dark brown or purple in a few minutes, perhaps owing to the presence of silver salts.

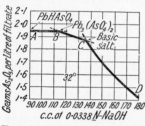

FIG. 29.—Equilibrium in the System : $PbO-As_2O_5-H_2O$ at 32°.

M. Amadori's lead oxyorthoarsenate, $4PbO.As_2O_5$, has been indicated in connection with Fig. 29. C. C. McDonnell and C. M. Smith reported **lead dihydroxytetrarsenate**, $Pb_5(PbOH)_2(AsO_4)_4$, or $7PbO.2As_2O_5.H_2O$, to be formed by pouring into 25·5 vols. of boiling water, a soln. of potassium or sodium hydroxide sat. with lead hydroarsenate. The washed product dried at 105° consists of small prismatic crystals which are doubly refractive, have a negative elongation, and an index of refraction of 2·07 for Na-light at 20°. The sp. gr. is 7·08 at 15°/15°.

The action of ammonia on lead hydroarsenate has been indicated above. J. J. Berzelius said that the normal arsenate is produced, but W. H. Volck said the product appears more basic than this, owing to the adsorption of other lead compounds. H. V. Tartar and R. H. Robinson said that with an excess of ammonia the basic arsenate $7Pb_3(AsO_4)_2.2Pb(OH)_2.5H_2O$ is formed—owing to an arithmetical error in calculating the formula from the analysis, they gave a more complex formula, namely 21 : 2 : 10. C. C. McDonnell and C. M. Smith's observations are summarized in Fig. 29. They found that when ammonia is distilled into water containing lead hydroarsenate, this is changed into what they called *hydroxymimetite*, $Pb_4(PbOH)(AsO_4)_3.H_2O$:

$$HO-Pb-AsO_4 {<}^{Pb-AsO_4-Pb}_{Pb-AsO_4-Pb}$$

that is, **lead hydroxytriarsenate**. They represented the reaction : $10PbHAsO_4 +nNH_3+Aq.=10PbO.3As_2O_5.mH_2O+4(NH_4)_3AsO_4+(n-12)NH_3+Aq.$ This is in agreement with the observations of G. E. Smith, who made the same compound by digesting lead hydroarsenate in 5 per cent. aq. ammonia for 3 hrs. on a water-bath, and filtering, washing, and drying the product at 110°. C. C. McDonnell and C. M. Smith recommended this procedure :

Lead hydroarsenate was added to a boiling 50 per cent. soln. of ammonium acetate mixed with about a quarter of its vol. of conc. aq. ammonia. Some of the lead salt passed into soln The filtered liquid was poured into 5–10 times its vol. of boiling water, when a voluminous white precipitate was formed. This was washed with boiling distilled water, and dried to a constant weight at 105°.

C. C. McDonnell and J. J. T. Graham said that the prolonged action of water on the hydroarsenate yields crystals of hydroxymimetite; and H. V. Tartar and L. A. Bundy found salts of the weak acids act in a similar way—*vide infra*. The preparation of this compound was studied by L. R. Streeter and R. W. Thatcher. G. E. Smith obtained the same salt by adding lead nitrate or acetate to a soln. of sodium hydroarsenate diluted to 0·001 mol per litre. The precipitate was immediately washed by decantation and dried. The analyses of products obtained by G. E. Smith, C. C. McDonnell and C. M. Smith, and H. V. Tartar and R. H. Robinson do not discriminate between the formulæ $Pb_4(PbOH)(AsO_4)_3.H_2O$ and $7Pb_3(AsO_4)_2.$ $2Pb(OH)_2.5H_2O$. The first one is taken to represent best the composition of the product. The white powder obtained by C. C. McDonnell and C. M. Smith consisted of hexagonal prisms terminated by the basal pinacoid frequently having the corners truncated by the second order pyramid. The crystals have parallel extinction, and are uniaxial. The average index of refraction is 2·09 at 20° with Na-light. These results closely resemble those obtained with artificial mimetite. The sp. gr. is 6·86 at 15°/15°.

The secondary salt, **lead hydroarsenate**, $PbHAsO_4$, has received many names —neutral lead arsenate, acid lead arsenate, lead hydrogen arsenate, secondary lead arsenate, diplumbic hydrogen arsenate, diplumbic arsenate, dilead orthoarsenate, and in commerce simply lead arsenate because this is the commonest form of the lead arsenates. J. J. Berzelius, G. C. Wittstein, H. Rose, G. E. Smith, H. Salkowsky, R. D. Holland and B. B. Reed, W. C. Ebaugh, produced this salt by adding an excess of lead nitrate to a soln. of sodium arsenate; E. Mitscherlich, J. Valentin, C. C. McDonnell and C. M. Smith, by adding lead acetate to a soln. of a dihydroarsenate—the product may be mixed with normal lead arsenate; E. Duvillier, by diluting with water a boiling soln. of lead arsenate in nitric acid; H. Goguel, by adding conc. arsenic acid to a boiling soln. of lead nitrate acidified with one per cent. of nitric acid; and A. de Schulten, and H. V. Tartar and R. H. Robinson, by slowly adding with constant stirring a 0·3 per cent. soln. of ammonia to a hot sat. soln. of lead arsenate in nitric acid. C. C. McDonnell and C. M. Smith found that if lead chloride be employed in place of the nitrate or acetate, a chloroarsenate is formed—*vide infra*. B. E. Curry and T. O. Smith allowed dil. soln. of lead nitrate and of sodium hydroarsenate to remain in contact for 3 months, and the results of the analysis of the filtrates is summarized in Fig. 30. They therefore concluded that in the system sodium hydroarsenate, lead nitrate, and water, at 25°, only one compound, lead hydroarsenate, exists. Working under other conditions, F. J. Smith, S. U. Pickering, J. K. Haywood, and H. V. Tartar and R. H. Robinson noted that the reaction

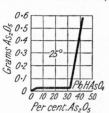

FIG. 30.—Equilibrium in the System: Na_2HAsO_4–$Pb(NO_3)_2$ –H_2O at 25°.

between lead nitrate and sodium hydroarsenate may give a product rather more basic than the hydroarsenate; but these systems may not have all been in equilibrium. C. C. McDonnell and C. M. Smith obtained salts more basic than the normal arsenate from lead acetate and sodium hydroarsenate. Analyses in agreement with the above formula were reported by L. J. Thénard, R. Chenevix. J. J. Berzelius, H. Goguel, H. V. Tartar and R. H. Robinson, A. de Schulten, H. Salkowsky, and C. C. McDonnell and C. M. Smith. L. J. Spencer found that the colourless, transparent, lustrous plates of a mineral from Tsumeb, Otavi, S.W. Africa, which he called **schultenite**—after A. de Schulten—were lead hydroarsenate.

Well-developed crystals of lead hydroarsenate were obtained by E. Duvillier, and C. C. McDonnell and C. M. Smith by pouring a boiling soln. of nitric acid (1 : 4) sat. with lead hydroarsenate into about 6 times its vol. of boiling water. Larger crystals were obtained by cooling the nitric acid soln. without dilution. L. J. Spencer said that the monoclinic crystals of schultenite have the axial ratios

$a:b:c=0.8643:1:0.7181$, and $\beta=84°\ 36'$. The crystallographic data for the mineral agree with those previously determined for the artificial hydroarsenate. The optic axial angles $2V_a=58°\ 14'$; and $2E_a=136°\ 38'$ for Na-light. The artificial crystals obtained by H. Goguel, and A. de Schulten were described as monoclinic leaflets with an acute angle about 84°. The former said extinction occurred at 21°–22°, the latter at 38°, while C. C. McDonnell and C. M. Smith gave 29°. The birefringence is high; the optical character positive; the indices of refraction $\alpha=1.90$, and $\gamma=1.97$. L. J. Spencer gave for schultenite $\alpha=1.8903$, $\beta=1.9077$, and $\gamma=1.9765$. P. Niggli said that the crystals are triclinic. A. de Schulten gave 6.076 for the sp. gr. of the crystals at 15°; H. V. Tartar and R. H. Robinson gave 5.786 at 20°/4° for the amorphous powder; and C. C. McDonnell and C. M. Smith, 6.053 at 15°/15° for the crystals, and 5.93 for the amorphous powder. L. J. Spencer gave for schultenite 5.943. H. Goguel said that the hydroarsenate can be heated to 200° without loss of weight, and it is not decomposed; H. V. Tartar and R. H. Robinson added that the formation of pyroarsenate occurs at a dull red-heat, while C. C. McDonnell and C. M. Smith found that the passage into pyroarsenate occurs at 280°. It melts at a bright red-heat, and on cooling forms a crystalline mass of the pyroarsenate. H. Goguel, and H. V. Tartar and R. H. Robinson found the hydroarsenate to be insoluble in cold water; C. C. McDonnell and co-workers showed that cold water has very little solvent action, while 100 c.c. of boiling water dissolved only 2 mgrms. of arsenic pentoxide in 6 hrs. W. H. Volck said that the prolonged action of fog, dew, and rain will convert the hydroarsenate into the orthoarsenate, but H. V. Tartar and R. H. Robinson could not confirm this. It was noted by W. P. Headden, and J. K. Haywood, and C. C. McDonnell and co-workers that when sprayed on tender foliage, the leaves may appear pitted owing to the decomposition of the arsenate by water; and, as indicated above, C. C. McDonnell and J. J. T. Graham showed that water slowly hydrolyzes lead hydroarsenate, forming hydroxymimetite: $5PbHAsO_4+H_2O \rightleftharpoons 2H_3AsO_4 +Pb_4(PbOH)(AsO_4)_3$. The reaction reaches equilibrium when the conc. of the arsenic acid is very low, but if the water be constantly changed, the end-product is lead hydroxytriarsenate. According to W. C. Ebaugh, hydrogen chloride acts on the heated hydroarsenate, forming lead chloride, and a volatile arsenic compound; hydrogen bromide acts similarly; C. C. McDonnell and C. M. Smith said that the hydroarsenate dissolves in hydrochloric acid, and that the soln. yields crystals of lead chloroarsenate, and lead chloride and hydroarsenate; while conc. and dil. soln. of alkali chlorides, and lead chloride also form the chloroarsenate; while sodium chloride and potassium bromide, and iodide act in an analogous manner. The action of aq. ammonia has been already discussed. J. J. Berzelius, and H. Goguel said that the hydroarsenate is soluble in nitric acid—*vide supra*. C. E. Bradley and H. V. Tartar found that soln. of calcium polysulphides form lead sulphide, and dissolve much of the contained arsenic. J. J. Berzelius, and J. Valentin said that the salt is not soluble in acetic acid; while G. E. Smith showed that salts of the weak acids—borax, sodium silicate, and sodium salts of the fatty acids—convert the hydroarsenate into lead hydroxytriarsenate. H. V. Tartar and L. A. Bundy found that 22.77–45.82 per cent. is dissolved by soap soln.

According to C. C. McDonnell and C. M. Smith, **lead dihydroarsenate,** $Pb(H_2AsO_4)_2$, is produced only when the conc. of the arsenic acid in soln. is high. The ordinary hydroarsenate is formed by the action of lead nitrate or acetate on an alkali dihydroarsenate: $Pb(NO_3)_2+KH_2AsO_4=PbHAsO_4+KNO_3+HNO_3$; likewise also when arsenic acid acts on lead nitrate and acetate at ordinary concentrations. A 50 per cent. soln. of arsenic acid does not convert the hydroarsenate into the dihydro-salt, but the transformation occurs when the conc. is raised above 86 per cent. arsenic acid. 400 grms. of an 86 per cent. soln. of arsenic acid, boiling at about 130°, with or without 2 per cent. nitric acid, was treated with 10 grms.

of lead hydroarsenate. The mixture was boiled a few minutes, and filtered through asbestos. The crystals were drained in the centrifuge, washed with alcohol, and dried at 110°. The Merrimac Chemical Co. treated 60 parts of lead and 25 parts of arsenic trioxide slowly with 25 kgrms. of nitric acid of sp. gr. 1·384, without allowing the temp. to rise above 90°. With these proportions the dihydro-salt is formed. C. C. McDonnell and C. M. Smith said that the crystals are long, narrow, rhomboidal plates. The acute angle is 68°. The crystals are biaxial, and probably negative. They are monoclinic or triclinic—probably the latter. The birefringence is strong; and the indices of refraction at 20° for Na-light are $\alpha=1\cdot74$, $\beta=1\cdot84$, and $\gamma=1\cdot82$. When the dihydro-salt is heated very slowly, it begins to lose water at 140°; and when kept 7 hrs. at 150°, it loses the eq. of a mol. of water, and the entire amount was not lost after heating 15 hrs. at 210°, but all was lost below a red-heat. When fused, some arsenic trioxide volatilizes. The salt is chemically very unstable, and when treated with water, it immediately forms lead hydroarsenate and arsenic acid. J. C. Brünnich and F. Smith said that lead dihydroarsenate $PbH_2As_2O_7$, occurs even in commercial arsenates, but C. C. McDonnell and C. M. Smith said that this is unlikely. The latter believe that the dehydration of lead dihydroarsenate takes place in two stages so that at 150° the reaction is $Pb(H_2AsO_4)_2=H_2O+PbH_2As_2O_7$. B. Brauner said that lead tetracetate forms by double decomposition with arsenates a very unstable lead dihydroarsenate, presumably $Pb(HAsO_4)_2$; and A. Hutchinson and W. Pollard obtained a salt of this composition by the action of arsenic acid on lead tetracetate.

According to J. J. Berzelius, L. J. Thénard, and H. Salkowsky, **lead pyroarsenate,** $Pb_2As_2O_7$, is formed when lead hydroarsenate is heated to whiteness; H. V. Tartar and R. H. Robinson said at a dull red-heat; and C. C. McDonnell and C. M. Smith, at 300°. C. Lefèvre obtained it in transparent rhombic leaflets by saturating fused potassium metarsenate with lead oxide; and C. C. McDonnell and G. M. Smith, by fusing a mixture of lead oxide and arsenic pentoxide, or lead nitrate and ammonium dihydroarsenate in eq. amounts. The fusion always results in a slight reduction to arsenite. M. Amadori's curve, Fig. 29, shows the conditions of stability. According to C. C. McDonnell and C. M. Smith, the statements of E. E. Luther and W. H. Volck that lead pyroarsenate is produced by the action of arsenic acid on basic lead carbonate, and of W. H. Volck, that it may occur in commercial "lead arsenate pastes," are not supported by facts. The mass which has been fused has a crystalline structure; the crystals are biaxial and positive with a medium birefringence, and an index of refraction $\beta=2\cdot03$ with Na-light at 20°. C. Lefèvre said that the rhombic leaflets are isomorphous with the pyrophosphates of the alkaline earths. The sp. gr. was found by C. C. McDonnell and C. M. Smith to be 6·85 at 15°/15°. M. Amadori gave 802° for the m.p. C. Lefèvre found that when heated at 500° in hydrogen, the salt is reduced to arsenic trioxide, arsenic, and lead. Cold water makes the crystals opaque; and, added C. C. McDonnell and C. M. Smith, forms lead hydroarsenate.

According to C. C. McDonnell and C. M. Smith, lead hydroarsenate loses its combined water below a red-heat and forms **lead metarsenate,** $Pb(AsO_3)_2$; the same salt is formed by heating a mixture of arsenic pentoxide and litharge, red-lead, or lead nitrate in the correct proportions. The mixture readily fuses to a mobile liquid which solidifies to a transparent glassy mass; if the glass be broken into fragments, and heated until incipient fusion occurs, the whole mass becomes crystalline. There is a slight reduction to arsenite during the preparation of this compound. Lead metarsenate consists of hexagonal tablets. The sp. gr. was 6·42 at 15°/15°. The salt is decomposed by water. The glass absorbs moisture rapidly from air and becomes opaque; the crystalline salt is less readily attacked.

C. Lefèvre treated a molten mixture of potassium chloride with over 25 per cent. of potassium orthoarsenate, or over 60 per cent. of the pyroarsenate, and obtained small transparent prisms of **potassium lead arsenate,** $KPbAsO_4$; similarly with **sodium lead arsenate,** $NaPbAsO_4$. If molten sodium metarsenate be treated with 15 per cent. of lead oxide, colourless plates of **sodium lead tripyroarsenate** $Na_4Pb_4(As_2O_7)_3$, are produced. The crystals are altered superficially by water A. H. Church[6] described a green mineral occurring in small mammillary concretions in Cornwall ; he named it **bayldonite**—after J. Bayldon. The analysis corresponds with **copper lead hydroxyarsenate,** $(Cu,Pb)_4As_2O_9.2H_2O$, analogous with libethenite, or, as P. Groth represents it, $(Cu,Pb)AsO_4(CuOH).\frac{1}{2}H_2O$. K. Bieh described a series of bayldonites which he called *cuproplumbites.* Their composition ranged over $R_3(AsO_4)_2.R(OH)_2.H_2O$ with $PbO : CuO : HO_2 = 1 : 3 ; 1 : 5 : 3 ;$ and $2 : 3$, with H_2O and $0.5H_2O$. He suggested the name *parabayldonite* for the mineral last indicated. In another series of bayldonites or cuproplumbites of the formula $2R_3(AsO_4)_2.3R(OH)_3$ the ratio $PbO : CuO = 2.5 : 1$; the monohydrate with $PbO : CuO = 4 : 5$; and the dihydrate with $PbO : CuO = 2.5 : 5$. E. S. Larsen gave for the indices of refraction $\alpha = 1.95$, and $\gamma = 1.99$. The optic axial angle is large, and the optical character positive. The hardness is 1.5–4.5 ; and the sp. gr. 5.21–5.504. O. Pufahl described a mineral from Tsumeb, South Africa, which he called **duftite**, and which occurs in small, pale olive-green, indistinct crystals soluble in hot, dil. hydrochloric acid, and which have the composition $2Pb_3(AsO_4)_2.Cu_3(AsO_4)_2.4Cu(OH)_2$, **copper lead octohydroxyhexaorthoarsenate.**

REFERENCES.

[1] S. J. Thugutt, *Zeit. anorg. Chem.*, **2.** 88. 1892 ; *Mineralchemische Studien*, Dorpat, 1891 ; H. Rose, *Ausführliches Handbuch der analytischen Chemie*, Braunschweig, **1.** 283, 1851.

[2] O. Kulka, *Beiträge zur Kenntnis einiger Verbindungen*, Bern, 1902 ; S. R. Paykull, *Bull. Soc. Chim.*, (2), **20.** 67, 1873 ; *Oefvers Akad. Förh.*, 22, 1873 ; M. Weibull, *Acta Univ. Lund.*, (2), **18.** 21, 1882 ; *Ber.*, **20.** 1394, 1887 ; E. Wedekind and H. Wilke, *Koll. Zeit.*, **34.** 83, 1924.

[3] J. J. Berzelius, *Pogg. Ann.*, **16.** 412, 1829 ; G. A. Barbieri, *Atti Accad. Lincei*, (5), **19. ii,** 643, 1910.

[4] E. Haeffely, *Phil. Mag.*, (4), **10.** 290, 1855 ; W. Prandtl and O. Rosenthal, *Ber.*, **40.** 2133, 1907 ; E. Lenssen, *Liebig's Ann.*, **114.** 113, 1860 ; C. W. Scheele, *Svenska Vet. Akad. Handl.*, **36.** 265, 1775 ; W. C. Williams, *Proc. Manchester Lit. Phil. Soc.*, **15.** 67, 1876.

[5] H. Salkowsky, *Journ. prakt. Chem.*, (1), **104.** 129, 1861 ; G. C. Wittstein, *Vollständiges etymologisch-chemisches Handwörterbuch*, München, **1.** 389, 1851 ; J. J. Berzelius, *Schweigger's Journ.*, **23.** 174, 1818 ; *Lehrbuch der Chemie*, Dresden, **3.** 72, 1845 ; *Ann. Chim. Phys.*, (2), **11.** 229, 1819 ; H. V. Regnault, *ib.*, (3), **1.** 129, 1841 ; C. Lefèvre, *ib.*, (6), **27.** 25, 1892 ; *Sur les arsénates cristallisés*, Paris, 1891 ; H. Goguel, *Contribution à l'étude des arsénates et des antimonates cristallisés préparés par voie humide*, Bordeaux, 53, 1894 ; *Mém. Soc. Phys. Nat. Bordeaux*, (5), **1.** 135, 1896 ; A. de Schulten, *Bull. Soc. Min.*, **27.** 113, 1904 ; F. J. Brinley, *Journ. Agric. Research*, **36.** 373, 1923 ; J. Valentin, *Zeit. anal. Chem.*, **54.** 83, 1915 ; L. Cambi and G. Bozza, *Giorn. Chim. Ind. Appl.*, **7.** 687, 1925 ; L. Cambi, *ib.*, **6.** 527, 1924 ; *Ital. Pat. No. 234998*, 1924 ; E. Duvillier, *Compt. Rend.*, **81.** 1251, 1875 ; H. Astruc, A. Couvergne, and J. Mahoux, *ib.*, **152.** 1860, 1911 ; L. Moureau and E. Vinet, *ib.*, **150.** 787, 1910 ; **151.** 1068, 1910 ; **156.** 906, 1913 ; J. C. Brünnich and F. Smith, *Queensland Agric. Journ.*, **26.** 333, 1911 ; C. W. Drury and C. W. Simmons, *Canadian Chem. Met.*, **9.** 179, 1925 ; A. Dexheimer, *Ueber die Darstellung anorganische Kolloide in kolloiden organischen Medien*, Erlangen, 47, 1910 ; A. Cutolo, *Boll. Chim. Farm.*, **53.** 692, 1914 ; G. Sonntag, *Arb. Kaiser. Ges. Amt.*, **49.** 502, 1914 ; S. J. Lloyd and A. M. Kennedy, *Chem. Met. Engg.*, **32.** 624, 1925 ; B. E. A. McGill, *Bull. Dept. Lab. Inland Revenue Ottawa*, 284, 1914 ; W. Middleton, *Journ. Agric. Research*, **20.** 741, 1921 ; A. L. Lovatt and R. H. Robinson, *ib.*, **10.** 199, 1917 ; B. T. Barreto, *Sugar*, **23.** 400, 1921 ; F. Herrmann, *Landw. Jahrb.*, **56.** i, 99, 1921 ; A. Hamilton, *Chem. Trade Journ.*, **65.** 365, 1915 ; E. O. Barstow and J. A. Cavanagh, *U.S. Pat. No. 1228516*, 1916 ; E. O. Barstow, *ib.*, 1014742, 1141920, 1911 ; N. Underwood, *ib.*, 1512432, 1924 ; Grasselli Chemical Co., *ib.*, 1529998, 1925 ; H. Howard, *ib.*, 1529998, 1925 ; J. Kirby, M. S. Hopkins, and C. B. Bernhardt, *ib.*, 1400167, 1921 ; E. O. Barstow and J. A. Cavanagh, *ib.*, 1228516, 1896 ; M. L. Tower and F. L. Begtrup, *ib.*, 1387212, 1387213, 1920 ; M. W. Butler, *ib.*, 1324300, 1917 ; M. L. Tower, *ib.*, 1387212, 1920 ; J. Kirby, M. S. Hopkins, and C. B. Bernhardt, *ib.*, 1398267, 1921 ; A. O. Allen, *ib.*, 1427049, 1921 ; T. A. Mitchell and K. Toabe, *ib.*, 1564093, 1925 ; E. E. Luther and W. H. Volck, *ib.*, 903389, 1908 ; R. E. Wilson, *ib.*, 1393473, 1919 ; C. H. Sakryd and H. M. Rosencrans, *ib.*, 1390647, 1390648, 1921 ; C. H. Hall, *ib.*, 1064639, 1913 ; C. B. Sprague, *ib.*, 1064023, 1909 ; O. F. Hedenburg and D. S. Pratt, *ib.*, 1344035, 1919 ; I. P. Lihme, *ib.*, 1267427, 1302186, 1918 ; *Met. Chem. Engg.*, **19.** 209, 1918 ; J. Lytle, *ib.*, **20.** 487, 1919 ; *Brit. Pat. No.* 121101, 1918 ; P. Denniston and J. McMillan, *ib.*, 3945, 1877 ; Merrimac Chemical Co., *French Pat. Nos.* 485509, 485510, 1918 ; G. R. Riches and W. C. Piver, *Canadian Pat., No.* 191628, 1919 ; L. J. Spencer, *Nature*, **118.** 411, 1926 ; *Min. Mag.*, **21.** 149, 1926 ; F. T. Shutt, *Chem. News*, **74.** 17,

1894 ; W. H. Volck, *Science*, (2), **33**. 868, 1911 ; O. Schairer, *Chem. Ztg.*, **28**. 15, 1904; E. Mit-
cherlich, *Svenska Akad. Handl.*, **4**, 1821 ; *Ann. Chim. Phys.*, (2), **19**. 405, 1821; V. Rose,
Schweigger's Journ.. **3**. 63, 1804; H. Rose, *Ausführliches Handbuch für analytischen Chemie*,
Braunschweig, **1**. 381, 1851 ; F. Wöhler, *Pogg. Ann.*, **4**. 161, 1825 ; M. Amadori, *Atti 1st. Veneto*,
76. 419, 1917 ; *Gazz. Chim. Ital.*, **49**. i, 38, 1919 ; C. C. McDonnell and C. M. Smith, *Amer. Journ.
Science*, (4), **42**. 139, 1916 ; *Journ. Amer. Chem. Soc.*, **38**. 2027, 2366, 1916 ; **39**. 938, 1917 ;
C. C. McDonnell and J. J. T. Graham, *ib.*, **39**. 1912, 1917 ; B. E. Curry and T. O. Smith, *ib.*,
37. 1687, 1915 ; G. E. Smith, *ib.*, **38**. 2014, 2366, 1916 ; H. V. Tartar and R. H. Robinson, *ib.*,
36. 1843, 1914 ; *Journ. Ind. Eng. Chem.*, **7**. 499, 1915 ; *Bull. Oregon Agric. Exp. Station*, 128,
1915 ; H. V. Tartar and L. A. Bundy, *Journ. Ind. Eng. Chem.*, **5**. 561, 1913 ; H. V. Tartar and
G. G. Grant, *ib.*, **14**. 311, 1922 ; C. E. Bradley and H. V. Tartar, *ib.*, **2**. 328, 1910 ; O. W. Brown,
C. R. Voris, and C. O. Henke, *ib.*, **13**. 531, 1921 ; R. H. Robinson, *ib.*, **14**. 313, 1922 ; J. F. Cullen
and T. E. Harper, *ib.*, **14**. 651, 1922 ; G. P. Gray and A. W. Christie, *ib.*, **8**. 1109,
1916 ; H. A. Scholz and P. J. Waldstein, *ib.*, **9**. 682, 1917 ; W. E. Ruth, *ib.*, **5**. 847, 1913 ;
L. R. Streeter and R. W. Thacker, *Journ. Ind. Eng. Chem.*, **16**. 941, 1924 ; B. Ormont, *Ukraine
Chem. Journ.*, **2**. 20, 1926 ; F. J. Smith, *Rep. Massachusetts Agric.*, **45**. 357, 1897 ; F. C. Moulton,
ib., **41**. 282, 1894 ; R. D. Holland and B. B. Reed, *ib.*, **24**. 204, 1912 ; W. P. Headden, *Bull.
Colorado Agric. Exp. Station*, 131, 1908 ; J. K. Haywood, *Bull. U.S. Dept. Agric.*, 105, 1907 ;
J. K. Haywood and C. C. McDonnell, *ib.*, 131, 1910 ; F. C. Cook and N. E. McIndoo, *ib.*, 1147,
1923 ; *Chem. News*, **127**. 35, 1923 ; I. McDougall and F. Holwes, *Brit. Pat. No.* 204223, 1922 ;
T. Graham, *Phil. Trans.*, **123**. 266, 1833 ; S. U. Pickering, *Journ. Chem. Soc.*, **91**. 309, 1907 ;
A. Hutchinson and W. Pollard, *ib.*, **69**. 224, 1896 ; D. Strömholm, *Zeit. anorg. Chem.*, **38**. 446,
1904 ; A. V. M. Kroll, *ib.*, **78**. 105, 1912 ; S. Motylewsky, *ib.*, **38**. 410, 1904 ; P. Niggli, *Zeit.
Kryst.*, **56**. 42, 1922 ; J. G. Hibbs, *The Action of Hydrochloric Acid Gas on Arsenates and Nitrates*,
Philadelphia, 1896 ; E. F. Smith and J. G. Hibbs, *Journ. Amer. Chem. Soc.*, **17**. 685, 1895 ;
W. C. Ebaugh, *ib.*, **24**. 489, 1902 ; *The Atomic Weight of Arsenic*, Philadelphia, 1901 ;
L. J. Thénard, *Ann. Chim. Phys.*, (1), **50**. 124 1804 ; R. Chenevix, *Phil. Trans.*, **91**. 199, 1801 ;
B. Zotier, *Bull. Soc. Chim.*, (4), **21**. 241, 191 ; B. Brauner, *Zeit. anorg. Chem.*, **7**. 2, 1894 ;
A. Hutchinson and W. Pollard, *Journ. Chem. Soc.*, **69**. 224, 1896.
   6 A. H. Church, *Journ. Chem. Soc.*, **18**. 265, 1865 ; P. Groth, *Tabellarische Uebersicht der
Mineralien*, Braunschweig, 174, 1898 ; K. Biehl, *Beiträge zur Kenntniss der Mineralien der
Erzlagerstätten von Tsumeb*, Münster, 1919 ; O. Pufahl, *Centr. Min.*, 289, 1920 ; E. S. Larsen,
Bull. U.S. Geol. Sur., 679, 1921.

§ 21. Arsenates of the Antimony-Vanadium Family

J. J. Berzelius [1] reported the formation of **antimony arsenate** as a white
precipitate on adding potassium metarsenate to a hydrochloric acid soln. of
antimony trichloride. P. Berthier heated an alloy of arsenic and antimony with
nitric acid, and diluted the soln. with water. He assumed that the white precipitate, soluble in nitric and hydrochloric acids, was *arsenatoantimonic acid.* If
the soln. in hydrochloric acid be evaporated, the antimonic acid is precipitated
while the arsenic acid remains in soln. There is here nothing to show that the
product was not a mixture.

According to C. W. Scheele,[2] and J. J. Berzelius, a soln. of arsenic acid or of
an alkali arsenate gives a white precipitate with a soln. of bismuth nitrate.
H. Salkowsky found that the composition of the precipitate agrees with **bismuth
orthoarsenate**, $BiAsO_4 \cdot \frac{1}{2}H_2O$, whether it is produced in soln. strongly or feebly
acidified with nitric acid, and whether the arsenic acid is in small or great excess.
M. Kuhara founded on this reaction a method for precipitating bismuth in
analytical work. R. Schneider added that this salt separates when arsenical
bismuth is treated with nitric acid. L. Vanino and F. Hartl obtained the same
precipitate when bismuth nitrate dissolved in a soln. of mannite is treated with
arsenic acid. H. Salkowsky said that the salt dried at 100°–120° is the *hemihydrate*, and that the water is expelled at a red-heat. A. de Schulten obtained
crystals of the anhydrous salt by heating on the water-bath a mixture of bismuth
nitrate, sodium arsenate, and nitric acid. A little water is added, and after some
days, microscopic, monoclinic prisms of sp. gr. 7·142 at 15° are obtained. According
to K. Haushofer, the hemihydrate is a white powder which appears under the
microscope as small, spherical, stellate, or octahedral forms, and if a large excess
of arsenic acid is employed in its preparation, the precipitate is inclined to be
amorphous. H. Salkowsky found that the salt is sparingly soluble in water, and

is less soluble in the presence of arsenic or nitric acid, but more soluble in a soln. of bismuth nitrate. On the other hand, R. Schneider said that bismuth ortho-arsenate is very sparingly soluble in a soln. of bismuth nitrate containing a little free nitric acid, and that it is more soluble in hot nitric acid than in the cold acid. L. J. Thénard said that bismuth orthoarsenate is soluble in hydrochloric acid ; and H. Salkowsky found that the arsenate is not completely decomposed by boiling alkali-lye or aq. ammonia ; the bismuth can be precipitated by repeatedly treating the hydrochloric acid with ammonia.

A. Cavazzi mixed ammoniacal soln. of sodium arsenate and bismuth citrate, and obtained a basic salt assumed to be *bismuth enneaoxydiarsenate*, $4Bi_2O_3.As_2O_5$, $3Bi_2O_3.2BiAsO_4$, or possibly $(BiO.O)_4As.O.As(O.BiO)_4$, *i.e.* **bismuthyl diarsenate,** $(BiO)_8As_2O_9$. If the alkali arsenate be added to the citrate soln., the basic salt is mixed with some citrate. The white product is sparingly soluble in water, but easily soluble in mineral acids. Another basic salt was found by G. vom Rath in a mine near Schneeberg, Saxony, and called by A. Breithaupt **atelestite**—from ἀτελής, incomplete, presumably because its composition was not known when described by G. vom Rath. It occurs in minute sulphur-yellow crystals which K. Busz assigned to the monoclinic system, with the axial ratio $a : b : c$ $=0.9334 : 1 : 1.5051$, and $\beta=70°$ 43'. The basal cleavage is indistinct. The analysis by K. Busz corresponds with $3Bi_2O_3.As_2O_5.2H_2O$, or $Bi_3H_2AsO_8$, which may be **bismuthyl orthoarsenate,** $(BiO)_3AsO_4.H_2O$, $AsO(O.BiO)_3.H_2O$, or $(BiO.O)_2As.O_2.Bi(OH)_2$. The hardness is 3·0–4·5 ; and the sp. gr. 6·4. Yet a third basic salt was reported by A. Weisbach in a mine at Neustädtel, Saxony, and named **rhagite**—from ῥάξ, a grape, in allusion to the colour and botryoidal grouping. The yellowish-green or yellow mineral occurs in crystalline mammillary or spherical aggregates. C. Winkler's analysis corresponds with $5Bi_2O_3.2As_2O_5.$ $8H_2O$, or better, according to C. F. Rammelsberg, with $5Bi_2O_3.2As_2O_5.9H_2O$. This may be represented as **bismuthyl tetrarsenate,** $(BiO)_{10}As_4O_9.9H_2O$, or $(BiO.O)_4As.O.AsO(O.BiO).O.AsO(OBiO).O.As(O.BiO)_4.9H_2O$; or as $BiAsO_4.$ $2BiO(OH)$. The hardness is 5 ; and the sp. gr. 6·82. The mineral fuses easily ; it is readily soluble in hydrochloric acid, but not so easily dissolved by nitric acid. A. H. Means described **arsenobismite**, $4Bi_2O_3.3As_2O.5H_2O$, as an impure mineral from the Mammoth Mine, Utah. Its sp. gr. is 5·70, and hardness about 3.

A. Schrauf found an emerald-green, bluish-green, or pale green mineral occurring with the bismuth ochre at Joachimsthal, and at Wittichen, Baden. The mineral was named **mixite**—after A. Mixa. According to W. F. Hillebrand and H. S. Washington, it also occurs in the Tintic district, Utah. The analyses agree with **copper bismuth arsenate,** $Cu_{20}Bi_2As_{10}O_{48}.22H_2O$. P. Groth writes the formula $BiCu_{10}(AsO_4)_5(OH)_8.7H_2O$. The slender acicular crystals are triclinic or monoclinic. The mineral also occurs as an incrustation in irregular particles, and spherical or reniform granules sometimes with a fibrous concentric structure. The mineral loses 4·08 per cent. of water at 100°, and 5·8 per cent. at 175°. The hardness is 3–4. A. Schrauf gave 2·66 for the sp. gr., while W. F. Hillebrand and H. S. Washington gave 3·79 at 23·5°. E. S. Larsen gave for the indices of refraction $\omega=1.730$, and $\epsilon=1.810$; the optical character is positive. When treated with nitric acid, the copper arsenate goes into soln., and white bismuth arsenate remains. A. Rosenheim and S. Thon could not prepare **bismutharsenates** like the aluminoarsenates.

According to J. J. Berzelius,[3] when aq. arsenic acid is sat. with vanadyl hydroxide, it yields on evaporation a gummy mass, easily soluble in water, and also crystalline grains of **vanadyl arsenate**, $V_2O_4.2As_2O_5.3H_2O$, or $V_2O_2(AsO_3)_4.$ $3H_2O$, *vanadyl metarsenate*. W. Schmitz-Dumont considered the water to be constitutional, and he wrote the formula (arsenic quinquevalent) :

$$\begin{matrix} HO \\ O \\ HO \end{matrix} {>} As {>} V_2O_2 {<} \begin{matrix} O . AsO(OH)_2 \\ O . AsO(OH)_2 \end{matrix}$$

J. J. Berzelius found the same compound was deposited on evaporating a soln. of vanadyl hydroxide in an excess of arsenic acid. W. Schmitz-Dumont made this salt by producing a hot soln. of vanadium arsenate with the theoretical quantity of arsenic trioxide. The dark green liquid absorbs oxygen from the air, forming a blue soln. of the vanadyl salt: $V_2O_5.As_2O_5+As_2O_3+O=V_2O_4.2As_2O_5$. The evaporation of the soln. yields the amorphous salt; but if an excess of arsenic acid is employed, the atm. oxidation proceeds rapidly and sky-blue crystals are deposited. The rectangular prismatic crystals can be melted without decomposition, but at a higher temp., say, 500°, arsenic trioxide volatilizes and red vanadium arsenate is formed: $V_2O_4.2As_2O_5.3H_2O=O+3H_2O+As_2O_3+V_2O_5.As_2O_5$. J. J. Berzelius said that the salt dissolves slowly when in boiling water, and in water containing arsenic acid, and when once dissolved, it does not separate on cooling the soln.; the addition of alcohol precipitates the salt from its aq. soln. The salt is freely soluble in hydrochloric acid.

J. J. Berzelius prepared vanadium arsenate by evaporating a soln. of vanadyl arsenate in nitric acid until the liquid turns red, and nitrous fumes are evolved. On cooling, a lemon-yellow compound separates which is analogous to vanadium phosphate. The analysis by W. Schmitz-Dumont agrees with the formula $V_2O_5.As_2O_5.nH_2O$. Vanadium pentoxide is a stronger base than arsenic pentoxide, and in harmony with the nomenclature for the phosphates, it is simplest to regard this compound as **vanadium arsenate**, $V_2O_2(AsO_4)_2$, or *vanadyl orthoarsenate*. P. F. y Chavarri prepared this compound by adding vanadium pentoxide in small quantities at a time, to a boiling conc. soln. of arsenic acid of sp. gr. 2. The red liquid is then diluted, filtered, and allowed to crystallize. If arsenic trioxide be present, the soln. will have a green colour. The crystals are washed with absolute alcohol to free them from mother-liquid. C. Friedheim and W. Schmitz-Dumont employed this process; and they also made the anhydrous compound by heating the preceding salt at 500° until arsenic trioxide is no longer evolved. The anhydrous salt is similarly formed by heating the hydrate to 440°. If the salt be crystallized from conc. nitric acid, the dihydrate, $V_2O_2(AsO_4)_2.2H_2O$, is formed; and if crystallized from aq. soln., the *decahydrate*, $V_2O_2(AsO_4)_2.10H_2O$. A. Ditte reported that the *tetradecahydrate* separates from a hot sat. soln., and the *octodecahydrate* by cooling a hot soln. W. Schmitz-Dumont suggested that A. Ditte's preparations were incompletely dried. The yellow, tabular crystals of the decahydrate belong to the tetragonal system. They lose water of crystallization when exposed to air—one-third being lost in 14 days, and over desiccating agents, 9 to $9\frac{1}{2}$ mols. are lost. At 100°, nine mols. of water are given off, but the tenth mol. is retained more tenaciously; all the water is lost at 440°. In agreement with this observation, C. Friedheim and W. Schmitz-Dumont represented the constitution of the anhydride and of the hydrates:

$$O=As<^{O.VO_2}_{O} \qquad O=As<^{O.VO_2}_{(OH)_2} \qquad O=As<^{O.VO_2}_{(OH)_2}.4H_2O$$

When the crystals are carefully warmed, they become brick-red, but the yellow colour is resumed on cooling. The crystals melt at a dull-redness, and arsenic trioxide is volatilized. The crystals dissolve in water, and this the more slowly, the less water of crystallization they contain. The aq. soln. has an acid reaction, and when warmed darkens in colour. When a conc. aq. soln. is heated, vanadic acid separates. The decomposition can be reversed by the addition of nitric acid, and it is prevented by the presence of arsenic acid. Hydrogen sulphide precipitates arsenic as sulphide from the soln. in hydrochloric acid, and the vanadium pentoxide is reduced to the tetroxide. The salt is insoluble in alcohol, but is not precipitated from its aq. soln. by alcohol. Alkaloids—brucine, quinine, strychnine, and nicotine—produce green, or yellowish-brown precipitates. G. Gain obtained the compound **vanadyl metahexarsenate**, $(V_2O_2)AsO_{17}.H_2O$, or $V_2O_4.3As_2O_5.H_2O$, in blue crystals by the action of arsenic acid on hydrated vanadium tetroxide. The salt becomes green when exposed to air.

O. W. Gibbs reported orange-red crystals of a compound of the composition $8V_2O_5.5As_2O_5.27H_2O$, to be formed by the addition of nitric acid to a hot soln. of sodium arsenate and vanadate, and evaporating the orange-red liquid on a water-bath ; also $6V_2O_5.7As_2O_5.3H_2O$ by oxidizing with nitric acid and potassium permanganate the residue obtained in the preparation of vanadyl vanadium arsenate. C. Friedheim and W. Schmitz-Dumont were unable to obtain either of these two products ; they were no doubt mixtures.

A number of complex arsenatovanadates have been reported ; and most of them can be represented as members of three series in which the ratios $R_2O : V_2O_5 : As_2O_5 : H_2O$, are as $1 : 1 : 1 : 1$; as $1 : 2 : 1 : 0$, or as $2 : 2 : 3 : 1$. C. Friedheim and W. Schmitz-Dumont represented typical members of each series by the formulæ

$$O=As{\Large\langle}\begin{array}{l}\text{O.VO}_2\\\text{OH}\\\text{OR}\end{array} \qquad O=As{\Large\langle}\begin{array}{l}\text{O.VO}_2\\\text{O.VO}_2\\\text{OR}\end{array} \qquad \begin{array}{l}\text{RO—AsO}{\langle}^{\text{O—VO}_2}_{\text{O}}\\\text{HO—AsO}{\langle}^{\text{O}}_{\text{O}}\\\text{RO—AsO}{\langle}^{\text{O}}_{\text{O—VO}_2}\end{array}$$

$$R_2O : V_2O_5 : As_2O_5 : H_2O \qquad R_2O : 2V_2O_5 : As_2O_5 \qquad 2R_2O : 2V_2O_5 : 3As_2O_5 : H_2O$$

The first series was obtained by C. Friedheim and W. Schmitz-Dumont by the decomposition of aq. soln. of salts of the third series ; from vanadium arsenate and the calculated quantity of either base ; and by adding a metavanadate to salts of the third series. The salts are decomposed at a red-heat, with the evolution of arsenic trioxide and oxygen. The original salt cannot always be obtained by treating with water the salt dehydrated at 150°. When the aq. soln. are warmed, or treated with alkali-lye, a yellow, gelatinous mass may be precipitated. C. Friedheim and W. Schmitz-Dumont described **copper hydroarsenatovanadate**, $Cu(HAsVO_6)_2.3H_2O$, in microscopic greenish-white needles which are sparingly soluble ; **magnesium hydroarsenatovanadate**, $Mg(HAsVO_6)_2.9H_2O$, in pale yellow needles, fairly soluble in water ; **zinc hydroarsenatovanadate**, $Zn(HAsVO_6)_2.H_2O$, in pale yellow needles which dissolve slowly in water ; and **cobalt hydroarsenatovanadate**, $Co(HAsVO_6)_2.8H_2O$, in microscopic, ochre-yellow needles, soluble in water.

The second series of salts prepared by C. Friedheim and W. Schmitz-Dumont represented by **ammonium arsenatodivanadate**, $NH_4(VO_2)_2AsO_4.2\frac{1}{2}H_2O$, was obtained by evaporating a soln. of ammonium arsenate sat. with vanadium pentoxide ; the first two crops of crystals were ammonium vanadate, and then followed a small yield of the arsenitodivanadate. A. Ditte obtained in this way yellow plates of a salt $5(NH_4)_2O.4As_2O_5.2V_2O_5.18H_2O$, but C. Friedheim and W. Schmitz-Dumont were unable to confirm this, and they suggested that A. Ditte's product is a mixture of ammonium arsenatodivanadate with ammonium dihydroarsenate, or a double salt of ammonium vanadate and arsenate. Analogous remarks apply to the sodium and potassium salts reported by A. Ditte. The ammonium salt was also prepared by C. Friedheim and W. Schmitz-Dumont by mixing vanadium pentoxide, ammonium vanadate, and a large excess of arsenic acid and allowing the liquid to stand for some weeks ; by mixing the theoretical quantities of vanadium arsenate and potassium or ammonium vanadate ; by the decomposition of an aq. soln. of the ammonium or potassium salt of the third series below ; and by mixing potassium metavanadate and arsenic acid. The ammonium salt forms small reddish-yellow needles, which acquire a superficial green tinge on exposure to air. It loses its water of crystallization in air dried by calcium chloride. It is sparingly soluble in cold water, readily soluble in hot water without precipitating vanadic hydroxide. Pale yellow **potassium arsenatodivanadate**, $K(VO_2)_2AsO_4.5H_2O$, was obtained as pale yellow microscopic needles which lose their water of crystallization at 100°.

The third series of salts reported by C. Friedheim and W. Schmitz-Dumont includes the ammonium salt and salts of the bivalent metals. They separate from a soln. of the carbonate, vanadium arsenate, and arsenic acid mixed in theoretical proportions. The soln. is liable to decompose, producing salts of the first series, but not if an excess of vanadium arsenate is present. P. F. y Chavarri first prepared a series of salts by this process. C. Friedheim and W. Schmitz-Dumont obtained salts of this series by the action of an excess of arsenic acid on a metavanadate—potassium metavanadate yields a salt of the second series, but the ammonium and magnesium salts are obtained in well-defined crystals. The barium and silver salts are not produced by double decomposition with the magnesium salt. These salts are usually red; they are decomposed by crystallization from aq. soln. and salts of the first series are usually formed, but with the ammonium salt, the arsenatodivanadate is formed. If vanadium arsenate be present in the aq. soln., the decomposition does not occur. **Ammonium triarsenatotetravanadate,** $2(NH_4)_2O.2V_2O_5.3As_2O_5.4H_2O$, is a red, crystalline powder; **sodium triarsenatotetravanadate** appears as a yellow, amorphous powder; **copper triarsenatotetravanadate,** $2CuO.2V_2O_5.3As_2O_5.nH_2O$, in greenish-white, microscopic needles, sparingly soluble in water; G. Canneri made the compounds in acidic soln. (1) by means of soln. containing a small proportion of an arsenate together with vanadic and molybdic (or tungstic) acids; (2) by addition of vanadic anhydride to a soln. of molybdoarsenates or tungsto-arsenates; (3) by addition of arsenic acid to soln. containing molybdates (or tungstates) and vanadates. The composition of the complex compound varies with the conc. and acidity of the soln. He stated that the variety of the ratios in which combination occurs between the constituent oxides in these compounds would appear to indicate that many of the compounds are mere isomorphous mixtures of far simpler true compounds. On the other hand, however, from the very small and but slightly variable proportions of arsenic present it may be assumed that the miscibility is effected between groupings of which the arsenic constitutes the central nucleus. The typical heterotri-arsenates may thus be represented by the

$$R_6'\left[As\frac{(R_2''O_6)m}{(R_2O_7)_n}\right]pH_2O$$

where R_6' represents six atoms of a monad, or three of a dyad radicle; R'' represents vanadium; and R''', molybdenum or tungsten. F. Rodolico found that for the end-member of the series $(NH_4)_6H[As(W_2O_7)_x(V_2O_6)_y].nH_2O$, the axial ratio is is $a : c = 1 : 0.9994$ for 40.26 per cent. WO_3 and 31.60 per cent. V_2O_5; and $1 : 1.0011$ for 63.28 per cent. WO_3 and 13.06 per cent. V_2O_5. The salts approximated to this scheme only in a few cases, **calcium triarsenatotetravanadate,** $2CaO.2V_2O_5.3As_2O_5.$ $21H_2O$, appears as an orange-red aggregate of tabular crystals; **strontium triarsenatotetravanadate,** $2SrO.2V_2O_5.3As_2O_5.21H_2O$, forms orange-red prisms; **magnesium triarsenatotetravanadate,** $2MgO.2V_2O_5.3As_2O_5.23H_2O$, furnishes red monoclinic crystals, **zinc triarsenatotetravanadate,** $2ZnO.2V_2O_5.3As_2O_5.23H_2O$, yields orange-red monoclinic crystals which lose 18 mols. of water at 150°; **cadmium triarsenatotetravanadate,** $2CdO.2V_2O_5.3As_2O_5.nH_2O$, as a compact granular mass; **manganese triarsenatotetravanadate,** $2MnO.2V_2O_5.3As_2O_5.nH_2O$, was obtained by P. F. y Chavarri in purple-red, rhombic crystals; **cobalt triarsenatotetravanadate,** $2CoO.2V_2O_5.3As_2O_5.nH_2O$; and **nickel triarsenatotetravanadate,** $2NiO.2V_2O_5.$ $3As_2O_5.24H_2O$, in yellowish-brown, probably tetragonal, crystals.

O. W. Gibbs reported a series of phosphatovanadylvanadates and also the **ammonium arsenatovanadylvanadates:** $5(NH_4)_2.12VO_2.6V_2O_5.12As_2O_5.7H_2O$, and $4(NH_4)_2O.9VO_2.8V_2O_5.9As_2O_5.11H_2O$. J. Meisel was unable to establish their chemical individuality, and concluded that the phosphato- and arsenato-vanadyl-vanadates are not chemical individuals. They are isomorphous mixtures of vanadates and phosphates or arsenates in which the vanadyl radicle plays the rôle of a base in part with strong bases like potash, or ammonia.

A series of **arsenatovanadatomolybdates** has been reported by O. Decker, E. Diem, and A. Rüdisüle, and by G. Canneri. They have been grouped in terms of the molar proportion of vanadium pentoxide they contain. Thus, (i) *The tetravanadates :* potassium arsenatotetravanadatohemipentamolybdate, $6\cdot5K_2O$. $As_2O_5.2V_2O_5.2\cdot5MoO_3.62H_2O$. (ii) *The hexavanadates :* yellow, microcrystalline ammonium arsenatohexavanadatoicosimolybdate, $5(NH_4)_2O.As_2O_5.3V_2O_5$. $20MoO_3.50H_2O$; potassium arsenatohexavanadatopentadecamolybdate, $6K_2O$. $As_2O_5.3V_2O_5.15MoO_3.nH_2O$; sodium arsenatohexavanadatopentadecamolybdate, $6Na_2O.As_2O_5.3V_2O_5.15MoO_3.nH_2O$; yellow barium arsenatohexavanadatohexacosimolybdate, $15BaO.As_2O_5.3V_2O_5.26MoO_3.62H_2O$. (iii) *The octovanadates :* red ammonium arsenatoctovanadatopentacosimolybdate, $11(NH_4)_2O.As_2O_5.4V_2O_5$. $25MoO_3.96H_2O$; potassium arsenatoctovanadatodimolybdate, $3K_2O.As_2O_5.4V_2O_5$. $2MoO_3.32H_2O$, yellow barium arsenatoctovanadatotricontamolybdate, $7BaO$. $As_2O_5.4V_2O_5.33MoO_3.34H_2O$. (iv) *The decavanadates :* ammonium arsenatodecavanadatohenamolybdate, $6(NH_4)_2.O.As_2O_5.5V_2O_5.11MoO_3.50H_2O$, as an orange-yellow microcrystalline powder ; ammonium arsenatodecavanadatotridecamolybdate, $6(NH_4)_2O.As_2O_5.5V_2O_5.13MoO_3.nH_2O$; ammonium arsenatodecavanadatopentadecamolybdate, $6(NH_4)_2.As_2O_5.5V_2O_5.15MoO_3.nH_2O$; ammonium potassium arsenatodecavanadatohexadecamolybdate, $7(NH_4)_2O.K_2O.As_2O_5.5V_2O_5.16MoO_3$. nH_2O ; potassium arsenatodecavanadatohexadecamolybdate, $7K_2O.As_2O_5.5V_2O_5$ $16MoO_3.nH_2O$; ammonium arsenatodecavanadatoheptadecamolybdate, $6(NH_4)_2O$. $As_2O_5.5V_2O_5.17MoO_3.nH_2O$; and ammonium arsenatodecavanadatoctodeca-molybdate, $7(NH_4)_2O.As_2O_5.5V_2O_5.18MoO_3.nH_2O$; and yellow thallium arsenatodecavanadatodotricontamolybdate, $3Tl_2O.As_2O_5.5V_2O_5.33MoO_3.45H_2O$. (v) *The dodecavanadates :* potassium arsenatododecavanadatoheptamolybdate, $6K_2O$. $As_2O_5.6V_2O_5.7MoO_3.5H_2O$; potassium arsenatododecavanadatododecamolybdate, $6K_2O.As_2O_5.6V_2O_5.12MoO_3.nH_2O$; ammonium potassium arsenatododecavana-datodecamolybdate, $6(NH_4)_2O.K_2O.As_2O_5.6V_2O_5.10MoO_3.nH_2O$; ammonium arsenatododecavanadatododecamolybdate, $6(NH_4)_2O.As_2O_5.6V_2O_5.12MoO_3.12H_2O$; sodium arsenatododecavanadatododecamolybdate, $6Na_2O.As_2O_5.6V_2O_5.12MoO_3$. nH_2O ; potassium arsenatododecavanadatododecamolybdate, $6K_2O.As_2O_5.6V_2O_5$. $12MoO_3.nH_2O$; and ammonium arsenatododecavanadatopentadecamolybdate, $6(NH_4)_2O.As_2O_5.6V_2O_5.15MoO_3.nH_2O$. (vi) *The tetradecavanadates :* ammonium arsenatotetradecavanadatohenamolybdate, $6(NH_4)_2O.As_2O_5.7V_2O_5.11MoO_3.nH_2O$ —O. Decker gave $6(NH_4)_2.As_2O_5.6V_2O_5.12MoO_3.nH_2O$ for the formula of this compound ; ammonium potassium arsenatotetradecavanadatododecamolybdate, $7(NH_4)_2O.K_2O.As_2O_5.7V_2O_5.12MoO_3.nH_2O$; potassium arsenatotetradecavanada-totridecamolybdate, $6K_2O.As_2O_5.7V_2O_5.13MoO_3.nH_2O$; and ammonium potassium arsenatotetradecavanadatotridecamolybdate, $6(NH_4)_2O.K_2O.As_2O_5.7V_2O_5$. $13MoO_3.nH_2O$. (vii) *The hexadecavanadates :* potassium arsenatohexadecavanadatododecamolybdate, $8K_2O.As_2O_5.8V_2O_5.12MoO_3.nH_2O$, where n is 15 and 28. (viii) *The octodecavanadates :* potassium arsenatodecavanadatopentamolybdate, $K_2O.As_2O_5.9V_2O_5.5MoO_3.34H_2O$. (ix) *The icosivanadates :* potassium arsenato-icosivanadatopentamolybdate, $7K_2O.As_2O_5.10V_2O_5.5MoO_3.77H_2O$, and potassium arsenatoicosivanadatohexamolybdate, $10K_2O.As_2O_5.10V_2O_5.6MoO_3.87H_2O$. (x) *The tetracosivanadates :* potassium arsenatotetracosivanadatoctomolybdate, $7K_2O.As_2O_5.12V_2O_5.8MoO_3.45H_2O$. (xi) *The octocosivanadates :* potassium arsenatoctoicosivanadatoheptamolybdate, $10K_2O.As_2O_5.14V_2O_5.7MoO_3.132H_2O$.

A. Rogers obtained a series of complex salts of arsenic, phosphoric, tungstic, and vanadic acids. The evidence in favour of the chemical individuality of the products is not decisive. There are the ammonium arsenatovanadatotungstate, $17(NH_4)_2O.14\cdot5V_2O_3.2As_2O_5.29WO_3.98H_2O$, which crystallizes in black octahedra sparingly soluble in cold water ; ammonium arsenatovanadatotungstate, $18(NH_4)_2O.13V_2O_5.2As_2O_5.39WO_3.88H_2O$, forming octahedral crystals soluble in water which appears to form a *copper salt* when treated with an ammoniacal soln. of copper nitrate ; black ammonium arsenatovanaditovanadatotungstate, $17(NH_4)_2O.4V_2O_3.7V_2O_5.2As_2O_5.32WO_3.73H_2O$; ammonium phosphatoarsenato-vanaditotungstate, $88(NH_4)_2O.9V_2O_3.12P_2O_5.2As_2O_5.148WO_3.484H_2O$, in greenish-black octahedral crystals soluble in water ; **ammonium phosphatoarsenatovanadatotungstate,** $82(NH_4)_2O.12P_2O_5.52V_2O_5.3As_2O_5.201WO_3.567H_2O$, in dark red octahedra ; and **ammonium phosphatoarsenatovanaditovanadatotungstate,** $99(NH_4)_2O.12P_2O_5.6V_2O_3.66V_2O_5.2As_2O_5.191WO_3.522H_2O$, in black octahedra. G. Canneri prepared **ammonium arsenatoctovanadatohenicositungstate,** $18(NH_4)_2O.As_2O_5.4V_2O_5.21WO_3.13H_2O$, as red prismatic crystals ; **barium arsenatodocosivanadatotetracontatungstate,** $12BaO.2As_2O_5.11V_2O_5.34WO_3.80H_2O$, in blood-red octahedra ; and **thallium arsenatoctovanadatohenicositungstate,** $6Tl_2O.As_2O_5.5V_2O_5.21WO_3.13H_2O$, as a red powder—*vide supra*, the corresponding molybdates, and phosphates.

REFERENCES.

[1] J. J. Berzelius, *Pogg. Ann.*, **7**. 28, 1826 ; *Schweigger's Journ.*, **32**. 162, 1821 ; P. Berthier, *Ann. Chim. Phys.*, (2), **22**. 239, 1823 ; (2), **25**. 379, 1824.

[2] A. de Schulten, *Bull. Soc. Chim.*, (3), **29**. 723, 1903 ; H. Salkowsky, *Journ. prakt. Chem.*, (1), **104**. 170, 1868 ; R. Schneider, *ib.*, (2), **20**. 418, 1879 ; L. Vanino and F. Hartl, *ib.*, (2), **74**, 142, 1906 ; C. Winkler, *ib.*, (2), **10**. 190, 1874 ; K. Busz, *Zeit. Kryst.*, **15**. 326, 25, 1889 ; A. Schrauf, *ib.*, **4**. 278, 1880 ; A. Frenzel, *Neues Jahrb. Min.*, 793, 1873 ; A. Weisbach, *ib.*, 869, 1871 ; 302, 1874 ; 404, 406, 407, 409, 1877 ; *Jahresb. Berg. Hütt.*, 42, 1877 ; G. vom Rath. *Pogg. Ann.*, 136, 422, 1869 ; M. Kuhara, *Chem. News*, **41**. 153, 1880 ; *Amer. Chem. Journ.*, **1**, 326, 1879 ; J. J. Berzelius, *Pogg. Ann.*, **7**. 137, 1826 ; C. W. Scheele, *Svenska Akad. Hand.*, **40**. 316, 1778 ; K. Haushofer, *Ueber einige mikroskopischechemische Reaktionen*, München, 140, 1885 ; A. Cavazzi, *Gazz. Chim. Ital.*, **14**. 289, 1885 ; L. J. Thénard, *Ann. Chim. Phys.*, (1), **50**. 117, 1804 ; W. F. Hillebrand and H. S. Washington, *Amer. Journ. Science*, (3), **35**. 298, 1888 ; A. H. Means, *ib.*, (4), **41**. 125, 1916 ; P. Groth, *Tabellarische Uebersicht der Mineralien*, Braunschweig, 99, 1898 ; A. Breithaupt, *Vollständige Charakteristik des Mineralsystems*, Dresden, 307, 1832 ; C. F. Rammelsberg, *Handbuch der Mineralchemie*, Leipzig, 348, 1875 ; E. S. Larsen, *Bull. U.S. Geol. Sur.*, 79, 1921 ; A. Rosenheim and S. Thon, *Zeit. anorg. Chem.*, **167**. 1, 1927.

[3] J. J. Berzelius, *Svenska Akad. Handl.*, 1, 1831 ; *Pogg. Ann.*, **22**. 1, 1831 ; C. Friedheim and W. Schmitz-Dumont, *Ber.*, **23**. 2600, 1890 ; W. Schmitz-Dumont, *Ueber die sogenannten Arsenvanadinsäuren und ihre Verbindungen*, Berlin, 1891 ; P. F. y Chavarri, *Ueber Arsenvanadinsäure*, Halle, 1886 ; *Ber.*, **17**. 1632, 1884 ; C. Friedheim, *ib.*, **23**. 1505, 1892 ; *Zeit. anorg. Chem.*, **2**. 319, 1892 ; A. Ditte, *Compt. Rend.*, **102**. 757, 1019, 1886 ; G. Gain, *ib.*, **144**. 1271, 1907 ; O. W. Gibbs, *Amer. Chem. Journ.*, **7**. 218, 1885 ; *Proc. Amer. Acad.*, **21**. 60, 1885 ; A. Rogers, *Journ. Amer. Chem. Soc.*, **25**. 298, 1903 ; A. Rüdisüle, *Beiträge zur Kenntnis der Arsenvanadinmolybdate*, Bern, 1906 ; E. Deim, *Beiträge zur Kenntnis der Arsenvanadin-molybdate*, Bern, 1904 ; J. Meisel, *Ueber die sogenannten Vanadylvanadinphosphate und arsenate*, Berlin, 1904 ; O. Decker, *Ueber Ammoniumarsenvanadin-molybdate*, Bern, 1902 ; G. Canneri, *Gazz. Chim. Ital.*, **53**. ii, 773, 1923 ; F. Rodolico, *Atti Accad. Lincei*, (6), **4**. 471, 1926.

§ 22. The Arsenates of the Sulphur-Chromium Family

For *sulphur arsenates, vide infra*, arsenic sulphate. R. F. Weinland and G. Barttlingck[1] obtained some complex selenium arsenates typified by **ammonium selenatoarsenate,** $2(NH_4)_2O.As_2O_5.2SeO_3.3H_2O$, or $(NH_4)_2H[AsO_3(SeO_4)_2].H_2O$, from a soln. containing a mol of selenic acid, and 2 mols each of arsenic acid and ammonia ; and **potassium selenatoarsenate,** $K_2H[AsO_3(SeO_4)_2].H_2O$, and **rubidium selenatoarsenate,** $Rb_2H[AsO_3(SeO_4)_2].H_2O$, were similarly prepared. The evaporation, over sulphuric acid, of a soln. of a mol each of selenic acid and potassium hydroxde and 2 mols of arsenic acid, furnishes prismatic crystals with the composition $35K_2O.As_2O_5.5SeO_3.5\cdot5H_2O$, which are stable in air, and easily soluble in water.

A. Oppenheim[2] did not obtain tellurium arsenate by fusing together a mixture of arsenic, tellurium, sodium carbonate, and charcoal ; but R. F. Weinland and H. Prause found that telluric acid unites with the alkali arsenates, forming complex salts. The rubidium and potassium salts could not be obtained, but by evaporating over sulphuric acid a mixture of a mol of telluric acid, and 4 mols of ammonium dihydroarsenate, dissolved in as little water as possible at ordinary temp. and mixed with enough ammonia to give a soln. neutral to litmus, triclinic prisms of **ammonium telluratoarsenate,** $2(NH_4)_2O.As_2O_5.TeO_3.4H_2O$, were obtained, with the axial ratios $a:b:c=0.7241:1:0.7468$, and $\alpha=90°\,34'$; $\beta=94°\,7'$; and $\gamma=92°\,17'$, isomorphous with the corresponding phosphate. By working with a more dil. soln., and one mol of ammonia, crystals of **ammonium telluratotriarsenate,** $4(NH_4)_2O.3As_2O_5.2TeO_3.11H_2O$, were obtained isomorphous with the corresponding phosphate. Six-sided plates of **sodium telluratoarsenate,** $2Na_2O.As_2O_5.2TeO_3.$ $9H_2O$, were obtained as in the case of the ammonium salt.

According to H. Moser,[3] soln. of chromic salts with soln. of potassium dihydroarsenate give an apple-green precipitate of **chromic arsenate.** C. Lefèvre reported **chromic pyroarsenate,** $Cr_4(As_2O_7)_3$, to be formed by melting chromic oxide with potassium or sodium dihydroarsenate. The green, prismatic crystals are not attacked by hot conc. acids. He also prepared **potassium chromic triorthoarsenate,** $K_3Cr_2(AsO_4)_3$, by adding chromic oxide to a molten mixture of potassium dihydroarsenate with 20 per cent. of potassium chloride. Green rhombic crystals of **sodium chromic triorthoarsenate,** $Na_3Cr_2(AsO_4)_3$, were produced in a similar way.

Some **arsenatochromates,** described by C. Friedheim, and N. Tarugi may be taken to be salts of heteropoly-acids, 6. 40, 50. They are formed by the action of arsenic acid on soln. of potassium or ammonium dichromate. They are considered to be condensation products of arsenic and chromic acids. They differ from what are usually regarded as double salts (i) in possessing a small proportion of water of crystallization; (ii) in not being formed directly from their components; and (iii) in not being resolved by water into their components. W. Meyerhofer, however, showed that the formation of these compounds takes place under conditions precisely analogous to those which generally hold for the formation of double salts usually regarded as molecular compounds. C. Friedheim said that the presence of free arsenic acid seems to be necessary for their formation. Two series of compounds have been prepared. These are typified by $2R'_2O.As_2O_5.4CrO_3$ and $3R'_2O.As_2O_5.8CrO_3$, which, according to the co-ordination theory, can be represented by the formulæ: $R'_3[As(CrO_4)_4]$ and $R'_2H[AsO_2(CrO_4)_2]$ respectively. C. Friedheim preferred to represent $R'_3[As(CrO_4)_4]$ by $(NH_4O.CrO_2.O)_2$ $=AsO-O.CrO_2.O.CrO_2.ONH_4$ rather than by $(NH_4)O_2=AsO-(OCr)(NH_4O)_2$ $=AsO-O-CrO_2.O.CrO_2.O.CrO_2.O.CrO_2.ONH_4$, because it has not been possible to replace the hydroxyl associated directly with the arsenic by another radicle. He represented the formation of the $R_2H[AsO_2(CrO_4)_2]$ series by the formula for the potassium salt:

$$HO-AsO\left\langle \begin{matrix} O.K \quad KO.CrO_2 \\ + \\ OK \quad KO.CrO_2 \end{matrix} \right\rangle O = K_2O+HO-AsO\left\langle \begin{matrix} O.CrO_2.O.CrO_2.OK \\ OK \end{matrix} \right.$$

and preferred the structure here indicated to $HO-AsO=(O.CrO_2.OK)_2$, because (i) arsenic acid and potassium chromate always form the dichromate; (ii) a mol of potassium hydroxide acting on a mol of the arsenatochromate produces potassium dichromate and dihydroarsenate; and (iii) the preparation of $(HO)_2$ $=AsO-O.CrO_2OK$, analogous to a well-defined molybdate, is not possible.

C. Friedheim reported **ammonium arsenatotetrachromate,** $(NH_4)_3[As(CrO_4)_4]$, or $3(NH_4)_2O.As_2O_5.8CrO_3$, to be formed by crystallization from a soln. containing a mol of chromic acid, and a mol of ammonium dihydroarsenate over sulphuric acid. The salt loses no water at 100°; water begins to come off at 120°; reduction begins at 130°; no ammonia is lost at 200°; and the salt detonates at 238°. When recrystallized from water, the salt is hydrolyzed: $2(NH_4)_3[As(CrO_4)_4]+H_2O$ $=(NH_4)_2Cr_2O_7+2(NH_4)_2H[AsO_2(CrO_4)_2]+2CrO_3$. C. Friedheim also obtained **ammonium hydroarsenatodioxydichromate,** $(NH_4)_2H[AsO_2(CrO_4)_2]$, or $2(NH_4)_2O.$ $As_2O_5.4CrO_3.H_2O$, from the mother-liquor obtained in the preparation of the preceding salt; and by crystallization from a soln. of two mols of arsenic acid and a mol of ammonium dichromate; if the chromate is substituted for the dichromate, no arsenatochromate is formed. The evaporation of the soln. over sulphuric acid yields dark red, prismatic crystals of sp. gr. 1·848 at 24°. The sart is not altered at 150°, but at 175° decomposition sets in and a residue of chromic oxide and arsenate is formed. By evaporating a soln. of one or two mols of arsenic acid and a mol of potassium dichromate in a similar manner, dark red crystals of **potassium arsenatodioxydichromate,** $K_2H[AsO_2(CrO_4)_2]$, are produced. The sp. gr. is 2·254 at 24°. There may be a mol. of water of crystallization since the salt loses 0·54 per cent. of water at 55°; 0·67 at 120°; 0·83 per cent. at 140°; 1·09 per cent. at 180°; and 2·06 per cent. at 200°. It melts at 280°, giving off oxygen. When recrystallized from water, the salt is hydrolyzed: $(NH_4)_2H[AsO_2(CrO_4)_2]+H_2O=H_3AsO_4+(NH_4)_2Cr_2O_7$, but if enough arsenic acid is present the decomposition does not occur; equimolar parts of this salt and potassium hydroxide form a mixture of potassium dichromate and dihydro-arsenate; and with three times as much alkali, potassium chromate and dihydro-arsenate are formed. The corresponding **sodium arsenatodioxydichromate,** $Na_2H[AsO_2(CrO_4)_2]$, has not been crystallized from aq. soln., although the aq. soln., if treated with potassium chloride, furnishes the potassium salt. A. Rosenheim and S. Thon also prepared **sodium dihydrochromiarsenate,** $NaH_2[Cr(AsO_4)_2].H_2O$; and **potassium dihydrochromiarsenate,** $KH_2[Cr(AsO_4)_2].nH_2O$, as a *heptahydrate*, and a *dodecahydrate*.

E. Schweizer found that when an aq. soln. of arsenic trioxide is added to a soln. of potassium dichromate, the liquid acquires a fine green colour, and in a few minutes coagulates to a jelly which, dried at 100°, has the composition $4K_2O.3CrO_3.3As_2O_3,20H_2O$. If the liquids be mixed in the reverse order, the green colour is produced, but no precipitate. N. Tarugi ascribed the formula $[Cr(OH)_4 : AsO_4]_2Cr(OH)_4.4K_2HAsO_4.12H_2O$, **potassium trichromatododecahydroxyhexarsenate,** to the compound obtained at ordinary temp. After heating to 60°, it has the constitution $(CrO_2 : AsO_4)_2CrO_2,4K_2HAsO_4,10H_2O$, whilst by heating at 120° the $10H_2O$ is expelled; these constitutions are assigned on the basis of determinations of water of crystallization. The compound of the composition $K_8Cr_3As_6O_{30}H_4$, obtained at 120°, is a green powder which, when boiled with potash, yields a pale green substance of the composition $K_4Cr_3As_2O_{16},12H_2O$, to which the constitution $(K_2AsO_4.CrO_2.O)_2CrO_2$ is assigned; when boiled with potassium hydroarsenite soln., it yields a substance of the composition $K_7As_3Cr_3O_{22},24H_2O$, and the constitution $[Cr(K_2AsO_4) : KAsO_4.O]_2(Cr(KAsO_4),24H_2O$. This, on boiling with potash, yields the compound $[Cr(HO)_2(K_2AsO_4).O]_2Cr(HO)_2$, which on heating at 150° is converted into a compound of the constitution $[CrO(K_2AsO_4).O]_2CrO$; on treating the latter with potassium hydroarsenite, it yields a substance of the constitution $[Cr(K_2AsO_4) : AsO_4]Cr_2$, which is readily oxidized by potassium ferricyanide with formation of chromium arsenite, $AsO_4 : Cr.AsO_4 : Cr : AsO_4.Cr : AsO_4$, as a dark green powder.

J. J. Berzelius[4] found that arsenic acid behaves like phosphoric acid towards molybdenum oxide; and by treating a soln. of molybdenum tetrachloride with sodium hydroarsenate, he obtained what is supposed to have been the secondary salt, **molybdenum bishydroarsenate,** $Mo(HAsO_4)_2.nH_2O$; and by dissolving molybdenum tetrahydroxide in an excess of arsenic acid, a soln. of what is supposed to have been **molybdenum quaterdihydroarsenate,** $Mo(H_2AsO_4)_4$. This soln. has a great inclination to turn blue; and, with ammonia, a deep red soln. is formed which gradually becomes colourless. G. Denigès reported a **molybdosic arsenate,** $[4MoO_3.MoO_2]_2$-$H_3AsO_4.4H_2O$, in sapphire-blue, hexagonal plates, to be formed by the action of sodium molybdate on sodium hydroarsenate.

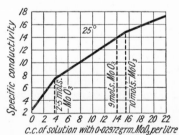

FIG. 31.—Electrical Conductivities of Mixed Solutions of Molybdic and Arsenic Acids.

A. Miolati and R. Pizzighelli measured the sp. electrical conductivity of soln. of arsenic acid (0·0456 grm. H_3AsO_4 per c.c.) and of molybdic acid (0·02972 grm. MoO_3 per c.c.); so that 1 c.c. of the MoO_3 soln. represents 0·643 mol of MoO_3. The results per mol of H_3AsO_4 are shown in Fig. 31. There are definite breaks corresponding with $As_2O_5 : MoO_3 = 1 : 5$ and $1 : 20$.

A series of arsenatomolybdates has been prepared analogous to the phosphatomolybdates, with the ratio As : Mo : 1 : 1 ; 1 : 2 ; 2 : 5 ; 1 : 3 ; 1 : 8; 1 : 9 ; and 1 : 12—with a possible 1 : 2½. They are represented by the co-ordination formulæ :

$R_3[AsO_3(MoO_4)].nH_2O$ . . . . . Arsenatomolybdates
$R_3[AsO_2(MoO_4)_2].nH_2O$ . . . . . Arsenatodimolybdates
$R_3[AsO(MoO_4)_3].nH_2O$ . . . . . Arsenatotrimolybdates
$R_3[(AsO_2)_2(MoO_4)]_5.nH_2O$ . . . . Arsenatohemipentamolybdates
$R_5[AsO(Mo_2O_7)_4].nH_2O$ . . . . Arsenatoctomolybdates
$R_{12}[(AsO)_2(Mo_2O_7)_9].nH_2O$ . . . . Arsenatoenneamolybdates
$R_7[As(Mo_2O_7)_6].nH_2O$ . . . . . Arsenatododecamolybdates

L. Forsén regards the arsenatomolybdic acids as members of three general series, (i) the *ortho-arsenatomolybdic acids* of the type $H_3[AsOMo_3O_{12}]$; (ii) the *meta-arsenatomolybdic acids* of the type $H_3[AsOMo_{12}O_{42}H_6]$; and the (iii) *leuteoarsenatomolybdic acids* of the type $AsO(Mo_3O_{12}H_5)H_3$ illustrated by the sodium salts with the graphic formula :

H. Seyberth described a salt which he obtained by boiling a soln. of molybdic and arsenic acids and an ammonium salt ; he represented it by the formula $(NH_4)_2O.As_2O_5.7MoO_3.H_2O$ —but gave no analysis. C. Friedheim and J. Meschoirer regarded it as the primary salt of the $H_3[AsO(MoO_4)_3]$-acid, namely, $(NH_4)H_2[AsO(MoO_4)_3].H_2O$—*vide infra*. C. Friedheim and J. Meschoirer also reported another *ammonium diarsenatoheptamolybdate*, $7(NH_4)_2O.2As_2O_5.14MoO_3.28H_2O$, to be formed as white amorphous powder by the action of 2 mols of ammonium dihydroarsenate, on a mol of $(NH_4)_3Mo_7O_{24}$; but they regard it as a mixture of 2 mols of ammonium arsenatotrimolybdate with ammonium molybdate, $(NH_4)_2Mo_2O_7$. They also reported a white amorphous powder to be precipitated when 3 mols of $(NH_4)_6Mo_7O_{24}$ were added to a soln. of 14 mols of ammonium dihydroarsenate ; and its composition corresponds with $7(NH_4)_2O.2As_2O_5.26MoO_3.47H_2O$. A white microcrystalline powder, with the composition $6(NH_4)_2O.As_2O_5.15MoO_3.3H_2O$, was obtained by the action of a mol of ammonia on a mol of ammonium dihydroarsenatotrimolybdate. By treating $(NH_4)_6Mo_7O_{24}$ with arsenic acid, a white amorphous powder with the composition $9(NH_4)_2O.2As_2O_5.24MoO_3.40H_2O$, was obtained.

According to C. Friedheim and J. Meschoirer, a mol of molybdic acid readily dissolves in a soln. containing a mol of ammonium dihydroarsenate. On evaporating the soln., the 1 : 2 compound separates out—*vide infra*—and the filtrate furnishes white prismatic crystals of **ammonium dihydroarsenatomolybdate**, $(NH_4)H_2[AsO_3(MoO_4)].\frac{1}{2}H_2O$. It is also obtained in a similar way from a soln. of equimolar parts of arsenic acid and ammonium molybdate. C. Friedheim and F. Mach obtained silky needles of **potassium dihydroarsenatomolybdate**, $KH_2[AsO_3(MoO_4)].1\frac{1}{2}H_2O$, by evaporating a soln. of equimolar parts of arsenic acid, potassium dihydroarsenate, and molybdic acid ; and quadratic prisms of **sodium dihydroarsenatomolybdate**, $NaH_2[AsO_3(MoO_4)].3H_2O$, were obtained in a similar way. C. Friedheim represented the constitution of these salts, $(HO)_2=AsO-O.MoO_2.ONa$. The free acid is unknown. The alkali salts at a bright red-heat give off arsenic trioxide, and molybdenum dioxide.

As indicated above, C. Friedheim and J. Meschoirer obtained **ammonium hydroarsenatodimolybdate**, $(NH_4)_2H[AsO_2(MoO_4)_2].1\frac{1}{2}H_2O$, by evaporating a soln. of equimolar parts of molybdic acid and ammonium dihydroarsenate ; it was also obtained by the action of arsenic acid on a soln. of ammonium molybdate ; and of molybdic acid on a soln. of ammonium hydroarsenate. C. Friedheim and F. Mach obtained **potassium hydroarsenatodimolybdate**, $K_2H[AsO_4(MoO_4)_2].nH_2O$, as a dihydrate, from a soln. of equimolar parts of molybdic acid and potassium dihydroarsenate ; and as a *hemiheptahydrate*, from a soln. of a mol of molybdic acid and 2 mols of potassium hydroarsenate—the first crop of crystals are those of the arsenatotrimolybdate. C. Friedheim represented the constitution by either $HO(KO) = AsO - O.MoO_2.OK$, or $HO - AsO = (O.MoO_2.OK)_2$. The potassium salt is decomposed by water, forming the arsenatoctomolybdate, etc.

C. Friedheim prepared **potassium hexahydroarsenatohemipentamolybdate,** $K_4H_6[(AsO_2)_2(MoO_4)_5].nH_2O$, where n ranged from 7 to 18; and also **potassium arsenatohemipentamolybdate,** $K_{10}[(AsO_2)_2(MoO_4)_5].19H_2O$, as white powders by evaporating a soln. of equimolar proportions of molybdic acid and potassium dihydroarsenate The second salt is found in the second crop of crystals. It is also obtained as a precipitate on mixing 2 mols of arsenic acid and a mol of potassium molybdate; or a mol of molybdic acid and 2 mols of potassium dihydroarsenate.

C. Friedheim also found **ammonium tetrahydroarsenatohemipentamolybdate,** $(NH_4)_4H_4[(AsO_2)_2(MoO_4)_5].7H_2O$, as an amorphous white powder, among the crystals obtained by the evaporation of a soln. of 2 mols of molybdic acid, and ammonium hydroarsenate; and **ammonium dihydroarsenatohemipentamolybdate,** $(NH_4)_6H_2[(AsO_2)_2(MoO_4)_5].4H_2O$. These products have not been definitely established as chemical individuals.

H. Seyberth first prepared a **hydroarsenatotrimolybdic acid,** $H_3[AsO(MoO_4)_3]$. nH_2O, by the action of aqua regia on the ammonium salt; J. H. Debray, by the action of aqua regia on ammonium arsenatododecamolybdate; C. Friedheim and F. Mach, from a soln. of one mol of arsenic acid, and 3 mols of molybdic acid, or from a soln. of arsenic acid sat. with molybdic acid; and O. Pufahl, by the action of sulphuric acid on a mixture of barium molybdate and arsenic acid in the theoretical proportions. O. Pufahl obtained the *hemitrihydrate* by slowly cooling a hot sat. soln. of the acid in nitric acid of sp. gr. 1·4. A. Scheibe said that the 4-sided prisms are probably monoclinic. O. Pufahl, and C. Friedheim said that when crystallized from **water** or dil. nitric acid (1 : 2), the *hemipentadecahydrate* is formed in tabular crystals which, according to A. Scheibe, belong to the trigonal system, and have the axial ratio $a : c = 1 : 0.8535$. The sp. gr. is 2·493 at 19·8°. The general properties of the two hydrates are otherwise similar. The crystals become matte and opaque; they lose all the water of crystallization in 8 hrs. at 150°; and in 8 days over sulphuric acid, all but one mol. The acid readily melts in its water of crystallization; and after heating to redness it forms a compact greenish-grey mass containing some arsenic trioxide. It forms a colourless soln. in water at ordinary temp.; the soln. sat. at 18·8° has a sp. gr. 2·21. The soln. has an acid reaction, and soon becomes yellow, especially on a water-bath. The acid is easily soluble in alcohol, and the soln. gradually becomes green owing to the reduction of the molybdic acid. The acid is insoluble in carbon disulphide, chloroform, and hydrocarbons. When treated with ether, the acid forms a thick, green liquid. The acid is coloured blue or green by many organic substances. Conc. or 50 per cent. sulphuric acid decomposes hydroarsenatotrimolybdic acid with the separation of molybdic acid, and when heated, a colourless soln. is produced. Boiling hydrochloric acid decomposes the acid, and nitric acid is without action. A conc. soln. of potassium or sodium carbonate gives a white precipitate which dissolves when warmed; alkalies give a white, gelatinous precipitate soluble in acids and alkalies; a cæsium or rubidium salt gives sparingly soluble crystalline precipitates; silver nitrate, a white precipitate easily soluble in nitric acid; magnesium salt in the presence of ammonia, a precipitate of ammonium magnesium arsenate and ammonium arsenatomolybdate; mercurous nitrate, a yellowish-white precipitate insoluble in excess, but freely soluble in nitric acid; lead nitrate, a sparingly soluble precipitate easily soluble in nitric acid; thallous nitrate, a similar result to that with lead nitrate; and thallic salts, a microcrystalline precipitate. No definite *mercurous or mercuric arsenatotrimolybdates* have been prepared by O. Pufahl.

C. Friedheim considers that the acid is better represented by the formula $(HO)_2 = AsO - O.MoO_2.O.MoO_2.O.MoO_2.OH$, than by $AsO(O.MoO_2.OH)_3$, because it agrees better with the properties of the salts, and with the tendency of the acid to polymerization. The aq. soln. gives reactions characteristic of both the constituent acids; and the acid is therefore dissociated in aq. soln. If an alkali is added to the soln., a salt of the acid is not formed at first, but with the excess of molybdic acid it forms an acid molybdate, and the molybdic acid then condenses with the arsenic acid. There are three series of salts: (i) primary, $RH_2[AsO(MoO_4)_3].nH_2O$; (ii) secondary, $R_2H[AsO(MoO_4)_3].nH_2O$; and (iii) tertiary, $R_3[AsO(MoO_4)_3].nH_2O$. C. Friedheim reported that there are two isomeric forms of the tertiary acid. J. H. Debray reported a salt $4(NH_4)_2O.As_2O_5.6MoO_3.nH_2O$, to be formed by adding ammonia to an aq. soln. of arsenatotrimolybdic acid, but he gave no analysis. O. Pufahl could not confirm the existence of the alleged salt; he always obtained the secondary salt, $(NH_4)_2H[AsO(MoO_4)_3].nH_2O$.

The primary salts were produced by J. H. Debray, and O. Pufahl by adding the calculated quantity of hydroxide, carbonate, nitrate, or acetate to the acid; by J. H. Debray, by mixing theoretical quantities of arsenic and molybdic acids and alkali carbonate, and by adding the theoretical quantity of the acid to the tertiary salt; and C. Friedheim, by mixing 3 or 4 mols of molybdic acid with 2 mols of potassium hydroarsenate, or by evaporating a soln. of 3 mols of molybdic acid with a mol of alkali dihydroarsenate. These salts are crystalline, stable in air, and are usually very soluble in water; and, added O. Pufahl, a soln. of the salt gives precipitates with mercurous nitrate, thallous salts, and thallic salts. A. Scheibe and O. Pufahl said the monoclinic crystals of the magnesium, zinc, cadmium, manganese, cobalt, and nickel salts are isomorphous. C. Friedheim found that the potassium salt loses oxygen but no molybdic acid when heated; he therefore argued that the molybdic acid must be united directly with the alkali.

O. Pufahl, J. H. Debray, and C. Friedheim and J. Meschoirer prepared **ammonium dihydroarsenatotrimolybdate**, $(NH_4)H_2[AsO(MoO_4)_3].H_2O$; and A. Scheibe showed that the tetragonal crystals have the axial ratio $a:c=1:1.0379$. O. Pufahl obtained tetragonal crystals of **lithium dihydroarsenatotrimolybdate**, $LiH_2[AsO(MoO_4)_3].6H_2O$. J. H. Debray, O. Pufahl, and C. Friedheim and F. Mach prepared colourless cubic crystals of **sodium dihydroarsenatotrimolybdate**, $NaH_2[AsO(MoO_4)_3].5H_2O$, which A. Scheibe referred to the tetragonal system. C. Friedheim and F. Mach obtained **potassium dihydroarsenatotrimolybdate**, $KH_2[AsO(MoO_4)_3].1\frac{1}{2}H_2O$, crystals which A. Scheibe referred to the tetragonal system. O. Pufahl also prepared cubic and octahedral crystals of **rubidium dihydroarsenatotrimolybdate**, $RbH_2[AsO(MoO_4)_3].nH_2O$, which were sparingly soluble in water; similarly also hexagonal crystals of **cæsium dihydroarsenatotrimolybdate**, $CsH_2[AsO(MoO_4)_3].nH_2O$. O. Pufahl obtained pale blue, rhombic, bipyramidal crystals of **copper dihydroarsenatotrimolybdate**, $Cu\{H_2[AsO(MoO_4)_3]\}_2.15H_2O$, which, according to A. Scheibe, had the axial ratios $a:b:c=0.788:1:-$. O. Pufahl prepared the salts of the three alkaline earths by dissolving the carbonates in the acid. According to A. Scheibe, **calcium dihydroarsenatotrimolybdate**, $Ca\{H_2[AsO(MoO_4)_3]\}_2.8H_2O$, furnishes rhombic crystals with the axial ratios $a:b:c=0.967:1:0.747$; the rhombic crystals of **strontium dihydroarsenatotrimolybdate**, $Sr\{H_2[AsO(MoO_4)_3]\}_2.8H_2O$, are isomorphous with the calcium and barium salts; and **barium dihydroarsenatotrimolybdate**, $Ba\{H_2[AsO(MoO_4)_3]\}_2.8H_2O$. They are all sparingly soluble in water. The monoclinic crystals of **magnesium dihydroarsenatotrimolybdate**, $Mg\{H_2[AsO(MoO_4)_3]\}_2.11H_2O$, made by O. Pufahl, were found by A. Scheibe to have the axial ratios $a:b:c=1.1286:1:1.0303$, and $\beta=120°16'$; similarly the ismorphous crystals of **zinc dihydroarsenatotrimolybdate**, $Zn\{H_2[AsO(MoO_4)_3]\}_2.11H_2O$, have $a:b:c=-:1:0.9117$, and $\beta=119°29'$; those of the **cadmium dihydroarsenatotrimolybdate**, $Cd\{H_2[AsO_4(MoO_4)_3]\}_2.11H_2O$, $a:b:c=-:1:0.9189$, and $\beta=119°44'$. Those of **manganese dihydroarsenatotrimolybdate**, $Mn\{H_2[AsO(MoO_4)_3]\}_2.11H_2O$, $a:b:c=1.12242:1:1.03199$, and $\beta=119°54'$; those of **cobalt dihydroarsenatotrimolybdate**, $Co\{H_2[AsO(MoO_4)_3]\}_2.11H_2O$, $a:b:c=1.12895:1:1.03039$, and $\beta=119°41'$; and those of **nickel dihydroarsenatotrimolybdate**, $Ni\{H_2[AsO(MoO_4)_3]\}_2.11H_2O$.

According to O. Pufahl, the only known salt is **ammonium hydroarsenatotrimolybdate**, $(NH_4)_2H[AsO(MoO_4)]_3.nH_2O$, which he obtained as a *hemipentahydrate*, by pouring a dil. soln. of the acid into an excess of 10 per cent. ammonia; and the *hemihenahydrate* which C. Friedheim and J. Meschoirer obtained by ˙aporating a mixture of ammonium arsenate and molybdate—the first crop of

:rystals were those of the arsenatoctomolybdate. The doubly refracting crystals
:re sparingly soluble in water and cannot be recrystallized from aq. soln.

The tertiary salts were obtained by O. Pufahl from a mixture of the acid with
3 mols of base ; and by C. Friedheim, from a mol of potassium or ammonium
orthoarsenate and 3 mols of molybdic acid. The condensation is supposed to
procced :

$$OAs\begin{cases} O\,H \\ O\,H \\ O\,H \end{cases} + \begin{matrix} HO\,-MoO_2-OK \\ HO\,-MoO_2-OK \\ HO\,-MoO_2-OK \end{matrix} = 3H_2O + OAs\begin{cases} O.MoO_2.OK \\ O.MoO_2.OK \\ O.MoO_2.OK \end{cases}$$

C. Friedheim also obtained a series of tertiary salts which he supposed to be
isomeric with those of O. Pufahl by the action of one or two mols of molybdic acid
on two mols of potassium dihydroarsenate ; of equimolar parts of molybdic acid
and sodium or potassium hydroarsenate ; of a soln. of a mol of sodium or ammonium
dihydroarsenate on one or two mols of $Na_6Mo_7O_{24}$, or $(NH_4)_6Mo_7O_{24}$, respectively
—in the last case the first crop of crystals is mixed with those of ammonium
molybdate, $(NH_4)_2Mo_2O_7$.

C. Friedheim and J. Meschoirer obtained **ammonium arsenatotrimolybdate,**
$(NH_4)_3[AsO(MoO_4)_3].4H_2O$, as a white crystalline powder by the action of 3 mols of
molybdic acid on a mol of ammonium orthoarsenate ; and the isomeric form,
$(NH_4)_3[AsO(MoO_4)_3].8H_2O$, as a white amorphous powder, by the action of ammonium
dihydroarsenate on $(NH_4)_2Mo_7O_{24}$. O. Pufahl obtained a soln. of **lithium arsenatotri-**
molybdate, $Li_3[AsO(MoO_4)_3]$, but could not crystallize the syrupy liquid. O. Pufahl, and
C. Friedheim and J. Meschoirer obtained **sodium arsenatotrimolybdate,** $Na_3[AsO(MoO_4)_3]$.
nH_2O, from the theoretical proportions of the acid and sodium carbonate ; and by evaporating a soln. of equimolar parts of acid sodium molybdate and arsenic acid. C. Friedheim
and J. Meschoir obtained the isomeric form by the action of 2 mols of sodium hydroarsenate on 2 mols of molybdic acid, or of a mol of sodium dihydroarsenate on one or 2
mols of $Na_6Mo_7O_{24}$. O. Pufahl obtained **potassium arsenatotrimolybdate,** $K_3[AsO(MoO_4)_3]$.
$4H_2O$, by the action of potassium carbonate on the theoretical proportion of the acid,
and C. Friedheim and F. Mach, by the action of potassium orthoarsenate on 3 mols of
molybdic acid. They also obtained the isomeric form with a high proportion of water of
crystallization, $25H_2O-44H_2O$, by evaporating a soln. of the arsenatodimolybdate in
hot water, and by evaporating a soln. of equimolar parts of molybdic acid and potassium
hydroarsenate. O. Pufahl could not crystallize the soln. of **copper arsenatotrimolybdate,**
$Cu_3[AsO(MoO_4)_3]_2$ He obtained a microcrystalline powder of sparingly soluble **calcium,**
strontium, and barium arsenatotrimolybdates, $Ca[AsO(MoO_4)_3]_2$.

O. W. Gibbs, O. Pufahl, and C. Friedheim and J. Meschoirer reported salts
of the hypothetical *hydroarsenatoctomolybdic acid,* $H_5[AsO(Mo_2O_7)_4].nH_2O$. They
obtained **ammonium arsenatoctomolybdate,** $(NH_4)_5[AsO(Mo_2O_7)_4].nH_2O$, where
n may be 5, 9, or 12, by precipitation from a mixture of soln. of equimolar parts
of ammonium dihydroarsenate and $3(NH_4)_6Mo_7O_{24}$; and by the action of
dil. aq. ammonia on hydroarsenatotrimolybdic acid. C. Friedheim and F. Mach
also obtained **potassium hydroarsenatoctomolybdate,** $K_5[AsO(Mo_2O_7)_4].3\frac{1}{2}H_2O$,
from a hot soln. of equimolar parts of potassium dihydroarsenate and molybdic
acid ; by the action of water on potassium arsenatomolybdate ; and when 2 mols
of molybdic acid are mixed with a mol of potassium hydroarsenate.

O. Pufahl prepared **hydroarsenatoenneamolybdic acid,** $H_{12}[(AsO)_2(Mo_2O_7)_9]$.
nH_2O, by decomposing barium molybdate by sulphuric acid in the presence of
arsenic acid ; J. H. Debray, by the action of aqua regia on ammonium arsenatododecamolybdate. J. H. Debray without publishing the analysis assigned the
formula $As_2O_5.20MoO_3.27H_2O$ to the product. C. Friedheim and F. Mach obtained
the acid from a sat. soln. of molybdic acid in one of hydroarsenatotrimolybdic acid ;
and from a soln. of 4 to 9 mols of molybdic acid in one of potassium dihydroarsenate.
If the aq. soln. of the acid be crystallized at ordinary temp. it forms the red
docosihydrate; and if below 8°, the yellow *dotricontahydrate.* C. Friedheim represented the composition by $AsO(O.MoO_2.O.MoO_2.O.MoO_2.OH)_3$, but the acid has a
higher basicity than this, namely, $H_{12}[(AsO)_2(Mo_2O_7)_9].22(or 32)H_2O$. F. Kehrmann

and E. Böhm called it *arsenatoluteomolybdic acid*. A. Scheibe said the red crystals of the lower hydrate are triclinic with the axial ratios $a:b:c=0.9448:1.1.1382$, and $a=86°\ 2'\ 10''$, $\beta=67°\ 21'\ 20''$, and $\gamma=122°\ 44'\ 20''$. The sp. gr. is 3·088 at 19·8°. These crystals are stable in air, but when kept over conc. sulphuric acid, they rapidly decompose, forming a brown powder ; if dried at 100°–110°, the acid loses 22 mols. of water, and O. Pufahl said that when heated to 150°–160°, it still retains 3 mols. of water of constitution, which are expelled at 300°. The salt is easily decomposed by moisture ; and when treated with water, two-thirds of the molybdic acid remains undissolved. The sat. soln. at 18·3° has a sp. gr. 2·450. It is soluble in alcohol, but insoluble in carbon disulphide, chloroform, and the hydrocarbons. The higher hydrate forms yellow triclinic crystals which, according to A. Scheibe, have the axial ratios $a:b:c=0.88:1:0.84$, and $a=100°\ 30'$, $\beta=101°\ 36'$, and $\gamma=79°\ 33'$. The sp. gr. is 2·822 at 19·8°. When the crystals are heated, they melt to a red liquid, which forms an orange-yellow mass ; if heated further, a brick-red powder is formed ; and when completely dehydrated, the product is greyish-green. When the acid is kept, it soon decomposes into hydroarsenatotrimolybdic and molybdic acids. If hot water be poured over the crystals the colour becomes red, and when recrystallized from water at ordinary temp., the red crystals of the lower hydrate are formed. When the very conc. soln. is warmed over 40°, it decomposes into molybdic acid, which is precipitated, and soluble hydroarsenatotrimolybdic acid. It also gradually decomposes at ordinary temp. in sunlight. The aq. soln. gives the reactions characteristic of molybdic acid. Hydrochloric, and sulphuric acids decompose this compound into its components, which form a colourless soln. The compound is freely soluble in cold nitric acid, and when evaporated, crystals of the hydrodiarsenatoctodecamolybdic acid are formed. At 40°, the soln. in nitric acid decomposes like the aq. soln. The acid decomposes carbonates, nitrates, and acetates, but with the latter, some molybdic acid separates ; and with solid chlorides, particularly in the presence of nitric acid, diarsenatoctodecamolybdates are formed. It behaves towards ether and many organic substances very like hydroarsenatotrimolybdic acid ; and, as shown by F. Kehrmann and E. Böhm, it gives coloured reactions with alkaloids and organic bases. Alkali carbonates give no precipitate with an aq. soln. of the acid ; aq. ammonia gives a precipitate soluble in excess ; silver nitrate, and lead, mercurous, and thallous salts give yellow precipitates ; copper, barium, zinc, cadmium, mercuric, and thallic salts are without action ; stannic, stannous, and arsenious chlorides give no precipitate, but the last two salts give a blue coloration.

O. Pufahl found that when equimolar parts of the acid and potassium carbonate are mixed together, **potassium decahydroarsenatoenneamolybdate**, $K_2H_{10}[(AsO)_2(Mo_2O_7)_9].20H_2O$, is formed together with the hexahydro-salt. C. Friedheim represented the formula $(HO.MoO_2.MoO_2.O.MoO_2.O)_2AsO(O.MoO_2.O.MoO_2.MoO_2.OK)$; and he prepared the salt by boiling with a soln. of potassium hydroarsenate an excess of molybdic acid ; the first crop of crystals is the dihydroarsenatotrimolybdate, the second crop the hexahydro-salt, and the third crop contains the required salt. The sulphur-yellow crystals were found by A. Scheibe to be trigonal, and to have the axial ratio $a:c=1.1.2066$. When heated, it gives off molybdic acid. The salt is soluble in water, and decomposes when evaporated, forming the hexahydro-salt and the red acid. Nitric acid converts it into potassium tetrahydroarsenatododecamolybdate. This is the only decahydroarsenatoenneamolybdate so far reported.

According to O. Pufahl, when a mol of the acid is mixed with one of ammonium carbonate, colourless crystals of **ammonium octohydroarsenatoenneamolybdate**, $(NH_4)_4H_8[(AsO)_2(Mo_2O_7)_9].14H_2O$, are formed. A. Scheibe gave for the axial angles of the triclinic crystals $a:b:c=0.604:1:0.974$, and $a=120°\ 22'$, $\beta=129°\ 39'$, and $\gamma=120°\ 9'$. This is the only octohydroarsenatoenneamolybdate so far reported.

O. Pufahl prepared a series of salts of the **hexahydroarsenatoenneamolybdates**, $R_6H_6[(AsO)_2(Mo_2O_7)_9].nH_2O$, by treating the acid with the carbonates, or hydroxides

)f the alkalies or alkaline earth metals, copper, zinc, cadmium, manganese, cobalt, or
nickel ; F. Kehrmann and E. Böhm, by treating the soln. of the acid in water
and nitric acid with a chloride of the metal; and C. Friedheim, by saturating soln.
)f some of the previous compounds or of the arsenates with molybdic acid. The
salts usually crystallize readily ; and are generally soluble in water. The aq. soln. of
the potassium salt is converted by nitric acid into the tetrahydrododecamolybdates.
The zinc, nickel, and cobalt salts were found by A. Scheibe to be isomorphous ;
probably the salts of magnesium, cadmium, and manganese should be included in
the list ; but not so with the salts of the alkaline earths. F. Kehrmann and
E. Böhm found that the reactions of this acid are like those of the corresponding
phosphatoenneamolybdate (q.v.).

F. Kehrmann obtained orange-yellow prisms of the unstable **ammonium hexahydroarsenatoctodecamolybdate,** $(NH_4)_6H_6[(AsO)_2(Mo_2O_7)_9].11H_2O$. The salt is easily soluble
in water, and alcohol. O. Pufahl obtained **lithium hexahydroarsenatoctodecamolybdate,**
$Li_6H_6[(AsO)_2(Mo_2O_7)_9].31H_2O$, in honey-yellow crystals, which A. Scheibe found to belong
to the monoclinic system, and to have the axial ratios $a : b : c = 1\cdot2982 : 1 : 0\cdot0381$, and
$\beta = 101° 28'$. The sat. aq. soln. has a sp. gr. 2·481 at 15°. O. Pufahl, and C. Friedheim
prepared **sodium hexahydroarsenatoctodecamolybdate,** $Na_6H_6[(AsO_2(Mo_2O_7)_9].nH_2O$. Usually
the salt has 21 mols. of water of crystallization ; but if a cold sat. soln. be allowed to
stand for some weeks, it has $27H_2O$. The sulphur-yellow *henicosihydrate* was found by
A. Scheibe to furnish monoclinic crystals with the axial ratios $a : b : c = 1\cdot7144 : 1 : 1\cdot7282$,
and $\beta = 100° 28'$. It loses 18 mols. of water when dried at 175°. The colourless crystals
of the *heptacosihydrate* were found by A. Scheibe to be hexagonal crystals with the
axial ratio $a : c = 1 : 0\cdot7475$, and to be isomorphous with the potassium salt.
O. Pufahl, and C. Friedheim prepared **potassium hexahydroarsenatoctodecamolybdate,**
$K_6H_6[(AsO)_2(Mo_2O_7)_9].23H_2O$. F. Kehrmann and E. Böhm obtained it by double decomposition between potassium chloride and the ammonium salt. A. Scheibe found the
hexagonal crystals have the axial ratio $a : c = 1 : 0\cdot7573$, and are isomorphous with the
sodium salt. O. Pufahl made orange-yellow, probably triclinic, crystals of what is probably **rubidium hexahydroarsenatoctodecamolybdate,** $Rb_6H_6[(AsO)_2(Mo_2O_7)_9].nH_2O$; and
similarly, yellow columns and plates of **cæsium hexahydroarsenatoctodecamolybdate,**
$Cs_6H_6[(AsO)_2(Mo_2O_7)_9].nH_2O$. O. Pufahl made grass-green crystals of **copper hexahydroarsenatoctodecamolybdate,** $Cu_3H_6[(AsO)_2(Mo_2O_7)_9].nH_2O$, or $3Cu(OH)_2.As_2O_5.18MoO_3.nH_2O$,
where n is 28 or 38. A. Scheibe gave $a : c = 1 : 1\cdot6355$ for the axial ratio of the hexagonal
crystals. O. Pufahl made yellow triclinic crystals of **calcium hexahydroarsenatoctodecamolybdate,** $Ca_3H_6[(AsO)_2(Mo_2O_7)_9].29H_2O$, which A. Scheibe found to have the axial ratios $a : o : c$
$= 0\cdot576 : 1 : 1\cdot0764$, and $a = 95° 12' 40''$, $\beta = 96° 7' 48''$, and $\gamma = 90° 32' 40''$. The sat.
aq. soln. had a sp. gr. 2163 at 18°. The isomorphous crystals of **strontium hexahydroarsenatoctodecamolybdate,** $Sr_3H_6[(AsO)_2(Mo_2O_7)_9].29H_2O$, had the axial ratios $a : b : c$
$= 0\cdot5837 : 1 : 1\cdot074$, and $a = 95° 46' 18''$, $\beta = 96° 3' 56''$, and $\gamma = 89° 48' 20''$. Small impure
crystals of **barium hexahydroarsenatoctodecamolybdate,** $Ba_3H_6[(AsO)_2(Mo_2O_7)_9]$, were
also prepared. Needle-like, triclinic crystals of **magnesium hexahydroarsenatoctodecamolybdate,** $Mg_3H_6[(AsO)_2(Mo_2O_7)_9].33H_2O$; yellow triclinic crystals of **zinc hexahydroarsenatoctodecamolybdate,** $Zn_3H_6[(AsO)_2(Mo_2O_7)_9].34H_2O$; and the triclinic crystals of
cadmium hexahydroarsenatoctodecamolybdate, $Cd_3H_6[(AsO)_2(Mo_2O_7)_9].33H_2O$; triclinic
needles of **manganese hexahydroarsenatoctodecamolybdate,** $Mn_3H_6[(AsO)_2(Mo_2O_7)_9].33H_2O$;
triclinic crystals of **cobalt hexahydroarsenatoctodecamolybdate,** $Co_3H_6[(AsO)_2(Mo_2O_7)_9].
30H_2O$; and yellowish-green triclinic crystals of **nickel hexahydroarsenatoctodecamolybdate,**
$Ni_3H_6[(AsO)_2(Mo_2O_7)_9].34H_2O$, with $a : b : c = 0\cdot7763 : 1 : 0\cdot6571$, and $a = 90° 29'$,
$\beta = 116° 40'$, and $\gamma = 84° 53'$, were prepared by O. Pufahl and examined by
A. Scheibe. F. Kehrmann also reported **mercurous hexahydroarsenatoctodecamolybdate,**
$Hg_6H_6[(AsO)_2(Mo_2O_7)_9.nH_2O$; **mercuric hexahydroarsenatoctodecamolybdate,** $Hg''_3H_6.
[(AsO)_2(Mo_2O_7)_9].nH_2O$; and **lead hexahydroarsenatoctodecamolybdate,** $Pb_3H_6[(AsO)_2.
(Mo_2O_7)_9].nH_2O$. O. Pufahl also made the mercurous salt.

According to O. Pufahl, **silver arsenatoctodecamolybdate,** $Ag_{12}[(AsO)_2.
(Mo_2O_7)_9].22H_2O$, is produced as a yellowish-white precipitate, when the theoretical
amount of silver nitrate is added to a dil. soln. of sodium hexahydroarsenatoennea-
molybdate. The amorphous precipitate furnishes microscopic needles in a few
days. The salt is sparingly soluble in water, and freely soluble in aq. ammonia
and in dil. nitric acid. C. Friedheim regarded it as a double salt, $(3Ag_2O.As_2O_5.
6MoO_3).3(Ag_2Mo_4O_{13})$. O. Pufahl prepared **thallous arsenatoctodecamolybdate,**
$Tl_{12}[(AsO)_2(Mo_2O_7)_9].6H_2O$, by treating the acid with a soln. of thallous nitrate.

The salt is decomposed by water, and it is easily soluble in nitric acid. The sal melts at a dull red-heat.

O. Pufahl reported $7Ag_2O.2As_2O_5.36MoO_3.30H_2O$ to be formed by mixing a conc. soln of hydroarsenatoenneamolybdic acid with a hot sat. soln. of nitric acid of sp. gr. 1·3. The orange-yellow precipitate was washed with dil. nitric acid (1 : 10), and dried on a porous tile The rhombic crystals melt at a red-heat. Their properties are like those of the last-named silver salt, and the salt may be a mixture.

F. L. Sonnenschein prepared the ammonium salt of the unknown *hydroarsenato-dodecamolybdic acid*, $H_7[As(Mo_2O_7)_6].4H_2O$. C. Friedheim represented the con stitution $AsO(O.MoO_2.O.MoO_2.O.MoO_2.O.MoO_2.OH)_3$. O. Pufahl made **ammonium tetrahydroarsenatododecamolybdate**, $(NH_4)_3H_4[As(Mo_2O_7)_6].10H_2O$, by adding ammonium nitrate to a soln. of ammonium molybdate and arsenic acid in nitric acid at 60°–70°; if the temp. be 100°, as recommended by F. L. Sonnenschein, O. Pufahl found that some molybdic acid is precipitated. It was also made by adding ammonium nitrate to a hot nitric acid soln. of any of the diarsenatoctodeca molybdates. J. H. Debray assigned to the ammonium salt the formula $3(NH_4)_2O.As_2O_5.20MoO_3$, but he did not give the analysis. The lemon-yellow powder consists of minute, rhombic dodecahedral crystals. The salt loses 10 mols. of water at 110°, and all is lost at 140°–150°; the dehydrated salt takes up 12 mols. of water from the air. H. Struve found that when heated in a glass tube, ammonia and arsenic trioxide are volatilized. O. Pufahl said that the salt is decomposed by water especially if boiled; and is freely soluble in aq. ammonia, in hot sulphuric acid, and in boiling arsenic acid. The salt is less soluble in a soln. of molybdic acid; in nitric acid; and a conc. soln. of ammonium nitrate. Aqua regia, said J. H. Debray, transforms it into hydroarsenatotrimolybdic and hydrodi-arsenatoctodecamolybdic acids. According to H. Struve, when the salt is treated with zinc and sulphuric acid, arsine is evolved. J. H. Debray prepared **potassium tetrahydroarsenatododecamolybdate**, $K_3H_4[As(Mo_2O_7)_6].10H_2O$, but he assigned to it the formula $3K_2O.As_2O_5.20MoO_3.nH_2O$. O. Pufahl's analysis agrees with the tetrahydro-salt, and he obtained it by warming a soln. of $(NH_4)_6Mo_7O_{24}$ with potash-lye until the ammonia is expelled, and then poured the soln. into an excess of nitric acid containing the theoretical amount of arsenic acid. The properties of the canary-yellow salt resemble those of the ammonium salt.

G. Canneri made a series of complex arsenates, some of them with the general formula $R'_6[(V_2O_6)_m(Mo_2O_7)_n].pH_2O$. A sat. soln. of ammonium molybdato-arsenate in dil. ammonia, when boiled, filtered, and cooled, to separate the excess of the ammonium salt, yields orange-yellow **ammonium vanadatomolybdato-arsenate**, $6(NH_4)_2O.As_2O_5.11MoO_3.5V_2O_5.50H_2O$; and on evaporating the mother-liquor a red powder of $11(NH_4)_2O.As_2O_5.25MoO_3.4V_2O_5.96H_2O$ was obtained; and when sodium vanadate was used, $5(NH_4)_2O.As_2O_5.20MoO_3.3V_2O_5.50H_2O$, was formed. If sodium vanadatomolybdatoarsenate be treated with barium chloride, **barium vanadatomolybdatoarsenate**, $15BaO.As_2O_5.26MoO_3.3V_2O_5.62H_2O$, separates as a white powder; and if the first part of the above ammonium salts be treated with barium nitrate, $7BaO.As_2O_5.33MoO_3.4V_2O_5.34H_2O$ is formed; and with thallium nitrate in place of barium nitrate, yellow **thallium vanadato-molybdatoarsenate**, $3Tl_2O.As_2O_5.32MoO_3.5V_2O_5.45H_2O$, is formed.

A large number of **arsenatotungstates** have been reported, but in some cases the formulæ assigned to them are based on inexact analyses, and are not therefore to be regarded as being definitely established. Representatives of arsenatotungstates with $As_2O_5 : WO_3 = 1 : 3$; $1 : 6$; $1 : 9$; $1 : 14$; $1 : 17$; $1 : 18$, $1 : 21$; $1 : 22$; $1 : 24$, have been reported. J. Lefort[5] reported **sodium diarsenato-tritungstate**, $3Na_2O.As_2O_5.3WO_3.20H_2O$, to be formed as a white amorphous powder by mixing conc. soln. of the sodium salts with one part of arsenic acid, and 4 parts of tungstic acid. It is easily soluble in water. J. L. Morris and A. G. Macleod recommended the use of arsenatotungstates in the colorimetric determination of urea. O. W. Gibbs treated the alkali dihydroarsenate with the paratungstate or

ARSENIC 213

the normal tungstate, and obtained a white crystalline powder of **ammonium diarsenatohexatungstate**, $4(NH_4)_2O.As_2O_5.6WO_3.5H_2O$. It is freely soluble in hot water, and on evaporating the aq. soln., a white amorphous mass remains which can be crystallized from nitric acid. He also reported **potassium diarsenatohexatungstate**, $3K_2O.As_2O_5.6WO_3.3H_2O$, as a white powder freely soluble in potash-lye. According to M. Fremery, no diarsenatoenneatungstates are known, but **hydrodiarsenatoenneatungstic acid**, $As_2O_5.9WO_3.14H_2O$, can be obtained by treating barium tungstate with a sulphuric acid soln. of arsenic acid so that the arsenic and tungstic acids are present in the theoretical proportions. It forms golden-yellow six-sided plates. The acid does not effloresce over sulphuric acid, but it loses all its combined water at a dull red-heat, and is then soluble neither in water nor in aq. ammonia. When exposed to air, the crystals acquire a greenish tinge owing to reduction. The acid dissolves freely in water without decomposition, and the aq. soln. sat. at 16° has a sp. gr. 3·279. Ammonia gives a gelatinous precipitate, but an ammoniacal soln. can be obtained by gradually adding ammonia to a soln. heated nearly to the b.p. When heated in hydrogen chloride, arsenic trichloride is formed ; the acid soln. is not reduced by potassium iodide or hydrogen sulphide ; magnesium salts precipitate ammonium magnesium arsenate from ammoniacal soln. When the attempt is made to prepare salts of this acid, higher tungstates are formed. Alkali nitrates, for example, as well as ammonium, zinc, and copper salts give a complex with the ratio $As_2O_5 : WO_3 = 1·18$; with nickel salts, $1 : 15$; and with cobalt salts, $1 : 16$. Alkali carbonates do not form salts of the acid. F. Kehrmann believed that this acid is really a mixture of the diarsenatoctodecatungstic acid with some other acid which has not been closely investigated, and that the two acids can be separated in the form of their potassium salts. The attempt to prepare the ammonium salt yields what has been regarded as *ammonium diarsenatotetradecatungstate*, $7(NH_4)_2O.As_2O_5.14WO_3.17H_2O$, which may be a complex salt, $(NH_4)_4W_5O_{17}.OAs(ONH_4)_2(O.WO_3.WO_3.NH_4).8·5H_2O$.

F. Kehrmann obtained **lead diarsenatohexadecatungstates**, $Pb_5(AsW_8O_{29})_2$, and $Pb_3(AsW_8O_{28})_2$, as insoluble white precipitates. F. Kehrmann prepared **ammonium diarsenatoheptadecatungstate**, $5(NH_4)_2O.As_2O_5.17WO_3.8H_2O$, by dropping a conc. soln. of ammonium carbonate into a soln. of ammonium diarsenatoctodecatungstate until the liquid is colourless. The white crystals which separate are washed with ice-cold water ; they can be recrystallized from the aq. soln. at 60°–90°. The corresponding **potassium diarsenatoheptadodecatungstate**, $5K_2O.As_2O_5.17WO_3.22H_2O$, was obtained in white crystals by a similar process. The salt is very sparingly soluble in cold water, and is converted by dil. acids into the arsenatoenneatungstate. These two salts are said to be isomorphous with the corresponding phosphates.

F. Kehrmann, and M. Fremery prepared what the former called **luteoarsenatotungstic acid**. F. Kehrmann first represented the composition by $H_3AsW_8O_{28}.16H_2O$, but this was afterwards corrected to $As_2O_5.18WO_3.42H_2O$, that is, **hydrodiarsenatoctodecatungstic acid**, $H_{10}[As_2(OH)_2(W_2O_7)_9].36H_2O$. The acid is obtained by boiling the ammonium salt with aqua regia. The yellow six-sided crystals are soluble in water ; alkali chlorides gave no precipitation ; barium chloride precipitates the barium salt; copper, mercuric, stannous, stannic, and antimonic chlorides, zinc and cadmium sulphates ; and silver and lead nitrates give no precipitate ; mercurous nitrate and thallous sulphate give a pale yellow precipitate; and quinoline, aniline, paratoluene, and β-naphthylamine also give a precipitate. Mineral acids are without action ; alkali-lye decomposes the acid ; and carbonates react : $3R_2CO_3+3R_2O.As_2O_5.18WO_3=R_2WO_4+3CO_2+5R_2O.As_2O_5.17WO_3$. Yellow alkali salts are formed by boiling sodium tungstate with an excess of arsenic acid ; by the action of the hydrodiarsenatoenneatungstic acid on nitrates, and of acids on the diarsenatoheptadecatungstates.

F. Kehrmann, and M. Fremery prepared *ammonium luteoarsenatotungstate*, or **ammonium diarsenatoctodecatungstate**, $3(NH_4)_2O.As_2O_5.18WO_3.14$ or $18H_2O$.

that is, $(NH_4)_6H_2[As_2(OH)_2(W_2O_7)_9].11$ or $15H_2O$. M. Fremery made it by boiling sodium tungstate with an excess of arsenic acid ; and by adding ammonium nitrate to a soln. of hydrodiarsenatoenneatungstic acid. F. Kehrmann employed a modification of the former process. The yellow or yellowish-green crystals are said by C. C. Stuhlmann to be isomorphous with those of the potassium salt, and of the corresponding phosphatotungstate. M. Fremery, and F. Kehrmann also prepared **potassium tetrahydrodiarsenatoctodecatungstate,** $K_6H_4[As_2(OH)_2(W_2O_7)_9].11H_2O$, in citron yellow, triclinic crystals which effloresce rapidly in air. F. Kehrmann said that the yellow salt obtained by J. Lefort by boiling a soln. of arsenic acid with 4 parts of sodium tungstate is **sodium tetrahydrodiarsenatoctodecatungstate,** $Na_6H_4[As_2(OH)_2(W_2O_7)_9].nH_2O$; it is easily soluble in water and alcohol. M. Fremery, and F. Kehrmann likewise prepared **copper tetrahydrodiarsenatoctodecatungstate,** $Cu_3H_4[As_2(OH)_2(W_2O_7)_9].27H_2O$. M. Fremery obtained a brown precipitate of unknown composition by treating a soln. of arsenatotungstic acid with silver nitrate ; and O. W. Gibbs obtained a complex salt approximating $6Ag_2O.As_2O_5.16WO_3.11H_2O$, which F. Kehrmann supposed to be a salt of luteoarsenatotungstic acid, or **silver diarsenatoctodecatungstate.** F. Kehrmann could not prepare **zinc and cadmium diarsenatoctodecatungstates** by precipitation. M. Fremery obtained the zinc salt. F. Kehrmann prepared yellow crystals of **mercurous diarsenatoctodecatungstate,** $3Hg_2O.As_2O_5.18WO_3.nH_2O$, fairly soluble in water ; and of **mercuric diarsenatoctodecatungstate,** $3HgO.As_2O_5.18WO_3.nH_2O$, soluble in water. F. Kehrmann also made pale yellow **thallous diarsenatoctodecatungstate.** M. Fremery reported red, monoclinic crystals of what was probably **cobalt diarsenatoctodecatungstate,** although he represented it by the formula $3CoO.As_2O_5.16WO_3.22H_2O$; likewise also with the rhombic crystals of **nickel diarsenatoctodecatungstate,** which he represented by $2NiO.As_2O_5.15WO_3.31H_2O$. F. Kehrmann could not obtain **stannous, stannic, and antimonic diarsenatoctodecatungstates** by precipitation. He found that **lead diarsenatoctodecatungstate** is not formed by precipitation of a salt of lead by the acid. The soln., however, soon decomposes with the separation of a white powder.

F. Kehrmann reported **ammonium diarsenatohenicositungstate,** $3(NH_4)_2O.$ $As_2O_5.21WO_3.nH_2O$, to be formed by adding a 5 per cent. soln. of ammonium carbonate to 20 grms. of ammonium diarsenatotetracositungstate suspended in 100 c.c. of water, until the precipitate is almost all dissolved. The soln. is acidified with hydrochloric acid, filtered, and treated with ammonium chloride. The white crystalline precipitate is easily soluble in water. It has been analyzed, but not otherwise investigated. According to F. Kehrmann, when ammonium diarsenatotetracositungstate is treated with a hot soln. of ammonium carbonate as just indicated, then treated with 5 grms. of dihydrated barium chloride, filtered while hot, and cooled, white, octahedral crystals of **barium arsenatohenidecatungstate,** $7BaO.As_2O_5.22WO_3.24H_2O$, are formed. They are purified by dissolving in hot water, and salting out with barium chloride. F. Kehrmann reported **ammonium diarsenatotetracositungstate,** $3(NH_4)_2O.As_2O_5.24WO_3.12H_2O$, to be formed when a conc. soln. of 8 mols of sodium tungstate is mixed at ordinary temp. with a mol of arsenic acid, and dil. hydrochloric acid added drop by drop with constant stirring. When the liquid is strongly acid, the cold liquid is mixed with solid ammonium chloride and slowly heated to boiling. The precipitate is washed by decantation with a soln. of ammonium chloride acidified with hydrochloric acid. The white, microcrystalline powder is analogous to the corresponding phosphatotungstate.

O. W. Gibbs found that potassium and ammonium arsenates react with a soln. of the arsenitotungstates with the precipitation of crystalline **ammonium arsenitoarsenatotungstate** and potassium arsenitoarsenatotungstate, $10K_2O.As_2O_3.$ $4As_2O_5.21WO_3.26H_2O$, respectively. He also obtained **mercurous arsenitoarsenatotungstate** by adding mercurous nitrate to a soln. of the potassium salt.

G. Canneri prepared some complex arsenatovanadates by the methods indicated in connection with the corresponding molybdato-salts ($q.v.$). Thus, **ammonium**

arsenatovanadatotungstate, $18(NH_4)_2O.As_2O_5.21WO_3.4V_2O_5.13H_2O$,   **barium**
arsenatovanadatotungstate, $6BaO.As_2O_5.17WO_3.5\cdot5V_2O_5.40H_2O$,   and   **thallium**
arsɜnatovanadatotungstate, $6Tl_2O.As_2O_5.21WO_3.5V_2O_5.15H_2O$,   were   obtained,
and he concluded that the arsenatovanadatotungstates are members of three
limiting series represented, respectively, by the compounds (1) $(NH_4)_6H[As(W_2O_7)_4$-
$(V_2O_6)_2].nH_2O$, (2) $(NH_4)_6H[As(W_2O_7)_3(V_2O_6)_3].25H_2O$, (3) $(NH_4)_6H[As(W_2O_7)_2$-
$(V_2O_6)_4].25H_2O$. The colour of these compounds increases in intensity with
increasing number of V_2O_6 groups in the complex anion. He did not find the
reproducibility of the salt satisfactory when prepared by crystallization, at constant temp., of soln., of various amounts of ammonium tungstate in soln.
containing a given ratio of $As_2O_5 : NH_4VO_3$. The differing compositions of
the complexes obtained from soln. containing the ratio $As_2O_5 : NH_4VO_3 = 3 : 2$
suggest that they are members of a series of mixed crystals of salts of the type
(1). From soln. in which the ratio $As_2O_5 : NH_4VO_3$ was, respectively, 3 : 4 and
1 : 2, salts were obtained approximating in composition to type (2) in the former
case, and to both types (2) and (3) in the latter.

C. F. Rammelsberg [6] found that **uranous arsenate,** $U_3(AsO_4)_4$, is precipitated
by ammonia from a soln. of the hydroarsenate in hydrochloric acid. It appears
as a green precipitate ; **uranous hydroarsenate,** $U(HAsO_4)_2.3H_2O$, is precipitated
by adding sodium hydroarsenate to a soln. of uranium tetrachloride. When
heated to redness, arsenic trioxide is evolved, and a little uranium trioxide is
formed. It is decomposed by potash-lye, and is soluble in hydrochloric acid.
J. Aloy and G. Auber also prepared this arsenate by double decomposition.

A mineral obtained by A. Weisbach from the uranium minerals at the Weisser
Hirsh mine, near Schneeberg, Saxony, and named **trögerite**—after R. Tröger—
was analyzed by C. Winkler, and found to be hydrated **uranyl orthoarsenate,**
$(UO_2)_3(AsO_4)_2.12H_2O$. According to A. Schrauf, it occurs in thin, tabular, monoclinic, lemon-yellow crystals, resembling those of gypsum, and with $a : b : c$
$= 0\cdot71 : 1 : 0\cdot42$, and $\beta = 100°$ nearly, but V. Goldschmidt showed that the crystals
are tetragonal with the axial ratio $a : c = 1 : 2\cdot16$. The (010)-cleavage is perfect.
According to C. Winkler, the water of crystallization can be expelled by heating
without changing the crystalline form. H. Morton and H. C. Bolton found that
the absorption spectrum of soln. of uranyl arsenate show bands at $\lambda = 4970$, 4820,
4670, 4570, 4370, 4240, and 4110. E. S. Larsen found the indices of refraction
of one variety to be $\alpha = 1\cdot585$, $\beta = 1\cdot630$, and $\gamma = 1\cdot630$, and of another variety
$\epsilon = 1\cdot580$, and $\omega = 1\cdot624$. The optical character is negative. When the calcined
mineral is moistened with water, it breaks up into shining scales. F. Bordas
observed that helium if given off by the mineral at a temp. above 250°.

According to G. Werther, when a soln. of uranyl acetate is treated with sodium
hydroarsenate, or arsenic acid, pale yellow, pulverulent **uranyl hydroarsenate,**
$(UO_2)HAsO_4.4H_2O$, is formed. It loses its water of crystallization at 120° ; and it
is insoluble in acetic acid. G. Werther also obtained **uranyl dihydroarsenate,**
$(UO_2)(H_2AsO_4)_2.3H_2O$, in small, yellow crystals, by evaporating an excess of
arsenic acid with uranyl oxide, nitrate, or acetate. The salt loses its water of
crystallization at 150°. R. E. O. Puller, and G. Werther said that if uranyl hydroarsenate, or ammonium uranyl arsenate be calcined, pale yellow **uranyl pyroarsenate,** $(UO_2)_2As_2O_7$, is formed. To prevent reduction to a greenish compound,
the calcination can be conducted in oxygen, or the mass can be moistened with
nitric acid and recalcined.

R. E. O. Puller prepared **ammonium uranyl arsenate,** $NH_4(UO_2)AsO_4.nH_2O$,
by adding uranyl acetate to a neutral or acetic acid soln. of an arsenate
mixed with ammonia or an ammonium salt. The slimy precipitate becomes
granular when boiled. The compound is insoluble in water, acetic acid, or aq.
ammonia. It is soluble in the mineral acids. Pale yellow **sodium uranyl arsenate,**
$Na(UO_2)AsO_4.2\cdot5H_2O$, is precipitated when sodium orthoarsenate in excess is added
to a soln. of uranyl nitrate. C. Winkler prepared **copper uranyl arsenate,**

$Cu(UO_2)_2(AsO_4)_2.8H_2O$, by mixing a soln. of freshly precipitated copper carbonate in an excess of arsenic acid, with a soln. of uranyl nitrate. In a short time, green, tabular crystals appear. The action is accelerated by warming the soln., but the crystals are then smaller. G. Werther also obtained this salt by boiling a soln. of uranyl arsenate with basic copper acetate. The water of crystallization is expelled by heat. A. G. Bergman measured the vap. press. of the octohydrate, and the results are summarized in Fig. 32. This salt occurs in grass-green or emerald-green crystals among the uranium minerals of the Weisser Hirsch mine, Schneeberg, and at Zinnwald, Saxony ; near Joachimsthal ; and at Wheal Gorland, Cornwall. A. Weisbach called the mineral **zeunerite**—after G. Zeuner. It has also been called *copper-uranite*, and *copper uranio-mica*. The mineral was analyzed by C. Winkler. The crystals were examined by G. C. Laube, B. Jezek, and

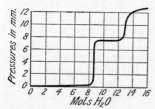

FIG. 32.—Vapour Pressure Curve of $Cu(UO_2)_2(AsO_4)_2.8H_2O$.

V. Goldschmidt ; A. Weisbach said that they belong to the tetragonal system, and have the axial ratio $a : c = 1 : 2.9125$. The (001)-cleavage is perfect, and that on the (100)-face is distinct. The hardness is 2·0–2·5 ; and the sp. gr. 3·2. E. S. Larsen gave for the indices of refraction $\omega = 1.635-1.643$, and $\epsilon = 1.623-1.651$. The optical character is negative. The mineral is soluble in nitric acid. The mineral, called by A. Weisbach **uranospinite**, occurs in siskin-green crystals among the uranium minerals at Neustädel, Saxony. The analysis by C. Winkler corresponds with **calcium uranyl arsenate**, $(UO_2)_2Ca(AsO_4)_2.8H_2O$, the arsenic analogue of autumite. A. H. Church said that the mineral may be decahydrated. C. Winkler synthesized the mineral by mixing uranyl nitrate with a soln. of lime in an excess of arsenic acid. The thin tabular crystals were found by A. Weisbach to be rhombic, and to have the axial ratios $a : b : c = 1 : 1 : 2.9136$ approximately. V. Goldschmidt said that the crystals are anomalous being really tetragonal ; according to A. Weisbach, the mineral is biaxial, but V. Goldschmidt said the artificial mineral is uniaxial. The (001)-cleavage is perfect. The hardness is 2–3, and the sp. gr. 3·45. E. S. Larsen found the optic axial angle of the rhombic variety to be $2V = 46°$; the indices of refraction $\alpha = 1.560, \beta = 1.582$, and $\gamma = 1.587$; and the optical character negative ; while for the tetragonal variety, $\omega = 1.586$, and $\epsilon = 1.56$. Another uranium mineral found in the Weisser Hirsch mine at Neustädtel, Saxony, was named *Walpurgin* by A. Weisbach. This name has been altered to **walpurgite**. Its analysis by C. Winkler corresponds with **bismuth uranyl arsenate**, $5Bi_2O_3.3UO_3.2As_2O_5.12H_2O$; C. F. Rammelsberg wrote this $(UO_2)_3(AsO_4)_2.2BiAsO_4.8Bi(OH)_3$; and P. Groth, $Bi_{10}(UO_2)_3As_4O_{28}.10H_2O$. The mineral occurs in thin scale-like crystals resembling gypsum ; the colour is orange-yellow. The crystals were considered by A. Weisbach, and A. Schrauf to belong to the triclinic system. The hardness is 3·5, and the sp. gr. 5·64–5·8. E. S. Larsen found the indices of refraction to be $\alpha = 1.90, \beta = 2.00$, and $\gamma = 2.05$; the optic axial angle $2V = 52°$; and the optical character negative. When calcined, the mineral becomes brown, and, on cooling, dark orange-yellow.

REFERENCES.

[1] R. F. Weinland and G. Barttlingck, *Ber.*, **3**. 1397, 1903.
[2] R. F. Weinland and H. Prause, *Zeit. anorg. Chem.*, **28**. 64, 1901 ; H. Prause, *Ueber Verbindungen der Tellursäure mit Jodaten, Phosphaten und Arsenaten*, München, 1901 ; A. Oppenheim, *Journ. prakt. Chem.*, (1), **71**. 266, 1857 ; *Beobachtung über das Tellur und einige seiner Verbindungen*, Göttingen, 1857.
[3] H. Moser, *Schweigger's Journ.*, **42**. 99, 1824 ; E. Schweizer, *Journ. prakt. Chem.*, (1), **39**. 257, 1846 ; C. Lefèvre, *Ann. Chim. Phys.*, (6), **27**. 45, 1892 ; *Compt. Rend.*, **111**. 3, 1890 ; *Sur les arsénates cristallisés*, Paris, 1891 ; C. Friedheim, *Zeit. anorg. Chem.*, **6**. 273, 1894 ; W. Meyerhofer, *Ber.*, **30**. 1804, 1810, 1897 ; N. Tarugi, *Gazz. Chim. Ital.*, **27**. 166, 1897 ; A. Rosenheim and S. Thon, *Zeit. anorg. Chem.*, **167**. 1, 1927.
[4] J. J. Berzelius, *Pogg. Ann.*, **6**. 34, 383, 1825 ; J. H. Debray, *Compt. Rend.*, **78**. 1408, 1874 ;

L. Forsén, *ib.*, **172**. 681, 1921 ; C. Friedheim and F. Mach, *Ueber die Einwirkung der Molybdän-säure auf Kalium und Natriumarsenate ; ein Beitrag zur Kenntnis der sogenannten Arsenmolybdän-säuren und ihrer Salze*, Berlin, 1892 ; *Zeit. anorg. Chem.*, **2**. 323, 1892 ; C. Friedheim and J. Meschoirer, *Ueber Arsenmolybdate und Phosphormolybdate des Ammoniums*, Berlin, 1894 ; *Zeit. anorg. Chem.*, **6**. 27, 1894 ; C. Friedheim, *ib.*, **2**. 362, 1892 ; F. Ephraim and H. Hersch-finkel, *ib.*, **65**. 233, 1909 ; H. Herschfinkel, *Ueber Molybdate, Sulfomolybdate, Phosphor- und Arsenmolybdate des Rubidiums und Cæsiums*, Bern, 1907 ; A. Rosenheim and J. Pinsker, *Zeit. anorg. Chem.*, **70**. 79, 1911 ; *Zeit. Elektrochem.*, **17**. 694, 1911 ; E. Bauer, *Ueber die Beständigkeit der Anionen der Heteropolysäuren*, Berlin, 1918 ; A. Rosenheim and E. Brauer, *Zeit. anorg. Chem.*, **93**. 284, 1915 ; A. Rosenheim and A. Traube, *ib.*, **91**. 96, 1915 ; F. Kehrmann, *Liebig's Ann.*, **245**. 50, 1888 ; *Zeit. anorg. Chem.*, **1**. 434, 1892 ; **4**. 142, 1893 ; **6**. 386, 1894 ; **7**. 410, 1894 ; **22**. 287, 1900 ; F. Kehrmann and E. Böhm, *ib.*, **7**. 419, 1894 ; *Ber.*, **20**. 1811, 1887 ; E. Dreschel, *ib.*, **20**. 1452, 1887 ; H. Seyberth, *ib.*, **7**. 391, 1874 ; O. Pufahl, *ib.*, **17**. 217, 1884 ; *Ueber die Arsenmolybdänsäure und ihre Salze*, Leipzig, 1888 ; A. Scheibe, *Zeit. Naturwiss. Halle*, **2**, 481, 1889 ; *Zeit. Kryst.*, **21**. 313, 1893 ; M. Seligsohn, *Dissertatio de acidi phosphoricomolybdici in nonnullas bases actione*, Berolini, 1856 ; *Journ. prakt. Chem.*, (1), **67**. 480, 1856 ; F. L. Sonnen-schein, *ib.*, (1), **53**. 343, 1851 ; A. Miolati, *ib.*, (2), **77**. 417, 1918 ; P. F. M. Sprenger, *Ueber Phosphorwolframsäure*, Berlin, 1880 ; *Journ. prakt. Chem.*, (2), **22**. 418, 1880 ; H. Struve, *ib.*, (1), **58**. 493, 1853 ; *Bull. Acad. St. Petersburg*, (2), **11**. 136, 1853 ; O. W. Gibbs, *Amer. Chem. Journ.*, **3**. 40, 1882 ; **7**. 317, 1885 ; G. Canneri, *Gazz. Chim. Ital.*, **53**. i, 773, 1923 ; A. Rogers, *Journ. Amer. Chem. Soc.*, **25**. 298, 1908 ; A. Miolati and R. Pizzighelli, *Journ. prakt. Chem.*, (2), **77**. 417, 1908 ; G. Denigès, *Compt. Rend.*, **184**. 687, 1927 ; *Bull. Soc. Pharm. Bordeaux*, **65**. 107, 1927.

  ⁵ O. W. Gibbs, *Amer. Chem. Journ.*, **2**. 217, 281, 1880 ; **7**. 313, 1885 ; *Proc. Amer. Acad.*, **16**. 134, 1880 ; M. Fremery, *Ber.*, **17**. 296, 1884 ; *Ueber Arsenwolframsäure und ihre Salze*, Freiburg, 1884 ; J. L. Morris and A. G. Macleod, *Journ. Biol. Chem.*, **1**. 55, 1922 ; F. Kehrmann, *Liebig's Ann.*, **245**. 50, 1888 ; *Zeit. anorg. Chem.*, **1**. 434, 1892 ; **4**. 142, 1893 ; **6**. 386, 1894 ; **7**. 410, 1894 ; **22**. 287, 1900 ; F. Kehrmann and E. Böhm, *Ber.*, **20**. 1811, 1887 ; *Zeit. anorg. Chem.*, **7**. 419, 1894 ; A. Rosenheim and J. Jaenicke, *ib.*, **101**. 286, 1917 ; J. Lefort, *Compt. Rend.*, **92**. 1461, 1881 ; *Ann. Chim. Phys.*, (5), **25**. 200, 1882 ; C. C. Stuhlmann, *Liebig's Ann.*, **245**. 54, 1888 ; G. Canneri, *Gazz. Chim. Ital.*, **53**. i, 773, 1923 ; **55**. ii, 883, 1925 ; **56**. 871, 1926.

  ⁶ C. F. Rammelsberg, *Pogg. Ann.*, **59**. 26, 1843 ; *Handbuch der Mineralchemie*, Leipzig, 354, 1875 ; A. Schrauf, *Tschermak's Mitt.*, (1), **2**. 181, 1872 ; C. Winkler, *Journ. prakt. Chem.*, (2), **7**. 7, 1873 ; E. S. Larsen, *Bull. U.S. Geol. Sur.*, 679, 1921 ; R. E. O. Puller, *Zeit. anal. Chem.*, **10**. 72, 1871 ; *Journ. Chem. Soc.*, **24**. 586, 1871 ; J. Aloy and G. Auber, *Bull. Soc. Chim.*, (4), **1**. 570, 1907 ; G. Werther, *Liebig's Ann.*, **68**. 313, 1848 ; *Journ. prakt. Chem.*, (1), **44**. 127, 1848 ; V. Goldschmidt, *Zeit. Kryst.*, **31**. 468, 1899 ; F. Bordas, *Compt. Rend.*, **146**. 896, 1908 ; A. Weis-bach, *Neues Jahrb. Min.*, 869, 1871 ; 206, 1872 ; 315, 1873 ; 1, 1877 ; G. C. Laube, *ib.*, 191, 18ᵀ3 ; *Lotos*, **22**. 210, 1873 ; P. Groth, *Tabellarische Uebersicht der Mineralien*, Braunschweig, 99, 1898 ; A. H. Church, *Min. Mag.*, **1**. 236, 1877 ; B. Jezek, *Rozp. Cesk.*, **31**. 15, 1924 ; H. Morton and H. C. Bolton, *Chem. News*, **28**. 47, 113, 167, 233, 244, 257, 268, 1873 ; A. G. Bergman, *Journ. Russ. Phys. Chem. Soc.*, **56**. 177, 1925.

§ 23. The Arsenates of the Manganese and Iron Families

Manganous salts, said C. H. Pfaff,[1] are not precipitated by sodium dihydro-arsenate. The Grasselli Chemical Co. prepared manganese arsenate heating a mixture of arsenic trioxide and water with a manganese oxide higher than the monoxide. A. Coloriano prepared chestnut-brown needles of **manganese ortho-arsenate**, $Mn_3(AsO_4)_2.H_2O$, by heating sodium orthoarsenate with an excess of manganese sulphate in a sealed tube at 175°. C. W. Scheele treated a manganese salt with alkali hydroarsenate and obtained a white, gelatinous precipitate, which, according to J. H. Debray, becomes crystalline when digested for a long time in the mother-liquor. H. Rose said that the precipitate is a mixture of normal manganese orthoarsenate, and **manganese hydroarsenate**, $MnHAsO_4.H_2O$. By the successive addition of ammonium sulphate, acetic acid, and sodium arsenate to a soln. of a manganous salt, E. O. Kraemer, H. B. Weiser, E. Deiss, and G. Klemp and J. von Gyulay obtained **colloidal manganese arsenate** as an opalescent jelly which slowly crystallized. H. B. Weiser and A. P. Bloxsom prepared the hydrogel of **manganese arsenate** by the method used for the zinc salt. F. Flade and co-workers found that glycerol retards the crystallization ; and by means of photographs demonstrated the fibrous structure of the gel, and the change of structure which accompanies ageing. A. Coloriano prepared the hydroarsenate, as a white crystalline powder, by treating manganese carbonate with not too much of a soln. of arsenic acid ; or by boiling the mixture. M. Amadori partially studied the conditions of equi-librium of the system $MnO-As_2O_5-H_2O$ at 25°, and his results are summarized in Fig. 33.   The *monohydrate* of the hydroarsenate, MnHAsO$_4$.H$_2$O, was obtained from soln. containing MnO : As$_2$O$_5$ in the ratio 3 : 1 ; or by precipitation by alcohol from a soln. of manganese carbonate in a sat. soln. of arsenic acid.   The salt is stable in water at 25°.   The monohydrate lost its water of hydration at 140°. According to C. W. Scheele, the hydroarsenate loses its combined water and forms the pyroarsenate when calcined ; and, according to C. Lefèvre, it loses all its arsenic when calcined for a long time at bright redness ; when heated in a current of

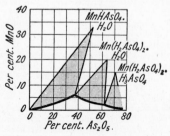

FIG. 33.—Equilibrium Conditions in the System: MnO–As$_2$O$_5$–H$_2$O at 25.°

hydrogen or carbon monoxide, the arsenic volatilizes and manganese oxide remains ; and, according to H. Rose, if heated with sulphur in a current of hydrogen, arsenic volatilizes, and manganese sulphide remains.   The salt is insoluble in cold water at ordinary temp.— M. Amadori said that 0·013 grm. is dissolved per 100 c.c. of water—and when treated with hot water, it forms manganic arsenate.   J. F. John said that it is soluble in arsenic acid.   Boiling potash-lye does not extract all the arsenic.   It is soluble in arsenic acid, and in the common mineral acids.   F. C. B. Schiefer reported that **manganese dihydroarsenate**, Mn(H$_2$AsO$_4$)$_2$, crystallizes from a soln. of manganese carbonate in the theoretical quantity of arsenic acid.   The rectangular plates deliquesce in air.   M. Amadori found the *monohydrate*, Mn(H$_2$AsO$_4$)$_2$.H$_2$O, is deposited in microscopic, rose-red crystals from soln containing an excess of arsenic acid.   It is readily hydrolyzed by water, and is stable only in an excess of arsenic acid.   Microcrystals of the acidic salt, **manganese heptahydrotriarsenate**, Mn(H$_2$AsO$_4$)$_2$.H$_3$AsO$_4$, are obtained from soln. containing a large excess of arsenic acid, are readily hydrolyzed by water, and are stable only in the presence of an excess of arsenic acid.

Some basic arsenates occur in nature.   Almost simultaneously L. J. Igelström reported a basic arsenate from the Sjömine, Orebro, Sweden, which he called *polyarsenite*, and A. Sjögren one from Pajsberg, Sweden, which he called **sarkinite**— from σάρκινος, made of flesh—in allusion to the blood-red colour and greasy lustre of the mineral.   G. Flink and A. Hamburg proved that the two minerals are of the same species.   The analyses reported by L. J. Igelström, and A. Sjögren correspond with (MnO)$_4$As$_2$O$_5$.H$_2$O, while G. Flink and A. Hamburg represent it as a **manganese hydroxyarsenate**, Mn=O$_2$=AsO—O—MnOH—*vide* adamite.   It can also be represented as *manganyl hydroarsenite*, (MnO)$_2$HAsO$_3$.   According to G. Flink and A. Hamburg, the crystals are monoclinic with the axial ratios $a : b : c$ =2·0017 : 1 : 1·5154, and β=62° 13½'.   The prismatic cleavage is distinct.   The optical axial angle $2E$=c. 83° ; the pleochroism is very feeble ; the optical character is negative ; and the birefringence strong.   G. Flink gave $2E$=99° 45' for light of wave-length 535$\mu\mu$; 108° 45' for 589$\mu\mu$; and 113° 30' for 671$\mu\mu$; the indices of refraction are α=1·8085 ; β=1·8065 ; and γ=1·7930 ; E. S. Larsen gave α=1·780, β=1·795, and γ=1·802.   The hardness is 4 to 5 ; and the sp. gr. 4·17 to 4·19. G. Flink gave 4·178 at 15°.   The mineral is easily soluble in nitric and hydrochloric acids.   L. J. Igelström described a yellow or reddish-yellow mineral from Pajsberg, Sweden, which resembled chondrodite in many respects, but contained an arsenate ; he called it *chondrarsenite*.   The analysis and general properties were found by H. Sjögren to be so like those of sarkinite that he thought it probable that chondrarsenite is more or less weathered sarkinite.   L. J. Igelström described a sulphur-yellow mineral occurring in masses or grains near chondarsenite.   He called it **xanthoarsenite**—from ξανθός, yellow—in allusion to the colour.   The analysis approximates 5(Mn,Fe,Mg,Ca)O.As$_2$O$_5$.5H$_2$O ;   W. C. Brögger favoured (Mn,Fe,Mg,Ca)$_5$(OH)$_4$(AsO$_4$)$_2$.3H$_2$O, by analogy with cornwallite, Cu(OH)$_4$(AsO$_4$)$_2$. 3H$_2$O ; and P. Groth favoured (Mn,Mg,Fe,Ca)(AsO$_4$)$_2$(MnOH)$_4$.2H$_2$O—in the idealized case this corresponds with **manganese tetrahydroxydiarsenate**, $(MnOH)_2 : AsO_4.Mn.AsO_4 : (MnOH)_2.2H_2O$. The crystals were found by E. Bertrand to be optically biaxial. L. J. Igelström reported a brownish-red, or garnet-red mineral occurring with the manganese minerals at Nordmark, Sweden. He called it *aimafibrite*, and it is now called *hemafibrite* or **hæmafibrite**—from *αἷμα*, blood, and *fibra*, fibre—in allusion to the blood-red colour, and the fibrous structure. Analyses reported by A. Sjögren, H. Sjögren, and L. J. Igelström agree with the formula $Mn_6As_2H_{10}O_{16}$, or, according to H. Sjögren, with $Mn_3(AsO_4)_2.3MnO.5H_2O$, because the water is easily expelled by heat. P. Groth regarded it as **manganese trihydroxyarsenate**, $(MnOH)_3AsO_4.H_2O$. The prismatic crystals are commonly aggregated into spherical radiating groups with a fibrous structure. H. Sjögren said that the crystals are rhombic, with the axial ratios $a : b : c = 0.5261 : 1 : 1.1510$; the (010)-cleavage is distinct, the (110)-cleavage less so. E. Bertrand found that the optic axial angle $2E = c$. 70°; the optical character is negative. According to A. Sjögren, the hardness is about 3; and the sp. gr. 3.50–3.65. E. S. Larsen gave for the indices of refraction $α = 1.87$, $β = 1.88$, and $γ = 1.93$. The mineral becomes black or brownish-black when exposed to air; it readily fuses; and dissolves in hydrochloric acid. The brownish-red mineral, found by A. Sjögren along with the manganese arsenates at Nordmark, Sweden, was named *allaktite*, or **allactite**—from *ἀλλάττειν*, to change—in allusion to its strong pleochroism. The analyses reported by A. and H. Sjögren correspond with $Mn_3O_6(AsO)_2.4Mn(OH)_2$, which they represented $3MnO.As_2O_5.4MnO.4H_2O$. It can be regarded as **manganese octohydroxydiarsenate**, $(HO)(MnOH.O)_3As.O.Mn.O.As(O.MnOH)_3(OH)$. G. Aminoff emphasized its relationship to pharmacolite. The water is expelled only at dull redness. The small, prismatic or tabular crystals were found by H. Sjögren to belong to the monoclinic system, and to have the axial ratios $a : b : c = 0.61278 : 1 : 0.33385$, and $β = 84° 16\frac{2}{3}'$. G. Aminoff gave $0.8206 : 1 : 0.4508$, and $β = 95° 37'$. J. A. Krenner gave for the optic axial angles $2H_a = 12° 22'$ for red light, 9° 2' for yellow light, 0° for green light, and 11° 36' for blue light; while $2V_a = 10° 12'$ for red light, and 7° 34' for yellow light. H. Sjögren found the optical character is negative, and the index of refraction $β = 1.778$ for red light, 1.786 for yellow light, and 1.795 for violet light. G. Aminoff gave $α = 1.75$; $β = 1.779$; and $γ = 1.78$; and E. S. Larsen, $α = 1.761$; $β = 1.786$; and $γ = 1.787$. The birefringence is strong. The (101)-cleavage is distinct, and the (100)-cleavage less so. J. A. Kenner, and C. F. Rammelsberg said that there is no physical or chemical support for H. Sjögren's suggestion that this mineral is isomorphous with vivianite. The hardness is 4.5, and the sp. gr. 3.83–3.85. Allactite is easily soluble in hydrochloric acid, and less soluble in sulphuric and nitric acids.

As indicated above, if manganese hydroarsenate be heated to redness, **manganese pyroarsenate**, $Mn_2As_2O_7$, is formed; and as F. J. Otto showed, the same result is obtained when ammonium manganese arsenate is similarly treated. C. Lefèvre found that the pyroarsenate is produced when manganese oxide or carbonate is dissolved in molten potassium dihydroarsenate. If over 8 or 9 per cent. of manganese oxide be added, potassium manganese arsenate is formed. The colourless, tabular crystals were found by H. Stallo to have a sp. gr. 3.683–3.693 at 23°; he obtained 3.662 at 25°. The salt melts to a dark red glass. Cold water is without action on the salt, but it is decomposed by hot water. A. Coloriano reported the formation of monoclinic or triclinic prismatic crystals of the *dihydrate* of **manganese tetrarsenate**, $Mn_5As_4O_{15}.2H_2O$, or $Mn_5H_2(AsO_4)_4.H_2O$, by heating a gram of manganic arsenate with 24 c.c. of water in a sealed tube at 150°; if the heating be continued for a longer time, monoclinic prisms of the *pentahydrate* are formed. M. Amadori could not confirm the existence of this salt.

O. T. Christensen prepared **manganic arsenate**, $MnAsO_4.H_2O$, as a dark grey powder, by decomposing the acetate with phosphoric acid, or, more conveniently, by adding a conc. soln. of manganese nitrate to a hot aq. soln. of arsenic acid. It forms the pyroarsenate when heated to redness. It is insoluble in nitric acid, but is slowly dissolved by hydrochloric acid; and is decomposed by alkalies and ammonium sulphide. E. Deiss obtained a similar compound in rose-red crystals by evaporating a soln. of manganic acetate in a cold, conc. soln. of arsenic acid; and by the action of potassium permanganate on manganous dihydroarsenate, and arsenic acid: $KMnO_4 + 4Mn(H_2AsO_4)_2 + 8H_3AsO_4 = KH_2AsO_4 + 4H_2O + 5H_6[Mn(AsO_4)_3]$. He showed that the crystallized salt is **triarsenatomanganic acid**, $H_6[Mn(AsO_4)_3].3H_2O$, which forms a stable, violet-red, crystalline powder; it can be recrystallized from acetic acid soln. The violet-coloured soln. observed by L. C. A. Barreswil to be formed when a soln. of a manganese salt containing arsenate or phosphate is oxidized, was shown to contain, in the former case, tri-arsenatomanganic acid. When triarsenatomanganic acid is rapidly heated over a bunsen burner, the compound is decomposed, but not so readily if the sample be first dried in vacuo over sulphuric acid. A conc. soln. of arsenic acid dissolves a little of the acid, forming a violet soln., and when warmed or diluted with water, it deposits O. T. Christensen's salt, $MnAsO_4.H_2O$. When the crystals are treated for a long time with water, manganic arsenate, soluble in nitric acid, is formed: $H_6[Mn(AsO_4)_3]=MnAsO_4+2H_3AsO_4$. Alcohol slowly decomposes triarsenato-manganic acid; acetic acid has no action, but an aq. soln. decomposes it with the liberation of arsenic acid; conc. hydrochloric acid of sp. gr. 1·12, dissolves it quickly with decomposition, the dil. acid acts more slowly; phosphoric acid of sp. gr. 1·7 dissolves it, forming a bluish-violet soln.; conc. sulphuric acid gives a bluish-violet soln., dil. sulphuric acid acts slowly, forming an olive-green soln.; fuming nitric acid of sp. gr. 1·52 has no perceptible action, but ordinary nitric acid becomes yellow, and a small quantity of arsenic acid passes into soln.; dil. nitric acid of sp. gr. 1·2–1·3 acts like dil. sulphuric acid; a 30 per cent. soln. of perchloric acid forms a green liquid.

A. Hamberg described a greenish-brown mineral from the Harstig mine, Pajsberg, Sweden, which he named **flinkite**—after G. Flink. Its composition corresponds with $4MnO.Mn_2O_3.AsO_5.4H_2O$, and this can be represented graphically as a **manganese tetrahydroxydimanganiarsenate**, $(HO)_2Mn—O—AsO=(O.MnOH)_2$, where the tervalent manganese can be partly replaced by tervalent iron or aluminium, and the bivalent manganese by calcium or magnesium. Flinkite occurs in minute tabular crystals, or in groups of feather-like aggregates. The rhombic crystals have the axial ratios $a : b : c = 0.41306 : 1 : 0.73862$. The optic axial angle is large; and the optical character positive. E. S. Larsen gave for the indices of refraction $a=1.783$, $\beta=1.801$, and $\gamma=1.834$; the pleochroism shows: a, pale brownish-green; β, yellowish-green; and γ, orange-brown. A. Hamburg gave orange-brown for a, yellowish to brownish-green for b, and yellowish-green for c. The hardness is 4·0–4·5, and the sp. gr. 3·87. Flinkite is not far removed from the mineral **syna-delphite**—from σύν, with; ἀδελφός, brother—so-named because of its close relation with other species. Synadelphite occurs at the Moss mine, Nordmark, Sweden. It was described by H. Sjögren. The analyses approximate $(Al,Fe,Mn)_2O_3.As_2O_5.5(Ca,Mg,Mn)(OH)_2$, and the idealized mineral with $Mn_2O_3.As_2O_5.5Mn(OH)_2$, that is, **manganese decahydroxydimanganidiarsenate**, $(MnOH).O.Mn(OH).O.Mn\{O.As(OH)_2(O.MnOH)_2\}_2$. The black or brownish-black prismatic crystals are monoclinic with the axial ratios $a : b : c = 0.8582 : 1 : 0.9192$, and $\beta=90°$. The crystals are feebly pleochroic; the optic axial angle is small; the optical character is positive; the hardness is 4·5; and the sp. gr. 3·45–3·50. E. S. Larsen gave for the indices of refraction $a=1.86$, $\beta=1.87$, and $\gamma=1.90$. The mineral is fusible; and it dissolves readily in acids, giving off chlorine with hydrochloric acid. L. J. Igelström described a brownish-red or garnet-red mineral from Nordmark, Sweden, which he called *aimatolite*, that is, *hematolite*, or **hæmatolite**—from αἷμα, blood—in allusion to the colour. A little later, H. Sjögren described what was apparently the same mineral as *diadelphite*—from δίς, twice, and ἀδελφός, brother—in allusion to its relationship with allactite. L. J. Igelström's analysis corresponds with $2(3MnO.As_2O_3).8MnO(OH).6H_2O$; and H. Sjögren's analysis, with $(Al,Fe,Mn)_2O_3.As_2O_5.8Mn(OH)_2$, or, in the idealized case, with Mn_2O_3. $As_2O_5.8Mn(OH)_2$, *i.e.* manganese hexahydroxymanganiarsenate, $(HO)_2Mn.O.$ $As(O.MnOH)_4.H_2O$. H. Sjögren found that the trigonal crystals have the rhombohedral habit, and the axial ratio $a : c = 1 : 0.8885$. E. Bertrand, and J. Lorenzen referred the crystals to the monoclinic system. According to H. Sjögren, the (0001)-cleavage is perfect ; the optic axial angle is small ; the optical character is negative ; optical anomalies are sometimes very marked ; the refractive indices are $\omega = 1.723$, and $\epsilon = 1.740$. E. S. Larsen gave $\omega = 1.733$, and $\epsilon = 1.714$. The hardness is 3.5 ; and the sp. gr. 3.30–3.40. The mineral is freely soluble in acids. W. F. Foshag and co-workers found what they called **chlorophoenicite** at Franklin Furnace, New Jersey. The mineral is pale green by daylight, purplish-red in artificial light ; and in general appearance it resembles willemite. The composition is $R_3(AsO_4)_2.7R(OH)_2$, *i.e.* $10RO.As_2O_5.7H_2O$, where R denotes bivalent Mn, Zn, Ca, Mg, and Fe, corresponding with **zinc manganese tetradecahydroxyarsenate.** The monoclinic crystals have the indices of refraction $\alpha = 1.682, \beta = 1.690$, and $\gamma = 1.697$; and the axial ratios $a : b : c = 2.357 : 1 : 2.153$, and $\beta = 105° 34'$. The cleavage is parallel to the front pinacoid (100). The sp. gr. is 3.55, and the hardness 3.0–3.5. C. Palache and E. V. Shannon obtained a pink mineral which they called **holdenite**—after A. F. Holden. The rhombic crystals from Franklin, New Jersey, approximate $12RO.As_2O_5.5H_2O$, where R is chiefly manganese and zinc in the ratio 2 : 1.

F. J. Otto obtained a flocculent precipitate of manganese arsenate which soon passes into crystalline **ammonium manganese arsenate,** $(NH_4)MnAsO_4.6H_2O$, by adding an ammoniacal soln. of manganese chloride to a soln. of arsenic acid or ammonium arsenate. This salt is washed with water freed from air by boiling. The reddish crystalline powder is permanent in air, and when heated it furnishes manganese pyroarsenate. With potash-lye, it gives off ammonia, forming potassium arsenate, and manganese hydroarsenate. It is insoluble in water, and alcohol, but soluble in acids. C. Lefèvre saturated with manganese carbonate a molten mixture of potassium dihydroarsenate with less than 80 per cent. potassium chloride, and obtained small, red, transparent, prismatic crystals of **potassium manganese arsenate,** $KMnAsO_4$. If more potassium chloride is employed, the product contains a chloro-compound, and if potassium orthoarsenate or hydroarsenate are used, the crystals are not so good. The product in the analogous case with the sodium salt is a mass of colourless lamellæ of **sodium manganese hexarsenate,** $Na_8Mn_2As_6O_{21}$. When molten sodium hydroarsenate, or a mixture of the orthoarsenate and chloride, is treated with manganese oxide, red, transparent dendritic crystals of **sodium manganese diorthoarsenate,** $Na_3AsO_4.NaMnAsO_4$, are formed. A. E. Nordenskjöld described a colourless or white mineral from the Harstig mine, Pajsberg, Sweden, which he called **brandtite**—after G. Brandt. The analysis agrees closely with normal dihydrated **calcium manganese arsenate,** $Ca_2Mn(AsO_4)_2.2H_2O$. The prismatic crystals are triclinic, and they were examined by G. Lindström ; P. Groth gave for the axial ratios $a : b : c = 2.20 : 1 : 1.44$, and $\alpha = 89°$, $\beta = 90° 30'$, and $\gamma = 89° 20'$; on the other hand, E. S. Larsen, and G. Aminoff said that the crystals are monoclinic. The latter gave for the axial ratios $a : b : c = 0.8720 : 1 : 0.4475$, and $\beta = 99° 37'$; and they have the indices of refraction $\alpha = 1.107$, and $\gamma = 1.729$ while the birefringence is 0.020. E. S. Larsen gave $\alpha = 1.709$, $\beta = 1.711$, and $\gamma = 1.724$; he also found the optic axial angle to be $2V = 23°$; and the optical character positive. The crystals may be united in radiated groups, and in rounded or reniform aggregates. Twinning occurs about the (001)-plane. The hardness is 5.0–5.5 ; and the sp. gr. 3.671–3.672. The mineral is easily fusible ; and it is soluble in nitric and hydrochloric acids.

H. Kühn [2] described a mineral from Längban, Sweden, which he called **berzeliite**—after J. J. Berzelius. It was called *magnesian pharmacolite* by J. D. Dana ; *chaux arsenatée anhydre*, by P. A. Dufrénoy ; *kühnite*, by H. J. Brookes and W. H. Miller ; and *pyrrharsenite*—from πυρρός, fire—in allusion to its fiery red colour, by L. J. Igelström. The mineral was analyzed by H. Kühn, G. Flink, A. G. Högbom, L. J. Igelström, A. H. Church, and H. Sjögren. L. J. Igelström, arid A. G. Högbom used the formula $(Ca,Mg,Mn)_{10}As_6O_{25}$, which is like that given by H. Kühn. G. Aminoff regarded it as a normal orthoarsenate, $R_3(AsO_4)_2$; and W. T. Schaller represented it by $(Ca,Mg,Mn)_3(AsO_4)_2$. The analyses show 5·68–19·18 per cent. MnO; 18·35–20·73 per cent. CaO; and 3·50–16·12 per cent. MgO; while in the case of a sample described by H. Sjögren, 5·14 per cent. of soda and potash —hence the name *soda-berzeliite*. Some samples also contain up to 6·54 per cent. of antimony pentoxide along with the 50·0 to 60·00 per cent. of arsenic pentoxide. The mineral may therefore be regarded as a **calcium magnesium manganese arsenate**, $(Ca,Mg,Mn)_3(AsO_4)_2$, in agreement with C. F. Rammeslberg's $R_3As_2O_8$. The mineral usually occurs massive, but G. Flink also described cubic crystals in trapezohedra. E. S. Larsen gave 1·727 for the index of refraction. The colour is various shades of yellow and yellowish-red. The hardness is 5; and G. Flink gave 4·07–4·09 for the sp. gr. The mineral can be easily fused; and it is soluble in nitric acid. L. J. Igelström, and E. Bertrand said that the mineral is normally isotropic, but doubly refracting patches may be found in the isotropic crystals. The doubly refracting variety was regarded by W. Lindgren as a distinct species, and called *pseudoberzeliite*. This variety was analyzed by L. W. McCay; W. T. Schaller represented it by $(Ca,Mg,Mn)_3(AsO_4)_2$. E. Bertrand held this mineral to be rhombic; the optic axial angle $2E=c. 140°$. The double refraction is positive. Pyrrharsenite is regarded as a variety of berzeliite, in which antimony pentoxide replaces part of the arsenic pentoxide. It was analyzed by L. J. Igelström, and A. G. Högbom. G. Flink described a **magnesium manganese tetrahydroxyarsenate**, $MgO.4MnO.As_2O_5.6H_2O$, or, according to G. K. Almström, $Mn_3(AsO_4)_2.Mn(OH)_2.Mg(OH)_2.4H_2O$, or $MgMn_4(AsO_5)_2.6H_2O$, from Langban, Sweden. G. Flink called the mineral **acrochordite**—from ἀκροχόρδων, a wart—in allusion to the warty excrescences on the crystals. The reddish-brown or yellowish-brown crystals belong to the mineral system; the sp. gr. is 3·194; and the hardness 3·5. W. Foshag and R. B. Gage described a mineral, which they called **chlorophoenicite**—from χλωρός, green; φονικὸς, blood-red—in allusion to the colour. It was found at Franklin Furnace, New Jersey. The composition corresponds with **zinc manganese hydroxyarsenate**, $R_3(AsO_4)_2.7R(OH)_2$, where R is mainly Mn : Zn=6 : 4. The indices of refraction are $a=1·682$, $\beta=1·690$, and $\gamma=1·697$. C. Palache and E. V. Shannon described a pink, red, or yellowish-red mineral which they called **holdenite**—after A. F. Holden—the composition of which approximated to **zinc manganese arsenate**, $4ZnO.8MnO.As_2O_5.5H_2O$. The rhombic crystals have the axial ratios $a : b : c=0·3802 : 1 : 0·2755$. The sp. gr. is 4·07; and the hardness is 4. The optical character is positive; the optical axial angle $2V=30° 21'$; and the indices of refraction $a=1·769$, $\beta=1·770$, and $\gamma=1·785$.

C. H. Lundström found a brown mineral among the manganese ores of Längban, Sweden. He named it *karynite, korginite*, or **caryinite**—from καρύινος, nut-brown. The analysis corresponds with the formula used by W. T. Schaller, $(Pb,Ca,Mg,Mn)_3(AsO_4)_2$; H. Sjögren added that if the contained water be regarded as basic, the general formula is $R_{10}As_6O_{25}$, otherwise the formula is $R_3(AsO_4)_2$—**calcium magnesium lead manganese orthoarsenate**. The mineral occurs massive, and in crystals which are biaxial, and may be monoclinic— E. S. Larsen said rhombic. A. des Cloizeaux gave $2E=41° 58'–47° 0'$ for the optic axial angle; the optical character is positive; the hardness is 3·0–3·5; and the sp. gr. 4·25. E. S. Larsen gave for the indices of refraction, $a=1·776$, $\beta=1·780$, and $\gamma=1·805$.

A mineral from Orebro, Sweden, was named *chloroarsenian* by L. J. Igelström. It was only qualitatively analyzed, and it may be related with caryinite. Another complex mineral, incompletely investigated, was called **arseniopleite**—from πλεῖον, more, because it adds one more to the number of arsenical minerals—by L. J. Igelström. He obtained it from Grythytte, Sweden. His analysis corresponds with $9R''O.R_{\bullet}'''O_x.3As_2O_5.3H_2O$, on the assumption that some of the manganese is tervalent, and can be replaced in part by ferric-iron. The mineral is also represented $(Ca,Mg,Pb,Mn)(Mn,Fe)(OH)_6(AsO_4)_6$. It occurs in brownish-red cleavable masses. According to E. Bertrand, the crystals are probably triclinic; optically uniaxial, and positive. E. S. Larsen gave $\omega=1\cdot794$ and $\epsilon=1\cdot803$ for the indices of refraction. The mineral is soluble in hydrochloric acid. Another basic calcium manganese arsenate containing 0·2 per cent. PbO, and 2·7 per cent. MgO, was called **retzian**—after A. J. Retzian—by H. Sjögren. It occurs at Nordmark, Sweden The prismatic or tabular, chocolate-brown or chestnut-brown crystals are rhombic, with the axial ratios $a:b:c=0\cdot4414:1:0\cdot7269$. The optic axial angle is large. The mineral is strongly pleochroic—brown-red and wine-red. The hardness is 4, and the sp. gr. 4·15. It is soluble in acids. A mineral called **rhodoarsenian** was obtained by L. J. Igelström from Orebro, Sweden. Its composition approximates $(Mn,Ca,Mg)_{20}O.As_2O_5.10H_2O$. It occurs in rose-red spherules embedded in arseniopleite. Its hardness is 4. It blackens when heated, and is soluble in hydrochloric acid. He also obtained a mineral which he called **elfstorpite** from the same locality. It is supposed to be a hydrated manganese arsenate. Similarly also with **pleurasite**—from πλευρά, side—in allusion to its occurrence in bluish-black bands on the side of arseniopleite. The composition of these three manganese arsenates is unknown.

R. Chenevix[3] reported a white precipitate of **ferrous orthoarsenate**, $Fe_3(AsO_4)_2.6H_2O$, to be formed when ammonium arsenate is added to a soln. of ferrous sulphate; and G. C. Wittstein obtained it by the reaction: $4Na_2HAsO_4 +4FeSO_4=Fe_3(AsO_4)_2+Fe(H_2AsO_4)_2+4Na_2SO_4$. G. Klemp and J. von Gyulay obtained **colloidal ferrous arsenate** by the successive addition of ammonium sulphate, acetic acid, and sodium arsenate to a soln. of a ferrous salt. The opalescent jelly slowly crystallizes. A. Breithaupt and C. F. Plattner found a mineral which he called **symplesite**—from σύν, together; and πλησιάζειν, to bring— in allusion to its relation to other minerals. It occurs at Lobenstein, Voigtland; Hüttenberg, Carinthia; at Pisek, Bohemia; and Felsöbanya; etc. Analyses reported by A. L. Parsons, E. Boricky, and C. F. Rammelsberg correspond with the *octohydrate*, $Fe_3(AsO_4)_2.8H_2O$; A. Breithaupt and C. F. Plattner obtained about 3 per cent. less than this proportion of water. T. L. Walker and A. L. Parsons described a related mineral from Cobalt, Ontario. Symplesite occurs in small prismatic or tabular crystals, or in crystal aggregates which are coloured pale indigo inclined to celadon-green; and they are sometimes mountain-green or leek-green. According to J. A. Krenner, the monoclinic crystals have the axial ratios $a:b:c =0\cdot7806:1:0\cdot6812$, and $\beta=72°43'$. The (010)-cleavage is perfect. The crystals are said to be isomorphous with vivianite. The optic axial angle for yellow light is $2E=107°28'$. The optical character is negative. E. S. Larsen gave $2V=86\frac{1}{2}°$; and, for the indices of refraction, $\alpha=1\cdot635, \beta=1\cdot668$, and $\gamma=1\cdot702$. The pleochroism for a is bluish-green to blue; for b, colourless to greenish-yellow; and for c, yellowish-green to oil-green. F. Ulrich studied the optical properties of the mineral. The hardness is 2·5–3; and the sp. gr. 2·957—C. Vrba gave 2·889. The mineral melts easily before the blowpipe. J. J. Berzelius said that the precipitated arsenate dissolves sparingly in aq. ammonia, forming a liquid which turns green when exposed to air; and G. C. Wittstein said that the ammoniacal soln. is greenish-yellow, and does not become turbid when exposed to air for several hours; the salt does not dissolve in a soln. of ammonium arsenate, or other ammonium salt soln. According to G. C. Wittstein, if the precipitated ferrous arsenate be washed and dried in air, it forms a grass-green mass with a composition corresponding with *ferrosic arsenate*, $6FeO.3Fe_2O_3.4As_2O_5.32H_2O$; most of the water is expelled at 100°, and the product is then greyish-green. At a red-heat, the compound loses all its water, but no arsenic. It is insoluble in water, but dissolves in hydrochloric acid, forming a yellow liquid. H. B. Weiser and A. P. Bloxsom prepared the **hydrogel of ferrous arsenate** by the method used for the zinc salt.

According to C. W. Scheele, iron dissolves in a soln. of arsenic acid, and N. W. Fischer added that if the acid acts on the metal for several weeks, out of contact with air, what is possibly *ferrous hydroarsenate* is deposited in asbestos-like threads united in spherical masses; black needles of arsenic also appear. As indicated in the above equation, G. C. Wittstein considered that the mother-liquor remaining after the precipitation of ferrous orthoarsenate contained **ferrous dihydroarsenate**, $Fe(H_2AsO_4)_2$. W. Duncan reported the formation of **ferrous ammonium arsenate**.

W. Duncan obtained anhydrous **ferric orthoarsenate**, $FeAsO_4$, by heating the hydrate at 100°; and B. Jezek and A. Simek observed that black, prismatic crystals of anhydrous ferric arsenate collected on the clay balls used in Deacon's process for chlorine at Hruschau, Silesia. The crystals are monoclinic, with the axial ratios $a:b:c=0.6155:1:0.3221$, and $\beta=77°\ 8'$. The (001)-cleavage is perfect; the sp. gr. is 4·32; and the mean refractive index is 1·78 for Na-light. N. H. Hartshorne measured the viscosity of soln. of ferric oxide in arsenic acid, for soln. with 2·6 to 23·13 per cent. As_2O_5, at 25°. Within this range, the results showed the existence of $FeAsO_4.nH_2O$, where n is not far from 3. This salt carries some adsorbed arsenic acid. Ferric trihydrodiarsenate was also formed—*vide infra*. No basic salts were observed. G. C. Wittstein, and H. Rose found that a yellowish-white precipitate of the *tetrahydrate*, $FeAsO_4.4H_2O$, gradually separated from a soln. of ferrous dihydroarsenate when exposed to air. G. Franceschi represented the reactions with ferric chloride and the potassium arsenates by the equations: $2K_3AsO_4+2FeCl_3=2Fe(AsO_4)_2+6KCl$; $3K_2HAsO_4+2FeCl_3=Fe_2(HAsO_4)_3+6KCl$; and $3KH_2AsO_4+2FeCl_3=Fe_2(HAsO_4)_3+3KCl+3HCl$. P. Kotschoubey reported the *hemipentahydrate*, $FeAsO_4.2\frac{1}{2}H_2O$, to be formed when the precipitation is made in the presence of acetic acid and sodium acetate, and the product dried at 100°; but H. Salkowsky could not confirm this. A. Verneuil and L. Bourgeois prepared the *dihydrate*, $FeAsO_4.2H_2O$, by heating iron wire and a conc. soln. of arsenic acid in a sealed tube at 150° for 8 days. The wire is then covered with bluish-green crystals of the dihydrate. H. Metzke found that ferric arsenate is formed under varying conditions by the action of a mol of ammonium ferric alum on 2 to 4 mols of sodium hydroarsenate. The appearance of the precipitate varies with the proportion of the salts employed; when a small quantity of the arsenate is added to the alum soln., a white precipitate is obtained, whilst on adding the alum soln. to the arsenate the precipitate is brownish; when the two salts are employed in equal proportions, a yellow precipitate is formed. The white precipitate turns yellow and finally brownish when washed with water. According to the conditions under which they are formed, the precipitates contain small quantities of ammonium and sodium arsenates. In the presence of a large excess either of disodium arsenate or of iron ammonium alum, a mixture is obtained consisting mainly of the basic ferric arsenate, $3Fe_2O_3.2As_2O_3.16$ or $17H_2O$—it is thought to be a mixture of basic salts. H. Metzke prepared the *hemihydrate* by heating precipitated ferric dihydroarsenate—*vide infra*—with arsenic acid, hydrogen dioxide, and water in a sealed tube at 170° for 14 days Yellowish-green, rhombic crystals of the hemihydrate mixed with the dihydrate are formed. Crystals of the *monohydrate* are produced from normal ferric arsenate treated in a similar manner. W. Duncan represented the air-dried salt as $FeAsO_4.H_2O$, and said that it becomes anhydrous at 100°. They represented the hydrated salt by the formula $AsO_2(FeO)(HO)_2$, the acidic character being shown by its effervescence with sodium hydrocarbonate. The *dihydrate* is formed by heating ferric arsenate with water and arsenic acid in a sealed tube at 80° for 4 days; and by the evaporation of a soln. of ferric arsenate acidified with hydrochloric acid. D. N. Chakravasti and N. R. Dhar discussed the viscosity of colloidal soln. of ferric arsenate. W. Ipatieff and co-workers heated ferric arsenate with water and hydrogen and obtained successively scorodite, ferric arsenite, arsine, ferrous arsenite, arsenic, and arsenious acid. H. B. Weiser discussed *colloidal ferric arsenate*. The dihydrate occurs in nature as the mineral **scorodite**—from σκόροδον, garlic—which was so named by A. Breithaupt in allusion to its odour before the blowpipe flame. J. L. Bournon called it *cupromartial arsenate;* R. J. Haüy, *cuivre arseniaté ferrifère;* and F. S. Beudant, scorodite and *néoctèse.*

ARSENIC   225

Analyses were reported by A. Damour, J. J. Berzelius, J. B. J. D. Boussingault,
R. Hermann, J. H. C. Martens, A. Raimondi, J. da Costa Sena, and A. Hague.
The results agree with the formula $FeAsO_4.2H_2O$. It has been reported from
many localities—Schwarzenberg, Saxony; Dernbach, Nassau; Hüttenberg,
Carinthia; Nerchinsk, Siberia; Chanteloube, Limoges; Minas Graes, Brazil;
Popayan, Peru; Edenville, New York; in Utah, and Nevada, Victoria, Australia,
etc. M. Piazza found it in the tungsten ores of Cerva, Portugal. A. Hague
found a deposit of ferric arsenate—scorodite—from a hot spring in the Yellowstone National Park. J. H. C. Martens, and R. P. D. Graham also described
some American deposits. M. Lippmann called a variety with cobalt, *cobalt-
scorodite*. R. L. Codazzi called a variety *loaisite*. E. Hussak observed scorodite
to be produced by the decomposition of auriferous arsenical pyrites; and it
is formed likewise in nature by the decomposition of other arsenical earths. The
mineral *jogynaite*, discussed by N. von Kokscharoff, is a variety of scorodite.
It occurs earthy and amorphous, when R. Hermann called it *arsenical sinter*, or
iron-sinter; it also occurs in irregular groups of crystals, and in octahedral,
prismatic, or tabular crystals. The colour is pale leek-green, or liver-brown.
According to G. vom Rath, the rhombic crystals have the axial ratios
$a:b:c=0.86578:1:0.95414$; and P. Groth gave $0.8687:1:0.9536$; and
R. P. D. Graham, $0.8785:1:0.0550$. The (120)-cleavage is imperfect; and
traces of cleavage appear on the (100)- and (010)-faces. E. F. Tschirva studied
the crystals of scorodite. A. des Cloizeaux gave for the optic axial angles with
red light, $2H_a=76°\ 43\frac{1}{2}'$, and $2E=130°\ 58'$; with yellow light, $2H_a=76°\ 5'$, and
$2E=129°\ 32'$; and with blue light, $2H_a=72°\ 44'$, and $2E=122°\ 25'$. When the
temp. was raised from 17° to 76·5°, $2E$ for red light altered from 115° 43' to
116° 56'. The optical character is positive. A. Verneuil and L. Bourgeois found
the artificial crystals were crystallographically and optically like the natural
crystals. The hardness is 3·5–4·0; and the sp. gr. 3·1–3·3. A. Damour gave
3·11; J. J. Berzelius, 3·18; J. H. C. Martens, 2·70–2·86; R. P. D. Graham, 3·235;
J. da Costa Sena, 3·2; and A. Verneuil and L. Bourgeois, 3·28 for the artificial
crystals. J. H. C. Martens found the index of refraction 1·775, and the birefringence, strong. Scorodite can be easily fused; and it is soluble in hydrochloric
acid. It is altered to limonite when weathered. E. S. Larsen gave 1·775 for the
index of refraction; and R. P. D. Graham, 1·76. In opposition to J. J. Berzelius,
H. Rose said that ferric arsenate is completely decomposed by potash-lye. Red or
yellow soln. were obtained by J. J. Berzelius, G. C. Wittstein, and J. W. Döbereiner
by treating the arsenate with aq. ammonia; and H. Rose said that the ammoniacal
soln. becomes blue when acidified. G. Lunge observed that ferric arsenate dissolves
in conc. arsenic acid, and is re-precipitated by diluting and warming the soln.

    According to H. Metzke, ferric orthoarsenate is a bright yellow powder in-
soluble in water. It is slowly decomposed by cold water, more quickly by hot
water, and is soluble in hydrochloric, sulphuric, nitric, dil. arsenic, and phosphoric
acids; the soln. in the last two acids decompose when boiled and diluted.
Neutral and acid ferric arsenate are quickly and completely dissolved by conc.
ammonia, yielding a blood-red soln.; the basic ferric arsenates, however, are not.
Yellow ammoniacal soln. are obtained in the presence of large quantities of
disodium arsenate and ammonium chloride. These arsenates are not decomposed
by a soln. of silver nitrate, are quickly decomposed by soln. of ammonium and
sodium acetates, and give the reaction of ferric salts with potassium ferrocyanide
and thiocyanate only in strongly acid soln., and never in ammoniacal soln. Cold
conc. potassium hydroxide precipitates ferric hydroxide from the neutral ferric
arsenate, but only an incomplete decomposition takes place when a hydrochloric
acid soln. of the arsenate is boiled with potassium hydroxide.

    According to C. H. Pfaff, a soln. of ferric chloride gives a white precipitate
when treated with sodium hydroarsenate. The precipitate was examined by
J. J. Berzelius, R. Chenevix, R. Brandes, J. W. Döbereiner, and G. C. Wittstein.

Analyses by J. J. Berzelius, and R. Chenevix correspond with **ferric hydroarsenate** $Fe_2(HAsO_4)_3.4\frac{1}{2}H_2O$. H. Metzke obtained the salt by dissolving ferric orthc arsenate in a soln. of arsenic acid and precipitating the filtered soln. with alcoho The white precipitate is quickly washed with 98 per cent. alcohol, and dried b press. between folds of bibulous paper. It dissolves in acids, forming a yellov soln., and in ammonia, a red soln. The white acid compound obtained by th action of sodium hydroarsenate on iron ammonium alum is quickly decompose when washed with water, dil. alcohol, or glycerol : it is not altered, however, b strong alcohol or ether, but these solvents do not wash out the impurities in th mother-liquor, so that it cannot be obtained pure. H. Metzke obtained **ferri dihydroarsenate,** $Fe(H_2AsO_4)_3.5H_2O$, by dissolving 4 grms. of artificial pharmaco siderite in syrupy arsenic acid (11·5 grms. As_2O_5), and heating the soln. White pulverulent ferric hydroarsenate is deposited. In 24 hrs., the precipitate wa washed with alcohol, and dried. It is decomposed by water and is readily dissolve by acids, forming a yellow soln., and in aq. ammonia, forming a red soln.

L. Dede found that when arsenic acid is added to a soln. of ferric chloride ther is a considerable increase in the sp. conductivity of the soln. ; an increase als occurs with the further addition of the acid soln. until equivalent proportions o acid and salt are mixed. It is therefore assumed that the complex **trichloro arsenatoferric acid,** $H_3[Fe(AsO_4)Cl_3]$, is formed ; neither the acid nor its salt could be isolated. Still further additions of arsenic acid had no appreciable effec on the conductivity, but the three chlorine atoms are replaced by another arsenato group so as to form **ferric trihydrodiarsenate,** or **diarsenatoferric acid,** $H_3[Fe(AsO_4)_2].2\frac{1}{3}H_2O$. The acid was readily isolated. N. H. Hartshorne als prepared this salt—*vide supra*.

J. J. Berzelius reported a basic salt, $16Fe_2O_3.As_2O_5.24H_2O$, to be formed by boiling one of the orthoarsenates with potash-lye ; but H. Metzke showed tha this product is probably a mixture. H. Metzke, however, prepared $4Fe_2O_3 3As_2O_5.nH_2O$ with $n=15\cdot4$, 20·5, and 33·5, and contaminated with small quantitie of sodium and ammonium salts by heating ferric orthoarsenate with water in a sealed tube at 200° ; or by boiling the orthoarsenate with a soln. of ammonium acetate acidified with acetic acid ; or by oxidizing with hydrogen dioxide the white precipitate obtained by mixing molar proportions of soln. of ferrous sulphate and sodium dihydroarsenate. The analysis $4Fe_2O_3.3As_2O_5.nH_2O$, can be repre sented by $Fe(AsO_4)_3.(FeOH)_3.mH_2O$, that is, **ferric trihydroxytriarsenate,** $Fe(AsO_4 : FeOH)_3.mH_2O$. A related product occurs in nature in various parts of Cornwall, and Cumberland ; Saxony ; Bohemia ; Hungary ; Dept. du Var, France ; Australia ; Utah, U.S.A. ; etc. It was probably the *fer minéralisé par l'acide arsenique* of J. L. Proust ; the arsenicated iron ore of R. Kirwan ; the *Olivenerz* or the *arseniksaures Eisen in Würfelnkrystallen,* of M. H. Klaproth ; the *Wurfelerz* or *cube ore,* of D. G. L. Lenz and D. L. G. Karsten. J. F. L. Hausmann called it **pharmacosiderite**—from φαρμακόν, poison ; and σίδηρος, iron. C. Vrba and A. d'Achiardi discussed the formation of the mineral in nature from arsenical pyrites. The mineral commonly occurs in cubes, and tetrahedra, and rarely granular. The colour varies from grass-green, emerald-green, olive-green, honey- yellow, to yellowish-brown—sometimes being hyacinth—red and blackish-brown. J. J. Berzelius' analysis corresponds with $4Fe_2O_3.3As_2O_2.15H_2O$, which P. Groth represented $Fe(AsO_4)_3.(FeOH)_3.6H_2O$. E. G. J. Hartley represented his analysis by $2FeAsO_4.Fe\{O(H,K)\}_3.5H_2O$. A. Kalecsinsky found some thallium in pharma- cosiderite from Ujbanya, Hungary. The hardness is 2·5, and the sp. gr. is nearly 3·0. C. Vrba found 2·873 for the sp. gr., and E. G. J. Hartley, 2·789. The last- named observed that when heated, the mineral lost 0·84–1·60 per cent. of water in dry air ; 9·82 per cent. at 100° ; 14·51 per cent. at 136° ; and 19·53 per cent. at a red-heat. The crystals are pyroelectric. The mineral was found by E. Bertrand to show an anomalous double refraction, and P. Gaubert gave for the index of refraction 1·676. The general properties are like those of orodite. Pharmacosiderite passes into psilomelane, limonite, and hæmatite when eathered.

A mineral called *pitchy iron ore, iron-sinter,* or *arsenical iron-sinter* was described by L. G. Karsten,[4] R. J. Häuy, and C. A. S. Hofmann. J. F. L. Hausmann called it *pittizite;* S. Beudant, *sideretine;* and later J. F. L. Hausmann called it **pitticite.** Analyses by Stromeyer, C. M. Kersten, C. F. Rammelsberg, A. H. Church, A. Frenzel, F. A. Genth, Kovar, E. W. Benecke and E. Cohen, etc., show that the mineral is rather indefinite, for e composition varies so much that a satisfactory guess at the idealized mineral has not en made. It appears to be a basic ferric arsenate—some varieties contain sulphates, hers also contain lime—*e.g.* the mineral described by P. P. Pilipenko. W. F. Foshag d H. G. Clinton regard it as a mixture of colloidal arsenate and sulphate of iron. S. Larsen found the index of refraction is near 1·635. The so-called iron sinter may pitticite or impure scorodite.

L. J. Curtman[5] found that when ammonium hydroarsenate is added to a strong id soln. of ferric chloride it furnished a white crystalline precipitate of **ferric mmonium arsenate,** $(NH_4)H_2AsO_4.FeAsO_4$. This salt readily hydrolyzes in the resence of water; it dissolves in mineral acids and in ammonia. A basic salt is recipitated from the ammoniacal soln. or by the addition of alcohol. A **ferric otassium arsenate** is formed in a similar way. C. Lefèvre dissolved about per cent. of ferric oxide in molten potassium metarsenate, and obtained colourless, ansparent, rhombic prisms of **potassium ferric pyroarsenate,** $KFeAs_2O_7$; with dium metarsenate, greenish, transparent prisms of **sodium ferric pyroarsenate,** aFeAs_2O_7$, were formed. He also obtained greenish lamellæ of **potassium rric triorthoarsenate,** $K_3Fe_2(AsO_4)_3$, by using a larger proportion of ferric oxide; nd green, transparent monoclinic prisms of **sodium ferric triorthoarsenate,** $_a_3Fe_2(AsO_4)_3$, were similarly obtained. A. Rosenheim and S. Thon prepared odium dihydroferriarsenate, $NaH_2[Fe(AsO_4)_2].H_2O$, and **potassium dihydro-** rr:arsenate, $KH_2[Fe(AsO_4)_2]$. The triclinic crystals of $CuFe_4As_4O_{17}$ obtained y A. Arzruni and E. Schütz in the brick-work of a furnace making chlorine y Deacon's process may be *copper ferric oxytetrarsenate.* The rare mineral amed **cheneviscite**—after R. Chenevix—occurs with the arsenical pyrites in ornwall, and Utah. Analyses by R. Chenevix, F. Pisani, G. S. Mackenzie, nd W. F. Hillebrand agree approximately with **copper ferryl arsenate,** $u(FeO)AsO_4.1\frac{1}{2}H_2O$. It occurs in dark green or greenish-yellow compact masses f hardness 3·5-4·5; and sp. gr. 3·93. E. S. Larsen found that the index of efraction approximates 1·88.

G. A. Koenig[6] described a basic arsenate from the Jesus-Maria mine, Mazapil, Iexico, and called it **mazapilite.** The analysis corresponds with $Ca_3Fe_2(AsO_4)_4$- FeO.OH)_2.5H_2O$, which P. Groth represented as **calcium ferric hexahydroxy-** etrarsenate, $Fe_4Ca_3(AsO_4)_4(OH)_6.3H_2O$; that is

$$Fe(OH){=}AsO_4.Ca$$
$$\phantom{Fe(OH){=}AsO_4.}Ca{>}\begin{matrix}AsO_4{-}Fe(OH)_2\\AsO_4{-}Fe(OH)_2\end{matrix}$$
$$Fe(OH){=}AsO_4.Ca$$

he slender prismatic crystals are black or deep brownish-red, but in thin splinters, y transmitted light, they are blood-red. The rhombic crystals have the axial ratios $: b : c = 0.8617 : 1 : 0.9980$; A. des Cloizeaux gave $0.57735 : 1 : 0.56443$. Accord- ng to G. A. Koenig, the hardness is 4·5; and the sp. gr. 3·567-3·562. E. S. Larsen ave for the index of refraction $\omega=1.898$, and $\epsilon=1.815$; the optical character is egative. About a mol. of water is lost at 360°, and the remainder at a red-heat. Iazapilite is soluble in warm hydrochloric acid. E. S. Larsen compared the roperties of the mineral with those of arsenosiderite. J. Barthoux obtained a elated mineral from Jebel Debar, Algeria. He named it **dussertite.** Its analysis orresponds with **calcium triferric enneahydroxydiarsenate,** $Ca_3Fe_3(OH)_9(AsO_4)_2$. he minute, green crystals are flattened parallel to the base and are either trigonal r hexagonal; they are optically uniaxial and negative; the indices of refraction, and ϵ, are between 1·80 and 1·88; and $\omega-\epsilon=0.012$. Thin sections are

yellowish-green and slightly pleochroic. The hardness is 3·5; and the sp. gr.
3·75. 0·3 per cent. of water is lost at 120°; 9·3 per cent. at 700°; and 9·8 per
cent. at 1000°. Dussertite is soluble in dil. hydrochloric acid. The related mineral
occurs at Mâcon, France, and at Schneeberg, Saxony. It was called by
P. A. Dufrénoy [7] **arseniosiderite,** which E. F. Glocker changed to *arsenocrocite*—
from κρόκη, a fibre—because the term arsenosiderite had been employed by him
for löllingite. Analyses were made by P. A. Dufrénoy, etc.   C. F. Rammelsberg
used the formula $2Ca_3(AsO_4)_2.6FeAsO_4.8Fe(OH)_3$; and A. H. Church
$2Ca_3(AsO_4)_2.2FeAsO_4.6Fe(OH)_3$.   P. Groth regarded it as **calcium tetraferric
enneahydroxyarsenate,** $Fe_4Ca_4(OH)_9AsO_4$. The yellowish-brown mineral occurs
in fibrous concretions, and the crystals belong to the tetragonal or hexagonal
system.   A. Lacroix said the crystals are uniaxial, negative, and strongly pleochroic.   The hardness is 1–2.   The sp. gr. given by P. A. Dufrénoy is 3·520;
by C. F. Rammelsberg, 3·88; and by A. H. Church, 3·36. It resembles scorodite
in many respects.   E. S. Larsen gave for the indices of refraction $\omega=1·870$, and
$\epsilon=1·792$.   J. B. Tyrrel and R. P. D. Graham described a yellowish-brown mineral
from the Yukon Territory, Canada, and called it **yukonite.** Its composition
approximates $(Ca_3,Fe_2''')(AsO_4)_2. 2Fe(OH)_3.5H_2O$. The sp. gr. was 2·65, and when
soaked in water, 2·86; and the hardness 2–3. Half the water is lost at 100°, or
in vacuo, and the remainder at a red-heat.   A. Rosenheim and S. Thon prepared
barium hexahydroferriarsenate, $Ba_3H_6[Fe(AsO_4)_3]_2$.

The mineral called *carmine spar* by F. Sandberger,[8] and **carminite,** by J. D. Dana
occurs in clusters of carmine-red or brick-red needles at Norhausen, Germany.
Other occurrences were noted by A. Russell, and W. F. Petterd. The analysis by
R. Müller corresponds with **lead ferric dodecarsenate,** $Pb_3(AsO_4)_2.10FeAsO_4$, the
prismatic crystals belong to the rhombic system. The hardness is 2·0–2·5; and
the sp. gr. 4·105. A. Russell found the refractive index to be over 1·74; and the
double refraction is strong and positive. The mineral is soluble in nitric acid.
L. J. Igelström described a yellow mineral from Sjö mine, Orebro, Sweden. He
called it **sjogrufvite.** The analysis corresponds with $2(RO)_3.2As_2O_5.R_2O_3.6H_2O$,
or **(calcium) manganese ferric triarsenate,** $FeMn_3(AsO_4)_3.3H_2O$. It contains about
3·61 per cent. of calcium oxide, and 1·74 per cent. of lead oxide. It resembles
arseniopleite in many ways. It is magnetic; it oxidizes rapidly in air; and is
readily soluble in cold hydrochloric acid. A. Frenzel found rhombohedral crystals
of a blackish, reddish, or yellowish-brown mineral at Schneeberg, Saxony, which
he called **miriquidite,** and which was regarded as a lead ferric phosphato-arsenate,
but it was not quantitatively analyzed. The rhombohedral crystals have a
hardness of 4.

In 1872, F. E. Bruckmann [9] described *Koboldblüthe,* or *cobalt bloom,* as a blood-
red mineral. J. G. Wallerius applied the term *Koboltblomma,* or *flos cobalti,* to
the *cobaltic minera colore rubra* when crystalline, and *Koboltbeslag,* when earthy.
A. Cronstedt called the same mineral *ochra cobalti rubra, red cobali,* or *cobalt
ochre;* T. Bergman, *cobaltum acido arsenico mineralisatum;* J. J. N. Huot, *rhodoise;*
and F. S. Beudant, *erythrine,* hence the usual term **erythrite**—from ἐρυθρός, red.
This mineral is supposed by G. la Valle, L. Buchrucker, etc., to be a decomposition
product of smaltite. It has been reported from Schneeberg, Saxony; Wolfach
and Wittichen, Baden; Riechelsdorf, Hesse; Saalfeld, Thuringia; Modum,
Norway; St. Just, Cornwall; Alston, Cumberland; Killarney, Ireland; Allemont,
Dauphiné; Messina, Sicily; in California, and Pennsylvania; and in several other
localities. It occurs as a pulverulent incrustation, in prismatic crystals, and in
globular and reniform shapes with a columnar structure, sometimes stellate. The
colour is crimson, and peach-red; pearl-grey or greenish-grey; and there is a
green variety at Platten, Bohemia, which sometimes has red and green on the
same crystal. Analyses have been reported by C. M. Kersten, J. F. Vogel,
C. F. Rammelsberg, F. Petersen, A. Laugier, and C. F. Bucholz. The results are
in agreement with what is required for **cobalt orthoarsenate,** $Co_3(AsO_4)_2.8H_2O$.

H. B. Weiser and A. P. Bloxsom prepared the **hydrogel of cobalt arsenate** by the method used for the zinc salt. The earthy variety of cobalt bloom—*Kobalt-beschlag*—was considered by C. M. Kersten to be a mixture of erythrite and arsenolite (1 : 1). Lavendulite (*q.v.*) has been regarded as a cupriferous erythrite. L. Gmelin obtained this arsenate as a precipitate, the colour of the peach-blossom, by adding sodium arsenate to a soln. of a cobalt salt. It dries to a dark horny mass. O. Ducru obtained the octohydrate by treating an aq. soln. of a cobalt salt with ammonia orthoarsenate, which may or may not contain ammonium chloride, but not free ammonia. The pale rose-red precipitate consists of microscopic needles. A. de Schulten obtained crystals of erythrite by allowing a soln. of heptahydrated sodium hydroarsenate (2 grms. per litre) slowly to drop into a soln. of anhydrous cobalt sulphate (2 grms. per 3 litres) heated on a water-bath for 40 days. G. Klemp and J. von Gyulay prepared **colloidal cobalt arsenate** by the successive addition of ammonium sulphate, acetic acid, and an excess of sodium arsenate to a soln. of a cobaltous salt. The opalescent jelly crystallizes when allowed to stand for some time.

The prismatic crystals of erythrite may be vertically striated. According to A. Brezina, they belong to the monoclinic system and have the axial ratios $a : b : c = 0.75 : 1 : 0.70$, and $\beta = c.\ 75°$; A. des Cloizeaux gave $0.7937 : 1 : 0.7356$, and $\beta = 105° 9'$. The (010)-cleavage is perfect; and the (100)- and ($\bar{1}$01)-cleavages indistinct. The crystals are isomorphous with vivianite. A. des Cloizeaux gave for the optic axial angle for red, yellow, and blue light, respectively $2H = 104° 41'$, $104° 31'$, and $102° 21'$. The optical character is positive. P. Gaubert gave for the indices of refraction $\alpha = 1.6263$, $\beta = 1.6614$, and $\gamma = 1.6986$ for Na-light; the birefringence $\gamma - \alpha = 0.0723$. E. S. Larsen gave $\alpha = 1.629$, $\beta = 1.663$, and $\gamma = 1.701$. The pleochroism is shown by the pale red colour of a, pale violet of b, and red of c. G. Lincio, and F. Ulrich studied the optical properties of the mineral. The hardness is 1·5 to 2·5, being smallest on the (010)-face. The sp. gr. given by C. M. Kersten is 2·912. A. de Schulten gave 3·178 for artificial erythrite. Erythrite dissolves in hydrochloric acid, forming a blue soln. which when diluted is rose-red. The mineral is decomposed by potash-lye leaving a black residue. J. Lemberg found that bromine-water slowly oxidizes the mineral; and J. R. Müller investigated the action of an aq. soln. of carbon dioxide. O. Ducru reported the formation of three ammines by the action of arsenic acid, or an arsenate on soln. of cobalt salts containing ammonium salts and free ammonia. The composition depends on the proportion of ammonia, but is not affected by the proportion of ammonium salts. The ammines are to be regarded as being formed by the substitution of water of crystallization by ammonia. If the mother-liquor contains 15 c.c. of 20 per cent. ammonia per litre, rhombic plates or needles of **cobalt monamminorthoarsenate**, $Co_3(AsO_4)_2(NH_3).7H_2O$, are formed; with 60 c.c. of 20 per cent. ammonia, **cobalt diamminorthoarsenate**, $Co_3(AsO_4)_2(NH_3)_2.6H_2O$, is formed; and with 350 c.c. of 20 per cent. ammonia, **cobalt triamminorthoarsenate**, $Co_3(AsO_4)_2(NH_3)_3.5H_2O$.

A basic arsenate of cobalt was once used commercially under the name *chaux métallique*. It was made by adding potassium carbonate to a soln. of smaltite in nitric acid so long as white ferric arsenate was precipitated, and more alkali carbonate was added to the filtrate to precipitate the basic cobalt arsenate. A reddish powder was also made by roasting cobalt arsenide. J. G. Gentele obtained **cobalt oxyarsenate**, $CoO.Co_3(AsO_4)_2$, by precipitating a soln. of cobalt arsenate in nitric acid by the addition of sodium carbonate, and fusing the product. The cold crystalline mass contained deep blue, prismatic crystals, soluble in acids. When powdered, the product is rose-red. It was used as a pigment. A. Coloriano prepared dichroic—blue and reddish-violet—rhombic, prismatic crystals of the *monohydrate*, $Co=O_2=AsO-O-CoOH$, by heating a mixture of sodium orthoarsenate with an excess of cobalt nitrate soln. in a sealed tube at 150°.

According to C. M. Kersten, the evaporation in vacuo of a soln. of cobalt hydroxide or cobalt orthoarsenate, dissolved in an excess of arsenic acid, furnished peach-coloured needles arranged in stellated groups. This product is supposed to be an acidic arsenate. A. Coloriano heated a mixture of cobalt carbonate and an excess of arsenic acid in a sealed tube at 235°, and obtained rose-red needles of $5CoO.2As_2O_5.3H_2O$, or **cobalt dihydrotetrarsenate**, $Co_3(AsO_4)_2.2CoHAsO_4.2H_2O$. The product is insoluble in water, and is dehydrated by heat. C. Lefèvre obtained **cobalt pyroarsenate**, $Co_2As_2O_7$, in violet crystals by dissolving cobalt oxide in molten potassium metarsenate; and H. Goguel obtained the *dihydrate*, $Co_2As_2O_7.2H_2O$, or $H_2(CoOH)_2As_2O_7$, in monoclinic crystals.

C. Lefèvre obtained blue, prismatic crystals of **potassium cobalt arsenate**, $KCoAsO_4$, by dissolving cobalt oxide in one of the molten potassium arsenates mixed with the alkali chloride; he also obtained blue prismatic crystals of **sodium cobalt arsenate**, $NaCoAsO_4$, in an analogous way; and violet plates of **sodium cobalt hexarsenate**, $Na_4Co_4As_6O_{21}$, from cobalt oxide and molten sodium metarsenate. A. Rosenheim and S. Thon could not prepare **cobaltiarsenates** like the ferriarsenates. A mineral obtained by A. Lévy from Schneeberg, Saxony, was called **roselite**—after G. Rose. It occurs in small crystals and in spherical aggregates coloured light or dark rose-red. Analyses were reported by C. Winkler, and A. Weisbach. A. Schrauf represented the results by formulæ ranging from $Ca_6Mg_2Co_4As_8O_{32}.10-12H_2O$ and $Ca_7Mg_2Co_3As_8O_{32}.10H_2O$; which can be generalized into $R_3(AsO_4)_2.3H_2O$, or $R_3(AsO_4)_2.2H_2O$, that is, $(Ca,Mg,Co)_3(AsO_4)_2.2H_2O$, or **calcium magnesium cobalt arsenate**. A. Schrauf gave for the axial ratios of the triclinic crystals $a : b : c = 0.45360 : 1 : 0.65604$, and $a=90° 34'$, $\beta=91°$, and $\gamma=89° 20'$; and P. Groth gave $2.2046 : 1 : 1.4463$, and $a=89° 0'$, $\beta=90° 34'$, and $\gamma=98° 21'$. E. S. Larsen said that the optic axial angle is moderate; the optical character, positive; the index of refraction, 1.725; the birefringence, 0.01; and the pleochroism b=pale rose-red, and c colourless. The hardness is 3.5; and the sp. gr. reported by A. Schrauf is 3.506–3.738; and by C. Winkler, and A. Weisbach, 3.460–3.561. The mineral is soluble in hydrochloric acid giving a blue conc. soln., or a red dil. soln.

C. Bergemann [10] described what he called *Nickelerz* as a sulphur-yellow mineral from Johanngeorgenstadt. The analysis corresponds with normal **nickel orthoarsenate**, $Ni_3(AsO_4)_2$. M. Adam called it **xanthiosite**—from $\xi\alpha\nu\theta\delta s$, yellow—in allusion to the colour. The anhydrous salt was made by A. Girard by heating the hydrate, or by the action of nitric acid on the hydrate; and by O. Ducru, by heating one of the ammines—*vide infra*. Xanthiosite is amorphous; its hardness is 4; and its sp. gr. 4.982. It is attacked by acids very slowly. R. Tupputi obtained the *dihydrate*, $Ni_3(AsO_4)_2.2H_2O$, by double decomposition with an alkali arsenate and a nickel salt; A. Coloriano obtained it as a by-product in the preparation of nickel dihydrotetraorthoarsenate—*vide infra*—from which it can be separated mechanically since the dihydrate is specifically heavier. The product appears as an apple-green powder, or in hexagonal plates. According to J. L. Proust, and R. Tupputi, when the dihydrate is heated, it gives off at first nothing but water, becoming first hyacinth-red; at a red-heat, it becomes pale yellow; and at a higher temp. it exhibits no further change unless it be in the presence of a reducing agent. J. W. Döbereiner observed that when heated with sulphur it gives off sulphur dioxide, then yellow arsenic sulphide, then the red sulphide, and leaves behind nickel sulphide. J. J. Berzelius reported it to be insoluble in water; soluble in arsenic acid, and in the stronger mineral acids; and freely soluble in aq. ammonia. When potassium hydroxide is added to the ammoniacal soln., potassium niccolate is precipitated free from arsenic unless some ferric salt is also present. The salt is decomposed by fused potassium hydroxide. If it be dissolved in an acidic soln. of cobalt arsenate, and a small proportion of potash-lye be added, cobalt arsenate is precipitated.

The *octohydrate*, $Ni_3(AsO_4)_2.8H_2O$, occurs in nature, as the mineral named **annabergite** by H. J. Brookes and W. H. Miller. It appears as an apple-green earth, or capillary crystals. It was called *ochra niccoli* and *niccolum calciforme* by A. Cronstedt, and it has been variously called nickel bloom, nickel ochre, and nickel green. Annabergite occurs at Annaberg and Schneeberg, Saxony; Kamsdorf, Thuringia; Allemont, Dauphiné; in Connecticut, Colorado, and Nevada; etc. Analyses, made by P. Berthier, F. Stromeyer, L. Buchrucker, A. Sachs, J. S. Newberry, C. M. Kersten, and F. A. Genth, are in agreement with the above formula. In some cases a little nickel is replaced by calcium, magnesium, or ferrous-iron. O. Ducru obtained the octohydrate, in microscopic needles, by precipitation by ammonium orthoarsenate from a soln. of nickelcus chloride and an ammonium salt, but no free ammonia; and A. de Schulten obtained artificial annabergite by a method similar to that employed for erythrite. He said that the crystals are monoclinic like those of erythrite. F. Ulrich studied the optical properties of the crystals. E. S. Larsen gave 82° for the optic axial angle; the optical character is positive; and the indices of refraction $a=1.622$, $\beta=1.658$, and $\gamma=1.687$. The sp. gr. was 3·300. Annabergite is soluble in acids. According to O. Ducru, a soln. containing a mixture of nickel and ammonium salts and free ammonia when treated with arsenic acid or a soluble arsenate, produces in the cold or on gently warming a gelatinous greenish-white precipitate which deepens in colour and becomes crystalline when the mixture is heated on the water-bath. The crystals are anisotropic and belong to the monoclinic system; they vary in composition according to the amount of ammonia present. When the soln. contains no free ammonia, the octohydrate is produced; with 1·38 per cent. of amroonia, **nickel monamminorthoarsenate,** $Ni_3(AsO_4)_2.(NH_3).7H_2O$; with 6·9 per cent. of ammonia, **nickel diamminorthoarsenate,** $Ni_3(AsO_4)_2(NH_3)_2.6H_2O$; and with more conc. soln., **nickel triamminorthoarsenate,** $Ni_3(AsO_4)_2(NH_3)_3.5H_2O$. When heated to dull redness, all these salts yield the anhydrous arsenate, but at 150°, $Ni_3(AsO_4)_2.8H_2O$ yields $Ni_3(AsO_4).1\frac{1}{2}H_2O$; $Ni_3(AsO_4)_2.7H_2O,NH_3$ yields $Ni_3(AsO_4)_2.H_2O.\frac{3}{4}NH_3$; $Ni_3(AsO_4)_2.6H_2O.2NH_3$ yields $Ni_3(AsO_4).\frac{1}{2}H_2O.\frac{3}{4}NH_3$; and $Ni_3(AsO_4)_2.5H_2O.3NH_3$ yields $Ni_3(AsO_4)_2.\frac{1}{2}H_2O.\frac{1}{2}NH_3$.

C. Bergemann reported a green or brownish-green nickel ore from Johanngeorgenstadt whose composition corresponded with **nickel dioxyarsenate,** $2NiO.Ni_3(AsO_4)_2$, or $Ni\{AsO(O.NiO)\}_2$. M. Adam called it **aerugite.** Its hardness is 4. It dissolves in acids very slowly, and resembles xanthiosite in many respects. J. F. L. Hausmann obtained monoclinic crystals approximating **nickel oxyarsenate,** $NiO.Ni_3(AsO_4)_2$, as a furnace product by the oxidation of smaltite at a high temp. A. Coloriano prepared **nickel hydroxyarsenate,** $(NiOH)Ni(AsO_4)$, by heating a conc. soln. of sodium arsenate and an excess of nickel nitrate in a sealed tube at 235°–260°. The pale green stellate groups of needle-like crystals belong to the hexagonal system. They are insoluble in water, and only slightly attacked by acids. He also heated nickel with an excess of a conc. soln. of arsenic acid in a sealed tube at 160°, and obtained pale green, rhombic prisms of **nickel hydroarsenate,** $NiHAsO_4.H_2O$. They are soluble in water, are decomposed by acids with difficulty; and lose their water at a high temp. When the filtrate from a soln. of nickel carbonate in an excess of arsenic acid is heated to 235° in a sealed tube, pale green needles of **nickel dihydrotetraorthoarsenate,** $5NiO.2As_2O_5.3H_2O$, or $Ni_3(AsO_4)_2 2NiHAsO_4.2H_2O$, are formed. They are insoluble in water; and only slightly attacked by acids.

M. F. Heddle described a mineral resembling annabergite, but with about one-third the nickel replaced by calcium, forming **calcium nickel arsenate,** $(Ni,Ca)_3(AsO_4)_2.8H_2O$. It was obtained from Creetown, Scotland. J. H. Ferber described a **magnesium nickel arsenate,** $(Ni,Mg)_3(AsO_4)_2.8H_2O$, with a little ferrous and cobaltous oxides in place of the nickel oxide. It was obtained from Sierra Cabrera, Spain, and hence J. D. Dana called it **cabrerite;** it also occurs in the zinc mines of Laurium, Greece. It results from the oxidation of the arsenides of nickel and cobalt. Analyses were reported by J. H. Ferber, A. Frenzel, A. Sachs, and A. Damour and A. des Cloizeaux. A. de Schulten synthesized the crystals of cabrerite by a method analogous to that employed for erythrite, and annabergite. Cabrerite appears in apple-green monoclinic crystals, and in masses with a fibrous, concentric, or radiated structure. It appears also reniform and granular. A. Sachs gave for the axial ratios $a : b : c = 0.82386 : 1 : 0.77677$ and $\beta = 106° 29'$. A. Damour and A. des Cloizeaux found the optic axial angle for red light to be $2H = 105° 30'$ to $112° 20'$. E. S. Larsen found that $2V$ is nearly $90°$. The optical character is negative. E. S. Larsen obtained for the indices of refraction $a = 1.620$, $\beta = 1.654$, and $\gamma = 1.689$. F. Ulrich studied the optical properties of the mineral. The hardness is 2 ; and the sp. gr. by A. des Cloizeaux and A. Damour, 3.11 ; by A. Sachs, 3.0104 ; by A. Frenzel, 2.92 ; and by J. H. Ferber, 2.96. A. de Schulten gave 2.288 for the artificial crystals. It loses all its water between $100°$ and $400°$. D. Forbes described what he called a hydrous dibasic arsenate of nickel and cobalt occurring at Atacama. G. A. Kenngott called it **forbesite**. The colour is greyish-white, and the mineral has a fibro-crystalline structure. D. Forbes' analysis corresponds with $2(Ni,Co)O.As_2O_5.9H_2O$, in agreement with **cobalt nickel hydroarsenate**, $(Ni,Co)(HAsO_4).4H_2O$. The hardness is 2.5 ; and the sp. gr. 3.086.

REFERENCES.

[1] A. Coloriano, *Compt. Rend.*, **103**. 273, 1886 ; *Recherches sur quelques arsénates cristallisés*, Paris, 1886 ; *Bull. Soc. Chim.*, (2), **45**. 707, 1886 ; C. Palache and E. V. Shannon, *Amer. Min.*, **12**. 82, 1927 ; W. F. Foshag, H. M. Berman, and R. B. Gage, *Proc. U.S. Nat. Museum*, **70**. 20, 1927 ; W. F. Foshag and R. B. Gage, *Journ. Washington Acad.*, **14**. 362, 1924 ; J. H. Debray, *ib.*, (1), 2. 14, 1864 ; L. C. A. Barreswil, *Compt. Rend.*, **44**. 677, 1857 ; H. Rose, *Zeit. anal. Chem.*, **1**. 414, 425, 1862 ; C. Lefèvre, *Ann. Chim. Phys.*, (6), **27**. 29, 1892 ; *Sur les arsénates crystallisés*, Paris, 1891 : M. Amadori, *Atti Ist. Veneto*, **81**. 603, 1922 ; F. C. B. Schiefer, *Zeit. ges. Naturw. Halle*, **23**. 365, 1864 ; C. W. Scheele, *Svenska Akad. Handl.*, **40**. 316, 1778 ; G. Kemp and J. von Gyulay, *Koll. Zeit.*, **15**. 202, 1914 ; **22**. 57, 1918 ; **28**. 262, 1921 ; E. Deiss, *ib.*, **14**. 139, 1914 ; **16**. 16, 1915 ; *Zeit. anorg. Chem.*, **145**. 365, 1925 ; F. Flade, H. Scherffig, and E. Deiss, *ib.*, **116**. 228, 1921 ; L. J. Igelström, *Geol. För. Förh. Stockholm*, **4**. 212, 1884 ; *Œfvers. Akad. Stockholm*, **22**. 3, 1865 ; **41**. 86, 1884 ; **42**. 257, 1885 ; *Bull. Soc. Min.*, **7**. 121, 237, 1884 ; **8**. 369, 1885 ; *Zeit. Kryst.*, **22**. 468, 1894 ; W. C. Brögger, *ib.*, **14**. 519, 1885 ; A. Sjögren, *Œfvers. Akad. Förh. Stockholm*, **8**. 3, 1884 ; *Œfvers. Akad. Stockholm*, **41**. 29, 1884 ; **44**. 109, 1887 ; *Geol. För. Förh. Stockholm*, **7**. 109. 724, 1885 ; H. Sjögren, *ib.*, **7**. 220, 386, 1884 ; **28**. 401, 1906 ; *Zeit. Kryst.*, **10**. 114, 142, 1885 ; G. Flink and A. Hamberg, *Geol. För. Förh. Stockholm*, **10**. 381, 1888 ; A. Hamberg, *ib.*, **11**. 212, 1889 ; G. Flink, *ib.*, **46**. 461, 1924 ; G. Lindström, *ib.*, **13**. 123, 1891 ; G. Aminoff, *ib.*, **41**. 161, 1919 ; **43**. 24, 1921 ; P. Groth, *Tabellarische Uebersicht der Mineralien*, Braunschweig, 96, 1898 ; E. S. Larsen, *Bull. U.S. Geol. Sur.*, 679, 1921 ; E. Bertrand, *Bull. Soc. Min.*, **7**. 124, 1884 ; H. B. Weiser and A. P. Bloxsom, *Journ. Phys. Chem.*, **28**. 26, 1924 ; J. A. Krenner, *Zeit. Kryst.*, **10**. 83, 1884 ; H. B. Weiser, *Colloid Symposium Wisconsin Univ.*, **38**, 1923 ; E. O. Kraemer, *ib.*, **62**. 1923 ; C. F. Rammelsberg, *Neues Jahrb. Min.*, ii, 72, 1884 ; H. Stallo, *Amer. Journ. Science*, (3), **14**. 285, 1877 ; O. T. Christensen, *Journ. prakt. Chem.*, (2), **28**. 23, 1883 ; F. J. Otto, *ib.*, (1), 2. 414, 1834 ; J. Lorenzen, *Œfvers. Akad. Stockholm*, **41**. 4, 1884 ; A. E. Nordenskjöld, *ib.*, **45**. 418, 1888 ; C. H. Pfaff, *Schweigger's Journ.*, **45**. 59, 1825 ; J. F. John, *ib.*, 4. 436, 1807 ; Grasselli Chemical Co., *Canadian Pat. No.* 260934, 1926 ; *U.S. Pat. No.* 1591795, 1926.

[2] H. Kühn, *Liebig's Ann.*, **34**. 211, 1840 ; J. D. Dana, *A System of Mineralogy*, New York, 239, 1844 ; P. A. Dufrénoy, *Traité de mineralogie*, Paris, 1844 ; H. J. Brookes and W. H. Miller, *Introduction to Mineralogy*, London, 481, 1852 ; L. J. Igelström, *Bull. Soc. Min.*, **9**. 218, 1886 ; *Zeit. Kryst.*, **22**. 468, 1894 ; *Geol. För. Förh. Stockholm*, **7**. 101, 1885 ; **15**. 471, 1893 ; A. G. Högbom, *ib.*, **9**. 397, 1887 ; W. Lindgren, *ib.*, **5**. 552, 1881 ; **7**. 291, 1884 ; L. W. McCay, *ib.*, **5**. 554, 1881 ; G. Flink, *ib.*, **44**. 773, 1922 ; G. K. Almström, *ib.*, **45**. 117, 1923 ; C. H. Lundström, *ib.*, **2**. 178, 223, 1874 ; G. Aminoff, *ib.*, **48**. 46, 1926 ; A. Sjögren, *ib.*, **2**. 533, 1874 ; H. Sjögren, *ib.*, **11**. 391, 1889 ; **15**. 472, 1893 ; **19**. 106, 1897 ; *Bull. Geol. Inst. Upsala*, **2**. 39, 54, 1894 ; *Zeit. Kryst.*, **22**. 469, 1893 ; A. H. Church, *Min. Mag.*, **11**. 11, 1895 ; G. Flink, *Bihang Svenska Akad. Handl.*, **12**. 2, 1886 ; *Nyt Mag.*, **29**. 300, 1885 ; E. Bertrand, *Bull. Soc. Min.*, **7**. 31, 1884 ; A. Wichmann, *Zeit. Kryst.*, **5**. 105, 1880 ; W. F. Foshag and R. B. Gage, *Journ. Washington Acad.*, **14**. 362, 1924 ; C. F. Rammelsberg, *Handbuch der Mineralchemie*, Leipzig, 335, 1875 ; A. des Cloizeaux, *Manuel de minéralogie*, Paris, 2. 409, 1893 ; E. S. Larsen, *Bull. U.S. Geol. Sur.*, 679, 1921 : W. T. Schaller, *ib.*, 610 (104), 1916 ; C. Palache and E. V. Shannon, *Amer. Min.*, **12**. 144, 1927.

[3] R. Chenevix, *Phil. Trans.*, **91**. 193, 1801 ; J. L. Bournon, *ib.*, **91**. 191, 1801 ; G. Klemp and J. von Gyulay, *Koll. Zeit.*, **15**. 202, 1914 ; **22**. 57, 1918 ; **28**. 262, 1921 ; J. A. Krenner, *Fermesz. Füzedek.*, **10**. 83, 1886 ; *Zeit. Kryst.*, **13**. 70, 1888 ; C. Vrba, *ib.*, **15**. 206, 1889 ; A. d'Achiardi, *ib.*, **1**. 618, 1877 ; A. Breithaupt, *Handbuch der Mineralogie*, Freiberg, **4**. ii, 182,

1817 ; **A.** Breithaupt and C. F. Plattner, *Journ. prakt. Chem.*, (1), **10**. 501, 1837 ; R. Hermann, *ib.*, (1), **33**. 95, 1844 ; *Bull. Soc. Nat. Moscow*, **1**. 254, 1845 ; W. Duncan, *Pharm. Journ.*, (4), **20**. 71, 1905 ; B. Jezek and A. Simek, *Zeit. Kryst.*, **54**. 88, 1914 ; *Rozpr. Ceske Akad. Prag.*, **20**. 16, 1911 ; N. H. Hartshorne, *Journ. Chem. Soc.*, 1759, 1927 ; E. Boricky, *Proc. Russ. Min. Soc.*, **3**. 98, 1868 ; C. F. Rammelsberg, *Handbuch der Mineralchemie*, Leipzig, 345, 1875 ; H. B. Weiser and A. P. Bloxsom, *Journ. Phys. Chem.*, **28**. 26, 1924 ; D. N. Chakravasti and N. R. Dhar, *ib.*, **30**. 1646, 1926 ; N. J. B. G. Guibourt, *Journ. Chim. Méd.*, (1), **15**. 306, 1839 ; G. C. Wittstein, *Repert Pharm.*, **63**. 329, 1854 ; *Pharm. Vierteljahr.*, **15**. 185, 1866 ; D. L. G. Karsten, *Mineralogische Tabellen*, Berlin, 66, 1808 ; J. J. Berzelius, *Akad. Handl. Stockholm*, 354, 1824 ; *Schweigger's Journ.*, **32**. 162, 1821 ; J. W. Döbereiner, *ib.*, **26**. 271, 1819 ; C. M. Kersten, *ib.*, **53**. 176, 1828 ; C. H. Pfaff, *ib.*, **22**. 255, 1818 ; **45**. 59, 1825 ; R. Brandes, *ib.*, **22**. 350, 1818 ; H. Metzke, *Zeit. anorg. Chem.*, **19**. 457, 1899 ; *Neues Jahrb. Min.*, i, 169, 1898 ; *Ueber einige Arsenate des Eisenoxydes*, Rostock, 1898 ; N. W. Fischer, *Pogg. Ann.*, **9**. 262, 1827 ; E. S. Larsen, *Bull. U.S. Geol. Sur.*, 679, 1921 ; J. B. J. D. Boussingault, *Ann. Chim. Phys.*, (3), **41**. 337, 1854 ; A. Damour, *ib.*, (3), **10**. 412, 1844 ; J. L. Proust, *ib.*, (1), **1**. 195, 1790 ; A. Hague, *Amer. Journ. Science*, (3), **34**. 171, 1887 ; J. da Costa Sena, *Bull. Soc. Min.*, **7**. 220, 1884 ; E. Bertrand, *ib.*, **4**. 256, 1881 ; P. Gaubert, *ib.*, **30**. 104, 1907 ; A. Verneuil and L. Bourgeois, *ib.*, **3**. 32, 1880 , *Compt. Rend.*, **90**. 223, 1880 ; *Bull. Soc. Chim.*, (2), **33**. 151, 1880 ; A. des Cloizeaux, *De l'emploi des propriétés optiques biréfringentes en minéralogie*, Paris, **1**. 60, 1857 ; *Ann. Mines*, (5), **11**. 261, 1857 ; (5), **14**. 339, 1858 ; *Ann. Chim. Phys.*, (3), **10**. 402, 1844 ; *Nouvelles recherches sur les propriétés optiques des cristaux*, Paris, 89, 1867 ; P. Groth, *Tabellarische Uebersicht der Mineralien*, Braunschweig, 95, 1898 ; A. Raimondi, *Minéraux du Pérou*, Paris, 228, 1875 ; T. L. Walker and A. L. Parsons, *Contributions to Canadian Mineralogy*, Toronto, 16, 1924 ; A. L. Parsons, *ib.*, 17, 1924 ; E. F. Tschirva, *Bull. Acad. Rep. Soviet.*, **19**. 731, 1925 ; C. W. Scheele, *Svenska Akad. Handl.*, **40**. 316, 1778 ; R. J. Haüy, *Tableau comparatif des résultats de la cristallographie*, Paris, 91, 1809 ; F. S. Beudant, *Traité élémentaire de mineralogie*, Paris, **2**. 605, 1832 ; M. Lippmann and M. von Hornberg, *Zool. Min. Ver. Regenberg*, **11**. 172, 1857 ; R. P. D. Graham, *Trans. Roy. Soc. Canada*, (3), **7**. 14, 1913 ; E. Hussak, *Tshermak's Mitt.*, (2), **14**. 395, 1894 ; R. L. Codazzi, *Mineralizadores y minerales metalicos de Columbia*, Bogota, 1905 ; J. H. C. Martens, *Amer. Min.*, **9**. 27, 1924 ; P. Kotschoubey, *Journ. prakt. Chem.*, (1), **49**. 182, 1850 ; H. Salkowsky, *ib.*, (1), **104**. 129, 1868 ; H. Rose, *Ausführliches Handbuch der analytischen Chemie*, Braunschweig, **2**. 401, 1867 ; *Zeit. anal. Chem.*, **1**. 414, 1862 ; G. Lunge, *ib.*, **6**. 185, 1867 ; E. S. Larsen, *Bull. U.S. Geol. Sur.*, 679, 1921 ; L. Dede, *Zeit. anorg. Chem.*, **125**. 28, 1922 ; N. R. Dhar and S. Ghosh, *ib.*, **152**. 409, 1926 ; G. Franceschi, *L'Orosi*, **15**. 192, 1892 ; H. B. Weiser, *Colloid Symposium Wisconsin Univ.*, 38, 1923 ; M. H. Klaproth, *Schrift. Ges. Nat. Berlin*, 161, 1786 : *Beiträge zur chemischen Kenntniss der Mineralkörper*, Berlin, **3**. 194, 1802 ; R. Kirwan, *Elements of Mineralogy*, London, **2**. 189, 1796 ; J. F. L. Hausmann, *Handbuch der Mineralogie*, Göttingen, 1065, 1813 ; D. G. L. Lenz, *Versuch einer vollständigen Anleitung zur Kenntniss der Mineralien*, Leipzig, **2**. 18, 151, 1794 ; E. G. J. Hartley, *Min. Mag.*, **12**. 153, 1899 ; A. Kalecsinsky, *Jahrb. Ungar. Geol. Landesanst.*, 128, 1888 ; N. von Kokscharoff, *Bull. Acad. St. Petersburg*, (4), **19**. 591, 1873 ; W. Ipatieff, *Ber.*, **59**. B, 1412, 1269 ; W. Ipatieff and W. N. Nikolaieff, *Journ. Russ. Phys. Chem. Soc.*, **58**. 664, 686, 692, 698, 1926 ; M. Piazza, *Atti Accad. Lincei*, (6), **6**. 70, 1927 ; G. vom Rath, *Neues Jahrb. Min.*, 396, 1876 ; F. Ulrich, *Zeit. Kryst.*, **64**. 143, 1926.

⁴ C. F. Rammelsberg, *Handbuch der Mineralchemie*, Leipzig, 355, 1875 ; *Pogg. Ann.*, **62** 139, 1844 ; F. Stromeyer, *Gilbert's Ann.*, **61**. 181, 1819 ; A. Laugier, *Ann. Chim. Phys.*, (2), **30**. 325, 1825 ; A. H. Church, *Chem. News*, **24**. 136, 1871 ; A. Frenzel, *Neues Jahrb. Min.*, 787, 1873 ; P. Groth, *Tabellarische Uebersicht der Mineralien*, Braunschweig, 100, 1898 ; C. M. Kersten, *Schweigger's Journ.*, **53**. 176, 1828 ; D. L. G. Karsten, *Mineralogische Tabellen*, Berlin, 66, 98, 1808 ; R. J. Häuy, *Tableau comparatif des résultats de la cristallographie*, Paris, 98, 1809 ; J. F. L. Hausmann, *Handbuch der Mineralogie*, Göttingen, 285, 1813 ; 1022, 1847 ; C. A. S. Hofmann, *Handbuch der Mineralogie*, Frieberg, **3**. b, 302, 1816 ; F. S. Beudant, *Traité élémentaire de minéralogie*, Paris, **2**. 609, 1832 ; E. W. Benecke and E. Cohen, *Geognostische Beschreibung der Umgebung von Heidelberg*, Strassburg, 1881 ; P. P. Pilipenko, *Bull. Univ. Tomsk*, **28**. 1, 1907 ; F. A. Genth, *Amer. Journ. Science*, (3), **40**. 205, 1890 ; F. Kovar, *Roz. Akad.*, 6, 1896 ; E. S. Larsen, *Bull. U.S. Geol. Sur.*, 679, 1921 ; W. F. Foshag and H. G. Clinton, *Amer. Min.*, **12**. 290, 1927.

⁵ R. Chenevix, *Phil. Trans.*, **91**. 193, 1801 ; F. Pisani, *Compt. Rend.*, **62**. 690, 1866 ; G. S. Mackenzie, *Min. Mag.*, **6**. 181, 1885 ; W. F. Hillebrand, *Proc. Colorado Scient. Soc.*, **1**. 115, 1884 ; C. Lefèvre, *Compt. Rend.*, **111**. 36, 1890 ; *Sur les arséniates cristallisés*, Paris, 1891 ; A. Arzruni and E. Schütz, *Zeit. Kryst.*, **23**. 529, 1894 ; L. J. Curtman, *Journ. Amer. Chem. Soc.*, **32**. 626, 1910 ; E. S. Larsen, *Bull. U.S. Geol. Sur.*, 679, 1921 ; A. Rosenheim and S. Thon, *Zeit. anorg. Chem.*, **167**. 1, 1927.

⁶ G. A. Koenig, *Proc. Acad. Philadelphia*, 192, 1888 ; P. Groth, *Tabellarische Uebersicht der Mineralien*, Braunschweig, 98, 1898 ; A. des Cloizeaux, *Bull. Soc. Min.*, **12**. 441, 1889 ; J. Barthoux, *Compt. Rend.*, **180**. 299, 1925 ; E. S. Larsen, *Bull. U.S. Geol. Sur.*, 679, 1921 ; *Amer. Min.*, **3**. 12, 1918.

⁷ P. A. Dufrénoy, *Ann. Mines*, (4), **2**. 243, 1842 ; *Compt. Rend.*, **16**. 22, 1843 ; E. F. Glocker, *Generum et specierum mineralium secundum ordines naturales digestorum synopsis*, Halle, 226, 1847 ; A. Lacroix, *Bull. Soc. Min.*, **9**. 3, 1886 ; C. F. Rammelsberg, *Pogg. Ann.*, **68**. 508, 1846 ; E. S. Larsen, *Bull. U.S. Geol. Sur.*, 679, 1921 ; A. H. Church, *Journ. Chem. Soc.*, **26**. 102, 1873 ;

P. Groth, *Tabellarische Uebersicht der Mineralien*, Braunschweig, 91, 1898 ; J. B. Tyrrel and R. P. D. Graham, *Trans. Roy. Soc. Canada*, (3), **7**. 4, 1913 ; A. Rosenheim and S. Thon, *Zeit. anorg. Chem.*, **167**. 1, 1927.

[8] F. Sandberger, *Pogg. Ann.*, **80**. 391, 1850 ; R. Müller, *ib.*, **103**. 345, 1858 ; A. Frenzel, *Neues Jahrb. Min.*, 939, 1872 ; 673, 1874 ; J. D. Dana, *A System of Mineralogy*, New York, 410, 1854 ; W. F. Petterd, *Proc. Roy. Soc. Tasmania*, 51, 1901 ; A. Russell, *Min. Mag.*, **15**. 285, 1910 ; L. J. Igelström, *Geol. För. Förh. Stockholm*, **14**. 309, 1892.

[9] F. E. Bruckmann, *Magnalia dei in locis subterraneis*, Helmstadt, 161, 1727 ; J. G. Wallerius, *Mineralogia*, Stockholm, 234, 1747 ; A. Cronstedt, *Mineralogie*, Stockholm, 212, 1758 ; T. Bergman, *Sciagraphia regni mineralis*, Lipsiæ, 134, 1782 ; F. S. Beudant, *Traité élémentaire de minéralogie*, Paris, **2**. 596, 1832 ; J. J. N. Huot, *Manuel de minéralogie*, Paris. **1**. 313, 1841 ; A. Brezina, *Tschermak's Mitt.*, (1), **2**. 19, 1872 ; A. Schrauf. *ib.*, (1), **4**. 137, 1874 ; A. des Cloizeaux, *Nouvelles recherches sur les propriétés optiques des cristaux*, Paris, 132, 1867 ; *Bull. Soc. Min.*, **1**. 76, 1878 ; A. de Schulten, *ib.*, **26**. 87, 1903 ; P. Gaubert, *ib.*, **30**. 107, 1907 ; F. Petersen, *Pogg. Ann.*, **134**. 86, 1868 ; C. M. Kersten, *ib.*, **60**. 251, 1843 ; C. F. Rammelsberg, *Handbuch der Mineralchemie*, Leipzig, 341, 1875 ; J. F. Vogel, *Gängverhältnisse und Mineralreichthum Joachimsthals*, Teplitz, 160, 1857 ; J. Lemberg, *Zeit. deut. geol. Ges.*, **46**. 788, 1894 ; P. Groth, *Tabellarische Uebersicht der Mineralien*, Braunschweig, 93, 1898 ; L. Buchrucker, *Zeit. Kryst.*, **19**. 113, 1891 ; J. R. Müller, *ib.*, **1**. 512, 1877 ; A. Laugier, *Mém. Mus. Hist. Nat.*, **9**. 233, 1807 ; L. Gmelin, *Handbook of Chemistry*, London, **5**. 350, 1851 ; C. F. Bucholz, *Gehlen's Journ.*, **9**. 308, 1810 ; G. la Valle, *Atti Accad. Lincei*, (5), **7**. ii, 68, 1898 ; O. Ducru, *Ann. Chim. Phys.*, (7), **22**. 185, 1901 ; *Recherches sur les arséniates ammoniacaux de cobalt et de nickel*, Paris, 1900 ; *Compt. Rend.*, **131**. 675, 1900 ; A. Coloriano, *Recherches sur quelques arséniates cristallisés*, Paris, 1886 ; *Compt. Rend.*, **103**. 274, 1886 ; C. Lefèvre, *ib.*, **110**. 407, 1890 ; *Sur les arséniates cristallisés*, Paris, 1891 ; F. Ulrich, *Zeit. Kryst.*, **64**. 143, 1926 ; G. Lincio, *Heidelberg. Akad. Wiss.*, 15, 1914 ; H. Goguel, *Contribution à l'étude des arséniates et des antimoniates cristallisés préparés par voie humide*, Paris, 1896 ; *Mém. Soc. Phys. Nat. Bordeaux*, (5), **1**. 135, 1896 ; J. G. Gentele, *Œfvers. Svenska Akad. Förh.*, 4, 1851 ; G. Klemp and J. von Gyulay, *Koll. Zeit.*, **15**. 202, 1914 ; **22**. 57, 1918 ; A. Lévy, *Ann. Phil.*, **8**. 439, 1824 ; *Edin. Journ. Science*, **2**. 177, 1825 ; C. Winkler, *Journ. prakt. Chem.*, (2), **10**. 190, 1877 ; A. Weisbach, *Jahrb. Berg. Hütt. Sachs.*, 42, 1877 ; *Neues Jahrb. Min.*, 407, 1877 ; E. S. Larsen, *Bull. U.S. Geol. Sur.*, 679, 1921 ; H. B. Weiser and A. P. Bloxsom, *Journ. Phys. Chem.*, **28**. 26, 1924 ; A. Rosenheim and S. Thon, *Zeit. anorg. Chem.*, **167**. 1, 1927.

[10] C. Bergemann, *Journ. prakt. Chem.*, (1), **25**. 239, 1858 ; P. Groth, *Tabellarische Uebersicht der Mineralien*, Braunschweig, 84, 1898 ; A. Girard, *Compt. Rend.*, **34**. 918, 1852 ; A. Coloriano, *ib.*, **103**. 274, 1886 ; *Bull. Soc. Chim.*, (2), **45**. 240, 1886 ; *Recherches sur quelques arséniates cristallisés*, Paris, 1886 ; J. L. Proust, *Ann. Chim. Phys.*, (1), **1**. 195, 1790 ; R. Tupputi, *ib.*, (1), **78**. 133, 1811 ; (1), **79**. 153, 1811 ; P. Berthier, *ib.*, (2), **13**. 52, 1820 ; O. Ducru, *ib.*, (7), **22**. 214, 1901 ; *Recherches sur les arséniates ammoniacaux de cobalt et de nickel*, Paris, 1900 ; *Compt. Rend.*, **131**. 702, 1900 ; J. J. Berzelius, *Akad. Handl. Stockholm*, 354, 1824 ; *Schweigger's Journ.*, **32**. 162, 1821 ; J. W. Döbereiner, *ib.*, **26**. 271, 1819 ; F. Stromeyer, *ib.*, **25**. 220, 1819 ; C. M. Kersten, *Pogg. Ann.*, **60**. 251, 1843 ; J. S. Newberry, *Amer. Journ. Science*, (3), **28**. 122, 1884 ; F. A. Genth, *Proc. Amer. Phil. Soc.*, **23**. 46, 1885 ; L. Buchrucker, *Zeit. Kryst.*, **19**. 113, 1891 ; J. D. Dana, *A System of Mineralogy*, New York, 561, 1868 ; G. la Valle, *Atti Accad. Lincei*, (5), **7**. ii, 68, 1898 ; M. F. Heddle, *Min. Mag.*, **8**. 200, 1889 ; A. Cronstedt, *Mineralogie*, Stockholm, 218, 1758 ; H. J. Brockes and W. H. Miller, *Introduction to Mineralogy*, London, 503. 1852 ; M. Adam, *Tableau minéralogique*, Paris, 42, 1869 ; A. de Schulten, *Bull. Soc. Min.*, **26**. 88, 1903 ; A. Damour and A. des Cloizeaux, *ib.*, **1**. 77, 1877 ; A. Sachs, *Centr. Min.*, 198, 1906 ; A. Frenzel, *Neues Jahrb. Min.*, 682, 1874 ; J. H. Ferber, *Berg. Hütt. Ztg.*, **22**. 306, 1863 ; D. Forbes, *Phil. Mag.*, (4), **25**. 103, 1863 ; G. A. Kenngott, *Uebersicht der Resultate mineralogischer Forschungen*, Leipzig, 46, 1868 ; J. F. L. Hausmann, *Beiträge zur metallurgischen Krystallkunde*, Göttingen, 50, 1852 ; E. S. Larsen, *Bull. U.S. Geol. Sur.*, 679, 1921 ; F. Ulrich, *Zeit. Kryst.*, **64**. 143, 1926.

§ 24. The Arsenates of the Platinum Family

Very little is known about these compounds. According to T. Thomson,[1] sodium arsenate gives a yellowish-white precipitate of *rhodium arsenate* when added to a hot aq. soln. of sodium chlororhodate ; J. J. Berzelius, a pale yellow precipitate of *palladious arsenate* from a neutral soln. of palladious nitrate ; T. Thomson, a brown precipitate of *iridium arsenate* from a hot soln. of iridium chloride ; and a pale brown precipitate of *platinic arsenate* from a soln. of platinic nitrate. D. Tivoli obtained platinic arsenate in red crystals by adding potassium chloroplatinate to a soln. of platinum hydroxyarsenide in aqua regia.

REFERENCES.

[1] T. Thomson, *Ann. Phil.*, **15**. 84, 1820 ; J. J. Berzelius, *Schweigger's Journ.*, **7**. 66, 1813 ; *Pogg. Ann.*, **13**. 454, 1828 ; D. Tivoli, *Gazz. Chim. Ital.*, **14**. 488, 1884.

§ 25. The Fluorides of Arsenic

Arsenic was found by H. Moissan [1] to unite directly with fluorine at ordinary temp. and the mass became incandescent. The product of the reaction is a mixture of the two fluorides of arsenic—AsF_3 and AsF_5. J. B. A. Dumas, in 1826, discovered **arsenic trifluoride**, AsF_3, while studying the action of a mixture of sulphuric acid and calcium fluoride on arsenic trioxide. H. Moissan found that this process is usually the most convenient; he prepared the liquid by heating a mixture of 2 kgrms. of sulphuric acid, and a kilogram of a powdered mixture of equal weights of precalcined calcium fluoride and dry arsenic trioxide in a 4-litre glass retort. The trifluoride is condensed in a lead receiver cooled by ice-water, and rectified by distillation on a water-bath at 65°. The liquid is best preserved in a platinum bottle. O. Unverdorben employed a platinum or lead retort. R. W. E. MacIvor also used this process. The trifluoride is formed in a number of reactions; H. Moissan obtained it by the action of gaseous or liquid fluorine on arsenic trichloride; by the action of iodine pentafluoride on arsenic; and by the action of silver fluoride or lead fluoride on arsenic. P. Lebeau obtained it by the action of fluorine on the arsenides of the alkalies or alkaline earths; J. B. A. Dumas, by the action of anhydrous hydrogen fluoride on arsenic trioxide; and R. W. E. MacIvor, by the action of ammonium fluoride on arsenic tribromide.

At ordinary temp., arsenic trifluoride is a colourless, mobile liquid, which fumes in air. It has not a garlic odour, but smells like silicon tetrafluoride. It evaporates from the skin like ether, but leaves a painful burn like hydrofluoric acid. O. Unverdorben gave 2·73 for the sp. gr.; R. W. E. MacIvor, 2·66; H. Moissan, 2·734; and T. E. Thorpe, 2·6659 at 0°/4°, and 2·4497 at the b.p. O. Masson, and J. A. Groshans studied the mol. vols. of the family of halides. H. Moissan found that the liquid forms a crystalline mass at −8·5°. O. Unverdorben gave 63° for the b.p.; R. W. E. MacIvor, 64°–66°; H. Moissan, 63° at 752 mm.; and T. E. Thorpe, 64° at 760 mm. According to T. E. Thorpe, the thermal expansion between 0° and 65° is given by $v=1+0{\cdot}0014430\theta+0{\cdot}0_62970\theta^2$, when v is the vol. at 0°. When the gas is heated in a glass vessel, it decomposes and attacks the glass: $4AsF_3+3SiO_2=3SiF_4+2As_2O_3$. H. Moissan said that the liquid is a bad conductor of electricity, but it can be electrolyzed, giving a deposit of arsenic at the cathode, and at the cathode evolving a gas which attacks platinum. Liquid arsenic trifluoride reddens blue litmus, but only when a trace of moisture is present. O. Unverdorben said that it mixes with **water** with a small rise of temp., forming a clear liquid which attacks zinc and tin slightly, and glass readily. J. B. A. Dumas found that the trifluoride is immediately decomposed by water, forming hydrofluoric acid and arsenic trioxide; and J. J. Berzelius thought that the arsenic trioxide reacts with the hydrofluoric acid, forming *hydrofluoarsenic acid*, which reacts with bases to form salts—*fluoarsenates*. H. Moissan found that arsenic trifluoride reacts with **bromine**, forming a crystalline substance; and the liquid dissolves **iodine**, forming a purplered soln. It does not react in the cold with **sulphur chloride**; but with **thionylchloride**, H. Moissan and P. Lebeau symbolized the reaction: $2AsF_3+3SOCl_2=3SOF_2+2AsCl_3$. O. Unverdorben found that arsenic trifluoride unites with **ammonia**, forming a white powder; ammonium carbonate can be used in place of ammonia. A. Besson also made this compound by vaporizing the trifluoride in an atm. of ammonia and showed that it is **arsenic triamminotrifluoride**, $As(NH_3)_3F_3$. O. Unverdorben represented its composition by $2AsF_3.5NH_3$, and said that it can be sublimed without decomposition, that it can be dissolved in boiling water, and recrystallized from the soln. on cooling. A. Besson, however, found that the compound is decomposed by water. According to A. Besson, **phosphine** reacts: $AsF_3+PH_3=3HF+AsP$. R. W. E. MacIvor, and H. Moissan found that with **phosphorus trichloride** there is a simple exchange of halogens: $PCl_3+AsF_3=AsCl_3+PF_3$; T. E. Thorpe observed an analogous reaction with **phosphorus pentachloride**: $3PCl_5+5AsF_3=5AsCl_3+3PF_5$; with **thiophosphoryl**

chloride, T. E. Thorpe and J. W. Rodger observed a similar reaction : $PSCl_3 + AsF_3 = AsCl_3 + PSF_3$. H. Moissan said that arsenic trifluoride does not react with **carbon tetrachloride** in the cold. O. Unverdorben said that the trifluoride may be mixed with more or less decomposition with **alcohol,** and **ether ;** and somewhat less readily with fixed and volatile **oils.** He also said that the trifluoride can be kept in **glass** vessels in which it slowly develops silicon fluoride— *vide supra*—it may also be evaporated without decomposition in glass vessels to which air has not access, but when exposed to air, the moisture reacts so that arsenic trioxide is left behind. At a dull red-heat, it acts on glass : $3SiO_2 + 4AsF_3 = 3SiF_4 + 2As_2O_3$; H. Moissan represented the reaction with **silicon tetrachloride :** $3SiCl_4 + 4AsF_3 = 4AsCl_3 + 3SiF_4$; and O. Ruff and K. Albert found that it reacts vigorously with **silico-chloroform** at ordinary temp. There are two simultaneous reactions one of which involves a simple exchange of halogens : $AsF_3 + SiHCl_3 = AsCl_3 + SiHF_3$, and the other reaction is symbolized : $4AsF_3 + 3SiHCl_3 = 3SiF_4 + 2AsCl_3 + 2As + 3HCl$. O. Unverdorben said that arsenic trifluoride has scarcely any action on **zinc** and **tin,** or on **calcium carbonate.**

H. Moissan found that arsenic trifluoride absorbs fluorine and becomes **warm ;** and O. Ruff and H. Graf prepared **arsenic pentafluoride,** AsF_5, by the action of bromine and antimony pentafluoride on arsenic trifluoride : $2SbF_5 + AsF_3 + Br_2 = 2SbBrF_4 + AsF_5$, in a platinum vessel, or in a well-dried glass vessel using dried reagents. The apparatus should be in one piece. 0.2 mol of well-cooled pentafluoride and 0.1 mol of arsenic trifluoride are mixed at $-20°$ with 0.25 mol of bromine. The retort is cooled by liquid air until it is fitted with a reflux condenser, etc. The retort is then warmed for half an hour on a water-bath at $55°$. The The arsenic pentafluoride collected in the well-cooled receiver is mixed with some bromine. To remove the bromine, the gas is passed over molten sulphur.

At ordinary temp., arsenic pentafluoride is a colourless gas with a vap. density in agreement with a mol. wt. 172.3–173—when the calculated value is 170.25. At $-53°$ and 760 mm. it forms a pale yellow liquid, and at $-80°$, it freezes to a white solid. The gas gives a dense white fume when exposed to **air.** It dissolves in **water** and alkali-lye with the development of heat. It reacts with **iodine** in the cold ; and slowly reacts with **sulphur** in the cold. O. Ruff found that **arsenic nitrosyl hexafluoride,** $AsF_5.NOF$, is obtained by passing **nitrosyl fluoride** through cooled arsenic trichloride until absorption is complete, the product being finally kept over fused sodium hydroxide in a vacuum for some time to absorb traces of nitrosyl chloride. The compound forms a white, crystalline mass, and is remarkably stable ; it is unaffected in dry air even at a high temp., but decomposes in moist air ; it is split up by water, by alkali, and by conc. hydrochloric aid, but is unacted on by phosphorus trichloride, carbon tetrachloride, silicon, copper, and lead. On warming gently with antimony pentafluoride, arsenic pentafluoride, and antimony nitrosyl hexafluoride are formed ; with **phosphorus** it produces a little phosphorus trifluoride ; and it dissolves in **arsenic trifluoride** developing a little heat—the gas escapes from the liquid when warmed. The gas is absorbed by **alcohol, ether,** and **benzene** with warming ; **turpentine** vapour gives a black cloud in contact with the gas ; dry **paper,** and **sugar** are not altered, but they are rapidly carbonized if moist ; and **paraffin,** and **wax** are gradually blackened. In the cold, the gas does not react with **silicon,** but when heated, arsenic and silicon tetrafluoride are formed ; when heated with dry **glass,** silicon tetrafluoride and probably arsenic pentoxide are produced. There is no reaction with **copper** in the cold, but the metal is blackened if heated ; **zinc, mercury, lead, bismuth,** and **iron** form fluorides ; **tungsten** is not attacked.

J. C. G. de Marignac prepared **potassium hexafluoarsenate,** $KF.AsF_5.\frac{1}{2}H_2O$, in small rhombic crystals, by evaporating a soln. of potassium arsenate in hydrofluoric acid. The axial ratios of the crystals are $a : b : c = 0.8401 : 1 : 2.5172$. The crystals are fairly stable when dry ; they are decomposed by water, forming an oxyfluoride (*vide infra*) ; and they melt when heated, giving off water and hydrogen fluoride. If a soln. of this salt, or of the oxyfluoride, in an excess of hydrofluoric acid and potassium fluoride, be evaporated, rhombic crystals of **potassium hepta-fluoarsenate**, $2KF.AsF_5.H_2O$, are formed ; they have the axial ratios $a:b:c = 0.8847:1:0.6453$; and are stable in dry air. The corresponding **ammonium hexafluoarsenate** was only obtained as a gum-like mass. H. von Hel-mont found that arsenic trioxide readily dissolves in a boiling soln. of ammonium fluoride, but on cooling the arsenic trioxide separates from the soln.

A compound of **arsenic oxyfluoride** or **arsenyl fluoride**, $AsOF_3$, with potassium arsenate was reported by J. C. G. de Marignac, but the oxyfluoride itself has not been prepared. If potassium hexafluoarsenate be crystallized from its aq. soln., or if potassium arsenate be dissolved in a dil. soln. of hydrofluoric acid, and the soln. crystallized, rhombic plates of **potassium oxytetrafluoarsenate**, $KF.AsOF_3.H_2O$, are formed. By repeatedly crystallizing potassium heptafluo-arsenate from its aq. soln., or by crystallizing a soln. of the oxytetrafluoarsenate from dil. hydrofluoric acid, a crystalline mass of **potassium oxydodecafluodi-arsenate**, $4KF.AsF_5.AsOF_3.3H_2O$, is produced. The right to the recognition of this product as a chemical individual has not been established.

REFERENCES.

[1] P. Lebeau, *Bull. Soc. Chim.*, (3), **23**. 250, 1900 ; *Compt. Rend.*, **130**. 502, 1900 ; H. Moissan and P. Lebeau, *ib.*, **130**. 1436, 1900 ; **99**. 874, 1884 ; **100**. 272, 1885 ; **136**. 786, 1903 ; H. Moissan, *Le fluor et ses composés*, Paris, 190, 1900 ; *Ann. Chim. Phys.*, (6), **24**. 253, 1891 ; J. B. A. Dumas, *ib.*, (2), **31**. 433, 1826 ; *Bull. Soc. Philomath.*, 71, 1826 ; *Quart. Journ. Science*, **22**. 211, 1827 ; R. W. E. MacIvor, *Chem. News*, **30**. 169, 1874 ; **32**. 258, 1875 ; T. E. Thorpe, *Proc. Roy. Soc.*, **25**. 122, 1877 ; *Liebig's Ann.*, **182**. 201, 1876 ; *Journ. Chem. Soc.*, **37**. 141, 327, 1880 ; T. E. Thorpe and J. W. Rodger, *ib.*, **53**. 766, 1888 ; **55**. 306, 1889 ; O. Unverdorben, *Pogg. Ann.*, **7**. 316, 1826 ; *Trommsdorff's Journ. Pharm.*, **9**. 22, 1824 ; O. Ruff and K. Albert, *Ber.*, **38**. 54, 1905 ; O. Ruff and H. Graf, *ib.*, **39**. 67, 1906 ; O. Ruff, *Zeit. anorg. Chem.*, **58**. 325, 1908 ; J. J. Berzelius, *Lehrbuch der Chemie*, Dresden, 2. i, 45, 1826 ; J. C. G. de Marignac, *Arch. Sciences Genève*, (2), **28**. 5, 1867 ; *Bull. Soc. Chim.*, (2), **8**. 327, 1867 ; O. Masson, *Phil. Mag.*, (5), **30**. 412, 1890 ; J. A. Groshans, *ib.*, (5), **20**, 197, 1885 ; *Ber.*, **19**. 974, 1886 ; H. von Helmont, *Zeit. anorg. Chem.*, **3**. 150, 1893 ; A. Besson, *Compt. Rend.*, **110**. 1258, 1890.

§ 26. The Chlorides of Arsenic

In 1648, J. R. Glauber [1] described the preparation of *butyrum arsenici—butter of arsenic*—by heating in a retort a powdered mixture of one part of white arsenic, two parts of common salt, and four parts of vitriol calcined white. A thick oil was collected in the receiver. N. Lemery obtained it by distilling a mixture of equal parts of white arsenic and corrosive sublimate. J. H. Pott, and T. Bergman found that white arsenic does not give so good results as arsenic itself. J. Davy's analysis showed that butter of arsenic is really **arsenic trichloride**, $AsCl_3$. It is doubtful if *arsenic pentachloride*, $AsCl_5$, has ever been isolated, and a similar remark applies to *arsenyl chloride*, $AsOCl$.

Arsenic trichloride can be obtained by chlorinating arsenic, arsenic tri- or penta-oxide, or arsenic sulphide. 1. *By chlorinating arsenic (q.v.).*—As previously indicated, powdered arsenic readily burns when projected in chlorine gas. J. B. A. Dumas [2] recommended making arsenic trichloride by the action of chlorine on arsenic contained in a retort. The neck of the retort was connected with a receiver cooled by a freezing mixture. The product was purified from the excess of chlorine by distillation from pulverized arsenic. B. H. Jacobson found the reaction accelerated if a trace of bromine be present, as well as alkali halide. E. W. Wescott also produced arsenic trichloride by treating arsenic ores with chlorine. Boiling hydrochloric acid slowly converts arsenic into the trichloride, and, as shown by R. Napoli, and A. Ditte and R. Metzner, particularly in the presence of oxygen. The trichloride is formed by the action of arsenic on numerous chlorides : thus M. Chevrier, and G. Oddo and E. Serra produced it by the action of arsenic on sulphur monochloride; K. Heumann and P. Köchlin, on chlorosulphonic acid or sulphuryl chloride; F. Selmi, ammonium chloride; A. Baudrimont, and B. Reinitzer and H. Goldschmidt, phosphorus pentachloride, or phosphoryl chloride; L. D. l'Hote, magnesium chloride; O. Ruff and K. Staib, aluminium chloride at 120°; and F. Selmi, H Capitaine, and H. Ludwig prepared the trichloride by heating arsenic with six times its weight of mercuric chloride. 2. *By chlorinating arsenic trioxide* (*q.v.*).—R. Weber, and C. L. Bloxam said that chlorine converts heated arsenic trioxide into arsenic trichloride and pentoxide. J. Davy made arsenic trichloride by heating a mixture of sulphuric acid and a sat. soln. of arsenic trioxide in conc. hydrochloric acid. Various modifications of this process have been used by W. Wallace and F. Penny, A. Negri, W. Böttger, etc. W. Wallace and F. Penny also passed dry hydrogen chloride over arsenic trioxide; J. B. A. Dumas heated arsenic trioxide with sodium chloride and sulphuric acid, and F. Selmi substituted lead chloride for the sodium chloride. Other chlorinating agents can be used with arsenic trioxide. Thus, H. Prinz, R. C. Smith, and G. Oddo and E. Serra used sulphur monochloride; V. de Luynes, ammonium chloride; A. Michaelis, phosphorus trichloride; L. Hurtzig and A. Geuther, phosphorus pentachloride; B. Reinitzer and H. Goldschmidt, phosphoryl chloride; and G. Rauter, silicon tetrachloride. L. H. Milligan and coworkers found that if carbonyl chloride be passed over a heated mixture of arsenic trioxide with 20 per cent. of carbon, at 200°-260°, an almost quantitative yield of arsenic trichloride is obtained. G. Oddo and U. Giarchery prepared the trichloride by passing chlorine over a heated mixture of sulphur and arsenic trioxide. 3. *By chlorinating arsenic pentoxide* (*q.v.*).—R. Weber showed that chlorine forms arsenic trichloride when passed over strongly heated arsenic pentoxide; and H. Rose, that hydrochloric acid will reduce arsenic acid to the volatile chloride. H. Rose, and J. von Liebig and F. Wöhler obtained a similar result by treating arsenic acid or an alkali arsenate with sodium chloride and sulphuric acid. The reducing action of hydrochloric acid or hydrogen chloride on arsenic acid has been studied by C. R. Fresenius and A. Souchay, K. Röhre, and J. Mayrhofer. E. Fischer showed that the reaction is greatly accelerated in the presence of ferrous chloride; A. Classen and R. Ludwig, in the presence of ferrous sulphate; F. A. Gooch and E. W. Danner, potassium iodide; F. A. Gooch and I. K. Phelps, potassium bromide; W. Böttger, hydrobromic acid; C. Friedheim and P. Michaelis, and L. Duparc and L. Ramadier, methyl alcohol; and W. Böttger, pyrogallol. Under these circumstances arsenic can be completely removed from a soln., and the process is utilized in analytical work for the separation from antimony, and tin—*vide supra*, arsenic trioxide, and arsenic acid. F. Hufschmidt showed that a current of hydrogen chloride through the liquid also favours the volatilization of the trichloride. H. Rose found that arsenic trichloride can be removed from alkali arsenates or arsenic acid by repeatedly heating them with ammonium chloride; L. Hurtzig and A. Geuther, by heating them with phosphorus pentachloride, but not, according to A. Michaelis, with phosphorus trichloride. 4. *By chlorinating arsenic sulphide* (*q.v.*).— L. N. Nilson converted arsenic di-, or tri-sulphide into the trichloride by heating it in a current of chlorine. For the action of hydrochloric acid, and hydrogen chloride, *vide infra*, arsenic sulphides. T. Reickher, A. Fyfe, E. R. Schneider, and J. Clark found that the presence of ferric chloride facilitates the chlorination of the sulphide by hydrochloric acid. C. R. Fresenius treated the sulphide with a mixture of ammonium chloride and nitrate; A. Baudrimont chlorinated the heated sulphide with sulphur monochloride; H. Ludwig, with mercuric chloride; and C. F. Rammelsberg, with cuprous chloride, or potassium antimonyl tartrate and hydrochloric acid. R. Napoli's observations on the action of conc. hydrochloric acid on arsine; and T. E. Thorpe's on the action of phosphorus pentachloride, etc., on arsenic trifluoride, have been previously discussed.

Arsenic trichloride, at ordinary temp., is a transparent, colourless, oily liquid, which fumes in air. It was analyzed by J. Davy, J. Mayrhofer, L. N. Nilson,

W. Wallace and F. Penny,[3] and K. Heumann and P. Köchlin. The results are in agreement with the empirical formula $AsCl_3$. J. B. A. Dumas found the vapour density to be 6·301 in agreement with 6·27, calculated for $AsCl_3$. H. Henstock discussed the electronic structure of the family of trihalides. According to P. Walden, the mol. wt. calculated from the f.p. of nitrobenzene is 127 instead of 180. L. Kahlenberg and A. T. Lincoln obtained a normal value. J. I. Pierre gave 2·205 for the **specific gravity** of the liquid at 0°; W. Wallace and F. Penny, 2·1766; H. Becquerel, 2·172; A. Stiefelhagen, 2·205; A. Haagen, 2·1668 at 20°; and T. E. Thorpe, 2·2050 at 0°/4°, and 1·91813 at the b.p. E. Rabinowitsch gave 92·4 for the mol. vol.; and O. Masson, and J. A. Groshans studied the mol. vols. of the family of halides. F. M. Jäger found the sp. gr., D, of the liquid at different temp., referred to water at 4°, can be represented by $D = 2·20511 - 0·001856\theta - 0·0_5 27\theta^2$; I. I. Saskowsky found the ratio of the mol. vol. to the at. vols. of the constituent elements to be 1·33. F. M. Jäger's observed results for the sp. gr. are indicated below along with values for the **specific cohesion,** a^2 in sq. mm.; the **surface tension,** σ, in dynes per cm.; and the mol. **surface energy** in ergs per sq. cm.; in an atm. of nitrogen,

	−21·0°	0·0°	20·8°	50·2°	75·7°	110·0°
Sp. gr. .	2·245	2·205	2·165	2·105	2·051	1·968
a^2 .	3·98	3·83	3·71	3·54	3·40	3·21
σ .	43·8	41·4	39·4	36·6	34·2	31·0
μ .	818·4	782·0	754·3	713·9	678·8	632·4

R. Lorenz and W. Herz studied some relationships of the surface tensions of the family of halides. J. B. A. Dumas gave 132° for the **boiling point**; J. I. Pierre, 133·5° at 756·9 mm.; P. Walden, 129° at 752 mm.; F. M. Jäger, 130·5° at 757 mm.; W. Biltz and E. Mienecke, between 130·1° and 130·3° at 758 mm.; A. Haagen, 128° at 754 mm.: G. P. Baxter and co-workers, 129·6° at 760 mm.; C. G. Maier, 121·9°; and T. E. Thorpe, 130·2° at 760 mm. N. de Kolossowsky gave 6·48 to 7·25 for the **ebulliscopic constant.** G. P. Baxter and co-workers found the **vapour pressure** of arsenic trichloride at 0° to be 2·44 mm.; at 25°, 11·65 mm.; at 35°, 19·53 mm.; at 50°, 40·90 mm.; and at 100°, 301 mm. The results at $\theta°$ can be represented by $\log p = 7·5183 - 1270(241·2 + \theta)^{-1}$ mm. C. G. Maier gave for the vap. press., p, in mm. of mercury:

	8·7°	27·1°	49·5°	61·1°	83·4°	101·1°	121·0°	122·0°	124·0°
p	21·7	29·7	90·4	145·1	270·6	452·2	749·1	776·0	798·9

A. Besson said that the trichloride freezes at −18° with a marked decrease in vol., forming acicular crystals. E. Haase gave −16° for the **melting point** of the solid: F. M. Jäger, −13°; C. Baskerville and H. H. Bennett, −18°; and W. Biltz and E. Meinecke, −16°; W. R. Smith and J. E. Hora, −16·2°—*vide* Fig. 34. J. I. Pierre represented the **thermal expansion** between −14·9° and 130·2° by $v = 1 + 0·000979070\theta + 0·0_6 96695\theta^2 + 0·0_8 17772\theta^3$ when the vol. is unity at 0°. T. E. Thorpe gave $v = 1 + 0·0009913380\theta + 0·0_6 84914\theta^2 + 0·0_8 27551\theta^3$. H. V. Regnault found the **specific heat** of the vapour to be 0·11224; and of the liquid, 0·17604, and the **heat of vaporization,** 69·741 cals. G. P. Baxter and co-workers calculated 7·42 Cals. per mol for the heat of vaporization at 0°; 7·29 Cals. at 50°; and 6·68 Cals. at 100°. C. G. Maier gave 7·63 Cals. per mol; and E. Beckmann, 44·51 cals. per gram. N. de Kolossowsky studied the relation between the thermal expansion and the heat of vaporization. C. M. Guldberg estimated 356·0° for the **critical temperature.** J. Thomsen gave 71·39 Cals. for the **heat of formation** of the liquid; M. Berthelot, 69·40 Cals.; and M. Berthelot and W. Louguinine, 74·6 Cals. According to A. Haagen, the **index of refraction** is 1·592 for red light; 1·6123, for green light; and 1·6248, for violet light. A. Stiefelhagen gave for the index of refraction, μ, for the wave-length $\lambda = 274\mu\mu$, 1·781; for $\lambda = 298$, 1·73023; for $\lambda = 394$, 1·64540; for $\lambda = 480$, 1·61949; for $\lambda = 589$, 1·60395: and for $\lambda = 768$, 1·59262. He also gave $\mu^2 = 1\cdot82577 + 0\cdot66457\lambda^2\{\lambda^2 - (195\cdot71)^2\}^{-1}$. A. Haagen found the **specific refraction** to be $0\cdot2732$; and the **refraction equivalent**, $49\cdot50$. A. K. Macbeth and N. I. Maxwell measured the **absorption of light** by a $0\cdot01N$-soln. of arsenic trichloride in N-HCl, and found the mol. extinction coeff. had a range from 5 to 30 in passing from light of wave-length $\lambda = 357$ to $\lambda = 227$. K. Natterer examined the **electrical conductivity** of the vapour ; and H. Buff found that if the liquid is free from moisture, it is a very bad electrical conductor. P. Walden said that the liquid has a small but appreciable conductivity of about $0\cdot00000124$ mho, and he suggested that it ionizes : $AsCl_3 \rightleftharpoons AsCl_2^{\cdot} + Cl'$; or $AsCl_3 \rightleftharpoons AsCl^{\cdot\cdot\cdot} + 2Cl'$; or $AsCl_3 \rightleftharpoons As^{\cdot\cdot\cdot} + 3Cl'$. According to L. Kahlenberg and A. T. Lincoln, the conductivity of a soln. of the trichloride in acetic ether is $\mu_{1\cdot8} = 0\cdot087$, and $\mu_{4\cdot8} = 0\cdot097$; and in nitrobenzene, $\mu_{8\cdot43} = 0\cdot026$, and $\mu_{16\cdot9} = 0\cdot042$. The soln. in dry benzene has no appreciable conductivity and yet it gives an immediate precipitation of cupric chloride with a soln. of cupric oleate in benzene. This is taken to show that ionization is not a necessary prelude to chemical reactions in soln. G. N. Guam and J. A. Wilkinson found that arsenic halide dissolved in liquid hydrogen sulphide is a conductor. P. Walden gave $0\cdot0_511$ mho for the sp. conductivity at $0°$; and W. Biltz and W. Klemm, $0\cdot0_430$ for the eq. conductivity. G. Hänsel found the following equilibrium values for the electrode potentials $As \mid 0\cdot33N\text{-}AsCl_3$ in $3N$-NaCl, $0\cdot3$ volt ; and in $3N$-HCl, $0\cdot305$ volt. W. Finkelstein found the **decomposition voltage** of arsenic trichloride in nitrobenzene soln. to be $0\cdot78$ volt. P. Walden said that arsenic trichloride is a good ionizing solvent for binary salts, but not for cobalt iodide and strong acids like tribromoacetic acid. He found the **dielectric constant** to be $12\cdot8$; and H. Schlundt gave $12\cdot35$ at $21°$.

According to A. Besson and L. Fournier,[4] when a mixture of arsenic trichloride **and hydrogen** is submitted to the electric discharge, the brown deposit which forms on the tube has the composition $As_{11}Cl$, and was thought to be a mixture of arsenic and an unknown *arsenic subchloride*. M. Berthelot showed that when the vap. of arsenic trichloride is mixed with **oxygen,** and passed through a red-hot tube, it decomposes into chlorine and an oxychloride. According to W. Wallace and F. Penny, a mol of arsenic trichloride requires 9 mols of **water** for its soln., and the liquid has the sp. gr. $1\cdot53$; if another 9 mols of water be added, the sp. gr. is $1\cdot346$; a little water changes arsenic trichloride into the oxychloride (*vide infra*), and with an excess of water, there is finally produced arsenious and hydrochloric acids. If enough water be added some arsenic trioxide may be deposited from the liquid. J. Thomsen gave for the heat of the reaction $AsCl_3 + Aq. = H_3AsO_{3aq.} + 3HCl_{aq.} + 17\cdot6$ Cals. A similar soln. is obtained by treating arsenic trioxide with hydrochloric acid. It is assumed that some arsenic chloride is present because more arsenic trioxide is dissolved by the acid than by water. As shown by A. Dupasquier, the liquid is volatile without residue, and hence when arseniferous hydrochloric acid is distilled, the arsenic collects in the distillate. This is the basis of a well-known analytical method of separating arsenic from antimony and tin—*vide supra*, action of hydrochloric acid on arsenic acid, and on arsenic trioxide. H. Moissan found that arsenic trichloride is vigorously attacked by **fluorine**—*vide* arsenic trifluoride. J. V. Janowsky, and J. Mayrhofer found that arsenic trichloride at a low temp. dissolves much **chlorine** which it gives off again at a higher temp., or by the passage of an inert gas like air. B. E. Sloan showed that at $-23°$, arsenic trichloride dissolves sufficient chlorine to give an at. ratio $As : Cl = 1 : 4\cdot45$, and at higher temp. the dissolved chlorine is slowly given off, but there is no evidence of the formation of a pentachloride. A. Besson found that arsenic trichloride carefully purified from excess of chlorine solidifies at $-18°$ with very considerable contraction, and crystallizes in white, nacreous needles. If, however, the chloride is sat. with chlorine at $0°$, the product does not solidify above $-30°$, but at this temp. it freezes with very great contraction. At $-30°$ the arsenic trichloride will absorb a much larger quantity of chlorine, yielding a yellow liquid which does not solidify at $-60°$. If this liquid, cooled to $-50°$, is thrown into water, a large vol. of chlorine is liberated.

and the soln. contains arsenious acid and not arsenic acid ; it follows that no arsenic pentachloride is formed. If liquid chlorine at —35° is brought in contact with arsenic trichloride at the same temp., and the temp. is allowed to rise slowly, the arsenic trichloride melts, and the two liquids gradually mix by diffusion without any development of heat or any other evidence of combination.

J. B. A. Dumas argued that when a large excess of dry chlorine is brought in contact with powdered arsenic, besides arsenic trichloride there is formed a small quantity of a white crystalline substance which was thought to be **arsenic pentachloride**, AsCl₅. H. Capitaine, however, showed that if the chlorine be very thoroughly dried, the alleged pentachloride is not produced. The white crystals obtained by J. B. A. Dumas were those of arsenic trioxide proceeding from traces of moisture in the inadequately dried gas. H. Rose also obtained nothing but the trichloride when arsenic is treated with an excess of chlorine. Nevertheless, C. Baskerville and H. H. Bennett said that arsenic pentachloride is produced when about 5 c.c. of purified arsenic trichloride, in a dry test-tube, are cooled by solid carbon dioxide loosely packed in a Dewar bulb, and sat. with chlorine. The crystalline trichloride assumes a greenish-yellow colour and becomes liquid. After distilling off the excess of chlorine at +31°, the residual liquid has the composition AsCl₅. Arsenic pentachloride is readily soluble in carbon disulphide and ether at —30°, and either crystallizes from these solvents, or solidifies alone at about —40° in yellow prisms. When heated above —25°, is begins to decompose, and on exposure to the air it evolves fumes of hydrogen chloride. The alleged pentachloride is only a mixture. For A. W. Cronander's complex AsCl₅.PCl₅, *vide infra.*

Results in opposition to those of C. Baskerville and H. H. Bennett, and in agreement with those of A. Besson, and B. E. Sloan were obtained by W. R. Smith and J. E. Hora by measuring the f.p. of mixtures of liquid chlorine and arsenic trichloride, and the results of W. Biltz and E. Meinecke are summarized in Fig. 34. There is no sign of a singular point on the curve as would be anticipated if a definite compound were produced under these conditions. The crystals obtained by freezing a mixture corresponding with the pentachloride consist of arsenic trichloride contaminated with liquid chlorine. The subject was discussed by W. Biltz and K. Jeep, and E. Kordes. A. G. Page observed that the presence of arsenic trichloride shows no signs of the stimulating action observed by some agents on the chlorination of organic compounds.

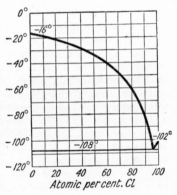

FIG. 34.—Freezing Points of Mixtures of Arsenic Trichloride and Chlorine.

T. Karantassis studied the interchange of the halogens—chlorine, bromine, and iodine. B. E. Sloan found that **iodine** readily dissolves in arsenic trichloride, the amount rapidly increasing with rise of temp. The surplus iodine separates out in crystals as the soln. is cooled ; 100 parts of the trichloride retain 8·42 parts of iodine at 0°, 11·88 parts at 15°, and 36·89 parts at 90°. There is no evidence of the formation of *arsenic diiodotrichloride,* although F. Gramp claimed to have made red crystals of a compound of the three elements by heating arsenic trichloride with iodine at 100°. W. Wallace and F. Penny found that arsenic trichloride is soluble in conc. **hydrochloric acid,** and when the soln. is treated with sulphuric acid an oily liquid is precipitated—*vide supra.* W. D. Treadwell and C. Mussler found that 100·3 grms. of arsenic trichloride can be dissolved by a litre of conc. hydrochloric acid at 100°. P. Hautefeuille found that **hydriodic acid** reacts with arsenic trichloride with the development of heat, forming arsenic triiodide and hydrochloric acid. B. Köhnlein said that **ethyl iodide** behaves similarly : and H. L. Snape found that **potassium iodide** and arsenic trichloride form arsenic triiodide when heated in a sealed tube at 240°. E. Bamberger and J. Philipp also showed that potassium iodide forms arsenic triiodide when treated with a hydrochloric acid soln. of arsenic trioxide.

According to P. Walden, arsenic trichloride dissolves many inorganic salts ; and E. Beckmann found arsenic trichloride can be used as a solvent for the ebullioscopic method of determining mol. wts. He used it for sulphur, etc. The ebullioscopic constant is 7·25. Thus, potassium iodide or rubidium iodide, tetramethylammonium or tetraethylammonium iodide, and trimethyl thioiodide dissolve in the cold, and when warmed, the soln. becomes yellow, or violet. The soln. with mercuric iodide, or antimony triiodide, is colourless ; with cobalt iodide, violet ; with sublimed ferric chloride, yellow ; and with arsenic triiodide, yellow. According to H. L. Snape, potassium bromide heated in a sealed tube with arsenic trichloride at 180°-200° forms some arsenic tribromide : $AsCl_3+3KBr=3KCl+AsBr_3$. L. Lindet observed that in the presence of hydrochloric acid, stannous chloride reduces the trichloride to arsenic, while gold chloride is dissolved without decomposition. The reaction with stannous chloride has been discussed in connection with allotropic arsenic. J. Davy said that hot arsenic trichloride copiously dissolves sulphur, and deposits the greater part on cooling. G. Vortmann and C. Padberg found that acidic soln. of arsenic trichloride are not altered by boiling with sulphur. L. Ouvrard found that hydrogen sulphide reacts with liquid arsenic trichloride, forming a series of thiochlorides (q.v.) ; F. Hurter, that the vap. of the trichloride is not attacked by hydrogen sulphide. According to W. Biltz and E. Keunecke, dry, liquid hydrogen sulphide thiohydrolyzes arsenic trichloride ; and, added O. Ruff, the hydrogen sulphide does not act on the boiling liquid, but if a little aluminium chloride be present, hydrogen chloride and arsenic trisulphide are formed ; and, working at a high temp., H. Arctowsky obtained the trisulphide in a crystalline form. G. N. Guam and J. A. Wilkinson, and A. W. Ralston and J. A. Wilkinson found the sp. conductivity of a sat. soln. of the arsenic trichloride in liquid hydrogen sulphide to be $11·510 \times 10^7$ mhos. N. R. Dhar found that the reaction between a thiosulphate and salts of antimony has an induction period dependent on the temp. and conc. of the soln. C. Hugot, and G. Gore observed that liquid ammonia reacts with arsenic trichloride. According to J. Persoz, ammonia is rapidly absorbed by arsenic trichloride forming a white or pale yellow solid, which has the composition $AsCl_3.4NH_3.$; H. Rose said $AsCl_3.3\frac{1}{2}NH_3$, and A. Besson, $AsCl_3.4NH_3$, i.e. arsenic tetramminotrichloride. L. Pasteur represented it by the formula $2As(NH)Cl.4NH_4Cl$; and C. Hugot suggested this alleged ammine is really a mixture of ammonium chloride and arsenic triamide (q.v.). L. Pasteur said that when the ammine is heated, ammonia is first given off, then the undecomposed compound, and finally ammonium chloride ; it dissolves in water with the evolution of heat, and the loss of ammonia, and the residue obtained on evaporation contains $As_4N_2Cl_2H_{10}O_7$. H. Rose said that ammonia in the aq. soln. is only partially precipitated by hydrochloroplatinic acid ; and, added L. Pasteur, hot water decomposes the ammine into ammonia, ammonium chloride, and arsenic trioxide. J. von Liebig and F. Wöhler said that conc. sulphuric acid expels ammonia from the ammine ; and aq. ammonia, said L. Pasteur, converts it into ammonium metarsenite. The tetrammine formed at −20°, when distilled in vacuo at 200°, was found by A. Besson and G. Rosset to pass into arsenic hemiheptamminotrichloride, $AsCl_3.3\frac{1}{2}NH_3$—vide arsenic imides. A. Ferratini found that when arsenic trichloride, in alcoholic soln., is boiled with hydrazine hydrochloride, a complex salt, hydrazine arsenochloride, is formed, but could not be isolated in a pure state. A. C. Vournazos obtained the complex sodium arsenoctoazidotrichloride, $Na_8[AsCl_3(N_3)_8]$. A. Geuther found that nitrogen peroxide oxidizes arsenic trichloride, forming arsenic pentoxide, and nitrogen oxychlorides. O. C. M. Davis found that nitrogen sulphide, N_4S_4, does not form a compound with arsenic trichloride. J. Davy showed that warm arsenic trichloride in the cold dissolves phosphorus, without becoming luminous, and deposits most of the phosphorus on cooling ; O. Ruff said that phosphorus does not react with arsenic trichloride, but if a little aluminium chloride be present, arsenic oxyphosphide, As_4PO_2, is formed. The reaction was studied by O. Ruff and K. Staib—vide infra.

W. Finkelstein found that yellow phosphorus, **antimony,** and **bismuth** precipitate arsenic from a soln. of the trichloride in nitrobenzene. According to A. Besson, and J. V. Janowsky, **phosphine** reacts with the trichloride : $AsCl_3+PH_3=3HCl+AsP$. A. W. Cronander found that with **phosphorus pentachloride** unstable complex arsenic phosphoctochloride, $PCl_5.AsCl_3$, and **arsenic phosphodecachloride,** $AsCl_5.PCl_5$, are produced. A. Geuther observed that **phosphorus trichloride** reduces arsenic trichloride to arsenic (q.v.) ; while T. Karantassis observed that **phosphorus triiodide** reacts with arsenic trichloride by double decomposition, but the reverse reaction does not occur. J. V. Janowsky, R. Engel, and J. Thiele found that the trichloride is reduced to arsenic by **hypophosphorous acid,** and by **phosphorous acid.** J. V. Janowsky found that **arsine** decomposes the trichloride : $AsCl_3+AsH_3$ $=3HCl+2As$. W. Wallace and F. Penny, and L. Hurtzig and A. Geuther, noted that the trichloride dissolves **arsenic trioxide,** forming the oxychloride ; **and L.** Ouvrard, that **arsenic trisulphide** converts the trichloride into thiochlorides.

J. Tarible found that **boron bromide** reacts with the trichloride : $AsCl_3+BBr_3$ $=BCl_3+AsBr_3+25$ cals. O. A. Dafert found that **acetylene** does not react to any considerable extent with arsenic trichloride at the ordinary temp. or at the b.p. of the latter ; in the presence of anhydrous aluminium chloride at the ordinary temp., however, **arsenic diacetylenotrichloride,** $AsCl_3.2C_2H_2$, is formed as a heavy oil of sp. gr. 1·6910 at 15°, and b.p. 250°. F. Oberhauser studied the reaction with **cyanogen bromide.** According to P. Walden, arsenic trichloride dissolves many organic compounds—e.g. **hydrocarbons, organic acids, ketones, esters, tertiary bases,** etc.—**quinoline** gives a colourless soln. ; and **dimethylaniline,** a yellowish-green liquid. H. Schiff, A. R. Leeds, and H. Grossmann prepared complex salts with **aniline,** and with quinoline. V. de Luynes said that absolute **alcohol,** and **ether** mix readily with the trichloride, and the soln. becomes warm. J. Davy found that the trichloride dissolves **turpentine, olive oil,** and **resin.** M. Centnerszwer found that the trichloride dissolves in liquid **cyanogen ;** J. Davy, that it dissolves ten times its vol. of **carbonyl chloride,** which is again set free on mixing the liquid with water ; G. Gustavson, that arsenic trichloride and **carbon tetrabromide** slowly react in a sealed tube at 150°–200° converting about 72 per cent. of the trichloride into tribromide in about 60 days ; and P. Miquel, that metal **thiocyanates** react, forming a small proportion of arsenic thiocyanate. For the interchange with **organic halides,** vide infra, arsenic triiodide. When arsenic trichloride acts on a Grignard reagent, **magnesium phenyl bromide,** in ethereal soln. in equimolar proportions, the product is triphenyl-arsine if the former is added gradually to the latter. If, however, magnesium phenyl bromide is added to arsenic trichloride, the product is diphenylchloroarsine. O. Ruff and K. Albert observed no change when arsenic trichloride and **silico-chloroform** are heated in a sealed tube at 150°.

A. C. Vournazos observed that the trichloride in boiling toluene soln. reacts with potassium furnishing potassium chloride and arsenic, but no arsenide. According to N. W. Fischer, when the metals **copper, zinc, cadmium, tin, lead, antimony, bismuth,** and **iron** are immersed in arsenic trichloride they acquire a crust of arsenic which prevents further decomposition, and J. B. A. Dumas found that **mercury** slowly decomposes the trichloride at ordinary temp., forming a greyish-brown powder. K. Seubert and A. Schmidt found that at a red-heat, **magnesium** reduces the trichloride to arsenic, and in acid soln., arsenic, arsine, and magnesium hydroxide and chloride are formed. Z. Roussin and R. Commaille also noted the production of arsine. F. Ducelliez examined the action of arsenic trichloride on **cobalt** at different temp. and obtained various arsenides (q.v.) ; A. Granger and G. Didier, and E. Vigouroux observed that when the vap. is passed over heated **nickel,** nickel arsenide is formed. According to L. Kahlenberg and J. V. Steinle, when sodium, magnesium, zinc, or aluminium is immersed in arsenic trichloride there is an immediate plating at ordinary temp., and a vigorous reaction at 100° ; with cadmium, iron, cobalt, and nickel, there is a slight plating on standing at ordinary temp., and a slight reaction at 100° ; with lead, and tin, there is an immediate plating at ordinary temp., and a strong reaction at 100° ; whilst bismuth and antimony are slightly tarnished after standing at ordinary temp. and there is a slight reaction at 100° ; with copper, there is a good plating after standing, and a strong reaction at 100° ; with mercury, there is a slight black deposit after standing, and no further reaction at 100° ; and with silver, platinum, gold, and molybdenum, there is no plating at ordinary temp., and no reaction at 100°. No effect was observed with acetone soln. of arsenic trichloride and bismuth or antimony.

According to H. L. Wheeler, if sat. soln. of rubidium chloride and of arsenic trioxide in 20 per cent. hydrochloric acid be mixed, and treated with conc. hydrochloric acid, pale yellow trigonal crystals of **rubidium enneachlorodiarsenite**, $3RbCl.2AsCl_3$, are formed having the axial ratio $a : c = 1 : 1.210$, and $\alpha = 88°\ 56'$. The salt can be recrystallized from 20 per cent. hydrochloric acid, but is hydrolyzed by 15 per cent. acid. 100 parts of hydrochloric acid, of sp. gr. 1·2, dissolve 2·935 parts of the salt. Trigonal crystals of **cæsium enneachlorodiarsenite**, $3CsCl.2AsCl_3$ were produced in an analogous way. The axial ratio is $a : c = 1 : 1.209$, and $\alpha = 89°\ 3'$. 100 parts of hydrochloric acid, of sp. gr. 1·2, dissolve 0·429 part of the salt. E. H. Ducloux used the complex salt in the microdetection of arsenic O. Ruff and K. Staib found that yellow phosphorus reduces arsenic trichloride in the presence of aluminium chloride, forming a red compound, **aluminium triarsenotrichloride**, $Al(AsCl)_3$, of sp. gr. 2·85 at 22°. The same substance is produced at 135°–140° by the action of **aluminium** powder on arsenic trichloride in the presence of a little aluminium chloride. Water decomposes the compound into aluminium chloride and black arsenic. Titanium tetrachloride and ammonia also decompose the compound, black arsenic being formed. It is stable in dry air, and when heated above 170° decomposes with formation of aluminium arsenide, arsenic, and arsenic trichloride thus : $AlAs_3Cl_3 = AlAs + As + AsCl_3$. S. Hilpert and F. Herrmann found that finely-divided, reduced **silver** and arsenic trichloride, when heated in a sealed tube, form **silver arsenochloride**, $7Ag.2AsCl_3$. By analogy with the corresponding bromide (q.v.), it is thought that the product is a solid soln. of silver and the compound Ag_3AsCl_3, or $[Ag_3As]Cl_3$. A substance with similar properties was obtained by the action of arsenic vapour on silver chloride at 500°. An analogous **copper arsenochloride** was likewise prepared.

J. J. Berzelius [5] reported a brown complex containing mercury, arsenic, and chlorine to be formed along with arsenic trichloride when arsenic is heated with mercurous chloride ; and R. Lochmann obtained a series of complexes, $As(HgCl)_3$; $AsH(HgCl)_2$; and $AsH_2(HgCl)$, by the action of arsine on mercuric chloride. A. Partheil and E. Amort reported **arsenic dihydrochloromercuriate**, $AsH_2(HgCl)$, to be formed when arsine, largely diluted with hydrogen, is passed into a soln. of mercuric chloride in alcohol. The pale yellow precipitate is decomposed by an excess of mercuric chloride, forming mercurous chloride, hydrochloric acid, and arsenic acid. F. Stromeyer observed these products in his study of the action of arsine on mercuric chloride. The next product of the reaction is **arsenic hydrobischloromercuriate**, $AsH(HgCl)_2$, obtained as a yellow precipitate by A. Partheil and E. Amort, and A. H. Gotthelf, when arsine acts on an aq. or alcoholic soln. of mercuric chloride. It, too, forms mercurous chloride, hydrochloric acid, and arsenic acid by the action of an excess of mercuric chloride. The next product of the action of arsine on mercuric chloride soln. is **arsenic trischloromercuriate**, $As(HgCl)_3$, or $HgCl_2.AsHg_2Cl$. H. Rose regarded this product as $3HgCl_2.As_2Hg_3$, but P. Lohmann said that this is wrong. E. Soubeiran obtained a similar product by the action of arsine on a 5 per cent. soln. of mercuric chloride ; P. Lohmann said that the product is less impure if an alcoholic soln. of mercuric chloride be employed. The reddish-brown product is decomposed into mercury and arsenic trichloride when heated in contact with its mother-liquor ; and, according to H. Rose it is decomposed by water : $2As(HgCl)_3 + 3H_2O = 6Hg + As_2O_3 + 6HCl$. P. Lohmann said that light accelerates, and the presence of ammonium chloride retards the decomposition by water.   A. Partheil and E. Amort said that an excess of mercuric chloride soln. decomposes it into arsenic and mercurous chloride. P. Lohmann observed that 20 grms. of the compound were decomposed by a 5 per cent. soln. of mercuric chloride in ten days.   H. Rose found that nitric acid converts it into mercurous chloride, etc.

H. Capitaine said that when an intimate mixture of arsenic with three times its weight of mercurous chloride is heated in a sand-bath until most has sublimed, the hard reddish residue has the composition of arsenic trischloromercuriate, $As(HgCl)_3$, but possibly $AsH(HgCl)_2$. It slowly blackens in sunlight; when heated it decomposes: $3As(HgCl)_2=6Hg+As+2AsCl_3$; and water breaks it down: $3As(HgCl)_2+3H_2O=6Hg+As+As_2O_3+6HCl$. G. Franceschi reported a *pentahydrate*, $As(HgCl)_3.5H_2O$, to be formed by the action of arsine on an alcoholic or ethereal soln. of mercuric chloride; it is decomposed by water into arsine, hydrochloric acid, arsenic trichloride, and mercurous oxide. D. Vitali reported a similar product to be formed by the action of nascent arsine on mercuric chloride. H. Capitaine also obtained **arsenic monochloromercuriate,** $As(HgCl)$, as a brown mass consisting of dendritic crystals as a by-product in the preparation of the bischloromercuriate.   The product is decomposed by sunlight; by heat: $3AsHgCl=3Hg+2As+AsCl_3$; and **by water**: $6AsHgCl+3H_2O=6Hg+As_2O_3+4As+6HCl$.

According to W. Wallace and F. Penny, and L. Hurtzig and A. Geuther, a mol of boiling arsenic trichloride dissolves a mol of arsenic trioxide, forming **arsenic oxychloride, or arsenyl monochloride,** $AsOCl$.   A similar soln. was obtained by passing hydrogen chloride into water with arsenic trioxide in suspension until the solid has disappeared.   If the soln. be distilled until it begins to foam, the residue forms a soln. of arsenic trioxide in arsenic trichloride, and beneath this is a brown, viscid mass of the oxychloride.   If the temp. of distillation be too high, the residue has the composition $AsOCl.As_2O_3$.   Again, if arsenic trichloride be mixed with sufficient water, and allowed to stand a few days, stellate masses of crystals of the *monohydrate*, $AsOCl.H_2O$, are formed.   If some ammonium chloride be placed in a soln. of arsenic trichloride in water acidified with hydrochloric acid to prevent the separation of arsenic oxychloride, snow-white needles of **ammonium oxy-arsenotrichloride,** $2NH_4Cl.AsOCl$, or $(NH_4)_2AsOCl_3$, are formed.   These observations need revision.

According to S. Delépine,[6] the inhalation of air charged with fumes of arsenic trichloride or the direct application of undiluted arsenic trichloride to the skin rapidly causes death by acute arsenic poisoning.   The application of the liquid to the skin results immediately in necrosis ; this is considerably retarded by washing within one minute of the application, but washing after five minutes has no effect.   The arsenic is rapidly absorbed by the tissues, and within a few hours can be recovered from most of the tissues and organs of the body, especially the brain, liver, and kidneys.   The symptoms of poisoning by arsenic trichloride include laryngeal obstruction, dyspnœa, and convulsions.

REFERENCES.

[1] J. R. Glauber, *Furni novi philosophici*, Amstelædami, 74, 1648 ; N. Lemery, *Cours de chymie*, Paris, 1675 ; J. H. Pott, *Dissertatio de auripigmento*, Berolini, 1720 ; T. Bergman, *De arsenico*, Upsala, 1777 ; J. Davy, *Phil. Trans.*, 102. 169, 1812.
[2] J. Davy, *Phil. Trans.*, 102. 169, 1812 ; W. Wallace and F. Penny, *Phil. Mag.*, (4), 4. 361, 1852 ; W. Wallace, *ib.*, (4), 16. 358, 1858 ; (4), 17. 261, 1859 ; *B.A. Rep.*, 69, 1858 ; M. Chevrier, *Compt. Rend.*, 63. 1003, 1866 ; L. D. l'Hote, *ib.*, 98. 1491, 1884 ; *Journ. Pharm. Chim.*, (5), 10. 254, 1884 ; H. Capitaine, *ib.*, (2), 25. 523, 1839 ; A. Ditte and R. Metzner, *Compt. Rend.*, 115, 936, 1892 ; V. de Luynes, *ib.*, 44. 1354, 1857 ; A. Baudrimont, *ib.*, 64. 369, 1867 ; *Ann. Chim. Phys.*, (4), 2. 11, 1864 ; J. B. A. Dumas, *ib.*, (2), 38. 337, 1828 ; F. Selmi, *Ber.*, 13. 579, 1880 ; *Riv. Chim. Med. Farm.*, 2. 444, 1884 ; A. Negri, *ib.*, 2. 385, 1884 ; K. Heumann and P. Köchlin, *Ber.*, 15. 418, 1736, 1882 ; F. Hufschmidt, *ib.*, 17. 2245, 1884 ; A. Classen and R. Ludwig, *ib.*, 18. 1110, 1885 ; C. Friedheim and P. Michaelis, *ib.*, 28. 1414, 1895 ; A. Michaelis, *Jena. Zeit.*, (1), 6. 239, 1870 ; B. Reinitzer and H. Goldschmidt, *Montash.*, 1. 427, 1881 ; E. W. Wescott, *Canadian Pat. No.* 223858, 223859, 1922 ; Metallurgical Development Co., *U.S. Pat. No.* 1512733, 1512734, 1924 ; R. Weber, *Pogg. Ann.*, 112. 624, 1861 ; E. R. Schneider, *ib.*, 85. 433, 1852 ; H. Rose, *ib.*, 52. 64, 1841 ; 116. 453, 1862 ; J. von Liebig and F. Wöhler, *ib.*, 11. 149, 1827 ;

F. Wöhler, *Liebig's Ann.*, **73.** 384, 1850; O. Ruff and K. Staib, *Zeit. anorg. Chem.*, **117.** 191, 1921; R. Lorenz and W. Herz, *ib.*, **120.** 320, 1921; G. Oddo and E. Serra, *Gazz. Chim. Ital.*, **29.** ii, 355, 1899; G. Oddo and U. Giachery, *ib.*, **53.** i, 56, 1923; L. Hurtzig, *Einige Beiträge zur näheren Kenntniss der Säuren des Phosphors und Arseniks*, Göttingen, 1859; L. Hurtzig and A. Geuther, *Liebig's Ann.*, **111.** 172, 1859; H. Prinz, *ib.*, **223.** 357, 1884; G. Rauter, *ib.*, **270.** 250, 1892; J. Mayrhofer, *ib.*, **158.** 326, 1871; E. Fischer, *ib.*, **208.** 182, 1881; *Ber.*, **13.** 1778, 1880; J. Clark, *Journ. Soc. Chem. Ind.*, **10.** 444, 1891; *Journ. Chem. Soc.*, **61.** 424, 1892; N. de Kolossowsky, *Journ. Chim. Phys.*, **24.** 56, 1927; W. Böttger, *Oester. Chem. Ztg.*, **27.** 24, 1924; C. R. Fresenius, *Zeit. anal. Chem.*, **25.** 200, 1886; C. R. Fresenius and A. Souchay, *ib.*, **1.** 448, 1862; K. Röhre, *ib.*, **56.** 109, 1925; B. H. Jacobson, *Brit. Pat. No.* 181385, 190688, 1922; C. F. Rammelsberg, *Sitzber. Akad. Berlin*, **79**, 1881; F. A. Gooch and E. W. Danner, *Amer. Journ. Science*, (3), **42.** 308, 1892; *Zeit. anorg. Chem.*, **6.** 268, 1894; F. A. Gooch and I. K. Phelps, *ib.*, **7.** 123, 1894; *Amer. Journ. Science*, (3), **48.** 216, 1894; R. Napoli, *ib.*, (2), **18.** 190, 1854; *Il Giamb. Vico*, **1.** 247, 1857; R. C. Smith, *Journ. Ind. Eng. Chem.*, **11.** 109, 1919; L. N. Nilson, *Akad. Handl. Stockholm*, **10**, 2, 1871; *Oefvers. Handl. Stockholm*, **28.** 303, 1871; *Journ. prakt. Chem.*, (2), **12.** 327, 1875; A. Fyfe, *Phil. Mag.*, (4), **2.** 487, 1851; E. Rabinowitsch, *Ber.*, **58.** 2790, 1925; T. Reickher, *Neues Jahrb. Pharm.*, **36.** 9, 1871; W. Böttger, *Oester. Chem. Ztg.*, **27.** 24, 1924; I. I. Saslawsky, *Zeit. anorg. Chem.*, **146.** 315, 1925; H. Ludwig, *Arch. Pharm.*, (2), **97.** 23, 1859; L. H. Milligan, W. A. Baude, and H. G. Boyd, *Journ. Ind. Eng. Chem.*, **12.** 221, 1920; L. Duparc and L. Ramadier, *Helvetica Chim. Acta*, **8.** 552, 1922; L. H. Milligan, *U.S. Pat. No.* 1421978, 1922; T. E. Thorpe, *Liebig's Ann.*, **182.** 201, 1876; *Proc. Roy. Soc.*, **25.** 122, 1877; *Journ. Chem. Soc.*, **37.** 141, 327, 1880; C. L. Bloxam, *ib.*, **18.** 62, 1865.

³ W. Wallace and F. Penny, *Phil. Mag.*, (4), **4.** 361, 1852; O. Masson, *ib.*, (5), **30.** 412, 1890; J. A. Groshans, *ib.*, (5), **20.** 197, 1885; *Ber.*, **19.** 974, 1886; J. I. Pierre, *Ann. Chim. Phys.*, (3), **15.** 325, 1845; (3), **20.** 5, 1848: H. Becquerel, *ib.*, (5), **12.** 34, 1877; H. Buff, *ib.*, (3), **59.** 122, 1860; J. B. A. Dumas, *ib.*, (2), **38.** 337, 1828; M. Berthelot, *ib.*, (5), **15.** 209, 1877; M. Berthelot and W. Louguinine, *Compt. Rend.*, **81.** 1011, 1017, 1072, 1875; A. Besson, *ib.*, **109.** 940, 1889; N. de Kolossowksy, *Journ. Chim. Phys.*, **23.** 353, 1926; C. M. Guldberg, *Christiania Vid. Selsk.*, 20, 1882; P. Walden, *Zeit. phys. Chem.*, **43.** 437, 1903; **46.** 103, 1904; *Zeit. anorg. Chem.*, **25.** 209, 1900; F. M. Jäger, *ib.*, **101.** 174, 1917; E. Beckmann, *ib.*, **51.** 96, 1908; W. Biltz and E. Meinecke, *ib.*, **131.** 1, 1923; W. Biltz and W. Klemm, *ib.*, **152.** 276, 1926; W. Biltz and K. Jeep, *ib.*, **162.** 32, 1927; E. Kordes, *ib.*, **168.** 177, 1927; H. Schlundt, *Journ. Phys. Chem.*, **5.** 503, 1901; L. Kahlenberg, *ib.*, **6.** 9, 1902; L. Kahlenberg and A. T. Lincoln, *ib.*, **3.** 26, 1899; A. T. Lincoln, *ib.*, **3.** 464, 1899; W. R. Smith and J. E. Hora, *Journ. Amer. Chem. Soc.*, **26.** 632, 1904; G. P. Baxter, F. K. Bezzenberger, and C. H. Wilson, *ib.*, **42.** 1386, 1920; E. Haase, *Ber.*, **26.** 1052, 1893; J. Thomsen, *ib.*, **16.** 39, 1883; C. G. Maier, *Vapor Pressures of the Common Metallic Chlorides and a Static Method for High Temperatures*, Washington, **42**, 1925; H. V. Regnault, *Mém. Acad.*, **26.** 200, 1862; *Phil. Mag.*, (4), **5.** 473, 1853; W. Finkelstein, *Zeit. phys. Chem.*, **115.** 303, 1925; G. Hänsel, *Wiss. Siemens-Konz.*, **4.** 111, 1925; A. Haagen, *Pogg. Ann.*, **131.** 117, 1867; **133.** 295, 1868; A. K. Macbeth and N. I. Maxwell, *Journ. Chem. Soc.*, **123.** 370, 1923; K. Natterer, *Wied. Ann.*, **38.** 663, 1889; *Monatsh.*, **10.** 605, 1889; A. Stiefelhagen, *Dispersion flüssiger Trichloride und Tetrachloride für ultraviolette Strahlen*, Berlin, 1905; S. Tolloczko and M. Meyer, *Kosmos*, **35.** 641, 1910; *Radzisewsky's Festband*, 641, 1910; G. N. Guam and J. A. Wilkinson, *Proc. Iowa Acad.*, **32.** 324, 1927; C. Baskerville and H. H. Bennett, *Journ. Amer. Chem. Soc.*, **24.** 1070, 1902; K. Heumann and P. Köchlin, *Ber.*, **15.** 418, 1736, 1882; E. Rabinowitsch, *ib.*, **58.** 2790, 1925; R. Lorenz and W. Herz, *Zeit. anorg. Chem.*, **120.** 320, 1921; T. E. Thorpe, *Liebig's Ann.*, **182.** 201, 1876; *Proc. Roy. Soc.*, **25.** 122, 1877; *Journ. Chem. Soc.*, **37.** 141, 327, 1880; H. Henstock, *Chem. News*, **126.** 337, 1923.

⁴ P. Walden, *Zeit. anorg. Chem.*, **25.** 214, 1900; W. Wallace and F. Penny, *Phil. Mag.*, (4), **4.** 361, 1852; H. Moissan, *Le fluor et ses composés*, Paris, 190, 1900; O. Ruff, *Ber.*, **34.** 1753, 1901; O. Ruff and K. Staib, *Zeit. anorg. Chem.*, **117.** 191, 1921; O. Ruff and K. Albert, *ib.*, **38.** 2235, 1905; G. Vortmann and C. Padberg, *ib.*, **22.** 2642, 1889; J. Thomsen, *ib.*, **16.** 39, 1883; F. Gramp, *Deut. Chem. Ges. Ber.*, **7.** 1723, 1874; J. V. Janowsky, *ib.*, **6.** 219, 1873; **8.** 1636, 1875; E. Bamberger and J. Philipp, *ib.*, **14.** 2643, 1881; S. Hilpert and F. Herrmann, *ib.*, **46.** 2218, 1913; M. Berthelot, *Compt. Rend.*, **86.** 863, 1878; L. Ouvrard, *ib.*, **116.** 1516, 1893; R. Engel, *ib.*, **77.** 1543, 1873; P. Hautefeuille, *ib.*, **64.** 704, 1867; E. Vigouroux, *ib.*, **147.** 426, 1908; F. Ducelliez, *ib.*, **147.** 424, 1908; T. Karantassis, *ib.*, **182.** 699, 1391, 1926; A. Besson, *ib.*, **109.** 940, 1889; **110.** 1258, 1890; A. Besson and G. Rosset, *ib.*, **146.** 1266, 1908; A. Besson and L. Fournier, *ib.*, **150.** 872, 1910; J. Tarible, *Sur les combinaisons du bromure de bore*, Paris, 1899; *Compt. Rend.*, **132.** 206, 1901; C. Hugot, *ib.*, **121.** 206, 1895; **139.** 54, 1904; V. de Luynes, *ib.*, **50.** 831, 1860; L. Lindet, *ib.*, **101.** 1492, 1885; *Ann. Chim. Phys.*, (6), **11.** 215, 1887; G. Geisenheimer, *ib.*, (6), **23.** 274, 1891; H. Schiff, *Compt. Rend.*, **56.** 1095, 1863; *Liebig's Ann.*, **131.** 116, 1864; B. Köhnlein, *ib.*, **225.** 176, 1884; J. Mayrhofer, *ib.*, **158.** 326, 1871; A. G. Page, *ib.*, **225.** 199, 1884; J. Thiele, *ib.*, **265.** 55, 1891; J. von Liebig and F. Wöhler. *ib.*, **11.** 149, 1834; K. Seubert and A. Schmidt, *ib.*, **267.** 237, 1892; L. Hurtzig and A. Geuther, *ib.*, **111.** 172, 1859; A. Geuther, *Journ. prakt. Chem.*, (2), **8.** 854, 1873; L. Hurtzig, *Einige Beiträge zur näheren Kenntniss der Säuren des Phosphors und Arseniks*, Göttingen, 1859; H. L. Snape, *Chem. News*, **74.** 27, 1896; R. E. Sloan, *ib.*, **44.** 203, 1881; **46.** 194, 1883; F. Hurter, *ib.*, **34.** 132, 162, 1876; W. D. Treadwell and C. Mussler, *Helvetica Chim. Acta*, **5.** 818, 1922; J. Davy, *Phil. Trans.*, **102.** 169, 1812;

H. Capitaine, *Journ. Pharm. Chim.*, (3), **25**. 524, 1839 ; L. Pasteur, *ib.*, (4), **13**. 395, 1848 ;
A. Dupasquier, *ib.*, (3), **27**. 717, 1841 ; C. Baskerville and H. H. Bennett, *Journ. Amer. Chem.
Soc.*, **24**. 1070, 1902 ; W. R. Smith and J. E. Hora, *ib.*, **26**. 632, 1904 ; A. R. Leeds, *ib.*, **3**. 112,
1882 ; H. Rose, *Pogg. Ann.*, **52**. 62, 1841 ; N. W. Fischer, *ib.*, **9**. 261, 1826 ; Z. Roussin and
A. Commaille, *Zeit. anal. Chem.*, **6**. 100, 1867 ; *Compt. Rend.*, **63**. 556, 1866 ; *Journ. Pharm.
Chim.*, (5), **3**. 413, 1866 ; G. Gustavson, *Ann. Chim. Phys.*, (5), **2**. 200, 1874 ; J. Persoz, *ib.*, (2),
44. 320, 1830 ; P. Miquel, *ib.*, (5), **11**. 352, 1877 ; J. B. A. Dumas, *ib.*, (2), **38**. 337, 1828 ;
M. Centnerszwer, *Journ. Russ. Phys. Chem. Soc.*, **33**. 545, 1901 ; A. W. Cronander, *Ber.*, **6**. 1466,
1873 ; *Oefrers. Akad. Stockholm*, **27**. 57, 1870 ; *Bull. Soc. Chim.*, (2), **19**. 499, 1873 ; A. Granger
and G. Didier, *ib.*, (3), **23**. 506, 1900 ; H. Grossmann, *Zeit. phys. Chem.*, **57**. 545, 1907 ; W. Finkelstein, *ib.*, **115**. 303, 1925 ; O. C. M. Davis, *Journ. Chem. Soc.*, **89**. 1575, 1906 ; E. Beckmann,
Zeit. anorg. Chem., **51**. 96, 1906 ; W. Biltz and E. Keunecke, *ib.*, **147**. 171, 1925 ; W. Biltz and
E. Meinecke. *ib.*, **131**. 1, 1923 ; A. C. Vournazos, *ib.*, **81**. 264, 1913 ; **164**. 263, 1927 ; H. Arctowsky,
ib., **8**. 213, 1895 ; N. R. Dhar, *ib.*, **128**. 207, 1923 ; H. L. Wheeler, *ib.*, **4**. 455, 1893 ; *Amer. Journ.
Science*, (3), **46**. 88, 1893 ; O. A. Dafert, *Monatsh.*, **40**. 313, 1919 ; K. Matsuniya, *Mem. Coll. Science
Kyoto*, **4**. 217, 1920 ; L. Kahlenberg and J. V. Steinle, *Trans. Amer. Electrochem. Soc.*, **44**. 493,
1923 ; G. Gore, *Proc. Roy. Soc.*, **20**. 441, 1872 ; **21**. 140, 1873 ; A. Ferratini, *Gazz. Chim. Ital.*,
42. i, 138, 1912 ; E. H. Ducloux, *Anal. Assoc. Quim. Argentina*, **9**. 215, 1921 ; G. N. Guam and
J. A. Wilkinson, *Proc. Iowa Acad.*, **32**. 324, 1925 ; *Journ. Amer. Chem. Soc.*, **47**. 989, 1925 ;
A. W. Ralston and J. A. Wilkinson, *ib.*, **50**. 259, 1928 ; F. Oberhauser, *Ber.*, **60**. B, 1434, 1927 ;
W. Biltz and K. Jeep, *Zeit. anorg. Chem.*, **162**. 32, 1927.
    [5] J. J. Berzelius, *Schweigger's Journ.*, **21**. 339, 1817 ; F. Stromeyer, *Comment. Soc. Gött.*, **16**.
141, 1808 ; R. Lochmann, *Zeit. öesterr. Apoth. Ver.*, **45**. 744, 1907 ; P. Lohmann, *Pharm. Ztg.*,
36. 749, 1891 ; H. Rose, *Pogg. Ann.*, **51**. 423, 1840 ; E. Soubeiran, *Ann. Chim. Phys.*, (2), **43**.
407, 1830 ; H. Capitaine, *Journ. Pharm. Chim.*, (3), **25**. 559, 1839 ; G. Franceschi, *L'Orosi*, **13**.
289, 1890 ; *Boll. Chim. Farm.*, **29**. 317, 1890 ; D. Vitali, *ib.*, **44**. 49, 1905 ; A. H. Gotthelf, *Journ.
Soc. Chem. Ind.*, **22**. 191, 1903 ; A. Partheil and E. Amort, *Arch. Pharm.*, **237**. 126, 1899 ; *Ber.*,
31. 594, 1898 ; W. Wallace and F. Penny, *Phil. Mag.*, (4), **4**. 361, 1852 ; L. Hurtzig and
A. Geuther, *Liebig's Ann.*, **111**. 172, 1859.
    [6] S. Delépine, *Journ. Ind. Hyg.*, **4**. 346, 410, 1923.

§ 27. The Bromides of Arsenic

Arsenic ignites as soon as it comes in contact with bromine burning with great
brilliancy. G. S. Sérullas [1] introduced dry powdered arsenic in small portions at a
time into a retort containing bromine ; and distilled the product from an excess of
arsenic. He thus obtained crystals of **arsenic tribromide**, $AsBr_3$. E. Jory passed
the bromine vapour into a column of arsenic contained in a long, hard glass tube.
J. Nicklès added powdered arsenic to a mixture of bromine with twice its weight
of carbon disulphide, and agitated the mixture until decolorized. On evaporating
the solvent, crystals of the tribromide remain. G. Oddo and U. Giachery obtained
the tribromide by heating a mixture of stoichiometrical proportions of arsenic
trioxide and sulphur in a current of bromine vapour ; and A. C. Vournazos, by
heating a mixture of arsenic trioxide, potassium bromide, and acetic acid at
100°.

G. S. Sérullas' analysis agrees with the formula $AsBr_3$, and E. Beckmann
found this to be in accord with the effect of the tribromide on the b.p. of bromine ;
and W. Finkelstein with the f.p. of bromine. There is an abnormal depression in
the f.p. of antimony trichloride by arsenic tribromide owing to chemical action—
vide infra, arsenic triiodide.

At ordinary temp., arsenic tribromide forms a mass of colourless, prismatic
crystals. W. Wallace and F. Penny obtained well-formed crystals by allowing the
molten mass partly to solidify, and then pouring off the still liquid portion.
P. Walden reported a few measurements of the crystal angles. The salt is stable
at ordinary temp. in air, but if a little moisture be present, a little fuming occurs.
P. Walden said that the smell is feebly aromatic, not arsenical ; J. Nicklès said the
smell is arsenical. C. H. D. Bödecker gave 3·66 for the sp. gr. at 15°/4°, and
J. W. Retgers gave 3·540 at 25°/4° for the tribromide which had been fused.
F. M. Jäger represented the sp. gr., D, of the liquid at θ, referred to water at 4°, by
$D = 3\cdot3972 - 0\cdot002822(\theta - 25) + 0\cdot00000248(\theta - 25)^2$. The cohesion, a^2 per sq. mm.,

the surface tension, σ dynes per cm., and the surface energy, μ ergs per sq. cm., were found to be :

	49·6°	74·5°	90°	121°	149·6°	165°	179·7°
Sp. gr.	3·328	3·261	3·234	3·143	3·076	3·041	3·008
A^2	3·04	2·96	2·82	2·66	2·53	2·48	2·45
σ	49·6	46·6	44·8	41·0	38·2	37·0	36·1
μ	1029·5	980·5	947·8	884·1	835·6	815·6	801·6

R. Lorenz and W. Herz studied some relations of the surface tensions of the family of halides. E. Rabinowitsch gave 111 for the mol. vol. I. I. Saskowsky found the ratio of the mol. vol. to the sum of the at. vols. of the constituent elements to be 1·21. G. S. Sérullas gave 20°–25° for the m.p. ; and P. Walden, S. Tolloczko and M. Meyer, N. A. Puschin and S. Löwy, and F. M. Jäger said that the tribromide melts sharply at 31°. G. S. Sérullas gave 220° for the b.p. ; J. Kendall and co-workers, 175° ; P. Walden, 221° at 760 mm., and 92° at 14 mm. ; and F. M. Jäger, 109° at 20 mm. S. Tolloczko and M. Meyer gave 9·83 cals. for the heat of fusion ; and W. Herz. 8·93 cals. per gram. M. Berthelot gave for the heat of formation $(As,3Br_{gas})=59·1$ Cals., and $(As,3Br_{liquid})=47·1$ Cals. For the mol. depression of the f.p., S. Tolloczko gave 206 ; F. Garelli and V. Bassani, 194·2 ; and P. Walden, 189. W. Finkelstein observed that the lowering of the f.p. of bromine by arsenic tribromide corresponds with theory, and the soln. is a non-conductor of electricity. P. Walden found the eq. electrical conductivity of a mol of the tribromide in 101·4 and 925·3 litres of liquid sulphur dioxide to be respectively 0·249 and 2·347. The ionizing power of the tribromide is said to be rather less than that of the trichloride. The dielectric constant at 35° is 9·3, and at 20°, 3·4. W. Finkelstein found that the decomposition voltage of arsenic tribromide in benzene soln. is 0·50 volt. W. Herz gave $1·99 \times 10^{12}$ for the vibration frequency.

Arsenic tribromide attracts moisture from the air, and, according to M. Berthelot, when mixed with oxygen it is decomposed by heat into free bromine and an oxybromide. According to G. S. Sérullas, the tribromide is rapidly decomposed by water into arsenic trioxide, bromine, and an oxybromide. W. Wallace and F. Penny found that one part of the tribromide dissolves in three parts of boiling water ; and less is dissolved in the presence of hydrobromic acid ; the boiling soln. in water on cooling deposits crystals of arsenic trioxide. C. Hugot found that liquid ammonia reacts with the tribromide. F. Oberhauser studied the reaction

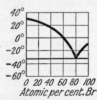

FIG. 35.—Freezing-point Curve of the Binary System : $AsBr_3$-Br_2.

with cyanogen bromide. S. Tolloczko found that antimony trichloride and arsenic tribromide probably interact chemically—*vide supra*. M. P. Cady and R. Taft found that the tribromide is appreciably soluble in phosphoryl chloride. M. Ussanowitsch studied the electrical conductivity of mixtures of arsenic tribromide and ether. Molten arsenic tribromide was found by P. Walden to dissolve potassium bromide, tetramethylammonium iodide, anhydrous aluminium and ferric chlorides, but rubidium iodide and tetrachloroiodide, mercuric iodide, stannic bromide and iodide, anhydrous cadmium, manganese, and cobalt iodides, and cobalt bromide are almost insoluble therein. W. Biltz and K. Jeep obtained the f.p. curve, Fig. 35, for the binary system : $AsBr_3$-Br_2. The subject was discussed by E. Kordes. J. W. Retgers also examined the soln. of stannic iodide, and mercuric iodide in this menstruum. A. C. Vournazos obtained the complex **sodium arsenoctoazidotribromide**, $Na_8[AsBr_3(N_3)_8]$. According to H. L. Wheeler, **rubidium diarsenoenneabromide**, $3RbBr.2AsBr_3$, is obtained by a method analogous to that used for the corresponding chloride. The amber-yellow trigonal crystals have the axial ratio $a:c=1:1·220$ and $\alpha=88°$ 42′. Similarly with **cæsium diarsenoenneabromide**, $3CsBr.2AsBr_3$, which furnishes trigonal crystals with the axial ratio $a:c=1:1·219$, and $\alpha=88°$ 43′. The properties of these salts resemble those of the corresponding chlorides. According to J. Nicklès, sodium thiosulphate first converts the tribromide into an oxybromide, and then into the trisulphide.

A. Besson, and W. Landau said that arsenic tribromide unites with ammonia and with many amines. The former obtained pale yellow **arsenic triamminotribromide,** $AsBr_3.3NH_3$, by treating arsenic tribromide with ammonia. W. Landau obtained **arsenic hemiheptamminotribromide,** $AsBr_3.3\frac{1}{2}NH_3$, by passing ammonia into a soln. of arsenic tribromide in benzene. The white precipitate can be recrystallized from hot absolute alcohol. The ammine loses ammonia and sublimes when heated. A. Besson said that at 300° the tribromide is decomposed into arsenic, nitrogen, and ammonium bromide. W. Landau found that cold water slowly dissolves the amine; while hot water decomposes it. A. Besson found that the tribromide reacts with phosphine: $PH_3 + AsBr_3 = 3HBr + AsP$. P. Walden said that the molten tribromide readily dissolves phosphoryl bromide, antimony trichloride, arsenic triiodide, and antimony triiodide. The soln. of arsenic and antimony triiodides and antimony tribromide were examined by J. W. Retgers. P. Walden found that molten arsenic tribromide dissolves ammonium thiocyanate very sparingly. J. W. Retgers observed that arsenic tribromide is soluble in methylene iodide, and in carbon disulphide. G. Gustavson observed that 29 per cent. of arsenic tribromide is converted into the trichloride when heated with carbon tetrachloride at 150°–200° for about 60 days. For the interchange with organic halides, *vide infra,* arsenic triiodide.

S. Hilpert and F. Herrmann heated finely-divided precipitated silver with molten arsenic bromide in a sealed tube and obtained **silver tribromoarsenite,** Ag_3AsBr_3; and when copper is used in place of silver, **copper bromoarsenite,** $7Cu.2AsBr_3$, is formed. This may be the compound Cu_3AsBr_3, in solid soln. with copper. The same products are obtained by the action of arsenic vapour on silver or cuprous bromide at 500°. J. Kendall and co-workers observed that arsenic tribromide and **aluminium tribromide** form no compound; the f.p. curve is shown in Fig. 36.

G. S. Sérullas, and M. Berthelot mentioned the formation of an arsenic oxybromide—*vide supra.* According to W. Wallace and F. Penny, molten arsenic tribromide easily dissolves arsenic trioxide, and when the tribromide in excess is distilled off, the residue separates into two layers—the upper layer is **arsenic oxybromide, or arsenyl bromide,** AsOBr, and the lower layer a mixture of that substance with arsenic trioxide. A. Michaelis made it by the action of phenylarsenic oxide on bromine; and W. Wallace and F. Penny, by evaporating a cold soln. of arsenic tribromide in water containing hydrobromic acid over sulphuric acid, when white crystals of the hemitrihydrate, $AsOBr.1\frac{1}{2}H_2O$, are formed. The oxybromide decomposes by heat into arsenic trioxide and tribromide. W. Wallace and F. Penny reported a complex **arsenic diarsenyl enneaoxydibromide,** $2AsOBr.3As_2O_3.12H_2O$, or $(AsO)_2As_6O_9Br_2.12H_2O$, to be formed when a hot sat. soln. of arsenic tribromide in dil. hydrobromic acid is cooled. This substance may be a mixture.

FIG. 36.—Freezing-point Curve of Mixtures: $AlBr_3$–$AsBr_3$.

REFERENCES.

[1] G. S. Sérullas, *Ann. Chim. Phys.,* (2), **38**. 319, 1828; G. Gustavson, *ib.,* **2**. 200, 1874; J. Kendall, E. D. Crittenden, and H. K. Miller, *Journ. Amer. Chem. Soc.,* **45**. 963, 1923; J. Nicklès, *Journ. Pharm. Chim.,* (3), **41**. 143, 1862; E. Jory, *ib.,* (6), **12**. 312, 1900; W. Wallace and F. Penny, *Phil. Mag.,* (4), **4**. 361, 1852; W. Wallace, *ib.,* (4), **16**. 358, 1858; (4), **17**. 261, 1859; *B.A. Rep.,* 69, 1858; J. W. Retgers, *Zeit. phys. Chem.,* **11**. 342, 1893; M. Ussanowitsch, *ib.,* **124**. 427, 1927; E. Beckmann, *ib.,* **46**. 853, 1903; W. Finkelstein, *ib.,* **105**. 10, 1923; P. Walden, *ib.,* **43**. 335, 1903; **46**. 103, 1904; *Zeit. anorg. Chem.,* **29**. 373, 1902; R. Lorenz and W. Herz, *ib.,* **120**. 320, 1921; **170**. 237, 1928; W. Biltz and K. Jeep, *ib.,* **162**. 32, 1927; F. M. Jäger, *ib.,* **101**. 174, 1917; I. I. Saskowsky, *ib.,* **146**. 315, 1925; N. A. Puschin and S. Löwy, *ib.,* **150**. 167, 1926; F. Garelli and V. Bassani, *Atti Accad. Lincei,* (5), **10**. i, 255, 1901; E. Rabinowitsch, *Ber.,* **58**. 2790, 1925; S. Tolloczko, *Bull. Acad. Cracovie,* **1,** 1901;

S. Tolloczko and M. Meyer, *Kosmos*, **35**. 64, 1910; *Radiszewsky's Festband*, 641, 1910; J. Tarible, *Sur les combinaisons du bromure de bore*, Paris, 1899; *Compt. Rend.*, **132**. 206, 1901; M. Berthelot, *ib.*, **86**. 862, 1875; A. Besson, *ib.*, **110**. 1258, 1890; A. C. Vournazos, *ib.*, **166**. 526, 1918; C. Hugot, *ib.*, **121**. 206, 1895; M. P. Cady and R. Taft, *Journ. Phys. Chem.*, **29**. 1057, 1925; A. Michaelis, *Ber.*, **10**. 625, 1877; S. Hilpert and F. Herrmann, *ib.*, **46**. 2218, 1913; W. Finkelstein, *Zeit. phys. Chem.*, **105**. 10, 1923; **115**. 303, 1925; W. Landau, *Ueber die Einwirkung von Ammoniak und Aminen auf Arsenbromür*, Berlin, 1888; C. H. D. Bödecker, *Beziehungen zwischen Dichte und Zusammensetzung bei festen und liquiden Stoffen*, Leipzig, 1860; G. Oddo and U. Giachery, *Gazz. Chim. Ital.*, **53**. i, 56, 1923; A. C. Vournazos, *Zeit. anorg. Chem.*, **164**. 263, 1927; E. Kordes, *ib.*, **168**. 177, 1927; F. Oberhauser, *Ber.*, **60**. B, 1434, 1927; H. L. Wheeler, *Zeit. anorg. Chem.*, **4**. 451, 1893; *Amer. Journ. Science*, (3), **46**. 88, 1893.

§ 28. The Iodides of Arsenic

Four arsenic iodides have been reported : monoiodide, diiodide, triiodide, and pentaiodide. F. M. Jäger and H. J. Doornbosch [1] obtained the thermal diagram, Fig. 37, for mixtures of arsenic and iodine. Two compounds are formed, however, AsI_3, melting at 140·7°, and As_2I_4, which at 135°–136° is transformed into a pair

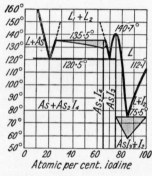

of immiscible liquids, one of which has a composition differing only slightly from As_2I_4, whilst the other contains 30·5 atomic per cent. of arsenic. The diiodide appears as a liquid layer at 135°–136° with a eutectic between the two compounds at 120·5°. It was not possible to isolate the diiodide either by extraction with solvents, or by the formation of solid soln. with the corresponding phosphorus diiodide. *L* in the diagram denotes a liquid melt. The diiodide is a definite compound formed by the dissociation of AsI_3 in accordance with $2AsI_3 \rightleftharpoons As_2I_4 + I_2$. It may also be formed by the interaction of AsI_3 and metallic arsenic in consequence of the occurrence of the reversible change represented by $8AsI_3 + 4As \rightleftharpoons 6As_2I_4$. There is no sign of a monoiodide ; and, as emphasized by E. Quercigh, there is no sign of a pentaiodide.

Fig. 37.—The Thermal Diagram of the Binary System : As–I.

He found the eutectic between iodine and arsenic triiodide to be at 71·5°.

A. Göpel reported that **arsenic monoiodide**, AsI, is formed as a chocolate-brown substance when a soln. of iodine in alcohol is saturated with arsine ; and H. Schiff found that the decomposition of arsenic trianilinotriiodide, by boiling alcohol results in the formation of the same compound : $AsI_3.3C_6H_5NH_2 = 2C_6H_5NH_2 + C_6H_4I.NH_3I + AsI$. F. Meurer said that the monoiodide is formed when an excess of arsine acts on an alcoholic soln. of iodine—*vide infra*, arsenic triiodide.

E. Bamberger and J. Philipp obtained **arsenic diiodide**, AsI_2, or As_2I_4, analogous with phosphorus and bismuth diiodides. The conditions of stability are indicated in connection with Fig. 37. J. T. Hewitt and T. F. Winmill found that while the analysis agreed with the formula AsI_2, the effect on the b.p. of carbon disulphide agrees with the formula As_2I_4. By heating arsenic with twice its weight of iodine in sealed tubes to 230°, a dark cherry-red crystalline mass is obtained, from which the diiodide is separated by crystallization from carbon disulphide, in an atm. of carbon dioxide. The diiodide forms thin prismatic crystals of a cherry-red colour, but, owing to their becoming opaque on exposure to the air, the measurement of their angles is rendered difficult ; one of the angles, however, seems to correspond with one of the angles of the analogous phosphorus compound. T. Karantassis made the compound by introducing one part of finely-powdered arsenic and 2 parts of iodine into a retort-shaped tube ; and after repeated evacuation and filling with pure, dry hydrogen, sealing the tube and heating the mixture to the b.p. for 2 hrs. On careful distillation, pure arsenic diiodide is obtained. The undistilled product melts at 117°–120°, the distilled compound at 130°, the change in m.p. proving the solubility of arsenic in the crude product. E. Frank gave 120° for the m.p. T. Karantassis said that the diiodide boils at 375°–380° in an atm. of hydrogen or carbon dioxide. E. Bamberger and J. Philipp said that the diiodide is readily oxidized, and in air, the crystals become brick-red. J. T. Hewitt and T. F. Winmill said that the compound should be recrystallized in an atm. of dry carbon dioxide since it is very sensitive to moisture and oxygen; they also found that cold conc. sulphuric acid is apparently without action, but some iodine is eliminated when the acid is raised near its b.p. Cold fuming nitric acid has apparently little immediate action, but, on heating, oxides of nitrogen and iodine vap. are given off, whilst eventually arsenic and iodic acids are produced. Pyridine decomposes the substance immediately, arsenic is liberated, and arsenic triiodide passes into soln. The substance dissolves in boiling acetic anhydride; the material which separates on cooling is mostly yellow, but evidently not homogeneous. It is very probable that the greater portion of the product is a derivative of arsenic triiodide. The compound is soluble in carbon disulphide, ether, alcohol, and chloroform. The soln. rapidly darkens in air owing to the formation of arsenic triiodide; and when evaporated in air, the diiodide is completely decomposed. When treated with water it turns black with the separation of rather less arsenic than corresponds with : $3AsI_2=2AsI_3+As$. This reaction distinguishes it from the triiodide. Alkaline liquids accelerate the decomposition. The alcoholic soln. is similarly decomposed by water. T. Karantassis could not prepare a complex of the diiodide with sulphur.

A. Plisson showed that **arsenic triiodide, AsI₃**, can be obtained by the direct union of the elements. When the mixture is warmed, union occurs with the evolution of heat. This method was used by A. Bette, G. S. Sérullas and M. Hottot, A. Göpel, and A. T. Thomson. The triiodide is also formed when arsenic acts on iodine in the presence of water as was found by A. Plisson, W. Duncan, and R. C. Cowley and J. P. Catford ; or on a soln. of iodine in ether or carbon disulphide as recommended by J. Nicklès, and J. W. Retgers. E. Bamberger and J. Philipp found J. Nicklès' method of heating arsenic and iodine in eq. proportions in carbon disulphide, to be the most convenient process. The product can be recrystallized from carbon disulphide or xylol. C. Brame obtained the triiodide by the action of iodine vap. on heated arsenic trioxide ; E. Richter, by heating a mixture of iodine and arsenic trioxide ; and A. Göpel, by sublimation from a mixture of arsenic trioxide, potassium iodide, and potassium hydrosulphate. J. F. Babcock treated arsenic trioxide with hydrogen iodide ; and E. Bamberger and J. Philipp found that the triiodide is precipitated when a conc. soln. of potassium iodide is added to a hot soln. of arsenic trioxide in hydrochloric acid. The yellowish-red, crystalline powder is washed with hydrochloric acid to remove potassium chloride. G. Oddo and U. Giachery obtained the triiodide by heating a mixture of stoichiometrical proportions of arsenic trioxide and sulphur in the vap. of iodine ; and A. C. Vournazos, by heating at 100° a mixture of arsenic trioxide, potassium iodide, and acetic acid. P. Hautefeuille also found that hydriodic acid reacts with arsenic chloride with the development of heat : $AsCl_3+3HI=3HCl+AsI_3$; the triiodide can be crystallized from the trichloride in which it is soluble. C. Husson found that arsine reacts with dry iodine forming the triiodide, and O. G. Jacobsen based a method of removing arsine from hydrogen sulphide on this reaction. F. Meurer obtained the triiodide by the action of arsine on an alcoholic soln. of iodine—an excess of arsine produces the monoiodide. According to E. R. Schneider, arsenic triiodide is formed when a mol of arsenic disulphide and six gram-atoms of iodine are heated together— with equimolar parts a sulphiodide is formed. The triiodide is also formed by the protracted heating of a mixture of iodine and the trisulphide. The product is dissolved in carbon disulphide, and on evaporation, the triiodide separates first, the sulphur last. E. R. Schneider made the triiodide by the action of arsenic disulphide or trisulphide on a soln. of iodine in carbon disulphide:

$As_2S_2 + 3I_2 = 2AsI_3 + 2S$. A. F. Duflos obtained the triiodide by sublimation from a mixture of mercuric iodide and arsenic trisulphide.

Analyses by A. Plisson, A. Bette, F. Meurer, and E. Bamberger and J. Philipp agree with the formula, AsI_3; and A. Wurtz found the vap. density to be 16·1 in agreement with 15·8 calculated for the simple formula. P. Walden also found the mol. wt., calculated from the lowering of the f.p. of arsenic tribromide, to be normal. S. Tolloczko found that the abnormal depression of the f.p. of arsenic triiodide in antimony trichloride can be explained by the increase in the number of mols of the solute owing to a reaction : $AsI_3 + SbCl_3 = AsCl_3 + 3SbCl_2I$. E. Beckmann obtained a mol. wt. about half the normal value. According to P. Friedländer, arsenic triiodide evaporates from its soln. in ether or carbon disulphide in red, hexagonal plates with the axial ratio $a : c = 1 : 2·998$. A. Bette said that the mass which has been fused is brick-red with a violet crystalline fracture ; the plates obtained by sublimation are also brick-red. According to E. R. Schneider, if the fused mass contains a little trisulphide it may freeze to an amorphous mass. The vapour is yellow. B. E. Sloan said that a partial dissociation occurs when the triiodide is heated to 165° in a sealed tube. A. Plisson said that during sublimation a small proportion is decomposed into iodine and arsenic. C. H. D. Bödecker gave 4·39 for the sp. gr. at 15°/4° ; and H. G. F. Schröder, 4·374. S. Motylewsky found the drop-weight to be 45 units when that of water at 0° is 100. T. Carnelley gave 146°, S. Horiba and R. Inouye 144°, and B. E. Sloan 149°, for the m.p.; F. M. Jäger and H. J. Doornbosch gave 140·7° for the f.p.; E. Quercigh, 135·5° ; and A. M. Wasiléeff, 146°. T. Carnelley and W. C. Williams gave 394°–414° for the b.p. S. Horiba and R. Inouye gave 19·2 Cals. for the mol. heat of vaporization ; the vap. press. the vap. press., p mm., of the liquid is :

	11·35°	34·73°	85·60°	130·98°	145·79°	160·39°	182·41°
p . . .	0·000	0·015	0·203	0·706	1·158	2·777	7·891

or $\log p = -4·2T^{-1} + 10·1$. The results for the vap. press., p mm., of the solid are somewhat irregular, due, it is supposed, to the presence of an allotropic form. If the reddish-orange variety is cooled by a mixture of solid carbon dioxide and alcohol, it forms a yellow modification stable only at a low temp. The first sublimate from the reddish-orange variety in vacuo is yellow, and this changes slowly into the reddish-orange variety at room temp. The vap. press. of the yellow variety is greater than that of the reddish-orange form. M. Berthelot gave for the heat of formation $(As,3I) = 28·8$ Cals. ; and $(As,3I_{solid}) = 12·6$ Cals. J. H. Mathews found that neither the solid nor the liquid conducts an electric current, but a sat. soln. in allyl isothiocyanate, at 60°, has a conductivity of $1·4 \times 10^{-4}$ mho.

A. Plisson said that arsenic triiodide has no smell; A. T. Thomson, that it has a metallic taste ; and A. Bette, that it gradually decomposes in air, forming iodine and arsenic trioxide. E. R. Schneider also found that the soln. in carbon disulphide gradually absorbs oxygen, and so acquires a dark colour owing to the liberation of iodine. M. Berthelot found that when the triiodide is heated in oxygen, it burns with a pale blue flame, forming arsenic trioxide and iodine. A. Plisson found that the triiodide dissolves freely in cold water, forming a yellow soln. which does not become brown when exposed to air. E. Bamberger and J. Philipp said that the triiodide is fairly stable in aq. soln. from which it may be recovered unchanged ; and E. Richter, that a one per cent. soln. of the triiodide in water, or a water containing 5–10 per cent. of alcohol, is stable. A. Plisson found that the aq. soln. tastes acidic ; but it does not turn starch-paper blue except on the addition of hydrochloric acid. If the aq. soln. be evaporated in an open vessel, crystals of the oxyiodide are formed ; but if evaporated after the addition of hydriodic acid, W. Wallace and F. Penny obtained only arsenic triiodide. A. Plisson reported that the aq. soln. furnishes iodine when treated with sulphuric or nitric acid ; arsenic trisulphide, when treated with hydrogen sulphide ; a brown precipitate, with bismuth nitrate; a yellow one, with lead nitrate; a green one, with copper ammoniosulphate; and none, with calcium sulphate. W. Wallace and F. Penny found that a boiling, sat., aq. soln. deposits arsenic triiodide unchanged; but the spontaneous evaporation of the cold aq. soln. yields colourless plates of what was regarded as **arsenic diarsenyl enneaoxydiiodide**, $2AsOI.3As_2O_3.12H_2O$, or $As_6(AsO)_2O_9I_2.12H_2O$. It was also obtained by slowly cooling a hot sat. aq. soln. of one part of the triiodide in 3·32 parts of hot water, and drying the colourless plates between bibulous paper. The water of crystallization is lost by desiccation over sulphuric acid, but, according to A. Plisson, not over calcium chloride in vacuo. When heated, arsenic triiodide sublimes, and the trioxide remains. The compound is only slightly soluble in cold water, and less so in alcohol. By repeatedly crystallizing the compound from a hot aq. soln., it becomes poorer in iodine; alcohol slowly removes all the iodine. The substance may or may not be a chemical individual.

S. Zinno reported that a hot, aq. soln. of arsenic trioxide, sat. with iodine, deposits on cooling **arsenic trioxytetraiodide**, $As_2O_3I_4$. M. Wegner, however, said that the crystals thus obtained are, however, nothing but arsenious oxide containing a trace of hydriodic acid. When iodine is dissolved in a hot soln. of arsenic trioxide, the latter is oxidized, and arsenic acid and hydriodic acid are formed, which act on each other again when the soln. is conc., free iodine and arsenic trioxide being regenerated.

V. Auger mixed carbon disulphide soln. of arsenic triiodide and sulphur, and obtained orange plates or prisms of **arsenic tetracosisulphoiodide**, $AsI_3.3S_8$, m.p.104°. L. Ouvrard found that when the triiodide is heated to 200° in a current of hydrogen sulphide, thioiodides are formed. According to E. Bamberger and J. Philipp, if ammonia be passed into a soln. of the triiodide in ether or benzene, a bulky white **arsenic hemienneamminotriiodide**, $AsI_3.4\frac{1}{2}NH_3$, is precipitated. A. Besson found that the triiodide absorbs ammonia and is gradually transformed into **arsenic tetramminotriiodide**, $AsI_3.4NH_3$. The two ammines are possibly the same. C. Hugot suggested that the alleged ammines are mixtures of ammonium iodide and arsenic triamide (*q.v.*). According to A. Besson, the tetrammine begins to lose ammonia at 50°, and at 300°, decomposes like the bromide. Water dissolves it with decomposition; hydrochloric acid removes the ammonia, and arsenic triiodide is precipitated. If left for a long time in contact with ammonia at 0°, **arsenic dodecamminotriiodide**, $AsI_3.12NH_3$, is formed. F. M. Jäger and H. J. Doornbosch showed that arsenic and phosphorus triiodides form an isodimorphous series of crystals with a transition point at 73·5°, as indicated in Fig. 35; the sat. solid soln. at that temp. contains respectively 18 and 75 per cent. of phosphorus triiodide, PT_3. L in the diagram denotes a liquid. A. C. Vournazos obtained a complex **sodium arsenoctoazidotriiodide**, $Na_8[AsI_3(N_3)_8]$.

A. Besson found that arsenic triiodide reacts with phosphine: $AsI_3+PH_3 =3HI+AsP$; and L. Ouvrard, that it reacts with molten arsenic trisulphide, forming thioiodides. For the interaction of arsenic triiodide and antimony trichloride, *vide supra*. J. Tarible found that boron tribromide is dissolved by arsenic triiodide. According to J. W. Retgers, arsenic triiodide is soluble in carbon disulphide, alcohol, ether, chloroform, benzene, toluene, xylene, and at 12°, 100 parts of methylene iodide dissolve 17·4 parts of arsenic triiodide, forming a dark red soln. with a sp. gr. 3·449; more is dissolved at a higher temp. E. Bamberger and J. Philipp said that with alcohol at 150°, ethyl iodide is formed; and H. Schiff observed that it forms with aniline the complex $AsI_3.3C_6H_5NH_2$. G. J. Burrows and E. E. Turner studied the action of arsenic triiodide on the tertiary amines. R. Brix, and B. Köhnlein studied the interchange of halogen between the arsenic trihalides and organic halides, and found that arsenic unites by preference with iodine rather than with bromine or chlorine, and with bromine rather than with chlorine.

J. Nicklès studied the action of arsenic triiodide on the alkali halides, but the complexes formed were not very stable; and H. L. Wheeler reported **rubidium enneaiodide**, $3RbI.2AsI_3$, to be formed as in the corresponding case of the chloride. The pseudohexagonal crystals have the axial ratio $a:c=1:2\cdot486$; and **cæsium**

diarsenoenneaiodide, $3CsI.2AsI_3$, is said to be formed in an analogous way. The hexagonal bipyramids have the axial ratio $a : c=1 : 2\cdot488$. A. Mosnier prepared **lead arsenoenneadiiodide,** $3PbI_2.AsI_3.12H_2O$, by adding a sat. soln. of lead iodide to a boiling sat. soln. of arsenic triiodide in fuming hydriodic acid. The heat of formation of the hydrate is $3\cdot6$ Cals., and the heat of soln. in 40 parts of water at $15°$, $-8\cdot2$ Cals. The salt is decomposed by water, alcohol, and ether. It becomes anhydrous at about $45°$; and the heat of formation of the anhydrous salt is $27\cdot1$ Cals.; and the heat of soln. in 40 parts of water at $15°$, $12\cdot5$ Cals. P. Lemoult made **arsenic trisiodomercuriate,** $As(HgI)_3$, or $HgI_2.AsHg_2I$, by passing arsine diluted with hydrogen or carbon dioxide into a soln. of potassium iodomercuriate. The pale brown crystalline precipitate is more stable than the corresponding phosphorus compound. According to A. M. Wasiléeff, there is a eutectic at $106\cdot2°$ with mixtures of **stannic iodide** and arsenic triiodide containing $SnI_4 : AsI_3$ $=1 : 0\cdot6936$.

B. E. Sloan reported **arsenic pentaiodide,** AsI_5, to be formed by heating the stoichiometrical proportions of the elements in an atm. of carbon dioxide in a sealed

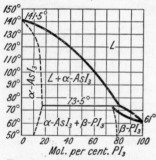

FIG. 38.—Fusion Curves of the Binary Mixtures : AsI_3–PI_3.

tube at $150°$. If a rather larger proportion of iodine be used, at $190°$, the excess is volatilized. The garnet-brown crystals are probably monoclinic prisms with a sp. gr. $3\cdot93$, and a m.p. of $70°$. The compound is more or less soluble in water, carbon disulphide, alcohol, ether, and chloroform. The compound is decomposed by soln. in carbon disulphide because on crystallization arsenic triiodide and iodine were obtained. The absorption spectrum of the soln. agrees with this assumption. The compound loses a little iodine when heated in nitrogen in a sealed tube at $100°$. There is no evidence of a pentaiodide on the fusion curve, Fig. 38, and, as pointed out by E. Quercigh, the supposed pentaiodide is really the eutectic which he found to have a f.p. at $73\cdot5°$. J. Tarible found that boron tribromide is dissolved by the alleged pentaiodide. R. Hanslian studied its mol. wt. from the f.p. of its soln. in iodine.

REFERENCES.

[1] A. Göpel, *Arch. Pharm.*, (2), **60**. 129, 141, 1849 ; F. Meurer, *ib.*, (2), **52**. 1, 1847 ; J. F. Babcock, *ib.*, (3), **9**. 455, 1877 ; E. Bamberger and J. Philipp, *Ber.*, **14**. 2644, 1881 ; O. G. Jacobsen, *ib.*, **20**. 1999, 1887 ; **21**. 2546, 1888 ; E. R. Schneider, *Journ. prakt. Chem.*, (2), **34**. 505, 1886 ; (2), **36**. 498, 1887 ; A. T. Thomson, *Lancet*, 176, 1838 ; *Repert. Pharm.*, (2), **17**. 360, 1839 ; S. Zinno, *ib.*, (3), **22**. 385, 1873 ; H. G. F. Schröder, *Dichtigkeitsmessungen*, Heidelberg, 1873 ; G. S. Sérullas, *Ann. Chim. Phys.*, (2), **38**. 319, 1828 ; G. S. Sérullas and M. Hottot, *Journ. Pharm. Chim.*, (2), **14**. 49, 164, 598, 1828 ; J. Nicklès, *ib.*, (3), **41**. 147, 1862 ; *Compt. Rend.*, **48**. 837, 1859 ; **50**. 872, 1880 ; A. Plisson, *ib.*, (2), **14**. 46, 592, 1828 ; *Ann. Chim. Phys.*, (2), **39**. 265, 1828 ; A. Mosnier, *ib.*, (7), **12**. 374, 1897 ; E. Mitscherlich, *Sitzber. Akad. Berlin*, 425, 1833 ; *Pogg. Ann.*, **29**. 193, 1833 ; *Liebig's Ann.*, **12**. 137, 1834 ; C. Brame, *Compt. Rend.*, **33**. 579, 1851 ; H. Schiff, *ib.*, **56**. 1096, 1863 ; C. Husson, *ib.*, **67**. 56, 1868 ; A. C. Vournazos, *ib.*, **166**. 526, 1918 ; L. Ouvrard, *ib.*, **117**. 107, 1893 ; V. Auger, *ib.*, **146**. 477, 1908 ; P. Lemoult, *ib.*, **139**. 479, 1904 ; P. Hautefeuille, *ib.*, **64**. 704, 1867 ; *Bull. Soc. Chim.*, (2), **7**. 189, 1867 ; T. Karantassis, *ib.*, (4), **37**. 853, 854, 1925 ; J. Tarible, *Compt. Rend.*, **132**. 206, 1901 ; *Sur les combinaisons du bromure de bore*, Paris, 1899 ; H. R. Doornbosch, *Proc. Acad. Amsterdam*, **14**. 625, 1911 ; F. M. Jäger and H. J. Doornbosch, *Zeit. anorg. Chem.*, **75**. 261, 1912 ; A. Wurtz, *Dictionnaire de chimie*, Paris, **1**. 463, 1868 ; R. C. Cowley and J. P. Catford, *Pharm. Journ.*, (4), **21**. 131, 1905 ; W. Duncan, *ib.*, (4), **18**. 8, 1904 ; G. Oddo and U. Giachery, *Gazz. Chim. Ital.*, **53**. i, 56, 1923 ; A. Bette, *Liebig's Ann.*, **33**. 349, 1840 ; M. Wegner, *ib.*, **174**. 129, 1874 ; A. M. Wasiléeff, *Journ. Russ. Phys. Chem. Soc.*, **44**. 1076, 1912 ; **49**. 88, 1917 ; P. Friedländer, *Zeit. Kryst.*, **3**. 214, 1879 ; E. Richter, *Apoth. Ztg.*, **26**. 728, 742, 1911 ; B. E. Sloan, *Chem. News*, **46**. 194, 1882 ; E. Quercigh, *Atti Accad. Ist. Veneto*, **70**. ii, 667, 1912 ; *Atti Accad. Lincei*, (5), **21**. i, 786, 1912 ; L. Ouvrard, *Compt. Rend.*, **117**. 107, 1893 ; M. Berthelot, **86**. 862, 1878 ; J. T. Hewitt and T. F. Winmill, *Journ. Chem. Soc.*, **91**. 962, 1907 ; T. Carnelley, *ib.*, **45**. 409, 1884 ; T. Carnelley and W. C. Williams, *ib.*,

37. 125, 1880 ; G. J. Burrows and E. E. Turner, *ib.*, **119.** 1448, 1921 ; J. H. Mathews, *Journ. Phys. Chem.*, **9.** 641, 1906 ; A. F. Duflos and A. G. Hirsch, *Das Arsenik*, Breslau, 1842 ; A. F. Duflos, *Pharmakologische Chemie*, Breslau, 153, 1842 ; P. Walden, *Zeit. anorg. Chem.*, **29.** 376, 1902 ; E. Beckmann, *ib.*, **51.** 111, 1906 ; S. Motylewsky, *ib.*, **38.** 410, 1904 ; J. W. Retgers, *ib.*, **3.** 344, 1893 ; H. L. Wheeler, *ib.*, **4.** 451, 1893 ; *Amer. Journ. Science*, (3), **46.** 88, 1893 ; E. Frank, *Zur Kenntnis des braunen und grauen Arsens*, Bern, 19, 1912 ; R. Hanslian, *Molekulargewichtsbestimmungen in çefierendem und siedendem Jod*, Weida i Th., 44, 1910 ; C. H. D. Rödecker, *Beziehungen zwischen Dichte und Zusammensetzung bei festen und liquiden Stoffen*, Leipzig, 1860 ; S. Tolloczko, *Bull. Acad. Cracovie*, 1, 1901 ; C. Hugot, *Compt. Rend.*, **121.** 206, 1895 ; E. C. Franklin and C. A. Kraus, *Amer. Chem. Journ.*, **20.** 820, 1898 ; G. Gore, *Proc. Roy. Soc.*, **20.** 441, 1872 ; **21.** 140, 1873 ; R. Brix, *Liebig's Ann.*, **225.** 146, 1884 ; B. Köhnlein, *ib.*, **225.** 171, 1884 ; A. C. Vournazos, *Zeit. anorg. Chem.*, **164.** 263, 1927 ; W. Wallace and F. Penny, *Phil. Mag.*, (4), **4.** 361, 1852 ; A. Besson, *Compt. Rend.*, **110.** 1258, 1890 ; S. Horiba and R. Inouye, *Osaka Celebration*, Kyoto, 279, 1927.

§ 29. Halogen Compounds of the Arsenites and Arsenates

A number of compounds of arsenic trioxide with the alkali and other halides has been reported. In the ternary systems : $As_2O_3-MX-H_2O$, or $As_2O_3-MX_2-H_2O$, where M stands for the metal and X for the halide, the conditions of equilibrium are represented by Fig. 39, when no compound is formed. In this case, *a* represents the solubility of arsenic trioxide in water ; *ab*, the solubility of the trioxide in soln. containing different proportions of the halide ; the area *abA* represents supersaturated soln. when the solid phase is arsenic trioxide ; *bd* represents the solubility of the halide in the presence of arsenic trioxide ; *f* represents soln. sat. with the halide, or the hydrated halide ; *d*, the composition of the hydrated halide—if the halide does not form a hydrate *d* and *D* coincide. If the halide forms one complex salt with arsenic trioxide, its composition is represented by *B*, Fig. 40 ; *cb* then

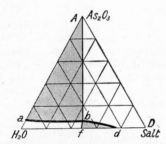

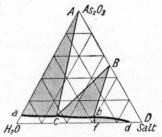

FIG. 39.—Equilibrium in the Ternary System : $As_2O_3-MX-H_2O$. (No complex salt.)

FIG. 40.—Equilibrium in the Ternary System : $As_2O_3-MX-H_2O$. (Complex salt.)

denotes the soln. sat. with the complex salt, and *cbB*, soln. supersaturated with respect to the complex salt. The curves *ab* and *bd* have the same meaning as they have in Fig. 39.

F. Rüdorff[1] prepared **ammonium chloroarsenite**, $NH_4Cl.As_2O_3$, by slowly cooling a soln. containing 147 grms. of arsenic trioxide, 17 grms. of ammonia, and 40 grms. of ammonium chloride. F. A. H. Schreinemakers and W. C. de Baat also obtained this salt in their study of the ternary system $As_2O_3-NH_4Cl-H_2O$ at 30°. The equilibrium diagram is of the type, Fig. 38, when *d* and *D* coincide. They also found that the system $As_2O_3-LiCl-H_2O$ at 30° is represented by Fig. 39, when *d* represents $LiCl.H_2O$; and there is no sign of the formation of a complex salt ; this was also the case with the system $As_2O_3-NaCl-H_2O$ at 30°. F. Rüdorff obtained **potassium chloroarsenite**, $KCl.As_2O_3$, by passing carbon dioxide into a soln. of 100 grms. of potassium arsenite in 200 grms. of water, and then mixing the sat. soln. with 30 grms. of potassium chloride dissolved in 150 grms. of water. The hexagonal plates decompose at 240°, and also when mixed with water. F. A. H. Schreinemakers and W. C. de Baat obtained this salt, and found the equilibrium curves of the system As_2O_3–KCl–H_2O at 30° were of the type shown in Fig. 39, when d and D coincide. F. Rüdorff also reported *potassium chlorobisarsenite*, $KCl(As_2O_3)_2$, but F. A. H. Schreinemakers and W. C. de Baat could not obtain this salt ; H. L. Wheeler reported **rubidium chloroarsenite**, $RbCl.As_2O_3$, to be formed from a soln. of the two components in 10 to 15 per cent. hydrochloric acid ; and he obtained **cæsium chloroarsenite**, $CsCl.As_2O_3$, in a similar manner. F. A. H. Schreinemakers and W. C. de Baat did not observe the formation of any complex salt in their study of the systems As_2O_3–$CaCl_2$–H_2O at 20°, when d, Fig. 39, represents $CaCl_2.6H_2O$; and As_2O_3–$SrCl_2$–H_2O at 30°, when d, Fig. 39, represents $SrCl_2.6H_2O$; **barium bischloroarsenite**, $Ba(Cl.As_2O_3)_2$. The curves were of the type, Fig. 39, when d represents, the hydrate, $BaCl_2.2H_2O$. P. Gruhl mixed hot, sat. soln. of the component salts, but found the constituents crystallized out separately on cooling.

F. Rüdorff reported **ammonium bromobisarsenite**, $NH_4Br.2As_2O_3$, to be formed when aq. ammonia at 60° is saturated with arsenic trioxide and then mixed with ammonium bromide. The six-sided prismatic crystals decompose at 200°. F. A. H. Schreinemakers and W. C. de Baat obtained the same salt in their study of the ternary system As_2O_3–NH_4Br–H_2O at 30°, when d and D coincide ; they also obtained **lithium bromobisarsenite**, $LiBr.2As_2O_3$, in their study of the ternary system As_2O_3–$LiBr$–H_2O at 30°, Fig. 40, when d represents $LiBr.nH_2O$; as well as **sodium bromobisarsenite**, $NaBr.2As_2O_3$, in their study of the ternary system As_2O_3–$NaBr$–H_2O at 30°, when d, Fig. 40, represents $NaBr.2H_2O$. This salt was also prepared in six-sided plates by F. Rüdorff from a mixed soln. of sodium bromide (120 parts), arsenic trioxide (20 parts), and water (350 c.c.). It is decomposed by water. He also made **potassium bromobisarsenite**, $KBr(As_2O_3)_2$, from a mixed boiling soln. of potassium arsenite, carbonate and bromide, and arsenic trioxide ; and H. Schiff and F. Sestini from a mixed soln. of potassium arsenite and bromide, but not from a mixed soln. of potassium bromide and arsenic trioxide. The six-sided prisms are stable in air ; and decompose at 300°. F. A. H. Schreinemakers and W. C. de Baat obtained this salt in their study of the ternary system As_2O_3–KBr–H_2O at 30°, when d and D, Fig. 40, coincide. H. L. Wheeler reported **rubidium bromoarsenite**, $RbBr.As_2O_3$, to be formed from a soln. of the components in dil. hydrobromic acid ; similarly with **cæsium bromoarsenite**, $CsBr.As_2O_3$. F. A. H. Schreinemakers and C. W. de Baat did not observe the formation of any complex salt in their study of the ternary system As_2O_3–$CaBr_2$–H_2O at 20°, when d, Fig. 40, represents $CaBr_2.6H_2O$; similarly, also with the ternary system As_2O_3–$SrBr_2$–H_2O at 30°, when d, Fig. 38, represents $SrBr_2.6H_2O$. P. Gruhl obtained a white crystalline mass—possibly **strontium bisbromoarsenite**, $Sr(Br.As_2O_3)_2$—which decomposed very readily ; he also obtained the analogous **barium bisbromoarsenite**, $Ba(Br.As_2O_3)_2$, which was also very unstable. The same salt was obtained by F. A. H. Schreinemakers and W. C. de Baat in their study of the ternary system As_2O_3–$BaBr_2$–H_2O at 30°, when d, Fig. 39, represents $BaBr_2.2H_2O$.

F. Rüdorff prepared **ammonium iodobisarsenite**, $NH_4I(As_2O_3)_2$, from a dil. soln. of ammonium dihydroarsenite, arsenic trioxide, and ammonium iodide. The six-sided prisms are not decomposed at 180°. P. Gruhl obtained tabular crystals of **lithium iodobisarsenite**, $LiI(As_2O_3)_2.3\frac{1}{2}H_2O$, by crystallization from a hot soln. of arsenic trioxide and an excess of lithium iodide. F. Rüdorff obtained six-sided plates of **sodium iodobisarsenite**, $NaI(As_2O_3)_2$, from a mixed soln. of sodium arsenite and iodide, and from a hot soln. of 60 parts sodium iodide, 25 parts arsenic trioxide, and 500 parts of water. The salt is decomposed by water. H. L. Wheeler obtained yellow plates of **potassium iodoarsenite**, $KI.As_2O_3$, from a hot soln. of arsenic triiodide and potassium iodide in dil. hydriodic acid. F. A. H. Schreinemakers and W. C. de Baat did not observe the formation of this salt in their study of the ternary system As_2O_3–KI–H_2O at 30°, when d and D, Fig. 40, coincide, and the complex salt is **potassium iodobisarsenite**, $KI(As_2O_3)_2$. This salt was obtained by H. Schiff and F. Sestini, and F. Rüdorff as a precipitate by mixing conc. soln. of potassium arsenite and iodide when the arsenite has been partially decomposed by carbon ioxide. The same salt was also obtained by saturating a boiling soln. of potassium iodide with arsenic trioxide. H. Schiff and F. Sestini obtained this salt rom a soln. of iodine in one of potassium arsenite. J. P. Emmet, E. Harms, and ℎ. Gruhl obtained impure salts—J. P. Emmet said $2KI.3As_2O_3$—by partly neutralizing potassium arsenite with acetic acid before mixing it with arsenic trioxide. The hexagonal, prismatic crystals are stable in air; and decompose at 50°. 100 parts of water at ordinary temp. dissolve 2·5 parts of salt; and with boiling water, twice as much salt. The salt is also soluble in soln. of potassium hydroxide, or carbonate; and is decomposed by acids with the separation of iodine. E. Harms reported **potassium dihydroxydiiodotriarsenite**, $2KOH.2KI.3As_2O_3$, to be precipitated on passing carbon dioxide into a hot, sat., aq. soln. of the iodobis-arsenite; and **potassium hexahydroxydiiodotrisarsenite**, $6KOH.2KI.3As_2O_3$, by dissolving the precipitate from potassium arsenite and iodide in hot alcohol, and passing into the soln. a current of carbon dioxide. H. L. Wheeler prepared six-sided plates of **rubidium iodoarsenite**, $RbI.As_2O_3$, by cooling a hot soln. of rubidium iodide and arsenic triiodide in dil. hydriodic acid; and **cæsium iodoarsenite**, $CsI.As_2O_3$, was obtained in an analogous manner.

P. Gruhl reported a white crystalline powder of **calcium diiodotrisarsenite**, $CaI_2.3As_2O_3.12H_2O$, to be formed from a soln. of arsenic trioxide in one of calcium iodide; similarly with **strontium diiodotrisarsenite**, $SrI_3.3As_2O_3.12H_2O$; with **barium diiodotrisarsenite**, $BaI_2.3As_2O_3.8H_2O$; with **beryllium diiodotrisarsenite**, $BeI_2.3As_2O_3.8H_2O$; and with **magnesium diiodotrisarsenite**, $MgI_2.3As_2O_3.12H_2O$; and with colourless **zinc diiodotrisarsenite**, $ZnI_2.3As_2O_3.10H_2O$. F. Ephraim and F. Moser added about 6 mols of ammonia at room temp., forming **zinc hexammino-diiodotrisarsenite**, and at —20°, formed **zinc heptamminodiiodotrisarsenite**. This passes to the hexammine at 70°; **zinc tetramminodiiodotrisarsenite** is formed at 57°, and at 200°, **zinc diamminodiiodotrisarsenite**. P. Gruhl also prepared colourless **aluminium triiodohexarsenite**, $AlI_3.6As_2O_3.16H_2O$; colourless **manganese diiodotetrarsenite**, $MnI_2.4As_2O_3.12H_2O$; colourless **ferrous diiodotetrarsenite**, $FeI_2.4As_2O_3.12H_2O$; pale red **cobalt diiodotetrarsenite**, $CoI_2.4As_2O_3.12H_2O$; and pale green **nickel diiodotetrarsenite**, $NiI_2.4As_2O_3.10H_2O$. F. Ephraim and F. Moser found that this salt could not be heated above 160° without decomposition, and at low temp. they prepared nickel amminodiiodotetrarsenite, carrying more than 10 mols of NH_3. Excepting the magnesium salt, these compounds are sparingly soluble in water. Soln. of chromic and stannous hydroxides in hydriodic acid take up arsenic trioxide, but the product is completely decomposed on evaporation. On the assumption that the compound is formed by the union of the mols. of arsenic trioxide with the iodine atoms, and the metal forms the cation, the constitution was represented:

$$Ca\!<^{O.As}_{O.As}\!\!>^{O.As=O_2=As-I}_{\ O\ \ \ \ \ \ \ \ \ \ \ \ \ \ \ }_{O\ .\ As=O_2=As-I}$$

$$CaI_2.3As_2O_3$$

$$Fe\!<^{O.As=O_2=As.O.As=O_2=As-I}_{O.As=O_2=As.O.As=O_2=As-I}$$

$$FeI_2.4As_2O_3$$

G. Aminoff[2] described a mineral from Langban, Sweden, which he called **finnemanite**—after K. J. Finneman. The analysis corresponds with **lead chlorotriorthoarsenite**, $Pb_5Cl(AsO_3)_3$. The colour is grey to black—in thin flakes, olive-green. The hexagonal crystals have the axial ratio $a : c = 1 : 0.6880$, or in alternate position $: 1.1917$. The cleavage is distinct and pyramidal. The optical character is negative. The indices of refraction $\omega = 2.295$, and $\epsilon = 2.285$ for the D-ray. The sp. gr. is 7·08 to 7·265; and the hardness 2·3. A. E. Nordenskjöld described a mineral from Langban, Sweden, which he called **ecdemite**, or rather *ekdemite*—from ἔκδημος, unusual. It occurs in yellow or green, coarsely foliated or granular masses; in tabular crystals; or as crystalline incrustations. A. E. Nordenskjöld represented his analysis by $2PbCl_2.2PbO.Pb_3(AsO_3)_2$; P. Groth wrote G. Flink's formula $(PbCl)_4Pb_2O(AsO_3)_2$, that is, $(PbCl)_2AsO_3.Pb.O.Pb.AsO_3(PbCl)_2$, or **lead**

oxytetrachlorodiarsenite. A. Hamberg used the more complex formula $4PbCl_2.Pb_2As_4O_{15}$. G. Flink obtained a mineral from Pajsberg, Sweden, which he called *heliophyllite*—from $\mathring{\eta}\lambda\iota os$, sun ; and $\phi\acute{v}\lambda\lambda o\nu$, leaf—in allusion to the colour and structure. G. Flink gave for heliophyllite $Pb_4As_2O_7.2PbCl_2$, and the deviation from this in the average analyses is within the limits of likely errors. G. Flink supposed the crystals of heliophyllite to be rhombic bipyramids with the axial ratio $a:b:c=0.96662:1:2.2045$, corresponding with ochrolite, the analogous antimonate. A. E. Nordenskjöld supposed ecdemite to be rhombic ; and A. Hamberg, tetragonal. The sections of ecdemite have a complex optical structure at first thought to be due to two different minerals. Heliophyllite also has a complex structure. A. Hamberg said that the basal cleavage sections of heliophyllite are in part uniaxial and in part biaxial ; while in the case of foliated masses, the lamellæ cross at right angles as if they were twinned about a prism of 90°. There are also acute, pyramidal, tetragonal crystals with sections parallel to c showing an isotropic matrix, and systems of birefringent lamellæ twinned as just indicated. The structure, however, is not yet satisfactorily established. The hardness of ecdemite is 2·5 to 3·0 ; that of heliophyllite, about 2·0. A. E. Nordenskjöld gave 7·14 for the sp. gr. of ecdemite ; and G. Flink, 6·885 for that of heliophyllite. Ecdemite is easily soluble in nitric acid, and in hot hydrochloric acid.

G. Lechartier [3] prepared **calcium chloroarsenate,** Ca_2AsO_4Cl, or Cl—Ca—O—AsO $=O_2=Ca$—analogous to wagnerite, and hence called *calcium chloroarsenato wagnerite*—by melting a mixture of calcium chloride and orthoarsenate as in the case of the corresponding chloroarsenatoapatite. C. Lefèvre also made it by melting calcium oxide with a mixture of potassium metarsenate and over 20 per cent. of potassium chloride. The corresponding **magnesium chloroarsenate,** Mg_2AsO_4Cl or *magnesium chloroarsenatowagnerite*, was obtained as well as mixed crystals $Mg_2AsO_4(Cl,F)$. H. Sjögren described a mineral from Langban, Sweden, and called it **tilasite**—after D. Tilas. The analyses by H. Sjögren, G. F. H. Smith and G. T. Prior, and G. Aminoff correspond with **calcium magnesium fluorthoarsenate** $CaAsO_4(MgF)$, or $(Mg,Ca)F(AsO_4).F.Mg$—$AsO=O_2=Ca$. Part of the fluorine may be replaced by hydroxyl and in the extreme case, the tilasite passes into adelite. Hence, tilasite can be called *fluoadelite*. G. F. H. Smith and G. T. Prior found a pale green tilasite from Kajlidongri, India, occurring in monoclinic crystals with the axial ratios $a:b:c=0.7503:1:0.8391$, and $\beta=59°0'30''$, and belonging to the clinohedral class, with a plane of symmetry, but no axis of symmetry. G. Aminoff gave $0.7436:1:0.8454$, and $\beta=121°00'$. It is grey with a tinge of violet. H. Sjögren gave for the optic axial angles, for red, yellow, and green light, $2H_a=98.4°$ 99·5°, and 100·2° ; and $2H_0=110°28'$, 111° 40', and 112° 20'. G. F. H. Smith and G. T. Prior found the optic axial angle $2V=82°44'$; and the indices of refraction with Na-light, are $\alpha=1.640$, $\beta=1.660$, and $\gamma=1.675$. G. Lechartier prepared **manganese chloroarsenate,** Mn_2AsO_4Cl, or *manganese chloroarsenatowagnerite*, as in the case of the calcium salt ; and E. Lenssen obtained **stannous chloroarsenate** $Sn_2(AsO_4)Cl.H_2O$, as a crystalline precipitate by adding an excess of stannous chloride to an acetic acid soln. of potassium arsenate.

A. Ditte made **calcium bromoarsenate,** Ca_2AsO_4Br, or *calcium bromoarsenatowagnerite*, as in the case of the corresponding chloro-compound. Similarly with **magnesium bromoarsenate,** Mg_2AsO_4Br, or *magnesium bromoarsenatowagnerite*, and **manganese bromoarsenate,** Mn_2AsO_4Br, or *manganese bromoarsenatowagnerite*.

F. Briegleb [4] reported a fluoarsenate to be formed by fusing a mixture of calcium fluoride, arsenic trioxide, and sodium nitrate and carbonate, and extracting with water the powdered product. He thus obtained octahedral crystals belonging to the cubic system. H. Baker obtained similar crystals from a mixed soln. of sodium orthoarsenate, and fluoride in soda-lye. According to H. Baker, F. Briegleb wrongly assigned the formula $Na_3AsO_4.NaF.12H_2O$ to the salt ; he claimed that it should be $2Na_3AsO_4.NaF.19H_2O$, **sodium fluodiorthoarsenate.** F. Briegleb said the sp. gr. is 2·85 at 25° ; and H. Baker found the refractive indices with Li-, Na-, and Tl-light respectively 1·4657, 1·4693, and 1·4726. The salt is isomorphous with the corresponding complex phosphate and vanadate. F. Briegleb found that 100 parts of water at 25° dissolve 10·47 parts of the salt, and at 75°, 50 parts of salt giving soln. with the respective sp. gr. 1·034, and 1·194.

A. Ditte [5] prepared **calcium fluotriorthoarsenate,** $Ca_5(AsO_4)_3F$, or *calcium fluoarsenatoapatite*, by melting together the halide of the alkaline earth with ammonium arsenate in sto:chiometrical proportions, or by melting the arsenate of the alkaline earth with the alkali fluoride and an excess of sodium chloride. The soluble matters were washed out with cold water. The hexagonal prisms and pyramids were freely soluble in dil. nitric and hydrochloric acids, and give off hydrogen fluoride when treated with sulphuric acids. H. Sjögren described a mineral from Pajsberg, and Jakobsberg, Sweden, and he called it **svavite,** or *svabite.* It occurs in colourless hexagonal prisms with the axial ratio $a : c = 1 : 0·7143$, and in fibrous crystalline aggregates. The formula calculated from the analysis is $Ca_5FAs_3O_{12}$, or calcium fluotriorthoarsenate, $CaF.Ca_4(AsO_4)_3$; G. Flink gave $(Cl,F,OH)Ca_5(AsO_4)_{12}$; H. Sjögren said that the calcium may be in part replaced by lead, magnesium, iron (ous), and MnO; and the fluorine, by chlorine and hydroxyl. The mineral is said to be isomorphous with apatite; and to have the axial ratio $a : c = 1 : 0·71094$. Its hardness is 5; and its sp. gr. 3·52. G. Flink gave 3·695. The birefringence is feeble and negative. The mineral is easily soluble in acids. A. Ditte made **strontium fluotriorthoarsenate,** $Sr_5(AsO_4)_3F$, in *strontium fluoarsenatoapatite*; **barium fluotriorthoarsenate,** $Ba_5(AsO_4)_3F$, or *barium fluoarsenatoapatite*; **magnesium fluotriorthoarsenate,** $Mg_5(AsO_4)_3F$, or *magnesium fluoarsenatoapatite*, by a process analogous to that employed for the calcium salt.

Orange-red crystals of a mineral occur in the Barranca tin mine, Durango, Mexico. The mineral was named **durangite** by G. J. Brush.[6] Analyses corresponded with the formula $(Na,Li)(Al,Fe)AsO_4F$, or, as C. F. Rammelsberg wrote it, $R'''AsO_4.NaF$, or, according to P. Groth, **sodium aluminium fluoarsenate,** $F—Al=AsO_4—Na$. W. T. Schaller regarded durangite, $NaAsO_4(AlF)$ as an amblygonite, and related to soda-amblygonite as indicated by the formula $NaPO_4(AlF)$, where some of the fluorine may be replaced by hydroxyl. According to G. J. Brush, and A. des Cloizeaux, the monoclinic crystals have the axial ratios $a : b : c = 0·77158 : 1 : 0·82499$ and $\beta = 64° 17'$; the (110)-cleavage is distinct.

A. des Cloizeaux gave for the optic axial angle for red and yellow light, $2H_a = 80° 53'$ and 80° 49', respectively; the optical character is negative: the hardness, 5; and the sp. gr., 3·94 to 4·07. It is decomposed by sulphuric acid with the evolution of hydrofluoric acid.

According to M. Amadori, when mixtures of lead fluoride and orthoarsenate are melted in the correct proportions, **lead fluotriorthoarsenate,** $3Pb_3(AsO_4)_2.PbF_2$, or $(PbF)Pb_4(AsO_4)_3$, is formed with a m.p. 1042°. The conditions of stability are indicated in Fig. 41. On account of the general resemblance of this compound to mimetite, it is called **fluomimetite.** C. C. McDonnell and C. M. Smith obtained it by boiling lead arsenate for 5 hrs. with a soln. of 35 grms. of sodium fluoride in a litre of water. M. Amadori found that mixtures of fluopyromorphite with 0, 10, 25, 50, 75, 90, and 100 per cent. of fluomimetite melted respectively at 1098°, 1092°, 1086°, 1092°, 1058°, 1050°, and 1042°. The mixtures have been called **lead fluotriorthophosphatoarsenates,** $(PbF)Pb_4\{(As,P)O_4\}_3$.

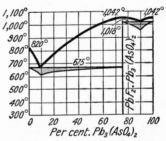

FIG. 41.—Freezing-point Curves in the System : PbF_2–$Pb_3(AsO_4)_2$.

E. F. Holden [7] reported a bright blue mineral from Bisbee, Arizona, with a fibrous structure. He called it *ceruleofibrite;* he at first regarded it as copper hydroxy-chloroarsenate, but later showed that it is a chlorosulphate—a variety of the

mineral connellite described by C. Palache and H. E. Merwin. G. Lechartier melted
a mixture of calcium arsenate and chloride, and obtained crystals of **calcium
chlorotriorthoarsenate,** $Ca_5(AsO_4)_3Cl$, isomorphous with apatite, and hence called
calcium chloroarsenatoapatite. J. H. Debray also made the salt by heating the
constituents with water in a sealed tube ; E. Weinschenk, by heating a mixture of
calcium chloride, ammonium dihydroarsenate, and chloride in a sealed tube at 150°–
180° ; and C. Lefèvre, by melting sodium dihydroarsenate with calcium chloride
and over 60 per cent. of sodium chloride. G. Lechartier found that if a mixture of
calcium chloride and fluoride be employed, mixed crystals are formed,
$Ca_5(AsO_4)_3(Cl,F)$. G. Lechartier, and C. Lefèvre prepared in an analogous way,
strontium chlorotriorthoarsenate, $Sr_5(AsO_4)_3Cl$, or *strontium chloroarsenatoapatite ;*
and A. Ditte, G. Lechartier, E. Weinschenk, and C. Lefèvre, **barium chlorotriorthoarsenate,** $Ba_5(AsO_4)_3Cl$, or *barium chloroarsenatoapatite ;* and A. de Schulten,
cadmium chlorotriorthoarsenate, $Cd_5(AsO_4)_3Cl$, or *cadmium chloroarsenatoapatite.*

J. G. Wallerius,[8] in 1748, described a green lead ore—*minera plumbi viridis*—
which he described as *plumbum arsenico mineralisatum ;* and partial analyses of
plomb vert arsenical were made by J. L. Proust, and A. F. de Fourcroy. The mineral
was also described by D. G. J. Lenz. F. S. Beudant called it *mimetèse*—from
μιμητής, an imitator—in allusion to its resemblance to pyromorphite. The term
mimetesite is wrongly formed, and A. Breithaupt, W. Haidinger, and E. F. Glocker
therefore called it **mimetite.** C. U. Shepard first called it mimetene and later mimetite.
Specimens have been reported from numerous localities : Cornwall, Devonshire,
and Cumberland, in England ; Leadhills and Wanlockhead, Scotland ; Saone, and
Puy de Dôme, France ; Nerchinsk, Siberia ; Zinnwald and Badenwerhr, Germany ;
Längban, Sweden ; Marqueza, Chili ; Phenixville, Pennsylvania, Cerro Gordo
mines, California ; etc. The colour may be white, pale yellow, passing into orange-
yellow and brown. The mineral usually occurs in crystals or rounded crystal
aggregates ; in capillary or filamentous crystals ; and in concretionary masses, and
mammillary crusts. Analyses were reported by F. Wöhler, J. L. Smith, A. Damour,
E. Jannettaz and L. Michel, P. A. Dufrénoy, G. A. König, O. Pufahl, K. Biehl,
C. C. McDonnell and C. M. Smith, C. Bergemann, A. Serra, L. E. Rivot,
A. F. de Fourcroy, F. A. Massie, F. A. Genth, C. F. Rammelsberg, P. von Jeremejeff,
D. Lovisato, H. Struve, C. M. Kersten, G. Lindström, W. Lindgren, etc. The
results correspond with $3Pb_3(AsO_4)_2.PbCl_2$, or **lead chlorotriorthoarsenate,**
$(PbCl)Pb_4(AsO_4)_3$. A. Werner represented it $[Pb\{(PbAsO_3O)_2\}_3]Cl_2$.

G. Lechartier prepared crystals of this compound by fusing lead arsenate with
an excess of lead chloride, and afterwards washing out the excess of chloride ;
the conditions of existence are illustrated in
M. Amadori's diagram, Fig. 40, showing the
freezing-point curve of binary mixtures of
these two components. L. Michel made this
mineral by heating to 1050° stoichiometrical proportions of the two components in a porcelain
crucible buried in magnesia contained in a
fireclay crucible. E. Weinschenk heated a
mixture of lead chloride and ammonium hydroarsenate ; and C. Lefèvre, a mixture of lead
chloride and sodium metarsenate together with
10 per cent. of sodium chloride. C. C. McDonnell
and C. M. Smith obtained this compound from
a sat. soln. of lead chloride in one of ammonium,

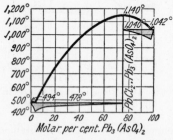

Fig. 42.—Freezing-point Curves in
the System : $PbCl_2$–$Pb_3(AsO_4)_2$.

sodium, or potassium arsenate with 0·04 mol of As_2O_5 per litre ; by boiling lead
hydroarsenate for 5 min. with a 2–10 per cent. soln. of sodium chloride ; and by
adding 30 grms. of arsenic acid to 2 litres of a boiling sat. soln. of sodium chloride,
then adding lead acetate until the precipitate no longer redissolves, and finally
600 c.c. of water. The precipitate is then washed with boiling water until the

washings are free from chlorine. Crystals were also formed from a soln. of lead arsenate in hydrochloric acid ; and a gelatinous precipitate of the composition of mimetite separated when a soln. of lead hydroarsenate in a boiling soln. of ammonium chloride was poured into a large vol. of cold water. Pseudomorphs after anglesite have been described by F. A. Genth, and G. vom Rath. The mineral is supposed to have been formed in nature as a secondary mineral by the action of soln. of arsenic acid or arsenates, and chlorides on lead minerals.

Mimetite is isomorphous with pyromorphite, vanadinite, and the fluophosphates. As emphasized by R. Brauns, there is a large family of isomorphous minerals of this type occurring as hexagonal pyramidal crystals with axial ratios $a : c$, nearly unity ; *apatite*, $Ca_5F(PO_4)_3$, and $Ca_5Cl(PO_4)_3$, $a : c = 0.7346$: *polysphœrite*, $(Pb,Ca)_5Cl(PO_4)_3$, 0.73544 ; *pyromorphite*, 0.72926 ; *svabite*, $Ca_5(F,Cl,OH)(AsO_4)_3$, 0.7143 ; *campylite*, $Pb_5Cl\{(As,P)O_4\}_3$, 0.725 ; *mimetite*, $Pb_5Cl(AsO_4)_3$, 0.73147 ; *hedyphane*, $(Ca,Pb)_5Cl(AsO_4)_3$, 0.7063 ; *endlichite*, $Pb_5Cl\{(As,V)O_4\}_3$, 0.7495 ; and *vanadinite*, $Pb_5Cl(VO_4)_3$, 0.7122. The crystals of mimetite are hexagonal, with pyramidal hemihedrism. W. Haidinger gave for the axial ratio $a : c = 1 : 0.7224$; A Serra, $1 : 0.7284$; R. Brauns, $1 : 0.73147$; J. Schabus, $1 : 0.71899$; W. H. Miller, $1 : 0.74956$; G. Aminoff and A. L. Parsons, $1 : 0.722$; and for the artificial crystals, M. Amadori gave $1 : 0.72754$. The crystals were also studied by J. F. L. Hausmann, W. H. Miller, P. von Jeremejeff, E. T. Wherry, O. Pufahl, E. S. Larsen, R. Brauns, K. Biehl, H. Ungemach, and V. Goldschmidt. M. Amadori found the axial ratios of artificial mixtures of pyromorphite and mimetite in agreement with the isomorphism of these salts. G. Carobbi and S. Restaino found that cerium, lanthanum, and didymium can replace the lead isomorphously. H. Baumhauer examined the corrosion figures. The $(10\bar{1}1)$-cleavage is imperfect ; twinning has not been observed. The artificial crystals were found by C. C. McDonnell and C. M. Smith to be optically uniaxial ; but mimetite may be optically anomalous, being often biaxial, and E. Bertrand found that mimetite from Johanngeorgenstadt had an optic axial angle $2E = 64°$; H. L. Bowman also gave $2E = 62°$ for a Cornish sample. E. Bertrand said that the basal section shows a division into six triangular sectors with uniaxial planes parallel to the sides of the hexagon. Pyromorphite is normally uniaxial, and E. Jannettaz and L. Michel showed that there is an increase in the biaxial character in an isomorphous series of phosphates and arsenates as the proportion of arsenate increases in the arsenical varieties of pyromorphite to pure mimetite. P. von Jeremejeff attributed the optical anomaly *auf einer Molekularumlagerung* of the substance. This means that the cause is unknown. W. Eissner found that in passing from $-160°$ to $650°$, the crystal angles show abrupt changes. The case of $(0001) : (10\bar{1}1)$ is indicated in Fig. 43. These are explained by the assumption that the mineral is dimorphous. The curve AB represents the variation of the crystal

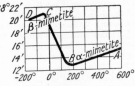

FIG. 43.—The Effect of Temperature on the Crystal Angles of Mimetite.

angles of α-mimetite with temp. ; and BC, the interval of transformation to β-mimetite ; so that CD represents the effect of temp. on the crystal angle of β-mimetite. Pyromorphite shows analogous changes. G. Aminoff and A. L. Parsons found the X-radiogram agrees with a space-lattice with 0.92 mol. per unit cell ; a c-axis of 7.28 A. ; an axial ratio $a : c = 1 : 0.727$; and a sp. gr. 7.25. The hardness of mimetite is about 3.5. C. F. Rammelsberg gave 7.218 for the sp. gr. of mimetite ; J. L. Smith, 7.32 ; F. Katzer, 7.126 ; O. Pufahl, 6.98 ; and H. Struve, 6.653. L. Michel gave for the artificial crystals 7.12, and C. C. McDonnell and C. M. Smith, 7.14 at $15°$. Calcareous varieties—hedyphane—have a smaller sp. gr. Thus, A. Damour gave 6.65 ; W. Lindgren, 5.85 ; G. Lindström, 5.82 ; and C. M. Kersten, and C. F. Rammelsberg, 5.49. M. Amadori found the m.p. of chloromimetite to be $1140°$, Fig. 42 ; and the f.p. of mixtures of chloromimetite and 0, 30, 50, and

100 per cent. of chloropyromorphite to be respectively 1156°, 1150°, 1145°, and 1140° ; the mixtures have been called **lead chlorotriorthophosphatoarsenates**, $(PbCl)Pb_4\{(As,P)O_4\}_3$; and for mixtures of fluomimetite with 0, 10, 30, 50, 80, and 100 per cent. of chloromimetite, the f.p. are 1042°, 1060°, 1087°, 1107°, 1128°, and 1140°. These mixtures have been called **lead fluochlorotriorthoarsenates,** $Pb(Cl,F)Pb_4(AsO_4)_3$ H. L. Bowman found the refractive indices for red, yellow, and blue light for a specimen of mimetite, from Wheal Alfred, Cornwall, $\omega=2\cdot1236$, $2\cdot1346$, and $2\cdot2053$ respectively ; and $\epsilon=2\cdot1392$, $2\cdot1488$, and $2\cdot2220$ respectively ; and for a specimen from Tintic, Utah, $\omega=2\cdot1178$, $2\cdot1286$, and $2\cdot1750$ respectively, and $\epsilon=2\cdot136$, $2\cdot1443$, and $2\cdot1932$ respectively. E. S. Larsen gave $\omega=2\cdot14$, $\epsilon=2\cdot13$; the negative birefringence for yellow light is $0\cdot0142$–$0\cdot019$; for red light, $0\cdot0148$–$0\cdot0214$; and for blue light, $0\cdot0153$–$0\cdot0182$. Earlier observers make the optical character positive. C. C. McDonnell and C. M. Smith found for the artificial mineral $\omega=2\cdot16$, and $\epsilon=2\cdot13$. W. G. Hankel studied the pyroelectricity of mimetite and found the basal surface becomes negative while the prismatic and pyramidal surfaces become positive. Mimetite is insoluble in water ; but soluble in nitric acid, and in dil. alkali-lye. H. C. Bolton also found that it is soluble in cold conc. citric acid. J. G. Hibbs found that the mineral is readily decomposed by hydrogen chloride.

The mineral **hedyphane,** so named by A. Breithaupt [*]—from $\dot{\iota}\delta\acute{\upsilon}\phi\alpha\nu\eta s$, ot attractive aspect—is a calcareous variety of mimetite so far as can be judged from the analyses of C. M. Kersten, I. Domeyko, C. F. Rammelsberg, G. Lindström, W. F. Foshag and R. B. Gage and L. J. Igelström, $(Ca,Pb)_5Cl(AsO_4)_3$. The white or yellow mineral occurs at Langban, and Pajsberg, Sweden. A. des Cloizeaux thought that the crystals are monoclinic, but H. Sjögren found them to be hexagonal dipyramids with the axial ratio $a:c=1:0\cdot7063$, and R. Brauns showed that they are isomorphous with mimetite. G. Aminoff examined the crystals. The hardness is $3\cdot5$–$4\cdot5$. A. Breithaupt gave $5\cdot404$ for the sp. gr. ; F. Gonnard, $6\cdot60$; A. Damour, $6\cdot65$; and G. Lindström, $5\cdot82$. W. F. Foshag and R. B. Gage found that the mineral is optically uniaxial and negative with the indices of refraction $\omega=2\cdot026$, and $\epsilon=2\cdot010$; and C. Palache and H. Berman gave $\epsilon=1\cdot958$, and $\omega=1\cdot948$ for Na-light. The optical character is positive. Another variety, partly described by L. J. Igelström, was called **pleonectite**—from $\pi\lambda\epsilon o\nu\epsilon\kappa\tau\epsilon\hat{\iota}\nu$, to have more—in allusion to the occurrence of several related minerals in the mine at Oerebro, Sweden. It is considered without proof to be an antimonial mimetite. According to R. P. Greg and W. G. Lettsom, the mineral **campylite**—from $\kappa\alpha\mu\pi\acute{\upsilon}\lambda o s$, curve—in allusion to the barrel-shaped crystals, occurs in Drygill, Cumberland. Analyses reported by A. Damour, H. Struve, W. Lindgren, C. F. Rammelsberg, and A. Lacroix show that it is an isomorphous mixture of pyromorphite and mimetite, $Pb_5Cl\{(As,P)O_4\}_3$. This subject was discussed by M. Amadori, E. Jannettaz and L. Michel, and F. Gonnard. L. Michel synthesized it as in the case of mimetite, but using variable proportions of lead phosphate and arsenate instead of arsenate alone. L. Michel said that some varieties are chromiferous ; and G. Lindström, that some are bariferous. The sp. gr., according to A. Breithaupt, is $6\cdot8$–$6\cdot9$; C. F. Rammelsberg gave $7\cdot218$. G. Aminoff found at Langban, Sweden, crystals of a mineral, which he called **finnemanite.** The analysis corresponds with **lead chlorotrimetarsenite,** $Pb_5Cl(AsO_3)_3$ or $3Pb_3(AsO_3)_2.PbCl_2$. The hexagonal prisms have the axial ratio $a:c=1:0\cdot6880$; the optical character is negative ; the sp. gr., $7\cdot08$ to $7\cdot265$; the hardness, 2 to 3 ; and the indices of refraction, $\omega=2\cdot2949$, and $\epsilon=2\cdot3847$. According to G. Aminoff and A. L. Parsons, the X-radiogram agrees with $0\cdot92$ mol. per unit cell ; a c-axis of $6\cdot97$ A. ; an axial ratio $a:c=1:0\cdot683$; and a sp. gr. $7\cdot26$.

A. Ditte [10] obtained **calcium bromotriorthoarsenate,** $Ca_5(AsO_4)_3Br$, or *calcium bromoarsenatoapatite,* by the method which he employed for the chloro-compound. Similarly also with **strontium bromotriorthoarsenate,** $Sr_5(AsO_4)_3Br$, or *strontium bromoarsenatoapatite ;* **barium bromotriorthoarsenate,** $Ba_5(AsO_4)_3Br$, or *barium bromoarsenatoapatite ;* A. de Schulten made **cadmium bromotriorthoarsenate,** $Cd_5(AsO_4)_3Br$, or *cadmium bromoarsenatoapatite* and A. Ditte, **manganese bromotriorthoarsenate,** $Mn_5(AsO_4)_3Br$, or *manganese bromoarsenatoapatite.*

A. Ditte reported complexes with bromine to be formed by melting a mixture of 2 parts of lead bromide with 3 parts of lead arsenate in the presence of an excess of sodium iodide, and afterwards washing out the soluble salts, when pale yellow hexagonal prisms and plates of **lead bromotriorthoarsenate,** $(PbBr)Pb_4(AsO_4)_3$ or $PbBr_2.3Pb(AsO_4)_3$, or, according to A. Werner, $[Pb\{(PbAsO_3.O)_2Pb\}_3]Br_2$, were

obtained. The salt was called *lead bromoarsenatoapatite,* or **bromomimetite.**
C. C. McDonnell and C. M. Smith obtained it by boiling lead hydroarsenate **for**
5 hrs. with a 3·5 per cent. soln. of potassium bromide.

A. Ditte prepared **calcium iodotriorthoarsenate,** $Ca_5(AsO_4)_3I$, or *calcium
iodoarsenatoapatite,* by a method analogous to that employed for the chloro-
compound; similarly with **strontium iodotriorthoarsenate,** $Sr_5(AsO_4)_3I$, or
strontium iodoarsenatoapatite; and **barium iodotriorthoarsenate,** $Ba_5(AsO_4)_3I$, or
barium iodoarsenatoapatite. By working in a manner analogous to that employed
for the bromo-compound, A. Ditte, and C. C. McDonnell and C M. Smith
obtained small yellow crystals of **lead iodotriorthoarsenate,** $(PbI)Pb_4(AsO_4)_3$, or
$PbBr_2.3Pb(AsO_4)_3$; *i.e. iodomimetite,* or *lead iodoarsenatoapatite.*

C. Haack [11] reported **mercuric oxychloroarsenate,** $8HgO.5HgCl_2.3Hg_3(AsO_4)_2.$
$3H_2O$, to be formed by dropping a soln. of 3 mols of mercuric chloride into one
containing 4 mols of sodium hydroarsenate. In 24 hrs., the yellow precipitate was
washed with cold water and dried in air. By dropping a soln. of one mol of
sodium hydroarsenate into a cold soln. of 3 mols of mercuric chloride, he obtained
a hydrate, $8HgO.5HgCl_2.3Hg_3(AsO_4)_2.62H_2O$, when the lemon-yellow precipitate
is washed and dried in air. C. C. McDonnell and C. M. Smith reported **lead
dichlorotetraorthoarsenate,** $PbCl_2.2Pb_3(AsO_4)_2.H_2O$, or $Pb_4(PbCl)_2(AsO_4)_4.H_2O$,
to be formed by adding to two litres of a boiling sat. soln. of sodium chloride,
30 grms. of arsenic acid, and lead arsenate until the precipitate formed no longer
dissolves, and pouring the clear filtrate into 5 times its vol. of water at 28°–30°.
The crystalline precipitate loses its water of crystallization when heated.

A. Lacroix and A. de Schulten [12] obtained a white or brownish-yellow, crystalline
mineral from the lead slags at Laurion, Greece; they called it **georgiadesite**—
after M. Georgiadès. Its composition corresponded with **lead trichlorortho-
arsenate,** $3PbCl_2.Pb_3(AsO_4)_2$, or $(PbCl)_3AsO_4$. The rhombic crystals have the
axial ratios $a : b : c = 0.5770 : 1 : 0.2228$. The hardness is 3·5, and the sp. gr. 7·1.

A. Hirsch [13] reported what he regarded as complex compounds of sodium chloride and
copper arsenate. Thus, **sodium copper chlorotetraorthoarsenate,** $NaCl.2Cu_3(AsO_4)_2.7\frac{1}{2}H_2O$,
was formed by adding an aq. soln. of 2 mols of sodium hydroarsenate to one containing an
excess of cupric chloride, say 30 mols, and washing the precipitate until the washings are
free from chlorides. He also obtained it by allowing the filtrate from a mixture of equimolar
parts of soln. of sodium hydroarsenate and cupric chloride to stand a few days.
The original precipitate corresponds with **sodium copper dichlorohexaorthoarsenate,**
$2NaCl.3Cu_3(AsO_4)_2.13\frac{1}{2}H_2O$; by using a rather smaller proportion of cupric chloride, he
obtained the hemihexacosihydrate. By using twice the molar proportion of cupric chloride,
he obtained products with $NaCl : Cu_3(AsO_4)_2 : H_2O$ as $3 : 5 : 19$, and as $3 : 5 : 23$, but
regarded them as mixtures. There is nothing to show that all are not mixtures.
J. W. Mallet [14] reported a sulphur-yellow, orange, red, or brown, massive, cryptocrystalline mineral from Guanacere, Mexico, which he named **achrematite**—from ἀχρήματος, useless,
in allusion to its being mistaken for a useful silver ore. The composition approximates to
lead oxymolybdatochloroarsenate, $3\{3Pb_3(AsO_4)_2.PbCl_2\}.4Pb_2MoO_5$. Its sp. gr. is 5·965
in lump, and 6·178 in powder; the hardness is 3–4.

REFERENCES.

[1] F. A. H. Schreinemakers and W. C. de Baat, *Chem. Weekbl.*, **14**, 141, 203, 244, 1917; *Proc.
Acad. Amsterdam*, **18**. 126, 1916; F. Rüdorff, *Ber.*, **19**. 2668, 1886; **21**. 3051, 1888; F. Ephraim
and F. Moser, *ib.*, **53**. 548, 1920; P. Gruhl, *Verbindungen des Arsen- und Antimontrioxydes mit
Halogenides mehrwertiger Metalle*, München, 1897; H. Schiff and F. Sestini, *Liebig's Ann.*, **228**.
72, 1885; E. Harms, *ib.*, **91**. 371, 1854; H. L. Wheeler, *Zeit. anorg. Chem.*, **4**. 457, 1893; *Amer.
Journ. Science*, (3), **46**. 88, 1893; J. P. Emmet, *ib.*, (2). **18**. 58, 1830; *Journ. Roy. Inst.*, **1**. 173,
1831.
[2] G. Flink, *Oefvers. Akad. Förh.*, **45**. 574, 1888; P. Groth, *Tabellarische Uebersicht der
Mineralien*, Braunschweig, 82, 1898; A. Hamberg, *Geol. För. Förh. Stockholm*, **11**. 229, 1889;
A. E. Nordenskjöld, *ib.*, **3**. 379, 1877; G. Aminoff, *ib.*, **45**. 160, 1923.
[3] A. Ditte, *Ann. Chim. Phys.*, (6), **8**. 502, 581, 1886; *Compt. Rend.*, **96**. 575, 864, 1883;
G. Lechartier, *ib.*, **65**. 172, 1867; C. Lefèvre, *ib.*, **108**. 1058, 1889; *Ann. Chim. Phys.*, (6), **27**.
23, 1890; *Sur les arséniates cristallisés*, Paris, 1891; E. Lenssen, *Liebig's Ann.*, **114**. 113, 1860;
H. Sjögren, *Geol. För. Förh. Stockholm*, **17**. 286, 1895; G. F. H. Smith and G. T. Prior, *Min. Mag.*,
16. 84, 1911; G. Aminoff, *Geol. För. Förh. Stockholm*, **45**. 160, 1923.

⁴ F. Eriegleb, *Liebig's Ann.*, 97. 112, 1856 ; H. Baker, *ib.*, 229. 293, 1885 ; *Journ. Chem. Soc.*, 47. 353, 1885.
⁵ H. Sjögren, *Geol. För. Förh. Stockholm*, 13. 789, 1891 ; G. Aminoff, *ib.*, 45. 144, 1923 ; G. Flink, *ib.*, 47. 127, 1925 ; J. H. Debray, *Ann. Chim. Phys.*, (3), 61. 429, 1861 ; A. Ditte, *ib.*, (6), 8. 502, 581, 1886 ; *Compt. Rend.*, 96. 575, 846, 1883 ; G. Lechartier, *ib.*, 65. 172, 1867.; C. Lefèvre, *ib.*, 108. 1058, 1889 ; *Ann. Chim. Phys.*, (6), 27. 23, 1892 ; *Sur les arséniates cristallisés*, Paris, 1891 ; E. Weinschenk, *Zeit. Kryst.*, 17. 486, 1890 ; M. Amadori, *Atti Accad. Lincei*, (5), 21. ii, 768, 1912 ; 27. i, 143, 1918 ; C. C. McDonnell and C. M. Smith, *Amer. Journ. Science*, (4), 42. 140, 1916 ; *Journ. Amer. Chem. Soc.*, 38. 2027, 1916.
⁶ G. J. Brush, *Amer. Journ. Science*, (2), 48. 179, 1869 ; (3), 11. 464, 1876 ; W. T. Schaller, *ib.*, (4), 31. 48, 1911 ; P. Groth, *Tabellarische Uebersicht der Mineralien*, Braunschweig, 88, 1898 ; C. F. Rammelsberg, *Handbuch der Mineralchemie*, Leipzig, 338, 1875 ; A. des Cloizeaux, *Ann. Chim. Phys.*, (5), 4. 404, 1875 ; C. C. McDonnell and C. M. Smith, *Amer. Journ. Science*, (4), 42. 140, 1916 ; *Journ. Amer. Chem. Soc.*, 38. 2027, 1916 ; M. Amadori, *Atti Accad. Lincei*, (5), 21. ii, 768, 1912 ; 27. i, 143, 1918.
⁷ E. F. Holden, *Amer. Min.*, 7. 80, 1922 ; 9. 55, 1924 ; C. Palache and H. E. Merwin, *Amer. Journ. Science*, (4), 28. 537, 1909 ; M. Amadori, *Atti Accad. Lincei*, (5), 21. ii, 768, 1912 ; (5), 27. i, 143, 1918 ; G. Lechartier, *Compt. Rend.*, 65. 172, 1867 ; A. de Schulten, *Bull. Soc. Chim.*, (3), 1. 472, 1889 ; E. Weinschenk, *Zeit. Kryst.*, 17. 486, 1890 ; C. Lefèvre, *Compt. Rend.*, 108. 1058, 1889 ; J. H. Debray, *Ann. Chim. Phys.*, (3), 61. 429, 1861.
⁸ E. Bertrand, *Bull. Soc. Min.*, 4. 35, 1881 ; 5. 254, 1882 ; F. Gonnard, *Compt. Rend.*, 106. 77, 1888 ; *Bull. Soc. Min.*, 5. 45, 1882 ; E. Jannettaz, *ib.*, 4. 39, 1881 ; E. Jannettaz and L. Michel, *ib.*, 4. 200, 1881 ; L. Michel, *ib.*, 10. 133, 1887 ; A. Damour, *ib.*, 6. 84, 1883 ; H. Ungemach, *ib.*, 33. 402, 1910 ; A. des Cloizeaux, *ib.*, 4. 93, 1881 ; L. E. Rivot, *Docimasie*, Paris, 4. 738, 1866 ; A. F. de Fourcroy, *Mém. Acad.*, 343, 1789 ; *Ann. Chim. Phys.*, (1), 2. 207, 1789 ; J. L. Proust, *Journ. Phys.*, 30. 394, 1787 ; F. A. Genth, *Proc. Amer. Phil. Soc.*, 24. 33, 1887 ; G. A. König, *Journ. Acad. Nat. Science*, 15. 405, 1915 ; P. von Jeremejeff, *Zeit. Kryst.*, 13. 191, 1888 ; *Proc. Russ. Min. Soc.*, 22. 179, 1886 ; H. Struve, *ib.*, 22. 332, 1886 ; H. Rose, *Ausführliches Handbuch der analytischen Chemie*, Braunschweig, 2. 387, 1851 ; C. F. Rammelsberg, *Handbuch der Mineralchemie*, Leipzig, 337, 1875 ; *Pogg. Ann.*, 91. 316, 1854 ; J. Schabus, *ib.*, 100. 297, 1856 ; O. Pufahl, *Centr. Min.*, 290, 1920 ; R. Brauns, *ib.*, 263, 1909 ; P. A. Dufrénoy, *Traité de minéralogie*, Paris, 3. 46, 1856 ; J. L. Smith, *Amer. Journ. Science*, (2), 20. 248, 1855 ; F. A. Massie, *Chem. News*, 14. 198, 1881 ; I. Domeyko, *Ann. Mines*, (4), 14. 115, 1848 ; C. M. Kersten, *Schweigger's Journ.*, 62. 1, 1831 ; V. Goldschmidt, *Krystallographische Winkeltabellen*, Berlin, 397, 1897 ; G. Lindström, *Geol. För. Förh. Stockholm*, 4. 266, 1880 ; W. Lindgren, *ib.*, 5. 262, 1881 ; *Neues Jahrb. Min.*, 21, 1882 ; H. Baumhauer, *ib.*, 411, 1876 ; H. Sjögren, *Bull. Geol. Inst. Upsala*, 1. 1, 1892 ; F. Katzer, *Tschermak's Mitt.*, (2), 16. 504, 1797 ; G. vom Rath, *Sitzber. niederrh. Ges. Bonn*, 34, 1886 ; J. G. Wallerius, *Mineralogia*, Stockholm, 296, 1748 ; F. S. Beudant, *Traité élémentaire de minéralogie*, Paris, 2. 594, 1832 ; A. Breithaupt, *Vollständiges Handbuch der Mineralogie*, Dresden, 2. 289, 291, 1841 ; W. Haidinger, *Treatise on Mineralogy*, Edinburgh, 2. 135, 1825 ; *Handbuch der bestimmenden Mineralogie*, Wien, 1847 ; E. F. Glocker, *Generum et specierum mineralium secundum ordines naturales digestorum synopsis*, Halle, 1847 ; D. G. J. Lenz, *Versuch einer vollständigen Anleitung zur Kenntniss der Mineralien*, Leipzig, 2. 224, 1794 ; C. U. Shepard, *Treatise on Mineralogy*, New Haven, 1835 ; C. C. McDonnell and C. M. Smith, *Amer. Journ. Science*, (4), 42. 140, 1916 ; *Journ. Amer. Chem. Soc.*, 38. 2027, 1916 ; G. Lechartier, *Compt. Rend.*, 65. 174, 1867 ; W. Eissner, *Die Aenderung der Winkel des Apatits, Vanadinits, Pyromorphits und Mimetesits, sowie der optischen Verhältnisse des Apatits im Temperaturbereich von −160° bis +650° und der Dimorphismus der Apatitgruppe*, Weida. i. Th., 27, 1913 ; C. Lefèvre, *Sur les arséniates cristallisés*, Paris, 1891 ; *Ann. Chim. Phys.*, (6), 27. 25, 1892 ; H. St. C. Deville and H. Caron, *ib.*, (3), 67. 447, 1863 ; *Compt. Rend.*, 47. 985, 1863 ; A. Lacroix and A. de Schulten, *ib.*, 145. 783, 1907 ; *Bull. Soc. Min.*, 31. 88, 1908 ; A. Werner, *Ber.*, 40. 4448, 1907 ; H. C. Bolton, *ib.*, 13. 732, 1880 ; O. Pufahl, *Centr. Min.*, 289, 1920 ; E. S. Larsen, *Amer. Min.*, 2. 20, 1917 ; E. T. Wherry, *Proc. U.S. Nat. Museum*, 54. 373, 1918 ; W. G. Hankel, *Wied. Ann.*, 18. 423, 1883 ; *Abhand. Sächs. Ges.*, 12. 551, 1870 ; F. Wöhler, *Pogg. Ann.*, 4. 161, 1825 ; C. Bergemann, *ib.*, 80. 401, 1850 ; G. Cesaro, *Bull. Accad. Belg.*, 327, 1905 ; K. Biehl, *Beiträge zur Kenntnis der Mineralien der Erzlager von Tsumeb*, Münster, 1919 ; A. Serra, *Atti Accad. Lincei*, (5), 18. 1, 361, 1909 ; D. Lovisato, *ib.*, (5), 13. ii, 43, 1904 ; M. Amadori, *ib.*, (5), 21. ii, 768, 1912 ; (5), 27. 1, 143, 1918 ; *Atti Ist. Veneto*, 76. 419, 1917 ; *Rend. Ist. Lombardo*, 49. 137, 1916 ; *Gazz. Chim. Ital.*, 49. i, 38, 69, 1919 ; G. Carobbi and S. Restaino, *ib.*, 56. i, 59, 1926 ; M. Amadori and E. Viterbi, *Mem. Accad. Lincei*, (5), 10. 386, 1914 ; H. L. Bowman, *Min. Mag.*, 13. 324, 1903 ; E. Weinschenk, *Zeit. Kryst.*, 17. 490, 1890 ; J. F. L. Hausmann, *Handbuch der Mineralogie*, Göttingen, 2. 1038, 1847 ; W. H. Miller, *Introduction to Mineralogy*, London, 481, 1852 ; J. G. Hibbs, *The Action of Hydrochloric Acid Gas upon Arsenates and Nitrates*, Philadelphia, 9, 1896 ; E. F. Smith and J. G. Hibbs, *Journ. Amer. Chem. Soc.*, 17. 685, 1895 ; G. Aminoff and A. L. Parsons, *Geol. För. Förh. Stockholm*, 49. 438, 1927.
⁹ R. P. Greg and W. G. Lettsom, *Manual of the Mineralogy of Great Britain and Ireland*, London, 1858 ; A. Damour, *Bull. Soc. Min.*, 6. 84, 1883 ; A. des Cloizeaux, *ib.*, 4. 93, 1881 ; L. Michel, *ib.*, 10. 133, 1887 ; E. Jannettaz and L. Michel, *ib.*, 4. 200, 1881 ; F. Gonnard, *ib.*, 5. 45, 1882 ; *Compt. Rend.*, 106. 77, 1888 ; H. Struve, *Proc. Russ. Min. Soc.*, 1, 1857 ; J. Igelström, *Oefvers. Akad. Stockholm*, 22. 229, 1865 ; *Geol. För. Förh. Stockholm*, 11. 15,

210, 1889 ; G. Aminoff and A. L. Parsons, *ib.*, **49.** 438, 1927 ; W. Lindgren, *ib.*, **5.** 262, 1880 ;
G. Aminoff, *ib.*, **45.** 124, 160, 1923 ; G. Lindström, *ib.*, **42.** 266, 1919 ; H. Sjögren, *ib.*, **14.** 250,
1892 ; *Bull. Geol. Inst. Upsala*, **1.** 1, 1893 ; C. M. Kersten, *Schweigger's Journ.*, **62.** 22, 1821 ;
A. Breithaupt, *ib.*, **60.** 310, 1830 ; C. F. Rammelsberg, *Handbuch der Mineralchemie*, Leipzig,
337, 1875 ; *Pogg. Ann.*, **91.** 316, 1854 ; A. Lacroix, *Minéralogie de la France et ses colonies*,
Paris, **4.** 407, 1905 ; W. F. Foshag and R. B. Gage, *Amer. Min.*, **10.** 351, 1925 ; C. Palache
and H. Berman, *ib.*, **12.** 180, 1927 ; M. Amadori, *Gazz. Chim. Ital.*, **49.** i, 38, 1919 ; I. Domeyko,
Ann. Mines, (4), **14.** 145, 1848 ; R. Brauns, *Centr. Min.*, 263, 1909.

  [10] A. Ditte, *Compt. Rend.*, **96.** 856, 1883 ; *Ann. Chim. Phys.*, (6), **8.** 523, 1886 ;
C. C. McDonnell and C. M. Smith, *Amer. Journ. Science*, (4), **42.** 140, 1916 ; A. Werner, *Ber.*,
40. 4448, 1907 ; A. de Schulten, *Bull. Soc. Chim.*, (3), **1.** 472, 1889 ; R. F. Weinland and
P. Gruhl, *Arch. Pharm.*, **255.** 467, 1917.

  [11] C. Haack, *Ueber Arsenate und Phosphate des Quecksilbers*, Halle a. S., **26**, 1890 ;
C. C. McDonnell and C. M. Smith, *Amer. Journ. Science*, (4) **42.** 140, 1916.

  [12] A. Lacroix and A. de Schulten, *Bull. Soc. Min.*, **31.** 88, 1908 ; *Compt. Rend.*, **145.** 783,
1907.

  [13] A. Hirsch, *Ein Beitrag zur Kenntnis der Arsenate des Kupfers*, Halle, 24, 1890.

  [14] J. W. Mallet, *Journ. Chem. Soc.*, **28.** 1141, 1875.

§ 30. The Sulphides of Arsenic—The Disulphide

Arsenic unites directly with sulphur when a mixture of the two elements is heated. The chemical individuality of the sulphides, As_2S_2, As_2S_3, and As_2S_5, is well established. The existence of As_3S and As_4S_3 is not so well established. J. J. Berzelius [1] reported a number of other sulphides ; thus, As_6S was said to be deposited as a brown powder when the di- or tri-sulphide is boiled with potash-lye, but A. Scott, O. B. Kühn, and L. F. Nilson showed that it is more likely to be a mixture of arsenic and arsenic sulphide. A. Schüller, as late as 1894, said the hexitasulphide is produced when molten As_4S_3 is exposed to the vap. of arsenic ; but there is no sign of such a compound on the thermal diagram, Fig. 44. As_2S_{10} was reported by O. B. Kühn, and As_2S_{18} by J. J. Berzelius as a result of treating potassium pyrosulpharsenite with alcohol. Both were shown by L. F. Nilson to be mixtures of arsenic sulphide and sulphur. J. J. Berzelius reported yet higher sulphides, for he said that arsenic trioxide may be fused with any excess of sulphur whatever, forming a brownish-yellow sulphide, and the evolution of sulphur dioxide. On distilling a persulphide of this nature, sulphur passes over accompanied by a continually increasing proportion of arsenic. L. Gmelin could even say that in his time, 1850, " much of the sulphur of commerce is of this nature." There is no sign on the thermal diagram of the arsenic sulphides, Fig. 44, or of a compound with an at. ratio As : S higher than 2 : 5.

A. Scott reported arsenic tritasulphide, As_3S, to be formed in the following manner :

Two hundred grms. of crystallized sodium arsenate were dissolved in 3½ litres of water, and then 150 c.c. of phosphorus trichloride added and allowed to stand till quite cold, the soln. filtered and sulphur dioxide passed in and allowed to stand for a day or two. The supernatant liquid is then poured off and the precipitate washed first with water, then with dil. ammonia soln., then warmed with stronger soln. of ammonia, and into this hydrogen sulphide is passed and the digestion continued for an hour or two ; the precipitate is then well washed with water by decantation, and finally with alcohol, and dried in a vacuum. The same sulphide is obtained from arsenites, but the yield is much smaller in proportion, owing to the precipitation of much arsenious oxide from the strongly acid soln. The corresponding antimony sulphide could not be prepared.

W. Farmer and J. B. Firth made arsenic tritasulphide by a reaction between a tervalent arsenic compound and sodium hyposulphite, while the trisulphide is produced by the interaction of the arsenic compounds with thiosulphate and other thio-decomposition products of the hyposulphite. A yellow precipitate of arsenic trisulphide is obtained when a soln. of sodium thiosulphate containing alkali arsenite is acidified with hydrochloric acid and warmed. Hence, an increased conc. of hydrochloric acid increases the rate of decomposition of the hyposulphite, and the quantity of subsulphide produced is diminished and that of the trisulphide increased. In the case of quinquevalent arsenic compounds, reduction to the tervalent compound first takes place with the production of thio-decomposition products ; the arsenic is subsequently precipitated, partly as subsulphide by the hyposulphite and partly as trisulphide by the thiosulphate, etc. In no case was the arsenic completely precipitated from soln., but in neutral soln., with 10 grms. of hyposulphite for 1 grm. of arsenic trioxide, 99·24 per cent. was precipitated. The maximum precipitation of arsenic from quinquevalent compounds was 57·25 per cent., obtained in the same series under similar conditions. A. Scott observed that the tritasulphide is insoluble in aq. soln. of ammonia or colourless ammonium sulphide, but it is readily dissolved by a yellow soln. of ammonium sulphide. Hydrochloric acid precipitates arsenic trisulphide from the soln. in yellow ammonium sulphide. When heated, it forms the disulphide which sublimes, and arsenic which remains. Alkali-lye acts on it as in the case of the disulphide. A. Schüller reported that arsenic tritetritasulphide, As_4S_3, is formed by melting a mixture of arsenic trisulphide and powdered arsenic, and purifying the powdered product either by carbon disulphide or sublimation in vacuo. The yellow or orange-yellow sulphide darkens when heated. J. A. Krenner showed that the crystals obtained by sublimation are rhombic with axial angles $a : b : c$ $=0·58787 : 1 : 0·88258$; and the optic axial angle $2H_a=108° 46'$; the optical character is positive ; and the sp. gr. 2·6 at 19°. A. Schüller gave 3·60 for the sp. gr. at 19°. According to E. C. Szarvasy and C. Messinger, the vap. density of this sulphide is 8·204 at 792°, and 6·588 at 1000°. The calculated value for As_4S_3 is 13·69. This was taken to mean that the vap. of the compound is dissociated. W. P. A. Jonker, and W. Borodowsky found no evidence of the tritetritasulphide on the f.p. curve of mixtures of the two elements.

A. Scacchi obtained orange-yellow crystals of an arsenic sulphide from a fumarole in the Phlegræan fields, Italy. He called it *dimorfina*, which was altered by J. D. Dana to **dimorphite**. The analysis corresponds with the tritetritasulphide. The sp. gr. is 3·58. The rhombic crystals of the sulphide were said to occur in two forms with the respective axial ratios, α-dimorphite $a : b : c=0·895 : 1 : 0·776$; and β-dimorphite $a : b : c$ $0·907 : 1 : 0·603$. J. D. Dana showed that if the crystals of orpiment and those of α-dimorphite are so compared that the (001)-face of the former corresponds with the (010)-face of the latter, the axial ratios and crystal angles are so much in agreement that he could say that α-dimorphite and orpiment " are probably identical." The relations of β-dimorphite are not so clear. G. A. Kenngott showed that if the crystals are so placed that the (011)-face of β-dimorphite corresponds with the (110)-face of orpiment, the angles of the two crystals agree fairly closely with one another. J. A. Krenner considers β-dimorphite to be a definite species, and he said that if the crystals be oriented so that the (011)-face of a crystal of β-dimorphite coincides with the (110)-face of a crystal of the sublimed tritetritasulphide. the angles of the two crystals " are closely identical." S. Stevanovic also made some observations on this subject.

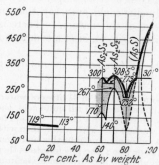

FIG. 44.—Freezing-point Curves of the Binary System : As–S.

W. Borodowsky, and W. P. A. Jonker studied the equilibrium diagram of mixtures of arsenic and sulphur. The results obtained by the former are summarized in Fig. 44. The temp. at which the melting of the mixtures begins M_1 and ends M_2, and the transition temp. T for different molar percentages of arsenic, are as follow :

As	0	10·70	40·07	43·92	50·05	54·88	57·12	63·23	69·19	74·08	91·14
M_1	119°	112°	300°	279°	308°	307°	305°	255·5°	261·5°	294°	466°
M_2	119°	113°	300°	293°	308°	308·5°	308°	232°	268°	301°	476°
T	—	—	170°	140°	367°	—	260°	—	—	—	—

Mixtures between 20 and 60 molar per cent. of arsenic were viscid, and did not crystallize quickly enough to enable the curves to be completed. The m.p. of sulphur drops from 119° to 118° with 0·21 molar per cent. of arsenic, and to 112°–113° with 10·7 molar per cent. The m.p. of red trisulphide is 300°, and there is a transition temp. from α-As$_2$S$_3$ (yellow) to β-As$_2$S$_3$ (red) at 170°; the m.p. of the disulphide is 308·5°, and the transition temp. from α-As$_2$S$_2$ (red) to β-As$_2$S$_2$ (black) is 267°. The corresponding eutectics are at 279°–293° for 64·7 molar per cent. of arsenic and 225·5°–232° for 80 molar per cent. of arsenic. The break at 301° may be due to the transformation of α- to β-arsenic, or to the formation of an unstable compound, *arsenic tritasulphide*, As$_3$S.

According to W. P. A. Jonker, arsenic sublimes at 616°, and a sat. soln. of realgar boils at 534°; and natural or artificial orpiment at 707°. The form of the sublimation curve, Fig. 45, shows that arsenic disulphide is largely dissociated as vap., while the trisulphide distils unchanged. No evidence of the pentasulphide was observed on the b.p. curves.

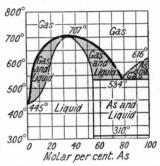

FIG. 45.—Boiling-point Curves of the Binary System : As–S.

The use of the words sandarach, arsenicon, and auripigmentum by the Greek and Roman writers has been discussed in connection with history of arsenic. The term *auripigmentum* was employed for the yellow sulphide—that is, arsenic trisulphide—and *sandarach*, for the red sulphide —that is, arsenic disulphide. A. Libavius [2] referred to the use of the term **realgar** for the red sulphide, by the Paracelsian school about the beginning of the sixteenth century, but the term appears to have been in use before this, for it was mentioned by Matthæus Sylvatieus in 1336, and, according to C. Hintze, the term also occurs in S. de Renzi's *Collectio salernitana*. F. von Kobell said the term is of unknown origin; J. B. Dana said that it comes from the Arabic *rahj al ghar*, meaning dust of the mine. According to C. Hintze, this meets with the approval of the Arabic scholars, but he added that this derivation is *ein wenig zutreffenden ware*. G. Agricola called the red sulphide *reuschgeel*, and *rosgeel ;* A. Libavius, *rosagallum*, and *Räuschgal ;* J. G. Wallerius, *Rauschgelb ;* A. G. Werner, and L. A. Emmerling, *rothes Rausch-gelb ;* and analogous terms were used by many subsequent writers for the red arsenic sulphide. The Italian word for realgar is *risigallo*, and the Spanish, *rejalgar*.

Realgar occurs in rose-red, orange-red, or orange-yellow prismatic crystals ; in coarse or fine granules, in compact masses or as an incrustation. Strabo, in the first century of our era, in his *Geographia* (**12**. iii, 40), said that there were sandarach mines at Pompeiopolis, in Paphlagonia ; and added :

The mountain is hollowed out by large trenches made by workmen in the process of mining. The work is always carried on at the public charge, and slaves were employed in the mine who had been sold on account of their crimes. Besides the great labour of the employment, the air is said to be destructive of life, and scarcely endurable in consequence of the strong odour issuing from the masses of mineral ; hence the slaves are short-lived. The mining is frequently suspended from its becoming unprofitable, for great expense is incurred by the employment of more than two hundred workmen, whose number is continually diminishing by disease and fatal accidents.

Realgar has been reported to be found at Goramis, and Tacht-i-Soleiman (Persia) ; Julamerk (Kurdistan) ; Allchar (Macedonia) ; Matra (Corcia) ; Plateau Central (France) ; Asturias (Spain) ; Aetna, Vulcano Casa Testi, Tolfa, and the Solfatara of the Phlegræan Fields (Italy) ; Binnenthal (Switzerland) ; Schwarz Mitterberg, Hall (Salzberg) ; Fohns-dorf (Styria) ; Keutschach, Sachsenberg, St. Stephan, and Luschari (Carinthia) ; Reichenberg (Carniola) ; Kresewo (Bosnia) ; Kovaczna, Nagyag, and Zalathna (Sieben-bürgen) ; Tajova, Nagybanya, Felsöbanya, Kapnik, and Neumoldova (Hungary) ; Schara-Dorna (Bukournia) ; Joachimsthal (Czechoslovakia) ; Beuthen (Silesia) ; Schneeberg, Freiberg, and Hänichen (Saxony) ; Wolfsberg and Andreasberg (Harz) ; Kahl (Bayern) ; Bieber (Hessen) ; Münslerthal, and Wiesloch (Baden) ; Markirch (Alsace) ; Semipalatinsk (Siberia) ; Kianfiu (China) ; Kiusiu (Japan) ; Nakety (New Caledonia) ; in Chili, Bolivia, and Peru ; Guadeloupe (Antilles) ; Zimapan (Mexico) ; and California, Utah, etc. (United States).

Up to the end of the eighteenth century, J. J. Becher's idea that the realgar and orpiment contained white arsenic seems to have been generally accepted. In 1801, J. L. Proust [3] proved that no oxygen is present in these compounds, and pointed out that the ratio of the constituent elements in these compounds is not accurately known. Indeed, the analyses available about this time were variable ; some gave more sulphur in realgar than in orpiment, and *vice versa*. A. Laugier, and M. H. Klaproth made the relations quite clear ; the red sulphide contains less sulphur than the yellow, and the results expressed in modern symbols correspond with **arsenic disulphide,** As_2S_2, for the red sulphide or realgar ; and arsenic trisulphide, As_2S_3, for the yellow sulphide, orpiment, or auripigmentum. This also is in agreement with the analyses of J. J. Berzelius, L. F. Nilson, and R. Bunsen.

Arsenic disulphide is prepared as a red-glass by distilling a mixture of iron pyrites and mispickel, or mispickel and sulphur, and remelting the distillate with arsenic or sulphur so as to obtain the desired tin for use as a pigment. If sulphur and arsenic are merely fused together, the product does not possess the desired colour, neither does the product obtained by J. J. Berzelius,[4] by fusing together arsenic trioxide and sulphur. To obtain a rich colour it seems necessary for the elements to combine in the state of vapour, although F. Faktor reported that he obtained a fiery-red product by melting arsenic trioxide or pentoxide with sodium thiosulphate. The preparation of the so-called *ruby-arsenic* or *ruby-sulphur*— trade names for realgar—has been described by C. R. Fresenius, A. Terreil, M. Buchner, E. Lampadius, J. F. L. Hausmann, and E. Kast and J. Bräuning. To obtain a rich colour it is not necessary to use sulphur and arsenic in the correct stoichiometrical proportions. The manufacturer finds the best proportions for any particular tint by the method of trial and failure. C. W. G. Fuchs, and F. Reich also mention the formation of realgar in the flues of furnaces roasting arsenical sulphide ores. F. Mayençon found realgar and several other sulphides amongst the sublimation products of a coal mine. W. H. Weed and L. V. Pirsson obtained realgar and orpiment from a deposit of the Norris Geyser, Yellowstone National Park ; and T. Bergman,[5] T. Monticelli and N. Covelli, and A. Scacchi observed it in the neighbourhood of volcanoes and solfatara. J. J. Berzelius, C. W. G. Fuchs, and A. Gélis obtained this sulphide by heating a mixture of the elements in the correct proportions. L. F. Nilson fused the mixture in an atm. of carbon dioxide. The conditions of equilibrium are shown in W. Borodowsky's diagram, Fig. 44. L. J. Thénard obtained realgar by melting the trisulphide with the correct proportion of arsenic. According to H. de Sénarmont, when pulverized realgar or orpiment is heated with a soln. of sodium hydrocarbonate in a sealed tube at 150°, the sulphide is dissolved and re-deposited as crystallized realgar ; L. F. Nilson also found that a boiling conc. soln. of alkali carbonate dissolves arsenic trisulphide, and deposits realgar crystals on cooling ; and W. Borodowsky heated a mixture of arsenic and sulphur in the required proportions with a 10 per cent. soln. of potassium carbonate in a sealed tube at 150°–300°. The homogeneous soln. deposits black needles of realgar on cooling. For **colloidal arsenic disulphide** and the formation of realgar in nature, *vide infra*.

J. B. L. Romé de l'Isle said that the **crystals** appear to be rhombic like the octahedral modification of sulphur, but R. J. Haüy later regarded them as mono- clinic, and F. Mohs likened them to the crystals of prismatic sulphur. According to A. des Cloizeaux, the monoclinic crystals have the axial ratios $a : b : c$ $=1·4403 : 1 : 0·9729$, and $\beta=66° 5'$; E. Liffa and K. Emszt gave $0·7201 : 1 : 0·4872$, and $\beta=66° 11'$; and R. Pilz and co-workers made a number of measurements agreeing with $0·7207 : 1 : 0·4859$, and $\beta=66° 15'$. The short prismatic crystals have the faces in the prismatic zone striated vertically. The (010)-**cleavage** is nearly perfect ; and the (100)-, (001)-, (210)-, and (110)-cleavages less clear. A. des

Cloizeaux gave for the **optic axial angle** $2H=96° 20'$, and $92° 58'$ respectively for red- and yellow-light. The **optical character** is negative. The crystals were also examined by V. R. von Zepharovich, A. Lévy, L. Fletcher, P. Groth, F. Büchler and V. Goldschmidt, L. Tokody, K. Vrba, J. A. Krenner, F. Hessenberg, A. Scacchi, A. Lacroix, H. von Foullon, V. Hackmann, E. Liffa and K. Emszt, M. Löw, R. Pilz and co-workers, V. Goldschmidt, L. Tokody, J. Orcel, etc. C. J. B. Karsten gave 3·5444 for the **specific gravity ;** F. E. Neumann, 3·240 ; and F. Mohs, and R. Böttger, 3·556. W. Borodowsky gave 3·506 at $19°/19°$ for the sp. gr. of a-As_2S_2 ; 3·254 at $19°/19°$ for β-As_2S_2 ; and 3·161 at $19°/19°$ for amorphous or γ-form. E. Szarvasy and C. Messinger found the **vapour density** to be 19·16 at 450° ; 18·5 at 503° ; 15·9 at 513° ; 13·89 at 574° ; 12·52 at 588 ; 7·51 at c. 1000° ; and 6·95 at c. 2000°. The theoretical value for As_2S_2 is 7·403. According to E. J. Houston, when powdered realgar is heated, the **colour** darkens and changes to brown ; the original colour is restored on cooling. L. F. Nilson, and H. Saito said that in the absence of air, fusion and **sublimation** occur at a temp. far below red-heat, without chemical change. The sublimate is reddish-yellow, and consists of minute prismatic crystals ; large crystals were produced by A. Schüller by subliming the sulphide in vacuo at a temp. below the m.p. L. F. Nilson said that the vapour is the colour of chlorine gas. W. Borodowsky gave 308·5° for the **melting point ;** W. P. A. Jonker, 320° ; and L. H. Borgström, 310°. W. Borodowsky observed that there is a **transition temp.** from the red a-As_2S_2 to the black β-As_2S_2 at 267° as illustrated in Fig. 42. The effect of arsenic and sulphur on the transition temp. is shown in the same diagram. The **boiling point** is 565° at 760°. W. P. A. Jonker gave 534° for the b.p. of the disulphide containing some dissolved arsenic. K. Jellinek and J. Zakowsky calculated the mol. **heat of formation** to be 40,300 cals. O. Weigel gave for the indices of refraction, at room temp., for light of wave-length λ :

λ		545μ	575μ	600μ	630μ	660μ	700μ	740μ	760μ
a		2·584	—	2·529	2·507	2·491	2·472	2·458	—
β		—	2·707	2·670	2·634	2·610	2·581	2·560	2·552
γ		—	2·728	2·688	2·654	2·627	2·600	2·578	—

The **absorption coefficients** are :

λ		$546·5\mu$	567μ	599μ	620μ	641μ	663μ	686μ	726μ
a		0·005	0·138	—	0·383	0·410	0·457	0·505	0·551
β		—	—	—	0·377	0·400	0·451	0·503	0·552
γ		—	—	0·115	0·262	—	—	0·447	—

where a and β refer to plates 0·957 mm. thick, and γ to one 0·588 mm. thick. A. des Cloizeaux found the **birefringence** is strong. O. Weigel gave for the relative **photoelectrical conductivity** :

λ		440μ	480μ	520μ	550μ	560μ	580μ	600μ	720μ
L		0	15	840	1360	1260	575	200	0

T. W. Case found that realgar is a non-conductor in light and darkness. F. Beijerinck said that the crystals are **pleochroic,** being yellow in the direction of the base, and red in the direction of the axis. A. de Gramont examined the **spark spectrum.** According to G. H. O. Volger, and G. A. Kenngott, exposure to **light** converts realgar into arsenic trisulphide and trioxide ; and A. Schüller added that arsenic tritetritasulphide is formed. O. Weigel said that the disintegration of realgar in light is connected with the photochemical conductivity which is attributed to the separation of electrons which loosens the atomic linkages and favours oxidation. C. Doelter said that the mineral is opaque to the **X-rays** even when in thin layers. T. W. Case, and F. Beijerinck said that the **electrical conductivity** is very small, although with a high potential difference the hygroscopic surface may conduct the current. M. Lapschine and M. Tichanowitsch studied the **electrodecomposition** of realgar.

L. F. Nilson showed that arsenic disulphide is reduced to arsenic when heated in a current of **hydrogen.** According to H. Pélabon, the interaction of realgar with hydrogen at temp. above 300° is reversible, $2H_2+As_2S_2 \rightleftharpoons 2H_2S+As_2$. Experiments at 610°, in tubes containing 0·5 grm. of realgar and about 8 c.c. of hydrogen measured under atm. press., show that the reaction is balanced when R, the ratio of the partial press. of hydrogen sulphide to the total press. in the tube on cooling, has a value 93·07. If more than 0·3 grm. of realgar is used (that is, so that some remains unvolatilized at 610°), increasing the amount of arsenic gradually diminishes the value of R until a constant value 78·69 is reached. The action of hydrogen sulphide on arsenic at 610° has a limit characterized by $R=64·90$. He also studied the reducing action of hydrogen on mixtures of realgar and antimony. The reaction was further investigated by K. Jellinek and J. Zakowsky who calculated the vap. press. of the sulphur, p, at 440° to be log $p= -5·24$, and at 610°, $-2·86$. A. Schüller, and L. F. Nilson found that the disulphide is oxidized in **air** : $3As_2S_2+3O=2As_2S_3+As_2O_3$; and H. V. Regnault said that this sulphide burns with a blue flame when heated in air. H. Saito found that with a rising temp. realgar begins to decrease in weight at 215° ; and after that oxidation to arsenic trioxide and sulphur dioxide occurs. The reaction is finished at about 400°. According to P. de Clermont and J. Frommel, boiling **water** resolves arsenic sulphide into hydrogen sulphide and arsenic trioxide—*vide* the trisulphide—and H. V. Regnault showed that when steam acts on the red-hot sulphide, a sublimate of arsenic trisulphide and trioxide is produced. H. Rose observed that in **chlorine** realgar forms a yellow liquid if a small proportion of chlorine be present, and a brown liquid with a large proportion of gas ; realgar inflames in a rapid current of chlorine producing arsenic trichloride and sulphur ; sulphur chloride furnishes the same end-products. A. Schüller found that an aq. soln. of **bromine** oxidizes the realgar to arsenic acid ; and, according to E. R. Schneider, when melted with **iodine** there is a reaction : $As_2S_2+3I_2=2AsI_3+2S$; a soln. of iodine in carbon disulphide is decolorized owing to the formation of these products. According to A. Geuther, when powdered realgar is heated with an aq. soln. of **sodium sulphide** in a sealed tube at 100°, sulpharsenate is formed ; and L. F. Nilson said that a sulphoarsenate is also formed by the action of a boiling soln. of **sodium sulphoarsenate** : $2As_2S +2Na_3AsS_4=6NaAsS_2$. H. V. Regnault found that with hot **sulphuric acid** sulphur dioxide and arsenic trioxide are formed. According to A. Gélis, dil. aq. **ammonia** does not attack realgar, but with a conc. soln., the surface becomes matte. G. Gore found that liquid ammonia dissolves realgar. H. V. Regnault observed that **nitric acid** oxidizes realgar to arsenic and sulphuric acids—*vide infra*, arsenic trisulphide— and it can be detonated when mixed with **potassium nitrate ;** the so-called *Indian fire* is a mixture of nitre, sulphur, and realgar (24 : 7 : 2). H. Zieler observed some hydrogen sulphide is given off when realgar is treated with boiling 5 per cent. HNO_3 ; with boiling 10 per cent. HNO_3, nitrous gases are evolved ; with 20 per cent. HNO_3, nitrous gases are given off only with the boiling acid ; cold agitated 30 per cent. HNO_3 gives a smell of nitric oxide, and with 40 per cent. and over, the agitated acid yields nitric oxide. C. R. Fresenius showed that when mixed with **ammonium chloride and nitrate,** and heated, arsenic trichloride is formed. L. F. Nilson said that when mixed with **arsenic trioxide** and heated, arsenic sublimes : $3As_2S_2+4As_2O_3=6SO_2+14As$. A. Schüller said that realgar is slightly soluble in **carbon disulphide,** and **benzene,** especially at a high temp. O. B. Kühn said that **alkali-lye** decomposes realgar : $3As_2S_2=2As+2As_2S_3$; and A. Geuther found that in a sealed tube at 100° an oxysulphide, $Na_2As_4O_5S_6$, is formed. L. F. Nilson said that no complex salts are formed analogous to those obtained by J. J. Berzelius with the trisulphide.

REFERENCES.

[1] J. J. Berzelius, *Schweigger's Journ.*, 34. 46, 1822 ; *Pogg. Ann.*, 7. 137, 1826 ; *Ann. Chim. Phys.*, (2), 11. 225, 1819 ; (2), 32. 166, 1826 ; A. Schüller, *Ber. Math. Naturw. Ungarn*, 12. 255, 1894 ; O. B. Kühn, *Arch. Pharm.*, (2), 71. 1, 1852 ; *Journ. Pharm. Chim.*, (3), 22. 75.

1852 ; **L. F.** Nilson, *Akad. Handl. Stockholm*, **10.** 2, 1871 ; *Oefvers. Akad. Stockholm*, **28.** 303, 1871 ; *Journ. prakt. Chem.*, (2), **12.** 327, 1875 ; (2), **14.** 19, 1876 ; L. Gmelin, *Handbook of Chemistry*, London, **4.** 280, 1850 ; W. Borodowsky, *Sitzber. Nat. Ges. Dorpat*, **14.** 159, 1905 ; F. C. Szarvasy and C. Messinger, *Ber.*, **30.** 1345, 1897 ; A. Scott, *Journ. Chem. Soc.*, **77.** 651, 1900 : W. Farmer and J. B. Firth, *ib.*, **119.** 1926 ; 2019, 1927 ; J. A. Krenner, *Zeit. Kryst.*, **43.** 476, 1907 ; S. Stevanovic, *ib.*, **39.** 18, 1904 ; A. Scacchi, *Compt. Rend.*, **31.** 263, 1850 ; *Zeit. deut. geol. Ges.*, **4.** 173, 1852 ; *Memorie geologische sulla Campania*, Napoli, 116, 1849 ; J. D. Dana, *A System of Mineralogy*, New York, 32, 1855 ; 35, 1892 ; W. P. A. Jonker, *Zeit. anorg. Chem.*, **62.** 89, 1909 ; G. A. Kenngott, *Neues Jahrb. Min.*, 537, 1870.

² A. Libavius, *Alchymia*, Francofurti, 1595 ; *De judicio aquarum mineralium*, Francofurti, 1597 ; M. Sylvaticus, *Pandectarum medicinæ*, Bonenien, 1336 ; S. de Renzi, *Collectio salernitana*, Napoli, **3.** 210, 1854 ; F. von Kobell, *Geschichte der Mineralogie*, München, 537, 1864 ; J. B. Dana, *A System of Mineralogy*, New York, 34, 1892 ; C. Hintze, *Handbuch der Mineralogie*, Leipzig, **1.** i, 352, 1924 ; G. Agricola, *Interpretatio Germanica vocum rei metallicæ*, Basiliæ, 468, 1529 ; J. J. Becher, *Physica subterranea*, Lipsiæ, 1669 ; J. G. Wallerius, *Mineralogia*, Stockholm, 224, 1747 ; L. A. Emmerling, *Lehrbuch der Mineralogie*, Giessen, **2.** 559, 1796 ; A. G. Werner, *Letztes Mineralsystem*, Freiberg, 25, 1817 ; C. A. Zipser, *Versuch eines topographisch-mineralogischen Handwörterbuchs von Ungarn*, Oedenburg, 87, 1817 ; J. Jonas, *Ungarn Mineralreich*, Wien, 198, 1920 ; A. Lévy, *Description de minéralogie*, Paris, **3.** 299, 1837 ; V. R. von Zepharovich, *Mineralogisches Lexikon für das Kaiserthum Oesterreich*, Wien, **1.** 374, 1859 ; M. Toth, *Magyar. Osvanyai*, 417, 1882.

³ J. L. Proust, *Journ. Phys.*, **53.** 89, 1801 ; *Nicholson's Journ.*, **1.** 109, 1802 ; M. H. Klaproth, *Beiträge zur chemischen Kenntniss der Mineralkörper*, Berlin, **5.** 234, 1810 ; T. Bergman, *Producta ignis subterranei chemice considerata*, Upsala, 1777 ; R. Kirwan, *Elements of Mineralogy*, London, 368, 1794 ; J. F. Westrumb, *Handbuch der Apothekerkunst*, Hannover, **3.** 383, 1801 ; L. J. Thénard, *Ann. Chim. Phys.*, (1), **59.** 284, 1806 ; *Nicholson's Journ.*, **19.** 74, 1808 ; B. G. Sage, *Analyse chimique et concordance des trois règnes de la nature*, Paris, **2.** 403, 1786 ; L. F. Nilson, *Journ. prakt. Chem.*, (2), **12.** 327, 1875 ; (2), **14.** 19, 1876 ; R. Bunsen, *Liebig's Ann.*, **192.** 320, 1878 ; J. J. Berzelius, *Schweigger's Journ.*, **34.** 46, 1822 ; *Pogg. Ann.*, **7.** 137, 1826 ; *Ann. Chim. Phys.*, (2), **11.** 225, 1819 ; (2), **32.** 166, 1826 ; A. Laugier, *Ann. Chim. Phys.*, (1), **85.** 46, 1813 ; J. Orcel, *Bull. Soc. Min.*, **44.** 98, 1921.

⁴ J. F. L. Hausmann, *Liebig's Ann.*, **74.** 197, 1850 ; *Ges. Wiss. Gött.*, 1, 1850 ; J. J. Berzelius, *Schweigger's Journ.*, **34.** 46, 1822 ; *Pogg. Ann.*, **7.** 137, 1826 ; L. F. Nilson, *Journ. prakt. Chem.*, (2), **12.** 327, 1875 ; (2), **14.** 19, 1876 ; F. Mayençon, *Compt. Rend.*, **86.** 491, 1878 ; **92.** 854, 1881 ; W. H. Weed and L. V. Pirsson, *Amer. Journ. Science*, (3), **42.** 401, 1891 ; S. S. Bhatnagar and B. L. Rao, *Koll. Zeit.*, **33.** 159, 1923 ; E. Kast and J. Bräuning, *Zeit. Berg. Hütt. Sal.*, **18.** 188, 1871 ; A. Gélis, *Ann. Chim. Phys.*, (4), **30.** 114, 1873 ; L. J. Thénard, *ib.*, (2), **59.** 284, 1835 ; W. Borodowsky, *Sitzber. Nat. Ges. Dorpat*, **14.** 159, 1905 ; F. Faktor, *Pharm. Post.*, **38.** 527, 1905 ; H. de Sénarmont, *Compt. Rend.*, **32.** 409, 1851 ; F. Reich, *Berg. Hütt. Ztg.*, **23.** 115, 1864 ; C. W. G. Fuchs, *Die künstlich dargestellten Mineralien nach Roses System geordnet*, Haarlem, 50, 1872 ; C. R. Fresenius, *Zeit. anal. Chem.*, **10.** 308, 1871 ; M. Buchner, *ib.*, **10.** 308, 1871 ; E. Lampadius, *Berg. Hütt. Ztg.*, **30.** 245, 1871 ; A Terreil, *Bull. Soc. Chim.*, (2), **45.** 484, 1886.

⁵ W. Borodowsky, *Sitzber. Nat. Ges. Dorpat*, **14.** 159, 1905 ; H. Pélabon, *Compt. Rend.*, **131.** 416, 1900 ; **132.** 774, 1901 ; **136.** 812, 1903 ; P. de Clermont and J. Frommel, *ib.*, **86.** 828, 1878 ; **87.** 330, 1878 ; V. H. Regnault, *Ann. Chim. Phys.*, (2), **62.** 536, 1838 ; H. de Sénarmont, (3), **32.** 158, 1851 ; A. Gélis, *ib.*, (4), **30.** 114, 1873 ; A. des Cloizeaux, *ib.*, (3), **10.** 422, 1844 ; *De l'emploi des propriétés biréfringentes en minéralogie*, Paris, **2.** 68, 1858 ; *Ann. Mines*, (5), **11.** 261, 1857 ; (5), **14.** 406, 1858 ; *Nouvelles recherches sur les propriétés optiques des cristaux*, Paris, 166, 1865 ; P. Groth, *Die Mineraliensammlung der Universität Strassburg*, Strassburg, 20, 1878 ; A. Lévy, *Description d'une collection de minéraux formée par M. Henri Heuland*, Paris, **3.** 277, 1837 ; A. Scacchi, *Memorie geologiche sulla Campania*, Napoli, 110, 1849 ; F. Beijerinck, *Neues Jahrb. Min. B.B.*, **11.** 423, 1897 ; C. Doelter, *Neues Jahrb. Min.*, ii. 91, 1896 ; A. de Gramont, *Bull. Soc. Min.*, **18.** 291, 1895 ; J. Orcel, *ib.*, **44.** 98, 1921 ; C. J. B. Karsten, *Schweigger's Journ.*, **65.** 394, 1832 ; R. Böttger, *Tabellarische Uebersicht der specifischen Gewichte der Körper*, Frankfort, 1837 ; J. B. L. Romé de l'Isle, *Cristallographie*, Paris, **3.** 33, 1783 ; R. J. Haüy, *Traité de minéralogie*, Paris, **4.** 229, 1801 ; **4.** 252, 1822 ; *Journ. Mines*, **29.** 161, 1810 ; F. Mohs, *Grundriss der Mineralogie*, Dresden, **2.** 616, 1824 ; V. R. von Zepharovich, *Mineralogisches Lexikon für das Kaiserthum Oesterreich*, Wien, 271, 1873 ; G. Grattarola, *Giorn. Min.*, **1.** 293, 1890 ; H. von Foullon, *Verh. Geol. Reichsanst. Wien*, 171, 1892 ; A. Lacroix, *Minéralogie de la France et de ses colonies*, Paris, **3.** 441, 1897 ; T. Monticelli and N. Covelli, *Prodromo della mineralogia Vesuviana*, Napoli, 36, 1825 ; T. Bergman, *Producta ignis subterranei chemice considerata*, Upsala, 1777 ; G. H. O. Volger, *Studien zur Entwicklungsgeschichte der Mineralien*, Zürich, 29, 1854 ; G. A. Kenngott, *Sitzber. Akad. Wien*, **11.** 988, 1853 ; W. P. A. Jonker, *Zeit. anorg. Chem.*, **62.** 89, 1909 ; K. Jellinek and J. Zakowsky, *ib.*, **142.** 1, 1925 ; M. Löw, *Math. Term. Tud. Erl.*, **29.** 830, 1911 ; *Zeit. Kryst.*, **51.** 132, 1912 ; L. Tokody, *ib.*, **61.** 553, 1924 ; R. Pilz, R. Schröder, and V. Thost, *Goldschmidt's Beiträge Kryst.*, 176, 1918 ; G. Gore, *Proc. Roy. Soc.*, **20.** 441, 1872 ; 21. 140, 1873 ; L. H. Borgström, *Oefvers Finska Vet. Soc. Förh.*, **57.** 24, 1915 ; O. Weigel, *Tschermak's Mitt.*, (2) , **38.** 288, 1925 ; M. Lapschine and M. Tichanowitsch, *Bull. Acad. St. Petersburg*, (3), **4.** 81, 1861 ; O. B. Kühn, *Arch. Pharm.*, (2), **71.** 2, 1852 ; *Journ. Pharm. Chim.*, (3), **22.** 75, 1852 ; E. R. Schneider, *Journ. prakt. Chem.*, (2), **34.** 505, 1886 ; L. F. Nilson, *ib.*, (2), **12.** 327,

1875 ; (2), **14**. 19, 1876 ; *Akad. Hand. Stockholm*, **10**. 2. 1871 ; *Oefvers. Akad. Stockholm*, **28** 303, 1871 ; J. J. Berzelius, *Schweigger's Journ.*, **34**. 46, 1822 ; *Pogg. Ann.*, **7**. 137, 1826 ; *Svenska Akad. Handl.*, 295, 1825 ; *Ann. Chim. Phys.*, (2), **11**. 225, 1819 ; (2), **32**. 166, 1826 ; C. R. Fresenius, *Zeit. anal. Chem.*, **25**. 200, 1886 ; H. Rose, *Pogg. Ann.*, **42**. 536, 1838 ; F. E. Neumann, *ib.*, **23**. 1, 1831 ; E. Szarvasy and C. Messinger, *Ber.*, **30**. 1344, 1897 ; E. J. Houston, *Chem. News*, **24**. 177, 1871 ; *Journ. Franklin Inst.*, **92**, 115, 1871 ; A. Schüller, *Ber. Math. Naturw. Ungarn*, **12**. 255, 1895 ; J. F. L. Hausmann, *Ges. Wiss. Gött.*, 1, 1850 ; *Liebig's Ann.*, **74**. 197, 1850 ; A. Geuther, *ib.*, **240**. 221, 1887 ; J. D. Dana, *A System of Mineralogy*, New York, 34, 1892 , F. Hessenberg, *Mineralogische Notizen*, Frankfurt, **1**. 14, 1856 ; 3. 3, 1860 ; W. H. Miller, *Introduction to Mineralogy*, London, 177, 1852 ; L. Fletcher, *Phil. Mag.*, (5), **9**. 189, 1880 ; K. Vrba, *Zeit. Kryst.*, **15**. 460, 1889 ; S. von Olshausen, *ib.*, **61**. 463, 1925 ; V. Hackmann, *ib.*, **27**. 609, 1897 ; L. Tokody, *ib.*, **61**. 553, 1925 ; V. Goldschmidt, *ib.*, **39**. 116, 1904 ; F. Büchler and V. Goldschmidt, *Beitr. Kryst. Min.*, **1**. 181, 1918 ; J. A. Krenner, *Földt. Közl.*, **12**. 210, 1882 ; **13**. 383, 1883 ; E. Liffa and K. Emszt, *ib.*, **50**. 21, 1920 ; T. W. Case, *Phys. Rev.*, (2), **9**. 305, 1917 ; H. Zieler, *Zeit. anorg. Chem.*, **162**. 161, 1927 ; H. Saito, *Science Rep. Tohoku Univ.*. **16**. 37, 1927 ; C. W. G. Fuchs, *Die kunstlich dargestellten Mineralien nach Roses System geordnet*, Haarlem, 50, 1872 ; L. J. Thénard. *Ann. Chem. Phys.*, (2), **59**. 284, 1835.

§ 31. Arsenic Trisulphide

As indicated in connection with the histories of arsenic, and realgar, the Greek and Roman writers used the names arrhenicum and auripigmentum—*arum*, gold ; *pigmentum*, paint—for the yellow arsenic sulphide. G. Agricola [1] mutilated auripigmentum into *operment*, which in French and English became **orpiment;** in Italian, *orpimento* ; and in Spanish, *oropimente*. The yellow sulphide was also called *arsenicum citrinum*, and *arsenicum fluvum*. It occurs in several shades of lemon-yellow in small crystals, or in foliated and fibrous masses. C. W. C. Fuchs [2] mentioned its formation as a product occurring in the flues of a furnace roasting arsenical ores. It has also been reported that arsenic trisulphide was found in the intestines of a person poisoned with arsenic trioxide.

Among the reported occurrences are the mine near Julamerk (Kurdistan) ; Allchar (Macedonia) ; Goramis (Turkey) ; Tolfa, and the Solfatara of the Phlegræan fields (Italy) ; Graubünden, St. Gothard, Tessin, and Binnenthal (Switzerland) ; Corsica, Luceram, and the Plateau Central (France) ; Hall (Tyrol) ; Schwarzleogang (Salzberg) ; Fohnsdorf (Steiermark) ; Keutschach (Carinthia) ; Kresewo (Bosnia) ; Olah Lepasbanya, Nagyag, Boieza, Porkura, and Kovaszna (Siebenbürgen) ; Tajova, Kapnik, Felsöbanya, and Neumoldova (Hungary) ; Wittichen (Baden) ; Andreasburg, and Wolfsberg (Harz) ; Hänichen (Saxony) ; Schara-Dorna (Bukowina) ; Elfdal, Sweden ; New York, Utah, Wyoming, Nevada (United States) ; Tlazcosantitlan (Mexico) ; Guadeloupe (Antilles) ; and Acobambillo (Peru). The occurrence of orpiment in Sweden was discussed by D. Wallerius, and N. Zenzen and co-workers.

Analyses reported by J. J. Berzelius, A. Laugier, M. H. Kalproth, R. Bunsen, and L. F. Nilson are in agreement with the empirical formula As_2S_3, **arsenic trisulphide.** E. Schmidt found that the precipitated trisulphide may contain both *arsenic hydrosulphide*, $As(SH)_3$, and the trioxide. Arsenic trisulphide is formed as a result of volcanic sublimation as noted by T. Bergman, T. Monticelli and N. Covelli, and A. Sacchi. W. H. Weed and L. V. Pirsson obtained it from a hot spring in the Yellowstone National Park, and G. F. Becker, from the sinter at Steamboat Springs, Nevada. F. Mayençon reported orpiment among the products of a burning coal-mine. The commercial product known as orpiment, or *King's yellow*, employed as an artist's pigment, is manufactured by subliming together mixtures of arsenic trioxide and sulphur in proportions determined by the particular tint required. The process is analogous to that employed for realgar (*q.v.*). The method of manufacture was described by N. J. B. G. Guibourt, and L. A. Buchner. L. J. Thénard made the trisulphide by melting realgar with the required proportion of sulphur ; and the conditions under which it is formed by fusing a mixture of the two elements are indicated in W. Borodowsky's diagram, Fig. 44. The trisulphide is produced by passing hydrogen sulphide into a hydrochloric acid soln. of arsenic trioxide ; and, added L. F. Nilson, if the precipitation is not allowed to be complete.

the product has a high degree of purity—*vide supra*, the action of hydrogen sulphide on arsenic trioxide. J. H. Reedy found that the precipitation of arsenic trisulphide from acid soln. of the arsenates is greatly hastened by the presence of a soluble iodide, presumably by the cyclic actions : $H_3AsO_4 + 2HI \rightarrow H_3AsO_3 + H_2O + I_2$; and $H_2S + I_2 \rightleftharpoons 2HI + S$. W. Spring said that if the precipitate be dried in a current of dry air, its composition corresponds with the *hexahydrate*, $As_2S_3.6H_2O$. Its colour is paler than that of the anhydrous sulphide, and its sp. gr. is 1·8806 at 25·6°. It is decomposed by a press. of 6000–7000 atm. into the anhydrous sulphide and water. Returning to anhydrous arsenic trisulphide, E. Weinschenk obtained it in crystals by heating a mixture of arsenic trioxide, ammonium thiocyanate, and hydrochloric acid in a sealed tube. If arsenic acid is used, sulphur is formed as well, owing to the reduction of the arsenic acid to arsenic trioxide. H. Vohl obtained it by treating a hydrochloric acid soln. of arsenic trioxide with sodium thiosulphate. A. Gages observed the formation of arsenic trisulphide by leaving arsenical pyrites to stand in dil. hydrochloric acid for some time. F. Sandberger observed its formation in nature from proustite, and K. F. Peters, from arsenic. The trisulphide can also be obtained by the decomposition of realgar (*q.v.*). For the colloidal trisulphide, and S. S. Bhatnagar and B. L. Rao's observations on the formation of orpiment in nature, *vide infra*. According to H. Winter, golden-yellow leaflets of arsenic trisulphide are formed in small amount when hydrogen sulphide is passed into an 0·2N-soln. of arsenic trioxide in water. The formation of this modification increases in amount with increase of conc. of arsenic trioxide up to 0·3N- ; as the conc. is still further increased, the amount diminishes. Traces only are formed with 0·05N-soln. of arsenic trioxide. H. Winter also found that the red modification of arsenic trisulphide was obtained by freezing the yellow colloidal soln., when the solid red form separated along with ice. It may also be conveniently obtained by evaporating the colloidal soln. on the water-bath. When yellow arsenic trisulphide, obtained by the addition of an electrolyte to the colloidal soln., was heated in an air oven at 100,° it was transformed into a red, vitreous mass ; the yellow arsenic trioxide in hydrochloric acid does not, however, undergo a similar change at 100° unless it is completely freed from hydrochloric acid. The red form is gradually transformed into the yellow on exposure to the atm. for 5 to 6 weeks at the ordinary temp., or by being heated for some time at 150°–160°.

I. S. R. I. Eques a Born [3] referred to the **crystals** as *crystallis polyedris*, and later called them *octaèdres complets ou tronqués*. Exact measurements were made by F. Mohs, who regarded them as belonging to the rhombic system, having the axial ratios $a : b : c = 0.60304 : 1 : 0.67427$. P. Groth at first regarded the crystals as rhombic and isomorphous with stibnite, but C. Hintze did not agree with this. Later, P. Groth, following A. Breithaupt, showed that the crystals are probably monoclinic and show *eine höchst auffallende Analogie mit Claudetit*. S. Stevanovic gave for the axial ratios of the crystals regarded as monoclinic prisms, $a : b : c = 0.5962 : 1 : 0.6650$, and $\beta = 90° 41'$. Observations on the crystals were made by A Lévy, O. Mügge, H. A. Miers, W. H. Miller, W. Phillips, and J. A. Krenner. The **cleavage** on the (010)-face is perfect; and that on the (100)-face shows in traces. According to O. Mügge, the (001)-face is a **gliding plane.** A. des Cloizeaux said that the **optic axial angle** is large ; and the **optical character** negative. W. Spring found that the precipitated sulphide passes into a microcrystalline powder when kept for many days at 150°. According to F. Mohs, the **specific gravity** of orpiment is 3·480 ; C. J. B. Karsten gave 3·459 ; and N. J. B. G. Guibourt, and R. Böttger, 3·44–3·45. J. F. L. Hausmann found the sp. gr. of a sample of the artificial citron-yellow pigment to be 2·762. The **hardness** of orpiment is 1·5-2·0 ; and the artificially prepared glass has a hardness of 3. There are two forms of orpiment. According to H. Winter, and W. Borodowsky, when ordinary or yellow α-As_2S_3 is kept in the vap. of carbon disulphide below 170° it suffers no change, but above that **transition temperature,** red β-As_2S_3 is formed. The effect of an excess of arsenic or sulphur on the transition temp. is illustrated in Fig. 44. H. Winter gave 150°–160° for the transition temp. The subject was studied by R. Lorenz and W. Herz. W. Borodowsky gave 300° for the **melting point** of arsenic trisulphide; R. Cusack, 325°; L. H. Borgström, 320°; and W. P. A. Jonker, 310°; he also found that an artificial preparation does not crystallize on cooling. H. Saito found that fusion and sublimation readily occur in a non-ozidizing gas. E. Mitscherlich said that the vap. is not decomposed if air be excluded and that the trisulphide has the **boiling point** 700°; W. P. A. Jonker gave 707°. F. Krafft found that the trisulphide, orpiment, distils unchanged at 240° in the vacuum of the cathode light; and C. Zenghelis observed signs of volatilization at ordinary temp. J. J. Berzelius said that when distilled, the first fractions are richest in sulphur, and the last fractions richest in arsenic. A. Schüller found that orpiment volatilizes in vacuo less readily than realgar, and the sublimation begins after the compound has melted. L. Merz said that in the vacuum of the cathode light, sublimation begins just over 220°. E. Szarvasy and C. Messinger found that the **vapour density** indicates that the trisulphide is dissociated at 1000°. E. Weinschenk said that the crystals are strongly **pleochroic,** a being greenish-yellow, and c, reddish-yellow. When heated to 150°, the crystals have the pleochroism of realgar—possibly, said C. Hintze, in virtue of the reversible reaction $3As_2S_3 \rightleftharpoons 2As_2S_2 + As_2S_5$—but the original state is restored on cooling provided the temp. has not exceeded 150°. C. Doelter found the crystals opaque to the **X-rays.** W. Herz gave 3.75×10^{12} for the **vibration frequency** of AsS (?). W. W. Coblentz examined the **photoelectric effect,** and found that at +20° to —50° the spectrophotoelectric sensitivity curve of proustite has a slight maximum at about 0.61μ, and a marked sensitivity with a maximum in the extreme violet. As the temp. is lowered (to —100°) the maximum in the ultra-violet is more or less obliterated by a new maximum (the 0.61μ band), which occurs at about 0.58μ. The position of this new maximum remains quite constant as the temp. is decreased to —170°. No photoelectric sensitivity was observed for radiation stimuli of wavelengths extending from 1μ to 2μ in the ultra-red. T. W. Case observed that light has no effect on the electrical conductivity of orpiment. R. Robl observed no **fluorescence** with the trisulphide in ultra-violet light. T. W. Case, and F. Beijerinck said that at ordinary temp. the **electrical conductivity** is inappreciable, but as the temp. rises above 60°, the conductivity becomes apparent. E. Jannettaz studied the electrical conductivity of the crystals. C. Tubandt and M. Haedicke found that up to the transition temp. arsenic trisulphide is an insulator.

D. Vitali[4] found that arsenic trisulphide is not poisonous; the commercial product, however, contains more or less arsenious trioxide, which is very poisonous. The administration of considerable quantities of the trisulphide to a dog is attended by an improvement in the health of the animal; the explanation of this lies in the fact that only a small proportion of the sulphide passes into the urine as arsenic acid. The effect is hence the same as that of administering very small doses of the latter substance; this, as is known, is beneficial. According to J. J. Berzelius, when **hydrogen** is passed over a red-hot mixture of alkali carbonate and arsenic sulphide, arsenic sublimes. H. Pélabon has studied the reduction of arsenic trisulphide by hydrogen—*vide supra*—when antimony is present, and also silver sulphide. G. H. O. Volger said that in **air,** the trisulphide is oxidized to arsenic trioxide; and E. Pollacci found that the oxidation of moist arsenic trisulphide to sulphur and arsenic trioxide, and the subsequent oxidation of the sulphur to sulphuric acid proceeds slowly in air; J. J. Berzelius showed that the trioxide is formed when the trisulphide is roasted in air. H. Saito found that with a rising temp., orpiment begins to decrease in weight at about 200°, forming arsenic trioxide and sulphur dioxide. The reaction is finished at about 750°. According to E. H. Riesenfeld and W. Haase, a colloidal soln. of arsenic trisulphide is decomposed by **ozone,** forming arsenic acid. M. Decourdemanche observed that when arsenic trisulphide is boiled with **water,** it evolves a very small quantity of hydrogen sulphide, and a trace of arsenic trioxide passes into soln.; indeed, this action goes on for several days at ordinary temp., and it is accelerated by sulphuric or hydrochloric acid. F. L. Hünefeld added that the native sulphide is also attacked by water, but only superficially. O. Weigel found that a litre of water at 18° dissolves $2 \cdot 1 \times 10^{-6}$ mol of precipitated arsenic trisulphide—*vide infra*, colloidal trisulphide. J. Roth found that water slowly converts arsenic trisulphide into the trioxide and hydrogen sulphide. P. de Clermont and J. Frommel believe that the sulphide is hydrated before it is attacked by the boiling water, for (i) the freshly precipitated sulphide gives off hydrogen sulphide more rapidly than the same sulphide previously dried at 125°; and (ii) if the dried sulphide be kept in contact with hot water in a closed vessel and then be boiled with water, it gives off hydrogen sulphide as rapidly as the freshly precipitated sulphide. K. Chodounsky suggested that the more rapid attack by water of the freshly precipitated trisulphide may be due to a soluble form of the trisulphide which reacts with water at ordinary temp. producing a hydroxysulphide. Contrary to S. E. Linder and H. Picton, and J. Billitzer, D. Vorländer and R. Häberle observed no hydrolysis of arsenic trisulphide suspended in water. E. Schmidt found that precipitated arsenic trisulphide is appreciably decomposed by water, and even by alcohol, forming hydrogen sulphide. He said that the trisulphide is appreciably attacked by water. P. de Clermont and J. Frommel found that when arsenic trisulphide is boiled with water in vacuo, it commences to decompose at 22°. The presence of arsenic trioxide impedes the dissociation of arsenic trisulphide by water, owing to the formation of an oxysulphide which dissociates more slowly. Crystallized arsenic trioxide does not retard the reaction so much as arsenic trioxide obtained by the dissociation of the sulphide. C. S. Ward observed that when carbon dioxide is passed through water in which arsenic trisulphide has been precipitated by hydrogen sulphide, hydrolysis sets in as soon as the temp. rises above 35°. At 100°, 24 per cent. of the trisulphide was decomposed in $2\frac{1}{2}$ hrs. More trisulphide was decomposed by water alone than by water in the presence of carbon dioxide. This statement wants confirmation. H. V. Regnault said that steam reacts with arsenic sulphide, forming arsenic oxysulphide of variable composition. A. Classen and O. Bauer found that arsenic trisulphide in an ammoniacal soln. is oxidized by **hydrogen dioxide** to arsenic and sulphuric acids.

H. Rose found that arsenic trisulphide deliquesces when placed in **chlorine,** much heat is evolved, and what appeared to be a complex $2AsCl_3.3SCl_2$ was formed; L. F. Nilson said that the product is really a mixture of arsenic and sulphur chlorides. R. Bunsen oxidized a soln. of arsenic trisulphide to arsenate by the action of chlorine. E. Reichardt showed that an aq. soln. of **bromine** oxidizes arsenic trisulphide quantitatively to arsenic acid ; and on evaporating the soln., arsenic tribromide appears. L. L. de Koninck observed that the trisulphide is similarly oxidized by a soln. of bromine in hydrochloric acid, or in aq. potassium bromide. According to E. A. Schneider, a soln. of **iodine** in carbon disulphide is without action on natural orpiment, but is decolorized by the precipitated sulphide, forming arsenic triiodide and sulphur. The attempt to prepare the complex $As_2S_3.2AsI_3$ was not successful. A mixture of the trisulphide and iodine fuses at a low temp. to a homogeneous, brown mass which dissolves in carbon disulphide and the soln. yields only arsenic triiodide and sulphur. He further showed that while arsenic trisulphide and iodine at moderate temp. form arsenic triiodide and sulphur, at higher temp., these products react to form the original trisulphide and iodine. This shows that the reaction $As_2S_3 + 3I_2 \rightleftharpoons 2AsI_3 + 3S$ is a reversible one. He was able to prepare a complex with sulphur iodide and arsenic iodide, As_4SI_{12}, as a reddish-brown powder melting at 72° ; while with a mixture of iodine, and arsenic trisulphide and trioxide, he obtained the complex : $As_{13}O_9I_9S_6$. In both cases where the chemical individuality of the products was not established, J. Kelley and E. F. Smith found that arsenic trisulphide is completely volatilized in a current of dry **hydrogen chloride ;** the reaction commences in the cold, and a liquid is formed which volatilizes when heated. Similar results were obtained with **hydrogen bromide.** L. Gmelin said that when the trisulphide is boiled with conc. **hydrochloric acid,** it is decomposed with difficulty, and the hydrogen sulphide and arsenic trichloride which are evolved from the containing retort, recombine in the receiver. E. Schmidt noted that the trisulphide is attacked by dil. acid. P. de Clermont and J. Frommel also found that when arsenic trisulphide is boiled with water containing a trace of hydrochloric acid, some arsenic trichloride is volatilized—*vide supra*, the chlorination of the sulphide for the preparation of arsenic trichloride ; and the analytical reactions of arsenic. The reaction with hydrochloric acid, or with sodium chloride and sulphuric acid, was studied by A. Fyfe, H. Becker, W. Wallace and F. Penny, H. Beckurts, J. A. Kaiser, H. Rose, and A. Lintner, and it was shown that the decomposition of the trisulphide is incomplete. The acceleration of the reaction in the presence of ferric chloride (T. Riekher), cuprous chloride (C. F. Rammelsberg, etc.), has been previously discussed. According to W. R. Lang and C. M. Carson, arsenic trisulphide may be treated with hydrochloric acid of sp. gr. 1·16 without danger of soln. provided the liquid be sat. with hydrogen sulphide. R. F. Weinland and P. Gruhl found arsenic trisulphide to be insoluble in a soln. of potassium iodide, and soln. of the sulphoarsenites and potassium iodide fail to give halide compounds with arsenic trisulphide like those with arsenic trioxide. C. R. Fresenius and C. H. L. von Babo oxidized the trisulphide by heating it with a mixture of hydrochloric acid and **potassium chlorate,** and R. Bunsen showed that some arsenic may be lost as trichloride during the process of volatilization.

S. E. Linder and H. Picton found that the precipitate formed by passing **hydrogen sulphide** into a hydrochloric or acetic acid soln. of arsenic trioxide contains rather more sulphur than corresponds with the trisulphide. They inferred that the product corresponds with *arsenic hydrosulphide*, $8As_2S_3.H_2S$, because (i) the sulphur content is not reduced by treatment with carbon disulphide, and (ii) a current of hydrogen removes hydrogen sulphide from the product at 115°. W. Biltz and E. Keunecke found that dry liquid hydrogen sulphide does not dissolve arsenic trisulphide. According to R. E. O. Puller, the trisulphide dissolves when digested with sulphur and **ammonium sulphide,** and is completely precipitated from the soln. as ammonium magnesium arsenate by magnesia-mixture. C. Eckert found that when the mixture of sulphur and arsenic trisulphide, precipitated by hydrogen sulphide from an arsenate, is digested with aq. ammonia, the trisulphide first dissolves, then the sulphur, and arsenic pentasulphide and ammonium thiosulphate are formed. H. Rose also showed that oxidation occurs in this reaction. R. Bunsen found that arsenic trisulphide dissolves when digested with an aq. soln. of **sulphur dioxide,** or of potassium hydrosulphite, forming arsenic trioxide and sulphur which dissolve in the liquid, and when boiled, sulphur dioxide escapes : $2As_2S_3+9K_2SO_3+3SO_2$ $=2As_2O_3+9K_2S_2O_3$. J. Milbauer and J. Tucek found that between 300° and 800°, arsenic trisulphide reacts with sulphur dioxide, forming sulphur and a sulphate. It is also soluble in a hot soln. of **potassium hydrosulphite.** H. Rose showed that conc. **sulphuric acid** dissolves the trisulphide faster than it does realgar, forming arsenic trioxide and sulphur dioxide. A. Baudrimont, and H. Feigel found that **sulphur monochloride** acts vigorously on the trisulphide, forming a molten mixture of arsenic trichloride and sulphur ; and J. Kelley and E. F. Smith found that complete decomposition occurs at about 140°. H. B. North and co-workers found that **thionyl chloride** at 150° in a sealed tube attacks arsenic trisulphide and also orpiment. E. A. Schneider found that when the **sulphur iodides** are fused with the trisulphide, arsenic trichloride and sulphur are produced.

According to J. J. Berzelius, finely divided arsenic trisulphide slowly absorbs **ammonia** without changing its colour ; and A. Bineau said that the product is saturated in about 3 weeks when its composition corresponds with **arsenic amminotrisulphide,** $As_2(NH_3)S_3$. The ammine, said J. J. Berzelius, rapidly loses ammonia on exposure to air, and when treated with water it forms ammonium arsenite and sulpharsenite. Arsenic trisulphide is easily dissolved by an aq. soln. of ammonia, and K. Heumann found that copper acts on the soln., forming a yellowish-brown precipitate containing copper, arsenic, and sulphur. G. Gore, and E. C. Franklin and C. A. Kraus found that the trisulphide is slightly soluble in liquid ammonia. The trisulphide is easily decomposed by **nitric acid** and by **aqua regia.** J. L. Proust found that a few drops of fuming nitric acid placed on melted orpiment produce a deflagration ; and R. Bunsen showed that with nitric acid of sp. gr. 1·42, the sulphur which separates during the oxidation fuses into globules which may entangle a little trisulphide and protect it from oxidation. This effect does not occur with fuming acid of sp. gr. 1·53. P. Askenasy and co-workers found that arsenic sulphides are oxidized by nitric acid and oxygen under press. to arsenic and sulphuric acids. When orpiment is treated with boiling 10 per cent. HNO_3, there is a faint smell of nitric oxide ; with boiling 20 per cent. acid, a little nitric oxide is given off ; cold 30 to 40 per cent. nitric acid, agitated, gives a faint smell of nitric oxide ; and with 50 per cent. acid, a little nitric oxide is given off. With oxygen at 20 atm. press., and at 120°, realgar is completely oxidized with twice its weight of 10 per cent. acid during 30 min. action, while orpiment requires 40 per cent. acid and 15 min. action. In the cases of arsenical pyrites, about 16 per cent. of the arsenic is not attacked, and some oxygen is used in oxidizing the iron. The amount of nitric acid required is in every case less than the amount that would theoretically be needed if no oxygen were used, and the losses are very small. Treatment of aq. suspensions of the sulphides with oxygen alone oxidizes some of the sulphur to sulphuric acid, but no arsenic acid is formed. Sulphuric acid may be removed as calcium sulphate from the arsenic acid soln. by addition of calcium carbonate or hydroxide, and subsequent conc. of the filtrate. O. Materne found that a 2 per cent. soln. of **borax** slowly dissolves arsenic trisulphide in the cold, and rapidly when heated. The sulphide is not quantitatively precipitated by acids unless hydrogen sulphide is introduced. A. Schüller found that arsenic trisulphide is insoluble in **carbon disulphide,** and in **benzene ;** and J. Spiller, that it is soluble in a soln. of **citric acid,** or **alkali citrates.** According to C. R. Fresenius and C. H. L. von Babo, when arsenic trisulphide is fused with **potassium cyanide,** the alkali thiocyanate is formed, and all the arsenic is sublimed. The reduction obtained by heating the sulphide with a mixture of potassium cyanide and sodium carbonate was studied by J. Haidlen and C. R. Fresenius, W. Fresenius, and H. Rose. The reduction of the sulphide by heating it with **carbon** and lime, or charcoal and potassium carbonate, was examined by J. von Liebig ; with **calcium oxalate,** by H. Rose ; and with **potassium oxalate** and calcium carbonate, by A. Duflos. J. Ossikowsky found that during the decomposition of organic bodies easily oxidizable bodies are oxidized, and that arsenic trisulphide under such circumstances is converted into arsenic trioxide, and to a small extent into arsenic pentoxide. The precipitated sulphide undergoes oxidation more readily than auripigmentum. In cases of poisoning by arsenic trisulphide, the oxidation products appear more or less quickly, according to the nature of the decomposing body ; the presence of water and heat also exerts much influence.

According to H. Rose, when the vap. of arsenic trisulphide is passed over red-hot **iron,** iron arsenide is formed ; and in the case of **silver,** silver arsenide. A. Taufflieb also noted the reducing action of silver on arsenic trisulphide. When arsenic trisulphide is suspended in water, and mixed with five times its weight of powdered **magnesium,** it furnishes at first a yellow soln., from which hydrochloric acid precipitates arsenic trisulphide ; if the reaction is prolonged, the whole of the arsenic may be removed from the soln. The addition of methyl alcohol tends to keep the arsenic trisulphide in soln. According to J. F. Simon, when the vap. of arsenic trisulphide is passed over red-hot **calcium oxide,** arsenic and calcium sulphide are formed as well as a little calcium sulphite, arsenite, and arsenate ; red-hot **magnesium oxide** had " little or no action." P. de Clermont and J. Frommel found that magnesia reacts with the trisulphide suspended in water : $2As_2S_3+6MgO=Mg_3(AsS_3)_2+Mg_3(AsO_3)_2$; and when the liquid is boiled,

$Mg_3(AsS_3)_2 + 6H_2O = 6H_2S + Mg_3(AsO_3)_2$.   J. J. Berzelius' observations on the solvent action of a soln. of an **alkali hydroxide** on the arsenic sulphides have been indicated above—alkali arsenite and sulpharsenite are formed as well as partially decomposed arsenic sulphides mixed with sulphur which he seems to have regarded as definite compounds. According to R. F. Weinland and P. Lehmann, sodium hydroxide and arsenic trisulphide yield arsenic, thioarsenate, and mono- and di-thioxyarsenates.   When alcoholic sodium hydroxide is employed, mono- and di-thioxyarsenates and arsenates are formed.   H. Rose said that when fused with **sodium carbonate**, arsenic, and the alkali arsenate and sulpharsenate, are formed. The reactions may be symbolized : $5As_2S_3 = 4As + 3As_2S_5$; and $3As_2S_5 + 15Na_2CO_3$ $= 15Na_2S + 3As_2O_5 + 15CO_2$, and the sodium sulphide and arsenic pentoxide form alkali salts : $8As_2S_5 + 24Na_2CO_3 = 10Na_3AsS_4 + 6Na_3AsO_4 + 24CO_2$; and, as shown by E. Soubeiran, the arsenate may be partly reduced by hydrogen, forming arsenite, and finally arsenic : $2Na_3AsO_4 + 5H_2 = 2As + 6NaOH + 2H_2O$.   Arsenic trisulphide dissolves rapidly and completely in a soln. of **alkali carbonate or hydrocarbonate** ; and, added E. Biltz, the alkali hydrocarbonate dissolves the sulphide in virtue of the carbonate it contains because carbon dioxide precipitates arsenic trisulphide from its soln. in alkali carbonate.   According to L. F. Nilson, a boiling soln. of the trisulphide in sodium carbonate gives off carbon dioxide and hydrogen sulphide, there is a separation of arsenic disulphide, and a sulpharsenate passes into soln. ; when cooled, the soln. deposits $NaAs_3S_5.4H_2O$.   If the soln. be evaporated, garnet-red plates or prisms of $Na_8As_{18}O_7S_{24}.30H_2O$ are deposited—K. Preis gives a different composition—*vide infra*.   J. S. F. Pagenstecher observed that when the trisulphide is placed in an aq. soln. of **mercuric chloride**, there is formed a white powder, mercuric sulphochloride, and a soln. of hydrochloric acid and arsenic trioxide ; F. Kessler symbolized the reaction : $As_2S_3 + 3HgCl_2 = 3HgS + 2AsCl_3$. According to E. Schürmann, arsenic trisulphide decomposes soln. of mercuric chloride and of **copper sulphate** completely ; and also **lead nitrate, zinc sulphate,** and **nickel sulphate** completely if heated under press. in a sealed tube ; a soln. of **ferrous sulphate** is only partially decomposed by the sulphide.   S. S. Bhatnagar and co-workers found that the reactions of **gold and silver salts** with arsenic trisulphide sol. are photosensitive.

Colloidal arsenic trisulphide.—H. O. Schulze [5] showed that colloidal arsenic trisulphide is probably the primary product of the action of hydrogen sulphide on soln. of arsenious salts ; while the crystalline trisulphide is produced by a secondary reaction of acids or salts on the colloid.   Amorphous arsenic trisulphide, if really non-crystalline, is the **hydrogel** of **arsenic trisulphide.**   According to J. J. Berzelius, finely divided arsenic sulphide obtained by precipitation from an aq. soln. of arsenic trioxide by hydrogen sulphide, after it has been washed with cold water, dissolves to a slight extent in hot water, forming a yellow soln.   It does not dissolve in an aq. soln. of hydrogen sulphide, and, according to C. G. C. Bischof, a dil. aq. soln. of arsenic trioxide does not give a precipitate with hydrogen sulphide —aq. soln. or gas—but forms a yellow soln—while a conc. soln. of arsenic trioxide gives a yellow precipitate under these conditions.   J. J. Berzelius added that " the yellow soln. is for the present to be regarded as a suspension of transparent particles because arsenic trisulphide gradually separates from the soln. as a precipitate." In modern language, the arsenic trisulphide is in a colloidal state, *i.e.* a **hydrosol** ; when flocculated or coagulated, the product is a **hydrogel.**   N. R. Dhar and S. Ghosh found arsenic trisulphide and the complex sulphides are peptized by alkali-lye, yellow ammonium sulphide, and sodium arsenite.   H. O. Schulze concluded that water actually dissolves the arsenic trisulphide.   He passed hydrogen sulphide into a soln. of 10 grms. of arsenic trioxide in a litre of water and found that the liquid became yellow and turbid, forming very thin golden-yellow flakes on the surface, which, on agitation, sank to the bottom in a flocculent state.   The remaining soln. was slightly turbid and of a reddish-yellow tint.   This turbidity, however, could not be removed by filtration, and on examination under the microscope no trace of solid matter could be detected. The liquid remained clear and yellow. When the soln. was rendered turbid by the addition of an acid or salt, insufficient to produce complete precipitation, solid particles in a yellow menstruum were seen under the microscope. The soln., moreover, was not turbid when viewed by transmitted light in thin layers between parallel plates of glass, but it appeared turbid only in reflected light—an effect attributed to fluorescence. Carbon dioxide was passed through che soln. to remove the excess of hydrogen sulphide, and the arsenic and sulphur were found to be in the ratio of $As_2 : S_3$. The arsenic trisulphide so obtained is a colloid, and the hydrogen sulphide cannot be readily removed from it by dialysis. On evaporation to dryness, an amount of arsenic trisulphide remains proportional to the amount of arsenic trioxide taken, this solid sulphide being no longer soluble in water. There is a limit to the conc. of the soln. of arsenic trisulphide prepared by passing hydrogen sulphide through an aq. soln. of arsenic trioxide on account of the sparing solubility of the latter, but by passing hydrogen sulphide and then dissolving fresh arsenic trioxide, and so on, H. O. Schulze obtained a 37·46 per cent. soln. of As_2S_3 (1 part of As_2S_3 in 1·67 parts of water). This soln. was like an intensely yellow milk, but perfectly transparent under the microscope. The more conc. soln. deposited a small quantity of solid matter on standing for a long time ; dil. soln. are more permanent, thus a soln. of 1 in 500 was quite unchanged after standing three months. Dil. soln. of arsenic trisulphide prepared from more conc. soln. by dilution are more turbid than dil. soln. of the same conc. prepared directly ; and they have a yellow rather than a reddish-yellow tint. V. Gazzi found that the colloidal soln. always contained some arsenic trioxide.

S. S. Bhatnagar and B. L. Rao inferred that the hydrosulphide ion, SH', and not the sulphide ion, S'', is the active agent in the precipitation of metallic sulphides by hydrogen sulphide. The colloidal soln. of sulphides obtained in this way can be regarded as soln. of hydrosulphides. When a colloidal soln. of arsenic sulphide sol is heated or when hydrogen is passed through it so that all the free and combined hydrogen sulphide is removed, the formula of the colloidal sulphide is not As_2S_3 but much more nearly As_2S_2, or AsS. It is shown that the action of heat on a red colloidal soln. converts it into a yellow sol with the precipitation of sulphur, according to the equation : $As_2S_2,xH_2S+xO=As_2S_3+xH_2O+(x-1)S$. When the content of combined hydrogen sulphide is small, no sulphur is precipitated. The action of heat and light consists mainly in the transformation of one variety into the other and may be represented by the equation : $As_2S_2+H_2S+O=As_2S_2S+H_2O$. By analysis and measurement of the absorption spectrum and the density, it is inferred that the red variety is identical with realgar and the yellow precipitate with orpiment, both in colour and other properties. According to S. G. Chaudhury and P. Kundu, the atomic ratio of arsenic to sulphur in an arsenious sulphide sol in which arsenious acid is in excess is 1 : 1·46, whilst in another sol prepared by the action of an excess of hydrogen sulphide on arsenious acid, but in which both free arsenious acid and hydrogen sulphide are absent, the ratio is 1 : 2. The constitution of the former sol, therefore, corresponds with arsenic trisulphide, and the latter either with As_2S_3,As_2S_5, or As_2S_3,H_2S, the latter being the more probable.

H. Picton prepared the colloidal soln. by allowing an aq. soln. of arsenic trioxide to flow into a sat. soln. of hydrogen sulphide through which a current of gas was passing. The uncombined hydrogen sulphide was then removed by a current of hydrogen. F. W. Küster and G. Dahmer showed that although no precipitation occurs in the preparation of these colloidal soln., the arsenic is quantitatively converted into the trisulphide. L. Gmelin also showed that the soln. may be kept for weeks with very little deposition. H. Picton said that conc. soln. containing 11 to 12 grms. of trisulphide per litre may be kept for 4 months with only a mere trace of a precipitate ; while dil. soln. under the same conditions are almost entirely unchanged. No change was observed with a 2 per cent. soln. when kept 3 years. F. W. Küster and G. Dahmer found a 2·3 per cent. soln. to be very stable.

D. Vorländer and R. Häberle found that with very dil. soln. arsenic trioxide and hydrogen sulphide do not appear to react because the product is devoid of colour; and they attributed the phenomenon to the hydrogen sulphide. N. P. Peskoff showed that the lack of colour is due (i) to the extremely small magnitude of the particles, and more especially (ii) to the complete individuality of these particles. A. Semler showed that the colour of arsenic sulphide sols varies from the orange-red of the coarser suspensions to the pure citron-yellow of the finely divided sols which show only a slight milkiness by transmitted light. Flocculation by an acid or a neutral salt gives a citron-yellow precipitate, but by drying at 100° the product precipitated by barium or calcium chloride becomes red. When heated, this red product behaves similarly to realgar, but its behaviour with water shows that its colour is probably due to the presence of barium thioarsenite. In agreement with H. O. Schulze, H. Picton said that although the soln. are clear by transmitted light, they appear turbid by reflected light; and on sending a beam of lime-light through the soln., the track of the beam is marked by a soft yellow glow, the light from which is completely polarized. This proves the existence of solid particles. F. Haber found that X-radiograms of the colloidal soln. show evidence of incipient crystallization. E. F. Burton and J. E. Currie studied the distribution of particles in a column of liquid and found no difference at the different levels. A. Dumansky measured the rate of settling. In cases where the particles are large enough to be variable under the microscope they exhibit the Brownian movement—provided their size does not exceed 5μ in diameter. In other cases, the existence of the particles may be revealed by the ultramicroscope. S. E. Linder and H. Picton suspected that the size of the particles of trisulphide is smaller the more dil. the soln. of arsenic trioxide used in their preparation, and G. Börjeson found that when the conc. was $10^{-2}N\text{-As}_2O_3$, the radius of the trisulphide particles was $39\mu\mu$; with $5 \times 10^{-4}N\text{-As}_2O_3$, $16\mu\mu$; and with $10^{-4}N\text{-As}_2O_3$, $11\mu\mu$. H. R. Kruyt and H. J. C. Tendeloo, and R. Zsigmondy and C. Carius also discussed this subject. A. Boutaric and M. Vuillaume observed that if the hydrogen sulphide is allowed to diffuse into the aq. soln. of arsenic trioxide the grain-size is less than when the gas is bubbled through the liquid. The grain size is also increased by a prolonged passage of the gas, and by a protracted boiling. H. Bechhold found that the ultra-filter will allow arsenic trisulphide to pass, but not Prussian blue, and it would hold back arsenic trisulphide when mixed with Prussian blue, presumably owing to mutual adsorption. From a study of the optical properties—the schlieren-effect— H. Freundlich inferred that the shape of the particles of arsenic trisulphide is almost spherical. S. E. Linder and H. Picton found that the relation between the specific gravity and the conc. of the colloidal soln. is represented by a straight line. Thus, with soln. containing

Per cent. As$_2$S$_3$	4·4	2·2	1·1	0·275	0·06875	0·01719
Sp. gr.	1·033810	1·016880	1·008435	1·002110	1·000535	1·000137

R. Wintgen, S. S. Bhatnagar and B. L. Rao, and A. Boutaric and R. Simonet also measured the sp. gr. of these soln. A. Dumansky gave 2·938 for the sp. gr. of the colloidal sulphide. R. Wintgen found the specific volume is a linear function of the conc. S. E. Linder and H. Picton observed that no change of vol. occurs when the arsenic trisulphide is coagulated and precipitated. No change in the surface tension was observed between water and the colloidal soln. S. E. Linder and H. Picton measured the diffusion of the arsenic trisulphide hydrosol into water, and this is in agreement with general observations which show that colloids and crystalloids are diffusible; and that the difference between colloids and crystalloids is one of degree and not of kind. The rate of diffusion of the colloids is much slower than that of crystalloids. H. Bechhold and J. Ziegler found that the diffusion of both electrolytes and non-electrolytes is diminished by gels, and this the more the greater the conc. of the gel. When a little soluble tartrate was present, the rate of diffusion was accelerated. There are three plausible explanations, (i) the dispersion or degree of fineness of the colloid is augmented by the trace of soluble salt; (ii) that the adsorbed salt in its tendency to rapid diffusion drags the colloidal particles with them ; or (iii) that movements in the liquid set up by the diffusion of the salts set up currents which carry along the colloidal particles by convection. H. Picton favoured the second hypothesis. J. Thovert calculated the molar weight of arsenic trisulphide in colloidal soln. from the diffusion constant, and found it to be over 6000. C. H. Pfaff observed that the arsenic trisulphide separates in yellow flakes during the **freezing** of the yellow soln. ; but, added S. E. Linder and H. Picton, if alcohol be added to prevent freezing no coagulation occurs when the temp. is lowered by a freezing mixture of ice and salt. Measurements of the **lowering of the freezing point** of water by colloidal arsenic trisulphide gave no perceptible result ; nor were they able to detect any permanent effect on the **osmotic pressure.** These results, added H. Picton, " might simply be due to very high mol. wt." A. Boutaric and R. Simonet, and D. N. Chakravarti and N. R. Dhar measured the **viscosity** of the hydrosol of the trisulphide. H. R. Kruyt and J. van der Spek found that the **heat of coagulation** of the colloidal trisulphide by alum or potassium chloride is small amounting to 0·01 to 0·05 cal. per gram of the trisulphide.

H. Freundlich and A. Nathansohn found that sols of arsenic trisulphide are **photochemically active ;** they sensitize the oxidation of colour substances, such as eosin and malachite-green, in light. The formation of colloidal sulphur by illuminating arsenic trisulphide sols depends on this photochemical sensitization, for the hydrogen sulphide which is set free by the hydrolysis of the arsenic trisulphide is oxidized to sulphur through the sensitizing action of the trisulphide micellæ. N. P. Peskoff found that anthracene added to colloidal arsenic sulphide causes precipitation in light in 5–8 hrs., but no such change occurs in darkness in 17 days. R. V. Murphy and J. H. Mathews showed that the electrical conductivity of the soln. increases on exposure to light, and the rate of change increases with decreasing conc. of the colloid. The increased photochemical activity is attributed to the greater dispersion of the more dil. soln. The chemical action involved is a photochemical oxidation of hydrogen sulphide to colloidal sulphur and a thionic acid, accompanied by a reaction between hydrogen sulphide and the thionic acid, which serve as stabilizing electrolytes for the micellæ of arsenic trisulphide and sulphur, respectively. Removal of the stabilizing electrolytes produces a de-stabilization of the two colloids which are consequently precipitated. The increase in electrical conductivity is explained as due to the building up of a concentration of the thionic acid sufficient to serve as the stabilizing electrolyte for the colloidal sulphur, the reaction between hydrogen sulphide and the thionic acid then proceeding at such a rate that the equilibrium is maintained between the several components of the system, further change in the electrical conductivity thus being prevented. S. S. Bhatnagar and B. L. Rao, and A. Boutaric and M. Vuillaume measured the **absorption spectrum** of the colloidal soln. There is an absorption due to diffusion, and one caused by a reflection of the incident rays from the surfaces of the colloidal particles. R. Wintgen, and I. Lifschitz and G. Beck measured the **refractive index,** and found the product of the sp. vol. into the refractive index is a linear function of the conc. K. Schaum and P. Friedrich observed that exposure to ultra-violet light and to light of long wave-length made no difference to the migration velocity of electrophoresis of arsenic trisulphide sols. B. Lange studied the polarization of light by the colloid ; and S. S. Bhatnagar and co-workers, the action of light.

S. E. Linder and H. Picton, and H. Freundlich noticed that the hydrosol of arsenic trisulphide is transported towards the anode by cataphoresis—*vide* **3.** 23, 8. The subject was discussed by K. von der Grinten, J. J. Bikermann, and by A. Ivanitzkaja and M. Proskurnin. A. Dumansky gave 136×10^{-6} mho for the **electrical conductivity** of colloidal arsenic trisulphide. Observations were made by W. Pauli and A. Semler on the electrical conductivity of the soln. and on the electrometric titration with baryta-water. According to A. Charriou, when arsenic trisulphide is precipitated by means of hydrogen sulphide in presence of a barium salt, the precipitate contains adsorbed barium. When the precipitate is washed with a soln. of sodium or potassium chlorides, no displacement of barium occurs, whilst with soln. of aluminium, ferric and chromic chlorides interchange of barium and tervalent metal takes place. A. J. Rabinovitsch measured the H'-ion concentration of sols of arsenic trisulphide, before and after coagulation with barium chloride, and in the filtrate from each coagulum the total H'-ion conc. was found to be unaltered ; but after correcting for dilution by the barium chloride soln., the filtrate was more acid than the original sol. The increase of acidity rises with the conc. of the sols. Arsenic trisulphide sols are considered to be fairly strong complex acids, ionizing as follows : $(As_2S_3).nSH_2 \rightleftharpoons (As_2S_3)nSH + H' \rightleftharpoons (As_2S_3)nS + 2H'$; the second ionization constant is less than the first. In the coagulum it was found that the hydrogen had been completely replaced by an eq. amount of barium ; there was no chlorine present. P. H. Boutigny found that the arsenic trisulphide in colloidal soln. is precipitated by boiling ; L. Gmelin added that the precipitation is incomplete ; W. Biltz observed the colour is darkened by boiling ; and H. Winter showed that the trisulphide may be converted into the red modification—*vide supra*. A. Dumansky found that flocculation slowly occurs when the soln. is rapidly centrifuged ; and P. B. Ganguly and N. R. Dhar, by exposure to sunlight. According to F. W. Küster and G. Dahmer, the hydrosol of arsenic trisulphide is only slowly precipitated by barium sulphate ; vigorous shaking is required, and precipitated barium sulphate causes the effect better than the powdered mineral. Furthermore, a large quantity of the solid is necessary. The precipitation is also brought about by charcoal, copper oxide, glass powder, and best of all by powdered Iceland spar. C. H. Hall observed no precipitation of arsenic trisulphide suspended in transformer oil of resistance 1.5×10^{16} ohms per c.c., and subjected to alternating and direct currents of voltages 10^4 to 2×10^5 for 3 hrs.

In 1832, P. H. Boutigny found that the addition of a small quantity of an acid precipitates arsenic trisulphide in yellow flakes from its colloidal soln. The greatest effect was produced by sulphuric, hydrochloric, or nitric acid ; then followed oxalic acid, then acetic acid, and even carbonic acid produced some effect. He also found that on adding certain salts—ammonium chloride, sodium nitrate or sulphate, or magnesium sulphate—the trisulphide was similarly precipitated. N. R. Dhar and A. C. Chatterji studied the adsorption of soln. and ions by arsenic trisulphide. H. O. Schulze found that the addition of a cold soln. of boric, tartaric, benzoic, or salicylic acid, arsenic trioxide, cane sugar, chloral hydrate, absolute alcohol, or glycerol occasioned no precipitation. The following caused the coagulation or flocculation of the arsenic trisulphide hydrosol when added in the given state of dilution :

HCl.aq., 1 : 555 ; HNO₃.aq., 1 : 276 ; H₂SO₄.aq., 1 : 255 ; H₂SO₃.aq., 1 : 138 ; H₂C₂O₄.aq., 1 : 65 ; H₃PO₄.aq., 1 : 26 ; HC₂H₃O₂.aq., 1 : 0·18 ; K₂SO₄.aq., 1 : 76 ; Na₂SO₄.aq., 1 : 129 ; (NH₄)₂SO₄.aq., 1 : 188 ; CaSO₄.aq., 1 : 2780 ; MgSO₄.aq., 1 : 2630 ; ZnSO₄.aq., 1 : 3330 ; MnSO₄.aq., 1 : 2860 ; NiSO₄.aq., 1 : 3440 ; FeSO₄.aq., 1 : 2380 ; Al₂(SO₄)₃.aq., 1 : 52600 ; Tl₂SO₄.aq., 1 : 799 ; KCl.aq., 1 : 137 ; KBr.aq., 1 : 103 ; KI.aq., 1 : 55 ; LiI.aq., 1 : 127 ; NaCl.aq., 1 : 212 ; NH₄Cl.aq., 1 : 207 ; BaCl₂+aq., 1 : 2860 ; CaCl₂.aq., 1 : 4370 ; MgCl₂.aq., 1 : 10000 ; FeCl₃.aq., 1 : 50000 ; AlCl₃.aq., 1 : 83000 ; CrCl₃.aq., 1 : 20000 ; KNO₂.aq., 1 : 84 ; NaNO₃.aq., 1 : 117 ; NH₄NO₃.aq., 1 : 138 ; Ba(NO₃)₂.aq., 1 : 2080 ; KClO₃.aq., 1 : 88 ; CaH₂(CO₃)₂.aq., 1 : 3120 ; K₂C₂H₄O.aq., 1 : 85 ; K₂C₂O₄.aq., 1 : 81 ; NaC₂H₃O₂.aq., 1 : 78 ; Urea.aq., 1 : 25 ; (NH₄)₂Fe(SO₄)₂.aq., 1 : 1160 ; K₂Al₂(SO₄)₄.aq., 1 : 50000 ; K₂Fe₂(SO₄)₄.aq., 1 : 55500 ; K₂Cr₂(SO₄)₄.aq., 1 : 25000 ; K₄Fe(CN)₆.aq., 1 : 67 ; K₃Fe(CN)₆.aq., 1 : 81. E. Herrmann studied the flocculation with organic anions.

All this is in agreement with the rule of H. O. Schulze that the active ion in coagulation has a charge of opposite sign to that of the colloid. This was discussed in connection with the gold hydrosol—3. 23, 8. There is a limiting conc. for the complete precipitation, and also a limiting conc. below which no precipitation occurs even after a long interval of time. Thus, H. Freundlich found that with a hydrosol containing 9·57 millimols of arsenic trisulphide per litre, and when 1·219 and 2·438 millimols of potassium chloride per litre were added, at the end of nearly a year, the soln. contained respectively 9·60 and 9·45 millimols of the trisulphide, and with a soln. containing 3·9 millimols of potassium chloride, almost complete precipitation had taken place. Again, the way the reagent is added has a marked influence. The more slowly the reagent is added, the greater the length of time and the greater the excess of reagent required for complete precipitation. In figurative language, the hydrosol seems to become acclimatized to the precipitant. This subject was studied by S. Ghosh and co-workers, W. Krestinskaja and W. Jakovleva, and V. V. Lepeshkin. As H. B. Weiser showed, the amount of electrolyte which when added all at once produces coagulation, will not do so if added drop by drop over a long period, owing to the adsorption of the precipitating ion by the neutralized colloidal particles. Likewise also the presence of one electrolyte may diminish the activity of a second one. Thus, if lithium chloride be added to the hydrosol of arsenic trisulphide, and then magnesium chloride, more magnesium chloride must be added if lithium chloride were absent. W. Biltz also observed that negatively charged colloids like arsenic trisulphide are precipitated by positively charged colloids like ferric oxide, added in the proper proportion. Thus, 24 mgrms. of arsenic trisulphide hydrosol are precipitated by the following hydrosols :

Hydrosol .	.	Fe_2O_3	ThO_2	CeO_2	ZrO_2	Al_2O_3	CeO_2
Milligrams.	.	12	6	4	2	2	0·5

J. Billiter observed that the soln. is negative or positive according as one or other component is in excess, and this holds whether precipitation has occurred or not. The results with hydrosols of ferric hydroxide and arsenic trisulphide, are shown in Table IX. The subject was studied by H. Freundlich and G. V. Stottman, and J. J. Bikermann. A. W. Thomas and L. Johnson studied the mutual precipitation

TABLE IX.—CATAPHORESIS OF ARSENIC TRISULPHIDE.

10 c.c. of the mixture contains in mgrms.		Result.	Charge on particles.	Cataphoresis.
Fe_2O_3	As_2S_3			
0·61	20·3	Opalescence	—	To anode
6·08	16·6	Precipitation immediate	—	To anode
9·12	14·5	Precipitation complete	0	Neutral
15·2	10·4	Precipitation immediate	+	To cathode
24·3	4·14	Opalescence slight	+	To cathode
27·4	2·07	No change	+	To cathode

of ferric hydroxide and arsenic trisulphide sols which is attributed to the chemical action $S''+2Fe'''=S+2Fe''$. A. Boutaric and G. Perreau found that the presence of lithium chloride protects arsenic trisulphide sol from flocculation by potassium, magnesium, barium, and ammonium chlorides, while the flocculation is accelerated by cadmium and aluminium chlorides. B. Papaconstantinou studied the protective action of soaps ; and J. Traube and E. Rackwitz, and S. Sugden and M. Williams, studied the action of protective colloids; and H. B. Weiser, the antagonistic action of ions.

S. E. Linder and H. Picton showed that when arsenic trisulphide hydrosol is coagulated by a metal salt, a sensible amount of metal is withdrawn from the soln. by the sulphide, while the acid radicle remains in soln. in undiminished amount. This was confirmed by W. R. Whitney and J. R. Ober, who inferred that the coagulant is hydrolyzed by the colloid, the base combining with the colloid while the acid remains in soln. On the other hand, S. E. Linder and H. Picton say that when a metallic salt is added to arsenious sulphide, an interchange takes place between the metal of the salt and the hydrogen of the hydrosulphide. The extent to which this interchange takes place is governed almost entirely by mass action, as the hydrosulphide itself is insoluble equally with the metallic derivatives in presence of excess of electrolyte, whether acid or salt. The reactions for potassium and barium chlorides are represented as follows : $m\mathrm{As_2S_3,H_2S+2KCl}\rightleftharpoons m\mathrm{As_2S_3,K_2S+2HCl}$; and $m\mathrm{As_2S_3,H_2S+BaCl_2}\rightleftharpoons m\mathrm{As_2S_3,BaS+2HCl}$. J. Duclaux assumed that when barium chloride is used as coagulent, it is probable that there is double decomposition between the barium chloride and the sulphide, perhaps by replacement of an AsO group existing in the sulphide by barium.

As indicated above, S. S. Bhatnagar and B. L. Rao, and S. E. Linder and H. Picton, regarded colloidal sulphides as hydrosulphides. A. J. Rabinovitch represented the colloid by $(\mathrm{As_2S_3})_n.\mathrm{H_2S}$. By precipitating arsenic trisulphide hydrosol with barium chloride, W. Pauli and A. Semler found four eq. of barium are present in the precipitate for each eq. of hydrogen ion found in the sol. The colloid is regarded as having the constituent $(x\mathrm{As_2S_3,H_2As_2S_4,HAs_2S_4})\mathrm{H^{\cdot}}$, only one of the hydrogen atoms being ionized in soln., but all four being replaced on precipitation. The flocculation of the hydrosol was examined by A. Dumansky, who observed that the precipitate contains a considerable proportion of silver and copper when the nitrates of these metals are used as coagulents ; lead acetate coagulates without forming lead sulphide ; alkali hydroxides and cyanides have no coagulating power ; iodine and potassium permanganate react chemically with the sulphide without coagulation. K. Matsuno, and H. Freundlich and H. P. Zeh examined the coagulating effect of cobalt-ammines. J. Mukhopadhyaya found that hydrogen sulphide renders colloidal soln. more stable towards electrolytes ; and he was unable to find any marked adsorption of the electrolytes by the colloidal trisulphide. H. R. Kruyt and C. F. van Duin observed that the coagulation of the hydrosol by electrolytes is influenced in the presence of ethyl, propyl, isobutyl, and isoamyl alcohols, and phenol, such that the limiting conc. of the electrolyte is diminished in the case of uni- and ter-valent inorganic cations, and increased for bi- and quadri-valent cations. The flocculation of arsenic trisulphide hydrosol was examined by H. R. Kruyt and J. van der Spek, H. R. Kruyt and P. C. van der Willigen, H. Freundlich and V. Birstein, S. Sugden and M. Williams, A. Boutaric and C. Simonet, A. J. Rabinovitch, N. P. Peskoff and V. I. Sokoloff, O. K. Rice, G. Rossi and B. Cecchetti, G. Rossi and co-workers, K. C. Sen, A. Ivanitzkaja and L. Orlova, F. Powis, E. F. Burton and co-workers, A. Boutaric and M. Vuillaume, J. N. Mukherjee and S. G. Chaudhury, J. N. Mukherjee and co-workers, H. D. Murray, W. R. Whitney and J. R. Ober, Wo. Ostwald, J. Mukhopadhyaya, N. Bach, N. Schiloff, C. K. Jablczynsky and H. Lorentz-Zienkovska, A. Janek and B. Jirgensons, S. Ghosh and co-workers, etc. N. R. Dhar and A. C. Chatterji observed the rhythmic coagulation of arsenic trisulphide. H. Freundlich and P. H. Zeh found that there is a close relationship between the precipitating value of an electrolyte and its effect on cataphoresis. With univalent to quadrivalent cations derived from complex cobalt salts, K. Matsuno noticed that eq. amounts have a similar coagulating effect on colloidal arsenic trisulphide, and cations of different valency are equally adsorbed from equimolar soln. H. B. Weiser has shown that H. O. Schulze's rule that the coagulating power of an electrolyte is greater the higher the valency of the precipitating ion is only a qualitative rule ; and in so far as this rule holds, the adsorbability of an ion is greater the higher the valency ; and that the observation of N. R. Dhar and co-workers that ions with the lowest precipitating power are adsorbed most, and conversely, is not true. He also showed that with strong electrolytes containing weakly adsorbed precipitating ions and the same stabilizing ion, there is a direct relationship between the relative adsorbability of the precipitating ions and the coagulating power of the electrolytes in the sense that the electrolyte containing the most readily adsorbed precipitating ion, coagulates a sol in lowest conc. The amount of various precipitating ions carried down on precipitating a sol are determined by (a) adsorption by the electrically charged particles during neutralization and (b) adsorption by the electrically neutral particles in case the adsorption of the stabilizing ions of the several electro lytes is constant or is negligibly small; but the amounts of (b) will vary with the nature and conc. of the electrolyte. M. Prasad and co-workers studied the adsorption of sugars. C. K. Jablczynsky and co-workers measured the rate of coagulation; H. Freundlich and F. Oppenheimer, the rate of crystallization; V. V. Lepeshkin the temp. coeff. of the rate of coagulation; A. J. Rabinovitsch and W. A. Dorfman, the electrometric changes during the coagulation; and S. S. Bhatnagar and co-workers, the effect of the size of the particles of the colloidal trisulphide.

C. K. Jablczynsky measured the rate of coagulation of arsenic trisulphide sols. H. Freundlich and S. K. Basu measured the effect of stirring on the coagulation of the hydrosol. J. N. Mukherjee found that a rise in temp. has different effects on the rate of coagulation, depending on the nature of the electrolyte, the quality of the sol, and the conc. of the electrolyte. These effects are not due to any irreversible change in the sol. The salts of the alkali metals show a stabilization at higher temp.; the salts of the alkaline earth metals always show a diminution in stability, the same being also the case with sulphuric and hydrochloric acids. The same results are obtained, even when the sol contains small quantities of alcohol or phenol in soln. H. Freundlich and V. Birstein studied the coagulation by salts of the amines ; A. J. Rabinovitsch, by barium chloride. A. Boutaric and M. Vuillaume found that the rapidity of the flocculation caused by potassium chloride or barium chloride diminishes as the granules increase in size, but the inverse is the case when the flocculating agent is aluminium chloride. In the latter case, the speed of floccula- tion increases, and in the former cases diminishes, as the conc. of the sol increases ; and A. Boutaric and Y. Manière found that light had little effect on the coagulation —the blue rays caused a slight acceleration with aluminium or potassium chloride as coagulant, and a slight retardation with barium chloride. Red light had no effect. P. B. Ganguly and N. R. Dhar also found that a sol of arsenic trisulphide is coagulated by exposure to tropical sunlight. H. P. Corliss observed that colloidal soln. of arsenic trisulphide containing alcohol and ether are more transparent, and less readily coagulated by salts than aq. soln. These soln. undergo a change on keeping, so that the amount of arsenic found in the filtrate after coagulation with acid increases. Under similar conditions the distribution of the arsenic between the two liquid phases varies continuously with the decomposition of the phases, and that, other things being equal, the fraction of the arsenic sulphide going into the upper layer decreases with an increase in the conc. of the sulphide. W. Reinders measured the distribution of colloidal arsenic trisulphide and other colloids between water and isobutyl alcohol, amyl alcohol, benzene, ether, carbon tetrachloride, and carbon disulphide. According to H. Freundlich and F. Moor, a mixture of silver and arsenious sulphide sols undergoes, in the dark, a change of colour from golden-brown through greenish-brown to lilac, and, with exposure to light, through green to a golden-yellow. Both changes are prevented in the presence of a gelatin gel. The reaction in the dark is regarded as a direct interchange between the particles of the two sols. The secondary change under the action of light is purely chemical and involves oxygen, with the probable formation of a silver sulphoarsenate. N. P. Peskoff found that while the presence of gelatin does not affect the velocity of reaction in true soln., it enormously reduces the velocity of dissolution of colloids by suitable reagents—e.g. the dissolution of colloidal arsenic trioxide by alkali-lye, and the reaction $3HgCy_2+As_2S_3=2AsCy_3+3HgS$. S. S. Bhatnagar and D. L. Shrivastava found that adsorbed sucrose, glucose, or galactose loses its optical activity, thus suggesting a chemical explanation of the protective action of these agents. N. P. Peskoff and V. I. Sokoloff found that at low conc., gelatin renders arsenic trisulphide sol unstable ; but larger quantities stabilize it. N. R. Dhar and S. Ghosh studied the ageing of the colloid.

J. J. Bikermann made organosols of arsenic trisulphide by passing a stream

of dry hylrogen sulphide through soln. of arsenic trichloride in anhydrous nitrobenzene, or acetoacetic ester, and removing hydrogen chloride, and the excess of
hydrogen sulphide with a current of dry air. The highest conc. obtained was
29 millimols of the trisulphide per litre. The conductivity of the soln. was less than
10^{-7} mho per c.c. The soln. are stable for an indefinitely long time at room temp.,
but, on boiling, a red coagulum separates. The soln. are not coagulated by freezing
and remelting, or by centrifuging at 2000 revs. per min. The soln. are red by
reflected light, and yellow by transmitted light. The arsenic trisulphide is not
removed from nitrobenzene by water, nor will organic liquids remove the trisulphide
from the hydrosol. Coagulation by ferric chloride, cupric acetoacetate, or tetra-
propylammonium iodide occurs when the electrokinetic potential has been reduced to
25×10^{-3} volts, and this value is nearly independent of the conc. of the soln., or of
the nature of the dispersion medium. The valency rule is applicable. If the
coagulation depended on the weakening of the electrostatic repulsion of the micelles,
the dielectric constant of the medium would be expected to influence the magnitude
of the precipitation value. This does not seem to be the case as the electrokinetic
potential at the coagulation point does not vary more than 20 per cent., while the
dielectric constant varies fivefold. W. L. Miller and R. H. McPherson found that
arsenic trisulphide forms a colloidal soln. with ether, and that on shaking the
hydrosol with ether, the trisulphide distributes itself between the two phases.

REFERENCES.

[1] G. Agricola, *Interpretatio Germanica vocum rei metallicæ*, Basileæ, 1546; D. Wallerius, *Geol. För. Förh. Stockholm*, **43**, 671, 1921; N. Zenzen, *ib.*, **44**. 172, 1922; N. Zenzen, H. G. Söder-baum, and H. Sjögren, *Ark. Kemi Min. Geol.*, **8**. 20, 1922.
[2] R. Bunsen, *Liebig's Ann.*, **192**. 320, 1878; H. Vohl, *ib.*, **96** 238, 1855; L. F. Nilson, *Journ. prakt. Chem.*, (2), **12**. 327, 1875; (2), **14**. 19, 1876; *Akad. Handl. Stockholm*, **10**. 2, 1871; *Oefvers. Akad. Stockholm*, **28**. 303, 1871; J. J. Berzelius, *Schweigger's Journ.*, **34**. 46, 1822; *Pogg. Ann.*, **7**. 137, 1826; *Ann. Chim. Phys.*, (2), **11**. 225, 1819; (2), **22**. 166, 1826; M. H. Klaproth, *Beiträge zur chemischen Kenntniss der Mineralkörper*, Berlin, **5**. 234, 1810; A. Laugier, *Ann. Chim. Phys.*, (1), **85**. 46, 1813; L. J. Thénard, *ib.*, (2), **59**. 284, 1825; G. F. Becker, *Monograph U.S. Geol. Sur.*, **13**. 344, 1888; W. H. Weed and L. V. Pirsson, *Amer. Journ. Science*, (3), **42**. 401, 1891; K. F. Peters, *Neues Jahrb. Min.*, 665, 1861; F. Sandberger, *ib.*, 403, 1868; T. Bergman, *Producta ignis subterranei chemice considerata*, Upsala, 1777; T. Monticelli and N. Covelli, *Prodromo della mineralogia vesuviana*, Napoli, 36, 1825; A. Scacchi, *Compt. Rend.*, **31**. 263, 1850; *Zeit. deut. geol. Ges.*, **4**. 173, 1852; *Memorie geologische sulla Campania*, Napoli, 116, 1849; F. Mayençon, *Compt. Rend.*, **86**. 491, 1878; **92**. 854, 1881; A. Gages, *Journ. Geol. Soc. Dublin*, **8**. 243, 1860; C. W. C. Fuchs, *Die künstliche dargestellten Mineralien nach Roses System geordnet*, Haarlem, **53**, 1872; E. Weinschenk, *Zeit. Kryst.*, **17**. 499, 1890; W. Spring, *Zeit. phys. Chem.*, **18**. 556, 1895; *Bull. Belg. Acad.*, (3), **30**. 199, 1895; *Zeit. anorg. Chem.*, **10**. 185, 1895; H. Winter, *ib.*, **43**. 228, 1905; N. J. B. G. Guibourt, *Journ. Chim. Méd.*, (1), **2**. 55, 106, 1826; W. Borodowsky, *Sitzber. Nat. Ges. Dorpat*, **14**, 159, 1905; L. A. Buchner, *Sitzber. Bayer. Akad.*, **404**, 1868; *Repert. Pharm.*, **17**. 386, 1868; *Berg. Hütt. Ztg.*, **30**. 245, 1871; *Zeit. anal. Chem.*, **10**. 308, 1871; J. H. Reedy, *Journ. Amer. Chem. Soc.*, **43**. 2419, 1921; S. S. Bhatnagar and B. L. Rao, *Koll. Zeit.*, **33**. 150, 1923; E. Schmidt, *Arch. Pharm.*, **255**. 45, 1917.
[3] I. S. R. I. Eques a Born, *Lythophylacium Bornianum*, Prague, **1**. 139, 1773; *Catalogue méthodique et raisonné de la collection des fossiles de Mlle. Eleonore de Raab*, Wien, **2**. 203, 1790; A. Breithaupt, *Berg. Hütt. Ztg.*, **25**. 194, 1866; *Mineralogische Studien*, Leipzig, 114, 1866; P. Groth, *Tabellarische Uebersicht der Mineralien*, Braunschweig, 74, 1874; 17, 1898; L. Merz, *Ueber das Verhalten der Elemente und Verbindungen der Schwefelgruppe in Vacuum*, Heidelberg, 1905; R. Robl, *Zeit. angew. Chem.*, **39**. 608, 1926; W. H. Miller, *Introduction to Mineralogy*, London, 176, 1852; W. Haidinger, *Treatise on Mineralogy*, Edinburgh, **3**. 48, 1825; F. Mohs, *Grundriss der Mineralogie*, Dresden, **2**. 613, 1824; H. Saito, *Science Rep. Tohoku Univ.*, **16**. 37, 1927; A. Lévy, *Description d'une collection de minéraux formée par M. Henri Heuland*, Londres, **3**. 280, 1837; C. Hintze, *Zeit. Kryst.*, **11**. 608, 1886; E. Weinschenk, *ib.*, **17**. 499, 1890; S. Stevanovic, *ib.*, **39**. 18, 1904; W. Phillips, *Introduction to Mineralogy*, London, 277, 1823; J. A. Krenner, *Földt. Közl.*, **12**. 210, 1882; **13**. 381, 1883; A. des Cloizeaux, *Bull. Soc. Min.*, **5**. 108, 1882; A. de Gramont, *ib.*, **18**. 291, 1895; H. A. Miers, *Min. Mag.*, **10**. 24, 1892; E. Jannettaz, *Compt. Rend.*, **116**. 317, 1893; F. Beijerinck, *Neues Jahrb. Min. B.B.*, **11**. 424, 1897; O. Mügge, *Neues Jahrb. Min.*, ii, 19, 1883; i, 81, 1898; C. Doelter, *ib.*, ii, 91, 1896; C. J. B. Karsten, *Schweigger's Journ.*, **65**. 394, 1832; J. F. L. Hausmann, *Liebig's Ann.*, **74**. 198, 1850; *Ges. Wiss. Gött.*, **1**, 1850; E. Mitscherlich, *ib.*, **12**. 137, 1834; *Sitzber. Akad. Berlin*, 425, 1833; *Pogg. Ann.*, **29**. 133, 1833; N. J. B. G. Guibourt, *Journ. Chim. Méd.*, (1), **2**. 55, 106, 1826;

J. J. Berzelius *Schweigger's Journ.*, **34**. 46, 1822 ; *Pogg. Ann.*, **7**. 137, 1826 ; *Ann. Chim. Phys.*, (2), **11**. 225, 1819 ; (2), **32**. 166, 1826 ; W. Spring, *Zeit. phys. Chem.*, **18**. 556, 1895 ; *Bull. Acad. Belg.*, (3), **30**. 199, 1895 ; *Zeit. anorg. Chem.*, **10**. 185, 1895 ; H. Winter, **43**. 228, 1905 ; W. P. A. Jonker, *ib.*, **62**. 89, 1909 ; A. Schüller, *Ber. Math. Naturw. Ungarn.*, **12**. 255, 1894 ; E. Szarvasy and C. Messinger, *Ber.*, **30**. 1344, 1897 ; W. Borodowsky, *Sitzber. Nat. Ges. Dorpat*, **14**. 159, 1905 ; R. Böttger, *Tabellarische Uebersicht der specifischen Gewichte der Körper*, Frankfort, 1837 ; C. Hintze, *Handbuch der Mineralogie*, Leipzig, **1**. i, 360, 1904 ; F. Krafft, *Ber.*, **40**. 4778, 1907 ; R. Lorenz and W. Herz, *Zeit. anorg. Chem.*, **135**. 374, 1924 ; C. Tubandt and M. Haedicke, *ib.*, **160**. 297, 1927 ; W. Herz, *ib.*, **163**. 220, 1927 ; W. W. Coblentz, *Phys. Rev.*, (2), **17**. 245, 1921 ; T. W. Case, *ib.*, (2), **9**. 305, 1917 ; C. Zenghelis, *Zeit. phys. Chem.*, **50**. 219, 1904 ; L. H. Borgström, *Oefvers. Finska Vet. Soc. Förh.*, **47**. 24, 1915 ; R. Cusack, *Proc. Irish Acad.*, **4**. 399, 1891.

⁴ T. Riekher, *Neues Jahrb. Pharm.*, **36**. 9, 1871 ; H. Ludwig, *Arch. Pharm.*, (2), **97**. 35, 1859 ; E. Reichardt, *ib.*, (3), **17**. 1, 1880 ; R. F. Weinland and P. Gruhl, *ib.*, **255**. 467, 1917 ; P. Gruhl, *Verbindungen des Arsen- und Antimontrioxydes mit den Halogeniden mehrwertiger Metalle*, München, 1897 ; H. Beckurts, *ib.*, (3), **22**. 654, 1884 ; L. Gmelin, *Handbook of Chemistry*, London, **4**. 274, 1850 ; A. Lintner, *Repert. Pharm.*, (4), **1**. 314, 1852 ; J. S. F. Pagenstecher, (2), **11**. 31, 1837 ; (2), **23**. 14, 1841 ; A. Fyfe, *Phil. Mag.*, (4), **2**. 487, 1851 ; W. Wallace and F. Penny, *ib.*, (4), **4**. 361, 1852 ; P. Berthier, *Ann. Chim. Phys.*, (2), **39**. 260, 1828 ; A. Bineau, *ib.*, (2), **70**. 264, 1839 ; H. V. Regnault, *ib.*, (2), **62**. 384, 1836 ; M. Decourdemanche, *Journ. Chim. Méd.*, (1), **3**. 229, 1827 ; *Journ. Pharm. Chim.*, (1), **13**. 217, 1827 ; E. Soubeiran, *ib.*, (2), **16**. 353, 1849 ; K. Chodounsky, *Listy Chem.*, **13**. 114, 1889 ; A. Schüller, *Ber. Math. Naturw. Ungarn*, **12**. 255, 1894 ; R. F. Weinland and P. Lehmann, *Zeit. anorg. Chem.*, **26**. 341, 1901 ; G. C. Winkelblech, *Liebig's Ann.*, **21**. 34, 1837 ; K. Preis, *ib.*, **257**. 178, 1890 ; J. von Liebig, *Pogg. Ann.*, **13**. 433, 1828 ; A. Duflos, *Breslau Schles. Ges.*, 65, 1835 ; D. Vitali, *L'Orosi*, **16**. 145, 1893 ; A. Taufflieb, *Journ. prakt. Chem.*, (1), **3**. 42, 1834 ; *Journ. Pharm. Chim.*, (1), **22**. 392, 1834 ; E. Pollacci, *Boll. Chim. Farm.*, **47**. 363, 1908 ; J. L. Proust, *Journ. Phys.*, **53**. 89, 1801 ; *Nicholson's Journ.*, **1**. 109, 1802 ; F. Kessler, *Pogg. Ann.*, **95**. 214, 1855 ; J. F. Simon, *ib.*, **40**. 411, 437, 1837 ; H. Rose, *ib.*, **42**. 536, 1837 ; **90**. 194, 565, 1853 ; **105**. 577, 1858 ; H. Becker, *ib.*, **74**. 303, 1848 ; C. Eckert, *Pharm. Viertelj.*, **13**. 357, 1864 ; E. Schmidt, *Arch. Pharm.*, **255**. 45, 1917 ; R. Bunsen, *Liebig's Ann.*, **106**. 10, 1858 ; **192**. 317, 1878 ; K. Heumann, *ib.*, **173**. 33, 1874 ; E. Schürmann, *ib.*, **249**. 326, 1888 ; C. R. Fresenius and C. H. L. von Babo, *ib.*, **49**. 298, 1844 ; W. Fresenius, *Zeit. anal. Chem.*, **20**. 522, 1881 ; C. R. Fresenius, *ib.*, **25**. 200, 1886 ; J. Haidlen and C. R. Fresenius, *Liebig's Ann.*, **43**. 129, 1842 ; J. J. Berzelius, *Schweigger's Journ.*, **34**. 46, 1822 ; *Pogg. Ann.*, **7**. 137, 1826 ; *Ann. Chim. Phys.*, (2), **11**. 225, 1819 ; (2), **32**. 116, 1826 ; O. Weigel, *Zeit. phys. Chem.*, **58**. 294, 1907 ; J. Billitzer, *ib.*, **51**. 129, 1905 ; W. Biltz and E. Keunecke, *Zeit. anorg. Chem.*, **147**. 171, 1925 ; E. H. Riesenfeld and W. Haase, *ib.*, **147**. 188, 1925 ; E. A. Schneider, *Journ. prakt. Chem.*, (2), **36**. 498, 1887 ; F. L. Hünefeld, *ib.*, (1), **7**. 235, 1836 ; J. Ossikowsky, *ib.*, (2), **22**. 323, 1880 ; C. F. Rammelsberg, *Sitzber. Akad. Berlin*, 79, 1881 ; H. Pélabon, *Compt. Rend.*, **136**. 454, 812, 1903 ; P. de Clermont and J. Frommel, *ib.*, **86**. 828, 1878 ; **87**. 330, 332, 1878 ; A. Baudrimont, *ib.*, **64**. 368, 1867 ; G. H. O. Volger, *Studien zur Entwicklungsgeschichte der Mineralien*, Zürich, 56, 1854 ; P. Askanasy, E. Elöd, and H. Zieler, *Zeit. anorg. Chem.*, **162**. 161, 1927 ; J. Roth, *Allgemeine und chemische Geologie*, Berlin, **1**. 262, 1879 ; H. Feigel, *Ueber die analytische Auswertung chemischer Reaktionen*, Erlangen, 1905 ; J. Kelley and E. F. Smith, *Amer. Chem. Journ.*, **18**. 1096, 1896 ; C. S. Ward, *Amer. Chemist.*, **4**. 10, 1873 ; L. F. Nilson, *Journ. prakt. Chem.*, (2), **12**. 327, 1875 ; (2), **14**. 19, 1876 ; *Akad. Handl. Stockholm*, **10**. 2, 1871 ; *Oefvers. Akad. Stockholm*, **28**. 303, 1871 ; A. Classen and O. Bauer, *Ber.*, **16**. 1061, 1883 ; D. Vorländer and R. Häberle, *ib.*, **46**. 1612, 1913 ; W. R. Lang and C. M. Carson, *Journ. Soc. Chem. Ind.*, **21**. 1018, 1902 ; J. A. Kaiser, *Zeit. anal. Chem.*, **14**. 255, 1875 ; L. L. de Koninck, *ib.*, **19**. 468, 1880 ; E. Biltz, *ib.*, **9**. 410, 1870 ; R. E. O. Puller, *ib.*, **10**. 41, 1871 ; *Journ. Chem. Soc.*, **24**. 586, 1871 ; S. E. Linder and H. Picton, *Journ. Chem. Soc.*, **61**. 114, 1892 ; J. Spiller, *ib.*, **10**. 110, 1858 ; *Chem. News*, **8**. 280, 1863 ; **19**. 166, 1869 ; G. Gore, *Proc. Roy. Soc.*, **20**. 441, 1872 ; **21**. 140, 1873 ; E. C. Franklin and C. A. Kraus, *Amer. Chem. Journ.*, **20**. 820, 1898 ; C. Pertusi, *Ann. Chim. Anal.*, **20**. 229, 1915 ; H. B. North and C. B. Connor, *Amer. Journ. Science*, (4), **40**. 640, 1915 ; *Journ. Amer. Chem. Soc.*, **37**. 2486, 1915 ; J. Milbauer and J. Tucek, *Chem. Ztg.*, **50**. 323, 1926 ; S. S. Bhatnagar, N. A. Yajnik, and V. D. Zadoo, *Journ. Indian Chem. Soc.*, **4**. 209, 1927 ; H. Saito, *Science Rep. Tohoku Univ.*, **16**. 37, 1927 ; O. Materne, *Bull. Soc. Chim. Belg.*, **20**. 46, 1906.

⁵ J. J. Berzelius, *Schweigger's Journ.*, **34**. 46, 1822 ; *Pogg. Ann.*, **7**. 137, 1826 ; *Svenska Akad. Handl.*, 295, 1825 ; *Ann. Chim. Phys.*, (2), **11**. 225, 1899 ; (2), **32**. 166, 1826 ; C. G. C. Bischof, *Brandes' Arch.*, **17**. 239, 1826 ; O. Faust, *German Pat.*, *D.R.P.* 424141, 1926 ; P. H. Boutigny, *Journ. Chim. Méd.*, (1), **8**. 449, 1832 ; F. Haber, *Ber.*, **55**. B, 1717, 1922 ; L. Gmelin, *Handbook of Chemistry*, London, **4**. 274, 1850 ; H. D. Murray, *Phil. Mag.*, (6), **40**. 578, 1920 ; (6), **44**. 401, 1922 ; F. W. Küster and G. Dahmer, *Zeit. anorg. Chem.*, **33**. 105, 1903 ; **34**. 410, 1903 ; H. Winter, *ib.*, **43**. 228, 1905 ; K. C. Sen, *ib.*, **149**. 135, 1925 ; H. Picton, *Journ. Chem. Soc.*, **61**. 137, 1892 ; S. E. Lindet and H. Picton, *ib.*, **61**. 148, 1892 ; **67**. 63, 1895 ; **71**. 568, 1897 ; **87**. 1906, 1905 ; S. Sugden and M. Williams, *ib.*, **129**. 2424, 1926 ; J. N. Mukherjee and S. K. Majumdar, *ib.*, **125**. 785, 1924 ; F. Powis, *ib.*, **109**. 734, 1916 ; J. N. Mukherjee, *Phil. Mag.*, (6), **44**. 305, 1922 ; *Journ. Chem. Soc.*, **117**. 350, 1920 ; J. N. Mukherjee and S. G. Chaudhury, *ib.*, **125**. 794, 1924 ; J. N. Mukherjee and B. C. Ray, *ib.*, **125**. 476, 1924 ; J. N. Mukherjee and N. N. Sen, *ib.*, **115**. 461, 1919 ; J. N. Mukherjee and B. N. Ghosh, *Journ. Indian Chem. Soc.*, **1**. 213, 1925 ;

J. N. Mukherjee. S. G. Chaudhury, and S. P. R. Choudhuri. *ib.*, 4. 493, 1927; J. N. Mukherjee and S. G. Chaudhury, *ib.*, 2. 296, 1925 ; J. N. and S. Mukherjee and S. G. Chaudhury, *ib.*, 3. 349, 1926; S. G. Chaudhury and P. Kundu, *ib.*, 3. 345, 1926 ; S. S. Bhatnagar, M. Prasad, and D. C. Bahl, *ib.*, 2. 11, 1925 ; E. F. Burton and J. E. Currie, *Phil. Mag.*, (6), 47. 721, 1924 ; E. F. Burton and E. D. MacInnes, *Journ. Phys. Chem.*, 25. 517, 1921 ; O. K. Rice, *ib.*, 30. 1660, 1926 ; H. B. Weiser, *ib.*, 30. 1526, 1926 ; E. F. Burton and E. Bishop, *ib.*, 24. 701, 1920 ; S. S. Bhatnagar, K. K. Mathur. and D. L. Shrivastava, *ib.*, 28. 387, 1924 ; H. P. Corliss, *ib.*, 18. 681, 1914 ; W. L. Miller and R. H. McPherson, *ib.*, 12. 706, 1908 ; H. B. Weiser, *ib.*, 25. 399, 665, 1921 ; 28. 237, 1924 ; 29. 955, 1253, 1925 ; 30. 20, 1926 ; H. B. Weiser and H. O. Nicholas, *ib.*. 25. 742, 1921 ; S. S. Bhatnagar and D. L. Shrivastava, *ib.*, 28. 730, 1924 ; M. Prasad, D. L. Shrivastava, and R. S. Gupta, *Zeit. Koll.*, 37. 101, 1925 ; S. S. Bhatnagar, K. K. Mathur and D. L. Shrivastava, *ib.*, 28. 392, 1924 ; K. C. Sen, *Journ. Indian Chem. Soc.*, 3. 81, 1926 ; *Zeit. Koll.*, 29. 376, 517, 1925 ; N. R. Dhar, K. C. Sen, and S. Ghosh, *ib.*. 28. 457, 1924 ; P. B. Ganguly and N. R. Dhar, *Koll. Zeit.*, 31. 16, 1922 ; S. Ghosh, A. K. Bhattacharya, and N. R. Dhar, *ib.*, 38. 141, 1926 ; D. N. Chakravarti and N. R. Dhar, *ib.*, 42. 120, 124, 1917 ; N. R. Dhar and A. C. Chatterji, *Zeit. anorg. Chem.*, 159. 186, 1927 ; *Koll. Zeit.*, 37. 2, 1925 ; S. S. Bhatnagar and B. L. Rao, *ib.*, 23. 159, 1923 ; S. S. Bhatnagar, N. A. Yajnik, and V. D. Zadoo, *Journ. Indian Chem. Soc.*, 4. 209, 1927 ; N. R. Dhar and S. Ghosh, *ib.*, 35. 144, 1924 ; 36. 129, 1925 ; *Koll. Zeit.*, 39. 346, 1926 ; 41. 229, 1927 ; *Zeit. anorg. Chem.*, 152. 408, 1926 ; *Journ. Phys. Chem.*, 29. 435, 658, 1925 ; 30. 628, 830, 1565, 1926 ; B. Papaconstantinou, *ib.*, 29. 323, 1925 ; D. Vorländer and R. Häberle, *Ber.*, 46. 1612, 1913 ; N. P. Peskoff and V. T. Sokoloff, *Journ. Russ. Phys. Chem. Soc.*, 58. 823, 1926 ; N. P. Peskoff, *ib.*, 46. 1619, 1914 ; *Koll. Zeit.*, 32. 238, 1923 ; R. Wintgen, *Koll. Beihefte*, 7. 251, 1915 ; A. Ivanitzkaja and L. Orlova, *ib.*, 18. 1, 1923 ; C. K. Jablczynsky and H. Lorentz-Zienkovska, *Bull. Soc. Chim.*, (4), 37. 612, 1925 ; C. K. Jablczynsky, *ib.*, (4), 35. 1277, 1924 ; G. Rossi and M. Andrearelli, 55. ii, 99, 1925 ; G. Rossi and B. Cecchetti, *ib.*, 55. ii, 900, 1925 ; G. Rossi and A. Marescotti, *Ann. Chim. Applicata*, 17. 167, 1927 ; V. V. Lepeshkin, *Koll. Zeit.*, 32. 166, 1923 ; 36. 41, 1926 ; J. Traube and E. Rackwitz, *ib.*, 37. 131, 1925 ; I. Lifschitz and G. Beck, *ib.*, 26. 10, 1920 ; 31. 13, 1922 ; H. R. Kruyt and H. J. C. Tendeloo, *Proc. Acad. Amsterdam*, 27. 377, 1924 ; H. J. C. Tendeloo, *Koll. Zeit.*, 41. 290, 1927 ; A. J. Rabinovitsch, *Zeit. anorg. Chem.*, 116. 97, 1925 ; *Journ. Russ. Phys. Chem. Soc.*, 58. 849, 1926 ; N. P. Peskoff and V. I. Sokoloff, *ib.*, 58. 823, 1926 ; N. P. Peskoff, *Koll. Zeit.*, 32. 24, 163, 1923 ; J. Mukhopadhyaya, *Journ. Amer. Chem. Soc.*, 37. 2031, 1915 ; C. K. Jablczynsky and A. P. Jedrzejowska, *Bull. Soc. Chim.*, (4), 37. 608, 1925 ; E. Herrmann, *Helvetica Chim. Acta*, 9. 785, 1926 ; K. Schaum and P. Friedrich, *Zeit. wiss. Photochem.*, 23. 98, 1924 ; H. O. Schulze, *Journ. prakt. Chem.*, (2), 25. 431, 1882 ; H. Freundlich and A. Nathansohn, *Koll. Zeit.*, 28. 258, 1920 ; H. Freundlich and F. Moor, *ib.*, 36. 7, 1925 ; H. Freund, lich and F. Oppenheimer, *Ber.*, 58. B, 148, 1925 ; H. Freundlich and V. Birstein, *Koll. Beihefte*, 22. 95, 1926 ; H. Freundlich, *Zeit. phys. Chem.*, 44. 129, 1903 ; H. Freundlich and H. P. Zeh, *ib.*, 114. 65, 1924 ; 57. 385, 1907 ; H. Freundlich and S. K. Basu, *ib.*, 115. 203, 1925 ; H. Freund-lich and G. V. Slottman, *ib.*, 129, 305, 1927 ; J. J. Bikerman, *ib.*, 115. 261, 1925 ; H. Zocher, *ib.*, 98. 293, 1921 ; N. Schiloff, *ib.*, 100. 455, 1922 ; W. Biltz, *Ber.*, 37. 1095, 1904 ; *Nachr. Gött.*, 1, 1904 ; W. Biltz and W. Geibel, *ib.*, 141, 1906 ; C. H. Pfaff, *Schweigger's Journ.*, 45. 95, 1825 ; H. Vogel, *German Pat.*, *D.R.P.* 411323, 1924 ; G. Börjeson, *Koll. Zeit.*, 27. 18, 1920 ; A. Dumansky, *ib.*, 9. 262, 1911 ; 36. 98, 1925 ; S. Utzino, *ib.*, 32. 149, 1923 ; Wo. Ostwald, *ib.*, 40. 201, 1926 ; A. Janek and B. Jirgensons, *ib.*, 41. 40, 1927 ; J. J. Bikermann, *ib.*, 42. 293, 1927 ; W. Reinders, *ib.*, 13. 235, 1923 ; *Proc. Akad. Amsterdam*, 16. 379, 1913 ; J. Duclaux, *Journ. Chim. Phys.*, 6. 592, 1908 ; N. Bach, *ib.*, 18. 46, 1920 ; T. Svedberg, *Die Methoden zur Herstellung kolloider Lösungen anorganischer Stoffe*, Dresden, 297, 1909 : J. Thovert, *Compt. Rend.*, 133. 1197, 1901 ; 134. 507, 1902 ; 135. 579, 1902 ; K. von der Grinten, *ib.*, 174. 2083, 1924 ; A. Charriou, *ib.*, 176. 1890, 1923 ; A. Boutaric and M. Dupin, *Bull. Soc. Chim.*, (4), 43. 44, 1928 ; A. Boutaric and M. Vuillaume, *Journ. Chim. Phys.*, 21. 247, 1924 ; *Compt. Rend.*, 172. 1291, 1921 ; 173. 229, 1921 ; 174. 1351, 1922 ; 177. 259, 1923 ; 178. 938, 1924 ; A. Boutaric and Y. Manière, *ib.*, 180. 1841, 1925 ; *Bull. Acad. Belg.*, (5), 10. 150, 1924 ; A. Boutaric and R. Simonet, *ib.*, (5), 10. 150, 1924 ; A. Boutaric, *ib.*, (5), 10. 560, 1924 ; *Rev. Gen. Colloid.*, 4. 268, 1926 ; *Journ. Chim. Phys.*, 25. 120, 1928 ; A. Boutaric and G. Perreau, *Compt. Rend.*, 179. 46, 1924 ; 181. 511, 1925 ; *Rev. Gen. Colloid.*, 3. 129, 167, 1925 ; 4. 33, 75, 1926 ; *Journ. Chim. Phys.*, 24. 496, 1927 ; W. R. Whitney and J. R. Ober, *Journ. Amer. Chem. Soc.*, 23. 842. 1901 ; *Zeit. phys. Chem.*, 39. 630, 1902 ; H. Bechhold and J. Ziegler, *ib.*, 56. 105, 1906 ; J. Billiter, *ib.*, 51. 142, 1905 ; H. Bechhold, *ib.*, 60. 299, 1907 ; K. Matsuno, *Journ. Coll. Science Tokoyo*, 41. 11, 1921 ; J. Mukhopadhyaya, *Journ. Amer. Chem. Soc.*, 37. 2034, 1915 ; R. V. Murphy and J. H. Mathews, *ib.*, 45. 16, 1923 ; A. W. Thomas and L. Johnson, *ib.*, 45. 2532, 1923 ; C. H. Hall, *ib.*, 44. 1246, 1922 ; H. R. Kruyt and C. F. van Duin, *Koll. Beihefte*, 5. 269, 1914 ; C. F. van Duin, *Koll. Zeit.*, 17. 123, 1915 ; H. R. Kruyt and J. van der Spek, *ib.*, 24. 145, 1919 ; 25. 1, 1919 ; *Proc. Acad. Amsterdam*, 17. 1158, 1915 ; H. R. Kruyt, *Koll. Zeit.*, 15. 1344, 1913 ; H. R. Kruyt and P. C. van der Willigen, *ib.*, 29. 484, 1926 ; *Zeit. phys. Chem.*, 130. 170, 1927 ; H. R. Kruyt, A. C. W. Roodvoets, and P. C. van der Willigen, *Fourth Colloid Symposium*, 304, 1926 ; H. R. van Kruyt and H. J. C. Tendeloo, *Proc. Acad. Amsterdam*, 27. 377, 1924 ; B. Lange,, *ib.*, 132. 1, 1928 ; A. J. Rabinowitsch and W. A. Dorfmann, *ib.*, 131. 313, 1928 ; R. Zsigmondy and C. Carius, *Ber.*, 60. B, 1047, 1927 ; W. Krestinskaja and W. Jakovleva, *Koll. Zeit.*, 44. 141, 1928 ; W. Pauli and A. Semler, *Zeit. Koll.*, 34. 145, 1924 ; A. Semler, *ib.*, 34. 209, 1924;

4. Ivanitzkaja and M. Proskurnin, *ib.*, **39**. 15, 1926; J. J. Bikermann, *ib.*, **42**. 293, 1927; V. Gazzi, *Zymol. Chim. Colloidi*, **2**. 1, 1927; *Ber. Ges. Physiol. Pharmakol.*, **41**. 425, 1927.

§ 32. The Complex Salts of Arsenic Trisulphide—The Sulpharsenites

Arsenic trisulphide plays the part of an acid anhydride in forming a series of complex salts with the basic sulphides, and the products may be regarded as derivatives of a series of hypothetical **sulpharsenious acids,** which A. Hilger and R. F. Weinland [1] tabulated in a slightly different form :

Orthosulpharsenious acid	H_3AsS_3
Metasulpharsenious acid	$HAsS_2$
Pyrosulpharsenious acid	$H_4As_2S_5$
Metasulphotriarsenious acid (*i.e.* $H_9As_3S_9$ less $4H_2S$) . . .	HAs_3S_5
Orthosulphotetrarsenious acid (*i.e.* $H_{12}As_4S_{12}$ less $3H_2S$) .	$H_6As_4S_9$
Metasulphotetrarsenious acid (*i.e.* $H_{12}As_4S_{12}$ less $5H_2S$) .	$H_2As_4S_7$
Metasulphoctarsenious acid (*i.e.* $H_{24}As_8S_{24}$ less $11H_2S$) .	$H_2As_8S_{13}$
Metasulphennearsenious acid (*i.e.* $H_{27}As_9S_{27}$ less $13H_2S$) .	HAs_9S_{14}
Metasulphododecarsenious acid (*i.e.* $H_{36}As_{12}S_{36}$ less $17H_2S$) .	$H_2As_{12}S_{19}$

They added that the ortho-acid has the greatest number of hydrogen atoms and is $H_{3n}As_nS_{3n}=H_{n+2}As_nS_{2n+1}+(n-1)H_2S$; the pyro-acid is formed when a mol. of hydrogen sulphide is abstracted from two mols. of the acid : $H_{3n}As_nS_{3n}=H_{2n}As_nS_{5n/2}+\frac{1}{2}nH_2S$; and the meta-acid has the smallest number of hydrogen atoms when derived according to the equation $H_{3n}As_nS_{3n}=H_{\frac{1}{2}}\{3+(-n)^n\}As_nS_{\frac{1}{2}(n+1)-\frac{1}{2}\{(-1)^{n+1}\{1+(-1)^n\}+\frac{1}{4}\{3(2n-1)}{-(-1)^n\}H_2S}.$

A fair number of salts of these acids occurs in nature. There are also compounds which can be regarded as products of these acids with hydrogen sulphide of crystallization instead of water of crystallization, *e.g.*, $H_3AsS_3.\frac{1}{2}H_2S$, and $H_3AsS_3.2H_2S$. A few basic salts have also been reported. A general study of the natural sulphosalts was made by G. Cesaro, W. F. Foshag, E. T. Wherry, F. Zambonini, and P. Niggli.

J. J. Berzelius obtained sulphoarsenites by heating the sulphoarsenites in the absence of air when some sulphur is driven off. They are obtained in an impure state by the fusing arsenic trisulphide with a mixture of carbon and sulphates. The unstable alkali ortho-salts are also precipitated when alcohol is added to a soln. of arsenic trisulphide in alkali sulphide in the proportions required for the pyro-salt : $K_4As_2S_5=K_3AsS_3+KAsS_2$. The sulpharsenites of the metals are produced by double decomposition with the alkali salts. L. F. Nilson made the sulpharsenites by saturating with arsenic trisulphide an aq. soln. of the alkali or alkaline earth hydrosulphides, and evaporating in vacuo or in air. The soln. of the alkali sulpharsenite may decompose during the evaporation : $5K_3AsS_3=3K_3AsS_4+2As+3K_2S$; and with the ammonium salt a condensation product may be formed, $(NH_4)As_3S_5$. J. J. Berzelius obtained sulpharsenites by the action of aq. soln. of the hydroxides of the alkalies or alkaline earths on arsenic trisulphide : $2As_2S_3+4KOH=3KAsS_2+KAsO_2+2H_2O$—the trisulphide is again precipitated on the addition of, say, hydrochloric acid. K. Preis obtained sulpharsenites by boiling arsenic trioxide with a soln. of sodium monosulphide ; and L. F. Nilson, with a soln. of alkali carbonate. Some of the condensed sulpharsenites are produced when water acts on the metasulpharsenites. O. B. Kühn, and L. F. Nilson obtained them by the action of hydrogen sulphide on arsenites ; and by boiling realgar with potassium hydroxide : $3As_2S_2+4KOH=3KAsS_2+KAsO_2+2As+2H_2O$; by J. B. Senderens, by the action of sulphur on soln. of alkali arsenites ; and by O. von der Pfordten by the action of arsine on potassium trisulphide at 300°–350° : $2AsH_3+3K_2S_3=2K_3AsS_3+3H_2S$. H. Sommerlad produced sulpharsenites by heating arsenic trisulphide with the metal chlorides.

The sulpharsenites are usually yellow or red ; they are sometimes blue, green, or colourless. Some of them crystallize well. They are usually stable when solid. J. J. Berzelius added that when calcined with the exclusion of air they usually lose arsenic trisulphide, though the alkali salts remain unchanged. L. F. Nilson said that only the alkali and alkaline earth salts can be obtained in soln. The soln. have a yellow colour, and a bitter taste. Soln. of the metasulpharsenates are obtained by direct saturation of soln. of the hydrosulphides with the required amount of arsenic trisulphide, but when solid, they are not easily dissolved in water, and are decomposed by that menstruum. The aq. soln. of the metasulphoarsenites can be evaporated in air without decomposition. Soln. of the orthosulpharsenites are obtained as in the case of the metasulpharsenites and, with the exception of the alkali salts, they cannot be evaporated in vacuo without decomposition into sulpharsenates and arsenic. Boiling the aq. soln. of the metasulpharsenites results in their decomposition—L. F. Nilson obtained the metasulphotriarsenite from potassium metasulpharsenite; and J. J. Berzelius obtained arsenic trisulphide from soln. of the alkaline earth salts. When the soln. are exposed to air, thiosulphates are formed. Acids liberate the complex acids, but there is an immediate decomposition into hydrogen sulphide and arsenic trisulphide which is precipitated , but, added L. F. Nilson, the condensed alkali and calcium salts may be decomposed incompletely by hydrochloric acid. E. Berglund found that a boiling soln. of a sulpharsenite is decomposed by copper oxide into arsenate and cuprous sulphide; and J. J. Berzelius, that cupric hydroxide forms copper sulpharsenites; and an excess of silver oxide desulphurizes the sulpharsenites. E. W. von Siemens and J. G. Halske observed that on electrolysis the alkali sulpharsenites deposit arsenic on the cathode and form alkali hydrosulphides.

J. J. Berzelius prepared **ammonium orthosulpharsenite,** $(NH_4)_3AsS_3$, by adding alcohol to a soln. of arsenic trisulphide and washing the product with water. The white, feathery crystals decompose in air, ammonium sulphide escapes, and arsenic trisulphide remains. L. F. Nilson obtained **ammonium metasulphotriarsenite,** $NH_4As_3S_5.2H_2O$, by evaporating a soln. of ammonium hydrosulphide sat. with arsenic trisulphide; and adding one or two mols of ammonium hydrosulphide to a soln. of ammonium metarsenite, and evaporating in vacuo over potassium hydroxide and sulphuric acid. The red powder consists of spherical aggregates; it is not attacked by water; potash-lye dissolves it with the evolution of ammonia and the formation of arsenic trisulphide; it is soluble in aq. ammonia especially when heated; it is stable towards hydrochloric acid even when boiling.

J. J. Berzelius reported that **potassium orthosulpharsenite,** possibly K_3AsS_3, can be prepared by a method analogous to that used for the ammonium salt; and likewise also with **sodium orthosulpharsenite,** Na_3AsS_3. An excess of alkali hydrosulphide transforms the sulpharsenite into sulpharsenate with the deposition of arsenic: $5K_3AsS_3=3K_3AsS_4+2As+3K_2S$. J. J. Berzelius, and L. F. Nilson prepared **potassium metasulpharsenite,** $KAsS_2.2\frac{1}{2}H_2O$, by evaporating in vacuo a soln. of potassium hydrosulphide sat. with arsenic trisulphide. L. F. Nilson obtained **sodium metasulpharsenite,** $NaAsS_2.\frac{1}{2}H_2O$, in a similar way and also by boiling a similar soln., and then allowing it to stand over sulphuric acid. The *hemitrihydrate,* $NaAsS_2.1\frac{1}{2}H_2O$, separates as an amorphous brown powder. The potassium salt is stable in air; it is partly dissolved by water with some decomposition; and it is slowly attacked by boiling hydrochloric acid. The sodium salt forms with water a red, gelatinous mass, and, when heated, it forms a red soln., but if dried over sulphuric acid, the product is no longer wholly soluble in water. J. J. Berzelius reported **potassium pyrosulpharsenite,** presumably $K_4As_2S_5$, by heating pyrosulpharsenate. The yellow mass melts to a dark red liquid, and is decomposed by water; **sodium pyrosulpharsenite,** $Na_4As_2S_5$, was prepared in a similar way. L. F. Nilson showed that when arsenic trisulphide is treated with a boiling soln. of sodium carbonate, arsenic disulphide is precipitated; and when the clear soln. is allowed to cool, a bulky brown precipitate of **sodium metasulphotri-arsenite,** $NaAs_3S_5.4H_2O$, gradually subsides: $4NaAsS_2+3H_2O=Na_3AsO_3+3H_2S+NaAs_3S_5$.

According to L. F. Nilson, if instead of allowing the soln. of arsenic trisulphide in a soln. of sodium carbonate to cool, it is kept for a long time at 70°–80°, a yellowish-brown crust of impure arsenic trisulphide is formed ; and when the soln. is evaporated until it solidifies on cooling, a brown amorphous mass is obtained which on standing deposits four crystalline substances : (i) yellow, monoclinic prisms of sodium sulpharsenate ; (ii) small white crystals of sodium hydrocarbonate ; (iii) colourless crystals of sodium hydroarsenate ; and (iv) garnet-red hexagonal crystals or short prisms of sodium pentoxyhexasulphotetrarsenite. In the case of potassium carbonate, the clear soln. remaining after the separation of arsenic disulphide was evaporated to dryness, and it furnished a yellowish-green amorphous mass, which, after standing for two months, gave a soln. containing a large amount of small globular red masses of potassium metasulphotriarsenite, $KAs_3S_5.H_2O$. These were washed with water, which decomposes the compound but very slightly. This substance is scarcely attacked by hydrochloric acid, but dissolves in caustic potash to a yellow liquid, which when boiled gives a blackish-brown deposit. The reddish-brown microscopic prisms of the potassium salt melt when heated, and the dark fluid burns leaving a white residue. Water has very little action ; boiling hydrochloric acid decomposes it very slowly ; potash-lye dissolves it in the cold, forming a yellow liquid which, when boiled, furnishes sulpharsenate and arsenic ; it is easily soluble in a soln. of sodium carbonate with the evolution of carbon dioxide. L. F. Nilson found that when a soln. of potassium metasulpharsenite is evaporated not quite to dryness, treated with water, and filtered from the blood-red mass of possibly *potassium metasulphotetrarsenite*, $K_2As_4S_7$, the filtrate, when evaporated over sulphuric acid, furnishes potassium orthosulphotetrarsenite, $K_6As_4S_9.8H_2O$. Dark brown sodium metasulphotetrarsenite, $Na_2As_4S_7.6H_2O$, is produced on evaporating a soln. of arsenic trisulphide in one of sodium hydrosulphide. When treated with water, the sodium salt furnishes a blood-red coagulum, and an orange-red soln. It is soluble in a large proportion of water ; when dried it is attacked by hydrochloric acid very slowly.

H. Sommerlad prepared cuprous orthosulpharsenite, Cu_3AsS_3, or $3Cu_2S.As_2S_3$, by heating the pyrosulpharsenite in a current of hydrogen sulphide so long as arsenic trisulphide sublimes. It looks like cuprous sulphide ; it gives up no arsenic trisulphide to aq. ammonia, although it is attacked by alkali sulphides. The mineral julianite reported by M. Websky from the Friedrich-Julian mine, Rudelstadt, Silesia, approximates closely in composition to this salt. It occurs in small reddish-grey crystals of sp. gr. 5·12. Julianite is one member of a group of minerals included in the general term fahlerz.

J. G. Wallerius [2] referred to fahlerz as *argentum arsenico cupro et ferro mineralisatum*, and as *falerts*, and *grauerts*. A. Cronstedt called it *pyrites cupri griseus*, and *Fahlkupfererz*. I. S. R. I. Eques a Born described it as *argentum cinereum crystallis pyramidatis trigonis*. There were also the *Antimonfahlerz* and the *Graugültigerz* of M. H. Klaproth, A. Breithaupt, L. A. Emmerling, and A. G. Werner. These ores were grouped together as *cuivre gris* by R. J. Häuy, and J. B. L. Romé de l'Isle. A. Breithaupt called a variety *clinohedrite* and *fahlite*. W. Haidinger called it *tetrahedrite ;* and F. S. Beudant, *panabas*—from " πάν, tout ; et βάσις, bases." The more antimonial varieties are now called tetrahedrite. Argentiferous varieties were called *argentum rude album* by G. Agricola : *weisgylden*, and *minera argenti alba*, by J. G. Wallerius, and A. Cronstedt ; *Weissgültigerz, Silberfahlerz*, etc., by J. F. L. Hausmann, A. Breithaupt, etc. ; *aphthorite*, by L. F. Svanberg ; *freibergite*, by G. A. Kenngott ; *polytelite*, by F. von Kobell ; and *leucargyrite*, by A. Weisbach. Mercurial varieties were called *Schwarzerz*, by A. G. Werner ; *mercurial fahlerz, Quecksilberfahlerz*, by E. F. Glocker, and A. Breithaupt ; *spaniolite*, by F. von Kobell ; *schwatzite*, by G. A. Kenngott ; and *hermesite*, by A. Breithaupt. Arsenical varieties were called *gray sulphuret of copper* by J. Sowerby ; tennantite—after S. Tennant—by W. and R. Phillips ; *sandbergite*, by A. Breithaupt ; *erythroconite*, by M. Adam ; and *fredricite*, by H. Sjögren. Bismuthiferous varieties were called *annivite* by D. Brauns ; *rionite*, by T. Petersen ; and *Kobaltwismuthfahlerz*, by F. Sandberger. Other varieties received various names. A plumbiferous variety was described as *malinowskite* by A. Raimondi. The *nepaulite*, regarded by H. Piddington as a carbonate of bismuth, copper, etc., was shown by F. R. Mallet to be tetrahedrite. The *falkenhaynite* of R. Scharizer, the *studerite* of L. R. von Fellenberg, the *frigidite* and *coppite* of A. d'Achiardi, the *Nickelfahlerz* of A. Arzruni, and the *Kobaltfahlerz* of F Sandberger, are varieties of tetrahedrite. The *fieldite* of G. A. Kenngott was described by F. Field, and C. Ettling. The *clayite* by W. J. Taylor —after J. A. and J. R. Clay—is an alteration product. The *dufrénoysite* of A. Damour, and W. S. von Waltershausen, or the *binnite* of A. des Cloizeaux was at first thought to be cubic. The crystals were examined by C. Heusser, G. A. Kenngott, W. S. von Waltershausen, F. Hessenberg, W. J. Lewis, H. Baumhauer, C. O. Trechmann, and G. T. Prior and L. J. Spencer. Analyses reported by W. S. von Waltershausen, C. F. Rammelsberg, T. Petersen, and G. A. Kenngott, and R. W. E. MacIvor, were represented by various formulæ : $Cu_2S.CuS.As_2S_3$; $3Cu_2S.2As_2S_3$; $3Cu_2S.As_2S_5$; $4CuS.Cu_2S.As_2S$, and $3Cu_2S.As_2S_3$. G. T. Prior and L. J. Spencer showed that the best representative formula is $3Cu_2S.As_2S_3$, or Cu_3AsS_3, and that the crystallographic, physical, and chemical properties of binnite have no essential difference from those of tennantite.

A very large number of analyses of fahlerz has been reported.[3] H. Rose represented the results by $4Cu_2S(Sb,As)_2S_3$, or generally, by $4R''S.R_2'''S_3$, where R'' denotes Cu_2, Ag_2, Fe, Zn, etc., and R''', Sb, As or Bi. It is assumed that the bivalent atoms Fe, and Zn can isomorphously replace Cu_2.   C. F. Rammelsberg attributed any deviations from the analysis to the contamination of the mineral by foreign matters. Actually, very few analyses of fahlerz agree closely with the formula, while many approach the 3 : 1 formula, *viz.*, $3Cu_2S(As,Sb)_2S_3$. G. A. Kenngott, in his memoir *Ueber die Fahlerzformel*, assumed that the mineral is a mixture of two others, $4R_2'S.R_2'''S_3 + n(3R''S.R_2'''S_3)$. G. Tschermak represented fahlerz as a combination of $3Cu_3(As,Sb)S_3 + CuZn_2(As,Sb)S_4$, while T. Petersen, and J. Palacios preferred 3 : 1 formula, *viz.*, $3Cu_2S.(As,Sb)_2S_3$, or $Cu_3(As,Sb)S_3$. A. N. Winchell doubted the accuracy of the $4Cu_2S.Sb_2S_3$ formula. E. T. Wherry and W. F. Foshag gave $Cu_{10}(Zn,Fe,Cu)_2Sb_4S_{13}$, in which part of the copper is bivalent. G. T. Prior and L. J. Spencer pointed out that the analyses which approach most nearly to the 4 : 1 formula have a high proportion of bivalent elements ; and where the proportion of these elements is small, the 3 : 1 formula is the best representative value. Their analyses agree with the assumption that fahlerz is a mixture : $3Cu_2S.(Sb,As)_2S_3 + n(R_6''Sb_2S_9)$. This formula suggests that R'' atoms may proxy for univalent copper, and that the extra three atoms of sulphur fall into the interspaces of the lattice. The antimonial mineral *tetrahedrite*, Cu_3SbS_3, is at one end of the series and the arsenic mineral *tennantite*, Cu_3AsS_3, is at the other end of the series. Usually both antimony and arsenic are present so that the two species gradually merge into one another without a sharp dividing line. Bismuth also appears in some varieties, chiefly at the arsenic end of the series. The copper can be in part replaced by silver, zinc, mercury, lead, iron, and rarely cobalt and nickel. F. Sandberger reported tin in one variety, and L. N. Vauquelin, platinum in another.

J. Durocher [4] obtained tetrahedral crystals which resembled fahlerz by passing the vapours of the metal chlorides, including arsenic and antimony trichlorides, and of hydrogen sulphide, through a red-hot porcelain tube. H. Sommerlad did not obtain satisfactory results by heating mixtures of cuprous chloride and arsenic trisulphide. B. Cotta observed the formation of fahlerz in the flues of some metallurgical furnaces. A. Daubrée noticed the formation of fahlerz as a crust on some Roman bronzes in the thermal springs of Bourbonne-les-Bains. The various occurrences of fahlerz in nature were described by C. Hintze.

Fahlerz occurs massive, and granular ; it also appears in cubic crystals with the tetrahedral habit. The crystals were examined by P. Groth,[5] A. Lacroix, J. Schweitzer, F. Sandberger, T. Petersen, C. Blömecke, L. Buchdrucker, F. Hessenberg, A. Sadebeck, O. Luedecke, M. Websky, K. Zimanyi, H. Baumhauer, W. J. Lewis, C. O. Trechmann, G. T. Prior and L. J. Spencer, W. Phillips, R. P. Greg and W. G. Lettsom, P. von Jeremejeff, G. Seligmann, A. Cathrein, F. Becke, G. vom Rath, L. Colombo, E. V. Shannon, A. Breithaupt, etc. There is no cleavage. The contact twins about the (111)-plane may have a composition face parallel or perpendicular to the twinning plane ; there may be penetration twins. There may be twins with axes parallel and symmetrical with reference to a cubic plane. H. Baumhauer examined the corrosion figures. J. Palacios [6] found that the X-radiogram corresponds with a space-lattice with a unit cell having

$a = 10.39$ **A.**, and is in agreement with the formula for tetrahedrite $3Cu_2S.Sb_2S_3$. Sp. gr., determined in most cases on the samples used for analysis, are 4·75 to 4·90 for antimonial fahlerz, 4·85 to 5·00 for argentiferous fahlerz; 4·73 to 5·35 for mercurial fahlerz; 4·37 to 5·12 for arsenical fahlerz. H. Fizeau gave for the coeff. of linear expansion at 40°, 0·000009 with an increase of 0.0_72 per degree. A. Sella found the sp. ht. to be 0·0987. L. H. Borgström gave 630° for the m.p.; and J. Joly, 460°–590° for the sublimation temp. A. de Gramont examined the spark spectrum of fahlerz. C. Friedel found that when warmed an electric current flows from the edges to the surfaces of the crystals. E. T. Wherry found the crystals to be good radio-detectors. The roasting of fahlerz was studied by C. F. Plattner, F. Janda, and M. de Florin. E. Schäfer found that the mineral is more readily decomposed when heated in a current of chlorine than in a current of carbon dioxide charged with bromine vap. J. Lemberg found that a soln. of bromine in alkali-lye attacks the mineral slowly. E. F. Smith found that there is a marked rise of temp. when the mineral is brought in contact with sulphur monochloride; the mineral is completely decomposed on heating to 140°. O. Gasparini said that the attack by nitric acid is much more energetic if made while the acid is being electrolyzed. C. A. Burghardt decomposed the mineral by fusion with ammonium nitrate. J. Lemberg found that the mineral is decomposed by a boiling soln. of potassium cyanide containing alkali-lye. C. Davies and A. D. Munro found that if arsenic trisulphide be associated with 0·200 grm. of copper as sulphide, and the mixture treated with 50 c.c. of yellow ammonium sulphide, $(NH_4)_2S_2$, the amount of copper dissolved rises steadily with increasing amounts of arsenic, and it may attain ten times its original value. Thus:

| As present | . | . | . | 0 | 83·3 | 113·6 | 253·2 | 349·7 | 613·5 mgrms. |
| Cu dissolved | . | . | . | 7·8 | 29·5 | 34·5 | 52·0 | 61·0 | 80·4 „ |

with sodium polysulphide soln. (Na_2S_2):

| As present | . | . | . | 0 | 149·2 | 237·7 | 365·5 | 480·0 | 620·2 mgrms. |
| Cu dissolved | . | . | . | 41·8 | 48·5 | 50·7 | 51·8 | 52·0 | 53·0 „ |

H. Sommerlad [7] heated to 200°–300° a mixture of 6 mols of cuprous chloride and 3 mols of arsenic trisulphide, some arsenic trichloride and trisulphide sublimed, and there remained a coke-like mass of sp. gr. 4·289. The analysis corresponded with **cuprous pyrosulpharsenite**, $Cu_4As_2S_5$. The product was decomposed by acids, and by soln. of alkali hydroxide or sulphides, but not by aq. ammonia. By heating a mixture of equimolar parts of arsenic trisulphide and cuprous chloride, he obtained a steel-grey mass approximating **cuprous metasulpharsenite**, $CuAsS_2$. J. J. Berzelius obtained what he considered to be a basic salt, $12CuS.As_2S_3$, as a reddish-brown mass by treating hydrated cupric oxide with a soln. of potassium metasulpharsenite until decolorized. There is nothing to indicate that a chemical compound is here involved. When hydrochloric acid is added to the resulting red soln. he said that **cupric orthosulpharsenite**, $Cu_3(AsS_3)_2$, is formed. He also said that when a soln. of a cupric salt is treated with sodium sulpharsenite, a brownish-black precipitate of **cupric pyrosulpharsenite**, $Cu_2As_2S_5$, is formed. It is decomposed by heat.

H. Sommerlad [8] reported two basic salts, $12Ag_2S.As_2S_3$ and $5Ag_2S.As_2S_3$, to be formed as black or grey crystalline masses by melting together the component sulphides in stoichiometrical proportions. The former had a sp. gr. 6·279, and the latter 5·517. There is no evidence of the chemical individuality of these products on the thermal diagram, Fig. 45, studied by F. M. Jäger and H. S. van Klooster. There are two maxima on the curve, one corresponding with **silver orthosulpharsenite**, or *proustite*, $3Ag_2S.As_2S_3$, m.p. 490°; and one with **silver metasulpharsenite**, or *arsenomiargyrite*, $Ag_2S.As_2S_3$, m.p. 417°. There are two eutectics at 469° and 399° respectively. The transition temp. is 179°—*vide* **3.** 22, 18. Silver orthosulpharsenite was prepared as a bright red mass by F. Wöhler by fusing together stoichiometrical proportions of the constituent sulphides ; H. Sommerlad, by fusing together the required proportions of silver chloride and arsenic trisulphide : $3AgCl+As_2S_3=AsCl_3+Ag_3AsS_3$; J. Margottet, by heating a mixture of powdered silver and arsenic with an excess of sulphur in an evacuated sealed tube, and distilling off the excess of sulphur ; H. de Sénarmont, by treating a soln. of a silver salt with sodium sulpharsenite in the presence of an excess of sodium hydrocarbonate ; and K. Preis, by treating sodium sulpharsenate first with potassium cyanide, and then with a quantity of silver nitrate insufficient for complete precipitation. If more potassium cyanide be added, and the mixture allowed to stand for a few days, the amorphous orange-red or brown precipitate becomes crystalline.

A red mineral was named *Rodtguldenerz*, or *Rothguldenerz*, by the early writers —*e.g.* G. Agricola, C. Gessner, and J. F. Henckel. J. G. Wallerius recognized eight varieties of the *minera argenti rubra pellucida*. J. Hill called the mineral *red silver ore*. J. F. Henckel, and T. Bergman showed that arsenic, sulphur, and silver are present. The former thought that the pale red mineral contained arsenic and the dark red mineral, sulphur. M. H. Klaproth found antimony, sulphur, and silver in two varieties of the red ore ; L. J. Thénard found antimony, but not arsenic in a variety ; W. A. Lampadius, both antimony and arsenic ; and J. L. Proust showed that there are varieties (i) with antimony and no arsenic ; (ii) with arsenic and no antimony ; and (iii) with both antimony and arsenic. He also showed that no oxygen was present. F. S. Beudant called the arsenical mineral **proustite**— after J. L. Proust. Even in 1824, F. Mohs regarded the light and dark *Rothgiltigerz*, or *Rubinbelnde*, as he called them, to be varieties of one species. A. Breithaupt called the dark *ruby ore*, or dark *red silver ore, antimonial silver blende*, and the light ruby ore or light red silver ore, *arsenical silver blende*. F. S. Beudant called the antimonial ore *argyrythrose ;* C. J. Selb, *œrosite ;* and E. F. Glocker, *pyrargyrite* —from πῦρ, fire ; and ἄργυρος, silver, in allusion to the colour. Analyses of proustite reported by H. A. Miers, H. Rose, F. Field, I. Domeyko, H. de Sénarmont, H. Sommerlad, A. Streng, F. Sandberger, and E. Rethwisch show that the composition approximates closely with that of **silver orthosulpharsenite**, Ag_3AsS_3, some varieties contain up to 3·74 per cent. of antimony. The mineral *sanguinite* reported by H. A. Miers to occur on the argentite of Chanarcillo is thought to be a variety of proustite. The various occurrences of proustite in nature are described by C. Hintze.

Proustite occurs in scarlet or vermillion, trigonal, hemimorphic crystals having, according to H. A. Miers, the axial ratio $a : c=1 : 0·80393$, and $\alpha=103° 32'$. It also occurs massive and compact. The crystals were described by A. Frenzel, P. Groth, A. L. Parsons, F. Sandberger, A. Lacroix, O. Luedecke, M. Fenoglio, etc. Twinning about the (10$\bar{1}$4)-, (1011)-, and the (0001)-planes is common ; and rarely about the (41$\bar{3}$0)-plane. The habit is often acute rhombohedral or scalenohedral. The (1011)-cleavage is distinct. The sp. gr. reported on many of the samples analyzed ranges from 5·555 to 5·64. The hardness is about 2. A. Sella gave 0·0807 for the sp. ht. F. M. Jäger and H. S. van Klooster gave 490° for the m.p.—Fig. 46. A. de Gramont examined the spark spectrum ; and A. des Cloizeaux found the indices of refraction to be $\omega=2·9789$ and $\epsilon=2·7113$ for Li-light ; and $\omega=3·0877$ and $\epsilon=2·7924$ for Na-light. The double refraction is strong ; and the optical character negative. The pleochroism is weak, ω

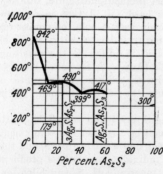

FIG. 46.—Freezing-point Curves of Mixtures of Arsenic Trisulphide and Silver Sulphide.

being blood-red, and ϵ, cochineal-red. W. W. Coblentz found that when proustite is exposed to thermal radiation with a wave-length extending from $0·3\mu$ to 2μ, the greatest photoelectric activity occurs between 0.5μ and 0.7μ, and there is then a rapid decrease, and no reaction was observed with wave-lengths exceeding 0.7μ. At 22°, the activity has a wide maximum in the ultra-violet with a weak ill-defined maximum near 0.6μ. Decreasing the temp. to $-167°$ increases the sensitivity throughout the spectrum, and the maximum at 0.6μ shifts to 0.578μ when, for low temp., the greatest photoelectric activity is localized. H. E. McKinstry observed a surface effect when the mineral is exposed to the electric arc-light. The electrical conductivity of proustite increases with increase in applied voltage; and with a constant voltage, the conductivity increases with time. T. W. Case observed that the resistance is less than a megohm, and light has no measurable influence. C. Tubandt and M. Haedicke observed that the pure salt is an ionic conductor, and that the silver ions are alone mobile. M. von Laue, and E. Giebe and A. Scheibe studied the piezoelectric properties of the crystals, and P. H. Geiger found that proustite shows a photoelectric effect. C. A. Burghardt found that the mineral is decomposed by fusion with ammonium nitrate; it is decomposed by nitric acid; and it is blackened by hot alkali-lye. H. B. North and C. B. Conover said that it is attacked by thionyl chloride at 150°-160° in a sealed tube.

J. J. Berzelius reported **silver pyrosulpharsenite**, $Ag_4As_2S_5$, to be formed when the metasulpharsenite is heated out of contact with air; and H. Sommerlad, by heating a mixture of silver chloride and arsenic trisulphide in the proportions: $12AgCl+5As_2S_3=3Ag_4As_2S_5+4AsCl_3$. It is a homogeneous mass with a conchoidal fracture, and a sp. gr. 4·886. The compound is not changed when heated out of contact with air; but when heated in a current of hydrogen sulphide, it slowly forms proustite. J. J. Berzelius found **silver metasulpharsenite**, $AgAsS_2$, to be formed by the action of a sat. soln. of arsenic trisulphide in one of sodium sulphide upon silver nitrate. H. Sommerlad prepared it by heating a mixture of silver chloride and arsenic trichloride in the proportions: $5AgCl+2As_2S_3=3AgAsS_2+AsCl_3$. The reaction begins at about 180°. The reddish-black crystalline mass has a sp. gr. 4·700. F. M. Jäger and H. S. van Klooster gave 417° for the m.p., Fig. 46. J. J. Berzelius said that when heated, arsenic trisulphide is given off and the pyro-salt is formed; H. Sommerlad said the ortho-salt.

According to J. J. Berzelius, the yellow precipitate formed by a soln. of sodium sulpharsenite and a gold salt consists of **gold sulpharsenite**, $2AuS_3.3As_2S_3$. It soon becomes black. It fuses in a glass retort, and gives off orpiment at a dull red-heat, and finally a residue of gold remains.

J. Voigt and J. F. A. Göttling,[9] and J. J. Berzelius prepared impure **calcium orthosulpharsenite**, $Ca_3(AsS_3)_2.15H_2O$, by digesting arsenic trisulphide with lime-water, and evaporating the filtrate. The product contained a brown mass of the pyrosulpharsenite, and crystals of the ortho-salt. J. J. Berzelius also obtained it by adding alcohol to a soln. of arsenic trisulphide in an excess of a soln. of calcium hydrosulphide. The colourless, feathery crystals are soluble in water. The corresponding **barium orthosulpharsenite**, $Ba_3(AsS_3)_2.14H_2O$, was obtained by J. J. Berzelius in an analogous way; and L. F. Nilson mixed a sat. soln. of arsenic trisulphide in a soln. of barium hydrosulphide with twice its vol. of the barium hydrosulphide soln., and evaporated the product in vacuo for crystallization. The mother-liquor deposits crystals of the pyrosulpharsenite. The barium salt appears in pale yellow prisms, sparingly soluble in water. The crystals soon turn brown on exposure to air. If a soln. of a mol of arsenic trisulphide and 3 mols of calcium hydrosulphide be evaporated in vacuo, L. F. Nilson found that colourless, four-sided prisms of the basic salt, **calcium tetrasulphorthosulpharsenit** $Ca_3(AsS_3)_3.4CaS.25H_2O$, are formed. The crystals are stable in air, sparingly soluble in hot and cold water, and are decomposed by hydrochloric acid. According to J. J. Berzelius, a brown mass of **calcium pyrosulpharsenite**, possibly $Ca_2As_2S_5.nH_2O$, is formed as a by-product in preparing the orthosalt as indicated above. It is easily soluble in water. L. F. Nilson found that **strontium pyrosulpharsenite**,

$Sr_2As_2S_5.15H_2O$, is obtained in large yellow crystals when a soln. of arsenic tri-sulphide and strontium hydrosulphide, in the molar proportions $1:1$ or $2:3$, is evaporated in vacuo. When a sat. soln. of arsenic trisulphide in one of barium hydrosulphide is mixed with an equal vol. of the soln. of the hydrosulphide, and evaporated in vacuo, hydrogen sulphide is evolved, and greyish-green **barium pyrosulpharsenite**, $Ba_2As_2S_5.5H_2O$, is formed. If this substance be allowed to remain in the mother-liquor for some time, it turns indigo-blue, and retains this colour even after washing with water, in which it is sparingly soluble. The blue salt has the same formula as the greyish-green salt. The blue salt probably contains a little colloidal sulphur. A *pentadecahydrate*, $Ba_2As_2S_5.15H_2O$, is obtained in monoclinic prisms as a by-product in the preparation of the ortho-salt as indicated above. L. F. Nilson found that **calcium metasulpharsenite**, $Ca(AsS_2)_2.11H_2O$, is deposited as a crystalline cake or yellow prisms on evaporating in vacuo a sat. soln. of arsenic trisulphide in one of calcium hydrosulphide. If the salt be exposed to air it absorbs water, and becomes brown. It is decomposed by water; and by hydrochloric acid. An orange-yellow crystalline mass of **strontium metasulph-arsenite**, $Sr(AsS_2)_2.2\frac{1}{2}H_2O$, was prepared in an analogous manner; likewise also with **barium metasulpharsenite**, $Ba(AsS_2)_2.2H_2O$. When calcium metasulph-arsenite is treated with cold water, it partially dissolves, leaving a brown residue of **calcium metasulphoctarsenite**, $CaAs_8S_{13}.10H_2O$; with boiling water, **calcium metasulphoennearsenite**, $Ca(As_9S_{14})_2.10H_2O$, is left. When barium metasulph-arsenite is treated for many hours with hydrochloric acid, **barium metasulpho-dodecarsenite**, $BaAs_{12}O_{19}$, is formed.

J. J. Berzelius reported **beryllium sulpharsenite** to be precipitated when a sat. soln. of arsenic trisulphide in one of sodium hydrosulphide is added to a soln. of a beryllium salt. L. F. Nilson made **magnesium orthosulpharsenite**, $Mg_3(AsS_3)_2.9H_2O$, by treating a sat. soln. of arsenic trisulphide in one of magnesium hydrosulphide. It appears as a yellow crystalline precipitate sparingly soluble in hot and cold water, but is decomposed by hydrochloric acid. According to P. de Clermont and J. Frommel, when magnesia is added to water holding arsenic trisulphide in sus-pension, soluble magnesium orthosulpharsenite, and insoluble magnesium hydro-arsenite are formed: $2As_2S_3+5MgO+H_2O=Mg_3(AsS_3)_2+2MgHAsO_3$. The soluble sulpharsenite is dissociated when boiled thus: $Mg_3(AsS_3)_2+7H_2O$ $=Mg_2HAsO_3+6H_2S+MgO$. Magnesia is an excellent antidote in cases of poisoning by arsenious acid, as the arsenite is completely insoluble; but if a portion of the arsenious acid becomes converted into trisulphide in the stomach or intestines, the magnesia would render this soluble. L. F. Nilson made **magnesium pyrosulpharsenite**, $Mg_2As_2S_5.8H_2O$, by evaporating in vacuo a soln. of equimolar parts of arsenic trisulphide and magnesium hydrosulphide. The salt is sparingly soluble in hot and cold water, but is decomposed by hydrochloric acid. J. J. Berzelius, and L. F. Nilson obtained a **magnesium metasulpharsenite**, $Mg(AsS_2)_2.5H_2O$, by evaporating a sat. soln. of arsenic trisulphide in one of mag-nesium hydrosulphide. The evaporation is best conducted in vacuo since J. J. Ber-zelius observed that the sulpharsenate is formed when the aq. soln. is evaporated and also when the conc. soln. is cooled to $-5°$. J. J. Berzelius reported **zinc sulpharsenite** to be formed as a bulky, lemon-yellow precipitate, when a sat. soln. of arsenic trisulphide in one of sodium hydrosulphide is treated with a zinc salt. The com-pound is decomposed by heat. According to J. Morozewicz, a mineral called **miedziankite**, from the copper mine at Miedzianka, Central Poland, is a **copper zinc sulpharsenite**, $3Cu_3AsS_3.ZnS$. It is grey in colour and compact or porous. Its sp. gr. is 4.700, and its hardness 3–4. According to J. J. Berzelius, **cadmium sulpharsenite** is formed by a process analogous to that used for the zinc salt; and similarly also with **mercurous pyrosulpharsenite**, $Hg_4As_2S_5$, which was deposited as a black precipitate from a soln. of mercurous nitrate. When heated, it furnishes a blackish sublimate of **mercuric pyrosulpharsenite**, $Hg_2As_2O_5$. If a soln. of mercuric chloride be treated with a sat. soln. of arsenic trisulphide in one of sodium sulphide, orange-yellow **mercuric metasulpharsenite**, $Hg(AsS_2)_2$, is formed.

According to J. Loczka,[10] thallium is not precipitated by hydrogen in acid soln., but in presence of dissolved arsenic, antimony, or tin, red precipitates are formed which contain thallium. The larger the amount of acid present, the less the amount of thallium precipitated, and, with a large excess of acid, no thallium is thrown down. J. W. Gunning has described the precipitates formed when a mixture of arsenious and thallous salts are treated with hydrogen sulphide in acid or alkaline soln. The composition of the precipitates varied widely with the mode of preparation, but in several cases the composition was near that required for **thallous metasulphoarsenite**, $TlAsS_2$. G. Canneri and L. Fernandes found the equilibrium conditions those indicated in Fig. 47. The meta-salt melts at 300°. According to L. F. Hawley, when the precipitates obtained in either acid or alkaline soln., are examined under the microscope, they are found to be perfectly homogeneous for all compositions between pure arsenic trisulphide and about 62 mol. per cent. arsenic trisulphide. The colour varies gradually from the light yellow of arsenic trisulphide through orange to a bright red as the amount of thallous sulphide increases. At about 62 mol. per cent. arsenic trisulphide, a second phase appears, the black

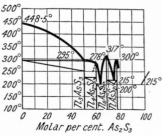

FIG. 47.—Freezing-point Curves of Binary Mixtures : $Tl_2S–As_2S_3$.

thallous sulphide, and from that point to pure thallous sulphide two phases are present. These observations show that thallous sulphide and arsenic trisulphide under the conditions named form a limited series of solid soln. extending from pure arsenic trisulphide to about 62 mol. per cent. of arsenic trisulphide, and that no compound is formed. From these precipitates acids will dissolve more or less thallous sulphide, depending on the conc. of the acid and the composition of the precipitate. Likewise soln. of alkaline sulphides will dissolve out varying amounts of arsenic trisulphide. The nearly constant composition of some of Gunning's precipitates obtained in acid soln. with excess of thallium present was probably due to the nearly constant conc. of the acid used. This agrees with the observations of L. Bruner and J. Zawadsky. G. Canneri and L. Fernandes obtained the results indicated in Fig. 45 for the f.p. curves of mixtures of thallous sulphide and arsenic trisulphide. **Thallous orthosulpharsenite**, Tl_3AsS_3, is unstable and decomposes on fusion at 295° ; **thallous pyrosulpharsenite**, $Tl_4As_2S_5$, also decomposes on fusion at 278°. The other part of the curve explored is normal. **Thallous orthosulphotetrarsenite**, $Tl_6As_4S_9$, melts at 317°. J. A. Krenner found crystals of a cochineal-red or carmine-red mineral on the realgar of Allchar, Macedonia. He named the mineral **lorandite**. The analyses by J. A. Krenner, J. Loczka, and P. Jannasch correspond with thallous metasulpharsenite. The tabular, or short prismatic crystals are monoclinic, and, according to V. Goldschmidt, have the axial ratios $a : b : c = 1\cdot3291 : 1 : 1\cdot0780$, and $\beta = 52° 27'$. The (100)-cleavage is perfect, while the (001)- and (101)-cleavages are good. A. S. Eakle, and L. Tokody consider lorandite to be isomorphous with miargyrite. The cleavage lamellæ are flexible like selenite. The refractive index is high. E. S. Larsen gave $+2\cdot72$ for Li-light. The hardness is $2\cdot0–2\cdot5$; and the sp. gr. $5\cdot529$. T. W. Case said that the poor conductivity of lorandite is not affected by light. The mineral is soluble in nitric acia.

J. J. Berzelius [11] prepared **cerous pyrosulpharsenite**, $Ce_4(As_2S_5)_3$, as an orange-yellow powder, by adding sodium pyrosulpharsenite to a soln. of a cerous salt. The product is sparingly soluble in water. He obtained **yttrium sulpharsenite** by the method employed for the beryllium salt. According to J. J. Berzelius, an orange-yellow precipitate of **zirconium sulpharsenite** is produced when a soln. of a zirconium

salt is treated with a sat. soln. of arsenic trisulphide in one of sodium hydrosulphide. For **copper germanium sulpharsenite,** *vide* germanite, **7.** 45, 1.
J. J. Berzelius obtained reddish-brown **stannous sulpharsenite,** and yellow **stannic
sulpharsenite,** by treating soln. of stannous and stannic chlorides respectively in a
similar way. J. J. Berzelius obtained reddish-brown **lead sulpharsenite** in an
analogous way. J. Fournet heated to whiteness a mixture of 10 parts of galena
and 5 parts of orpiment, and obtained one part of ductile lead. H. Sommerlad
found that lead sulpharsenites can be obtained by melting mixtures of lead
sulphide or chloride and arsenic trisulphide. The occurrence of metallic grey
mineral in *le dolomie de Binnen* was mentioned by C. Lardy in 1833, as *une
substance métallique d'un gris de plomb;* and D. F. Wiser observed that this substance contained sulphur, lead, silver, copper, antimony, and arsenic. This term
" binnite " was at first given indiscriminately to the grey minerals; they were
later distinguished as *pea-shaped binnite—Kugelbinnit,* and *rod-shaped binnite—
Stangenbinnit.* A. Damour analyzed the Stangenbinnet, but described the crystals
of Kugelbinnet. He called the combination *dufrénoysite.* W. S. von Waltershausen
pointed out A. Damour's mistake, but curiously he himself made a similar blunder.
The confusion was accentuated by J. C. Heusser, and A. des Cloizeaux and J. C. G. de
Marignac. The subject was cleared up by the work of G. vom Rath,[12] H. Baumhauer,
and R. H. Solly. As a result, crystals of nearly a dozen lead sulpharsenites have
been since reported from the dolomite region of Binnenthal, Switzerland. They
have the ratio PbS : As$_2$S$_3$ ranging from 4 : 1 to 1 : 1. The constitution was discussed
by G. Cesaro.

Two basic salts with the mol. ratio 4 : 1 and 7 : 2 are represented by the minerals
ordanite and legenbachite. G. vom Rath discovered **jordanite**—named after
J. Jordan—in cavities of the dolomite of Imfield, Binnenthal, Switzerland.
Analyses reported by L. Sipöcz, A. Sachs, C. Guillemain, R. H. Solly, E. Ludwig,
and H. Sommerlad correspond with 4Pbs.As$_2$S$_3$, or **lead disulphopyrosulpharsenite,**
(Pb.S.Pb)$_2$As$_2$S$_5$. S. S. Smirnoff gave 4PbS.(As,Sb)$_2$S$_3$. L. Sipöcz regarded this
mineral as a salt of pyrosulpharsenious acid, H$_4$As$_2$S$_5$, in which each pair of
hydrogen atoms is replaced by the dyad radicle—Pb.S.Pb. C. F. Rammelsberg
represented it

$$S<{Pb-S \atop Pb-S}>As-S-As<{S-Pb \atop S-Pb}>S$$

and V. Wartha regarded it as a salt of pyrosulpharsenic acid, H$_4$As$_2$S$_7$, with each
pair of hydrogen atoms replaced by the dyad group—Pb.Pb—

$$Pb-S \atop Pb-S}>As-S-S-S-As<{S-Pb \atop S-Pb}$$

H. Sommerlad prepared a substance of the same composition by fusing stoichiometrical proportions of lead sulphide and arsenic trisulphide in a current of hydrogen
sulphide, and by strongly heating lead metasulpharsenite in a current of hydrogen
sulphide until no more arsenic trisulphide is evolved. The lead-grey, six-sided
crystals often have the (001)-face predominating, or they may be tabular with the
pyramidal planes narrow and striated. G. vom Rath supposed the crystals to be
rhombic, and to have the axial ratios $a : b : c = 0.53747 : 1 : 2.0305$; but H. Baumhauer showed that they are more probably monoclinic prisms with the axial ratios
$a : b : c = 0.4945 : 1 : 0.2655$, and $\beta = 90° 33\frac{1}{2}'$. The oft-repeated lamellar twinning
about the (10$\overline{1}$)-plane may furnish pseudohexagonal forms like those of aragonite.
The (010)-cleavage is perfect. The crystals were examined by W. J. Lewis,
R. H. Solly, and G. Tschermak. The possible isomorphism of the crystals with
those of meneghinite, 4PbS.Sb$_2$S$_3$, was discussed by A. Schmidt, J. A. Krenner,
H. A. Miers, C. Hintze, G. d'Archiadi, P. Groth, and G. vom Rath. The hardness

is 3. G. vom Rath gave 6·393 for the sp. gr.; R. H. Solly, 6·413; C. Guillemain, 5·480; L. Sipöcz, 6·3842; H. Baumhauer, 6·339 at 25°; S. S. Smirnoff, 6·38; and H. Sommerlad, for the artificial crystals, 6·101. H. Sommerlad found that aq. ammonia has no action on the salt, but it is decomposed by hot alkali-lye. R. Bunsen found that potassium sulphide extracts arsenic from the natural sulpharsenites, and L. Sipöcz represented the reaction with jordanite: $Pb_3(AsS_3)_2.PbS+K_2S$ =$4PbS+2KAsS_2$.

R. H. Solly [13] described a steel-grey mineral from the Lengenbach quarry, Binnenthal, Switzerland, which he named **lengenbachite**. Analyses by A. Hutchinson correspond with $7PbS.2As_2S_3$, or $PbS.2Pb_3(AsS_3)_2$, or **lead trisulphobispyrosulpharsenite**, $(Pb.S.Pb)_3(As_2S_5)_2Pb$. The mineral also contains small amounts of copper, silver, and antimony. The thin-bladed crystals are sometimes curled up like paper; they are probably triclinic. The cleavage parallel to the large face of the crystal is perfect. R. H. Solly gave 5·80 for the sp. gr., and A. Hutchinson, 5·85. This mineral is thought to be identical with the mineral *jentschite* described by R. Köchlin.

W. F. Hillebrand [14] found a massive bluish-grey mineral mixed with zunyite in the zuni mine, Silverton, Colorado, and named it **guitermanite**—after F. Guiterman. The analysis corresponded with $10PbS.3As_2S_3$, which is so very near **lead orthosulpharsenite**, $3PbS.As_2S_3$, that it is probably this compound with a trace of lead sulphide as an impurity. The sp. gr. is 5·94 at 17·5°; and the hardness 3. A. de Gramont examined the spark spectrum. T. W. Case observed that the mineral is a non-conductor of electricity, and light had no measurable effect. E. T. Wherry studied the crystals as rectifiers of alternating currents, or as radio-detectors. H. Sommerlad obtained a product of the composition of guitermanite by melting together the constituent sulphides. The sp. gr. was 5·86. He thought that the product might not be a chemical individual because aq. ammonia extracted from it arsenic trisulphide; but A. Terreil observed that a boiling 10 per cent. soln. of sodium sulphide gradually extracts arsenic trisulphide from all the lead sulpharsenites. H. Baumhauer described small crystals of a lead-grey mineral from the Lengenbach quarry, Binnenthal, Switzerland. He named it **seligmannite**—after G. Seligmann. The qualitative analysis, and the apparent isomorphism of the crystals with bournonite, and aikinite, indicate that the composition is probably $CuPbAsS_3$, **cuprous lead orthosulpharsenite**, in agreement with G. T. Prior's analysis. W. F. Foshag gave $Cu_2S.2PbS.As_2S_3$. H. Baumhauer gave $a:b:c$ =0·92804 : 1 : 0·87568 for the axial ratios of the rhombic crystals, and R. H. Solly, 0·92332 : 1 : 0·87338. The hardness is 3.

J. J. Berzelius [15] obtained what is thought to have been **lead pyrosulpharsenite**, $Pb_2As_2S_5$, as a reddish-brown precipitate, by the action of sodium sulpharsenite on a soln. of a lead salt. H. Sommerlad also obtained it by melting a mixture of the constituent sulphides; and also a mixture of six mols of lead chloride and five mols of arsenic trisulphide. A lead-grey mineral found by A. Damour in the dolomite of Binnenthal, Switzerland, was named **dufrénoysite**—after P. A. Dufrénoy. The analyses reported by A. Damour, J. Berendes, G. vom Rath, H. Baumhauer, and C. Guillemain correspond with $2PbS.As_2S_3$. G. Cesaro said that dufrénoysite corresponds with the general formula $As_2S_3(1+2n-1)R''S$, for these minerals were $n=2$. The corresponding hypothetical acid is $(HS)_2=As-S-As=(SH)_2$. A. Brun found thallium to be present. At first, A. Damour assumed the mineral to belong to the cubic system, and since W. S. von Waltershausen obtained it in rhombic crystals, he called the rhombic form *binnite*—*vide supra*. J. C. Heusser used these two terms. Later, W. S. von Waltershausen reported two other minerals, *arsenomelane* and *sclerodase*. G. vom Rath found three rhombic minerals in this locality; one he identified with A. Damour's dufrénoysite; another with W. S. von Waltershausen's scleroclase, which later came to be called *sartorite*; and the third he named *jordanite*. R. H. Solly added that the arsenomelane of W. S. von Waltershausen is the mineral now called *rathite*. C. F. Rammelsberg's *gottardite*, T. Petersen's

Skleroklas, and P. Groth's *Bleiarsenit* were no doubt samples of dufrénoysite. The measurements of the crystals by A. des Cloizeaux and J. C. G. de Marignac were shown by G. vom Rath to belong to the mineral sartorite. The crystals of dufrénoysite were also examined by R. H. Solly, and H. Baumhauer. G. vom Rath gave $a:b:c=0\cdot9381:1:1\cdot5309$ for the axial ratios of the rhombic crystals ; but R H. Solly said that the crystals are monoclinic with the axial ratios $a:b:c=0\cdot650987:1:0\cdot612576$, and $\beta=90°\ 33\frac{1}{2}'$. The cleavage parallel to the (010)-plane is perfect. J. L. C. Schröder van der Kolk studied the colour of these minerals ; and L. J. Spencer, the isomorphism with zinckenite, etc. A. Damour gave 5·549 for the sp. gr. ; G. vom Rath, 5·555–5·569, at 21° ; H. Baumhauer, 5·553 ; W. S. von Waltershausen, 5·52 ; R. H. Solly, 5·50 ; and H. Sommerlad, for the artificial crystals, 5·505. The hardness is 3. The compound is readily fused, and at a higher temp., it gives off arsenic trisulphide. A. de Gramont examined the spark spectrum. The compound is somewhat attacked by aq. ammonia : and is decomposed by potash-lye ; and by soln. of the alkali sulphides, and acids.

H. Baumhauer [16] obtained a lead-grey mineral, allied to dufrénoysite, from the dolomite of Binnenthal, Switzerland. It was called **rathite**—after G. vom Rath. Analyses reported by H. Baumhauer, W. S. von Waltershausen, G. vom Rath, T. Petersen, G. A. Kenngott, R. H. Solly, and H. Jackson correspond with $3PbS.2As_2S_3$, or **lead orthosulphotetrarsenite**, $Pb_3As_4S_9$. G. Cesaro gave the constitutional formula $As(S.R.S.As:S)_3$. The prismatic crystals belong to the rhombic system, and H. Baumhauer gave for the axial ratios $a:b:c=0\cdot668099:1:1\cdot057891$, and R. H. Solly, $0\cdot4782:1:0\cdot5112$. The twinning about the (074)-plane is indicated by numerous fine lamellæ ; and there is also a juxtaposed twin about the (0, 15, 1)-plane. H. Baumhauer regards the fine striæ of the macrodomes to be produced by alternate bands of lead sulpharsenite and sulphantimonite, but since the bands occur with crystals containing no antimony, R. H. Solly said that the fine striæ are caused by twin lamellæ parallel to (074). The cleavage parallel to the (010)-face is perfect, and there is a parting parallel to (100). The sp. gr. given by H. Baumhauer is 5·32, and by R. H. Solly, 5·412–5·421. The hardness is 3. T. W. Case found the resistance is greater than a megohm, and that light has no measurable influence. The mineral is soluble in hot nitric acid. W. J. Lewis reported a mineral from the same locality as rathite, and he named it *wiltshireite*—after T. Wiltshire. It is said to occur in tin-white or lead-grey, monoclinic crystals with the axial ratios $a:b:c=1\cdot5869:1:1\cdot0698$, and $\beta=79°\ 16'$. G. T. Prior showed the similarity of wiltsherite with dufrénoysite. According to R. H. Solly, this mineral is identical with rhandite, and if this is so, the crystals are probably rhombic. Another lead-grey or steel-grey mineral from Binnenthal was called **baumhauerite**—after H. Baumhauer—by R. H. Solly.[17] The analysis corresponds with $4PbS.3As_2S_3$, that is, with **lead sulphohexarsenite**,

$$\text{Pb}\!\!\begin{array}{c}\cdot\text{S}\\{\cdot}\text{S}\end{array}\!\!>\text{As}-\text{S}-\dot{\text{As}}\ \dot{\text{S}}\qquad\begin{array}{c}\text{S}-\text{As}-\text{S}-\text{As}-\text{S}\\ \dot{\text{S}}\ \ \dot{\text{As}}-\text{S}-\text{As}<\begin{array}{c}\text{S}\\ \text{S}\end{array}>\text{Pb}\\ \text{Pb}-\dot{\text{S}}\end{array}$$
$$\text{S}.\,\dot{\text{Pb}}$$

The crystals are monoclinic prisms or plates with the axial ratios $a:b:c=1\cdot136817:1:0\cdot947163$, and $\beta=82°\ 42\frac{3}{4}'$. The (100)-cleavage is perfect. The sp. gr. is 5·330, and the hardness 3. The monoclinic crystals of a mineral, called *liveingite*—after G. D. Liveing—from Binnenthal had an analysis corresponding with $4PbS.3As_2S_3$, or better with $5PbS.4As_2S_3$. E. V. Shannon regards this as analogous with plagionite. The axial angle of the monoclinic crystals is $89°\ 45\frac{1}{2}'$. G. E. Uhrlaub's mineral of sp gr. 5·405 is probably the same thing.

H. Sommerlad [18] prepared **lead metasulpharsenite**, $Pb(AsS_2)_2$, by melting stoichiometrical proportions of the component sulphides in an atm. of hydrogen sulphide ; or by melting a mixture of 3 mols of lead chloride and 4 mols of arsenic trisulphide. The Binnenthal mineral *scleroclase*—from σκληρός, hard ; and κλάειν, to break—of W. S. von Waltershausen, and G. vom Rath has been mentioned in connection with dufrénoysite. J. D. Dana called it **sartorite**—after W. Sartorius von Waltershausen. Analyses reported by W. S. von Waltershausen, G. A. Kenngott, T. Petersen, H. Baumhauer, and R. H. Solly are in agreement with the formula $Pb(AsS_2)_2$, favoured by P. Groth and K. Mieleitner, and C. F. Rammelsberg ; H. Baumhauer favoured $3(PbS.As_2S_3).2(PbS)$. The crystals were examined by G. vom Rath, C. O. Trechmann, and H. Baumhauer ; they belong to the rhombic system having the axial ratios $a : b : c = 0.5389 : 1 : 0.6188$. The colour is dark lead-grey. The crystal faces may be striated or channelled. The (001)-cleavage is distinct. J. Königsberger studied the anisotropy of the crystals ; and L. J. Spencer, the isomorphism with zinckenite (*q.v.*), etc. The hardness is 3. W. S. von Waltershausen gave 5.074–5.469 for the sp. gr. ; H. Baumhauer, 5.05 ; R. H. Jolly, 4.980 ; G. A. Kenngott, 5.074–5.355 ; and H. Sommerlad, for the artificial crystals, 4.585. T. W. Case found the mineral is a non-conductor of electricity, and light has no appreciable effect. The mineral is soluble in nitric acid. When the artificial compound is heated in hydrogen sulphide, it forms lead pyrosulpharsenite, and then passes into lead disulphopyrosulpharsenite. It is decomposed by soln. of alkali sulphides or hydroxides, and by hydrochloric or nitric acid.

R. H. Solly [19] discovered a mineral at Lengenbach, Switzerland, and he named it **hutchinsonite**—after A. Hutchinson. Its analysis reported by G. F. H. Smith and G. T. Prior corresponds with **silver thallium lead metasulpharsenite,** $(Tl,Ag)_2S.As_2S_3.PbS.As_2S_3$, or $Pb(Tl,Ag)_2(AsS_2)_4$. Up to 3 per cent. of copper (ous), and 2.0 per cent. of antimony are present in some samples. The colour is vermilion-scarlet or cherry-red, and it occurs in flattened prisms with numerous small faces of domes and pyramids. R. H. Solly gave for the axial ratios of the rhombic crystals $a : b : c = 0.8172 : 1 : 0.7549$, and G. F. H. Smith and G. T. Prior, 1.6343 : 1 : 0.7549. The (100)-cleavage is good. The hardness is 1.5–2.0, and the sp. gr. 4.6. The optic axial angle $2E = 63° 22'$; $2H = 35° 19'$ for red-light, and 71° 58' for yellow-light ; and $2V = 19° 44'$, and 37° 34'. The corresponding indices of refraction were $\alpha = 2.799$, $\beta = 3.063$, and $\gamma = 3.073$; and $\alpha = 3.087$, $\beta = 3.176$, and $\gamma = 3.188$. The birefringence is strong ; the optical character negative ; and the pleochroism weak.

For **germanium sulpharsenite,** *vide* germanite, 7. 44, 1. J. J. Berzelius [20] found that a mixture of antimony and arsenic trisulphides fuses to an orange-yellow, transparent liquid, but there is here no evidence of the formation of an **antimony sulpharsenite.** When a soln. of a bismuth salt is treated with sodium sulpharsenite, the reddish-brown precipitate was considered to be **bismuth pyrosulpharsenite,** $Bi_4(As_2S_5)_3$. It fuses readily, and gives off arsenic trisulphide when heated to a higher temp. No precipitate of **vanadium sulpharsenite** is formed when an aq. soln. of sodium sulpharsenite is added to a soln. of vanadic sulphate, but the blue liquid becomes colourless. With soln. of chromic salts and sodium sulpharsenite, a dingy, greenish-yellow precipitate is formed which is assumed to be **chromic sulpharsenite.** This precipitate melts when heated, and at a higher temp., gives off arsenic trisulphide. The mixture readily burns when heated in air. Molybdenum salts under similar conditions give a dark brown precipitate of **molybdenum sulpharsenite,** which gives off arsenic trisulphide at an elevated temp. Uranyl salts also give a yellow precipitate of **uranium sulpharsenite** under similar conditions, and it melts when heated and gives off arsenic trisulphide at a higher temp. With manganese salts an aurora-red precipitate of **manganese sulpharsenite** is formed. It behaves when heated like the other sulpharsenites. A soln. of a ferrous salt yields a dark brown precipitate of **ferrous sulpharsenite** soluble in excess of sodium sulpharsenite, forming a yellowish-brown soln. ; and a soln. of a ferric salt yields an olive-green precipitate of **ferric sulpharsenite** which dissolves in an excess of sodium sulpharsenite, forming a black soln. Both salts fuse when heated, and decompose at a higher temp. Cobalt salts under similar conditions give a dark brown **cobalt sulpharsenite** which is soluble in an excess of the sodium sulpharsenite, and decomposes when heated, forming what was thought to be cobaltite or cobalt glance. Nickel salts give a black precipitate of **nickel sulpharsenite** which is also decomposed by heat leaving nickel sulphide as a residue. A soln. of platinic chloride and sodium sulpharsenite gives a dark brown precipitate of **platinum sulpharsenite** which is decomposed by heat.

REFERENCES.

[1] J. J. Berzelius, *Schweigger's Journ.*, **34**. 46, 1822 ; *Pogg. Ann.*, **7**. 137, 1826 ; *Svenska Akad. Handl.*, 295, 1825 ; *Ann. Chim. Phys.*, (2), **11**. 225, 1819 ; (2), **32**. 166, 1826 ; L. F. Nilson, *Journ. prakt. Chem.*, (2), **12**. 295, 1875 ; (2), **14**. 145, 1876 ; (2), **16**. 93, 1877 ; *Akad. Handl. Stockholm*, **10**. 2, 1871 ; *Oefvers. Akad. Stockholm*, **28**. 303, 1871 ; **34**. 5, 1877 ; E. W. von Siemens and J. G. Halske, *German Pat.*, *D.R.P.* 67973, 1892 ; K. Preis, *Liebig's Ann.*, **257**. 180, 1890 ; R. Bunsen, *ib.*, **192**. 305, 1878 ; E. Berglund, *Ber.*, **17**. 95, 1884 ; O. von der Pfordten, *ib.*, **17**. 2897, 1884 ; J. B. Senderens, *Bull. Soc. Chim.*, (3), **7**. 511, 1892 ; H. Sommerlad, *Zeit. anorg. Chem.*, **15**. 173, 1897 ; **18**. 420, 1898 ; L. Sipöcz, *Tschermak's Mitt.*, (1), **3**. 132, 1873 ; O. B. Kühn, *Arch. Pharm.*, (2), **71**. 2, 1852 ; *Journ. Pharm. Chim.*, (3), **22**. 75, 1852 ; A. Hilger and R. F. Weinland in L. Gmelin, *Handbuch der anorganischen Chemie*, Heidelberg, 2. ii, 590, 1897 ; M. Websky, *Zeit. deut. geol. Ges.*, **23**. 486, 1871 ; G. Cesaro, *Bull. Soc. Min.*, **38**. 38, 1915 ; W. F. Foshag, *Amer. Journ. Science*, (5), **1**. 444, 1921 ; E. T. Wherry, *Journ. Washington Acad.*, **10**. 487, 1920 ; **11**. 1, 1921 ; F. Zambonini, *Riv. Min. Crist. Ital.*, **41**. 3, 1912 ; **47**. 40, 1916 : P. Niggli, *Zeit. Kryst.*, **60**. 477, 1924.

[2] M. Websky, *Zeit. deut. geol. Ges.*, **23**. 486, 1871 ; J. G. Wallerius, *Mineralogia*, Stockholm, 313, 1747 ; A. Cronstedt, *Mineralogie*, Stockholm, 157, 175, 1758 ; I. S. R. I. Eques a Born, *Lythophylacium Bornianum*, Prague, **1**. 82, 108, 1772 ; A. G. Werner, *Letztes Mineralsystem*, Freiberg, 18, 1817 ; L. A. Emmerling, *Lehrbuch der Mineralogie*, Giessen, **2**. 180, 195, 238, 1796 ; J. R. Haüy, *Traité de minéralogie*, Paris, **3**. 537, 1801 ; J. B. L. Romé de l'Isle, *Cristallographie*, Paris, **3**. 315, 1783 ; A. Breithaupt, *Handbuch der Mineralogie*, Freiberg, **3**. b, 78, 119, 124, 127, 1818 ; *Mineralogische Studien*, Leipzig, 102, 105, 1866 ; *Pogg. Ann.*, **9**. 613, 1827 ; *Vollständiges Charakteristik des Mineralsystems*, Dresden, 131, 251, 1823 ; *Berg. Hütt. Ztg.*, **25**. 187, 1866 ; F. S. Beudant, *Traité élémentaire de minéralogie*, Paris, **2**. 438, 1832 ; W. Haidinger, *Handbuch der bestimmenden Mineralogie*, Wien, 563, 1845 ; M. H. Klaproth, *Beiträge zur chemischen Kenntniss der Mineralkörper*, Berlin, **1**. 166, 177, 1795 ; **4**. 54, 1807 ; *Samml. Abh. Akad. Berlin*, 3, 1790 ; E. F. Glocker, *Handbuch der Mineralogie*, Nürnberg, 406, 1831 ; *Generum et specierum mineralium secundum ordines naturales digestorum synopsis*, Halle, 31, 1847 ; A. Weisbach, *Synopsis mineralogica*, Freiberg, 62, 1875 ; G. A. Kenngott, *Das Mohs'sche Mineralsystem*, Wien, 117, 1853 ; *Uebersichte der Resultate mineralogischer Forschungen*, Wien, 174, 1859 ; *Die Minerale der Schweiz nach ihren Eigenschaften und Fundorten*, Leipzig, 373, 1866 ; F. von Kobell, *Tafeln zur Bestimmung der Mineralien*, München, 10, 1853 ; *Die Mineralnamen*, München, 98, 1853 ; M. L. Frankenheim, *System der Krystalle*, Breslau, 29, 1842 ; A. d'Achiardi, *Atti Soc. Toscana*, 172, 1881 ; *Mineralogia della Toscana*, Pisa, **2**. 347, 1873 ; G. Agricola, *De natura fossilium*, Basileæ, 362, 1546 ; F. Sandberger, *Untersuchungen über Erzgänge*, Wiesbaden, 392, 1885 ; *Neues Jahrb. Min.*, 584, 1865 ; J. Sowerby, *British Mineralogy*, London, 1817 ; G. Rose, *Das krystallochemischen Mineralsystem*, Leipzig, 23, 1852 ; H. Rose, *Pogg. Ann.*, **15**. 582, 1829 ; R. Phillips, *Quart. Journ. Science*, **7**. 95, 100, 1819 ; W. Phillips, *Introduction to Mineralogy*, London, 227, 1819 ; J. F. L. Hausmann, *Handbuch der Mineralogie*, Göttingen, 179, 1847 ; M. Adam, *Tableau minéralogique*, Paris, 59, 1869 ; H. Sjögren, *Geol. För. Förh. Stockholm*, **5**. 82, 1880 ; R. Scharizer, *Jahrb. geol. Reichsanst. Wien*, **40**. 433, 1890 ; D. Brauns, *Mitt. Naturf. Ges. Bern*, **57**, 1854 ; L. R. von Fellenberg, *ib.*, 178, 1864 ; T. Petersen, *Neues Jahrb. Min.*, 590, 1870 ; *Ber. Offenbach, Ver. Naturk.*, **7**. 131, 1866 ; A. Arzruni, *Zeit. Kryst.*, **7**. 629, 1884 ; H. Baumhauer, *ib.*, **21**. 202, 1893 ; **28**. 545, 1897 ; W. J. Lewis, *ib.*, **2**. 192, 1878 ; *Phil. Mag.*, (5), **5**. 139, 1877 ; *Proc. Crystal. Soc.*, **1**. 52, 1877 ; H. Piddington, *Journ. Asiatic Soc.*, **23**. 170, 1854 ; G. T. Prior and L. J. Spencer, *Min. Mag.*, **12**. 184, 1899 ; C. O. Trechmann, *ib.*, **10**. 220, 1893 ; L. F. Svanberg, *Oefvers. Akad. Handl. Stockholm*, **4**. 85, 1847 ; *Journ. prakt. Chem.*, (1), **43**. 313, 1847 ; W. J. Taylor, *Proc. Acad. Philadelphia*, 306, 1859 ; A. Raimondi, *Minéraux du Pérou*, Paris, 122, 1878 ; F. R. Mallet, *A Manual of the Geology of India*, Calcutta, 30, 1887 ; *Rec. Geol. Sur. India*, **18**. 235, 1885 ; C. Ettling, *Journ. Chem. Soc.*, **6**. 140, 1854 ; F. Field, *ib.*, **4**. 332, 1851 ; C. F. Rammelsberg, *Pogg. Ann.*, **68**. 515, 1846 ; *Handbuch der Mineralchemie*, Leipzig, 86, 1860 ; 107, 1875 ; 95, 1886 ; 46, 1895 ; W. S. von Waltershausen, *Pogg. Ann.*, **94**. 119, 1865 ; E. Uhrlaub, *ib.*, **94**. 120, 1855 ; C. Heusser, *ib.*, **94**. 334, 1855 ; **97**. 115, 1856 ; A. des Cloizeaux, *Ann. Mines*, (5), **8**. 389, 1855 ; F. Hessenberg, *Mineralogische Notizen*, Frankfurt, 6, 1875 ; A. Damour, *Ann. Chim. Phys.*, (3), **14**. 379, 1845 ; R. W. E. McIvor, *Chem. News*, **30**. 103, 1874.

[3] J. Loczka, *Zeit. Kryst.*, **34**. 86, 1901 ; L. F. Nilson, *ib.*, **1**. 421, 1877 ; *Oefvers. Akad. Stockholm*, **34**. 5, 1877 ; G. A. Kenngott, *Uebersicht der Resultate mineralogischer Forschungen*, Leipzig, 175, 1858 ; 289, 1868 ; *Neues Jahrb. Min.*, ii, 228, 1881 ; R. W. E. MacIvor, *Chem. News*, **30**. 103, 1874 ; L. R. von Fellenberg, *Mitt. Naturf. Ges. Bern*, 178, 1864 ; D. Brauns, *ib.*, 57, 1854 ;

. d'Achiardi, *Mineralogia della Toscana*, Pisa, **2**. 342, 1873 ; *Atti Soc. Toscana*, **171**, 1881;
. Bechi, *Amer. Journ. Science*, (2), **14**. 60, 1852 ; W. J. Comstock, *ib.*, (3), **17**. 401, 1879 ;
. S. Burton, *ib.*, (2), **45**. 320, 1868 ; S. L. Penfield, *ib.*, (3), **44**. 18, 1892 ; A. Lacroix, *Minéralogie
e ta France, et de ses colonies*, Paris, **2**. 722, 1897 ; C. F. A. Tenne and S. Calderon, *Mineral-
undstätten der iberischen Halbinsel*, Berlin, 80, 1902 ; F. Gonnard, *Bull. Soc. Min.*, **5**. 89, 1882 ;
. L. Ungemach, *ib.*, **29**. 194, 1906 ; A. Lamy, *Bull. Ind. Min.*, **13**. 422, 1869 ; C. Méne, *Compt.
Rend.*, **51**. 463, 1860 ; **52**. 1326, 1861 ; A. Daubrée, *ib.*, **80**. 461, 1875 ; G. C. Wittstein, *Viertelj.
rakt. Chem.*, **4**. 72, 1855 ; J. H. Collins, *A Handbook to the Mineralogy of Cornwall and Devon.
London*, 45, 1876 ; R. Phillips, *Quart. Journ. Science*, **7**. 95, 1819 ; J. Hemming, *Phil. Mag.*,
3), **10**. 157, 1831 ; D. Forbes, *ib.*, (4), **34**. 350, 1867 ; F. Field, *Journ. Chem. Soc.*, **4**. 332, 1851 ;
. Rose, *Reise nach dem Ural, dem Atlai, und dem kaspischen Meere*, Berlin, **1**. 198, 1837 ;
I. Sjögren, *Geol. För. Förh. Stockholm*, **5**. 82, 1880 ; J. D. Dana, *A System of Mineralogy*, New
York, 102, 1868 ; H. Rose, *Pogg. Ann.*, **15**. 577, 1829 ; A. Hilger, *ib.*, **124**. 500, 1863 ; *Liebig's
Ann.*, **185**. 205, 1877 ; H. Peltzer, *ib.*, **126**. 340, 1863 ; P. Berthier, *Ann. Mines*, (1), **11**. 121,
825 ; (3). **10**. 529, 1836 ; J. J. Ebelmen, *ib.*, (4), **11**. 47, 1847 ; J. M. Leitao, *ib.*, (5), **1**. 107, 1852 ;
. Domeyko, *ib.*, (4), **6**. 183, 1844 ; *Elementos de Mineralojia*, Santiago, 229, 1879 ; A. Raimondi,
Minéraux du Pérou, Paris, 115, 1878 ; M. H. Klaproth, *Beiträge zur chemischen Kenntniss der
Mineralkörper*, Berlin, **4**. 73, 1807 ; G. T. Prior and L. J. Spencer, *Min. Mag.*, 12. 184, 1899 ;
. Petersen, *Neues Jahrb. Min.*, 458, 1870 ; i, 262, 1881 ; F. Sandberger, *ib.*, 592, 1865 ; 275, 1877 ;
, 96, 1887 ; C. Schindling, *ib.*, 335, 1856 ; F. Sandmann, *Liebig's Ann.*, **89**. 364, 1854 ; *Journ. prakt.
Chem.*, (1), **62**. 90, 1854 ; W. J. Jordan, *ib.*, (1), **9**. 92, 1837 ; E. von Bibra, *ib.*, (1), **96**. 204, 1865 ;
. F. Rammelsberg, *Handbuch der Mineralchemie*, Leipzig, 88, 1860 ; 107, 1875 ; 95, 1886 ;
46, 1895 ; *Pogg. Ann.*, **77**. 247, 1849 ; C. F. Plattner, *ib.*, **67**. 422, 1846 ; H. Weidenbusch, *ib.,
76*. 86, 1849 ; W. S. von Waltershausen and E. Uhrlaub, *ib.*, **94**. 120, 1855 ; C. M. Kersten, *ib.,
59*. 131, 1843 ; J. Kudernatsch, *ib.*, **38**. 397, 1836 ; T. Scheerer, *ib.*, **65**. 298, 1845 ; T. Bromeis,
ib., **55**. 117. 1842 ; G. Tschermak, *Lehrbuch der Mineralogie*, Wien, 366, 1897 ; C. W. Paijkull,
Oefvers. Akad. Stockholm, 85, 1866 ; *Journ. prakt. Chem.*, (1), **100**. 62, 1867 ; L. F. Svanberg,
ib., (1), **43**. 313, 1848 ; *Oefvers. Akad. Stockholm*, **4**. 85, 1847 ; A. Breithaupt, *Mineralogische
Studien*, Leipzig, 108, 1866 ; F. A. Genth, *The Minerals of North Carolina*, Washington, 27, 1891 ;
Proc. Amer. Phil. Soc., **23**. 38, 1885 ; *Amer. Journ. Science*, (2), **16**. 83, 1853 ; (2), **19**. 15, 1855 ;
2), **45**. 320, 1868 ; L. J. Smith, *ib.*, (2), **43**. 67, 1867 ; G. C. Hofmann, *ib.*, (3), **50**. 273, 1895 ; *Ann.
Rep. Geol. Sur. Canada*, **7**. 12, 1895 ; J. B. Harrington, *Trans. Roy. Soc. Canada*, **1**. 80, 1883 ;
. H. Swallow, *Proc. Boston Soc.*, **17**. 465, 1875 ; F. W. Clarke and M. E. Owens, *Journ. Amer.
Chem. Soc.*, **2**. 173, 1880 ; E. T. Wherry and W. F. Foshag, *Journ. Washington Acad.*, **11**. 1, 1921 ;
. R. Mallet, *A Manual of the Geology of India*, Calcutta, 30, 1887 ; *Rec. Geol. Sur. India*, **18**.
235, 1885 ; V. Novarese, *Boll. Comit. Geol. Ital.*, (4), **3**. 319, 1903 ; E. Tacconi, *Atti Accad.
Lincei*, (5), **13**. ii. 337, 1904 ; A. Schwager and C. W. von Gümbel, *Geognost. Jahrb.*, **7**. 57, 1899 ;
Neues Jahrb. Min., i, 8, 1899 ; L. N. Vauquelin, *Ann. Chim. Phys.*, (1), **60**. 317, 1806 ; *Nicholson's
Journ.*, **17**. 128, 1807 ; *Phil. Mag.*, **27**. 335, 1807 ; **29**. 278, 1807 ; C. H. Scheidhauer, *ib.*, **58**.
161, 1843 ; G. vom Rath., *ib.* **96**. 322, 1855 ; *Niederrh. Ges. Bonn*, **15**. 73, 1858 ; F. M. Baumert,
ib., **15**. 73, 1858 ; B. Kerl, *Berg. Hütt. Ztg.*, **12**. 20, 1853 ; J. Löwe, *ib.*, **13**. 24, 1854 ; M. von
Lill, *ib.*, **13**. 24, 1854 ; P. Kröber, *ib.*, **23**. 130, 1864 ; W. Hampe, *Chem. Ztg.*, **17**. 1691, 1893 ;
. Kuhlemann, *Zeit. Ges. Naturw.*, **8**. 500, 1865 ; F. Wandesleben, *Liebig's Ann.*, 87. 248, 1853 ;
M. Websky, *Zeit. deut. geol. Ges.*, **23**. 489. 1871 ; F. Babanek, *Tschermak's Mitt.*, (2), **6**. 85, 1885 ;
C. Hidegh, *ib.*, (2), **2**. 356, 1880 ; F. Becke, *ib.*, (1), **7**. 274, 1877 ; C. von Hauer, *Jahresb. geol.
Reichsanst. Wien*, **3**. 98, 1852 ; C. Untchj, *Mitt. Naturw. Ver. Steiermark*, 60, 1872 ; *Neues Jahrb.
Min.*, 874, 1872 ; A. N. Winchell, *Amer. Min.*, **11**. 181, 1926 ; J. Palacios, *Anal. Fis. Quim.*,
25. 246, 1927.

⁴ J. Durocher, *Compt. Rend.*, **32**. 825, 1851 ; A. Daubrée, *ib.*, **80**. 462, 1875 ; B. Cotta, *Neues
Jahrb. Min.*, 432, 1860 ; H. Sommerlad, *Zeit. anorg. Chem.*, **15**. 173, 1897 ; **18**. 420, 1898 ;
C. Hintze, *Handbuch der Mineralogie*, Leipzig, **1**. i, 1087, 1904.

⁵ P. Groth, *Die Mineraliensammlung der Universität Strassburg*, Strassburg, 66, 1878 ;
A. Lacroix, *Minéralogie de la France et de ses colonies*, Paris, **2**. 730, 1897 ; J. Schweitzer,
Krystallographische Beschreibung des Eisenglanzes und des Fahlerzes von Framont, Strassburg, 18,
1892 ; F. Sandberger, *Untersuchungen über Erzgänge*, Wiesbaden, 392, 1885 ; *Neues Jahrb. Min.*,
223, 1864 ; 585. 1865 ; 301, 1869 ; 275, 1877 ; T. Petersen, *ib.*, 464, 1870 ; C. Blömecke, *Zeit. prakt.
Geol.*, **3**. 74, 171, 208, 250, 1895 ; L. Buchdrucker, *ib.*, **3**. 393, 1895 ; L. Colombo, *Atti Accad.
Lincei*, (5), **15**. ii. 636, 1906 ; F. Hessenberg, *Mineralogische Notizen*, Frankfurt, **4**. 36, 1868 ;
O. Luedecke, *Die Minerale des Harzes*, Berlin, 162, 1896 ; A. Sadebeck, *Zeit. deut. geol. Ges.*, **24**.
427, 1872 ; M. Websky, *ib.*, **23**. 486, 1871 ; G. vom Rath, *Ber. niederrh. Ges. Bonn*, 190, 1884 ;
K. Zimanyi, *Zeit. Kryst.*, **34**. 78, 1901 ; H. Baumhauer, *ib.*, **21**. 202, 1893 ; **28**. 545, 1897 ;
W. J. Lewis, *Phil. Mag.*, (5), **5**. 139. 1877 ; *Proc. Crystal. Soc.*, **1**. 52, 1877 ; *Zeit. Kryst.*, **2**. 192,
1878 : G. Seligmann, *ib.*, i. 335, 1877 ; A. Cathrein, *ib.*, **9**. 353, 1844 ; *Tschermak's Mitt.*, (2),
10. 56, 1888 ; F. Becke, *ib.*, (2), **5**. 331, 1882 ; E. V. Shannon, *Proc. U.S. Nat. Museum*, **58**.
437, 1921 ; *Amer. Min.*, **13**. 18, 1928 ; C. O. Trechmann, *Min. Mag.*, **10**. 220, 1893 ; G. T. Prior
and L. J. Spencer, *ib.*, **12**. 184, 1899 ; A. Breithaupt, *Mineralogische Studien*, Leipzig, 105, 1866 ;
W. Phillips, *Introduction to Mineralogy*, London, 227, 1819 ; R. P. Greg and W. G. Lettsom, *Manual
of the Mineralogy of Great Britain and Ireland*, London, 334, 1858 ; P. von Jeremejeff, *Proc.
Russ. Min. Soc.*, **3**. 106, 1868 ; **19**. 179, 1884 ; **20**. 323, 1885.

⁶ M. de Florin, *Erz Bergbau*, **3**. 99. 1907 : F. Janda. *Oesterr. Zeit. Berg. Hütt.*. **53**. 235. 1905 ;

E. Schäfer, *Zeit. anal. Chem.*, **45**. 145, 1906; E. F. Smith, *Journ. Amer. Chem. Soc.*, **20**. 289, 1898; L. H. Borgström, *Oefvers. Finska Vet. Soc. Forh.*, **59**. 16, 1917; J. Lemberg, *Zeit. deut* *geol. Ges.*, **46**. 798, 1894; **52**. 490, 1900; C. A. Burghardt, *Min. Mag.*, **9**. 233, 1891; O. Gaspa rini, *Gazz. Chim. Ital.*, **37**. ii. 426, 1907; A. Sella, *Gött. Nachr.*, 311, 1891; H. Fizeau, *Compt* *Rend.*, **66**. 1005, 1072, 1868; J. Joly, *Phil. Mag.*, (6), **27**. 1, 1914; *Chem. News*, **107**. 241, 1913 A. de Gramont, *Bull. Soc. Min.*, **18**. 309, 1895; C. Friedel, *Ann. Chim. Phys.*, (4), **17**, 93, 1869 C. F. Plattner, *Die metallurgischen Röstprocesse theoretisch betrachtet*, Freiberg, 91, 1856 E. T. Wherry, *Min. Mag.*, **10**. 28, 1925; H. Saito, *Science Rep. Tohoku Univ.*, **16**. 37, 1927 C. Davies and A. D. Munro, *Journ. Chem. Soc.*, 2385, 1927; J. Palacios, *Anal. Fis. Quim.*, **25**. 246, 1927.

[7] J. J. Berzelius, *Schweigger's Journ.*, **34**. 46, 1822; *Pogg. Ann.*, **7**. 137, 1826; *Svenska Akad Handl.*, 295, 1925; *Ann. Chim. Phys.*, (2), **11**. 225, 1819; (2), **32**. 166, 1826; H. Sommerlad, *Zeit. anorg. Chem.*, **15**. 173, 1897; **18**. 420, 1898.

[8] H. Sommerlad, *Zeit. anorg. Chem.*, **15**. 173, 1897; **18**. 420, 1898; F. M. Jäger and H. S. van Klooster, *ib.*, **78**. 245, 1912; H. de Sénarmont, *Ann. Chim. Phys.*, (3), **32**. 129, 1851; *Compt. Rend.*, **32**. 409, 1851; J. Margottet, *ib.*, **85**. 1142, 1877; F. Wöhler, *Liebig's Ann.*, **27**. 159, 1838; K. Preis, *ib.*, **257**. 178, 1890; H. Rose, *Pogg. Ann.*, **15**. 472, 1829; J. J. Berzelius, *ib.*, **7**. 150, 1826; H. B. North and C. B. Conover, *Amer. Journ. Science*, (4), **40**. 640, 1915; F. Field, *Journ. Chem. Soc.*, **12**. 12, 1859; F. Sandberger, *Untersuchungen über Erzgänge*, Wiesbaden, 372, 1885; *Neues Jahrb. Min.*, 402, 1868; A. Streng, *ib.*, i, 60, 1886; I. Domeyko, *Elementos de Mineralojia*, Santiago, 389, 1879; E. Rethwisch, *Neues Jahrb. Min. B.B.*, **4**. 94. 1886; *Zur mineralogischen und chemischen Kenntnis des Rothgultigerzes*, Göttingen, 1885; H. A. Miers, *Min. Mag.*, **8**. 37, 1888; **9**. 182, 1890; C. A. Burghardt, *ib.*, **9**. 230, 1891; A. des Cloizeaux, *Nouvelles recherches sur les propriétés optiques des cristaux*, Paris, 714, 1867; F. S. Beudant, *Traité élémentaire de minéralogie*, Paris, **2**. 430, 445, 1832; G. Agricola, *Interpretatio Germanica vocum rei metallicæ*, Basileæ, 462, 1546; *De natura fossilium*, Basileæ, 362, 462, 1546; *De re metallica*, Basileæ, 565, 703, 1557; J. Hill, *Fossils Arranged according to their Obvious Characters*, London, 1771; E. F. Glocker, *Handbuch der Mineralogie*, Nürnberg, 388, 1831; A. Breithaupt, *Vollständiges Charakteristik des Mineralsystems*, Dresden, 282, 1832; *Schweigger's Journ.*, **51**. 348, 1827; **62**. 375, 1831; M. H. Klaproth, *Beiträge zur chemischen Kenntniss der Mineral körper*, Berlin, **1**. 146, 155, 1795; *Berg. Journ.*, **1**. 147, 1792; L. N. Vauquelin, *Journ. Mines*, **4**. 1796; W. A. Lampadius, *Handbuch der chemischen Analyse der Mineralkörper*, Freyberg, 254, 1801; F. Mohs, *Grundriss der Mineralogie*, Dresden, **2**. 504, 1824; C. J. Selb, *Denks. Ges. Aerzte Naturf. Schwabens*, **1**. 311, 1805; C. Hintze, *Handbuch der Mineralogie*, Leipzig, **1**. i, 1071, 1904; O. Luedecke, *Die Minerale des Harzes*, Berlin, 130, 1896; A. Lacroix, *Minéralogie de la France et de ses colonies*, Paris, **2**. 744, 1897; P. Groth, *Die Mineraliensammlung der Universität Strass burg*, Strassburg, 66, 1878; A. Frenzel, *Mineralogisches Lexikon für das Königreich Sachsen*, Leipzig, 241, 1874; W. W. Coblentz, *Science Papers Bur. Standards*, **17**. 179, 1921; **18**. 353, 1922; E. Giebe and A. Scheibe, *Zeit. Physik*, **33**. 760, 1925; P. H. Geiger, *Phys. Rev.*, (2), **22**. 461, 1923; A. L. Parsons, *Univ. Toronto Geol. Stud.*, 14, 1922; M. von Laue, *Zeit. Kryst.*, **63**. 312, 1926; J. G. Wallerius, *Mineralogia*, Stockholm, 311, 1747; M. Fenoglio, *Atti Accad. Torino*, **61**. 357, 1926; J. L. Proust, *Journ. Phys.*, **59**. 403, 1804; L. J. Thénard, *ib.*, **51**. 68, 1800; A. de Gramont, *Bull. Soc. Min.*, **18**. 294, 1895; A. Sella, *Gött. Nachr.*, 311, 1891; A. Made lung, *Zeit. Kryst.*, **7**. 75, 1883; C. Gessner, *De omni rerum fossilium genere, gemmis, lapidus, et metallis*, Tiguri, 62, 1555; J. F. Henckel, *Pyritologia oder Kiesshistorie*, Leipzig, 1725; T. Berg man, *De arsenico*, Upsala, 1777; T. W. Case, *Phys. Rev.*, (2), **9**. 365, 1917; C. Tubandt and M. Haedicke, *Zeit. anorg. Chim.*, **160**. 297, 1927; H. E. McKinstry, *Econ. Geol.*, **22**. 669, 1928.

[9] J. Voigt and J. F. A. Göttling, *Almanach Scheidekünstler*, **2**. 49, 1781; J. J. Berzelius, *Schweigger's Journ.*, **34**. 46, 1822; *Pogg. Ann.*, **7**. 137, 1826; *Svenska Akad. Handl.*, 295, 1825; *Ann. Chim. Phys.*, (2), **11**. 225, 1819; (2), **32**. 166, 1826; L. F. Nilson, *Journ. prakt. Chem.*, (2), **12**. 295, 1875; (2), **14**. 145, 1876; (2), **16**. 93, 1877; *Akad. Handl. Stockholm*, **10**. 2, 1871; *Oefvers. Akad. Stockholm*, **28**. 303, 1871; **34**. 5, 1877; P. de Clermont and J. Frommel, *Compt. Rend.*, **87**. 330, 1878; J. Morozewicz, *Compt. Rend. Congrès Géol. Belg.*, **3**. 1619, 1922; *Bull. Serv. Geol. Pologne*, **2**. 1, 1923.

[10] J. W. Gunning, *Chem. News*, **17**. 138, 1868; *Arch. Néerl.*, (1), **3**. 86, 1868; A. S. Eakle, G. Canneri, and L. Fernandes, *Atti Accad. Lincei*, (6), **1**. i, 671, 1925; *Zeit. Kryst.*, **31**. 215, 1899; E. S. Larsen, *Bull. U.S. Geol. Sur.*, 102, 1921; L. Tokody, *Zeit. Kryst.*, **59**. 83, 1924; R. Böttger, *Liebig's Ann.*, **128**. 250, 1863; L. F. Hawley, *Journ. Amer. Chem. Soc.*, **29**. 1011, 1907; J. A. Krenner, *Math. Term. Mayi Ertösitö*, **12**. 473, 1895; **13**. 258, 1895; J. Loczka, *Magyar Chem. Foly.*, **3**. 1, 1899; V. Goldschmidt, *Zeit. Kryst.*, **30**. 272, 1898; L. Tokody, *ib.*, **59**. 250, 1924; P. Jannasch, *ib.*, **39**. 123, 1904; L. Bruner and J. Zawadsky, *Bull. Acad. Cracovie*, 312, 1909; T. W. Case, *Phys. Rev.*, (2), **9**. 305, 1917.

[11] J. J. Berzelius, *Schweigger's Journ.*, **34**. 46, 1822; *Pogg. Ann.*, **7**. 137, 1826; *Svenska Akad. Handl.*, 295, 1825; *Ann. Chim. Phys.*, (2), **11**. 225, 1819; (2), **32**. 166, 1826; J. Fournet, *Ann. Chim. Phys.*, (2), **56**. 412, 1834; A. Damour, *ib.*, (3), **14**. 579, 1845; *Compt. Rend.*, **20**, 1121, 1845; *L'Inst.*, 141, 1845; C. Lardy, *Acta Soc. Helvét.*, **1**. b, 244, 1833; D. F. Wiser, *Neues Jahrb. Min.*, 414, 559, 1839; 216, 1840; R. H. Solly, *Min. Mag.*, **12**. 283, 1900; **13**. 77, 151, 336, 1902; **14**. 186, 1904; **18**. 259, 1919; A. des Cloizeaux and J. C. G. de Marignac, *Ann. Mines*, (5), **8**. 389, 1855; W. S. von Waltershausen, *Sitzber. Akad. Wien*, **14**. 291, 1854; *Pogg. Ann.*, **94**. 115, 1855; J. C. Heusser, *ib.*, **94**. 334, 1855; **97**. 120, 1856; *Ber. Zürich. Na†*

Ges., **3.** 431, 1854 ; G. vom Rath, *Zeit. deut. geol. Ges.*, **16.** 186, 1864 ; *Pogg. Ann.*, **122.** 373, 1864 ; G. Cesaro, *Bull. Soc. Min.*, **38.** 53, 1915 ; H. Sommerlad, *Zeit. anorg. Chem.*, **18.** 442, 1898. ¹² G. vom Rath, *Ber. niederrh. Ges. Bonn*, **21.** 34, 1864 ; **30.** 155, 1873 ; *Pogg. Ann.*, **122.** 387, 1864 ; *Pogg. Ann. Ergbd.*, **6.** 363, 1873 ; L. Sipöcz, *Tschermak's Mitt.*, (1), **3.** 29, 132, 1873 ; E. Ludwig, *ib.*, (1), **3.** 216, 1873 ; G. Tschermak, *ib.*, (1), **3.** 215, 1873 ; V. Wartha, *ib.*, (1), **3.** 131, 1873 ; *Jahresb. geol. Reichsanst. Wien*, **23.** 131, 1873 ; H. Baumhauer, *Sitzber. Akad. Berlin*, 697, 711, 915, 1891 ; *Zeit. Kryst.*, **21.** 207, 1893 ; **24.** 78, 1895 ; **38.** 635, 1904 ; R. Bunsen, *Liebig's Ann.*, **192.** 305, 1878 ; W. J. Lewis, *Phil. Mag.*, (5), **5.** 139, 1877 ; *Proc. Crystal Soc.*, **1.** 52, 1877 ; *Zeit. Kryst.*, **2.** 192, 1878 ; C. Guillemain, *Beiträge zur Kenntniss der natürlichen Sulfosalze*, Breslau, 40, 1878 ; A. Sachs, *Centr. Min.*, 723, 1904 ; R. H. Solly, *Min. Mag.*, **12.** 282, 1900 ; H. A. Miers, *ib.*, **5.** 330, 1884 ; A. Schmidt, *Zeit. Kryst.*, **8.** 613, 1887 ; J. A. Krenner, *ib.*, **8.** 623, 1887 ; G. Hintze, *ib.*, **9.** 294, 1888 ; P. Groth, *Tabellarische Uebersicht der Mineralien,* Braunschweig, 37, 1898 ; G. d'Archiardi, *Atti Soc. Toscana*, **18.** 15, 1901 ; H. Sommerlad, *Zeit. anorg. Chem.*, **18.** 442, 1898 ; S. S. Smirnoff, *Proc. Russ. Min. Soc.*, (2), **54.** 21, 1925; C. F. Rammelsberg, *Handbuch der Mineralchemie*, Leipzig, 2. 37, 1886. ¹³ R. H. Solly, *Nature*, **71.** 118, 1904 ; *Bull. Soc. Min.*, **28.** 283, 1905 ; *Min. Mag.*, **14.** 78, 1905 ; A. Hutchinson, *ib.*, **14.** 204, 1905 ; R. Köchlin, *Tschermak's Mitt.*, (2), **23.** 551, 1904. ¹⁴ W. F. Hillebrand, *Bull. U.S. Geol. Sur.*, 20, 1885 ; *Proc. Colorado Scient. Soc.*, **1.** 129, 1884 ; F. W. Clarke, *ib.*, 419, 1910 ; *Bull. Soc. Min.*, **9.** 146, 1886 ; A. de Gramont, *ib.*, **18.** 291, 1895 ; T. W. Case, *Phys. Rev.*, (2), **9.** 305, 1917 ; W. F. Foshag, *Amer. Journ. Science*, (5), **1.** 444, 1921 ; H. Baumhauer, *Sitzber. Akad. Berlin*, 110, 1901 ; 611, 1902 ; R. H. Solly, *Min. Mag.*, **13.** 336, 1903 ; **14.** 186, 1904 ; G. T. Prior, *ib.*, **15.** 385, 1910 ; H. Sommerlad, *Zeit. anorg. Chem.*, **18.** 446, 1898 ; A. Terreil, *Bull. Soc. Chim.*, (2), **13.** 116, 1870 ; E. T. Wherry, *Min. Mag.*, **10.** 28, 1925. ¹⁵ J. J. Berzelius, *Pogg. Ann.*, **7.** 147, 1826 ; G. vom Rath, *Zeit. deut. geol. Ges.*, **16.** 186, 1864 ; *Pogg. Ann.*, **122.** 373, 1864 ; W. S. von Waltershausen, *ib.* **94.** 115, 1855 ; *Sitzber. Akad. Wien*, **14.** 291, 1854 ; J. C. Heusser, *Ber. Zürich. Nat. Ges.*, **3.** 431, 1854 ; *Pogg. Ann.*, **94.** 334, 1855 ; **97.** 120, 1856 ; A. Damour, *Ann. Chim. Phys.*, (3), **14.** 379, 1845 ; *Compt. Rend.*, **20.** 1121, 1845 ; *L'Inst.*, 141, 1845 ; H. Baumhauer, *Zeit. Kryst.*, **24.** 78, 1895 ; **28.** 551, 1897 ; J. Berendes, *De dufrénoysite Vallis Binnensis,* Bonn, 1864 ; C. Guillemain, *Beiträge zur Kenntniss der natürlichen Sulfosalze*, Breslau, 1898 ; H. Sommerlad, *Zeit. anorg. Chem.*, **18.** 445, 1898 ; A. des Cloizeaux and J. C. G. de Marignac, *Ann. Mines*, (5), **8.** 389, 1855 ; R. H. Solly, *Min. Mag.*, **13.** 77, 160, 1902 ; L. J. Spencer, *ib.*, **11.** 1, 1896 ; C. F. Rammelsberg, *J. J. Berzelius' neues chemisches Mineralsystem*, Nürnberg, 229, 1847 ; *Handbuch der Mineralchemie*, Leipzig, 85, 1875 ; P. Groth, *Tabellarische Uebersicht der Mineralien*, Braunschweig, 18, 1874 ; T. Petersen, *Ber. Offenbach Ver. Naturk.*, **7.** 13, 1867 ; *Neues Jahrb. Min.*, 203, 1867 ; J. L. C. Schröder van der Kolk, *Centr. Min.*, 79, 1901 ; A. de Gramont, *Bull. Soc. Min.*, **18.** 292, 1895 ; A. Brun, *ib.*, **40.** 110, 1917 ; G. Cesaro, *ib.*, **38.** 53, 1915 ; F. Field, *Journ. Chem. Soc.*, **14.** 153, 1862. ¹⁶ H. Baumhauer, *Zeit. Kryst.*, **26.** 593, 1896 ; H. Jackson, *Min. Mag.*, **12.** 287, 1900 ; R. H. Solly, *ib.*, **13.** 77, 1901 ; **16.** 121, 1913 ; W. J. Lewis, *ib.*, **16.** 197, 1913 ; *Phil. Mag.*, (6), **20.** 474, 1910 ; G. T. Prior, *Centr. Min.*, 351, 1914 ; G. A. Kenngott, *Uebersicht der Resultate mineralogischer Forschungen*, Wien, 176, 1857 ; T. W. Case, *Phys. Rev.*, (2), **9.** 305, 1917 ; T. Petersen, *Neues Jahrb. Min.*, 203, 1867 ; G. vom Rath, *Pogg. Ann.*, **122.** 374, 1864 ; W. S. von Waltershausen, *Pogg. Ann.*, **100.** 540, 1857 ; G. Cesaro, *Bull. Soc. Chim.*, **38.** 53, 1915. ¹⁷ R. H. Solly, *Nature*, **64.** 577, 1901 ; *Min. Mag.*, **13.** 151, 339, 1902 ; R. H. Solly and H. Jackson, *ib.*, **13.** 160, 1902 ; *Proc. Cambridge Phil. Soc.*, **11.** 239, 1901 ; E. V. Shannon, *Amer. Journ. Science*, (5), **1.** 424, 1921 ; G. E. Uhrlaub, *Pogg. Ann.*, **100.** 540, 1857. ¹⁸ H. Sommerlad, *Zeit. anorg. Chem.*, **18.** 442, 1898 ; W. Sartorius von Waltershausen, *Sitzber. Akad. Wien*, **14.** 291, 1854 ; *Pogg. Ann.*, **94.** 115, 1855 ; **100.** 540, 1857 ; G. vom Rath, *ib.*, **122.** 380, 1864 ; *Zeit. deut. geol. Ges.*, **16.** 186, 1864 ; J. D. Dana, *A System of Mineralogy,* New York, 87, 1868 ; 112, 1892 ; H. Baumhauer, *Sitzber. Akad. Berlin*, 243, 1895 ; *Zeit. Kryst.* **29.** 159, 1898 ; G. F. H. Smith and R. H. Solly, *Min. Mag.*, **18.** 259, 1919 ; R. H. Solly. *ib.*, **12.** 287, 1900 ; L. J. Spencer, *ib.*, **11.** 188, 1896 ; C. O. Trenchmann, *ib.*, **14.** 212, 1907 ; *Zeit. Kryst.*, **43.** 548, 1907 ; G. A. Kenngott, *Uebersicht der Resultate mineralogischer Forschungen,* Wien, 176, 1857 ; T. Petersen, *Neues Jahrb. Min.*, 203, 1867 ; *Ber. Offenbach. Ver. Naturk.*, **7.** 13, 1867 ; C. F. Rammelsberg, *Handbuch der Mineralchemie,* Leipzig, 37, 1876 ; P. Groth and K. Mieleitner, *Mineralogische Tabellen,* München, 25, 1921 ; J. Königsberger, *Centr. Min.*, 397, 1918 ; T. W. Case, *Phys. Rev.*, (2), **9.** 305, 1917. ¹⁹ R. H. Solly, *Proc. Cambridge Phil. Soc.*, **12.** 277, 1904 ; *Min. Mag.*, **14.** 72, 1905 ; G. F. H. Smith and G. T. Prior, *ib.*, **14.** 284, 1907 ; G. T. Prior, *Nature*, **71.** 534, 1905 ; R. Köchlin, *Tschermak's Mitt.*, (2), **23.** 551, 1904. ²⁰ J. J. Berzelius, *Schweigger's Journ.*, **34.** 46, 1822 ; *Pogg. Ann.*, **7.** 137, 1826 ; *Svenska Akad. Handl.*, 295, 1825 ; *Ann. Chim. Phys.*, (2), **11.** 225, 1899 ; (2), **32.** 166, 1826.

§ 33. The Sulphoarsenides, Sulpharsenides, or Arsenosulphides

A. Frenzel [1] described a mineral from the copper mines at Lauta, Marienberg ; and called it **lautite.** Analyses reported by A. Frenzel, and A. Weisbach agreed with the formula CuAsS, **copper sulpharsenide,** but about one-fifth of the copper was replaced by silver, (Cu,Ag)AsS. The crystals of the dark steel-grey mineral belong either to the rhombic or the monoclinic system. W. F. de Jong found the X-radiogram to be totally different from that of the arsenopyrite-glaucodote family, so that it is doubtful if isomorphism exists. The hardness is 3·0–3·5, and the sp. gr. 4·96. L. Dürr gave 4·53 at 18°. A. Weisbach considered lautite to be a mixture of arsenic with julianite.

H. and G. Rose [2] described an arsenical polybasite from Mexico, and S. L. Penfield applied the name **pearceite**—after R. Pearce—to a similar mineral from Aspen, Colorado. Analyses reported by S. L. Penfield, S. H. Pearce, H. Rose, and I. Domeyko agree with the formula $9Ag_2S.As_2S_3$, or **silver hexasulpharsenide,** Ag_9AsS_6, or $(Ag,Cu)_9AsS_6$. The black crystals are monoclinic, and, according to S. L. Penfield, have the axial ratios $a : b : c = 1·7309 : 1 : 1·6199$, and $\beta = 89°\ 51'$. The tabular crystals appear to be pseudo-rhombohedral, and have triangular markings on the basal faces ; the twinning is thought to be like that of the micas and chlorites. No cleavage has been observed. The hardness is 3, and the sp. gr. ranges from 6·125 to 6·166. T. W. Case found that the mineral has an electrical resistance less than one megohm, and light has no measurable effect. H. E. McKinstry found that the surface of the mineral is roughened by exposure to the light of an electric arc. Pearceite is readily oxidized, and the powder dissolved by nitric acid.

G. Agricola [3] described a mineral which he called *mistpuckel* as *lapis substilis atque non fere aliter ac argenti spuma splendens et friabilis ;* C. Gesner called the same mineral *Wasserkies* or *pyrites candidus ;* J. F. Henckel, **mispickel** or *arsenikalischer Kies ;* J. G. Wallerius, *mispikkel, pyrites albus, arsenicum ferro mineralisatum,* etc. ; A. G. Werner, A. Cronstedt, C. A. S. Hofmann, and L. A. Emmerling used various designations—*Rauschgelbkies, Giftkies, Glanzarsenikkies, Weisserz, dalarnite,* etc. A. Breithaupt called it *plinian ;* and E. F. Glocker, **arsenopyrite.** The names mispickel and arsenopyrite are in common use. A very large number of analyses has been reported.[4] Some specimens contain little or no cobalt, others —danaite—contain up to 10 per cent., and gradually merge into glaucodote. Some specimens contain up to 0·28 per cent. of antimony ; some bismuth ; and some are niccoliferous. The early analyses—e.g. W. A. Lampadius—missed the sulphur, and thus R. J. Haüy called the mineral *fer arsenical.* The presence of iron, sulphur, and arsenic as essential constituents was demonstrated by M. E. Chevreul, F. Stromeyer, and T. Thomson, who regarded it as a mixture of FeS_2 and $FeAs_2$; while C. F. Rammelsberg regarded it as a mixture of $FeS_2 + nFe_xAs_y$, i.e. of FeAs, Fe_3As_4, Fe_2As_5, or $FeAs_3$. J. Loczka, and P. Groth represented the constitution of mispickel as marcasite with part of the sulphur replaced by arsenic, or as löllingite with part of the arsenic replaced by sulphur :

$$Fe<^{S-S}_{S-S}>Fe \qquad Fe<^{S-S}_{As-As}>Fe \qquad Fe<^{As=As}_{As=As}>Fe$$

Marcasite, $(FeS_2)_2$ Mispickel, $(FeAsS)_2$ Löllingite, $(FeAs_2)_2$

N. S. Kurnakoff and N. S. Konstantinoff held similar views. According to F. W. Starke, H. L. Shock, and E. F. Smith, (i) when mispickel is heated in hydrogen, all the sulphur is expelled as hydrogen sulphide, whilst the iron and practically all the arsenic remain ; this indicates that the sulphur is less intimately combined with the iron than is the arsenic. Pyrites and marcasite lose half their sulphur when heated in hydrogen. (ii) Heating with ammonium chloride in nitrogen, and dissolving in water, gives indications of the presence of much ferrous, but only a little ferric iron. (iii) Heating with copper sulphate soln. in sealed tubes and titrating with permanganate shows the presence of much ferrous iron and arsenious acid. (iv) Heating in a current of dry hydrogen bromide showed the presence of about 28 per cent. of ferrous iron, and in dry hydrogen chloride of 30·86, 30·55, 30·16 per cent. Since there is 34·35 per cent. of iron in mispickel, this leaves about 4 per cent. for ferric iron. Consequently, the formula of mispickel is given provisionally as $14Fe''As'''S,2Fe'''As'''S$. Experiments to determine the mol. wt. by observing the influence of mispickel on the solidification point of alloys were without result. G. A. Behncke, and A. Breithaupt considered the difference in chemical composition, density, and crystal angles is founded on essential differences in composition ; and A. Arzruni, and A. Arzruni and C. Barwäld showed that the differences cannot be regarded as being produced by varying proportions of FeS_2 and $FeAs_2$ regarded as isomorphous compounds ; and G. Magel found that as the proportion of sulphur increased so did the axial ratio $a : b$ increase. J. W. Retgers, as well as A. Arzruni, did not consider the FeS_2 and $FeAs_2$ to be isomorphous, but rather morphotropic. H. de Sénarmont heated, in a sealed tube at 300°, a mixture of iron sulphide with sodium sulpharsenite, and hydrocarbonate and water ; or a mixture of precipitated iron sulpharsenite, and sodium hydrocarbonate, and water, and obtained crystals of iron sulpharsenide (mispickel). W. Ipatieff and W. Nikolaieff obtained the crystals by the prolonged action of hydrogen, at a high temp. and press., on iron arsenate. A. N. Winchell discussed the isomorphism of the tetrahedrite-tennantite system.

Mispickel is the most important of the arsenic ores. It occurs in well-defined fissure veins in beds, or threaded bands, and as impregnation deposits in crystalline rocks. It is commonly associated with ores of silver, lead, and tin, and also with pyrite, chalcopyrite, and sphalerite. Mispickel occurs compact and granular, as well as in prismatic or tabular crystals. C. Hintze has given a review of the more important occurrences of the mineral. The colour of mispickel varies from silverwhite to steel-grey. C. Linnæus [5] referred to the cubic crystals, and so did J. B. L. Romé de l'Isle, and J. J. Bernhardi. R. J. Haüy, however, showed that the crystals are rhombic prisms. A. Arzruni found the axial ratios of the rhombic crystals to be $a : b : c = 0.677726 : 1 : 1.18817$; H. Bücking, $0.6734 : 1 : 1.1921$; and F. Scherer gave $0.69764 : 1 : 1.201$. Twinning occurs about the (110)-plane with contact or penetration twins repeated as with marcasite ; and there may be cruciform twins about the (101)-plane. There may be star-shaped trillings crossing at angles 59° and 62°. The brachydomes may be horizontally striated and the (110)-faces may also be finely striated. The (110)-cleavage is distinct ; and the (001)-cleavage faint. The crystals were examined by A. Frenzel, P. Groth, F. Scherer, A. Breithaupt, G. Magel, H. Bücking, V. R. von Zepharovich, A. Schmidt, A. des Cloizeaux, M. Weibull, P. von Jeremejeff, K. Jimbo, etc. The effect of variations in the composition on the crystal form were studied by A. Arzruni, A. Arzruni and C. Bärwald, G. Magel, A. Breithaupt, G. A. Behncke, M. Weibull, F. Scherer, L. J. Wallmark, and F. Sandberger. F. Scherer studied the corrosion figures ; M. L. Huggins, the space-lattice ; and P. F. Kerr,[6] the X-radiograms. W. F. de Jong found the constants of the space-lattice of the rhombic crystals are $a = 6.44$ A., $b = 4.76$ A., and $c = 5.63$ A. ; and if there are 4 mols. per cell, the calculated density, 6.28, agrees with the observed value. The hardness is 5–6, and the sp. gr. 5.9–6.2. G. A. Kenngott gave 6.269 for the sp. gr. ; A. Vogel, 6.21 ; J. Potyka, 6.004 for the powder, and 6.095 for the solid ; D. Forbes, 6.255 ; V. R. von Zepharovich, 6.16 ; L. W. McCay, 6.05–6.07 ; and A. Breithaupt, 5.84–5.911. E. Madelung and R. Fuchs found for the compressibility, 2.86×10^{12} dynes per sq. cm. F. E. Neumann gave 0.1012 for the sp. ht. ; A. Sella, 0.103 ; and P. E. W. Oeberg, 0.1210. The mineral easily fuses ; L. H. Borgström gave 700° for the m.p. of arsenopyrite. At a higher temp., P. Berthier found that in the absence of air mispickel loses half its sulphur, and three-quarters of its arsenic ; and J. Loczka observed that almost all the arsenic is sublimed, and ferrous sulphamide remains. C. Schubert gave 220° for the temp. at which the decomposition, $FeAsS = FeS + As$, begins, and he found that the reaction is not completed at 670°. A. de Gramont examined the spark spectrum. T. W. Case observed that in darkness arsenopyrite and tetrahedrite have a resistance less than a megohm, and exposure to light has no effect on the conductivities. Mispickel is a conductor of electricity; and H. Bäckström observed that the thermoelectric force of a combination of two crystals with a copper strip between them gives an e.m.f. of 0·0002410 volt per degree with the (110)-faces; and 0·0002429 volt per degree with the (110)-faces. C. Schubert found that when heated, dissociation begins at 220°. V. Goldschmidt examined some magnetic properties of mispickel. E. T. Wherry found the crystals poor radiodetectors. H. Saito said that arsenopyrite is rapidly oxidized from about 500° subliming arsenic trioxide, and that the best temp. for the trioxide sublimation is 600°. Slower heating and low temp. give iron arsenate which reduces the yield of trioxide. The mineral is attacked by nitric acid with the separation of sulphur and arsenic acid; and with aqua-regia, only a little sulphur separates. F. Scherer observed the corrosion figures with aqua regia. H. Zieler observed a feeble reaction with boiling 10 and 20 per cent. HNO_3; with 30–40 per cent. HNO_3, there is a feeble reaction in the cold when the mixture is shaken, and a vigorous reaction with the boiling acid; and with 50 per cent. acid, agitated, there is a vigorous reaction in the cold. E. F. Smith found that with sulphur monochloride, there is a great rise of temp., but the mineral is decomposed completely only on heating to 140°; and H. B. North and C. B. Conover, that it is decomposed slowly by heating it with thionyl chloride in a sealed tube at 150°–175°. J. Lemberg found that the mineral is oxidized by soln. of bromine in alkali-lye. For the observations of F. W. Starke and co-workers on the action of hydrogen, ammonium chloride, hydrogen bromide, and a soln. of copper sulphate, vide supra. V. Lenher found that arsenopyrite is slowly attacked in the cold by selenium oxydichloride; the reaction is faster with hot soln. J. Lemberg found that when mispickel is warmed with a sulphuric acid soln. of silver nitrate at 75°, it is coloured bluish-violet, and some silver is deposited. E. Thomson studied the etching reactions with nitric acid and with soln. of mercurous and ferric chlorides.

The mineral *pacite* obtained by A. Breithaupt [7] from La Paz, Bolivia, resembles mispickel in general appearance. Its composition approximates $Fe_5S_2As_8$, *i.e.* $Fe(As,S)_2$. The sp. gr. is 6·297–6·008. The *glaucopyrite* obtained by F. Sandberger from Guadalcanal, Spain, approximates $Fe_{13}S_2As_{24}$ in composition, and is usually regarded as a variety of löllingite. Its sp. gr. is 7·181.

J. G. Wallerius,[8] and A. Cronstedt referred to *cobaltum cum ferro sulfurato et arsenicato mineralisatum* as *Glantzkobolt*, or *cobolt glance*, *Kobolterz*, or *Koboltmalm*. J. B. L. Romé de l'Isle called it *mine de cobalt arsenicosulfureuse;* R. J. Haüy, *cobalt gris;* E. F. Glocker, *Kobaltkies*, and **cobaltite;** and F. S. Beudant, *cobaltine*. It is the *sehta* of the Indian jewellers. The first quantitative analyses was made by M. H. Klaproth,[9] and his analyses as well as that of B. M. Tassert, gave too small a proportion of sulphur. F. Stromeyer's analysis came nearer the mark, and this with numerous others corresponded with the idealized $CoS_2.CoAs_2$, or **cobalt sulpharsenide,** CoAsS. Iron is present in some samples, and was called *Stahlcobalt* by C. F. Rammelsberg; *Staglerz*, by T. Münster; and *ferrocobaltite*, by J. D. Dana. According to P. Groth, the sp. gr. favours the view that ferrocobaltite is a variety of cobaltite. The crystals of cobaltite were mentioned by C. Linnæus,[10] and B. G. Sage; while J. B. L. Romé de l'Isle, and R. J. Haüy observed that the cubic crystals are pyritohedral. They commonly occur in cubes or pyritohedra or combinations of these, and with the faces striated as with pyrites. The cubic cleavage is nearly perfect. The crystals were examined by A. von Hubert, P. Groth, F. von Kobell, G. A. Kenngott, W. H. Miller, C. F. Naumann, etc. L. S. Ramsdell found the X-radiograms corresponded with the pyritic structure with arsenic occupying alternate positions with respect to the sulphur. The unit cubic cell has a side 5·58 A.; this agrees with the results obtained by W. H. and W. L. Bragg, and M. Mechling. H. Schneiderhöln found that all the crystals he examined were rhombic. This may mean that the rhombic structure of cobaltite is so near cubic that the X-ray data cannot distinguish the one from the other; or it may mean that cobaltite is dimorphous and that one form is metastable at ordinary temp. The data were discussed by M. L. Huggins. The colour may be silver-white, inclining to red ; steel-grey with a violet tinge : or greyish-black when much iron is present. P. F. Kerr examined the X-radiogram of cobaltite. W. Flörke found the anisotropic mineral became isotropic when heated for an hour at 800°–900°—the reverse change was not observed. The hardness is between 5 and 6 ; the sp. gr. between 6·0 and 6·4. According to A. Schrauf and E. S. Dana, crystals with a higher sp. gr. than 6·30 are usually octahedral, and those with a smaller sp. gr. than 6·1 are cubes. E. Madelung and R. Fuchs gave for the compressibility, $3 \cdot 06 \times 10^{12}$ dynes per sq. cm. P. W. Bridgman represented the linear compressibility at 30° by $\delta l/l_0 = 0 \cdot 0_6 2519 p$ $-0 \cdot 0_{11} 101 p^2$; and at 75°, by $\delta l/l_0 = 0 \cdot 0_6 2559 p - 0 \cdot 0_{11} 101 p^2$; and the vol. compressibility at 30° by $\delta v/v_0 = 0 \cdot 0_6 756 p - 0 \cdot 0_{11} 285 p^2$; and at 75° by $\delta v/v_0 = 0 \cdot 0_6 768 p$ $-0 \cdot 0_{11} 282 p^2$ for press., p ranging up to 12,000 kgrms. per sq. cm. H. Fizeau gave for the linear coeff. of thermal expansion, $0 \cdot 0_5 919$ at 40°. F. E. Neumann found the sp. ht. to be 0·107 ; P. E. W. Oeberg, 0·097 ; and A. Sella, 0·099. A. de Gramont studied the spark spectrum. T. W. Case said that the mineral is practically a non-conductor of electricity in the dark, and light has no measurable influence. W. G. Hankel found the octahedral crystals from Tunaberg to be thermoelectrically positive towards copper, the cubic crystals negative. This subject was investigated by H. Marbach, G. Rose, and P. Curie. According to A. Schrauf and E. S. Dana, generally, not always, the denser crystals richer in cobalt are usually octahedral, and negative, while the less dense crystals are cubic and positive. H. Bäckström showed that the (111)- and (100)-faces have the same thermoelectric force towards copper. E. T. Wherry found the crystals to be poor radio-detectors ; and J. Forrest studied their magnetic qualities. Warm nitric acid dissolves the mineral with the separation of sulphur and arsenic acid. E. F. Smith found that cobaltite must be heated to 180° before it is completely decomposed by sulphur monochloride. J. Lemberg observed that cobaltite is oxidized by a soln. of bromine in alkali-lye, forming cobalt peroxide ; that with a soln. of potassium ferricyanide and hydrochloric acid, cobalt ferricyanide is formed ; and that with a sulphuric acid soln. of silver sulphate there is very little action until the soln. is boiled—the reaction of smaltite with this soln., resulting in the deposition of silver, is much faster. E. Thomson studied the etching reactions with nitric acid, and soln. of mercurous and ferric chlorides. H. B. North and C. B. Conover said that it is not attacked by thionyl chloride at 150°–175°.

The cobaltiferous mispickel from Franconia, New Hampshire, was called *danaïte* —after J. D. Dana—by A. Hayes ;[11] T. Scheerer, and F. Wöhler called the cobaltiferous mispickel from Skutterud, *Kobaltarsenikies* ; A. Breithaupt called the cobaltiferous mispickel from Hausco, Chili, **glaucodotite**—from γλαυκός, blue —in allusion to its use for making smalt, and another variety from Hakansboda, Sweden, *akontite*. Analyses were reported by A. Hayes, F. Wöhler, T. Scheerer, C. F. Rammelsberg, G. Tschermak, C. Schnabel, F. von Kobell, G. C. Hoffmann, A. Breithaupt, I. Domeyko, and J. D. Dana. Hence, G. Tschermak showed that glaucodotite and danaite are members of an isomorphous series with FeAsS and CoAsS as terminal members. The members of the series are represented by the formula (Fe,Co)AsS. F. Becke gave for the axial ratios of the rhombic crystals of danaite $a:b:c = 0 \cdot 6732:1:1 \cdot 1871$; and W. J. Lewis for those of glaucodotite, $0 \cdot 6942:1:1 \cdot 1925$. The habit of the crystals resembles that of mispickel, being commonly prismatic. The (100)-faces are usually striated vertically, the brachydomes, horizontally. Twinning occurs about the (110)- and (101)-planes ; these are cruciform twins, and also trillings. The (001)-cleavage is nearly perfect, the (110)-cleavage less so. The crystals were also examined by M. Weibull, A. Sadebeck, W. H. Miller, G. A. Kenngott, A. Breithaupt, and I. Domeyko. The X-radiogram was examined by L. S. Ramsdell, and M. L. Huggins. W. F. de Jong found that the space-lattice of glaucodotite resembles that of arsenopyrite, but with $a = 6 \cdot 67$ A., $b = 4 \cdot 81$ A., and $c = 5 \cdot 73$ A., with the calculated density, 6·0, in agreement with that observed on the assumption that there are 4 mols. per unit cell. The hardness is 5 ; and the sp. gr. is usually between 5·9 and 6·0—T. Münster gave 5·958–5·983 ; G. Tschermak, 5·973 ; A. Breithaupt, 5·975–6·059 ; A. Hayes, 6·214 ; and G. C. Hofmann, 5·988. L. H. Bergström gave 480°–700° for the m.p. ; and J. Joly, 190° for the temp. at which sublimation occurs. F. Beijerinck found that the mineral is a good conductor of electricity ; the increase of conductivity is regular as the temp. rises from 17° to 215°. A. Schrauf and E. S. Dana found the thermoelectric force of danaite from Franconia is positive, and negative with glaucodotite from Modum, Skutterud, and Hakansboda. Crystals from Hakansboda have a negative skin of sp. gr. 6·011 and a positive core of sp. gr. 5·905. E. T. Wherry found the crystals to be fair radio-detectors. J. Lemberg said that when the mineral is heated to 60° with a sulphuric acid soln. of silver sulphate, it is rapidly coloured blue ; and it is rapidly oxidized with a soln. of bromine in alkali-lye.

A. Cronstedt [12] described *niccolum ferro et cobalto arsenicatis et sulphuratis mineralisatum*, or kupfernickel as he called it ; but in 1818, C. H. Pfaff showed that *ein neues Nickelerz* is involved which was called *nickel glance* or *white nickel ore*. F. von Kobell called a variety *Nickelarsenikglanz*, and *amoibite*—from ἀμοιβή, exchange ; E. F. Glocker, *Nickelarsenikkies* ; F. S. Beudant, *sulfoarséniure de nickel*, and *disomose* ; A. Breithaupt, *tombazite* ; J. D. Dana, *dobschauite*, and *plessite* ; and A. Löwe, **gersdorffite**—after A. von Gersdorff. According to C. H. Pfaff's analysis, the composition was $2NiAs_2.FeS_2$, but J. J. Berzelius [13] represented his analysis by $NiS_2 + NiAs_2$. Numerous other analyses have been reported, and the results agree with the idealized formula NiAsS, **nickel sulph-arsenide**. M. Hörnes showed that some varieties have a significant proportion of iron, and a small proportion of sulphur. The analyses are somewhat discordant —the nickel, for example, ranges from 19·59 to 37·34 per cent., and some indeed approach smaltite or chloanthite in composition. This is taken to mean that the normal gersdorffite is mixed with other minerals. There is probably a trimorphous series FeAsS–CoAsS–NiAsS.

The mineral varies in colour from tin-white to steel-grey. It occurs massive in various imitative shapes, and crystalline. J. C. L. Zincken [14] described the first crystals ; he regarded them as tetragonal, but G. Rose, and F. von Kobell showed that the crystals are pyritohedral and belong to the cubic system. The cubic cleavage is nearly perfect. S. von Olshausen studied the X-radiograms, and inferred that there is a simple cubic lattice of side $a=5·719$ A. L. S. Ramsdell found the X-radiogram to be in agreement with the pyritic pattern with arsenic atoms occupying alternate positions with the sulphur. The unit cube had a side of length 5·68 A. The lattice structure was also examined by M. L. Huggins. The hardness is near 5. J. C. L. Zincken gave for the sp. gr. 6·097–6·300 ; C. F. Rammelsberg, 5·61–6·415 ; A. Bäumler, 6·2 ; M. Hörnes, 6·72–6·87 ; F. Pless, 6·641 ; L. Sipöcz, 6·1977 ; D. Forbes, 5·49–5·65 ; C. H. Pfaff, 6·129 ; and G. C. Hofmann, 6·231 ; and V. R. Zepharovich, 6·514. J. Jolly said sublimation occurs at 450°–480°. A. de Gramont examined the spark spectrum. The mineral is a good conductor of electricity ; T. W. Case said that the resistance is less than a megohm, and exposure to light has no effect. It is decomposed by nitric acid, forming a green soln. with the separation of sulphur and arsenic acid. E. F. Smith found that gersdorffite is completely decomposed when heated to 170° with sulphur monochloride. J. Lemberg found that the mineral is oxidized by a soln. of bromine in alkali-lye, and with a sulphuric acid soln. of silver sulphate there is a separation of silver, and the colour becomes dark blue. E. Thomson studied the etching reactions with nitric acid, and with soln. of mercurous and ferric chlorides.

REFERENCES.

¹ A. Frenzel, *Tschermak's Mitt.*, (2), **3**. 515, 1881 ; (2), **4**. 97, 1882 ; (2), **14**. 125, 1895 ; A. Weisbach, *Neues Jahrb. Min.*, ii, 250, 18%₂ ; L. J. Spencer, *Min. Mag.*, **11**. 78, 1897 :

L. Dürr, *Mitt. geol. Landesanst. Elsass-Lothr.*, **6**. 249. 1909 ; P. Groth, *Tabellarische Uebersicht der Mineralien*, Braunschweig, 28, 1898 ; W. F. de Jong, *Physica*, **6**. 325, 1926.

[2] H. Rose, *Pogg. Ann.*, **15**. 575, 1829 ; **28**. 158, 1833 ; G. Rose, *Elemente der Krystallographie*, Berlin, 147, 1833 ; *Das krystallochemischen Mineralsystem*, Leipzig, 23, 1852 ; S. H. Pearce, *Amer. Journ. Science*, (3), **44**. 16, 1892 ; S. L. Penfield, *ib.*, (4), **2**. 17, 1896 ; I. Domeyko *Elementos de Mineralojia*, Santiago, 393, 1879 ; P. Groth, *Tabellarische Uebersicht der Mineralien*, Braunschweig, 38, 1898 ; T. W. Case, *Phys. Rev.*, (2), **9**. 305, 1917 ; H. E. McKinstry, *Econ. Geol.*, **22**. 669, 1927.

[3] G. Agricola, *Interpretatio Germanica vocum rei metallica*, Basileæ, 465, 1546 ; C. Gesner, *De omni rerum fossilium genere, gemmis, lapidis, et metallis*, Tiguri, 1565 ; J. F. Henckel, *Pyritologia oder Kiesshistorie*, Leipzig, 1725 ; J. G. Wallerius, *Mineralogia*, Stockholm, 227, 1747 ; A. G. Werner, *Letztes Mineralsystem*, Freiberg, 227, 1747 ; E. F. Glocker, *Generum et specierum mineralium secundum ordines naturales digestorum synopsis*, Halle, 38, 1847 ; A. Cronstedt, *Mineralogie*, Stockholm, 168, 1760 ; L. A. Emmerling, *Lehrbuch der Mineralogie*, Giessen, **2**. 552, 1796 ; C. A. S. Hofmann, *Handbuch der Mineralogie*, Freiberg, **4**. a, 211, 1817 ; A. Breithaupt, *Berg. Hütt. Ztg* , **25**. 168, 1866 ; *Pogg. Ann.*, **69**. 430, 1846 ; *Journ. prakt. Chem.*, (1), **4**. 259, 1835.

[4] G. Rose, *Das krystallochemischen Mineralsystem*, Leipzig, 56, 1852 ; G. A. Behncke, *Pogg. Ann.*, **98**. 184, 1856 ; C. F. Plattner, *ib.*, **69**. 430, 1846 ; J. Potyka, *ib.*, **107**. 302, 1859 ; T. Scheerer, *ib.*, **42**. 546, 1837 ; F. Wöhler, *ib.*, **43**. 391, 1838 ; A. Arzruni, *Zeit. Kryst.*, **2**. 327, 1878 ; A. Arzruni and C. Bärwald, *ib.*, **7**. 340, 1882 ; M. Weibull, *ib.*, **20**. 8, 1892 ; F. Scherer, *ib.*, **21**. 360, 1893 ; **22**. 62, 1894 ; G. Magel, *Ber. oberhess. Ges.*, **22**. 297, 1882 ; *Zeit. Kryst.*, **11**. 162, 1885 ; A. Thiel, *ib.*, **23**. 295, 1894 ; K. Oebbeke, *ib.*, **17**. 386, 1890 ; V. R. von Zepharovich, *ib.*, **5**. 271, 1881 ; G. Zimmermann, *ib.*, **13**. 94, 1888 ; *Ber. Akad. München*, 385, 1885 ; J. Loczka, *Zeit. Kryst.*, **11**. 269, 1885 ; **14**. 574, 1888 ; **15**. 41, 1889 ; **23**. 501, 1894 ; *Földt. Közl.*, **22**. 353, 1892 . *Term. Füz.*, **9**. 285, 1885 ; F. A. Genth, *Proc. Amer. Phil. Soc.*, **23**. 39, 1885 ; L. W. McCay, *Chem. News*, **48**. 7, 1883 ; *Beitrag zur Kenntniss der Kobalt-, Nickel- und Eisenkiese*, Freiberg, 1884 ; M. E. Chevreul, *Ann. Mus. Hist. Nat.*, **18**. 156, 1812 ; F. Stromeyer, *Anz. gel. Gött.*, 733, 1814 ; A. Breithaupt, *Mineralogische Studien*, Leipzig, 95, 1866 ; C. F. Rammelsberg, *Handbuch der Mineralchemie*, Leipzig, 55, 1853 ; 28, 1875 ; 12, 1895 ; *Neues Jahrb. Min.*, ii, 45, 1897 ; *Zeit. deut. geol. Ges.*, **25**. 266, 1873 ; I. Domeyko, *Elementos de mineralojia*, Santiago, 164, 1879 ; G. C. Hoffmann, *Ann. Rep. Geol. Sur. Canada*, **8**. 13, 1897 ; A. Brunlechner, *Die Minerale des Herzogtums Kärnten*, Klagenfurt, 68, 1884 ; A. Frenzel, *Mineralogisches Lexikon für das Königreich Sachsen*, Leipzig, 29, 1874 ; *Neues Jahrb. Min.*, 517, 1872 ; F. Sandberger, *ib.*, i, 99, 1890 ; A. Vogel, *ib.*, 674, 1855 ; J. F. L. Hausmann, *Handbuch der Mineralogie*, Göttingen, 73, 1847 ; C. J. B. Karsten, *Handbuch der Eisenhüttenkunde*, Berlin, **2**. 19, 1841 ; A. Baentsch, *Zeit. Ges. Naturw. Halle*, **7**. 372, 1856 ; J. B. Ragosky, *Jahrb. geol. Reichsanst. Wien*, **4**. 828, 1853 ; C. von Hauer, *ib.*, **4**. 400, 1853 ; **9**. 294, 1858 ; F. Amelung, *Naturh. Ver. Rheint.*, **10**. 221, 1853 ; F. Katzer, *Tschermak's Mitt.*, (2), **16**. 505, 1897 ; J. Rumpf, *ib.*, (1), **4**. 178, 235, 1874 ; P. Groth, *Tabellarische Uebersicht der Mineralien*, Braunschweig, 21, 1898 ; F. W. Starke, H. L. Shock, and E. F. Smith, *Journ. Amer. Chem. Soc.*, 19. 948, 1897 ; N. S. Kurnakoff and N. S. Konstantinoff, *Journ. Russ. Phys. Chem. Soc.*, **40**. 227, 1908 ; *Zeit. anorg. Chem.*, **58**. 1, 1908 ; J. W. Retgers, *Zeit. phys. Chem.*, **6**. 234, 1890 ; L. Baldo, *Sitzber. Akad. Wien*, **53**. 221, 1866 ; A. Carnot, *Compt. Rend.*, **79**. 479, 1874 ; D. Forbes, *Phil. Mag.*, (4), **29**. 6, 1865 ; P. Kröber, *ib.*, (4), **29**. 8, 1865 ; *Berg. Hütt. Ztg.*, **23**. 130, 1864 ; C. Hintze, *Handbuch der Mineralogie*, Leipzig, **1**. i, 838, 1904 ; A. N. Winchell, *Amer. Min.*, **11**. 181, 1926 ; W. A. Lampadius, *Handbuch der chemischen Analyse der Mineralkörper*, Freyberg, 309, 1801 ; R. J. Haüy, *Traité de minéralogie*, Paris, **4**. 59, 1801 ; T. Thomson, *System of Chemistry*, Edinburgh, 1810 ; W. Ipatieff and W. Nikolaieff, *Journ. Russ. Phys. Chem. Soc.*, **58**. 664, 686, 692, 698, 1926 ; H. de Sénarmont, *Compt. Rend.*, **32**. 409, 1851 ; *Ann. Chim. Phys.*, (1), **32**. 129, 1851 ; *Edin. Phil. Journ.*, **52**. 326, 1852 ; **57**. 344, 1854.

[5] C. Linnæus, *Systema naturæ*, Holmiæ, 118, 1768 ; R. J. Haüy, *Traité de minéralogie*, Paris, **4**. 59, 1801 ; **4**. 28, 1822 ; *Ann. Mus. Hist. Nat.*, **12**. 306, 1808 ; J. B. L. Romé de l'Isle, *Cristallographie*, Paris, **3**. 28, 1783 ; J. J. Bernhardi, *Gehlen's Journ.*, **3**. 80, 1807 ; A. Arzruni, *Zeit. Kryst.*, **2**. 430, 1878 ; A. Arzruni and C. Bärwald, *ib.*, **7**. 337, 1883 ; M. Weibull, *ib.*, **20**. 1, 1892 ; F. Scherer, *ib.*, **21**. 383, 1893 ; G. Magel, *ib.*, **11**. 162, 1885 ; *Ber. oberhess. Ges.*, **22**. 297, 1882 ; L. J. Wallmark, *Förh. Skand. Naturf.*, 519, 1842 ; *Journ. prakt. Chem.*, (1), **31**. 169, 1844 ; M. L. Huggins, *Journ. prakt. Chem. Soc.*, **44**. 1841, 1922 ; *Phys. Rev.*, (2), **19**. 369, 1922 ; W. F. de Jong, *Physica*, **6**. 325, 1926 ; F. Sandberger, *Sitzber. Akad. München*, 139, 1873 ; G. A. Behncke, *Pogg. Ann.*, **98**. 184, 1856 ; A. Breithaupt, *Mineralogische Studien*, Leipzig, 95, 1866 ; *Journ. prakt. Chem.*, (1), **4**. 258, 1835 ; A. Frenzel, *Mineralogisches Lexikon für das Königreich Sachsen*, 27, 1874 ; J. L. C. Schröder van der Kolk, *Centr. Min.*, 77, 1901 ; P. Groth, *Die Mineraliensammlung der Universität Strassburg*, Strassburg, 39, 1878 ; *Sitz. Bayr. Akad.*, 384, 1875 ; *Zeit. Kryst.*, **13**. 94, 1888 ; H. Bücking, *Mitt. Comm. geol. Landesanst Elsass-Lothr.*, **1**. 114, 1887 ; *Zeit. Kryst.*, **17**. 218, 1890 ; A. Schmidt, *ib.*, **12**. 116, 1887 ; P. von Jeremejeff, *ib.*, **15**. 553, 1889 ; V. R. von Zepharovich, *Mineralogisches Lexikon für das Kaiserthum Oesterreich*, Wien, 279, 1859 ; 210, 1873 ; 167, 1893 ; A. des Cloizeaux, *Manuel de minéralogie*, Paris, **2**. 346, 1893 ; K. Jimbo, *Journ. Coll. Science Univ. Tokyo*, **11**. 222, 1899.

[6] G. A. Kenngott, *Sitzber. Akad. Wien*, **9**. 584, 1852 ; V. R. von Zepharovich, *ib.*, **56**. 42, 1867 ; E. T. Wherry, *Amer. Min.*, **10**. 28, 1925 ; A. Vogel, *Neues Jahrb. Min.*, 674, 1855 :

V. Goldschmidt, *ib.*, ii, 205, 1880 ; D. Forbes, *Phil. Mag.*, (4), **29.** 6, 1865 ; J. Potyka, *Pogg. Ann.*, **107.** 302, 1859 ; F. E. Neumann, *ib.*, **23.** 1, 1831 ; H. Saito, *Science Rep. Tohoku Univ.*, **16.** 37, 1927 ; L. W. McCay, *Beitrag zur Kenntniss der Kobalt, Nickel-, und Eisenkiese*, Freiberg, 1883 ; E. Madelung and R. Fuchs, *Ann. Physik*, (4), **65.** 289, 1921 ; A. Sella, *Nach. Gött.*, 311, 1891 ; *Zeit. Kryst.*, **22.** 180, 1894 ; J. Loczka, *ib.*, **15.** 41, 1889 ; F. Scherer, *ib.*, **21.** 376, 1893 ; P. E. W. Oeberg, *Oefvers. Vet. Akad. Förh.*, 8, 1885 ; E. Thomson, *Univ. Toronto Geol. Studies*, **20.** 54, 1925 ; P. F. Kerr, *Econ. Geol.*, **19.** 1, 1924 ; L. H. Borgström, *Oefvers. Finska Vet. Soc. Forh.*, **59.** 16, 1917 ; H. Bäckström, *ib.*, 553, 1888 ; A. de Gramont, *Bull. Soc. Min.*, **18.** 302, 1895 ; J. Lemberg, *Zeit. deut. geol. Ges.*, **46.** 795, 1894 ; E. F. Smith, *Journ. Amer. Chem. Soc.*, **20.** 289, 1898 ; F. W. Starke, H. L. Shock, and E. F. Smith, *ib.*, **19.** 948, 1897 ; H. B. North and C. B. Conover, *Amer. Journ. Science*, (4), **40.** 640, 1915 ; P. Berthier, *Ann. Chim. Phys.*, (2), **62.** 113, 1836 ; A. Breithaupt, *Mineralogische Studien*, Leipzig, 94, 1866 ; C. Schubert, *Beiträge zur Kenntnis der Dissoziation einiger Oxyde, Karbonate, und Sulfide*, Weida i. Thür., **68,** 1910 ; V. Lenher, *Journ. Amer. Chem. Soc.*, **43.** 29, 1921 ; T. W. Case, *Phys. Rev.*, (2), **9.** 305, 1917 ; H. Zieler, *Zeit. anorg. Chem.*, **162.** 161, 1927 ; C. Schubert, *Beiträge zur Kenntnis der Dissoziation siniger Oxyde, Karbonate, und Sulfide*, Weida i. Thür., **68,** 1910 ; W. F. de Jong, *Physica*, **6.** 325, 1920.

⁷ A. Breithaupt, *Berg. Hütt. Ztg.*, **25.** 167, 1866 ; F. Sandberger, *Journ. prakt. Chem.*, (2), **1.** 230, 1870.

⁹ J. G. Wallerius, *Mineralogia*, Stockholm, 231, 1747 ; A. Cronstedt, *Mineralogie*, Stockaolm, 213, 1758 ; E. F. Glocker, *Handbuch der Mineralogie*, Nürnberg, 447, 1831 ; *Generum et specierum mineralium secundum ordines naturales digestorum synopsis*, Halle, 37, 1847 ; F. S. Beudant, *Traité élémentaire de minéralogie*, Paris, **2.** 450, 1832 ; R. J. Haüy, *Traité de minéralogie*, Paris, **4.** 204, 1801 ; J. B. L. Romé de l'Isle, *Essai de cristallographie*, Paris, 333, 1772 ; *Cristallographie*, Paris, **3.** 123, 1783.

⁹ C. F. Rammelsberg, *Handbuch der Mineralchemie*, Leipzig, 65, 1847 ; 89, 1875 ; *Pogg. Ann.*, **71.** 516, 1847 ; V. R. von Zepharovich, *Mineralogisches Lexikon für das Kaiserthum Oesterreich*, Wien, **2.** 170, 1873 ; J. D. Dana, *A System of Mineralogy*, New York, 58, 1854 ; 72, 1865 ; 89, 1892 ; A. von Haubert, *Ber. Mitt. Freund. Nat.*, **3.** 389, 1848 ; A. Patera, *ib.*, **3.** 389, 1848 ; G. Flink, *Bihang. Svenska Akad. Handl.*, **12.** 2, 1886 ; F. R. Mallet, *Rec. Geol. Sur. India*, **14.** 190, 1880 ; I. Domeyko, *Elementos de mineralojia*, Santiago, 180, 1879 ; G. A. Kenngott, *Uebersicht der Resultate mineralogischer Forschungen*, Wien, 140, 1853 ; T. Münster, *Zeit. Kryst.*, **30.** 668, 1899 ; L. W. McCay, *Chem. News*, 48, 7, 1883 ; *Beitrag zur Kenntnis der Kobalt-, Nickel- und Eisenkiese*, Freiberg, 1884 ; F. Stromeyer, *Schweigger's Journ.*, **19.** 336, 1817 ; M. H. Klaproth, *Beiträge zur chemischen Kenntniss der Mineralkörper*, Berlin, **2.** 307, 1797 ; B. M. Tassaert, *Ann. Chim. Phys.*, (1), **28.** 92, 1798 ; F. Stromeyer, *Anz. Gel. Gött.*, 715, 1817 ; *Schweigger's Journ.*, **19.** 336, 1817 ; W. H. and W. L. Bragg, *X-Rays and Crystal Structure*, London, 144, 1924 ; M. Mechling, *Abhand. Akad. Leipzig*, 37, 1921 ; H. Schneiderhölm, *Anleitung zur mikroskopischen Bestimmung von Erzen in auffallenden Licht*, Berlin, 1922 ; M. L. Huggins, *Journ. Amer. Chem. Soc.*, **44.** 1841, 1922 ; J. Forrest, *Phil. Mag.*, (6), **50.** 1009, 1925 ; P. Groth, *Tabellarische Uebersicht der Mineralien*, Braunschweig, 24, 1898 ; E. T. Wherry, *Amer. Min.*, **10.** 28, 1925 ; L. S. Ramsdell, *Amer. Min.*, **10.** 281, 1925.

¹⁰ C. Linnæus, *Systema naturæ*, Holmiæ, 129, 1768 ; B. G. Sage, *Elémens de minéralogie docimastique*, Paris, **2.** 87, 1772 ; J. B. L. Romé de l'Isle, *Essai de cristallographie*, Paris, 333, 1772 ; *Cristallographie*, Paris, **3.** 129, 1783 ; R. J. Haüy, *Traité de minéralogie*, Paris, **4.** 208, 1801 ; **4.** 228, 1822 ; A. von Hubert, *Ber. Mitt. Fr. Nat.*, **3.** 389, 1848 ; P. Groth, *Die Mineraliensammlung der Universität Strassburg*, Strassburg, 42, 1878 ; F. von Kobell, *Anz. Gel. München* **78.** 648, 1849 ; G. A. Kenngott, *Uebersicht der Resultate mineralogischer Forschungen*, Wien, 140, 1853 ; C. F. Naumann, *Pogg. Ann.*, **16.** 486, 1829 ; F. E. Neumann, *ib.*, **23.** 1, 1831 W. G. Hankel, *ib.*, **62.** 197, 1844 ; W. H. Miller, *Introduction to Mineralogy*, London, 190, 1852 ; G. Rose, *Monatsber. Akad. Berlin*, 359. 1870 ; *Pogg. Ann.*, **142.** 39, 1871 ; H. Marbach, *Compt. Rend.*, **45.** 707, 1857 ; H. Fizeau, *ib.*, **66.** 1005, 1072, 1868 ; H. Schneinderhöln, *Anleitung zur mikroskopischen Bestimmung und Untersuchungen von Erzen und Aufbereitungsprodukten besonders im auffallenden Licht*, Berlin, 1922 ; L. S. Ramsdell, *Amer. Min.*, **10.** 281, 1925 ; W. H. and W. L. Bragg, *X-rays and Crystal Structure*, London, 144, 1924 ; T. W. Case, *Phys. Rev.*, (2), **9.** 305, 1917 ; W. Flörke, *Centr. Min.*, 337, 1926 ; A. Schrauf and E. S. Dana, *Sitzber. Akad. Wien*, **69.** 156, 1874 ; P. Curie, *Bull. Soc. Min.*, **8.** 131, 1885 ; A. de Gramont, *ib.*, **18.** 304, 1895 ; J. Lemberg, *Zeit. deut. geol. Ges.*, **46.** 796, 1894 ; H. Bäckström, *Oefvers. Akad. Förh. Stockholm*, 553, 1888 ; P. E. W. Oeberg, *ib.*, 8, 1885 ; E. Madelung and R. Fuchs, *Ann. Physik*, (4), **65.** 289, 1921 ; A. Sella, *Gött. Nachr.*, 311, 1891 ; *Zeit. Kryst.*, **22.** 180, 1894 ; P. W. Bridgman, *Amer. Journ. Science*, (5), **10.** 483, 1925 ; E. F. Smith, *Journ. Amer. Chem. Soc.*, **20.** 289, 1898 ; H. B. North and C. B. Conover, *ib.*, (4), **40.** 640, 1915 ; E. Thomson, *Univ. Toronto Geol. Studies*, **20.** 54, 1925 ; P. F. Kerr, *Econ. Geol.*, **19.** 1, 1924 ; M. L. Huggins, *Journ. Amer. Chem. Soc.*, **44.** 1841, 1922 ; M. Mechling, *Abhand. Akad. Leipzig*, 37, 1921 ; E. T. Wherry, *Amer. Min.*, **10.** 28, 1925 ; J. Forrest, *Phil. Mag.*, (6), **50.** 1009, 1925.

¹¹ A. Hayes, *Amer. Journ. Science*, (1), **24.** 386, 1833 ; T. Scheerer, *Pogg. Ann.*, **42.** 546, 1837 ; F. Wöhler, *ib.*, **43.** 591, 1838 ; L. H. Borgström, *Oefvers. Finska. Vet. Soc. Forh.*, **59.** 16, 1917 ; C. Schnabel, *Verh. Nat. Hist. Ver. Rheinl.*, 159, 1850 ; C. F. Rammelsberg, *Handbuch der Mineralchemie*, Leipzig, 149, 1853 ; 31, 1875 ; J. D. Dana, *A System of Mineralogy*, New

York, 79, 1868; I. Domeyko, *Elementos de mineralojia*, Santiago, 180, 1879; F. von Kobell, *Ber. Akad. München*, 276, 1867; *Journ. prakt. Chem.*, (1), 102. 409, 1867; G. Tschermak, *Sitzber. Akad. Wien*, 55. 447, 1867; A. Schrauf and E. S. Dana, *ib.*, 69. 152, 1874; G. A. Kenngott, *ib.*, 9. 583, 1852; G. C. Hoffmann, *Ann. Rep. Geol. Sur. Canada*, 5. 19, 18?2; A. Breithaupt, *Die Paragenesis der Mineralien*, Freiberg, 207, 1849; *Pogg. Ann.*, 77. 127, 1849; *Journ. prakt. Chem.*, (1), 4. 258, 1835; F. Beijerinck, *Neues Jahrb. Min. B.B.*, 11. 437, 1897; F. Becke, *Tschermik's Mitt.*, (1), 7. 101, 353, 1877; A. Sadebeck, *ib.*, (1), 7. 353, 1877; J. Lemberg, *Zeit. deut. geol. Ges.*, 46. 796, 1894; W. H. Miller. *Introduction to Mineralogy*, London, 190, 1852; W. J. Lewis, *Proc. Crystal. Soc.*, 1. 67, 1877; *Phil. Mag.*, (5), 3. 354, 1877; J. Joly, *ib.*, (6), 27. 1, 1914; *Chem. News*, 107. 241, 1913; M. Weibull, *Zeit. Kryst.*, 20. 18, 1892; T. Münster, *ib.*, 30. 668, 1899; E. T. Wherry, *Amer. Min.*, 10. 28, 1925; L. S. Ramsdell, *ib.*, 10. 294, 1925; M. L. Huggins, *Journ. Amer. Chem. Soc.*, 44. 1841, 1922; W. F. de Jong, *Physica*, 6. 325, 1926.

¹² J. D. Dana, *A System of Mineralogy*, New York, 73, 1868; C. H. Pfaff, *Schweigger's Journ.*, 22. 260, 1818; A. Cronstedt, *Mineralogie*, Stockholm, 218, 1758; *Akad. Handl. Stockholm*, 15. 38, 1754; *Abh. Svenska Akad.*, 13. 293, 1755; F. S. Beudant, *Traité élémentaire de minéralogie*, Paris, 430, 1824; 2. 448, 1832; F. von Kobell, *Grundzüge der Mineralogie*, Nürnberg, 297, 1838; *Journ. prakt. Chem.*, (1), 33. 402, 1844; A. Breithaupt, *ib.*, (1), 15. 330, 1838; A. Löwe, *Pogg. Ann.*, 55. 503, 1842; *Berg. Hütt. Ztg.*, 1. 439, 1842; *Ber. Mitt. Freund. Naturw.*, 3. 82, 1847; E. F. Glocker, *Handbuch der Mineralogie*, Nürnberg, 443, 1831; 315, 1839.

¹³ J. J. Berzelius, *Akad. Handl. Stockholm*, 251, 1820; C. F. Rammelsberg, *Handbuch der Mineralchemie*, Leipzig, 104, 1845; 37, 1875; *Zeit. deut. geol. Ges.*, 25. 284, 1873; *Pogg. Ann.*, 25. 494, 1846; G. C. Hoffmann, *ib.*, 25. 494, 1832; M. Hörnes, *ib.*, 55. 505, 1842; H. Laspeyres, *Ber. Nat. Hist. Ver. Rheinl.*, 50. 204, 1893; C. Schnabel, *ib.*, 8. 572, 1851; D. Forbes, *Phil. Mag.*, (4), 35. 184, 1868; C. Bergemann, *Journ. prakt. Chem.*, (1), 75. 244, 1858; (1), 79. 412, 1860; F. von Kobell, *ib.*, (1), 33. 404, 1844; J. W. Döbereiner, *Schweigger's Journ.*, 26. 270, 1819; F. A. Genth, *Amer. Chem. Journ.*, 1. 324, 1880; C. W. von Gumbel, *Geognostische Beschreibung des Konigreichs Bayerns*, Gotha, 3. 404, 1844; G. Bodländer, *Zeit. prakt. Geol.*, 1. 387, 1893; L. F. Bley, *Arch. Apoth. Ver.*, 30. 278, 1831; *Neues Jahrb. Min.*, 84, 1831; A. Bäumler, *Zeit. Ges. Naturw.*, 10. 70, 1857; *Zeit. deut. geol. Ges.*, 9. 41, 1857; F. Stromeyer, *Anz. gel. Gött.*, 514, 1820; L. Zerjäu, *Anz. Akad. Wien*, 3. 173, 1866; A. Löwe, *Ber. Mitt. Freund. Naturw.*, 3. 83, 1847; A. Eschka, *Berg. Hütt. Jahrb.*, 13. 23, 1864; L. Sipöcz, *Zeit. Kryst.*, 11. 213, 1886; F. Pless, *Liebig's Ann.*, 51. 250, 1844; *Ann. Mines*, (4), 8. 677, 1844; A. von Kraynag and A. Löwe, *Jahrb. geol. Reichsanst. Wien*, 1. 556, 1850; J. J. Berzelius, *Akad. Handl. Stockholm*, 251, 1820; G. C. Hoffmann, *Ann. Rep. Geol. Sur. Canada*, 5. 22, 1890.

¹⁴ J. C. L. Zincken, *Pogg. Ann.*, 13. 165, 1828; G. Rose, *ib.*, 13. 167, 1828; *Elemente der Krystallographie*, Berlin, 144, 1833; M. Hörnes, *ib.*, 55. 505, 1842; F. von Kobell, *Journ. prakt. Chem.*, (1), 1. 95, 1834; C. F. Rammelsberg, *Zeit. deut. geol. Ges.*, 25. 284, 1873; *Handbuch der Mineralchemie*, Leipzig, 12, 1841; F. Pless, *Ann. Mines*, (4), 8. 677, 1844; *Liebig's Ann.*, 51. 250, 1844; G. C. Hoffmann, *Ann. Rep. Geol. Sur. Canada*, 5. 22, 1890; V. R. von Zepharovich, *Mineralogisches Lexikon für das Kaiserthum Oesterreich*, Wien, 3. 107, 1893; D. Forbes, *Phil. Mag.*, (4), 35. 184, 1868; L. Sipöcz, *Zeit. Kryst.*, 11. 215, 1886; S. von Olshausen, *ib.*, 61. 463, 1924; A. Bäumler, *Zeit. Ges. Naturw.*, 10. 70, 1857; *Zeit. deut. geol. Ges.*, 9. 41, 1857; J. Lemberg, *ib.*, 46. 797, 1894; C. H. Pfaff, *Schweigger's Journ.*, 22. 260, 1818; A. de Gramont, *Bull. Soc. Min.*, 18. 296, 1895; E. F. Smith, *Journ. Amer. Chem. Soc.*, 20. 289, 1898; M. L. Huggins, *ib.*, 44. 1841, 1922; L. S. Ramsdell, *Amer. Min.*, 10. 281, 1925; E. Thomson, *Univ. Toronto Geol. Studies*, 20. 54, 1925; J. Joly, *Phil. Mag.*, (6), 27. 1, 1914; *Chem. News*, 107. 241, 1913; T. W. Case, *Phys. Rev.*, (2), 9. 305, 1917.

§ 34. Arsenic Pentasulphide

There is an unexplored gap in the f.p. curves of the binary system: As–S, Fig. 43, corresponding with **arsenic pentasulphide**, As_2S_5. A. Gélis[1] said that the dark yellowish-green, plastic mass obtained by fusing stoichiometrical proportions of the constituent elements, gradually hardens and forms a lemon-yellow powder. By digesting the product with aq. ammonia, pale yellow flocculent sulphur remains undissolved, and when the yellow soln. is treated with acids, arsenic pentasulphide is deposited. If the horny product of the fusion of the two elements be distilled, sulphur first passes off, then arsenical sulphur, and the colour of the distillate changes in colour from yellow to orange and then to red. If the distillation be stopped as soon as the colour change begins, and the residue be digested with aq. ammonia, it is almost completely soluble in aq. ammonia, and consists of arsenic pentasulphide. Numerous investigations have been made on the conditions which favour the formation of arsenic pentasulphide by precipitation from a soln. containing arsenic acid, or an arsenate. For instance, J. J. Berzelius,

B. Brauner and F. Tomicek, R. Bunsen, L. W. McCay, F. Neher, E. W. Parnell, H. Rose, J. Thiele, F. L. Usher and M. W. Travers, and H. W. F. Wackenroder have worked on this subject, and the results of their work are discussed in connection with the action of hydrogen sulphide on arsenic acid. J. J. Berzelius, and A. F. Fuchs found that the pentasulphide is also precipitated when hydrochloric acid is added to a boiling dil. soln. of sulpharsenate. L. F. Nilson said that the decomposition is here not quantitative since soluble oxysulpharsenates are formed. If the precipitation is made in the cold, the product may contain free sulphur. R. Bunsen washed out the free sulphur with hydrogen sulphide, but B. Brauner and F. Tomicek said the extraction is incomplete. F. V. von Hahn did not obtain a colloidal soln. of arsenic pentasulphide by the hydrolysis of alkali arsenic thiosulphates owing to the instability of these compounds.

The formula As_2S_5 is in agreement with the analyses of A. Gélis, R. Bunsen, and B. Brauner and F. Tomicek. According to L. F. Nilson, arsenic pentasulphide appears as a lemon-yellow powder somewhat paler than the trisulphide ; it can be heated to 95° without change, but if heated to 100° in air for a long time it acquires a surface film of crystals of arsenic trioxide—B. Brauner said that it can be dried at 107° without decomposition ; and R. Bunsen, and F. Neher said at 110°. J. J. Berzelius found that the pentasulphide melts at a higher temp. than does sulphur, and when distilled the residue becomes poorer and poorer in sulphur until, as A. Gélis found, the trisulphide is formed. According to V. and C. Meyer, the pentasulphide dissociates at 500° into the trisulphide and sulphur. The pentasulphide holds adsorbed water very tenaciously ; L. F. Nilson found that the water is expelled at 90° to 95°, and he suggested that a hydrate, $As_2S_5.H_2O$, is formed, or possibly the acids $HAsS_3$ and $HAsOS_2$, but L. W. McCay could not confirm this. H. Rose said that the pentasulphide is reduced by hydrogen, and this also occurs when the pentasulphide is melted with sodium carbonate in hydrogen gas. R. Bunsen found that the pentasulphide is insoluble in water, and J. J. Berzelius observed that blue litmus paper is reddened by the pentasulphide warmed in a current of steam. When the pentasulphide is boiled in water, P. de Clermont and J. Frommel observed that a soln. of arsenic trioxide is formed with the separation of sulphur, and since arsenic acid is not formed by the hydrolysis of the pentasulphide, they doubted if the pentasulphide is a definite compound. R. Bunsen said that the pentasulphide is insoluble in hydrochloric acid. H. Zieler observed no reaction with 10 per cent. HNO_3 ; with 20 per cent. HNO_3, nitric oxide could be detected only with the boiling acid ; with 30–40 per cent. acid, agitated, nitric acid could be detected in the cold, and the gas is given off by the boiling acid ; and with over 60 per cent. acid, agitated, nitric oxide was given off. H. Rose showed that the pentasulphide is reduced when heated with carbon, or when fused with potassium cyanide and sodium carbonate ; and R. Bunsen, that it is insoluble in alcohol, and in carbon disulphide. J. Spiller observed that the pentasulphide is soluble in soln. of citric acid, or alkali citrates. J. J. Berzelius found that the pentasulphide absorbs ammonia, forming a pale yellow solid which loses the whole of its ammonia when exposed to air. The *arsenic amminopentasulphide* is soluble in water, and the soln. gradually deposits a red powder. L. F. Nilson showed that the pentasulphide is soluble in aq. ammonia, and in soln. of alkali hydroxides, carbonates, or hydrosulphides, forming sulpharsenates and oxysulpharsenates. He added that it dissolves in a soln. of potassium arsenate with the separation of sulphur, forming an oxysulpharsenate, and in a soln. of sodium arsenate, forming arsenic trisulphide.

REFERENCES.

¹ A. Gélis, *Ann. Chim. Phys.*, (4), **30**. 114, 1873 ; *Compt. Rend.*, **76**. 1205, 1873 ; P. de Clermont and J. Frommel, *ib.*, **87**. 330, 1878 ; H. Rose, *Pegg. Ann.*, **90**. 194, 568, 1853 ; **107**. 186, 1859 ; J. J. Berzelius, *ib.*, **7**. 2, 1826 ; H. Ludwig, *Arch. Pharm.*, (2), **97**. 32, 1859 ; R. Bunsen, *Liebig's*

Ann., **192**. 305, 1878 ; J. Thiele, *ib.*, **265**. 65, 1891 ; **H. W. F.** Wackenroder, *ib.*, **13**. 241, 1835;
Journ. prakt. Chem., (1), **2**. 340, 1834 ; *Kleine analytisch-chemische Tabellen*, Jena, 1847 ;
E. W Parnell, *Chem. News*, **21**. 133, 1870 ; F. Neher, *Zeit. anal. Chem.*, **32**. 45, 1893 ; A. F. Fuchs,
ib., **1**. 189, 1861 ; L. W. McCay, *ib.*, **26**. 635, 1887 ; **27**. 632, 1888 ; **34**. 728, 1895 ; *Amer. Chem.
Journ.*, **7**. 375, 1887 ; **9**. 174, 1888 ; **10**. 459, 1889 ; **12**. 547, 1891 ; *Zeit. anorg. Chem.*, **29**. 46,
1902 ; *Journ. Amer. Chem. Soc.*, **24**. 661, 1902 ; *Chem. News*, **54**. 287, 1886 ; B. Brauner and
F. Tomicek, *Monatsh.*, **8**. 607, 1887 ; B. Brauner, *Journ. Chem. Soc.*, **67**. 532, 1895 ; F. L. Usher
and M. W. Travers, *ib.*, **87**. 1370, 1905 ; J. Spiller, *ib.*, **10**. 110, 1858 ; *Chem. News*, **8**. 280, 1863 ;
19. 166, 1869 ; L. F. Nilson, *Akad. Handl. Stockholm*, **10**. 2, 1871 ; *Oefvers. Akad. Stockholm*, **28**.
303, 1871 ; *Journ. prakt. Chem.*, (2), **12**. 327, 1876 ; (2), **14**. 19, 1876 ; V. and C. Meyer, *Ber.*,
12. 1112, 1879 ; F. V. von Hahn, *Koll. Zeit.*, **31**. 200, 1922 ; H. Zieler, *Zeit. anorg. Chem.*, **162**.
161, 1927.

§ 35. The Complex Salts of Arsenic Pentasulphide—The Sulpharsenates

Arsenic pentasulphide plays the part of an acid anhydride in forming a series
of complex salts with the basic sulphides, and the products can be regarded as
derivatives of a series of hypothetical **sulpharsenic acids** :

Orthosulpharsenic acid	H_3AsS_4
Metasulpharsenic acid	$HAsS_3$
Pyrosulpharsenic acid	$H_4As_2S_7$
Penterasulphotriarsenic acid ($H_{15}As_3S_{15}$ less $5H_2S$)	$H_5As_3S_{10}$
Penterasulphotetrarsenic acid ($H_{20}As_4S_{20}$ less $5H_2S$)	$H_{10}As_4S_{15}$

A small number of the corresponding salts occur in nature—epigenite, enargite, and
xanthocone. H. Rose [1] said that the sulpharsenic acids are stronger than the sulpharsenious acids because they develop more heat in combining with ammonium
sulphide. J. J. Berzelius, and L. F. Nilson prepared a number of these salts by
dissolving the pentasulphide in a warm soln. of the hydrosulphide of the base, and
evaporating the soln. in vacuo. Sulpharsenates were also prepared by J. J. Berzelius,
and C. Eckert by dissolving arsenic trisulphide in soln. of the alkali polysulphides, or
in soln. of sulphur in the alkali hydroxides. L. W. McCay said that J. J. Berzelius,
erred in supposing that the sulpharsenates can be produced by dissolving arsenic
pentasulphide in soln. of the alkali hydroxides or carbonates or in aq. ammonia
because oxysulpharsenates are produced. This was confirmed by R. F. Weinland
and P. Lehmann, and F. A. Flückiger. Sulpharsenates were made by J. J. Berzelius
by the action of hydrogen sulphide on aq. soln. of the alkali arsenates. The gas
is at first slowly absorbed, but afterwards, more quickly. L. W. McCay studied this
reaction and found that arsenic pentasulphide is formed when hydrogen sulphide
in excess is passed rapidly into a soln. of alkali dihydroarsenate, some trisulphide
and sulphur may also be formed. With the ortho-sulpharsenates and dihydrosulph-
arsenates, the decomposition of the oxysulpho-arsenate which is always formed
may produce potassium arsenite and sulphur. The former then yields arsenic
trisulphide. J. J. Berzelius also obtained the sulpharsenates by mixing soln. of
the alkali arsenates with an excess of ammonium hydrosulphide, and distilling until
the free ammonia and excess of ammonium hydrosulphide are expelled ; if the
arsenate is insoluble in water—*e.g.* copper arsenate—it is dissolved in hydrochloric
acid and the sulpharsenate precipitated by hydrogen sulphide. J. J. Berzelius,
and K. Preis obtained some of these sulpharsenates by double decomposition with
soln. of sodium sulpharsenate, and a soln. of the metal salt. Impure sulpharsenates
were produced by J. J. Berzelius by fusing a mixture of arsenic penta- or trisulphide
with an excess of alkali hydroxide, carbonate, or sulphide ; L. F. Nilson, by
evaporating soln. of arsenic trisulphide in one of alkali carbonate or hydrosulphide ;
K. B. Edwards, by treating arsenic trisulphide with ammonium or alkali polysulphides ; A. Geuther, by heating arsenic disulphide and a soln. of sodium sulphide
in a sealed tube at 100° ; and R. F. Weinland and P. Lehmann, by the action of
sodium ethoxide on arsenic pentasulphide. In most cases, oxysulpharsenates are
produced at the same time.

J. J. Berzelius reported that the sulpharsenates are yellow, red, or brown salts. The orthosulpharsenates have a tendency to crystallize, but not so with the pyro- or meta-sulpharsenates. They are permanent in air ; and when soluble they taste first hepatic and afterwards bitter. The ortho-salts of the alkalies and alkaline earths can be heated white-hot without decomposition if air be excluded ; while the pyro- and meta-sulpharsenates give off sulphur and form sulpharsenites. When heated in air, arsenic trioxide and trisulphide, and sulphur dioxide are evolved and either the metal oxide or sulphate is formed. L. F. Nilson found that the salts are reduced, forming a mirror of arsenic when they are heated in a current of hydrogen. The sulpharsenates of the alkalies and alkaline earths, magnesium, beryllium, and yttrium were found by J. J. Berzelius to be soluble in water, forming colourless or pale yellow liquids ; and, added L. F. Nilson, and J. J. Berzelius, the aq. soln. are slowly decomposed, yielding sulphur, arsenic, arsenic pentasulphide, arsenite, thiosulphate, and sulphate when exposed to air : the oxidation proceeds more slowly, the more conc. the soln., and the lower the temp. J. J. Berzelius said that acids, even carbonic acid, decompose the alkali sulpharsenates, forming arsenic pentasulphide and hydrogen sulphide. Copper hydroxide partly decomposes alkali sulpharsenate, forming alkali arsenate and copper sulphide, and some copper sulpharsenate is produced. L. Storch found that some of the heavy metal sulphides—copper, iron, mercury, cadmium, etc., are soluble in a soln. of alkali sulpharsenate.

According to J. J. Berzelius, when a soln. of arsenic pentasulphide is gently treated with an excess of ammonium hydrosulphide, and agitated with hot alcohol, colourless prisms of **ammonium orthosulpharsenate,** $(NH_4)_3AsS_4$, are deposited. These are washed with alcohol, and dried by press. between bibulous paper. The salt is fairly stable in air, but acquires a yellow film on the surface. When heated, the crystals melt and then decompose : $2(NH_4)_3AsS_4=3(NH_4)_2S+As_2S_3+2S$. The alcoholic soln. remaining after the separation of the ortho-salt was stated to contain **ammonium metasulpharsenate,** NH_4AsS_3, but the salt was not isolated ; and it was also said that if aq. soln. of the ortho-salt be boiled ammonium hydrosulphide is given off, and the hot liquid deposits an acid salt, $(NH_4)_2As_{24}S_{61}$, but the product was probably a mixture of ammonium sulpharsenate and arsenic sulphides. J. J. Berzelius reported **ammonium pyrosulpharsenate,** $(NH_4)_4As_2S_7$, to be formed by allowing a soln. of arsenic pentasulphide in aq. ammonia to evaporate spontaneously. The reddish-yellow glutinous mass cannot be dried without decomposing ; and when heated, it behaves like the ortho-salt. L. F. Nilson allowed a filtered soln. of arsenic pentasulphide in a soln. of ammonium hydrosulphide to evaporate in vacuo over sulphuric acid, and obtained a yellow amorphous mass of **ammonium penterasulphotriarsenate,** $(NH_4)_5As_3S_{10}$.

J. J. Berzelius reported crystals of **sodium orthosulpharsenate,** $Na_3AsS_4.8H_2O$, to be formed by evaporating a sat. soln. of arsenic pentasulphide in an excess of sodium hydrosulphide. L. F. Nilson used a similar mode of preparation. J. J. Berzelius also prepared it by evaporating spontaneously a soln. of pyrosulpharsenate in sodium hydrosulphide ; by adding alcohol to an aq. soln. of the pyrosulpharsenate ; by digesting an alcoholic soln. of sodium pentasulphide with arsenic trisulphide ; and by crystallizing a soln. of arsenic pentasulphide in soda-lye. L. F. Nilson made it by boiling a soln. of arsenic trisulphide and sodium carbonate ; J. J. Berzelius, H. Heubach, and C. F. Rammelsberg, by boiling a mixture of sulphur, arsenic trisulphide and a soln. of sodium carbonate ; A. Geuther, by heating arsenic disulphide with a soln. of sodium sulphide at 100° : $5As_2S_2+6Na_2S=6As+4Na_3AsS_4$; K. B. Edwards, by the action of a polysulphide on arsenic trioxide or trisulphide, or by the action of a monosulphide on arsenic pentasulphide ; H. Heubach, by the action of hydrogen sulphide on a soln. of sodium orthoarsenate : $Na_3AsO_4+4H_2S=Na_3AsS_4+4H_2O$; and L. W. McCay, by mixing an alkaline soln. of sodium hydroarsenate with hydrogen sulphide, pouring the clear liquid into absolute alcohol, and washing the crystals with absolute alcohol. The analyses of J. J. Berzelius, L. W. McCay, H. Heubach, L. F. Nilson, A. Geuther,

nd C. F. Rammelsberg correspond nearly with the octohydrate—though in the last
cases some results corresponded more nearly with $7 \cdot 5H_2O$; and that of H. Heubach
with $7H_2O$. According to C. F. Rammelsberg, the colourless or pale yellow crystals
are monoclinic with the axial ratios $a : b : c = 0 \cdot 6676 : 1 : 1 \cdot 0393$, and $\beta = 100° 00'$.
J. J. Berzelius found the dry salt to be stable in air, and even over sulphuric acid,
in vacuo, the salt does not give up water until gently heated. H. Heubach said that
the crystals of sodium orthosulpharsenate soon acquire a yellow film on their
surface when they are exposed to air ; when heated, the crystals melt in their water
of crystallization and are hydrolyzed : $Na_3AsS_4 + 4H_2O = 4H_2S + Na_3AsO_4$. If
more strongly heated, J. J. Berzelius, and H. Heubach found that some hydrogen
sulphide is given off and the salt becomes yellow, and at a still higher temp., the salt
melts to a dark red liquid, which, on cooling, solidifies to the anhydrous salt.
H. Heubach said that the aq. soln. of sodium orthosulpharsenate is decomposed by
air with the separation of sulphur ; the separation of arsenic sulphide mentioned
by J. J. Berzelius was not observed. When the soln. is boiled hydrogen sulphide is
given off without forming sulphuric acid. Alcohol added to the conc. aq. soln. of
sodium orthosulpharsenate gives a yellow precipitate which J. J. Berzelius considered
to be a basic salt. When carbon dioxide is passed through the soln., hydrogen
sulphide is given off, and sulphur is simultaneously precipitated, and then arsenic
sulphide is deposited. J. J. Berzelius said that the aq. soln. of sodium orthosulpharsenate is decomposed when heated with copper sulphate, and K. Preis added that
when heated cupric sulphide is formed, and in the cold copper sulpharsenate is
produced—*vide infra ;* and with lead acetate, C. F. Rammelsberg said that a mixture
of lead sulphide and arsenate is produced. J. J. Berzelius prepared colourless
crystals of **lithium orthosulpharsenate,** $Li_3AsS_4.nH_2O$, by adding alcohol to an aq.
soln. of the pyrosulpharsenate. The salt is soluble in water, and when the hot aq.
soln. is rapidly cooled six-sided prisms are formed, and when slowly cooled, four-
sided prisms. By adding alcohol to a soln. of potassium pyrosulpharsenate,
J. J. Berzelius obtained a liquid which, when evaporated, furnished a crystalline
mass of **potassium orthosulpharsenate,** $K_3AsS_4.H_2O$. L. F. Nilson also made it by
evaporating in vacuo the liquid obtained by adding to a sat. soln. of arsenic trisulphide in potassium hydrosulphide or sulphide as much again alkali hydrosulphide
or sulphide. The pale yellow, four-sided, probably rhombic, prisms are hygroscopic.
J. J. Berzelius prepared **sodium pyrosulpharsenate,** $N_4As_2S_7$, by spontaneously
evaporating an aq. soln. of sodium hydroarsenate sat. with hydrogen sulphide. The
pale lemon-yellow mass readily fuses to a yellow liquid. The corresponding
lithium pyrosulpharsenate, $Li_4As_2S_7$, is citron-yellow and non-hygroscopic. It is
readily soluble in water. Likewise also with **potassium pyrosulpharsenate,**
$K_4As_2S_7$, which forms rhombic plates. The soln. is decomposed by carbon dioxide
with the precipitation of arsenic pentasulphide. J. J. Berzelius said that **sodium
metasulpharsenate,** $NaAsS_3$, is precipitated when alcohol is added to a soln. of the
ortho-salt ; likewise also with **lithium metasulpharsenate,** $LiAsS_3$; and **potassium
metasulpharsenate,** $KAsS_3$. A soln. of two mols of potassium hydrosulphide
dissolves between a half and one mol of arsenic pentasulphide, and when evaporated
in air, acquires a film of sulphur, arsenic pentasulphide separates, and a soln. of the
pyrosulpharsenate is formed.
J. J. Berzelius evaporated a mixed aq. soln. of sodium and potassium ortho-
sulpharsenates, and obtained pale yellow or colourless, four-sided plates of the
double salt **potassium sodium orthosulpharsenate** ; but not so with the mixture of
sodium and ammonium salts. The double salt, **ammonium sodium orthosulpharsenate,** $Na_3(NH_4)_3(AsS_4)_2$, however, was made by adding alcohol to a mixture of
the two salts in the correct proportions, and also by evaporating a mixed soln. of
sodium orthosulpharsenate and ammonium chloride. The salt furnishes colourless
or pale yellow six-sided prisms.
A. Breithaupt [2] reported what he regarded *als neues Mineral,* from Morococha,
in the Cordilleras of Peru. He called it **enargite**—from ἐναργής, clearly visible—

in allusion to its perfect cleavage. The analyses corresponded with **cuprous ortho-sulpharsenate,** Cu_3AsS_4. C. R. Rammelsberg, and C. Guillemain considered it to be more complex—the former gave $4CuS.Cu_2S.As_2S_3$, or $5CuS.Cu_2S.As_2S_3$. Analyses of enargite have been reported by F. Sandberger, V. R. von Zepharovich, R. de Neufville, I. Domeyko, A. Knop, F. Field, F. von Kobell, A. Raimondi, C. Guillemain, W. J. Taylor, A. Breithaupt, W. F. Hillebrand, B. S. Burton, P. Krusch, V. Zsivny, F. A. Genth, W. Semmons, B. Silliman, E. W. Root, C. F. Rammelsberg, A. d'Achiardi, A. W. Stelzner, etc. Specimens have been reported from many localities, and some varieties have received special names. Enargite may occur massive, and granular and in prismatic crystals coloured greyish-black to iron-black. The rhombic crystals, according to H. Dauber, have the axial ratios $a : b : c = 0.8711 : 1 : 0.8248$; V. Zsivny gave $0.8711 : 1 : 0.8248$ and L. J. Spencer, $0.8694 : 1 : 0.8308$. The prismatic planes may be vertically striped. Twins may occur about the (320)-plane, and there are sometimes star-shaped trillings resembling chrysoberyl. The (110)-cleavage is perfect; the (100)- and (010)-cleavages are distinct; and the (001)-cleavage indistinct. The crystals were also examined by F. Sandberger, V. R. von Zepharovich, L. V. Pirsson, C. F. Rammelsberg, M. Zettler, A. W. Stelzner, and G. vom Rath. P. F. Kerr studied the X-radiogram. The hardness is 3, and the sp. gr. 4·3–4·5. A. W. Stelzner gave 4·35–4·37. A. Sella gave 0·1202 for the sp. ht. J. Joly gave 290° for the temp. at which sublimation occurs. A. de Gramont examined the spark spectrum. T. W. Case said that the mineral is a non-conductor of electricity and light has no measurable effect. E. T. Wherry, and H. S. Roberts and L. H. Adams examined the properties of the crystals as rectifiers of alternating currents, and as radio-detectors. The compound decomposes when heated; it is soluble in aqua regia. H. Saito found that when enargite is heated in air, most of the arsenic is expelled at a comparatively low temp., and the copper sulphide is then oxidized. The oxidation is analogous to that of a mixture of its components, arsenic pentasulphide being oxidized first, and then the cuprous sulphide. Nearly 75 per cent. of the dearsenicating reaction occurs below 350°, and to complete this action, rapid oxidation at 500°–600° is necessary because at higher temp. the reaction is hindered. The ore fuses at about 400°, and the amount of copper arsenate which is produced varies with the conditions.

F. Field called a sample of enargite from the Cordilleras of Chili, *guayacanite;* W. Semmons, an arsenical copper ore from Montana, *garbyite.* A. Frenzel's *lautite* from Lauta, Saxony, was shown by A. Weisbach to be a mixture of arsenic with a mineral resembling enargite. A. Weisbach's *luzonite,* from the Island of Luzon, Philippines, was found to have a composition approaching enargite, but to be monoclinic instead of rhombic. G. Bodländer obtained a specimen with the same composition from Famatina, Argentine. The *clarite* of F. Sandberger was obtained from the Clara mine, Baden. It too occurs in monoclinic crystals with the composition of enargite. The analyses of some samples of binnite (*q.v.*) approach that of enargite.

K. Preis[3] reported **cupric orthosulpharsenate,** $Cu_3(AsS_4)_2$, to be formed by mixing soln. of one part of sodium sulpharsenate and three parts of cupric sulphate, and drying the washed precipitate at 100°. A boiling soln. of cupric sulphate furnishes cupric sulphide. The reddish-brown salt when heated loses arsenic trisulphide and sulphur. J. J. Berzelius reported that soln. of sodium sulpharsenate and a cupric salt give a dark brown precipitate of **cupric pyrosulpharsenate,** $Cu_2As_2S_7$; and he said that same substance is precipitated by passing hydrogen sulphide through acidic soln. containing copper and arsenic. If arsenic acid is in excess, the brown sulpharsenate is first precipitated, and then yellow arsenic pentasulphide. When the precipitate is treated with ammonium hydrosulphide, E. F. Anthon said that both arsenic and copper sulphide are dissolved. A. Carnot found that ammonium hydrosulphide gives a precipitate of cupric sulphide when added to a soln. of arsenic acid and a copper salt; and the clear liquid gives an orange-yellow precipitate with hydrochloric acid. **L.** Gmelin observed that dil. aq. ammonia extracts arsenic sulphide while a conc. soln. dissolves both arsenic and copper sulphides. As a matter of fact the reaction between copper sulphate and alkali sulpharsenate is not so simple —*vide supra*. H. Heubach represented the reaction by a set of equations involving : $3CuSO_4+2Na_3AsS_4=Cu_3(AsS_4)_2+3Na_2SO_4$, and $3CuSO_4+2Na_3AsS_4=3CuS$ $+As_2S_5+3Na_2SO_4$; the arsenic pentasulphide reacts : $As_2S_5+5CuSO_4+8H_2O$ $=2H_3AsO_4+5CuS+5H_2SO_4$; and the sulphuric acid reacts : $2Na_3AsS_4+3H_2SO_4$ $=3Na_2SO_4+As_2S_5+3H_2S$; and the arsenic acid is reduced by the hydrogen sulphide : $H_3AsO_4+H_2S=H_3AsO_3+H_2O+S$, etc., as in the case of silver nitrate —*vide infra*.

J. J. Berzelius prepared **silver orthosulpharsenate,** Ag_3AsS_4, by adding a soln. of sodium sulpharsenate to one of a silver salt. When the dark brown precipitate is heated in air, it forms silver sulphide by the combustion of the arsenic sulphide ; and when heated in a closed vessel, it fuses with the evolution of sulphur and arsenic trisulphide. According to L. F. Nilson, and K. Preis, when a soln. of silver nitrate is added to one of sodium orthosulpharsenate, the reaction is different according as the reaction takes place in aq. or acidic soln., or in ammoniacal soln. of the sodium sulphoarsenate, silver sulphide is precipitated, and the soln. contains arsenic acid, sodium nitrate, and nitric acid, the reaction taking place according to the equation : $Na_3AsS_4+8AgNO_3+4H_2O=4Ag_2S+H_3AsO_4+3NaNO_3+5HNO_3$. When, however, silver nitrate is added to an aq. soln. of sodium sulphoarsenate or if the soln. contains nitric acid, silver sulphide is precipitated as before, and arsenious but no arsenic acid is found in the soln., nitric acid and sodium nitrate being formed as before. This reaction takes place according to the two following equations : (i) $Na_3AsS_4+8AgNO_3+4H_2O=4Ag_2S+H_3AsO_3+5HNO_3+3NaNO_3+O$, and (ii) $Na_3AsS_4+6AgNO_3+3H_2O=3Ag_2S+H_3AsO_3+3HNO_3+3NaNO_3+S$. The larger the amount of free acid present the more nearly does the reaction conform to equation (i), but in aq. soln., which is neutral at the commencement of the reaction, it conforms more closely to the second equation. The oxygen which is formed according to the first equation is not liberated in the free state, but as the two reactions always take place simultaneously it combines with some of the sulphur thrown down according to the second equation, and is found as sulphuric acid. These reactions take place immediately, and are not affected by the length of time allowed for the precipitation. It is suggested that arsenic acid is a strong acid, whose thermal effect is equal to that of the strongest acids, whilst on the contrary arsenic trioxide possesses feeble acidic properties, and even under certain conditions exhibits basic properties. Therefore, if the reaction takes place in the presence of ammonia, arsenic acid is formed, whilst in the presence of free acid the feebly basic arsenic trioxide is formed. This theory corresponds with the decomposition of silver nitrate by arsine ; on passing this gas through neutral silver nitrate soln., arsenious acid goes into soln., whilst if the silver soln. is ammoniacal arsenic acid is formed. The reaction was also examined by H. Heubach, who suggested that the first stage of the reaction proceeds : $2Na_3AsS_4+6AgNO_3=3Ag_2S+As_2S_5$ $+6NaNO_3$; the pentasulphide then reacts with the silver nitrate : $As_2S_5+10AgNO_3$ $+8H_2O=5Ag_2S+2H_3AsO_4+10HNO_3$; the nitric acid then decomposes sodium sulpharsenate : $6HNO_3+2Na_3AsS_4=3H_2S+As_2S_5+6NaNO_3$; the hydrogen sulphide reduces the arsenic acid : $H_3AsO_4+H_2S=H_3AsO_3+H_2O+S$; the sulphur reacts partly with the silver nitrate : $2AgNO_3+S+H_2O=Ag_2S+2HNO_3+O$; and is partly oxidized to sulphuric acid.

A. Breithaupt [4] applied the term **xanthoconite**—from ξανθός, yellow ; κόνις, powder—to a yellow pulverulent mineral from the Himmelsfürst mine, Freiberg. Analyses reported by A. Breithaupt, and H. A. Miers agree with the formula Ag_3AsS_4. F. X. M. Zippe reported crystals of another mineral with a similar composition but containing a little selenium, $Ag_3As(Se,S)_4$, and he called it **rittingerite**— after P. Rittinger. The observations of A. Breithaupt, A. L. Parsons, P. Groth, G. A. Kenngott, A. Streng, A. Schrauf, and H. A. Miers have proved that rittingerite

and xanthoconite are the same mineral species. A. Breithaupt regarded xantho
conite as a trigonal mineral with the axial ratio $a:c=1:2.3163$, bu
H. A. Miers proved that the mineral is monoclinic with the axial ratios $a:b:$
$=1.9187:1:1.0152$, and $\beta=88°47'$; and A. Schrauf gave $0.52801:1:0.52934$
and $\beta=89°26'$. The colour is brown or orange-red, and by transmitted ligh
lemon-yellow, or hyacinth-red. According to H. A. Miers, the crystals are isomor
phous with those of pyrostilpnite. Twinning occurs about the (001)-plane; th
(001)-cleavage is well-defined; the optic axial angle $2E=125°$ (nearly); and th
double refraction is strong. The hardness is between 2 and 3. A. Breithaupt gav
5·158–5·191 for the sp. gr.; H. A. Miers, 5·40–5·68; and A. Schrauf, 5·63. Th
mineral melts and decomposes when heated, giving a sublimate of arsenic sulphide.

According to J. J. Berzelius,[5] **gold orthosulpharsenate**, $AuAsS_4$, is precipitatec
when a soln. of a gold salt is treated with sodium orthosulpharsenate. The dark
brown precipitate is soluble in water, and the soln. is decolorized by ferrous sulphate
and a yellowish-brown precipitate is formed. If sodium pyrosulpharsenate is the
precipitant, then **gold pyrosulpharsenate**, $Au_4(As_2O_7)_3$, is obtained as a reddish
brown precipitate, soluble in water.

J. J. Berzelius reported **calcium orthosulpharsenate**, $Ca_3(AsS_4)_2.20H_2O$, to be
formed by evaporating the clear liquid obtained by digesting calcium sulphide with
a soln. of calcium pyrosulpharsenate, or by precipitation from the same liquid with
alcohol. The formula is based on the analysis of L. F. Nilson, who made the salt
by crystallization from a soln. of a mol of arsenic trisulphide and 5 mols of arsenic
hydrosulphide. The pale-yellow, rhombic crystals are soluble in water, insoluble in
alcohol. J. J. Berzelius prepared **strontium orthosulpharsenate**, $Sr_3(AsS_4)_2.nH_2O$,
by a method similar to that used for the calcium salt; he obtained **barium orthosulpharsenate**, $Ba_3(AsS_4)_2.nH_2O$, in a similar way, and also by heating the pyro-salt
to redness in a retort when arsenic trisulphide and sulphur sublime. J. J. Berzelius
made **calcium pyrosulpharsenate**, $Ca_2As_2S_7.nH_2O$, by adding alkali pyrosulpharsenate to a soln. of a calcium salt. The soln. on evaporation forms a yellow,
opaque mass which loses water at 60°, but recovers it again on exposure to air. It
is decomposed by heat. The salt is soluble in water and alcohol, and the boiling
aq. soln. dissolves very little arsenic pentasulphide. He also made **strontium
pyrosulpharsenate**, $Sr_2As_2S_7.nH_2O$, in a similar way; and also lemon-yellow **barium
pyrosulpharsenate**, $Ba_2As_2S_7.nH_2O$. He also reported that barium metasulpharsenate, $Ba(AsS_3)_2$, remains in soln. when alcohol is added to a soln. of the pyro-
salt; but it is decomposed when the soln. is conc. by evaporation. L. F. Nilson
evaporated in vacuo a sat. soln. of arsenic pentasulphide in one of calcium hydrosulphide, and obtained a crystalline mass of **calcium penterasulphotetrarsenate**,
$Ca_5As_4S_{15}.12H_2O$, which is freely soluble in water, and decomposed by hot hydrochloric acid. L. F. Nilson also reported that he had made a complex salt, **barium
orthosulphopyroarsenate**, $Ba_3(AsS_4)_2.Ba_2As_2O_5.8H_2O$, by crystallization from the
mother-liquor used in preparing barium pyrosulpharsenite; **strontium ortho-
sulphopyroarsenitoarsenate**, $Sr_3(AsS_4)_2.Sr_2As_2S_5.8H_2O$, was prepared in a similar
way. L. F. Nilson at first considered the barium salt to be $5BaS.2As_2S_3.6H_2O$.
He also obtained it from a conc. soln. of barium hydrosulphide sat. with arsenic
pentasulphide. The salt can be recrystallized from hot water. It gives yellow
monoclinic prisms isomorphous with barium pyrosulpharsenite, $Ba_2As_2S_5.15H_2O$.
L. F. Nilson represented the constitution of the salt by the formula :

$$Ba{<}^O_S{>}As{-}S{-}Ba{-}S{-}As{<}^{S-\rceil}_{}{}_{S\ \ S}$$
$$Ba{<}^O_S{>}As{-}S{-}Ba{-}S{-}As{<}_{S-\rfloor}$$

J. J. Berzelius obtained a soln. of **beryllium sulpharsenate** by digesting the
hydroxide with arsenic pentasulphide suspended in water. He reported **magnesium**

orthosulpharsenate, $Mg_3(AsS_4).nH_2O$, to be formed by treating a soln. of the pyro-salt with magnesium hydrosulphide so long as hydrogen sulphide is evolved, and evaporating in vacuo, or cooling the clear liquid. This compound may be formed as a white porous mass by heating the pyro-salt in a retort. The colourless crystals are hygroscopic. Alcohol extracts arsenic sulphide and leaves a sparingly soluble basic salt as a residue. When a soln. of magnesium and ammonium sulpharsenates is treated with alcohol, needle-like crystals of **ammonium magnesium ortho-sulpharsenate,** $(NH_4)MgAsO_4.nH_2O$, are deposited. They lose ammonia and hydrogen sulphide on exposure to air. They are freely soluble in water; alcohol precipitates the original salt from the aq. soln. When the aq. soln. is evaporated, it decomposes, giving off hydrogen sulphide. J. J. Berzelius obtained **magnesium pyrosulpharsenate,** $Mg_2As_2S_7.nH_2O$, as a non-crystallizable lemon-yellow mass by the action of sodium pyrosulpharsenate on a soln. of a magnesium salt. The pyro-salt is freely soluble in water, and it is not precipitated on adding alcohol to the aq. soln. L. F. Nilson prepared **magnesium penterasulphotetrarsenate,** $Mg_5As_4S_{15}.3H_2O$, by the method employed for the corresponding calcium salt. The crystals are freely soluble in water, and are decomposed by hydrochloric acid.

According to J. J. Berzelius, **zinc orthosulpharsenate,** $Zn_3(AsS_4)_2$, is precipitated, in pale yellow flakes, when a zinc salt is treated with sodium orthosulpharsenate, and, according to K. Preis, it is formed by mixing a cold soln. of three parts of zinc sulphate with two parts of sodium orthosulpharsenate. He also obtained light yellow **cadmium orthosulpharsenate** by treating a cadmium salt with a sat. soln. of arsenic trisulphide in one of ammonium hydrosulphide. H. Heubach represented the reaction : $2Na_3AsS_4+3CdSO_4=Cd_3(AsS_4)_2+3Na_2SO_4$. J. J. Berzelius observed that yellow flakes of **zinc pyrosulpharsenate,** $Zn_2As_2S_7$, are precipitated by adding the corresponding sodium salt to a soln. of a zinc salt; similarly also with **cadmium pyrosulpharsenate.** According to F. Wöhler, hydrogen sulphide precipitates the whole of the zinc as **zinc metasulpharsenate,** $Zn(AsS_3)_2$, from a soln. of zinc and an excess of arsenic acid in an excess of hydrochloric or sulphuric acid ; but if the arsenic be in the form of arsenic trioxide, arsenic trisulphide is precipitated without the zinc. H. Heubach found that when sodium orthosulpharsenate is added to a soln. of mercurous nitrate, no hydrogen sulphide is evolved and a black precipitate of mercurous sulphide is deposited, he assumed that the **mercurous orthosulph-arsenate,** Hg_3AsS_4, is immediately decomposed by the action of the excess of mer-curous nitrate : $5HgNO_3+Hg_3AsS_4+4H_2O=4Hg_2S+5HNO_3+H_3AsO_4$. K. Preis obtained **mercuric orthosulpharsenate,** $Hg_3(AsS_4)_2$, by mixing soln. of equal parts of mercuric chloride and sodium orthosulpharsenate ; washing the orange-yellow precipitate with cold water, and drying at 100°. H. Heubach represented the reaction : $3HgCl_2+2Na_3AsS_4=6NaCl+Hg_3(AsS_4)_2$. The olive-green powder is decomposed by heat. J. J. Berzelius obtained a black precipitate by adding sodium sulpharsenate to a soln. of a mercurous salt ; he assumed that **mercurous pyrosulpharsenate,** $Hg_4As_2S_7$, is formed which, when heated, loses mercury and sublimes as **mercuric pyrosulpharsenate,** $Hg_2As_4S_7$. He also obtained this salt, as a dark yellow precipitate, by adding a soln. of sodium meta- or pyro-sulpharsenate to a soln. of a mercuric salt.

According to L. F. Hawley,[6] when thallous salts and salts of quinquevalent arsenic are precipitated together by alkaline sulphides. the precipitate varies in colour and properties according to the composition, and mixtures varying from yellow arsenic pentasulphide to a crystalline orange phase can be prepared. Only one phase is present when the composition is that of **thallous orthosulpharsenate,** Tl_3AsS_4, and from that point onwards, the precipitate is mixed with black thallous sulphide. With acidic soln. it is difficult to prevent the reduction of the arsenic salt. Solid soln. of thallous sulphide and arsenic trisulphide can be transformed into thallous orthosulpharsenate by treatment with sodium polysulphide. Thallous ortho-sulpharsenate is an orange-coloured precipitate insoluble in dil. alkaline sulphides. On boiling with a conc. soln. of sodium sulphide it is partially decomposed, some arsenic pentasulphide going into soln. and thallous sulphide remaining. Dil. acids decompose it with the evolution of hydrogen sulphide, thallium going into soln. and arsenic pentasulphide remaining. When washed with water and dried it is perfectly stable in the air at ordinary temp., but it melts with slight decomposition at about 250°. This compound may also be used in the gravimetric determination of thallium in a manner similar to the thallium sulphostannate method.

J. J. Berzelius reported **cerous orthosulpharsenate** to be formed by precipitating a cerous salt soln. with alkali orthosulpharsenate ; if alkali hydrosulpharsenate be used then **cerous pyrosulpharsenate** is formed. Both salts appear as pale yellow precipitates. If a ceric salt be treated with the alkali sulpharsenate, then ceric sulpharsenate is formed as a yellowish-white precipitate. He also obtained a soln. of **yttrium sulpharsenate** by digesting yttrium hydroxide with water in which arsenic pentasulphide is suspended. Yttrium salts do not give any turbidity with soln. of sodium sulpharsenates. J. J. Berzelius reported **zirconium sulpharsenate** to be formed as a lemon-yellow precipitate when a soln. of a zirconium salt is treated with sodium sulpharsenate. It is not decomposed by acids. He also obtained **stannous sulpharsenate** as a chestnut-brown precipitate by adding a soln. of sodium sulpharsenate to one of stannous chloride ; with stannic chloride a pale yellow, slimy precipitate of **stannic sulpharsenate** is formed. Sodium orthosulpharsenate gives a red precipitate of **lead orthosulpharsenate** when added to a soln. of a lead salt ; and with sodium pyrosulpharsenate, dark brown **lead pyrosulpharsenate** is formed —*vide supra*, jordanite. H. Heubach represented the former reaction : $2Na_3AsS_4+3Pb(NO_3)_2=Pb_3(AsS_4)_2+6NaNO_3$.

J. J. Berzelius obtained **antimony sulpharsenate** as a brownish-yellow, fusible precipitate by mixing soln. of sodium orthosulpharsenate and an antimonious salt. He also obtained a dark brown precipitate of **bismuth pyrosulpharsenate,** $Bi_4(As_2O_7)_3$, by adding sodium sulpharsenate to a soln. of a bismuth salt. The precipitate is soluble in an excess of the alkali sulpharsenate. No **vanadium sulpharsenate** is precipitated when a soln. of vanadyl sulphate is treated with sodium sulpharsenate, but the blue liquid becomes colourless. J. J. Berzelius said that chromic salt soln. give a dirty yellow precipitate of **chromic sulpharsenate** when treated with a soln. of sodium sulpharsenate ; molybdic salt soln. under similar conditions form a yellowish-brown soln. of **molybdic sulpharsenate,** but no precipitate is formed. According to R. F. Weinland and K. Sommer,[7] a series of **metasulpharsenatosulphomolybdates** with the general formula $R_2S.As_2S_5.2MoO_3$, analogous to the corresponding $R_2O.As_2O_5.2MoO_3$, is known, and can be represented graphically :

$$\begin{array}{c} S \\ S \end{array}\!\!>\!As\!-\!S\!-\!Mo\!<\!\!\begin{array}{c} S \\ S \\ S \end{array}$$

Another series of **pyrosulpharsenatosulphomolybdates,** with the general formula $2R_2S.As_2S_5.2MoS_3.nH_2O$, is known. They can be regarded as double salts of metasulpharsenates and pyrosulphomolybdates, $2RAsS_3.R_2Mo_2S_7$, or as complex salts with the graphic formula $(RS)_2AsS.S.AsS(S.MoS_3S)_2$. There are two representatives of the first series, **sodium metasulpharsenatosulphomolybdate,** $NaAsS_3(MoS_3).6H_2O$, formed by triturating a mol of sodium pyrosulphoarsenatosulphomolybdate with 1·5 mols of salicylic acid, and water ; warming the mixture at 40°–50° ; and treating the clear soln. with alcohol. The brick-red precipitate was washed with dil. alcohol, and finally with as little cold water as possible. The amorphous powder is insoluble in water, and freely soluble in dil. soda-lye, and aq. ammonia. The other member of the series, **potassium metasulpharsenatosulphomolybdate,** $KAsS_3(MoS_3).4H_2O$, was obtained in a similar manner.

R. F. Weinland and K. Sommer prepared **sodium pyrosulpharsenatosulphomolybdate,** $Na_4As_2S_7(MoS_3)_2.14H_2O$, by adding molybdenum trisulphide (2 mols) to a soln. of sodium sulpharsenate (1 mol) heated on the water-bath ; a portion of the trisulphide remains undissolved, and a brown by-product is also formed. The filtrate, on evaporation, yields the salt mixed with the brown, amorphous by-product, which, although insoluble in water, is easily soluble in a soln. of the salt; the two are most conveniently separated by dissolving the crude salt in a large quantity of ice-cold water, when the brown by-product remains for the most part undissolved. The salt is also formed on boiling a soln. of sodium pyrosulpharsenate with molybdenum trisulphide, but large quantities of by-products are formed at the same time. It can, however, be easily obtained in a pure state by adding salicylic acid (1 mol) to a soln. of molybdenum trisulphide (1 mol) in sodium sulpharsenate (1 mol), and precipitating the clear filtrate with alcohol. It crystallizes in lustrous, dark red, six-sided prisms, gradually decomposes when dry, and is then no longer entirely soluble in water, is not hygroscopic, and loses its water of crystallization at 105°. It is decomposed by dil. mineral acids with evolution of hydrogen sulphide and precipitation of a reddish-brown sulphide, and gives characteristic coloured precipitates with soln. of metallic salts. This salt is also produced by the action of arsenic pentasulphide on sodium sulphomolybdate. The **potassium pyrosulpharsenatosulphomolybdate,** $K_4As_2S_7(MoS_3)_2.8H_2O$, which can be prepared in a similar manner to the sodium salt, crystallizes in bright red, slender needles, is easily soluble in water, insoluble in alcohol, and has properties like those of the sodium salt. The **ammonium pyrosulpharsenatosulphomolybdate,** $(NH_4)_4As_2S_7(MoS_3)_2.5H_2O$, is best prepared by adding salicylic acid (4 mols) to a conc. soln. of ammonium pyrosulpharsenate and ammonium sulphomolybdate, and then precipitating with alcohol; it crystallizes in slender, scarlet needles, is very unstable, and cannot be obtained pure. The aq. soln. quickly decomposes with evolution of ammonia and hydrogen sulphide. The **barium pyrosulpharsenato-sulphomolybdate,** $Ba_2As_2O_7(MoS_3)_2.14H_2O$, is obtained by dissolving arsenic pentasulphide in a soln. of barium sulphomolybdate, and cooling the filtrate to $-15°$. It cannot be obtained by the action of molybdenum trisulphide on barium sulpharsenate, as under these conditions sulphur is precipitated, and a double salt of barium sulpharsenate and barium sulpharsenite is formed. It crystallizes in slender, red needles, and when recrystallized partially decomposes with separation of sulphur. A reddish-brown precipitate of the **copper salt** was obtained by treating a soln. of a copper salt with the potassium salt. It is soluble in aq. ammonia. Similarly a dark red, **silver salt** insoluble in aq. ammonia and ammonium sulphide; the dark brown **mercuric salt,** and the dark red **zinc salt,** soluble in aq. ammonia were also formed; the **cobalt salt** is brown and does not dissolve in an excess of the complex salt, in aq. ammonia, or ammonium sulphide; the **nickel salt** is reddish-brown. At first ferrous salts give no precipitate, but a dark brown **ferrous salt** forms after some time. No **manganese salt** is precipitated.

According to J. J. Berzelius,[8] a soln. of sodium sulpharsenate gives a dingy yellow precipitate of **uranyl sulpharsenate** when added to a soln. of a uranyl salt; it dissolves in an excess of the sodium sulpharsenate. An aq. soln. of sodium sulpharsenate does not give a precipitate with manganese salts. If freshly precipitated manganese sulphide and arsenic pentasulphide be suspended in water, **manganese pyrosulpharsenate,** $Mn_2As_2S_7$, is formed—part passes into soln., and part is precipitated as a yellow powder which is soluble in a larger proportion of water. The evaporation of the aq. soln. deposits first sulphur and then a lemon-yellow mass which is the partly decomposed pyrosulpharsenate and does not all dissolve in water. Acids precipitate arsenic pentasulphide from the aq. soln., and hydrogen sulphide is evolved. Manganese pyrosulpharsenate is produced when manganese carbonate and arsenic pentasulphide are boiled in water, but some manganese arsenate is formed at the same time. When the pyrosulpharsenate is digested with conc. aq. ammonia, some arsenic pentasulphide is extracted and a brick-red basic salt is formed. J. J. Berzelius made **ferrous sulpharsenate** as a dark brown precipitate by the action of sodium sulpharsenate on a soln. of ferrous sulphate. It forms a dark brown soln. with an excess of the sodium salt; and when dried in air it forms a mixture of ferric hydroxide and **ferric sulpharsenate**. A soln. of sodium sulpharsenate precipitates greenish-grey ferric sulpharsenate from soln. of ferric salts, and the precipitate forms a dark brown soln. with an excess of the sodium salt. The precipitate does not decompose on drying; it fuses readily; and decomposes at a higher temp. giving off sulphur.

A steel-grey mineral, from the Neuglück mine, Wittchen, was described by F. Sandberger [9] as an *Arsenwismuthkupfererz*, and was afterwards named **epigenite**—from ἐπιγενής, born afterwards—in allusion to its occurring implanted on barite vein-masses. The analysis by T. Petersen corresponds with **cuprous ferrous sulpharsenate**, $3Cu_2S.3FeO.As_2S_5$; P. Groth gave $4Cu_2S.3FeS.As_2S_5$; and C. F. Rammelsberg, $9CuS.3Cu_2S.6FeS.2As_2S_5$. The rhombic prisms resemble those of arsenopyrite. The hardness is 3 to 4; and the sp. gr. 4·45. A. d'Achiardi described a mineral from the Jucud mine, Cajamarca, Peru, which he called *regnolite* —after C. Regnoli. Its analysis corresponds with **cupric zinc ferrous sulpharsenate**, $5CuS.FeS.ZnS.As_2S_5$. The tetragonal crystals were considered by L. J. Spencer to be related to those of binnite.

J. J. Berzelius [10] obtained a dark brown precipitate of **cobalt pyrosulpharsenate**, $Co_2As_2S_7$, by adding sodium sulpharsenate to a soln. of a cobalt salt; the precipitate is soluble in excess; with a nickel salt soln., sodium pyrosulpharsenate furnishes **nickel pyrosulpharsenate**, $Ni_2As_2S_7$, and sodium orthosulpharsenate, **nickel ortho-sulpharsenate**, $Ni_3(AsS_4)_2$, as dark brown precipitates. When a soln. of nickel arsenate in hydrochloric acid is treated with ammonium hydrosulphide, the precipitate is a mixture of nickel sulphide and sulpharsenate. The dark yellow precipitate obtained when sodium ortho- or meta-sulpharsenate is added to hydrochloroplatinic acid is **platinic sulpharsenate**.

REFERENCES.

[1] J. J. Berzelius, *Schweigger's Journ.*, **34**. 46, 1822; *Pogg. Ann.*, **7**. 4, 1826; *Ann. Chim. Phys.*, (2), **11**. 225, 1819; (2), **32**. 166, 1826; C. F. Rammelsberg, *Pogg. Ann.*, **52**. 238, 1844; H. Rose, *ib.*, **90**. 194, 568, 1853; **107**. 186, 1859; R. F. Weinland and P. Lehmann, *Zeit. anorg. Chem.*, **26**. 322, 1902; K. B. Edwards, *Canadian Pat. No.* 234917, 1923; C. R. Fresenius, *Zeit. anal. Chem.*, **1**. 192, 1862; L. W. McCay, *ib.*, **26**. 635, 1887; **27**. 632, 1888; **34**. 728, 1895; *Beitrag zur Kenntnis der Kobalt-, Nickel- und Eisenkiese*, Freiberg, 1883; *Amer. Chem. Journ.*, **7**. 375, 1887; **9**. 174, 1888; **10**. 459, 1889; **12**. 547, 1891; *Journ. Amer. Chem. Soc.*, **24**. 661, 1902; *Chem. News*, **54**. 287, 1886; *Zeit. anorg. Chem.*, **25**. 459, 1900; **29**. 36, 1902; **41**. 452, 1904; F. A. Flückiger, *Pharm. Viertelj.*, **12**. 330, 1862; C. Eckert, *ib.*, **13**. 357, 1864; K. Preis, *Liebig's Ann.*, **257**. 196, 1890; A. Geuther, *ib.*, **240**. 221, 1887; L. Storch, *Ber.*, **16**. 2015, 1883; L. F. Nilson, *Journ. prakt. Chem.*, (2), **12**. 295, 1875; (2), **14**. 145, 1876; (2), **16**. 93, 1877; *Akad. Handl. Stockholm*, **10**. 2, 1871; *Oefvers. Akad. Stockholm*, **28**. 303, 1871; **34**. 5, 1877; H. Heubach, *Ueber das sulfarsensaure Natron und dessen Verhalten zu einigen Metallsalzen*, Berlin, 1890; K. B. Edwards, *Brit. Pat. No.* 162747, 1920.

[2] F. Sandberger, *Neues Jahrb. Min.*, 960, 1874; 382, 1875; A. Knop, *ib.*, **70**, 1875; M. Zettler, *ib.*, i, 159, 1880; V. R. von Zepharovich, *Lotos*, **17**. 20, 1867; *Verh. geol. Reichsanst. Wien*, 182, 1879; A. d'Achiardi, *Nuovo Cimento*, (2), **3**. 314, 1870; A. Raimondi, *Minéraux de Pérou*, Paris, 122, 1878; I. Domeyko, *Elementos de mineralojia*, Santiago, 226, 1879; C. F. Rammelsberg, *Handbuch der Mineralchemie*, Leipzig, 119, 1875; 84 1886; *Zeit. deut. geol. Ges.*, **18**. 243, 1866; W. F. Hillebrand, *Amer. Journ. Science*, (4), **7**. 56, 1899; F. A. Genth, *ib.*, (2), **23**. 420, 1857; B. S. Burton, *ib.*, (2), **45**. 34, 1868; B. Silliman, *ib.*, (3), **6**. 127, 1873; L. V. Pirsson, *ib.*, (3), **47**. 212, 1894; H. Saito, *Science Rep. Tohoku Univ.*, **16**. 37, 1927; F. Field, *Journ. Chem. Soc.*, **12**. 8, 1860; *Amer. Journ. Science*, (2), **27**. 52, 1859; E. W. Root, *ib.*, (2), **46**. 201, 1868; W. J. Taylor, *ib.*, (2), **26**. 349, 1858; *Proc. Acad. Philadelphia*, 168, 1857; P. Krusch, *Zeit. prakt. Geol.*, **9**. 215, 1901; A. Breithaupt, *Pogg. Ann.*, **80**. 383, 1850; H. Dauber, *ib.*, **92**. 237, 1854; W. Semmons, *Min. Mag.*, **6**. 51, 1884; L. J. Spencer, *ib.*, **11**. 71, 1895; F. von Kobell, *Sitzber. Akad. München*, **1**. 161, 1865; A. W. Stelzner, *Tschermak's Mitt.*, (1), **3**. 242, 1873; A. Frenzel, *ib.*, (2), **3**. 515, 1881; (2), **4**. 97, 1881; A. Weisbach, *ib.*, (1), **4**. 257, 1874; *Neues Jahrb. Min.*, ii, 250, 1882; R. de Neufville, *Zeit. Kryst.*, **19**. 76, 1891; G. vom Rath, *ib.*, **4**. 426, 1880; V. Zsivny, *ib.*, **62**. 489, 1926; A. de Gramont, *Bull. Soc. Min.*, **18**. 300, 1895; J. L. C. Schroeder van der Kolk, *Centr. Min.*, **79**, 1901; T. W. Case, *Phys. Rev.*, (2), **9**. 305, 1917; H. S. Roberts and L. H. Adams, *Amer. Min.*, **7**. 131, 1922; A. Sella, *Nachr. Gött.*, 311, 1891; *Zeit. Kryst.*, **22**. 180, 1894; C. Guillemain, *Beiträge zur Kenntnis der naturalichen Sulfosalze*, Dresden, 1898; E. T. Wherry, *Amer. Min.*, **10**. 28, 1925; P. F. Kerr, *Econ. Geol.*, **19**. 1, 1924; J. Joly, *Phil. Mag.*, (6), **27**. 1, 1914; *Chem. News*, **107**. 241, 1913; G. Bodländer, *Zeit. Kryst.*, **19**. 275, 1891.

[3] H. Heubach, *Ueber das sulfarsensaure Natron und dessen Verhalten zu einigen Metallsalzen*, Berlin, 1890; K. Preis and B. Rayman, *Bull. Soc. Chim.*, (2), **47**. 892, 1887; K. Preis, *Liebig's Ann.*, **257**. 196, 1890; J. J. Berzelius, *Pogg. Ann.*, **7**. 29, 1826; E. F. Anthon, *Repert. Pharm.*, **76**. 125, 1836; L. Gmelin, *Handbook of Chemistry*, London, **5**. 474, 1851; A. Carnot, *Compt. Rend.*, **105**. 121, 1887; L. F. Nilson, *Journ. prakt. Chem.*, (2), **12**. 295, 1875; (2), **14**. 145, 1876; (2), **16**. 93, 1877; *Akad. Handl. Stockholm*, **10**. 2, 1871; *Oefvers. Akad. Stockholm*, **28**. 303, 1871; **34**. 5, 1877.
[4] A. Breithaupt, *Pogg. Ann.*, **64**. 272, 1845; *Journ. prakt. Chem.*, (1), **20**. 67, 1840; *Berg. Hütt. Ztg.*, **12**. 16, 1853; H. A. Miers, *Min. Mag.*, **10**. 212, 1893; A. Schrauf, *Sitzber. Akad. Wien*, **65**. 227, 1872; *Neues Jahrb. Min.*, 189, 1872; A. Streng, *ib.*, 917, 1878; 547, 1879; i, 57, 1886; F. Sandberger, *ib.*, 167, 1877; *Untersuchungen über Erzgänge*, Wiesbaden, 373, 1885; F. Becke, *Tschermak's Mitt.*, (2), **2**. 94, 1880; F. X. M. Zippe, *Sitzber. Akad. Wien*, **9**. 345, 1852; *Lotos*, **3**. 45, 1853; A. L. Parsons, *Univ. Toronto Geol. Stud.*, **17**. 11, 1924; P. Groth, *Tabellarische Uebersicht der Mineralien*, Braunschweig, 35, 1898; G. A. Kenngott, *Uebersicht der Resultate mineralogischer Forschungen*, Wien, 129, 1853.
[5] J. J. Berzelius, *Schweigger's Journ.*, **34**. 46, 1822; *Pogg. Ann.*, **7**. 4, 1826; *Ann. Chim. Phys.*, (2), **11**. 225, 1819; (2), **32**. 166, 1826; L. F. Nilson, *Journ. prakt. Chem.*, (2), **12**. 295, 1875; (2), **14**. 145, 1876; (2), **16**. 93, 1877; *Akad. Handl. Stockholm*, **10**. 2, 1871; *Oefvers. Akad. Stockholm*, **28**. 303, 1871; **34**. 5, 1877; H. Heubach, *Ueber das sulfarsensaure Natron und dessen Verhalten zu einigen Metallsalzen*, Berlin, 1890; K. Preis, *Liebig's Ann.*, **257**. 196, 1890; F. Wöhler, *Berzelius' Jahresb.*, **21**. 150, 1842.
[6] L. F. Hawley, *Journ. Amer. Chem. Soc.*, **29**. 1013, 1907; J. J. Berzelius, *Schweigger's Journ.*, **34**. 46, 1822; *Pogg. Ann.*, **7**. 4, 1826; *Ann. Chim. Phys.*, (2), **11**. 225, 1819; (2), **32**. 166, 1826; H. Heubach, *Ueber das sulfarsensaure Natron und dessen Verhalten zu einigen Metallsalzen*, Berlin, 1890.
[7] R. F. Weinland and K. Sommer, *Zeit. anorg. Chem.*, **15**. 42, 1897.
[8] J. J. Berzelius, *Schweigger's Journ.*, **34**. 46, 1822; *Pogg. Ann.*, **7**. 4, 1826; *Ann. Chim. Phys.*, (2), **11**. 225, 1819; (2), **32**. 166, 1826.
[9] F. Sandberger, *Untersuchungen über Erzgänge*, Wiesbaden, 1885; *Neues Jahrb. Min.*, 414, 1868; 205, 1869; T. Petersen, *Pogg. Ann.*, **136**. 502, 1869; P. Groth, *Tabellarische Uebersicht der Mineralien*, Braunschweig, 39, 1898; C. F. Rammelsberg, *Handbuch der Mineralchemie*, Leipzig, 122, 1875; A. d'Achiardi, *I Metalli*, **1**. 293, 1883; *Nuovo Cimento*, (2), **3**. 314, 1870; L. J. Spencer, *Min. Mag.*, **11**. 77, 1895.
[10] J. J. Berzelius, *Schweigger's Journ.*, **34**. 46, 1822; *Pogg. Ann.*, **7**. 4, 1826; *Ann. Chim. Phys.*, (2), **11**. 225, 1819; (2), **32**. 166, 1826.

§ 36. The Oxysulpharsenites and Oxysulpharsenates

The **arsenic oxysulphides** reported by H. V. Regnault [1] to be formed by the action of steam on arsenic trisulphide; and by C. Cross and A. Higgin, by dissolving arsenic trisulphide in a hot aq. soln. of arsenic trioxide and evaporating the filtrate, are not recognized as chemical individuals. J. F. L. Hausmann, and L. F. Nilson were unable to isolate any definite oxysulphide by melting mixtures of arsenic trioxide and trisulphide.

It is possible to imagine that in the sulpharsenic acids, the sulphur atoms can be replaced by oxygen atoms one by one, so as to give a series of, say, **oxysulpharsenious acids**: H_3AsO_3, H_3AsO_2S, H_3AsO_2S, and H_3AsS_3. This exhibition has not been taken very far with the sulpharsenious acids, as is represented by the following sodium and barium salts. L. F. Nilson [2] reported **sodium oxysulpharsenite**, $Na_8As_{18}O_7S_{24}.30H_2O$, to be formed when arsenic trisulphide is boiled with a soln. of sodium carbonate. K. Preis obtained the same salt by boiling a soln. of a mol of sodium hydrosulphide and arsenic trioxide, and pouring alcohol over the filtered liquid. The alcoholic soln. on evaporation gives crystals of this salt. He also obtained it by boiling a mixture of a 16 per cent. soln. of one part of sodium hydroxide sat. with hydrogen sulphide, 4 parts of arsenic trioxide, and one part of sulphur. The hot filtrate was cooled; warmed with sodium hydroxide until all was dissolved; and allowed to crystallize. R. F. Weinland and A. Gutmann mixed conc. soln. of equimolar parts of sodium dihydroarsenite and sodium thiosulphate, and allowed the filtrate to concentrate on a water-bath. The liquid furnished garnet-red or purple-red hexagonal plates. The salt is decomposed by water, by hydrochloric acid, boiling soda-lye, and by heating with sodium carbonate. L. F. Nilson's analysis agrees with the above formula, but he gave $Na_2O.2As_2S_3O_2.7H_2O$.

R. F. Weinland and A. Gutmann say that the salt is derived from the ortho-acid, $H_3As(S,O)_3]_{18}$, by the abstraction of $23(H_2S,H_2O)$. L. F. Nilson also reported **barium oxysulpharsenite,** $Ba_5As_4O_2S_9.6H_2O$, to be formed from the mother-liquid remaining after the preparation of barium pyrosulpharsenite. It appears in red needle-like crystals, stable in air, and sparingly soluble in water.

More work has been done on the **oxysulpharsenic acids,** or rather on their salts. None of the acids has been isolated in the solid state, but H_3AsO_3S, and $H_3AsO_2S_2$ are known in soln., while H_3AsOS_3 seems to decompose immediately it is formed. Salts of these and of more complex acids are known. L. W. McCay [3] prepared a soln. of **trioxysulpharsenic acid,** H_3AsO_3S, by the action of hydrogen sulphide on an excess of a cold, dil., acidified soln. of arsenic acid. The finely-divided sulphur formed at the same time was removed by shaking the liquid with finely-divided asbestos and filtration ; and some free hydrogen sulphide was removed by a current of air or by adding copper sulphate which does not attack the trioxysulpharsenic acid. He also obtained the acid by decomposing a cold soln. of the salt with an acid. The aq. soln. of the acid remains clear for a long time after addition of sulphuric or hydrochloric acid ; it gives no immediate precipitate with hydrogen sulphide, but ultimately yields one. When boiled, it gives a precipitate of pure sulphur, without evolution of hydrogen sulphide or sulphurous anhydride. With hydrogen sulphide, the boiled and cooled liquid gives an immediate precipitate of arsenic trisulphide ; it gives no precipitate with copper sulphate ; with mercuric chloride it gives immediately a heavy yellowish-white precipitate ; with silver sulphate it gives a heavy black precipitate, the filtrate from which contains no arsenious acid. The properties of the soln. of J. Bouquet and S. Cloez's potassium oxysulpharsenate agree with those of trioxysulpharsenic acid.

L. W. McCay prepared **dioxydisulpharsenic acid,** $H_3AsO_2S_2$, by the action of hydrogen sulphide on a soln. of sodium arsenate acidified with mineral acids ; by the action of an excess of hydrogen sulphide on a soln. of arsenic acid. A soln. of **oxytrisulpharsenic acid,** H_3AsOS_3, has not been prepared.

Trioxysulpharsenic acid forms primary, secondary, and tertiary salts, while the other acids have hitherto furnished only the tertiary salts. Salts of ammonium, the alkali and alkaline earth metals are known, but not so with the salts of the heavy metals. The salts of the heavy metals decompose at once into the metal sulphide. The sodium salts are easiest to isolate ; the potassium and ammonium salts are very soluble. Salts of a few condensed acids are known. The primary trioxysulpharsenates were prepared by J. Bouquet and S. Cloez by the action of hydrogen sulphide on a cold aq. soln. of the primary arsenate ; by L. F. Nilson, by the action of a boiling soln. of arsenic trisulphide and potassium carbonate ; by L. W. McCay, by dissolving arsenic pentasulphide in aq. ammonia ; by R. F. Weinland and O. Rumpf, by boiling a soln. of a tertiary arsenate with the stoichiometrical proportion of sulphur, by treating the tertiary or secondary salt with thiosulphates, by the action of arsenic pentasulphide or a mixture of arsenic trisulphide and sulphur on the hydroxides of the alkalies or alkaline earths, and by triturating a mixture of the tertiary salt with salicylic acid. K. Preis showed that the secondary and tertiary salts are formed together when arsenic trioxide is boiled with a soln. of sodium monosulphide.

The alkali and alkaline earth salts furnish colourless crystals which are soluble in water ; acids liberate the oxysulpharsenic acid as just indicated. An excess of silver nitrate was found by K. Preis to furnish a precipitate containing brown arsenic ; and J. Bouquet and S. Cloez said that lead salts give a white precipitate which soon becomes black. Other reactions are indicated in Table X copied from L. W. McCay and W. Foster's memoir. The reagent indicated in the last column of the table is that recommended by R. L. Weinland and P. Lehmann, namely, a soln. of 0·03 grm. of the sodium salt in 10 c.c. of water treated with 2 c.c. of a soln. of 10 grms. of potassium antimonyl tartrate, 20 grms. of potassium sodium hydrotartrate, and 170 grms. of water.

ARSENIC

TABLE X.—REACTIONS OF THE TERTIARY SODIUM OXYSULPHARSENATES.

Acid.	A solution of the tertiary sodium salt.					
	HCl	BaCl$_2$	SrCl$_2$	Magnesia mixture.	AgNO$_3$	Weinland's reagent.
H$_3$AsO$_4$, white crystals	—	white pp. in dil. soln.	white pp.	white pp.	brown-red pp.	—
H$_3$AsO$_3$S, known in dil. soln.	turbidity	white pp. in dil. soln.	white pp.	no pp.	black pp.	turbidity with 3 min. boiling
H$_3$AsO$_2$S$_2$, known in every dil soln.	H$_2$S, yellow pp.	0·3 per cent.soln. white pp.	no pp.	no pp.	black pp.	turbidity with 1 min. boiling
H$_3$AsOS$_3$, not known in soln.	H$_2$S+As$_2$S$_5$ in cold	0·3 per cent.soln. turbidity 0·5 per cent. soln.	no pp.	no. pp.	black pp.	At 75° orange-red pp.
H$_3$AsS$_4$, not known in soln.	H$_2$S+As$_2$S$_5$ in cold	no pp.	no pp.	no pp.	black pp.	in dil. soln. orange-red pp.

L. W. McCay obtained a soln. of **ammonium trioxysulpharsenate,** (NH$_4$)$_3$AsO$_3$S, mixed with ammonium sulpharsenate, by dissolving arsenic pentasulphide in aq. ammonia; and R. F. Weinland and O. Rumpf obtained crystals of the *trihydrate,* (NH$_4$)$_3$AsO$_3$S.3H$_2$O, by heating under press. on a water-bath a mixture of a soln. of ammonium arsenite and the calculated quantity of finely-divided sulphur. The liquid also contains sulpharsenate and arsenate. The salt can be purified by fractional crystallization from dil. alcohol. The small, colourless plates readily lose ammonia when exposed to air, probably forming **ammonium dihydrotrioxy-sulpharsenate,** (NH$_4$)H$_2$AsO$_3$S. The salt is readily soluble in water, and the soln. decomposes when boiled, forming arsenic trioxide and sulphur with the escape of ammonia. W. H. McLauchlan fused a mixture of equal parts of sulphur and arsenic trioxide, digested the mass in aq. ammonia, and fractionally precipitated the soln. with alcohol. He represented the salt as a *tetrahydrate,* (NH$_4$)$_3$AsSO$_3$.4H$_2$O; and on adding more alcohol to the mother-liquor, obtained crystals of **ammonium bydrotrioxysulpharsenate,** (NH$_4$)$_2$HAsO$_3$S, which lose ammonia and become yellow when exposed to air. The white colour is restored in an atm. of ammonia.

K. Preis boiled arsenic trioxide with a soln. of sodium sulphide, and, on fraction-ally crystallizing the resulting liquid, obtained **sodium trioxysulpharsenate,** Na$_3$AsO$_3$S.12H$_2$O, as well as the hydrotrioxysulpharsenate, dioxysulpharsenate, orthoarsenate, and a condensed salt—*vide infra.* R. F. Weinland and O. Rumpf prepared the trioxysulpharsenate by crystallization from the filtered liquid obtained by boiling a conc. soln. of sodium orthoarsenate with the calculated amount of precipitated sulphur; also, by treating sodium arsenite with sodium polysulphide: Na$_2$S$_4$+3Na$_3$AsO$_3$=Na$_2$S+3Na$_3$AsO$_3$S, and allowing the warm alcoholic soln. to crystallize—K. B. Edwards used an analogous process; R. F. Weinland and A. Gutmann, by mixing a conc. soln. of sodium orthoarsenite with an equimolar proportion of sodium thiosulphate: Na$_3$AsO$_3$+Na$_2$S$_2$O$_3$=Na$_2$SO$_3$+Na$_3$AsO$_3$S, and crystallizing the aq. soln. of the resulting product—they also used calcium thiosulphate in place of the sodium salt, and sodium hydroarsenite in place of the normal salt: Na$_2$HAsO$_3$+Na$_2$S$_2$O$_3$=NaHSO$_3$+Na$_3$AsO$_3$S; and L. W. McCay, by passing a rapid current of hydrogen sulphide through a soln. of 10 grms. of hemihydrated arsenic acid in a litre of water, allowing the mixture to stand 20 mins., filtering the turbid liquid through asbestos, shaking the liquid with magnesia, precipitating the magnesia from the filtered liquid by potash-lye, adding a barium salt, and converting the soln. of barium trioxysulpharsenate into the sodium salt by means of sodium carbonate ; he also prepared sodium trioxysulph-arsenate by dissolving 7 grms. of arsenic pentasulphide in 100 c.c. of a 10 per cent. soln. of sodium hydroxide, shaking the product with strontium chloride, and, after standing 24 hrs., boiling with a soln. of sodium carbonate. The required salt was precipitated from the soln. by alcohol. The colourless, four-sided prisms belong to the rhombic system, and, according to R. F. Weinland and O. Rumpf, have the axial ratios $a : b : c = 0.9199 : 1 : 0.6602$. The salt is freely soluble in water, and the aq. soln. reacts as indicated in Table X. R. F. Weinland and co-workers obtained colourless, six-sided, prismatic crystals of **potassium trioxysulpharsenate**, $K_3AsO_3S.2H_2O$, in an analogous manner to the method used for the sodium salt.

K. Preis obtained **sodium hydrotrioxysulpharsenate**, $Na_2HAsO_3S.8H_2O$, as indicated above. The clear, colourless, tabular, triclinic crystals had the axial ratios $a : b : c = 1.0334 : 1 : 1.07065$, and $\alpha = 94° 25'$, $\beta = 114° 7'$, and $\gamma = 87° 28'$. The salt loses three-fourths of its water of crystallization when confined over sulphuric acid, and if the product is heated to 100°, it melts, and, when cold, forms an orange-red mass. It is easily soluble in water. R. F. Weinland and O. Rumpf obtained **potassium hydrotrioxysulpharsenate**, $K_2HAsO_3S.2\frac{1}{3}H_2O$, in colourless, hygroscopic, prismatic crystals, by evaporating over sulphuric acid and potassium hydroxide, a soln. of the dihydrotrioxysulpharsenate with one-seventh more than the stoichiometrical quantity of potassium hydroxide.

R. F. Weinland and O. Rumpf prepared **sodium dihydrotrioxysulpharsenate**, NaH_2AsO_3S, by triturating the normal salt with two molar proportions of salicylic acid, treating the product with 96 per cent. alcohol, in a closed flask so long as the alcohol shows the presence of salicylic acid. The primary salt was separated from the undecomposed tertiary salt by levigation, and dried on a porous tile. The crystalline powder is composed of colourless prisms, and reddens moist litmus-paper. It contains no water of crystallization. The salt is decomposed by water with the separation of sulphur ; and it decomposes in the dry state in a few hours : $NaH_2AsO_3S = NaAsO_2 + S + H_2O$—this reaction is hastened by raising the temp. J. Bouquet and S. Cloez reported **potassium dihydrotrioxysulpharsenate**, $KH_2AsO_3S.H_2O$, to be formed by passing a brisk current of hydrogen sulphide through a cold sat. soln. of potassium hydroarsenate; L. W. McCay used potassium dihydroarsenate, and he also passed hydrogen sulphide through the boiling soln., and continued the passage of the gas until the soln. was cold. The product was washed with alcohol, and then with ether. L. F. Nilson found that the pale yellow mass obtained by boiling arsenic trisulphide in a conc. soln. of potassium carbonate, when washed with alcohol and allowed to stand in a closed vessel, gradually forms crystals of the dihydrotrioxysulpharsenate ; he also made the same salt by crystallization from a filtered soln. of arsenic pentasulphide in a sat. soln. of arsenic acid in one of potassium carbonate. R. F. Weinland and O. Rumpf made it by the action of the calculated quantity of salicylic acid on a conc. soln. of the normal salt, and precipitating the salt with alcohol. The colourless, four-sided crystals are stable in air ; they lose water at 170° without melting, but they melt at a higher temp., and decompose into arsenic trisulphide, arsenic, etc. The salt is sparingly soluble in cold water, freely soluble in hot water, but not without decomposition. L. W. McCay found that the free acid is obtained by the action of acids on a cold, dil. soln. of the salt, and no hydrogen sulphide is evolved. L. F. Nilson found that the salt is decomposed by acids with the separation of, presumably, sulphur. The salt is soluble in alkali-lye, and decomposed by silver nitrate, forming a soln. of arsenic acid.

According to A. Gutmann, when ammonia is added to a mixed soln. of 3 mols of lithium chloride and one mol of sodium trioxysulpharsenate, prismatic or acicular crystals of **sodium lithium trioxysulpharsenate**, $Na_2LiAsO_3S.5H_2O$, are formed.

L. W. McCay prepared a colourless, crystalline powder of **barium trioxysulpharsenate**, $Ba_3(AsO_3S)_2.6H_2O$, from a soln. of potassium dihydrotrioxysulpharsenate in baryta-water; and K. Preis, and R. F. Weinland and O. Rumpf, by mixing a warm soln. of sodium trioxysulpharsenate with an excess of a soln. of barium chloride, and allowing the mixture to stand for 24 hrs. K. Preis obtained **barium hydrotrioxysulpharsenate**, $BaHAsO_3S.10H_2O$, in colourless crystals, from a conc. soln. of barium chloride and sodium hydrotrioxysulpharsenate. L. W. McCay reported **ammonium strontium trioxysulpharsenate**, $(NH_4)SrAsO_3S.nH_2O$, to be formed by adding strontium chloride to a filtered soln. of 5 grms. of arsenic pentasulphide in 20 c.c. of conc. aq. ammonia, after standing 12 hrs., the crystalline precipitate was washed with dil. aq. ammonia, and dried rapidly between bibulous paper because the salt rapidly loses ammonia when exposed to air and becomes yellow; the white colour is restored in an atm. of ammonia. F. R. Weinland and O. Rumpf obtained **sodium barium trioxysulpharsenate**, $NaBaAsO_3S.9H_2O$, by mixing a hot, very dil., aq. soln. of sodium trioxysulpharsenate, free from carbon dioxide, with a dil. soln. of barium chloride so long as the precipitate first formed disappears. In the course of cooling for 24 hrs., colourless crystals of the complex salt appear.

A. Gutmann observed that when sodium trioxysulpharsenate is treated with copper sulphate a black precipitate is formed; zinc sulphate gives a white precipitate—presumably **zinc trioxysulpharsenate**, $Zn_3(AsO_3A)_2.nH_2O$—soluble in excess, and the soln. decomposes when concentrated on a water-bath, forming zinc sulphide, and arsenite, and sodium sulphate. Cadmium sulphate likewise gives a white precipitate—presumably **cadmium trioxysulpharsenate**, $Cd_3(AsO_3S)_2.nH_2O$—which decomposes in a few hours; mercurous nitrate gives a black precipitate; and mercuric chloride a yellow precipitate—presumably **mercuric trioxysulpharsenate**, $Hg_3(AsO_3S)_2.nH_2O$—which quickly turns brown, and black. A dil. soln. of the sodium salt forms a white precipitate of **manganese trioxysulpharsenate**, $Mn_3(AsO_3S)_2.nH_2O$, when treated with manganese sulphate; with ferrous sulphate a dirty green precipitate, presumably of **ferrous trioxysulpharsenate**, $Fe_3(AsO_3S)_2.nH_2O$, is formed, and it rapidly darkens in colour; cobalt nitrate gives a violet precipitate of **cobalt trioxysulpharsenate**, $Co_3(AsO_3S)_2.nH_2O$; and a nickel salt a greenish-white precipitate of **nickel trioxysulpharsenate**, $Ni_3(AsO_3S)_2.nH_2O$.

As indicated above, K. Preis prepared **sodium dioxydisulpharsenate**, $Na_3AsO_2S_2.10H_2O$, by the action of a soln. of sodium sulphide on arsenic trioxide; he also made it by the action of soda-lye on a hot soln. of sodium sulpharsenate: $Na_3AsS_4+4NaOH=Na_3AsO_2S_2+2Na_2S+2H_2O$; R. F. Weinland and O. Rumpf, by the action of equimolar proportions of sodium metarsenite or trioxysulpharsenate and disulphide: $NaAsO_2+Na_2S_2=Na_3AsO_2S_2$; and L. W. McCay, by treating the filtrate from the strontium trioxysulpharsenate, obtained in the preparation of sodium trioxysulpharsenate, with barium chloride, and treating the precipitated barium dioxydisulpharsenate with sodium carbonate so as to convert it into the sodium salt. This was precipitated by alcohol from its aq. soln. L. W. McCay also prepared the salt by pouring a soln. of 5 grms. of arsenic acid into a litre of water sat. with hydrogen sulphide; allowing the mixture to stand for 2 hrs.; removing the hydrogen sulphide by a current of air; treating the filtrate with solid strontium hydroxide; allowing the mixture to stand for 12 hrs.; treating the filtrate with barium hydroxide; and treating the resulting barium salt with sodium carbonate. According to K. Preis, the tabular or prismatic crystals belong to the rhombic system and have the axial ratios $a:b:c=0.769:1:0.555$. A soln. of barium chloride precipitates the barium salt. The action of acids, etc., has been indicated in Table VIII. R. F. Weinland and O. Rumpf prepared **potassium dioxydisulpharsenate**, $K_3AsO_2S_2.nH_2O$, by passing hydrogen sulphide into a soln. of potassium ortharsenate; treating the product with an excess of potash-lye; and evaporating to soln. so as to obtain yellow, hygroscopic crystals of the impure salt. When the attempt is made to recrystallize the salt from water, it decomposes into arsenate and sulpharsenate. They also prepared **barium dioxydisulpharsenate,** $Ba(AsO_2S_2)_2.4$ or $6H_2O$, as a white precipitate, by the action of a soln. of the alkali salt on barium chloride; and by boiling a soln. of sodium sulpharsenate with baryta-water.

L. W. McCay and W. Foster prepared **sodium oxytrisulpharsenate,** $Na_3AsOS_3.11H_2O$, by mixing 45 grms. of magnesia, and 26 grms. of freshly precipitated arsenic pentasulphide with water so as to form a thick slurry, and then with 800 c.c. of water; allowing the mixture to stand at 18° for about 6 hrs. until the pentasulphide has disappeared; precipitating the magnesia by an excess of soda-lye; adding alcohol to the filtered soln. until a faint turbidity appears; and cooling the soln. in an ice-chamber. The crystals contain a little trioxysulpharsenate but no dioxydisulpharsenate. To purify the crystals, they are washed in 50 per cent. alcohol; dissolved in 375 c.c. of water; and mixed with strontium chloride. After standing 12 hrs., the filtrate was mixed with barium chloride, treated with the theoretical quantity of sodium sulphate and heated for 15 mins. on a water-bath; allowed to stand 20 hrs.; filtered; and treated with alcohol, etc., as before. He also made this salt by shaking for 20 mins. a mixture of 8 grms. of arsenic pentasulphide, 1·5 grms. of sodium hydroxide in 145 grms. of water, or an eq. amount of aq. ammonia, and treating the strongly alkaline filtrate with alcohol, etc., as before. L. W. McCay and W. Foster also obtained this salt from the products of the action of magnesia on a mixture of arsenic trisulphide and sulphur. The white, feathery crystals rapidly effloresce in a dry, warm atm. When the salt is kept in a closed vessel for some days, it becomes yellow, and then contains sodium sulpharsenate, but it can be kept for a week without change out of contact with air in an ice-chamber. For the general reactions, *vide* Table VIII. Yellow crystals of **potassium oxytrisulpharsenate,** $K_3AsOS_3.7H_2O$, were obtained in an analogous manner. L. W. McCay and W. Foster also prepared **sodium strontium oxysulpharsenate,** $NaSrAsOS_3.10H_2O$, by the action of magnesia on arsenic pentasulphide as in preparing sodium oxytrisulpharsenate; treating the product with soda-lye, and then with strontium chloride; adding more strontium chloride to the filtrate; mixing the soln. with alcohol; and cooling. The white crystals are washed first with water, then with alcohol, and dried at 18°. The salt becomes straw-yellow in air in 20 mins., but it can be preserved many days in a closed vessel cooled by ice. A soln. of 3 grms. of the potassium salt in 40 c.c. of recently-boiled water when mixed with a 10 per cent. soln. of barium chloride, and cooled in an ice-chamber, furnishes yellow crystals of **potassium barium oxytrisulpharsenate,** $KBaAsOS_3.7H_2O$.

Some oxysulpharsenates of what appear to be condensed acids have been reported. Thus, K. Preis obtained what he represented as a **sodium oxysulphotetrarsenate,** $Na_{12}As_4O_{11}S_5.48H_2O$, by the action of a soln. of sodium sulphide on arsenic trioxide; and fractional crystallization. This salt was the least soluble of the products of the reaction— *vide supra,* sodium trioxysulpharsenate. A. Geuther represented the composition $2(Na_3AsO_3S.12H_2O)Na_2As_2O_5S_3.24H_2O$. He also obtained **sodium pentoxytrisulphodiarsenate,** $Na_6As_2O_5S_3.24H_2O$, or $Na_3AsO_4.Na_3AsOS_3.24H_2O$, or

$$NaO\!\!>\!\!As\!\!<\!\!{O \atop O}\!\!>\!\!As\!\!<\!\!{-SNa \atop SNa}.24H_2O \qquad or \qquad NaS\!\!>\!\!As\!\!<\!\!{S \atop O}\!\!>\!\!As\!\!<\!\!{-SNa \atop -ONa}.24H_2O$$

by heating a mixture of arsenic disulphide and soda-lye in a sealed tube at 100°. By rapidly recrystallizing the product from water, and finally precipitating the conc. aq. soln. with alcohol, he obtained the salt in long, colourless needles. L. W. McCay and W. Foster obtained white crystals of **sodium barium oxysulphopentarsenate,** $Na_2Ba_7As_5O_7S_{14}.12H_2O$, by mixing a soln. of sodium or sodium strontium oxytrisulpharsenate with barium chloride, washing the product with water and alcohol, and drying at room-temp. The reactions of the salt are like those of the oxytrisulpharsenates.

R. F. Weinland and K. Sommer prepared **sodium pyrosulpharsenatoxy-molybdate,** $Na_4As_2Mo_2O_3S_{10}.15H_2O_2$, or

$$\underset{S}{\overset{NaS}{>}}As\text{—}S\text{—}Mo\underset{O}{\overset{SNa}{<}}$$

$$\begin{array}{cc} | & \wedge \\ S & S\,O \end{array}$$

$$\begin{array}{cc} \underset{NaS}{\overset{S}{>}}As\text{—}S\text{—}Mo\underset{SNa}{\overset{O}{<}} \end{array}$$

A mol of arsenic pentasulphide was boiled with a soln. containing two mols of ammonium sulphomolybdate and four mols of sodium hydroxide to eliminate ammonium sulphide. The filtrate was evaporated when a crop of the meta-salt, $NaAsS_3.MoO_2S.5H_2O$, was first deposited, and afterwards, on slowly evaporating the mother-liquid, a crop of yellow needles of the required pyro-salt appeared. The product was recrystallized until the salt furnished a clear soln. when dissolved in water. The properties of the sodium salt closely resemble those of the potassium salt. R. F. Weinland and K. Sommer prepared what they called **potassium pyro-sulpharsenatoxymolybdate,** $K_4As_2Mo_2O_3S_{10}$, or $K_4As_2S_7.Mo_2S_3O_3$, as follows: A mol of arsenic pentasulphide was boiled with a soln. containing two mols of molybdenum trisulphide and four mols of potassium hydroxide, and the liquid filtered from the remaining sulphur. The conc. soln. furnishes red, acicular crystals of potassium pyrosulpharsenatosulphomolybdate, and the mother-liquor yields a crop of yellow, six-sided, needle-like crystals of the hexahydrate. They also obtained it by warming a mol of arsenic pentasulphide with a soln. of two mols of molybdenum trioxide and four mols of potassium hydrosulphide—the first crop of crystals consists of the meta-salt, $KAsS_3.MoO_2S.2\frac{1}{2}H_2O$, and the next crop is the required pyro-salt. The product is purified by recrystallization. When a soln. of two mols of potassium sulphomolybdate, prepared by warming ammonium sulphomolybdate with potassium sulphide, is boiled for a long time with potassium hydroarsenate, a dark red fluid and a brown amorphous precipitate are produced. The filtrate yields a crop of crystals of potassium molybdate, KMo_3O_{10}, and the yellow needles of the decahydrate, $K_4As_2Mo_2O_3S_{10}.10H_2O$. The hexahydrate is not hygroscopic, it is freely soluble in water, forming a yellow soln. Hydrochloric acid gives a yellowish-brown flocculent precipitate ; and acetic acid gives no precipitate, but colours the liquid dark red. A reddish-brown precipitate is obtained with a soln. of a *copper* salt and a dark brown, with a *silver* salt—both precipitates are insoluble in ammonia. Soln. of the *alkaline earths* give no precipitation ; and a small proportion of *zinc* sulphate gives no precipitation, but an excess yields a dirty reddish-brown precipitate, soluble in aq. ammonia, and in potash-lye. *Manganese, ferrous, cobalt,* and *nickel* salts slowly form dark brown flocculent precipitates. R. F. Weinland and K. Sommer prepared **magnesium pyrosulpharsenatoxymolybdate,** $Mg_2As_2Mo_2O_3S_{10}.16H_2O$, by a process analogous to that used for the sodium salt. The yellow, acicular crystals have properties similar to those of the alkali salts.

R. F. Weinland and K. Sommer prepared **sodium metasulpharsenatoxy-molybdate,** $NaAsS_3.MoO_2S.5H_2O$, or

$$\underset{S}{\overset{S}{>}}As\text{—}S\text{—}Mo\underset{O}{\overset{O}{<}}SNa$$

as indicated above as a by-product in the preparation of potassium pyro-salt. The lemon-yellow product is purified by recrystallization a number of times when it appears reddish-yellow. It consists of microscopic cubes somewhat soluble in cold water, freely soluble in hot water. They obtained a fine, orange-red powder, consisting of microscopic crystals of **potassium metasulpharsenatoxymolybdate,** $KAsS_3.MoO_2S.2\frac{1}{2}H_2O$, by the method employed for the sodium salt. It is rather less soluble in cold water than the sodium salt, but is freely soluble in hot water. The hot conc. soln. deposits the salt as a crystalline powder, the dil. soln. forms a gelatinous mass. Hydrochloric acid deposits a reddish-yellow flocculent precipitate, and the filtrate is free from molybdenum and arsenic ; acetic acid gives neither a precipitate nor a colour change.   The salt is slowly decomposed at 100° giving off sulphur dioxide. *Ammonium* salts, and salts of the *alkaline earths*, give an amorphous, yellow precipitate insoluble in cold water, but sparingly soluble in hot water, and which is again precipitated as the hot soln. cools ; *magnesium, zinc,* and *manganese* salts give no precipitate ; *ferrous, cobalt,* and *nickel* salts in excess give a dirty yellow precipitate ; *copper* and *silver* salts give a dirty or brownish-yellow precipitate, and, in excess, a dark brown precipitate.

REFERENCES.

[1] H. V. Regnault, *Ann. Chim. Phys.*, (2), 62. 386, 1836 ; L. F. Nilson, *Journ. prakt. Chem.*, (2), 12. 297, 1875 ; J. F. L. Hausmann, *Liebig's Ann.*, 74. 199, 1850 ; C. Cross and A. Higgin, *Ber.*, 16. 1198, 1883.

[2] L. F. Nilson, *Journ. prakt. Chem.*, (2), 12. 297, 1875 ; (2), 14. 10, 1876 ; (2), 16. 93, 1877 ; K. Preis, *Liebig's Ann.*, 257. 178, 1890 ; R. F. Weinland and A. Gutmann, *Zeit. anorg. Chem.*, 17. 412, 1898 ; A. Gutmann, *Ueber den Abbau der Thiosulfate und einiger Polythionate zu Sulfiten durch reducierende Salze in alkalischer Lösung und über einige Monosulfoxyarsenate*, München, 1897.

[3] L. W. McCay. *Zeit. anal. Chem.*, 26. 635, 1887 ; 27. 632, 1888 ; 34. 728, 1895 ; *Beitrag zur Kenntnis der Kobalt-, Nickel- und Eisenkiese*, Freiberg, 1883 ; *Amer. Chem. Journ.*, 7. 375, 1887 ; 9. 174, 1888 ; 10. 459, 1889 ; 12. 547, 1891 ; *Journ. Amer. Chem. Soc.*, 24. 661, 1902 ; *Chem. News*, 54. 287, 1886 ; *Zeit. anorg. Chem.*, 25. 459, 1900 ; 29. 36, 1902 ; 41. 452, 1904 ; L. W. McCay and W. Foster, *Ber.*, 37. 573, 1904 ; *Zeit. anorg. Chem.*, 41. 452, 1904 ; R. F. Weinland and O. Rumpf, *ib.*, 14. 45, 1897 ; R. F. Weinland and P. Lehmann, *ib.*, 26. 327, 1901 ; R. F. Weinland and A. Gutmann, *ib.*, 17. 410, 1898 ; R. F. Weinland and K. Sommer, *ib.*, 15. 48, 1897 ; A. Gutmann, *Ueber den Abbau der Thiosulfate und einiger Polythionate zu Sulfiten durch reducierende Salze in alkalischer Lösung und über einige Monosulfoxyarsenate*, München, 1897 ; J. Bouquet and S. Cloez, *Ann. Chim. Phys.*, (3), 13. 44, 1845 ; K. Preis, *Liebig's Ann.*, 257. 180, 1890 ; A. Geuther, *ib.*, 240. 223, 1887 ; L. F. Nilson, *Journ. prakt. Chem.*, (2), 12. 295, 1875 ; (2), 14. 145, 1876 ; (2), 16. 93, 1877 ; *Akad. Handl. Stockholm*, 10. 2, 1871 ; *Oefvers. Akad. Stockholm*, 28. 303, 1871 ; 34. 5, 1877 ; W. H. McLauchlan, *Ber.*, 34. 2166, 1901 ; K. B. Edwards, *Brit. Pat. No.* 162747, 1920.

§ 37. Arsenic Sulphates

Arsenic trioxide behaves like a base towards the stronger acids ; but the earlier chemists did not succeed in making an arsenic sulphate. According to A. Vogel,[1] when sulphuric acid is heated with arsenic, sulphur dioxide is given off, and a residue containing arsenic trioxide, but no pentoxide, is formed ; arsenic trioxide crystallizes from a soln. of that oxide in sulphuric acid ; and the distillation of sulphuric acid containing some arsenic trioxide in soln. gives a distillate free from arsenic, and a residue of arsenic trioxide but no arsenic pentoxide—C. F. Bucholz said that a little arsenic pentoxide is formed, and H. W. F. Wackenroder, that a little arsenic is carried into the distillate. According to R. H. Adie, there is an upper and an under limit to the number of SO_3-groups that can combine with arsenic trioxide, for when this oxide is dissolved in excess of hot, liquid sulphur trioxide, under increased press., the compound obtained on cooling is probably $As_2O_3.8SO_3$; when acid of the conc. approximately represented by the formula H_2SO_4,H_2O is used, the compound obtaining on cooling is $As_2O_3.SO_3$; if the acid is more dil. than this, no compound of the two oxides is formed. When a considerable excess of arsenic trioxide is dissolved in hot conc. sulphuric acid, the excess of the trioxide separates, on cooling, in combination with sulphur dioxide, the quantity of which varies in accordance with the relative masses of the oxide and acid used ; on agitating the mother-liquor, deposition of a definite compound occurs. On recrystallization of the definite compounds from the same acids, the same phenomena are repeated. 100 grms. of H_2SO_4 can hold in soln. and combination 1 grm. of As_2O_3 ; if there be more As_2O_3 than this, the excess separates on cooling. As regards the action of heat, the most stable compound of the series examined is $As_2O_3.SO_3$; this compound is probably partially volatile without decomposition. The compounds of arsenic trioxide and sulphur dioxide do not belong to the category of salts, understanding by this term the metallic derivatives of acids ; the method of their production, and their instability towards sulphuric acid, water, and heat, points to a constitution analogous to that of the double salts.

F. Reich, B. Kosmann, F. Ulrich, and C. E. Schafhäutl mentioned the existence of a compound of sulphuric acid and arsenic trioxide occurring in the flues leading from the pyrites burners to the lead-chamber of a sulphuric acid factory. The composition approximated to that of **arsenic sulphatotrioxide**, $As_2O_3.SO_3$, or

$$SO_4{<}{\begin{smallmatrix}As=O\\As=O\end{smallmatrix}} \quad \text{or} \quad {\begin{smallmatrix}O\\O\end{smallmatrix}}{\gg}S{<}{\begin{smallmatrix}O.As=O\\O.As=O\end{smallmatrix}}$$

A. Stavenhagen obtained a product with the same composition by dissolving arsenic trioxide in warm, conc. sulphuric acid ; evaporating the soln. ; and heating the product so long as sulphur trioxide vap. is given off. R. H. Adie said that the same compound is obtained by crystallization from sulphuric acid between $9H_2SO_4.2H_2O$, and $H_2SO_4.H_2O$. According to F. Reich, the tabular crystals become moist in air and form sulphuric acid which runs away leaving arsenic trioxide behind ; and, according to R. H. Adie, the compound, at $225°$, gradually loses sulphur trioxide. A. Laurent obtained perhaps the same compound, contaminated with sulphuric acid, by heating arsenic trioxide with conc. sulphuric acid, and pouring off the partially cooled liquor. Crystals with the composition $3As_2O_3.4SO_3.H_2O$, or $As_2O_3.SO_3.\frac{1}{3}H_2SO_4$, were formed. The mother-liquor deposits octahedral crystals of arsenic trioxide.

According to R. H. Adie, crystals of **arsenic disulphatotrioxide**, $As_2O_3.2SO_3$, are formed from a soln. of 98 per cent. sulphuric acid, sat. with arsenic trioxide ; and by crystallizing the trisulphatotrioxide from conc. sulphuric acid. The compound is stable at $150°$, but decomposes at $170°$. A. Stavenhagen found crystals of **arsenic trisulphatotrioxide**, or **arsenic sulphate**, $As_2O_3.3SO_3$, or $As_2(SO_4)_3$, occurring in the flues of a pyrites-burner of a sulphuric acid works ; and R. Weber obtained the crystals by warming arsenic trioxide with sulphur trioxide at $100°$, and driving off the excess of sulphur trioxide at this temp. C. Schultz-Sellack reported needle-like crystals of **arsenic tetrasulphate**, or **arsenic tetrasulphatotrioxide**, $As_2O_3.4SO_3$, to be formed by heating arsenic trioxide and sulphuric acid which, according to R. H. Adie, should contain 88.3 per cent. of sulphuric anhydride. R. Weber reported **arsenic hexasulphatotrioxide**, $As_2O_3.6SO_3$, to be formed by warming at $60°$ a mixture of arsenic trioxide and sulphur trioxide ; and R. H. Adie, **arsenic octosulphatotrioxide**, or **arsenic octosulphate**, $As_2O_3.8SO_3$, by heating a mixture of arsenic trioxide and sulphur trioxide in a sealed tube at $100°$. G. Karl considered that *les anhydrides mixtés* are represented by :

$As_2O_3.SO_3$ $As_2O_3.2SO_3$ $As_2O_3.3SO_3$ $As_2O_3.4SO_3$ $As_2O_3.6SO_3$ $As_2O_3.8SO_3$

A. Stavenhagen obtained hexagonal prisms of **potassium decasulphatarsenite**, $K_3AsO_3.10K_3SO_4$, by evaporating and slowly cooling an aq. soln. of 21.8 grms. of potassium sulphate and 3 grms. of potassium arsenite. H. Kühl obtained **potassium tetrasulphatarsenite**, $2K_2O.As_2O_3.4SO_3$, by heating a soln. of arsenic trioxide and potassium sulphate in conc. sulphuric acid so as to drive off the sulphuric acid. Similarly with **calcium trisulphatarsenite**, $CaO.As_2O_3.3SO_3$, but the corresponding *barium and strontium trisulphatarsenites* could not be so obtained. Lead sulphate, however, gave **lead disulphatarsenite**, $PbO.As_2O_3.2SO_3$. C. Freidheim and J. Mozkin prepared **ammonium hydrosulphatarsenate**, $2(NH_4)_2O.As_2O_5.2SO_3.3H_2O$, or $NH_4(H_2AsO_4).NH_4(HSO_4)$, or $(NH_4)_2H[AsO_3(SO_4)]$, or $HO.AsO(ONH_4).O.SO_2.$ ONH_4+H_2O, or $(NH_4O)(NH_4SO_4)As(OH)_3$, by crystallizing from a soln. of two mols of ammonium dihydroarsenate and a mol of sulphuric acid. The first crop of crystals is ammonium hydrosulphate. They also prepared **ammonium hydro-sulphatarsenate**, $NH_4(H_2AsO_4).H_2SO_4$. They obtained in a similar manner **potassium hydrosulphatarsenate**, $2K_2O.As_2O_5.2SO_3.3H_2O$, or $HO.AsO(OK).O.SO_2OK+H_2O$, or $K_2H[AsO_3(SO_4)].H_2O$, from a soln. of 2 mols of potassium dihydrarsenate and a mol of sulphuric acid ; from equimolar parts of potassium dihydroxarsenate and sulphuric acid ; **potassium tetrasulphatarsenate**, $5K_2O.As_2O_5.8SO_3.6H_2O$, or $KO.As(KSO_4)_4.3H_2O$, from equimolar parts of potassium dihydrarsenate and sulphuric acid ; and **sodium hydrosulphatarsenate**, $2Na_2O.As_2O_5.3SO_3.3H_2O$, or $Na_2H[AsO_3(SO_4)].H_2O$. J. Setterberg reported a double salt, $Na_2SO_4.2Na_2HAsO_4$, to be deposited by a soln. of eq. quantities of sodium sulphate and hydroarsenate ; and E. Mitscherlich, $2Na_2SO_4.Na_8As_6O_{19}$, from a soln. of 3 mols of sodium hydrarsenate and a mol of sulphuric acid. J. Setterberg also obtained **silver sulphatarsenate**, $3Ag_2O.As_2O_5.SO_3$, by driving off the excess of acid from a mixture of sulphuric acid and silver ortharsenate. It is decomposed by water with the formation of sulphuric acid and silver ortharsenate.

J. F. Vogl [2] reported a mineral from Eliaszeche, Joachimsthal, which he called **lindackerite**. Its analysis corresponded with **copper nickel hydroxysulphat-arsenate**, $Cu_6Ni_3(OH)_4SO_4(AsO_4)_4.5H_2O$. The rhombic crystals occur in rhombohedral plates grouped in rosettes and reniform masses. The colour is verdigris-green or apple-green. E. S. Larsen said the optical axial angle is 73°, the optical character negative, and the indices of refraction $\alpha=1.629$, $\beta=1.662$, and $\gamma=1.727$. The hardness is 2·0–2·5 ; and the sp. gr., 2·0–2·5. It is slowly dissolved by hydrochloric acid. Another brownish-red mineral from Laurion, Greece, was described by L. Milch ; [3] he called it **lossenite**. The analysis corresponds with **lead iron hydroxysulphatarsenate**, $2PbSO_4.6As_2O_3(FeOH)_3.24$ or $27H_2O$; that is, $PbSO_4(FeOH)_9(AsO_4)_6.12H_2O$. The rhombic crystals occur in acute pyramids resembling scorodite. The axial ratios are $a : b : c = 0.843 : 1 : 0.945$. The crystals are optically positive. E. S. Larsen gave $\alpha=1.783$, $\beta=1.788$, and $\gamma=1.818$; the optical character is positive ; the optic axial angle $2V=50°$. The mineral named **beudantite**—after F. S. Beudant—was described by A. Lévy ; [4] and a variety from Cork, Ireland, was called *corkite* by M. Adam, and a variety from Dernbach, *dernbachite*. Analyses were reported by J. Percy, C. F. Rammelsberg, R. Köchlin, F. Sandberger, and E. G. J. Hartley. The formula is doubtful. C. F. Rammelsberg regarded it as a **lead ferric hydroxysulphatophosphatarsenate**, $4Fe_2O_3.2PbO.3SO_3.(As,P)_2O_5.9H_2O$; F. Sandberger gave $PbSO_4.Pb_3(PO_4)_2.3FePO_4.24H_2O$; E. G. J. Hartley, $3PbSO_4.2FePO_4.6Fe(OH)_3$; and G. T. Prior, $PbSO_4.FePO_4.2Fe(OH)_3$. The colour may be olive-green, yellowish-green, brown, or black. The acute rhombohedral crystals belong to the trigonal system, and were found by H. Dauber to have the axial ratio $a : c = 1 : 1.1842$. The (0001)-faces are flat and dull ; the (10$\bar{1}$1)-faces, bright and curved. The (0001)-cleavage is easy to distinguish. E. S. Larsen gave for the index of refraction of beudantite, 1·96 ; the optical character is negative. W. T. Schaller regarded beudantite as one member of an isomorphous group of trigonal crystals with the following axial ratios for $a : c$:

Svanbergite	•	•	•	$2SrO, 3Al_2O_3, 2SO_3, P_2O_5, 6H_2O$	1 : 1·2063
Hinsdalite .	•	•	•	$2PbO, 3Al_2O_3, 2SO_3, P_2O_5, 6H_2O$	1 : 1·2677
Corkite	•	•	•	$2PbO, 3Fe_2O_3, 2SO_3, P_2O_5, 6H_2O$	1 : 1·1842
Beudantite	•	•	•	$2PbO, 3Fe_2O_3, 2SO_3, As_2O_5, 6H_2O$	1 : 1·1842

Following A. Lacroix, and E. Bertrand, corkite is here regarded as a phosphate ; beudantite as an arsenate. E. Bertrand found that the optical character is positive ; and the index of refraction, medium. The optical character was also examined by E. G. J. Hartley, and H. A. Miers. The sp. gr. is 4·0–4·3 ; and the hardness, 3·5–4·5. The mineral readily fuses ; and it is soluble in hydrochloric acid.

REFERENCES.

1 C. F. Bucholz, *Schweigger's Journ.*, **15**. 337, 1815; *Beiträge zur Erweiterung und Berichtigung der Chemie*, Erfurt, **1**. 61, 1799; A. Vogel, *Journ. prakt. Chem.*, (1), **4**. 232, 1835; F. Reich, *ib.*, (1), **90**. 176, 1863; H. W. F. Wackenroder, *ib.*, (1), **2**. 340, 1834; *Liebig's Ann.*, **13**. 241, 1835; H. Kühl, *Arch. Pharm.*, **245**. 377, 1907; R. H. Adie, *Journ. Chem. Soc.*, **55**. 157, 1889; E. V. Shannon, *Amer. Journ. Science*, (5), **7**. 31, 1924; G. Karl, *Sur quelques anhydrides mixtes de l'acide sulfurique*, Genève, 1908; F. Ulrich, *Berg. Hütt. Ztg.*, **13**. 98, 1854; A. Stavenhagen, *Zeit. angew. Chem.*, **6**. 284, 1893; R. Weber, *Ber.*, **19**. 3186, 1886; C. Schultz-Sellack, *ib.*, **4**. 109, 1871; A. Laurent, *Journ. Pharm. Chim.*, (3), **55**. 184, 1863; B. Kosmann, *Vortrag Naturf. Versamml. Stettin*, 1, 1863; C. E. Schafhäutl, *B.A. Rep.*, **69**, 1840; *Chemist.*, **1**. 363, 1840; *Journ. prakt. Chem.*, (1), **23**. 298, 1841; J. Setterberg, *Oefvers. Vet. Akad. Förh.*, **3**. 25, 1846; *Journ. Pharm. Chim.*, (3), **12**. 142, 1847; C. Freidheim and J. Mozkin, *Zeit. anorg. Chem.*, **6**. 273, 1894: **69**. 262, 1911; E. Mitscherlich, *Lehrbuch der Chemie*, Berlin, 1829.
2 E. S. Larsen, *Bull. U.S. Geol. Sur.*, 679, 1921; J. F. Vogl, *Jahresb. geol. Reichsanst. Wien*, **3**. 552, 153.
3 L. Milch, *Zeit. Kryst.*, **29**. 102, 1895; E. S. Larsen, *Bull. U.S. Geol. Sur.*, 679, 1921.
4 J. Percy, *Phil. Mag.*, (3), **37**. 161, 1850; A. Lévy, *Ann. Phil.*, **11**. 195, 1826; F. Sandberger *Pogg. Ann.*, **100**. 611, 1857; H. Dauber, *ib.*, **100**. 579, 1857; C. F. Rammelsberg, *ib.*, **100**. 581, 1857; *Handbuch der Mineralchemie*, Leipzig, 332, 1875; G. T. Prior, *Min. Mag.*, **12**. 251, 1900; E. G. J. Hartley, *ib.*, **12**. 234, 1900; H. A. Miers, *ib.*, **12**. 242, 1900; R. Köchlin, *Tschermak's Mitt.*, (2), **35**. 1, 1921; E. Bertrand, *Bull. Soc. Min.*, **4**. 237, 1881; A. Lacroix, *Minéralogie de la France et de ses colonies*, Paris, **4**. 596, 1910; W. T. Schaller, *Amer. Journ. Science*, (4), **32**. 251, 1911; M. Adam, *Tableau minéralogique*, Paris, 49, 1869; G. vom Rath, *Verh. Ver. Rheinl.*, **34**. 177, 1877; E. S. Larsen, *Bull. U.S. Geol. Sur.*, 679, 1921.

§ 38. The Arsenic Sulphohalides, or Halogenosulphides

According to O. Ruff and K. Thiel,[1] sulphur tetrachloride reacts with arsenic trifluoride, forming yellow crystals of $2AsF_3.SCl_4$, or **arsenic sulphohexafluotetrachloride**, $As_2SF_6Cl_4$. It attacks glass slowly, but decomposes or chars thionyl chloride, carbon tetrachloride, carbon disulphide, alcohol, ether, benzene, and light petroleum.

H. Rose treated arsenic disulphide or trisulphide with dry chlorine, and obtained a brown liquid with a composition approximating $2AsCl_3.3SCl_2$. It dissolved in nitric acid, giving off nitrous fumes and forming sulphuric, hydrochloric, and arsenic acids; with water, it forms a soln. of hydrochloric, sulphuric, hyposulphurous, and arsenious acids—the hyposulphurous acid is quickly decomposed into sulphur and sulphurous acid; the ammoniacal soln. is rendered turbid by sulphuric acid. L. F. Nilson regarded the product of the action of chlorine on arsenic di-, tri-, or penta-sulphide as a mixture, not a chemical individual.

L. Ouvrard found that dry hydrogen sulphide acts on arsenic trichloride at the ordinary temp., with evolution of hydrogen chloride and formation of a yellow precipitate, which, if the action is continued until the evolution of hydrogen chloride ceases, and the precipitate is washed with carbon disulphide, consists partly of crystalline, and partly of amorphous, material. The proportion of the latter varies, and it can be removed by levigation with carbon disulphide. Both the amorphous and crystalline products consist of **arsenic pentasulphodichloride**, $As_4S_5Cl_2$. This compound is slowly decomposed by boiling water, with formation of arsenic trichloride and amorphous arsenious trisulphide. It melts at about 120°, and volatilizes at about 300° (out of contact with air), with decomposition into arsenic trichloride and trisulphide. If 1 part of the trisulphide and 5 parts of the trichloride are heated at 180° for 24 hrs., and cooled slowly, the pentasulphodichloride, $As_4S_5Cl_2$, is obtained in very small, pale-yellow crystals. If the hydrogen sulphide used in the preparation of the chlorosulphide is not quite dry, the product is simply the ordinary trisulphide, and the same result follows if the reacting substances are heated. Arsenious trisulphide dissolves in the trichloride when heated, but is deposited unchanged on cooling. If, however, a mixture of the two substances is heated in sealed tubes at 150, the trichloride being in excess, the **arsenic sulphochloride**, AsSCl, is obtained in microscopic crystals, which melt and volatilize readily when heated out of contact with air. It is decomposed by water in the same way as the preceding compound, and is dissolved by soln. of ammonia and alkali carbonates.

V. Auger prepared **arsenic tetracosisulphotriiodide**, $AsI_3.3S_8$, by mixing soln. of the two components in carbon disulphide. According to L. Ouvrard, dry hydrogen sulphide has no action on dry arsenic triiodide in the cold, but at 200°, some of the triiodide volatilizes in a current of hydrogen sulphide, and crystals of **arsenic pentasulphodiiodide**, $2AsSI.As_2S_3$, are formed; they are less soluble than arsenic triiodide in carbon disulphide. If arsenic trisulphide be melted with an excess of the triiodide, out of contact with air, and the product crystallized from its soln. in carbon disulphide, small acicular crystals of **arsenic sulphotetraiodide**, $AsI_3.AsSI$, are formed. If the arsenic trisulphide be in excess, then **arsenic sulphoiodide**, AsSI, or $As_2S_3.AsI_3$, is formed. E. R. Schneider obtained it by heating together either a mixture of realgar (1 mol) and iodine (2 atoms) with the least possible access of air, or a mixture of 3 parts arsenious triiodide with 1·6 parts of arsenic trisulphide. N. Tarugi obtained lemon-yellow crystals by heating arsenic triiodide with thioacetic acid. The sulphiodide forms an amorphous, vitreous mass with conchoidal fracture, and is of a dark red or reddish-brown colour. It is not acted on by the air at ordinary temp. When heated at 100°, it softens, and boils at a higher temp. without evolution of iodine vapour, but with partial decomposition into arsenious triiodide and trisulphide. It is insoluble in hot and cold alcohol, ether, carbon disulphide, chloroform, and benzene. E. R. Schneider found that hot water slowly decomposes it with formation of hydriodic acid. Boiling hydrochloric acid slowly decomposes it with evolution of iodine. When boiled with conc. sulphuric acid, it gives off iodine, sulphur, and sulphur dioxide. Potassium and ammonium hydroxides dissolve arsenious sulphiodide to a colourless liquid, from which dil. acids precipitate arsenic trisulphide, whilst the whole of the iodine and parts of the arsenic remain in soln. When treated with an ammoniacal soln. of silver nitrate, it is decomposed, forming silver iodide, sulphide, and arsenite.

According to E. R. Schneider, a soln. of iodine in carbon disulphide is without action on natural arsenic trisulphide (orpiment), but reacts with that precipitated by hydrogen sulphide, forming arsenious iodide and sulphur. Attempts to prepare the compound $As_2S_3,2AsI_3$, by heating a mixture of iodine and arsenic trisulphide in the ratio $As_2S_2 : 6I$, were not successful. The mixture fused at a low temp. to a homogeneous mass of a brown colour, which dissolved almost entirely in carbon disulphide; on evaporation of the solvent nothing but arsenic iodide and sulphur crystallized out. On distilling a mixture of arsenic trisulphide and iodine in the ratio $As_2S_3 : 6I$, until two-thirds of the material had passed over, the distillate was found to contain 58·63 per cent. of free iodine, 40 per cent. of arsenic iodide, and 1·37 per cent. of sulphur; the residue consisted of 55·32 per cent. of arsenic trisulphide and 44·04 per cent. of arsenic triiodide. When in place of the former, a mixture of arsenic triiodide and sulphur in the ratio of $2AsI_3 : 3S$ was employed, and the distillation continued until half the material had passed over, the distillate contained 69·44 per cent. of free iodine, 28 per cent. of arsenic triiodide, and 2·56 per cent. of sulphur. It therefore follows that whilst a mixture of arsenic trisulphide and iodine is converted at moderate temp. into arsenic triiodide and sulphur, these products again react at a higher temp., reproducing their generators. If the distillate, rich in iodine, is sealed up in a glass tube, which is slightly inclined so that the distillate occupies the higher portion of the tube, and gently heated in a water-bath to a temp. of about 72°, a dark-brown liquid which solidifies on cooling trickles to the bottom of the tube. By repeated liquations in sealed tubes this dark brown mass becomes perfectly homogeneous, crystallizing in hard, brittle plates of a greyish-black colour, and dull lustre. The pure substance melts at 72°, and is **arsenic sulphododecaiodide**, $S_6,2As_2I_3$. On pulverizing, it forms a reddish-brown powder which by exposure to the air rapidly loses iodine, whilst the residue, consisting of a mixture of arsenic triiodide and sulphur, assumes a bright red colour. On fusing a mixture of arsenic trisulphide with iodine in the ratio $As_2S_2 : 4I$, the iodine reacts with only two-thirds of the arsenic trisulphide present. When, as not infrequently happens, the arsenic trisulphide contains arsenious acid, there remains behind, after fusion with iodine and treatment with carbon disulphide, an insoluble pale-yellow powder of arsenic **enneaoxyhexasulphoenneaiodide,** $2As_2S_3,3(AsI_3,As_2O_3)$. This substance can also be prepared by heating a mixture of arsenic trisulphide (1 part) and arsenic triiodide (0.2 part) with a large excess 8–10 parts) of arsenic triiodide, or by heating a mixture of arsenic triiodide (4 mols) with arsenic trisulphide (1 mol) with free access of air. Under the microscope, the compound appears to be indistinctly crystalline. On gently heating it, arsenious iodide first sublimes, then arsenious acid, and lastly, arsenic trisulphide. The compound is completely dissolved by soln. of potassium hydroxide and ammonia, and is readily decomposed by the common mineral acids and by boiling water.

REFERENCES

[1] H. Rose, *Pogg. Ann.*, **42**. 535, 1837; L. Ouvrard, *Compt. Rend.*, **116**. 1516, 1893; **117**. 107, 1893; V. Auger, *ib.*, **146**. 477, 1908; L. F. Nilson, *Oefvers. Akad. Stockholm*, **28**. 303, 1871; *Stockholm. Akad. Handl.*, **10**. 2, 1871; *Journ. prakt. Chem.*, (2), **12**. 327, 1875; (2), **14**. 145, 1876; E. R. Schneider, *ib.*, (2), **34**. 507, 1886; (2), **36**. 505, 1887; O. Ruff and K. Thiel, *Ber.*, **37**. 4520, 1904; N. Tarugi, *Gazz. Chim. Ital.*, **27**. ii, 153, 1897.

§ 39. Arsenic Carbonates, Nitrates, and Phosphates

No *arsenic carbonate* has yet been prepared, although a number of salts with organic acids are known—*e.g.* arsenic acetate, tartrate, cyanide, thiocyanate, have been prepared. *Arsenic nitrate* is unknown; but some complex nitrato-salts are known. J. F. Simon [1] found that mercurous **dinitratarsenate,** $2HgNO_3.Hg_3AsO_4.2H_2O$, is produced when a soln. of mercurous hydrarsenate in conc. nitric acid is covered with an equal vol. of water; aq. ammonia poured on that; and all left to stand for some time. The given salt is deposited in warty masses and needles. When the liquids are mixed too rapidly, the product is mixed with a grey powder and with mercurous hydrarsenate. He also made it by adding aq. ammonia with constant agitation to a warm soln. of mercurous hydrarsenate in nitric acid until the hydrarsenate is just about to be precipitated. On cooling the liquid, the complex salt appears in warty masses. This salt is also obtained as a white powder on adding a very small proportion of arsenic acid to a soln. of mercurous nitrate. If too much arsenic acid be used the precipitate turns yellow or orange. The yellowish-white salt gives off nitrous acid—salpetrige Säure—when heated alone or with conc. sulphuric acid, and when its soln. in nitric acid is treated with aq. ammonia, mercurous hydrarsenate is precipitated. K. Haack reported a basic salt, mercurous **dioxydinitratotriarsenate,** $2(Hg_2O.HgNO_3)_2.3Hg_3(AsO_4)_2$, to be formed by dropping a cold soln. of a mol of sodium hydrarsenate into a cold soln. of nine mols of mercurous nitrate, washing the product with cold water, and drying it in air. The dirty yellow powder is soluble in hydrochloric acid.

J. V. Janowsky [2] found that when arsenic phosphide is acted on by water, it yields arsenic **dioxydiphosphide,** $As_3P_2O_2$, which is decomposed by chlorine. O. Ruff obtained a violet-black substance, arsenic **dioxyphosphide,** As_4PO_2, by the action of water on the product obtained by the action of phosphorus on arsenic in the presence of aluminium chloride. No *arsenic phosphate* has been reported, but in view of the isomorphous relationship of the phosphates and arsenates, as might be anticipated, many phosphate-minerals also contain arsenates, and conversely—*e.g.* beudantite, veszelyite, and fermorite previously described.

E. Glatzel obtained **arsenic sulphophosphate,** $AsPS_4$, by heating a mixture of arsenic trisulphide and phosphorus pentasulphide—*vide supra*, thiophosphates. The co-precipitation of arsenic with ammonium phosphomolybdate was studied by A. Frank and F. W. Hinrichsen,[3] and J. R. Cain and J. C. Hostetter.

REFERENCES.

[1] J. F. Simon, *Pogg. Ann.*, **40**. 442, 1837 ; **41**. 424, 1837 ; K. Haack, *Ueber Arsenate und Phosphate des Quecksilbers*, Halle, 1890 ; *Liebig's Ann.*, **262**. 190, 1891.

[2] E. Glatzel, *Zeit. anorg. Chem.*, **4**. 186, 1893 ; J. V. Janowsky, *Ber.*, **8**. 1636, 1875 ; O. Ruff, *ib.*, **34**. 1749, 1901.

[3] A. Frank and F. W. Hinrichsen, *Stahl Eisen*, **28**. 295, 1908 ; J. R. Cain and J. C. Hostetter, *Journ. Amer. Chem. Soc.*, **43**. 2557, 1921.

CHAPTER LII

ANTIMONY

§ 1. The History of Antimony

ANTIMONY sulphide was known as a mineral to the people of ancient times, and it was used by them as a medicine, and as a cosmetic. For example, in the Vulgate edition of the *Bible*, *Ezekiel* (**23**. 40), it says : *te lavisti, et circumlinisti stibio oculos tuos*—thou didst wash thyself, and didst paint thine eyes with stibium ; in *II Kings* (**9**. 30) : *Jezebel depinxit oculos suos stibio*—Jezebel painted her eyes with stibium ; and in *Jeremiah* (**4**. 30) : *tu pinxeris stibio oculos tuos*. According to X. Fischer,[1] finely-divided lead sulphide was used more frequently than antimony sulphide by the women of ancient Egypt for painting the eyes. In the first century of our era, Dioscorides, in his *De materia medica* (**5**. 49), applied the term στίμμι, *stimmi*, or *stibium*, to the mineral sulphide, and said that in allusion to its use by women for painting their eyes, it was called πλατυόφθαλμον, or eye-expander ; καλλιβλέφαρον, or eye-beautifier ; γυναικείον, or womankind ; etc. About the same time, Pliny, in his *Historia naturalis* (**33**. 34), described seven remedies derived from *stimmi ;* and he spoke of two kinds of *stimmi*—also called *stibium*, *alabastron*, or *larbasis*—which were regarded respectively as male and female. Some commentators have argued that native antimony and antimony sulphide were denoted respectively as female and male *stimmi ;* others, that the metal and its oxide were in question.

M. Berthelot obtained a fragment of a vase from some excavations at Tello, and found it to consist of metallic antimony ; thus showing that this metal was known to the ancient Chaldeans perhaps 4000 B.C. R. Forrer reported vessels of antimony from old burial grounds near Tiflis ; O. Helm and H. V. Hilprecht, and E. Mayer found 3 per cent. of antimony in some bronze vessels of the oldest Babylonian period ; O. Stoll found antimony in some old Abyssinian alloys ; A. F. von Parly and A. Nies observed 15 per cent. of antimony in some bronzes of the old lake-dwellers ; W. Hommel reported antimony in some old Japanese bronzes ; H. Oldenberg, in some old Indian bronzes ; and B. Bucher, in some old Peruvian alloys.

The scholars tell us that the Hebrew and Arabic word for antimony is *kohol* or *kohl*, which was translated *alcool* or *alkohol* in other languages. E. O. von Lippmann has quoted a number of examples from the writings of the Middle Ages, where the term *alcohol* was used for substances in the state of a fine powder ; only later was the term used for spirit of wine. According to H. Kopp, the word *antimonium* appeared in the Latin translations of Geber's *Summa perfectionis magisterii ;* but, added M. Berthelot, it is *une circonstance singulière* that the term antimony does not appear in the reputed twelfth and thirteenth century translations of the Arabian chemists. It does not occur in the writings of Geber, the pseudo-Aristotle, or Avicenna reproduced in the *Theatricum chemicum*, or in the *Bibliotheca chemica*. The terms *marcassite* or *magnesia* are sometimes applied to antimony sulphide, as well as to the other metal sulphides. The term ἀντεμόνιον appears in a practical treatise on the goldsmith's art, written in the Greek characteristic of the Middle Ages, and reproduced in M. Berthelot and C. E. Ruelle's *Collection des anciens alchimistes grecs* (Paris, **2**. 6, 1888). The mineral sulphide is called *antimonium*, and not *stimmi*, or *stibium*, in the *Speculum naturale* (**8**. 49) of Vincent de Beauvais, written towards the middle of the thirteenth century; while Constantinus Africanus, in his *De gradibus*, is said to have employed the same term a century and a half earlier. The word *antimonium* also appears in the *Circa instans* of M. Platearius, about 1150; in the *Tabulæ* of M. Salernus, about 1200; and in the *Antidotatium*, or *Isagogica introductio in artem apothecariatus* of P. Nicolas, about the middle of the twelfth century. Hence, added M. Berthelot, the term *antimonium* appeared in Western Europe about the middle of the eleventh century, and it ultimately displaced the older words.

The origin of the word *antimony* has been the subject of some speculation. It is said that certain monks experimented with antimony on some pigs and discovered that it hastened their fattening. With the desire of avoiding the effects of fasting on themselves, they partook of the same medicament, but with fatal results. Hence the origin of the term αντί, against ; μόνος, one who lives alone, a monk. It has also been suggested that the μόνος means solitude, and that *antimonos* means opposed to solitude, in allusion to the fact that antimony always occurs in nature associated with other minerals. M. Berthelot said it was not worth while discussing *l'etemologie puerile*, which refers the term antimony to *anti-moine* in allusion to the accidental poisoning of some monks by a preparation of antimony. M. Berthelot continued : E. Littre favours the suggestion that *anti-moine* is derived from the Arabian *athmoud, othmoud*, or *ithmid*, eye-paint which in turn is derived from *stimmi* with the addition of the article *al*. Possibly also the Greek word is of Oriental origin, and not borrowed by the Arabians from the Greeks. Many examples of the adaptation of Arabian words to Latin or Greek forms will be found in M. Ruland's *Lexicon alchemiæ* (Francofurti, 1612). For example, the word *tinkar* becomes *attinkar*, and *anticar*, and *antimonium* is given with the synonym *antistini*.

According to H. Kopp, up to the time of the antiphlogistians, the word *stibium* or *antimonium* was employed in alchemical and chemical writings in place of antimony sulphide. Pliny described a process for preparing *stimmi* for medical purposes by heating it with organic matter in such a way as *ne plumbum fiat*—not to become lead. This is taken to mean that the metal was occasionally obtained by the ancients but not recognized by them as anything different from lead. Dioscorides also mentioned that *stimmi* could be roasted by heating it in a current of air ; but if too strongly heated, it melted like lead. Here again it is thought that metallic antimony was formed.

The metal antimony was known to A. Libavius in 1615, to G. E. Stahl, and to D. G. Morhof ; while, according to H. von Peters, G. W. von Leibniz made some observations on the metal. A. Libavius obtained antimony by adding iron to a molten mixture of antimony sulphide, salt, and potassium tartrate. The *regulus* so produced had a crystalline or starred surface—hence the terms : *the wonderful star, stella antimonii, antimonium stellatum, regulus stellatus, the royal star, the philosopher's signet star*, etc. The anonymous Basil Valentine, at the beginning of the seventeenth century, showed that starred and unstarred antimony had the same composition ; and he attributed the effect to the use of iron—Mars—in the reduction of the sulphide. Robert Boyle, in his essay *On the unsuccessfulness of experiments* (Oxford, 1661), said :

It may perhaps be from some diversity either in antimonies or irons, that eminent chemists have often failed in their endeavours to make the starry regulus of Mars and antimony. Insomuch that divers artists fondly believe and teach (what our experience will not allow) that there is a certain respect to times and constellations requisite to the producing of this (I confess admirable) body. Upon this subject, I must not omit to tell you that a while since an industrious acquaintance of ours was working on an antimony, which, unawares to him, was, as we then supposed, of so peculiar a nature, that making a regulus of it alone without iron, the common way (for this manner of operation I inquired of him), he found, to his wonder, and showed me his regulus adorned with a more conspicuous star than I have seen in several stellate reguluses of both antimon and Mars.

N. Lemery, in his *Cours de chymie* (Paris, 1675), argued against the idea that the planet Mars had anything to do with the stellate crystals on the surface of metallic antimony. In 1546, G. Agricola described the preparation of antimony by heating the sulphide in a belly-shaped pot with perforations in the bottom. This vessel rested on an empty pot. The two vessels were surrounded by earth and coal-dust, and heated from above by burning logs. The metal ran into the lower vessel. In 1574, L. Ercker, and in 1650, B. Rössler, described methods of reducing the sulphide to metal.

A. Libavius said that *antimonium triplex est*, for it is compounded of mercury, arsenic, and sulphur. A. Sala knew that antimony is often associated with arsenic, and cautioned users of medicinal preparations of antimony against that impurity. Basil Valentine called antimony an *Abart des Bleis*, thus regarding it as a degenerate form of a true metal. Analogous views as to the semi-metallic nature of antimony were held by A. von Suchten in 1613 ; by H. Poppe in 1625 ; by J. J. Becher in 1669 ; by N. Lemery in 1675 ; by J. Kunckel in 1690 ; and by E. Ettmüller in 1693. In 1732, H. Boerhaave classed the sulphide as a *semi-metalla sulphurea*. According to N. Lemery, the fact that antimony comes after gold in resisting attack by aqua regia led to its being regarded by some alchemists as imperfect gold. The use of additions of antimony for purifying molten gold, said J. Chartier, is because the antimony can unite with impurities, thereby forming a scum which can be easily removed. This, and the fact that antimony united with or devoured all the metals then known, with the exception of gold, led to *stimmi, kohl,* or *antimonium* being called in the alchemical literature of the Middle Ages, *judex ultimus, lupus repax, pupus metallorum*—the wolf of the metals—the *red lion,* the *fiery dragon,* the *fiery satan,* the *son of satan, balneum regis*—the bath of the king—*der hochste, Richter,* etc. A fanciful analogy with lead—Saturn—and the likening of the mythological appetite of Saturn for infants with the appetite of antimony for other metals, led some alchemists to call antimony *the sacred lead, the lead of the philosophers,* or the *lead of the sages.* Antimony was also called *radix metallorum,* the root of the metals, because it occurs associated with other metals in mines, and it was sometimes designated *protheus* because of the varying colours associated with the products derived from antimony. *Spiessglas* or *Spiessglanz* was a miners' term for antimony.

J. R. Glauber showed that when antimony sulphide is heated with mercuric chloride, owing to the *attractio electiva duplex,* the metals exchange places to form mercuric sulphide and antimony chloride. With the advent of the antiphlogistian theory, it was recognized that antimony is an element forming sulphides, oxides, etc., as in the case of other metals. According to H. Hyman,

> The part played by antimony in the early history of chemistry is generally overlooked, its claim to an all-important position being overshadowed by its great rival, gold. There is a considerable amount of evidence, however, that antimony and its compounds must have proved of fascinating interest to many of the early chemists, and it is indeed probable that the study of this metal led to more developments in the early history of the science than did that of the precious metal. This fascination became in some cases so absorbing that entire life-times were devoted to its study, and the specialization which we are inclined to attribute to the economic conditions of the present era was in force several centuries ago. The result of this intensive study was the publication of several books dealing entirely with this metal, all of which remain as landmarks in the steady progress of the science.

The following monographs on antimony were published after Basil Valentine's *Triumphwagen antimonii* (Leipzig, 1604) :

N. Lemery, *Traité sur l'antimoine,* Paris, 1707 ; E. P. Meuder, *Analysis antimonii,* Paris, 1738 ; A. von Suchten, *Antimonii mysteria gemina,* Leipzig, 1604 ; H. Poppe, *Basilica antimonii,* Franckfurt, 1617 ; T. Bergman, *De antimonialibus sulphuratis,* Upsala, 1782 ; G. Rolfinck, *De antimonio,* Jenæ, 1691 ; Le Pere Lamy, *Dissertation sur l'antimoine,* Paris, 1682 ; G. Pearson, *Experiments and Observations to Investigate the Composition of James's Powder,* London, 1791 ; R. G. Renault, *Histoire de l'antimoine,* Paris, 1868 ; L. de Launay, *De la faculte et vertu admirable de l'antimoine, avec response a certaine calomnies,* La Rochelle, 1564 ; A. Sala, *Anatomia antimonii,* Francofurti, 1617 ; G. D. Traverso,

L'Antimonio, Alba, 1897 ; A. Guntz, *Antimoine*, Paris, 1884 ; C. Y. Wang, *Antimony*, London, 1909 ; A. Nicolas, *L'Antimoine et ses principaux composés*, Montpellier, 1880. F. Fittica [2] said that antimony is a nitrogen derivative of phosphorus, and can be obtained in small quantities together with arsenic by heating amorphous phosphorus with ammonium nitrite and potassium nitrate with or without the addition of ammonium carbonate. He also said that antimony can be similarly obtained from arsenic. C. Winkler, and C. Arnold and F. Murach showed that the arsenic and antimony which F. Fittica obtained must have been derived from impurities in the materials he used—*vide* arsenic.

REFERENCES.

[1] H. Kopp, *Geschichte des Chemie*, Braunschweig, 4. 104, 1847 ; M. Berthelot, *Compt. Rend.*, 104. 265, 1887 ; *Ann. Chim. Phys.*, (6), 12. 134, 1887 ; (6), 30. 285, 1894 ; *Introduction à l'étude de chimie des anciens et du moyen-âge*, Paris, 279, 1889 ; M. Ettmüller, *Nouvelle chimie raisonée*, Lyon, 187, 1693 ; E. O. von Lippmann, *Entstehung und Ausbreitung der Alchemie*, Berlin, 629, 1919 ; X. Fischer, *Arch. Pharm.*, 230. 9, 1892 ; O. Helm and H. V. Hilprecht, *Chem. Ztg.*, 25. 250, 1901 ; *Verh. Berlin. Ges. Anthropologie, Ethnologie, Urgeschichte*, 157, 1901 ; R. Forrer, *Real-Lexicon der prähistorischen, klassischen, und frühchristlichen Altertümer*, Berlin, 32. 1907 ; *Urgeschichte des Europaërs*, Stuttgart, 410, 1908 ; O. Stoll, *Das Geschlechtsleben in der Völkerpsychologie*, Leipzig, 321, 376, 1908 ; E. Mayer, *Geschichte des Alterthums*, Stuttgart, 1. 416, 1894 : B. Bucher, *Geschichte der technischen Künste*, Stuttgart, 2. 406, 1893 ; A. F. von Pauly and A. Nies, in G. Wissowa, *Real Enzyklopädie der klassischen Altertumswissenschaft*, Stuttgart, 1. 2346, 1894 ; W. Hommel, *Zeit. angew. Chem.*, 25. 97, 1912 ; *Chem. Ztg.*, 36. 918, 1912 ; H. Oldenberg, *Lehrbuch der Upanischaden und die Anfänge des Buddhismus*, Göttingen, 143, 1915 ; J. R. Glauber, *Novi furni philosophici*, Amstelodami, 1648 ; E. Littre, *Dictionaire de la langue française*, Paris, 1. 156, 1873 ; and M. Devie's supplement, 10, 1897 ; A. Libavius, *Alchymia*, Francofurti, 1595 ; J. J. Becher, *Physica subterranea*, Leipzig, 659, 1669 ; D. G. Morhof, *Polyhistor*, Lübeck, 1. 84, 1714 ; G. E. Stahl, *Zufällige Gedanken und nützlichen Bedencken über den Streit von dem sogennanten Sulphure*, Halle, 48, 1718 ; H. von Peters, *Leibniz als Chemiker—Arch. Gesch. nat. Tech.*, 7. 279, 1916 ; G. Agricola, *Bergmannus sive de re metallica*, Basileæ, 1546 ; *De re metallica*, Basileæ, 1556 ; London, 428, 1912 ; B. Rössler, *Speculum metallurgiœ politissimum*, Dresden, 1700 ; L. Ercker, *Beschreibung aller fürnemsten mineralische Ertzt und Berckwercksarten*, Prag, 1574 ; J. Chartier, *Scientia plumbi sacri seu cognitio rararum potestatum et virtutum antimonii*, *in Theatrum chemicum*, Argentorati, 6. 569, 1659 : H. Boerhaave, *Elementa chemiœ*, Lugduni Batavorum, 1. 20, 1732 ; 2. 199, 1732 ; J. Kunckel, *Vollständiges Laboratorium chymicum*, Hamburg, 432, 1722 ; H. Poppe, *Basilica antimonii*, Franckfurt, 1617 ; A. von Suchten, *Antimonii mysteria gemina*, Leipzig, 1604 ; Basil Valentine, *Triumphwagen antimonii*, Leipzig, 1604 ; London, 1893 ; N. Lemery, *Traité sur l'antimoine*, Paris, 1707 ; A. Sala, *Anatomia antimonii*, Francofurti, 1617 ; A. Duflos, *Kastner's Arch.*, 1. 56, 1830 ; H. Hyman, *Journ. Soc. Chem. Ind.—Chem. Ind.*, 43. 1006, 1924.

[2] F. Fittica, *Leopoldina*, 36. 3, 40, 1900 ; *Chem. Ztg.*, 24. 483, 561, 991, 1900 ; 25. 41, 259, 1901 ; C. Arnold and F. Murach, 16. 25. 131, 1901 ; C. Winkler, *Ber.*, 33. 1693, 1900.

§ 2. The Occurrence of Antimony

Antimony is regarded as one of the common elements, but it is neither widely nor abundantly distributed in nature. F. W. Clarke and H. S. Washington [1] estimate that the igneous rocks of the earth's crust contain $n10^{-7}$ per cent. of antimony, and J. H. L. Vogt, $n10^{-5}$ per cent. W. Vernadsky gave 0.05_7 for the percentage amount of antimony, and 0.04_5 for the atomic proportion. According to H. Rowland,[2] and M. N. Saha, the spectral lines of antimony have not been detected in the spectrum of the sun. Antimony has been observed by G. Trottorelli, B. Silliman and F. S. Hunt, E. Cohen, and E. Cohen and E. Weinschenk in meteorites.

Elemental antimony occurs in nature too rarely for the deposits to be of any commercial importance. The earliest definite record of the occurrence of the element is the *gediget Spitsglas* found at Sala, Sweden, by A. von Swab [3] in 1748 ; and in 1780, J. G. Schreiber found it at Allemont, France. The following analyses of native antimony were reported by M. H. Klaproth, A. Eschka, A Raimondi, R. A. A. Johnston, and G. F. Kunz, respectively :

	Sb	As	Fe	Ag
Andreesberg . . .	98·00	—	0·25	1·00
Pribram . . .	95·15	4·85	—	—
Macata, Peru . .	96·36	3·63	—	0·0
Madoc, Ontario . .	99·80	0·02	trace	—
York County, U.S.A. (fine)	98·19	0·86	0·11	—
,, ,, (coarse)	94·15	0·47	0·34	—

The French occurrences of native antimony have been described by R. Hörnes. The deposits in Germany—Andreesberg, Harz; Goldkronach, Bayern; and Pribram, Bohemia—were described by M. H. Klaproth, J. F. L. Hausmann, O. Luedecke, E. Schulze, G. Rose, F. A. Roemer, C. Greifenhagen, W. von Gümbel, C. Hahn, A. E. Reuss, A. Eschka, V. R. von Zepharovich, and F. Katzer; at Kapruk, and Pozsony, in Hungary, by V. R. von Zepharovich, and S. Koch; at Waldenstein, Carinthia, by E. Döll; at Sarrabus, Sardinia, by A. des Cloizeaux; at Chang-Sha, China, by F. R. Tegengren; at Lucknow, New South Wales, by A. Liversidge; in Queensland, by B. Dunstan, and R. W. E. MacIvor; in Chili, by I. Domeyko; in Peru, by A. Raimondi; in Mexico, by G. Leonhard, I. Domeyko, and C. F. de Landero; in California and New Jersey, by J. D. Dana, and C. H. Behre; in North Carolina, by F. A. Genth; in Canada, by C. H. Hitchcock, W. E. Logan, R. A. A. Johnston, and A. Weisbach; and in New Brunswick, by G. F. Kunz.

The chief minerals containing antimony are the sulphides, various antimonides and sulphantimonides of the heavy metals, and oxidized compounds of secondary origin. The arsenic minerals include :

Antimonides.—Breithauptite, NiSb; arite or arsenantimonial nickel, Ni(As,Sb); dycrasite or antimonial silver, Ag₃Sb; chanarcillite, Ag₂(As,Sb)₃; antimonial copper; allemontite, SbAs₃—vide arsenic; sperrylite, (Pt,Rh)(As,Sb)₂; horsfordite, Cu₃Sb. Sulphides.—Stibnite, antimonite, or antimony glance, Sb₂S₃; metastibnite, Sb₂S₃. Mixed antimonides and sulphides.—Pyrargyrite, Ag₃SbS₃; polybasite, Ag₁₆Sb₂S₁₁; miargyrite, AgSbS₂; polyargyrite, Ag₂₄Sb₂S₁₅; stephanite, Ag₅SbS₄; pyro-stilpnite, Ag₃SbS₃; wolfsbergite, CuSbS₄; guejarite, Cu₈Sb₄S₇; famatinite, Cu₃SbS₄; tetrahedrite, Cu₃Sb₂S₇; chalcostibite, CuSbS₂; etromeyerite, (Ag,Cu)S; stylotypite, (Cu₂,Ag₂,Fe)₃Sb₂S₆; livingstonite, HgSb₄S₇; zinkenite, PbSb₂S₄; brongniardtite, (Pb,Ag₂)Sb₂S₅; boulangerite, Pb₃Sb₂S₆; epiboulangerite, Pb₃Sb₂S₃; geokronite, Pb₅Sb₂S₈; warrenite, or domingite, Pb₃Sb₄S₉; plagionite, Pb₅Sb₈S₁₇; meneghinite, Pb₄Sb₂S₇; kobellite, Pb₂(Bi,Sb)S₅; jamesonite, Pb₂Sb₂S₅; freieslebenite, or diaphorite, (Pb,Ag₂)₅Sb₄S₁₁; bournonite, (Pb,Cu₂)₃Sb₂S₆; semseyite, Pb₇Sb₆S₁₆; kylindrite, Pb₆Sn₆Sb₂S₂₁; franckeite, Pb₅Sn₂Sb₂S₁₂; kilbruckenite, Pb₆Sb₂S₉; steinmannite, antimonial galena; berthierite, FeSb₂S₄; dürfeldtite, a sulphantimonide of lead, silver, copper, iron, and manganese; plumbostannite, a sulphantimonide of lead, tin, and iron; ullmannite, NiSbS; wolfachite, Ni(As,Sb)S; korynite, (Ni,Fe)(As,Sb)S; ammiolite, mercury copper tellurantimonide.

Oxides, and oxidized salts.—Senarmontite, Sb₂O₃; valentinite, Sb₂O₃; cervantite, Sb₂O₄; volgerite, hydrated antimonic acid, stibiconite or stiblite, Sb₂O₄.H₂O; arsenostibnite, an arsenical hydrate of antimony; partzite, hydrated antimonious oxide mixed with copper, lead, and silver oxides; romeite, CaSb₂O₄; atopite, Ca₂Sb₂O₇, or (Ca,Na₂,Fe,Mn)₂Sb₂O₇; thrombolite, Cu₃(SbO₃)₂.6H₂O; barcenite, mercury antimonate; bindheimite, Pb₃Sb₂O₈.4H₂O; coronguite, silver lead antimonate; monimolite, (Pb,Fe,Mn)₃ (SbO₄)₂; tanzite, bismuth arsenantimonate; hematostibiite, Mn₈Sb₂O₁₃; manganostibnite, Mn₁₀Sb₂O₁₅; tripuhyite, Fe₂Sb₂O₇; ochroite, Pb₄Sb₂O₇.2PbCl₂; nadorite, PbSbO₂Cl; rivotite, a copper silver antimonate with carbon dioxide; sarawakite, antimony chloride; schneebergite, calcium antimony sulphate; stetefeldtite, hydrated silver copper oxysulphantimonate; kermesite, Sb₂S₂O; stibiatil, and ferrostibian, ferrous manganese antimonate; langbanite, manganese iron antimonatosilicate; arequipite, lead antimonatosilicate.

There are upwards of fifty minerals containing antimony, but only a few are worked commercially. Stibnite is by far the most important ore of antimony, and metallic antimony not infrequently occurs with stibnite. Thus, antimony is abundant in the lower levels of the stibnite at West Gore, Nova Scotia, and it predominates over the stibnite of Wolfe Co., Quebec; it occurs massive near Sandon, New South Wales; and in nodular masses, at Erskine Creek, Cal. Native antimony impregnates the shales near Vinuela, Spain; and it occurs in the antimony veins and detritus of Bidi, British Borneo. Stibnite is associated with cinnabar at San Martino, Corsica; Rohonez, Hungary; Selvena, Italy; Cemernitsa and Prozer, Yugoslavia ; Sandjak-Kale, Asia Minor ; Djebel Tayo, etc., Algeria ; Tegora, British B⁓neo ; Pulganbar, New South Wales ; at Rio Blanco, Mexico ; etc. Antimony itself is regarded as an alteration product of stibnite, etc. The antimony ores are often associated with volcanic activity, and were deposited near the surface—e.g. Monte Amiata, Italy ; Hsi-Ku'ang-Shan, China ; Thabyu, Burma ; Bridge River, British Columbia ; West Gore, Nova Scotia ; Huitzuco, Mexico ; and in South Utah. In other cases, particularly with the sulphantimonides, the ores were deposited at intermediate depths at moderate temp., and under great press.—e.g. the antimony ores in Cobalt, Ontario ; Slocan, British Columbia ; Aspen, Colorado ; Park City, Utah ; Black Hills, South Dakota ; Hillgrove, New South Wales · Bendigo, Victoria ; Andreesberg, Harz ; Clausthal, Germany ; and Pribram, Czechoslovakia. The antimony ores of Bolivia ; Zimapan, Mexico ; Arabia, Nevada ; and Western Australia are thought to have been deposited at high temp. and under great press. The stibnite ores commonly occur in fissure veins with a quartz gangue, and they may or may not be argentiferous and auriferous ; they may occur in faults or shear zones in limestone, sandstone, or schist ; as irregular masses in limestone being formed by substitution ; as impregnations in porous beds of limestone or sandstone ; and as sporadic occurrences in lead, zinc, copper, mercury, gold, or silver minerals. The geographical distribution of the ores is illustrated by the map, Fig. 1.

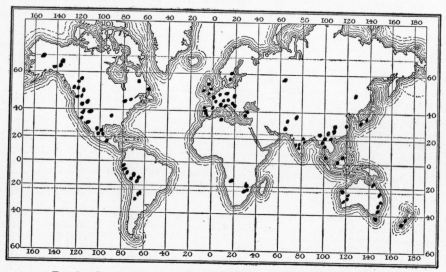

FIG. 1.—Geographical Distribution of the Antimony-bearing Districts.

Europe.—Comparatively little antimony ore was raised in *Great Britain* [4] from the end of the eighteenth century to 1893, when the mining of antimony ore virtually ceased. The ores occur in Cornwall, Devon, Cumberland, Derbyshire, and the Isle of Man ; in the past, in Scotland, ores were mined in Dumfriesshire, and in Ayrshire ; and in Ireland, in Monaghan. Before the war, *France* [5] was the largest producer in Europe ; it occurs at La Lucette, Mayenne, Semmon, Isle-et-Vilaine ; Massiac, Brioude, etc., Central Plateau ; Bresnay, Souvigny ; Freycenet, Mercoeur, Valadau, La Licoulne, Haute Loire ; Malbosc, Ardèche ; Luri Castello, Meria, Metra, and Ersa, Corsica. In *Portugal*,[6] it occurs in the Basin of the Douro, Braganza, Prata, and Alcoutim. In *Spain*,[7] Ribas valley, Caurel, Orense, Alemtejo, Estremadura, and Vinuela. In *Switzerland*, at Lessnig. In *Italy*,[8] Sardinia, Monte Annata, Selvena, San Martino, Percia Fiorentina, Montauto, Cetine di Cotorniano, Pari, Su Suergiu, and Soana di Campiglia. In *Greece*,[9] Mytilene, and Chios. In *Russia*,[10] Urals, Amur, and Siberia. In *Austria*,[11] Rohoncz. *Czechoslovakia*,[12] Pricov, Schönberg, Mileschen, Kritz, Punnau, Joachimsthal. There are several mines in Slovakia, and ores occur in Ruthenia. In *Yugoslavia*,[13] there are deposits in Kostainic-Krapanj, in Slovenia, Crovatia, Bosnia, Dalmatia, and Serbian Macedonia. In *Germany*,[14] Mobendorf, Brück, Westphalia, Nuttler, Böhmsdorf, Wolfsgalgen, and Goldkronach. In *Sweden*, Sala, Westmannland, and Gladhammar.

Asia.—In *Asia Minor*,[15] antimony ores occur in Anatolia, Brusa, Smyrna, and Kordilio. In *Persia*,[16] Afshar. In *Afghanistan*, Kil' Abdullo, Kinchak, and Duligird. In *India*,[17] Mysore, Madras, Bihar, Orissa, Baluchistan, Punjaub, in the North-West Provinces. *Burma* In *British Borneo*,[18] Bidi, Busan, Jambusan, Piat, Orogo, Siktingit, and in the basin of the River Rejang. In *French Indo-China*, near Tonkin. *China*[19] has been the principal producer of antimony for the last quarter of a century ; the more important deposits occur in the provinces of Hunan, Hupeh, Yunnan, Kweichow, and Kwangsi. In *Japan*,[20] the principal antimony deposits extend from the Province of Yamato in Honshu, through Tosa and Iyo in Shikoku, to Hyuga and Osumi in Kyushu.

Africa.—There has been a small production of antimony from the ore deposits— *Southern Rhodesia*[21]—extending from Hartley to Belingive, and from Gwelo to Selukwe. Ore occurs at Octavi in *Damaraland ;* and in the *Transvaal* district in a line of hills extending north-east of Leydsdorp. In *Algeria*,[22] Djebel Nador, Sidi-Rgheiss.

North America.—There are deposits of antimony ore in *Alaska*[23]—Fairbanks, Kantiohna, and Seward Peninsula. In *Canada*,[24] British Columbia, Ontario, Quebec, Yukon, Nova Scotia, New Brunswick. In *Newfoundland*,[25] New World Island, Notre Dame Bay. In the *United States*,[26] Arizona, Arkansas, California, Idaho, Montana, Nevada, Oregon, Utah, and Washington. In *Cuba*,[27] there is a deposit of argentiferous stibnite in the Isle of Pines. In *Mexico*,[28] there are mines in the district of Catorce, Charcas, Altar, and Aueretars. There are deposits in Durango ; Tlaxiaco, Oaxaca ; and Zimapan, Hidalgo.

South America.—In *Argentina*,[29] antimony ore occurs at Charillos, and near La Higuera. In *Bolivia*, in the districts of Oruru, Pulacayo, and Portugalete. In *Peru*, Cajamarca, Liberlad, Ancachs, Junin, Huanaco, Huancavelica, Arequipa, Cuzeo, and Puno.

Australia.—In *Australia*,[30] there are deposits in Queensland—Chillagoe mineral field ; Hungary Hill, Neerdie, in the vicinity of Gympie. New South Wales, in a north-east line from Forbes to Buller. Victoria, in the vicinity of Bendigo, Western Australia, West Oilbara, and East Murchison. Tasmania, Mount Bischoff, Mount Zeehan, Heazelwood River, and Table Cape. *New Caledonia* ; [31] *New Zealand*,[32] Endeavour Inlet, Marlborough ; Waipori, Cromwell, Alexandra, and Mt. Stoker, Otago ; Reefton, Greymouth, Westland ; Kawau Island ; Bay of Islands, and the Thames and Coromandel Districts.

The World's production of antimony ore, so far as data are available, amounted to 24,114 metric tons in 1913 ; 83,449 metric tons in 1916 ; 32,283 metric tons in 1918 ; 23,363¼ metric tons in 1920 ; 17,301¾ metric tons in 1921 ; and 32,000 metric tons in 1926. The results for individual countries are indicated in Table I. The highest price since 1800 was reached in 1906, *viz.* £135 per ton, and

TABLE I.—THE WORLD'S PRODUCTION OF ANTIMONY ORE.

Country.	1800.	1890.	1900.	1916.	1920.	1926.
Great Britain	—	—	—	4	—	—
India	—	—	—	520	nil	—
S. Africa	—	—	—	344	nil	29
Canada	41	27	—	354	nil	1
Australasia	61	728	255	2,047	163	95
Austria-Hungary	785	994	2574	—	348	30
Czechoslovakia	—	—	—	—	131	—
France	1781	4962	7936	3,033	873	2,800
Germany	—	—	—	—	—	—
Serbia or Macedonia	—	—	267	—	131	—
Italy	540	891	7609	4,334	465	442
Portugal	—	—	38	1,000	—	—
Spain	11	821	30	170	—	—
Asia Minor	—	—	—	4	400	400
China	—	—	—	42,800	19,040	17,799
Japan	—	3224	81	280	—	—
Indo-China	—	—	—	642	50	—
Algeria	—	—	—	4,550	236	250
Mexico	—	—	2313	2,647	775	2,572
United States	—	327	300	310	33	38
Argentina	—	—	—	812	—	—
Bolivia	—	—	1174	12,860	751	4,284
Peru	—	—	—	450	nil	—

the lowest in 1903, *viz.* £25 10*s.* per ton. The highest and lowest prices in London per ton of 2240 lbs. in pounds sterling were :

	1918.		1920.		1922.		1924.	
	Max.	Min.	Max.	Min.	Max.	Min.	Max.	Min.
English regulus	85	80	72	45	36	25¾	—	—
Chinese regulus	82	60	70	34	26	23½	—	—
Crude regulus .	70	57½	56	25	18½	14	—	—

In England, antimony sulphide ore is bought at so much per unit. On April 18, 1916, it was 11*s.* per unit, less 2·5 per cent. According to H. K. Masters,[33] the penalties are : Lead, up to 0·3 per cent. free, with an allowance to buyers of 5*s.* per ton of ore for every one-tenth of 1 per cent. over 0·3 per cent. up to 1½ per cent. ; arsenic, 0·1 per cent. free, with an allowance to buyers of 7*s.* 6*d.* per ton of ore for every one-tenth of 1 per cent. in excess of 0·1 per cent. up to 0·5 per cent. Should the ore fall below 60 per cent. in antimony content, an allowance to be made to buyers of 3*d.* per unit down to 55 per cent. If below 55 per cent. and down to 50 per cent. an allowance of 6*d.* per unit. If above 60 per cent. an allowance to be made to sellers of 3*d.* per unit. Copper carries the same deductions as arsenic. Zinc and bismuth should not be present in more than traces.

Antimony is common in the arsenical minerals where part of the arsenic is replaced by antimony—*e.g.* A. Carnot,[34] D. Campbell, E. Schmid, W. Hampe, and A. Hilger found it in native arsenic, laucopyrite, and arsenical pyrites ; D. Campbell, P. Berthier, T. Petersen, L. Sipöcz, C. F. Rammelsberg, G. Tschermak, C. Winkler, G. T. Prior, F. Sandberger, and C. Bergemann, in arsenical cobalt, and löllingite ; L. Sipöcz, in arsenical nickel ; G. T. Prior, and G. Tschermak, in jordanite, and proustite—*vide* arsenic. L. Sipöcz, W. Petz, and R. Scharizer found antimony in a number of tellurium minerals, thus, he represented nagyadite by the formula $Au_2Pb_{14}Sb_3(S,Te)_{24}$; C. F. Rammelsberg, L. Sipöcz, F. Becke, and W. Hampe, in zinc blende ; F. Sandberger, W. Hampe, D. Forbes, and P. Kröber, in galena ; C. Winkler, T. Petersen, and A. Carnot, in bismuthinite ; W. Hampe, in copper pyrites ; C. Winkler, in argyrodite ; E. Ebler, in ochre ; F. Mauro, in spinel ; F. Sandberger, in rubellan biotite ; and H. Reinsch, in hausmannite. A. Daubrée found 0·03 grm. of antimony per kilogram in the basalt of Kaiserstuhl, and in some coals. As in the case of arsenic, the presence of antimony in many ores explains its occurrence in many commercial metals—thus, W. Hampe found it in zinc, tin, lead, and copper as well as in electrolytic copper ; A. Ledebur, in iron ; S. P. L. Sörensen, in nickel ; T. Poleck, in phosphorus ; E. R. Schneider, in bismuth ; and G. S. Sérullas, and H. Ramage, in the flue-dust of South Yorkshire coals. Arsenic has been found by A. Buchner in a number of commercial antimonial preparations derived from the use of arsenical antimony sulphide.

A. Daubrée found antimony in sea-water ; and D. Campbell, in a number of rivers and streams. The element has also been detected in a number of springs, thermal water, and in the ochreous deposits therefrom by H. de Sénarmont,[35] L. F. Bley, T. Poleck, C. R. Fresenius, E. Ludwig and J. Mauthner, H. Will, F. A. Walchner, E. F. von Gorup-Besanez, N. B. Hardin, F. Garrigou, H. von Fehling, and H. Göttl. W. von Gümbel found the sediment from the Bormio spring had 1·27 per cent. of antimonic oxide ; C. R. Fresenius found the ochre of the springs at Driburg contained 0·007–0·009 per cent. Sb_2O_3 ; E. Reichardt, 0·011 per cent. of Sb_2O_3 in that from Liebenstein, Thüringia ; C. P. Williams found 0·021–0·022 per cent. Sb_2O_3 in 10 litres of the waters of the lead mines of Jasper County, Missouri.

REFERENCES.

[1] F. W. Clarke and H. S. Washington, *The Composition of the Earth's Crust,* Washington, 1924 ; *Proc. Nat. Acad. Sciences,* 8. 108, 1922 ; J. H. L. Vogt, *Zeit. prakt. Geol.,* 6. 225, 374, 377.

13, 1898 ; **7**. 10, 274, 1899 ; **W. Vernadsky,** *Essai de minéralogie descriptive*, St. Petersburg.
1. 121, 740, 1914 ; *Geochimie*, Paris, 16, 1924 ; A. E. Fersman, *Bull. Acad. St. Petersburg*, (6).
6. 367. 1912.
    ² H. Rowland, *Amer. Journ. Science*, (3), **41.** 243, 1891 ; *Johns Hopkins Univ. Circulars*, 8ᶠ,
1891 ; *Chem. News*, **63.** 133, 1891 ; G. Trottorelli, *Gazz. Chim. Ital.*, 20. 611, 1890 ; M. N. Saha,
Phil. Mag., (6), **40.** 808, 1920 ; B. Silliman and F. S. Hunt, *Amer. Journ. Science*, (2), **2.** 374,
1846 ; E. Cohen and E. Weinschenk, *Ann. Naturhist. Hofmuseums*, **6.** 131, 1891 ; E. Cohen, *ib..*
7. 143, 1892 ; **9.** 97, 1894.
    ³ O. Luedecke, *Die Minerale des Harzes*, Berlin, 7, 1896 ; F. R. Tegengren, *Bull. China Geol.
Sur.*, 3, 1921 ; E. Schulze, *Lithia Hercynia*, Leipzig, 2, 1895 ; W. von Gümbel, *Geognostische
Beschreibung des Königreichs Bayern*, Gotha, **3.** 301, 389, 1879 ; B. Dunstan, *Queensland Min.
Journ.*, 67, 1917 ; A. des Cloizeaux, *Manuel de minéralogie*, Paris, 324, 1893 ; A. Liversidge,
Proc. Roy. Soc. New South Wales, **25.** 234, 1888 ; R. W. E. MacIvor, *Chem. News*, 57. 64, 1888 ;
S. Koch, *Földt. Közl.*, 55. 162, 1926 ; E. Döll, *Verh. geol. Reichsanst. Wein*, 45, 1876 ; A. von
Swab, *Akad. H ndl. Stockholm*, **10.** 99, 1748 ; A. Cronstedt, *Mineralogie*, Stockholm, 201, 1758 ;
A. G. Werner, *Letztes Mineralsystem*, Freiberg, 23, 1817 ; J. G. Schreiber, *Journ. Phys.*, 34. 380.
1784 ; A. E. Reuss, *Lotos*, 10. 211, 1860 ; *Sitzber. Akad. Wein*, 47. 63, 1863 ; *Neues Jahrb. Min.*,
326, 1861 ; G. F. Kunz, *Amer. Journ. Science*, (3), **30.** 275, 1885 ; C. H. Hitchcock, *ib.*, (2), 37.
405, 1864 ; C. H. Behre, *ib.*, (5), **2.** 330, 1921 ; W. E. Logan, *Rep. Geol. Sur. Canada*, 876, 1863 ;
R. A. A. Johnston, 11, 1900 ; A. Weisbach, *Neues Jahrb. Min.*, 609, 1867 ; C. Greifenhagen
ib., 48, 1856 ; F. A. Roemer, *ib.*, 310, 1848 ; R. Hörnes, *ib.*, 781, 1846 ; M. H. Klaproth, *Beiträge
zur chemischen Kenntniss der Mineralkörper*, Berlin, **3.** 170, 1802 ; J. D. Dana, *A System of
Mineralogy*, New York, 13, 1892 ; J. F. L. Hausmann, *Handbuch der Mineralogie*, Göttingen,
12, 1847 ; C. F. de Landero, *Sinopsis mineralogica o catalogo descriptios de los minerales*, Mexico,
32, 1888 ; I. Domeyko, *Elementos de mineralojia*, Santiago, 268, 1879 ; A. Raimondi, *Minéraux
du Pérou*, Paris, 191, 1878 ; G. Leonhard, *Handwörterbuch der topographischen Mineralogie*,
Heidelberg, 24, 1843 ; F. A. Genth, *The Minerals of North Carolina*, Washington, 20, 1891 ;
V. R. von Zepharovich, *Mineralogisches Lexicon für das Kaiserthum Oesterreich*, Wien, 19, 1873 ;
C. Hahn, *Berg. Hütt. Ztg.*, **6.** 97, 1855 ; A. Eschka, *ib.*, **13.** 23, 1862 ; G. Rose, *Sitzber. Akad.
Berlin*, 72, 1849 ; *Pogg. Ann.*, **77.** 144, 1849 ; F. Katzer, *Geologie von Böhmen*, Prag., 786, 1892.
    ⁴ W. J. Henwood, *Trans. Roy. Geol. Soc. Cornwall*, **5.** 461, 1843 ; W. Pryce, *Mineralogia
Cornubiensis*, London, 47, 1778 ; H. T. de la Beche, *Report of the Geology of Cornwall, Devon,
and West Somerset*, London, 616, 1839 ; H. Dewey, *Mem. Geol. Sur.—Special Reports*, 15, 1920 ;
Anon., *Bull. Imp. Inst.*, **14.** 389, 1916 ; E. Halse, *Antimony Ores*, London, 1925 ; G. A. J. Cole,
Mem. Geol. Sur. Ireland, 14, 1922.
    ⁵ E. Bellanger, *Ann. Mines*, (11), **12.** 83, 1921 ; A. Carnot, *ib.*, (7), **13.** 394, 1878 ; P. L. Burthe,
ib., (9), **4.** 15, 1893 ; M. Nentien, *ib.*, (9), **12.** 251, 1897 ; L. N. Vauquelin, *Ann. Chim. Phys.*,
(1), **83.** 32, 1817 ; C. Manière, *Mém. Acad.*, **4.** 108, 1858 ; M. Michel, *Bull. Soc. Min.*, 27. 79,
1904 ; L. de Launay, *Compt. Rend. Internat. Geol. Congress*, **8.** 953, 1950 ; T. Lesalle, *Rev. Scient.*,
9. 18, 1896 ; A. Lacroix, *Minéralogie de la France et de ses colonies*, Paris, **2.** 449, 1896 ; D. Hol-
lauce, *Bull. Soc. Géol.*, (4), **4.** 30, 1876 ; G. Hynert, *Une ancienne mine d'antimoine*, Paris, 1, 1906.
    ⁶ T. Breidenbach, *Gluckauf*, 29. 1095, 1141, 1893 ; Orey d'Albuquerque, *Berg. Hütt. Ztg.*,
40. 270, 1881 ; E. Ackermann, *Chem. Ztg.*, **30.** 677, 1906.
    ⁷ L. de Launay, *Traité de métallogénie gites minéraux et metallifères*, Paris, **1.** 749, 1913 ;
J. Phillips, *A Treatise on Ore Deposits*, London, 505, 1896 ; R. Beck, *The Nature of Ore Deposits*,
New York, 1905.
    ⁸ A. d'Achiardi, *Mineralogie della Toscana*, Pisa, 1872 ; *I Metalli*, 2. 584, 1883 ; *Proc. Verb.
Soc. Toscana*, **7.** 7, 1901 ; L. Baldacci, *Mem. Geol. Italia*, 1. 138, 1886 ; C. Baldracco, *Consti
tuzione metallifera della Sardegna*, Torino, 1854 ; M. Nentien, *Ann. Mines*, (9), **12.** 251, 1897 ;
H. Coquand, *Bull. Soc. Géol.*, (2), **6.** 91, 1849 ; Denti, *Giorn. Min. Crist.*, 2. 211, 1891 ; C. Decastro,
Descrizione geologico mineraria del Sarrabus, Roma, 1890 ; A. Haupt, *Berg. Hütt. Ztg.*, **45.** 313,
333, 1886 ; W. P. Jervis, *I Tesori sotteranei dell' Italia*, Torino, 1881 ; B. Lotti, *Zeit. deut. geol.
Geo.*, **53.** 41, 1901 ; D. Lovisato, *Rend. Accad. Lincei*, (5), i. **3.** 82, 1894 ; V. Novarese, *Boll.
Comt. Geol. Ital.*, **33.** 319, 1902 ; V. E. Rimbotti, *I filoni di stibma a gangha di fluorina a calcite
di San Martino*, Firenze, 1884 ; D. Pantanelli, *Rend. Accad. Lincei*, (3), **8.** 35, 1880 ; P. Tosco,
Revista del Servizeo Minerario, 144, 1899.
    ⁹ A. Foniakoff, *Zeit. prakt. Geol.*, **7.** 54, 1899.
    ¹⁰ H. G. Ferguson, *Min. Res. U.S. Geol. Sur.*, 1, 1919.
    ¹¹ R. Beck, *The Nature of Ore Deposits*, New York, 1905.
    ¹² B. von Cotta, *Berg. Hütt. Ztg.*, **20.** 123, 1861 ; *A Treatise on Ore Deposits*, New York, 1870 ;
A. von Groddeck, *Die Lehre von den Lagerstätten der Erze*, Leipzig, 179, 1879 ; J. Schwarz, *Oesterr.
Zeit. Berg. Hütt.*, **29.** 595, 608, 1881 ; J. Grimm, **16.**. 8. 3, 1860 ; F. Posepny, *Arch. prakt. Geol..*
165, 1895 ; A. Irmler, *Verh. geol. Reichsanst. Wien*, 27. 85, 1899 ; A. Hofmann, *Zeit. prakt. Geol.*,
9. 94, 1901 ; R. Helmhacker, *Leob. Jahrb.*, 22. 340, 1874.
    ¹³ R. Beck and W. von Fircke, *Zeit. prakt. Geol.*, **8.** 33, 1900 ; A. D. Wray, *The Geology and
Mineral Resources of the Serb-Croat-Slovene State*, London, 1921 ; A. Bordeaux, *Rev. Gén. Mines*,
30. 254, 1895 ; L. de Launay, *Ann. Mines*, (9), **13.** 196, 1898 ; H. B. von Foullon, *Verh. geol.
Reichsanst. Wien*, 318, 1890 ; R. Hofmann, *Oesterr. Zeit. Berg. Hütt.*, 39. 167, 1891.
    ¹⁴ A. W. Arndt, *Ueber den Bergbau auf Spiessglanz am Silberberge bei Arnsberg*, Elberfeld,
1834 ; B. von Cotta, *Die Lehre von den Erzlagerstäffen*, Freiberg, **2.** 154, 1861 ; A. Buff, *Karsten's*

Arch., **16**. 54, 1827; A. Erbeich, *ib.*, **16**. 44, 1827; Anon., *ib.*, **8**. 272, 1824; **76**. 54, 1827; **W. von** Gümbel, *Geognostische Beschreibung des Fichtelgebirges*, Gotha, 386, 1879; O. Luedecke, *Die Minerale des Harzes*, Berlin, 1896; R. Schmidt, *Die Mineralien des Fichtelgebirges*, Nürnberg, 1903; E. R. von Warnsdorff, *Berg. Hütt. Ztg.*, **17**. 304, 1858.

[15] K. E. Weiss, *Zeit. prakt. Geol.*, **9**. 249, 1901; W. F. A. Thomas, *Trans. Amer. Inst. Min. Eng.*, **28**. 208, 1898; N. F. Penzer, *Min. Mag.*, 218, 1919.

[16] L. Hennecke, *Zeit. Berg. Hütt. Sal.*, **47**. 272, 1889.

[17] J. C. Brown, *Bull. Indian Indust. Lab.*, 6, 1921; V. Ball, *A Manual of the Geology of India*, Calcutta, 1881; W. R. Criper, *Rec. Geol. Sur. India*, **18**. 151, 1885; A. M. Heron, *ib.*, **53**. 34, 1921; H. C. Jones, *ib.*, **53**. 44, 1921; L. L. Fermor, *ib.*, **33**. 234, 1906; T. H. D. la Touche, *Mem. Geol. Sur. India*, **39**. 366, 1913.

[18] T. Rosewitz, *Borneo : Its Geology and Mineral Resources*, London, 1892; F. Gräger, *Verh. geol. Reichsanst. Wien*, **4**. 87, 1876.

[19] F. R. Tegengren, *Bull. Chim. Geol. Sur.*, 3, 1921; G. D. Hubbard, *Amer. Min.*, **7**. 137, 1922.

[20] P. Jordan, *Ann. Mines*, (9), **14**. 530, 1898; E. S. Dana, *Amer. Journ. Science*, (3), **26**. 214, 1883; T. Wada, *Sitzber. Akad. Berlin*, **79**, 1884; J. J. Rein, *The Industries of Japan*, London, 305, 1889.

[21] H. Merensky, *Zeit. prakt. Geol.*, **13**. 208, 1905; J. P. Johnson, *The Mineral Industry of Rhodesia*, London, 41, 1911; *The Ore Deposits of South Africa*, London, 1908; A. L. Hall, *Mem. Geol. Sur. S. Africa*, 6, 1912; 9, 1918; L. Hennecke, *Trans. Inst. Min. Eng.*, **17**. 30, 1900; L. de Launay, *Les richesses minérales de l'Afrique*, Paris, 335, 1903.

[22] H. Coquand, *Bull. Soc. Géol.*, (2), **9**. 342, 1852; L. Ville, *Ann. Mines*, (6), **16**. 161, 1869; A. Lacroix, *Minéralogie de la France et de ses colonies*, Paris, **2**. 457, 1893; **3**. 22, 1895.

[23] A. H. Brookes, *Bull. U.S. Geol. Sur.*, 649, 1916; 714, 1921; J. B. Mertie, *ib.*, 662, 1918; S. R. Capps, *ib.*, 662, 1918.

[24] L. W. Bailey, *Amer. Journ. Science*, (2), **35**. 150, 1863; G. F. Kunz, *ib.*, (3), **30**. 275, 1885; C. W. Drysdale, *Rept. Canada Geol. Sur. Dept. Mines*, **84**, 1915; W. H. Collins, *ib.*, 251, 1911; J. Keele, *ib.*, 16, 1904; W. S. McCann, *Mem. Canada. Geol. Sur. Dept. Mines*, 130, 1922; R. W. Ellis, *ib.*, 92, 1907; W. Malcolm, *ib.*, 20, E, 1912; J. A. Dresser, *ib.*, 22, 1913; W. R. Askwith, *Trans. Nova Scotia Min. Soc.*, **6**. 80, 1902; E. L. Frebeck, *Ontario Bur. Mines*, 16, 1907; H. V. Ellsworth, *ib.*, 24, 1916; D. D. Cairnes, *Bull. Can. Min. Inst.*, 10, 1910; G. Mailhiot, *Rep. Quebec Bur. Mines*, 55, 1917; J. Obabski, *Mines and Minerals of the Province of Quebec*, Quebec, 1890.

[25] J. P. Hawley, *Mineral Resources of Newfoundland*, St. Johns, 9, 1909; *Mineral Statistics for Newfoundland*, St. Johns, 24, 1898; *Report on the Mineral Statistics and Mines of Newfoundland*, St. Johns, 15, 1900.

[2] W. H. Emmons, *Bull. U.S. Geol. Sur.*, 625, 1917; F. L. Hess, *ib.*, 340, 1908; E. L. Jones, *ib.*, 710, 1919; A. Knopf, *ib.*, 660, 1918; G. B. Richardson, *ib.*, 340, 1908; G. J. Mitchell, *Eng. Min. Journ.*, **114**. 455, 1922; A. J. McDermid, *ib.*, **114**. 538, 1922; J. F. Kemp, *The Ore Deposits of the United States*, New York, 259, 1893; *Eng. Min. Journ.*, **53**. 6, 1892; W. P. Blake, *Report upon the Antimony Deposits of Southern Utah*, New Haven, 1881; E. Halse, *Trans. Amer. Inst. Min. Eng.*, **6**. 290, 1894; C. E. Waite, *ib.*, **7**. 42, 1895; W. Lindgren, *ib.*, **36**. 27, 1906; C. P. Williams, *ib.*, **3**. 150, 1895; G. F. Becker, *ib.*, **36**. 389, 1906; C. Upham, *Amer. Journ. Science*, (2), **37**. 405, 1864; J. C. Branner, *Ann. Rep. Arkansas Geol. Sur.*, **1**. 136, 1888; G. H. Ashley, *Proc. Amer. Phil. Soc.*, **36**. 306, 1897.

[27] E. S. Murias, *Eng. Min. Journ.*, **114**. 198, 1922.

[28] E. Halse, *Trans. Amer. Inst. Min. Eng.*, **6**. 290, 1893; **18**. 370, 1900; J. G. Aguilera, *ib.*, **32**. 307, 1902; M. Rangel and A. Terrones, *Eng. Min. Journ.*, **111**. 170, 1921; J. Douglas, *ib.*, **31**. 350, 1881; J. F. Kemp, *ib.*, **53**. 6, 1892; W. Lindgren and W. L. Whitehead, *Econ. Geol.*, **9**. 435, 1914; E. T. Cox, *Amer. Journ. Science*, (3), **20**. 421, 451, 1880.

[29] G. Bodenbender, *Anales Geol. Min. Agric. Argentina*, **1**. 2, 1905; B. L. Miller and J. T. Singewald, *The Mineral Deposits of South America*, London, 1919; E. S. Bastin, *Min. Res. U.S. Geol. Sur.*, 1, 1918; E. Weckwarth, *Bol. Ing. Minas Peru*, 68, 1908; F. M. Santolalla, *ib.*, 46, 1906; E. I. Duenas, *ib.*, 53, 1907; G. Preumont, *Min. Journ.*, **83**. 282, 1908.

[30] J. E. Carne, *Bull. N.S.W. Dept. Mines*, 15, 16, 1912; E. J. Kenny, *ib.*, 5, 1924; E. C. Andrews, *ib.*, 8, 1900; *Mem. N.S.W. Dept. Mines*, **8**, 1922; G. W. Card, *Rec. Geol. Soc. New South Wales*, **7**. 43, 1904; E. F. Pittman, *The Mineral Resources of New South Wales*, Sydney, 1901; A. Liversidge, *Trans. Roy. Soc. New South Wales*, **9**. 181, 1876; B. Dunstan, *Queensland Govt. Min. Journ.*, 67, 1917; *Publ. Queensland Dept. Mines*, 241, 1913; H. I. Jensen, *ib.*, 274, 1923; L. C. Ball, *ib.*, 223, 1909; E. C. Saint-Smith, *Queensland Govt. Min. Journ.*, 270, 404, 1917; A. M. Howitt, *Mem. Victoria Dept. Mines*, 11, 1913; *Rec. Victoria Dept. Mines*, 2, 1908; S. Hunter, *ib.*, 2, 1908; O. A. L. Whitelaw, *Mem. Victoria Dept. Mines*, 3, 1905; J. Phillips, *A Treatise on Ore Deposits*, London, 1896; A. G. Maitland, *Mem. Geol. Sur. Western Australia*, 1, 1919; R. M. Johnston, *Guide to the Rocks and Minerals of Tasmania*, Hobart, 19, 1888; L. Hennecke, *Trans. Inst. Min. Eng.*, **18**. 30, 1900.

[31] A. Bernard, *Zeit. prakt. Geol.*, **5**. 259, 1897; E. Glasser, *Ann. Mines*, (10), **5**. 536, 1904; A. Lacroix, *Minéralogie de la France et de ses colonies*, Paris, **2**. 443, 1897.

[32] G. L. Binns, *Trans. Fed. Inst. Min. Eng.*, **4**. 59, 1892; P. Marshall, *Geology of New Zealand*, Wellington, 11, 1912; J. Park, *The Geology of New Zealand*, Wellington, 1910; S. H. Cox, *Rept. Geol. Explor. New Zealand*, 2, 1877.

[33] H. K. Masters, *Eng. Min. Journ.*, **118**. 498, 1924 ; F. T. Havard, *New Zealand Mines Record*, 381, 1907 ; W. V. Smitheringale, *Bull. Canada Min. Met.*, 180, 1927 ; L. de Launay, *Statistique de la production des gîtes métallifères*, Paris, 1893 ; L. H. Quin, *Metal Handbook and Statistics*, London, 1925.
[34] S. P. L. Sörensen, *Zeit. anorg. Chem.*, **5**. 354, 1894 ; D. Campbell, *Chem. News*, **2**. 218, 360 ; *Phil. Mag.*, (4), **20**. 304, 1860 ; D. Forbes, *ib.*, (4), **29**. 1, 1865 ; H. Ramage, *Nature*, **119**. 83, 1927 ; P. Kröber, *Berg. Hütt. Ztg.*, **23**. 130, 1864 ; W. Hampe, *Chem. Ztg.*, **17**. 66, 1893 ; *Zeit. Anal. Chem.*, **13**. 176, 1874 ; **32**. 85, 1893 ; A. Carnot, *Compt. Rend.*, **79**. 303, 479, 1874 ; C. F. Rammelsberg, *Handbuch der Mineralchemie*, Leipzig, **2**. 20, 1895 ; *Zeit. deut. geol. Ges.*, **25**. 84, 1873 ; G. T. Prior, *Min. Mag.*, **8**. 98, 1888 ; R. Scharizer, *Jahrb. geol. Reichsanst. Wien*, **30**. 404, 1880 ; L. Sipöcz, *Tschermak's Mitt.*, (2), **7**. 277, 1886 ; F. Becke, *ib.*, (2), **14**. 278, 1894 ; *G*. Tschermak, *ib.*, (1), **3**. 215, 1873 ; W. Petz, *Pogg. Ann.*, **57**. 472, 1842 ; T. Petersen, *ib.*, **136**. 600, 1869 ; **137**. 396, 1869 ; E. Schmid, *Zeit. Kryst.*, **11**. 268, 1886 ; A. Hilger, *Neues Jahrb. Min.*, **99**, 1899 ; G. S. Sérullas, *Journ. Phys.*, **91**. 123, 170, 1820 ; **93**. 115, 1820 ; *Ann. Chim. Phys.*, (2), **18**. 217, 1821 ; F. Sandberger, *Neues Jahrb. Min.*, 222, 1864 ; 291, 1878 ; *Journ. prakt. Chem.*, (2), **1**. 230, 1870 ; *Chem. News*, **21**. 251, 1874 ; C. Winkler, *Ber.*, **19**. 210, 1886 ; E. Ebler, *ib.*, **40**. 1807, 1907 ; *Verh. Nat. Hist. Ver. Heidelberg*, **8**. 435, 1907 ; F. Mauro, *Gazz. Chim. Ital.*, **9**. 70, 1879 ; P. Berthier, *Ann. Mines*, (2), **4**. 467, 1819 ; (3), **7**. 537, 1835 ; A. Daubrée, (4), **19**. 469, 1851 ; *Compt. Rend.*, **32**. 827, 1851 ; A. Ledebur, *Stahl Eisen*, **4**. 634, 1884 ; T. Poleck, *Arch. Pharm.*, (3), **25**. 190, 1887 ; C. R. Schneider, *Journ. prakt. Chem.*, (2), **44**. 23, 1891; H. Reinsch, *ib.*, (2), **22**. 111, 1880 ; C. Bergemann, *ib.*, (1), **75**. 244, 1858 ; A. Buchner, *Repert. Pharm.*, **44**. 264, 1833 ; *Kastner's Arch.*, **24**. 253, 1832.
[35] H. de Sénarmont, *Ann. Chim. Phys.*, (3), **31**. 504, 1851 ; C. R. Fresenius, *Journ. prakt. Chem.*, (1), **90**. 36, 1863 ; (1), **92**. 456, 1864 ; (1), **95**. 151, 1865 ; (1), **98**. 321, 1866 ; (1), **103**. 425, 1867 ; (2), **7**. 20, 1873 ; E. F. von Gorup-Besanez, *ib.*, (2), **17**. 371, 1878 ; T. Poleck, *Chemische Analysen schlesischer Mineralquellen*, Breslau, 1885 ; *Ber.*, **12**. 1905, 1879 ; *Arch. Pharm.*, (3), **25**. 190, 1887 ; L. F. Bley, *ib.*, (2), **82**. 129, 1855 ; E. Reichardt, *ib.*, (2), **98**. 257, 1859 ; W. von Gümbel, *Ber. Bayr. Akad.*, **79**, 1891 ; C. P. Williams, *Amer. Chemist*, **7**. 246, 1877 ; N. B. Hardin, *ib.*, **4**. 427, 1874 ; E. Ludwig and J. Mauthner, *Tschermak's Mitt.*, (2), **2**. 269, 1880 ; *Arch. Pharm.*, (2), **51**. 145, 1847 ; F. Garrigou, *Compt. Rend.*, **84**. 963, 1877 ; H. von Fehling, *Jahresb. Württ. Naturw.*, **16**. 129, 1860 ; H. Göttl, *Oesterr. Zeit. Pharm.*, 253, 1853 ; *Viertelj. prakt. Pharm.*, **5**. 161, 1856 ; H. Will, *Liebig's Ann.*, **61**. 192, 1847; F. A. Walchner, *b.*, **61**. 205, 1847.

§ 3. The Extraction of Antimony

Stibnite is the commonest ore of antimony ; senarmontite and ratentinite are the chief ones at Sidi-Rgherss and Senga in Algeria ; stibiconite has been mined at El Altar, Sonora, Mexico ; kermesite, in Tuscany, Italy ; jamesonite, in South Rhodesia, and Ontario ; jamesonite, and tetrahedrite, Ourro, Bolivia, and Santa Rosa, Peru ; nadorite, at Djebel Nador, Algeria ; and livingstonite, and barcenite, at Huitzuco, Mexico. In the last case mercury was once extracted from the ore and the antimony rejected.

The *concentration of stibnite* by washing with water is costly because the ore is soft, and of a low sp. gr., 4·5. The crushing produces a large proportion of lime which makes the loss so great that the water concentration is then satisfactory only when the precious metals are present in payable quantities. J. Daniels and C. R. Corey [1] found that low-grade stibnite ores can be successfully concentrated by flotation methods. Fine grinding, and the creosote oils with sulphuric acid give the highest yields with the lowest cost of production.

The more important methods for the extraction of antimony from sulphide ores are : (i) Fusion with iron ; (ii) Roasting in shaft furnace, and reducing the oxide with charcoal and alkali ; and (iii) Electrolysis of the sulphide dissolved in alkali sulphide. The extraction of antimony from its ores is discussed in the usual books on the metallurgy of the non-ferrous metals. In addition there are a few special monographs on antimony :

W. Borchers, *Zinn, Wismuth, Antimon*, Halle (Saale), 1924; G. D. Traverso, *L'antimonio*, Alba, 1897; A. Guntz, *Antimoine*, Paris, 1884; C. Y. Wang, *Antimony*, London, 1909; J. Oehme, *Die Fabrikation der wichtigsten Antimon-Präparate*, Wien, 1884; G. Hyvert, *Technologie de l'antimoine*, Carcassonne, 1906.

Liquation processes.—Ores containing over 90 per cent. antimony sulphide are considered to be *crude antimony* or *needle antimony* ; those containing more than

40 per cent. and less than 90 **per cent.** can be liquated for the production of crude antimony. This liquation is possible because of the comparatively low melting temp. of the sulphide. Small-grained ore is not suitable for liquation, presumably because the grains are so close together that the molten sulphide is unable to escape. Pieces the size of a walnut are considered most suited for the liquation process. Fine-grained ore with a low percentage of metal is best reduced to regulus. If the temp. of liquefaction be too high, some antimony sulphide is lost by volatilization ; and if too low, a relatively large proportion of sulphide is retained by the residue. Since merchants prefer crude antimony with a radiating structure, the liquated sulphide is allowed to cool slowly. If rapidly cooled, the required crystalline structure is not developed. The liquefaction can be conducted in pots or crucibles made of fireclay and perforated at the base to allow the molten sulphide to trickle into a fireclay receiver placed below. The pots can be heated by direct contact with the fuel, or by flames with the receiver inside or outside the furnace. The process is intermittent ; the pots require recharging every 10 hrs. In the continuous process of liquation, tubes are fitted over a perforated slab below which is the receiver. The tube is so arranged that the exhausted charge can be raked from the bottom, and a new charge inserted at the top. Continuous liquation is also conducted in reverberating furnaces. There is a tap-hole at the deepest part of the bed of the furnace for the removal of the liquated sulphide. The liquation residues, if sufficiently rich, are worked up for regulus.

Iron reduction process.—The production of metallic antimony or regulus from crude antimony, or from rich ores, with over 60 per cent. antimony, can be effected by the so-called *precipitation process*, or *iron reduction process :* $Sb_2S_3 + 3Fe$ $= 2Sb + 3FeS$. As indicated in connection with the history, this method was used in the Middle Ages. It is not possible to separate the iron sulphide from the antimony, and therefore sodium sulphate and carbon must be added. The resulting sodium sulphide forms a fusible slag with the ferrous sulphide which floats on the surface of the antimony. Common salt can be used instead of sodium sulphate and carbon. The iron is introduced in the form of turnings, shavings, or tin-plate cuttings, for the tin they contain does no harm. The proportion of iron is kept low since arsenides and lead sulphides are reduced by the excess, and the antimony is then unduly contaminated, not only with iron, but also with lead and arsenic. With ores free from arsenic and lead, an excess of iron is used in order to ensure the separation of all the antimony in the ore. The excess of iron is removed by subsequent fusion with crude antimony. The process was discussed by P. Berthier,[2] J. von Liebig, C. J. B. Karsten, E. Hering, C. Schnabel, E. Rodger, T. C. Sanderson, N. C. Cookson, R. Helmhacher, G. Pautrat, A. H. Imbert, N. Baraboschkin, etc.

The operation on a large scale is carried out in crucibles or in reverberatory furnaces. In the crucible process, the metal produced by the reduction with wrought iron is known as *singles*. It contains, maybe, 91·6 per cent. of antimony, about 7 per cent. of iron, and less than one per cent. of sulphur. The singles is mixed with some liquated or crude antimony and common salt, and heated. The operation is called *doubling*. The product is known as *star bowls*, and contains, say. 99·5 per cent. of antimony, nearly 0·2 per cent. each of iron and sulphur. The refining or *frenching* of the star bowls is effected again by heating the metal with liquated sulphide and a flux. The product is known as *star antimony*, or *French metal*. The reverberatory furnace process involves the fusion with scrap iron to produce crude metal, and a refining fusion.

Formerly the metal or regulus obtained by reducing the grey sulphide was called *regulus antimonii simplex* or *regulus antimonii vulgario*. When the metal was cast in a mould and the upper surface of the ingots had a stellated structure, it was called *regulus antimonii stellatus*, Fig. 2. When the antimony contained much iron, it was called *regulus antimonii martialis*. When the sulphide was reduced with tin, the product was called *regulus antimonii jovialis ;* with lead, *regulus antimonii saturninus ;* with copper, *regulus antimonii venereus ;* and with silver, *regulus antimonii lunaris*.

Reduction processes.—Formerly the grey sulphide was mixed with charcoal and roasted. There remained a mixture of the trioxide and pentoxide called *calx antimonii grisea*, or *cinis antimonii*. This was then mixed with cream of tartar, or with a mixture of charcoal and sodium carbonate and fused in a crucible at a low red-heat. The slag floated on the surface of the metal, which was then cast in a mould. Modifications of the process were described by P. L. Geiger and A. Reimann,[3] J. von Liebig, and A. Duflos. Heating the sulphide with lime and carbon does not give good results : $Sb_2S_3+3CaCO_3+6C=2Sb+3CaS+9CO$, but C. G. Fink obtained good results in an electrically heated vacuum furnace. A. Levol reduced antimony sulphide by melting it with twice its weight of potassium ferrocyanide. H. C. Geelmuyden reduced the sulphide with calcium carbide ; and N. Tarugi employed this agent with other antimonial compounds. M. G. Bachimont heated the sulphide with ferric chloride and obtained ferrous sulphide and volatile antimony trichloride. A. Germot heated the sulphide to its temp. of dissociation while protected from oxygen ; the sulphur was recovered by sublimation. R. Jahn passed the fumes from the roaster through a reducing flame.

Roasting for tetroxide.—Poor ores, and liquation residues can be roasted to the tetroxide or to the volatile trioxide. In the past, the roasting for the tetroxide has been carried out in muffles, or reverberatory furnaces with rabbling. At about 350°, air converts antimony sulphide into antimony trioxide and sulphur dioxide ; a part of the trioxide forms the pentoxide, which, uniting with the trioxide forms the tetroxide. In the presence of metal oxides, antimonates are formed ; no antimony sulphate is produced. If the ore contains foreign sulphides which, when roasted alone, form sulphates, antimonates are produced in place of the sulphates. According to L. Bidou,[4] if the temp. of roasting be less than 350°, the sulphide is not decomposed ; if it exceeds 350° a little, the mass sinters together, thereby retarding the access of air to the interior of the mass ; and if the temp. be raised still higher, the trioxide volatilizes. The rabbling of the mass hinders the sintering. The richer the ore the more difficult it is to roast it in this way because of the tendency to sinter ; the presence of gangue hinders the balling or sintering. If the admission of air be restricted during the roasting, the volatile trioxide, not the tetroxide, is formed.

Roasting for volatile trioxide.—In 1844, A. Bobierre, F. A. H. F. de Ruobz and M. Rousseau proposed to obtain antimony trioxide by the volatilization process ; and the idea was applied by M. de Franceschi, W. Glass, H. L. Herrenschmidt, J. Oehme, E. Hering, R. Helmhacker, E. Chatillon, J. Woolford, A. S. Plews, E. Rasse-Courbet, and the Miniere e Fonderie d'antimonie Società Anonima, Genoa, Italy. The process was studied by J. A. de Cew. In the volatilization process poor ores and residues from the manufacture of crude antimony can be treated by roasting them in a furnace at a sufficiently high temp. to volatilize the antimony as trioxide, and collect it in suitable chambers. The product contains very little antimony tetroxide, or pentoxide, and is used partly in the preparation of paint, and partly for reduction to antimony by melting it with coal and fluxes. J. Oehme prepared the trioxide for use as paint by roasting the sulphide in a restricted supply of air and steam. The air roasting for the volatile sulphide is effected (i) in E. Chatillon's furnace. This consists of two rectangular cupolas charged with alternate layers of fuel and ore ; these cupolas communicate with two smaller cupolas where hot air is produced and where the last traces of antimony trioxide are produced from scoriæ. The volatile trioxide is collected in sheet-iron tanks acting as a filtration chamber, or bag-house. The roasting is also effected (ii) in H. L. Herrenschmidt's furnace which consists of a rectangular shaft which is fitted with a step-grate of iron bars. The upper part of the furnace communicates with a series of condensing chambers provided with condensation tubes of corrugated iron. The air and dust is drawn through these chambers by an exhaust fan. Beyond the condensing chamber is a coke-tower down which water trickles so as to arrest the last traces of uncondensed oxide.

Reducing the oxides to regulus.—The products obtained in the roasting of sulphide ores—tetroxide, or volatile trioxide—or the natural oxidized ores are reduced to antimony regulus. Coal alone is unsuitable as a reducing agent because so much antimony is lost by volatilization as trioxide, and any sulphide which has escaped oxidation will also escape reduction. Hence, fluxing agents are added to form a protective cover preventing undue volatilization, to assist in the formation of fusible slags, and to help the separation of the metal from the sulphide. Fluxes like alkali sulphates and carbonates also help to remove impurities from the antimony, and to serve as a refining medium. With rich ores, crude antimony, or the volatilized oxide, when only a small quantity of metal is required, the reduction is carried out in crucibles or pots; the reduction, however, is more economically effected in reverberatory furnaces or in shaft furnaces. The processes were described by E. Hering, L. and G. Simonin, J. Rössner, A. F. Wendt, C. Winkler, C. A. M. Balling, L. A. Pelatan, E. Basse, etc.

The direct reduction of the ore in a blast-furnace.—W. R. Schoeller described a process for the direct smelting of stibnite, slag, and liquation residues containing 25–40 per cent. of antimony. No iron is used in the reduction. The molten sulphide dissolves the trioxide formed in the blast: $2Sb_2S_3+9O_2=Sb_4O_6+6SO_2$, and there is then a reaction: $Sb_4O_6+Sb_2S_3=6Sb+3SO_2$. This self-reduction also occurs during the roasting of lead sulphide ores. The current of sulphur dioxide which is at the same time evolved acts as inert gas in that it does not reduce antimony trioxide, and it takes no active part in the liberation of the metal. The reaction does not occur in an inert gas, for if the oxide-sulphide mixture be melted under a layer of salt, the metal is not obtained. The fused mixture of oxide and sulphide is the so-called *antimony glass*. In order to reduce the loss by volatilization, a tall shaft is required, and it should be connected with a suitable condenser. E. Hering observed that no antimony is formed when a mixture of the sulphide and tetroxide is heated in the roasting furnace, but the mixture forms a red glass; K. Brückner made some observations on this reaction. Water-jacketed furnaces were used by H. L. Herrenschmidt, and A. Germot used a converter. R. Jahn described a process in which the volatilized oxide is at once reduced by a reducing gas; and A. P. Hernandez heated the sulphide with carbon and nitrate: $Sb_2S_3+8KNO_3+6C=2Sb+3K_2SO_4+K_2CO_3+4CO_2+CO+4N_2$. W. Buddëus reduced the ore with silicon or silicides.

Extraction by lixiviation processes.—Many proposals have been made for the extraction of antimony, from poor ores and liquation products, by wet methods, but none has yet had much success. J. Hargreaves and T. Robinson [5] extracted the powdered ore with hot hydrochloric acid, neutralized the liquid with lime; and precipitated the antimony with tin or zinc. The precipitated metal was washed, and fused with alkali. R. F. Smith employed a somewhat similar process; and E. Hering treated the hydrochloric acid soln. of liquation residues either with water to precipitate the oxychloride, or with hydrogen sulphide to precipitate the sulphide. J. S. MacArthur treated the pulverized ore with a 2 per cent. soln. of sodium hydroxide at 100°; and passed carbon dioxide through the filtered soln. The precipitated antimony sulphide was collected on a filter, and the alkali carbonate was causticized for further use by the lime from the kiln furnishing the carbon dioxide. The process was therefore continuous. F. Leyser also extracted the ore with alkali-lye. J. Simpson and E. W. Parnell proposed soln. of alkali sulphides as solvent. N. W. Edwards lixiviated the ores with a 7 per cent. soln. of sodium sulphide; the antimony sulphide in the filtered soln. was precipitated by carbon dioxide, and the hydrogen sulphide evolved was used to regenerate calcium sulphide by bubbling it through milk of lime. Any gold or silver in the antimony ore remained undissolved and was recovered by ordinary methods. H. L. Herrenschmidt also employed a soln. of sodium sulphide as solvent, but precipitated the antimony sulphide by sulphur dioxide. L. A. Pelaton and D. Lévat reported on this process. F. Kessler, and A. Loir also used sodium sulphide as solvent:

evaporated the filtered soln. to dryness ; fused the product, and precipitated the antimony with iron. R. Koepp used a soln. of ferric chloride as solvent for the antimony sulphide : $6FeCl_3+Sb_2S_3=6FeCl_2+2SbCl_3+3S$. The presence of hydrochloric acid or of halide salts hastens the process of dissolution. The antimony can be readily precipitated from the soln. The antimony was recovered by electrolysis. J. Gitsham used a soln. of alkali cyanide lye. M. Haremann roasted the ore with alkali carbonate and carbon, and on lixiviating the product with water, lead and the precious metals remained undissolved, while antimony sulphide was precipitated from the soln. by adding sulphuric acid. F. M. Lyte roasted the ore with chlorides and condensed the vapour of antimony chloride in a soln. of common salt. The antimony was precipitated from the liquid by iron or zinc.

Electrolytic processes.—Several methods have been proposed for the extraction of antimony electrolytically, but with no marked commercial success. According to W. Borchers,[6] low-grade antimony ores can be leached with soln. of sulphides of the alkalies or alkaline earths, to form a soln. of sulphantimonite or sulphanti-monate. He found that with the same expenditure of current, the same quantity of antimony is deposited whether the soln. of sulphantimonite or sulphantimonate is used. Hydrogen was liberated along with antimony at the cathode ; and at the anode, oxidation products of sodium sulphide, oxygen, sulphur, and antimony sulphide are formed. The reactions occurring during the electrolytic process are not clear ; they have been studied by F. W. Durkee, A. Scheurer-Kestner, H. Ost and W. Klapproth, A. Engelenberg, and D. I. Demorest. R. Koepp leached the ore with a soln. of ferric chloride as indicated above, and electrolyzed the soln. at 50° between lead plates. A. G. Betts studied a similar process. E. W. von Siemens and J. G. Halske extracted the ore with alkali sulphides, hydrosulphides, or poly-sulphides : $3Sb_2S_3+6NaHS=6NaSbS_2+3H_2S$. The liquor was then electrolyzed in diaphragm chambers with carbon or platinum anodes, and copper or antimony cathodes. At the cathode, the soln. of hydrosulphide is regenerated, and antimony deposited. E. W. von Siemens also used soln. of magnesium or alkaline earth sulphides as the extraction liquid. Modifications were devised by I. Izart, and J. von der Ploeg. J. H. Vogel, and T. C. Sanderson used as electrolyte a soln. of antimony trichloride and alkali or ammonium chloride, acidified with hydrochloric acid. F. C. Mathers and K. S. Means recommended a soln. of antimony fluoride in water mixed with an excess of hydrofluoric acid, with a small addition of aloin, resorcinol, α-naphthol, β-naphthol, or salicylic acid, as the best electrolyte for the electrodeposition of antimony ; and F. von Hemmelmayr, and J. C. Ghosh and A. N. Kappana, a hydrochloric acid soln. of tartar emetic—the last-named added that if oil of bergamot be present, this bath gives a very smooth, uniform white deposit, which on polishing assumes a silvery appearance. Thin deposits of thick-ness 0·025 mm. have been found to be quite adhesive ; this thickness is quite sufficient for plating purposes. High current densities can be employed (50 milli-amperes per cm.) and the current efficiency is as high as 97 per cent.—*vide infra.*

J. Lukas and A. Jilek showed that to obtain bright, firmly-adherent deposits of anti-mony from acid soln., the substance, containing less than 0·3 g. of antimony, is dissolved in 3 c.c. of conc. sulphuric acid ; water is added and the soln. treated with 12·5 g. of ammonium citrate, 2 g. of sodium hydrophosphate, and 2 c.c. of hydrazine hydrate, and electrolyzed for 2 hrs. at 70°–90°, using a current of 1 amp. at 1·6–2·1 volts and a rotating anode. If a stationary anode is employed, the electrolysis should be con-ducted with 0·5 amp. for 3 hrs. The citrate may be replaced by 11 g. of sodium potassium tartrate, but the deposits then obtained are not quite so brilliant. Good deposits are produced also by using ammonium instead of sodium phosphate and neutralizing the soln. (to methyl-orange) with ammonia before adding the hydrazine hydrate.

The refining of antimony.—R. Helmhacker found unrefined antimony prepared by the iron precipitation process had 84·0–94·5 per cent. of antimony ; 2·0–5·0 per cent. of sulphur ; 3·0–10·0 per cent. of iron ; 0·25–1·0 per cent. of arsenic ; and traces of gold. That prepared by the reduction of oxidized ores in a shaft-furnace had 95·0–97·2 per cent. antimony ; 0·2–0·75 per cent. sulphur ; 2·5–4·0 per cent iron ; and 0·1–0·25 per cent. arsenic. Unrefined antimony contains sulphur, iron, arsenic, copper, and frequently lead. These impurities with the exception of lead can be eliminated partly by oxidizing and slagging agents, and partly by sulphurizing agents, and partly by chlorinating agents. Fusion with alkali, or antimony-glass —*i.e.* antimony oxysulphide—removes sulphur, and converts arsenic with the alkali arsenate. Fusion with antimony sulphide converts copper and iron into sulphides, and the reaction is facilitated by the addition of alkalies or Glauber's salt and charcoal, which form sodium sulphide. These sulphides are removed by antimony glass. Common salt, cryolite, or magnesium chloride volatilize some of the foreign metals as chlorides, and slag others, but at the same time much antimony may be lost by volatilization. The lead can be partly eliminated by the chloridizing agents, but not by the oxidizing or sulphurizing agents since antimony reduces lead from its oxide or sulphide. The refining of antimony is conducted in pot furnaces or in a reverberatory furnace. The refinery slags are treated with the original ore. L. and M. Meyer recovered antimony from its alloys with other metals by adding enough sulphur to form sulphides with all the metals except antimony. The molten antimony can then be separated from the molten sulphides.

R. Helmhacker [7] studied the purification of antimony by oxidizing agents like manganese dioxide, potassium permanganate, antimony tetroxide and antimony-glass. J. von Liebig purified small quantities of antimony in the following manner :

Fuse in a fireclay crucible a mixture of powdered antimony with one-eighth its weight of sodium carbonate and one-sixteenth its weight of antimony sulphide. The button of metal so obtained is again fused with sodium carbonate for two hours ; and a third time with sodium carbonate mixed with a small proportion of potassium nitrate. The sulphur of the antimony sulphide transforms the foreign metals, except lead, into sulphides which dissolve in the scoria. The arsenic compounds form arsenates and sulpharsenates. The nitrate added by J. Schill in the last fusion is to complete the conversion of arsenic with arsenate. If the sample to be purified contains much iron, the proportion of antimony sulphide should be increased. A. Bensch recommended adding iron sulphide to the mixture in cases where the antimony was free from iron, and contained much arsenic. The presence of iron was said to facilitate the removal of arsenic. E. F. Anthon said that the fusions should not be made in carbon crucibles because carbon would reduce arsenates to arsenic.

The subject was discussed by J. A. Buchner, J. A. Buchner and J. E. Herberger, J. F. A. Göttling, A. Duflos, T. Martius, C. Meyer, and F. Wöhler. F. Winkler, W. Artus, G. C. Wittstein, and F. Kessler obtained antimony of a high degree of purity by reducing the purified oxychloride with carbon in the presence of alkali ; A. Popper reduced the oxychloride with hydrogen. B. Unger purified antimony by first converting it into sodium sulphantimonate. H. Capitaine, F. Kessler, and G. C. Friend and E. F. Smith purified potassium antimonyl tartrate by repeated crystallization, and reduced the product for antimony. T. Martius did not recommend the process. W. P. Dexter reduced sodium antimonate with carbon. J. B. A. Dumas, and J. P. Cooke purified the trichloride by fractional distillation ; and F. Mylius and K. Hüttner recommended purifying the penta-chloride by first extraction with ether. E. Groschuff examined the different methods used for preparing antimony of a high degree of purity. Technically purified antimony has a higher degree of purity than that obtained by the electrolysis of soln. of antimony sulphide. He recommended the following mode of preparing antimony of a high degree of purity :

Antimony trichloride or pentachloride is purified by distillation, and is then transformed into chlorantimonic acid. This compound is specially adapted to the separation of anti-mony from all likely metallic impurities. After purification by recrystallization, the chlor-antimonic acid is readily hydrolyzed to antimonic acid, which is reduced to metal preferably by melting with potassium cyanide. In a large preparation (about a kilogram) purified in this way, no impurities at all could be detected by qualitative methods.

J. Bongartz, and A. Classen electrolyzed a soln. of a sulphantimonite ; and J. B. Alzugaray, a soln. of antimony trichloride. The electro-deposition of antimony has been discussed above. The difficulty is to obtain a deposit which adheres well to the cathode. The electro-deposition of antimony has also been discussed by many others [8]—*vide infra*, explosive antimony. According to A. Mazzucchelli, the presence of antimony trichloride, tribromide, or triiodide, cannot be prevented by electrolyzing the halide with a soln. containing a colloid. Many colloids, including resorcinol, tannin, molybdic acid, starch, and gum, have no influence on the aspect and properties of the metallic deposit, but the presence of proteins, especially of gelatin, results in the separation of antimony which exhibits increased lustre and fragility and is explosive towards heat, but only slightly so towards shock. Quinine, with which antimony chloride forms a double chloride, sparingly soluble in conc. hydrochloric acid, has an effect similar to that of the proteins ; the cationic function of the alkaloid appears to depend on its absorption by the metal. Lowering of the temp. at which the electrolysis takes place renders the metallic deposit pitted and less adherent, owing to an increase in the cathodic evolution of hydrogen. G. F. Taylor described the manufacture of thin filaments of antimony.

The refined metal usually contains over 99 per cent. of antimony, and the surface is covered by a fern-like appearance, Fig. 2. This effect appears only when

FIG. 2.—Star Antimony, or *Regulus antimonii stellatus.*   FIG. 3.—Crystals from a Cavity in Cast Antimony.

the purified molten metal is allowed to solidify slowly beneath a layer of slag. The slag is easily detached from the cold metal by scrubbing with water and sand. This is the commercial *star-metal* or *star-antimony*, and is considered the best quality of refined antimony. Fig. 3 shows some crystals from a cavity in the cast metals. Analyses were quoted by R. Engelhardt,[9] F. Herz, J. M. M. Dormaar, and A. L. Day, R. B. Sosmann, and E. T. Allen. The main impurities occurring in commercial antimony in appreciable and varying quantities are lead, arsenic, iron, copper, and sulphur. There are also present, in nearly all cases, traces of tin, bismuth, zinc, nickel, cobalt, and other elements ; but these impurities are usually present only in negligible quantities, and are rarely included in commercial analysis of the metal. Two of the following analyses are quoted by C. Schnabel ; the others have been supplied from private sources.

	Sb	Cu	Fe	Pb	As	Bi	S	Co,Ni
C. . .	99·75	0·02	0·04	0·04	0·07	—	0·05	—
Tyne . .	99·63	0·04	0·07	0·06	0·08	—	0·08	—
H. . .	99·662	—	0·110	0·061	0·038	—	0·129	—
La Lucitte .	99·35	0·01	0·06	0·13	0·20	—	0·20	—
Brioude . .	98·3	0·03	0·03	0·03	1·3	—	0·03	—
W.C.C. . .	99·35	tr.	0·03	0·14	0·08	—	0·35	—
California .	98·34	0·021	0·144	0·410	1·008	—	0·064	0·013
Hungary .	98·27	0·54	0·63	—	—	0·36	—	—

356   INORGANIC AND THEORETICAL CHEMISTRY

The commercial brands are " A.S.P.," St. Helen's Smelting Co. (Fig. 2); " C.," and
" Tyne," Cookson and Co., Newcastle-on-Tyne ; " H.," Hallett and Son, London ;
" W.C.C.," Wah Chang Trading Corporation, Chang-Sha, China ; Lucette Brioude, La
Société France-Italienne, Brioude, France.   The continental and Chinese brands are very
variable in quality.   E. A. Smith reported from a trace to 0·0054 per cent. of gold, and
0·008–0·0191 per cent. of silver in star antimony.

REFERENCES.

[1] J. Daniels and C. R. Corey, Eng. Min. Journ., 103. 185, 1917 ; C. S. Parsons, Canada Dept.
Mines, 643, 1924 ; W. V. Smitheringale, Bull. Canada Min. Met., 180, 1927.
[2] P. Berthier, Ann. Chim. Phys., (2), 25. 379, 1824 ; E. Hering, Dingler's Journ., 230. 253,
262, 1878 ; C. Schnabel, Handbuch der Metallhüttenkunde, Berlin, 2. 572, 1904 ; London, 2.
559, 1907 ; J. von Liebig, Mag. Pharm., 35. 120, 1831 ; Liebig's Ann., 22. 60, 1837 :
C. J. B. Karsten, System der Metallurgie, Berlin, 4. 561, 1831 ; E. Rodger, Journ. Soc. Chem. Ind.,
11. 16, 1892 ; Eng. Min. Journ., 52. 299, 1892 ; G. Pautrat, ib., 84. 493, 1907 ; T. C. Sanderson,
U.S. Pat. No. 714040, 1902 ; N. C. Cookson, Brit. Pat. No. 20981, 1902 ; French Pat. No.
324864, 1902 ; A. H. Imbert, ib., 384717, 1907 ; R. Helmhacher, Berg. Hütt. Ztg., 42. 1, 23, 44,
145, 172, 191, 1885 ; 43. 394, 1884 ; N. Baraboschkin, Met., 9. 335, 1912 ; German Pat., D.R.P.
237552, 1910 ; R. A. Sembdner, ib., 359744, 1917.
[3] P. L. Geiger and A. Reimann, Mag. Pharm., 17. 136, 1827 ; J. von Liebig, ib., 35. 120, 1831 ;
Liebig's Ann., 22. 62, 1837 ; J. H. McLean, Chem. Eng. Mining Rev., 19. 93, 1926 ; A. Duflos,
Brandes' Arch., 36. 277, 1843 ; 38. 158, 1844 ; Kastner's Arch. Chem., 1. 56, 1830 ; A. Levol,
Ann. Chim. Phys., (3), 46. 471, 1856 ; M. G. Bachimont, German Pat., D.R.P. 80225, 1895 ;
H. C. Geelmuyden, Compt. Rend., 130. 1036, 1900 ; N. Tarugi, Gazz. Chim. Ital., 29. 509, 1899 ;
C. G. Fink, Trans. Amer. Electrochem. Soc., 21. 452, 1912 ; A. Germot, U.S. Pat. No. 1475294,
1924 ; R. Jahn, Montan. Rund., 17. 565, 1925 ; Austrian Pat. No. 102293, 1925.
[4] L. Bidou, Génie civil, 2. 534, 1882 ; E. Hering, Dingler's Journ., 230. 253, 262, 1878 ;
J. Rössner, ib., 166. 449, 1862 ; A. F. Wendt, Berg. Hütt. Ztg., 33. 237, 1874 ; Eng. Min. Journ.,
ib., 387, 1873 ; K. Brückner, Monatsh., 27. 49, 1906 ; J. Oehme, Die Fabrikation der wichtigsten
Antimon-Präparate, Wien, 61, 1884 ; E. Chatillon, French Pat. No. 189974, 1888 ; 382504,
1907 ; Eng. Min. Journ., 85. 991, 1908 ; C. Y. Wang, Min. Journ., 84. 108, 1908 ; Antimony,
London, 67, 1909 ; H. L. Herrenschmidt, French Pat. Nos. 296200, 1900 ; 324860, 1902 ;
333306, 333340, 1903 ; 339980, 350013, 1904 ; 356917, 1905 ; 386107, 1908 ; New South Wales
Pat. Nos. 533, 1876 ; 997, 1881 ; Brit. Pat. No. 2736, 1876 ; A. Bobierre, F. A. H. F. de Ruobz,
and M. Rousseau, French Pat. No. 8084, 1844 ; E. T. Havard, Min. Ind., 59, 1907 ; Eng.
Min. Journ., 82. 1014, 1906 ; W. Glass, Brit. Pat. No. 2565, 1862 ; A. Germot, Rev. Prod. Chim.,
12. 375, 1907 ; French Pat. No., 379143, 1907 ; E. Hering, Dingler's Journ., 230. 253, 262, 1878 ;
R. Helmhacker, Berg. Hütt. Ztg., 42. 1, 23, 44, 145, 172, 191, 1883 ; 43. 394, 1884 ; A. S. Plews,
Brit. Pat. No. 5440, 1901 : M. de Franceschi, French Pat. No. 20257, 1858 ; J. Woolford,
Brit. Pat. No. 7257, 1888 ; E. Rasse-Courbet, French Pat. No. 362455, 1906 ; Miniere e Fonderie
d'antimonie Società Anonima, ib., 381517, 1907 ; L. A. Pelatan, ib., 210331, 1890 ; E. Basse,
ib., 319534, 1902 ; 368745, 1906 ; W. R. Schoeller, Trans. Inst. Min. Met., 27. 237, 1918 ; Journ.
Soc. Chem. Ind., 33. 169, 1914 ; L. Simonin, Bull. Soc. Ind. Min., (1), 3. 577, 1858 ; Berg. Hütt.
Ztg., 18. 195, 200, 1859 ; G. Simonin, French Pat. No. 203882, 1890 ; C. A. M. Balling, Chem.
Ztg., 9. 1825, 1885 ; C. Winkler, Amt. Ber. deut. Reichs Wein. Weltausstellung, (3), 1. 975, 1873 ;
in A. W. Hoffmann's Bericht über die Entwicklung der chemischen Industrie, Braunschweig, 975,
1875 ; Monit. Scient., (3), 7. 1190, 1877 ; J. A. de Cew, Chem. Met. Engg., 16. 444, 1917 ;
R. Jahn, Montan. Rund., 17. 565, 1925 ; Austrian Pat. No. 102293, 1925 ; A. P. Hernandez,
Anal. Soc. Quim. Argentina, 6. 306, 1918 ; Anal. Fis. Quim., 16. 302, 1918 ; F. H. Mason, Min.
Scient. Press, 92. 280, 1906 ; Met., 3. 706, 1906 ; K. Pietrusky, ib., 2. 7, 1905 ; A. Lissner and
R. Eichelter, Metall Erz, 19. 373, 1922 ; R. A. Sembdner, German Pat., D.R.P. 359744, 1917 ;
360820, 1918 ; W. Buddëus, Brit. Pat. No. 264834, 1927.
[5] F. M. Lyte, Brit. Pat. No. 4635, 1882 ; N. W. Edwards, ib., 15791, 1897 ; J. Simpson and
E. W. Parnell, ib., 11827, 11882, 1884 ; 9918, 1886 ; J. Hargreaves and T. Robinson, ib., 184,
1881 ; J. S. MacArthur, ib., 11123, 1904 ; Mineral Industry, 14. 26, 1905 ; E. Hering, Dingler's
Journ., 230. 253, 262, 1878 ; 286. 287, 1893 ; F. Kessler, Journ. Pharm. Chim., (3), 40. 308,
1861 ; Pogg. Ann., 95. 220, 1855 ; 113. 134, 1860 ; A. Loir, Bull. Soc. Chim., (1), 2. 73, 1861 ;
R. F. Smith, ib., (2), 16. 389, 1871 ; Brit. Pat. No. 205, 1871 ; R. Koepp, German Pat., D.R.P.
66547, 1892 ; M. Haremann, Rev. Prod. Chim., 1. 196, 1898 ; H. L. Herrenschmidt, French Pat.
No. 339980, 350013, 1904 ; F. Leyser, German Pat., D.R.P. 360429, 1921 ; L. A. Pelaton and
D. Lévat, Sur le traitement des minérais auro-antimonieux par le procédé de M. Herrenschmidt,
Paris, 1904 ; J. Platten and C. R. Barnett, U.S. Pat. No. 880752, 1908 ; Met., 5. 302, 1908 ;
J. Gitsham, French Pat. No. 430852, 1911 ; U.S. Pat. No. 1068646, 1913.
[6] W. Borchers, Elektrometallurgie, Braunschweig, 148, 1891 ; 485, 1903 ; London, 476, 1904 ;
Chem. Ztg., 11. 1011, 1023, 1887 ; J. Lukas and A. Jilek, Chem. Listy, 20. 63, 130, 170, 1926 ;
F. W. Durkee, Zeit. Elektrochem., 3. 153, 1896 ; A. Scheurer-Kestner, ib., 4. 215, 1897 ; H. Ost
and W. Klapproth, ib., 7. 376, 1900 ; J. H. Vogel, Zeit. angew. Chem., 4. 327, 1891 ; R. Koepp,
German Pat., D.R.P. 66547, 1892 ; J. von der Ploeg, ib., 138198, 1903 ; Brit. Pat. No. 12308.

1903 ; **E. W. von Siemens and J. G. Halske**, *ib.*, 67973, 1892 ; E. W. von Siemens, *Zeit. Elektro-chem.*, **2**. 130, 1897 ; *Brit. Pat. No.* 7123, 1896 ; A. G. Betts, *ib.*, 15294, 1904 ; *Trans. Amer. Electrochem. Soc.*, **8**. 187, 1905 ; F. C. Mathers and K. S. Means, *ib.*, **31**. 289, 1917 ; D. I. Demorest, *Eng. Min. Journ.*, **105**. 105, 1918 ; F. von Hemmelmayr, *Monatsh.*, **23**. 262, 1908 ; I. Izart, *L'Électricien*, **22**. 33, 1902 ; *Journ. Soc. Chem. Ind.*, **21**. 1237, 1902 ; T. C. Sander-son, *Brit. Pat. No.* 6882, 1889 ; J. C. Ghosh and A. N. Kappana, *Journ. Phys. Chem.*, **28**. 149, 1924 ; A. Engelenberg, *Elektro-analytische Methoden zur Bestimmung von Metallen aus salzsaurer Lösung*, Aachen, 1922 ; L. and M. Meyer, *Brit. Pat. No.* 264139, 1926 ; R. Helmhacker, *Berg. Hütt. Ztg.*, **42**. 1, 44, 145, 172, 191, 1883 ; 43. 394, 1884.
[7] W. Artus, *Journ. prakt. Chem.*, (1), **8**. 127, 1836 ; W. P. Dexter, *Pogg. Ann.*, **100**. 563, 1857 ; F. Kessler, *ib.*, **95**. 220, 1855 ; **113**. 134, 1860 ; *Journ. Pharm. Chim.*, (3), **40**. 308, 1861 ; A. Bensch, *ib.*, (3), **14**. 444, 1848 ; J. Lefort, *ib.*, (3), **28**. 95, 1855 ; F. Wöhler, *ib.*, (2), **19**. 358, 1833 ; *Pogg. Ann.*, **27**. 628, 1832 ; *Liebig's Ann.*, **5**. 20, 1833 ; J. von Liebig, *ib.*, **19**. 22, 645, 1836 ; J. Schill, *ib.*, **104**. 223, 1857 ; A. Popper, *ib.*, **233**. 154, 1886 ; C. Meyer, *ib.*, **27**. 628, 1838 ; **64**. 238, 1848 ; G. C. Wittstein, *ib.*, **60**. 216, 1846 ; J. Struthers, *Eng. Min. Journ.*, **76**. 14, 1903 ; R. Helmhacker, *Berg. Hütt. Ztg.*, **42**. 1, 44, 145, 172, 191, 1883 ; **43**. 394, 1884 ; J. A. Buchner and J. E. Herberger, *Repert. Pharm.*, **38**. 381, 1831 ; J. A. Buchner, *ib.*, **44**. 253, 1833 ; E. F. Anthon, *ib.*, **59**. 240, 1837 ; H. Capitaine, *Journ. prakt. Chem.*, (1), **18**. 449, 1839 ; *Pogg. Ann.*, **100**. 563, 1857 ; *Journ. Pharm. Chim.*, (2), **25**. 516, 1839 ; A. Duflos, *Schweigger's Journ.*, **60**. 353, 1830 ; **62**. 501, 1831 ; *Arch. Apoth.*, **36**. 277, 1843, ; **38**. 158, 1844 ; *Kastner's Arch.*, **19**. 56, 1830 ; T. Martius, *ib.*, **24**. 253, 1832 ; J. F. A. Göttling, *Taschenbuch*, 1. 96, 1780 ; J. B. A. Dumas, *Ann. Chim. Phys.*, (3), **55**. 175, 1859 ; J. Bongartz, *Ber.*, **16**. 1944, 1883 ; A. Classen, *ib.*, **14**. 1629, 1881 ; F. Mylius and K. Hüttner, *ib.*, **44**. 1315, 1324, 1911 ; G. C. Friend and E. F. Smith, *Journ. Amer. Chem. Soc.*, **23**. 502, 1901 ; J. B. Alzugaray, *Brit. Pat. No.* 15713, 1892 ; E. Groschuff, *Zeit. anorg. Chem.*, **103**. 164, 1918 ; B. Unger, *Arch. Pharm.*, **197**. 193, 1871 ; J. P. Cooke, *Proc. Amer. Acad.*, **13**. 1, 1877 ; **15**. 251, 1880 ; **17**. 1, 1881 ; F. Winkler, *Das Atomgewicht des Antimons. Neubestimmung durch Ueberführung des Metalls in Antimon-Tetroxyd*, München, 1917.
[8] F. Wrightson, *Zeit. anal. Chem.*, **15**. 300, 1876 ; G. Parodi and A. Mascazzini, *ib.*, **18**. 588, 1879 ; C. Luckow, *ib.*, **19**. 13, 1880 ; A. Classen, *Quantitative Chemical Analysis by Electrolysis*, New York, 208, 1908 ; *Ber.*, **27**. 2060, 1894 ; A. Classen and M. A. von Reiss, *ib.*, **14**. 1622, 1881 ; **17**. 2467, 1884 ; A. Classen and R. Ludwig, *ib.*, **18**. 1104, 1885 ; G. Vortmann, **24**. 2762, 1891 ; A. Fischer, *ib.*, **36**. 2348, 1903 ; *Zeit. anorg. Chem.*, **42**. 363, 1904 ; F. Henz, *ib.*, **37**. 29, 1904 ; J. M. M. Dormaar, *ib.*, **53**. 349, 1907 ; A. Lecrenier, *Chem. Ztg.*, **13**. 1219, 1888 ; W. Borchers, *ib.*, **12**. 1021, 1887 ; E. F. Smith, *Electroanalysis*, Philadelphia, 171, 1907 ; E. F. Smith and F. Muhr, *Journ. Anal. Chem.*, **5**. 448, 1891 ; 7. 189, 1893 ; J. Langness and E. F. Smith, *Journ. Amer. Chem. Soc.*, **27**. 1524, 1905 ; F. F. Exner, *ib.*, **25**. 905, 1903 ; N. K. Chaney, *ib.*, **35**. 1482, 1913 ; R. H. Chittenden and J. A. Blake, *Trans. Conn. Acad. Science*, **7**. 276, 1886 ; H. Daneel and H. Nissenson, *Proc. Internat. Congress Appl. Chem.*, 4. 678, 1903 ; A. Mazzucchelli, *Gazz. Chim. Ital.*, **44**. ii, 404, 1914 ; H. D. Law and F. M. Perkin, *Trans. Faraday Soc.*, 1, 262, 1905 ; A. Hollard, *Bull. Soc. Chim.*, (3), **29**. 262, 1903 ; *Chem. News*, **87**. 282, 1903 ; *Eclair. Électro.*, **26**. 165, 1900 ; G. F. Taylor, *Phys. Rev.*, (2), **23**. 655, 1924 ; F. Förster and J. Wolf, *Zeit. Elektrochem.*, **13**. 205, 1907 ; V. Engelhardt, *ib.*, 2. 524, 1896 ; H. J. S. Sand, *Journ. Chem. Soc.*, **93**. 1572, 1908 ; *Zeit. Elektrochem.*, **13**. 326, 1907 ; A. Fischer and R. J. Boddarrt, *ib.*, **10**. 950, 1904 ; H. Ost and W. Klapproth, *ib.*, 7. 376, 1900 ; *Zeit. angew. Chem.*, **13**. 827, 1900 ; F. Rüdorff, *ib.*, **5**. 199, 1892 ; R. Böttger. *Journ. prakt. Chem.*, (1), **73**. 484, 1856 ; G. Gore, *Journ. Chem. Soc.*, **17**. 365, 1863 ; *Proc. Roy. Soc.*, **12**. 185, 1858 ; B. Neumann, *Theorie und Praxis der analytischen Elektrolyse der Metalle*, Halle a. S., 146, 1897. I am indebted to The Cookson Lead and Antimony Co., Newcastle-on-Tyne, for the photographs Figs. 2 and 3.
[9] C. Schnabel, *Handbuch der Metallhüttenkunde*, Berlin, 2. 572, 1904 ; London, 2. 550, 1907 ; E. Groschuff, *Zeit. anorg. Chem.*, **103**. 164, 1918 ; F. Henz, *ib.*, **37**. 3, 1903 ; M. J. M. Dormaar, *ib.*, **53**. 349, 1907 ; A. L. Day, R. B. Sosmann, and E. T. Allen, *Amer. Journ. Science*, (4), **29**. 158, 1910 ; R. Engelhardt, *Zeit. Elektrochem.*, 2. 524, 1896 ; W. A. Cowan, *Journ. Amer. Inst. Metals*, **8**. 196, 1914 ; E. A. Smith, *Journ. Soc. Chem. Ind.*, **12**. 315, 1893.

§ 4. The Allotropic Forms of Antimony

The ordinary or metallic form of antimony furnishes trigonal or rhombohedral crystals—**trigonal antimony**, or **grey antimony**. G. Rose [1] obtained them by allowing molten antimony to cool in the crucible until a crust had formed on the sides and surface, and after breaking the surface skin, pouring off the molten metal. The sides of the resulting cavity often furnish aggregates of large crystals. J. P. Cooke observed microscopic crystals of antimony are produced when a current of hydrogen and stibine is heated ; and J. Durocher, when antimony trichloride is reduced by hydrogen at a high temp. The antimony obtained by electro-deposition from various soln. has a crystalline structure—*vide supra*. The *stella antimonii* is produced by the formation of dendritic skeletons during the solidification of the surface layer, and these are thrown into relief by the irregular contraction which occurs during the cooling of the later growth—*vide* Figs. 2 and 3. *Amorphous antimony* is obtained by condensing the vapour of the metal rapidly by contact with a surface cooled by liquid air. According to A. Stock and W. Siebert, and V. Köhlschütter, the effect is due to a deposition of a film, forming minute globules whose size is such that their form is governed by surface tension; similarly with the minute globule obtained by electrical dispersion—sublimation. The properties of ordinary grey antimony are discussed later.

According to E. Cohen and J. C. van den Bosch, when metallic antimony, which has been melted and rapidly cooled, is powdered and examined in a dilato-meter, it shows a transition point at about 101°, in agreement with the observation that the sp. gr. of antimony is lowered by heating it for 4 days at 102·5°; a dilato-meter containing antimony which had been heated for 50 mins. at 150° and then examined at 96° showed at first a decrease in vol. followed by a steady increase. It was inferred that at 96°, ordinary antimony is really a mixture of at least three allotropic forms—*vide* 3. 21, 8. E. Jänecke measured the heating and cooling curves of antimony while exposed to a press. of about 3000 kgrms., and observed that in 9 mins. the heating curve rose from 80° to 124°; there was then a break such that in 13 mins. more the temp. was 178°; the metal cooled from 148° to 137° in 4½ mins. when there was a break, and it then cooled to 111° in 9½ mins. more. These breaks in the two curves at 124° and 137° are taken to represent a transition from an α- to a β-form of antimony. P. W. Bridgman also found a discontinuity in the electrical resistance at about 145°. P. N. Laschtschenko observed no sign of a break on the cooling curve between 680° and 200°.

In virtue of the relationship between the members of this family of elements —phosphorus, arsenic, antimony, and bismuth—G. E. Linck[2] inferred that an allotropic form should correspond eutropically with yellow phosphorus, and yellow arsenic. A. Stock and O. Guttmann obtained **yellow antimony** by leading a current of air or oxygen into liquid stibine at −90°. The product is very unstable and rapidly changes into ordinary antimony at −50°. The yield of yellow antimony is very small. It is not possible to work at a lower temp. because the stibine freezes at −91°. Purified and dried oxygen has scarcely any action, but if a little ozone be present, the action is faster; if the oxygen contains 2 per cent. of ozone, an explosion occurs. A better yield of the yellow modification of antimony is obtained by the interaction of stibine with a soln. of chlorine in liquid ethane at −100° in red-light : $2SbH_3 + 3Cl_2 = 2Sb + 6HCl$. The reaction is completed at the temp. of liquid air. The product is not an antimony hydride because under water it passes into a black modification of antimony without giving off hydrogen; and its mode of preparation shows that it does not contain water. The light yellow form of antimony is much more changeable than yellow arsenic; and it blackens above −90°, even in the dark, but more quickly when exposed to light. It dissolves slightly in carbon disulphide at a little above −90°. When yellow antimony, below −50°, is shaken with carbon disulphide, a suspension of insoluble yellow antimony in a colloidal state is produced which above −50° changes in a few seconds into the black modification. H. Staudinger and W. Kreis could not make solid yellow antimony by cooling the vapour to −190°. Yellow antimony probably corresponds with cubic or yellow arsenic.

A. Stock and W. Siebert prepared **black antimony** either by rapidly cooling the vapour of ordinary antimony, or by the action of air or oxygen on liquid stibine at about −40°. The stibine is allowed to evaporate, and freed from oxide by washing it with hydrochloric acid; it is then washed with alcohol, and ether, and dried in vacuo. In the former method of preparation, the metal is distilled from an electrically-heated porcelain tube, at about 300°, in vacuo, and arranged so that the vapour impinges on a surface cooled by liquid air. The black powder appears to be amorphous ; its sp. gr. is 5·3. It is more volatile than ordinary grey antimony because when the latter is heated in an evacuated glass tube, a mirror of black antimony appears, and afterwards, a mirror of ordinary antimony is formed between the black antimony and the mass being heated. Black antimony is more chemically active than the grey antimony ; it oxidizes and burns in air at ordinary temp. Black antimony is labile at ordinary temp., and at 400°, it passes instantaneously into the grey form ; and in boiling water, the same change occurs more slowly. A. Stock and W. Siebert said that the black antimony obtained by R. Böttger by reducing a soln. of antimony trichloride with aluminium ; and by P. Lebeau, by treating antimonial magnesium with hydrochloric acid, or antimonial sodium with water is a mixture of black and grey antimony. The same remark probably applies to the black powder produced by H. N. Warren by the action of zinc, aluminium, tin, or iron on a soln. of a salt of tervalent antimony—*vide infra*, explosive antimony. Black antimony probably corresponds with monoclinic black arsenic.

G. Gore [3] discovered that when a hydrochloric acid soln. of antimony trichloride is electrolyzed with a feeble current, with a copper or platinum cathode, and antimony anode, a form of antimony—**explosive antimony**—is obtained with very peculiar properties. G. Gore used a 17 per cent. soln. of antimony trioxide in hydrochloric acid of sp. gr. 1·12 ; R. Böttger, a 33 per cent. soln. of antimony trichloride in hydrochloric acid ; and F. Pfeifer said that the soln. may have a conc. between 22 and 60 per cent. of antimony trichloride, and a current density between 0·043 and 0·2 ampère. A soln. containing 7 per cent. of antimony trichloride gave only ordinary crystalline antimony with both strong and weak currents ; and soln. with over 60 per cent. of the chloride were bad conductors. E. Cohen and W. E. Ringer obtained explosive antimony with soln. containing between 10 and 86 per cent. of antimony trichloride at 15°. Wide variations in the proportion of hydrochloric acid present were found by F. Pfeifer, A. Popper, and E. Cohen and W. E. Ringer to have little influence on the result ; similarly also with variations of temp. M. y Hernandez said that the current from one Leclanché cell gave the explosive antimony, but that with two such cells, ordinary antimony was deposited ; and R. Böttger added that if the anode is separated from the cathode by a porous cell, no explosive antimony is deposited. G. Gore obtained an *antimony tree*, consisting of branches of amorphous and crystalline nodules, by suspending a horizontal copper wire as cathode on the surface of the trichloride soln. He also found that if the electrolyte is of unequal density, from long-continued working and neglected stirring, and the receiving surface rough or unclean, the smooth deposit of explosive antimony will appear in the lower and denser part of the liquid, while a warty deposit of ordinary antimony will be formed in the upper and lighter part of the liquid. G. Gore obtained explosive antimony by the electrolysis of a soln. of one part antimony trichloride and 3–4 parts of potassium antimonyl tartrate in water and from hydrochloric acid soln. of antimony chloride in the presence of ammonium chloride, or, according to R. Böttger, in the presence of sodium chloride, but A. Bertrand did not obtain explosive antimony by using soln. containing ammonium salts. G. Gore also obtained explosive antimony from hydrobromic acid soln. of antimony tribromide, and hydriodic acid soln. of antimony triiodide. E. Cohen and W. E. Ringer obtained explosive antimony from soln. with 4·3–68·4 per cent. of antimony tribromide. Soln. of antimony trifluoride were found by G. Gore, and E. Cohen and W. E. Ringer to give ordinary, crystalline antimony. According to F. Pfeifer, and A. Popper, the quantity of antimony deposited by the current, from soln. of the trichloride, is proportional to the quantity of silver deposited in the voltameter with the same current. This ratio was independent of the conc. of the antimony trichloride enclosed in the deposited antimony. E. Cohen and co-workers found that the influence of temp. and of the conc. of the hydrochloric acid are negligible ; but the ratio Sb : Ag increases with the conc. of the trichloride in the electrolyte ; thus, as the conc. rises from 2·3 to

83·3 per cent., the electrochemical eq. of the antimony appears to rise from 40·29 to 40·63. A similar increase was found with soln. of antimony trichloride in methyl alcohol, and of the tribromide and trifluoride in water. According to H. N. Warren, when a zinc rod wrapped in a few coils of asbestos-paper is dipped into a soln. of antimony trichlòride, containing enough tartrate to prevent the precipitation of basic salts, part of the antimony is deposited in crystals on the asbestos, and part falls as an amorphous black powder of explosive antimony.

The explosive antimony is always associated with combined or occluded antimony halide. G. Gore said that explosive antimony contains about 6 per cent. of antimony chloride ; R. Böttger, 3·03–5·8 per cent. ; and F. Pfeifer, 4·8–7·9 per cent. E. Cohen and W. E. Ringer found that a minimum proportion of antimony halide must be present before the antimony acquires its explosive properties. If much less than 3 per cent. is present, the electro-deposit is no longer explosive. Besides antimony trichloride, F. Pfeifer found small quantities of hydrogen chloride and water are present, and E. Cohen and W. E. Ringer observed that other substances—sulphuric acid, and ammonium chloride—may be mechanically entangled in the deposit of antimony during electrolysis. R. Böttger, H. Reckleben and J. Scheiber, and F. Pfeifer observed no occluded hydrogen in explosive antimony ; the reducing action which it exercises on potassium ferricyanide was attributed by the latter to the antimony trichloride, not to hydrogen. H. Reckleben and J. Scheiber found only traces of free chlorine in explosive antimony. The halide is not mechanically associated with antimony because, said E. Cohen and W. E. Ringer, a mixture of ether and alcohol does not remove the halide from explosive antimony in the finest state of subdivision ; and because, said G. Gore, the powdered substance does not redden moist litmus paper. According to F. Pfeifer, the amount of antimony trichloride associated with the explosive antimony increases with the conc. of the soln., with a rise of temp. and with a decrease in the current density. E. Cohen and W. E. Ringer found that the influence of the current density is small but recognizable ; while under constant conditions—15°, and current density 0·2–0·3 amp.—the relationship between the conc. of the soln. and the proportion of antimony trichloride by the deposited antimony is :

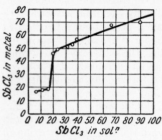

FIG. 4.—Relation between the Concentration of the Electrolyte and the Composition of the Deposited Metal.

| SbCl$_3$ in soln. | 3·08 | 8·06 | 11·92 | 18·07 | 33·05 | 55·35 | 86·70 |
| SbCl$_3$ in deposit | 1·64 | 1·82 | 4·82 | 5·35 | 6·75 | 8·24 | 10·51 |

The conc. of the trichloride in soln. and deposit are expressed as percentages. The curve obtained by plotting these numbers is discontinuous, Fig. 4, near the point corresponding with a 10 per cent. soln. of the trichloride—the metal deposited from soln. with a smaller proportion of the trichloride is non-explosive. As the temp. is raised, the proportion of the halide retained by the metal decreases as follows :

	0°	30·0°	50·3°	93·5°	0°	30·0°	50·5°	96
SbCl$_3$ in deposit	3·81	1·76	1·90	0·17	5·22	5·54	2·64	0·76
SbCl$_3$ in soln.		15·6				21·24		

It will be observed that the metal deposited from a 15·6 per cent. soln. at 30° is non-explosive, while that deposited from a 21·24 per cent. soln. at the same temp. is explosive.

G. Gore favoured the hypothesis that explosive antimony is formed by the " comparatively feeble " union of the antimony *in statu nascendi* " with the elements of the electrolyte, in an indefinite and somewhat variable proportion." He added that " another explanation which has nearly an equal weight of evidence in its **favour, is** that the antimony is deposited in the amorphous **state, and** the chloride or other salt is enclosed with it mechanically in the process of deposition, and that the change consists in the assumption by the metal of the crystalline state, whereby it is converted with an inconceivable number of crystals of insensible size and the imprisoned salt is set free." E. Jordis assumed that explosive antimony is an alloy of antimony with an unknown metallic form of chlorine which when converted with the metalloid form produces an explosion ; antimony trifluoride does not give an explosive compound because fluorine has no tendency to form a metallic modification. According to E. Cohen and T. Strengers, explosive antimony is to be regarded as a solid soln. of antimony trichloride, tribromide, or tri-iodide in a metastable form of the metal, referred to as α-**antimony.** The explosion is the transformation of this α-antimony into ordinary antimony, and the heat of transformation amounts to about 20 cals. per gram. Explosive antimony and non-explosive electrolytic antimony are simply solid soln. of the trichloride, tribromide, or tri-iodide in ordinary antimony. The α-antimony is to be regarded as a monotropic form, for it has been observed that a soln. which ordinarily deposits explosive antimony on electrolysis will deposit the stable form if the latter acts as cathode in the soln. A. Stock and W. Siebert suggested that their black modification of antimony is the same as E. Cohen and T. Strengers' α-antimony. J. Böhm showed that the X-radiogram of explosive antimony shows no crystalline structure ; but after it has exploded the product is crystalline.

Explosive antimony is an example of *monotropic allotropy ;* for it is in an unstable form at all temp., and the change is not reversible. Other examples are graphite, and the diamond. G. Gore said that explosive antimony has the colour of polished steel, and its fracture is amorphous, smooth, conchoidal, and waxy ; F. Pfeifer added that under the microscope the fracture does not show the slightest trace of a crystalline structure. G. Gore said that the texture of explosive antimony is soft and weak, that of ordinary grey antimony is hard and strong. The amorphous metal files easily, the grey with more difficulty. The grey metal, if struck by a hard substance, emits a clear metallic sound, whilst the dark variety gives a more dull tone. The crystallization lines of grey antimony are at right angles to the receiving surface ; and, in several experiments where antimony was deposited upon magnets, the direction of those lines did not seem to be altered by the magnetism. The amorphous variety, if gently struck by a hard substance, undergoes *a rapid and intense change* throughout its mass, attended by development of considerable heat ; the crystalline kind undergoes no such change, apparently under any circumstances. The change appears to be mol. in its character ; and according to this view the crystalline variety of metal must be regarded as being in a state of comparatively stable mol. equilibrium. Fumes of antimony trichloride are evolved during the explosion. The explosion can be produced by scratching the metal, by friction, by contact with a red-hot wire, by an electric spark, or by warming it to about 125°. When gradually heated under water to 100°, or immersed in boiling water, no change could be observed. Explosive antimony can be powdered by trituration under water at 12°, but when scratched under water at 10°, R. Böttger found that an explosion occurs and the water becomes turbid owing to the formation of the oxychloride. E. Cohen and W. E. Ringer found that thin pieces can be pulverized without explosion at ordinary temp. but thick pieces should be cooled to the temp. of solid carbon dioxide. According to G. Gore, light has no action, and specimens showed no perceptible change when kept for a couple of years. If gradually warmed specimens may lose their explosive property, and then they react acid to litmus, and impart a turbidity to water. F. Pfeifer said that the sp. gr. of explosive antimony is smaller the more antimony trichloride it contains ; G. Gore gave 5·74–5·83 for the sp. gr. ; F. Pfeifer, 5·64–5·907. E. Cohen and T. Strengers observed that the monotropic change of explosive into ordinary antimony is attended by a decrease in vol. of 0·0047 c.c. per gram with a sample containing 5·17 per cent. $SbCl_3$. The formation of a solid soln. of ordinary antimony with this amount of antimony trichloride is attended by a vol. increase of 0·58 c.c. per gram.   G. Gore gave 0·06312 for the sp. ht. of explosive antimony, and 0·0543 for the same substance after it had exploded.   According to L. von Pebal and H. Jahn, the sp. ht. of explosive antimony between −21° and −75° is 0·0540 ; between 0° and −21°, 0·0516 ; and between 0° and 38°, 0·0559.   The heat of the explosion was found by L. von Pebal to be 21 cals. per gram ; E. Cohen and T. Strengers gave 19·4 cals. per gram, and found that the difference in the heat of reaction between a gram of ordinary and explosive antimony with a soln. of bromine in carbon disulphide, amounts to 19·6 cals.   G. Gore found that explosive antimony is electropositive to the crystalline variety when immersed in dil. phosphoric, sulphuric, hydrochloric, and nitric acids ; and in aq. soln. of ammonia, potassium hydroxide, sodium carbonate, or ammonium chloride.   Explosive antimony is thermoelectrically positive to ordinary antimony. E. Cohen and T. Strengers found that the cell $^+\mathrm{Sb_{grey}} \mid 18$ per cent. soln. $\mathrm{SbCl_3} \mid \mathrm{Sb_{explosive}}^-$ is 19·4 millivolts.   Both explosive and ordinary antimony were found by G. Gore to acquire a coating of dendritic crystals of silver by immersion in a soln. of silver nitrate.   The varieties of explosive antimony prepared from soln. of antimony tribromide and triiodide had properties analogous to those of the product obtained from the trichloride.

According to F. Hérard,[4] when antimony is heated to dull redness in a current of nitrogen, the greenish vapour condenses on the cool parts of the tube in agglomerations of small spheres.   This form of antimony is said to melt at 614°, and to have a sp. gr. of 6·22 at 0°, whereas ordinary antimony melts at 440°, and has a sp. gr. 6·73.   The fact that this variety of amorphous antimony is not produced by heating antimony in a current of hydrogen is explained by assuming that, in nitrogen, a nitride is formed which decomposes in the cooler parts of the tube.   According to E. Cohen and J. Olie, the phenomena described by F. Hérard are not to be observed when pure antimony and pure nitrogen are used.   If, on the other hand, the nitrogen is insufficiently purified, these phenomena are reproduced. What F. Hérard described as " amorphous antimony " appears to be nothing else than the ordinary stable antimony contaminated with more or less trioxide.

According to A. Gutbier and N. Kräutle,[5] colloidal solutions of antimony, prepared by the action of sodium hyposulphite on a soln. of potassium antimonate acidified slightly by the addition of tartaric acid, have their stability considerably increased in presence of the extract of *Tubera salep*.   The dialyzed soln. may be evaporated to give solid colloids containing about 10 per cent. of antimony which dissolve completely in water.   The stability of the protected soln. is not affected by the addition of acids and neutral salts, but alkalinity reduces the stability to a large extent.   A. Gutbier and co-workers obtained the colloid by reducing a fine suspension of antimony trichloride in water by means of titanous chloride. G. Wegelin obtained colloidal antimony by a prolonged grinding in an agate mortar. E. Fouard obtained the colloid by electrolyzing a soln. of a salt of the metal containing a pure organic colloid (albumin, starch, or gelatin) with a current of a few milliampères.   At the cathode the metal ions are neutralized by the repelled negatively-charged colloid micelles.   A colloidal organo-metallic complex is thus formed.   The anode is separated by immersion in a collodion cell rendered semipermeable by precipitated copper ferrocyanide.   The cathode should be a bad conductor so as to reduce the frequency with which formation of the complex occurs on the cathode.   T. Svedberg obtained a colloidal soln. of antimony in isobutyl alcohol by suspending a thin foil of antimony in liquid and using electrodes of iron or aluminium with a potential difference of 110 volts, and a current density so small that it can scarcely be measured by an ordinary ammeter—3. 23, 10.   The soln. is brownish-red in transmitted light, and black in reflected light.   It can be kept for 24 hrs.   T. Svedberg also prepared a colloidal soln. of antimony in ethyl ether by connecting a glass condenser of 225 sq. cm. surface with an induction coil and attaching the secondary poles to the electrodes, which are immersed in the liquid contained in a porcelain dish.   The antimony is used in a granular form or as wire clippings.   When the current is passed, sparks play between the metal particles, and in the course of a few minutes dark-coloured soln. are obtained.   These contair no large particles and hence need not be filtered. Colloidal soln. of magnesium, zinc, aluminium, tin, antimony, iron, nickel, and even alkali metals in ether have been obtained. S. S. Bhatnagar and co-workers found that sols of gold or silver are photosensitive in association with antimony trisulphide.

REFERENCES.

[1] G. Rose, *Sitzber. Akad. Berlin*, **72**, 1849; *Pogg. Ann.*, **77**. 144, 1849; V. Köhlschütter, *Zeit. Elektrochem.*, **18**. 373, 1912; A. Stock and W. Siebert, *Ber.*, **38**. 3837, 1905; E. Cohen and J. C. van den Bosch, *Proc. Acad. Amsterdam*, **17**. 645, 1914; E. Jänecke, *Zeit. phys. Chem.*, **90**. 313, 1915; J. P. Cooke, *Amer. Journ. Science*, (2), **31**. 191, 1861; P. W. Bridgman, *Proc. Amer. Acad.*, **52**. 573, 1917; J. Durocher, *Compt. Rend.*, **32**. 823, 1851; P. N. Laschtschenko, *Journ. Russ. Phys. Chem. Soc.*, **46**. 311, 1914.

[2] G. E. Linck, *Ber.*, **32**. 881, 1899; A. Stock and O. Guttmann, *ib.*, **37**. 899, 1904; A. Stock and W. Siebert, *ib.*, **38**. 3840, 1905; W. Siebert, *Zur Kenntnis der Modifikation des Arsens und Antimons*, Berlin, 1905; P. Lebeau, *Compt. Rend.*, **134**. 231, 284, 1902; R. Böttger, *Zeit. Phys. Ver. Frankfurt*, 16, 1879; H. N. Warren, *Chem. News*, **61**. 183, 1890; H. Staudinger and W. Kreis, *Helvetica Chim. Acta*, 8. 71, 1925.

[3] G. Gore, *Phil. Mag.*, (4), **9**. 73, 1855; *Journ. Chem. Soc.*, **17**. 365, 1863; *Proc. Roy. Soc.*, **12**. 185, 1858; *Phil. Trans.*, **148**. 185, 797, 1858; **152**. 323, 1862; M. y Hernandez, *Cronica Cientifica*, 3. 86, 1879; F. Pfeifer, *Liebig's Ann.*, **209**. 161, 1881; A. Popper, *ib.*, **233**. 155, 1886; G. Vosmaer, *Met. Chem. Engg.*, **13**. 535, 1915; R. Böttger, *Journ. prakt. Chem.*, (1), **73**. 484, 1858; *Pogg. Ann.*, **97**. 334, 1856; **104**. 292, 1858; E. Cohen and W. E. Ringer, *Zeit. phys. Chem.*, **47**. 1, 1904; E. Cohen, E. Collins, and T. Strengers, *ib.*, **50**. 291, 1905; E. Cohen and T. Strengers, *ib.*, **52**. 129, 1905; E. Jänecke, *ib.*, **90**. 313, 1915; H. N. Warren, *Chem. News*, **61**. 183, 1890; A. Bertrand, *Bull. Soc. Chim.*, (2), **27**. 383. 1877; E. Jordis, *Zeit. Elektrochem.*, **11**. 787, 1906; L. von Pebal and H. Jahn, *Weid. Ann.*, **27**. 602, 1886; L. von Pebal, *ib.*, **31**. 925, 1887; A. Stock and W. Siebert, *Ber.*, **38**. 3840, 1905; H. Reckleben and J. Scheiber, *Zeit. anorg. Chem.*, **70**. 275, 1911; A. Mazzucchelli, *Gazz. Chim. Ital.*, **44**. ii, 404, 1914; J. Böhm, *Zeit. anorg. Chem.*, **149**. 217, 1925.

[4] F. Hérard, *Compt. Rend.*, **107**. 420, 1888; E. Cohen and J. Olie, *Zeit. phys. Chem.*, **61**. 588, 1908.

[5] T. Svedberg, *Ber.*, **38**. 3619, 1905; A. Gutbier and N. Kräutle, *Koll. Zeit.*, **20**. 194. 1917; G. Wegelin, *ib.*, **14**. 65, 1914; E. Fouard, *Compt. Rend.*, **184**. 328, 1927; A. Gutbier, B. Ottenstein, and F. Allam, *Zeit. anorg. Chem.*, **164**. 287, 1927; A. Gutbier and H. Weithase, *ib.*, **169**. 264, 1928; S. S. Bhatnagar, N. A. Yajnik, and V. D. Zadoo, *Journ. Indian Chem. Soc.*, **4**. 209, 1927.

§ 5. The Physical Properties of Antimony

Antimony is a tin-white, or silver-grey crystalline mass, as indicated above; the colloid, in transmitted light is brownish-red. G. E. Linck [1] said that the green vapour of antimony is probably finely-divided cubic antimony. According to F. Hérard, the vapour is grey. R. J. Haüy supposed that native antimony occurs in octahedral and dodecahedral crystals belonging to the cubic system, but F. Mohs showed that they are trigonal. The crystals were described by C. M. Marx, F. Hessel, F. C. L. Elsner, G. W. Zenger, O. Mügge, G. W. A. Kahlbaum, J. W. Retgers. F. A. Römer, C. W. C. Fuchs, F. Fouqué and A. Michel-Lévy, C. F. Rammelsberg, H. C. H. Carpenter, etc. G. Rose gave for the axial ratio $a:c=1:1\cdot3068$; and H. Laspeyres, $1:1\cdot32362$. Twinning occurs about the (0112)-plane in complex groups—fourlings, sixlings, and polysynthetic. O. Mügge produced lamellæ about the (0112)-plane by percussion or pressure. H. Laspeyres said that the (0001)-cleavage is perfect; (0112)-, distinct; (0221)-, sometimes distinct; and (1120)-, indistinct. M. L. Huggins studied the relation between the cleavage and the electronic structure. I. V. Obreimoff and L. V. Schubnikoff obtained large single crystals of antimony when the molten metal is contained in a capillary tube, or in a vessel with a capillary exit below, and is cooled from below. Crystallization starts at a single centre in the capillary and extends uniformly throughout, producing a single individual with the external shape of the containing vessel. G. Tammann and Q. A. Mansuri studied the velocity of crystallization of molten antimony. W. H. and W. L. Bragg concluded that the atoms of antimony are arranged like those in the diamond, but with the whole structure distorted along the trigonal axis; but **X-radiograms** by R. W. James and N. Tunstall, showed that the atoms of antimony lie in two interpenetrating face-centred lattices. If for one of the lattices diagonals are drawn parallel to the trigonal axis for each of the eight equal rhombohedral cells into which the unit lattice may be divided, from considerations of symmetry, the atoms of the second lattice must lie in these diagonals; if they lay at the unoccupied corners of the first lattice, the structure would become a simple rhombohedron. This is not in accord with the facts, but if the atoms of the second lattice are all displaced from these corners along the diagonals in the same direction by a distance equal to 0·074 of the length of the diagonal of one of the small cells, all the facts are explained. For the sake of clearness, only one of the small cells is shown in Fig. 5. According to A. Ogg. the edge of the unit antimony rhomb is 6·20 A., and the shortest distance between two atoms 2·92 A., and the longest distance 3·37A. ; $a=86°$ 58'. M. L. Huggins made some observations on the electronic structure— *vide* arsenic, Table II, **9.** 51, 5 ; and for the poly-morphism of phosphorus, arsenic, antimony, and bismuth. *vide* arsenic, Tables III and IV, **9.** 51, 5.

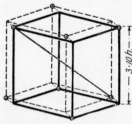

FIG. 5.—Arrangement of the Eight Atoms in a Unit Rhomb of the Space-lattice of Antimony.

P. P. Ewald and C. Hermann collected data respecting the polymorphism of antimony; and the subject was discussed by P. Möller, G. Linck and H. Jung, F. Roll, and R. Neumann. The fracture of antimony depends on the rate of cooling, and on the purity of the metal. If rapidly cooled, the fracture is granular, and if slowly cooled, flaky. E. Bekier found the ratio of the spontaneous crystallizing power to the linear velocity of crystallization increases with the velocity of cooling ; the number of crystallites in a given area increases with the degree of undercooling from 600° to −70°. The size of the crystallites increases at a low temp. The spontaneous crystallizing power thus diminishes, and it is possible that with sufficient undercooling the antimony might be obtained in an amorphous condition, as in the black antimony obtained by condensing its vapour or by oxidizing hydrogen antimonide at −40°. J. A. M. van Liempt discussed the production of single crystals.

The **specific gravity** of native antimony ranges from 6·6 to 6·8—A. Breithaupt [2] gave 6·6101 ; A. Eschka, 6·20 ; F. Mohs, 6·646 ; G. A. Kenngott, 6·62–6·65 ; G. F. Kunz, 6·606–6·693 ; M. J. Brisson, 6·702 ; and J. F. L. Hausmann, and M. H. Klaproth, 6·720. P. van Muschenbrock's, and T. Bergman's values are rather high, being respectively 6·852, and 6·860. C. J. B. Karsten gave 6·7006 for the sp. gr. of ordinary antimony ; C. Hatchett, 6·712 ; J. Dalton, 6·7–6·8 ; G. Wert-heim, 6·697 ; R. F. Marchand and T. Scheerer, 6·715 at 16° ; W. P. Dexter, 6·6987 to 6·7102, or the mean of three determinations : 6·705 at 3·75°. A. Matthiessen gave 6·713 at 14° ; H. G. F. Schröder, 6·697 at 3·9° in vacuo ; J. P. Cooke, 6·6957 to 6·7070 with the average of six determinations, 6·7022 ; H. Fay and H. E. Ashley, 6·693 ; E. Maey, 6·67 at 17·5°/4° ; H. G. Dorsey, 6·88 at 20° for cast antimony ; F. Winkler, 6·7137 at 4°/4° ; R. von Dallwitz-Wegner, 6·62 ; and W. Gaede, 6·627. I. I. Saslowsky gave 6·690 for the sp. gr. at room temp., and 18·0 for the at. vol. C. del Fresno studied this subject. W. Herz estimated the sp. gr. of antimony at −273° to be 7·59. According to R. F. Marchand and T. Scheerer, subjecting antimony to a press. of 75,000 kgrms. per sq. mm. makes no appreci-able difference to its sp. gr., since a sample before compression had a sp. gr. 6·715, and after, 6·714 ; on the contrary, W. Spring noticed a marked difference, for a sample not compressed had a sp. gr. 6·675 at 15·5° ; after one compression at 20,000 atm. the sp. gr. was 6·733 at 15° ; and after two compressions, 6·740 at 16°. G. W. A. Kahlbaum and co-workers also found that antimony cast in a mould has a sp. gr. 6·690 at 20°/4° ; antimony distilled in vacuo, 6·61781 at

$20°/4°$, and after compression at 10,000 atm., 6·6909 under the same conditions. T. M. Lowry and R. G. Parker found the sp. gr. of antimony *en masse* is 6·6908, and in the form of filings 6·6585. E. Cohen gave 6·678 at $25°/4°$ for the sp. gr. of antimony which had been cast and then annealed at 102·5°. T. M. Lowry said that the sp. gr. is increased by annealing at 100°. According to F. Nies and A. Winkelmann, the sp. gr. of antimony is greater in the liquid state than when solid, at the same temp., though C. M. Marx said that antimony does not expand on freezing. M. Toepler said that there is a 1·4 per cent. contraction when antimony fuses at the m.p. L. Playfair and J. P. Joule gave 6·529–6·646 for the sp. gr. of liquid antimony; G. Quincke, 6·620 for the sp. gr. at 0°, and 6·528 for the molten metal. J. M. Guinchant and H. Chrétien found the sp. gr. to be 6·75 at 13°; 6·55 at 698°; and 6·45 at 1156°; L. L. Bircumshaw gave 6·49 at 640°; 6·45 at 700°; 6·38 at 800°; and 6·29 at 970°; and P. Pascal and A. Jouniaux gave 6·55 at 631°; 6·48 at 800°; 6·36 at 1000°. J. J. van Laar calculated b of J. D. van der Waals' equation, 0·00250; $\sqrt{a}=0·089$; and the valency attraction A, $\sqrt{A}=34$. R. M. Bozorth calculated the **atomic radius** of antimony to be 1·57 A. when that of oxygen is 0·65 A. W. L. Bragg gave 1·40 A. for the at. radius, E. N. Gapon, 1·79 A.; M. L. Huggins, 2·58 A.; and W. F. de Jong and H. W. V. Willems, 1·34 A. H. G. Grimm made observations on the ionic radius.

V. Meyer and H. Biltz [3] measured the **vapour density** of antimony and found 12·31 (air unity) at 1437°; 10·74 at 1572°; and 9·78 at 1640°—when the value calculated for Sb_3 is 12·43; and that for Sb_2 is 8·29. According to H. von Wartenberg, antimony has monatomic molecules at 2070°. J. M. Guinchant and H. Chrétien found the **molecular weight** of antimony in melted antimony trichloride is 113; and from the effect of antimony on the f.p. of cadmium, C. T. Heycock and F. H. Neville inferred that the molecules are monatomic; and with lead in place of cadmium, diatomic. A. Jouniaux found that calculations based on Trouton's rule agree with the assumption that antimony is monatomic between the m.p. and the b.p., while the b.p. of antimony amalgams show that antimony is monatomic at 357°, but the effect of antimony on the f.p. and b.p. of iodine indicate a polymerization at lower temp.

The **hardness** of antimony on Mohs' scale is 3·0 to 3·5, so that the metal is a soft one. J. R. Rydberg [4] gave 3·0 for the hardness. P. Ludwik found the pressure hardness with a load applied for 300 seconds at 17°, 64·4; at 51°, 45·6; at 140°, 26·5; at 262°, 14·8; at 306°, 10·0; at 445°, 4·05; and with a load applied for 15 seconds at 17°, 73·0; 20°, 72·8; at 49°, 58·1; at 81°, 45·0; at 128°, 35·2; at 201°, 22·5; at 298°, 14·4; at 434°, 6·20; and at 448°, 5·85. C. A. Edwards and A. M. Herbert gave 58·0 for Brinell's hardness number; F. Sauerwald gave 125·6 at 13°; 105·1 at 113°; 87·3 at 212°; 67·5 at 313°; 45·3 at 412°; and 28·9 at 514°. The subject was also studied by F. Sauerwald and K. Knehans. K. Honda and R. Yamada studied the abrasive hardness. The metal is brittle, easily pulverized, and, when compressed, W. Spring found that it takes on its former lustre. C. I. Burton and W. Marshall observed that there is a rise of temp. of 0·248° when the metal is subjected to a press. of 300 atm.; and a fall of temp. of 0·191° when the press. is suddenly released. T. W. Richards gave $2·4\times10^{-6}$ for the average **compressibility** of antimony between 100 and 500 megabars at 20°. P. W. Bridgman found with antimony cooled slowly in graphite, at 30°, $\delta v/v_0=$ $-10^{-7}(14·69-6·2\times10^{-5}p)p$; and at 75°, $-10^{-7}(14·80-6·3\times10^{-5}p)p$; while for another sample rapidly chilled in iron, at 30°, $-10^{-7}(20·41-12·9\times10^{-5}p)p$; and at 75°, $-10^{-7}(20·50-12·9\times10^{-5}p)p$. He also found for the compressibility of simple crystals over the range 12,000 kgrms. per sq. cm.; he found $26·99\times10^{-7}p-31·6$ $\times10^{-12}p^2$ at 30°; and $26·55\times10^{-7}p-25·3\times10^{-12}p^2$ at 75°. P. W. Bridgman gave for the compressibility, β, of two samples at 30°, $0·0_51469$ and $0·0_42041$; $\delta\beta/\beta\delta p=0·0_584$, and $0·0_4126$; and $-\delta a/a\delta p=0·0_561$, and $0·0_575$, where a denotes the coeff. of thermal expansion. L. H. Adams gave $\delta\beta=-0·65$. E. Madelung and R. Fuchs gave for the compressibility $0·84\times10^{12}$ dynes per sq. cm

P. W. Bridgman found the **modulus of elasticity**, or Young's modulus, for antimony wires to be 7.8×10^{-11} c.g.s. units, and the **rigidity**, 2.0×10^{-11} c.g.s. units—the magnitude is thus of the same order as for ordinary glass. With the compressibility 2.4×10^{-12} c.g.s. units, **Poisson's ratio** becomes 0.18—a value which is probably far too low. He also measured the elastic constants of single crystals. B. MacNutt and A. Concilio measured the load at which a noise was heard in stressed antimony. W. Widder studied the relation between the elastic modulus, the temp., and the m.p. E. Jänecke observed a discontinuity in the press.-temp. curve at 124°–137°. G. Quincke found the **specific cohesion** to be $a^2 = 9.90$ sq. mm., and the **surface tension**, 317.2 dynes per cm. G. Drath and F. Sauerwald gave:

	750°	800°	900°	1000°	1100°
a^2	11.79	11.71	11.63	11.54	11.44 sq. mm.
σ	368	367	361	355	348 dynes per cm.

and for the temp. coeff. $d\sigma/d\theta = -0.063$. Observations were made by Y. Matuyama. R. von Dallwitz-Wegner calculated for the **cohesion pressure**, 167,184 atm. at 0°, and 130,543 at 100°. L. L. Bircumshaw gave for the surface tension, 350 dynes per cm. at 640°; 348, at 700°; 346, at 800°; and 342, at 970°; for the sp. cohesion a^2 per sq. cm., 0.1100, at 640°; 0.1103, at 700°; 0.1105, at 800°; and 0.1111, at 970°; and for the surface energy, 2605 dynes per cm. at 640°; 2619, at 700°; 2634, at 800°; and 2663, at 970°. The temp. coeff. of the surface tension is -0.02. A. Saito and K. Hayashi measured the fluidity of molten antimony. A. Bienias and F. Sauerwald found the **viscosity** of antimony, η grms. per cm. per sec., to be:

	702°	801°	900°	1002°
η	0.01296	0.01113	0.00999	0.00905

H. Kopp [5] found the cubical **coeff. of thermal expansion** to be 0.000033 between 12° and 13° and 41° to 43°. A. Matthiessen gave for the vol., v, at $\theta°$, between 0° and 100°, $v = v_0(1 + 0.000027700 + 0.0_7 397\theta^2)$; and for the coeff. of linear expansion, $0.0_5 976$ at 20°; and F. C. Calvert and co-workers made some measurements of this constant. According to H. Fizeau, the linear coeff. of crystals parallel to the chief axis is $0.0_4 1692$ at 40°; and $0.0_4 1683$ at 50°; perpendicular to the chief axis, $0.0_5 882$ at 40°, and $0.0_5 895$ at 50°; while the average value is $0.0_4 1152$ at 40°, and $0.0_4 1158$ at 50°. M. de Hemptinne gave $0.0_4 1150$ for the coeff. of expansion of antimony highly purified. R. von Dallwitz-Wegner gave for the coeff. of cubical expansion $0.0_4 277$ at 0° and $0.0_4 356$ at 100°. H. G. Dorsey gave for cast antimony of sp. gr. 6.88:

	−170°	−150°	−130°	−110°	−90°	−50°	−10°	10°
a	$0.0_6 747$	$0.0_5 791$	$0.0_5 841$	$0.0_5 886$	$0.0_5 913$	$0.0_5 956$	$0.0_5 988$	$0.0_6 1009$

A. Schrauf found the ratio of the expansion coeff. for the directions $a : c$ to be as $3 : 2$. P. Braesco gave for the linear coeff. between 100° and 300°, $0.0_5 93$; and E. Grüneisen, $0.0_4 1088$ between 17° and 100°, and $0.0_4 1022$ between 17° and $-190°$. S. Lussana found between 9° and 72°, $0.0_4 1177$ at 1 atm. press.; $0.0_4 1097$ at 1000 atm.; and $0.0_4 1055$ at 2000 atm. press. For single crystals at room temp. P. W. Bridgman found the coeff. of thermal expansion to be 15.56×10^{-6} when parallel, and 7.96×10^{-6} when perpendicular to the chief axis. According to A. Mattheissen, if the **thermal conductivity** of silver is 100, that of antimony is 26.5. A. Berget found the coeff. of thermal conductivity, k, in absolute units to be 0.042; L. Lorenz, 0.0442 at 0°, and 0.0396 at 100°. G. Gehlhoff and F. Neumeier gave for the metal in the form of compressed powder, 0.0328 at $-80°$, 0.0290 at 0°, and 0.0250 at 100°; and for cast electrolytic antimony, 0.106 at $-190°$, 0.0628 at $-77°$, 0.0538 at 0°, and 0.0515 at 100°. A. Eucken and co-workers gave 0.0593 at $-190°$, 0.0445 at $-77°$, and 0.0381 at 0°. S. Konno obtained:

	0°	100°	200°	300°	400°	500°	600°	650°	700°
k	0.045	0.040	0.038	0.040	0.043	0.048	0.057	0.052	0.05(

S. Lussana found the thermal conductivity to be 3·65 per cent. greater at 1500 atm., and 6·34 per cent. greater at 3000 atm. than at 1 atm. S. Lussana found that the relation between pressure and thermal conductivity is not linear since the coeff. at atm. press. is $+0·0_5251$, and at 3000 atm., $+0·0_5164$. P. W. Bridgman, on the other hand, found the thermal conductivity decreases with press., and the press. relation to be linear with the coeff. $-0·0_421$—a value larger than that for any other metal except bismuth. E. Jannetaz found the sq. root of the ratio of the thermal conductivity in the direction of the base to that in the direction of the chief axis to be 1·591. The thermal conductivity of fine-grained crystals of antimony, $1·41 \times 10^{-4}$ sq. cm., at $-183°$ and at $0°$ was found by A. Eucken and O. Neumann to be respectively 0·1925 and 0·1716 watts per cm. per degree; for another sample, $2·27 \times 10^{-4}$ sq. cm., 0·2025 and 0·1716 watts per cm. per degree respectively; for medium-sized grains, $6·35 \times 10^{-4}$ sq. cm., 0·2205 and 0·1820 watts per cm. per degree respectively; and for coarse-grained crystals, 0·143 sq. cm., 0·4519 and 0·2452 watts per cm. per degree respectively. Thus, the heat conductivity decreases as the size of grain decreases. It is assumed that the heat-conductivity is composed of a true metallic conductivity, and a non-metallic conductivity due to the crystal structure, and in the limit with extremely fine-grained material, only the metallic conductivity comes into play.

P. L. Dulong and A. J. Petit [6] found the **specific heat** of antimony to be 0·0507; H. V. Regnault gave 0·05078 between 12° and 97°; E. Bède, 0·04861 between 13° and 106°; and 0·04989 between 15° and 27·5° or $c = 0·0466 + 0·0000020\theta$; H. Kopp, 0·0518 between 0° and 100°; R. Bunsen, 0·0528 between 0° and 100°; L. Lorenz, 0·05162 at 0°; 0·05174 at 50°; 0·05070 at 75°; L. von Pebal and H. Jahn, 0·0495 between 0° and $-76°$, and 0·0499 between $-21°$ and $-76°$; A. Naccari, 0·05004 from 15° to 99°; 0·05027 from 18° to 172°; 0·05070 from 22° to 251°; and 0·05157 from 21° to 322°—or $0·048896 + 0·016718(\theta - 15)$; P. Schübel, 0·0502 between 18° and 100°; 0·0516 between 18° and 300°; and 0·0561 between 18° and 600°; W. Gaede gave for antimony of sp. gr. 6·627, 0·050248 at 17·1°; 0·050558 at 33°· 0·050823 at 47·2°; 0·051028 at 62·4°; 0·051160 at 77·3°; and 0·051321 at 92·5°. S. Umino gave:

	150°	250°	350°	450°	550°	650°	850°	950°
Sp. ht. .	0·0505	0·0520	0·0537	0·0552	0·0569	0·0656	0·0656	0·0656

H. Jahn gave:

	$-72°$ to 13·1°	$-21°$ to 15°	55° to 21·7°	303° to 26·3°	500° to 26·5°	625° to 27·7°
Sp. ht. . .	0·049315	0·049368	0·049517	0·050205	0·050496	0·050834

and for temp. between 22° and $\theta°$, sp. ht. $= 0·04941078 - 0·0_513097(\theta - 22°)$ $-0·0_55171207(\theta - 22)^2 + 0·0_{10}245733(\theta - 22)^3$; and $a\theta/a\theta = 0·04941078 - 0·0_526164 - (\theta - 22) - 0·0_7155136(\theta - 22)^2 + 0·0_{10}982932(\theta - 22)^3$. L. Schüz, 0·05060 and 0·05192, J. Laborde, 0·0509, and U. Behn, 0·0484 for the range between 18° and $-79°$; 0·0472 between 18° and $-186°$; and 0·0462 between $-79°$ and $-186°$; R. Ewald found 0·0477 at $-28°$, 0·0462 at $-39°$, and $-0·0423$ at $-135°$; J. Dewar, 0·0240 between $-196°$ and $-253°$; T. W. Richards and F. G. Jackson, 0·0469 between 20° and $-188°$; H. Schimpf, 0·0503 between 17° and 100°, 0·0482 between 17° and $-79°$, 0·0450 between 17° and $-190°$. J. H. Awbery and E. Griffiths also obtained values for the sp. ht. of antimony. For powdered crystals of antimony P. Günther gave 0·0428 at 188°. G. W. A. Kahlbaum and co-workers gave 0·0497 for distilled antimony, and 0·0496 for the same metal after compression at 10,000 atm. The corresponding **atomic heat** ranges from J. Dewar's value 2·89 near $-253°$ to P. Schübel's 6·74 near 600°. P. Günther gave 5·19 for the at. ht. at $-194·6°$; 5·22 at $-187·4°$; 5·33 at $-181°$; and 5·47 at $-174·9°$. G. N. Lewis gave $C_p = 6·0$; $C_v = 5·9$ at 20°; and E. D. Eastman and co-workers examined the effect of temp. on the relation $C_p - C_v$; and A. Simon and M. Ruhemann gave $C_v = 3·87$ and $C_p = 3·89$ at $-201·70°$; $C_v = 3·90$ and $C_p = 3·92$ at $-200·93°$; $C_v = 4·21$ and $C_p = 4·21$ at $-191·79°$; and $C_v = 4·20$ and $C_p = 4·24$ at $-191·42°$.

The older determinations of the **melting point** of antimony by J. Dalton,[7] L. B. G. de Morveau, R. Pictet, and A. Ledebur were far too low ; they ranged from 7. Dalton's 432° to L. B. G. de Morveau's 513°. H. Capitaine made the questionable observation that the higher the degree of purity of antimony the more easily does it fuse. C. T. Heycock and F. H. Neville gave 629·54° ; **L.** Holborn and A. L. Day, 630·5° ; L. Holborn, 630·3° ; A. L. Day and R. B. Sosman, 629·8°–630° ; E. van Aubel, 630° ; W. R. Mott, 630·7° ; H. Callendar, 629·5° ; A. Gautier, 632° ; F. Krafft, 635° ; F. Winkler, 630°–635° ; P. N. Laschtschenko, and J. H. Awbery and E. Griffiths, 630° ; E. Groschuff, 630·3° ; C. W. Waidner and G. K. Burgess, 630·23°–630·7° ; K. Scheel, 630° ; and H. Chrétien, 628°. L. I. Dana and P. D. Foote gave 630° for the best representative value ; and W. Guertler and M. Pirani, 630·5°. W. Reinders found the metal is much inclined to undercooling. H. Fay and H. E. Ashley gave 624° for the f.p. H. Pélabon found the **freezing point constant** to be 1240°. According to E. Karrer, when antimony is heated at a temp. above its m.p. it becomes bright red ; on cooling, the brightness decreases with the temp. until solidification commences, when a sudden increase in brightness occurs, accompanied by an increase in temp. Moreover, the brightness after the flash appears greater for a given temp. than the brightness at the same temp. before the flash. It thus appears to be a case of **crystal luminescence ;** the phenomenon is not due to oxidation of the antimony, since it takes place in hydrogen or in a vacuum.

J. von Liebig [8] said that antimony volatilizes out of contact with air only at elevated temp., but, in a current of air, less heat is required. Antimony volatilizes at a bright red heat or in a current of an inert gas, but not when fused under a layer of salt ; if antimony trioxide be ignited with charcoal and alkali carbonates, metallic antimony is formed, but if the alkali be omitted most of the antimony will be volatilized as trioxide, and only a small part will be reduced to the metallic state. When covered with a flux, antimony lost only one-thousandth part of its weight at the strongest white-heat, but in a current of hydrogen, antimony can be distilled at a white-heat. J. A. M. van Liempt found that the **vapour pressure,** p mm., is :

	1075°	1135°	1175°	1225°	1265°	1325°
p . .	54	107	206	302	407	745

The values can be represented by $\log_{10} p = 6·20 - 9888 T^{-1}$. J. Johnston gave for the vap. press., $\log p = -9010 T^{-1} + 8·12$. T. Carnelley and W. C. Williams gave 1090°–1450° for the **boiling point** of antimony at ordinary press. H. F. Wiebe's relation furnished 1961°. V. Meyer and H. Mensching said that evaporation proceeds very vigorously at 1437° ; V. Meyer and H. Biltz said that the b.p lies between 1500° and 1700°, but the metal is volatile at lower temp. F. Winkler gave 965° for the b.p. of antimony at 10 mm. press. ; W. R. Mott, 1440° ; H. C. Greenwood, 1440° for the b.p. at 760 mm. ; J. A. M. van Liempt, 1322° ; and O. Ruff and B. Bergdahl, 1325° at 745 mm., and 1330° at 760 mm. E. Demarçay said that antimony readily volatilizes in vacuo at 292° ; A. Schuller found that antimony can be readily sublimed in vacuo ; and F. Krafft distilled the element at 775°–780° in vacuo ; and E. Tiede and E. Birnbräuer, and F. Krafft and L. Bergfeld said that antimony volatilizes readily in the vacuum of the cathode light at 290°–292°, and evaporation occurs even at lower temp. J. Johnston gave 540° for the b.p. at 10^{-3} mm. ; 620° at 10^{-2} mm. ; 720° at 0·1 mm. ; 840° at 1 mm. ; 990° at 10 mm. ; 1130° at 50 mm. ; 1200° at 100 mm. ; and 1440° at 760 mm. C. Zenghelis observed that when antimony was placed near a piece of silver-foil in a desiccator, in a few months the surface of the silver was discoloured by the vapour of antimony. W. G. Duffield made estimates of the **rate of vaporization** of liquid antimony. F. Wüst and co-workers found the **heat of fusion** to be 38·9 cals. per gram, or 4·6 Cals. per gram-atom ; S. Umino, 40·75 cals. per gram ; and J. H. Awbery and E. Griffiths, 24·3 cals. per gram ; and W. Herz gave 24·2 cals. per gram. P. N. Laschtschenko gave 4·85 Cals. per gram-atom. J. W. Richards calculated, with different standard formulæ, 16–27·25 cals. per gram. J. Tate found the latent heat of vaporization to be 320 cals. per gram, or 38·5 Cals. per gram-atom. F. S. Mortimer calculated 41·15 Cals.; and J. Johnston, 41·3 Cals. J. A. M. van Liempt gave 45·28 Cals. per gram-atom, and 28·39 for Trouton's constant. W. G. Mixter [9] found the heat of oxidation of antimony to the trioxide, $(2Sb,3O)$ $=163·0$ Cals. per mol; $(2Sb,4O)=209·8$ Cals.; and $(2Sb,5O)=229·5$ Cals. J. C. Thomlinson compared the thermochemistry of antimony and arsenic. E. Kordes gave 5·16 (cals.) for the entropy of antimony; and B. Brugs, 12·6 for the entropy at 25°, and 19·6 at the m.p. M. Kawakami measured the heat of mixing pans of the following metals: sodium, potassium, zinc, cadmium, mercury, lead, antimony, and bismuth.

G. Quincke [10] found the index of refraction, ω, to be 3·027 for the C-ray; 2·398 for D-ray; 1·832 for E-ray; 1·429 for F-ray; and 1·110 for G-ray; G. Horn gave 2·965 for C-ray; 2·571 for D-ray; 1·962 for E-ray; 1·578 for F-ray; and 1·246 for G-ray; and P. Drude gave 3·19 for C-ray; and 3·04 for D-ray. For the absorption coefficient, k, G. Quincke gave 1·490 for the C-ray; 1·899 for D-ray; 2·329 for E-ray; 2·762 for F-ray; and 2·937 for G-ray; G. Horn gave 1·875 for C-ray; 2·090 for D-ray; 2·534 for E-ray; and 3·260 for G-ray. P. Drude found 1·56 for C-ray, and 1·63 for D-ray. The optical dispersion of antimony is very large, and the curve shows a point of inflection. W. W. Coblentz found that the percentage reflecting power of antimony, 53 per cent. for light of wave-length 0·06μ; 55 per cent. for 1·0μ; 60 per cent. for 2μ; 68 per cent. for 4μ; and 72 per cent. for 10μ. P. Drude gave 70 per cent. for $\lambda=0·589\mu$; and 4·94 for the extinction coeff. A. Ghira gave for the atomic refraction 23·69–25·27 for tervalent antimony from the μ-formula, and 11·18–13·01 from the μ^2-formula. J. H. Gladstone gave 24·5 for the at. refraction. S. Procopiu studied the electro-optical effect and the magneto-optical effect of antimony powder suspended in toluene.

J. Piccard and E. Thomas [11] discussed the colour of antimony ions. Antimony salts give no characteristic flame spectrum in the colourless gas flame, although R. Bunsen [12] found that the upper part of the reducing zone acquires a green tinge. H. W. Vogel found that antimony trichloride in the colourless gas-flame gives a continuous spectrum, which shows a few feeble lines in the green; antimony trichloride volatilized in hydrogen also gives a continuous spectrum in the colourless gas-flame. O. Vogel found that antimony and many of its compounds give a band spectrum—vide infra—in the oxy-coal gas flame. The spark spectrum of antimony was first described by A. Masson in 1851, and since then numerous observations have been made by A. J. Angström, D. Alter, G. Kirchhoff, T. R. Robinson, W. A. Miller, W. Huggins, R. Thalén, L. de Boisbaudran, R. Capron, H. Schippers, A. Hagenbach and H. Konen, L. and E. Bloch, E. O. Hulburt, J. C. McLennan and

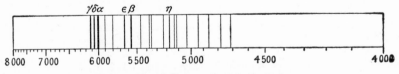

FIG. 6.—Spark Spectrum of Antimony.

co-workers, G. Ciamician, J. Parry and A. E. Tucker, W. N. Hartley and co-workers, A. de Gramont, M. C. W. Buffam and H. J. C. Ireton, F. Exner and E. Haschek, J. M. Eder and E. Valenta, P. G. Nutting, J. Herpertz, S. R. Milner, C. E. Gissing, H. Nagaoka and co-workers, and A. Kretzer. The principal lines in the visible spectrum are: 6129—γ, Fig. 6—6079—δ, Fig. 6—6005—α, Fig. 6 —and 5792 in the orange-yellow; 5792, and 5639—ϵ, Fig. 6—in the yellow; 5568—β, Fig. 6—5464, 5379, 5353, 5242, 5176—η, Fig. 6—5140, 5113, 5036, and 4949 in the green; 4878, 4786, and 4711 in the blue; with numerous lines in the ultra-violet. The orange-yellow α-line, and the green β-line, are characteristic in qualitative spectral analysis. The spark spectrum underwater was examined by M. C. W. Buffam and H. J. C. Ireton, and E. O. Hulburt ; and *les raies ultimes*, by A. de Gramont. The arc spectrum was studied by R. Capron, G. D. Liveing and J. Dewar, J. M. Eder and E. Valenta, F. Exner and E. Haschek, T. Royds, A. Kretzer, J. C. McLennan and co-workers, S. L. Malurkar, J. B. Green, F. M. Walters, etc. ; the intermittent arc spectrum by M. Kimura ; the ultra-violet spectrum, by W. A. Miller, G. D. Liveing and J. Dewar, V. Schumann, L. and E. Bloch, R. J. Lang, F. Exner and E. Haschek, M. Kimura, etc. ; the ultra-red spectrum, by H. M. Randall, and V. P. Lubovich and E. M. Pearen ; and the band spectrum, by J. N. Lockyer, W. N. Hartley, J. Stark and R. Küch, C. de Watteville, E. Paterno and A. Mazzucchelli, L. Janicki, A. Kretzer, J. M. Eder and E. Valenta, etc. The absorption spectrum of the vapour was examined by J. N. Lockyer and W. C. Roberts-Austen, J. C. McLennan and A. B. McLay, J. G. Frayne and A. W. Smith, A. Terenin, R. V. Zumstein, W. Grotrian, and J. J. Dobbie and J. J. Fox. A. L. Narayan and K. R. Rao found that absorption spectrum of the vapour showed fine lines at 2312 and at 2306 ; and there was a banded spectrum extending from 2305 to 2250 with a constant interval of 15 A. The banded spectrum is taken to mean that the molecules are polyatomic. A. Terenin examined the spectrum of the light emitted by the vapour at 1100°. According to J. Formanek, the salt soln. do not react with alkanna. C. R. Crymble examined the absorption spectrum of soln. of antimony chlorides and antimoniates. The influence of *pressure* was examined by W. J. Humphreys ; the *self-induction*, by A. de Gramont, E. Néculcéa, and G. A. Hemsalech ; the *enhanced lines*, by J. Steinhausen, and M. Kimura and G. Nakamura ; and the influence of a *magnetic field*, or the Zeeman effect, by J. E. Purvis, and P. A. van der Harst. Attempts to find regularities and series spectra were made by A. Ditte, J. C. McLennan and A. B. McLay, G. Ciamician, H. Kayser and C. Runge, R. J. Lang, and T. van Lohuizen. No series have been identified, although H. Kayser and C. Runge observed several constant difference lines.

The K-series of X-ray spectra was found by F. C. Blake,[13] W. Duane, B. B. Ray, A. Leide, J. M. Cork and B. R. Stephenson, B. Walter, and M. Siegbahn to have the lines a_2a^1, 0·472 ; a_2a, 0·468 ; $\beta_1\beta$, 0·416 ; and $\beta_2\gamma$, 4·008 ; the L-series, by H. Hirata, D. Coster, K. Chamberlain, K. Chamberlain and G. A. Lindsay, G. Kellstrom, G. I. Pokrowsky, B. B. Ray, A. Dauvillier, A. Jönsson, D. Coster and F. P. Mulder, G. A. Lindsay, Y. Nishina, E. Hjalmar. M. J. Druyvesteyn, and M. Siegbahn to have the lines a_2a^1, 3·44075 ; a_1a, 3·43177 ; $\beta_1\beta$, 3·21836 ; $\beta_2\gamma$, 3·017 ; $\gamma_1\delta$, 2·84507 ; β_4v, 3·184 ; and $\beta_3\phi$, 3·14514. D. Coster and F. P. Mulder also studied the M-, N-, and O-series ; P. Günther, the absorption of the K-rays ; and A. L. Foley, the effect on the spectrum of antimony of exposing the element to X-rays, or to ultra- violet light.

P. D. Foote and co-workers found 8·5 volts for the ionizing potential, and 1·7 and 5·7 volts for the inelastic collision potential of antimony. G. Piccardi gave 8·46 volts for the ionizing potential. C. G. Barkla and co-workers found that the K-series of X-rays of wave-length 1·172 A., from an antimony radiator, have the ratios of the absorption coeff. μ, divided by the density of the absorber carbon, 0·31 ; aluminium, 1·21 ; and silver, 56·1. J. Thibaud measured the β-ray spectrum of antimony. W. Herz gave $2·90 \times 10^{12}$ for the vibration frequency. A. Bouers measured the intensity of the X-rays from antimony ; K. Chamberlain studied the fine structure of the X-ray absorption edges. A. L. Foley observed no definite change occurs when antimony is exposed for a long time to the X-rays in an atm. of nitrogen. E. T. Wherry classed antimony as a poor radio-detector. M. Hake, and A. Predvoditeleff and A. Witt, studied the photoelectric effect with antimony. M. de Broglie examined the photoelectric effects of the γ-rays. M. Levin and R. Ruer found that ordinary antimonic acid exhibits a feeble **radioactivity.** J. E. P. Wagstaff gave 3.0×10^{12} for the **vibration frequency ;** and W. Herz gave 2.90×10^{12}.

K. F. Herzfeld [14] studied the metallic condition of antimony. A. Mattheissen and M. von Bose found that if the **electrical conductivity** of silver be 100, that of antimony is 4·29 at 18·7°. A. Berget gave 2.48×10^4 mhos for the electrical conductivity of antimony at 0°–30° ; A. Oberbeck and J. Bergmann, 2610 mhos at 0° ; A. Eucken and G. Gehlhoff, 2565 mhos at 0°, 3568 mhos at −79°, and 9560 mhos at −190° ; and L. de la Rive, 620 mhos for the solid and 890 mhos for the liquid at the m.p., and 830 mhos for the liquid at 860°. H. Tsutsumi gave 0·67 for the ratio of the resistance of the liquid to that of the solid. The conductivity is very sensitive to the degree of purity of the metal, and A. Eucken and G. Gehlhoff's results may be taken as representing a metal of a high degree of purity. A. Mattheissen and M. von Bose gave for the **electrical resistance** at θ between 12° and 100°, $R = R_0(1 - 0.0039826\theta + 0.0_4103640^2)$. The data were reviewed by A. Schulze. E. F. Northrup and V. A. Suydam measured the electrical resistance of four samples of antimony. The results for two are illustrated by Fig. 7. The other two curves fall within these extremes. With two curves for

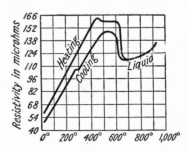

FIG. 7.—The Effect of Temperature on the Electrical Resistance of Antimony.

the solid, on a rising temp., there are breaks near 450°, and with two others, for the solid, on a falling temp., there are breaks between 117° and 107°. H. Tsutsumi observed no such singular points in his observations. E. F. Northrup and V. A. Suydam gave for the resistance of the liquid, R in microhms per c.c. :

	20°	627°	650°	700°	750°	800°	850°	900°
R .	43·47	117·00	117·07	117·65	118·53	120·31	123·54	131·00

W. Haken gave 43·48 microhms at 18°. Y. Matsuyama gave 115.0×10^{-6} ohm for the sp. resistance of molten antimony. H. Tsutsumi found the ratio of the sp. resistance in the liquid and solid states to be 0·67—*vide* bismuth. W. J. de Haas gave 0·00511 for the *temperature* coeff. of the resistance, and P. W. Bridgman, 0·00478, between 0° and 100° ; and he observed a discontinuity in the curve at about 145°. H. Perlitz studied the relation between the space-lattice and the change of resistance with fusion. S. Lussana found the electrical conductivity increases under *pressure* as with normal metals, and the press. coeff. for 3000 atm. at 25° is 0.0_5874. On the other hand, P. W. Bridgman obtained converse results ; he found for the effect of press. over the range 12,000 kgrms. per sq. cm., at 0°, 25°, 50°, 75°, and 100°, the respective values 1·000, 1·113, 1·229, 1·349, and 1·473, with the respective press. coeff., 0.0_41220, 0.0_41107, 0.0_5994, 0.0_5881, and 0.0_5768. There was a discontinuity in the curve at about 145°. E. D. Williamson gave 1·1461 for the ratio of the resistance at 12,000 kgrms. per sq. cm. press. to that at 1 kgrm. per sq. cm. P. W. Bridgman found that the electric resistance of antimony wires increases linearly with *tension*. The tension coeff. was $+0.0_545$ for loads up to 80 grms. ; with another sample the coeff. was $+0.0_420$, and with another one, 0.0_575 For single crystals at 20° he found the sp. resistance to be 35.6×10^{-6} ohm when parallel and 42.6×10^{-6} ohm . when perpendicular to the chief axis. O. Jaamaa and Y. E. G. Leinberg studied the resistance of powdered antimony mixed with marble, sulphur, etc. P. Fischer found that cylinders made from compressed mixtures of antimony sulphide and up to 30 per cent. of antimony do not conduct direct or alternating currents ; with 40 per cent. antimony, the mixture is non-conducting with a direct current, but has a conductivities of 2.2×10^{-4} mhos with the alternating current, and the cylinder then conducts the direct current.

Mixtures with 50 and 60 per cent. antimony show a similar phenomenon. So also does a mixture of cupric oxide with 50 per cent. antimony. G. Tammann and H. Bredemeier, of thin films ; A. Schulze found antimony has a higher resistance for alternating than for direct currents. T. W. Case said that the conductivity of antimony is not affected by *light*. G. Eucken and O. Neumann found that the *grain-size* of the antimony but slightly affected the electrical conductivity, for with fine-grained material, 1.41×10^{-4} sq. cm., the conductivities at $-183°$ and $0°$ are respectively 8.34×10^{-4} and 2.43×10^{-4} mhos ; material of grain-size 2.27×10^{-4} sq. cm., 8.13×10^{-4} mhos respectively ; material of mean-sized grain, 6.35×10^{-4} sq. cm., 8.08×10^{-4} and 2.35×10^{-4} mhos respectively ; and coarse-grained material, 0.143 sq. cm., 7.89×10^{-4} and 2.32×10^{-4} mhos. The relation of G. Wiedemann and R. Franz—3. 21, 5—was for the finest-grained, fine-grained, medium-grained, and coarse-grained material 2.31, 2.46, 2.73, and 5.72 respectively at $-183°$, and 7.09, 7.20, 7.73, and 10.55 respectively at $0°$—*vide infra*, thermal conductivity. Z. A. Epstein, and A. Günther-Schulze studied the relation between conductivity of various metals and the periodic system ; P. W. Bridgman, the electrical resistance and thermal e.m.f.

The **thermoelectric force** of antimony against platinum at $100°$ was found by W. H. Steele [15] to be 4.70 millivolts, and by E. Rudolfi, 4.86 millivolts. The current passes from the cold junction at $0°$ to the platinum. A. Matthiessen found the thermoelectric power of antimony wire with respect to lead, at $20°$, to be 6.0 microvolts ; with crystals axially disposed, 22.6 microvolts ; and with crystals equatorially disposed, 26.4 microvolts. J. Svanberg found a rod cut parallel to the chief axis is more negative, and one cut perpendicular to that axis is more positive than a rod cut in any other way. R. Franz found a current is produced by warming the junction of a crystal with the (0001)-surface in contact with another surface. C. Matteucci also made observations on this subject. G. Todesco studied the effect of light ; and T. Terada and co-workers, the effect with thin films. F. P. le Roux found the **Peltier effect with** the copper-antimony couple to be -5.64 millivolts. For the **Hall effect**, *vide* bismuth. M. Campa found that X-rays of maximum frequency $\gamma = 1.46 \times 10^{19}$ produce a decrease in the Hall coeff. of antimony during solidification. This causes a thermoelectric current in a circuit containing the unexposed metal. The e.m.f. of the couple is 2×10^{-6} volt at $0°$ to $18.5°$, M. Campa also studied the Hall effect with weak fields ; C. W. Heaps, the relation between the Hall effect and the thermoelectric power of antimony ; and P. W. Bridgman, the relation between the four transverse electro- and thermomagnetic effects. In Table V, 9. 51, 5, N. C. Little has compared the **thermomagnetic effect** and the **galvanomagnetic effect** of the arsenic family of elements.

The electrodeposition of antimony has been previously discussed. B. Neumann [16] found that the absolute **electrode potential** of antimony in a normal soln. of the chloride is -0.376 volt ; K. Jellinek and H. Gordon gave 0.244 volt. K. Elbs and H. Thümmel found that an antimony anode in a soln. of sodium chloride or hydrochloric acid dissolves in the tervalent form. G. Grube and F. Schweigardt obtained a similar conclusion with conc. soln. of alkali hydroxide, without the antimony becoming passive. If the current density exceeds 7.5 amp. per sq. dcm., the anode becomes passive by acquiring a film of white non-conducting oxide. A soln. of potassium antimonite is a strong reducing agent and readily absorbs oxygen from the air. The process of its electrolytic oxidation at a polished platinum electrode is not, however, reversible, and it is shown that production of potassium antimonate in this manner is effected, not by a direct process of anodic oxidation, but by the oxidizing action of oxygen evolved in the form of gas at the electrode. The **electrode potential,** ϵ, of antimony in a $10N$-soln. of potassium hydroxide at $20°$, the process of soln. being represented by $Sb + 4OH' + 3(+) \rightarrow SbO_2' + 2H_2O$, is given by $\epsilon = -0.675 + 0.058/3 \log C_{SbO_3}$. For the oxidation process to antimonate, the corresponding equation is

$SbO_2'+2OH'+2(+)\rightarrow SbO_3'+H_2O$, and the value of ϵ is given by $\epsilon=-0.589$ $+0.058 \log (C_{SbO_2'}/C_{SbO_3'})/2$. The value of the electrode potential of antimony in a soln. containing a gram-ion of SbO_3' in $10N$-potassium hydroxide soln. is -0.641 volt. The value of the antimonite-antimonate potential difference is reduced as the alkalinity of the soln. is increased, and is determined by the OH' conc. of the soln. N. T. M. Wilsmore gave <-0.466 volt. for the electrode potential of antimony in contact with normal soln. when the hydrogen electrode is zero. M. le Blanc and D. Reichenstein measured the electrode potential of antimony in soln. of potassium hydroxide, and sulphuric acid. R. Schuhmann found the e.m.f. of the cell $Sb \mid Sb_2O_3,HClO_{4soln.} \mid H_2$ to be -0.152 volt at $25°$; and the mol. reduction potential, corresponding with the reaction $Sb+H_2O+3(+)=SbO'+2H'$, was found to be -0.212 volt. From measurements of the e.m.f. of cells with antimony in combination with a soln. of a tartrate, K. Jellinek and H. Gordon observed that in acidic soln., antimony and tartrate ions form the complex $(SbO)COO.CH(OH).CH(OH).COOH$. G. Tammann and J. Hinnüber studied the cell $SbnHg \mid SbCl_{3aq.}$, N-$KCl,HgCl \mid Hg$. A. Günther-Schulze found that antimony exhibits the electrolytic valve action with nearly all electrolytes, and the valve effect is due to a layer of oxide on the surface of the anodic antimony which holds in some cases with a voltage of $600-700$. H. von Steinwehr gave 3.8×10^{-12} atm. for the electrolytic **solution pressure** $Sb\rightarrow Sb'''$. S. Berberich studied the anodic behaviour of antimony in sulphuric, acetic, nitric, and hydrochloric acid, and in potash-lye—*vide infra*, antimony trioxide and pentoxide. N. R. Dhar studied the effect of dilution on the electrode potential of antimony in salt soln. W. Isbekoff studied the decomposition voltages of a number of metal bromides, and hence deduced the **electrochemical series** : Al, Zn, Cd, Ag, Hg, **Sb**, Bi. F. W. Bergstrom found for soln. in liquid ammonia the series : Pb, Bi, Sn, **Sb**, As, P, Te, Se, S, I. A. Thiel and W. Hammerschmidt found the **overvoltage** of antimony to be 0.233 volt with $2N$-H_2SO_4 at $25°$. H. J. S. Sand and co-workers found that the polarization overvoltage of the antimony cathode is lowered by a high concentration of sulphuric acid or alkali-lye ; and in alkaline soln., the polarization overvoltage, $\omega=A-2h$, where a is a constant, and h is the p_H voltage. E. Newbery observed a black film is formed on antimony in both acidic and alkaline soln. S. Glasstone measured the cathodic overvoltage of antimony in N-H_2SO_4, and in N-NaOH. H. J. S. Sand and co-workers found that in alkaline soln., the over-voltage-current density curves obtained by the direct method show an arrest of inflexion which usually takes place at a voltage not far removed from the maximum given by the commutator method. The decay curves representing the overvoltage at successive short intervals after breaking the current also give indications of this same value, for they sink to, and become constant for a considerable time at, a potential not far removed from it. E. Newbery, A. Günther-Schulze, and W. Winter studied the **electrolytic valve action** ; V. Bayerle found that the deposition of antimony from hydrochloric acid soln. proceeds reversibly ; but with alkaline soln., it is irreversible. The **solubility product** is $[Sb'''][OH']^3=4\times10^{-42}$. G. C. Schmidt examined the **passivity** of antimony. W. B. Nottingham studied the characteristic curves of the antimony arc ; H. F. Vieweg, the frictional electricity ; and E. Blechschmidt, and A. Günther-Schulze, the cathodic spluttering of antimony.

In 1827, M. le Bailiff [17] observed that antimony is repelled by a magnet, and later, M. Faraday found that antimony is diamagnetic like bismuth. According to H. Knoblauch and J. Tyndall, if the crystals of antimony are ferruginous, the metal may appear to be paramagnetic. A. von Ettingshausen gave -4.5×10^{-6} to -5.6×10^{-6} vol. units for the **magnetic susceptibility** of antimony ; L. Lombardo, -3.8×10^{-6} vol. units; S. Meyer, -0.57×10^{-6} mass units; K. Honda, -0.94×10^{-6} mass units at $18°$; M. Owen, -0.815×10^{-6} mass units ; and H. Isnardi and R. Gans, -1.346×10^{-6}. C. Nusbaum studied the magnetic susceptibility of single crystals and found 0.497×10^{-6} for the value of the constant parallel to the principal axis, and $1·38\times10^{-6}$ when vertical thereto. S. Meyer gave $-2·28\times10^{-6}$ for the **magnetization number** of antimony in the powdered state, and $-33·1\times10^{-6}$ for compact antimony; and he gave $-0·069\times10^{-6}$ and $-0·59\times10^{-6}$ respectively for the **atomic magnetism** of antimony. P. Pascal gave for the at. susceptibility of tervalent antimony, -259×10^{-7} to -263×10^{-7}; and for quinquevalent antimony, -669×10^{-7}. J. Forrest studied the variations in the transverse and parallel components of magnetization of crystals of antimony. W. Gerlach studied the magnetic moment of the atoms. B. H. Wilson calculated the magnetic constants from theoretical principles.

REFERENCES.

[1] F. Hérard, *Compt. Rend.*, 107. 420, 1888; R. J. Haüy, *Traité de minéralogie*, Paris, 4. 253, 1801; F. Mohs, *Grundriss der Mineralogie*, Dresden, 2. 496, 1824; H. Laspeyres, *Zeit. deut. geol. Ges.*, 26. 318, 1874; 27. 574, 1875; *Journ. prakt. Chem.*, (2), 9. 314, 1874; F. C. L. Elsner, *ib.*, (1), 20. 71, 1840; I. V. Obreimoff and L. V. Shubnikoff. *Trans. Phys. Lab. Leningrad*, 100. 21, 1925; *Zeit. Physik*, 25. 31, 1924; G. Rose, *Sitzber. Akad. Berlin*, 72, 1849; *Pogg. Ann.*, 77. 144, 1849; C. M. Marx, *Schweigger's Journ.*, 59. 211, 1830; F. Hessel, *Neues Jahrb. Min.*, 56, 1833; O. Mügge, *ib.*, ii, 40, 1884; i, 183, 1866; F. A. Römer, *ib.*, 310, 1848; G. W. Zenger, *Sitz. Akad. Wien*, 44. 312, 1861; *Verh. geol. Reichsanst. Wien*, 10, 1861; C. W. C. Fuchs, *Die künstlich dargestellen Mineralien nach Roses System geordnet*, Haarlem, 24, 1872; F. Fouqué and A. Michel-Lévy, *Synthèse des minéraux des roches*, Paris, 284, 1882; C. F. Rammelsberg, *Handbuch der krystallographisch-physikalischen Chemie*, Leipzig, i, 110, 1881; W. H. and W. L. Bragg, *X-rays and Crystal Structure*, London, 227, 1914; G. Tammann and Q. A. Mansuri, *Zeit. anorg. Chem.*, 126. 104, 1925; R. W. James and N. Tunstall, *Phil. Mag.*, (6), 40. 233, 1920; A. Ogg, *ib.*, (6), 42. 163, 1921; P. Möller, *Ueber den roten Phosphor und die eutropische Reihe Phosphor, Arsen, Antimon, Wismuth*, Langensalza, 1908; R. Neumann, *Beiträge zur Kenntnis der Phosphor-Arsen-Antimon-Gruppe*, Heidelberg, 1900; G. E. Linck, *Ber.*, 32. 888, 1899; 33. 2284, 1900; 41. 822, 1908; *Zeit. anorg. Chem.*, 56. 400, 1908; *Grundriss der Kristallographie*, Jena, 1913; G. W. A. Kahlbaum, *Zeit. anorg. Chem.*, 29. 292, 1902; J. W. Retgers, *ib.*, 4. 403, 435, 1893; E. Bekier, *ib.*, 78. 178, 1912; G. Linck and H. Jung, *ib.*, 147. 288, 1925; M. L. Huggins, *Journ. Amer. Chem. Soc.*, 44. 1481, 1922; *Phys. Rev.*, (2), 19. 369, 1922; *Amer. Journ. Science*, (5), 5. 303, 1923; P. P. Ewald and C. Hermann, *Zeit. Kryst.*, 65. Suppl., 27, 1927; F. Roll, *ib.*, 65. 119, 1927; J. A. M. van Liempt, *Tech. Publ. Amer. Inst. Min. Eng.*, 15, 1927; H. C. H. Carpenter, *Metal Ind.*, 32. 405, 1928.

[2] A. Matthiessen, *Proc. Roy. Soc.*, 10. 207, 1860; *Phil. Trans.*, 150. 177, 1860; *Pogg. Ann.*, 110. 21, 1860; W. P. Dexter, *ib.*, 100. 567, 1857; G. Quincke, *ib.*, 135. 621, 1868; H. G. F. Schröder, *ib.*, 106. 226, 1859; 107. 113, 1859; R. F. Marchand and T. Scheerer, *Journ. prakt. Chem.*, (1), 27. 207, 1842; W. Spring, *Ber.*, 16. 2723, 1883; W. L. Bragg, *Phil. Mag.*, (6), 40. 169, 1920; L. L. Bircumshaw, *ib.*, (7), 3. 1286, 1927; G. W. A. Kahlbaum, K. Roth, and P. Siedler, *Zeit. anorg. Chem.*, 29. 177, 1902; W. Herz, *ib.*, 105. 171, 1919; G. A. Kenngott, *Sitzber. Akad. Wien*, 10. 184, 1853; M. Toepler, *Wied. Ann.*, 53. 343, 1894; F. Nies and A. Winkelmann, *ib.*, 13. 70, 1881; H. G. Grimm, *Zeit. phys. Chem.*, 122. 177, 1925; W. Gaede, *Phys. Zeit.*, 4. 105, 1902; J. M. Guinchant and H. Chrétien, *Compt. Rend.*, 142. 702, 1906; P. Pascal and A. Jouniaux, *ib.*, 158. 414, 1914; *Bull. Soc. Chim.*, (4), 15. 312, 1914; *Zeit. Elektrochem.*, 22. 71, 1916; E. Maey, *Zeit. phys. Chem.*, 50. 200, 1905; E. Cohen and J. C. van den Bosch, *ib.*, 89. 757, 1915; J. Dalton, *A New System of Chemical Philosophy*, Manchester, 2. 263, 1880; I. I. Saslowsky, *Zeit. anorg. Chem.*, 145. 315, 1925; C. del Fresno, *ib.*, 152. 25, 1926; F. Mohs, *Grundriss der Mineralogie*, Dresden, 2. 496, 1824; H. Fay and H. E. Ashley, *Amer. Chem. Journ.*, 27. 95, 1902; T. Bergman, *De antimonialibus sulphuratis*, Upsala, 1782; J. F. L. Hausmann, *Handbuch der Mineralogie*, Göttingen, 12, 1847; A. Eschka, *Berg. Hütt. Ztg.*, 13. 23, 1862; G. F. Kunz, *Amer. Journ. Science*, (3), 30. 275, 1885; M. H. Klaproth, *Beiträge zur chemischen Kenntniss der Mineralkörper*, Berlin, 3. 170, 1802; G. Wertheim, *Ann. Chem. Phys.*, (3), 12. 385, 581, 1844; *Compt. Rend.*, 19. 229, 1844; J. J. van Laar, *Die Zustandsgleichung von Gasen und Flussigkeiten*, Leipzig, 1924; *Proc. Acad. Amsterdam*, 18. 1220, 1915; 19. 2, 1916; R. M. Bozorth, *Journ. Amer. Chem. Soc.*, 47. 1621, 1925; T. M. Lowry, *Journ. Inst. Metals*, 19. 259, 1919; T. M. Lowry and R. G. Parker, *Journ. Chem. Soc.*, 107. 1005, 1915; F. Winkler, *Das Atomgewicht des Antimons. Neubestimmung durch Ueberführung des Metalls in Antimon-Tetroxyd*, München, 1917; E. N. Gapon, *Zeit. Physik*, 44. 535, 1927; M. J. Brisson, *Pésanteur spécifique des corps*, Paris, 49, 1787; C. Hatchett, *Phil. Trans.*, 93. 43, 1883; P. van Muschenbrock, *ib.*, 33. 370, 1726; J. P. Cooke, *Proc. Amer. Acad.*, 13. 11, 1877; L. Playfair and J. P. Joule, *Mem. Chem. Soc.*, 3. 77, 1848; G. Gore, *Phil. Mag.*, (4), 9. 73, 1855; *Journ. Chem. Soc.*, 17. 365, 1863; *Proc. Roy. Soc.*, 12. 185, 1858; *Phil. Trans.*, 148. 185, 797, 1858; 152. 323, 1862; C. J. B. Karsten, *Schweigger's Journ.*, 65. 394, 1832; A. Breithaupt, *ib.*, 52. 167, 1828; C. M. Marx, *ib.*, 58. 464, 1830; H. G. Dorsey, *Phys. Rev.*, (1), 25. 88, 1907; M. L. Huggins, *ib.*, (2), 28. 1086, 1926; E. N. Gapon, *Zeit. Physik*, 44. 535, 1927; R. von Dallwitz-Wegner, *Zeit. Elektrochem.*, 33. 42, 1927; W. F. de Jong and H. M. V. Willems, *Physica*, 7. 74, 1927.

⁸ V. Meyer and H. Biltz, *Ber.*, **22.** 725, 1889 ; J. M. Guinchant and H. Chrétien, *Compt. Rend.*, **138.** 1269, 1904 ; C. T. Heycock and F. H. Neville, *Journ. Chem. Soc.*, **49.** 158, 1890 ; **50.** 145, 1892 ; A. Jouniaux, *Bull. Soc. Chim.*, (4), **35.** 463, 1924 ; H. von Wartenberg, *Zeit. anorg. Chem*, **56.** 320, 1907.
⁴ J. R. Rydberg, *Zeit. phys. Chem.*, **33.** 353, 1900 ; P. Ludwik, *ib.*, **91.** 232, 1916 ; *Zeit. anorg. Chem.*, **94.** 161, 1915 ; W. Spring, *Ann. Chim. Phys.*, (5), **22.** 186, 1881 ; W. Widder, *Phys. Zeit.*, **26.** 618, 1925 ; C. I. Burton and W. Marshall, *Proc. Roy. Soc.*, **50.** 130, 1891 ; L. L. Bircumshaw, *Phil. Mag.*, (7), **3.** 1286, 1927 ; D. Saito and K. Hayashi, *Mem. Coll. Eng. Kyoto*, **2.** 83, 1919 ; K. Honda and R. Yamada, *Science Rep. Tohoku Univ.*, **14.** 63, 1925 ; E. Madelung and R. Fuchs, *Ann. Physik*, (4), **65.** 289, 1921 ; C. A. Edwards and A. M. Herbert, *Metal Ind.*, **18.** 221, 1921 ; *Journ. Inst. Metals*, **25.** 175, 1921 ; *Proc. Manchester Assoc. Eng.*, 225, 1919 ; T. W. Richards, *Journ. Amer. Chem. Soc.*, **37.** 1643, 1915 ; G. Quincke, *Pogg. Ann.*, **135.** 642, 1868 ; P. W. Bridgman, *Proc. Amer. Acad.*, **58.** 166, 1923 ; **57.** 48, 1922 ; **60.** 358, 1925 ; *Phys. Rev.*, (2), **9.** 138, 1917 ; *Proc. Nat. Acad.*, **10.** 411, 1924 ; B. MacNutt and A. Concilio, *ib.*, (2), **20.** 95, 1922 ; E. Jänecke, *Zeit. phys. Chem.*, **90.** 313, 1915 ; F. Sauerwald, *Zeit. Metallkunde*, **16.** 315, 1924 ; F. Sauerwald and K. Knehans, *Zeit. anorg. Chem.*, **140.** 227, 1924 ; A. Bienias and F. Sauerwald, *ib.*, **161.** 51, 1927 ; G. Drath and F. Sauerwald, *ib.*, **162.** 301, 1927 ; Y. Matuyama, *Science Rep. Tohoku Univ.*, **16.** 555, 1927 ; R. von Dallwitz-Wegner, *Zeit. Elektrochem*, **33.** 42, 1927 ; L. H. Adams, *Journ. Washington Acad.*, **17.** 529, 1927.
⁵ H. Kopp, *Liebig's Ann.*, **81.** 1, 1852 ; *Pogg. Ann.*, **86.** 156, 1852 ; A. Matthiessen, *ib.*, **130.** 50, 1867 ; *Ann. Chim. Phys.*, (3), **54.** 255, 1858 ; H. Fizeau, *Compt. Rend.*, **68.** 1125, 1869 ; A. Berget, *ib.*, **110.** 76, 1890 ; P. Braesco, *ib.*, **170.** 103, 1920 ; M. de Hemptinne, *Bull. Acad. Belg.*, (5), **12.** 797, 1926 ; F. C. Calvert, R. Johnson, and G. C. Lowe, *Proc. Roy. Soc.*, **10.** 315, 1860 ; *Chem. News*, **3.** 315, 357, 371, 1861 ; G. Gehlhoff and F. Neumeier, *Verh. deut. phys. Ges.*, **15.** 876, 1069, 1913 : A. Eucken and G. Gehlhoff, *ib.*, **14.** 169, 1912 ; A. Eucken and O. Neumann, *Zeit. phys. Chem.*, **111.** 431, 1924 ; A. Schrauf, *Zeit. Kryst.*, **12.** 374, 1867 ; E. Jannetaz, *Compt. Rend.*, **114.** 1352, 1892 ; *Bull. Soc. Min..* **15.** 136, 1892 ; *Ann. Chim. Phys.*, (4), **29.** 38, 1873 ; L. Lorenz, *Wied. Ann.*, **13.** 422, 582, 1881 ; *Vid. Selsk. Skr. Kopenhagen*, (6), **2.** 37, 1881 ; P. W. Bridgman, *Proc. Amer. Acad.*, **57.** 77, 1922 ; *Proc. Nat. Acad.*, **10.** 411, 1924 ; E. Grüneisen, *Ann. Physik*, (4), **33.** 33, 65, 1910 ; S. Lussana, *Nuovo Cimento*, (5), **19.** 182, 1910 ; (6), **15.** 130, 1918 ; S. Konno, *Science Rep. Tohoku Univ.*, **8.** 169, 1919 ; *Phil. Mag.*, (6), **40.** 542, 1920 ; H. G. Dorsey, *Phys. Rev.*, (1), **25.** 88, 1907 ; (1), **27.** 1, 1908 ; R. von Dallwitz-Wegner, *Zeit. Elektrochem.*, **33.** 42, 1927.
⁶ P. L. Dulong and A. J. Petit, *Ann. Chim. Phys.*, (2), **7.** 146, 1818 ; H. V. Regnault, *ib.*, (2), **73.** 5, 1840 ; *Compt. Rend.*, **10.** 658, 1840 ; E. Bède, *Mém. Cour. Savants Acad.*, **27.** 1, 1856 ; H. Kopp, *Liebig's Ann. Suppl.*, **3.** 289, 1865 ; R. Bunsen, *Pogg. Ann.*, **141.** 1, 1870 ; L. Lorenz, *Vid. Selsk. Skr. Kopenhagen*, (6), **2.** 37, 1881 ; *Wied. Ann.*, **13.** 422, 1881 ; L. von Pebal and H. Jahn, *ib.*, **27.** 584, 1886 ; L. Schüz, *ib.*, **46.** 177, 1892 ; F. Wüst, A. Meuthen and W. R. Durrer, *Ver. deut. Ing. Forsch.*, 204, 1918 ; A. Naccari, *Atti Accad. Torino*, **23.** 107, 1887 ; J. Laborde, *Journ. Phys.*, (3), **5.** 547, 1896 ; J. H. Awbery and E. Griffiths, *Proc. Phys. Soc.*, **38.** 378, 1926 ; U. Behn, *Ann. Physik*, (4), **1.** 257, 1900 ; R. Ewald, *ib.*, (4), **44.** 1213, 1914 ; P. Günther, *ib.*, (4), **63.** 476, 1920 ; G. W. A. Kahlbaum, K. Roth, and P. Siedler, *Zeit. anorg. Chem.*, **29.** 177, 1902 ; P. Schübel, *ib.*, **87.** 81, 1914 ; W. Gaede, *Phys. Zeit.*, **4.** 105, 1902 ; H. John, *Viertelj. Nat. Ges. Zürich*, **53.** 186, 1908 ; *Die Abhängigkeit der spezifischen Wärme des festen Antimons und des festen Wismuts von der Temperatur.*, Zürich, 1908 ; H. Schimpff, *Zeit. phys. Chem.*, **71.** 257, 1910 ; T. W. Richards and F. G. Jackson, *ib.*, **70.** 414, 1910 ; J. Dewar, *Proc. Roy. Soc.*, **89.** A, 158, 1913 ; E. D. Eastman, A. M. Williams, and T. F. Young, *Journ. Amer. Chem. Soc.*, **46.** 1184, 1924 ; G. N. Lewis, *ib.*, **29.** 1165, 1907 ; S. Umino, *Science Rep. Tohoku Univ.*, **15.** 597, 1926 ; A. Simon and M. Ruhemann, *Zeit. phys. Chem.*, **129.** 337, 1927.
⁷ L. B. G. de Morveau, *Mém. l'Inst.*, **12.** 89, 1811 ; C. T. Heycock and F. H. Neville, *Journ. Chem. Soc.*, **67.** 186, 1895 ; A. Gautier, *Compt. Rend.*, **123.** 112, 1896 ; E. van Aubel, *ib.*, **132.** 1266, 1901 ; H. Chrétien, *ib.*, **142.** 1340, 1906 ; H. Pélabon, *ib.*, **142.** 207, 1906 ; L. Holborn, *Zeit. Elektrochem.*, **23.** 287, 1917 ; L. Holborn and A. L. Day, *Ann. Physik*, (4), **2.** 534, 1900 ; A. L. Day and R. B. Sosman, *ib.*, (4), **38.** 849, 1912 ; *Amer. Journ. Science*, (4), **33.** 517, 1912 ; J. H. Awbery and E. Griffiths, *Proc. Phys. Soc.*, **38.** 378, 1926 ; E. Karrer, *Phys. Rev.*, (2), **19.** 437, 1922 ; F. Winkler, *Das Atomgewicht des Antimons. Neubestimmung durch Ueberführung des Metalls in Antimon-Tetroxyd*, München, 1917 ; H. Callendar, *Phil. Mag.*, (5), **48.** 519, 1899 ; H. Fay and H. E. Ashley, *Amer. Chem. Journ.*, **27.** 95, 1902 ; K. Scheel, *Zeit. angew. Chem.*, **32.** 347, 1919 ; F. Krafft, *Ber.*, **36.** 1712, 1903 ; H. Capitaine, *Journ. Pharm. Chim.*, (2), **25.** 516, 1839 ; W. Reinders, *Zeit. anorg. Chem.*, **25.** 119, 1900 ; E. Groschuff, *ib.*, **103.** 164, 1918 ; A. Ledebur, *Wied. Ann. Beibl.*, **5.** 650, 1881 ; J. Dalton, *A New System of Chemical Philosophy*, Manchester, **2.** 263, 1810 ; R. Pictet, *Compt. Rend.*, **88.** 1315, 1829 ; P. N. Laschtschenko, *Journ. Russ. Phys. Chem. Soc.*, **46.** 311, 1914 ; W. Guertler and M. Pirani, *Zeit. Metallkunde*, **11.** 1, 1919 ; L. I. Dana and P. D. Foote, *Trans. Faraday Soc.*, **15.** 186, 1920 ; C. W. Waidner and G. K. Burgess, *Bull. Bur. Standards*, **6.** 149, 1909 ; W. R. Mott, *Trans. Amer. Electrochem. Soc.*, **34.** 255, 1918 ; H. Carlsohn, *Ber.*, **59.** B, 1916, 1926.
⁸ S. Umino, *Science Rep. Tohoku Univ.*, **15.** 597, 1926 ; J. von Liebig, *Handwörterbuch der reinen und angewandten Chemie*, Braunschweig, **1.** 416, 1837 ; F. Krafft and L. Bergfeld, *Ber.*, **38.** 258, 1905 ; F. Krafft, *ib.*, **36.** 1704, 1903 ; H. F. Wiebe, *ib.*, **12.** 788, 1879 ; V. Meyer and H. Biltz, *ib.*, **22.** 725, 1889 ; *Zeit. phys. Chem.*, **4.** 249, 1889 ; C. Zenghelis, *ib.*, **57.** 90, 1906 ;

F. Winkler, *Das Atomgewicht des Antimons Neubestimmung durch Ueberführung des Metalls* in *Antimon-Tetroxyd*, München, 1917; V. Meyer and H. Mensching, *Liebig's Ann.*, 240. 321, 1887; *Ber.*, 20. 500, 1833, 1887; A. Schuller, *Wied. Ann.*, 18. 321, 1883; E. Demarçay, *Compt. Rend.*, 95. 183, 1882; F. S. Mortimer, *Journ. Amer. Chem. Soc.*, 44. 1431, 1922; T. Carnelley and W. C. Williams, *Journ. Chem. Soc.*, 55. 563, 1879; J. H. Awbery and E. Griffiths, *Proc. Phys. Soc.*, 38. 378, 1926; W. R. Mott, *Trans. Amer. Electrochem. Soc.*, 34. 255, 1918; P. N. Laschtschenko, *Journ. Russ. Phys. Chem. Soc.*, 46. 311, 1914; W. G. Duffield, *Phil. Mag.*, (6), 45. 641, 1104, 1923; O. Ruff and B. Bergdahl, *Zeit. anorg. Chem.*, 106. 76, 1919; O. Ruff and S. Mugdan, *ib.*, 117. 147, 1921; E. Tiede and E. Birnbräuer, *ib.*, 87. 129, 1914; H. von Wartenberg, *ib.*, 56. 320, 1908; J. A. M. van Liempt, *ib.*, 114. 105, 1920; H. C. Greenwood, *Proc. Roy. Soc.*, 82. A, 396, 1909; 83. A, 483, 1910; F. Wüst, A. Meuthen, and R. Durrer, *Ver. deut. Ing. Forsch.*, 204, 1918; J. W. Richards, *Chem. News*, 75. 278, 1897; *Journ. Franklin Inst.*, 143. 379, 1897; J. Tate, *Die experimentelle Bestimmung der Verdampfungswärme einiger Metalle*, Berlin, 42. 1914; M. Kawakami, *Zeit. anorg. Chem.*, 167. 345, 1927; W. Herz, *ib.*, 170. 237, 1928; J. Johnston, *Journ. Ind. Eng. Chem.*, 9. 873, 1917.
⁹ W. G. Mixter, *Amer. Journ. Science*, (4), 28. 108, 1909; E. Kordes, *Zeit. anorg. Chem.*, 160. 67, 1927; B. Brugs, *Journ. Phys. Chem.*, 31. 681, 1927; J. C. Thomlinson, *Chem. News*, 99. 133, 1909.
¹⁰ W. W. Coblentz, *Bull. Bur. Standards*, 2. 457, 1906; 7. 197, 1911; *Journ. Franklin Inst.*, 170. 182, 1910; J. H. Gladstone, *Proc. Roy. Soc.*, 16. 439, 1868; 18. 49, 1870; *Journ. Chem. Soc.*, 23. 101, 1870; *Phil. Trans.*, 160. 9, 1870; S. Procopiu, *Compt. Rend.*, 174. 1170, 1922; P. Drude, *Wied. Ann.*, 39. 481, 1890; G. Quincke, *Pogg. Ann. Jubelbd.*, 336, 1874; G. Horn, *Neues Jahrb. Min. B.B.*, 12. 341, 1899; A. Ghira, *Gazz. Chim. Ital.*, 24. i, 309, 324, 1894.
¹¹ J. Piccard and E. Thomas, *Helvetica Chim. Acta*, 6. 1040, 1923.
¹² A. Masson, *Ann. Chim. Phys.*, (3), 31. 295, 1851; L. de Boisbaudran, *Spectres lumineux*, Paris, 1874; A. J. Angström, *Pogg. Ann.*, 94. 141, 1855; D. Alter, *Amer. Journ. Science*, (2), 18. 55, 1854; T. R. Robinson, *Phil. Trans.*, 152. 939, 1862; W. A. Miller, *ib.*, 152. 861. 1862; G. D. Liveing and J. Dewar, *ib.*, 174. 187, 1883; R. J. Lang, *Proc. Nat. Acad.*, 13. 341, 1927; *Phil. Trans.*, 224. A, 371, 1924; W. Huggins, *ib.*, 154. 139, 1864; J. N. Lockyer, *ib.*, 163. 253, 1873; *Proc. Roy. Soc.*, 22. 371, 1874; J. N. Lockyer and W. C. Roberts-Austen, *ib.*, 23. 344, 1875; J. C. McLennan, J. F. T. Young, and H. J. C. Ireton, *ib.*, 98. A, 95, 1920; T. Royds, *ib.*, 107. A, 360, 1925; W. N. Hartley and H. W. Moss, *ib.*, 87. A, 38, 1912; W. N. Hartley, *Trans. Roy. Soc. Dublin*, (2), 1. 231, 1883; *Journ. Chem. Soc.*, 41. 84, 1882; *Proc. Roy. Soc.*, 54. 5, 1893; *Phil. Trans.*, 175. 325, 1884; 185. 161, 1894; W. N. Hartley and W. E. Adney, *ib.*, 175. 63, 1884; S. R. Milner, *ib.*, 209. A, 91, 1908; R. Capron, *Photographed Spectra*, London, 1877; E. Demarçay, *Spectres électriques*, Paris, 1895; F. Exner and E. Haschek, *Sitzber. Akad. Wien*, 106. 337, 1897; *Wellenlangentabellen für spectralanalytische Untersuchungen auf Grund der ultravioletten Funkenspectren der Elemente*, Leipzig, 1902; *Wellenlangentabellen für spectralanalytische Untersuchungen auf Grund der ultravioletten Bogenspectren der Elemente*, Leipzig, 1904; *Die Spectren der Elemente bei normalen Druck*, Leipzig, 1912; J. M. Eder and E. Valenta, *Atlas typischer Spectren*, Wien, 1911; *Denkschr. Akad. Wien*, 68. 531, 1899; 118. 511, 1909; 119. 519, 1910; G. Ciamician, *ib.*, 76. 499, 1877; 82. 425, 1880; G. Kirchhoff, *Sitzber. Akad. Berlin*, 63, 1861; 227, 1863; H. Kayser and C. Runge, *ib.*, 3, 1893; *Wied. Ann.*, 52. 93, 1894; J. C. McLennan, J. F. T. Young, and H. J. C. Ireton, *Proc. Roy. Soc.*, 98. A, 95, 1920; J. J. Dobbie and J. J. Fox, *ib.*, 98. A, 147, 1920; A. Hagenbach and H. Konen, *Atlas der Emissionsspectra*, Jena, 1905; H. Schippers, *Messungen in Antimonspectrum*, Bonn, 1912; E. Néculcéa, *Recherches théoriques et expérimentales sur la constitution des spectres ultraviolettes d'étincelles oscillantes*, Paris, 1906; G. A. Hemsalech, *Recherches expérimentales sur les spectres d'étincelles*, Paris, 1901; A. de Gramont, *Analyse spectres d'étincelles des minéraux*, 1895; *Compt. Rend.*, 118. 591, 746, 1894; 134. 1205, 1902; 146. 1260, 1908; 170. 31, 1920; A. Ditte, *ib.*, 73. 738, 1871; L. and E. Bloch, *ib.*, 171. 709, 1920; 178. 472, 1924; *Journ. Phys. Rad.*, 2. 229, 1921; J. Parry and A. E. Tucker, *Engg.*, 27. 127, 429, 1879; 28. 141, 1879; R. Thalén, *Om spectralanalys*, Upsala, 1866; *Nova Acta Soc. Upsala*, (3), 6. 9, 1868; V. Schumann, *Phot. Rund.*, 41. 71, 1890; W. J. Humphreys, *Astrophys. Journ.*, 6. 169, 1897; P. Lewis, *ib.*, 16. 31, 1902; *Phys. Zeit.*, 3. 498, 1902; J. Stark and R. Küch, *ib.*, 6. 438, 1905; P. G. Nutting, *Astrophys. Journ.*, 22. 131, 1905; J. Herpertz, *Die Spektra von Arsen und das Geisslerrohrspektrum von Antimon*, Bonn, 1906; *Zeit. wiss. Photochem.*, 4. 175, 1906; J. Steinhausen, *ib.*, 3. 45, 1905; C. de Watteville, *ib.*, 7. 279, 1909; M. Kimura, *Science Papers Japan Inst. Phys. Chem. Research*, 3. 71, 1925; A. Kretzer, *Untersuchungen über das Antimonspektrum*, Leipzig, 1909; *Zeit. wiss. Photochem.*, 8. 45, 1910; H. M. Randall, *ib.*, 34. 1, 1911; T. van Lohuizen, *ib.*, 11. 397, 1912; *Proc. Acad. Amsterdam*, 15. 31, 1912; J. E. Purvis, *Proc. Cambridge Phil. Soc.*, 13. 82, 1908; 14. 216, 1907; E. Paterno and A. Mazzucchelli, *Rend. Accad. Lincei*, (5), 17. 428, 1908; L. Janicki, *Ann. Physik*, (4), 29. 833, 1909; C. E. Gissing, *Spark Spectra of the Metals*, London, 1910; J. Formanek, *Die qualitative Spektralanalyse anorganischer und organischer Körper*, Berlin, 152, 1905; P. A. van der Harst, *Proc. Acad. Amsterdam*, 22. 300, 1920; *Arch. Néerl.*, (3), 9. 1, 1925; A. Grünwald, *Monatsh.*, 10. 829, 1889; R. Bunsen, *Liebig's Ann.*, 138. 276, 1886; H. W. Vogel, *Practische Spectralanalyse irdischer Stoffe*, Berlin, 1. 243, 1889; O. Vogel, *Zeit. anorg. Chem.*, 5. 61, 1895; C. R. Crymble, *Proc. Chem. Soc.*, 30. 179, 1914; A. L. Narayan and K. R. Rao, *Phil. Mag.*, (6), 50. 645, 1925; J. G. Frayne and A. W. Smith,

ib., (7), 1. 732, 1926 ; M. Kimura and G. Nakamura, *Science Papers Inst. Phys. Chem. Research,* 3. 51, 1925 ; M. Kimura, *Japan. Journ. Phys.*, 3. 217, 1924 ; E. O. Hulburt, *Phys. Rev.*, (2), 24. 129, 1924 ; (2), 25. 888, 1925 ; R. V. Zumstein, *ib.*, (2), 29. 209, 1927 ; V. P. Lubovich and E. M. Pearen, *Trans. Roy. Soc. Canada*, (3), 16. 195, 1922 ; J. C. McLennan and A. B. McLay, *ib.*, (3), 19. 89, 1925 ; *Phil. Mag.*, (7), 4. 407, 1927 ; M. C. W. Buffam and H. J. C. Ireton, *ib.*, (3), 19. 113, 1925 ; W. Grotrian, *Zeit. Physik*, 18. 169, 1923 ; A. Terenin, *ib.*, 37. 98, 1926 ; F. M. Walters, *Bur. Standards Scient. Papers*, 17. 161, 1921 ; A. Terenin, *Zeit. Physik*, 31. 26, 1925 ; 37. 98, 1926 ; H. Nagaoka, D. Nukiyama, and T. Futagami, *Proc. Acad. Tokyo*, 3. 392, 398, 403, 409, 415, 1927 ; S. L. Malurkar, *Proc. Cambridge Phil. Soc.*, 24. 85, 1928 ; J. B. Green, *Phys. Rev.*, (2), 31. 707, 1928 ; T. van Lohuizen, *Proc. Akad. Amsterdam*, 15. 31, 1912.

[13] M. de Broglie, *Nature*, 115. 461, 1925 ; W. Herz, *Zeit. anorg. Chem.*, 163. 220, 1927 ; F. C. Blake and W. Duane, *Phys. Rev.*, (2), 10. 697, 1917 ; J. M. Cork and B. R. Stephenson, *ib.*, (2), 27. 530, 1926 ; K. Chamberlain, *ib.*, (2), 26. 525, 1925 ; *Nature*, 114. 500, 1924 ; K. Chamberlain and G. A. Lindsay, *Phys. Rev.*, (2), 30. 369, 1927 ; D. Coster, *Phil. Mag.*, (6), 43. 1070, 1923 ; *Zeit. Physik*, 25. 83, 1924 ; *Compt. Rend.*, 174. 378, 1922 ; A. Leide, *ib.*, 180. 1203 1925 ; A. Dauvillier, *ib.*, 173. 1458, 1921 ; G. A. Lindsay, *ib.*, 175. 150, 1922 ; P. Günther, *Naturwiss.*, 14. 1118, 1926 ; A. Predvoditeleff and A. Witt, *Zeit. Physik*, 35. 783, 1926 ; D. Coster, *ib.*, 25. 83, 1924 ; D. Coster and F. P. Mulder, *ib.*, 38. 264, 1926 ; B. Walter, *ib.*, 30. 357, 1924 ; A. Leide, *ib.*, 39. 686, 1926 ; J. Thibaud, *Journ. Phys. Rad.*, 6. 82, 1925 ; M. Levin and R. Ruer, *Phys. Zeit.*, 10. 576, 1909 ; A. Bouers, *Physica*, 5. 8, 1925 ; E. Hjalmar, *Zeit. Physik*, 3. 262, 1920 ; G. I. Pokrowsky, *ib.*, 35. 390, 1926 ; M. Siegbahn, *Jahrb. Rad. Elektron.*, 13. 296, 1916 ; A. Günther-Schulze, *Zeit. Elektrochem.*, 33. 360, 1927 ; A. E. Ruark, F.L. Mohler, P. D. Foote, and R. L. Cherault, *Bull. Bur. Standards*, 19. 463, 1924 ; *Phys. Rev.*, (2), 23. 770, 1924 ; *Journ. Franklin Inst.*, 199. 541, 1924 ; C. G. Barkla, *Phil. Mag.*, (6), 5. 685, 1903 ; C. G. Barkla and V. Collier, *ib.*, (6), 23. 987, 1912 ; J. E. P. Wagstaff, *ib.*, (6), 47. 84, 1924 ; B. B. Ray, *ib.*, (6), 48. 707, 1924 ; C. G. Barkla and C. A. Sadler, *ib.*, (6), 17. 739, 1909 ; E. T. Wherry, *Amer. Min.*, 10. 28, 1925 ; A. L. Foley, *Proc. Indiana Acad.*, 34. 185, 1925 ; M. Hake, *Zeit. Physik*, 15. 110, 1923 ; A. Jönsson, *ib.*, 35. 387, 1926 ; 41. 221, 1927 ; M. J. Druyvesteyn, *ib.*, 43. 707, 1927 ; G. Kellström, *ib.*, 44. 269, 1927 ; B. B. Ray, *Phil. Mag.*, (6), 48. 707, 1924 ; Y. Nishina, *ib.*, (6], 49. 521, 1925 ; H. Hirata, *Proc. Roy. Soc.*, 104. A, 40, 1924 ; W. Herz, *Zeit. anorg. Chem.*, 170. 237, 1928 ; G. Piccardi, *Atti Accad. Lincei*, (6), 6. 428, 1927.

[14] A. Matthiessen and M. von Bose, *Pogg. Ann.*, 115. 353, 1862 ; *Proc. Roy. Soc.*, 11. 516, 1862 ; *Phil. Trans.*, 152. 1, 1862 ; H. Tsutsumi, *Science Rep. Tohoku Univ.*, 7. 93, 1918 ; P. Fischer, *Zeit. Elektrochem.*, 33. 172, 1927 ; E. D. Williamson, *Journ. Franklin Inst.*, 193. 491, 1922 ; A. Eucken and G. Gehlhoff, *Verh. deut. phys. Ges.*, 14. 169, 1912 ; A. Eucken and O. Neumann, *Zeit. phys. Chem.*, 111. 431, 1924 ; H. Perlitz, *Phil. Mag.*, (7), 2. 1148, 1926 ; A. Oberbeck and J. Bergmann, *Wied. Ann.*, 31. 792, 1887 ; N. R. Dhar, *Zeit. anorg. Chem.*, 118. 75, 1921 ; G. Tammann and H. Bredemeier, *ib.*, 143. 64, 1925 ; A. Berget, *Compt. Rend.*, 100. 36, 1890 ; L. de la Rive, *ib.*, 56. 588, 1863 ; A. Schulze, *Zeit. Metallkunde*, 15. 158, 1923 ; A. Schulze, *ib.*, 16. 48, 1924 ; O. Jaamaa and Y. E. G. Leinberg, *Comment. Soc. Fenn.*, 1. 21, 1922 ; P. W. Bridgman, *Proc. Amer. Acad.*, 52. 573, 1917 ; 57. 48, 1922 ; *Phys. Rev.*, (2), 19. 114, 1922 ; *Proc. Nat. Acad.*, 10. 411, 1924 ; T. W. Case, *Phys. Rev.*, (2), 9. 305, 1917 ; K. F. Herzfeld, *ib.*, (2), 29. 703, 1927 ; W. J. de Haas, *Versl. Akad. Amsterdam*, 22. 1110, 1914 ; G. Grube and F. Schweigart, *Zeit. Elektrochem.*, 29. 257, 1923 ; S. Lussana, *Nuovo Cimento*, (6), 15. 130, 1918 ; E. F. Northrup and V. A. Suydam, *Journ. Franklin Inst.*, 175. 153, 1913 ; W. Haken, *Ann. Physik*, (4), 32. 336, 1910 ; Y. Matsuyama, *Kinzoku no Kenku*, 3. 254, 1926 ; *Science Rep. Tohoku Univ.*, 16. 447, 1927 ; H. Tsutsumi, *ib.*, 7. 93, 1918 ; Z. A. Epstein, *Zeit. Physik*, 31. 620, 1925 ; P. W. Bridgman, *Proc. Amer. Acad.*, 61. 101, 1926.

[15] E. Rudolfi, *Zeit. anorg. Chem.*, 67. 65, 1910 ; W. H. Steele, *Phil. Mag.*, (5), 37. 218, 1894 ; G. Todesco, *Atti Accad. Lincei*, (6), 5. 434, 1927 ; M. Campa, *ib.*, (6), 3. 177, 1926 ; *Nuovo Cimento*, (7), 4. 28, 1927 ; *Rend. Accad. Napoli*, (3), 32. 170, 1926 ; T. Terada, S. Tanaka, and S. Kusaba, *Proc. Acad. Tokyo*, 3. 200, 1927 ; J. Svanberg, *Oefvers. Akad. Förh. Stockholm*, 93, 1850 ; *Compt. Rend.*, 31. 250, 1850 ; *Pogg. Ann. Ergbd.*, 3. 153, 1853 ; P. W. Bridgman, *Proc. Amer. Acad.*, 52. 573, 1917 ; 57. 48, 1922 ; *Phys. Rev.*, (2), 19. 114, 1922 ; *Proc. Nat. Acad.*, 10. 411, 1924 ; R. Franz, *Pogg. Ann.*, 83. 374, 1851 ; 85. 388, 1852 ; A. Mattheissen, *ib.*, 103. 412, 1858 ; *Phil. Trans.*, 148. 369, 383, 1858 ; *Phil. Mag.*, (4), 16. 219, 1858 ; C. Matteucci, *Ann. Chim. Phys.*, (3), 43. 470, 1855 ; F. P. le Roux, *ib.*, (4), 10. 201, 1867 ; H. Zahn, *Ann. Physik*, (4), 14. 886, 1904 ; C. W. Heaps, *Phil. Mag.*, (6), 50. 1001, 1925 ; *Phys. Rev.*, (2), 27. 252, 1926 ; N. C. Little, *ib.*, (2), 28. 418, 1926.

[16] A. Thiel and W. Hammerschmidt, *Zeit. anorg. Chem.*, 132. 15, 1923 ; N. R. Dhar, *ib.*, 118. 75, 1921 ; K. Elbs and H. Thümmel, *Zeit. Elektrochem.*, 10. 364, 1904 ; G. Tammann and J. Hinnüber, *Zeit. anorg. Chem.*, 160. 254, 1927 ; S. Glasstone, *Journ. Chem. Soc.*, 123. 1745, 1923 ; P. Pascal, *Compt. Rend.*, 174. 1698, 1922 ; G. Grube and F. Schweigardt, *ib.*, 29. 257, 1923 ; V. Bayerle, *Rec. Trav. Chim. Pays-Bas*, 44. 514, 1925 ; R. Schuhmann, *Journ. Amer. Chem. Soc.*, 46. 52, 1924 ; K. Jellinek and H. Gordon, *Zeit. phys. Chem.*, 112. 207, 1924 ; W. Isbekoff, *ib.*, 116. 304, 1925 ; T. M. Wilsmore, *ib.*, 35. 291, 1900 ; A. Günther-Schulze, *Zeit. Physik*, 36. 563, 1926 ; *Ann. Physik*, (4), 24 43, 1907 ; (4), 65. 223, 1921 ; H. Isnardi and R. Gans, *ib.*, (4), 61. 585, 1920 ; H. von Steinwehr, *Zeit. Instrk.*, 33. 321, 1913 ; H. J. S. Sand and E. J. Weeks, *Journ. Chem. Soc.*, 125. 160, 1924 ; H. J. S. Sand, J. Grant, and W. V. Lloyd, *ib.*, 131. 378, 1927 ; H. J. S. Sand, E. J. Weeks, and

S. W. Worrell, *ib.*, 123. 456, 1923; E. Newbery, *ib.*, 109. 1066, 1916; *Proc. Roy. Soc.*, 114. A, 103, 1927; F. W. Bergstrom, *Journ. Amer. Chem. Soc.*, 47. 1503, 1925; W. Winter, *Phys. Zeit.*, 14. 823, 1923; W. B. Nottingham, *Phys. Rev.*, (2), 27. 806, 1926; (2), 28. 764, 1926; S. Berberich, *Ueber das anodische Verhalten des Jods, Arsens und Antimons*, München, 1913; W. Gerlach, *Phys. Zeit.*, 23. 618, 1924; H. F. Vieweg, *Journ. Phys. Chem.*, 30. 865, 1926; E. Blechschmidt, *Ann. Physik*, (4), 81. 999, 1926; G. C. Schmidt, *Zeit. phys. Chem.*, 106. 105, 1923; B. Neumann, *ib.*, 14. 218, 1914; K. Jellinek and H. Gordon, *ib.*, 112. 207, 1924; M. le Blanc and D. Reichenstein, *Zeit. Elektrochem.*, 15. 261, 1909.

[17] M. Faraday, *Phil. Trans.*, 136. 21, 1846; H. Knoblauch and J. Tyndall, *Phil. Mag.*, (2), 36. 178, 1850; (2), 37. 1, 1850; *Pogg. Ann.*, 79. 233, 1850; 81. 481, 1850; A. von Ettinghausen, *Sitzber. Akad. Wien*, 96. 777, 1887; *Wied. Ann.*, 17. 272, 1882; S. Meyer, *ib.*, 68. 325, 1899; L. Lombardi, *Mem. Accad. Torino*, (2), 47. 1, 1897; K. Honda, *Science Rep. Tohoku Univ.*, 1. 1, 1912; 2. 25, 1913; 3. 139, 223, 1914; 4. 215, 1915; *Ann. Physik*, (4), 32. 1027, 1910; M. Owen, *ib.*, (4), 37. 657, 1912; H. Isnardi and R. Gans, *ib.*, (4), 61. 585, 1920; B. H. Wilson, *Phil. Mag.*, (6), 49. 1145, 1925; J. Forrest, *Trans. Roy. Soc. Edin.*, 54. 601, 1927; C. Nusbaum, *Phys. Rev.*, (2), 29. 370, 905, 1927; P. Pascal, *Compt. Rend.*, 174. 1698, 1922; W. Gerlach, *Phys. Zeit.*, (4), 81. 999, 1926; M. le Bailiff, *Bull. Soc. Math.*, 7. 87, 1827.

§ 6. The Chemical Properties of Antimony

The solubility of the common gases in antimony is probably very small. P. Goerens and J. Paquet [1] found that antimony retained only a small trace of occluded gas—E. Groschuff said that about 0·005 per cent. of gas was present in ordinary antimony; and 0·0005 per cent. in the purified metal. F. Fischer and co-workers observed that no combination occurs when antimony is sparked below liquid **argon**; W. Ramsay and J. N. Collie observed no reaction with **helium** at a red-heat. H. Caron found that molten antimony absorbs **hydrogen,** and gives it up incompletely when further heated. T. Graham observed that when antimony is exposed to hydrogen, both above and below the m.p. of the metal, and after-wards exhausted at dull redness, there is no evidence of the absorption or occlu-sion of hydrogen. F. H. Newman observed that hydrogen is adsorbed by antimony in an electric discharge tube. R. Böttger found that in the electrolysis of water with an antimony cathode, a little hydrogen was absorbed by the metal; but neither R. Böttger, nor F. Pfeifer observed an appreciable amount of hydrogen in explosive antimony. K. Iwase studied the absorption of hydrogen by antimony. A. J. J. Van-develde said that antimony does not unite directly with hydrogen under the influence of heat, and that antimony volatilizes unchanged in an atm. of hydrogen. F. Winkler observed a slight absorption of hydrogen by antimony. W. P. Dexter said that no difference in the values for the at. wt. were observed with antimony melted in hydrogen, and in **air.** H. Wölbling said that appreciable quantities of **oxygen** are found only in electrolytic antimony. C. F. Schönbein [2] found that crystalline antimony is not affected by dry air, but, as noted by T. Bergman, J. J. Berzelius, and J. L. Proust, when antimony is exposed to moist air, particularly in light, the surface becomes matte and grey—particularly, said A. Ditte and R. Metzner, if the metal is finely divided. Antimony prepared by the reduction of potassium antimonyl tartrate may contain some potassium, and this behaves differently from ordinary antimony towards air and water. When antimony is heated in air until it boils, it takes fire, and burns with a bright bluish-white flame, and, at a moderate red-heat, with a reddish light yielding antimony trioxide which condenses on cold bodies in the form of *flores antimonii*—flowers of antimony; or *nix stibii*, antimony snow. If the burning antimony contains some arsenic, the odour resembles that of garlic; J. von Liebig, and H. Capitaine said that there is no odour if the antimony is pure; while F. Wöhler, and C. H. Pfaff said that the smell is peculiar but different from that of garlic, and it reminded T. Martius of that of nitric acid. G. Tammann and N. I. Nikitin found that the metal obtained by reducing the oxide at temp. as low as 125° is not pyrophoric since crystallization occurs at a low temp. When strongly ignited and molten antimony is poured on the ground, it separates into small globules which continue to burn. H. B. Baker also found that antimony burns when heated in thoroughly dried oxygen. C. F. Schönbein found that antimony is oxidized to the pentoxide by **ozone,** and by ozonized ether or turpentine. A. Ditte and R. Metzner showed that antimony precipitated from soln. of its salts by metals, is slowly attacked by **water** exposed to air ; and if distilled water comes in contact with purified antimony, in air, the oxide is always found in the liquid. J. Thiele also found that with the precipitated metal, even when the water has been previously boiled, a considerable quantity of antimony passes into soln. ; the metal also undergoes oxidation to such an extent that, in spite of the loss experienced in washing, the results sometimes come out too high. According to J. Milbauer and B. Slemr, if air be passed through a boiling suspension of antimony in water, 45 per cent. of the metal is oxidized ; at room temp., only 8 per cent. is oxidized, but if tartrates or citrates be present nearly 45 per cent. is oxidized at room temp. O. Ruff and K. Albert also found that antimony is attacked by distilled water, as well as by alcohol and ether, but not, according to E. Cohen and W. E. Ringer, by a mixture of alcohol and ether. A. Barillé found that alloys of lead or antimony with tin are more readily attacked by seltzer water than is either metal alone. J. J. Berzelius, and H. V. Regnault found that water vapour when passed over red-hot antimony forms hydrogen and antimony trioxide. J. Clark found that neutral **hydrogen dioxide** is without action on antimony, but in the presence of alkalies, an antimonate is formed. L. J. Thénard also observed that hydrogen dioxide has no action on bismuth.

H. Moissan [3] found that antimony burns vigorously in **fluorine,** forming a white solid. Powdered antimony takes fire in **chlorine,** burning with a reddish light and the emission of sparks, forming antimony pentachloride ; and, added H. Rose, antimony trichloride is never formed in this way. Liquid chlorine, at its b.p., was found by V. Thomas and P. Dupuis to have no action on antimony. R. Cowper found that chlorine, thoroughly dried by fused calcium chloride, acts immediately on antimony with the evolution of heat and light. V. Thomas and P. Dupuis found that liquid chlorine, at the b.p., has no action on antimony. C. Willgerodt found antimony and several of its compounds are good catalytic agents in chlorination reactions. According to A. J. Balard, and G. S. Sérullas, antimony takes fire when brought in contact with **bromine,** the metal running about in fused globules on the surface of the bromine—the tribromide is formed. R. Brandes said that antimony and **iodine** unite at ordinary temp., the reaction is accompanied by a great rise of temp., and the evolution of iodine vapour, and even by an explosion if large quantities are used. G. S. Sérullas, J. B. Berthemot, as well as R. Brandes, obtained the triiodide as a product of this reaction. H. Reckleben found that iodine in the presence of a soln. of tartaric acid readily converts antimony into antimonic acid : $2Sb+5I_2+8H_2O=2H_3SbO_4+10HI$, and free antimony may be readily estimated in this way. L. B. Parsons observed no reaction with iodine and antimony in the presence of water, alcohol, ether, benzene, heptane, quinoline, pyridine, acetone, carbon disulphide, carbon tetrachloride, or chloroform. F. A. Flückiger said that conc. **hydrofluoric acid** has no action on antimony. Neither **hydrogen chloride** nor **hydrochloric acid** acts on antimony in the absence of air ; if commercial antimony is attacked by hydrochloric acid, L. J. Chaudet, and H. von der Planitz showed that this is due to the presence of impurities—e.g. antimony sulphide, lead, etc. A. Ditte and R. Metzner showed that antimony, precipitated by tin from an acid soln. of antimony trichloride, is not attacked by hydrochloric acid of any conc. at any manageable temp., even in the presence of platinum or gold chloride ; but in the presence of air, W. P. Dexter, and J. P. Cooke found that the metal is slowly dissolved—even by water alone. W. L. Clasen, and J. Thiele made similar observations. P. J. Robiquet, and J. P. Cooke found that **aqua regia,** or hydrochloric acid containing a little nitric acid, dissolves antimony. N. A. E. Millon found that if the aqua regia is cold, and dilute, it does not attack the metal unless nitrous acid be present. J. W. Retgers observed that **antimony** is not dissolved by **methylene iodide.**

When a mixture of antimony and **sulphur** is heated, black antimony trisulphide (*q.v.*) is formed. W. Guertler [4] studied the affinity of antimony for sulphur. J. Spiller said that if a tube containing sulphur and stibine be exposed to sunlight, orange-coloured antimony sulphide is formed. C. Geitner noticed that when a mixture of the two elements with water is heated to 200° in a sealed tube, the black trisulphide is formed; and W. Spring also obtained the same product by compressing a mixture of the elements at 6500 atm. According to H. Pélabon, the reaction with **hydrogen sulphide** is reversible above 360 ° : $2Sb+3H_2S \rightleftharpoons 3H_2+Sb_2S_3$. When the temp. is below the m.p. of the sulphide, the reaction depends only on the temp., and is independent of the press. and of the mass of the solids. When the temp. is above the m.p. of antimony sulphide, this compound dissolves the liberated antimony, and equilibrium is established between two homogeneous systems; the final composition of the gas depends on the conc. of the soln. of antimony in the trisulphide, and therefore on the amount of trisulphide originally present. If an excess of antimony be present, the soln. of metal in its sulphide is always saturated, providing that all the sulphide is not decomposed. The amount of hydrogen sulphide then produced depends solely on the temp. J. Uhl found that when antimony is heated in a current of dry **sulphur dioxide**, antimony trioxide and trisulphide are formed—H. Schiff said that only the trisulphide is produced; and C. Geitner observed that when an aq. soln. of sulphur dioxide and antimony are heated in a sealed tube at 200°, microcrystalline antimony trisulphide is obtained. According to R. Brandes, when antimony is heated with **sulphuric acid,** the products are sulphur dioxide, sublimed sulphur, and antimony sulphate or basic sulphate; cold sulphuric acid, dil. or conc., is without action on antimony. According to R. H. Adie, when sulphuric acid acts on antimony, sulphur dioxide appears at 90°–95° and no hydrogen sulphide is formed. As previously indicated, the resistance of antimony to attack by acids led some alchemists to regard this element as imperfect gold. M. G. Levi and co-workers observed the formation of oxide or basic sulphate by the action of a soln. of **alkali persulphate.** N. Domanicky discussed the reaction with **sulphur monochloride.** According to K. Heumann and P. Köchlin, antimony forms the volatile trichloride, and a non-volatile antimony compound, when it is heated with **chlorosulphonic aicd ;** with **sulphuryl chloride,** the reaction is symbolized : $2Sb+3SO_2Cl_2=2SbCl_3+3SO_2$; with **thionyl chloride** : $6Sb+6SOCl_2=4SbCl_3+Sb_2S_3+3SO_2$; and with **pyrosulphuryl chloride** : $2Sb+3S_2O_5Cl_2=2SbCl_3+3SO_2+3SO_3$. E. B. Hutchins found that hot, conc. soln. of **telluric acid** attack antimony.

No compound of antimony and **nitrogen** has been obtained by the union of the two elements—*vide* **8.** 49, 12. F. H. Newman [5] studied the adsorption of nitrogen in discharge tubes; and K. Iwase found that antimony does not occlude nitrogen. G. Gore found antimony to be insoluble in liquid **ammonia.** C. A. Kraus observed complex ion formation with antimony in ammonia soln. E. B. Peck showed that the metal dissolves in a soln. of sodium in liquid ammonia—*vide* sodium antimonide. F. W. Bergstrom found that antimony is attacked by **potassium amide.** T. Curtius and A. Darapsky found that an aq. soln. of **hydrazoic acid** slowly attacks antimony, and when the soln. is evaporated in vacuo, antimony trioxide remains. According to J. J. Berzelius, when antimony is treated with **nitric acid,** nitric oxide is given off, and a basic antimony nitrate as well as antimony tetroxide or pentoxide are formed. The colder and the less the conc. of the nitric acid, the greater the proportion of antimony nitrate, and the less the proportion of antimony tetroxide produced. The antimony nitrate will then be mixed with antimony, which remains undissolved when the products of the reaction are digested with hydrochloric acid. H. Rose said that antimony tetroxide is always produced along with the trioxide; and C. P. Conrad found that the oxidation is never complete. The reaction was also studied by J. Lefort. N. A. E. Millon made the remarkable observation that if nitric acid of sp. gr. 1·42–1·51 is completely freed from nitrous acid the attack by nitric acid is very slight at 20° ; if a little nitrous acid be added the reaction progresses continuously—see the action of nitric acid on copper, silver, etc. An acid weaker than that of sp. gr. 1·42 has no marked action on antimony even if it contains nitrous acid. C. Montemartini said that, contrary to the statements of J. Personne, and E. J. Maumené, the action on antimony of nitric acid, varying in concentration from 2 to 70·27 per cent., does not yield appreciable quantities of ammonia ; 2 per cent. acid has very little action on the metal. Antimony is not dissolved by nitric acid ; a white powder always remains ; when 70 per cent. acid is used, this residue seems to have the composition $(SbO)NO_3$. Nitrogen peroxide is practically the sole gas produced when this metal is used. N. A. E. Millon found that a mixture of nitric and hydrochloric acids has no action if dilute, or at a low temp., but when very dilute, and potassium nitrate is added, the action will begin. A. Quartaroli studied the period of induction. C. C. Palit and N. R. Dhar observed no action with 13 per cent. nitric acid, and a slow action with 26 per cent. acid during 3 hrs. at ordinary temp. There was a slight formation of nitrous acid. P. T. Austen found that antimony does not burn in the vapour of nitric acid. A. Streng found that antimony readily dissolves in a mixture of nitric and tartaric acids ; and A. Czerwek obtained a similar result with mixtures of nitric acid and other polybasic organic acids. P. Sabatier and J. B. Senderens found that nitrogen peroxide converts reduced antimony into the trioxide. According to J. J. Sudborough, nitrosyl chloride transforms antimony, at ordinary temp., into antimony pentachloride, and the complex $NOCl.SbCl_5$, antimony nitrosyl hexachloride..

Antimony was shown by B. Pelletier,[6] and G. Landgrebe to unite readily with phosphorus, forming phosphides. E. Baudrimont found that when antimony is heated with phosphorus pentachloride it forms antimony and phosphorus trichlorides ; and A. Michaelis found that when antimony is heated in a sealed tube with phosphorus trichloride at 160°, red phosphorus and antimony trichloride are formed. F. Krafft and R. Neumann obtained an analogous result at 200° ; and they found that when antimony is heated for 6 hrs. with phosphorus trioxide, 96 per cent. of the theoretical amount of antimony trioxide is formed; with phosphorus trisulphide, for 9 hrs. at 325°, almost the theoretical amount of antimony trisulphide is formed ; with arsenic trichloride, at 200° for 6 hrs., 97 per cent. of the theoretical antimony trichloride is formed ; W. Finkelstein found that antimony precipitates arsenic from a soln. of arsenic trichloride in nitrobenzene with arsenic trioxide, at 360°, 90 per cent. of the theoretical trioxide is formed : $2Sb+As_2O_3=Sb_2O_3+2As$; and with arsenic trisulphide, at 360°, a 90 per cent. yield of antimony trisulphide is obtained. J. J. Berzelius found that antimony reduces antimony tetroxide to the trioxide ; and a similar result is obtained with antimony pentoxide.

F. von Bacho found that antimony begins to react with carbon dioxide at about 830°, and at 1100° the reaction is found to occur in accordance with $2Sb+3CO_2=Sb_2O_3+3CO$. The antimony trioxide sublimes at this temp. No evidence of the formation of higher oxides was obtained. K. Iwase found that carbon dioxide and carbon monoxide are not dissolved by antimony. W. Fränkel studied the reduction of carbon dioxide by antimony between 400° and 900°. The equilibrium : $3CO_2+2Sb=Sb_2O_3+3CO$ is attained in some weeks at 400° ; in some days at 500° ; in 60 hrs. at 650° ; and in 24 hrs. at 900°. A. Cahours found that some organic compounds react with antimony—e.g. the alkyl iodides which furnish stibines. Antimony was also found by B. Moritz and C. Schneider to be readily attacked by many organic compounds in the presence of air ; for instance, by oxalic, malic, tartaric, or citric acid, but not by malonic, succinic, benzoic, or salicylic acid, or by phenol. According to A. Czerwek, antimony trisulphide is soluble in a mixture of nitric acid with tartaric acid, or other organic polybasic acid ; E. Cohen found that it is not attacked by a mixture of alcohol and ether ; and C. B. Gates, that 0·0014 grm. is dissolved by a c.c of oleic acid in 6 days. According to J. Milbauer and B. Slemr, very finely ground antimony dissolves fairly rapidly in soln. of tartaric acid, alkali tartrates, citric acid, and alkali citrates if a rapid current of air is passed through the soln., and much more slowly in lactic, hydrofluosilicic, and oxalic acids under the same conditions. Y. Shibata and H. Kaneko studied the oxidation of pyrogallol in the presence of colloidal antimony. A. Korezynsky studied the catalytic action of antimony on the halogenization of aromatic hydrocarbons. H. Moissan observed that boron is not attacked when heated with antimony. E. Vigouroux found that when antimony is heated with silicon, a silicide is formed; but L. Kahlenberg and W. J. Trautmann observed no reaction at high temp.

A. Joannis [7] observed the formation of sodium tritantimonide when a soln. of sodium in liquid ammonia acts on antimony, and the reaction was studied by E. B. Peck, and C. A. Kraus and H. F. Kurtz. The action of antimony on the metals is discussed in connection with the antimonides. The partition coeff. of antimony between zinc and lead was found by G. Tammann and P. Schafmeister to be 1·28 at 535°; between zinc and bismuth, 0·66 at 550°; and between aluminium and lead, 2·22 at 725°. W. Guertler discussed the affinity of antimony for some of the other metals. J. J. Berzelius found that when mercuric oxide is heated with antimony, green mercuric antimonate is first formed, and afterwards antimony pentoxide. O. Ruff and K. Albert found that antimony is attacked by aq. soln. of the alkalies, and of their salts. K. Jellinek and J. Wolff studied the equilibrium of the molten chlorides of sodium, potassium, barium, and strontium in contact with antimony. Molten potassium hydrosulphate was found by M. Websky to attack antimony, forming a basic sulphate and an antimonate. Powdered antimony mixed with an alkali nitrate detonates when heated, forming an antimonate. R. Böttger observed the reduction of a soln. of potassium nitrate by antimony. J. B. Senderens found that soln. of copper nitrate are reduced covering the antimony with a thin layer of copper. C. Strzyzowsky observed that Fehling's soln. is reduced by antimony. M. Kohn found that the reaction with antimony and ammoniacal soln. of copper salt containing tartaric acid resembles that with arsenic (q.v.). T. Poleck and K. Thümmel observed that, unlike arsenic, phosphorus, and sulphur, when antimony is placed in a soln. of silver nitrate, it does not form a complex salt, but furnishes silver tritantimonide, which is soon converted into antimony trioxide and silver. R. Bartels said that some hydrogen is evolved; but with 0·05N-AgNO₃, J. B. Senderens observed no evolution of gas, and the soln. is incompletely reduced since the antimony acquires a protective film of a basic nitrate; with 0·25N- or 0·5N-AgNO₃, antimony gives a quantitative precipitate of silver, and the soln. contains nitric acid with very little ammonium nitrate. W. P. Dexter found that antimony reduces gold trichloride completely to the metal gold. J. B. Senderens observed no reduction of a soln. of lead nitrate by antimony. N. W. Fischer said that antimony does not precipitate mercury from soln. of mercuric chloride. J. W. Slater found that antimony reduces a soln. of potassium permanganate, forming manganese dioxide, and a soln. of potassium antimonate. J. Attfield observed that antimony reduces ferric chloride, forming antimony trichloride; and R. Böttger also found that soln. of ferric sulphate and of potassium ferricyanide are reduced by antimony. H. Lessheim and co-workers discussed the co-ordination number of antimony in its complex salts.

Some reactions of analytical interest.—Soln. of antimonious salts give a precipitate of a basic salt when treated with water. According to F. Jackson,[8] the presence of one part of antimony in 2000 parts of liquid can be so detected. Alkali hydroxides and carbonates precipitate antimony trioxide from soln. of its salts; the precipitate is soluble in an excess of the alkali-lye; the precipitate with aq. ammonia is not soluble in an excess—vide infra, antimony trioxide. H. Demarçay found that the carbonates of the alkali earths, and magnesium carbonate precipitate antimony trioxide from salt soln.; the precipitation is incomplete with barium carbonate, some barium antimonite being formed. Soln. of antimonious or antimonic salts do not give a precipitate with hydrochloric acid.

The acid soln. precipitates orange-red antimony trisulphide when treated with hydrogen sulphide : $3H_2S+2SbCl_3 \rightleftharpoons Sb_2S_3+6HCl$. The trisulphide is soluble in hydrochloric acid, and in the 1 : 1-acid it is soluble under conditions where arsenic trisulphide does not dissolve. Consequently, the soln. from which the trisulphide is to be precipitated must be weakly acidic—*vide infra*, antimony trisulphide. F. Neher said that in the presence of 27·69 per cent. hydrochloric acid antimony salts soln. gave no precipitate with hydrogen sulphide. In practice, the soln. of antimony trichloride is not diluted too much at first because of the precipitation of the oxychloride, rather is the gas passed into the liquid, and the soln. then diluted and again treated with gas. The precipitated sulphide is soluble in a soln. of ammonium sulphide, forming ammonium sulphantimonite ; antimony trisulphide is also soluble in alkali-lye, forming a mixture of a soluble antimonite and sulphantimonite. The soln. of the sulphantimonites are decomposed by acids with the precipitation of antimony trisulphide. According to C. H. Pfaff, hydrogen sulphide gives an appreciable effect with one part of the salt in 20,000 parts of water ; F. Jackson said 1 in 512,000 parts ; and H. Reinsch found that one part of potassium antimonyl tartrate in 10,000 parts of water and 5000 parts of hydrochloric acid gives a perceptible cloudiness with hydrogen sulphide ; with 15,000 parts of water and 7500 parts of hydrochloric acid, a yellow coloration ; and with 30,000 parts of water and 15,000 parts of acid, no visible effect is produced —*vide infra*, antimony trisulphide.

With soln. of antimonic salts, H. Rose assumed that hydrogen sulphide precipitates a mixture of antimony trisulphide and sulphur ; but R. Bunsen, G. C. Wittstein, and A. Classen said that the pentasulphide is formed. O. Klenker, T. Willm, and J. Thiele were unable to confirm R. Bunsen's results. O. Bosek studied the action of hydrogen sulphide on antimonic acid by the methods employed by B. Brauner and F. Tomicek with arsenic acid. He found that when an excess of hydrogen sulphide in the form of an aq. soln. acts at once on antimonic salt soln. at ordinary temp., antimony pentasulphide alone is precipitated ; and that when hydrogen sulphide acts on soln. of antimonic salts under otherwise similar conditions, the proportion of pentasulphide precipitated is greater the lower the temp., and the more rapid the stream of gas ; and the proportion of trisulphide is increased by reversing these conditions. The proportion of pentasulphide increases as the amount of hydrochloric acid increases up to a maximum lying between 10 and 20 per cent. HCl ; after that limit the proportion of pentasulphide rapidly decreases as the amount of hydrochloric acid increases. In the presence of chromic salt soln., acidic soln. of antimonic acid are reduced more easily and completely than without such an addition. Antimony trisulphide alone is obtained from antimonic salt soln. only in the presence of chromic acid, and with a slower current of hydrogen sulphide, for a longer time, at a higher temp., the black trisulphide is formed. B. Brauner added that whereas arsenic acid is first converted by hydrogen sulphide into oxysulpharsenic acid, antimonic acid gives a precipitate of the sulphide almost immediately ; oxysulpharsenic acid and its stable salts are known, but not so with the oxyantimonates. These facts are, à *priori*, against a complete analogy in the mechanism of the action of hydrogen sulphide on arsenic and antimonic acids. When a soln. of antimonic acid is treated with insufficient quantity of hydrogen sulphide, in a few hours, the antimonic acid is reduced to antimonious acid with the separation of free sulphur. B. Brauner said that the action cannot be explained as a direct reduction: $H_3SbO_4+H_2S+Aq.=H_3SbO_3+H_2O+S+Aq.$, because (i) hydrogen sulphide as such does not reduce antimonic acid, and that its sulphur probably combines with the antimony as sulphantimonic acid ; and (ii), even in the presence of such a strong reducing agent as sulphur dioxide, acting for a long time, only about 75 per cent. of the antimonic acid is reduced to antimonious acid. It is possible that when an excess of hydrogen sulphide is present along with free mineral acid, sulphantimonic acid is first formed : $2H_3SbO_4+8H_2S+Aq.=2H_3SbS_4$ $+8H_2O+Aq.$; followed by the formation of antimony pentasulphide : $2H_3SbS_4$

$+n\text{HCl}+\text{Aq.}=\text{Sb}_2\text{S}_5+3\text{H}_2\text{S}+n\text{HCl}+\text{Aq}$. B. Brauner preferred the assumption that when the antimonic acid is in excess, sulphantimonic acid is first formed, but this, in contact with the excess of free antimonic acid, forms trioxysulphantimonic acid : $\text{H}_3\text{SbS}_4+3\text{H}_3\text{SbO}_4+\text{Aq.}=4\text{H}_3\text{SbO}_3\text{S}+\text{Aq.}$; this, however, must be a very unstable compound and decompose at once into antimonious acid and sulphur : $n\text{H}_3\text{SbO}_3\text{S}+m\text{HCl}+\text{Aq.}=n\text{H}_3\text{SbO}_3+n\text{S}+m\text{HCl}+\text{Aq}$. The existence of the trioxysulphantimonious acid corresponds with the deep orange colour of the liquid first formed, before the formation of antimonious acid and sulphur which occurs when the soln. is allowed to stand for some time. A soln. of an **alkali sulphide** with antimonious salts gives a precipitate of orange-red antimony trisulphide ; and orange antimony pentasulphide from soln. of antimonic salts. All salts of antimony when warmed with **sodium thiosulphate** give a precipitate of the sulphide : $2\text{SbCl}_3+3\text{Na}_2\text{S}_2\text{O}_3+3\text{H}_2\text{O}=\text{Sb}_2\text{S}_3+3\text{Na}_2\text{SO}_4+6\text{HCl}$.

Antimonic salt soln. are reduced by **hydriodic acid** or **alkali iodides** in acid soln. : $\text{SbCl}_5+2\text{HI}=2\text{HCl}+\text{SbCl}_3+\text{I}_2$, but not so with soln. of antimonious salts. Alkali iodides gave a yellow precipitate of antimony triiodide when added to a not too strongly acidic soln. of an antimonious salt. According to G. von Knorre, **sulphur dioxide** reduces antimonic to antimonious salts. Unlike the corresponding case with arsenic salts, **stannous chloride** also reduces antimonic to antimonious salts without ever precipitating the metal. Antimonious salts reduce **chromates** to chromic salts ; and acid soln. of antimonious salts reduce **manganates** and permanganates to manganous salts. An aq. soln. of silver nitrate gives a heavy black precipitate of silver when treated with a soln. of an antimonious compound in fixed alkali, but with ammoniacal silver nitrate, no precipitate occurs until the ammonia has been expelled. R. Bunsen found that an ammoniacal soln. of **silver nitrate** gives a black precipitate with a soln. of an antimonious salt when evaporated on a water-bath. Antimonates with silver nitrate give a precipitate of silver antimonate soluble in aq. ammonia. Antimonious salt soln. give a white precipitate with **potassium cyanide**, soluble in excess ; antimonious chloride, not tartrate, gives a white precipitate, with **potassium ferrocyanide**—soluble in hydrochloric acid or alkali-lye ; alkaline soln. of antimonious salts reduce **potassium ferricyanide** to ferrocyanide ; soln. of **sodium phosphate** give no precipitate with soln. of antimony salts. The reduction of antimony salts by **nascent hydrogen** resulting in the formation of stibine has been discussed in connection with arsine in the analytical reactions of arsenic. According to A. Pinkus and F. Martin, **cupferron** (nitrosophenylhydroxylamine) gives no precipitate with antimonic salts.

The metallic precipitation of antimony.—According to N. W. Fischer,[9] **copper** precipitates antimony incompletely from a hydrochloric soln. ; K. Seubert and A. Schmidt, F. Faktor, and Z. Roussin found that **magnesium** precipitates black flecks of antimony with the evolution of hydrogen and stibine ; if the soln. be too acid, the precipitation is incomplete. H. Rose, J. J. Berzelius, and N. W. Fischer observed that **zinc** precipitates antimony as a black powder, and C. R. Fresenius observed that a 1 : 1000-soln. gives a brown film in 2 mins. ; a 1 : 20,000-soln., in 15 mins. ; and a 1 : 30,000-soln., in half an hour—*vide infra*, H. N. Warren on explosive antimony. A. Dupasquier observed that some antimony may be evolved as stibine during the reaction with zinc, but not so with iron. H. Hager found that zinc also precipitates antimony from soln. of the alkali antimonites with the evolution of hydrogen, not of stibine. N. W. Fischer found that **cadmium** acts like zinc. W. Schulte, and R. Böttger showed that **aluminium** gives a fine black precipitate and stibine is evolved. The precipitation of antimony by **tin** was observed by N. W. Fischer, E. Pieszczek, J. L. Gay Lussac, A. Carnot, and J. H. Mengin ; by **lead**, by N. W. Fischer ; by **iron**, by J. J. Berzelius, H. Rose, N. W. Fischer, C. Tookey, O. Low, A. Thiel and K. Keller, M. Hoffmann, J. Attfield, W. L. Clasen, J. Thiele, and S. Rideal ; by **cobalt**, by N. W. Fischer ; and by **manganese**, by O. Prelinger. N. W. Fischer said that the precipitation by **bismuth** is incomplete.

The physiological action of antimony.—There is a traditional belief with some raisers of cattle that a daily dose of antimony (sulphide) will improve the condition and hasten the fattening of, say, horses and pigs. In Brunswick, for example, the breeders of fat geese add a little antimonious oxide to the food as a traditional custom. The old Roman *pocula emetica*, or everlasting emetic cups, were made from an alloy containing much antimony. When wine was allowed to stand therein for a few days, it dissolved some of the metal, and this acted as an emetic, causing any one drinking it to vomit violently. The available evidence is not unequivocal. J. Wohlgemuth and B. Rewald [10] discussed the toxicity of antimony compounds when used in the manufacture of iron enamels. The use of antimony in medicinal preparations was prohibited in France in 1566 because it was considered so poisonous. The edict was repealed in 1650. There is a marked analogy between the symptoms of poisoning by arsenic and by antimony, particularly in cases of acute poisoning. Potassium antimonyl tartrate—tartar emetic—is the commonest antimonial preparation. The first result of swallowing tartar emetic is vomiting due to the direct action of the drug on the walls of the stomach. It is, however, quickly absorbed. The action of the heart is at first quickened, and afterwards slowed, weakened, and paralyzed. The respiration is depressed—inspiration is shortened, and expiration lengthened. Moderate doses cause a feeling of languor, inaptitude for mental exertion, and sleepiness. Antimony is excreted by the urine, bile, sweat, bronchial secretion, milk, and particularly by the fæces. The long-continued used of tartar emetic in small doses may produce fatty degeneration, especially of the liver, and a suppression of the glycogenic function of the liver. The medicinal dose of a soluble antimony salt does not exceed 97·2 mgrms.; a dose of 129·6 mgrms. has proved fatal, and a dose of 48·5 mgrms. has killed a child. A healthy adult, however, can usually take doses up to 194·4 mgrms. Horses can take 5·832 grms. three times a day; and 3·8 grms. are not considered excessive for cattle; 0·38 grm. has been prescribed as an emetic for pigs, and half this quantity for dogs.

According to M. Cloetta, in chronic antimony poisoning, there is, in contradistinction to arsenic poisoning, not only no decrease in absorption, but an absolute and relative increase, which grows with the length of time the administration lasts, and with the strength of the dose. R. G. Fargher and W. H. Gray studied the toxic action of a number of organic compounds of antimony on mice. O. Brunner found that all the more powerfully-acting compounds contain tervalent antimony, and all the feebly-acting ones quinquevalent antimony. No evidence of habituation to either group was observed. According to G. Pouchet, when antimony in the form of tartar emetic is administered for a long time to rabbits and dogs by ingestion, it tends to accumulate in the digestive tract and is found only in very small quantities in the organs and other parts of the body. It therefore differs markedly from arsenic. If antimony is administered with small quantities of arsenic, the toxic effect of the latter seems to be increased, but the distribution of the two elements in the organism is not affected. According to J. Morgenroth and O. Rosenthal, the action of tartar emetic on trypanosomes is more rapid and powerful than any other preparation yet tried, as 0·2 c.c. of a soln. of 1 in 1000 causes a disappearance of this organism. The acquisition of a noticeable resistance to the drug by repeated treatment was not observed. Various antimony compounds, like those of arsenic, are fatal to trypanosomes. According to J. D. Thompson and A. R. Cushny, the best results were obtained with ethyl antimonyl tartrate. The trypanocidal activity of antimony compounds was also studied by C. Voegtlin and H. W. Smith. J. Morgenroth and O. Rosenthal found that potassium hexatantalate counteracts the trypanocidal activity of antimony compounds on mice. G. T. Morgan and E. A. Cooper studied the germicidal action of antimony compounds on the bacillus typhosus. E. von Knaffl-Lenz was unable to find any evidence of the formation of volatile antimony compounds by moulds. In this respect, there is a difference between antimony and the similar elements arsenic, selenium, and tellurium. The possibility that chronic antimony poisoning is due to the formation of volatile substances is excluded. A. Wöber found antimony compounds are less poisonous to phanerogams than arsenic compounds. J. A. Smorodinceff and F. E. A. Iliin studied the action of antimony compounds on the fermentative action of ptyalin in the organism. H. Eulenberg found that workmen, exposed for long periods to the vapour of antimony oxide, suffer pain in the bladder, and a burning sensation in the urethra; the continued inhalation leads to impotence and wasting of the testicles. There are a few cases on record of poisoning by antimony chloride. A. Stock and co-workers found that stibine is a violent poison. It transforms the oxyhæmoglobin into hæmoglobin and hæmolysis occurs. The action was studied by F. Joly and B. de Nabais. F. Jones said that fishes placed in water through which the gas is passing die in about 2 hrs., but a fish on the point of death is revived when placed in fresh water. A. Stock and co-workers observed that a mouse in an atm. of the gas dies at once; in an atm. with one part of stibine in a 100 parts of air, death occurs in a few seconds; with an atm. having 1 : 1000 of the gas, death occurs in two minutes; and when two mice were placed in an atm. with 1 : 10,000 for 20 mins., one died in 6½ hrs., and the other in 12 hrs. F. Flury [11] discussed the noxious properties of enamels containing antimony for cooking vessels.

The antidotes for antimony are infusions containing tannin or allied astringent principles—decoctions of tea, oak-bark, tannic or gallic acid, etc. Unless vomiting is free, it may be encouraged by zinc sulphate or subcutaneous injections of apomorphine, or the stomach-pump may be used. Stimulants may be required as well as hot-water bottles and warm blankets.

Some uses of antimony.—Antimony is used in making a number of alloys—*e.g.* Britannia metal, bearing or antifriction metal; type-metal; and hard-lead—largely because of its property of hardening the softer metals. It is used in making pigments and paints—*e.g.* antimony white as a substitute for white-lead; antimony black as a bronzing powder for metals or plaster; antimony reds—red or orange-red; and kermes, a brownish-yellow pigment; pharmaceutical preparations—tartar emetic, quinine antimonate, etc.; antimony oxide, or sodium antimonate as an opacifying agent for enamels, etc.—this subject was discussed by K. Fuwa, R. R. Danielson and M. K. Frehafer, etc. Naples yellow—a lead antimonate—is used for colouring pottery, tiles, etc.; colouring matter for cloth and paper; as a mordant—*e.g.* antimony oxychloride, potassium antimony oxalate, antimony tannate, and sodium antimony fluoride; and in vulcanizing rubber [12]—antimony pentasulphide; bronzing copper and iron—*e.g.* antimony chloride or fluoride. The sulphide is used in some paints, in making matches, percussion caps, and fireworks. The so-called Bengal signal light used at sea is a mixture of antimony trisulphide with twice its weight of sulphur, and six times its weight of nitre—*cf.* gunpowder. Antimonic acid is used in the manufacture of aniline red and yellow. Antimony sulphochloride is used as a macerating agent for wood; antimony salts are used in conjunction with the colloidal pastes fibrocol; for the manufacture of antiseptic washes, and the *papier couchés* of painters.[13]

REFERENCES.

[1] A. J. J. Vandevelde, *Des affinités de l'hydrogène moléculaire á chaud*, Bruxelles, 1895; *Bull. Acad. Belg.*, (3), **30**. 78, 1895; W. P. Dexter, *Pogg. Ann.*, **100**. 566, 1857; F. H. Newman, *Proc. Phys. Soc.*, **33**. 73, 1921; H. Caron, *Compt. Rend.*, **63**. 1129, 1868; F. Pfeifer, *Liebig's Ann.*, **209**. 161, 1881; R. Böttger, *Journ. prakt. Chem.*, (1), **107**. 43, 1869; P. Goerens and J. Paquet, *Ferrum*, **12**. 61, 1915; H. Wölbling, *Die Bestimmungsmethoden des Arsens, Antimons und Zinns*, Stuttgart, 198, 1914; E. Groschuff, *Zeit. anorg. Chem.*, **103**. 164, 1918; F. Winkler, *Das Atomgewicht des Antimons. Neubestimmung durch Ueberführung des Metalls in Antimon-Tetroxyd*, München, 1917; F. Fischer and G. Iliovici, *Ber.*, **41**. 4449, 1908; F. Fischer and F. Schrötter, *ib.*, **43**. 1442, 1454, 1910; W. Ramsay and J. N. Collie, *Proc. Roy. Soc.*, **60**. 57, 1896; K. Iwase, *Science Rep. Tohoku Univ.*, **15**. 531, 1926; T. Graham, *Phil. Trans.*, **156**. 399, 1866.

[2] C. F. Schönbein, *Verh. Nat. Ges. Basel*, **1**. 237, 1857; *Pogg. Ann.*, **75**. 362, 1855; *Journ.*

prakt. Chem., (1), **66**. 272, 1855 ; J. von Liebig, *Handwörterbuch der reinen und angewandten Chemie*, Braunschweig, **1**. 414, 1837 ; J. J. Berzelius, *Schweigger's Journ.*, **6**. 144, 1812 ; **22**. 69, 1818 ; J. L. Proust, *Journ. Phys.*, **59**. 260, 1804 ; *Phil. Mag.*, **21**. 208, 1805 ; G. Tammann and N. I. Nikitin, *Journ. Russ. Phys. Chem. Soc.*, **56**. 115, 1925 ; H. B. Baker, *Proc. Roy. Soc.*, **45**. 1, 1888 ; H. V. Regnault, *Ann. Chim. Phys.*, (2), **62**. 362, 1836 ; T. Bergman, *ib.*, (1), **26**. 84, 1798 ; A. Ditte and R. Metzner, *Compt. Rend.*, **115**. 936, 1892 ; A. Barillé, *ib.*, **153**. 351, 1911 ; J. Thiele, *Liebig's Ann.*, **263**. 361, 1891 ; O. Ruff and K. Albert, *Ber.*, **38**. 54, 1905 ; E. Cohen and W. E. Ringer, *Zeit. phys. Chem.*, **47**. 12, 1904 ; J. Clark, *Journ. Chem. Soc.*, **63**. 886, 1893 ; H. Capitaine, *Journ. Pharm. Chim.*, (2), **25**. 516, 1839 ; T. Martius, *Kastner's Arch.*, **24**. 253, 1832 ; F. Wöhler, *Pogg. Ann.*, **27**. 628, 1832 ; *Liebig's Ann.*, **5**. 20, 1833 ; C. H. Pfaff, *Pogg. Ann.*, **42**. 339, 1837 ; J. Milbauer and B. Slemr, *Chem. Listy*, **20**. 392, 1926 ; L. J. Thénard, *Traite de chimie*, Paris, **2**. 67, 1824.

³ H. Moissan, *Ann. Chim. Phys.*, (6), **12**. 523, 1887 ; (6), **24**. 247, 1891 ; P. J. Robiquet, *ib.*, (2), **4**. 165, 1817 ; N. A. E. Millon, *ib.*, (3), **6**. 101, 1842 ; L. J. Chaudet, *ib.*, (2), **3**. 376, 1816 ; A. J. Balard, *ib.*, (2), **32**. 337, 1826 ; G. S. Sérullas, *ib.*, (2), **38**. 322, 1828 ; *Journ. Pharm. Chim.*, (2), **14**. 19, 1828 ; J. B. Berthemot, *ib.*, (2), **14**. 615, 1828 ; J. W. Retgers, *Zeit. anorg. Chem.*, **3**. 350, 1893 ; V. Thomas and P. Dupuis, *Compt. Rend.*, **143**. 282, 1906 ; J. P. Cooke, *Proc. Amer. Acad.*, **13**. 1, 172, 1877 ; *Amer. Journ. Science*, (3), **19**. 469, 1880 ; *Chem. News*, **44**. 221, 233, 245, 268, 1880 ; R. Cowper, *Journ. Chem. Soc.*, **43**. 153, 1883 ; C. Willgerodt, *Journ. prakt. Chem.*, (2), **31**. 540, 1885 ; (2), **35**. 394, 1887 ; W. L. Clasen, *ib.*, (1), **92**. 477, 1864 ; F. A. Flückiger, *Pogg. Ann.*, **87**. 250, 1852 ; H. Rose, *ib.*, **3**. 443, 1824 ; H. von der Planitz, *Bull. Soc. Chim.*, (2), **24**. 69, 1875 ; *Ber.*, **7**. 1664, 1875 ; *Dingler's Journ.*, **215**. 442, 1875 ; A. Ditte and R. Metzner, *Compt. Rend.*, **115**. 936, 1893 ; V. Thomas and P. Dupuis, *ib.*, **143**. 282, 1906 ; R. Brandes, *Brandes' Arch.*, **14**. 135, 1838 ; **17**. 283, 1839 ; **21**. 319, 1840 ; H. Reckleben, *Ber.*, **42**. 1458, 1909 ; L. B. Parsons, *Journ. Amer. Chem. Soc.*, **47**. 1830, 1925 ; J. Thiele, *Liebig's Ann.*, **263**. 361, 1891 ; W. P. Dexter, *Pogg. Ann.*, **100**. 563, 1857 ; *Journ. prakt. Chem.*, (1), **71**. 242, 1857.

⁴ C. Geitner, *Ueber das Verhalten des Schwefels und der schwefligen Säure zu Wasser bei hohen Druck und hohen Temperatur*, Göttingen, 1863 ; *Liebig's Ann.*, **129**. 359, 1864 ; H. Schiff, *ib.*, **117**. 95, 1861 ; W. Guertler, *Metall Erz*, **22**. 199, 1925 ; H. Pélabon, *Compt. Rend.*, **130**. 911, 1900 ; M. G. Levi, E. **Migliorini**, and G. Ercolini, *Gazz. Chim. Ital.*, **38**. i, 598, 1908 ; E. B. Hutchins, *Journ. Amer. Chem. Soc.*, **27**. 1157, 1905 ; N. Domanicky, *Journ. Russ. Phys. Chem. Soc.*, **48**. 1724, 1916 ; J. Spiller, *Journ. Photogr. Soc. Great Britain*, (1), **16**. 157, 1876 ; J. Uhl, *Ber.*, **23**. 2154, 1890 ; W. Spring, *ib.*, **16**. 999, 1883 ; K. Heumann and P. Köchlin, *ib.*, **15**. 419, 1737, 1882 ; **16**. 482, 1625, 1883 ; R. Brandes, *Arch. Pharm.*, (2), **21**. 156, 1840 ; R. H. Adie, *Proc. Chem. Soc.*, **15**. 133, 1899 ; *Chem. News*, **79**. 261, 1899.

⁵ T. Curtius and A. Darapsky, *Journ. prakt. Chem.*, (2), **61**. 408, 1900 ; N. A. E. Millon, *Ann. Chim. Phys.*, (3), **6**. 101, 1842 ; E. J. Maumené, *ib.*, (4), **3**. 343, 1865 ; G. Gore, *Proc. Roy. Soc.*, **20**. 441, 1872 ; **21**. 140, 1873 ; H. Rose, *Pogg. Ann.*, **53**. 161, 1841 ; J. Lefort, *Journ. Pharm. Chim.*, (3), **28**. 93, 1855 ; P. Sabatier and J. B. Senderens, *Bull. Soc. Chim.*, (3), **7**. 504, 1892 ; J. Personne, *ib.*, (2), **1**. 163, 1864 ; *Chem. News*, **9**. 242, 1864 ; P. T. Austen, *Amer. Chem. Journ.*, **11**. 80, 1889 ; *Chem. News*, **59**. 208, 1889 ; C. P. Conrad, *ib.*, **40**. 197, 1879 ; J. J. Sudborough, *Journ. Chem. Soc.*, **59**. 655, 1891 ; A. Streng, *Dingler's Journ.*, **151**. 389, 1859 ; *Berg. Hütt. Ztg.*, **19**. 128, 1860 ; A. Czerwek, *Zeit. anal. Chem.*, **45**. 505, 1906 ; J. J. Berzelius, *Schweigger's Journ.*, **6**. 144, 1912 ; **22**. 69, 1818 ; E. B. Peck, *Journ. Amer. Chem. Soc.*, **40**. 335, 1918 ; C. Montemartini, *Gazz. Chim. Ital.*, **22**. 384, 1892 ; A. Quartaroli, *ib.*, **53**. i, 345, 1923 ; F. W. Bergstrom, *Journ. Phys. Chem.*, **30**. 15, 1926 ; K. Iwase, *Science Rep. Tohoku Univ.*, **15**. 531, 1926 ; C. A. Kraus, *ib.*, **44**. 1216, 1922 ; C. C. Palit and N. R. Dhar, *ib.*, **30**. 1125, 1926 ; F. H. Newman, *Proc. Phys. Soc.*, **33**. 73, 1921.

⁶ B. Pelletier, *Ann. Chim. Phys.*, (1), **13**. 132, 1792 ; E. Baudrimont, *ib.*, (4), **2**. 12, 1864 ; *Compt. Rend.*, **55**. 277, 1862 ; G. Landgrebe, *Schweigger's Journ.*, **53**. 469, 1828 ; A. Korezynsky, *Bull. Soc. Chim.*, (4), **29**. 283. 1921 ; Y. Shibata and H. Kaneko, *Journ. Japan. Chem. Soc.*, **45**. 155, 1924 ; L. Kahlenberg and W. J. Trautmann, *Trans. Amer. Electrochem. Soc.*, **39**. 377, 1921 ; K. Iwase, *Science Rep. Tohoku Univ.*, **15**. 531, 1926 ; E. Vigouroux, *Compt. Rend.*, **123**. 115, 1895 ; H. Moissan, *ib.*, **114**. 619, 1892 ; A. Cahours, *ib.*, **49**. 87, 1859 ; B. Moritz and C. Schneider, *Zeit. phys. Chem.*, **41**. 129, 1902 ; E. Cohen, *ib.*, **47**. 12, 1904 ; W. Finkelstein, *ib.*, **115**. 303, 1925 ; C. B. Gates, *Journ. Phys. Chem.*, **15**. 143, 1911 ; A. Czerwek, *Zeit. anal. Chem.*, **45**. 507, 1906 ; F. Krafft and R. Neumann, *Ber.*, **34**. 565, 1901 ; W. Fränkel, *Festschrift zur Jahrhundertfeier des physikalischen Vereins*, Frankfurt a. M., 136, 1924 ; A. Michaelis, *Journ. prakt. Chem.*, (2), **4**. 425, 1871 ; J. J. Berzelius, *Schweigger's Journ.*, **6**. 144, 1812 ; **22**. 69, 1818 ; F. von Bacho, *Montash.*, **37**. 119, 1916 ; J. Milbauer and B. Slemr, *Chem. Listy*, **20**. 392, 1926 .

⁷ N. W. Fischer, *Pogg. Ann.*, **9**. 258, 1827 ; O. Ruff and K. Albert, *Ber.*, **38**. 54, 1905 ; T. Poleck and K. Thümmel, *ib.*, **16**, 2446, 1883 ; M. Kohn, *Monatsh.*, **42**. 83, 1921 ; J. B. Senderens, *Bull. Soc. Chim.*, (3), **15**. 218, 1896 ; *Compt. Rend.*, **104**, 504, 1887 ; C. Strzyzowsky, *Oesterr. Chem. Ztg.*, **7**. 77, 1904 ; M. Websky, *Zeit. anal. Chem.*, **11**. 124, 1872 ; J. Attfield, *Pharm. Journ.*, (2), **10**. 512, 1869 ; E. B. Peck, *Journ. Amer. Chem. Soc.*, **40**. 339, 1918 ; C. A. Kraus and H. F. Kurtz, *ib.*, **47**. 43, 1925 ; R. Böttger, *Journ. prakt. Chem.*, (2), **9**. 195, 1874 ; J. W. Slater, *ib.*, (1), **60**. 247, 1853 ; G. Tammann and P. Schafmeister, *Zeit. anorg. Chem.*, **138**. 219, 1924 ; H. Lessheim, J. Meyer, and R. Samuel, *ib.*, **165**. 253, 1927 ; K. Jellinek and J. Wolff, *ib.*, **146**. 329, 1925 ; W. P. Dexter, *Pogg. Ann.*, **100**. 568, 1857 ; W. Guertler, *Metall Erz*, **22**. 199, 1925 ; A. Joannis, *Compt. Rend.*, **113**. 745, 1891 ; **114**. 585,

1892; J. J. Berzelius, *Schweigger's Journ.*, 16. 144, 1813; 22. 69, 1818; R. Bartels, *Ueber die Einwirkung des Antimonwasserstoffs auf Metallsulzlösungen*, Berlin, 1889; A. Pinkus and F. Martin, *Journ. Chim. Phys.*, 24. 83, 137, 1927.

[8] F. Jackson, *Journ. Amer. Chem. Soc.*, 25. 992, 1903; T. G. Wormley, *Microchemistry of Poisons*, New York, 1867; H. Reinsch, *Journ. prakt. Chem.*, (1), 24. 244, 1841; O. Klenker, *ib.*, (2), 59. 150, 353, 1899; G. von Knorre, *Zeit. angew. Chem.*, 1. 155, 1888; H. Rose, *Pogg. Ann.*, 107. 186, 1859; C. H. Pfaff, *Handbuch der analytischen Chemie*, Altona, 1. 113, 1822; O. Bosek, *Journ. Chem. Soc.*, 67. 515, 1895; B. Brauner, *ib.*, 67. 527, 1895; B. Brauner and F. Tomicek, *ib.*, 53. 145, 1888; T. Willm, *Zeit. anal. Chem.*, 30. 443, 1891; F. Neher, *ib.*, 32. 50, 1893; R. Bunsen, *Liebig's Ann.*, 106. 1, 1855; 192, 305, 1878; J. Thiele, *ib.*, 263, 71, 1891; H. Demarçay, *ib.*, 11. 241, 1834; G. C. Wittstein, *Pharm. Viertelj.*, 18. 531, 1869; A. Classen, *Ber.*, 16. 1067, 1883; H. Rose, *Pogg. Ann.*, 3. 441, 1834; A. Pinkus and F. Martin, *Journ. Chim. Phys.*, 24. 83, 137, 1927.

[9] Z. Roussin, *Journ. Pharm. Chim.*, (4), 3. 413, 1886; *Chem. News*, 14. 27, 1886; J. H. Mengin, *Compt. Rend.*, 117. 224, 1894; 119. 224, 1894; *Chem. News*, 70. 93, 1894; W. L. Clasen, *Journ. prakt. Chem.*, (1), 92. 477, 1864; O. Low, *Viertelj. prakt. Pharm.*, 14. 406, 1864; A. Carnot, *Compt. Rend.*, 114. 587, 1892; A. Dupasquier, *ib.*, 14. 514, 1842; J. L. Gay Lussac, *Ann. Chim. Phys.*, (2), 46. 222, 1831; M. Hoffmann, *Beiträge zur Kenntnis der analytischen Chemie des Zinns, Antimons und Arsens*, Berlin, 27, 1911; J. Attfield, *Pharm. Journ.*, (2), 10. 512, 1870; C. Tookey, *Journ. Chem. Soc.*, 15. 462, 1862; 23. 107, 1870; A. Thiel and K. Keller, *Zeit. anorg. Chem.*, 68. 42, 1910; W. Schulte, *Met.*, 6. 214, 1909; N. W. Fischer, *Das Verhältnis der chemischen Verwandtschaft zur galvanischen Electricität in Versuchen dargestellt*, Berlin, 1830; *Pogg. Ann.*, 8. 499, 1826; 9. 284, 1826; H. Rose, *ib.*, 3. 41, 1824; J. J. Berzelius, *Schweigger's Journ.*, 6. 144, 1812; 22. 69, 1818; K. Seubert and A. Schmidt, *Liebig's Ann.*, 267. 237, 1892; J. Thiele, *ib.*, 263. 361, 1891; C. R. Fresenius, *Zeit. anal. Chem.*, 1. 443, 1862; H. Hager, *ib.*, 11. 82, 1872; F. Faktor, *Pharm. Post*, 38. 153, 1905; E. Pieszczek, *Arch. Pharm.*, 229. 667, 1891; O. Prelinger, *Monatsh.*, 14. 369, 1893; S. Rideal, *Chem. News*, 51. 292, 1885; H. N. Warren, *ib.*, 62. 183, 1890; R. Böttger, *Jahresb. Phys. Ver. Frankfurt*, 16, 1879.

[10] M. Cloetta, *Arch. Exp. Path. Pharm.*, 64. 352, 1911; O. Brunner, *ib.*, 68. 186, 1912; E. von Knaffl-Lenz, *ib.*, 72. 224, 1913; J. Morgenroth and O. Rosenthal, *Berlin. Klin. Woch.*, 48. 2, 1911; *Zeit. Hyg. Infekt. Krankh.*, 68. 506, 1911; F. Jones, *Journ. Chem. Soc.*, 29. 641, 1876; G. Pouchet, *Compt. Rend.*, 133. 526, 1901; F. Joly and B. de Nabais, *ib.*, 110. 667, 1890; H. Eulenberg, *Handbuch der Gewerbehygiene*, Berlin, 1876; A. Stock, O. Guttman, and P. Bergell, *Ber.*, 37. 893, 1904; J. D. Thompson and A. R. Cushny, *Proc. Roy. Soc.*, 82. B, 249, 1910; G. T. Morgan and E. A. Cooper, *Proc. Internat. Congress Appl. Chem.*, 7. iv, 365, 1909; J. Wohlgemuth and B. Rewald, *Sprech.*, 57. 160, 1924; *Chem. Trade Journ.*, 77. 356, 1925; C. Voegtlin and H. W. Smith, *Journ. Pharm. Exp. Ther.*, 15. 453, 1920; R. G. Fargher and W. H. Gray, *ib.*, 18. 341, 1921; A. Wöber, *Angew. Botanik*, 2. 161, 1920; J. A. Smorodinceff and F. E. A. Iliin, *Biochem. Zeit.*, 141. 297, 1923.

[11] K. Fuwa, *Journ. Japan. Cer. Assoc.*, 241, 1923; R. R. Danielson and M. K. Frehafer, *Journ. Amer. Cer. Soc.*, 6. 634, 1923; B. Rewald, *Chem. Ztg.*, 48. 280, 1924; H. F. Staley, *Trans. Amer. Cer. Soc.*, 17. 173, 1915; H. E. Mausen, *Journ. Amer. Cer. Soc.*, 8. 437, 1925; B. Bock, *Chem. Ztg.*, 32. 446, 1908; R. Rickmann, *Sprech.*, 45. 115, 1912; J. Wohlegemath and B. Rewald, *ib.*, 57. 160, 1924; E. Svagr, *Chem. Listy*, 20. 21, 1926; L. Vielhaber, *Die Konstrucktion der Emailleversatze*, Meissen, 1925; *Ker. Rund.*, 35. 516, 1927; L. R. Mernagh, *Journ. Soc. Chem. Ind.—Chem. Ind.*, 45. 805, 1926; H. Haupt and G. Popp, *Zeit. angew. Chem.*, 40. 218, 1927; H. Melzer, *Ker. Rund.*, 34. 801, 1926; F. Flury, *Zeit. angew. Chem.*, 40. 1134, 1927.

[12] E. Anderson and W. M. Ames, *Journ. Soc. Chem. Ind.*, 42. 136, T, 1923.

[13] J. C. Brown, *Bull. Indian Ind. Labour*, 6, 1921; M. E. Manson, *Journ. Amer. Cer. Soc.*, 8. 437, 1925; T. T. Read, *Metal Ind.*, 17. 391, 1920.

§ 7. The Atomic Weight of Antimony

In 1812, J. J. Berzelius [1] recognized that the oxygen contents of the three antimony oxides were related as 3 : 4 : 5, and represented these compounds by the formulæ SbO_3, SbO_4, and SbO_5 respectively. On the oxygen 16 basis, and from the ratio $Sb : SbO_4$, he calculated the at. wt. of antimony to be 258·0; and from the ratio $Sb : SbS_3$, 257·8. In 1826, he recognized that the lowest oxide has the nature of a sesquioxide, and he therefore represented the three oxides by the formulæ Sb_2O_3, Sb_2O_4, and Sb_2O_5. This reduced his values for the at. wt. of antimony one-half. Later workers found J. J. Berzelius' value for the at. wt. to be too large, and that 120 would have been nearer the mark. This number is in agreement with the vapour densities of the volatile antimony compounds; with the sp. ht. rule; with the isomorphism of the antimony compounds of the same family of

ANTIMONY389

elements ; and with the position of antimony in the periodic table.   J. Dalton gave
40 for the chemical equivalent of antimony.

Antimony is undoubtedly *tervalent* in such compounds as stibine, SbH_3 ; the
trihalides, $SbCl_3$, $SbBr_3$, and SbI_3 ; trimethylstibine, $Sb(CH_3)_3$; and triethylstibine,
$Sb(C_2H_5)_3$.   It is *quinquevalent* in the stibonium salts—*e.g.* tetraethylstibonium
iodide, $Sb(C_2H_5)_4I$, and hydroxide, $Sb(C_2H_5)_4OH$—in pentamethylstibine, $Sb(CH_3)_5$,
and pentaethylstibine, $Sb(C_2H_5)_5$; and in antimony pentafluoride, SbF_5.   The
compounds SbF_5Br, $(SbF_5)_2I$, SbF_5I, and SbF_5S, may involve antimony in a
valency greater than fire ; but more probably, fluorine is not always univalent,
and the bromine, iodine, and sulphur are attached to the fluorine, not the antimony.
Chlorine does not form complexes with the pentafluoride, and this is in agreement
with (i) the failure of P. Lebeau to prepare chlorine fluoride, and (ii) the known
combinations of fluorine with bromine, iodine, and sulphur.   The *quadrivalency* of
antimony is discussed in connection with antimony tetroxide.   M. Padoa discussed
the valency of antimony.

F. Kessler calculated 120·86 for the at. wt. of antimony from the ratio
$Sb_2O_3 : O_2$; W. P. Dexter, 122·46, from the ratio $2Sb : Sb_2O_4$, and J. Knop,
122·04 ; F. Kessler, 121·31, from the ratio $2Sb : 3O$; and F. Winkler, 121·448 from
the ratio $Sb : Sb_2O_4$.   F. Kessler obtained 121·21, from the ratio $2SbCl_3 : 2O$; and
119·59, from the ratio $3\{K(SbO)C_4H_4O_6.\frac{1}{2}H_2O\} : K_2Cr_2O_7$; and 124·26 from the
ratio $SbCl_3 : 3AgCl$.   Assuming the at. wt. of silver to be 107·92, J. P. Cooke obtained
121·86 from the same ratio $SbCl_3 : AgCl_3$; 119·90–119·91 from the ratio $SbBr_3 : 3AgBr$;
and 119·86 from the ratio $SbI_3 : 3AgI$.   H. Rose obtained 120·63 from analyses of
the trichloride ; J. B. A. Dumas, 121·88 from the ratio $SbCl_3 : 3Ag$; and J. P. Cooke,
119·90 from the ratio $SbBr_3 : 3Ag$.   E. R. Schneider obtained 120·41–120·53 from
the ratio $Sb_2S_3 : 2Sb$, and J. P. Cooke, 120·22 from the ratio $2Sb : Sb_2S_3$ with the
red sulphide, and 120·54 with the black sulphide.   B. Unger calculated 119·71
from his value for the ratio $3Na_2SO_4 : Sb_2S_3$.   F. Pfeifer computed 122·36 from his
value for the ratio $3Cu : 2Sb$, and 121·36 from the ratio $3Ag : Sb$, while A. Popper
obtained 121·20 from the ratio $3Ag : Sb$.   E. Cohen and co-workers showed that the
electrolytic results obtained by A. Popper, and F. Pfeifer are invalid because the
eq. of antimony increases with the conc. of the soln. electrolyzed.   J. Bongartz
obtained 120·64 from the ratio $2Sb : 3BaSO_4$; and G. C. Friend and E. F. Smith,
120·43, from the ratio $K(SbO)C_4H_4O_6 : KCl$.   H. H. Willard and R. K. McAlpine,
and O. Hönigschmid and co-workers obtained 121·76 by converting the purified
metal into the chloride or bromide—Ag, 107·88 ; Cl, 35·457 ; and Br, 79·916 ;
P. F. Weatherill gave 121·748 from the ratio $SbCl_3 : 3Ag$ with Ag, 107·880 ; and
Cl, 35·458.   H. H. Willard and R. K. McAlpine obtained 121·773 ; and T. Schreiner,
121·73 from the ratio $SbBr_3 : 3AgBr$ when the at. wt. of silver is 107·88.   Working
with the results available in 1907, B. Brauner considered that 120 was the best
representative value for the at. wt. of antimony ; and F. W. Clarke, in 1910, gave
120·048.   The International Table for 1925 gave 120·2 as the best representative
value.   K. R. Krishnaswami found that the at. wt. of antimony from different
sources ranged from 121·744 to 121·754, so that the variation is less than the
experimental error.

The **atomic number** of antimony is 51.   F. W. Aston found that the mass
spectrum of antimony obtained from the trimethide gives lines corresponding with
isotopes with at. wt. 121 and 123 respectively—the former being 10–20 per cent.
more intense than the latter.   The results agree with the value obtained by
H. H. Willard and R. K. McAlpine.   S. D. Muzaffar determined the at. wt. of
antimony derived from stibnite from various sources.   From the ratio
$3SbCl_3 : KBrO_3$, he found with Hungarian stibnite, 121·144 ; Bornean stibnite,
121·563 ; Peruvian stibnite, 121·720 ; and Bolivian, 122·374, pointing to a different
distribution of the isotopes in different localities.   N. Bohr represented the
electronic structure of antimony by (2) (4, 4) (6, 6, 6,) (6, 6, 6) (4, 1).   C. D. Niven,
M. L. Huggins, J. H. W. Booth, and H. Collins have made some speculations on this

subject. M. Padoa discussed the valencies of the crystal lattices ; H. G. Grimm and A. Sommerfeld, the electronic structure ; and H. Pettersson and G. Kirsch, **atomic disintegration** by bombardment with α-rays. H. Müller obtained negative results by exposing antimony to an intense α-radiation, and testing for induced radioactivity.

REFERENCES.

[1] J. J. Berzelius, *Afhand. Fysik. Kemi*, **5.** 490, 1812 ; *Akad. Handl. Stockholm*, **189,** 1812 ; *Schweigger's Journ.*, **6.** 149, 1812 ; **22.** 70, 1818 ; **23.** 200, 1818 ; *Gilbert's Ann.*, **42.** 283, 1812 ; *Pogg. Ann.*, **8.** 1, 1826 ; F. Kessler, *ib.*, **95.** 204, 1855 ; **113.** 134, 1860 ; *Ber.*, **12.** 1044, 1879 ; F. Kessler and A. Stumpf, *1st das Atomgewicht des Antimons* 120 *oder* 122 ? Bochum, 1879 ; E. R. Schneider, *Journ. prakt. Chem.*, (2), **18.** 402, 1878 ; (2), **22.** 131, 1880 ; (2), **31.** 420, 1885 ; *Ueber das Atomgewicht des Antimons*, Berlin, 1880 ; *Pogg. Ann.*, **97.** 483, 1856 ; **98.** 293, 1856 ; H. Rose, *ib.*, **98.** 455, 1856 ; W. P. Dexter, *ib.*, **100.** 563, 1857 ; *Journ. prakt. Chem.*, (1), **71.** 242, 1857 ; O. Brunck, *Zeit. anal. Chem.*, **34.** 171, 1895 ; H. Pettersson and G. Kirsch, *Atomzertrüm-merung*, Leipzig, 104, 1926 ; *Sitzber. Akad. Wien*, **134.** 491, 1925 ; H. Baubigny, *Compt. Rend.*, **124.** 499, 560, 1897 ; P. Lebeau, *ib.*, **143.** 425, 1906 ; J. B. A. Dumas, *Ann. Chim. Phys.*, (3), **55.** 175, 1859 ; B. Unger, *Arch. Pharm.*, (2), **147.** 194, 1871 ; J. P. Cooke, *Proc. Amer. Acad.*, **13.** 1, 1877 ; **15.** 251, 1880 ; **17.** 1, 13, 1881 ; *Amer. Journ. Science*, (3), **15.** 41, 107, 1878 ; (3), **19.** 382, 1880 ; (3), **21.** 220, 1881 ; *Ber.*, **12.** 2123, 1879 ; **13.** 951, 1880 ; J. Bongartz, *ib.*, **16.** 1942, 1883 ; P. Pfeifer, *Liebig's Ann.*, 209, 174, 1881 ; A. Popper, *ib.*, **233.** 153, 1886 ; J. Dalton, *A New System of Chemical Philosophy*, Manchester, **2.** 263, 1810 ; G. C. Friend and E. F. Smith, *Journ. Amer. Chem. Soc.*, **23.** 502, 1901 ; H. H. Willard and R. K. McAlpine, *ib.*, **43.** 797, 1921 ; S. D. Muzaffar, *ib.*, **45.** 2009, 1923 ; P. F. Weatherill, *ib.*, **46.** 2437, 1924 ; E. Cohen and T. Strengers, *Proc. Acad. Amsterdam*, **5.** 543, 1903 ; E. Cohen, E. Collins, and T. Strengers, *Zeit. phys. Chem.*, **50.** 291, 1905 ; B. Brauner and R. Abegg, *Handbuch der anorganischen Chemie*, Leipzig, **3.** iii, 556, 1907 ; F. W. Clarke, *A Recalculation of the Atomic Weights*, Washington, 314, 1910 ; F. W. Aston, *Phil. Mag.*, (6), **42.** 141, 1921 ; (6), **45.** 943, 1923 ; *Phil. Mag.*, (6), **42.** 140, 1921 ; (6), **49.** 1191, 1925 ; *Nature*, **110.** 732, 1922 ; N. Bohr, *ib.*, **112.** Suppl., 1923 ; C. D. Niven, *Phil. Mag.*, (7), **3.** 1314, 1927 ; J. Knop, *Zeit. anal. Chem.*, **63.** 181, 1923 ; O. Hönigschmid, E. Zintl, and M. Linhard, *Zeit. anorg. Chem.*, **136.** 257, 1924 ; H. Collins, *Chem. News*, **129.** 267, 1924 ; J. H. W. Booth, *ib.*, **130.** 237, 1925 ; M. L. Huggins, *Journ. Phys. Chem.*, **26.** 601, 1922 ; F. Kessler, *Das Atomgewicht des Antimons. Neubestimmung durch Ueberführung des Metalls in Antimontetroxyd*, München, 1917 ; M. Padoa, *Gazz. Chim. Ital.*, **52.** ii, 189, 1922 ; T. Schreiner, *Tids. Kemi Bergvaesen*, **4.** 63, 89, 1924 ; H. G. Grimm and A. Sommerfeld, *Zeit. Physik*, **36.** 36, 1926 ; K. R. Krishnaswami, *Journ. Chem. Soc.*, 2534, 1927 ; H. Müller, *Sitzber. Akad. Wien*, **135.** 563, 1926 ; F. Winkler, *Das Atomgewicht des Antimons*, München, 1917.

§ 8. The Antimony Hydrides

While studying the electrolytic decomposition of water by means of an antimony cathode, R. L. Ruhland [1] obtained a brownish-black substance which he regarded as a *solid antimony hydride.* R. F. Marchand likewise obtained black flecks in the electrolysis of a soln. of ammonium chloride with an antimony cathode, and with a large current density there was a development of gas which burnt in air with a white flame—maybe with feeble detonations. He regarded the gas as spontaneously inflammable antimony hydride, but R. Böttger showed that the self-accendible properties and the detonations are due to the formation of some nitrogen chloride ; the gases evolved at the negative pole are hydrogen and ammonia. E. Wiederhold obtained a powder resembling graphite when an alloy of zinc with one-fifth of its weight of antimony is treated with dil. sulphuric acid. The residue was washed with tartaric acid soln. to remove the antimony trioxide. The analysis corresponded with SbH_2. Dil. acids and dil. alkali-lye are without action ; the hydride decomposes with the evolution of hydrogen at 200°. An alloy of zinc with one-thirtieth of its weight of antimony gave only metallic antimony as a powder. In repeating these experiments, R. C. Engel obtained only arsenic in place of the alleged antimony hydride. A. Stock and O. Güttmann observed no solid antimony hydride was produced by the spontaneous decomposition of liquid stibine ; and H. Reckleben and J. Scheiber observed none in their study of the action of the silent discharge on stibine. E. J. Weeks and J. G. F. Druce did not succeed in preparing a solid hydride of antimony by reducing a soln. of the tri-chloride by stannous chloride. H. J. S. Sand and co-workers showed that the amounts of stibine formed at an antimony cathode during the electrolysis of soln. of sulphuric acid and sodium hydroxide were related to the temp. and conc. of the electrolyte. Besides stibine, an amorphous deposit containing antimony was deposited in the alkali-electrolyte. E. J. Weeks and J. G. F. Druce showed that the amorphous deposit is **antimony dihydride**, Sb_2H_2, analogous to arsenic dihydride. When mixtures of stibine and hydrogen are passed through soln. of sodium hydroxide over 5N-conc., poor yields of the dihydride were obtained: $SbH_3+3NaOH=Na_3Sb+3H_2O$; followed by $2Na_3Sb+6H_2O=6NaOH+Sb_2H_2$ $+2H_2$. Negative results were obtained with soln. of potassium hydroxide. Better yields were obtained by passing stibine over solid sodium hydroxide, which soon became covered with a grey deposit. This was decomposed by water when hydrogen was evolved. The residual antimony dihydride was treated with dil. hydrochloric acid, washed with water, and dried over calcium chloride in vacuo. The same hydride is produced when stibine is prepared by dropping a soln. of antimony trichloride in conc. hydrochloric acid, diluted with its own vol. of water, into a flask containing zinc and dil. hydrochloric acid. A grey residue of antimony dihydride was formed: $2SbCl_3+8H\rightarrow6HCl+Sb_2H_2$. Antimony dihydride is soluble in moderately conc. nitric acid, but is insoluble in other dil. mineral acids, and in conc. sulphuric or hydrochloric acid. It is readily attacked by conc. nitric acid, and dil. aqua regia, and it is insoluble in alkali-lye. At a dull red-heat, there is a slight decomposition, and at a sufficiently high temp. it becomes incandescent, and glows until it is converted into elemental antimony. There is no abrupt change in vol. when heated between 12° and 112° in xylene in a dilatometer. The dihydride reacts vigorously with fused potassium nitrate, while reduced antimony dissolves in the same solvent very slowly.

In 1837, L. Thompson,[2] and C. H. Pfaff, almost simultaneously discovered gaseous **antimony trihydride, or stibine,** SbH_3. It is formed when dil. hydro-chloric or sulphuric acid acts on a suitable antimonial alloy. Thus, L. Thompson, H. Capitaine, J. L. Lassaigne, M. Berthelot and P. Petit, J. P. Cooke, R. H. Brett, H. Halle, K. Olschewsky, H. A. von Vogel, R. Bartels, and A. Stock and W. Doht, used an alloy of zinc and antimony. The proportions Sb : Zn recommended varied from L. Thompson's 1 : 1 to A. Stock and W. Doht's 1 : 4. E. J. Weeks showed that there is no actual best composition since the same amount of stibine can be obtained from alloys varying from 1 : 1 to 1 : 4. J. Schiel, and H. Capitaine used an alloy of potassium and antimony; A. van Bijlert, and T. Poleck and C. Thümmel, an amalgam of sodium and antimony; T. Humpert, an alloy of antimony and magnesium; and H. von der Planitz, an alloy of antimony and lead with conc. hydrochloric acid, or, according to A. Harding, with hydrobromic acid. D. Vitali found that the presence of mercuric chloride seriously interferes with the formation of stibine, in the reaction with zinc, acid, and antimony. H. Caron treated an alloy of antimony with barium, strontium, or calcium with water; H. Moissan said that an alloy of calcium and antimony of a high degree of purity gives hydrogen, not stibine, with dil. acids. The best yield obtained by A. Stock and W. Doht with the zinc-antimony alloy (3 : 1) and dil. sulphuric acid was a mixture of hydrogen with 0·98 vol. per cent. of stibine; the sodium-antimony alloy gave even worse results; a calcium-antimony alloy with dil. hydrochloric acid gave a gas with 9–16 vol. per cent. of stibine; substituting strontium or barium for the calcium did not improve the yield. The very best yield was obtained when an alloy of magnesium with 33 per cent. of antimony was treated with 12 per cent. hydro-chloric acid in a vessel cooled by a freezing mixture. The resulting hydrogen con-tained 14 per cent. of stibine. Alloys of antimony with aluminium, iron, lead, or thallium were found to be unsuitable for the preparation of stibine—aluminium and iron alloys gave a gas with only a little stibine; and lead and thallium alloys, a gas with only a trace of stibine. T. Humpert found that hydrogen iodide acting on the dry alloy of zinc or sodium and antimony forms no stibine ; nor does hydrogen sulphide acting on the sodium-antimony alloy.

F. Paneth and co-workers, and H. Blumenberg observed that stibine is produced when activated hydrogen is developed electrolytically, using antimony rods as electrodes. Stibine is also formed when soln. containing antimony are treated with nascent hydrogen. For example, soln. of the compounds of antimony with oxygen or chlorine, or potassium antimony tartrate, were found by L. Thompson, C. H. Pfaff, H. A. von Vogel, and J. F. Simon to give stibine in the presence of zinc and dil. hydrochloric or sulphuric acid ; Z. Roussin, and K. F. O. Seubert and A. Schmidt used magnesium in place of zinc ; and R. Böttger, aluminium. J. F. Simon found that stibine is formed when kermes is treated with zinc and hydrochloric acid ; and W. Skey, when stibnite is treated in a similar way. A. Dupasquier, and J. Thiele found that no trace of stibine is formed if iron is used in place of zinc, while very little is obtained with tin. According to V. A. Jacquelain, only a very small proportion of the antimony is converted into stibine by these processes—T. Rieckher said 4–8 per cent. T. Humpert found that the gas obtained by adding a soln. of antimony trichloride to a mixture of zinc and dil. sulphuric acid contained 10–12 per cent. by vol. of stibine. F. Jones, and E. J. Weeks and J. G. F. Druce obtained a gas rich in stibine by dropping a soln. of antimony trichloride in conc. hydrochloric acid, diluted with its own vol. of water, into a flask containing zinc and dil. hydrochloric acid. H. Capitaine obtained stibine by treating an alloy of zinc and antimony (2 : 1) with dil. sulphuric acid in which antimony trioxide was suspended ; but J. Schiel said that here the presence of antimony trioxide is not necessary. Sodium amalgam and water can be used as the source of nascent hydrogen. This mixture was found by T. Poleck and C. Thümmel, and O. Brunn to give stibine in the presence of reduced antimony ; by T. Humpert, with antimony trichloride ; and by F. A. Flückiger, with potassium antimonyl tartrate. On the other hand, no stibine was obtained by T. Fleitmann, and H. Hager when an alkaline soln. of an antimony salt was treated with zinc ; or by J. W. Gatehouse, when the soln. was treated with aluminium.

Advantage can be taken of nascent electrolytic hydrogen for the production of stibine. Thus, E. Newbery observed stibine may be associated with the hydrogen liberated from an antimony cathode ; and F. Paneth said that this method of preparing stibine can be usefully adopted in preference to that involving the treatment of a magnesium-antimony alloy with acids. H. J. S. Sands and co-workers found that the most favourable conditions involve a compact antimony electrode in a $4N$-soln. of sulphuric acid, at a low temp. and with the current density greater than the critical value of 10 milliampères per sq. cm. A yield of about 15 per cent. by vol. may be thus obtained. For a given electrolyte at a given temp., the overvoltage becomes practically independent of current density after a certain critical value has been reached. Below this value no stibine whatever is produced, above it is obtained a yield that is influenced only very slightly by further increase of current density. The curves for acidic and alkaline soln. are quite analogous. In both cases, at a low conc., the overvoltage is high and there is practically no yield of stibine ; with increasing conc. of the acid or alkali, the overvoltage diminishes to a value almost constant at each temp. while the yield slowly increases. This is taken to mean that both acid and alkali act as catalysts, promoting the union between the antimony of the cathode and the hydrogen which is being produced with a large amount of free energy. Such catalysts might be expected to cause the decomposition of the stibine formed, when it has passed from the electrode into the liquid, where it is unstable. In agreement with this, some of the stibine is decomposed in the most conc. acid soln., and in all the alkaline ones. With rise of temp. the overvoltage decreases, the yield of stibine becoming smaller and finally zero. It is probable that these two facts are closely connected, the free energy of the nascent hydrogen gradually becoming too small with rise of temp. to allow it to form stibine. The yields of stibine obtained by the electrolysis of soln. of sodium carbonate or sulphate using an antimony cathode and its dependence on the temp., voltage, and conc. were studied by E. J. Weeks. H. J. S. Sand and co-workers found that the formation of stibine proceeds somewhat more readily in alkaline than in acid soln., and the conditions favourable to it are similar in the two cases. To obtain appreciable yields of the gas, however, it is necessary to blow a rapid current of hydrogen past the electrode, in order to carry away the nascent gas before it has been decomposed by the alkaline soln. The decomposition product formed, when this is not done, has the properties of metallic antimony. The formation and decomposition of stibine in the corona discharge was observed by C. Montemartini.

O. Brunn recommended drying the gas by passing it over calcium chloride ; and he found that it is better to confine the gas over petroleum than over mercury or water. A. Stock and O. Guttmann said that the calcium chloride should be free from lime because the gas is decomposed by the hydroxides of the alkalies or alkaline earths, by the alkali carbonates, and by soda-lime. Phosphorus pentoxide can be employed as a desiccating agent. A. Stock and W. Doht obtained stibine free from hydrogen by condensing the dried mixture of hydrogen and stibine in a U-tube surrounded by liquid air. The stibine condenses to a white or colourless crystalline solid, which melts at a higher temp. to a colourless liquid. The liquid vaporizes without leaving a residue at a higher temp.

The composition of stibine was determined—directly and indirectly—by J. L. Lassaigne, F. Jones, T. Poleck and C. Thümmel, R. Bartels, and A. Stock and W. Doht. The results agree with the formula $(SbH_3)_n$. A. Stock and O. Guttmann found the vapour density at 15°, air unity, was 4·360, that is, about 2·95 per cent. higher than the value calculated for SbH_3. H. Remy discussed the structure of stibine ; and H. Henstock, the electronic structure. H. Capitaine, and R. Bartels found the mixed gas obtained by treating an alloy of antimony and zinc with dil. sulphuric acid has no smell. The observations on the smell made by the early workers—L. Thompson, C. H. Pfaff, J. L. Lassaigne, and K. Olschewsky —were probably made with a gas contaminated with arsine or other impurities. A. Stock and W. Doht said that the gas has a faint smell, not unlike that of hydrogen sulphide, but quite different from that of arsine or phosphine. F. Jones said that the gas, freed from arsine, has a distinct, nauseating odour, and an intensely disagreeable taste. Some say that the stibine is as poisonous as arsine, others that it is much less dangerous, and the only poisonous action it exerts is due only to the antimony it contains, for the gas is decomposed by contact with the organism. A. Stock and W. Doht found that gas is a violent poison, being quite as toxic as arsine—*vide infra*, physiological action of antimony.

K. Olschewsky found that when the colourless gas is cooled by liquid ethylene, it forms a snow-white mass, and A. Stock and W. Doht observed that it yields colourless crystals when cooled by liquid air. D. Rabinowitsch gave 54·5 for the mol. vol. B. H. Wilsdon studied the electronic structure of stibine. K. Olschewsky gave −91·5° for the melting point, but the gas was probably impure, perhaps moist, for A. Stock and W. Doht gave −88° for the m.p. Above this temp., stibine forms a water-white liquid with a boiling point of −17° at 760 mm. A. Stock and O. Guttmann found the specific gravity of the liquid at −25° to be 2·26, and at −50°, 2·34. M. Berthelot and P. Petit found that the heat of formation is strongly negative, being −81·8 Cals. per mol. ; A. Stock and F. Wrede found this result about two and a half times too small, being −34·27 Cals. per mol. at constant vol., and −33·98 Cals. per mol. at constant press. The subject was studied by R. de Forcrand. H. J. S. Sand and co-workers found the free energy, F, of the reaction : $2Sb+3H_2=2SbH_3$ to be $F=6\times96540\pi$, where π denotes the overvoltage, which at 90° was 0·402 in an acidic soln. when stibine at a partial press. of 0·01 atm. was produced. Hence, the free energy is $F=6\times96540\times0·402\times2·389\times10^{-4}=55·6$ Cals. for 2 mols ; at atm. press., the free energy is 62·1 Cals. for 2 mols. A similar value,

62·0 Cals. for 2 mols, is obtained with alkaline soln. At 20°, the results for acidic and alkaline soln. were respectively 74·2 and 77·0 Cals. for 2 mols. From A. Stock and F. Wrede's datum, the internal energy of 2 mols of stibine is 68·5 Cals. Again, $dF/dT=(F-U)/T$, which corresponds with a value almost zero at 100°. J. C. Thomlinson discussed the heat of formation of this family of hydrides.

The decomposition of stibine.—K. Olschewsky found that liquid stibine readily decomposes at very low temp.; and, added A. Stock and O. Guttmann, liquid stibine decomposes more readily than the gaseous compound. K. Olschewsky found that the decomposition begins between −65° and −56°. Gaseous stibine explodes at ordinary temp. if there be any local heating of the containing vessel; and if the temp. of the gas at any point exceeds 200°, an explosion occurs. In the evaporation of liquid stibine, an explosion may occur without a rise of temp. The glass containing vessel may be shattered, but the force of the explosion is not great; and the temp. is so low that the hydrogen is not inflamed, and the antimony is not oxidized. R. Böttger found that stibine, presumably slightly diluted with hydrogen, is decomposed by an electric spark, forming a black deposit of antimony; A. Stock and O. Guttmann found that stibine alone is instantly exploded by an electric spark; this also occurs if the stibine is diluted with 40 per cent. of hydrogen, but not so with 75 per cent. hydrogen. During the explosion, A. Stock and W. Doht found that the antimony separates as a grey powder, whereas the thermal decomposition of stibine furnishes a lustrous film of antimony. H. Reckleben and J. Scheiber found that the silent electric discharge yields only antimony and hydrogen. H. A. von Vogel studied the spontaneous decomposition of stibine at ordinary temp., and C. H. Pfaff said that the larger the proportion of free hydrogen present, the slower the decomposition. C. Montemartini studied the decomposition and formation of stibine when exposed to the corona electric discharge. K. Olschewsky found that gaseous stibine decomposes at a temp. not far removed from its b.p., −17°; and T. Humpert, and F. Jones said that the gas decomposes at ordinary temp., only if it is not diluted with much hydrogen, but A. Stock and W. Doht did not agree. If air be excluded from stibine confined in a clean glass vessel, free from alkali, it can be kept for some hours without decomposition; and if air be present decomposition quickly sets in; similar results were obtained with aerated water, but water free from dissolved air has no perceptible effort. J. L. Lassaigne said that the decomposition of stibine is accelerated by the sun's rays, but A. Stock and co-workers could not detect any such effect.

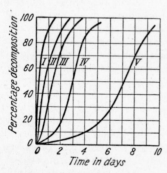

FIG 8.—The Progress of the Decomposition of Stibine in Different Containing Vessels.

The curves representing the relation between the percentage amount of stibine decomposed and the time vary considerably with the nature of the inner surface of the containing vessel. With a clean, smooth surface, the curve V, Fig. 8, has an S-shape: when the inner surface is etched with hydrofluoric acid, the curve has the appearance shown in III, Fig. 8; and if the inner surface of the containing vessel has a film of arsenic, the result is that indicated by IV, Fig. 8. If the vessel be filled with stibine, and the gas is warmed, the inner surface acquires a bright film of antimony, and when this vessel is refilled with stibine, the course of the decomposition is represented by curve II, Fig. 8. In another vessel coated with antimony first by warming, and by introducing another charge of stibine and allowing it to decompose slowly for 8 hrs. at ordinary temp., the introduction of another charge of stibine gave the results represented by the hyperbolic curve, I, Fig. 8. The deposited antimony (I) accelerated the decomposition of the stibine quite differently from the acceleration (IV) produced by arsenic. The deposit of antimony loses its activity after it has stood for some time. The progress of the reaction was measured by the change of press. in the containing vessel, and it is supposed that the reaction occurs instantly at the surface of antimony, and the time actually measured is occupied by the diffusion of more stibine from within to the antimony film. This is in agreement with the view of M. Bodenstein. A. Stock and O. Guttmann found that the equation employed for arsine, $kt = \log \{P_0/(3P_0 - 2P)\}$, does not apply, and they obtained better results with $V = 2(x_1 - x_2)/(x_1 + x_2)(t_2 - t_1)$, where V represents its amount of stibine decomposed in unit time—one hour—and calculated as the mean of the amounts present at the beginning and end of the time. In calculating x, an allowance of 15 mm. in 760 mm. must be made at 15° for the deviation of stibine from the normal gas-law. A. Stock, F. Gomolka, and H. Heynemann found that with a given vessel and a mirror deposited at 150°, the initial velocity of reaction is fairly constant, but in successive experiments in the same vessel the initial velocity is constant only after the superposition of three mirrors upon one another, they did not find that the activity of the film of antimony is dependent on the conc. of the stibine from which the film is produced ; and they inferred that the measurements are really those of a chemical reaction and not of diffusion phenomena, because the temp. coeff. is 2·050 between 15° and 25°, and 1·909 between 25° and 35°.; the temp. coeff. of chemical reactions lie between 2 and 3 at the ordinary temp. The addition of hydrogen does not affect the rate of decomposition, and under given conditions, the relative velocity of the reaction is nearly proportional to the square root of the conc. of the stibine. In the presence of oxygen, the antimony mirror is poisoned completely for several hours ; then it recovers and the reaction proceeds with increased velocity. The mirror is unaffected by oxygen in the complete absence of stibine ; hence the poisoning is due to oxidation, not of the mirror itself, but of the hydride or of some compound formed intermediately, by which a layer of oxide is formed and destroys contact between the hydride and the catalyst. The "revivifying" of the mirror may be due to the reduction of this oxide by the stibine ; the increased velocity of the reaction is not due to the water so produced, but may be consequent on changes in the surface of the catalyst caused by successive oxidation and reduction. Black antimony is not poisoned by oxygen, and is changed into the ordinary metallic mirror after the decomposition of the stibine has been in progress for a few minutes. A. Stock and M. Bodenstein found that the observed results can be represented by the equation $dx/dt = -kxp$, where x denotes the conc. of the stibine, and k and p are constants dependent on the nature of the reaction substance and the temp.—p was found to vary from 0·5 to 0·6— the results then agree with the assumption that the reaction occurs in two phases : (i) a rapid adsorption of the stibine by the antimony ; and (ii) a slowly progressing chemical reaction at the surface. A. Stock, E. Echeandia and P. R. Voigt tested the relation $dx/dt = -kxp$ at different temp., and found that p increases with temp. from 0·4 at 0° to 0·7 at 75°. The relative decomposition velocities at 0°, 25°, 50°, and 75° are 1, 5·8, 23·8, and 86·4 ; and the temp. coeff. are 2·05 from 0° to 10° ; 1·80 from 30° to 40° ; and 1·66 from 60° to 70°. The reaction was studied by S. Dushman, and M. Trautz.

The decomposition of stibine by heat was noticed by L. Thompson, C. H. Pfaff, and J. L. Lassaigne ; and J. F. Simon found that under these conditions stibine is decomposed more readily than arsine. O. Brunn found that stibine mixed with hydrogen begins to decompose at 150°, while A. Stock and W. Doht said that the decomposition takes place rapidly at this temp. Arsine was found by O. Brunn to begin to decompose at about 230°, so that by passing a mixture of stibine and arsine through a tube heated to 200°, the arsine alone escapes decomposition. A. van Bijlert based a method of analysis on this reaction. When a mixture of stibine and hydrogen is passed through a glass tube heated by a gas flame, a mirror of antimony is deposited on the glass before and behind the heated part. A comparison of the properties of the films of antimony and arsine has been given in connection with arsenic.

The chemical properties of stibine.—L. Vallery studied the action of traces of stibine in the combustion of **hydrogen** with palladized asbestos as catalyst. L. Thompson found that when stibine—presumably admixed with hydrogen—is mixed with **oxygen,** it is exploded violently by the electric spark. A. Stock and O. Guttmann found that oxygen or **air** decomposes stibine in 24 hrs.: $4SbH_3+3O_2=4Sb+6H_2O$, a part of the stibine also decomposes spontaneously with the separation of hydrogen. Black antimony is produced; and if the reaction occurs at $-90°$, yellow antimony is formed. According to H. A. von Vogel, and L. A. Buchner, when stibine, mixed with hydrogen, is set on fire in contact with air, white flakes of antimony trioxide are formed, but no elemental antimony is produced. In the analogous case with arsine, arsenic is formed. L. Thompson said that if a stream of the gas be inflamed, it burns with a bluish-green light producing dense, white clouds of antimony trioxide, and glass or porcelain held in the flame becomes covered with a metallic film, which R. H. Brett found to be darker than those produced with burning arsine. The older observations on the solubility of stibine in **water** were based on those made with hydrogen containing a small proportion of stibine; accordingly, J. F. Simon could say that stibine is not sensibly absorbed by water. F. Jones also working with a mixture of the two gases said that under these conditions water absorbs 4·12 to 5·32 c.c. per litre at $10°-10·5°$. A. Stock and O. Guttmann found that at room temp. 100 vols. of water absorb 20 vols. of the gas. H. A. von Vogel, and C. H. Pfaff noticed that the gas in contact with water is decomposed with the precipitation of antimony; and A. Stock and W. Doht found that while air-free water has very little action on stibine, aerated water quickly decomposes the gas; and A. Stock and O. Guttmann, and A. Güttich observed that stibine is rapidly decomposed in contact with **hydrogen dioxide.**

According to H. A. von Vogel, and L. A. Buchner, at ordinary temp. **chlorine** acts slowly on stibine, forming antimony trichloride and hydrogen chloride, without the separation of antimony; and J. F. Simon noticed that when the gas is passed through chlorine-water, hydrochloric acid and white flakes of antimony oxychloride are produced. The stibine in question was mixed with a large proportion of hydrogen, and L. Thompson accordingly said that a mixture of the gas with chlorine can be exploded by the electric spark. A. Stock and O. Guttmann found that purified stibine decomposes with detonation in contact with chlorine, and similarly also with chlorine-water. A. Stock found that stibine reacts with liquid chlorine to form antimony and antimony pentachloride. J. F. Simon found that an aq. soln. of **bromine** decomposes the stibine (and hydrogen) with the separation of white flecks; while A. Stock and O. Guttmann found that stibine alone is instantly attacked without explosion by gaseous and liquid bromine. O. Brunn found that stibine is completely decomposed by **iodine,** and A. Stock and O. Guttmann showed that the reaction is slower than with bromine, and that hydrogen iodide and antimony triiodide are formed. With heated iodine, C. Husson observed that an orange or brown substance is formed, and a little antimony. J. F. Simon observed that when an aq. soln. of iodine is treated with stibine, it becomes colourless and deposits white flakes which, if the current of gas be continued, become brown and finally black, being converted into antimony. A. Stock and O. Guttmann found that **hydrogen chloride** raises the speed of decomposition of stibine. A. Güttich found that **sodium hypochlorite** soln. slowly oxidize stibine; and that **iodic acid** also oxidizes it: $5SbH_3+8HIO_3=5H_3SbO_4+4I_2+4H_2O$, and also $5SbH_3+6HIO_3 =5H_3SbO_3+3I_2+3H_2O$. Stibine does not act on neutral soln. of the **iodates** even if iodine or silver nitrate be used as catalysts.

According to F. Jones, when stibine is passed over **sulphur** it is decomposed: $2SbH_3+6S=Sb_2S_3+3H_2S$. The reaction occurs at ordinary temp. only in the presence of light, being slow in diffused daylight, rapid in sunlight. The reaction is also brought about by the electric light, light from burning magnesium, and even the light of a good oil-lamp. The same decomposition occurs at $100°$, but is rapid at higher temp. **The reaction with paper coated with sulphur, by dipping in a** soln. of sulphur in carbon disulphide, is coloured by stibine at a rate proportional to the brightness of the light, and F. Jones based a photometric process on the reaction. The reaction with stibine affords an extremely delicate test for antimony. The development of the orange tint is perceptible in the presence of 0·0001 grm. of antimony. A. Stock and O. Guttmann found that stibine alone reacts with finely-divided sulphur, forming hydrogen and antimony sulphides, and antimony. G. B. Buckton found that triethyl stibine readily reacts with sulphur, forming the sulphide, $(C_2H_5)_3SbS$. A. Stock and O. Guttmann also found that stibine does not react with **hydrogen sulphide,** and the contrary observation by O. Brunn is attributed to the presence of impurities in the gas. J. F. Simon, and F. Jones observed that in light, stibine and hydrogen sulphide react: $2SbH_3 + 3H_2S = Sb_2S_3 + 6H_2$. J. F. Simon found that an aq. soln. of hydrogen sulphide does not react with stibine. When stibine is passed into conc. **sulphuric acid,** T. Humpert, and R. Bartels observed a black metallic separation and the formation of hydrogen sulphide, but not sulphur dioxide—R. Bartels supposed the black substance to be antimony, and T. Humpert, antimony hydride. O. Brunn also found stibine is decomposed by dil. sulphuric acid. F. Jones also found that stibine reacts slowly with **selenium** in sunlight, and at 100°, but not in darkness; while **tellurium** reacts with stibine in sunlight; very slowly at 100°; and not at all in darkness.

A. Stock and O. Guttmann found that **nitrogen** is without action on stibine; similarly, with **ammonia,** as was also observed by J. F. Simon; and R. Bartels added that purified ammonia does not react with stibine in darkness, but the impure gas reacts with stibine in light. The presence of ammonia, however, was found by A. Stock and O. Guttmann to accelerate the decomposition of stibine, and when a mixture of the two gases is heated, an explosion occurs. The action of **nitrous oxide** is like that of oxygen; similarly also with **nitric oxide.** At ordinary temp. the reactions with nitric oxide are represented by the equations, $6NO + 2SbH_3 = 3N_2O + 3H_2O + 2Sb$; $3NO + 2SbH_3 = 3N + 3H_2O + 2Sb$; and $3NO + 5SbH_3 = 3NH_3 + 3H_2O + 5Sb$. A. Güttich found stibine is readily oxidized by a 20 per cent. soln. of **nitrous acid,** and by a 30 per cent. soln. of **nitric acid.** C. F. Ansell found that hot nitric acid oxidizes stibine, admixed with hydrogen, forming antimony pentoxide; conc. nitric acid was found by A. Stock and O. Guttmann to act explosively on stibine. R. Mahn observed no reaction between **phosphorus trichloride** and stibine, but **phosphorus pentachloride** is slowly reduced to the trichloride. A. Stock and O. Guttmann showed that **phosphorus triiodide** reacts with stibine producing the diiodide; and the **phosphorus diiodide** reacts: $3P_2I_4 + 4SbH_3 = 4PH_3 + 4SbI_3 + 2P$; and the **antimony triiodide** then reacts: $SbH_3 + SbI_3 = 2Sb + 3HI$. R. Bartels found that **arsenic tribromide,** dissolved in carbon disulphide, gives a brown precipitate of arsenic and antimony; while R. Mahn observed that with **antimony trichloride,** a precipitate of antimony formed. R. Bartels found that an aq. soln. of **arsenic trioxide** is gradually blackened by stibine without forming a precipitate. The black soln. does not change in an atm. of carbon dioxide, but the colour gradually disappears on standing in air, and rapidly when warmed with nitric acid. When heated with hydrochloric acid, a brown precipitate is formed. A soln. of **bismuth nitrate** in nitric acid gives with stibine a metallic mirror on the walls of the containing vessel; a piece of filter-paper soaked in a soln. of bismuth nitrate is browned by stibine, the brown colour disappears on exposure to air. A soln. of **bismuth chloride** gives with stibine a steel-grey precipitate and a metallic mirror; a **bismuth acetate** soln. gives a black, pulverulent precipitate; **bismuth hydroxide** is blackened by stibine. No complex compound is formed between stibine and **boron tribromide;** arsine does form a complex.

According to A. Stock and O. Guttmann, **carbon dioxide** is without action on stibine, but when a mixture of the gases is sparked for some time the reaction can be symbolized : $2SbH_3+3CO_2=2Sb+3H_2O+3CO$.   A. Stock and O. Guttmann said that **carbon disulphide** is the best solvent for stibine, since one vol. of the liquid dissolves 250 vols. of stibine at 0°—it is said that no chemical compound is formed because when the soln. boiled, stibine is given off and carbon disulphide remains. J. Schiel showed that when stibine is passed through carbon disulphide, and then through a glowing porcelain tube, antimony trisulphide is deposited along with sulphur and a trace of carbon, while the escaping gas contains hydrogen, methane, hydrogen sulphide, and some undecomposed carbon disulphide.   A. W. Hofmann found that triethylstibine is without action on carbon disulphide even at 100° ; F. Jones showed that **mercaptan** decomposes stibine with the separation of a black powder.   One vol. of **alcohol** dissolves 15 vols. of stibine ; and stibine is freely soluble in **ether, benzene,** and **petroleum ether.**   Stibine has no action on soln. of **sodium acetate,** or of **ammonium oxalate.**

According to G. Dragendorff, stibine is decomposed when passed over solid **potassium hydroxide,** and the alkali acquires a metallic film which separates in black flecks when the product is treated with water ; the colourless filtrate contains antimony.   The film also becomes colourless on exposure to air—presumably the film is an alloy of potassium and antimony which in both cases passes into the alkali antimonate.   A. Stock and O. Guttmann said that stibine is rapidly decomposed by aq. soln. of potassium or **sodium hydroxide ;** a similar result was observed by O. Brunn, G. Dragendorff, and R. Bartels.   A. Guttich represented the reaction : $SbH_3+3KOH=K_3Sb+3H_2O$.   According to F. Jones, when stibine is passed through soln. of sodium or potassium hydroxide, the liquid is tinged yellowish-brown, then deep brown, and finally a black powder separates out.   This brown soln. is extremely oxidizable ; the simple shaking of an open flask containing it causes the colour to disappear almost instantly ; it forms indeed a delicate test for the presence of oxygen.   The soln. rapidly decolorizes one of potassium permanganate.   The composition of the black precipitate which separates out from such alkaline soln. has been assumed to be an antimonide of sodium or potassium, but F. Jones found its composition to be H_3SbO, or Sb_2O.   W. Meissner found that alcoholic potassium or sodium hydroxide is coloured brownish-yellow by stibine, and then dark brown with the separation of dark brown flecks ; arsine does not act on the alcoholic soln.   I. Guareschi found that stibine is absorbed by **soda-lime.** R. Bartels found that soln. of **potassium and sodium chlorides** have no perceptible influence on stibine—*vide infra,* the desiccation of stibine.

A. Lionet found that when stibine and hydrogen are passed over **copper,** the whole of the antimony is retained ; and a similar result was obtained with **cuprous oxide** and with **cupric oxide.**   R. Bartels found that moist cupric hydroxide is blackened by stibine, and that a soln. of **cupric sulphate** is very slowly attacked by stibine, depositing, according to J. F. Simon, a few black flecks of copper antimonide, or, according to R. Bartels, a mixture of copper and antimony.   By using a small proportion of soln., and a large proportion of gas, the deposit can be augmented. A. Güttich also studied this reaction.   R. Bartels found that a soln. of **cupric chloride** gives a similar deposit, and leaves behind a soln. of cuprous chloride.   A soln. of **cuprous chloride** in hydrochloric acid gives a reddish deposit which appears to be similar to that obtained with cupric salt soln.   J. Riban obtained a black precipitate.   In contrast with arsine, E. Dowzard found that stibine is absorbed by a 15 per cent. soln. of cuprous chloride in hydrochloric acid.   R. Bartels found that moist **silver oxide** is blackened by stibine.   J. F. Simon said that a dil. aq. soln. of **silver nitrate** precipitates all the antimony as silver antimonide, and if arsine be also present, the soln. will contain arsenic trioxide.   The reaction was examined by C. H. Pfaff, J. L. Lassaigne, H. Halle, A. W. Hofmann, T. Humpert, A. Houzeau, F. Jones, and R. Bartels.   The clear liquid has an acidic reaction, and contains very little antimony ; the black precipitate was considered by T. Poleck and C. Thümmel, and R. Bartels to be a mixture of silver and antimony trioxide ; by J. L. Lassaigne, and F. Jones as a silver antimonide alone or mixed with silver. D. Vitali found the action of stibine on an aq. soln. of silver nitrate to be in all respects like that of arsine : $SbH_3+6AgNO_3+3H_2O=H_3SbO_3+6Ag+6HNO_3$, except that antimonious acid, being insoluble, separates with the silver from which it can be extracted by hydrochloric acid. H. Reckleben agrees with J. L. Lassaigne's conclusion that the first action of stibine is : $SbH_3+3AgNO_3=Ag_3Sb+3HNO_3$, while the excess of silver nitrate causes the further reaction : $Ag_3Sb+3AgNO_3+3H_2O=6Ag+H_3SbO_3+3HNO_3$. The final precipitate, therefore, consists of silver, antimony hydroxide, and a little metallic antimony—some antimony at the same time passes into soln. A. Güttich agrees with this view of the reaction. W. J. Russell, and E. Schobig found that silver nitrate reduced by the hydrogen usually accompanying the stibine is negligibly small. According to T. Poleck and C. Thümmel, with conc. soln. of silver nitrate, say a gram of the salt in 0·7 grm. of water, the soln. is coloured yellow ; if the stibine is very much diluted with hydrogen, a green coloration first appears, and grey silver is deposited. The yellow colour could not be isolated, and it is thought to be $SbAg_3.3AgNO_3$, being formed by the reaction : $SbH_3+6AgNO_3=SbAg_3.3AgNO_3+3HNO_3$. and it is hydrolyzed by water : $SbAg_3.3AgNO_3+3H_2O=H_3SbO_3+6Ag+3HNO_3$. R. Bartels thought the yellow coloration to be due to the formation of $SbH_3.AgNO_3$, which reduces the remaining silver nitrate : $SbH_3.AgNO_3+5AgNO_3+3H_2O=H_3SbO_3+6Ag+6HNO_3$. If stibine acts on a piece of filter-paper with a spot wetted with a conc. soln. of silver nitrate, the periphery is coloured dark brown or black, and the interior is either coloured grey, or not coloured at all ; if the spot be wetted with a 1 : 2-soln. of silver nitrate and water, the interior will be coloured brownish-red ; and if with a dil. soln., black. According to R. Bartels, moist **gold hydroxide** is blackened by stibine. V. A. Jacquelain found a soln. of **gold chloride** is decomposed by stibine ; R. Bartels said the precipitate which first forms is black, the colour then changes to brown, and it then consists of gold mixed with a little antimony ; antimonious acid passes into soln. The composition of the black body has not yet been determined.

R. Bartels found that aq. soln. of the **alkaline earth hydroxides** are coloured brown by stibine ; and similarly with an alcoholic soln. of barium hydroxide—*vide infra*, the desiccation of stibine. He also found that the soln. of the **alkaline earth chlorides** have no perceptible action on stibine ; similarly also with soln. of **magnesium chloride,** and of **zinc chloride.** J. F. Simon observed no effect with aq. soln. of **zinc sulphate.** R. Bartels observed that moist **zinc hydroxide** is but slightly affected by stibine, but after an hour's action, it acquires a yellowish-green colour ; moist **cadmium hydroxide** is blackened ; a black precipitate mixed with white or brass-coloured particles is slowly formed with neutral and ammoniacal soln. of **cadmium sulphate**—the precipitate with neutral soln. has very little cadmium, while that with ammoniacal soln. has 53·08 per cent. of antimony and 38·46 per cent. of cadmium. R. Bartels found that moist **mercuric oxide** is blackened by stibine. According to J. F. Simon, when stibine, admixed with hydrogen, is slowly passed into a soln. of **mercuric chloride,** the whole of the antimony collects in the precipitate, which is first white, then grey, and finally black. According to R. Bartels, the white precipitate is a mixture of mercurous chloride and antimony oxychloride, the filtrate contains antimonious acid ; he represented the reaction : $6HgCl_2+SbH_3=6HgCl+SbCl_3+3HCl$; the trichloride is then hydrolyzed by water. The grey and black colorations are due to the reduction of the mercurous chloride to mercury. A. Güttich also studied this reaction. Filter-paper soaked with a soln. of mercuric chloride was found, by M. Mayençon and M. Bergeret, to be coloured greyish-brown by stibine ; F. A. Flückiger obtained this result only when the stibine is present in not too small a proportion. D. Vitali made some observations on the formation of antimonial mercury compound by stibine and mercuric chloride. R. Bartels found that soln. of **mercuric sulphate** and of **mercuric nitrate** behave in a manner analogous to that of mercuric chloride ; and P. Lemoult found that a soln. of **potassium tetriodomercuriate**—Nessler's reagent—is slowly coloured brown as in the analogous cases with phosphine and arsine. R. Bartels found that soln. of **mercurous salts** immediately give a black precipitation when treated with stibine; the black precipitate is a mixture of antimony trioxide and mercury.

R. Bartels found that a soln. of **potash-alum** has no perceptible action on stibine. R. Mahn observed no reaction between soln. of **stannic chloride** and stibine; and R. Bartels, none with soln. of **stannous chloride**; while **lead hydroxide** suspended in water is immediately blackened. E. Dowzard said that a soln. of **lead acetate** does not absorb stibine, while R. Bartels, and J. F. Simon observed no reaction between stibine and soln. of **lead salts**. R. Bartels found that a soln. of **chrome-alum**, or of **potassium dichromate**, is rapidly blackened by stibine; and E. Varenne and E. Herbé, that a mixture of potassium dichromate and sulphuric acid oxidizes stibine completely. R. Bartels said that a dil. soln. of **ammonium molybdate** is coloured blue by stibine; and that a soln. of **sodium tungstate** is indifferent towards stibine. Moist **manganese hydroxide** is blackened by stibine if air be excluded, while a soln. of **manganese sulphate** has no action on the gas. F. Jones found that stibine reacts with a neutral soln. of **potassium permanganate** giving a precipitate of manganese oxide while antimonic acid passes into soln.:
$2KMnO_4 + SbH_3 = Mn_2O_3 + K_2HSbO_4 + H_2O$; E. Schobig said that in neutral and acidic soln., antimony trioxide and pentoxide are formed; and R. Bartels added that with dil. neutral soln., the change is not very marked; the violet soln. becomes brownish-red. J. F. Simon found that a soln. of **ferrous chloride**, and R. Bartels that **ferrous hydroxide**, is indifferent towards stibine; while soln. of **ferric chloride**, and of **potassium ferricyanide**, are slowly reduced. A soln. of **cobaltous chloride** is indifferent towards stibine; while **cobaltous hydroxide** is blackened if air be excluded; and a soln. of **cobalt hydroxypentamminochloride** gives white flecks, and finally a black precipitate which oxidizes in air, forming a pale blue mass. Moist **nickelous hydroxide** is blackened by stibine when air is excluded; and a soln. of **nickelous chloride** is indifferent towards the gas. Moist **platinum oxide** is blackened by stibine; a soln. of **platinum tetrachloride** decomposes stibine completely, producing, according to J. F. Simon, platinum antimonide; according to P. Christofle, a mixture of the antimonide, platinous chloride, and antimony; and, according to R. Bartels, a mixture of platinum and antimony trioxide.

REFERENCES.

[1] R. L. Ruhland, *Schweigger's Journ.*, **15**. 418, 1815; R. F. Marchand, *Journ. prakt. Chem.*, (1), **34**. 383, 1845; R. Böttger, *ib.*, (1), **68**. 374, 1856; *Pogg. Ann.*, **97**. 333, 1856; **104**. 292, 1858; E. Wiederhold, *ib.*, **122**. 481, 1864; R. C. Engel, *Ber.*, **7**. 121, 1874; H. Reckleben and J. Scheiber, *Zeit. anorg. Chem.*, **70**. 275, 1911; A. Stock and O. Güttmann, *Ber.*, **37**. 885, 1904; J. G. F. Druce, *Chem. Listy*, **19**. 156, 1925; E. J. Weeks and J. G. F. Druce, *Chem. News*, **129**. 31, 1924; **130**. 403, 1925; *Journ. Chem. Soc.*, **127**. 1069, 1925; H. J. S. Sand, E. J. Weeks, and S. W. Worrell, *ib.*, **123**. 456, 1923; F. Flury, *Zeit. angew. Chem.*, **40**. 1134, 1927.
[2] L. Thompson, *Phil. Mag.*, (3), **10**. 353, 1837; C. H. Pfaff, *Pogg. Ann.*, **42**. 339, 1837; J. F. Simon, *ib.*, **42**. 563, 1837; T. Humpert, *Journ. prakt. Chem.*, (1), **94**. 398, 1865; H. A. von Vogel, *ib.*, (7), **13**. 57, 1838; W. Meissner, *ib.*, (1), **25**. 243, 1842; E. Schobig, *ib.*, (2), **14**. 291, 1876; R. Böttger, *ib.*, (1), **90**. 34, 1863; J. Schiel, *Liebig's Ann.*, **104**. 223, 1857; K. F. O. Seubert and A. Schmidt, *ib.*, **267**. 237, 1892; J. Thiele, *ib.*, **265**. 62, 1891; T. Fleitmann, *ib.*, **77**. 126, 1851; A. W. Hofmann, *ib.*, **115**. 287, 1860; *Journ. Chem. Soc.*, **13**. 289, 1861; G. B. Buckton, *ib.*, **13**. 115, 1861; A. van Bijlert, *Ber.*, **23**. 2968, 1890; H. Reckleben, *ib.*, **42**. 1458, 1909; H. von der Planitz, *ib.*, **7**. 1664, 1874; T. Poleck and C. Thümmel, *ib.*, **16**. 2435, 1883; A. Harding, *ib.*, **14**. 2092, 1881; O. Brunn, *ib.*, **21**. 2548, 1888; **22**. 3205, 1889; F. Paneth, M. Matthies, and E. Schmidt-Hebbel, *ib.*, **55**. B, 775, 1922; C. Montemartini, *Gazz. Chim. Ital.*, **52**. ii, 96, 1922; H. Capitaine, *Journ. Pharm. Chim.*, (2), **25**. 516, 1839; K. Olschewsky, *Monatsh.*, **7**. 371, 1886; *Ber.*, **34**. 3592, 1901; E. Rabinowitsch, *Ber.*, **58**. 2790, 1925; M. Bodenstein, *Zeit. phys. Chem.*, **49**. 41, 1904; **50**. 611, 1905; A. Stock, *ib.*, **50**. 111, 1905; A. Stock and M. Bodenstein, *ib.*, **40**. 570, 1907; A. Stock and O. Guttmann, *ib.*, **37**. 885, 1904; A. Stock and W. Doht, *ib.*, **34**. 2339, 3592, 1901; **35**. 2270, 1902; A. Stock, F. Gomolka, and H. Heynemann, *ib.*, **40**. 532, 1907; A. Stock, E. Echeandia, and P. R. Voigt, *ib.*, **41**. 1309, 1908; P. R. Voigt, *Neue Untersuchungen über die Zersetzung des Antimonwasserstoffs*, Berlin, 1908; E. Echeandia, *Ueber den Gang des Arsen- und Antimon-Wasserstoffzerfalls*, Berlin, 1909; A. Stock and F. Wrede, *Ber.*, **41**. 540, 1908; A. Stock, *ib.*, **53**. 837, 1920; F. Gomolka, *Beiträge zur Kenntnis der Antimonwasserstoff-*

zersetzung, Berlin, 1906 : H. Heynemann, *Ueber die Zersetzung des Antimonwasserstoffs*, Berlin, 1906 ; A. Güttich, *Ueber Bestimmungsmethoden für Arsen- und Antimonwasserstoff*, Leipzig, 1909 ; H. Reckleben, *Ber.*, 42. 1458, 1909 ; J. Guareschi, *Atti Accad. Lincei*, 51. 4, 59, 263, 1916 : H. Reckleben and A. Güttich, *Zeit. anal. Chem.*, 49. 73, 1910 ; H. Halle, *Ueber Antimon und Arsen*, München, 1893 ; S. Dushmann, *Journ. Amer. Chem. Soc.*, 43. 397, 1921 ; M. Trautz, *Zeit. anorg. Chem.*, 104. 69, 1918 ; H. Caron, *Compt. Rend.*, 48. 440, 1859 ; H. Moissan, *ib.*, 127. 584, 1898 ; V. A. Jacquelain, *ib.*, 16. 28, 1843 ; A. Dupasquier, *ib.*, 14. 514, 1842 ; P. Lemoult, *ib.*, 139. 478, 1904 ; M. Mayençon and M. Bergeret, *ib.*, 79. 118, 1874 ; J. Riban, *ib.*, 88. 582, 1879 ; A. Lionet, *ib.*, 89. 440, 1879 ; A. Houzeau, *ib.*, 75. 1823, 1872 ; C. Husson, *ib.*, 67. 56, 1868 ; P. Lebeau, *ib.*, 134. 284, 1902 ; T. Rieckher, *Neues Jahrb. Pharm.*, 28. 10, 1867 ; J. L. Lassaigne, *Journ. Chem. Méd.*, (2), 6. 638, 1839 ; (2), 7. 440, 1840 ; R. Böttger, *Jahrb. Phys. Ver. Frankfurt*, 16, 1879 ; Z. Roussin, *Journ. Pharm. Chim.*, (4), 3. 413, 1866 ; *Chem. News*, 14. 27, 1866 ; *Zeit. anal. Chem.*, 6. 100, 1867 ; H. Hager, *ib.*, 11. 82, 1872 ; G. Dragendorff, *ib.*, 5. 200, 1866 ; J. W. Gatehouse, *Chem. News*, 27. 189, 1873 ; H. Henstock, *ib.*, 136. 337, 1923 ; W. Skey, *ib.*, 34. 147, 1876 ; J. C. Thomlinson, *ib.*, 99. 133, 1909 ; E. J. Weeks, *ib.*, 127. 87, 1923 ; H. Blumenberg, *U.S. Pat. No.* 1375819, 1921 ; R. de Forcrand, *Journ. Chim. Phys.*, 15. 516, 1907 ; R. Bartels, *Ueber die Einwirkung des Antimonwasserstoffs auf Metallsalzlösungen*, Berlin, 1889 ; M. Berthelot and P. Petit, *Ann. Chim. Phys.*, (6), 18. 65, 1889 ; *Compt. Rend.*, 109. 546, 1889 ; F. Jones, *Proc. Chem. Soc.*, 23. 164, 1907 ; *Journ. Chem. Soc.*, 29. 641, 1876 ; 33. 95, 1878 ; G. F. Ansell, *ib.*, 5. 210, 1852 ; E. Newbery, *ib.*, 109. 1361, 1916 ; W. J. Russell, *ib.*. 27. 3, 1874 ; E. Dowzard, *ib.*, 79. 715, 1901 ; H. J. S. Sand, E. J. Weeks, and S. W. Worrell, *ib.*, 123. 456, 1923 ; H. J. S. Sand, J. Grant, and W. V. Lloyd, *ib.*, 378, 1927 ; E. J. Weeks and J. G. F. Druce, *ib.*, 127. 1069, 1925 ; E. J. Weeks, *Rec. Trav. Chim. Pays-Bas*, 44. 261, 795, 1925 : R. Mahn, *Jena. Zeit.*, 5. 162, 1869 ; E. Varenne and E. Herbé, *Bull. Soc. Chim.*, (2), 28. 523, 1877 ; F. A. Flückiger, *Arch. Pharm.*, (3). 27. 26, 1889 ; D. Vitali, *Boll. Chim. Farm.*, 44. 49, 1905 ; *L'Orosi*, 15. 397, 1892 ; P. Christofle, *Recherches sur les combinaisons de l'antimoine avec les métaux*, Göttingen, 1863 ; H. Reckleben and J. Scheiber, *Zeit. anorg. Chem.*, 70. 275, 1911 ; R. H. Brett, *Phil. Mag.*, (3), 20. 403, 1842 ; *Proc. Liverpool Lit. Phil. Soc.*, 1. 26, 1844 ; L. A. Buchner, *Repert. Pharm.*, 63. 250, 1838 ; F. Paneth, *Zeit. Elektrochem.*, 26. 452, 1920 ; B. H. Wilsdon, *Phil. Mag.*, (6), 49. 336, 1925 ; L. Vallery, *Compt. Rend.*, 185. 538, 1927 ; J. P. Cooke, *Proc. Amer. Acad.*, 13. 1, 1877 ; 15. 251, 1880 ; 17. 13, 1881 ; *Amer. Journ. Science*, (3), 15. 41, 107, 1878 ; (3), 19. 382, 1880 ; (3), 21. 220, 1881 ; H. Remy, *Zeit. anorg. Chem.*, 116. 255, 1921.

§ 9. The Antimonides

P. Lebeau [1] found that an alloy of lithium and antimony is formed with violence when the two elements are fused together ; he obtained **lithium tritantimonide**, Li_3Sb, by electrolyzing a fused mixture of equal parts of lithium and potassium chlorides with a current of 15 amps. using an antimony cathode ; it is also formed when a small fragment of antimony is heated with lithium in a sealed tube containing liquid ammonia ; the reaction is completed when the blue colour of the lithium ammonium disappears ; or finely powdered antimony may be suspended in liquid ammonia at −80°, and lithium added in successive small portions until a permanent blue coloration is obtained. Lithium antimonide, thus prepared, is a brownish-grey powder in a very fine state of division, having a density 3·2 at 17°. It fuses a little above 950°, and is therefore less fusible than either of its components. It reacts readily with chlorine, bromine, iodine, sulphur, selenium, or tellurium, and burns in oxygen with a violet flame. When heated with arsenic, it yields lithium arsenide. It is more easily decomposed by carbon than the corresponding arsenide. It decomposes hydrogen chloride, bromide, and iodide, the oxides of nitrogen, and sulphur dioxide with incandescence. At a red-heat, ammonia is decomposed, hydrogen being evolved. The antimonide dissolves in liquid ammonia, forming a reddish-brown liquid which contains **lithium amminotritantimonide**, Li_3Sb,NH_3. With water, the antimonide reacts at the ordinary temp., pure hydrogen being evolved, and antimony being formed as a black, flocculent mass ; with aq. acids, a little hydrogen antimonide is also formed. The chlorides, sulphides, and oxides of the metals are reduced by the antimonide.

J. L. Gay Lussac and L. J. Thénard obtained an alloy of sodium and antimony by fusing mixtures of the two elements ; E. Wiederhold, by heating a mixture of antimony trioxide and sodium in a covered crucible ; and G. S. Sérullas, by heating

2 D

a mixture of sodium tartrate, sodium carbonate, and charcoal for some hours.
H. Caron also made a sodium antimonide. E. B. Peck showed that the electrolytic
properties of soln. of antimony and sodium in liquid ammonia indicate that a
series of compounds is formed, that antimony forms the anion, and that more
than one atom of antimony is associated with each negative charge. C. H. Mathewson found the two metals unite quietly at the m.p. of sodium, but at higher temp.
the reaction is violent. The f.p. curve, Fig. 9, has two maxima, at 856° and 75 at.
per cent. of sodium, and 465° with 50 at. per cent. of sodium, corresponding
respectively with the trita- and mono-antimonides. The two eutectics are at
435° and 55·5 at. per cent. of sodium, and 400° and 39·4 at. per cent. of sodium.
E. Kordes studied the eutectic mixtures. J. A. Joannis obtained **sodium tritantimonide,** Na₃Sb, by the action of an excess of a soln. of sodium in liquid ammonia

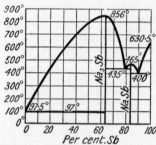

FIG 9.—Freezing-point Curves of
the Sodium-Antimony Alloys.

on antimony; and P. Lebeau, by the method
employed for the corresponding arsenide. The
conditions of equilibrium, studied by C. H. Mathewson, are shown in Fig. 9. The deep blue compound has the m.p. 856°. It is decomposed by
water giving off hydrogen; and inflames when
heated in air. C. H. Mathewson also obtained
sodium antimonide, NaSb, Fig. 9. The colour
is like that of antimony; its hardness is like
that of gypsum; and it is softer and less easily
oxidized than the tritantimonide. R. Kremann
and E. Preszfreund found that the e.m.f. curve
of the sodium-antimony alloys showed a break
corresponding with the tritantimonide; but the
potential of the compound could not be distinguished from that of the
monoantimonide.

J. L. Gay Lussac and L. J. Thénard found that antimony alloys with potassium,
and the reaction is accompanied by incandescence. E. Wiederhold, indeed, found
that when warmed, the two elements unite with explosive violence, and he obtained
alloys by heating a mixture of antimony trioxide and potassium in a covered
porcelain crucible; G. S. Sérullas, by heating a mixture of antimony, potassium
carbonate, and carbon; L. N. Vauquelin, by heating a mixture of antimony or
roasted antimony sulphide with potassium tartrate for 2 hrs. in a covered crucible
at a red-heat; by heating potassium antimonyl tartrate which has been roasted
in air until it appears incandescent, or the unroasted tartrate with one-tenth its
weight of potassium nitrate; and C. Löwig and E. Schweizer, by slowly heating
a mixture of antimony and potassium tartrate in a covered crucible. The greyish-

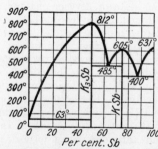

FIG. 10.—Freezing-point Curves of
the Potassium-Antimony Alloys.

white, soft, brittle, fine-grained, fusible alloys are
best preserved in stoppered bottles under the form
of naphtha. The alloys oxidize rapidly in air,
and when in powder disengage so much heat that
paper is ignited; under water, the alloys give
off much hydrogen, and if arsenic be present,
arsine. The alloys rich in potassium assume the
spheroidal state when placed on the surface of
mercury moistened with water. N. Parravano
found the m.p. diagram of the alloys to be
simple. The formation of the alloys is accompanied by the evolution of much heat, and with
the high potassium alloys, the union occurs
with almost explosive violence. There are
three eutectics at 485°, 400°, and 63°. No solid soln. are formed. The eutectic
K₃Sb–KSb at 485° solidifies with supercooling in the presence of the tritantimonide,
but not in the presence of the monantimonide. T. Seebeck studied the thermo-

electric properties of the potassium-antimony alloys. One of the two maxima corresponds with **potassium tritantimonide**, K_3Sb, which is yellowish-green and iridescent; melts at 812°, undergoes rapid change in air, and usually ignites spontaneously when broken in air. The other maximum corresponds with **potassium monantimonide**, KSb, which forms long, slender prisms of the colour of antimony; m.p. 605°; oxidizes in air less readily than the tritantimonide, and does not ignite spontaneously when struck with a hammer. G. Bredig and F. Haber made colloidal sodium and potassium antimonides by the submerged arc process.

The alloys of antimony and copper have been discussed in connection with the latter element—**3.** 21, 6 ; A. A. Baikoff's[2] diagram of the f.p. curves there indicated shows the existence of two compounds—the hemi- and trita-antimonides. The equilibrium diagram was studied by N. S. Kurnakoff and K. F. Beloglazoff, and K. Honda and T. Ishigaki. A. Mazzucchelli and L. Tonini prepared those alloys electrolytically ; H. Weiss studied the rate of formation of homogeneous alloys from the heterogeneous alloy ; and M. Chikashige studied the colour of the alloys. A silver-white mineral occurring massive near Mytilene, Asia Minor, was named *horsfordite*—after E. N. Horsford—and described by A. Laist and T. H. Norton. The analysis corresponds with **copper hexitantimonide**, Cu_6Sb— or possibly Cu_5Sb. The sp. gr. is 8·12—the value calculated from the mixture rule is 8·19. The hardness is 4–5. G. Drath and F. Sauerwald studied the surface tension of the alloys ; A. Mallock, the hardness ; and A. Bienias and F. Sauerwald, the viscosity. The mineral tarnishes easily in air. A. Brand described octahedral crystals containing the hexitantimonide apparently in isomorphous association with lead nickel sulphantimonide and copper lead sulphantimonide. The conditions of stability of **copper tritantimonide**, Cu_3Sb, are indicated in A. A. Baikoff's diagram. S. Stevanovic found octahedral crystals in a lead furnace associated with lead, iron, nickel, and cobalt ; and some rhombic crystals associated with antimonial lead. Copper tritantimonide is pale grey with a feeble greenish tinge. It is dimorphous. W. M. Jones and E. J. Evans studied the X-radiogram. When the compound at 600° is quenched in water, β-Cu_3Sb is obtained in a stable form at ordinary temp.; it melts at 687°, and at 407° it passes into α-Cu_3Sb with the development of 2·5 Cals. The sp. gr. of the α-form is 8·48. β-Cu_3Sb forms solid soln. with antimony and copper, but α-Cu_3Sb does not form solid soln. Of all the alloys of copper, this was found to be the hardest. E. Sauerwald found that the degree of dissociation at 900° is 50 per cent.; at 1000°, 46 per cent.; at 1100°, 41 per cent.; and at 1200°, 37 per cent. It is oxidized by water more rapidly than the hemiantimonide. P. Braesco studied the transformation point of the tritantimonide. F. Sauerwald said that at 900°, the tritantimonide is 50 per cent. dissociated ; at 1000°, 46 per cent.; at 1100°, 41 per cent.; and 1200°, 37 per cent. The conditions of formation of **copper hemiantimonide**, Cu_2Sb, are indicated in A.' A. Baikoff's diagram. The compound was prepared by P. Christofle, G. Kamensky, and E. J. Ball. A. Mazzucchelli and A. Vercillo made it by the action of a hydrochloric acid soln. of antimony trichloride on copper. The hard, violet or purple alloy is the *regula veneris* of the alchemists. P. Christofle gave 7·463 for the sp. gr.; G. Kamensky, 8·339 ; and W. Biltz and C. Haase gave 8·75 at 25°/4°. It has a fine-grained crystalline fracture. A. A. Baikoff found that the compound melts at 587° with decomposition into the tritantimonide, etc. W. Biltz and C. Haase give for the heat of formation $(3Cu,Sb)=2-3$ Cals. G. Kamensky measured the e.m.f. of the alloy. F. Sauerwald said that the degrees of dissociation of **copper dipentitantimonide,** Cu_5Sb_2, at 900°, 1000°, 1100°, and 1200° are respectively 53, 51, 46, and 36 per cent. H. Reimann gave 682° for the m.p.

E. J. Ball prepared a white alloy of copper and antimony with a conchoidal fracture. It was considered to be **copper tetritantimonide**, Cu_4Sb. The sp. gr. was 8·871. G. Kamensky found that it conducted electricity worse than antimony. E. Elsässer obtained **copper ditritantimonide**, Cu_3Sb_2, by melting the two elements under borax.

The fine-grained, brittle, violet alloy has a sp. gr. 8·00–8·05; P. Christofle gave 7·387. E. Elsässer found the alloy conducted the electric current without decomposition. R. Christofle, and F. C. Calvert and R. Johnson found copper monantimonide, CuSb, collected on the surface of the alloy in needle-like crystals of sp. gr. 7·119 according to the former, and 7·99 according to the latter. P. Christofle found copper diantimonide, CuSb₂, collected in rhombohedral crystals in druses in molten alloys. The sp. gr. is 6·825.

The alloys of silver and antimony were discussed in connection with the chemical properties of silver, 3. 22, 7. They were prepared by P. Berthier,[3] P. Christofle, C. R. A. Wright, and P. A. von Bonsdorff. H. Weiss studied the rate of formation of the homogeneous alloy from the heterogeneous state. H. Gautier, C. T. Heycock and F. H. Neville, and G. I. Petrenko studied the f.p. curve; W. Campbell, and G. Charpy, the microstructure; E. Maey, the sp. gr.; H. Weiss, the rate of diffusion or cementation of the two elements; A. M. Portevin, the structure of the eutectics; G. Sachs and F. Saeftel, the hardness; and also the mechanical properties of these alloys; E. Elsässer, and M. Hansen and G. Sachs, the electrical conductivity; N. A. Puschin, the electrochemical behaviour; R. Kremann and K. Bayer, the electrolysis of the alloys; E. van Aubel, and W. Haken, the thermoelectric force; G. Tammann, the potential; H. Rose, the action of ammonium chloride. G. I. Petrenko's f.p. curves there shown indicate the existence of only one compound, silver tritantimonide, Ag₃Sb. It was obtained by P. Christofle by melting together the calculated quantities of the two elements. P. A. von Bonsdorff said that this compound is produced when pyrargyrite is heated to redness in a current of hydrogen. N. W. Fischer prepared the tritantimonide when antimony is placed in a soln. of silver nitrate, and, as shown by T. Poleck and C. Thümmel, the antimonide is soon converted into a mixture of antimony trioxide and silver. J. F. Simon, and A. W. Hofmann said that the tritantimonide is precipitated when stibine is passed into a soln. of silver nitrate, but, added F. Jones, the precipitate is always mixed with some metallic silver; and, according to H. Reckleben, with a little antimony and antimonious acid. E. J. Weeks also obtained the tritantimonide by the action of stibine on a cold dil. soln. of silver nitrate; E. J. Weeks and W. V. Lloyd used a similar process and found that the product is not oxidized by the nitric acid formed if the action be conducted in an atm. of hydrogen. E. J. Weeks said that the properties of silver antimonide are remarkable by the fact that it is totally insoluble in both hot and cold, conc. and dil., sulphuric and hydrochloric acids. It is, however, soluble in boiling dil. nitric acid, giving off nitrous fumes, but is insoluble in the cold dil. acid.

The compound is represented in nature by a mineral called by B. G. Sage, and J. B. L. Romé de l'Isle, mine d'argent blanche antimoniale; by T. Bergman, as argentum nativum antimonio adunatum; by C. J. Selb, Spiesglanzsilber; and by L. A. Emmerling, Spiesglassilber. A. Breithaupt used a similar term. Terms corresponding with antimonial silver were used by J. F. L. Hausmann, R. J. Haüy, and C. C. von Leonhard. J. D. Dana gave stöchiolith as an old name for the mineral. F. S. Beudant called it discrase—from δυσκράσις, a bad alloy— and E. F. Glocker dyskrasit, that is, dyscrasite. The mineral occurs near Wolfach, Baden; Andreasberg, Harz; Casalla, Spain; Allemont and Isère, France; and in Norway, Chili, Bolivia, Mexico, Canada, New South Wales, etc. H. Wurtz called a variety from Thunder Bay, Lake Superior, Ontario, animikite—from an Indian word for thunder; and J. D. Dana, a variety from Chanarcillo, Chili, chanarcillite. Analysis were reported by C. J. Selb, M. H. Klaproth, C. F. Rammelsberg, T. Petersen, R. A. Abich, R. J. Haüy, I. Domeyko, and H. Wurtz. Some of the analyses agree with the tritantimonide, others with silver hexitantimonide, Ag₆Sb; and T. Petersen called the former stibiotriargentite; and the latter, stibiohexargentite; and he suggested that the observed results represent variable mixtures of these two minerals. Some analyses correspond with Ag₂S.Ag₄(Sb,As); and the analysis of chanercillite, with Ag₄(Sb,As)₃. T. Liebisch found a specimen from Andreasberg with the composition Ag_3Sb. G. Rose, and C. F. Rammelsberg assumed that the similarity of the crystalline form of the different varieties of the antimonial silver showed that they are isomorphous mixtures. G. A. Kenngott, and P. Groth argued that the similarity in the crystalline form of stromeyerite, chalcocite, etc., shows that dyscrasite is a mechanical mixture of silver *hemiantimonide*, Ag_2Sb, with other elements; and P. Groth later regarded dyscrasite as a mechanical mixture of the tritantimonide with silver or antimony. C. W. C. Fuchs discussed the synthesis of dyscrasite.

The mineral occurs massive, granular, and foliated; as well as in silver-white or tin-white crystals, sometimes tarnished yellow or black. J. B. L. Romé de l'Isle, and R. J. Haüy supposed the crystals of dyscrasite to be hexagonal, but J. F. L. Hausmann, C. C. von Leonhard, A. Breithaupt, F. Mohs, and F. Sandberger showed that they belong to the rhombic system; and J. F. L. Hausmann found the axial ratios to be $a : b : c = 0.5775 : 1 : 0.6718$. G. Smith made some observations on the crystals. The twinning about the (110)-plane produces stellate and pseudohexagonal forms. The (001)- and (011)-cleavages are distinct; and the (110)-cleavage, imperfect. The crystals were studied by T. Liebisch. C. F. Rammelsberg gave 9·611–10·027 for the sp. gr.; T. Petersen, 9·611–9·960; and H. Wurtz, 9·45. E. Maey studied the sp. vol. of the alloys. The hardness is between 3 and 4. L. Jordan and co-workers studied the hardness, elongation, and tensile strength of the silver-antimony alloys. M. de Hemptinne found a maximum in the thermal expansion curves of the alloys corresponding with 73 per cent. Ag when $a = 0.0_42459$. A. Sella found the sp. ht. to be 0·0558; and J. Joly said that dyscrasite sublimes at 520°. G. I. Petrenko found a break in the f.p. curve at 559°–560° corresponds with the tritantimonide which dissociates into a solid soln. and a molten liquid by a reversible reaction. Some observations on this subject were made by C. T. Heycock and F. H. Neville. A. de Gramont examined the spark spectrum. H. E. McKinstry observed no change when the mineral is exposed to the light of an electric arc. C. A. Kraus, and E. Elsässer studied the electrical conductivity; W. Haken, the thermoelectric properties; and N. A. Puschin, the electrochemical behaviour. F. Sandberger found dyscrasite altered to pyrargyrite, and native silver; and T. Liebisch found the mineral becomes richer in silver by weathering. Dyscrasite is not attacked by alkali-lye; but it is soluble in nitric acid, and it leaves antimony trioxide as a residue. T. Poleck and C. Thümmel found that a current of stibine passed into a conc. soln. of silver nitrate forms a yellow soln. with an acidic reaction: $SbH_3 + 6AgNO_3 = 3HNO_3 + Ag_3Sb.3AgNO_3$; the alleged **silver trinitratoantimonide**, $Ag_3Sb.3AgNO_3$, was not isolated because it is decomposed by water with the separation of silver tritantimonide.

As indicated in connection with the chemical properties of gold—**3.** 23, 6—the two elements form alloys. The alloys were prepared by C. Hatchett.[4] H. Weiss studied the formation of homogeneous alloys from the heterogeneous state. C. T. Heycock and F. H. Neville, and R. Vogel studied the f.p. of these alloys, and W. C. Roberts-Austen and F. Osmond, and L. Nowack, the structure. The equilibrium diagram, worked out by R. Vogel, shows the existence of an unstable **gold diantimonide**, $AuSb_2$, which is brittle and hard and which dissociates at about 460°. P. Christofle obtained what he regarded as **gold monantimonide**, AuSb, by fusing a mixture of the two elements in the correct proportions. The sp. gr. is 11·13. Nitric acid oxidizes the alloy superficially; hydrochloric acid has no action; and aqua regia dissolves it easily. There is no satisfactory evidence that the monantimonide is a chemical individual; similar remarks apply to the gold tritantimonide, Au_3Sb, obtained by F. Rössler in grey crystals, when the alloy is digested with a mixture of nitric and tartaric acids. The crystals soon turn red or bronze-colour. C. Hatchett made the ternary alloys Au–Cu–Sb. G. Tammann studied the potential of these alloys.

H. Caron[5] prepared alloys of *calcium and antimony* as indicated below.

J. D. Reidel obtained an antimonide by fusing an intimate mixture of sand, calcium, and antimony. L. Donsky examined the f.p. of alloys with up to 9 per cent. of calcium, and the results are illustrated by Fig. 11. The f.p. of antimony is lowered to the eutectic at 585° by the addition of 22 per cent. of calcium. Alloys containing a small proportion of calcium are less brittle than antimony ; the 9 per cent. calcium alloy is brittle and porous ; and alloys with up to 6 per cent. of calcium are not

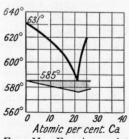

FIG. 11.—Freezing - point Curve of Calcium-Antimony Alloys.

acted on by hot water. O. Ruff and H. Hartmann studied the velocity of absorption of nitrogen by the alloy at 400°–520°. H. Caron prepared alloys of *strontium and antimony ;* and of *barium and antimony* by treating the alkaline earth chloride with a sodium-antimony alloy containing less than 33 per cent. of sodium. The alloys oxidize rapidly in air, and if more than 5 per cent. of the alkaline earth metal be present, they are decomposed by water, forming antimony and stibine. S. Parkinson [6] made magnesium-antimony alloys. J. D. Reidal obtained an antimonide by fusing an intimate mixture of sand, magnesium, and antimony. R. Kremann and co-workers studied the electrode potentials of these alloys. The alloys were indicated in connection with the chemical properties of magnesium—**4.** 29, 5. G. Grube's diagram, there indicated, shows that only one compound is formed, namely, **magnesium ditritantimonide,** Mg_3Sb_2. This substance appears in steel-grey needles, easy to pulverize. It melts at 961° ; and decomposes on exposure to air, forming a greyish-black powder. E. Becquerel studied the thermo-electric power of the alloys ; and E. Kordes, the eutectic mixtures. The alloys of zinc and antimony were discussed in connection with the chemical properties of zinc—**4.** 30, 6—and the f.p. curve of S. F. Schemtschuschny [7] is there shown. J. P. Cooke obtained large crystals of **zinc ditritantimonide,** Zn_3Sb_2, by slowly cooling an alloy of the correct proportions of the two elements. S. F. Schemt-schuschny, T. Takei, and K. Mönkmeyer also obtained this compound. C. T. Heycock and F. H. Neville, and T. Takei made observations on the f.p. of these alloys. J. P. Cooke gave 6·48 for the sp. gr. ; and C. F. Rammelsberg, 6·327. F. Sauerwald studied the sp. vol. S. F. Schemtschuschny gave 565° for the m.p. M. Kawakami gave for maximum heat of admixture at 700°, 681 cals. with 46·77 at. per cent. Sb. E. Elsässer examined the electrical conductivity—*vide* the general properties of these alloys. F. Sauerwald found that at 700°, 38 per cent. of the ditritantimonide is dissociated, and at 800°, 35 per cent. Rhombic crystals of **zinc monoantimonide,** ZnSb, were reported by J. P. Cooke, T. Takei, and K. Mönkmeyer to be formed by cooling an alloy of the two elements in the correct proportions. J. P. Cooke gave for the axial ratios $a : b : c = 0·9597 : 1 : 0·7610$. C. F. Rammelsberg gave 6·384 for the sp. gr., and K. Mönkmeyer, 6·41. The last-named gave 544° for the m.p., and S. F. Schemtschuschny showed that the alloy dissociates at 539°. T. Takei also found **zinc tetritatriantimonide,** Zn_4Sb_3, in alloys with between 35 and 45 per cent. of zinc. A. V. Saposhnikoff measured the hardness of these alloys ; G. Tammann and K. Dahl, the brittleness ; A. Eucken and G. Gehlhoff, the thermal and electrical conductivities ; K. Herrmann, the photoelectric effects ; G. Tammann, the potential. R. Kremann and J. Gmachl-Pammer examined the e.m.f. of the cadmium-antimony alloys ; W. Jenge, the electrode potentials ; F. Fischer and G. Pfleiderer, the thermo-electric power ; H. Endo, and K. Honda and T. Sone, the magnetic susceptibility ; A. Schleicher, the ternary system Cu–Cd–Sb. W. Heike found that silver mixed with zinc monanti-monide made the crystals good radio-detectors. A. Battelli, E. Becquerel, and J. Beattie studied the thermoelectric properties. The alloys of cadmium and antimony were discussed in connection with the chemical properties of the former element—**4.** 30, 6. The alloys were made by B. Wood. C. T. Heycock and

F. H. Neville made observations on the f.p. N. S. Kurnakoff and N. S. Konstantinoff's equilibrium diagram, there shown, indicates the existence of two compounds. W. Treitschke, and N. S. Kurnakoff and N. S. Konstantinoff obtained prismatic crystals and plates of **cadmium ditritantimonide,** Cd_3Sb_2, from alloys with the proper proportions of the two elements. The axial ratios of the rhombic crystals are $a:b:c=0.75909:1:0.96872$; and the crystals were also examined by W. Isküll. The alloy dissociates at about 400°. E. Maey found a break in the sp. vol. curve of the alloys corresponding with the compound. W. Biltz and C. Haase gave 7·03 for the sp. gr. at 25°/4°; and for the heat of formation $(3Cd,2Sb)=c.$ 4 Cals. Columnar crystals of **cadmium monantimonide,** CdSb, were obtained by W. Treitschke, and N. S. Kurnakoff and N. C. Konstantinoff from alloys with the correct proportions of the two elements. The m.p. is 455°. W. Biltz and C. Haase gave 6·95 for the sp. gr. at 25°/4°; and for the heat of formation $(Cd,Sb)=c.$ 3 Cals. G. Tammann, and W. Jenge studied the electrode potentials; A. Schulze, and M. Jakob and S. Erk, the heat conductivity; H. Endo, and K. Honda and T. Sone, the magnetic susceptibility.

C. H. Pfaff,[8] J. F. Simon, A. Partheil and E. Mannheim, and H. Rose said that mercury antimonide cannot be made by passing arsine through a soln. of mercuric chloride. J. G. Wallerius, G. Tammann and J. Hinnüber, and J. Nicklès observed that mercury does not act on antimony at ordinary temp., but if hot mercury be triturated with melted antimony for a short time, *antimony-amalgam* is formed; and a similar product is obtained if the two elements be triturated with a little hydrochloric acid. J. Schumann triturated moistened antimony powder with sodium amalgam. R. Böttger found that when sodium-amalgam is immersed in a sat. soln. of potassium antimonyl tartrate, hydrogen gas is evolved having a peculiar odour—possibly owing to the formation of stibine—and burning with a dazzling white flame; antimony, but not the amalgam, is formed. A. J. J. Vandevelde obtained the amalgam by the action of sodium-amalgam and antimony; but J. Schumann found that a poor yield of impure antimony-amalgam is produced by the action of a 6 per cent. zinc-amalgam on a conc. soln. of antimony trichloride. J. Schumann also prepared the amalgam by the electrolysis of a soln. of antimony trichloride for two days using a mercury cathode and a platinum anode. G. Tammann and J. Hinnüber used a similar process. G. Vortmann obtained the amalgam by electrolyzing a soln. of mercury and antimony oxides (2 : 1) in sodium sulphide. J. Regnauld also studied these alloys. Antimony amalgam appears as a steel-grey soft mass with a metallic lustre. J. Schumann found that a 56·6 per cent. amalgam had a sp. gr. 7·17, when the calculated value was 8·9. W. J. Humphreys measured the rate of diffusion of antimony in mercury. W. Ramsay measured the vap. press. of the amalgams and found the calculated mol. wt. of antimony to be 136·5 with 1·117 per cent. soln. of antimony in mercury, and 301·2 with 3·289 per cent. soln.— the theoretical value for Sb is 120·2. The amalgams are stable in air, but with long trituration in air, or shaking in water, black pulverulent antimony separates out. G. Vortmann said that antimony amalgam is soluble in nitric acid; and J. B. Baille and C. Féry, that when mixed with aluminium-amalgam, the antimony separates out, and the aluminium is oxidized. According to A. Partheil and E. Mannheim, when dried stibine is passed through a mixture of dry mercuric chloride and sand, contained in a rotating cylinder at ordinary temp., there is a slow reaction resulting in the formation of **mercuric ditritantimonide,** Hg_3Sb_2. This compound is a dark grey, heavy powder, which when pure is liable to decompose, but when mixed with sand is stable. Warm nitric acid converts it into mercuric nitrate and antimony tetroxide; and when heated in air, the antimony burns to the trioxide, and mercury sublimes. Ethyl iodide, at about 185°, converts the antimonide into *ethylstibonium iodomercuriate,* $Sb(C_2H_5)_4.I.HgI_2$, in white crystals melting at 93°–95°.

C. R. A. Wright[9] concluded that antimony forms no commercially valuable alloy with aluminium. He found that when antimony is dropped into molten aluminium it falls to the bottom and melts ; no combination takes place until the mixture is stirred, when part solidifies owing to the formation of an alloy with 81·6 per cent. of antimony of high m.p. Considering the m.p. of the component elements, it is remarkable that the alloy should melt over 1000° ; and H. Gautier observed that the m.p. of nearly all these alloys are above the m.p. of either constituent. H. Gautier gave for the f.p. of these alloys :

Al	0	1·13	5·42	8·40	10·28	14·66	18·65	25·0 per cent.
F.p.	632°	630°	855°	945°	1030°	1048°	1035°	1010°

Al	36·42	54·47	60	66	68·52	84·89	91·9	100 per cent.
F.p.	983°	950°	945°	950°	940°	800°	734°	650°

There is a maximum corresponding with 15·0 per cent. of aluminium and another with 68 per cent. The former corresponds with AlSb, and the other with $Al_{10}Sb$. W. Campbell and J. Mathews obtained analogous results but placed the first maximum nearer 18 per cent. of aluminium. D. A. Roche, G. G. Urazoff, and E. van Aubel agree that **aluminium monoantimonide,** AlSb, is formed ; but the equilibrium diagram has not yet been definitely established. K. Bornemann based a diagram

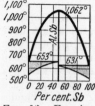

FIG. 12.—Freezing-point Curves of Aluminium - Antimony Alloys.

on these observations ; the results of G. G. Urazoff are summarized in Fig. 12. According to G. Tammann, the existence of the maximum with 68 per cent. of aluminium is doubtful. He showed that the speed of combination of the two elements is very slow. In preparing the AlSb-alloy, only one-tenth of the mixture had combined in 100 mins. at 715° ; and three-fourths in 30 mins. at 1100°. In cases like this, if two metals enter into combination very slowly, the melting-point curve may show a maximum at a point where no chemical compound exists, and its position will depend on how long the alloy has been heated. C. T. Heycock and F. H. Neville made some X-ray photographs ; and E. A. Owen and G. D. Preston found that the X-radiogram corresponded with face-centred cubic cells of antimony atoms with a side 6·126 A. intermeshed with an identical lattice of aluminium atoms. L. Pauling discussed the space-lattice. L. Guillet, and W. Campbell and J. Mathews studied the microstructure of these alloys ; alloys with 18 per cent. of aluminium are homogeneous ; but alloys with more or less aluminium consist of crystals of the monantimonide, decreasing in amount the more the composition of the alloy deviates from the one with 18 per cent. aluminium, and finally disappearing. E. van Aubel said that the monantimonide melts at 1078°–1080°, and has a sp. gr. 4·2176 at 16°/4°, when the value calculated from the mixture rule is 5·2246. Consequently when the compound is formed, there is a large increase in vol. which manifests itself at the moment of solidification. H. Pécheux gave 2·736 for the sp. gr. at 23° of the $SbAl_{30}$ alloy, 2·700 for $SbAl_{35}$, 2·662 for $SbAl_{38}$, and 2·598 for $SlAl_{40}$. F. Sauerwald studied the sp. vol. D. A. Roche

FIG. 13 —Magnetic Susceptibility of Al-Sb Alloys.

said that the alloy with 5 per cent. aluminium is malleable, and superior in elasticity, tenacity, and hardness to aluminium alone. The hardness and tenacity diminished as the proportion of antimony is increased to 10 per cent. when the alloy crystallizes in brilliant laminæ. C. R. A. Wright, and J. W. Richards added that all these alloys disintegrate in a few months. H. Schirmeister studied the tensile strength and elongation. H. Pécheux found that the alloys are stable in the air at the temp. of fusion, bluish-grey in colour, do not decompose water in the cold, but the alloy $SbAl_{30}$ decomposes water at 100° ; they are attacked by conc., hot sulphuric acid, by cold dil. sulphuric acid, by cold, conc. nitric or hydrochloric acid or aqua regia ; and by cold, conc. potassium hydroxide soln. K. Honda studied the magnetic susceptibility, Fig. 13; and R. Kremann and J. Dellacher, the electrolysis of the alloys. The observations of E. Carstanjen [10] on the thallium-antimony alloys, of M. Chikashige, and R. S. Williams on the f.p. curves, and of R. Kremann and A. Lobinger, and E. Bekier on the chemical properties, have been indicated in connection with the chemical properties of thallium—**5**. 36, 4. There is evidence on the f.p. curve of the formation of an unstable **thallium tritantimonide,** Tl_3Sb, at 225°—Fig. 4, **5**. 36, 4. T. Barth obtained no evidence of the existence of this compound in his study of the X-radiograms of these alloys; but he found that alloys with 30 molar per cent. of antimony have a second type of crystal—presumably thallium antimonide, $TlSb$. The side of the cubic lattice has $a = 3\cdot86 \times 10^{-8}$ cm. T. Barth gave 10·66, D. Omodei 10·143 for the sp. gr. of a 20 per cent. antimony alloy at the m.p. 194°, and 9·915 for the sp. gr. of the liquid at the same temp. He also found the cubic expansion coeff. to be 0·000227. G. Winogoroff and G. Petrenko measured the electrode potentials of the alloys. For the alloys of *cerium and antimony, vide* **5**. 38, 10; and of *silicon and antimony, vide* **6**. 40, 12. For **tin monantimonide,** $SnSb$, and **tin ditritantimonide,** Sn_3Sb_2, see the chemical properties of tin, **7**. 46, 5. R. A. Morgan studied the ternary system : Pb–Cu–Sb ; and W. Bonsack, and L. Losana, the systems : Sn–Cu–Sb, and Sn–Cu–Sb–Pb. For

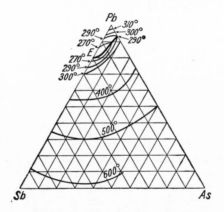

FIG. 14.—Freezing-point Curves of the
Ternary System : Pb-As-Sb

the **lead antimonides,** see the chemical properties of lead—**7**. 47, 5. R. Kremann and A. Tröster studied the electrolysis of these alloys ; Y. Matuyama, the electrical conductivity ; E. Kordes, the eutectic ; and E. E. Schumacker and G. M. Bouton, the solubility of antimony in lead. R. A. Morgen and co-workers studied the effect of copper, bismuth, and tin on the Pb–Sb alloys. E. Abel and O. Redlich's f.p. curves of the ternary system : Pb–As–Sb, are summarized in Fig. 14. The eutectic line is indicated by E. For **nitrogen antimonide,** *vide* antimony nitride, **8**. 49, 12 ; for **phosphorus antimonide,** see antimony phosphide, **8**. 50, 12 ; and for **arsenic antimonide,** see antimony arsenide, **9**. 51, 10. C. M. Marx,[11] and F. Rudberg showed that antimony and bismuth melt and form brittle alloys in all proportions. No *bismuth antimonide* appears to be formed. A. Mazzucchelli and L. Tonini prepared these alloys electrolytically ; but A. Mazzucchelli and A. Vercillo could not make them by the action of hydrochloric acid soln. of the trichlorides on bismuth or antimony respectively. The f.p. curves were studied by H. Gautier, M. Cook, C. T. Heycock and F. H. Neville, B. Otani, and K. Hüttner and G. Tammann. The results are shown in Fig. 15. From molten masses rich in antimony, crystals rich in antimony first separate ; the main amount of this molten mass solidifies about 50° below the temp. at which crystallization begins. Molten masses which contain less than 70 per cent. of antimony do not crystallize until the m.p. of bismuth is reached, and finally bismuth itself separates in almost a pure state. When alloys of antimony and bismuth are allowed to cool very slowly, the structure of the solid which separates is homogeneous ; it is very probable that the two metals are miscible in all proportions. In molten masses containing antimony up to 60 per cent., the temp. at the beginning of the crystallization remains constant for a time. G. Charpy, and W. Campbell studied the structure of these alloys. A. Matthiessen and M. Holzmann found that the Sb : Bi=2 : 1-alloy has a sp. gr. 7·864 at 9·7° ; 1 : 1, 8·392 at 11·0° ; 1 : 2, 8·886 at 14·0° ; 1 : 4, 9·227 at 12·1° ; 1 : 6, 9·434 at 9·4°. The values calculated from the mixture rule are rather less than this. E. Maey, and F. C. Calvert and R. Johnson studied the sp. gr., and the thermal and electrical conductivities ; G. Gehlhoff and F. Naumaier, and A. Schulze the thermal conductivity—Fig. 16 ; W. Haken, K. Bädeker, Y. Matuyama, and A. Matthiessen, the electrical conductivities—Fig. 17, and the temp. coeff. of the resistance—Fig. 18.

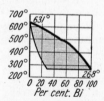

FIG. 15.—Freezing-point Curve of Bismuth - Antimony Alloys.

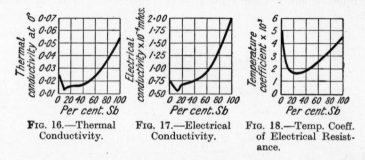

FIG. 16.—Thermal Conductivity.

FIG. 17.—Electrical Conductivity.

FIG. 18.—Temp. Coeff. of Electrical Resistance.

The curve is characteristic of alloys which are solid soln. ; J. P. Joule, C. Hutchins, E. Becquerel, A. Matthiessen, W. Rollmann, W. Haken, T. Seebeck, A. Sundell, and A. Battelli, the thermoelectric properties—Fig. 20 ; N. A. Puschin, and M. Herschkowitsch, the e.m.f. ; R. Kremann and A. Tröster, the electrolysis of the alloys ; H. Endo, J. Beattie, and K. Honda and T. Sone, the magnetic susceptibility—Fig. 21, the curve is linear until the alloy contains about 90 per cent.

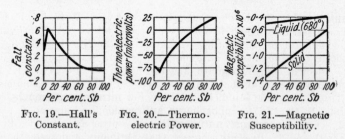

FIG. 19.—Hall's Constant.

FIG. 20.—Thermo-electric Power.

FIG. 21.—Magnetic Susceptibility.

of antimony when the proportionality fails ; and A. W. Smith, Hall's constant—Fig. 19, the curve is related with that for the thermoelectric power. N. A. Puschin, and E. Bekier studied the potential of the bismuth-antimony alloys ; N. Parravano and E. Viviani, the Bi–Sb–Cu alloys. C. R. A. Wright, and R. Kremann and co-workers studied the ternary Bi–Sb–Zn alloys.

R. S. Williams [12] obtained the curves, Fig. 22, for the f.p. of alloys of chromium and antimony. Two compounds are formed : **chromium diantimonide,** $CrSb_2$, is stable below its m.p. 675°, and above that temp. it decomposes. It is silver-white in colour, very brittle, and is slightly acted upon by dil. acids. The other compound, **chromium monantimonide,** CrSb, melts at 1125°; it is dark-grey, very brittle, and readily attacked by acids. There are two series of mixed crystals. The components of one series are the monantimonide and chromium, and it extends from

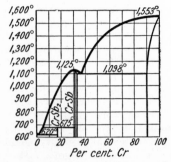

FIG. 22.—Freezing-point Curves of the Chromium-Antimony Alloys.

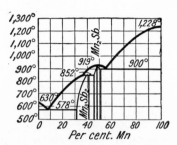

FIG. 23.—Freezing-point Curves of Manganese-Antimony Alloys.

50 to 52·5 at. per cent. of chromium ; the other series extends from 95 to 100 at. per cent. of chromium and its components are chromium and antimony. W. F. de Jong and H. W. V. Willems found that the X-radiogram agrees with a hexagonal lattice with $a=4·14$ A., and $c=5·51$ A. ; and a sp. gr. of 7·08 ; I. Oftedal gave $a=4·107$ A., $c=5·468$ A., and $a:c=1·331$. J. J. and F. de Elhuyar, and F. A. Bernoulli prepared a *tungsten-antimony* alloy. A. Colani said that when antimony is heated with uranous chloride, a binary compound of *uranium and antimony* is formed.

L. Troost and P. Hautefeuille obtained an alloy of manganese and antimony by heating manganese carbide with antimony. R. S. Williams found that antimony and manganese form two compounds—**manganese hemiantimonide,** Mn_2Sb, melting at 919°, and **manganese ditritantimonide,** Mn_3Sb_2, melting at 852°, and stable below its m.p., but not above. There are two series of mixed crystals, one of which, having the components antimony and the ditritantimonide, extends from 65 to 69 at. per cent. of manganese ; and the other series having the components antimony, manganese, and the hemiantimonide, extends from 65 to 69 at. per cent. of manganese. Both antimonides are silver-grey, and the hemiantimonide is less brittle than its components. Both alloys are magnetic—like F. Heusler's non-ferrous magnetic alloys. The hemiantimonide loses its magnetic permeability at 250°–260° ; and the ditritantimonide, at 320°–330°. E. Wedekind found the alloys to be less magnetic than manganese boride. P. Martin measured the magnetic-optical effect. I. Oftedal found that Mn_3Sb_2 has a lattice of the NiAs-type with $a=4·131$ A., $c=5·744$ A., and $a:c=1:390$. E. Wedekind prepared the hemianti-monide, and also an alloy which he regarded as **manganese monantimonide,** MnSb, by the thermite process, and removing the excess of manganese by dil. hydrochloric acid, and the excess of antimony by heating in a current of chlorine. S. Hilpert and T. Dieckmann also made the monantimonide by heating manganese amalgam with the necessary amount of antimony in an atm. of hydrogen, and distilling off the mercury. W. F. de Jong and H. W. V. Willems found that the X-radiogram of the monantimonide agrees with a hexagonal lattice with $a=4·14$ A., and $c=5·90$ A. ; and a sp. gr. 6·71. I. Oftedal gave $a=4·120$ A., $c=5·784$ A., and $a:c=1:1·404$. The monoantimonide can dissolve considerable amounts of manganese and of antimony. E. Wedekind found that the black, crystalline powder had a sp. gr. 5·6 at 17° ; it was soluble in aqua regia ; and had stronger magnetic qualities than the boride. S. Hilpert and T. Dieckmann said that it is soluble in hot hydro-chloric acid and in nitric acid. It burns in air giving non-magnetic products.

It loses its magnetic properties at 320°–330°. E. Wedekind found that the magnetic permeability is diminished by the presence of impurities.

An alloy of antimony and iron is the *regulus antimonii martialis* of the alchemists. According to A. F. Gehlen,[13] iron and antimony readily unite by fusion, producing hard, brittle, white, easily fusible alloys, of lower sp. gr. than the value calculated by the mixture rule. G. Tammann and E. Schaarwächter found that the reaction begins at about 725°. P. Berthier, C. F. Rammelsberg, J. Percy, and C. J. B. Karsten obtained alloys of these two elements. The last-named said that the addition of one per cent. of antimony to a charge of cast-iron, being converted into malleable iron in the charcoal hearth, acts far more injuriously than tin on the metal. J. Percy said that it acts far more injuriously on the magnetic properties of iron than any other metal. An alloy of antimony with twice its weight of iron produces sparks when filed. According to P. Berthier, alloys with more than 70·5 per cent. of antimony lose antimony by volatilization at a white-heat, leaving a residuum of **iron monantimonide**, FeSb. W. F. de Jong and H. W. V. Willems said that iron monantimonide is a definite entity ignored in phase diagrams. X-radiograms of the crystals agree with a hexagonal lattice with $a=4·06$ A., and $c=5·13$ A.; and a sp. gr. 8·05. I. Oftedal gave $a=4·064$ A., $c=5·130$ A., and $a:c=1:1·262$. P. Christofle also prepared the monantimonide and reported the formation of others: *iron tritantimonide*, Fe_3Sb, as a grey, hard regulus which gives sparks when filed; **iron ditritantimonide**, Fe_3Sb_2, as a black, brittle alloy. N. S. Kurnakoff and N. S. Konstantinoff showed that this compound melts at 1014°, Fig. 22. I. Oftedal found the space-lattice is of the NiAs-type with $a=4·123$ A., $c=5·168$ A., and $a:c=1:1·253$. P. Christofle obtained *iron tetratritantimonide*, Fe_3Sb_4, as a crystalline mass;

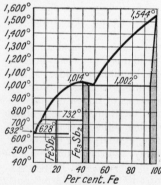

FIG. 24.—Freezing-point Curves of Iron-Antimony Alloys.

and **iron diantimonide**, $FeSb_2$, as a hard, grey mass with a crystalline fracture; it gives no sparks when filed. N. S. Kurnakoff and W. S. Konstantinoff obtained the f.p. curve shown in Fig. 24. They found that the f.p. curve has four branches representing four solid phases, there being eutectic points at 628° and 1·5 per cent. iron and 1002° and 49·5 per cent. iron respectively, and a transition point at 732° and 7·0 per cent. iron. The conc. of solid soln. of antimony in iron never exceeds 5 per cent. At 1014° the compound Sb_2Fe_3 separates, and forms solid soln. in iron up to the composition 46·0 per cent. The compound $FeSb_2$ at its m.p. (732°) decomposes partly, thus: $3FeSb_2 \rightleftharpoons Fe_3Sb_2+4Sb$.

In general, the antimonides of the eighth group are somewhat inert chemically, and have a tendency to form unstable compounds. In the case of the antimonides of iron and nickel, the solid substances which have escaped reaction in the liquid state retain their composition when further cooled rapidly; thus, the diantimonide, when cooled at the rate of 1000–300° in one or two hours, shows a microstructure composed of three elements, and only on heating an alloy of this composition for 30 hrs. at a temp. of 710° could the homogeneous diantimonide be obtained. The raw antimony obtained in the commercial extraction of antimony contains diantimonide in well-formed, rhombic crystals. Compounds such as FeSAs belong to the same type, the arsenic and sulphur being united directly with one another, and the structural formulæ thus obtained are in complete accord with those deduced by other methods. The rhombic prismatic crystals have the axial ratios $a:b:c=0·5490:1:1·1237$; W. Isküll gave $0·5490:1:1·1212$; the (110)-cleavage is incomplete. The hardness is 3. The crystals are isomorphous with löllingite and safflorite. The constitution is possibly $Fe<^{Sb}_{Sb}$.

P. Goerens and K. Ellingen found that antimony greatly lowers the solubility of carbon in iron, whilst tin has less effect. In an alloy containing 3·5 per cent. carbon, antimony lowers the initial f.p. of the austenite, and also the eutectic temp., until the latter coincide at 1090° and 5 per cent. antimony. The ternary eutectic, composed of austenite, cementite, and the hemitriantimonide, solidifies at 950°. In an alloy containing 3 per cent. carbon, the austenite curve meets that of the binary eutectic at 1070° and about 14 per cent. antimony. The freezing-point surface is thus made up of three surfaces, corresponding with the separation of austenite (containing some antimony in solid soln.), cementite, and antimonide. The formation of pearlite at 690° is unaffected by the presence of antimony. A. Portevin said that the temp. at which pearlite is formed in alloys of iron and carbon is not appreciably altered by the presence of 1–9 per cent. of antimony. The antimony is retained in solid soln. up to 6·5 per cent.; richer alloys show distinct crystals of an antimonide. E. Maey, and J. Laborde measured the sp. gr.; J. Laborde, and E. van Aubel, the sp. ht. of the alloys; J. Seebeck, and E. Becquerel, the thermoelectric power; and P. Weiss, and L. Cailletet, the magnetic qualities. G. Tammann and K. Dahl studied the brittleness of the FeSb, and Fe₂Sb₃ alloys. G. S. Sérullas reported a **potassium iron antimonide** is formed as a brittle alloy when a mixture of equal parts of iron turnings, powdered antimony, and potassium tartrate is heated in a covered crucible to a high temp.

A. F. Gehlen [14] said that when a powdered mixture of cobalt and antimony (1 : 2) is heated, the two elements unite with incandescence, forming an iron-grey mass which acquires metallic lustre by press. C. F. Rammelsberg applied the term Spieses to some furnace-products with the composition $(Cu,Fe,Co)_5Sb_2$. F. Ducelliez observed that cobalt and antimony furnish three classes of alloys which can be made by the direct union of the elements at 500° in a current of hydrogen. (i) Magnetic alloys containing less than 67·04 per cent. antimony. When heated with antimony trichloride at 800°, or when treated with sulphuric acid, these lose their magnetic properties, and leave a residue of the monoantimonide. (ii) Alloys containing 64·04–80·27 per cent. of antimony, which decompose readily on heating, and form the monoantimonide when heated at 1200° in hydrogen. Substitution of antimony trichloride for hydrogen gives the same compound together with antimony and cobalt chloride. (iii) Alloys containing more than 80·27 per cent. antimony, which, on treatment with nitric acid followed by hydrogen chloride, give the diantimonide. N. S. Kurnakoff and N. I. Podkapajeff, and K. Lewkonja studied the f.p. diagram. K. Lewkonja's curve is shown in Fig. 25. While the two elements are completely miscible in the liquid state, two compounds are formed during the freezing of the alloys. The one, **cobalt monantimonide,** CoSb, melts at 1191°—N. S. Kurnakoff and N. I. Podkapajeff gave 1237°, and F. Ducelliez, about 1200°. Besides being formed by the direct union of the elements, F. Ducelliez

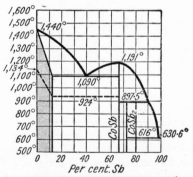

FIG. 25.—Freezing-point Curves of Cobalt-Antimony Alloys.

found that the monantimonide is produced when cobalt at 700°–1200° is submitted to the action of the vapour of antimony trichloride; at 1200°, the antimony trichloride converts cobalt into a magnetic alloy containing less antimony than the monantimonide, but if the product be treated with sulphuric acid, it loses its magnetic qualities and leaves the monantimonide as a residue. W. F. de Jong and H. W. V. Willems found that the X-radiogram agrees with a hexagonal lattice with $a=3·91$ A., and $c=5·30$; and sp. gr. 8·72. I. Oftedal gave $a=3·866$ A., $c=5·188$ A., and $a:c=1:1·342$. F. Ducelliez observed that

cobalt monantimonide is a crystalline non-magnetic powder of sp. gr. 8·12 at 0°.
It undergoes slight oxidation in air, and burns readily in oxygen ; hydrogen chloride
has little action on it, but hot conc. sulphuric acid dissolves it rapidly. At 700°–1250°
it attacks antimony trichloride, forming antimony and cobalt chloride ; the composition of the residual substance, however, remains unaltered. K. Lewkonja prepared
cobalt diantimonide, $CoSb_2$, by the direct union of its elements, and F. Ducelliez,
by treating alloys with over 80·27 per cent. of antimony as indicated above. The
grey crystalline powder has a sp. gr. 7·76 at 0°, and melts about 700°. K. Lewkonja found that the diantimonide melts with decomposition at 879·5°—N. S. Kurnakoff and N. I. Podkapajeff gave 888°. The first eutectic, Fig. 24, is at 1090°, and
the last one at 616°. Antimony is soluble to the extent of 12·5 per cent. in cobalt.
A. M. Portevin studied the structure of the eutectics. The magnetic transformation
temp. from 1134° to 924° for alloys with up to 67 per cent. of antimony represents
the temp. at which the alloys lose their magnetic permeability.

According to A. F. Gehlen,[15] if a powdered mixture of nickel and antimony
(1 : 2) be heated, a dark grey metallic powder is formed. The combination is
attended by the emission of a red light.

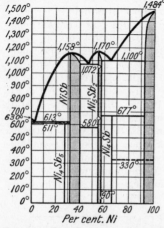

F. Rössler obtained needle-like crystals when an
alloy of the two elements is digested with a
mixture of nitric and tartaric acids. According
to K. Losseff, the freezing-point curve, Fig. 26,
shows two maxima at 1158° and 32·83 per cent.
and 1170° and 55 per cent. by weight of nickel
respectively, corresponding with the monantimonide and the dipentitantimonide, and there
are three eutectic points at 2 to 3, 47·6, and 66·1
per cent. by weight of nickel respectively. From
32·8 to 40 per cent., 55 to 57 per cent. and 92·5
to 100 per cent. of nickel, mixed crystals
separate out. In the alloys with from 3 to 32·8
per cent. of nickel, microscopic observation
shows a third crystalline form in addition to the
monantimonide and the eutectic mixture ; there

Fig. 26.—Freezing-point Curve of
Nickel-Antimony Alloys.

are indications that these crystals represent the
pentatetritantimonide, but conclusive evidence
on this point could not be obtained. From 57
to 92·5 per cent. of nickel, the two series of sat. mixed crystals existing within
these limits interact when the temp. falls to 677° with formation of the tetritantimonide : this reaction proceeds in the reverse direction at higher temp. The
transition temp.—namely, 90° and 330°—at which the magnetic alloys lose their
permeability are shown in the diagram. The subject was studied by W. Guertler
and H. Schack.

The evidence for the existence of **nickel pentatetritantimonide,** Ni_4Sb_5, is not
conclusive, on account of experimental difficulties. It decomposes on melting into
the monantimonide and a liquid. P. Christofle reported **nickel ditritantimonide,**
Ni_3Sb_2, to be formed by melting nickel powder with the required proportion of
antimony. The violet product does not lose antimony when strongly heated in an
indifferent gas, but it loses antimony when heated in air ; it is soluble in nitric acid,
but insoluble in hydrochloric acid. There is no sign of this product on the f.p.
diagram, Fig. 25. N. A. Puschin studied the e.m.f. of these alloys ; and also
N. S. Kurnakoff and N. S. Podkopajeff, and of K. Losseff. There are three very well-
defined nickel antimonides indicated on the thermal diagram, and their existence is
confirmed by microscopic observation of polished sections of the alloys. T. Seebeck
studied the thermoelectric power of the alloys. Alloys containing 57–92·5 per
cent. of nickel contain **nickel tetritantimonide,** Ni_4Sb. It decomposes at 677°
into two solid soln. with about 57 and 92·5 per cent. of nickel respectively. The

alloy becomes non-magnetic at 90°. The maximum in the f.p. curve at 1170° represents the m.p. of **nickel pentitadiantimonide**, Ni_5Sb_2. This alloy is a grey colour, and not so hard as the monantimonide, but it behaves towards reagents like that alloy. There is a transition temp. at 580°. The conditions for the formation of **nickel monantimonide**, NiSb, are shown in Fig. 26. This compound was prepared by F. Stromeyer by fusing together eq. proportions of the two elements. Light and heat are emitted during the combination. E. Vigouroux made the monantimonide by the action of antimony trichloride on nickel powder at 800°; by the action of antimony vapour on pulverized nickel in hydrogen at 1300°; and by heating a powdered mixture of the two elements in hydrogen at 1200°. It was also made by P. Christofle, and by F. Stromeyer and J. F. L. Hausmann. W. Herz gave $4·91 \times 10^{12}$ for the vibration frequency of NiSb.

Nickel antimonide is represented in nature by the *antimonial nickel* obtained from Andreasberg by F. Stromeyer and J. F. L. Hausmann; E. J. Chapman called it *hartmannite*, and W. Haidinger, **breithauptite**—after A. Breithaupt. It has also been observed as a furnace-product by J. F. L. Hausmann, F. Sandberger, and A. Brand, although F. Fouqué and A. Michel-Lévy thought that natural breithauptite might be different from the furnace-product. A. Brand, however, showed that the two are identical. The mineral has been also found in Italy, France, and in Connecticut, U.S.A. Analyses were reported by F. Stromeyer, L. N. Vauquelin, P. Berthier, C. F. Rammelsberg, E. Mattirolo, F. Pisani, and A. Brand. Arsenic is sometimes present—*vide* aarite, or arite. The native copper-red, or violet-blue crystals are tabular, the artificial crystals are prismatic. The mineral may also occur massive, and in arborescent, and disseminated forms. The crystals belong to the hexagonal system; A. Breithaupt gave for the axial ratio $a : c = 1 : 0·8586$; and K. Busz, $1 : 1·2940$. They have been described by A. des Cloizeaux. W. F. de Jong and co-workers' study of the X-radiogram of breithauptite showed that it has the same structure as niccolite, with $a = 3·938$ A. and $c = 5·138$ A. The smallest distance between the Ni–Sb atoms is 2·61 A. I. Oftedal found the X-radiogram corresponded with a space-lattice of the NiAs-type, having $a = 3·907$ A., $c = 5·133$ A., and $a : c = 1 : 1·314$. Twinning has been observed about the $(10\bar{1}1)$-plane. The basal cleavage is distinct. A. Breithaupt gave 7·541 for the sp. gr.; A. des Cloizeaux, 8·42; and F. Pisani, 7·19. E. Vigouroux gave 7·70 at 0° for the artificial crystals. The hardness of the mineral is 5. K. Losseff gave 1158° for the m.p. E. Vigouroux said that the compound melts at 1100° and begins to decompose at 1400°. J. Joly found that sublimation occurs at 520° in air. A. de Gramont studied the spark spectrum. F. Beijerinck found the mineral is a conductor of electricity; while T. W. Case said that the resistance is greater than a megohm and is not affected appreciably by light. The monantimonide was found by K. Losseff to be easily soluble in nitric acid; but it is not attacked by sulphuric and hydrochloric acids, or by strong bases. E. Vigouroux said that the monantimonide is vigorously acted on by chlorine and by oxygen when heated to dull redness. It is not affected by conc. hydrochloric acid, but is decomposed by warm conc. sulphuric acid and by warm nitric acid. It is scarcely affected even by fused alkalis. E. Vigouroux also discussed the Ni–Sn–Sb alloys.

An alloy of platinum and antimony was made by A. F. Gehlen [16] by heating a powdered mixture (1 : 2) of the two elements; the combination is attended by vivid incandescence, and when the temp. is further raised, it furnishes a steel-grey, brittle, fine-grained alloy; and R. W. Fox found that at a still higher temp., the antimony is almost wholly expelled, leaving malleable platinum. The alloys were also made by J. Murray, W. Lewis, P. Christofle, H. Landolt, and F. Rössler. Those rich in antimony are inclined to liquation; and F. Rössler found that the presence of platinum makes the crystals of antimony smaller. C. Barus found the sp. electrical resistance of an alloy of sp. gr. 20·75 at 0° to be 29·5 ohms, with the temp. coeff. 0·00111 between 0° and 100°, and 0·00109 between 0° and 357°. The alloys readily fuse before the blowpipe, and K. Friedrich and A. Leroux represented their observations on the f.p. of the alloys by Fig. 27. The f.p. of antimony is not appreciably lowered by the addition of platinum. The f.p. curve rises to a maximum at 1226° and 44·7 per cent. Pt, corresponding with **platinum diantimonide,** PtSb₂. A second compound, **platinum monantimonide,** probably PtSb, is formed at 1045°. The curve then falls to a eutectic point at 685° and 77 per cent. Pt, and rises to the

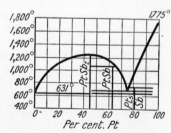

FIG. 27.—Freezing-point Curve of Platinum-Antimony Alloys.

f.p. of platinum. Two reactions take place in the solid state, the monantimonide being transformed into one richer in antimony, and a third compound, **platinum dipentitantimonide,** Pt₅Sb₂, being formed from alloys rich in platinum at 644°, the eutectic structure disappearing when the alloys are maintained for some hours at this temp. The diantimonide was made by F. Rössler by melting a mixture of antimony and platinum (40 : 1) under glass, and digesting the regulus for a long time with a mixture of nitric and tartaric acids ; J. F. Simon reported it to be formed by the action of stibine on a soln. of platinic chloride ; according to P. Christofle, the admixed platinous chloride and antimony can be removed by soln. of potassium cyanide, and potassium sulphide. R. Bartels found very little diantimonide is formed in this reaction, but he obtained it from an acid soln. of Na₂Pt(SO₂)₂. The cubic or octahedral crystals are hard, and brittle. The m.p. is 631°. P. Christofle said that the antimony can be all removed by chlorine at a red-heat. H. Landolt said that boiling aqua regia does not remove all the antimony from the platinum antimony alloys. The alloy is insoluble in nitric and hydrochloric acids, and is soluble in aqua regia. J. Murray made alloys of Pt–Sb–Sr ; Pt–Sb–Be ; Pt–Sb–Al ; and Pt–Sb–Si.

N. W. Fischer [17] found that when a mixture of antimony and palladium is heated, the two elements unite with the evolution of light and heat, and the formation of a brittle alloy. F. Rössler also prepared

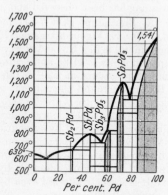

FIG. 28.—Freezing-point Curves of the Palladium-Antimony Alloys.

some of these alloys. W. Sander prepared alloys by heating mixtures of the two elements in nitrogen in porcelain tubes ; and he measured the f.p. of the alloys. His results are summarized in Fig. 28. He found that undercooling could occur to the extent of 40°–50°. The f.p. curve has two maxima at 805° and 1220°, corresponding respectively with **palladium monantimonide,** PdSb, and **palladium tritantimonide,** Pd₃Sb. There are also breaks in the curves at 680° and 839° due to **palladium diantimonide,** PdSb₂, and **palladium tripentitantimonide,** Pd₅Sb₃, respectively. Palladium retains antimony in solid soln. up to 15 per cent., and the tritantimonide also forms solid soln. between 68·5 and 72·5 per cent. Pd, and the tripentitantimonide

forms solid soln. between 57·5 and 61·5 per cent. Pd. Between 57·5 and 65 per cent. a thermal arrest occurs at 524°–532°, and is accompanied by a change from a polyhedral to a lamellar structure. The change is attributed to a transformation of the tripentitantimonide. The triantimonide, which also undergoes a transformation at 1070°, is less readily attacked by aqua regia than the palladium solid soln. The alloys are brittle up to 85 per cent. Pd, the maximum brittleness occurring at the composition of the triantimonide.

REFERENCES.

¹ J. L. Gay Lussac and L. J. Thénard, *Recherches physicochimiques*, Paris, 1. 219, 1811 ; E. Wiederhold, *Pogg. Ann.*, 122. 488, 1864; T. Seebeck, *ib.*, 6. 148, 1826 ; *Sitzber. Akad. Berlin*, 265, 1823 ; L. N. Vauquelin, *Ann. Chim. Phys.*, (2), 7. 32, 1818 ; G. S. Sérullas, *ib.*, (2), 18. 217, 1821 ; (2), 21. 198, 1822 ; *Journ. Phys.*, 91. 123, 1820 ; 93. 115, 1921 ; G. Bredig and F. Haber, *Ber.*, 31. 2741, 1898 ; E. Kordes, *Zeit. Chem., anorg.* 154. 97, 1926 ; 168. 177, 1927 ; C. Löwig and E. Schweizer, *Mitt. Naturf. Ges. Zürich*, 2. 97, 1852; *Liebig's Ann.*, 75. 316, 1850; P. Lebeau, *Bull. Soc. Chim.*, (3), 27. 254, 256, 1902 ; *Compt. Rend.*, 134. 231, 284, 1902; J. A. Joannis, *ib.*, 114. 587, 1892 ; H. Caron, *ib.*, 48. 440, 1859 ; C. H. Mathewson, *Zeit. anorg. Chem.*, 50. 192, 1906 ; E. B. Peck, *Journ. Amer. Chem. Soc.*, 40. 335, 1918 ; R. Kremann and E. Preszfreud, *Zeit. Metallkunde*, 13. 19, 1921 ; N. Parravano, *Gazz. Chim. Ital.*, 45. i, 485, 1915.

² A. Laist and T. H. Norton, *Amer. Chem. Journ.*, 10. 60, 1888 ; A. Brand, *Zeit. Kryst.*, 17. 264, 1889 ; S. Stevanovic, *ib.*, 40. 321, 1905 ; P. Christofle, *Recherches sur les combinaisons de l'antimoine avec les différentes métaux*, Göttingen, 16, 1863 ; A. A. Baikoff, *Journ. Russ. Phys. Chem. Soc.*, 36. 111, 1904 ; H. Reimann, *Zeit. Metallkunde*, 12. 321, 1920 ; E. Maey, *Zeit. phys. Chem.*, 50. 214, 1905 ; N. S. Kurnakoff and K. F. Beloglazoff, *Ann. Inst. Phys. Chem. Leningrad*, 2. 490, 1924 ; E. J. Ball, *Journ. Chem. Soc.*, 53. 167, 1888 ; G. Tammann and K. Dahl, *Zeit. anorg. Chem.*, 123. 104, 1923 ; G. Tammann, *ib.*, 118. 93, 1921 ; W. Biltz and C. Haase, *ib.*, 129. 141, 1923 ; M. Chikashige, *ib.*, 154. 333, 1926 ; G. Drath and F. Sauerwald, *ib.*, 162. 301, 1927 ; A. Bienias and F. Sauerwald, *ib.*, 161. 51, 1927 ; G. Kamensky, *Proc. Phys. Soc.*, 6. 53, 1884 ; *Phil. Mag.*, (5), 17. 270, 1884 ; F. C. Calvert and R. Johnson, *ib.*, (4), 18. 354, 1859 ; *B.A. Rep.*, 66, 1859 ; P. Braesco, *Compt. Rend.*, 170. 103, 1920 ; *Ann. Chim. Phys.*, (9), 14. 5, 1920 ; H. Weiss, *ib.*, (9), 20. 131, 1923 ; H. Weiss and P. Henry, *Compt. Rend.*, 174. 1421, 1922 ; E. Elsässer, *Wied. Ann.*, 8. 458, 1879 ; A. Mazzucchelli and L. Tonini, *Atti Accad. Lincei*, (5), 32. ii, 290, 1923 ; A. Mazzucchelli and A. Vercillo, *ib.*, (6), i, 1. 233, 1925 ; A. Mallock, *Nature*, 119. 669, 1927 ; F. Sauerwald, *Zeit. Elektrochem.*, 29. 85, 1923 ; F. Sauerwald and K. Bornemann, *Zeit. Metallkunde*, 14. 254, 1922 ; K. Honda and T. Ishigaki, *Science Rep. Tohoku Univ.*, 14. 219, 1925 ; W. M. Jones and E J. Evans, *Phil. Mag.*, (7), 4. 1302, 1927.

³ C. T. Heycock and F. H. Neville, *Phil. Trans.*, 189. A, 25, 1897 ; G. I. Petrenko, *Zeit. anorg. Chem.*, 50. 133, 1906 ; G. Tammann, *ib.*, 118. 93, 1921 ; P. A. von Bonsdorff, *Schweigger's Journ.*, 34. 225, 1822 ; E. J. Weeks, *Chem. News*, 127. 319, 1923 ; E. J. Weeks and W. V. Lloyd, *Chem. News*, 127. 362, 1923 ; J. F. Simon, *Pogg. Ann.*, 42. 563, 1837 ; N. W. Fischer, *ib.*, 10. 603, 1827 ; *Kastner's Arch.*, 13. 224, 1827 ; T. Poleck and C. Thümmel, *Ber.*, 16. 2435, 1883 ; H. Reckleben, *ib.*, 42. 1458, 1909 ; P. Christofle, *Recherches sur les combinaisons de l'antimoine avec les différentes métaux*, Göttingen, 15, 1863 ; A. W. Hofmann, *Liebig's Ann.*, 115. 287, 1860 ; A. de Gramont, *Bull. Soc. Min.*, 18. 287, 1895 ; J. Joly, *Phil. Mag.*, (6), 25. 856, 1913 ; C. R. A. Wright, *Journ. Soc. Chem. Ind.*, 13. 1014, 1894 ; L. A. Emmerling, *Lehrbuch der Mineralogie*, Giessen, 2. 162, 1796 ; J. B. L. Romé de l'Isle, *Cristallographie*, Paris, 3. 460, 1783 ; T. Bergman, *Sciagraphia regni mineralis*, Lipsiæ, 159, 1782 ; F. S. Beudant, *Traité élémentaire de minéralogie*, Paris, 2. 613, 1832 ; A. Breithaupt, *Vollständiges Charakteristik des Mineralsystems*, Dresden, 119, 1823 ; H. Wurtz, *Eng. Min. Journ.*, 27. 124, 1879 ; B. G. Sage, *Élémens de minéralogie decimastique*, Paris, 2. 323, 1777 ; C. C. von Leonhard, *Handbuch der Oryktognosie*, Heidelberg, 204, 1821 ; R. J. Haüy, *Traité de minéralogie*, Paris, 3. 391, 1801 ; G. Rose, *Das krystallochemisches Mineralsystem*, Leipzig, 20, 45, 1852 ; J. F. L. Hausmann, *Handbuch der Mineralogie*, Göttingen, 126, 1813 ; 57, 1847 ; M. H. Klaproth, *Beiträge zur chemischen Kenntniss der Mineralkörper*, Berlin, 2. 301, 1797 ; 3. 175, 1802 ; C. F. Rammelsberg, *Handbuch der Mineralchemie*, Leipzig, 29, 1860 ; 26, 1875 ; *Zeit. deut. geol. Ges.*, 16. 621, 1864 ; *Pogg. Ann.*, 120. 54, 1863 ; 128. 441, 1866 ; R. A. Abich, *Crell's Ann.*, ii, 3, 1798 ; T. Petersen, *Pogg. Ann.*, 137. 381, 1869 ; I. Domeyko, *Elementos de mineralojia*, Santiago, 364, 1879 ; F. Mohs, *Grundriss der Mineralogie*, Dresden, 2. 499, 1824 ; E. F. Glocker, *Generum et specierum mineralium secundum ordines naturales digestorum synopsis*, Halle, 44, 1847 ; C. J. Selb, *Lempe's Mag. Bergbaukunde*, 3, 5, 1786 ; A. Sella, *Gött. Ges. Wiss.*, 311, 1891 ; F. Sandberger, *Untersuchungen über Erzgänge*, Wiesbaden, 2. 293, 1885 ; J. D. Dana, *A System of Mineralogy*, New York, 36, 1877 ; P. Groth, *Tabellarische Uebersicht der Mineralien*, Braunschweig, 23, 1889 ; 25, 1898 ; G. A. Kenngott, *Sitzber. Akad. Wien*, 9. 548, 1852 ; C. W. C. Fuchs, *Die künstlich dargestellten Mineralien nach Roses System geordnet*, Haaslem, 39, 1872 ; E. Maey, *Zeit. phys. Chem.*, 50. 203, 1905 ; N. A. Puschin, *Journ. Russ. Phys. Chem. Soc.*, 37. 302, 1905 ; W. Haken, *Ann. Physik*, (4), 32. 325, 1910 ; E. Elsässer, *Wied. Ann.*, 8. 455, 1879 ; T. Liebisch, *Sitzber. Akad. Berlin*, 365, 1910 ; W. Campbell, *Journ. Franklin. Inst.*, 154. 1, 131, 201, 1902 ; L. Jordan, L. H. Grenall, and H. K. Herschman, *Trans. Amer. Inst. Min. Met. Eng.*, . , 1927 ; R. Kremann and K. Bayer, *Monatsh.*, 46. 649, 1927 ; G. Charpy, *Journ. Phys.*, (3), 7. 145, 1898 ; *Contribution à l'étude des alliages*, Paris, 149, 1901 ; *Bull. Soc. Enc. Nat. Ind.*, (5), 2. 384, 1897 ; H. Gautier, *ib.*, (5), 1. 1309, 1896 ; *Contribution à l'étude des alliages*, Paris, 110, 1901 ; *Compt. Rend.*, 123. 172, 1896 ; P. Berthier, *Traité des essais par la voie sèche*, Liége, 2. 681, 1847 ; H. Rose, *Chem. Gaz.*, 6. 412, 1848 ; G. Sachs and F. Saeftel, *Naturwiss.*, 13. 744, 1925 ; *Zeit. Metallkunde*, 17. 155, 258, 294, 1925 ; G. Smith, *Amer. Journ. Science*, (4), 49. 278, 1920 ; H. Weiss, *Ann. Chim. Phys.*, (9), 20. 131, 1923 ;

H. Weiss and P. Henry, *Compt. Rend.*, **174**. 292, 421, 1922 ; A. M. Portevin, *Metal Ind.*, **22**. 334, 1923 ; *Journ. Inst. Metals*, **29**. 239, 1923 ; C. A. Kraus, *Journ. Amer. Chem. Soc.*, **44**. 1232, 1922 ; E. van Aubel, *Bull. Acad. Belg.*, (5), **12**. 559, 1926 ; M. de Hemptinne, *ib.*, (5), **12**. 797, 1926 ; H. E. McKinstry, *Econ. Geol.*, **22**. 669, 1927 ; M. Hansen and G. Sachs, *Zeit. Metallkunde*, **20**. 151, 1928 ; F. Jones, *Journ. Chem. Soc.*, **29**. 641, 1876.
    [4] C. Hatchett, *Phil. Trans.*, **93**. 43, 1803 ; C. T. Heycock and F. H. Neville, *Journ. Chem. Soc.*, **61**. 897, 1892 ; W. C. Roberts-Austen and F. Osmond, *Bull. Soc. Enc. Nat. Ind.*, (5), **1**. 1137, 1896 ; *Phil. Trans.*, **187**. A, 417, 1896 ; F. Osmond, *Engg.*, **66**. 756, 1898 ; W. C. Roberts-Austen, *Phil. Trans.*, **179**. 339, 1838 ; P. Christofle, *Recherches sur les combinaisons de l'antimoine avec les différentes métaux*, Göttingen, 1863 ; R. Vogel, *Zeit. anorg. Chem.*, **50**. 147, 1906 ; G. Tammann, *ib.*, **118**. 93, 1921 ; F. Rössler, *ib.*, **9**. 31, 1895 ; *Synthese einiger Erzmineralien und analoger Metallverbindungen*, Berlin, 1895 ; H. Weiss, *Ann. Chim. Phys.*, (9), **20**. 131, 1923 ; L. Nowack, *Zeit. Metallkunde*, **19**. 238, 1927.
    [5] H. Caron, *Compt. Rend.*, **48**. 440, 1859 ; L. Donsky, *Zeit. anorg. Chem.*, **57**. 185, 1908 ; O. Ruff and H. Hartmann, *ib.*, **121**. 167, 1922 ; J. D. Reidel, *German Pat.*, *D.R.P.* 300152, 305025, 1917.
    [6] G. Grube, *Zeit. anorg. Chem.*, **49**. 87, 1906 ; E. Kordes, *Zeit. anorg. Chem.*, **154**. 97, 1926 ; R. Kremann and G. Machl-Pammer, *Internat. Zeit. Metallog.* **12**. 241, 1920 ; S. Parkinson, *Journ. Chem. Soc.*, **20**. 117, 1867 ; E. Becquerel, *Ann. Chim. Phys.*, (4), **8**. 389, 1866 ; J. D. Riedel, *German Pat.*, *D.R.P.* 300152, 305025, 1917.
    [7] S. F. Schemtschuschny, *Internat. Zeit. Metallog.*, **4**. 229, 1913 ; *Zeit. anorg. Chem.*, **49**. 386, 1906 ; W. Heike, *ib.*, **118**. 255, 1921 ; K. Mönkmeyer, *ib.*, **43**. 187, 1905 ; W. Treitschke, *ib.*, **50**. 217, 1906 ; N. S. Kurnakoff and N. S. Konstantinoff, *ib.*, **58**. 16, 1908 ; N. S. Kurnakoff and A. N. Achnasaroff, *ib.*, **125**. 185, 1922 ; G. Tammann and K. Dahl, *ib.*, **126**. 104, 1923 ; W. Biltz and C. Haase, *ib.*, **129**. 141, 1923 ; W. Jenge, *ib.*, **118**. 105, 1921 ; G. Tammann, *ib.*, **118**. 93, 1921 ; *Journ. Russ. Phys. Chem. Soc.*, **40**. 227, 1908 ; A. V. Saposhnikoff, *ib.*, **40**. 665, 1908 ; C. F. Rammelsberg, *Pogg. Ann.*, **120**. 61, 1863 ; M. Jakob and S. Erk, *Zeit. Physik*, **35**. 670, 1926 ; E. Elsässer, *Wied. Ann.*, **8**. 457, 1879 ; J. P. Cooke, *Amer. Journ. Science*, (2), **18**. 229, 1854 ; (2), **20**. 222, 1855 ; (2), **30**. 194, 1860 ; E. Becquerel, *Ann. Chim. Phys.*, (4), **8**. 389, 1866 ; C. T. Heycock and F. H. Neville, *Chem. News*, **62**. 280, 1890 ; *Journ. Chem. Soc.*, **61**. 888, 1892 ; B. Wood, *Journ. Franklin. Inst.*, **73**. 61, 1862 ; *Chem. News*, **6**. 135, 1862 ; C. R. A. Wright, *Journ. Soc. Chem. Ind.*, **13**. 1014, 1894 ; K. Honda and T. Sone, *Journ. Inst. Metals*, **37**. 29, 1927 ; *Science Rep. Tokyo Univ.*, **2**. 5, 1913 ; H. Endo, *ib.*, **16**. 201, 1927 ; W. Isküll, *Zeit. Kryst.*, **42**. 374, 1906 ; E. Maey, *Zeit. phys. Chem.*, **50**. 202, 1905 ; A. Schleicher, *Internat. Zeit. Metallog.*, **3**. 102, 1913 ; R. Kremann and J. Gmachl-Pammer, *ib.*, **12**. 241, 1920 ; F. Sauerwald, *ib.*, **14**. 457, 1922 ; *Zeit. Elektrochem.*, **29**. 85, 1923 ; K. Bornemann and F. Sauerwald, *Zeit. Metallkunde*, **14**. 145, 1922 ; R. Kremann and H. Eitel, *ib.*, **12**. 363, 1920 ; R. Kremann and H. Ruderer, *ib.*, **12**. 403, 1920 ; F. Fischer and G. Pfleiderer, *Ges. Abhand. Kennt. Kohle*, **4**. 440, 1919 ; A. Eucken and G. Gehlhoff, *Ber. deut. phys. Ges.*, **14**. 169, 1912 ; K. Herrmann, *ib.*, **14**. 573, 1912 ; A. Battelli, *Mem. Accad. Torino*, (2), **36**. 487, 1885 ; J. Beattie, *Proc. Roy. Soc. Edin.*, **20**. 481, 1895 ; A. Schulze, *Zeit. anorg. Chem.*, **159**. 325, 1927 ; M. Kawakami, *ib.*, **167**. 345, 1927 ; *Science Rep. Tohoku Univ.*, **16**. 915, 1927 ; T. Takei, *ib.*, **16**. 1031, 1927.
    [8] J. G. Wallerius, *Physische Chemie*, Schleusingen, **2**. i, 84, 1772 ; J. Schumann, *Untersuchungen über Amalgame*, Leipzig, 1891 ; *Wied. Ann.*, **43**. 102, 1891 ; G. Vortmann, *Ber.*, **24**. 2762, 1891 ; A. J. J. Vandevelde, *Bull. Acad. Belg.*, (3), **30**. 92, 1895 ; W. Ramsay, *Journ. Chem. Soc.*, **55**. 533, 1899 ; W. J. Humphreys, *ib.*, **69**. 1686, 1896 ; R. Böttger, *Journ. prakt. Chem.*, (1), **12**. 350, 1837 ; J. Nickles, *Compt. Rend.*, **36**. 154, 1853 ; J. Regnauld, *ib.*, **52**. 533, 1861 ; A. Partheil and E. Mannheim, *Arch. Pharm.*, **238**. 168, 1900 ; J. B. Baille and C. Féry, *Ann. Chim. Phys.*, (6), **17**. 249, 1889 ; C. H. Pfaff, *Pogg. Ann.*, **42**. 344, 1837 ; H. Rose, *ib.*, **51**. 423, 1840 ; J. F. Simon, *ib.*, **42**. 566, 1837 ; G. Tammann and J. Hinnüber, *Zeit. anorg. Chem.*, **160**. 255, 1927.
    [9] E. A. Owen and G. D. Preston, *Proc. Phys. Soc.*, **36**. 341, 1924 ; J. W. Richards, *Aluminium*, Philadelphia, 495, 1896 ; L. Guillet, *Génie Civil*, **41**. 139, 156, 169, 188, 1902 ; G. G. Urazoff, *Journ. Russ. Phys. Chem. Soc.*, **51**. 461, 1919 ; H. Gautier, *Compt. Rend.*, **123**. 109, 1896 ; *Contribution à l'étude des allaiges*, Paris, 112, 1901 ; *Bull. Soc. Enc. Nat. Ind.*, (5), **1**. 1315, 1896 ; J. Mathews, *Eng. Min. Journ.*, **72**. 819, 855, 1901 ; R. Kremann and J. Dellacher, *Monatsh.*, **46**. 547, 1926 ; W. Campbell and J. Mathews, *Journ. Amer. Chem. Soc.*, **24**. 259, 1902 ; L. Pauling, *ib.*, **49**. 765, 1927 ; W. Campbell, *Journ. Franklin Inst.*, **154**. 1, 131, 201, 1892 ; C. T. Heycock and F. H. Neville, *Journ. Chem. Soc.*, **73**. 714, 1898 ; G. Tammann, *Zeit. anorg. Chem.*, **48**. 53, 1906 ; C. R. A. Wright, *Journ. Soc. Chem. Ind.*, **11**. 492, 1892 ; **13**. 1014, 1894 ; E. van Aubel, *Journ. Phys.*, (3), **7**. 223, 1898 ; *Compt. Rend.*, **132**. 1266, 1901 ; D. A. Roche, *Monit. Scient.*, (4), **7**. 269, 1893 ; H. F. Hoeveler, *Brit. Pat. No.* 22997, 1893 ; *Chem. Ztg.*, **17**. 1000, 1893 ; H. Pécheux, *Compt. Rend.*, **138**. 1606, 1904 ; K. Bornemann, *Die binären Metallegierungen*, Halle a. S., **2**. 77, 1912 ; *Met.*, **7**. 572, 1910 ; H. Schirmeister, *Beiträge zur Kenntnis der binären Aluminiumlegierungen hinsichtlich ihrer technischen Eigenschaften*, Dusseldorf, 1914 ; *Stahl Eisen*, **35**. 649, 873, 996, 1915 ; F. Sauerwald, *Zeit. Metallkunde*, **14**. 457, 1922 ; K. Honda, *Science Rep. Univ. Tokyo*, **2**. 9. 1913 ; *Journ. Inst. Metals*, **37**. 29, 1927.
    [10] E. Carstanjen, *Journ. prakt. Chem.*, (1), **102**. 82, 1867 ; R. Kremann and A. Lobinger, *Zeit. Metallkunde*, **12**. 246, 1820 ; R. Kremann and A. Tröster, *Monatsh.*, **47**. 285, 1926 ; R. A. Morgan, *Journ. Amer. Chem. Soc.*, **49**. 39, 1927 ; E. E. Schumacher and G. M. Bouton, *ib.*,

49. 1667, 1927; L. Losana, *Notiz. Chim. Ind.*, **2.** 63, 121, 1927; W. Bonsack, *Zeit. Metallkunde.* **19.** 107, 1927; T. Barth, *Zeit. phys. Chem.*, **127.** 113, 1927; M. Chikashige, *Zeit. anorg. Chem.*, **51.** 328, 1906; R. S. Williams, *ib.*, **50.** 129, 1906; D. Omodei, *Atti Fis. Siena*, **4.** 2, 1890; E. Bekier, *Chem. Polski*, **15.** 119, 1917; G. Winogoroff and G. Petrenko, *Zeit. anorg. Chem.*, **150.** 258, 1926; E. Abel and O. Redlich, *ib.*, **161.** 221, 1927; E. Kordes, *ib.*, **167.** 97, 1927; Y. Matuyama, *Science Rep. Tohoku Univ.*, **16.** 447, 1927; R. A. Morgan, L. G. Swenson, F. C. Nix, and E. H. Roberts, *Trans. Amer. Inst. Min. Eng.*, . , 1927.
11 K. Hüttner and G. Tammann, *Zeit. anorg. Chem.*, **44.** 131, 1905; R. Kremann, A. Langsbauer, and H. Rauch, *ib.*, **127.** 289, 1923; B. Otani, *Science Rep. Tohoku Univ.*, **13.** 293, 1925; C. M. Marx, *Schweigger's Journ.*, **58.** 464, 1830; N. Parravano and E. Viviani, *Atti Accad. Lincei*, (5), **19.** i, 835, 1910; (5), **19.** ii, 69, 197, 243, 343, 1910; A. Mazzucchelli and L. Tonini, *ib.*, (5), **32.** ii, 290, 1923; A. Mazzucchelli and A. Vercillo, *ib.*, (6), **1.** i, 233, 1925; K. Bädeker, *Ueber die elektrische Leitfähigkeit und die thermoelektrische Kraft einiger Schwermetallverbindungen,* Leipzig, 1906; A. Matthiessen and M. Holzmann, *Phil. Trans.*, **150.** 85, 1860; *Chem. News*, **2.** 217, 1860; *Pogg. Ann.*, **110.** 222, 1860; A. Matthiessen, *ib.*, **103.** 412, 428, 1858; **110.** 21, 1860; *Phil. Trans.*, **148.** 369, 383, 1858; **150.** 177, 1860; M. Cook, *Journ. Metals*, **28.** 421, 1922; *Metal Ind.*, **22.** 77, 104, 1923; N. A. Puschin, *Journ. Russ. Phys. Chem. Soc.*, **39.** 528, 1907; E. Bekier, *Chem. Polski*, **15.** 119, 1917; C. R. A. Wright, *Journ. Soc. Chem. Ind.*, **13.** 1014, 1894; *Proc. Roy. Soc.*, **52.** 540, 1893; A. Battelli, *Mem. Accad. Torino*, (2), **36.** 487, 1885; T. Seebeck, *Sitzber. Akad. Berlin*, 265, 1823; *Pogg. Ann.*, **6.** 148, 1826; A. Sundell, *ib.*, **149.** 144, 1873; K. Honda and T. Sone, *Journ. Inst. Metals*, **37.** 29, 1927; *Science Rep. Tokyo Univ.*, **2.** 5, 1913; H. Endo, *ib.*, **16.** 201, 1927; A. W. Smith, *Phys. Rev.*, (1), **32.** 178, 1911; G. Gehlhoff and F. Naumaier, *Verh. deut. phys. Ges.*, **15.** 876, 1913; W. Campbell, *Journ. Franklin Inst.*, **154.** 1, 131, 201, 1902; J. Beattie, *Proc. Roy. Soc. Edin.*, **20.** 481, 1895; E. Becquerel, *Ann. Chim. Phys.*, (4), **8.** 389, 1868; F. C. Calvert and R. Johnson, *Phil. Mag.*, (4), **18.** 354, 1859; *Phil. Trans.*, **148.** 349, 1858; **149.** 831, 1859; J. P. Joule, *ib.*, **14.** 91, 1859; G. Charpy, *Contribution à l'étude des alliages*, Paris, 119, 1901; *Bull. Soc. Enc. Nat. Ind.*, (5), **2.** 384, 1897; H. Gautier, *ib.*, (5), **1.** 1293, 1896; *Contribution à l'étude des alliages*, Paris, 93, 1901; R. Kremann and A. Tröster, *Monatsh.*, **47.** 285, 1926; R. Kremann, *ib.*, **47.** 295, 1926; M. Herschkowitsch, *Zeit. phys. Chem.*, **27.** 123, 1897; E. Maey, *ib.*, **38.** 289, 1901; C. T. Heycock and F. H. Neville, *Chem. News*, **62.** 280, 1890; *Journ. Chem. Soc.*, **61.** 888, 1892; C. Hutchins, *Amer. Journ. Science*, (3), **48.** 226, 1894; W. Rollmann, *Pogg. Ann.*, **83.** 77, 1851; **84.** 275, 1851; **89.** 90, 1853; F. Rudberg, *ib.*, **18.** 280, 1830; *Svenska Akad. Handl.*, 157, 1829; A. Schulze, *Zeit. anorg. Chem.*, **159.** 325, 1927; Y. Matuyama, *Science Rep. Tohoku Univ.*, **16.** 447, 1927; W. Haken, *Ber. deut. phys. Ges.*, **12.** 229, 1910.
12 R. S. Williams, *Zeit. anorg. Chem.*, **55.** 1, 1907; F. A. Bernoulli, *Pogg. Ann.*, **111.** 573, 1860; L. Troost and P. Hautefeuille. *Ann. Chim. Phys.*, (5), **9.** 65, 1876; A. Colani, *ib.*, (8), **12.** 59, 1907; E. Wedekind, *Ber.*, **40.** 1259, 1907; *Zeit. phys. Chem.*, **66.** 614, 1909; *Zeit. Elektrochem.*, **11.** 850, 1905; *Ber.*, **40.** 1259, 1907; S. Hilpert and T. Dieckmann, *ib.*, **44.** 2831, 1911; T. Dieckmann, *Ueber einige Mono- und Bi-arsenide des Eisens, Mangans, und Chroms, über ihre chemischen und magnetischen Eigenschaften, sowie über die magnetischen Eigenschaften einiger Mangan-Wismuth Legierungen*, Berlin, 1911; F. Heusler, *Zeit. angew. Chem.*, **17.** 260, 1904; P. Martin, *Ann. Physik*, (4), **39.** 625, 1912; W. F. de Jong and H. W. V. Willems, *Physica*, **7.** 74, 1927; I. Oftedal, *Zeit. phys. Chem.*, **128.** 135, 1927; J. J. and F. de Elhuyar, *Análisis quimico del volfram y exámen de un nuevo metal que entra en su composicion*, Bascongada, 1783; *A Chemical Examination of Wolfram and Examination of a New Metal which enters into its Composition*, London, 1785; *Chemische Zerkliederung des Wolframs*, Halle, 1786; *Mém. Acad. Toulouse*, **2.** 141, 1784.
13 A. F. Gehlen, *Schweigger's Journ.*, **15.** 501, 1815; **20.** 353, 1817; P. Weiss, *Aimantation des alliages der fer et d'antimoine*, Paris, 1896; *Éclair. Elect.*, **8.** 248, 306, 436, 1896; L. Cailletet, *Compt. Rend.*, **48.** 1113, 1859; J. Laborde, *ib.*, **123.** 227, 1896; *Journ. Phys.*, (3), **5.** 547, 1896; E. Maey, *Zeit. phys. Chem.*, **38.** 292, 1901; C. F. Rammelsberg, *Pogg. Ann.*, **128.** 441, 1866; T. Seebeck, *ib.*, **10.** 203, 1827; P. Berthier, *Traité des essais par la voie seche*, Paris, **2.** 217, 1834; J. Percy, *The Metallurgy of Iron*, London, 170, 1864; W. F. de Jong and H. W. V. Willems, *Physica*, **7.** 74, 1927; I. Oftedal, *Zeit. phys. Chem.*, **128.** 135, 1927; C. J. B. Karsten, *System der Metallurgie*, Berlin, **4.** 34, 1831; P. Christofle, *Recherches sur les combinaisons de l'antimoine avec les différentes métaux*, Göttingen, 1863; N. S. Kurnakoff and N. S. Konstantinoff, *Journ. Russ. Phys. Chem. Soc.*, **40.** 227, 1908; *Zeit. anorg. Chem.*, **58.** 1, 1908; G. Tammann and K. Dahl, *ib.*, **126.** 104, 1923; G. Tammann and E. Schaarwächter, *ib.*, **167.** 404, 1927; G. S. Serullas. *Journ. Phys.*, **91.** 123, 1820; **93.** 115, 1821; *Ann. Chim. Phys.*, (2). **18.** 217 1821; (2), **21.** 198, 1822; W. Isküll, *Zeit. Kryst.*, **42.** 377, 1906; E. van Aubel, *Journ. Phys.*, (3), **9.** 493, 1900; *Phys. Zeit.*, **1.** 452, 1900; E. Becquerel, *Ann. Chim. Phys.*, (4), **8.** 389, 1866; P. Goerens and K. Ellingen, *Met.*, **7.** 72, 1910; A. Portevin, *Rev. Mét.*, **8.** 312, 1911.
14 A. F. Gehlen, *Schweigger's Journ.*, **15.** 501, 1815; **20** 353, 1817; C. F. Rammelsberg, *Pogg. Ann.*, **128.** 441, 1866; N. S. Kurnakoff and N. I. Podkapajeff, *Journ. Russ. Phys. Chem. Soc.*, **38.** 463, 1906; I. Oftedal, *Zeit. phys. Chem.*, **128.** 135, 1927; K. Lewkonja, *Zeit. anorg. Chem.*, **59.** 305, 1908; F. Ducelliez, *Compt. Rend.*, **147.** 1048, 1908; A. M. Portevin, *Metal Ind.*, **22.** 334, 1923; *Journ. Ind. Metals*, **29.** 239, 1923; W. F. de Jong and H. W. V. Willems, *Physica*, **7.** 74, 1927.
15 A. F. Gehlen, *Schweigger's Journ.*, **15.** 501, 1815; **20.** 353, 1817; F. Stromeyer, *ib.*, **69**.

252, 1833 ; F. Stromeyer and J. F. L. Hausmann, *Gött. Gel. Anz.*, 2001, 1883 ; *Pogg. Ann.*, **31.** 134, 1834 ; *Liebig's Ann.*, **14.** 82, 1835 ; J. F. L. Hausmann, *Gött. Gel. Anz.*, 177, 1852 ; *Neues Jahrb. Min.*, 179, 1853 ; P. Christofle, *Recherches sur les combinaisons de l'antimoine avec les différentes métaux*, Göttingen, 1863 ; K. Losseff, *Zeit. anorg. Chem.*, **49.** 58, 1906 ; F. Rössler, *ib.*, **9.** 73, 1895 ; *Synthese einiger Erzmineralien und analoger Metallverbindungen*, Berlin, 1895 ; A. Brand, *Zeit. Kryst.*, **12.** 234, 1887 ; H. Laspeyres, *ib.*, **25.** 592, 1896 ; K. Busz, *ib.*, **24.** 496, 1895 ; *Ber. Niederrh. Ges. Bonn.*, 33, 1894 ; F. Sandberger, *Jahrb. Ver. Nat. Nassau*, **9.** 40, 1854 ; *Pogg. Ann.*, **103.** 526, 1858 ; *Neuesl. Jahrb. Min.*, i, 90, 1886 ; F. Beijerinck, *Neues Jahrb. Min. B.B.*, **11.** 431, 1897 ; E. Mattirolo, *Atti Accad. Lincei*, (5), 98, 1891 ; D. Lovisato, *ib.*, (5), 3. 82, 1894 ; F. Pisani, *Compt. Rend.*, **76.** 239, 1873 ; E. Vigouroux, *ib.*, 147, 976, 1909 ; M. Vigouroux, *Génie Ind.*, **30.** 230, 1865 ; A. Breithaupt, *Pogg. Ann.*, **53.** 631, 1841 ; T. Seebeck, *ib.*, **10.** 203, 1827 ; A. de Gramont, *Bull. Soc. Min.*, **18.** 289, 1895 ; C. F. Rammelsberg, *Ber.*, **7.** 152, 1874 ; *Handbuch der Mineralchemie*, Leipzig, 33, 1875 ; *Pogg. Ann.*, **128.** 441, 1866 ; *Sitzber. Akad. Berlin*, 188, 1863 ; F. Fouqué and A. Michel-Lévy, *Synthèse des minéraux et des roches*, Paris, 287, 1882 ; T. W. Case, *Phys. Rev.*, (2), **9.** 305, 1927 ; E. J. Chapman, *Practical Mineralogy*, London, 1843 ; W. Haidinger, *Handbuch der bestimmenden Mineralogie*, Wien, 559, 1845 ; A. des Cloizeaux, *Manuel de minéralogie*, Paris, 2. 326, 1893 ; L. N. Vauquelin, *Ann. Chim. Phys.*, (2), **20.** 421, 1822 ; P. Berthier, *ib.*, (2), **13.** 52, 1820 ; *Ann. Mines*, (1), **4.** 467, 1819 ; (3), 7. 538, 1835 ; N. A. Puschin, *Journ. Russ. Phys. Chem. Soc.*, **39.** 528, 1907 ; N. S. Kurnakoff and N. I. Podkopajeff, *ib.*, **37.** 1280, 1905 ; N. F. de Jong, *Physica*, **5.** 241, 1925 ; J. Joly, *Phil. Mag.*, (6), **27.** 1, 1914 ; *Chem. News*, **107.** 241, 1913 : W. F. de Jong, *Physica*, **5.** 241, 1925 ; W. F. de Jong and H. W. V. Willems, *ib.*, **7.** 74, 1927 ; W. Guertler and H. Schack, *Metall Erz*, **20.** 162, 1923 ; W. Herz, *Zeit. anorg. Chem.*, **163.** 220, 1927 ; I. Oftedal, *Zeit. phys. Chem.*, **128.** 135, 1927.

[16] A. F. Gehlen, *Schweigger's Journ.*, **20.** 353, 1817 ; F. Rössler, *Synthese einiger Erzmineralien und analoger Metallverbindungen*, Berlin, 1895 ; *Zeit. anorg. Chem.*, **9.** 73, 1895 ; W. Lewis, *Commercium Philosophico-Technicum*, London, 521, 1763 ; P. Christofle, *Recherches sur les combinaisons de l'antimoine avec les différentes métaux*, Göttingen, 1863 ; K. Friedrich and A. Leroux, *Met.*, **6.** 1, 1909 ; K. Bornemann, *ib.*, **8.** 686, 1911 ; J. Murray, *Edin. Phil. Journ.*, **4.** 202, 1921 ; 6. 387, 1822 ; H. Landolt, *Liebig's Ann.*, **84.** 61, 1852 ; C. Barus, *Amer. Journ. Science*, (3), **36.** 434, 1888 ; R. W. Fox, *Ann. Phil.*, **13.** 467, 1819 ; J. F. Simon, *Pogg. Ann.*, **42.** 63, 1832 ; R. Bartels, *Ueber die Einwirkung des Antimonwasserstoffs und Metallsalzlösungen*, Berlin, 1889 ; T. W. Case, *Phys. Rev.*, (2), **9.** 305, 1927.

[17] N. W. Fischer, *Kastner's Arch.*, **11.** 224, 1827 ; W. Sander, *Zeit. anorg. Chem.*, **75.** 96, 1912 ; F. Rössler, *ib.*, **9.** 31, 1895 ; *Synthese einiger Erzmineralien und analoger Metallverbindungen*, Berlin, 1895.

§ 10. Antimonious Oxide, or Antimony Trioxide

It is not known if the *stibia femina*—female antimony—referred to by Pliny, in his *Historia naturalis* (**33.** 33), written in the first century of our era, was antimony oxide, or antimony sulphide. The *vitrium antimonii*, or the *Spiessglanzglas* of Basil Valentine [1] in the seventeenth century, was a mixture of oxide and sulphide obtained by incompletely roasting the sulphide ore. This subject was also discussed by A. Libavius, and N. Lemery. It was also mentioned in the first century by Dioscorides, in his *De materia medica*, and by Pliny, in the work just cited ; it is also mentioned in the twelfth-century Latin translation of Geber—*De investigatione magisterii*. In the seventeenth century, Basil Valentine described the preparation of *flores antimonii* which is the calx of antimony now known as antimony trioxide. Some antimony oxide of commerce is a potassium antimonate. Basil Valentine also described another preparation obtained by igniting a number of times a mixture of antimony and nitre, and treating the product with an acid—sulphuric or acetic. The preparation—antimony pentoxide —was called *antimonium diaphoreticum ablutum*, or *calx antimonii clota*, and it acquired some fame, amongst the Iatro-chemists, for its medicinal properties. It was also called *materia perlata Kerkringii*—after T. Kerkring, who edited Basil Valentine's work ; and *fondant de Rotrou*—after a medical practitioner at St. Cyr. A. Libavius, and O. Croll called it *antimonium diaphoreticum ;* M. Ettmüller gave a clear history of this subject in 1693. O. Croll obtained diaphoretic antimony by repeatedly evaporating antimony trichloride with nitric acid ; and he called it *bezoar ;* R. J. Glauber, *bezoardecium minerale*. At the beginning of the nineteenth century, L. J. Thénard [2] supposed that antimony formed half a dozen different oxides. J. L. Proust limited the number to two—the ordinary trioxide, and one with a higher proportion of oxygen which J. J. Berzelius referred to as antimonious and antimonic oxides. Only three oxides are now recognized—**antimony trioxide,** or *antimonious oxide,* Sb_2O_3; *antimony tetroxide,* Sb_2O_4; and *antimony pentoxide,* or *antimonic oxide,* Sb_2O_5.

J. J. Berzelius [3] said that *antimony suboxide,* or **antimony hemioxide,** Sb_2O, is formed as a thin, grey film when antimony is exposed to moist air ; and as a bluish-grey flocculent powder when powdered antimony is immersed in water, and connected by a platinum wire so that the antimony forms the anode in the electrolysis of the water. The suboxide is resolved into antimonic oxide and antimony, when treated with hydrochloric acid. J. L. Proust supposed that the alleged suboxide is itself a mixture of oxide and metal. F. Jones obtained a black substance, with nearly this composition, by the action of stibine on alkali-lye. A. Ludwig reported the suboxide to be formed by cooling molten antimony in the presence of water at about 6000 atm. R. F. Marchand reported another suboxide— antimony ditritoxide, Sb_3O_2, to be deposited on the platinum anode when a conc. soln. of potassium antimonyl tartrate is electrolyzed. R. Böttger obtained a somewhat similar product. The individuality of these two oxides has not been established.

A native form of antimony trioxide, occurring in *rhombic crystals,* was found by J. A. Mongez [4] in the Mine des Chalanches, *Allemont,* and the mineral was also described by R. J. Haüy as *chaux d'antimoine native.* A deposit of the mineral at Pribram was described by B. Rössler, and B. Hacquet and called *antimonium spatosum album splendens;* A. G. Werner and C. A. S. Hoffmann named it *Weissspiessglanzerz.* M. H. Klaproth's analysis showed that the mineral is antimony trioxide. R. Kirwan called the mineral *white antimonial ore;* C. C. von Leonhard, *Antimonblüthe;* A. Breithaupt, *Antimonspath;* F. S. Beudant, *exitèle*—from ἐξίτηλος, vaporizable ; E. J. Chapman, *exitelite;* and W. Haidinger, **valentinite**—after Basil Valentine. Another form of antimony trioxide occurring in *cubic crystals* at Haraclas, Algeria, was called by H. de Sénarmont,[5] *antimoine oxydé octaédrique,* and by J. D. Dana, **sénarmontite**—after H. de Sénarmont. It was also found by G. A. Kenngott at Perneck, Hungary. F. Wöhler, and P. Groth emphasized the dimorphism of antimony trioxide, and the isodimorphism of arsenic and antimony trioxides—*vide* arsenic trioxide, **9.** 52, 11.

Antimony trioxide, calx antimonii, can be prepared by burning antimony in an inclined crucible exposed to air, and passing the products of combustion through wide glass or earthenware tubes, in which the *flores antimonii* are deposited. The antimony can be heated to redness in a wide crucible, inclined and loosely covered. The oxide collects in the cooler parts of the crucible in the form of brilliant needles. H. Debray [6] obtained the oxide in this way. H. Rose found that the trioxide prepared by combustion contains some tetroxide, and this makes it fuse with difficulty. H. V. Regnault also made the trioxide by passing steam over red-hot antimony. R. Brandes, and J. Preuss obtained the trioxide by boiling pulverized antimony with moderately conc. nitric acid until it is converted into a white powder which is a mixture of a basic nitrate, antimony trioxide, and antimony. Some higher oxides are also present. The nitric acid is removed by repeated boiling with water. R. Brandes found that when one part of powdered antimony is digested with two parts of aqua regia, and four parts of water, 96·6 per cent. of antimony trioxide is obtained. J. Preuss projected a mixture of 74 parts of antimony ; 39, of nitric ; and 34, of potassium hydrosulphate in small portions at a time into a red-hot crucible ; the mass is kept red-hot in a covered crucible for some time ; and, when cold, boiled first with water, then with sulphuric acid, and finally with water. Any arsenic oxide present is washed out by the water, but iron oxide is not removed by the washing. S. Berberich found that antimony trioxide is formed at the antimony electrode during the electrolysis of sulphuric and hydrochloric acid, or potash-lye, and this the more the greater the conc. of the electrolyte.

Antimony trioxide is produced by roasting the trisulphide—*vide supra,* the history and the extraction of antimony.   J. J. Berzelius showed that the product of roasting the sulphide is largely the tetroxide, and if the product is fused with one-sixteenth to one-twentieth of its weight of the trisulphide, antimony trioxide is formed.   If but a small excess of the trisulphide is present, transparent and colourless *Spiessglanzglas* is formed as an oxysulphide ; if too little sulphide be produced, some tetroxide remains undecomposed and the *Spiessglanzglas* will be opaque.   E. G. Hornung obtained antimony trioxide by treating the trisulphide with conc. sulphuric acid ; washing the product with water ; and then treating the residue with a soln. of sodium carbonate.   M. Durand employed a somewhat similar process.   S. Metzl treated the trisulphide with alkali sulphate and sulphuric acid, and digested the resulting complex salt with water.   W. Lindner boiled the trisulphide with a soln. of ferric chloride and dil. hydrochloric acid, diluted the liquid with water, washed the precipitate with water and then with a soln. of sodium carbonate.   A. Germot made the trioxide for use as a paint by blowing air into the molten metal, and collecting the fumes in suitable chambers.

According to H. Rose, antimonious salt soln. give white, voluminous precipitates when treated with alkali-lye or aq. ammonia—in the case of the alkali-lye, the precipitate is soluble in excess, but not so with the aq. ammonia.   Similarly with soln. of alkali carbonates, and, according to C. Arnold, the precipitates are not soluble in an excess.   The precipitates are thoroughly washed and dried.   G. von Knorre, A. Guntz, and E. Mitscherlich obtained the trioxide in this manner.   H. Debray prepared the oxide by decomposing the oxychloride with water at 150° ;   and A. Guntz, by treating the oxychloride with sodium carbonate.   According to J. H. Long, an aq. soln. of potassium antimonyl tartrate is decomposed by the salts of many of the feeble acids—boric, acetic, thiosulphuric, phosphoric, sulphurous, or tungstic—with the separation of the hydrated trioxide.   G. von Knorre showed that the trioxide is formed by reducing antimony pentoxide, with sulphur dioxide, etc.   H. Baubigny found that the tetroxide, at a high temp. passes into the trioxide.   W. Spring obtained a **colloidal solution** of antimony trioxide ;   and V. Kohlschütter and J. L. Tüscher obtained highly dispersed, or colloidal antimony trioxide by vaporization in the electric arc.   R. W. Gray and co-workers studied the formation of the dispersed oxide—smoke.   S. Wosnessensky discussed the coagulation of the antimony trioxide sol.

Rhombic antimony trioxide—valentinite—is the commoner form.   The rhombic crystals appear when the trioxide is slowly cooled.   J. Weber also obtained valentinite mixed with a little sénarmontite by cooling molten valentinite or sénarmontite.   Rhombic crystals are formed when the trioxide is sublimed. According to R. Brauns, molten sénarmontite or valentinite, on cooling, furnishes crystals of valentinite as well as of amorphous trioxide ;   and when the trioxide is sublimed, both sénarmontite and valentinite may be found beside one another. According to A. Terreil, E. Mitscherlich, and F. Wöhler, valentinite is formed at a higher temp. than sénarmontite.   C. W. C. Fuchs, and J. Weber showed that the rhombic crystals are formed when the trioxide is obtained by the action of steam on red-hot antimony ;   and, according to C. W. C. Fuchs, when prepared by the action of a hot soln. of alkali carbonate on a soln. of antimony trichloride in hydrochloric acid.   Thus, E. Mitscherlich obtained the rhombic crystals by pouring a boiling hydrochloric acid soln. of the trichloride into a boiling soln. of alkali carbonate.   H. Debray said that valentinite appears when the trioxide is formed by wet processes at a temp. above 100°.   The crystals may also appear in the flues of furnaces in which antimony trisulphide has been roasted ;   thus, A. Arzruni found valentinite as well as sénarmontite in the flues of an antimony furnace at Schlaining, Hungary.

Octahedral crystals of antimony trioxide—sénarmontite—were obtained by E. Mitscherlich, and F. Wöhler by heating antimony for a long time exposed to air.   A. Terreil obtained sénarmontite by subliming antimony trioxide at as low a temp. as possible—say dull redness—in an inert gas.   He also observed that when antimony is heated in a porcelain tube in a stream of dry air, the sublimate has crystals of valentinite nearest the antimony, then follow a mixture of crystals of valentinite and sénarmontite, and finally of sénarmontite alone. If antimony be laid on a piece of charcoal and heated in the blowpipe flame until it oxidizes to a white substance, the fine powder, when examined under a microscope, will show both a mass of needle-like latticed crystals, and a mass of perfect cubic and octahedral crystals. A. Schrauf also said that when the molten trioxide is cooled, crystals of valentinite are first formed, and at a lower temp. sénarmontite appears. The crystals of both forms of the trioxide may be found in the flues of furnaces roasting antimony trisulphide—*vide supra.* H. Fischer, and G. A. Kenngott made analogous observations. H. Debray, and A. Terreil found that sénarmontite appears when the trioxide is formed by wet processes at a temp. below 100°. L. Pasteur obtained the octahedral crystals by digesting the oxychloride for many days with an excess of a soln. of sodium carbonate ; and E. Mitscherlich, by treating a soln. of potassium antimonyl tartrate with aq. ammonia, or a soln. of an alkali hydroxide or carbonate ; and by treating a hydrochloric acid soln. of antimony trichloride with alkali carbonate.

The natural forms of antimony trioxide are produced by the oxidation of antimonial ores. J. R. Blum observed pseudomorphs of valentinite after antimony, and stibnite ; and H. Laspeyres, pseudomorphs after allemontite. T. Carnelley and J. Walker found the precipitated trioxide is anhydrous after drying in air for five months. Analyses of antimony trioxide, made by J. J. Berzelius, J. Davy, T. Thomson, and J. L. Proust, are in agreement with the formula Sb_2O_3. Sénarmontite was analyzed by L. E. Rivot ; and analyses of valentinite were reported by M. H. Klaproth, L. J. Spencer, G. Suckow, F. Sandberger, and A. Schuller. Both minerals have the same composition. V. Meyer and H. Mensching found that at 1560°, the vapour density 19·60–19·98 is in agreement with 19·90, the calculated value for $(Sb_2O_3)_2$ or Sb_4O_6. H. Biltz showed that dissociation occurs at a higher temp. R. M. Bozorth found that the unit mol in the solid trioxide is Sb_4O_6. The degree of purity of commercial white antimony oxide is 96–98 per cent. Sb_2O_3. The chief impurities are antimony tetroxide and sulphide ; and the sulphides and oxides of iron, lead, copper, arsenic, nickel, cobalt, and bismuth.

The physical properties of antimony trioxide.—The **colour** of antimony trioxide is snow-white, but as a mineral it may appear peach-blossom red, ash-grey, or brown. Valentinite may occur in lamellar, columnar, or granular masses, or in prismatic **crystals,** which may appear in fan-shaped or stellar groups, in bundles, and as aggregates of thin plates ; while sénarmontite may occur in granular masses, and incrustations, as well as in octahedral crystals—the *antimoine oxydé octaédrique* of H. de Sénarmont. W. Phillips, and F. Mohs made observations on the rhombic or prismatic crystals of valentinite ; and H. Laspeyres gave for the axial ratios $a : b : c = 0·3910 : 1 : 0·3364$; L. J. Spencer, $0·3938 : 1 : 0·4344$; A. Brezina, $0·3925 : 1 : 0·4205$; and F. Millosevich, $0·39122 : 1 : —$. Observations were also made by A. Brezina, E. S. Dana, W. Haidinger, G. Cesaro, A. des Cloizeaux, A. Pelloux, J. Nöggerath, D. Lovisato, P. Groth, etc. The **cleavage** on the (010)- and the (110)-face of valentinite is perfect ; sénarmontite shows traces of octahedral cleavage. The octahedral crystals of sénarmontite were shown by A. des Cloizeaux to be **optically anomalous** like boracite ; and this property was investigated by P. Groth, E. Mallard, E. Bertrand, A. Grosse-Bohle, J. Weber, R. Brauns, and R. Prendel. E. Mallard attributed the effect to the crystal being compounded of triclinic individuals, and A. Grosse-Bohle, of monoclinic individuals. R. Brauns thought that the existence of twinned groupings is very unlikely ; the crystals become isotropic when warmed, and the isotropism remains when the crystals are cooled ; the anomalous state can be produced by press. ; and the sublimed crystals are isotropic. A. Pelloux gave for the **optic axial angle** of valentinite, $2E = c. 60°$. A. des Cloizeaux found that the optic axes parallel to c converge slightly when the crystals are heated to 75°, while those perpendicular to c open slightly.

A. Grosse-Bohle found the **corrosion figures** of sénarmontite, with warm hydro-chloric acid, are triangular with the apices towards the corners of the octahedra. R. M. Bozorth examined the **X-radiogram** of the octahedral crystals of antimony trioxide, and found the corresponding space-lattice is of the diamond type with a mol of Sb_4O_6 in place of one carbon atom. The case is analogous to that of arsenic trioxide (*q.v.*). The unit cube, with 8 mols of Sb_4O_6, has a side 11·14 A. ; and the shortest distance between the antimony and oxygen atoms in the same group is 2·22 A., and in a neighbouring group 2·61 A.—*vide* Fig. 13, **9**. 52. 11. The X-radiogram was also studied by A. Simon, and U. Dehlinger and co-workers.

The **specific gravity** of antimony trioxide was found by C. J. B. Karsten to be 6·6952. For sénarmontite, A. Terreil gave 5·20 ; H. de Sénarmont, 5·22–5·30 ; and for the artificial crystals, A. Terreil gave 5·11 ; and L. Playfair and J. P. Joule, 5·251. For valentinite, A. Breithaupt gave 5·558–5·577 ; F. Mohs, 5·566 ; D. Lovisato, 5·807 ; A. Terreil, 5·70 ; L. J. Spencer, 5·76 ; and for the artificial crystals, P. F. G. Boullay gave 5·778 ; and A. Terreil, 5·72. The best representative values are 5·25 for sénarmontite and 5·72 for valentinite. A. Simon found that the sp. gr. of the trioxide sublimed in vacuo at 1000° is 5·19 ; while the value calculated from the X-radiogram is 5·49. For the **vapour density**, *vide supra*. The **hardness** of sénarmontite is 2–2·5 ; and of valentinite, 2–3. The cubical coeff. of **thermal expansion** of sénarmontite was found by H. Fizeau to be 0·00002501 at 40° ; and the linear coeff. 0·00001963. H. V. Regnault found the **specific heat** of artificial crystals of sénarmontite, between 15° and 99°, to be 0·09009 ; and C. F. Neumann, 0·0927 between 17° and 19°. F. Winkler gave 25·9 for the mol. ht. of the solid, and 20 for the mol. ht. of the gas. Hot antimony trioxide is yellow, and when cold, white. H. Debray's work would make the **transition temp.** run over 100°, but this datum has not been established. E. Quercigh gave 656° for the **melting point** of the trioxide. The molten oxide is yellow or grey, and it freezes to a white mass resembling asbestos. The trioxide volatilizes when heated out of contact with air, without passing into the tetroxide, and forms a sublimate with needle-like crystals. A. A. Read found that the trioxide volatilizes freely at 1750°. M. R. Mott calculated 1570° for the **boiling point.** A. Simon and E. Thaler gave for the **dissociation pressure :** 26·4 mm. at 2127° ; 73 mm. at 2227° ; and 184 mm. at 2327°—*vide* Fig. 31. F. Winkler gave 0·09 atm. for the partial press. of the oxygen at 820° ; and 44·850 Cals. for the **heat of vaporization** of a mol of the trioxide. A. Ditte and R. Metzner gave for the **heat of formation,** $(2Sb,3O)=167\cdot4$ Cals. ; A. Simon and E. Thaler, 167·4 Cals. ; W. Biltz, 167·4 Cals. ; W. G. Mixter, 163·0 Cals. ; and J. Thomson, for the rhombic form, 166·9 Cals. From the heat of soln. of the trioxides in hydrofluoric acid, A. Guntz obtained 1·2 Cals. for the **heat of transformation** of the rhombic into the cubic form. From the e.m.f. of cells with antimony oxide and perchloric acid and the hydrogen electrode, R. Schuhmann calculated the **free energy** of the formation of antimony trioxide from its elements at 25° to be —148,600 cals. C. Hensgen observed that the trioxide obtained by the hydrolysis of antimony sulphate is **photo-sensitive ;** and C. Renz made a similar observation, for, when exposed to sunlight in the presence of glycerol, benzaldehyde or tartaric acid in alcoholic soln., it becomes grey and ultimately black owing to the formation of a suboxide of the metal. H. S. Patterson and R. Whytlaw studied the photophoresis of particles of the trioxide suspended in air. A. des Cloizeaux gave for the **index of refraction** of sénarmontite 2·073 for red-light, and 2·087 for sodium-light. A. de Gramont examined the **spark spectrum** of sénarmontite. W. Heintze observed a maximum **photoelectric effect** at $\lambda=313\mu\mu$; and found the trioxide is opaque to waves shorter than $313\mu\mu$. F. Beijerinck found both forms of the trioxide to be **non-conductors of electricity ;** while T. W. Case said that the resistance is not appreciably affected by light. R. W. Gray, J. B. Speakman and E. Thomsen measured the tendency of the oxide dispersed in air to condense in string-like aggregates under the influence of an electrostatic field.

The chemical properties of antimony trioxide.—According to A. Terreil,[7] valentinite is more easily attacked than sénarmontite, since the former is coloured brownish-red by ammonium sulphide and then dissolved, while the latter is not attacked ; and the rhombic form dissolves more easily in acids and in alkali-lye. Antimony trioxide is amphoteric ; it reacts with acids, forming salts in which antimony, or the univalent radicle *antimonyl*, SbO, acts as cation ; while with bases, antimony trioxide acts as an acidic anhydride, forming a series of salts, **antimonites.** W. Metzener studied the amphoteric qualities of antimony trioxide. According to J. von Liebig, the trioxide is reduced by **hydrogen** at a red-heat. V. Ipatieff found that when the trioxide is heated with hydrogen under press., stibine and antimony are formed. J. J. Berzelius found that when heated in **air,** the finely divided trioxide burns like tinder, forming the tetroxide. According to T. Carnelley and J. Walker, the trioxide is stable in air until a temp. approaching 360° is attained ; between 360° and 400°, oxygen is rapidly absorbed, forming a product Sb_5O_8, which gains only 0·11 per cent. as the temp. rises from 415° to 440° ; there is a rapid absorption of oxygen between 440° and 500°, and the product Sb_4O_7 is comparatively stable between 500° and 565°. There is again a rapid absorption of oxygen between 565° and 585°, forming the tetroxide which is stable as the temp. rises 590° to over 775°. H. Baubigny found that the tetroxide at still higher temp. passes into the trioxide. For the hydrates of antimony trioxide, *vide infra,* antimonious acids. J. J. Berzelius said that the trioxide is but slightly soluble in **water,** and H. Capitaine observed that it also dissolves sparingly in hot water without separating as the liquid cools. According to H. Schulze, 100 parts of water at 15° dissolve 0·0016 part of the trioxide ; and at 100°, 0·01 part. P. Edgerton, in opposition to J. B. Tingle, found that antimony trioxide is not oxidized when aqueous-alcoholic soln. are boiled. L. J. Thénard found that **hydrogen dioxide** has no action on antimony trioxide.

When antimony trioxide is heated in a current of **chlorine,** R. Weber found that antimony tri- and pentachlorides are formed as well as the tetroxide, which at a higher temp. is decomposed. K. H. Butler and D. McIntosh observed that the trioxide is insoluble in liquid chlorine ; and C. Willgerodt found the trioxide is a good *Ueberträger*, or catalyst, in chlorinating organic compounds. R. F. Weinland and P. Gruhl could not obtain compounds with the metal iodides analogous to those obtained with arsenic trioxide, but a soln. of antimony trioxide in fused potassium iodide gave crystals of **potassium oxyiodoantimonite,** $K_2O.2KI.8Sb_2O_3$. The trioxide is soluble in **hydrochloric acid**—*vide* antimony oxychloride. R. Schuhmann found that soln. containing 0·2310, 0·4970, 0·8610, and 1·1330 mols of **perchloric acid** per litre dissolve respectively the eq. of 0·000236, 0·000317, 0·000575, and 0·000752 gram-atoms of antimony per litre at 25°. According to J. L. Proust, when the trioxide is melted with a little **sulphur** it forms *Spiessglanzglas* —*vide* the oxysulphides—while with an excess of sulphur it forms the trisulphide : $2Sb_2O_3+9S=2Sb_2S_3+3SO_2$. E. Mitschlerlich obtained sodium sulphantimonate and antimonate by boiling the trioxide with sulphur and soda-lye. O. Schumann found that in the cold, antimony trioxide is coloured yellow by **hydrogen sulphide,** but when heated, an oxysulphide is formed. J. J. Berzelius found that **ammonium sulphide** first produces an orange oxysulphide, then brownish-red trisulphide, and finally dissolves that sulphide ; A. Terreil, as indicated above, found that the rhombic trioxide is more quickly attacked than the cubic trioxide. With **sulphur dioxide,** a sulphite is produced. J. Milbauer and J. Tucek found that when sulphur dioxide is passed over heated antimony oxide, sulphate and sulphur are formed. As shown by A. Terriel, dil. **sulphuric acid** does not dissolve the trioxide, but the conc. acid forms a soln. of antimony sulphate (*q.v.*). G. Oddo and E. Serra observed that **sulphur monochloride** converts the trioxide into the trichloride ; and H. Prinz represented the reaction at 120° in a sealed tube : $6S_2Cl_2+2Sb_2O_3=4SbCl_3+3SO_2+9S$. F. Faktor obtained antimony trisulphide by the action of the trioxide on fused **sodium thiosulphate ;** and M. Meyer observed that the reaction between a soln. of antimony trioxide in alkali-lye and sodium thiosulphate may be used as a clock reaction, in that the conc. of the soln. may be regulated so that the orange sulphide appears after definite intervals of time.

G. Gore said that the trioxide is insoluble in liquid **ammonia**. E. R. Schneider, and R. H. Brett found the trioxide to be soluble in a cold soln. of **ammonium chloride** or **ammonium nitrate.** J. J. Berzelius prepared what he regarded as **antimony aminotrioxide,** $Sb_2O_3.nNH_3$, by the action of aq. ammonia on antimonyl chloride at ordinary temp. ; the white powder is slightly soluble in water. F. Ephraim found that when the trioxide is heated with **sodamide,** antimony and sodium antimonite are formed. According to J. J. Berzelius, **nitric acid** dissolves a little antimony trioxide and converts it into the pentoxide (q.v.). A. Terreil said the trioxide is insoluble in dil. nitric acid ; and E. M. Péligot, that, with the conc. acid, a mixture of tetra- and penta-oxides is formed. Fuming nitric acid dissolves more trioxide. Fused **alkali nitrates** transform the trioxide into an alkali antimonate. E. Berger and L. Delmas found that the presence of the trioxide facilitates the combustion of **carbon** in air. W. Bulgrin studied the complex salts.

T. Köhler found that the trioxide dissolves in a soln. of **phosphoric acid,** forming a phosphate. A. Michaelis represented the reaction with **phosphorus trichloride** at 160° in a sealed tube : $5Sb_2O_3+6PCl_3=3P_2O_5+6SbCl_3+4Sb$, and the antimony reduces a little of the trichloride to red phosphorus. For the action of phosphorus halides on the trioxide, see N. N. Sen's observations with arsenic trioxide. J. L. Proust observed no reaction between **antimony** and antimony trioxide ; E. R. Schneider said that 100 parts of boiling **antimony trichloride** dissolve 6·7 parts of the trioxide ; for the reaction between **antimony trisulphide** and trioxide, vide infra, the oxysulphides. W. R. Schoeller observed that antimony trioxide is reduced to antimony when heated to incipient fusion, or to 965°, in an atm. of an inert gas.

L. Möser and W. Eidmann found that **boron nitride** reduces the trioxide to antimony ; the trioxide dissolves in fused **borax.** J. J. Berzelius found that the trioxide is readily reduced by **carbon** at a red-heat ; and J. F. Gmelin, by **carbon monoxide** at a red-heat—vide antimony. W. Fränkel and co-workers studied the reduction of the trioxide by carbon monoxide at 400°, 500°, 600°, and 900°. J. von Liebig found that fused **potassium cyanide** reduces the trioxide, forming antimony and potassium cyanate ; and, added F. Nelissen, some sodium formate is also produced. Dittler and Co., and T. Köhler found the trioxide to be slightly soluble in **alcohol,** and in **glycerol** in the presence of alkalies. H. Gordon studied this subject ; and H. Meerwein, the formation of alkoxides $H[Sb(OR)_4]$. H. Schulze observed that the trioxide prepared in the wet-way dissolves more easily in a soln. of **tartaric acid** than if it had been made by a sublimation process. A. Naumann, and W. Eidmann reported that the trioxide does not dissolve in **acetone.** Antimony trioxide dissolves in **acetic, benzoic, or pyrotartaric acid.** C. N. Waite, and M. Kretzschmar found the trioxide to be soluble in **lactic acid ;** W. Vogel, in a soln. of **grape sugar** containing a little lime water ; G. G. Henderson and D. Prentice, a soln. of **potassium citrate, malate, mucate, lactate, and tartrate.** Observations were also made by E. Jordis, and A. Rosenheim. A. C. Vournasos found that at 400°, antimony oxide is reduced by **sodium formate** without the production of stibine. H. Causse studied compounds with the **catechols.** L. Lévy observed that **phenols** and **alkaloids** give coloured reactions with antimony trioxide. L. Kahlenberg and W. J. Trautmann observed a very slow reaction with **silicon** at high temp. G. Rauter found that when heated with **silicon tetrachloride** in a sealed tube at 360°–370°, antimony trioxide forms antimony trichloride and silica. K. Fawa examined the effect of the trioxide on **glass.** O. Ruff and K. Albert observed that **trichlorosilane** reacts with antimony trioxide in the presence of sodium hydroxide or hydrocarbonate : $Sb_2O_3+9NaOH+3SiHCl_3$ $=9NaCl+3Si(OH)_4+2Sb$.

J. J. Berzelius found that at a gentle heat **potassium** reduces antimony tri-

ANTIMONY 427

oxide to antimony—light and heat are developed during the reaction. **L. Guillet** observed that **magnesium,** and **aluminium** also reduce the trioxide to **the metal.** A series of antimonites is produced by the action of aq. soln. of the **alkali or alkaline earth hydroxides** on antimony trioxide. The composition of the products depends on the temp. and conc. of the soln.—*vide infra,* the antimonites. R. Bunsen found that an ammoniacal soln. of **silver oxide** is reduced by antimony trioxide.

REFERENCES.

[1] A. Libavius, *Alchymia,* Francofurti, 1595 ; N. Lemery, *Cours de chymie,* Paris, 1675 ; Basil Valentine, *Triumphwagen Antimonii,* Nürnberg, 1676 ; London, 1893 ; *Von dem grossen Stein der Uhralten,* Strassburg, 1651 ; O. Croll, *Basilica chymica,* Frankfort, 1609 ; R. J. Glauber, *Pharmacopœa spagyrica,* Amstelodami, 1656 ; H. Kopp, *Geschichte der Chemie,* Braunschweig, 4. 108, 1847 ; M. Ettmüller, *Nouvelle chimie raisonnée,* Lyon, 187, 1693 ; L. J. Thénard, *Ann. Chim. Phys.,* (1), 32. 257, 1799.

[2] L. J. Thénard, *Ann. Chim. Phys.,* (1), 32. 257, 1799 ; J. L. Proust, *Journ. Phys.,* 55. 325, 1802 ; 64. 150, 1807 ; J. J. Berzelius, *Schweigger's Journ.,* 6. 144, 1812 ; 22. 69, 1818.

[3] J. J. Berzelius, *Schweigger's Journ.,* 6. 144, 1812 ; 22. 69, 1818 ; J. L. Proust, *Journ. Phys.,* 55. 325, 1802 ; 64. 150, 1807 ; F. Jones, *Journ. Chem. Soc.,* 29. 642, 1876 ; R. F. Marchand, *Journ. prakt. Chem.,* (1), 34. 381, 1845 ; R. Böttger, *ib.,* (1), 68. 372, 1856 ; A. Ludwig, *Journ. Amer. Chem. Soc.,* 31. 1130, 1909.

[4] J. A. Mongez, *Journ. Phys.,* 23. 66, 1783 ; B. Rössler, *Crell's Chem. Ann.,* i, 334, 1787 ; B. Hacquet, *ib.,* i, 523, 1788 ; M. H. Klaproth, *ib.,* i, 9, 1789 ; *Beiträge zur chemischen Kenntniss der Mineralkörper,* Berlin, 3. 183, 1802 ; R. J. Haüy, *Traité de minéralogie,* Paris, 4. 275, 1801 ; A. G. Werner and C. A. S. Hoffmann, *Berg. Journ.,* 385, 398, 1789 ; A. Rose, *Pogg. Ann.,* 53. 167, 1841 ; A. Breithaupt, *Vollständiges Charakteristik des Mineralsystems,* Dresden, 62, 1832 ; F. S. Beudant, *Traité élémentaire de minéralogie,* Paris, 2. 615, 1832 ; E. J. Chapman, *Practical Mineralogy,* London, 39, 1843 ; W. Haidinger, *Handbuch der bestimmenden Mineralogie,* Wien, 506, 1845 ; C. C. von Leonhard, *Handbuch der Oryktognosie,* Heidelberg, 160, 1821 ; R. Kirwan, *Elements of Mineralogy,* London, 1. 251, 1796.

[5] H. de Sénarmont, *Ann. Chim. Phys.,* (3), 31. 504, 1851 ; J. D. Dana, *Amer. Journ. Science,* (2), 12. 209, 1851 ; G. A. Kenngott, *Sitzber. Akad. Wien,* 9. 587, 1852 ; F. Wöhler, *Pogg. Ann.,* 26. 177, 1832 ; P. Groth, *ib.,* 137. 426, 1869.

[6] S. Berberich, *Ueber das anodische Verhalten des Jodes Arsens und Antimons,* Munchen, 1913 ; R. Brandes, *Brandes' Arch.,* (2), 21. 156, 1840 ; E. G. Hornung, *ib.,* (2), 50. 47, 1847 ; *Journ. Pharm. Chim.,* (3), 13. 355, 1848 ; M. Durand, *ib.,* (3), 2. 364, 1842 ; H. de Sénarmont, *ib.,* (3), 19. 444, 1851 ; *Ann. Chim. Phys.,* (3), 31. 504, 1851 ; (3), 32. 129, 1851 ; L. E. Rivot, *ib.,* (3), 31. 504, 1851 ; H. V. Regnault, *ib.,* (2), 62. 362, 1836 ; (3), 1. 129, 1841 ; W. Lindner, *Chem. Tech. Repert.,* 1. 92, 1868 ; *Zeit. Chem.,* (2), 5. 442, 1869 ; *Bull. Soc. Chim.,* (1), 12. 455, 1869 ; J. L. Proust, *Journ. Phys.,* 55. 325, 1802 ; 64. 150, 1807 ; J. Preuss, *Liebig's Ann.,* 31. 197, 1839 ; R. Bunsen, *ib.,* 106. 1, 1858 ; A. Terreil, *Compt. Rend.,* 62. 302, 1866 ; *Ann. Chim. Phys.,* (4), 7. 350, 1866 ; L. Pasteur, *ib.,* (3), 24. 442, 1848 ; (3), 28. 56, 1850 ; (3), 31. 67, 1851 ; P. F. G. Boullay, *ib.,* (2), 43. 266, 1832 ; H. Fizeau, *ib.,* (4), 8. 360, 1866 ; *Compt. Rend.,* 62. 1101, 1133, 1866 ; H. Baubigny, *ib.,* 124. 499, 560, 1897 ; G. von Knorre, *Zeit. angew. Chem.,* 1. 155, 1888 ; J. Thomsen, *Thermochemische Untersuchungen,* Leipzig, 2. 329, 1882 ; J. J. Berzelius, *Schweigger's Journ.,* 6. 144, 1812 ; 22. 69, 1818 ; C. J. B. Karsten, *ib.,* 65, 394, 1832 ; S. Metzl, *German Pat.,* D.R.P. 161776, 1905 ; E. S. Dana, *Amer. Journ. Science,* (2), 17. 88, 1854 ; W. G. Mixter, *ib.,* (4), 28. 103, 1909 ; H. Debray, *Compt. Rend.,* 58. 1209, 1864 ; T. Thomson, *System of Chemistry,* London, 1. 533, 1817 ; A. Simon and E. Thaler, *Zeit. anorg. Chem.,* 162. 253, 1927 ; A. Simon, *ib.,* 165. 31, 1927 ; U. Dehlinger and R. Glocker, *ib.,* 165. 41, 1927 ; U. Dehlinger, *Zeit. Kryst.,* 66. 109, 1927 ; W. Biltz, *Nachr. Gött.,* 298, 1908 ; A. Ditte and R. Metzner, *ib.,* 115. 936, 1892 ; A. Guntz, *ib.,* 98. 303, 1884 ; *Antimoine,* Paris, 1884 ; E. Mitscherlich, *Journ. prakt. Chem.,* (1), 19. 455, 1840 ; *Pogg. Ann.,* 15. 453, 1828 ; A. Rose, *ib.,* 53. 167, 1841 ; H. Rose, *ib.,* 3. 441, 1824 ; 26. 180, 1832 ; C. F. Neumann, *ib.,* 126. 123, 1865 ; P. Groth, *ib.,* 137. 426, 1869 ; H. Fischer, *Verh. Geol. Reichsanst. Wien,* 255, 1873 ; C. Hensgen, *Rec. Trav. Chim. Pays-Bas,* 4. 401, 1885 ; J. H. Long, *Journ. Amer. Chem. Soc.,* 17. 87, 1895 ; A. Schuller, *Math. Term. Tad. Ertesito,* 6. 163, 1884 ; A. Grosse-Bohle, *Zeit. Kryst.,* 5. 222, 1881 ; A. Arzruni, *ib.,* 18. 58, 1891 ; A. Schrauf, *ib.,* 20. 433, 1892 ; J. Weber, *ib.,* 44. 236, 1907 ; H. Laspeyres, *ib.,* 9. 162, 1884 ; *Zeit. deut. geol. Ges.,* 27. 608, 1875 ; H. Biltz, *Zeit. phys. Chem.,* 19. 385, 1896 ; L. Playfair and J. P. Joule, *Mem. Chem. Soc.,* 3. 83, 1846 ; T. Carnelley and J. Walker, *Journ. Chem. Soc.,* 53. 86, 1888 ; A. A. Read, *ib.,* 65. 313, 1894 ; S. Rideal, *Ber.,* 19. 589, 1886 ; W. Spring, *ib.,* 16. 1142, 1883 ; V. Meyer and H. Mensching, *ib.,* 12. 1282, 1879 ; W. Haidinger, *Treatise on Mineralogy,* Edinburgh, 2. 152, 1825 ; F. Mohs, *Grundriss der Mineralogie,* Dresden, 2. 169, 1824 ; W. Phillips, *Introduction to Mineralogy,* London, 331, 1823 ; A. de Gramont, *Bull. Soc. Min.,* 18. 232, 1895 ; R. W. Gray, J. B. Speakman, and J. H. P. Campbell, *Proc. Roy. Soc.,* 102. A, 600, 1923 ; A. des Cloizeaux, *Manuel de minéralogie,* Paris, 2. 330, 1893 ; *Nouvelles recherches sur les propriétés optiques des cristaux,* Paris, 520, 1867 ; *Mémoire sur l'emploi du microscope polarisant,* Paris, 124, 1864 ; *Ann. Mines,* (5), 14. 339, 1858 ; (6), 6. 557, 1864 ; *Mém.*

Savants Etrang., **18**. 511, 1868; *Compt. Rend.*, **62**. 987, 1866; S. Wosnessensky, *Koll. Zeit.*, **33**. 32, 1923; E. Mallard, (7), **10**. 108, 1876; E. Bertrand, *Bull. Soc. Min.*, **5**. 11, 1881; A. Germot, *U.S. Pat. No.* 1504685, 1924; R. Prendel, *Tschermak's Mitt.*, (2), **11**. 7, 1889; R. Brauns, *Die optischen Anomalien der Krystalle*, Leipzig, 190, 1891; V. Kohlschütter and J. L. Tüscher, *Zeit. Elektrochem.*, **27**. 225, 1921; W. Heintze, *Zeit. Physik*, **15**. 339, 1923; C. F. Rammelsberg, *Handbuch der krystallographischphysikalschen Chemie*, Leipzig, **1**. 110, 1881; R. W. Gray, J. B. Speakman, and E. Thomson, *Nature*, **107**. 619, 1920; F. Winkler, *Das Atomgewicht des Antimons. Neubestimmung durch Ueberführung des Metalls in Antimon-Tetroxyd*, München, 1917; A. Breithaupt, *Vollständiges Charakteristik des Mineralsystems*, Dresden, 62, 1832; *Vollständiges Handbuch der Mineralogie*, Dresden, **2**. 185, 1841; A. Brezina, *Ann. Naturhist. Hofmus. Wien*, **1**. 149, 1886; C. Arnold, *Ber.*, **38**. 1175, 1905; C. Renz, *Helvetica Chim. Acta*, **4**. 961, 1921; C. W. C. Fuchs, *Die künstlich dargestellten Mineralien nach Roses System geordnet*, Haarlem, 83, 1872; G. Suckow, *Die Verwitterung im Mineralreiche*, Leipzig, 12, 1848; H. S. Patterson and R. Whytlaw, *Proc. Leeds Lit. Phil. Soc.*, **1**. 70, 1926; T. W. Case, *Phys. Rev.*, (2), **9**. 305, 1917; Anon., *Continental Met. Chem. Engg.*, **2**. 27, 1927; F. Millosevich, *Atti Accad. Lincei*, (5), **9**. i, 336, 1900; A. Pelloux, *ib.*, (5), **10**. 10, 1901; (5), **13**. 34, 1904; D. Lovisato, *ib.*, (5), **3**. 82, 1894; E. Quercigh, *ib.*, (5), **21**. i, 415, 1912; F. Sandberger, *Neues Jahrb. Min.*, 316, 1869; F. Beijerinck, *Neues Jahrb. Min. B.B.*, **11**. 442, 1897; J. Davy, *Phil. Trans.*, **102**, 169, 1812; M. H. Klaproth, *Beiträge zur chemischen Kenntniss der Mineralkörper*, Berlin, **3**. 183, 1802; *Crell's Chem. Ann.*, i, 9, 1789; L. J. Spencer, *Min. Mag.*, **14**. 308, 1907; G. A. Kenngott, *Sitzber. Akad. Wien*, **9**. 587, 1852; J. Nöggerath, *Ber. Niederrh. Ges. Bonn*, 26, 1856; J. R. Blum, *Die Pseudomorphosen des Mineralreichs*, Stuttgart, 31, 1843; G. Cesaro, *Mém. Acad. Belg.*, **8**. 4, 1925; W. R. Mott, *Trans. Amer. Electrochem. Soc.*, **34**. 255, 1918; R. Schumann, *Journ. Amer. Chem. Soc.*, **46**. 59, 1924; R. M. Bosworth, *ib.*, **47**. 1621, 1925; F. Wöhler, *Po₀g. Ann.*, **27**. 628, 1833; *Liebig's Ann.*, **5**. 20, 1833.

⁷ A. Terreil, *Ann. Chim. Phys.*, (4), **7**. 350, 1886; P. Gruhl, *Verbindungen des Arsen- und Antimontrioxydes mit den Haloqeniden mehrwertiger Metalle*, München, 1897; R. F. Weinland and P. Gruhl, *Arch. Pharm.*, **255**. 467, 1917; J. von Liebig, *Handwörterbuch der reinen und angewandten Chemie*, Braunschweig, **1**. 414, 1837; J. J. Berzelius, *Schweigger's Journ.*, **6**. 144, 1812; 22. 69, 1818; L. J. Thénard, *Traité de chimie*, Paris, **8**. 478, 1833; T. Carnelley and J. Walker, *Journ. Chem. Soc.*, **53**. 86, 1888; H. Baubigny, *Compt. Rend.*, **124**. 499, 560, 1897; E. M. Péligot, *ib.*, **23**. 709, 1846; L. Lévy, *ib.*, **103**. 1195, 1886; H. Causse, *ib.*, **114**. 1072, 1892; H. Schulze, *Journ. prakt. Chem.*, (2), **27**. 320, 1883; C. Willgerodt, *ib.*, (2), **31**. 539, 1885; A. Michaelis, *ib.*, (2), **4**. 425, 1871; E. Mitscherlich, *ib.*, (1), **19**. 455, 1840; H. Capitaine, *Journ. Pharm. Chim.*, (3) **25**. 516, 1839; J. L. Proust, *Journ. Phys.*, **55**. 325, 1802; 64. 150, 1807; O. Schumann, *Liebig's Ann.*, **187**. 312, 1877; H. Prinz, *ib.*, **223**. 356, 1884; G. Rauter, *ib.*, **270**. 251, 1892; R. Bunsen, *ib.*, **106**. 1, 1858; R. Weber, *Pogg. Ann.*, **112**. 625, 1861; E. R. Schneider, *ib.*, **108**. 407, 1859; G. Oddo and E. Serra, *Gazz. Chim. Ital.*, **29**. ii, 355, 1899; G. Gore, *Proc. Roy. Soc.*, **20**. 441, 1872; 21. 140, 1873; T. Köhler, *Dingler's Journ.*, **258**. 520, 1885; J. F. Gmelin, *Gilbert's Ann.*, **8**. 319, 1801; F. Nelissen, *Bull. Acad. Belg.*, (3), **13**. 258, 1887; R. H. Brett, *Phil. Mag.*, (3), **10**. 97, 1837; M. Kretzschmar, *Chem. Ztg.*, **12**. 943, 1888; W. Metzener, *Zur Kenntnis der amphoteren Metalloxyde*, München, 1906; C. N. Waite, *Brit. Pat. No.* 6070, 1886; Dittler and Co., *German Pat.*, *D.R.P.* 31688, 1884; W. Vogel, *ib.*, 30194, 1884; W. Eidmann, *Ein Beitrag zur Erkenntnis des Verhaltens chemischer Verbindungen in nichtwässrigen Lösungen*, Geissen, 1899; G. G. Henderson and D. Prentice, *Journ. Chem. Soc.*, **67**. 1030, 1895; **81**. 658, 1902; E. Berger and L. Delmas, *Bull. Soc. Chim.*, (4), **29**. 68, 1921; E. Jordis, *Zeit. angew. Chem.*, **15**. 906, 1902; A. Rosenheim, *Zeit. anorg. Chem.*, **20**. 281, 1899; P. Ephraim, *ib.*, **44**. 193, 1905; W. Fränkel and K. Snipschsky, *ib.*, **125**. 235, 1922; W. Fränkel, *Festschrift zur Jahrhundertfeier des physikalischen Vereins*, Frankfurt a. M., 136, 1924; J. Milhauer and J. Tucek, *Chem. Ztg.*, **50**. 323, 1926; L. Kahlenberg and W. J. Trautmann, *Trans. Amer. Electrochem. Soc.*, **39**. 377, 1921; A. Naumann, *Ber.*, **37**. 4329, 1904; O. Ruff and K. Albert, *ib.*, **38**. 2234, 1905; L. Möser and W. Eidmann, *ib.*, **35**. 525, 1902; F. Faktor, *Pharm. Post*, **38**. 527, 1905; L. Guillet, *Contribution à l'étude des alliages d'aluminium*, Paris, 1902; P. Edgerton, *Journ. Amer. Chem. Soc.*, **35**. 1769, 1913; J. B. Tingle, *ib.*, **33**. 1762, 1911; R. Schuhmann, *ib.*, **46**. 52, 1924; M. Meyer, *ib.*, **44**. 1498, 1922; W. R. Schoeller, *Journ. Soc. Chem. Ind.*, **34**. 6, 1915; N. N. Sen, *Proc. Asiatic Soc.*, **15**. 263, 1919; K. Fawa, *Journ. Japan. Cer. Assoc.*, 241, 1923; A. C. Vournasos, *Ber.*, **43**. 2264, 1910; H. Gordon, *Ueber die Komplexität verschiedener Metalltartrationen und die Löslichkeit verschiedener Metallhydroxyde und Sulfide*, Danzig, 1924; V. Ipatieff, *Ber.*, **59**. B, 1412, 1926; W. Bulgrin, *Ueber innerkomplexe Verbindungen des drei- und fünfwertigen Antimons*, Berlin, 1926; K. H. Butler and D. McIntosh, *Trans. Roy. Soc. Canada*, (3), **21**. 19, 1927; H. Meerwein, *Liebig's Ann.*, **455**. 227, 1927.

§ 11. The Antimonious Acids, and the Antimonites

The compounds of antimony trioxide with the bases are called **antimonites**; the antimonites can be regarded as salts of ortho-, pyro-, and meta-antimonious acids.

or of the more complex, hypothetical acids, HSb_3O_5, $H_2Sb_4O_7$, $H_4Sb_6O_{11}$, $H_2Sb_6O_{10}$, and $H_2Sb_{16}O_{25}$. These salts were specially investigated by H. Rose,[1] E. Frémy, etc. E. Mitscherlich found that the precipitate obtained by the action of cold soln. of sodium carbonate on antimony trichloride usually changes in the cold, and always on boiling, into a white powder consisting of small octahedra of the trioxide. F. W. Clarke and H. Stallo prepared **orthoantimonious acid,** H_3SbO_3, by decomposing barium antimonyl tartrate with the calculated quantity of sulphuric acid ; warming the soln. of antimonyl tartrate ; and drying the white precipitate at 100°. C. Lea and J. K. Wood showed that the composition of the product obtained by this process does not correspond with orthantimonious acid. They also found that conc. sulphuric, hydrochloric, or nitric acid, or alkali-lye precipitates orthantimonious acid from soln. of potassium antimonyl tartrate. A. Guntz said that antimony trioxide and not the hydrate is precipitated by acids from soln. of potassium antimonyl tartrate. In opposition to F. W. Clarke and H. Stallo, A. Guntz found that the precipitate obtained by the addition of an acid to potassium antimonyl tartrate, even after washing until the filtrate gave no acidic reaction, still retained as much as 5 per cent. of tartaric acid. R. Lorenz found antimony acquires a grey film of hydroxide when made the anode in the electrolysis of soln. of alkali chlorides, sulphates, or nitrates. T. Carnelley and J. Walker made a similar observation with respect to alkali-lye, and aq. ammonia. The white powder was stated by F. W. Clarke and H. Stallo to be stable in air, even at 150°, but to pass into the trioxide at a higher temp. H. Remy discussed the structure of antimonious acid. A. Simon and H. Pöhlmann studied the dehydration and rehydration of the **hydrogels** of antimony trioxide at 18°, and the results are summarized in Fig. 29. There is no evidence of the formation of a definite hydrate. T. Carnelley and J. Walker found that precipitated antimony trioxide is always anhydrous after being kept in air a few months. L. Schaffner heated to boiling a soln. of recently precipitated antimony sulphide in potash-lye, and added a soln. of copper sulphate until the liquid gives a white precipitate without a tinge of orange. The filtered liquid was then treated with acetic acid so long as a precipitate was formed. The washed and dried precipitate was supposed to be **pyroantimonious acid,** $H_4Sb_2O_5$, or $Sb_2O_3.2H_2O$; but C. Sereno showed that the product is really orthoantimonic acid, H_3SbO_4, formed at the expense of a portion of the oxygen of the cupric salt—a cuprous salt is present among the products of the reaction. According to J. H. Long and H. E. Sauer, **metantimonious acid,** $HSbO_2$, is produced when potassium antimonyl tartrate is decomposed by an alkali carbonate, phosphate, tungstate, or acetate. C. Lea and J. K. Wood found that the composition of the product depends on the mode of preparation, being at ordinary temp. $Sb_2O_3.\frac{1}{2}H_2O$.

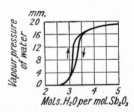

FIG. 29.—Vapour Pressure of Hydrated Antimony Trioxide at 18°.

The individuality of none of the antimonious acids, or hydrates of antimonious acids has been definitely established. C. Lea and J. K. Wood concluded : when hydrated antimonious oxide is liberated, as by the action of a mineral acid on a soln. of tartar emetic, the finely-divided precipitate tends to adsorb some of the added acid or some of the liberated tartaric acid, forming an adsorption product in equilibrium with the soln. On removing the supernatant liquid by decantation and replacing it with fresh water, the equilibrium conditions are disturbed, and some of the adsorbed acid is removed ; this operation is repeated at each decantation, until eventually it becomes impossible to detect the acid in the soln. by the ordinary methods. Although antimony trioxide is amphoteric, so long as an appreciable quantity of an acid is present the behaviour of the hydrated oxide in an acidic capacity is impossible. As the acid is removed, however, the hydrated oxide begins to act as an acid in addition to behaving as a base ; interaction between molecules acting in these two capacities will lead to the formation of a condensation product of a salt-like nature. If the solid is left in contact with water for a considerable period, the last traces of adsorbed acid are slowly removed and the process of condensation continues until an almost anhydrous product is eventually obtained. Hydrated antimonious oxide is more feeble as an acid than as a base. When, therefore, the substance is precipitated by an alkaline reagent, there is little tendency for the formation of adsorption compounds with the alkali employed ; on filtering and washing the product, therefore, condensation can proceed unchecked and the almost anhydrous oxide is obtained more readily than when an acid precipitant is employed. When a soln. of antimony trichloride is titrated with sodium hydroxide, the precipitate begins to separate before the neutral point is reached and may at this stage be regarded as a hydrated basic chloride. As the addition of the alkali is slowly continued, the chlorine is gradually removed, the removal of the last traces of halogen by the practically neutral soln. taking place slowly ; the small amount of acid retained by the precipitate makes no appreciable difference to the titration, but retards the process of condensation. If a slight excess of alkali is added, the whole of the halogen is eliminated, condensation can then proceed unhindered, and the nearly anhydrous oxide results. A. Simon and H. Pöhlmann studied the adsorption of potassium hydroxide by the trioxide prepared in different ways, and attributed the different results solely to differences in the grain-size of the trioxides. They also studied the peptization of the colloid by acids. While phosphoric acid peptizes the colloidal trioxide, an excess of that acid coagulates it. They also prepared **alcogels** of hydrated antimony trioxide ; and **acetonegels** in which the water of the hydrate is completely replaced by acetone.

E. Mitscherlich [2] obtained **sodium metantimonite**, $NaSbO_2$, by melting antimony trioxide with an excess of sodium carbonate ; an eq. amount of carbon dioxide is expelled ; and the antimonite isolated by washing away the soluble salts. A. Terreil found that the *trihydrate*, $NaSbO_2.3H_2O$, crystallized from a soln. of antimony trioxide in soda-lye ; and it was obtained by H. Cormimbœuf by saturating with antimony trioxide a boiling soln. of sodium hydroxide in twice its weight of water ; pouring the liquid into a large proportion of boiling water ; and on cooling the filtered liquid, quadratic plates of the metantimonite were deposited. H. Cormimbœuf said that the crystals are clear, colourless, octahedra with square bases. The trihydrate was found by A. Terreil to have a sp. gr. 2·864, and when heated, the salt loses its water of crystallization and becomes opaque. H. Cormimbœuf said that the salt is decomposed by moist air, forming antimony trioxide and sodium carbonate ; with hot or cold water the salt is hydrolyzed and rhombic antimony trioxide is formed. According to H. Rose, E. Frémy, and E. Mitscherlich, the alkaline soln. of antimony trioxide is oxidized by exposure to air, and the antimonites are oxidized when fused with alkali hydroxide in air. If an excess of alkali-lye is present, the clear soln. does not become turbid by dilution or by boiling. H. Hager said that the antimonites are oxidized by hydrogen dioxide and by the halogens. A. Terreil said that hydrogen sulphide transforms the antimonite into a sulphantimonite ; and R. Weinland and A. Gutmann, that sodium thiosulphate is reduced to sulphite, and unlike the corresponding case with arsenites, only antimonates and sulphantimonates are formed ; no oxysulphantimonate could be detected. O. Brunck found that sodium hyposulphite in alkaline soln. reduces the trioxide to antimony ; likewise also in neutral or feebly acidic soln. if a large excess of reducing agent is employed. A. C. Vournasos found that sodium antimonite mixed with sodium formate is reduced to antimony at 800°, and a little stibine is formed. A. Terreil obtained a precipitate soluble in nitric acid when a copper salt is treated with an antimonite. According to M. C. Harding, an alkaline soln. of cupric sulphate precipitates copper antimonite. According to A. Terreil, silver nitrate gives a white precipitate with alkali antimonites ; but H. Rose found that in alkaline soln. silver nitrate gives a black precipitate which R. Bunsen regarded as a suboxide, but which was shown by W. Pillitz to be a mixture of silver oxide, silver, and antimony: $6NaSbO_2+Ag_2O=4NaSbO_3+2Sb$ $+2Ag+Na_2O$; and also $NaSbO_2+Ag_2O=NaSbO_3+2Ag$. H. Rose said that gold chloride gives a black precipitate with antimonites, and M. C. Harding added that if the gold chloride be in excess, aurous oxide is formed, and if the antimonite be in excess, an aurous antimonite is produced. A. Terreil found that an ammoniacal soln. of barium chloride gives a precipitate with antimonites; and mercurous salts also give a precipitate with the antimonites. M. C. Harding found that a soln. of antimony trioxide in alkali-lye in excess gives with mercuric chloride a precipitate of mercuric oxide with no free mercury, but with the antimonite in excess free mercury is formed on standing or on warming. The alkaline soln. of antimonite reduces stannous chloride. A. Terreil found that lead salts give a precipitate with a soln. of an antimonite; similarly also with ferric salts. M. C. Harding found that an alkaline soln. of an antimonite gives a precipitate with ferric chloride which slowly dissolves, forming a red soln. An alkaline soln. of an antimonite is oxidized by potassium dichromate or permanganate to antimonate; and J. Quincke obtained a similar result with potassium ferricyanide. M. C. Harding found that a soln. of platinic chloride gives a brown liquid from which a black precipitate settles—the precipitate contains platinous oxide, and antimony trioxide.

H. Cormimbœuf obtained **sodium triantimonite**, $NaSb_3O_5$, by keeping an excess of antimony trioxide in contact with 33 per cent. soda-lye at 100° for a long time. A. Terreil obtained the *monohydrate*, $NaSb_3O_5.H_2O$, from a soln. of antimony trioxide in conc. soda-lye. The rhombic crystals are almost insoluble in water, and have a sp. gr. 5·05. H. Cormimbœuf found that when a soln. of sodium hydroxide with twice its weight of water is boiled with an excess of antimony trioxide, the warm liquid deposits rhombic plates of **sodium tetrantimonite**, $Na_2Sb_4O_7$.

A number of observers have recorded the formation of **potassium antimonite** without stating definitely the composition of the product. Thus, J. J. Berzelius obtained a grey powder by digesting antimonyl chloride with potash-lye; the powder dissolves in boiling potash-lye, and separates out in crystals on cooling; R. Brandes, and H. Rose and F. Varrentrapp obtained a similar result with a soln. of antimony trioxide in potash-lye. J. von Liebig fused antimony trioxide with potasium carbonate and found that carbon dioxide is driven off; if the trioxide is in excess, the product is more fusible than if the carbonate be in excess, and in the latter case some free antimony is formed as well as antimonate. H. Cormimbœuf found that when a soln. of two parts of potassium hydroxide in an equal weight of water holding in suspension one part of precipitated antimony trioxide, is boiled for a few minutes, prismatic crystals of **potassium triantimonite**, KSb_3O_5, are formed. They are decomposed by water, and by the carbon dioxide of the atm. Rectangular lamellæ of the *hydrate*, $KSb_3O_5.1\frac{1}{2}H_2O$, are formed by saturating a boiling soln. of equal parts of water and potassium hydroxide with antimony trioxide, and allowing the liquid to cool. H. Cormimbœuf said that when water is added gradually to the anhydrous or hydrated triantimonite, the salt is decomposed with separation of prismatic antimony trioxide, but as soon as the water, by decomposition of the salt, has become charged with the 5 per cent. of potassium hydroxide, octahedral antimony trioxide is formed, and when the proportion of hydroxide in soln. reaches 20·9 per cent., decomposition ceases. The octahedral trioxide obstinately retains 0·6–0·2 per cent. of alkali. It is noteworthy that sodium hydroxide yields three antimonites, all of which yield antimony oxide in the crystalline form of valentinite when they are decomposed by water, whereas potassium hydroxide yields only one antimonite, but this, when treated with water, yields antimony oxide crystallized in the forms of both valentinite and sénarmontite. H. Cormimbœuf obtained small crystals of **potassium hexadecantimonite**, $K_2Sb_{16}O_{25}.7H_2O$, by passing carbon dioxide into the mother-liquor from the preceding salt, until a turbidity appears. This salt is stable in contact with cold water, but is decomposed by boiling water.

G. Tammann [3] heated mixtures of copper oxide and antimony trioxide, and observed that a reduction of the former occurs at 420°, presumably, $4CuO + Sb_2O_3 = 2Cu_2O + Sb_2O_5 - 10\cdot6$ cals. It is probable that some antimonite is formed at the same time. The subject was discussed by D. Balareff. According to M. C. Harding, **copper metantimonite,** $Cu(SbO_2)_2$, is obtained by adding a dil. soln. of copper sulphate to an excess of a sat. soln. of antimony trioxide in potash-lye; or by adding copper sulphate to a soln. of potassium antimonyl-tartrate in 8 per cent. aq. potassium hydroxide; it is a green, crystalline powder, is soluble in hydrochloric, tartaric, or citric acid, and when heated in an open crucible at first evolves antimony oxide and then explodes, leaving a residue of antimony trioxide and copper oxide; when heated in a closed vessel, the residue contains metallic copper. The mineral **thrombolite** was found by A. Breithaupt in the limestone of Rezbanya, Hungary. The first incomplete analysis indicated that it is a phosphate, but A. Schrauf showed that its composition can be represented by $10CuO.3Sb_2O_3.19H_2O$. A. Breithaupt gave $3\cdot381-3\cdot401$ for the sp. gr., and A. Schrauf gave $3\cdot668$. It may be a mixture, and not a definite individual—*vide* cuprous antimonate. I. Domekyo described a copper antimonite resembling the mineral stetefeldite—*vide infra*—occurring in the Potochi copper mine of Peru. As indicated above, **silver antimonite** is not formed by the action of silver nitrate on a soln. of alkali antimonite. M. C. Harding treated gold chloride with an excess of an alkaline soln. of an antimonite and obtained a precipitate which may be a **gold antimonite,** $Au_2O.Sb_2O_3$, or $AuSbO_2$—*vide supra.*

The antimonites of *barium, strontium, and calcium* have not been examined. G. Tammann [4] found that when a mixture of equimolar parts of calcium oxide and antimony trioxide is heated, an acceleration is indicated on the heating curve at about 570°, and the residue remaining after extractions with ammoniacal acetic acid, and with dil. tartaric acid, seems to contain a mixture of two calcium antimonites. The reaction was discussed by D. Balareff. A. Terreil found that barium chloride gives a precipitate with a soln. of alkali antimonite only when aq. ammonia is present. A hyacinth-yellow or honey-yellow mineral obtained by A. Damour from St. Marcel, Piedmont, was called *roméine*—after J. B. L. Romé de l'Isle—a term subsequently altered to **romeite.** A. Damour's analysis corresponds with $3RO.Sb_2O_3.Sb_2O_5$, where $R = Ca$, Mn, and Fe—*vide infra,* calcium hypoantimonate. P. Groth regarded the idealized mineral as *calcium metantimonite,* $Ca(SbO_2)_2$. W. T. Schaller found that A. Damour's analysis was probably in error, that the formula corresponds with *calcium hexantimonate,* $Ca_5Sb_6O_{20}$—or $(Ca,Na_2,Fe,Mn)_5Sb_6O_{20}$—in which the mineral is considered to be the salt of a partially dehydrated hexantimonic acid, $H_{12}Sb_6O_{21}$ less H_2O. A. Damour's tetragonal crystals have the axial ratio $a:c = 1:1\cdot0257$. The double refraction is strong; and E. Bertrand discussed the optical anomaly. W. T. Schaller reported the index of refraction to be $1\cdot83-1\cdot87$. The crystals were also examined by A. Pelloux, E. Hussak, W. T. Schaller, and E. R. Schröder. The crystals are really octahedra belonging to the cubic system; and they possess an imperfect octahedral cleavage. W. T. Schaller added that the mineral is probably dimorphous with the high temp. form cubic. The sp. gr. is 4·713; W. T. Schaller gave 5·074; and E. Hussak, 5·1. The hardness is 5·5. Romeite is insoluble in acids. It fuses to a black slag. W. T. Schaller supposes that the Swedish and Brazilian atopites are romeite. The *antimonites of beryllium, magnesium, zinc, and cadmium* have not been prepared in the wet way. G. Tammann observed that with mixtures of magnesia and antimony trioxide, **magnesium metantimonite,** $Mg(SbO_2)_2$, is formed at 500°; and with zinc oxide and antimony trioxide, **zinc metantimonite,** $Zn(SbO_2)_2$, is formed at 485°. The reactions were discussed by D. Balareff. The *mercurous and mercuric antimomites* have not been prepared. A. Terreil obtained a precipitate with a mercurous salt and alkali antimonite; and M. C. Harding, one with mercuric chloride. No *tin antimonite* has been prepared—*vide supra.* A. Terreil, and A. Streng obtained a precipitate with a lead salt and alkali antimonite. G. Tammann found that when a mixture of lead oxide and antimony trioxide is heated lead metantimonite, $Pb(SbO_2)_2$, is formed at 400° : with mixtures of calcium dioxide and antimony trioxide, a reduction of the former occurs at 300°. The reaction was discussed by D. Balareff. The mineral *lewisite*—after R. J. Lewis—was found at Ouro Preto, Brazil, and described by E. Hussak and G. T. Prior.[5] The analysis approximates $5CaO.2TiO_2.3SbO_3$, or $3Ca(SbO_2)_2.2CaTiO_3$, calcium dititanatohexametantimonite. It crystallizes in minute octahedra belonging to the cubic system. The sp. gr. is 4·9, the hardness 5·5. The mineral mauzeliite—named after R. Mauzelius—was obtained by H. Sjögren from Jakobsberg, Sweden. It is a light yellow calcium lead ortho-titanatotetrantimonite, $4(Ca,Pb)O.TiO_2.2Sb_2O_3$, or $2(Ca,Pb)(SbO_2)_2.Ca_2TiO_4$. The octahedral crystals belong to the cubic system and have a sp. gr. 5·11, and hardness 5–6—*vide* derbylite.

T. Thomson [6] obtained a brownish-yellow precipitate and a green soln. by adding potassium chromate to a soln. of antimony trichloride. The observations of M. C. Harding, and F. Kessler show that the antimony trioxide is oxidized. O. W. Gibbs [7] obtained alkali antimonitomolybdates by dissolving freshly precipitated antimony trioxide, or antimonyl chloride in a boiling soln. of alkali molybdate. There is a partial reduction of the molybdate during the action ; and the conc. of the soln. is attended by decomposition with the separation of antimony trioxide. If ammonium molybdate be employed, pale greenish-yellow crystals of ammonium antimonitomolybdate, $6(NH_4)_2O.3Sb_2O_3.17MoO_3.21H_2O$, are formed. They are insoluble in cold water. O. W. Gibbs reported platinum antimonitomolybdate to be formed like the corresponding arsenite. Alkali and ammonium tungstates, under similar conditions, give alkali and ammonium antimonitotungstates as yellow oils. When treated with a barium salt, crystals of barium antimonitotungstate, $2BaO.3Sb_2O_3.11WO_3.18H_2O$, are formed. The salt under hot water melts to a yellow oil which with a large proportion of water dissolves to a yellow, acidic liquid which gives pale yellow flocculent precipitates with *mercurous nitrate, silver nitrate*, or *thallous nitrate*. O. W. Gibbs reported platinum antimonitotungstate to be formed like the corresponding arsenite. O. W. Gibbs obtained antimonitophosphatotungstates by the action of metal salts on a soln. obtained by the action of phosphates on antimonitotungstates, or of phosphatotungstates on hydrated antimony oxide. Pale yellow crystals of potassium antimonitophosphatotungstate, $12K_2O.5Sb_2O_3.6P_2O_5.22WO_3.48H_3O$, were obtained by mixing sodium antimonitophosphatotungstate with potassium phosphate. The salt is insoluble in hot or cold water.

J. J. Berzelius [8] obtained ferrous antimonite by the action of a ferrous salt on an alkali antimonite. For the action of ferric salts on soln. of alkali antimonites, *vide supra*. J. J. Berzelius obtained a violet precipitate of cobalt antimonite from a soln. of a cobalt salt and an alkali antimonite. The precipitate is slightly soluble in water, and when heated gives off water, becoming dark green ; at a higher temp., it emits a glimmering light and afterwards appears white. G. Tammann observed the formation of nickel metantimonite, $Ni(SbO_2)_2$, when mixtures of antimony trioxide and nickel oxide are heated to 600°. The reaction was discussed by D. Balareff.

REFERENCES.

[1] H. Rose, *Pogg. Ann.*, 3. 441, 1824 ; *Phil. Mag.*, 67. 124, 1826 ; *Ann. Phil.*, 10. 416, 1825 ; E. Frémy, *Ann. Chim. Phys.*, (3), 23. 404, 1848 ; *Journ. prakt. Chem.*, (1), 45. 209, 1848 ; F. W. Clarke and H. Stallo, *Ber.*, 13. 1787, 1880 ; *Amer. Chem. Journ.*, 2. 319, 1881 ; A. Guntz, *Compt. Rend.*, 102. 1472, 1886 ; T. Carnelley and J. Walker, *Journ. Chem. Soc.*, 53. 60, 1888 ; C. Lea and J. K. Wood, *ib.*, 123. 259, 1923 ; A. Simon and H. Pöhlmann, *Zeit. anorg. Chem.*, 149. 101, 1925 ; D. Balareff, *ib.*, 160. 92, 1927 ; G. Tammann, *ib.*, 160. 101, 1927 ; H. Remy, *ib.*, 116. 255, 1921 ; R. Lorenz, *ib.*, 12. 436, 1896 ; J. H. Long and H. E. Sauer, *Journ. Amer. Chem. Soc.*, 17. 87, 1895 ; *Chem. News*, 63. 269, 1891 ; L. Schaffner, *Liebig's Ann.*, 51. 168, 1844 ; C. Serono, *Gazz. Chim. Ital.*, 24. ii, 274, 1894 ; E. Mitscherlich, *Journ. prakt. Chem.*, (1), 19. 445, 1840.

[1] E. Mitscherlich, *Journ. prakt. Chem.*, (1), **19**. 455, 1840 ; A. Terreil, *Ann. Chim. Phys.*, (4), **7**. 352, 1866; E. Frémy, *ib.*, (3), **23**. 404, 1848 ; *Journ. prakt. Chem.*, (1), **45**. 209, 1848; H. Cormimbœuf, *Compt. Rend.*, **115**. 1306, 1892 ; *Rev. Chim. Anal. App.*, **3**. 53, 1895 ; H. Rose, *Pogg. Ann.*, **3**. 441, 1824 ; H. Rose and F. Varrentrapp, *ib.*, **47**. 326, 1839 ; A. Gutmann, *Ueber den Abbau der Thiosulfate und einiger Polythionate zu Sulfiten durch reducierende Salze in alkalischer Lösung und über einige Monosulfoxyarsenate*, München, 1897 ; R. Weinland and A. Gutmann, *Zeit. anorg. Chem.*, **17**. 413, 1898 ; M. C. Harding, *ib.*, **20**. 235, 1899 ; J. Quincke, *Zeit. anal. Chem.*, **31**. 35, 1892 ; H. Hager, *ib.*, **11**. 82, 1872 ; W. Pillitz, *ib.*, **21**. 27, 496, 1882 ; O. Brunck, *Liebig's Ann.*, **336**. 281, 1905 ; R. Bunsen, *ib.*, **106**. 1, 1858 ; R. Brandes, *Schweigger's Journ.*, **62**. 199, 1831 ; J. J. Berzelius, *ib.*, **6**. 144, 1812 ; **22**. 69, 1818 ; J. von Liebig, *Handworterbuch der reinen und angewandten Chemie*, Braunschweig, **1**. 414, 1837 ; A. C. Vournasos, *Ber.*, **43**. 2264, 1910.

[3] M. C. Harding, *Zeit. anorg. Chem.*, **20**. 235, 1899 ; A. Breithaupt, *Journ. prakt. Chem.*, (1), **15**. 320, 1838 ; A. Schrauf, *Zeit. Kryst.*, **4**. 28, 1880 ; I. Domekyo, *Elementos de Mineralojia*, Santiago, 1871 ; G. Tammann, *Zeit. anorg. Chem.*, **149**. 68, 1925 ; **160**. 101, 1927 ; D. Balareff, *ib.*, **160**. 92, 1927.

[4] A. Terreil, *Ann. Chim. Phys.*, (4), **7**. 350, 1866 ; A. Streng, *Liebig's Ann.*, **129**. 238, 1864 ; M. C. Harding, *Zeit. anorg. Chem.*, **20**. 235, 1899 ; G. Tammann, *ib.*, **149**. 68, 1925 ; **160**. 101, 1927 ; D. Balareff, *ib.*, **160**. 92, 1927 ; A. Damour, *Ann. Mines*, (3), **20**. 247, 1841 ; (5), **3**. 179, 1853 ; E. Bertrand, *Bull. Soc. Min.*, **4**. 240, 1881 ; P. Groth, *Tabellarische Uebersicht der Mineralien*, Braunschweig, **71**, 1889 ; A. E. Nordenskjöld, *Geol. För. Förh. Stockholm*, **3**. 376, 1877 ; E. R. Schneider, *Pogg. Ann.*, **108**. 407, 1859 ; E. Hussak, *Centr. Min.*, 240, 1905 ; A. Pelloux, *Ann. Mus. Storia Nat. Geneva*, (3), **6**. 22, 1913 ; R. Schröder, *Goldschmidt's Atlas der Kristallformen*, **1**. 121, 1913 ; W. T. Schaller, *Bull. U.S. Geol. Sur.*, 610, 1916.

[5] E. Hussak and G. T. Prior, *Min. Mag.*, **11**. 80, 176, 1895 ; H. Sjögren, *Geol. För. Förh. Stockholm*, **17**. 313, 1895.

[6] T. Thomson, *Phil. Trans.*, **117**. 159, 1827 ; F. Kessler, *Zeit. anal. Chem.*, **2**. 383, 1863 ; M. C. Harding, *Zeit. anorg. Chem.*, **20**. 235, 1899.

[7] O. W. Gibbs, *Proc. Amer. Acad.*, **21**. 69, 89, 105, 1885 ; **8**. 289, 1886 ; *Amer. Chem. Journ.*, **7**. 209, 313, 392, 1885.

[8] J. J. Berzelius, *Schweigger's Journ.*, **6**. 144, 1812 ; **22**. 69, 1818 ; G. Tammann, *Zeit. anorg. Chem.*, **149**. 68, 1925 ; **160**. 101, 1927 ; D. Balareff, *ib.*, **160**. 92, 1927.

§ 12. Antimony Tetroxide, and the Hypoantimonates

As indicated in connection with the history of antimony trioxide, at the beginning of the nineteenth century, quite a number of antimony oxides were supposed to exist. J. J. Berzelius [1] recognized the suboxide, Sb_2O ; the trioxide, or anti-monious oxide, Sb_2O_5 ; the tetroxide, Sb_2O_4 ; and the pentoxide or antimonic oxide, Sb_2O_4. The oxide between antimonious and antimonic oxide was called *hypoantimonic oxide*, and later **antimony tetroxide**, Sb_2O_4, or *antimony dioxide*, SbO_2. Analyses were made by J. J. Berzelius, T. Thomson, L. J. Thénard, J. L. Proust, W. P. Dexter, C. F. Rammelsberg, and E. Bechi. Antimony tetroxide can be regarded as a definite oxide which furnishes the hydrate, **hypoantimonic acid**, $H_2Sb_2O_5$, and the corresponding salts, **hypoantimonates**. The oxide may also be regarded as *antimony metantimonate*, $(SbO)SbO_3$, a salt of metantimonic acid, $HSbO_3$, and the acid as a derivative of orthantimonic acid, $H_2(SbO)SbO_4$. P. Groth represented it as *antimony orthantimonate*, $SbSbO_4$, that is, $Sb\equiv O_3\equiv Sb=O$. E. Mitscherlich, and E. Frémy regarded it as a mixed antimonite and antimonate, $HSbO_2.HSbO_3$; or as a mixed oxide, $Sb_2O_3.Sb_2O_5$, *antimonious antimonate*, $O=Sb-O-Sb\equiv O_2$. If the tetroxide be a definite individual, like the tri- and penta-oxides, antimony would appear to be quadrivalent in the tetroxide, $O=Sb=O_2=Sb=O$, or $O=Sb-O-Sb\equiv O_2$; tervalent in the trioxide, $O=Sb-O-Sb=O$; and quinquevalent in the pentoxide, $O_2\equiv Sb-O-Sb\equiv O_2$. The brown liquid obtained by mixing equimolar proportions of antimony tri- and penta-chlorides is supposed to contain antimony tetrachloride, and, like other tetrachlorides, C. Setterberg, R. F. Weinland and H. Schmid, and F. Ephraim and S. Weinberg said that it forms a series of salts—*e.g.* Cs_2SbCl_6, Rb_2SbCl_6, etc.—isomorphous with K_2PtCl_6, $(NH_4)_2PtCl_6$, K_2SnCl_6, and $(NH_4)_2SnCl_6$. H. Biltz found that the valency diminishes with rising temp. ; thus antimony pentoxide passes into the tetroxide at 450° ; the tetroxide into the trioxide at 1060° ; and the trioxide into antimony, etc., at 2490°.

J. J. Berzelius obtained antimony tetroxide by heating antimony or antimony trioxide or pentoxide in air for a long time. J. von Szilagyi recommended this process. From the observations of T. Carnelley and J. Walker, the tetroxide is the stable oxide between 585° and 775°—*vide supra*, antimony trioxide—and H. Biltz said that the tetroxide passes into the trioxide at temp. exceeding 1060°. J. J. Berzelius, J. von Szilagyi, and W. P. Dexter obtained it by treating antimony with nitric acid, and calcining the residue at a red-heat until it has a constant weight. R. Bunsen treated antimony trisulphide in a similar way, and also by heating a mixture of the sulphide with 30–40 times its weight of mercuric oxide. H. Capitaine roasted the sulphide on a gradually rising temp., without fusion, until sulphur dioxide is no longer evolved ; but the sulphur cannot be all expelled by this procedure. J. von Liebig melted antimony with potassium sulphate and obtained a mixture of potassium sulphantimonite, and hypoantimonate ; and M. Websky obtained a similar product by fusing antimony or its sulphide with potassium hydrosulphate. A. Simon observed that in the transformation of antimony pentoxide into the trioxide, at 430°, there is formed **antimony hexitatridecoxide,** Sb_6O_{13} ; at 700°, this forms antimony tetroxide ; and this at 910°, yields the trioxide. No other intermediate oxides were observed. A. Simon and E. Thaler represented this compound by $Sb_2O_3.2Sb_2O_5$, or $2Sb_2O_4.Sb_2O_5$, or $(SbO_3)_2{=}Sb{-}O{-}Sb{=}(SbO_3)_2$; or as the anhydride of a *hydropyroantimonic acid,* $SbHSb_2O_7$, being equivalent to $2SbH.Sb_2O_7$ less $H_2O{=}Sb_2Sb_4O_{13}$. The formation of this compound is shown on the heating curve, Fig. 30. The vap. press. is 21·7 mm. at 630° ; 59·4 mm. at 670° ; and 23·2 mm. at 730°— *vide* Fig. 31. The heat of formation is represented by $2Sb_6O_{13}{=}6Sb_2O_4{+}O_2{-}39.274$

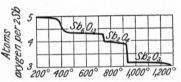

FIG. 30.—The Action of Heat on Antimony Pentoxide.

Cals. ; and $3Sb_2O_5{=}Sb_6O_{13}{+}O_2{-}25.47$ Cals. U. Dehlinger and R. Glocker, and A. Simon studied the X-radiogram. A. Simon found the sp. gr. after 3 hrs.' calcination to be 5·70 ; and after 6 months at 690°, 6·22.

The early mineralogists, D. L. G. Karsten,[2] L. A. Emmerling, A. G. Werner, and C. A. S. Hoffmann, described a *Spiessglanzocker* which J. F. L. Hausmann regarded as a *Spiessglanzoxydul.* C. C. von Leonhard called it *Antimonocker ;* A. Breithaupt, *Gelbantimonerz ;* F. S. Beudant, *stibiconise*—from στίβι, antimony ; and κόνις, powder ; and G. L. Brush, *stibiconite.* J. R. Blum and W. Delffs described a hydrated tetroxide which they called *stiblith*—from στίβι, antimony ; and λίθος, stone—in allusion to its hardness. P. A. Dufrénoy had previously described an *antimony ochre* from Cervantes, Galicia, as *un acide antimonieux anhydre,* with the formula Sb_2O_4. E. Bechi also described some small needlelike crystals of the same composition occurring at Pereta, Tuscany. E. S. Dana, and G. A. Kenngott showed that both minerals are the same species, and J. D. Dana called them **cervantite.** Subsequent writers—J. D. Dana, M. Bauer, F. Klockmann, P. Groth, G. Tschermak, and F. Zirkel—confined the term cervantite to the anhydrous mineral, and stibiconite or antimony ochre to the monohydrate. These minerals occur in several localities where they have been produced by the weathering of stibnite or other antimony minerals.

Artificial antimony tetroxide is a white powder ; cervantite occurs massive, as an incrustation, or in powder as well as in acicular crystals belonging to the rhombic system. The colour of the mineral is white with a yellow or red tinge, and sulphur-yellow. U. Dehlinger and R. Glocker [3] found that the X-radiogram corresponds with a lattice like that of the trioxide ; but rather more compact. A. Simon discussed this subject. C. J. B. Karsten gave 6·7 for the sp. gr., but this is too high ; F. Winkler gave 6·641 for the sp. gr. of the tetroxide which had been heated at 740°–830° for 21 hrs. ; and 6·643 when heated for 42 hrs. L. Playfair and J. P. Joule gave 4·07 for the sp. gr. ; and P. A. Dufrénoy, 4·08. A. Simon found the sp. gr. at 25°/4° of the tetroxide calcined at 840° for

Time .	1	2	48	60	72	96	100	150 hrs.
Sp. gr.	5·99	6·21	6·65	6·71	6·73	7·26	7·50	7·50

The hardness of cervantite is 4–5. H. V. Regnault gave 0·0951 for the sp. ht. ; and F. Winkler gave 28 for the mol. ht. R. Bunsen said that the tetroxide is reduced to the trioxide, and volatilized at a temp. a little higher than that at which it is formed ; A. Guntz also observed a loss when the tetroxide is calcined at dull redness. O. Brunck showed that the tetroxide is not reduced when ignited in a crucible provided reducing gases from the flame are excluded. In an uncovered crucible neither reduction nor loss of weight occurs, but with a covered crucible reduction occurs even when the flame surrounds only the lower half of the crucible. J. J. Berzelius said that the white tetroxide becomes yellow when hot, and the white colour returns on cooling ; the tetroxide emits a vivid light in the oxidizing blowpipe flame without fusing, and in the reducing flame it is slowly dissipated. W. P. Dexter said that the tetroxide is not decomposed when heated many hours at a bright red-heat ; T. Carnelley and J. Walker observed no decomposition at 775° ; H. Biltz said that decomposition occurs towards 1060° ; and H. Baubigny, below the m.p. of gold (1068°). A. A. Read found that at 1750°, the tetroxide volatilizes freely, and that which had not volatilized was the trioxide showing that the trioxide was volatilizing. H. Halle studied this subject. H. W. Foote and E. K. Smith could not measure the dissociation press. accurately because an appreciable loss of weight occurred at about 950°. This is taken to mean that at that temp. the dissociation press. is nearly equal to the partial press. of the oxygen in atm. air. A. Simon and E. Thaler gave 19·42 mm. at 930° ; 137·8 mm. at 1080° ; and 224·9 mm. at 1110°—vide Fig. 30. F. Winkler calculated the vap. press. of the oxygen to be $1·2 \times 10^{-11}$ atm. at 820° ; and for the heat of formation, $2Sb_2O_{3solid} + O_2 = 2Sb_2O_4 + 89,700$ cals. W. G. Mixter gave $(2Sb, 2O_2) = 209·8$ Cals. and $(Sb_2O_3, O) = 46·8$ Cals. ; W. Biltz gave $(2Sb, 2O_2) = 192·65$, and $(Sb_2O_3, O) = 25·25$ Cals. ; while A. Simon and E. Thaler gave $(2Sb, 2O_2) = 195·29$ Cals., and $(Sb_2O_3, O) = 27·89$ Cals. T. W. Case said that the tetroxide is a non-conductor, and its resistance is not appreciably affected by light.

H. Rose found that antimony tetroxide is sparingly soluble in water ; and it reddens moist litmus-paper rather less intensely than the pentoxide. The tetroxide also forms a hydrate—vide infra. R. Weber found that the heated oxide is decomposed by chlorine. H. Rose said that the tetroxide is but sparingly soluble in acids ; even boiling hydrochloric acid attacks it very slowly ; and R. Bunsen said that it liberates iodine from a mixture of potassium iodide and hydrochloric acid ; J. von Szilagyi represented the reaction : $Sb_2O_4 + 6HCl + 2HI = 2SbCl_3 + 4H_2O + I_2$, and said that metastannic acid does not liberate iodine under these conditions. H. Capitaine found that when the tetroxide is heated with potassium iodide, iodine is evolved, and potassium antimonite is formed. J. L. Proust observed that when the tetroxide is heated with sulphur, Spiessglanzglas is formed : $Sb_2O_4 + 5S = Sb_2S_3 + 2SO_2$; and J. J. Berzelius, that alkali hydrosulphides do not attack the tetroxide in the cold, but when heated, the oxide dissolves with the evolution of hydrogen sulphide. J. J. Berzelius found the tetroxide to be slightly soluble in sulphuric acid. The oxide is reduced when heated with carbon ; and also, according to J. von Liebig, when treated with fused potassium cyanide. H. Rose said that potassium antimonyl tartrate is not produced when the tetroxide is boiled with a soln. of potassium hydrotartrate ; E. Mitscherlich found that some potassium antimonyl tartrate is formed with the separation of antimony pentoxide. J. L. Proust found the tetroxide is reduced to the trioxide when heated with antimony : $2Sb + 3Sb_2O_4 = 4Sb_2O_3$; and J. J. Berzelius showed that when the tetroxide is fused with antimony trisulphide, Spiessglanzglas is formed : $9Sb_2O_4 + Sb_2S_3$

$=10Sb_2O_3+3SO_2$. W. R. Schoeller studied the reaction. **J. L. Gay Lussac and L. J. Thénard** found that when heated with potassium or sodium, the tetroxide is reduced, with incandescence, to antimony. R. Bunsen showed that the oxide blackens ammoniacal silver nitrate.

J. J. Berzelius [4] obtained **monohydrated antimony tetroxide,** $Sb_2O_4.H_2O$, or **hypoantimonic acid,** $H_2Sb_2O_5$, by precipitation with strong acids from a soln. an alkali hypoantimonate. As indicated above, this same compound occurs in nature as the mineral **stibiconite.** Analyses were reported by J. R. Blum and W. Delffs, J. R. Santos, C. F. Rammelsberg, C. Schnabel, and S. P. Sharples. The mineral occurs in pale yellow compact masses ; in powder, or in crusts. H. C. Lewis obtained artificial crystals of sp. gr. 4·9 ; J. R. Blum and W. Delffs gave 5·28 for the sp. gr ; A. Frenzel, 5·08 ; F. P. Dunnington, 5·58. The hardness is 4·5–5·0.

A number of other minerals containing antimony oxide has been reported. O. Volger [5] found white antimony ochre to be a common product of the alteration of stibnite. E. Cumenge analyzed a variety from Constantine, Algeria, and the results corresponded with $Sb_2O_5.4H_2O$. G. A. Kenngott called the mineral *cumengite,* and J. D. Dana, *volgerite.* A mineral obtained from Sierra del Cadi, Spain, was analyzed by H. Ducloux, and called *rivotite*—after L. E. Rivot. The analysis approximates to $Sb_2O_5.4(Cu,Ag_2)CO_3$. The sp. gr. is 3·55–3·62 ; and the hardness 3·5–4·0. It is considered to be a mixture of antimony ochre, and silver copper carbonate. The so-called *partzite*—named after A. F. W. Partz— was obtained by A. Arrents from the Blind Spring Mountains, California. The sp. gr. is 3·8 ; and the hardness, 3–4. J. M Blake regarded partzite as a hydrated antimony oxide mixed with different metal oxides—*e.g.* Cu_2O, Ag_2O, FeO, and PbO. E. Riotte described a mineral from Nevada, U.S.A., which he called *stetefeldtite*—after C. Stetefeldt. It is a variety of partzite. The sp. gr. is 4·12–4·24, and the hardness 3·5–4·5. E. Goldsmith applied the term *stibioferrite* to an amorphous incrustation on the antimonial ores of Santa Clara Co., California. It is a hydrated antimony oxide mixed with 31·85 per cent. of ferric oxide, and 8·84 per cent. of silica. The sp. gr. is 3·598, and the hardness 4.

J. J. Berzelius [6] prepared what he regarded as **potassium hypoantimonate,** $K_2Sb_2O_5$, by fusing antimony tetroxide with an excess of potassium hydroxide or carbonate ; removing the excess of alkali with cold water ; and dissolving the residue in boiling water. The aq. soln. does not crystallize on evaporation, but dries to a yellow mass, freely soluble in water. When the aq. soln. is treated with carbon dioxide, a white powder is deposited, and it has the composition of **potassium bishypoantimonate,** $K_2Sb_4O_9$. J. von Liebig reported potassium hypoantimonate to be present in the product obtained by fusing potassium sulphate with antimony ; and M. Websky fused antimony or antimony trisulphide with potassium hydrosulphate at a red-heat ; the cold mass dissolves in water, and was said to contain hypoantimonate because it reduced gold chloride : $3Sb_2O_4+2AuCl_3 +3H_2O=3Sb_2O_5+2Au+6HCl$. Sulphuric acid precipitates hydrated antimony tetroxide from the aq. soln. These observations do not discredit E. Frémy's opinion that the alleged hypoantimonites are mixtures of antimonites and anti-monates. J. J. Berzelius obtained **sodium hypoantimonate** in a similar way, but E. Mitscherlich melted antimony tetroxide with sodium carbonate, and extracted the cold mass with water. He found that the main product was sodium hypo-antimonate which dissolved, and a little sodium metantimonate most of which remained as a residue. J. J. Berzelius said that **barium hypoantimonate**—pre-sumably $BaSb_2O_5$—is produced by slowly adding a boiling dil. soln. of potassium hypoantimonate to one of barium chloride. Small, flat, needle-like crystals were deposited ; the crystals were permanent in air ; sparingly soluble in water ; and gave up baryta to acids. He made **calcium hypoantimonate,** $CaSb_2O_5$, in a similar way. The white crystalline powder was insoluble in water. The mineral *romeite*—*vide supra*—can be regarded as calcium hypoantimonate.

I. Domeyko [7] also described what he called *antimonite de mercure* obtained from the Chilian mines. This red or scarlet powder was called by J. D. Dana *ammiolite*—from ἄμμιον, vermilion—is of doubtful composition. It may be *copper hypoantimoniate* or antimonate mixed with cinnabar ; or *mercury hypoantimoniate* or antimonate mixed with copper oxide. I. E. Rivot, and F. Field analyzed Chilian red earths which may be related to ammiolite.

A dark grey mineral from Huitzucco, Mexico, was analyzed by J. R. Santos, and named, by J. W. Mallet, *barcenite*—after M. Barcena. J. W. Mallet supposed it to be a mixture of mercuric sulphide and a calcium antimonate and antimony trioxide, $(Sb_2O_3.4RO)(Sb_2O_5)_5$; while P. Groth supposed it to be a mixture of mercury and calcium antimonate with antimonic acid. Its sp. gr. is 5·34 at 20°, and its hardness 5·5.

REFERENCES.

J. J. Berzelius, *Schweigger's Journ.*, **6**. 144, 1812 ; **22**. 69, 1818 ; W. P. Dexter, *Pogg. Ann.*, **100**. 564, 1857 ; C. F. Rammelsberg, *Handbuch der Mineralchemie*, Leipzig, 175, 1875 ; E. Bechi, *Amer. Journ. Science*, (2), **14**. 61, 1852 ; J. L. Proust, *Journ. Phys.*, **55**. 325, 1802 ; **64**. 150, 1807 ; L. J. Thénard, *Ann. Chim. Phys.*, (1), **32**. 257, 1799 ; T. Thomson, *Ann. Phil.*, (2), **2**. 125, 1821 ; A. Simon and E. Thaler, *Zeit. anorg. Chem.*, **162**. 253, 1927 ; A. Simon, *ib.*, **165**. 31, 1927 ; H. Biltz, *Zeit. phys. Chem.*, **19**. 385, 1896 ; C. Setterberg, *Octvers. Akad. Förh.*, 6, 1882 ; R. F. Weinland and H. Schmid, *Zeit. anorg. Chem.*, **44**. 37, 1905 ; *Ber.*, **38**. 1080, 1905 ; F. Ephraim and S. Weinberg, *ib.*, **42**. 4447, 1909 ; E. Mitscherlich, *Journ. prakt. Chem.*, (1), **19**. 457, 1840 ; E. Frémy, *Ann. Chim. Phys.*, (3), **23**. 404, 1848 ; T. Carnelley and J. Walker, *Journ. Chem. Soc.*, **53**. 86, 1888 ; A. Simon, *Oesterr. Chem. Ztg.*, **28**. 195, 1925 ; H. Capitaine, *Journ. Pharm. Chim.*, (3), **25**. 516, 1839 ; J. von Liebig, *Handwörterbuch der reinen und angewandten Chemie*, Braunschweig, **1**. 414, 1837 ; R. Bunsen, *Liebig's Ann.*, **192**. 315, 1878 ; M. Websky, *Zeit. anal. Chem.*, **11**. 124, 1872 ; P. Groth, *Tabellarische Uebersicht der Mineralien*, Braunschweig, 85, 1898 ; J. von Szilagyi, *Zeit. anal. Chem.*, **57**. 23, 1918 ; F. Winkler, *Das Atomgewicht des Antimons. Neubestimmung durch Ueberführung des Metalls in Antimon-Tetroxyd*, München, 1917.

² D. L. G. Karsten, *Museum Leskeanum*, Leipzig, **1**. 534, 1789 ; *Tabellarische Uebersicht der mineralogisch-einfachen Fossilien*, Berlin, 1791 ; 54, 78, 1800 ; L. A. Emmerling, *Lehrbuch der Mineralogie*, Giessen, **2**. 485, 1796 ; **3**. 414, 1797 ; C. A. S. Hoffmann, *Handbuch der Mineralogie*, Freiberg, **4**. 124, 1817 ; A. G. Werner, *Letztes Mineralsystem*, Freiberg, 24, 1817 ; J. F. L. Hausmann, *Handbuch der Mineralogie*, Göttingen, **1**. 339, 1813 ; F. S. Beudant, *Traité élémentaire de minéralogie*, Paris, **2**. 616, 1832 : C. C. von Leonhard, *Handbuch der Oryktognosie*, Heidelberg, 151, 1821 ; G. A. Kenngott, *Das Mohs'sche Mineralsystem*, Wien, 141, 1855 ; *Uebersichte der Resultate mineralogischer Forschungen*, Wien, 33, 1851 ; 41, 1852 ; 60, 1857 ; J. R. Blum and W. Delffs, *Journ. prakt. Chem.*, (1), **40**. 318, 1847 ; G. L. Brush, *Amer. Journ. Science*, (2), **34**. 207, 1862 ; E. S. Dana, *ib.*, (2), **14**. 61, 1852 ; E. Bechi, *ib.*, (2), **14**. 61, 1852 ; P. A. Dufrénoy, *Traité de minéralogie*, Paris, **2**. 655, 1845 ; A. Breithaupt, *Vollständige Charakteristik des Mineralsystems*, Dresden, 98, 1823 ; 224, 1832 ; *Vollständiges Handbuch der Mineralogie*, Dresden, **3**. 896, 1847 ; A. des Cloizeaux, *Manuel de minéralogie*, Paris, **2**. 332, 1893 ; J. D. Dana, *A System of Mineralogy*, New York, 417, 1850 ; 203, 1892 ; G. Tschermak, *Lehrbuch der Mineralogie*, Wien, 404, 1897 ; P. Groth, *Tabellarische Uebersicht der Mineralien*, Braunschweig, 85, 1898 ; F. Zirkel, *Elemente der Mineralogie*, Leipzig, 618, 1901 ; F. Klockmann, *Lehrbuch der Mineralogie*, Stuttgart, 342, 365, 1903 ; M. Bauer, *Lehrbuch der Mineralogie*, Stuttgart, 561, 571, 1904.

³ L. Playfair and J. P. Joule, *Mem. Chem. Soc.*, **2**. 401, 1845 ; H. V. Regnault, *Ann. Chim. Phys.*, (3), **1**. 129, 1841 ; J. J. Berzelius, *Schweigger's Journ.*, **6**. 144, 1812 ; **22**. 69, 1818 ; C. J. B. Karsten, *ib.*, **65**. 394, 1832 ; J. L. Proust, *Journ. Phys.*, **55**. 325, 1802 ; **64**. 150, 1807 ; H. Capitaine, *Journ. Pharm. Chim.*, (3), **25**. 516, 1839 ; J. von Liebig, *Handwörterbuch der reinen und angewandten Chemie*, Braunschweig, **1**. 414, 1837 ; W. P. Dexter, *Pogg. Ann.*, **100**. 564, 1857 ; H. Rose, *ib.*, **3**. 441, 1824 ; R. Weber, *ib.*, **112**. 625, 1861 ; A. A. Read, *Journ. Chem. Soc.*, **65**. 313, 1894 ; T. Carnelley and J. Walker, *ib.*, **53**. 86, 1888 ; H. Baubigny, *Compt. Rend.*, **124**. 560, 1897 ; A. Guntz, *ib.*, **101**. 161, 1885 ; H. Biltz, *Zeit. phys. Chem.*, **19**. 385, 1896 ; R. Bunsen, *Liebig's Ann.*, **106**. 1, 1858 ; **192**. 315, 1878 ; J. von Szilagyi, *Zeit. anal. Chem.*, **57**. 23, 1918 ; O. Brunck, *ib.*, **34**. 171, 1895 ; P. A. Dufrénoy, *Traité de minéralogie*, Paris, **2**. 655, 1845 ; J. L. Gay Lussac and L. J. Thénard, *Recherches physicochimiques*, Paris, **1**. 272, 1811 ; E. Mitscherlich, *Journ. prakt. Chem.*, (1), **19**. 455, 1840 ; H. W. Foote and E. K. Smith, *Journ. Amer. Chem. Soc.*, **30**. 1344, 1908 ; F. Winkler, *Das Atomgewicht des Antimons. Neubestimmung durch Ueberführung des Metalls in Antimon-Tetroxyd*, München, 1917 ; H. Halle, *Ueber Antimon und Arsen*, München, 1893 ; W. R. Schoeller, *Journ. Soc. Chem. Ind.*, **34**. 6, 1915 ; W. G. Mixter, *Amer. Journ. Science*, (4), **28**. 103, 1909 ; T. W. Case, *Phys. Rev.*, (2), **9**. 305, 1917 ; W. Biltz, *Gött. Nachr.*, **298**, 1908 ; A. Simon and E. Thaler, *Zeit. anorg. Chem.*, **162**. 253, 1927 ; U. Dehlinger and R. Glocker, *Ann. Phil.*, **165**. 41, 1927 ; U. Dehlinger, *Zeit. Kryst.*, **66**. 108, 1927 ; A. Simon, *Zeit. anorg. Chem.*, **165**. 31, 1927.

⁴ J. J. Berzelius, *Schweigger's Journ.*, **6**. 144, 1912 ; **22**. 69, 1818 ; J. R. Blum and W. Delffs, *Journ. prakt. Chem.*, (1), **40**. 318, 1847 ; J. R. Santos, *Chem. News*, **36**. 167, 1877 ; S. P. Sharples, *Amer. Journ. Science*, (3), **20**. 423, 1880 ; H. C. Lewis, *Amer. Nat.*, 608, 1882 ; C. Schnabel, *Pogg. Ann.*, **105**. 146, 1858 ; A. Frenzel, *Zeit. Kryst.*, **2**. 629, 1877 ; *Tschermak's Mitt.*, (1), **7**. 298, 1877 ; C. F. Rammelsberg, *Handbuch der Mineralchemie*, Leipzig, 175, 188, 1875 ; E. Frémy, *Ann. Chim. Phys.*, (3), **12**. 498, 1844 ; (3), **23**. 404, 1848 ; F. P. Dunnington, *Proc. Amer. Assoc.*, 182, 1877.

⁵ O. Volger, *Studien zur Entwicklungsgeschichte der Mineralien*, Zürich, 77, 1854 ; G. A. Kenngott, *Das Mohs'sche Mineralsystem*, Wien, 29, 1853 ; *Uebersichte der Resultate mineralogischer Forschungen*, Wien, 33, 1851 ; 60, 1857 ; E. Cumenge, *Ann. Mines*, (4), **20**. 80, 1851 ; J. D. Dana,

A System of Mineralogy, New York, 142, 1854; H. Ducloux, *Compt. Rend.*, **78**. 1471, 1874; E. Goldsmith, *Proc. Acad. Philadelphia*, 366, 1873; 154, 1878; A. Arrents, *Berg. Hütt. Ztg.*, **26**. 119, 1867; *Amer. Journ. Science*, (2), **43**. 362, 1867; J. M. Blake, *ib.*, (2), **44**. 119 1867; E. Riotte, *Berg. Hütt. Ztg.*, **26**. 253, 1867.
    ⁶ J. J. Berzelius, *Schweigger's Journ.*, **6**. 144, 1812; **22**. 69, 1818; J. von Liebig, *Handwörterbuch der reinen und angewundten Chemie*, Braunschweig, **1**. 414, 1837; E. Mitscherlich, *Journ. prakt. Chem.*, (1), **19**. 457, 1840; M. Websky, *Zeit. anal. Chem.*, **11**. 124, 1872; E. Frémy, *Ann. Chim. Phys.*, (3), **12**. 498, 1844; (3), **23**. 404, 1848.
    ⁷ I. Domeyko, *Elementos de mineralojia*, Santiago, 129, 1860; *Ann. Mines*, (4), **6**. 183, 1844; L. E. Rivot, *ib.*, (4), **6**. 556, 1844; F. Field, *Journ. Chem. Soc.*, **12**. 27, 1860; J. R. Santos, *Amer. Journ. Science*, (3), **16**. 308, 1878; J. W. Mallet, *ib.*, (2), **16**. 309, 1878; P. Groth, *Tabellarische Uebersicht der Mineralien*, Braunschweig, 96, 1898; J. D. Dana, *A System of Mineralogy*, New York, 142, 1854.

§ 13. Antimony Pentoxide and the Antimonic Acids

The history of antimony pentoxide, and *antimonium diaphoreticum*, dating from the end of the sixteenth century, has been discussed in connection with antimony trioxide. J. J. Berzelius [1] prepared **antimony pentoxide,** or *antimonic oxide,* Sb_2O_5, by heating antimony, or one of its lower oxides, with nitric acid or aqua regia. In the latter case, the soln. is evaporated to dryness, mixed with conc. nitric acid, again evaporated to dryness, and then heated sufficiently to drive off the nitric acid, but not to redness. J. Bourson found that antimony precipitated by zinc is more easily oxidized by nitric acid than ordinary antimony. H. Rose said that complete oxidation to the pentoxide is attained only by repeatedly evaporating the product with conc. nitric acid, although C. P. Conrad reported that the complete oxidation of antimony cannot be effected with nitric acid, and O. Bosek, too, was unable to complete the oxidation by means of nitric acid, or by a mixture of hydrochloric acid and potassium chlorate. O. Bosek also found that bromine does its work slowly. The temp. to which the product is heated is of importance. H. Biltz said that the pentoxide passes into the tetroxide at 450°—*vide infra.* The same remarks apply when the pentoxide is obtained by heating one of its hydrates— say that produced by the hydrolysis of antimony pentachloride (H. Rose). J. S. F. Pagenstecher has described the preparation of the diaphoretic antimony. L. Zambelli and E. Luzzatto transformed antimony trisulphide into the hydrated pentoxide by treatment with hydrogen dioxide. J. J. Berzelius heated a mixture of antimony and mercuric oxide whereby the mercury antimonate first produced is transformed into the pentoxide. S. Berberich observed the formation of antimony pentoxide in the electrolysis of sulphuric, nitric, hydrochloric, or acetic acid, or potash-lye using an antimony electrode. An alkali antimonate was obtained by J. Clark by the action of an alkaline soln. of hydrogen dioxide on antimony—*vide infra,* sodium antimonates—and by W. Hampe, by the action of sodium dioxide on antimony. J. J. Berzelius also produced the alkali antimonate by projecting a mixture of alkali nitrate with antimony, antimony oxide or sulphide, or potassium antimonyl tartrate in small portions at a time into a red-hot crucible; when the deflagration has ceased, the temp. is raised; the cold powdered mass is extracted with water, and the filtrate which contains potassium antimonate treated with an excess of nitric acid gives a precipitate of hydrated antimony pentoxide, which is to be washed with water and dried. When the residue is boiled with dil. nitric acid, and washed with water, the hydrated pentoxide results. J. W. Slater oxidized antimony to antimonate by the action of potassium permanganate; and M. C. Harding oxidized antimony trioxide or the antimonites by potassium permanganate, dichromate, or ferricyanide. E. Frémy found that the antimonites are slowly converted into antimonates when heated in air. E. Berglund converted the alkali sulphantimonites into antimonates by boiling the aq. soln. with copper oxide—cuprous sulphide is formed; and C. Serono boiled copper oxide with a soln. of antimony trisulphide in alkali-lye—complete oxidation to the antimonate occurred; H. Rose added that oxidation is complete only if sulphur be present. T. Rieckher, and M. Duyk used copper hydroxide as the desulphurizing and oxidizing agent.

Antimony pentoxide is a pale yellow powder which becomes deeper in tint as the temp. is raised. A. Simon, and U. Dehlinger and R. Glocker studied the X-radiogram, and found that it corresponds with a cubic lattice. P. F. G. Boullay gave 6·525 for the sp. gr., but this number is far too high since L. Playfair and J. P. Joule obtained 3·78 for the sp. gr. at 3·9°. A. Simon gave for the sp. gr. of the pentoxide calcined at 840°, 5·41 ; and for $Sb_2O_{4·98}.O.4H_2O$, calcined one hour at this temp. 3·799 ; for $Sb_2O_{4·95}.O.14H_2O$, calcined 3 hrs., 4·147 ; $Sb_2O_{4·95}.O.2H_2O$, calcined 4 hrs., 4·309 ; and $Sb_2O_{4·98}.O.5H_2O$, calcined many weeks, 5·116. D. Balareff, and C. del Fresno studied the mol. vol. H. Biltz showed that the pentoxide changes into the tetroxide at about 450° ; A. A. Read, and J. J. Berzelius examined the action of heat on this oxide. A. Geuther said that the decomposition occurs at 300°, but H. Daubrawa found this temp. too low. H. Baubigny reported that the oxide is stable at 357°, but slowly decomposes at 440° ; the decomposition is slow even at dull redness, but is rapid at 750°–800° when $2Sb_2O_5=2Sb_2O_4+O_2$. E. Weidenbach observed the same reaction occurs at 1000° and 1100°. A. Simon said that when the pentoxide is heated, there is a transformation at 430° corresponding with the formation of an *antimony hexitatridecaoxide*, Sb_6O_{13}, which, at 700°, decomposes into the tetroxide, and at 910°, into the trioxide—*vide supra*, Fig. 30. A. Simon and E. Thaler gave for the vap. press :

	70°	90°	130°	190°	350°	400°
p . .	0·1	0·4	1·1	6·3	29·6	224 mm.

The results are plotted in Fig. 31. W. G. Mixter gave for the heat of formation $(2Sb,5O)=229·36$ Cals., $(Sb_2O_3,2O)=66·6$ Cals., and $(Sb_2O_4,O)=19·8$ Cals. ; W. Biltz

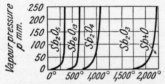

FIG. 31.—Dissociation Pressure Curves of the Antimony Oxides.

gave respectively, 205·65, 38·25, and 13 Cals. ; and A. Simon and E. Thaler, 210·325, 42·925, and 15·035 Cals. S. Glixelli studied the electro-osmosis of the pentoxide.

The composition of antimony pentoxide was established by the analyses of J. J. Berzelius, J. L. Proust, L. J. Thénard, and T. Thomson. J. J. Berzelius said that antimony pentoxide has no taste ; and H. Rose added that it reddens moist litmus-paper ; and that it is sparingly soluble in **water**—*vide infra*. R. Weber found that at a high temp. **chlorine** converts the pentoxide (trioxide) into antimony trichloride ; and H. Rose observed that **hydrochloric acid** dissolves it in the cold with difficulty without the evolution of chlorine ; the action is faster when the temp. is raised ; presumably the soln. contains antimony pentachloride. According to E. Stelling, antimony pentoxide is readily dissolved by conc. hydrochloric acid in the presence of sulphurous acid. R. Bunsen observed that the pentoxide oxidizes **hydriodic acid**—*i.e.* a soln. of potassium iodide in an acid—liberating iodine, and, added J. Klein, if starch-paste be present, one part of the pentoxide in 633,000 parts of liquid can be detected. A. Kolb and R. Formhals discussed the mechanism of the reversible reaction : $Sb_2O_5+4HI \rightleftharpoons Sb_2O_3+2H_2O+2I_2$. The reaction has been utilized by H. Giraud, F. A. Gooch and H. W. Gruener, F. E. Herroun, G. von Knorre, M. Rohmer, and A. Weller. The reaction with **potassium iodide** was symbolized by C. F. Schönbein : $3Sb_2O_5+4KI=4KSbO_3+Sb_2O_3+2I_2$; and H. Schulze found that with an **alkali chloride** in the presence of oxygen, chlorine is evolved. C. F. Rammelsberg observed that when the pentoxide is heated with a small proportion of **sulphur** it is reduced to the trioxide : $Sb_2O_5+S=SO_2+Sb_2O_3$; and with a large proportion of sulphur, antimony trisulphide is formed : $2Sb_2O_5+11S=2Sb_2S_3+5SO_2$. O. Schumann obtained an oxysulphide, Sb_4OS_5, by heating the pentoxide in a current of **hydrogen sulphide ;** while H. Rose found that an aq. soln. of hydrogen sulphide slowly transforms the pentoxide into orange-red **penta-**

sulphide, while a soln. of **ammonium sulphide** slowly dissolves the pentoxide. J. J. Berzelius said that the pentoxide dissolves in a warm soln. of **alkali hydrosulphide,** and that from the soln. acids precipitate the pentasulphide. H. Rose found that the pentoxide is but sparingly soluble in dil. and conc. **sulphuric acid.** H. Prinz represented the reaction with **sulphur monochloride** when heated in a sealed tube : $6S_2Cl_2+2Sb_2O_5=4SbCl_3+5SO_2+7S$.

G. Gore found hydrated antimony pentoxide to be sparingly soluble in liquid **ammonia.** According to H. Rose, antimony pentoxide is insoluble in aq. ammonia ; and A. Rosenheim and F. Jacobsohn found that it is not attacked by liquid ammonia. V. Thomas found that when **nitrogen peroxide** is passed into a soln. of antimony tribromide in chloroform, or antimony triiodide in ether, there is precipitated white, crystalline, **antimony nitropentoxide,** $2Sb_2O_5.N_2O_5$, which is not decomposed by water. L. Rosenstein said that red **phosphorus** does not reduce antimony salts. A. Michaelis represented the reaction with **phosphorus trichloride** at 160° in a sealed tube : $Sb_2O_5+2PCl_3=2SbCl_3+P_2O_5$. For the action of **phosphorus halides,** vide N. N. Sen's observations with arsenic trioxide. J. J. Berzelius observed that when heated with **antimony** or with **antimony trisulphide,** the pentoxide is reduced to the trioxide ; he also found that the pentoxide is reduced to a lower oxide which glows brightly when heated on **carbon** before the blowpipe ; H. Rose added that reduction to antimony occurs in the presence of sodium carbonate. The pentoxide is reduced when heated with **potassium cyanide,** or **sodium formate.** W. Müller said that the pentoxide is not reduced by **carbon disulphide.** H. Rose found that the pentoxide is insoluble in **alcohol ;** and J. J. Berzelius, that it is sparingly soluble in **tartaric acid.** W. Bulgrin studied the complex salts of quinquevalent antimony. G. Rauter observed that when the pentoxide is heated with **silicon tetrachloride** in a sealed tube, a. 260°–270°, antimony trichloride and silica are formed and chlorine is set free.

Aq. soln. of **alkali hydroxides** slowly dissolve antimony pentoxide ; soln. of **alkali carbonates** react even more slowly. When the pentoxide is fused with alkali hydroxides or carbonates, antimonates are produced—vide infra. According to C. F. Rammelsberg, **copper, silver, and lead sulphides** reduce the pentoxide to the trioxide with the elimination of sulphur dioxide. R. Bunsen found that antimony pentoxide is darkened by an ammoniacal soln. of **silver nitrate ;** G. Tammann studied the reduction of silver nitrate in light, and H. Schiff, by a soln. of **stannous chloride.** M. Mengin obtained antimony by treating the pentoxide with a mixture of tin and hydrochloric acid.

The hydrates of antimony pentoxide.—J. J. Berzelius [2] obtained hydrated antimony pentoxide, as indicated above, by treating alkali antimonate with dil. nitric acid. L. Heffter said that the alkali is very tenaciously retained by the hydrate and is not removed by washing with dil. acid. H. Rose obtained the hydrate by the hydrolysis of antimony pentachloride ; when the hydrochloric acid has been washed away, the hydrate diffuses through the wash-water in so finely-divided a state that it passes through the filter-paper, and the liquid is opalescent. The hydrate is also produced when antimony is treated with aqua regia—vide supra, preparation of antimony pentoxide. Analyses of the air-dried product by C. P. Conrad, H. Daubrawa, E. Frémy, A. Geuther, L. Heffter, J. B. Senderens, and C. Serono, give results ranging from 15·77 to 20·02 per cent. of water, corresponding with the tetrahydrate. Analyses by C. P. Conrad, H. Daubrawa, A. Geuther, and J. B. Senderens of the product dried over conc. sulphuric acid show 12·87–14·53 per cent. of water in agreement with the trihydrate, $Sb_2O_5.3H_2O$. J. B. Senderens regarded the trihydrate as orthoantimonic acid, H_3SbO_4, and obtained it by drying the hexahydrate for 3 weeks over conc. sulphuric acid. F. Raschig, and others question the existence of the ortho-acid ; H. Remy discussed its structure. According to J. B. Senderens, when antimony trichloride is treated with conc. nitric acid, a vigorous action occurs, and a clear red liquid is obtained which, on dilution, yields a white deposit, and which has the composition of the *hexahydrate*, $Sb_2O_5.6H_2O$, when exposed to air for 3 months at ordinary temp. 100 c.c. of water dissolve 2·2 grms. of Sb_2O_5, but the soln. gradually becomes turbid, and a precipitate of the *tetrahydrate*, $Sb_2O_5.4H_2O$, appears which increases until the conc. of the soln. is 0·3 grm. of the pentoxide per 100 c.c. This hydrate is less readily dehydrated by heat than in the case with hydrates prepared in other ways. These results were confirmed by the work of H. Baubigny. E. Frémy represented the tetrahydrate as dihydrated pyroantimonic acid, $H_4Sb_2O_7.2H_2O$— *vide infra*. The dehydration curves of the hydrate obtained by the hydrolysis of the pentachloride were found by A. Simon and E. Thaler to be of the continuous type characteristic of hydrated metal oxides of the hydrogel type. At lower temp., the hydrogel holds its water more tenaciously the greater the dispersity—*i.e.* the lower the temp. of preparation ; as the temp. rises, the differences become smaller ; at 200°, the composition of all the gels approximates *tritapentahydrate*,$3Sb_2O_5.5H_2O$, and the curve has a point of inflexion, indicating that hydrated antimony pentoxide begins to crystallize, and a similar result occurs when the hydrate is kept for some time—*ageing*. This hypothesis is confirmed by X-radiograms. The crystallization of the hydrogel is favoured by heating it with water under press. The product then gives a definite indication of the existence of the $3Sb_2O_5.5H_2O$-hydrate, and also less clear indications of a dihydrate and a hemihydrate. In the absence of the treatment with water under press., which aids in the breaking down of the gel structure, the indications of the hydrates on the vap. press. curves is masked by capillary effects. Analyses by C. P. Conrad, H. Daubrawa, and A. Geuther of the product dried at 100° show 9·698–11·44 per cent. of water corresponding with the *dihydrate*, $Sb_2O_5.2H_2O$. J. B. Senderens regarded the dihydrates as *pyroantimonic acid*, $H_4Sb_2O_7$, and obtained it by heating the trihydrate to 200°. Analyses by J. J. Berzelius, H. Daubrawa, and A. Geuther of the product dried between 175° and 200°, show 5·09–6·20 per cent. of moisture corresponding with the *monohydrate*, $Sb_2O_5.H_2O$. J. B. Senderens regarded the monohydrate as *metantimonic acid*, $HSbO_3$, and obtained it by heating the trihydrate to 300°. According to E. Goldsmith, the massive mineral *stibianite* from Victoria, Australia, has an analysis corresponding with $Sb_2O_5.H_2O$. The hardness is 5, and the sp. gr. 3·67. According to C. P. Conrad, the product dried at 300° has the composition of the *hemihydrate*, $Sb_2O_5.\frac{1}{2}H_2O$, and only at dull redness is all the water expelled, and at the same time the pentoxide begins to decompose into the tetroxide. J. B. Senderens said that the hydrated pentoxide becomes anhydrous at 400°. A. Naumann said metantimonic acid is insoluble in acetone.

If the red liquid obtained by J. B. Senderens by the action of conc. nitric acid on antimony trichloride be heated, and the white precipitate which forms be washed with dil. nitric acid, then with water, and dried in air, the *hemienneahydrate*, $Sb_2O_5.4\frac{1}{2}H_2O$, is formed. Again, if the same red liquid be evaporated to dryness on a sand-bath until acid fumes are no longer evolved, the white residue has the composition of the *pentahydrate*, $Sb_2O_5.5H_2O$. E. Frémy found that the tetra-hydrates obtained by the hydrolysis of antimony pentachloride, and by the action of acids on soln. of the antimonites, have different properties. The former was supposed to be $H_4Sb_2O_7.2H_2O$, and the latter, $2H_3SbO_4.H_2O$. The former was said to dissolve in much water, and to be precipitated by acids from the aq. soln. The precipitate dissolved in conc. ammonia whereas that obtained from the latter acid was not so dissolved. F. F. Beilstein and O. von Bläse, and C. P. Conrad showed that there is no real difference between the two products. J. B. Senderens, and A. E. Delacroix agreed that a soluble and an insoluble form of antimonic acid exists, and they called them ortho- and pyro-acids ; but they differed as to which was which. The conductivity observations of E. S. Tomula show that the soluble acid is orthoantimonic acid, whether prepared by J. B. Senderens' or A. E. Delacroix's method. The eq. conductivities of the potassium salts of both acids were nearly the same, and in agreement with those of the dihydro-antimonates. A conc. soln. of antimonic acid is not a true soln. but a supersaturated, colloidal pseudo-solution from which the acid soon separates in an insoluble form.

A. E. Delacroix reported what he first called *pyroantimonic acid*, and later **tetrantimonic acid**, because it forms salts of the type $K_2O.4Sb_2O_5$, or $K_2Sb_8O_{21}$. The acid is prepared by adding antimony pentachloride to 20–25 times its weight of cold water, the excess of chlorine being removed by drawing air through the liquid, and, after remaining for an hour or so, the precipitated hydroxide is transferred to a filter; it is extremely difficult to remove the last traces of hydrogen chloride. By freezing the aq. soln., the acid is obtained in thin scales which are optically active. The ultimate composition is $Sb_2O_5.4H_2O$; when dried over sulphuric acid, $Sb_2O_5.3H_2O$; and when dried at 100°, $Sb_2O_5.2H_2O$. When left in contact with cold water, the hydroxide slowly dissolves, yielding a soln. of pyroantimonic acid. At 15°, the soln. contains 5·88 grms. of Sb_2O_5 per litre; at 25°, 8·55 grms.; at 60°, 21·30 grms. When treated with mineral acids, a precipitate is obtained, but organic acids have no action. The hydroxides yield white precipitates soluble in water, but insoluble in an excess of alkali. When titrated with alkali, using methyl-orange as indicator, neutralization is reached when the ratio of alkali to Sb_2O_5 is 0·25 : 1. With phenolphthalein, the ratio is 0·5 : 1. It was not possible to isolate the salt $K_2O,4Sb_2O_5$, but $Na_2O.4Sb_2O_5$ was obtained, and the salt $K_2O,2Sb_2O_5$ is produced when the acid is treated with a slight excess of potassium hydroxide or acetate. The observations of G. Jander show that the so-called tetrantimonic acid is a hydrosol of small stability.

A. E. Delacroix could not make **ammonium tetrantimonate**, $(NH_4)_2Sb_4O_{11}$, by neutralizing the free acid, but it is produced when the acid is treated with ammonium acetate. A. E. Delacroix prepared **sodium tetrantimonate**, $2Na_2O.4Sb_2O_5,18H_2O$, by neutralizing the free acid with sodium hydroxide, and freezing the soln. The salt is decomposed into the triantimonate by water. A crystalline powder, with the composition $Na_2O.4Sb_2O_5.20H_2O$, was obtained by freezing a soln. of a mol of antimony pentoxide and 3 mols of sodium chloride; or a soln. of a mol of antimony pentoxide and half a mol of sodium hydroxide. By neutralizing a soln. of the free acid with potash-lye, using phenolphthalein as indicator, and treating the liquid with alcohol, and by freezing a soln. obtained by neutralizing tetrantimonic acid with potash-lye, **potassium tetrantimonate**, $2H_2O.4Sb_2O_5.18H_2O$, was obtained; **copper** tetrantimonate, $2CuO.4Sb_2O_5.18H_2O$, was produced in a similar way. A. E. Delacroix also obtained evidence of the formation of **barium tetrantimonate**, $BaO.4Sb_2O_5.15H_2O$, by freezing a soln. of a mol of antimony pentoxide and 2 mols of barium chloride; and of $BaO.2Sb_2O_5.5H_2O$, from a soln. of tetrantimonic acid and barytawater. The chemical individuality of these products has not been established.

A. E. Delacroix also made what he first called *orthoantimonic acid*, and later **triantimonic acid**, because it forms salts of the type $R_2O.3Sb_2O_5$, or RSb_3O_8. The acid was made by heating tetrantimonic acid for some minutes at 100°; the same transformation occurs slowly at ordinary temp., and the soln. so obtained are feebly opalescent. By freezing its soln., triantimonic acid was obtained in crystals with the ultimate composition $Sb_2O_5.3H_2O$, or $Sb_2O_5.2H_2O$, when dried over conc. sulphuric acid. The potassium salt KSb_3O_8 is indicated when the acid is titrated with the alkali, using methyl-orange as indicator. Triantimonic acid forms salts of the type $R_2O.3Sb_2O_5$, $2R_2O.3Sb_2O_5$, and $3R_2O.3Sb_2O_5$, and other more complex derivatives. The alkali salts are alone soluble in water, and those containing one eq. of base are soluble in alcohol. G. Jander showed that the alleged triantimonic acid is a hydrosol of small stability.

A. E. Delacroix obtained an aq soln. of **lithium triantimonate** by neutralizing free triantimonic acid with lithium hydroxide, using phenolphthalein as indicator; if the hot soln. be neutralized, the liquid deposits the metantimonate after standing some hours. The lithium salt resembles that of potassium. By a similar process, using sodium hydroxide, a soln. of **sodium triantimonate**, $2Na_2O.3Sb_2O_5.10H_2O$, was produced; and if the free acid be treated with an excess of sodium chloride, sulphate, or nitrate, the crystalline powder which is precipitated has the composition $Na_2O.3Sb_2O_5.11H_2O$. It is also obtained by freezing the soln. obtained by half neutralizing the free acid with sodium hydroxide. Where potassium hydroxide is employed in neutralizing the free acid—with phenolphthalein as indicator—the soln. contains **potassium triantimonate**, $K_2O.3Sb_2O_5.nH_2O$—

A. E. Delacroix gave the formula $K_2O.2Sb_2O_5.nH_2O$. If a soln. of the free acid be treated with an excess of potassium hydroxide, and then with alcohol, an amorphous precipitate of potassium triantimonate, $2K_2O.3Sb_2O_5.10H_2O$, is produced. A. E. Delacroix obtained from the triantimonic acid **barium triantimonate**, $BaO.3Sb_2O_5.5H_2O$; as well as the salts $4BaO.5Sb_2O_5.nH_2O$; $9BaO.10Sb_2O_5.18H_2O$; and $BaO.Sb_2O_5.2H_2O$; **copper triantimonate**, $2CuO.3Sb_2O_5.10H_2O$, was obtained from copper acetate and triantimonic acid. Likewise also *copper hexantimonate*, $CuO.6Sb_2O_5.16H_2O$. Analogous evidence of the existence of **strontium and calcium triantimonates** was obtained. The chemical individualities of the triantimonates was not established.

G. Jander and A. Simon prepared hydrates of antimony pentoxide by these methods : (i) the hydrolysis of the pentachloride at $0°-1°$; (ii) hydrolysis at $100°$; and (iii) oxidation of the trichloride by conc. nitric acid and hydrolysis of the product at $60°$. The products were dried on porous plates in the air, and were found to contain (i) 30·57, (ii) 9·97, (iii) 7·91 mols of water to one mol of the pentoxide. After drying over sulphuric acid, the water contents were (i) 3·68, (ii) 2·17, (iii) 0·60 mols per mol Sb_2O_5. Drying at $105°$ reduced the molecules of water per mol of the pentoxide to (i) 2·43, (ii) 1·02, (iii) 0·45. The behaviour of the three hydrates towards alkalies and phosphoric acid was investigated, and their vapour tension isotherms were measured. No definite hydrates were formed, but gels were present, the behaviour of which depend on grain size, which varies with the method of

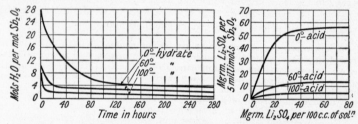

FIG. 32.—Speeds of Dehydration of the Hydrates of Antimony Pentoxide.

FIG. 33.—Adsorption of Alkali by the Hydrates of Antimony Pentoxide.

preparation. Alcogels of the pentoxide were also prepared, and these were de-alcoholated by placing them over glycerol; the curves of dealcoholation were similar to those of dehydration. The pentoxide was also able to take up benzene when kept in an atm. of the latter. The speeds of dehydration of the acids prepared at $0°$, $60°$, and $100°$, in vacuo over conc. sulphuric acid at room-temp., are indicated by the curves shown in Fig. 32 ; and the adsorption of alkali from soln. of lithium sulphate of different conc., in Fig. 33. G. Jander showed that the hydrates of antimony pentoxide show a marked selective adsorption towards dil. alkalies, forming what appear to be alkali antimonates. Conc. soln. of the alkalies dissolve the hydrates of antimony pentoxide, and the evaporation of the soln. at low temp. furnishes crystals of various alkali antimonates, but the nature of the salt depends on the conc. of the mother-liquor. The compound $1·71K_2O.Sb_2O_5.8H_2O$ was obtained in this way. Analogous results were obtained for the adsorption of phosphoric acid by hydrated antimony pentoxide. In no case is there any evidence of the formation of definite hydrates. The vap. press. curves support this conclusion. The results for the hydration and dehydration of the acid prepared at $0°$ are given in Fig. 34, and they are analogous with those obtained with other colloids —*e.g.* silica acid, stannic acid, etc. The results depend on the grain-size and mode

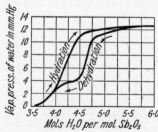

FIG. 34.—Hydration and Dehydration of Antimony Pentoxide.

of preparation of the hydrates. A. Lottermoser found that the **electrical** conductivity of a mixture of antimony pentoxide rises to a maximum, corresponding with the clarification of the soln., and then slowly falls. It is thought that the clear soln. represents a soln. of $Sb(OH)_5$, and that subsequently dehydration occurs, and a colloid is formed.

The hydrates of antimony pentoxide, or the antimonic acids, are therefore **hydrogels** of antimony pentoxide; this agrees with the observed properties of the hydrates—peptization with alkalies and water; flocculation with acids. H. Lachs and F. Lachmann studied the coagulation of colloidal antimonic acid. The soluble antimonic acid of J. B. Senderens, for instance, is the **hydrosol** of antimony pentoxide. G. Jander and A. Simon also prepared **alcogels** of antimony pentoxide which were dealcoholated by placing them over glycerol. The dealcoholation and dehydration curves were similar. S. Glixelli and M. Deniszczukowna prepared antimonic acid by the hydrolysis of a conc., aq. soln. of antimony pentachloride at 0° for 12–14 hrs., and subsequently removing the hydrochloric acid with iced water. A soln. containing 150 grms. per litre is slightly opalescent, and stable at 0°. It is coagulated by cations in the usual way. The mol. wt. determined by the f.p. method is influenced by the conc. of the soln. Measurements of the conc. of the H'-ion show the number of ions associated with the colloidal anion in each micelle, and the electrical conductivity is attributed to the decomposition of these micelles, and their subsequent ionization on dilution. For conc. soln., the conductivity decreases with time; but for dil. soln., it rises to a maximum and then falls. The soln. are not susceptible of ultra-filtration, but they can be made so by prolonged heating. Stable colloidal soln. are then obtained which give a mol. wt. of the order of 10,000. The mol. conductivities are small and increase with time, especially in dil. soln. where the micelles are split up into molecules. H. Lachs and F. Lachmann studied the coagulating effect of soln. of electrolytes on hydrosols of antimonic acid.

P. F. G. Boullay gave 6·6 for the sp. gr. of the tetrahydrate. H. Rose said that the hydrates of antimony pentoxide have a metallic taste; that they strongly redden moist litmus-paper; and that they slowly dissolve in cold hydrochloric acid, and rapidly when heated, with the evolution of chlorine and the formation of antimony trichloride. The soln. initially turbid becomes clear on standing. The hydrate is gradually transformed by hydrogen sulphide into antimony pentasulphide; H. Capitaine observed that hydrogen sulphide colours the soln. yellow, and the addition of an acid gives a precipitate of antimony pentasulphide. H. Rose found that a soln. of ammonium sulphide gradually dissolves the hydrate; while the hydrate is insoluble in sulphuric acid, and also in aq. ammonia. E. Frémy reported that one hydrate prepared as indicated above dissolves slowly by prolonged contact with conc. ammonia in the cold; but F. F. Beilstein and O. von Bläse observed no difference in the behaviour of the different hydrates towards the aq. ammonia. H. Rose found that nitric acid does not dissolve the hydrate; and H. Schiff, that phosphorus pentachloride yields phosphorus oxychloride and antimony pentachloride. According to F. Schultze, and G. Jander and A. Simon, the hydrates of antimony pentoxide adsorb phosphoric acid from aq. soln. According to J. J. Berzelius, the hydrate dissolves in tartaric acid; according to H. Rose, and C. Luckow, in oxalic acid; and, according to H. Rose, in a soln. of potassium oxalate. G. Jander and A. Simon found that the pentoxide adsorbs benzene vapour, and alcohol vapour. H. Rose showed that by the prolonged contact of the hydrate with an aq. soln. of potassium hydroxide or carbonate only a small amount of the hydrated pentoxide passes into soln.; while the molten alkali hydroxide or carbonate yields alkali antimonate. According to H. Schiff, when the hydrate is digested with a feebly (hydrochloric) acid soln. of stannous chloride, brick-red stannous antimonate is formed.

REFERENCES.

[1] H. Biltz, *Zeit. phys. Chem.*, 19. 385, 1896 ; J. J. Berzelius, *Schweigger's Journ.*, 6. 144, 1812 ; 22. 69, 1818 ; J. S. F. Pagenstecher, *Trommsdorff's Journ.*, 3. 394, 1819 ; H. Rose, *Pogg. Ann.*, 3. 441, 1824 ; C. F. Rammelsberg, *ib.*, 52. 241, 1841 ; C. F. Schönbein, *ib.*, 78. 513, 1849 ; R. Weber, *ib.*, 112. 625, 1861 ; W. Müller, *ib.*, 127. 404, 1866 ; J. Bourson, *Ann. Chim. Phys.*, (2), 70. 109, 1839 ; P. F. G. Boullay, *ib.*, (2), 43. 264, 1830 ; L. J. Thénard, *ib.*, (1), 32. 257, 1799 ; E. Frémy, *ib.*, (3), 23. 404, 1851 ; C. P. Conrad, *Chem. News*, 40. 197, 1879 ; F. E. Herroun, *ib.*, 45. 101, 1882 ; J. Clark, *ib.*, 67. 249, 1893 ; *Journ. Chem. Soc.*, 63. 886, 1893 ; O. Bosek, *ib.*, 67. 515, 1895 ; A. A. Read, *ib.*, 65. 313, 1894 ; L. Playfair and J. P. Joule, *Mem. Chem. Soc.*, 2. 401, 1845 ; L. Zambelli and E. Luzzatto, *Ann. Chem. Farm.*, (4), 3. 229, 1886 ; G. von Knorre, *Zeit. angew. Chem.*, 1. 155, 1888 ; T. Rieckher, *Dingler's Journ.*, 145. 313, 1857 ; T. Thomson, *Ann. Phil.*, 4. 171, 1814 ; M. Duyk, *Bull. Soc. Pharm. Belg.*, 37. 109, 1893 ; J. L. Proust, *Journ. Phys.*, 55. 325, 1802 ; 64. 150, 1807 ; W. Hampe, *Chem. Ztg.*, 18. 1899, 1894 ; S. Berberich, *Ueber das anodische Verhalten des Jodes, Arsens und Antimons*, München, 1913 ; E. Berglund, *Ber.*, 17. 95, 1884 ; M. Rohmer, *ib.*, 34. 1565, 1901 ; J. W. Slater, *Journ. prakt. Chem.*, (2), 9. 107, 1870 ; A. Geuther, *ib.*, (2), 4. 438, 1871 ; A. Michaelis, *ib.*, (2), 4. 454, 1871 ; H. Schulze, *ib.*, (2), 21. 437, 1880 ; D. Balareff, *ib.*, (2), 102. 283, 1921 ; C. del Fresno, *Anal. Fis. Quim.*, 24. 707, 1926 ; L. Rosenstein, *Journ. Amer. Chem. Soc.*, 42. 883, 1920 ; M. C. Harding, *Zeit. anorg. Chem.*, 20. 235, 1899 ; A. Rosenheim and F. Jacobsohn, *ib.*, 50. 307, 1906 ; A. Kolb and R. Formhals, *ib.*, 58. 189, 1908 ; C. Serono, *Gazz. Chim. Ital.*, 24. ii, 274, 1894 ; H. Daubrawa, *Liebig's Ann.*, 186. 118, 1877 ; O. Schumann, *ib.*, 187. 312, 1877 ; H. Prinz, *ib.*, 223. 358, 1884 ; R. Bunsen, *ib.*, 106. 1, 1858 ; H. Schiff, *ib.*, 120. 55, 1861; G. Rauter, *ib.*, 270. 250, 1892 ; A. Weller, *ib.*, 213. 364, 1882 ; H. Giraud, *Bull. Soc. Chim.*, (2), 46. 504, 1886 ; F. A. Gooch and H. W. Gruener, *Zeit. anal. Chem.*, 32. 472, 1893 ; *Amer. Journ. Science*, (4), 44. 117, 1893 ; J. Klein, *Arch. Pharm.*, (3), 27. 922, 1899 ; V. Thomas, *Compt. Rend.*, 120. 1116, 1895 ; H. Baubigny, *ib.*, 124. 560, 1897 ; M. Mengin, *ib.*, 119. 224, 1894 ; A. Simon and E. Thaler, *Zeit. anorg. Chem.*, 161. 113, 1927 ; 162. 253, 1927 ; A. Simon, *ib.*, 165. 31, 1927 ; U. Dehlinger and R. Glocker, *ib.*, 165. 41, 1927 ; U. Dehlinger, *Zeit. Kryst.*, 66. 1, 1927 ; A. Simon, *Oesterr. Chem. Ztg.*, 28. 195, 1925 ; E. Goldsmith, *Proc. Acad. Philadelphia*, 154, 1878 ; E. Weidenbach, *Untersuchungen über die Komplexbildung beim dreiwertigen Arsen*, Berlin, 1915 ; G. Gore, *Proc. Roy. Soc.*, 20. 441, 1872 ; 21. 140, 1873 ; N. N. Sen, *Proc. Asiatic Soc.*, 15. 263, 1919 ; W. G. Mixter, *Amer. Journ. Science*, (4), 28. 103, 1925 ; E. Stelling, *Journ. Ind. Eng. Chem.*, 16. 346, 1924 ; S. Glixelli, *Anz. Akad. Cracow*, 102, 1917 ; G. Tammann, *Zeit. anorg. Chem.*, 114. 151, 1920 ; W. Biltz, *Gött. Nachr.*, 298, 1908 ; W. Bulgrin, *Ueber innerkomplexe Verbindungen des drei- und fünfwertigen Antimons*, Berlin, 1926.

[2] L. Heffter, *Pogg. Ann.*, 86. 419, 1852 ; H. Rose, *ib.*, 3. 441, 1824 ; F. F. Beilstein and O. von Bläse, *Bull. Acad. St. Petersburg*, (4), 1. 97, 201, 209, 1889 ; G. Jander, *Koll. Zeit.*, 23. 122, 1918 ; A. Simon and T. Schmidt, *ib.*, 36. 65, 1926 ; G. Jander and A. Simon, *Zeit. anorg. Chem.*, 127. 68, 1923 ; A. Simon and H. Pöhlmann, *ib.*, 149. 101, 1925 ; A. Simon and E. Thaler, *ib.*, 161. 113, 1927 ; H. Remy, *ib.*, 116. 255, 1921 ; E. S. Tomula, *ib.*, 118. 81, 1921 ; *Studien über die Antimonsäuren und deren Alkalisalze zur Bestimmung des Antimons neben Zinn*, Helsingfors, 1920 ; A. E. Delacroix, *Journ. Pharm. Chim.*, (6), 6. 337, 1897 ; *Bull. Soc. Chim.*, (3), 21. 1049, 1899 ; (3), 25. 288, 1901 ; J. B. Senderens, *ib.*, (3), 21. 47, 1899 ; H. Daubrawa, *Liebig's Ann.*, 186. 110, 1877 ; H. Schiff, *ib.*, 102. 111, 1857 ; F. Schultze, *ib.*, 109. 171, 1859 ; C. P. Conrad, *Chem. News*, 40. 197, 1879 ; H. Baubigny, *Compt. Rend.*, 124. 499, 1897 ; S. Glixelli and M. Deniszczukowna, *ib.*, 182. 521, 1926 ; H. Capitaine, *Journ. Pharm. Chim.*, (3), 25. 516, 1839 ; C. Luckow, *Zeit. anal. Chem.*, 26. 14, 1897 ; A. Geuther, *Journ. prakt. Chem.*, (2), 4. 438, 1871 ; J. J. Berzelius, *Schweigger's Journ.*, 6. 144, 1812 ; 22. 69, 1818 ; F. Raschig, *Ber.*, 18. 2743, 1885 ; A. Naumann, *ib.*, 37. 4329, 1904 ; E. Frémy, *Ann. Chim. Phys.*, (3), 12. 361, 457, 1844 ; (3), 23. 385, 1848 ; P. F. G. Boullay, *ib.*, (2), 43. 266, 1830 ; H. Lachs and F. Lachmann, *Zeit. phys. Chem.*, 123. 303, 1926; A. Lottermoser, *Zeit. Elektrochem.*, 33. 514, 1927; C. Serono, *Gazz. Chim. Ital.*, 24. ii, 274, 1894 ;' E. Goldsmith, *Proc. Acad. Philadelphia*, 154, 1878.

§ 14. The Antimonates

A review of the antimonates shows that our knowledge of these compounds is in an unsatisfactory state. The main difficulty encountered by previous workers turns on the constitutional water. An antimonate with the ratio R : Sb=1 : 1 may be an orthoantimonate, $RH_2SbO_4.nH_2O$; a pyroantimonate, $R_2H_2Sb_2O_7.nH_2O$, or a metantimonate, $RSbO_3.(n+1)H_2O$. J. J. Berzelius,[1] and E. Frémy found that **ammonium metantimonate**, $NH_4SbO_3.nH_2O$, where n may be zero, 2, 2·5, or 3, separates on cooling a soln. of metantimonic acid in warm aq. ammonia. E. Frémy obtained it by adding alcohol to a soln. of pyroantimonic acid, or by adding ammonium chloride to the gum-like soln. of potassium metantimonate ; and

J. B. Senderens, by treating an aq. soln. of antimony pentoxide with ammonium acetate. F. Raschig found that when freshly precipitated antimony sulphide, from 30 grms. of potassium antimonyl tartrate, is treated with 500 c.c. of conc. aq. ammonia, and 900 c.c. of a 2·5 per cent. soln. of hydrogen dioxide, about one-sixth is converted into antimonic acid which forms a flaky precipitate. The soln. contains ammonium sulphate and antimonate ; the latter salt is precipitated by the addition of alcohol, and when dried at the ordinary temp., has the composition $NH_4SbO_3,3H_2O$, and is therefore identical with E. Frémy's ammonium dihydro-pyroantimonate, $H_2(NH_4)_2Sb_2O_7.5H_2O$. The white, crystalline powder precipitated by alcohol contains 3 mols. of water of crystallization, and it is soluble in water ; that obtained by cooling the ammoniacal soln. contains 2 mols. of water of crystallization and is insoluble in water ; while that obtained by precipitation with ammonium acetate contains 2·5 mols. of water of crystallization when dried for several months in air ; it contains one mol. of water when dried over conc. sulphuric acid ; and it becomes anhydrous at 300°. The crystals of the trihydrate lose a mol. of water at ordinary temp. ; and also when boiled with water. E. Frémy found that the aq. soln. of the crystalline salt is a good reagent for sodium—a soln. with one of sodium chloride in 1000 parts of soln. precipitates sodium antimonate on standing a few days ; with a 1 : 100 soln., a precipitate is produced in a short time. No precipitation occurs with potassium chloride ; but magnesium salt soln. precipitate magnesium metantimonate ; and ammoniacal soln. of copper salts were found by F. Raschig to give crystalline cupric ammonium antimonate. W. Müller showed that the vapour of carbon disulphide converts warm ammonium metantimonate into antimony and ammonium sulphides. According to F. Raschig, the **ammonium pyroantimonate,** $(NH_4)_4Sb_2O_7$, of E. Frémy is probably something else—*vide supra*. E. Frémy made it by the action of conc. ammonia on the anti-monic acid obtained by the hydrolysis of antimony pentachloride.

According to J. B. Senderens,[2] the white precipitate obtained by treating an aq. soln. of antimony pentoxide with potassium acetate and drying over sulphuric acid, approximates to **potassium dihydroantimonate,** $KH_2SbO_4.2\frac{1}{2}H_2O$. It is stable up to 100° ; loses its water at 300° ; and does not decompose at a red-heat. F. F. Beilstein and O. von Bläse regarded many of the antimonates as salts of ortho-antimonic acid, H_3SbO_4—and J. B. Senderens, as salts of the same acid with a doubled molecule, $H_5Sb_2O_8$—because many of the antimonates when dried over sulphuric acid can be represented by the formula RH_2SbO_4. The alternative view is that they are metantimonates $RSbO_3.H_2O$. The analogy of the orthophosphates, orthoarsenates, does not apply to the so-called orthoantimonates. Soln. of these salts have an alkaline reaction. F. Raschig found that the product of the reaction with molten alkali hydroxide and antimony pentoxide ; of antimony trisulphide and ammoniacal hydrogen dioxide ; and of sodium thiorthoantimonate with copper oxide has the ratio $R : Sb = 1 : 1$, not $3 : 1$; and F. Ebel regarded most of the antimonates as metantimonates, but the sparingly soluble sodium salt, and the granular potassium salt are considered to be dihydropyroantimonates because they retain a mol. of water when heated to 200°–350°.

E. Frémy found that **sodium dihydropyroantimonate,** $Na_2H_2Sb_2O_7.5$ or $6H_2O$, is obtained when a soln. of potassium dihydropyroantimonate, or metantimonate is added to one of a sodium salt—say chloride, or acetate. The reaction was employed by H. Rose, C. R. Fresenius, T. H. Behrens, F. F. Beilstein and O. von Bläse, etc., in analytical work. E. Frémy showed that the precipitation occurs with one part of the sodium salt in 500 parts of water, even when potassium salts are also present—organic salts should be absent. E. Frémy's method of preparing the salt was used by L. Heffter, F. Ebel, and G. von Knorre and P. Olschewsky. W. P. Dexter recommended washing the salt by decantation since it is liable to choke up the filter-paper ; and F. F. Beilstein and O. von Bläse recommended washing it with 25 per cent. alcohol mixed with a little sodium acetate to prevent the peptization of the precipitate and its passage through the filter-paper. G. von

Knorre and P. Olschewsky obtained this salt by oxidizing a soln. of antimony trioxide in hot soda-lye by means of hydrogen dioxide, potassium dichromate, or potassium ferrocyanide—if the permanganate be employed, the product is contaminated with manganese dioxide ; R. Robl found that the salt does not show fluorescence when exposed to ultra-violet light. E. S. Tomula measured the electrical conductivity of the salt at 25°, and found for the eq. conductivity, λ, for soln. with a mol of the salt in v litres :

v		32	64	128	256	512	1024
λ		93·5	93·8	95·5	95·2	93·7	103·4

which by the Ostwald-Walden rule—**1.** 15, 13—makes the basicity unity. The salt in soln. cannot therefore be the dihydropyroantimonate, $K_2H_2Sb_2O_7$, and since it has an acidic reaction it cannot be the metantimonate. It must therefore be the orthoantimonate—**potassium dihydroantimonate**, KH_2SbO_4: The ionization constant is 0·957 ; and the hydrogen ion conc. for $v=1024$ is $C_H=10^{-6·3}$. F. E. Brown and J. E. Snyder observed no reaction with vanadium oxytrichloride and anhydrous potassium pyroantimonate. E. Mitscherlich, and B. Unger prepared the salt by boiling a soln. of antimony trioxide or trisulphide with sulphur—sodium ortho-sulphantimonate is formed at the same time. E. Mitscherlich obtained the same product by the action of soda-lye on antimony pentasulphide. Some of the commercial *kermes mineral* is sodium dihydropyroantimonate. It is formed by boiling antimony sulphide with a 10 per cent. aqueous soln. of sodium carbonate. The corresponding potassium compound is more difficult to crystallize than the sodium compound. W. Hampe obtained the product by treating antimony trisulphide with sodium dioxide, or a soln. of antimony trisulphide in soda-lye with hydrogen dioxide. G. Jander and L. Brandt added that the hydrated crystalline precipitates of sodium and lithium antimonates obtained by oxidizing alkaline soln. of antimony trisulphide with hydrogen dioxide, are not of fixed composition, the alkali content varying with the alkalinity of the mother-liquor and the temp. of precipitation. B. Unger said that some dihydropyroantimonate is formed by the action of soda-lye itself on the trisulphide which is simultaneously reduced ; and E. Mitscherlich observed that the salt separates when a soln. of antimony trisulphide in aq. sodium carbonate is exposed to air.

The salt usually appears in the form of a white, crystalline powder. C. von Haushofer made crystals 0·5 mm. in length by allowing soln. of potassium metantimonate and sodium chloride to diffuse slowly into one another. The tetragonal crystals had the axial ratio $a:c=1:10079$. The crystals were also examined by E. Mitscherlich, L. Heffter, T. H. Behrens, and G. von Knorre and P. Olschewsky. Analyses by E. Frémy, G. von Knorre and P. Olschewsky, L. Heffter, and F. Ebel, agree with the formula $Na_2H_2Sb_2O_7.6H_2O$ for the air-dried salt, or of the salt precipitated between 50° and 80° ; and the analyses of G. von Knorre and P. Olschewsky, and B. Unger of the salt precipitated at 100° agree with $Na_2H_2Sb_2O_7.5H_2O$. The percentage losses in weight of the hexa- and pentahydrates, at different temp., were found, by G. von Knorre and P. Olschewsky, to be :

	100°	125°	150°	165°	185°	200°	250°	350°	Red-heat.
$6H_2O$	0·58	1·11	4·96	8·42	15·28	17·92	18·71	20·64	20·30
$5H_2O$	0·00	0·01	0·39	0·87	9·13	16·29	16·72	18·69	22·39

Observations were also made by L. Heffter. E. S. Tomula found the eq. electrical conductivities of soln. of a mol of the sodium salt in 512 and 1024 litres of water were slightly smaller, but of the same order as those of the potassium salt—*vide infra*—being respectively 80·2 and 81·0 ; the low solubility of the salt prevented more conc. soln. being examined. By analogy with the potassium salt, it was therefore inferred that the soln. contains **sodium dihydroantimonate**, $Na(H_2SbO_4)$, and not the dihydropyroantimonate, $Na_2H_2Sb_2O_7$, or the metantimonate, $NaSbO_3$. The hydrogen-ion conc. for $v=1024$ is $C_H=10^{-6·4}$. According to F. Ebel, and

L. Heffter, 100 parts of boiling water dissolve rather less than 0·3 part of salt; while F. F. Beilstein and O. von Bläse found that at 12·3°, 100 parts of water dissolve 0·031 part of the hexahydrate; 100 parts of 15·8 per cent. alcohol, 0·013 part of the salt; and 100 parts of 25·6 per cent. alcohol, 0·007 part of the salt. E. S. Tomula found that the solubilities of sodium antimonate, $Na_2O.Sb_2O_5.6H_2O$, in water at 18°, 25°, and 33·5° are respectively 56·4, 73·8, and 101·8 mgrms. per 100 c.c. of soln.; with methyl alcohol of sp. gr. 0·9734, 12·0, 19·3, and 27·0 mgrms.; sp. gr. 0·9559, 4·4, 9·5, and 15·0 mgrms.; sp. gr. 0·9298, 0·6, 3·1, and 6·2 mgrms. respectively; with ethyl alcohol of sp. gr. 0·9774, 11·8, 15·0, and 40·3 mgrms.; sp. gr. 0·9618, 3·8, 6·0, and 14·0 mgrms.; and sp. gr. 0·9370, 0·1, 0·4, and 0·8 mgrms. respectively. With a one per cent. soln. of sodium acetate, 6·1, 14·6, and 20·5 mgrms.; with a 2·5 per cent. soln., 3·1, 4·0, and 9·4 mgrms.; and with a 5 per cent. soln., a feeble opalescence appeared at 18° and 25°, and at 33·5°, 4·2 mgrms. were dissolved per 100 c.c. of soln. The salt is less soluble in a 2·5 to 10 per cent. soln. of sodium hydroxide or carbonate than it is in water; while ammonium or potassium salt soln. have a greater solvent action than water. Thus, 100 parts of a soln. of 160 parts of potassium carbonate in 250 c.c. of water, dissolve 0·514 part $NaSbO_3$; 48 parts of potassium nitrate, 0·132 part $NaSbO_3$; and 27, 40, and 60 of potassium chloride, respectively 0·063, 0·079, and 0·145 part $NaSbO_3$. Observations were made by E. Frémy, G. von Knorre and P. Olschewsky, H. Rose, E. S. Tomula, F. F. Beilstein and O. von Bläse, C. R. Fresenius, L. Garnier, and F. J. Otto. E. C. Franklin and C. A. Kraus found it to be insoluble in liquid ammonia. According to B. Unger, and W. Feit and C. Kubierschky, the dihydropyroantimonate dissolves slowly in a soln. of sodium sulphide, and acids precipitate antimony pentasulphide from the colourless soln. G. von Knorre and P. Olschewsky found the salt to be insoluble in acetic acid. A. Naumann said that it is insoluble in methyl and ethyl acetates, and in acetone.

E. Frémy obtained what might be **potassium pyroantimonate**, $K_4Sb_2O_7.nH_2O$, by melting antimony pentoxide or potassium metantimonate with three times its weight of potassium hydroxide; and evaporating an aq. soln. of the product. G. von Knorre and P. Olschewsky, and A. E. Delacroix were unable to establish the chemical individuality of the product. It may be a mixture of the metantimonate and alkali. E. Frémy said that when the dihydroantimonate is decomposed with cold water, it forms **potassium dihydropyroantimonate**, $K_2H_2Sb_2O_7.4H_2O$, but G. von Knorre and P. Olschewsky were unable to verify this. E. Frémy heated antimony with four times its weight of nitre in a fireclay crucible at a red-heat, and extracted the nitrate and nitrite from the cold mass by cold water. The residue was boiled with water for 2 to 3 hrs., when almost all passed into the soln. The liquid was evaporated for crystallization; and the crystals were drained on a porous tile, and washed with cold water. The result was supposed to be the dihydropyroantimonate, but G. von Knorre and P. Olschewsky obtained the metantimonate by this process. L. Heffter also obtained poor yields of salt by this process; C. F. Rammelsberg used a somewhat similar process, and C. Brunner deflagrated a mixture of nitre and potassium antimonyl tartrate, but G. von Knorre and P. Olschewsky did not obtain a pure product by this process. A. E. Delacroix precipitated this salt by adding alcohol to a 2–2·5 per cent. soln. of potassium metantimonate, and A. Reynoso, by treating a soln. of potassium antimonite with potassium permanganate. J. D. van Leeuwen made potassium pyroantimonate for the determination of sodium by heating to redness a mixture of 20 grms. potassium antimonyl tartrate with an equal weight of potassium nitrate. When reaction has ceased, the lid is placed on the crucible, and heating continued for 15 mins. After cooling, 50 c.c. of warm water are added, and the mass stirred until it becomes powdery. It is then filtered through a porcelain vacuum filter, the residue is treated with 100 c.c. of cold water, and transferred with the filter-paper to a flask containing 500 c.c. of boiling water. After boiling for one minute and rapidly cooling, some aluminium hydroxide is added, the mixture is shaken, and finally passed through an ordinary filter-paper. S. A. Schou prepared this salt as follows :

Grey stibnite is boiled with potassium hydroxide soln., cupric oxide is added, and the whole stirred and boiled for $\frac{1}{2}$ hr., and then filtered. The filtrate (which should be quite free from sulphur and give a pure white precipitate with lead acetate soln.) is evaporated to one-tenth of its original vol. and treated with alcohol. The precipitated potassium antimonate is filtered off, washed with 50 per cent. alcohol, left for 24 hrs., and then ground in a mortar and dried on filter-paper. This method gives a yield of 90 per cent. of the theoretical, whilst a yield of 98 per cent. can be obtained if very finely divided antimony trisulphide, prepared by the careful ignition of the pentasulphide, is used instead of the ore. The antimony trisulphide and potassium hydroxide react to form a mixture of antimonite and thioantimonite, which are then oxidized by the cupric oxide with the formation of an intermediate oxysulphide, K_3SbO_3S, which cannot be isolated.

The analyses of the white powder by G. von Knorre and P. Olschewsky, and C. F. Rammelsberg corresponded with a tetrahydrate ; A. E. Delacroix represented the compound as a pentahydrate ; and E. Frémy, L. Heffter, and C. Jander and W. Brüll, as a hexahydrate. G. von Knorre and P. Olschewsky, and A. E. Delacroix represented the salt dried at 100° as a trihydrate ; and the salt dried at 100° lost 0·47 per cent. in weight at 122° ; 1·04, at 150° ; 1·64, at 170° ; 5·23, at 200° ; 9·26, at 225° ; 10·51, at 280° ; 10·70, at 330° ; and 15·80, at a red-heat. 100 parts of water at 20° dissolve 2·81 parts of the anhydrous salt ; and the sp. gr. of the soln. is 1·0263 at 18°. G. Jander and W. Brüll found that the solubility of the *hexahydrated* sodium pyroantimonate, dried at room temp., is $3·01 \times 10^{-3}$ mols per litre ; and when dried at 100° the resulting *trihydrate* has the solubility of $2·52 \times 10^{-3}$ to $2·55 \times 10^{-3}$ mols per litre. The transition point is 10°. The mol. lowering of the f.p. is 27·3° for a 0·1970N-soln., and 33·9° for a 0·395N-soln. The effects of sodium chloride and of potassium antimonate on the solubility, S, of this sodium antimonate, are :

NaCl	0·03	0·01	0·003	0·001
S	0·00025	0·00066	0·00149	0·00213
K antimonate	0·03	0·01	0·003	0·001
S	0·00005	0·00067	0·000148	0·00208

The aq. soln. of this sodium pyroantimonate contains sodium ortho- or meta-antimonate involving either $Na^{·}+H_2SbO_4{'}=NaH_2SbO_4$; or else $Na^{·}+SbO_3{'}=NaSbO_3$. Likewise also with aq. soln. of potassium ortho- or meta-antimonate ; both salts have similar ions in aq. soln., and hence they are assumed to be either ortho- or meta-antimonates—which is not evident. The conc. of the $H^{·}$-ions in 0·1N-, 0·01N-, 0·005N-, and 0·002N-soln. are respectively $10^{-8·7}$, $10^{-8·2}$, $10^{-7·8}$, and $10^{-7·7}$ for the potassium salt, and for the 0·004N- and 0·0004N-soln. of the sodium salt, respectively, $10^{-7·8}$ and $10^{-7·7}$. The diffusion coeff. of the antimonate ion in N- and 0·1N-HCl are 0·44, and in strongly acid soln., a tetrantimonate is probably formed. When the cold sat. soln. is evaporated in vacuo, the original salt is obtained as a white, crystalline mass ; but if the hot, sat., aq. soln. is evaporated to dryness on a water-bath, the metantimonate is formed. E. Mitscherlich obtained a similar product by the action of soda-lye on antimony pentasulphide. E. Frémy, and G. von Knorre and P. Olschewsky found that the dil. or conc. aq. soln. gives a white crystalline precipitate of sodium dihydropyroantimonate, with a soln. of sodium acetate. Unlike the metantimonate, the dihydropyroantimonate is decomposed when calcined 2 or 3 times with ammonium chloride. W. Ipatieff and co-workers observed that potassium hydropyroantimonate gives potassium hydroxide and antimony when heated with hydrogen under press. J. W. Thomas said that the action of hydrogen chloride on potassium antimonate is energetic, forming antimony and potassium chlorides.

F. F. Beilstein and O. von Bläse treated a soln. of potassium metantimonate with lithium sulphate and, after the liquid had stood some time, obtained a white powder consisting of hexagonal plates of lithium metantimonate, $LiSbO_3.3H_2O$. It loses all its water of crystallization when ignited, and neither darkens in colour,

nor becomes calorescent. The product obtained by deflagrating and fusing antimony, or antimony pentoxide or trisulphide with sodium nitrate and an alkali furnishes an impure *sodium metantimonate*, which occurs in commerce under the trade name *leukonium*. The use of this substance as an opacifying agent for enamels, glasses, and glazes was discussed by P. Askenasy, and R. Rickmann. W. G. Mixter gave for the heat of formation of a possible sodium orthantimonate : $3Na_2O + 2Sb + 5O = 2Na_3SbO_4 + 393 \cdot 3$ Cals.

The two important potassium antimonates are the granular dihydropyroantimonate, $K_2H_2Sb_2O_7.4H_2O$; and the gummy **potassium metantimonate,** $KSbO_3.nH_2O$. The sodium salt eq. to the former has just been described, but the existence of a sodium eq. of the latter has not been established. Potassium metantimonate was prepared by J. J. Berzelius, and E. Frémy by melting a mixture of antimony, or antimony trioxide or trisulphide with 3–4 times its weight of potassium nitrate for an hour at dull redness. The mass is then washed with cold water to remove alkali nitrate and nitrite ; boiled with water for 2–3 hrs., replacing the water as it evaporates, and the potassium antimonate is thereby converted into a gummy soluble antimonate. W. P. Dexter, and F. F. Beilstein and O. von Bläse treated a mixture of potassium antimonyl tartrate in an analogous way. G. Jander and L. Brandt found that the antimonate obtained by oxidizing alkaline soln. of antimony trioxide by hydrogen dioxide is difficult to crystallize. The value of the ratio $K_2O : Sb_2O_5$ is nearly unity. F. F. Beilstein and O. von Bläse purified potassium metantimonate by washing the powder with cold water ; shaking it up with conc., aq. ammonia and allowing the mixture to stand in a closed flask for two days ; and boiling the mixture diluted with much water to drive off the ammonia. T. Rieckher prepared potassium metantimonate by adding sufficient copper hydroxide to a boiling soln. of antimony pentasulphide in potash-lye to desulphurize the mixture ; filtering off the precipitated copper sulphide ; and evaporating the soln. ; the product was washed with a little cold water, and dried on a porous tile. M. Duyk used a modification of this process. G. von Knorre and P. Olschewsky obtained the metantimonate by treating the dihydropyroantimonate with boiling water ; and by adding alcohol to a soln. of antimony pentoxide or potassium antimonate in potash-lye. Analyses of air-dried potassium metantimonate by E. Frémy, L. Heffter, and G. von Knorre and P. Olschewsky correspond with $KSbO_3.nH_2O$, where n ranges from 5·66 to 7·99 ; and of the product dried at 100°, with $KSbO_3.1\cdot5H_2O$. According to G. von Knorre and P. Olschewsky, the salt prepared by E. Frémy's process and dried at 100° lost the following percentage amounts of water at the given temp. :

	125°	150°	175°	200°	225°	250°	280°	350°	Red-heat.
Loss	1·26	2·64	4·43	4·29	5·14	5·71	6·39	6·79	11·77

Observations were also made by E. Frémy. J. J. Berzelius found that the air-dried salt dissolves slowly in cold and quickly in hot water ; G. von Knorre and P. Olschewsky, that the salt dried at 100° dissolves with difficulty in cold water, but readily in hot water ; and E. Frémy, that the salt dried at 160° is insoluble in cold water, but is slowly dissolved by boiling water. L. Heffter, and G. von Knorre and P. Olschewsky found that acids precipitate hydrated antimony pentoxide from the aq. soln., and carbon dioxide, an acid salt containing no carbonate— L. Heffter thought a carbonate was present. The alkali antimonates were found by B. Unger to be converted into antimony trisulphide and alkali sulphate when fused with sulphur ; and H. Rose, into sodium sulphantimonate when fused with sodium thiosulphate ; or with a mixture of sulphur and sodium carbonate. E. Frémy said that soln. of ammonium chloride gave a precipitate with aq. soln. of the metantimonate. H. Rose, and F. Ebel found that ignition with ammonium chloride volatilizes the antimony completely from alkali and alkaline earth antimonates, but not completely from other antimonates. G. von Knorre and P. Olschewsky found that the salt is decomposed, but not completely unless the metantimonate has been previously evaporated with hydrochloric acid. H. Rose, and O. Brunck showed that fused potassium cyanide reduces the antimonates to antimony. W. Müller found that when heated in a current of carbon disulphide, potassium metasulphantimonate is produced. According to H. Rose, soln. of potassium metantimonate with acids—hydrochloric, nitric, or sulphuric acid—precipitate a hydrate soluble in an excess of hydrochloric acid ; hydrogen sulphide precipitates antimony pentasulphide ; carbon dioxide precipitates $3K_2O.3Sb_2O_5.nH_2O$; oxalic acid and potassium oxalate give no precipitate—although after long standing oxalic acid gives a flocculent precipitate ; aq. ammonia has no effect or gives only a slight precipitation ; most salts of the alkaline earths and of the heavy metals give precipitates—magnesium sulphate acts in the presence of ammonia ; copper sulphate gives a bluish-green precipitate ; silver nitrate, a white or pale yellow precipitate soluble in aq. ammonia ; and auric chloride gives a precipitate only after standing a long time. Sodium salts give a flocculent precipitate when added to a soln. of potassium antimonate. Soln. of the metantimonate prepared in the cold give a flocculent precipitate with sodium acetate ; if the soln. has been boiled and cooled before adding the acetate, a crystalline precipitate appears. A. Bartoli and G. Papasogli electrolyzed a soln. of potassium metantimonate with electrodes of wood-charcoal or gas-carbon, and found much gas evolved at the cathode, and very little at the anode. They obtained a black deposit and a liquid which when filtered and concentrated on the water-bath, and treated with hydrochloric acid, gives a black precipitate which, after washing and drying at 100°, (i) contains carbon, oxygen, hydrogen, and antimony ; (ii) it dissolves in water and in alkaline hydrates, forming deep black soln., from which it is completely precipitated by mineral acids ; (iii) it dissolves with rise of temp. in aq. potassium hypochlorite, forming mellic acid and other benzocarboxylic acids, together with potassium antimonate. This substance being analogous in modes of formation and in properties to mellogen, was called *stibiomellogen*. The graphite anode was much disintegrated ; and the product corresponding with stibiomellogen was called *stibiographitic acid*. E. F. Smith and D. L. Wallace, and S. C. Schmucker found that in the presence of alkali tartrates, antimony is not precipitated by electrolysis, and may thus be separated from copper, cadmium, tin, bismuth, and mercury. L. Kahlenberg and W. J. Trautmann observed a strong reaction when the pyroantimonate is heated with silicon.

The alchemists obtained what they called *antimonium diaphoreticum ablutum*, *cerussa antimonii*, or *calx antimonii alba* by mixing antimony or antimony sulphide with an excess of nitre, projecting the mixture in small portions at a time into a red-hot crucible, and igniting the mass for some time after the deflagration has ceased. The mass is extracted with water to remove soluble impurities. The residue is boiled with 3 or 4 parts of water, and the soln. of metantimonate is treated with carbon dioxide ; this yields a white precipitate with the composition $2K_2O.3Sb_2O_5.nH_2O$, usually represented $K_2H_3Sb_3O_{10}.nH_2O$—**potassium trihydrotriantimonate,** or $K_2HSb_3O_9.6.11H_2O$. The salt was so prepared by J. J. Berzelius, E. Frémy, O. Figuier, G. von Knorre and P. Olschewsky, and A. E. Delacroix. Instead of using carbon dioxide, J. A. Buchner recommended adding sufficient acetic acid to give the soln. a feeble acidic reaction ; and L. Heffter, adding a soln. of potassium sulphate to one of potassium metantimonate. J. A. Buchner boiled hydrated antimony pentoxide with a soln. of potassium hydroxide; evaporated the soln. to dryness ; heated the product to redness ; and extracted the cold mass with boiling water. There remained undissolved a small yield of this salt. C. F. Rammelsberg prepared the salt by treating antimony pentasulphide with conc. potash-lye, when dioxydisulphantimonate passes into soln. Analyses of the air-dried, white powder by L. Heffter, and G. von Knorre and P. Olschewsky show between 19·05 and 24·09 per cent. of water ; and for that dried at 100°, $K_2H_3Sb_3O_{10}.2H_2O$. The percentage losses of water at higher temp. are :

	125°	150°	175°	200°	225°	250°	280°	350°	Red-heat.
Loss	1·02	2·13	3·18	4·00	4·81	5·46	6·30	6·47	9·80

L. Heffter found that the powder reddens moist litmus-paper. According to G. von Knorre and P. Olschewsky, it is sparingly soluble in cold and hot water ; and when heated with water in a sealed tube, at 180°, much potassium antimonate passes into soln. The **sodium trihydrotriantimonate,** $Na_2H_3Sb_3O_{10}.2.78H_2O$, can also be represented $Na_2HSb_3O_9.3.78H_2O$. The sat. soln. of the potassium salt at 20° contains 2.69×10^{-3} gram-atoms per litre ; while with the sodium salt there are 3.8×10^{-5} gram-atoms per litre. If the formula is $R_2HSb_3O_9.nH_2O$, the solubility of the potassium salt is 0.9×10^{-3} mols per litre, and that of the sodium salt, 1.3×10^{-5} mols per litre. G. Jander and W. Brüll found the diffusion coefficient for the two salts is equally great and amounts to 0.55 at 11.8° ; the acid residue, in strongly acid soln., has a smaller diffusion coeff. due, it is assumed, to polymerization resulting in the formation of alkali tetrantimonate, $4Sb_3O_{10}''''' + 2H^. = 3Sb_4O_3''''' + H_2O$. The conc. of the $H^.$-ions in the aq. soln. of the potassium salt in 0.001N-soln. is $10^{-3.63}$; and the three hydrogen-ions are 69 per cent. ionized, so that it is a very strong acid—the dissociation constant is 0.00053. The *antimony oxide* used in glass painting and for enamels is really a potassium antimonate.

W. Hampe reported **copper orthoantimonate,** $Cu_3(SbO_4)_2$, to be formed as a dark red mass by heating a mixture of copper oxide and an excess of antimony trioxide to 1100° in an atm. of carbon dioxide. It is slowly soluble in hydrochloric acid ; and is decomposed by nitric acid, and by heating in an atm. of carbon dioxide. J. J. Berzelius obtained a pale green crystalline powder by the action of a soln. of potassium metantimonate on one of copper sulphate ; and C. L. Allen obtained a similar product—**copper metantimonate,** $Cu(SbO_3)_2.5H_2O$, by using eq. quantities of these two salts. F. Ebel used a somewhat similar process. J. B. Senderens treated antimony pentoxide with an aq. soln. of copper acetate, washed the product with cold water, and dried it in air. G. von Knorre and P. Olschewsky boiled antimony pentasulphide with potash-lye, precipitated the sulphur as cupric sulphide by the addition of copper hydroxide, and allowed the filtrate to stand for some time. Pale green crystals were deposited from the liquid. The above formula is based on the analyses of F. Ebel, and J. B. Senderens. J. B. Senderens found that it loses 3 mols. of water over conc. sulphuric acid, and the remainder at 300°, while at a red-heat it begins to decompose. C. L. Allen observed that at 100°, the salt loses a mol. of water ; at 260°, 3 mols. ; and at 360°, it is virtually freed from water and becomes yellowish-green. According to F. Ebel, the salt dried at 100° has 7.10 per cent. of water ; at 125°, 5.45 per cent. ; at 150°– 200°, 4.13 per cent. ; and at 300°, 1.99 per cent. According to J. J. Berzelius, and C. L. Allen, when heated by a gas-blowpipe flame, dehydrated copper antimonate becomes incandescent, without losing weight. J. J. Berzelius said that the mass blackens when heated, but C. L. Allen attributed this to the presence of copper hydroxide, since the purified salt becomes pale greenish-grey. F. Ebel said that when melted with sodium carbonate and sulphur, the antimony is not completely removed by washing ; nitric acid decomposes the salt incompletely ; and it is completely soluble in hydrochloric acid provided it has been ignited. A. E. Delacroix obtained a basic salt approximating $5CuO.2Sb_2O_5.7H_2O$, by heating to 80° the green soln. of copper oxide, antimony pentoxide, and potash-lye ; washing the precipitate with water, and drying at 100°. F. F. Beilstein and O. von Bläse obtained $3CuO.2Sb_2O_5.13H_2O$ as a pale green precipitate from a soln. of cupric sulphate and potassium antimonate. The more the product is washed the more basic the product. Both these substances are probably mixtures.

H. Schiff treated the precipitate, obtained by adding cupric sulphate to a soln. of potassium antimonate, with aq. ammonia, and found that it gradually passed into a pale blue granular powder of **copper tetramminopyroantimonate,** $Cu_2Sb_2O_7.4NH_3.4H_2O$, which was washed with aq. ammonia, and dried over conc. sulphuric acid. A. E. Delacroix crystallized a soln. of copper triantimonate in aq. ammonia, and found that after drying in air, the **copper triamminometanti-monate** had the composition $Cu(SbO_3)_2.3NH_3.9H_2O$. R. F. Weinland and H. Schmid found that when copper pentamminometachlorantimonate is allowed to stand in its mother-liquor, the triamminometantimonate separates out in hexagonal prisms or plates. F. Raschig found that a soln. of copper tetramminoxide and ammonium metantimonate furnishes dark blue crystals of **ammonium copper ammoniohydroxyantimonate**, $2NH_4SbO_3.Cu(ONH_4)(OH).4H_2O$.

J. J. Berzelius obtained a white precipitate of **silver metantimonate**, $AgSbO_3$, by adding silver nitrate to a soln. of alkali metantimonate ; and F. Ebel obtained the same salt by using an excess of silver nitrate. The precipitate obtained with soln. at $80°-86°$ had $2.5H_2O$; and when dried at $100°$, $0.625H_2O$; at $125°$, $0.5H_2O$; and at $150°-200°$, $0.3H_2O$. F. F. Beilstein and O. von Bläse obtained the trihydrate by this process. It is completely soluble in aq. ammonia when freshly precipitated, and only imperfectly soluble after drying. Gaseous ammonia reacts with the air-dried salt producing **silver diamminometantimonate,** $AgSbO_3.2NH_3.2H_2O$. T. Thomson found that a soln. of antimony pentoxide in alkali-lye gives with auric chloride a black precipitate thought to be **aurous antimonate.**

J. J. Berzelius precipitated a soln. of potassium metantimonate by the addition of a calcium salt. The mineral *romeite* has been already described as a calcium antimonite; the mineral *schneebergite* obtained by A. Brezina from Schneeberg, Tyrol, occurs in honey-yellow, octahedral crystals with a dodecahedral cleavage. This agrees with W. T. Schaller, who found that schneebergite is cubic in its geometrical symmetry. The mineral is probably dimorphous where the high temp. form is cubic. A. Brezina gave 4.1 for the sp. gr. ; and W. T. Schaller, 5.41. The hardness is 6.5. C. Hlawatsch gave 2.10 for the refractive index of schneebergite, and W. T. Schaller, 2.09. The crystals may have an anomalous birefringence, but they become optically isotropic when heated. A. Brezina found that schneebergite is insoluble in acids; and is slowly decomposed by molten alkali carbonate. The paragenesis of schneebergite was discussed by R. Köchlin, and W. T. Schaller. Schneebergite is sometimes considered to be a calcium metantimonate admixed with traces of iron, copper, bismuth, magnesium, zinc, and sulphate. W. T. Schaller's analysis agrees with the empirical formula $CaSbO_3$. He regards the mineral as a mixture of calcium pyroantimonite, $Ca_2Sb_2O_5$, and calcium pyro-antimonate, $Ca_2Sb_3O_7$, because the contained antimony exists in two states of oxidation, and "to regard tervalent antimony as a base to be added on to the calcium throws too heavy a burden on quadrivalent antimony, which must then serve as an acid for an overwhelming base." According to P. Groth, schneebergite is probably identical with atopite—*vide infra*. The samples of schneebergite analyzed by A. von Elterlein, and A. S. Eakle and W. Muthmann were probably lime-iron garnet. J. B. Senderens obtained what may be **calcium metantimonate,** $Ca(SbO_3)_2.6H_2O$, or *calcium dihydroantimonate*, $Ca(H_2SO_4)_2.4H_2O$, by treating an aq. soln. of antimony pentoxide with calcium acetate. The white precipitate loses 4 mols. of water over conc. sulphuric acid, and the residue at $100°$ is stable. All the water is expelled at a higher temp., and the residue is stable at a red-heat. L. Heffter treated a soln. of sodium dihydropyroantimonate with calcium chloride and obtained a white, flocculent precipitate with the composition $Ca(SbO_3)_2.5H_2O$. It lost 6.17 per cent. of its water at $100°$, 11.4 per cent. at $200°$, 14.7 per cent. at $300°$, and 18.6 per cent. at dull redness. He obtained **strontium metantimonate,** $Sr(SbO_3)_2.6H_2O$, in an analogous manner as a white, amorphous powder which lost 8.17 per cent. of water at $100°$, 12.42 per cent. at $200°$, 14.62 per cent. at $300°$, and 19.81 per cent. at a dull red-heat. L. Heffter obtained **barium metantimonate,** $Ba(SbO_3)_2.6H_2O$, in an analogous way, and the same salt was also prepared by J. J. Berzelius, and F. Ebel. If the precipitate is allowed to stand for a long time in contact with the mother-liquid at $0°$, small needle-like crystals are formed. The precipitate dried over sulphuric acid contained $6H_2O$, and dried at $80°-100°$, $5H_2O$. The loss at $125°-175°$ was 1.66 per cent. ; at $225°-250°$, 3.07 per cent. ;

at 300°, 5·36 per cent. ; and at a red heat, 8·48 per cent. When calcined, the salt becomes calorescent. It is sparingly soluble in water ; dissolves in hydrochloric acid ; and is not decomposed by carbon dioxide. H. Rose said that when the antimonates of the alkalies and alkaline earths are heated with ammonium chloride, the whole of the antimony is volatilized as chloride. The reaction is incomplete with the other metal chlorides. H. Rose, and O. Brunck found that when fused with potassium cyanide, antimony is produced. The yellow or resin-brown mineral **atopite**—from ἄτοπος, unusual—occurs at Langban, Sweden. It was described by A. E. Nordenskjöld. The analysis corresponds with **calcium pyroantimonate**, $Ca_2Sb_2O_7$, or, according to P. Groth, with **sodium calcium pyroantimonate**, $CaNa_2Sb_2O_8$, or $(Ca,Na_2,Mn,Fe)_2Sb_2O_7$. C. F. Rammelsberg gave $Na_4Sb_2O_7.5(Ca,Fe,Mn)_2Sb_2O_7$. W. T. Schaller showed that atopite is probably the same mineral species as romeite (*q.v.*). Atopite furnishes octahedral and dodecahedral crystals of sp. gr. 5·03, and hardness 5·5–6·0. H. Rose found that the average index of refraction for Na-light is 1·836.

F. Ebel reported **beryllium metantimonate**, $Be(SbO_3)_2.6H_2O$, to be formed as a white powder by precipitating a boiling soln. of sodium dihydropryoantimonate, with an excess of beryllium sulphate. The air-dried product has $6H_2O$; when dried at 100°, $4H_2O$; and the percentage losses at higher temp. are 4·56 at 125° ; 7·01 at 175°–225° ; 7·71 at 250° ; 10·56 at 300° ; and 16·71 at a red-heat. It is somewhat soluble in hot water, and is readily dissolved by hot hydrochloric acid. M. Obajdin prepared **magnesium dihydroantimonate**, $Mg(H_2SbO_4)_2.10H_2O$, by the addition of a magnesium salt to a soln. of dipotassium dihydropyroantimonate. According to the conc. of the soln., it is obtained as hexagonal or monoclinic crystals or in the amorphous form. From a soln. containing 1 per cent. of the pyroantimonate, both hexagonal and monoclinic crystals and a large quantity of the amorphous precipitate are deposited ; from a soln. containing 0·35 per cent. of the pyroantimonate, monoclinic crystals are alone deposited ; whilst a soln. containing 0·07 per cent. of the potassium pyrantimonate yields hexagonal crystals only. The composition of both hexagonal and monoclinic crystals is the same. The crystals lose $8H_2O$ if heated at 176°. When heated further, they lose $2H_2O$, and change their colour successively from colourless to pink, orange-yellow, yellowish-green, greyish-green, greyish-blue, and violet, a fact which is probably due to the formation of various polymerides. Finally, the crystals spontaneously incandesce and turn white, forming magnesium metantimonate, $Mg(SbO_3)_2$. The magnesium dihydrorthantimonate has a sp. gr. 2·57 ; it is insoluble in alcohol ; and the solubility in water at 16° is 0·7075 grm. in 1000 grms. of soln. L. Heffter prepared **magnesium metantimonate**, $Mg(SbO_3)_2.10–12H_2O$, by treating a hot soln. of sodium dihydropyroantimonate with magnesium salt. H. Goguel used potassium dihydropyroantimonate. F. Raschig, prepared this salt by treating ammonium metantimonate with a magnesium salt. H. Goguel argued from his observations on the dehydration at different temp. that the salt is *magnesium dihydroantimonate*, $Mg(H_2SbO_4)_2.10H_2O$.

$$O<^{SbO_4<^{H_2}_{Mg}}_{SbO_4<^{Mg}_{H_2}}$$

C. von Haushofer obtained the salt by adding a magnesium salt to a conc. soln. of potassium metantimonate ; he added that the salt is dimorphous, furnishing hexagonal and monoclinic crystals. The hexagonal form is obtained by precipitating the salt at a temp. between 80° and 100°, or by cooling the soln. to 100°. He was unable to obtain the monoclinic form alone. G. Rose found the salt obtained by L. Heffter's process is hexagonal ; while H. W. F. Wackenroder obtained the monoclinic form. H. Goguel attributed the behaviour of the monoclinic or rhombic crystals in polarized light to *macles multiple*. The hexagonal crystals consist of six sectors, and the cross or hyperbolas produced in parallel polarized light is a result of *la compensation de ces trois zones à leur contact.* The hexagonal crystals were stated by C. von Haushofer, and G. Rose to be isomorphous with the corresponding salts of zinc, cobalt, and nickel. L. Heffter said that the air-dried salt is dodecahydrated, and C. von Haushofer, decahydrated. At 100°, it loses $3H_2O$. L. Heffter said that the loss at 100° is 24·82 per cent.; at 200°, 32·29 per cent.; at 300°, 33·39 per cent.; and at a red-heat, 36·55 per cent. without showing any calorescence. H. Rose found that the whole of the antimony cannot be driven off by heating a mixture of the salt with ammonium chloride.

G. Aminoff described a mineral from Langban, Sweden, which he named **swedenborgite**—after E. Swedenborg. The analysis corresponds with $Na_2O.2Al_2O_3.Sb_2O_5$, **sodium dialuminyl antimonate,** $Na(AlO)_2SbO_4$, analogous with nordenskjöldine, $Ca(BO)_2SnO_4$; or it can be regarded as an aluminate, $NaSb(AlO_3)_2$. The mineral may be colourless or wine-yellow; the hexagonal prisms have the axial ratio $a : c = 1 : 1·6309$. The (0001)-cleavage is distinct. The hardness is 8. The mineral is uniaxial, and negative. The X-radiogram corresponds with an elementary parallelopiped with $a = 8·81$ A., and $c = 5·40$. The indices of refraction are $\omega = 1·7724$, and $\epsilon = 1·7700$ for the Na-light. The dispersion is strong. B. Gossner suggested that swedenborgite is an intergrowth of two corundum-like networks of alumina and sodium metantimonate.

J. J. Berzelius, and L. Heffter treated a soln. of zinc sulphate with potassium metantimonate, allowed the liquid to stand a few hours, and obtained a crystalline mass of **zinc metantimonate,** $Zn(SbO_3)_2.5H_2O$. J. B. Senderens said that the *hexahydrate* is produced from a soln. of antimonic acid and zinc acetate, by allowing the white precipitate to dry in air; it passes into the *dihydrate* when dried over conc sulphuric acid; and becomes anhydrous at 300°. F. Ebel obtained the *pentahydrate* by treating a boiling soln. of sodium dihydropyroantimonate with zinc sulphate, washing the precipitate, and drying it in air. At 100°, it loses 8·03 per cent. of water. The hydrate dried at 100° loses 2·41 per cent. of water at 125°; 4·49 per cent. at 150°–200°; 4·79 per cent. at 250°; 5·83 per cent. at 300°–350°; and 8·03 per cent. at a red-heat. J. B. Senderens said the salt decomposes at a red-heat. F. Ebel found that the salt is not insoluble in cold water and is fairly soluble in hot water. F. Ebel obtained **cadmium metantimonate,** $Cd(SbO_3)_2.3\frac{1}{2}H_2O$, by the action of a boiling soln. of sodium dihydropyroantimonate on an excess of a boiling soln. of a cadmium salt; J. B. Senderens regarded the salt as a *pentahydrate;* if produced at 35°, F. Ebel found the salt to be a *hexahydrate.* At 100°, the salt loses 8·66 per cent. of water, and the remainder at 125° loses 1·75 per cent. of water; at 150°–200°, 4·37 per cent., at 250°, 5·24 per cent.; at 300°–350°, 6·11 per cent.; and at a red-heat, 8·66 per cent. The salt is sparingly soluble in water; and soluble in hydrochloric acid.

J. J. Berzelius obtained an orange-yellow precipitate of **mercurous metantimonate** by adding mercurous nitrate to a soln. of potassium metantimonate; a similar precipitate of **mercuric metantimonate,** $Hg(SbO_3)_2.nH_2O$, is obtained with soln. of a mercuric salt and potassium metantimonate; while F. Ebel obtained only a yellow turbidity but no precipitate with sodium dihydropyroantimonate and an excess of mercuric chloride. According to J. J. Berzelius, when a mixture of antimony with 8 times its weight of mercuric oxide is heated, calorescence occurs, metallic mercury distils off, and mercuric antimonate is formed as a dark olive-green powder. It can be heated to redness without decomposition, but is decomposed at a higher temp. It is scarcely attacked by alkali-lye and by a number of acids; sulphuric acid acts on it very slowly, and hydrochloric acid dissolves very little. J. B. Senderens said that the *pentahydrate* is formed by treating a soln. of antimony pentoxide with mercuric acetate, and allowing the washed precipitate to dry for some months in air. The ochre-yellow product loses 3 mols. of water over conc. sulphuric acid; 4 mols. at 170°; and 5 mols. at 300°. It does not alter at a red-heat. F. F. Beilstein and O. von Bläse obtained the *hexahydrate* as a yellow flocculent precipitate by adding mercuric chloride to a soln. of potassium antimonate. There is no calorescence at 100° when the salt loses its water.

F. Ebel made **aluminium orthantimonate,** $AlSbO_4.4\frac{1}{2}H_2O$, by the action of a boiling soln. of sodium dihydropyroantimonate on a boiling soln. of potash-alum. The voluminous white powder when dried at 100°, contains 1·5 mols. of water, and with a rise of temp., the salt loses 2·21 per cent. at 125° ; 4·75 at 150°–200° ; 6·62 at 250° ; 7·57 at 300°–350° ; and 11·38 per cent. at a red-heat. The calcined salt is pale yellow. The hydrated salt is freely soluble in hot, dil. hydrochloric acid, but the calcined salt in incompletely soluble. F. F. Beilstein and O. von Bläse found that a conc. soln. of potassium metantimonate precipitates **aluminium metantimonate,** $Al(SbO_3)_2.15H_2O$, when added to a soln. of potash- or ammonia-alum. When the precipitate is allowed to stand some days in contact with the mother-liquid, it becomes crystalline. It contains when dried at 100°, 7 mols. of water ; at 150°, 4·5 mols. ; at 200°, 3 mols. It shows a calorescence when ignited. F. F. Beilstein and O. von Bläse made **thallous metantimonate,** $TlSbO_3.2H_2O$, by precipitation from a soln. of potassium metantimonate and thallous sulphate. The colourless, needle-like crystals are soluble in water when freshly precipitated, but insoluble when dried. The salt gradually loses its water above 150°, when it becomes lemon-yellow when cold, dark orange when hot.

O. Kulka [3] prepared **zirconyl pyroantimonate,** $ZrO_2.Sb_2O_5.7\cdot5H_2O$, or $(ZrO)_2Sb_2O_7.7\cdot5H_2O$, by treating a soln. of zirconium sulphate with potassium metantimonate ; the precipitate is slimy and difficult to wash ; the precipitate with potassium pyroantimonate is easy to wash with hot water. It is an amorphous, white powder ; insoluble in water, soluble in hydrochloric acid. E. Lenssen made **stannous pyroantimonate,** $Sn_2Sb_2O_7$, by adding potassium antimonate to an excess of a soln. of stannous chloride acidified with acetic acid ; washing the precipitate with cold water, and drying it in air. H. Schiff made **stannous metantimonate,** $Sn(SbO_3)_2.2H_2O$, by digesting hydrated antimony pentoxide with a feebly acid soln. of stannous chloride at 60°–80° for 12–24 hrs. The brick-red product becomes yellowish-grey when dehydrated in a current of carbon dioxide ; and when heated in air, it oxidizes, becoming pale yellow. It is attacked by acids and alkalies very slowly ; most readily by conc. sulphuric acid. If hydrated antimony pentoxide be digested with a soln. of stannous chloride for 8–10 hrs. at 35°–40°, the product has the composition $Sn_2Sb_6O_{17}.4H_2O$, **stannous hexantimonate ;** and with a 4 hrs.' digestion at 30°–40°, stannous tetrantimonate, $SnSb_4O_{11}$. L. J. Thénard obtained **stannic antimonate,** by adding water to a soln. of the two oxides in hydrochloric acid ; A. Levol mixed the liquids obtained by treating antimony and tin each with an excess of hot nitric acid, and obtained a yellow powder with the evolution of nitrous fumes owing to the union of antimony nitrate with the stannic oxide.

J. J. Berzelius [4] treated a soln. of potassium antimonate with lead nitrate and obtained a white curdy precipitate of **lead antimonate ;** the same compound was produced by the action of hot nitric acid on an alloy of lead and antimony. The product turns yellow and gives off water when heated ; charcoal reduces it to lead antimonide ; it is insoluble in water ; and is partially decomposed by nitric acid. The so-called *Naples' yellow,* or *gialliolino,* is produced by igniting, in a fireclay crucible for 2 hrs., a mixture of potassium antimonyl tartrate, with twice its weight of lead nitrate, and four times its weight of sodium chloride. The cold mass is lixiviated with water. If the temp. of fusion has been too high, the product remains as a hard mass when treated with water, otherwise it disintegrates to a fine powder. The lower the temp. of preparation, the lighter the tint of the product. The proportion of lead oxide, affects the shade ; too much lead oxide dulls the tint. Commercial Naples' yellow is graded into about six shades of colour, ranging from a pale greenish yellow to a pale orange colour with a pink tinge. C. Brunner made it by mixing a pulverized alloy of equal parts of lead and antimony with three times its weight of potassium nitrate, and six times its weight of sodium chloride. There are many other recipes. The simplest mode of preparation is to roast an intimate mixture of antimony oxide and lead oxide until it has acquired the desired tint. J. B. Guimet made it by similarly roasting a mixture of potassium antimonate with twice its weight of red-lead. When ground with oil, Naples' yeilow is used as a paint ; and the pigment is largely used for producing yellow enamels ; and in glass painting. This subject was discussed by J. Stenhouse and G. Hallett. The colour is an old one. J. Percy said that he found lead and antimony in the yellow enamel of an enamelled brick from the Kasr ruins of Babylon, and inferred that the colour was therefore due to lead antimonate. In 1548, C. Piccolpassi gave directions for making the colour ; it was also described by G. Passeri, A. D. Fougeroux de Bondaroy, and J. J. le F. de la Lande in the eighteenth century. The commercial product varies in composition and tint. Some varieties fuse at a red-heat, others require 3 or 4 times their weight of lead flux before fusion. Some varieties contain basic lead chromate, or ochre. Hydrochloric acid or nitric acid slowly acts on Naples' yellow, forming a colourless soln.

Lead antimonates occur in nature. For example, there is the *Bleiniere* of D. L. G. Karsten, altered to *bleinierite* by J. Nicol. Probably the same ore, contaminated with galena, was called by E. F. Glocker, *stibiogalenite* ; and by M. Adam, *pfaffite*—after C. H. Pfaff. It is now generally called **bindheimite**—after J. J. Bindheim. The ore has been found at Nerchinok, Siberia ; Endellion, Cornwall ; Arkansas, Nevada, etc. It is a product of the decomposition of other antimonial ores. E. V. Shannon showed that it is of widespread occurrence. It occurs in white, greyish, brownish, or yellowish masses, as earth, and as an incrustation. Analyses were reported by J. J. Bindheim, C. H. Pfaff, R. Hermann, C. Stamm, M. F. Heddle, C. F. Rammelsberg, M. Tscherne, L. Fletcher, W. G. Mixter, W. F. Hillebrand, F. P. Dunnington, and C. E. Wait. The results show that it is a hydrated **lead orthoantimonate,** $Pb_3(SbO_4)_2.4H_2O$—*vide infra*, monimolite. W. F. Hillebrand, P. Groth, and C. E. Wait gave $3PbO.2Sb_2O_5.6H_2O$. M. F. Heddle gave $3PbO.2Sb_2O_5.10H_2O$; some varieties approximate $Pb_2Sb_2O_7.3H_2O$; and W. T. Schaller gave $Pb_2Sb_2O_7.nH_2O$. R. Hermann gave for the sp. gr. 4·60–4·76 ; M. F. Heddle, 4·707–5·05 ; W. F. Hillebrand, 5·01 ; F. Gonnard, 4·75 ; M. Tscherne, 5·6. The hardness is 4. H. Leroux found that in an oxidizing atm., lead oxide reacts with antimony trioxide, forming **lead pyroantimonate,** $Pb_2Sb_2O_7$, thus : $6PbO+2Sb_2O_3+O_2=2Pb+2Pb_2Sb_2O_7$; and if heated in a closed vessel, $2PbO+Sb_2O_3=2Pb+Sb_2O_5$. When lead and the pyroantimonate are heated together : $2Pb+Pb_2Sb_2O_7=4PbO+Sb_2O_3$. In the oxidation of the mixed metals, antimony oxidizes first ; and the lead oxide, when formed, serves as a carrier of oxygen oxidizing more antimony as it mixes with the salt.

F. F. Beilstein and O. von Bläse treated potassium metantimonate with lead acetate, and after washing the product by decantation, and drying in air, they obtained colourless lead oxytetrametantimonate, $PbO.2Pb(SbO_3)_2.11H_2O$. It retains $4H_2O$ at 100° : $2H_2O$ at 150° ; H_2O at 250° ; and none at a red-heat. It shows a calorescence when ignited, and is then yellow. J. B. Senderens made lead metantimonate, $Pb(SbO_3)_2.9H_2O$, as a white precipitate, by treating metantimonic acid with lead acetate. It becomes the *dihydrate* when kept a few months over sulphuric acid. F. Ebel obtained the *hexahydrate* by treating potassium metantimonate with lead nitrate ; at 25° it becomes the *pentahydrate ;* at 100°, the *hemitrihydrate ;* and at 125°, the *monohydrate*. He obtained the *tetrahydrate* by mixing a boiling soln. of lead nitrate and sodium dihydropyroantimonate. The salt is somewhat soluble in hot water.

A variety of bindheimite found by A. Raimondi in Corongo, Peru, was called *coronguite*. It is a greyish-yellow earth with an analysis Sb_2O_5, 58·97 ; PbO, 21·48 ; Ag_2O, 7·82 ; Fe_2O_3, 0·52 ; and H_2O, 11·21, so that if homogeneous, it is silver lead antimonate. Its sp. gr. is 5·05 ; and its hardness, 2·5–3·0. L. J. Igelström reported a mineral from Pajsberg, Sweden, which he called **monimolite**—from μόνιμος, permanent, stable. Analyses by L. J. Igelström, and G. Flink indicate two varieties : one, free from calcium, corresponds with lead orthoantimonate, $Pb_3(SbO_4)_2$, or, as P. Groth represented it, $(Pb,Fe,Mn)_3(SbO_4)_2$; and the other, containing calcium, corresponds with $(Pb,Ca)_3(SbO_4)_2$, or **calcium lead orthoantimonate.** The colour ranges from yellow to brown, to black. It occurs massive, as an incrustation, and in octahedral and cubic crystals which have an indistinct octahedral cleavage. A. E. Nordenskjöld considered the crystals to be tetragonal with the axial ratio $a:c=1:0.9950$. The sp. gr. of the calciferous variety is 6·579, and the hardness 6; and the sp. gr. of the other variety is 7·287, and the hardness 5. The mineral is insoluble in strong acids, and is not decomposed by fusion with alkali carbonates and hydroxides—excepting in the case of the variety free from calcium. The mineral is reduced by hydrogen at a red-heat, and the product is soluble in acids.

For *tellurium antimonates*, *vide* antimony tellurates. F. F. Beilstein and O. von Bläse [5] prepared **chromium metantimonate,** $Cr(SbO_3)_3.14H_2O$, as a bluish-green precipitate, by the action of chrome-alum on a soln. of potassium metantimonate. The precipitate should be rapidly washed. When ignited, the salt becomes grey without showing any calorescence.

According to O. W. Gibbs, **ammonium antimonatomolybdate,** $5(NH_4)_2O.4Sb_2O_5.7MoO_3.12H_2O$, is a representative of the antimonatomolybdates. The **alkali antimonatomolybdates** are formed by the action of freshly precipitated, hydrated antimony pentoxide on acid molybdates; by the action of molybdic acid on antimonates; and by gradually adding a hydrochloric acid soln. of antimony pentachloride to a basic molybdate. The ammonium salt crystallizes from a boiling soln. of ammonium molybdate, sat. with hydrated antimony pentoxide. The colourless crystals are freely soluble in hot water; the salt decomposes when the aq. soln. is evaporated. The aq. soln. gives a canary-yellow precipitate with manganese sulphate.

O. W. Gibbs obtained **potassium antimonatotungstate,** $3K_2O.2Sb_2O_5.6WO_5.12\frac{1}{2}H_2O$, by boiling a soln. of potassium dihydropyroantimonate for a long time with potassium tungstate. The colourless crystals are sparingly soluble in water. The alkali salt is also obtained by oxidizing the antimonitotungstate, and by the action of tungstic acid on an antimonate. According to A. L. Hallopeau, when an excess of antimonic acid is boiled for several hours with a soln. of potassium paratungstate, it dissolves, and, on filtering, crystals of potassium antimonato-tungstate are deposited having the composition $2WO_3.3KSbO_3.8H_2O$, and differing from the antimonatotungstate described by O. W. Gibbs. This compound forms small botryoidal masses, composed of a very large number of prismatic, twinned crystals, which are highly refractive and act powerfully on polarized light. They are permanent in the air, lose $6H_2O$ at $100°$, and, on ignition, yield potassium tungstate, tungstic acid, and antimonic acid. When fused with an excess of sodium carbonate, carbon dioxide is evolved and sodium tungstate, potassium tungstate, and sodium antimonate are formed. On treating the fused mass with water, a crystalline sodium metantimonate is left. Potassium antimonatotungstate is decomposed by hydrochloric, sulphuric, and nitric acids with the formation of tungstic acid; and by hydrogen sulphide, with the precipitation of antimony and tungsten. When well-washed silver antimonatotungstate is treated with the theoretical quantity of hydrochloric acid, and the soln. evaporated in vacuo, a transparent, vitreous residue of **antimonatotungstic acid,** $4WO_3.3Sb_2O_5.11H_2O$, remains, which does not lose weight at $100°$. O. W. Gibbs obtained **copper antimonatotungstate** by the action of copper sulphate on a soln. of the potassium salt; O. W. Gibbs, and A. L. Hallopeau, **silver antimonatotungstate** by the action of silver nitrate; and O. W. Gibbs obtained **barium antimonatotungstate** by the action of barium chloride; and **mercurous antimonatotungstate,** by the action of mercurous nitrate.

C. F. Rammelsberg obtained **uranyl antimonate,** $UO_2.1.22Sb_2O_5.6.4H_2O$, by treating a hydrochloric acid soln. of uranium tetrachloride with an excess of potassium metantimonate. The green gelatinous precipitate becomes yellowish-brown when calcined with nitric acid, there is a separation of antimony pentoxide and the formation of uranyl nitrate ; potash-lye precipitates uranium dioxide.

According to J. F. L. Mérimée, when a mixture of bismuth with 8 times its weight of antimony sulphide, and 21 times its weight of nitre, is projected into a heated crucible in small portions at a time, then fused, powdered, washed, and dried, bismuth antimonate is produced. When one part of this is mixed with 8 parts of ammonium chloride, and 128 parts of litharge, and fused, it furnishes a yellow glass. The tint depends on the time and temp. The product is used as a pigment—*Mérimée's yellow*. W. Hampe obtained bismuth metantimonate, $Bi(SbO_3)_3$, as a residue when copper containing these two elements is dissolved in nitric acid. A. Cavazzi made bismuth orthoantimonate, $BiSbO_4.H_2O$, or bismuthyl metantimonate, $(BiO)SbO_3.H_2O$, as a white, amorphous precipitate by adding a conc. soln. of potassium metantimonate to a dil. soln. of ammonium bismuth citrate. The precipitate is washed with boiling water. The product is insoluble in water ; soluble in hydrochloric acid ; and fusible only at a high temp. It is not decomposed by boiling water ; and it becomes yellow when heated. If the preparation is conducted in the presence of an excess of ammonia, bismuthyl orthoantimonate, $(BiO)_3SbO_4.H_2O$, is produced as a gelatinous precipitate, insoluble in water, and soluble in hydrochloric acid. He obtained evidence of the possible existence of *potassium bismuthyl metantimonate*, $K(BiO)(SbO_3)_2$, in the unwashed precipitate of bismuthyl metantimonate, *vide stibiotantalite*.

J. J. Berzelius,[6] and F. F. Beilstein and O. von Bläse prepared manganous metantimonate, $Mn(SbO_3)_2.nH_2O$, by the action of manganous sulphate on a soln. of potassium metantimonate ; F. Ebel, by the action of manganous sulphate on a soln. of sodium dihydropyroantimonate ; and J. B. Senderens, by the action of manganous acetate on an aq. soln. of antimony pentoxide. Analyses of the white amorphous powder by F. F. Beilstein and O. von Bläse corresponded with the *heptahydrate ;* J. B. Senderens, with the *hexahydrate ;* and F. Ebel, with the *pentahydrate.* The salt dried at 100° is the *dihydrate,* and F. Ebel found that the loss when the salt is heated to 125° is 2·63 per cent. ; to 150°–200°, 5·49 per cent. ; to 250°, 5·82 per cent. ; to 300°–350°, 6·15 per cent. ; and at a red-heat, 8·61 per cent. F. Ebel said that the action of heat on the salt supports the hypothesis that it is a metantimonate. J. J. Berzelius said that the salt is sparingly soluble in water ; and when ignited it turns grey, but at a higher temp. becomes white without exhibiting any glow ; after this, acids do not separate manganous oxide. When exposed to air, the salt becomes reddish-grey. A steel-blue mineral found by L. J. Igelström at Oerebro, Sweden, was named basilite—after Basil Valentine. According to C. F. Rammelsberg, the analyses correspond with manganic antimonate, $11(Mn_2O_3,Fe_2O_3).Sb_2O_5.21H_2O$; P. Groth represented it by $(Mn_3O_4)_4.Sb_2O_5.7Mn_2O_3.3H_2O$. It dissolves in warm hydrochloric acid with the evolution of chlorine. L. J. Igelström described two manganese oxyantimonates : black *manganostibiite*, $10MnO.Sb_2O_5$, from Nordmark, Sweden ; and black *hæmatostibiite* or *hematostibiite*, $8MnO.Sb_2O_5$. or $9MnO.Sb_2O_5$, from Oerebro, Sweden. The two minerals are optically negative, and the optic axial angle is small. E. S. Larsen gave for the indices of refraction of monoclinic manganostibiite $\alpha=\beta=1·92$, and $\gamma=1·96$; and said that the optical character is positive. Some arsenic may replace the antimony.

J. J. Berzelius reported ferrous metantimonate to be formed by the action of potassium antimonate on a ferrous salt. The white powder becomes yellowish-grey on drying, and at a red-heat gives off water, and becomes red. It is slightly soluble in water. This salt was also prepared by J. B. Senderens, and F. Ebel. According to F. F. Beilstein and O. von Bläse, the salt does not glow when ignited. E. Hussak and G. T. Prior described greenish-yellow, microcrystalline aggregates of a mineral from Tripuhy, Mines Geraco, which they called *tripuhyite*. Its sp. gr. is 5·82 ; and the index of refraction and birefringence are high. E. S. Larsen gave $\alpha=2·19$, $\beta=2·20$, and $\gamma=2·33$. The analyses correspond with ferrous pyroantimonate, $Fe_2Sb_2O_7$. L. J. Igelström described black, monoclinic crystals of a weakly magnetic mineral from Oerebro, Sweden ; they called it *ferrostibian.* Its hardness is 4. The analysis is Sb_2O_5, 11·80 ; FeO, 22·60 ; MnO, 46·97 ; MgO, CaO, 2·14 ; H_2O, 10·34 ; SiO_2, 2·24. It is therefore a **manganese ferrous antimonate.** Similar remarks apply to *stibiatile* from the same locality. It occurs in black prisms, presumably monoclinic. It is not magnetic. The hardness is 5·0–5·5 The analyses is Sb_2O_5, 30 ; Mn_2O_3, 44 ; and FeO, 26. The **ferrous pentametatitanatodimetantimonate,** $Fe(SbO_3)_2.5FeTiO_3$, or $3FeTiO_5.Fe_3(SbO_4)_2$, named *derbylite*—after O. A. Derby—is a brownish-black mineral from Ouro Preto, Brazil. It was described by E. Hussak and G. T. Prior. The axial ratios of the rhombic crystals are $a : b : c = 0.9661 : 0.5502$; the sp. gr. is 4·5 ; and its hardness, 5—*vide* derbylite, and mauzeliite. G. Flink described honey-yellow, cubic crystals of a mineral frɔm Langban, Stockholm ; he called the mineral **weslienite**—after J. G. H. Weslien. Its analysis corresponds with **sodium calcium ferrous tetrantimonate,** $Na_2O.FeO.3CaO.2Sb_2O_5$, or $5RO.2Sb_2O_5$. The crystals are optically anomalous ; the sp. gr. is 4·967 ; and the hardness, 6·5. The corresponding **ferric metantimonate** was found by J. J. Berzelius to be light yellow. A. Lacroix obtained a lemon-yellow, compact or earthy mineral from Constantine, Algeria. It was named *flajolotite*—after M. Flajolot. The analysis agrees with **ferric orthoantimonate,** $FeSbO_4.\frac{3}{4}H_2O$. J. J. Berzelius obtained **cobalt metantimonate,** $Co(SbO_3)_3.nH_2O$, as a rose-coloured, crystalline powder, from a soln. of a cobalt salt and of potassium metantimonate ; L. Heffter, from boiling a soln. of sodium antimonate and cobalt sulphate ; F. Ebel, from boiling soln. of sodium dihydropyroantimonate and cobalt nitrate ; and J. B. Senderens, from soln. of cobalt acetate and hydrated antimony pentoxide. F. Ebel found that the microscopic, monoclinic crystals are *dodecahydrated* when dried in air ; the crystals precipitated from the boiling soln. are *hexahydrated.* J. B. Senderens' crystals were *pentahydrated,* and when dried over sulphuric acid, *dihydrated.* F. Ebel said that when dried at 100°, the crystals are *hemipentahydrated ;* and when heated to 120°–175°, have $2H_2O$; and at 225°, $1\frac{3}{4}H_2O$. He therefore argued that no constitutional water is present, and the salt is the metantimonate. J. J. Berzelius found that the crystals become violet-blue when heated, and blackish-grey when the water is all removed. The salt glows vividly when ignited, and appears reddish-white when cold. It is slightly soluble in water. H. Goguel inferred from the loss of water on ignition that the hexagonal, or pseudohexagonal, crystals, obtained from boiling soln. of cobalt chloride and potassium dihydropyroantimonate, are really **cobalt dihydroantimonate,** $Co(H_2SbO_4)_2.10H_2O$. J. J. Berzelius prepared **nickel metantimonate,** $Ni(SbO_3)_2.nH_2O$, as a greenish-white, insoluble precipitate by the action of nickel salt on a soln. of potassium metantimonate. L. Heffter obtained the *hexahydrate* by precipitation from boiling soln. of sodium metantimonate and nickel sulphate. When ignited it glows vividly and loses all its water. The *dodecahydrate* separates in crystals slowly from the mother-liquid of the preceding operation. The crystals lose 22·96 per cent. of water at 100° ; 27·91 per cent. at 200° ; 31·49 per cent. at 300° ; and 34·9 per cent. at a red-heat. H. Goguel inferred that the hexagonal plates, obtained by the action of boiling soln. of nickel chloride and potassium dihydropyroantimonate, are really **nickel dihydroantimonate,** $Ni(H_2SbO_4)_2.10H_2O$. The salt glows when ignited.

REFERENCES.

[1] J. J. Berzelius, *Schweigger's Journ.,* **6.** 144, 1812 ; **22.** 69, 1818 ; E. Frémy, *Ann. Chim Phys.,* (3), **12.** 361, 457, 1844 ; (3), **23.** 385, 1848 ; W. Müller, *Pogg. Ann.,* **127.** 412, 1866 ; R. Robl, *Zeit. angew. Chem.,* **39.** 608, 1926 ; F. Raschig, *Ber.,* **18.** 2743, 1885 ; J. B. Senderens, *Bull. Soc. Chim.,* (3), **21.** 56, 1899 ; A. E. Delacroix, *ib.,* (3), **21.** 1049, 1899 ; (3), **25.** 288, 1901 ; *Journ. Pharm. Chim.,* (6), **6.** 337, 1897.

[2] J. B. Senderens, *Bull. Soc. Chim.,* (3), **21.** 57, 1899 ; A. E. Delacroix, *ib.,* (3), **21.** 1049, 1899 ; (3), **25.** 288, 1901 ; *Journ. Pharm. Chim.,* (6), **6.** 337, 1897 ; O. Figuier, *ib.,* (3), **25.** 92, 1839 ; L. Garnier, *ib.,* (5), **28.** 97, 1893 ; J. J. Berzelius, *Schweigger's Journ.,* **6.** 144, 1812 ; **22.**

69, 1818; E. Frémy, *Ann. Chim. Phys.*, (3), **12**. 361, 457, 1844; (3), **23**. 385, 1848; *Compt. Rend.*, **16**. 187, 1843; G. von Knorre and P. Olschewsky, *Ber.*, **18**. 2353, 1885; **20**. 3044, 1887; W. Feit and C. Kubierschky, *ib.*, **21**. 1662, 1888; F. Raschig, *ib.*, **18**. 2743, 1885; F. Ebel, *ib.*, **22**. 3044, 1889; *Ueber einige Salze der Antimonsäure*, Berlin, 1890; S. A. Schou, *Zeit. anorg. Chem.*, **133**. 104, 1924; A. Reynoso, *Compt. Rend.*, **32**. 644, 1851; H. Rose, *Centr. Min.*, 268, 1919; C. Brunner, *Dingler's Journ.*, **159**. 356, 1861; *Pogg. Ann.*, **44**. 137, 1838; *Journ. prakt. Chem.*, (1), **10**. 196, 1837; T. Rieckher, *ib.*, **145**. 313, 1857; A. Geuther, *ib.*, (2), **4**. 438, 1871; G. Hallett and J. Stenhouse, *ib.*, **162**. 373, 1861; *Brit. Pat. No.* 215, 1861; L. Heffter, *Pogg. Ann.*, **86**. 437, 1852; C. F. Rammelsberg, *ib.*, **52**. 197, 1841; W. P. Dexter, *ib.*, **100**. 564, 1857; W. Müller, *ib.*, **127**. 413, 1866; E. Mitscherlich, *ib.*, **49**. 410, 1840; H. Rose, *ib.*, **3**. 441, 1824; **71**. 302, 1847; **73**. 582, 1848; **90**. 201, 1853; G. Rose, *ib.*, **86**. 426, 1852; M. Duyk, *Bull. Soc. Pharm. Belg.*, **37**. 109, 1893; J. D. van Leeuwen, *Chem. Weekbl.*, **16**. 1462, 1919; F. F. Beilstein and O. von Bläse, *Bull. Acad. St. Petersburg*, (4), **1**. 97, 201, 1889; A. Bartoli and G. Papasogli, *Gazz. Chim. Ital.*, **13**. 22, 1883; J. A. Buchner, *Repert. Pharm.*, **66**. 168, 1836; H. W. F. Wackenroder, *Arch. Pharm.*, (2), **34**. 279, 1843; B. Unger, *ib.*, (2), **147**. 193, 1871; *Journ. Chem. Soc.*, **25**. 41, 1872; T. H. Behrens, *Zeit. anal. Chem.*, **30**. 104, 1891; C. R. Fresenius, *ib.*, **20**. 536, 1881; O. Brunck, *ib.*, **34**. 171, 1895; C. von Haushofer, *Zeit. Kryst.*, **4**. 49, 1880; F. J. Otto, *Anleitung zur Ausmittelung der Gifte*, Braunschweig, 164, 1884; P. Askenasy, *Sprech.*, **46**. 403, 1913; R. Rickmann, *ib.*, **46**. 464, 1913; *German Pat.*, *D.R.P.* 134774, 1901; W. Hampe, *Chem. Ztg.*, **18**. 1899, 1894; *Zeit. Berg. Hütt. Sal.*, **22**. 106, 1874; C. L. Allen, *Chem. News*, **42**. 193, 1880; H. Schiff, *Liebig's Ann.*, **120**. 55, 1861; **123**. 39, 1862; E. Lenssen, *ib.*, **114**. 113, 1860; R. F. Weinland and H. Schmid, *Zeit. anorg. Chem.*, **44**. 55, 1905; S. C. Schmucker, *ib.*, **5**. 199, 1894; E. F. Smith and D. L. Wallace, *ib.*, **4**. 273, 1893; G. Jander and L. Brandt, *ib.*, **147**. 5, 1925; W. Brüll, *Ueber die Sauerstoffsäuren des fünfwertigen Antimons und ihre Alkalisalze*, Göttingen, 1926; G. Jander and W. Brüll, *Zeit. anorg. Chem.*, **158**. 321, 1926; C. P. Conrad, *Chem. News*, **40**. 197, 1879; R. Schneider, *Wied. Ann.*, **5**. 265, 1878; *Journ. prakt. Chem.*, (2), **18**. 402, 1878; (2), **22**. 131, 1880; H. Daubrawa, *Liebig's Ann.*, **186**. 110, 1877; J. W. Thomas, *Journ. Chem. Soc.*, **33**. 367, 1878; F. Raschig, *Ber.*, **18**. 2745, 1885; A. Naumann, *ib.*, **37**. 3601, 4329, 1904; **42**. 3790, 1909; T. Thomson, *Ann. Phil.*, **4**. 171, 1814; A. Brezina, *Verh. geol. Reichsanst. Wien*, 313, 1880; P. Groth, *Tabellarische Uebersicht der Mineralien*, Braunschweig, 73, 1889; 85, 1898; M. Obajdin, *Rad. Accad. Science Zagreb*, 226, 220, 1922; A. E. Nordenskjöld, *Geol. För. Förh. Stockholm*, **3**. 376, 1877; C. F. Rammelsberg, *Handbuch der Mineralchemie*, Leipzig, **2**. 183, 1895; F. E. Brown and J. E. Snyder, *Journ. Amer. Chem. Soc.*, **47**. 2671, 1925; A. Levol, *Ann. Chim. Phys.*, (3), **1**. 504, 1841; L. J. Thénard, *ib.*, (1), **32**. 257, 1800; H. Goguel, *Contribution à l'étude des arséniates et des antimoniates cristallisés préparés par voie humide*, Paris, 61, 1894; L. Kahlenberg and W. J. Trautmann, *Trans. Amer. Electrochem. Soc.*, **39**. 377, 1921; E. S. Tomula, *Studien über die Antimonsäuren und deren Alkalisalze zur Bestimmung des Antimons neben Zinn*, Helsingfors, 1920; *Zeit. anorg. Chem.*, **118**. 81, 1921; W. T. Schaller, *Bull. U.S. Geol. Sur.*, 610, 1916; A. von Elterlein, *Jahrb. geol. Reichsanst. Wien*, **41**. 289, 1891; R. Köchlin, *Tschermak's Mitt.*, (2), **21**. 15, 1902; C. Hlawatsch, *ib.*, (3), **21**. 21, 1902; A. S. Eakle and W. Muthmann, *Amer. Journ. Science*, (3), **50**. 244, 1895; *Zeit. Kryst.*, **24**. 581, 1895; E. C. Franklin and C. A. Kraus, *Amer. Chem. Journ.*, **20**. 829, 1898; W. G. Mixter, *Amer. Journ. Science*, (4), **28**. 103, 1909; G. Aminoff, *Zeit. Kryst.*, **60**. 262, 1924; W. Ipatieff, *Ber.*, **59**. B, 1412, 1926; W. Ipatieff and W. Nikolaieff, *Journ. Russ. Phys. Chem. Soc.*, **58**. 664, 686, 692, 698, 1926; R. Robl, *Zeit. angew. Chem.*, **39**. 608, 1926.

³ O. Kulka, *Beiträge zur Kenntnis einiger Zirkoniumverbindungen*, Bern, 1902; E. Lenssen, *Liebig's Ann.*, **114**. 113, 1860; H. Schiff, *ib.*, **120**. 55, 1861; L. J. Thénard, *Ann. Chim. Phys.*, (1), **32**. 257, 1800; A. Levol, *ib.*, (3), **1**. 604, 1841.

⁴ J. J. Berzelius, *Schweigger's Journ.*, **6**. 144, 1812; **22**. 69, 1818; C. H. Pfaff, *ib.*, **27**. 1, 1819; J. B. Guimet, in J. F. L. Mérimée, *De la peinture à l'huile*, Paris, 113, 1830; J. B. Senderens, *Bull. Soc. Chim.*, (3), **21**. 57, 1899; F. Ebel, *Ueber einige Salze der Antimonsäure*, Berlin, 1890; *Ber.*, **22**. 3044, 1889; F. F. Beilstein and O. von Bläse, *Bull. Acad. St. Petersburg*, (4), **1**, 97, 201, 1889; J. J. Bindheim, *Schrift. Ges. Nat. Berlin*, **10**. 374, 1792; M. Adam, *Tableau minéralogique*, Paris, 37, 1869; E. F. Glocker, *Generum et specierum mineralium secundum ordines naturales digestorum synopsis*, Halle, 257, 1847; D. L. G. Karsten, *Mineralogische Tabellen*, Berlin, 50, 77, 1800; J. Nicol, *Manual of Mineralogy*, Edinburgh, 383, 1849; R. Hermann, *Journ. prakt. Chem.*, (1), **34**. 179, 1845; C. Stamm, *Pogg. Ann.*, **100**. 618, 1857; M. F. Heddle, *Phil. Mag.*, (4), **12**. 126, 1856; F. P. Dunnington, *Proc. Amer. Assoc.*, 182, 1877; C. E. Wait, *Trans. Amer. Inst. Min. Eng.*, **8**. 51, 1880; W. F. Hillebrand, *Proc. Colorado Scient. Soc.*, **1**. 119, 1884; E. V. Shannon, *Econ. Geol.*, **15**. 88, 1920; W. G. Mixter, *Rep. U.S. Geol. Sur.*, **2**. 759, 1877; C. F. Rammelsberg, *Handbuch der Mineralchemie*, Leipzig, **2**. 184, 1895; M. Tscherne, *Verh. geol. Reichsanst. Wien*, 211, 1891; F. Gonnard, *Bull. Soc. Min.*, **5**. 50, 1882; A. Raimondi, *Minéraux du Pérou*, Paris, 88, 1878; P. Groth, *Tabellarische Uebersicht der Mineralien*, Braunschweig, 83, 96, 1898; J. Percy, *The Metallurgy of Lead*, London, 88, 1870; F. Sandberger, *Untersuchungen über Erzgänge*, Wiesbaden, 1882; L. Fletcher, *Min. Mag.*, **8**. 171, 1889; L. J. Igelström, *Oefvers. Akad. Stockholm*, **22**. 227, 1865; A. E. Nordenskjöld, *ib.*, **27**. 550, 1870; G. Flink, *Bihang Svenska Akad. Handl.*, **12**. 35, 1887; W. T. Schaller, *Bull. U.S. Geol. Sur.*, 10, 1916; H. Leroux, *Metall. Erz*, **21**. 421, 1924; B. Gossner, *Centr. Min.*, 289, 1925; J. Stenhouse and G. Hallett, *Brit. Pat. No.* 49, 215, 1861; C. Brunner, *Journ. prakt. Chem.*, (1). **10**. 196, 1837; A. Chambers and J. F. Rigg, *Journ. Cer. Soc.*, **25**. 101, 1926; F. Rose, *Die*

Mineralfarben, Leipzig, 307, 1916; C. Piccolpassi, *I tre libei dell'arte del Vasajo*, Rome, 28, 1857; G. Passeri, *Nuovo Raccolta d'Opuscoli Scientifica e Filologici*, Venezia, 4. 1, 1758; A. D. Fougeroux de Bondaroy, *Mém. Acad.*, 303, 1766; J. J. le F. le la Lande, *Voyage d'un François en Italie*, Paris, 9. 504, 1786.
  [5] F. F. Beilstein and O. von Bläse, *Bull. Acad. St. Petersburg*, (4), 1. 97, 201, 1889; O. W. Gibbs, *Proc. Amer. Acad.*, 21. 105, 1885; *Amer. Chem. Journ.*, 7. 313, 392, 1885; L. A. Hallopeau, *Compt. Rend.*, 123. 1065, 1896; C. F. Rammelsberg, *Pogg. Ann.*, 59. 27, 1846; A. Cavazzi, *Gazz. Chim. Ital.*, 15. 37, 1885; W. Hampe, *Zeit. Berg. Hütt. Sal.*, 27. 205, 1873; *Zeit. anal. Chem.*, 13. 192, 1874; J. F. L. Mérimée, *De la peinture à l'huile*, Paris, 1830.
  [6] J. J. Berzelius, *Schweigger's Journ.*, 6. 144, 1812; 22. 69, 1818; L. J. Igelström, *Geol. För. Förh. Stockholm*, 7. 210, 1884; 8. 143, 1886; 11. 389, 391, 1889; 14. 307, 1892; *Bull. Soc. Min.*, 7. 120, 1884; *Neues Jahrb. Min.*, i, 250, 254, 1890; C. F. Rammelsberg, *Handbuch der Mineralchemie*, Leipzig, 2. 185, 1895; G. Flink, *Geol. För. Förh. Stockholm*, 45. 567, 1923; F. Ebei, *Ueber einige Salze der Antimonsäure*, Berlin, 1890; *Ber.*, 22. 3044, 1889; F. F. Beilstein and O. von Bläse, *Bull. acad. St. Petersburg*, (4), 1. 97, 201, 1889; A. Lacroix, *Minéralogie de la France et de ses colonies*, Paris, 4. 509, 1910; W. T. Schaller, *Bull. U.S. Geol. Sur.*, 610, 1916; E. Hussak and G. T. Prior, *Min. Mag.*, 11. 80, 176, 302, 1895; J. B. Senderens, *Bull. Soc. Chim.*, (3), 21. 57, 1899; C. L. Allen, *Chem. News*, 42. 193, 1880; P. Groth, *Tabellarische Uebersicht der Mineralien*, Braunschweig, 92, 1898; L. Heffter, *Pogg. Ann.*, 86. 448, 1852; H. Goguel, *Contribution à l'étude des arséniates et des antimoniates cristallisés préparés par voie humide*, Paris, 1896; E. S. Larsen, *Bull. U.S. Geol. Sur.*, 679, 1921.

§ 15. Antimony Trifluoride

In 1824, J. J. Berzelius [1] first prepared **antimony trifluoride**, SbF_3, by crystallization from a soln. of antimony trioxide is an excess of hydrofluoric acid. The soln. is concentrated on a water-bath, and cooled. The crystals are separated from the mother-liquor, and dried between bibulous paper. F. A. Flückiger, and A. Guntz used this process. The product is preserved in bottles of guttapercha, or platinum. T. Swarts sublimed the crystals in a platinum vessel. F. A. Flückiger could not prepare the trifluoride by the action of hydrofluoric acid on antimony, or of a mixture of calcium fluoride and sulphuric acid on antimony or antimony trioxide. J. B. A. Dumas, however, made the trifluoride by distillation from a mixture of powdered antimony and mercuric fluoride. A. Rosenheim and H. Grünbaum found that the trifluoride prepared from antimony trioxide and hydrofluoric acid, is best stored in white celluloid vessels. Salts containing the trifluoride can be used as mordants. C. and H. Sunder mixed the hydrofluoric acid soln. of antimony trioxide with 3 mols of anhydrous sodium sulphate per mol of trifluoride and dried the resulting white crystalline mass.

According to F. A. Flückiger, antimony trifluoride obtained by the slow evaporation of the soln. at 79°–90° appears in colourless, transparent, rhombic plates; and when obtained by rapid evaporation, it appears in small prisms or scales. O. Ruff and W. Plato gave 4·379 for the sp. gr. at 20·9°; and W. Biltz and E. Rahlfs gave 4·385 at 25°/4°, and for the mol. vol., 40·78. The trifluoride was found by J. B. A. Dumas to volatilize more easily than sulphuric acid; and T. Swarts said that the salt is readily sublimed. T. Carnelley gave 292°±8° for the b.p. A. Guntz found the heat of formation to be $Sb_{solid}+3F=SbF_{3solid}+144\cdot3$ Cals.; H. von Wartenberg gave for the molar heat of formation, 210·6 Cals. A. Guntz found that the heat of soln. of a mol of rhombic antimony trioxide in hydrofluoric acid is 19 Cals.; and of the octahedral trioxide, 20·2 Cals. The heat of soln. of a mol. of the trifluoride in 58 mols of water is −1·16 Cals., and in 407 mols of water, −2·0 Cals. The eq. electrical conductivity, λ, for soln. containing one-third of a mol in v litres was found by H. Grünbaum to be at 0°, and at 25°:

v	8	16	32	64	128	256	512	1024
$\lambda\{$ 0°	20·31	25·0	32·0	42·5	58·6	82·8	115·8	156·6
25°	25·84	33·20	43·14	52·74	74·14	105·4	146·2	—
λHF_{25}.	35·8	44·3	59·5	76·6	104·7	138·0	177·0	—

The great increase in the conductivity with increasing dilution is supposed to be conditioned by hydrolysis and not by the ionization of the trifluoride. This is confirmed by the eq. conductivity of that acid included in the above table. The electrical conductivities of mixtures of antimony trifluoride with various salts —potassium fluoride, nitrate, sulphate, oxalate, hydroxalate, tartrate, and antimonioxalate, and ammonium oxalate—are often smaller than the values calculated by the mixture rule. This shows that complex salts are formed. Unlike the other three halides, antimony trifluoride is not dissolved by electrolytic antimony deposited from trifluoride soln.—vide supra, explosive antimony.

F. A. Flückiger found that antimony trifluoride tastes acid, and later is styptic ; it does not form in air ; but in the presence of air it cannot be volatilized without some decomposition—leaving a residue of antimony trioxide. The trifluoride is freely soluble in water, and the soln. can be diluted without appreciable hydrolysis. H. Grünbaum found that 100 grms. of water at 0° dissolve 384·7 grms. of the trifluoride ; at 20°, 444·7 grms. ; at 22·5°, 452·8 grms. ; at 25°, 492·4 grms. ; and at 30°, 563·6 grms. The effect of various additions on the solubility—expressed in grams of trifluoride per 100 grms. of the given soln. at 0°—is indicated in Table II.

TABLE II.—THE SOLUBILITY OF ANTIMONY TRIFLUORIDE IN SALT SOLUTIONS.

Solution.	Normality of the dissolved salt.				
	2N-	N-	$\frac{1}{2}N$-	$\frac{1}{4}N$-	$\frac{1}{8}N$-
Hydrofluoric acid	474·9	432·5	404·0	—	—
Potass. chloride	—	461·8	448·3	431·9	407·3
Potass. bromide	—	448·7	450·0	455·6	417·2
Potass. nitrate	—	458·2	451·9	418·3	401·4
Potass. sulphate	—	419·9	408·5	406·6	—
Potass. oxalate	—	465·7	481·2	451·3	405·2
Amm. oxalate	—	—	431·9	442·3	433·3
Potass. tartrate	—	461·4	430·5	430·8	435·2

F. A. Flückiger found that the trifluoride is very hygroscopic, and rapidly deliquesces, and decomposes on exposure to air. The product no longer forms a clear soln. with water. According to P. Redenz, when antimony pentoxide is dissolved in hydrofluoric acid, and the soln. evaporated, a hygroscopic syrupy mass is formed which is not completely soluble in water, and which may be antimony tetrahydroheptafluoride, $SbF_3.4HF$—this statement is not well supported by evidence. The trifluoride form complex salts with antimony pentafluoride ; and with antimony pentachloride. T. Swarts observed the formation of antimony difluotrichloride. According to O. Ruff and K. Albert, the aq. soln. of the trifluoride forms with bromine a colourless liquid ; and in the solid state it absorbs bromine slowly, forming antimony tribromide ; and similarly with chlorine. G. Gore found antimony fluoride to be insoluble in liquid ammonia. W. Biltz and E. Rahlfs found that antimony hexamminotrifluoride, $SbF_3.6NH_3$, has a vap. press. of 13·0 mm. at —78·5°; 46·5 mm. at —65°; 72·0 mm. at —60° ; 108·0 mm. at —55°; and 158·2 mm. at —50° ; and a heat of formation of 7·5 Cals. ; and antimony tetramminotrifluoride, $SbF_3.4NH_3$, has a vap. press. of 52·7 mm. at —60°; 79·5 mm. at —55°; and 118·0 mm. at —50°, and a heat of formation of 7·6 Cals. ; while antimony triamminotrifluoride, $SbF_2.3NH_3$, has a sp. gr. of 2·324 at 25°/4° ; a mol. vol. of 98·92 ; a vap. press. of 42·0 mm. at —21° ; 85·0 mm. at —11° ; and 174 mm. at 0° ; and a heat of formation of 9·2 Cals. O. Ruff obtained antimony diamminotrifluoride, $SbF_3.2NH_3$, by the action of liquid ammonia on antimony trifluoride. The yellow powder loses ammonia in contact with moist air, and is less stable than the product with antimony pentafluoride—vide infra. W. Biltz and E. Rahlfs found the sp. gr. to be 2·95 at 625°/4° ; the mol. vol. 79·00 ; the vap. press. at 17°, 3·0 mm. ; at 25°, 13 mm. ; at 34°, 24 mm. ; and at 62°, 107·5 mm. ; while the heat of formation is 12·0 Cals. They also found that antimony monammino-

trifluoride, SbF$_3$.NH$_3$, has a sp. gr. of 3·302 at 25°/4°; **a** mol. vol. of 59·3; **a** vap press. of 7·5 mm. at 61·5°; 9·0 mm. at 64°; 25·5 mm. at 80°; 70·5 mm. at 100°, and 114·5 at 110°; and a heat of formation of 14·1 Cals. T. Swarts observed that with carbon tetrachloride, carbon fluotrichloride is produced; with chloroform, carbon hydrofluodichloride is formed; and with carbon hydrochlorodibromide, carbon hydrofluochlorodibromide is produced. O. Ruff and K. Albert represented the reaction with silicon-chloroform by the equation: $3SiHCl_3 + 4SbF_3 = 3SiF_4 + 2Sb + 2SbCl_3 + 3HCl$. F. A. Flückiger found that a soln. of auric chloride is reduced by antimony trifluoride.

Antimony trifluoride forms a number of complex salts with the metal fluorides. Complex salts were obtained by F. A. Flückiger from aq. soln. of the component salts; and from a soln. of antimony trioxide and the metal carbonate in hydrofluoric acid. A. von Rad and G. Hauser obtained them from a soln. of antimony trioxide and the metal hydrophosphate in hydrofluoric acid; O. Frölich, by the action of sulphuric acid on a mixture of antimony trisulphide, calcium fluoride, and alkali nitrate. F. A. Flückiger obtained **ammonium pentafluoantimonite,** (NH$_4$)$_2$SbF$_5$, by crystallization from a soln. of antimony trioxide and ammonium carbonate in an excess of hydrofluoric acid; and H. von Helmolt, from a soln. of antimony trioxide in one of ammonium fluoride. F. Ephraim also obtained this salt. F. A. Flückiger said that the colourless plates or prisms belong to the rhombic system; when heated, sublimation occurs with some decomposition. No ammonia is lost at 140°. After lying in air for some time, the crystals do not all dissolve in water, but the residue dissolves in dil. hydrofluoric acid. 100 parts of water dissolve 111·1 parts of salt with a considerable lowering of the temp. The aq. soln. reacts acid; attacks glass; and gives a precipitate with alcohol and ether. Sulphuric acid decomposes the salt. Glass containing vessels are attacked by the salt. A. von Rad and G. Hauser prepared **ammonium tridecafluotetrantimonite,** NH$_4$Sb$_4$F$_{13}$, or NH$_4$F.4SbF$_3$. The crystals are stable in dry air; 100 parts of water dissolve 150 parts of salt. H. Grünbaum tried to obtain f.p. curves of fused mixtures of the alkali fluorides and antimony trifluoride, but the volatility of the latter was too great to allow satisfactory measurements to be made. G. Stein prepared six-sided plates of **lithium tetrafluoantimonite,** LiSbF$_4$; F. A. Flückiger, colourless prisms of **lithium enneafluodiantimonite,** Li$_3$Sb$_2$F$_9$, which require over 20 times their weight of water for dissolution. F. Ephraim studied this salt. G. Stein prepared **lithium hydropentafluoantimonite,** LiSbHF$_5$. G. Stein also made crystals of **sodium tetrafluoantimonite,** NaSbHF$_4$; 93 parts of which require 100 parts of cold water, while 166 parts require 100 parts of hot water for dissolution. A. von Rad and G. Hauser made **sodium tridecafluotetrantimonite,** NaSb$_4$F$_{13}$; and F. A. Flückiger rhombic prisms of **sodium hexafluoantimonite,** Na$_3$SbF$_6$. 100 parts of cold water dissolve 7·1 parts of salt and hot water, 25 parts of salt. F. Ephraim studied this salt. A. von Rad and G. Hauser made **potassium tridecafluotetrantimonite,** KF.4SbF$_3$; F. A. Flückiger, **potassium tetrafluoantimonite,** KSbF$_4$, 36·3 parts of which dissolve in 100 parts of water; and F. A. Flückiger, **potassium penta-fluoantimonite,** K$_2$SbF$_5$, with which 100 parts of water dissolve 11·1 parts of salt at ordinary temp., and 50 parts of salt when the water is boiling. F. Ephraim studied this salt. H. L. Wells and F. J. Metzger prepared **cæsium decafluotrianti-monite,** CsSb$_3$F$_{10}$, in transparent prisms; **cæsium heptafluodiantimonite,** CsSb$_2$F$_7$, in transparent needles; **cæsium pentacosifluoheptantimonite,** Cs$_4$Sb$_7$F$_{25}$, in transparent plates; **cæsium tetrafluoantimonite,** CsSbF$_4$, in regular prisms; and **cæsium pentafluoantimonite,** Cs$_2$SbF$_5$, in rhombic prisms. According to F. A. Flückiger, these salts are generally free from water of crystallization; when dry they are usually stable in air; and dissolve in water easily without turbidity. The aq. soln. can be diluted without turbidity; it reacts acid; it attacks glass; and on evaporation furnishes the original salt. When triturated with sodium, a feeble detonation may occur; zinc and tin precipitate antimony from the soln., but not completely. The ammonium salt gives precipitates with soln. of salts of

466   INORGANIC AND THEORETICAL CHEMISTRY

lithium, the alkaline earths, mercury(ic), aluminium, tin(ic), lead, manganese, iron(ic), cobalt, and nickel; no change occurs with salts of copper, zinc, cadmium, tin(ous), and iron(ous). Hydrochloroplatinic acid gives a precipitate of potassium or ammonium chloroplatinate respectively with potassium or ammonium fluoantimonite; silver and mercurous salts give white precipitates, but reduction soon occurs : and auric chloride is reduced. Tannin gives a precipitate, but not so with salts of morphine, quinine, etc. F. Ephraim and L. Heymann prepared crystals of thallous tetrafluoantimonite, TlF.SbF₃; thallous heptafluodiantimonite. TlSb₂F₇; and thallous decafluotriantimonite, TlSb₃F₁₀.

Antimony trifluoride produces complex salts with alkali chlorides. G. Stein made lithium chlorotrifluoantimonite, LiCl.SbF₃, from a soln. of the component salts; E. de Häen, sodium chlorotrifluoantimonite, NaCl.SbF₃, freely soluble in water; and potassium chlorotrifluoantimonite, KCl.SbF₃, in crystals. 100 parts of water at ordinary temp. dissolve 51 parts of the salt, and 300 parts at 100°. H. Grünbaum prepared potassium trinitratotrifluoantimonite, 3KNO₃.SbF₃; and potassium tetranitratoënneafluotriantimonite, 4KNO₃.3SbF₃. O. Frölich, and H. Grünbaum made a number of oxalatofluoantimonites.

Antimony trifluoride forms complex salts with several sulphates. E. de Häen, and F. Hasslacher obtained the complex salts from an aq. soln. of the component salts; F. Hasslacher, from a soln. of basic antimony sulphate in one of the given fluoride; T. Meyer, from a soln. of the component salts in hydrochloric acid; O. Frölich, by the action of sulphuric acid on a mixture of antimony trisulphide, calcium fluoride, and alkali nitrate; and A. von Rad, by the action of an excess of sodium hydrosulphate on the double fluoride. T. Meyer obtained ammonium sulphatohexafluodiantimonite, (NH₄)₂SO₄.2SbF₆. F. Hasslacher, ammonium trisulphatododecafluotetrantimonite, 3(NH₄)₂SO₄.4SbF₃, in trigonal crystals which, according to A. Fock, have the axial ratio a : c=1 : 0·4413 ; and E. de Häen, ammonium sulphatotrifluoantimonite, (NH₄)₂SO₄.SbF₃, in rhombic prisms which, according to A. Fock, have the axial ratios a : b : c=0·6245 : 1 : 0·5008. E. de Häen said that 100 parts of water at 24° dissolve 140 parts of the salt, and at the b.p., 1500 parts of salt. H. Grünbaum also made this salt. E. de Häen also prepared sodium sulphatotrifluoantimonite, Na₂SO₄.SbF₃, in small prisms; he also made potassium sulphatotrifluoantimonite, K₂SO₄.SbF₃ ; T. Meyer, potassium sulphatohexafluodiantimonite, K₂SO₄.2SbF₃ ; and A. Rosenheim and H. Grünbaum also prepared complexes with ammonium or sodium oxalate, and with potassium antimonyl oxalate.

REFERENCES.

¹ J. J. Berzelius, Pogg. Ann., 1. 34, 1824 ; F. A. Flückiger, ib., 87. 249, 1852 ; Liebig's Ann., 84. 248, 1851 ; Ann. Chim. Phys., (3), 39. 495, 1853 ; H. L. Wells and F. J. Metzger, Amer. Journ. Science, (4), 11. 453, 1901 ; A. Guntz, Ann. Chim. Phys., (6), 3. 47, 1884 ; J. B. A. Dumas, ib., (2), 31. 435, 1826 ; G. Gore, Proc. Roy. Soc., 20. 441, 1872 ; 21. 140, 1873 ; O. Ruff and W. Plato, Ber., 37. 680, 1904 ; O. Ruff, ib., 39. 4310, 1906 ; O. Ruff and K. Albert, ib., 38. 53, 1905 ; F. Ephraim, ib., 36. 1815, 1913 ; F. Ephraim and L. Heymann, ib., 42. 4456, 1909 ; A. Fock, Zeit. Kryst., 19. 454, 1891 ; T. Carnelley, Journ. Chem. Soc., 33. 275, 1878 ; C. and H. Sunder, Bull. Soc. Ind. Mulhouse, 90. 273, 1924 ; T. Swarts, Bull. Belg. Acad., (3), 24. 309, 474, 1892 ; (3), 26. 102, 1893 ; (3), 29. 874, 1895 ; Zeit. anorg. Chem., 12. 71, 1896 ; H. von Helmolt, ib., 3. 141, 1893 ; H. von Wartenberg and O. Fitzner, ib., 151. 313, 1926 ; H. von Wartenberg, ib., 151. 326, 1926 ; A. von Rad and G. Hauser, German Pat., D.R.P. 50281, 1888 ; A. von Rad, ib., 85626, 1894 ; O. Frölich, ib., 53618, 1890 ; 86668, 1894 ; E. de Häen, ib., 45222, 45224, 1887 ; F. Hasslacher, ib., 57615, 1890 ; T. Meyer, ib., 76168, 1892 ; H. Grünbaum, Ueber Verbindungen des Antimontrifluorids, Berlin, 1908 ; A. Rosenheim and H. Grünbaum, Zeit. anorg. Chem., 61. 187, 1909 ; P. Redenz, Arch. Pharm., 236. 268, 1898 ; G. Stein, Chem. Ztg., 11. 1298, 1887 ; 13. 357, 1889 ; Oester. Zeit. Wollind., 698, 1887 ; W. Biltz and E. Rahlfs, Zeit. anorg. Chem., 166. 351, 1927.

§ 16. The Higher Antimony Fluorides

In addition to antimony fluoride, J. J. Berzelius ¹ also mentioned the existence of antimony tetrafluoride, SbF₄, which he said unites with alkali fluorides to form double salts. F. A. Flückiger showed that it is doubtful if the tetrafluoride or its complex salts really exist. J. J. Berzelius likewise mentioned **antimony pentafluoride**, SbF_5, which also forms a series of complex salts, but F. A. Flückiger was unable to confirm this statement. According to P. Redenz, when antimonic acid is dissolved in pure hydrofluoric acid, and the soln. evaporated, a very hygroscopic, syrupy mass is left which is not completely soluble in water ; neither by this method nor by dissolving antimonic oxide in hydrofluoric acid could a crystalline antimony pentafluoride be obtained. J. C. G. de Marignac evaporated in vacuo a soln. of hydrated antimony pentoxide in hydrofluoric acid, and obtained a gummy mass which, when heated, formed an oxyfluoride. He obtained a number of complex salts with antimony pentafluoride. H. Moissan obtained the pentafluoride by burning powdered antimony in fluorine gas. O. Ruff and W. Plato prepared the pentafluoride by boiling at 25°–30° a mixture of anhydrous hydrogen fluoride with about half the calculated quantity of antimony trifluoride, sat. with chlorine, in a vessel fitted with a reflux condenser cooled by iced-water. The boiling is continued until hydrogen chloride is no longer given off. This occupies about three days. The hydrogen fluoride is then distilled off, and the b.p., rising to 155°, enables the antimony pentafluoride to be distilled off.

According to O. Ruff and co-workers, antimony pentafluoride is a colourless, viscid liquid which freezes in the cold. Its sp. gr. is 2·993 at 22·7°/4° ; and the b.p. 149°–150°. The pentafluoride dissolves in **water** with a hissing noise, forming a clear soln. which, when sat. with sodium hydrocarbonate, does not decolorize iodine. The pentafluoride is very hygroscopic, forming *dihydrated* antimony pentafluoride, $SbF_5.2H_2O$, when exposed to humid air. Antimony pentafluoride is not attacked by **chlorine** ; **bromine** forms a viscid, dark brown mass, possibly SbF_5Br ; **iodine** forms some mixed halides (*q.v.*) ; **sulphur** forms sulphopentafluoride ; **hydrogen sulphide** produces sulphur, hydrogen fluoride, and antimony thiofluoride. The pentafluoride reacts with **sulphur dichloride.** When a current of dry **ammonia** is passed over the pentafluoride, there is a vigorous reaction and a protective yellowish-red crust is formed. With liquid ammonia there is a vigorous reaction, and when the product is heated 12 hrs. at 100°, the product has the composition of **antimony hemitriamminotetrafluoride**, $2SbF_4.3NH_3$, but it is considered to be **antimony imidohydrofluoamidotrifluoride**, $NH(SbF_3.NH_2.HF)_2$. This product is a white powder very readily decomposed by atm. moisture ; is slowly hydrolyzed by water, and the aq. soln. is acid to litmus. Antimony pentafluoride reacts with **nitrogen sulphide.** O. Ruff made **antimony fluonitrosylpentafluoride**, $SbF_5.NOF$, by the action of **nitrosyl fluoride** on the pentafluoride as in the case of the corresponding arsenic compound or by the interaction of solid antimony chlorofluoride and nitrosyl fluoride at −80°. The compound occurs in slender, colourless needles, which sublime without decomposition below a red-heat ; it is very hygroscopic, and is decomposed by water and by alcohol. On warming with arsenic trifluoride, it gives arsenic pentafluoride mixed with excess of the trifluoride, and, on heating with potassium fluoride, it yields nitrosyl fluoride and a compound of antimony pentafluoride and potassium fluoride. **Phosphorus** inflames in contact with antimony pentafluoride producing a yellow vapour which sublimes ; with **phosphorus trichloride** it forms phosphorus trifluoride ; with **phosphorus pentoxide** it forms phosphorus oxyfluoride ; with **arsenic trifluoride** it forms crystalline compounds ; with **antimony** it forms antimony trifluoride ; with **antimony trifluoride** it forms compounds varying in composition from $SbF_5.2SbF_3$ to $SbF_5.5SbF_3$—*vide infra*. The pentafluoride quickly attacks **organic substances**, *e.g.* the skin, filter-paper, cork, wood, and india-rubber. It attacks **hydrocarbons**—thus, with **benzene** hydrogen fluoride is evolved. It also reacts with **alcohol, ether, acetone,** glacial **acetic acid, ethyl acetate, carbon disulphide,** light **petroleum, toluene,** and **chloroform.** P. Redenz made a number of complex salts with the chlorides of a number of organic bases—pyridine, picoline, *p*-toluidine, and quinine. A gas—possibly CCl_3F—is evolved by the action of the pentafluoride on **carbon tetrachloride** at 45°. The pentafluoride reacts with **silicon tetrachloride.** Colloidal **silicic acid** forms antimonic acid and silicon tetrafluoride when warmed with the pentafluoride. The dry purified pentafluoride does not attack dry **glass**— if hydrogen fluoride be present as an impurity, glass is attacked. **Copper** and **lead** are attacked very slowly by the pentafluoride ; indeed, if the substances are all dry, the **metals** do not usually react with the pentafluoride. When heated with **sodium,** rapid combustion with the formation of a white vapour occurs. With sodium hydroxide or carbonate, the pyroantimonite is formed. The pentafluoride reacts with **chromyl chloride ;** with **molybdenum pentachloride,** above 100°, molybdenum fluoride and antimony pentachloride are formed, and the latter parting with some of its chlorine forms a complex compound with the excess of pentafluoride. The pentafluoride reacts with **tungsten hexachloride,** forming the hexafluoride ; and it reacts with **tin and titanium tetrachlorides.**

O. Ruff and W. Plato prepared some complex compounds of antimony tri- and penta-fluorides. By boiling a mixture of anhydrous hydrogen fluoride and antimony pentachloride for about 8 hrs., in an apparatus fitted with a well-cooled reflux condenser and distilling the product so as to collect the fraction boiling at 390°, **antimonidiantimonious henafluoride,** $SbF_5.2SbF_3$, is produced. The same compound was obtained by distilling a mixture of the component chlorides. This compound is a colourless, transparent, crystalline substance, with a sp. gr. 4·188 at 21°/4°. It boils at 390°. It dissolves completely in water ; but if distilled in the presence of traces of moisture, some antimony tri- or tetra-oxide is formed. The vapour density shows that a considerable contraction takes place in the formation of this compound, and if heated to about 445°, the vapour dissociates. If a mixture of antimony pentafluoride with an excess of the trifluoride be distilled, the fraction boiling at 384° is **antimonipentantimonious icosifluoride,** $SbF_5.5SbF_3$. The colourless liquid solidifies when cold. Fractions corresponding with **antimoni-tetrantimonious heptadecafluoride,** $SbF_5.4SbF_3$, and **antimonitriantimonious tetradecafluoride,** $SbF_5.3SbF_3$, were obtained, but their b.p. were too close together to enable their existence to be established with certainty.

J. C. G. de Marignac prepared a series of complex alkali fluorides by adding alkali (or ammonium) hydroxide to an acid soln. of antimony pentafluoride ; or by dissolving the proper antimonate in hydrofluoric acid. According to **H.** von Helmolt, freshly precipitated hydrated antimony pentoxide dissolves freely in a soln. of ammonium fluoride, but no crystalline salt can be separated from the liquid. J. C. G. de Marignac obtained **ammonium heptafluoantimonate,** $2NH_4F.SbF_5.\frac{1}{2}H_2O$, in rhombic crystals with the axial ratios $a:b:c=0.9827:1:1.142$, from a soln. of the component salts with the ammonium fluoride in excess ; otherwise, small hexagonal prisms of **ammonium hexafluoantimonate,** $NH_4F.SbF_5$, are formed. The salt is deliquescent. J. C. G. de Marignac obtained cubic deliquescent crystals of **sodium hexafluoantimonate,** $NaF.SbF_5$; **potassium hexafluoanti-monate,** $KF.SbF_5$, in rhombic plates freely soluble in water ; and when potassium fluoride is in excess, monoclinic prisms of **potassium heptafluoantimonate,** $2K_2F.SbF_5.2H_2O$. The axial ratios are $a:b:c=1.805:1:1.136$, and $\beta=91°$ 30'. The salt melts in its water of crystallization at 90°, and loses water and hydro-fluoric acid at the same time. The fluoantimonates can be preserved in a dry atm. They are freely soluble in water, and deliquesce in air. By repeatedly evaporating the aq. soln., an oxyfluoride is formed. The aq. soln. are not at once affected chemically by hydrogen sulphide, by acids, or by alkali hydroxides or carbonates. In attempting to make *copper fluoantimonate,* and *zinc fluoantimonate,* only viscid products were obtained.

REFERENCES.

[1] J. J. Berzelius, *Pogg. Ann.,* **1.** 34, 1824 ; F. A. Flückiger, *ib.,* **87.** 245, 1852 ; *Liebig's Ann.,* **84.** 248, 1851 ; *Ann. Chim. Phys.,* (3), **39.** 495, 1853 ; H. Moissan, *ib.,* (6), **24.** 247, 1891 ; J. C. G. de Marignac, *ib.,* (4), **10.** 371, 1867 ; *Bull. Soc. Chim.,* (1), **8.** 323, 1869 ; *Liebig's Ann.,*

145. 239, 1868 ; *Bibl. Univ. Genève*, 28. 13, 1867 ; O. Ruff and W. Plato, *Ber.*, 37. 673, 1904 ; O. Ruff, *ib.*, 39. 4310, 1906 ; 58. 325, 1908 ; P. Redenz, *Arch. Pharm.*, 236, 267, 1898 ; H. von Helmolt, *Zeit. anorg. Chem.*, 3. 151, 1893.

§ 17. Antimony Trichloride

In the seventeenth century, J. R. Glauber,[1] and Basil Valentine prepared **antimony trichloride**, $SbCl_3$, by distillation from a mixture of antimony sulphide with mercuric chloride, salt and clay, or hydrochloric acid. The product was named *butyrum antimonii*—butter of antimony ; and also *causticum antimoniale, Spiessglanzbutter*, and, from the idea that it contained mercury, *cinnabaris antimonii*. J. R. Glauber showed that no mercury is present ; and he gave a correct interpretation of the reaction between mercuric chloride (sublimed mercury) and antimony sulphide (antimony) :

Butyrum antimonii is nothing else but the regulus of antimony dissolved with spirit of salt ; for sublimed mercury, being mixed with antimony, feeling the heat of the fire, is forsaken by the corrosive spirits associating themselves with the antimony, whence comes the thick oyle ; whilest which is done the sulphur of antimony is joyned to the quick-silver, and yields a cinnabar, sticking to the neck of the retort ; but the residue of the mercury remains in the bottom with the *caput mortuum*, because a little part thereof doth distill off : and if thou hast skill thou mayst recover the whole weight of the mercury again. . . . Whence it doth necessarily follow that the thick oyle is nothing else but antimony dissolved in spirit of salt.

The theory of J. R. Glauber was accepted by J. C. Barchusen, and H. Boerhaave. C. Hensgen obtained the trichloride by passing chlorine through a tube containing antimony, and joined on to a bulb. The mixture of antimony tri- and penta-chlorides which collects in the bulb was mixed with antimony and distilled for the trichloride.

The antimony trichloride to be distilled is placed in a distillation-flask provided with a side-tube, and of about 1½ to 2 litres capacity ; the flask is placed on a water-bath with the neck inclined downwards, and fitted by means of a good cork into a smaller flask serving as a receiver ; the side tube passes vertically upwards, and is then bent and fitted with a drying tube. The water-bath is of such a size that the part of the flask containing liquid antimony trichloride is completely immersed in water-vapour when the sublimation is going on. The upper part of the flask is cooled by cold water dropped on to a piece of filter-paper. When a sufficient quantity of the long, lanceolate crystals of the sublimate has collected on the cooled portion of the flask, the whole is allowed to cool slowly ; and as soon as the trichloride on the bottom of the flask has solidified, the sublimate is shaken carefully into the receiver. The operation is then repeated until the whole of the charge has been sublimed.

P. S. Brallier used a modification of the process. A. W. Hofmann also described an apparatus for this purpose. B. H. Jacobson obtained the chloride by the action of chlorine on the metal with a trace of bromine as catalyst, and in the presence of alkali halides to keep the product liquid. P. J. Robiquet obtained the trichloride by dissolving antimony in a mixture of four parts of hydrochloric acid and one part of nitric acid. The latter is to be added in small portions at a time and a gentle heat applied. If too much chlorine is given off on evaporation, too much nitric acid is present, and more hydrochloric acid and antimony should be added. It is advisable to have a little antimony in excess at the bottom of the retort. G. Oddo and E. Serra prepared antimony trichloride by heating the trioxide with sulphur monochloride in an apparatus fitted with a reflux condenser ; and G. Oddo and U. Giarchery, by passing chlorine through a heated mixture of the trioxide and powdered sulphur. As indicated in connection with the chemical properties of antimony, some trichloride is formed by the slow action of hydrochloric acid, in the presence of air, on antimony ; and also by the action of phosphorus trichloride, chlorosulphonic acid, and sulphur oxychlorides on antimony. As indicated above, Basil Valentine obtained the trichloride by distillation from a mixture of mercuric chloride and antimony ; P. J. Malouin, from a mixture of silver chloride and antimony ; and L. D. l'Hôte, by the action of other metal chlorides on antimony.

Antimony trioxide is chlorinated by heating it in a current of chlorine, or in the presence of the chlorides of phosphorus, sulphur, etc.—*vide supra*, antimony trioxide. J. R. Glauber, and P. L. Robiquet obtained a soln. of the trichloride by the action of hydrochloric acid on antimony trioxide, or oxychloride. The excess of hydrochloric acid can be removed from the soln. by a current of air, and the buttery residue distilled for the trichloride. H. Rose found that the trichloride is produced by distilling a soln. of antimony pentoxide in hydrochloric acid. H. Rose obtained the trichloride, by the action of chlorine on heated antimony trisulphide, but separated the sulphur monochloride produced simultaneously, by volatilization at a gentle heat. E. Mitscherlich added that the affinity of sulphur monochloride for chlorine prevents the trichloride from passing into the pentachloride. The Rhenania Verein Chemische Fabrik heated the sulphide with chlorine. Gaseous hydrogen chloride also converts antimony trisulphide into the trichloride ; and, according to J. R. Glauber, when antimony trisulphide is heated with hydrochloric acid, the trichloride is formed ; and, according to F. Göbel, J. von Liebig, A. Larocque, R. Brandes, and P. L. Geiger and L. Reimann, the presence of a little nitric acid favours the reaction. The Hooker Electrochemical Co. passed chlorine into hydrochloric acid in the presence of antimony. J. R. Glauber distilled the antimony trisulphide with sodium chloride and sulphuric acid ; C. R. Fresenius, and P. de Clermont heated it with ammonium chloride ; Basil Valentine, with mercuric chloride ; and J. Linder, with ferric chloride. J. M. Scherer, A. Classen and O. Bauer, and G. C. Wittstein heated antimony pentasulphide with hydrochloric acid ; and J. J. Berzelius heated antimony sulphate with sodium chloride. Antimony trichloride is formed when chlorine, or phosphorus pentachloride, etc., acts on stibine (*q.v.*), and when antimony acts on the pentachloride.

Fairly pure antimony trichloride is obtained by the action of hydrochloric acid on the oxychloride. If the antimony trichloride is contaminated with arsenic trichloride (*q.v.*), the impurity can be volatilized by the action of hydrogen chloride ; lead chloride as an impurity remains behind when the antimony trichloride is sublimed ; and ferric chloride can be removed by subliming the antimony trichloride mixed with powdered antimony. H. Rose [2] obtained well-developed crystals by cooling a hot soln. of antimony trichloride in sulphur monochloride, and J. P. Cooke used carbon disulphide as solvent. Good crystals can also be obtained by sublimation, and by pouring the molten chloride from a partially solidified mass.

The analyses of J. Davy, F. Göbel, H. Rose, J. B. A. Dumas, and J. P. Cooke are in agreement with the empirical formula $SbCl_3$. E. Mitscherlich gave 7·8 for the vapour density when the value calculated for $SbCl_3$ is 7·82 ; and C. P. Worcester, 7·96. P. Walden found the mol. wt. of antimony trichloride from its effect on the f.p. of arsenic tribromide to be $(SbCl_3)_2$; and with nitrobenzene, the mol. wt. was 256 when the normal value is 225·1. L. Kahlenberg and A. T. Lincoln also measured the effect of antimony trichloride on the f.p. of nitrobenzene. S. Tolloczko measured the effect of bismuth chloride, sulphur, iodine, arsenic bromide and iodide, xylene, anthracene, diphenylmethane, acetophenone, and benzophenone on the f.p. of antimony trichloride ; and E. Beckmann, the effect of arsenic triiodide and trioxide, antimony triiodide, and stannic iodide. H. Henstock discussed the electronic structure of the family of trihalides.

Antimony trichloride forms colourless, prismatic, or octahedral **crystals** or a colourless, crystalline mass. The crystals examined by H. Töpsöe, and J. P. Cooke, belong to the rhombic system. J. Kendall and co-workers found three breaks in the cooling curves, corresponding with three allotropic forms : $\alpha\text{-}SbCl_3 \rightleftharpoons \beta\text{-}SbCl_3 \rightleftharpoons \gamma\text{-}SbCl_3$. The **specific gravity** given by J. P. Cooke is 3·064 at 26°, and E. Cohen and T. Strengers, 3·14 at 20°/4° ; and Z. Klemensiewicz, 2·681 at 75°, and 2·647 at 97°. H. Kopp found that the compound melts to a colourless or yellow oil of sp. gr. 2·675 at 73·2°/4°. W. Biltz, R. Lorenz and W. Herz, O. Masson, and J. A. Groshans studied the mol. vols. of this family of elements. I. I. Saslawsky found a 1·11 per cent. contraction in the formation of this compound from its elements. J. D. Sullivan discussed the use of the tri-chloride as a heavy liquid in mineral analyses. F. M. Jäger found the sp. gr. of the liquid at different temp. indicated below, and he represented the sp. gr., D, at θ, by $D=2\cdot6712-0\cdot002166(\theta-75)-0\cdot0_672(\theta-75)^2$. F. M. Jäger found the specific cohesion, a^2 sq. mm., to be 3·79 at 74·5°, 3·43 at 137·0°, and 3·20 at 178·0°; and the surface tension, σ dynes per cm., and the mol. surface energy, $\sigma(mv)^{\frac{2}{3}}$ ergs per sq. cm.—1. 13, 22—at different temp. to be:

	74·5°	90·4°	105°	120·6°	137°	149·8°	165°	178°
σ	49·6	47·8	46·0	44·3	42·6	41·2	39·6	38·3
$\sigma(mv)$	957·4	930·3	902·8	899·3	851·8	830·2	805·2	785·2

S. Motylewsky found the drop-weight to be 67 when that of water at 0° is 100. R. Lorenz and W. Herz studied the relations of the surface tensions of this family of halides. Z. Klemensiewicz measured the viscosity of antimony trichloride between 797° and 200°. The viscosity is 0·0241 at 79·1°; 0·01955 at 99·1°; 0·0148 at 119·0°; 0·0124 at 139·2°; 0·0108 at 159·7°; 0·0097 at 181·2°; and 0·0091 at 191·6°. He found there is a slight change of direction at 120°. He also measured the viscosities of soln. of antimony trichloride and potassium, rubidium, thallium, and mercuric chlorides. N. S. Kurnakoff and co-workers measured the viscosity of binary systems of antimony trichloride with ethyl ether and acetone. F. Schuster gave 220 atm. for the internal pressure. According to H. Kopp, the thermal expansion represented by the vol. of the liquid at different temp., $\theta°$, is given by $v=1+0\cdot0008054(\theta-73\cdot2)+0\cdot000001033(\theta-73\cdot2)^2$. R. Lorenz and W. Herz gave 0·000811; the sp. ht. found by L. von Pebal and H. Jahn is 0·110 between 0° and 33°; 0·100 between 0° and —21°; and 0·102 between —21° and —77°. H. Capitaine, G. B. Bernardis, and J. P. Cooke gave 72° for the melting point; H. Kopp, and F. M. Jäger, 73·2°; W. Biltz and K. Jeep, 72·5°; J. Kendall and co-workers, 73·4°; R. Lorenz and W. Herz, 73°; and E. K. Rideal, 73°. J. P. Cooke said that when heated near its m.p., antimony trichloride can be readily triturated to a powder. H. Braune and W. Tiedje found the vap. press., p mm., of antimony trichloride to be:

	100·2°	115·1°	121·7°	130·0°	141·2°	155·1°
p	13·7	25·0	33·0	44·1	66·1	100·3

For the boiling point H. Capitaine gave 230°; H. Kopp, 223° at 748 mm.; J. P. Cooke, 216°; P. Walden, 219·0°–219·5° at 757 mm.; F. M. Jäger, 111° at 20 mm.; T. Carnelley and W. C. Williams, 221°; C. G. Maier, 220·2°; and R. Anschütz and P. N. Evans, 233° at 760 mm., 143°–144° at 70 mm., and 102° at 11 mm., and L. Rotinjanz and W. Suchodsky, 223°. W. Böttger found that antimony trichloride can be distilled from conc. sulphuric acid soln. if 47 per cent. hydrobromic acid be continually dropped into the liquid. C. G. Maier gave for the vap. press., p mm.:

	50·3°	84·4°	112·0°	145·3°	173·3°	204·5°	216·9°	226·4°
p	12·6	20·2	45·0	112·0	263·5	538·8	718·9	797·3

L. Rotinjanz and W. Suchodsky gave 524° for the critical temperature, and $T_m/T_c=0\cdot622$ for the ratio of the m.p. to the critical temp. M. Prud'homme, and E. van Aubel found the relation between the m.p., the b.p., and the critical temp., to be normal. S. Tolloczko calculated the mol. latent heat of fusion to be 3010 cals. per mol, or 12·9 to 13·27 cals. per gram; W. Herz gave 13·29 cals. per gram; S. Tolloczko and M. Meyer gave 13·29 cals.; and the freezing-point constant, 184; H. Braune and W. Tiedje gave 11,050 cals. for the heat of vaporization at 123°; and E. K. Rideal gave for the mol. heat of vaporiza-tion, 3·0 Cals.; and C. G. Maier, 10·7 Cals. J. Thomsen gave for the heat of formation, $Sb_{solid}+3Cl_{gas}=SbCl_{3solid}+91\cdot39$ Cals.; and A. Guntz, $Sb_2O_{3solid}+6HCl_{gas}=2SbCl_{3solid}+3H_2O_{solid}+90\cdot90$ Cals. H. Becquerel found the refractive index for Na-light to be 1·460; and the electromagnetic rotatory

power of a soln. in conc. hydrochloric acid, 0·703. A. K. Macbeth and N. I. Maxwell measured the **absorption of light** by hydrochloric acid soln. of antimony trichloride; C. R. Crymble, the **absorption spectrum**; and O. Gosmann, the emission of positive ions by the trichloride. W. Herz gave $2·60 \times 10^{12}$ for the **vibration frequency.**

H. Buff found antimony trichloride to be a bad conductor of electricity; Z. Klemensiewicz found the **electrical conductvity** to be $0·0_685$ mho at 75°. This is smaller than the value obtained by P. Walden, and L. Graetz, 0·000109 mho at 80°. Possibly the latter preparations were moist. P. Walden assumed that the salt is ionized step by step: $SbCl_3 \rightleftharpoons SbCl'_2 + Cl' \rightleftharpoons SbCl'' + 2Cl' \rightleftharpoons Sb''' + 3Cl'$. L. Kahlenberg and A. T. Lincoln found the molar conductivity in methyl alcohol soln. to be $\mu_{8·15} = 15·7$, and $\mu_{1044} = 156·3$; for ethyl alcohol, $\mu_{8·1} = 4·2$, and $\mu_{260} = 29·4$. They also measured the conductivity in soln. of the trichloride in acetone, ethyl acetate, ethyl acetoacetate, benzaldehyde, nitrobenzene, nitrotoluene, paraldehyde, and ethyl monochloracetate. G. N. Guam and J. A. Wilkinson found antimony halide dissolved in liquid hydrogen sulphide is a conductor. S. Tolloczko found that ionization occurs with soln. of potassium chloride and bromide. Z. Klemensiewicz measured the electrical conductivities of soln. of thallium, ammonium, potassium, and rubidium in antimony trichloride at different temp., and he found the conductivities in dil. soln. greater, and in conc. soln. less than for the corresponding aq. soln. The conductivity increases regularly with temp. from 70°–200°. The degree of ionization for soln. in antimony trichloride is less than for water, but the ionic velocity is greater with the trichloride. K. Frycz and S. Tolloczko found that with soln. of ammonium and potassium chlorides in antimony trichloride at 90°, with increasing dilution the transport numbers of the Cl'-ions increase more rapidly than with aq. soln. In general, the ions which have the higher transport numbers are those which are common to the electrolyte and solvent. T. C. Sanderson separated gold from antimony by electrolyzing the soln. of the chlorides of the two elements in hydrochloric acid and sodium chloride. For the absorption of antimony trichloride by electrolytic antimony, *vide supra*, explosive antimony. G. Hänsel found the electrode potential $Sb \mid 0·33N\text{-}SbCl_3$ in 0·3N-HCl to be 0·131 volt, and in 3N-HCl, 0·101 volt. W. Finkelstein measured the **decomposition potential** of the trichloride in nitrobenzene soln. H. Schlundt found the **dielectric constant** to be 5·4 at 18°, and 33·2 at 75°.

J. P. Cooke [3] found that antimony trichloride can be distilled without decomposition in a current of **hydrogen.** W. D. Bancroft and H. B. Weiser observed that when added to the colourless gas-flame, antimony trichloride furnishes a bright metallic mirror and also pulverulent black antimony, but no yellow antimony. J. P. Cooke found that a soln. of antimony trichloride in hydrochloric acid is rapidly oxidized by exposure to **air.** The soln. which at first has no action on iodized starch paste, will strike the blue colour after it has been exposed a few minutes. This property was also noticed by W. P. Dexter. Antimony trichloride is very hygroscopic, and it rapidly absorbs moisture from the atm. to form a liquid. R. Brandes said that antimony chloride absorbs more than its own weight of **water** from the atm. in 70 days; and H. Rose added that deliquescence without turbidity occurs only if the trichloride contains hydrochloric acid. H. von Wartenberg devised the reaction as a demonstration experiment to illustrate the law of mass action. E. Baudrimont found that the composition of the oxychloride depends on the temp. and the proportion of water which is present. If hydrochloric acid be added, the turbidity disappears, and if water be again added, the turbidity reappears. When the trichloride is hydrolyzed by water, the acid liquid simultaneously formed was once called *spiritus vitrioli philosophicus*, and also *liquor stibiimuriatici.* According to A. Sabaneeff, the nature of the precipitate depends on the relative amounts of water and trichloride; a mol of the solid trichloride is dissolved by 2 mols of water, and can be recovered unchanged by evaporating the soln.; with a larger proportion of water, the trichloride is hydrolyzed, forming various oxychlorides ranging from SbOCl to $Sb_4O_5Cl_2$ with 8–27 mols of water to a mol of the solid trichloride ; with still higher proportions of water, the amorphous products supposed to be mixtures of antimony trioxide and $Sb_4O_5Cl_2$ were produced, but the complete removal of the chlorine can be affected only by prolonged washing with a very large proportion of water. The change from SbOCl to $Sb_4O_5Cl_2$ occurred with soln. more dil. than 2·5N-HCl ; and the change from $Sb_4O_5Cl_2$ to Sb_2O_5 occurred with soln. less conc. than 0·25N-HCl. H. le Chatelier gave 2·12N-HCl for the former transition point at 15° ; and C. Lea and J. K. Wood gave 8·0N-HCl for the former transition point and 0·1N-HCl for the latter. The errors in observation are due to the slowness of the change from the metastable to the stable solid phases. They noted that the following proportions of antimony trichloride were dissolved by soln. of hydrochloric acid in 1000 grms. of water, at 15° :

HCl .	8·6	19·3	40·5	56	72·5	88	95	97·5	104	105
$SbCl_3$.	0·11	0·18	0·36	2·10	9·9	34	111	319	590	850

The soln. were allowed to stand for 3 months. At a higher temp., 50°, the soln. were allowed to stand for a week. Antimony trichloride is decomposed at the higher temp. The results at 50° were :

HCl . .	3·65	32	40·2	56	68	77·2	84·5	88
$SbCl_3$ . .	0·1	1	1·5	5·8	21·8	50·5	136·5	337

Observations were also made by A. Ditte, M. Berthelot, and E. Baudrimont. H. E. Causse found the following proportions of antimony trioxide were dissolved by 100 c.c. of hydrochloric acid :

HCl	5	10	15	20	25	30	35
Sb_2O_3 . .	0·28	2·13	5·53	13·0	18·77	24·30	30·80
HCl { bound . .	0·21	1·62	4·85	9·93	14·26	18·47	23·42
HCl { free . .	4·79	8·38	10·15	10·07	10·74	11·53	11·57

Expressing the results in mols of $SbCl_3$ per 100 mols of water, J. M. van Bemmelen gave for the solubility of antimony trichloride in water at different temp. :

	0	15	20	25	30	35	40	50	60	72
$SbCl_3$.	47·9	64·9	72·8	78·6	84·9	91·6	108·8	152·5	360·4	∞

The equilibrium diagram for the ternary system $SbCl_3$–HCl–H_2O at 20° has four curves, Fig. 35, with the solid phases $SbCl_3$, DE ; $SbCl_3$.SbOCl, or $SbCl_3$.2SbOCl, BC ; SbOCl, AB ; and $Sb_4O_5Cl_2$, OA. The three quadruple points are A, B, and C. The curve DE represents the saturation curve of $SbCl_3$ in dil. hydrochloric acid. The solubility of the trichloride decreases with increasing conc. of the acid. The part CE is stable, the part DC is labile. J. M. van Bemmelen and co-workers said that the oxychloride $SbCl_3$.SbOCl, or Sb_2OCl_4, is deposited from soln. with between 1·38 and 4 mols. of water to a mol. of $SbCl_3$, but C. Lea and J. K. Wood said that this substance is really the oxychloride, $Sb_4O_5Cl_2$, and

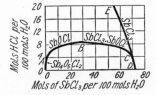

FIG. 35.—Equilibrium in the Ternary System: $SbCl_3$–HCl–H_2O at 20°.

that the only stable oxychlorides at 25° are SbOCl and $Sb_4O_5Cl_2$. The addition of a sufficient amount of water to antimony trichloride brings about the complete hydrolysis of that compound, with the formation of hydrochloric acid and a highly-hydrated form of antimony trioxide, which forms a bulky, white precipitate. The precipitate tends to adsorb hydrochloric acid from the surrounding liquid, the amount of acid adsorbed and the composition of the absorption product depending on the conc. of the soln. The amorphous oxychloride, SbOCl, referred to in literature is an adsorption product whose composition depends on the conc. of the soln. with which it is in contact. C. Lea and J. K. Wood continue : The adsorption product then tends to change into an oxychloride of antimony as a result of interaction between the adsorbed acid and the adsorbent ; the oxychloride so formed, however, may not be able to exist in stable equilibrium with the soln., but may in its turn suffer slow conversion into a crystalline product of different composition ; probably the adsorption product changes first into that oxychloride the composition of which most nearly approximates to its own. One of these metastable substances is J. P. Cooke's oxychloride to which the formula $Sb_4O_3(OH)_5Cl$ has been assigned, whilst the other is the compound deposited in the form of fine needles from the more conc. mixtures ; as the latter can apparently suffer change into either SbOCl or $Sb_4O_5Cl_2$, according to the conditions, it would appear to have the composition intermediate between those of the substances mentioned, and the formula $Sb_4O_3(OH)_3Cl_3$ is suggested as suitable for this substance. The process of conversion of these metastable compounds into the stable ones varies according to the nature of the final product ; thus, the conversion of $Sb_4O_3(OH)_3Cl_3$ into SbOCl and $Sb_4O_5Cl_2$, respectively, will take place in accordance with the following equations : $Sb_4O_3(OH)_3Cl_3 + HCl = 4SbOCl + 2H_2O$; and $Sb_4O_3(OH)_3Cl_3 = Sb_4O_5Cl_2 + H_2O + HCl$. In the second reaction the solid simply gives up acid to the soln. until the necessary equilibrium is established, but in the first it is necessary for interaction between the solid and the soln. to occur ; this difference in the nature of the process probably accounts for the more rapid attainment of equilibrium when the stable solid phase is $Sb_4O_5Cl_2$ than when it is SbOCl. In a similar manner, when a smaller proportion of hydrochloric acid is contained in the adsorption product, the latter suffers change into J. P. Cooke's oxychloride, and subsequently, according to the conc., into $Sb_4O_5Cl_2$ or antimonious oxide. The non-production of any appreciable quantity of J. P. Cooke's oxychloride from boiling soln. is probably due to dehydration of the amorphous adsorption product at the higher temp., which makes the separation of a crystalline hydrated oxychloride impossible. The dehydration adsorption product was, in the most conc. soln. investigated, mixed with crystals of $Sb_4O_5Cl_2$, and from this it would appear that the latter oxychloride may, under certain conditions, be formed directly from the adsorption compound.

The hydrolysis of antimony trichloride by water is retarded by the presence of hydrochloric acid, by the alkali and alkaline earth chlorides, and by tartaric acid. H. E. Causse obtained a neutral soln. by saturating a hydrochloric acid soln. of the trichloride with sodium chloride, and then neutralized the acid with sodium carbonate. G. Watson found that antimony trichloride forms clear soln. with sat. soln. of sodium, ammonium, calcium, and magnesium chlorides ; while potassium and barium chlorides gave turbid soln. He compared the effect of sodium, ammonium, and magnesium chlorides in preventing the decomposition of antimony trichloride by water. He also said (cf. 2. 19, 12) :

If some antimony trichloride be dissolved in a sat. soln. of sodium chloride, a liquid is obtained which is quite clear at first, but which, being in a state of instability, deposits, on standing, a portion of its antimony as basic salt. If scratches be made on the glass, however, in the newly-prepared liquid, such scratches are in a very short time—indeed almost at once—coated by a deposit of basic salt, the liquid otherwise remaining clear. This result is due to the slight increase of surface energy produced locally by the scratching, and inasmuch as a certain quantity of muscular energy is expended in producing an abrasion, causing the disappearance of its equivalent of cohesive force, and the appearance of the same amount of surface energy, it is evident that the surface energy of all solids is dependent on their intrinsic cohesive force ; for any mass of solid may be viewed as having been originally part of a larger mass, and as having been formed from it by breaking or sub-division. Increase of surface is the inevitable concomitant of comminution, and comminution is the disappearance of so much cohesive force.

H. Moissan found that **fluorine** reacts vigorously with antimony trichloride, forming the trifluoride. T. Karantassis studied the interchange of halogens—chlorine, bromine, and iodine. J. von Liebig showed that **chlorine** converts the tri- into the penta-chloride. W. Biltz and E. Meinecke, and K. H. Butler and D. McIntosh said that the trichloride is insoluble in liquid chlorine ; and W. Biltz and K. Jeep observed that the f.p. curve of antimony trichloride and chlorine, Fig. 36, shows the presence of the pentachloride, as well as of a complex $SbCl_5.2Cl_2$, or **antimony enneachloride**, $SbCl_9$. The action of **hydrochloric acid** on the hydrolysis of antimony trichloride has just been discussed. H. Rose, and M. Schleier found that when the hydrochloric acid soln. of the trichloride is heated, hydrochloric acid is first evolved ; then follows the acid containing some antimony trichloride ; and later, the trichloride alone. E. Fischer found that unlike arsenic trichloride (q.v.) the volatility of antimony trichloride is very much reduced if ferrous chloride be present in the soln. F. Hufschmidt, and F. A. Gooch and co-workers observed that no antimony trichloride is volatilized when a current of hydrogen chloride is passed through a hot dil. soln. L. Duparc and L. Ramadier showed that the presence of methyl alcohol favoured the volatility of antimony trichloride. M. Berthelot said that molten antimony trichloride, at as low a temp. as possible absorbs 8–10 vols. of hydrogen chloride, which is retained during the solidification ; but is expelled by heat, and re-absorbed on cooling. A deliquescent, crystalline mass is produced when antimony trichloride and one-fifth of its weight of conc. hydrochloric

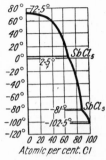

FIG. 36. — Freezing-point Curve of the System : $SbCl_3$–Cl_2.

acid, $HCl.3.73H_2O$, is cooled below 0°. A. Ditte believed that with hydrogen chloride, **antimony trichlorotrihydrochloride**, $SbCl_3.3HCl$, is formed ; while R. Engel passed dry hydrogen chloride at ordinary temp. into a soln. of antimony trichloride sat. at 0° so long as gas was absorbed. On cooling the liquid to 0°, crystals of **antimony trichlorohemihydrochloride**, $2SbCl_3.HCl.2H_2O$, were formed. The crystals melt at 16°, and give off hydrogen chloride when warmed. H. L. Snape[4] found that when the solid trichloride and **potassium iodide** are heated while being protected from oxygen, antimony triiodide is formed ; and A. Naumann found that a similar reaction occurs when in acetone soln. ; similarly, silver nitrate forms antimony nitrate and silver chloride. For reactions with various chlorides, vide infra. F. Feigl and O. Schummer represented the reaction with **sodium hypochlorite** : $SbCl_3 + NaOCl + 2HCl = NaCl + H_2O + SbCl_5$; and with **potassium bromate** : $3SbCl_3 + KBrO_3 + 6HCl = KBr + 3H_2O + 3SbCl_5$.

H. A. von Vogel found that antimony trichloride decomposes when heated with **sulphur**, and grey trisulphide is formed ; but, according to G. Vortmann and C. Padberg, a boiling soln. of the trichloride is not affected by sulphur. The action of **hydrogen sulphide** is discussed in part in connection with the analytical reactions of antimony, and in part in connection with the trisulphide—vide infra, sulphurochlorides. W. Biltz and H. Keunecke observed that dry liquid hydrogen sulphide has no action on antimony trichloride. A. Naumann observed no precipitation occurs when hydrogen sulphide acts on an acetone soln. of the trichloride. G. N. Guam and J. A. Wilkinson, and A. W. Ralston and J. A. Wilkinson measured the conductivity of soln. of antimony trichloride in liquid hydrogen sulphide, and found that it is about 10,000 times that of phosphorus chloride—the sp. conductivity of the sat. soln. is 4244×10^7 mhos. H. A. von Vogel said that conc. **sulphuric acid** does not act on antimony trichloride in the cold, but when heated, hydrogen chloride is evolved, and antimony sulphate formed. H. Friedrich also found that while tin and germanium tetrachlorides can be distilled from their sulphuric acid soln., the higher chlorides of iron and antimony are decomposed with the evolution of hydrogen chloride. H. Rose found that when a hydrochloric acid soln. of the trichloride is heated with conc. sulphuric acid, hydrogen chloride is first evolved, then antimony trichloride, and when the sulphuric acid distils over, the distillate is free from antimony. Antimony sulphate remains in the retort. If more hydrochloric acid is added, the sequence is repeated ; and by repeating the addition of hydrochloric acid a number of times, all the antimony may be distilled as chloride. F. Clausnizer found that **chloro-sulphonic acid** dissolves a little antimony trichloride at ordinary temp. ; and when heated in a sealed tube, the trichloride melts without mixing the acid, but as the temp. is raised, the two fluids mix, and the trichloride crystallizes out unchanged on cooling. H. Rose, and P. Walden found the trichloride to be soluble in **sulphur monochloride.**

G. Gore [5] found antimony trichloride to be insoluble in liquid **ammonia ;** and J. Persoz, and P. Grouvelle observed that the trichloride absorbs ammonia. H. Rose added that the absorption by this solid is very slow, and when the molten trichloride is cooled in an atm. of ammonia, **antimony amminotrichloride,** $SbCl_3.NH_3$, is formed. All the ammonia is expelled when the ammine is heated ; and on exposure to air, the ammine is decomposed more slowly than the trichloride alone. P. P. Déherain said that hydrochloric acid converts it into ammonium tetra-chlorantimonite, and he prepared **antimony diamminotrichloride,** $SbCl_3.2NH_3$, by passing ammonia into the melted trichloride, or into warm pentachloride. The yellowish-white, crystalline diammine is stable, and volatile ; and is converted by hydrochloric acid into ammonium pentachlorantimonite. A. Naumann supposed **antimony triamminotrichloride,** $SbCl_3.3NH_3$, to be the chief product of the action of ammonia on a soln. of antimony trichloride in **acetone.** The white compound ·s stable in air, and the ammonia is expelled by heat. O. C. M. Davis found that **nitrogen sulphide** yields **antimony nitrogen sulphopentachloride,** $N_4S_4.SbCl_5$. H. Rheinboldt and R. Wasserfuhr, and H. Gall and H. Mengdehl found that antimony trichloride reacts with **nitrosyl chloride,** forming **antimonic nitrosyl chloride,** $SbCl_5.NOCl$. V. Thomas said that **nitric oxide** is without action on a chloroform or carbon disulphide soln. of antimony trichloride, and **nitrogen peroxide** forms a moderately stable compound approximating $Sb_4O_{11}Cl_4N_2$; or $Sb_2O_4.2SbOCl_2.N_2O_5$; or **nitroxyl tetrantimonyltetrachloride,** $(SbO.O)_2 : NO$. $O.O.NO : (O.SbOCl_2)_2$. The product is decomposed by warming ; by water ; and is dissolved by hydrochloric acid. The soln. liberates iodine from potassium iodide ; and in alkaline soln., blackens silver nitrate. A. Besson found that antimony trichloride reacts with nitrogen peroxide, forming an unstable compound ; V. Thomas said that very little nitrogen peroxide is absorbed in the cold, but at the m.p. it readily absorbs the gas, becoming pale yellow, dark yellow, and finally red. If the product be slowly cooled, it drops its yellow colour and retains a certain quantity of peroxide ; the gas is given off when the product is placed in vacuo, or exposed for some time to dry air. The vap. press. of the product varied from 3 mm. to 491 mm. for the same temp., thus indicating that the peroxide forms no definite compound with antimony trichloride, but remains simply dissolved. H. A. von Vogel found that conc. **nitric acid** oxidizes antimony trichloride to the hydrated pentoxide ; and H. Rose added that when a soln. of the trichloride in hydrochloric acid is distilled with nitric acid, after hydrogen chloride and nitrogen oxides have passed over, antimony pentachloride partially dissociated distils over, and the pentoxide remains as a residue. O. Ruff found that **phosphorus** scarcely reacts with antimony trichloride at 200°, but in the presence of aluminium trichloride the phosphorus is rapidly dissolved, and when the product is digested with carbon disulphide, an unstable red substance is formed. P. Walden found antimony trichloride is readily soluble in **phosphorus trichloride and tribromide.** H. Köhler observed that with **phosphorus pentachloride,** a complex, $SbCl_5.PCl_5$, is formed (*q.v.*). T. Karantassis observed that **phosphorus triiodide** reacts with antimony trichloride by double decomposition, but the reverse reaction does not occur. According to R. Mahn, **stibine** reacts with the molten trichloride, forming a black substance, which, after washing with hydrochloric acid and water, con-tained 76·86 per cent. of Sb ; 12·85, P ; 3·45, Cl ; and 6·84, O. The hot tri-chloride dissolves **antimony trioxide**—*vide* oxychlorides—and **antimony trisulphide** —*vide* sulphochlorides. P. Walden said that antimony trichloride is readily dis-solved by **arsenic trichloride.** L. Kahlenberg and J. V. Steinle observed that no replacement of the antimony could be observed when an acetone soln. of antimony trichloride is treated with arsenic or bismuth.

J. Tarible found that with **boron tribromide**, antimony tribromide and boron trichloride are formed: $SbCl_3 + BBr_3 = SbBr_3 + BCl_3 + 20\cdot9$ cals. L. Schäffer found that when antimony trichloride is heated with **alcohol** in a sealed tube at 160°, an oxychloride is formed. E. R. Schneider, and J. P. Cooke observed the solubility of the trichloride in absolute alcohol; A. Sabaneeff, in **chloroform**; J. P. Cooke, in **carbon disulphide**; M. Centnerszwer, in liquid **cyanogen**; and F. Oberhauser studied the reaction with **cyanogen chloride**. J. P. Cooke found the trichloride dissolves in **alcohol** without decomposition. A. Naumann found that 100 grms. of **acetone** dissolve 537·6 grms. of the trichloride at 18°, and the soln. has a sp. gr. of 2·216 at 18°/4°; the soln. is at first yellow, and it then becomes black. At 18°, the sat. soln. has 532 grms. of salt per 100 grms. of solvent. F. Swarts found it to be insoluble in **carbon tetrachloride**. A. Naumann found that the trichloride is soluble in **benzonitrile**; and that 100 parts of **ethyl acetate** dissolve 5·89 parts of the trichloride at 18°, and the sp. gr. of the sat. soln. is 1·7968 at 18°/4°. W. Eidmann found the trichloride to be soluble in **methylal**. J. Nicklès, and A. Sabaneeff found that the trichloride reacts with **ether,** forming a sticky liquid. W. Smith and G. W. Davis, and A. Rosenheim and W. Stellmann found that a complex compound, $3SbCl_3.C_6H_6$, is formed with **benzene**. B. N. Menschutkin measured the solubility of the trichloride in a number of organic liquids. Expressing the results in mols of trichloride per 100 mols of solvent, he found for benzene:

	5·6°	4°	20°	40°	60°	73°
$SbCl_3$ . .	0	2·6	13·1	21·4	34·7	100

chlorobenzene :

	−45·2°	−20°	0°	20°	40°	73°
$SbCl_3$ . .	0	9·0	28·1	38·7	56·2	100

bromobenzene :

	−31°	−15°	0°	20°	40°	73°
$SbCl_3$ . .	0	14·1	26·6	43·2	59·2	100

iodobenzene :

	−28·6°	−15°	5°	25°	55°	73°
$SbCl_3$ . .	0	24·7	44·5	53·9	76·2	100

paradichlorobenzene :

	54·5°	39·5°	50°	60°	70°	73°
$SbCl_3$ . .	0	29·5	46·4	66·5	91·1	100

paradibromobenzene :

	88°	75°	49·5°	60°	70°	73°
$SbCl_3$ . .	0	25·7	64·9	79·8	95·2	100

nitrobenzene :

	6°	−18°	5°	25°	65°	73°
$SbCl_3$ . .	0	(26·2)	55·8	63·0	87·2	100

metadinitrobenzene :

	90°	−60°	−11°	20°	60°	73°
$SbCl_3$ . .	0	33·8	(62·2)	65·2	85·8	100

toluene :

	−93°	−30°	0°	30°	60°	73°
$SbCl_3$ . .	0	7·2	22·1	47·6	83·8	100

ethylbenzene :

	−93°	−30°	0°	30°	60°	73°
$SbCl_3$ . .	0·1	1·1	5·6	27·2	85·5	100

propylbenzene :

		−70°	−20°	0°	30°	60°	73°
$SbCl_3$	. .	(0·6)	(14·8)	26·2	60·6	81·0	100

isoamylbenzene :

		−80°	−25°	0°	30°	60	73°
$SbCl_3$	. .	3	(34·4)	(52·3)	57·3	8? ⌐	100

W. Smith and G. W. Davis observed the formation of a complex compound with naphthalene : J. P. Claësson, one with mercaptan ; C. Vincent, one with dimethylamine ; G. Bruni and A. Manuelli, with formamide, a product with a composition ranging between $SbCl(NH.COH)_2$ and $Sb(NH.COH)_3$; and similarly with acetamide. N. S. Kurnakoff studied the viscosity and m.p. of mixtures of antimony trichloride with benzene, naphthalene, diphenylmethane, triphenylmethane, aniline, ethyl ether and acetone. F. Feigl and O. Schummer represented the reaction with potassium ferricyanide : $2K_3FeCy_6 + SbCl_3 + 4HCl = K_4FeCy_6 + H_4FeCy_6 + SbCl_5 + 2KCl$. L. Belladen and R. Astengo obtained a compound with benzamide ; F. Ephraim and S. Weinberg, with methylamine ; and L. Vanino and F. Mussgnug, with thiocarbamide. W. Smith observed the colour reactions with aromatic hydrocarbons, and with alkaloids. The trichloride also reacts with many other organic compounds ; thus, E. Vanstone, P. May, B. N. Menschutkin, observed that it reacts with benzaldehyde, benzonitrile, chlorotoluene, nitrotoluene, methyl-, ethyl-, propyl, and isoamyl-benzenes, xylenes, toluenes, and various other substitution products, mesitylene, ψ-cumene, anisole, phenol, aniline, propylbenzene, etc.; S. Hakomori, complex with tartaric acid; P. May, azonium chlorides; J. Hasenbäumer, A. Michaelis and A. Günther, P. May, G. T. Morgan and F. M. G. Micklethwait, and G. Grüttner and M. Wiernik studied the action of antimony trichloride on triphenylstibine ; V. Auger and M. Billy, on organomagnesium compounds ; W. H. Gray, on diazotized diamines ; L. Barthe and A. Minet, on cacodylic acid and methylarsenic acid ; and A. M. Wasilieff, chloronaphthalenes and nitronaphthalenes. This subject is discussed in G. T. Morgan's *Organic Compounds of Arsenic and Antimony* (London, 1918) ; and in W. G. Christiansen's *Organic Derivatives of Antimony* (New York, 1925). For the action of antimony trichloride on organic halides, *vide infra*, antimony triiodide. The use of antimony trichloride as a chlorinating agent for organic compounds was discussed by Lassar Cohn.

A. C. Vournasos [6] found that antimony trichloride in boiling toluene soln. reacts with potassium, forming antimony and potassium chloride. K. Seubert and A. Schmidt observed that the vapour of antimony trichloride passed over red-hot magnesium furnishes magnesium chloride and antimony—*vide supra*, metallic precipitation of antimony. V. A. Jacquelain noticed that when small pieces of the trichloride are laid on mercury, they revolve about for some time until the mercury is covered with a film of the trichloride. A. Mazzucchelli and A. Vercillo found that a soln. of antimony trichloride in hydrochloric acid is almost inert towards copper at ordinary temp., but at 100°, a protective film is formed on the copper, if cuprous chloride be present, Cu_2Sb is formed ; with tin in place of copper, Sn_2Sb_2 is formed ; with bismuth, no alloy is formed. F. Ducelliez found that cobalt reacts with the trichloride at 700°–1200°, forming antimonides ; E. Vigouroux obtained a similar result with nickel. A. Levallois observed that when heated with lead sulphide (galena) in a sealed tube at 160°, a crystalline substance is formed which was not investigated ; and when a dil. soln. is allowed to stand in contact with plumbiferrous iron sulphide (pyrites) for a long time—5 years—E. Masing noticed that needle-like crystals containing Sb_2O_3, Fe_2O_3, and PbO are formed. F. Kessler observed that manganese dioxide oxidizes the trichloride to the hydrated pentoxide ; similarly also with potassium permanganate.

Antimony trichloride forms a number of complex salts with various other halides. Thus, A. Ferratini [7] boiled an alcoholic soln. of antimony trichloride with hydrazine hydrochloride, and obtained silky needles of **hydrazine hexachlorantimonite,** $SbCl_3.3N_2H_5Cl$. J. Kendall and co-workers observed no evidence of the existence of the 2 : 1 and the 3 : 1 compounds in their study of the f.p. curve of $NH_4Cl-SbCl_3$ mixtures. They did obtain evidence of the existence of the 1 : 1 compound, and of **ammonium enneachlorodiantimonite,** $(NH_4)_3Sb_2Cl_9$. The α-, β-, and γ-forms of antimony trichloride are represented by breaks on the curve. P. P. Déherain obtained **ammonuim tetrachlorantimonite,** $NH_4Cl.SbCl_3$, in colourless, deliquescent needles, by the action of hydrochloric acid on the monammine—*vide supra.* V. A. Jacquelain prepared **ammonium pentachlorantimonite,** $2NH_4Cl.SbCl_3$, from a soln. containing theoretical proportions of the two salts ; A. B. Poggiale said that crystals of ammonium hexachlorantimonite, $3NH_4Cl.SbCl_3.1\frac{1}{2}H_2O$, separates before the crystals of the pentachlorantimonite appear. P. P. Déherain obtained the pentachlorantimonite by the action of hydrochloric acid on the diammine—*vide supra.* A. B. Poggiale said that the salt is *monohydrated.* The crystals belong to the cubic system, and are decomposed by water. F. Ephraim studied this salt, he also prepared **lithium pentachlorantimonite,** $2LiCl.SbCl_3.5H_2O$, as a *penta-hydrate,* from a conc. hydrochloric acid soln. of a mol of antimony trichloride and three or more mols of lithium chloride. The acicular crystals are deliquescent ; they melt when warmed ; decompose at 110° ; dissolve sparingly in hydrochloric

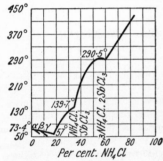

FIG. 37.—Freezing-point Curves of Mixtures of Ammonium and Antimonious Chlorides.

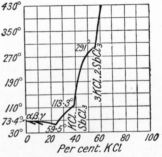

FIG. 38.—Freezing-point Curves of Mixtures of Potassium and Anti-monious Chlorides.

acid ; and are decomposed by water. If 8 mols of lithium chloride are used in the preparation, the *hexahydrate* is formed. The same hydrate is produced by evaporating over sulphuric acid a soln. of equimolar parts of antimony trichloride and lithium chloride ; heating the syrup on a water-bath when antimony trichloride volatilizes and the required crystals are formed. J. Kendall and co-workers could not obtain a thermal diagram for the $LiCl-SbCl_3$ system because clear soln. containing more than 0·6 per cent. of lithium clhloride were not obtained at 300°. A. B. Poggiale, and J. von Liebig obtained tabular crystals of **sodium tetrachloro-antimonite,** $NaCl.SbCl_3$, from a soln. of the component salts. F. Ephraim studied this salt. J. Kendall and co-workers found that sodium chloride is virtually insoluble in antimony trichloride at 300°.

K. Seidel found the f.p. of antimony trichloride to be 67°–68° ; and when a mol of the trichloride is mixed with 0·1, 0·2, 0·3, 0·4, and 0·5 mol of potassium chloride, the respective f.p. are 59°, 53°, *c.* 45°, 47°, and 50°, showing that there is a eutectic temp. below 50°. He also examined in part the ternary system $SbCl_3-KCl-H_2O$ at temp. between 0° and 70°, more particularly the conc. of the potassium chloride soln. when a turbidity appears. J. Kendall and co-workers' observations on the f.p. of the $KCl-SbCl_3$ system are indicated in Fig. 38. There is no evidence of the existence of the 1 : 2, 3 : 7, or 1 : 3 compound, but there is shown **potassium etrachloroantimonite,** $KSbCl_4$, and **potassium enneachlorodiantimonite,** $K_3Sb_2Cl_9$.

There are transition temp. representing α-, β-, and γ-forms of antimony trichloride R. Benedikt obtained *hexagonal* crystals of **potassium pentachlorantimonite**. $2KCl.SbCl_3$, from a conc. soln. of the component salts—with or without hydrochloric acid. O. Bosek found this salt amongst the products of the action of potassium chlorate on a soln. of antimony in hydrochloric acid. The tabular crystals are stable in air ; they lose antimony trichloride when heated in a current of carbon dioxide ; they are decomposed by water ; they can be recrystallized from their soln. in hydrochloric acid—but the first crop of crystals consists of potassium chloride. The salt is soluble in tartaric acid. F. Ephraim studied this salt. If potassium pentachlorantimonite be allowed to stand in its mother-liquor for some days, prismatic and tabular crystals belonging to the *monoclinic* system were obtained by R. Benedikt. The axial ratios are $a : b : c = 0.7241 : 1 : 0.7222$, and $\beta = 111° 3'$. The salt is therefore dimorphous. C. F. Rammelsberg described what he regarded as rhombic crystals of this salt. The hexagonal crystals were also obtained by V. A. Jacquelain. R. Benedikt obtained tabular monoclinic prisms of the *dihydrate* by crystallizing the soln. at about $-10°$. A. B. Poggiale seems to have obtained this salt in crystals, which he supposed belonged to the cubic system. The crystals do not lose their lustre at $-5°$; but they do so at $15°$ in consequence of the loss of water ; all the water is lost over sulphuric acid, or at $105°$, and hydrogen chloride is given off at $110°$. C. H. Herty evaporated a soln. of a mol of antimony trichloride and 3 mols of potassium chloride at $35°$ and obtained six-sided colourless crystals of a complex salt, $23KCl.10SbCl_3.27H_2O$; H. L. Wells and H. W. Foote favoured the formula $7KCl.3SbCl_3.8H_2O$—**potassium hexadecachlorotriantimonite**. S. Miyake studied the system $KCl-SbCl_3-HCl-H_2O$ at $25°$ with the conc. of the hydrochloric acid constant, and this acid was ignored. The solubilities of potassium chloride in water and 10·55 per cent. hydrochloric acid at $25°$ were respectively 26·27 and 12·75 grms. per 100 grms. of soln. The solubilities of antimony trichloride in the same menstrua were respectively 90·90 and 90·07 grms. respectively. Only two complex salts were found to be stable—prisms or plates of potassium penta-chlorantimonite, $2KCl.SbCl_3$, and hexagonal plates of potassium hexadecachloro-triantimonite, $7KCl.3SbCl_3$. According to E. Jordis, when a mixed soln. of the component salts is evaporated, potassium chloride first separates, the next crop of crystals had the composition $23KCl.SbCl_3$, after that there appeared a crop with the composition $0.78KCl.SbCl_3$. The solid products are crystallographically uniform, and are not mixtures. S. Miyake could not confirm the existences of E. Jordis' mixtures. A. B. Poggiale reported crystals of **potassium hexachlorantimonite**, $3KCl.SbCl_3$; but R. Benedikt believed that the product was really the salt indicated above.

F. Godeffroy first prepared complex salts with rubidium and cæsium chlorides. H. J. Wheeler reported crystals of **rubidium heptachlorodiantimonite**, $RbCl.2SbCl_3.H_2O$, from a hydrochloric acid soln. of a mol of rubidium chloride and 6–10 mols of antimony trichloride. The tabular crystals belong to the monoclinic system, and have the axial ratios $a : b : c = 1.699 : 1 : 0.820$, and $\beta = 90° 31.5'$. The m.p. is $77°$; with a hydrochloric acid soln. containing a mol of rubidium chloride and 2·5–4 mols of antimony trichloride, I. Remsen and A. P. Saunders, and H. J. Wheeler obtained colourless, monoclinic crystals of rubidium tetrachloranti-monite, $KCl.SbCl_3$, with the axial ratios $a : b : c = 1.732 : 1 : 1.085$, and $\beta = 114° 26'$. The m.p. was not definite. H. J. Wheeler prepared crystals of rubidium enneachlorodiantimonite, $3RbCl.2SbCl_3$, by crystallization from a hydrochloric acid soln. of rubidium chloride and antimony trichloride in the molar proportions 1 : 1·5 to 2·0. I. Remsen and A. P. Saunders also prepared this salt. The pale yellow, trigonal crystals have the axial ratio $a : c = 1 : 0.5625$, and $a = 110° 54'$. They are stable in dry air. F. Godeffroy obtained a salt to which he attributed the formula $6PbCl.SbCl_3$, but which was shown by H. L. Wells and H. W. Foote, and I. Remsen and A. P. Saunders to be more probably **rubidium hexadecachloro-triantimonite**, $7RbCl.3SbCl_3$, or $23RbCl.10SbCl_3$. The crystals separate from a hydrochloric acid soln. of rubidium chloride and antimony trichloride in the mol. proportions 1·4–1·6RbCl : SbCl₃. The colourless, hexagonal plates can be heated to 200° without decomposition ; dissociation begins at 230°. The salt is decomposed by water ; it is soluble in hydrochloric acid, or in alcoholic hydrogen chloride, from which it can be crystallized unchanged. It is less soluble in conc. hydrochloric acid. The crystals become opaque in air. When crystallized from dil. hydrochloric acid, the salt passes into an oxychloride. F. Ephraim, F. Godeffroy, and I. Remsen and A. P. Saunders obtained **cæsium enneachlorodiantimonite,** 3CsCl.2SbCl₃, by precipitation by adding a conc. hydrochloric acid soln. of antimony trichloride to a soln. of cæsium chloride. F. Godeffroy first gave CsCl.SbCl₃ for the formula, and later altered it to 6CsCl.SbCl₃, but C. Setterberg, W. Muthmann, and I. Remsen and A. P. Saunders showed that this is not correct. The salt can be obtained in very pale yellow prisms or needles by recrystallization from hydrochloric acid. I. Remsen and A. P. Saunders, and T. H. Behrens said that the crystals belong to the rhombic system and appear hexagonal because of trilling. The plates are stable in air ; and are decomposed by heat, and by water. They are sparingly soluble in conc. hydrochloric acid, but readily soluble in the dil. acid. The salt was studied by F. Ephraim ; and employed by E. H. Duclaux in the micro-detection of antimony.

J. Kendall and co-workers did not succeed in measuring the f.p. curve of *cuprous and antimonious chlorides* because of the low solubility—less than 0·3 per cent.— of the former in the latter at 300° ; similar remarks apply to the system *silver and antimonious chlorides*. R. Benedikt obtained an unstable **calcium pentachloroantimonite,** CaCl₂.SbCl₃.8H₂O, by evaporating a hydrochloric acid soln. of the component salts over sulphuric acid at 0°. The colourless plates are probably triclinic ; they decompose at ordinary temp. into their component salts. A. B. Poggiale made needle-like crystals of **barium pentachloroantimonite,** BaCl₂.SbCl₃.2½H₂O, by evaporating a hydrochloric acid soln. of the component salts, at a low temp. J. Kendall and co-workers did not measure the f.p. curve of the system *barium and antimonious chlorides*, because the solubility of the former in the latter is less than 0·4 per cent. at 300°. F. Ephraim prepared a crystalline mass of crystals of **beryllium pentachloroantimonite,** BeCl₂.SbCl₃.3H₂O, by evaporating a hydrochloric acid soln. of the equimolar parts of the component salts over conc. sulphuric acid. The crystals are very hygroscopic ; are freely soluble in hydrochloric acid, and are decomposed by water ; besides the *trihydrate*, a *tetrahydrate* was made by evaporating a similar soln. containing the component salts in the molar ratio BeCl₃ : SbCl₃=3 : 2. A. B. Poggiale first prepared a complex salt with magnesium chloride ; and F. Ephraim obtained **magnesium octochlorodiantimonite,** MgCl₂.2SbCl₃.10H₂O, by evaporating on a water-bath a hydrochloric acid soln. of the component salts in theoretical proportions, and cooling the syrup to 40°. The crystals are very hygroscopic ; melt at a gentle heat ; dissolve freely in hydrochloric acid ; and are decomposed by water. He also obtained **magnesium pentachloroantimonite,** MgCl₂.SbCl₃.5H₂O, from a soln. of the component salts in the proportions MgCl₂ : SbCl₃=1·0 to 1·5 : 1. The salt can be recrystallized from hydrochloric acid. The crystals are deliquescent, and are decomposed by water. Part of the contained antimony is volatilized at a red-heat.

P. Lohmann [8] found that at the first moment of the action of stibine on a 5 per cent. soln. of mercuric chloride containing 10 per cent. of ammonium chloride, brown flecks of **antimony trichloromercuriate,** Sb(HgCl)₃, are formed. The compound is immediately decomposed into mercury or mercurous chloride and antimony trichloride and oxychloride. G. Franceschi obtained **antimony hydrobischloromercuriate,** SbH(HgCl)₂.3H₂O, by the action of stibine on an aq. or alcoholic soln. of mercuric chloride. The precipitate is decomposed by water—*vide* the corresponding arsenic compounds. D. Vitali obtained this compound by the action of nascent stibine on mercuric chloride soln.

F. Ephraim [9] could not prepare a complex *aluminium chloroantimonite.*

J. Kendall and co-workers found that in the system *mercurous and antimonious chlorides*, 0·42 and 0·61 per cent. of the former in the latter gave clear soln. at 74° and 235°, but complete soln. was not obtained with 2 per cent. of $HgCl$ at 300°. With the system *mercuric and antimonious chlorides*, there was no evidence of the formation of a compound on the f.p. curve shown in Fig. 39. Similar remarks apply to the f.p. curve of the system *aluminium and antimonious chlorides*, Fig. 40.

Fig. 39.—Freezing-point Curve of the System : $HgCl_2$–$SbCl_3$.

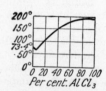

Fig. 40.—Freezing-point Curve of the System : $AlCl_3$–$SbCl_3$.

F. Ephraim and P. Barteczko prepared **thallous pentacholroantimonite**, Tl_3SbCl_6, in light yellow, lustrous scales, by dissolving thallous chloride in molten antimony trichloride, and adding conc. hydrochloric acid. J. Kendall and co-workers found that the f.p. curves of the system *stannous and antimonious chlorides*, show the existence of no compound, but there is a two-liquid region extending from 1·4 to 91·2 per cent. of stannous chloride in equilibrium with the solid phase $mSnCl_2.nSbCl_3$, at 243·1°—*vide* Fig. 41. The f.p. curve of mixtures of *stannic and antimonious chlorides* is shown in Fig. 42. No complex salt is formed. A coalescence temp. in a metastable two-liquid region was observed with between 35·8 and 73·5 per cent. of stannic chloride.

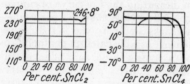

Fig. 41.—Freezing-point Curve of Mixtures : $SnCl_2$–$SbCl_3$.

Fig. 42.—Freezing-point Curve of Mixtures : $SnCl_4$–$SbCl_3$.

REFERENCES.

[1] L. D. l'Hôte, *Compt. Rend.*, **98**. 1491, 1884 ; P. J. Robiquet, *Ann. Chim. Phys.*, (2), **4**. 165, 1817 ; P. S. Brallier, *Trans. Amer. Electrochem. Soc.*, **49**. 65, 1926 ; J. D. Sullivan, *Heavy Liquids for Mineralogical Analyses*, Washington, 1927 ; P. J. Malouin, *Mém. Acad.*, 46, 1740 ; *Chymie médicinale*, Paris, 1750 ; C. Hensgen, *Rec. Trav. Chim. Pays-Bas*, **10**. 301, 1891 ; A. W. Hofmann, *Liebig's Ann.*, **115**. 267, 1860 ; B. H. Jacobson, *Brit. Pat. No.* 181385, 190688, 1922 ; Anon., *Crell's Chem. Journ.*, **6**. 76, 1781 ; A. Classen and O. Bauer, *Ber.*, **16**. 1067, 1883 ; H. Rose, *Pogg. Ann.*, 3. 445, 1824 ; **105**. 571, 1858 ; Hooker Electrochemical Co., *U.S. Pat. No.* 1425565, 1922 ; P. L. Geiger and L. Reimann, *Mag. Pharm.*, **17**. 126, 1827 ; J. von Liebig, *Handwörterbuch der reinen und angewandten Chemie*, Braunschweig, **1**. 414, 1837 ; F. Göbel, *Brandes' Arch.*, **2**. 216, 1822 ; R. Brandes, *Repert. Pharm.*, **11**. 289, 1821 ; *Schweigger's Journ.*, **51**. 437, 1827 ; G. C. Wittstein, *Pharm. Viertelj.*, **18**. 534, 1869 ; J. J. Berzelius, *Schweigger's Journ.*, **6**. 144, 1812 ; **22**. 69, 1818 ; Rhenania Ver⌋in Chemische Fabrik, *German Pat.*, *D.R.P.* 406673, 1923 ; E. Mitscherlich, *Journ. prakt. Chem.*, (1), **19**. 455, 1840 ; J. P. Cooke, *Amer. Journ. Science*, (3), **19**. 469, 1880 ; *Chem. News*, **44**. 221, 223, 245, 255, 268, 1880 ; *Proc. Amer. Acad.*, **13**. 1, 2, 1877 ; A. Larocque, *Journ. Pharm. Chim.*, (3), **15**. 161, 1849 ; G. Oddo and E. Serra, *Gazz. Chim. Ital.*, **29**. 355, 1899 ; G. Oddo and U. Giachery, *ib.*, **53**. i, 56, 1923 ; Basil Valentine, *Triumphwagen Antimonii*, Nürnberg, 1676 ; London, 1893 ; H. Boerhaave, *Elementa chemiæ*, Lugduni Batavorum, **2**. 521, 1732 ; J. C. Barchusen, *Pyrosophia*, Lugduni Batavorum, 222, 1698 ; J. R. Glauber, *Novis furnis philosophicis*, Amstelodami, 1648 ; London, 7, 1689 ; J. Linder, *Zeit. Chem.*, (2), **5**. 442, 1869 ; P. de Clermont, *Compt. Rend.*, **88**. 972, 1879 ; C. R. Fresenius, *Zeit. anal. Chem.*, 25. 200, 1886 ; J. M. Scherer, *ib.*, 3. 206, 1864 ; F. Schuster, *Zeit. anorg. Chem.*, **146**. 299, 1925.

[2] W. Finkelstein, *Zeit phys. Chem.*, **115**. 303, 1925 ; H. Töpsöe, *Sitzber. Akad. Wien*, **66**. 42, 1872 ; *Arch. Science Genève*, (2), **45**. 76, 1872 ; J. P. Cooke, *Amer. Journ. Science*, (3), **19**. 469, 1880 ; *Chem. News*, **44**. 221, 233, 245, 268, 1880 ; *Proc. Amer. Acad.*, 13, 1, 72, 1878 ; C. P. Worcester, *ib.*, **18**. 61, 1883 ; T .C. Sanderson, *Brit. Pat. No.* 6882, 1889 ; G. B. Bernardis, *Atti Accad. Lincei*, (5), **21**. ii, 438, 1912 ; E. Cohen and T. Strengers, *Zeit. phys. Chem.*, **52**. 164, 1905 ; W. Böttger, *Oesterr. Chem. Ztg.*, **27**. 24, 1924 ; H. Capitaine, *Journ. Pharm. Chim.*, (3),

25. 516, 1839 ; N. S. Kurnakoff, S. I. Perlmutter, and K. P. Kanoff, *Journ. Russ. Phys. Chem. Soc.*, **48**. 1658, 1916 ; H. Kopp, *Liebig's Ann.*, **95**. 348, 1855 ; H. Buff, *ib.*, **105**. 145, 1858 ; *Ann. Chim. Phys.*, (3), **59**. 122, 1860 ; E. K. Rideal, *Phil. Mag.*, (6), **42**. 156, 1921 ; J. Kendall, E. D. Crittenden and H. E. Miller, *Journ. Amer. Chem. Soc.*, **45**. 963, 1923 ; T. Carnelley and W. C. Williams, *Journ. Chem. Soc.*, **33**. 281, 1878 ; A. K. Macbeth and N. I. Maxwell, *ib.*, **123**. 370, 1923 ; C. R. Crymble, *Proc. Chem. Soc.*, **30**. 179, 1914 ; F. Göbel, *Brandes' Arch.*, **2**. 216, 1822 ; Z. Klemensiewicz, *Bull. Acad. Cracovie*, 485, 1908 ; R. Anschütz and P. N. Evans, *Ber.*, **19**. 1994, 1886 ; J. Thomsen, *ib.*, **16**. 39, 1883 ; *Bull. Soc. Chim.*, (2), **39**. 598, 1883 ; E. Beckmann, *Zeit. anorg. Chem.*, **51**. 111, 1906 ; I. I. Saslawsky, *ib.*, **146**. 315, 1925 ; R. Lorenz and W. Herz, *ib.*, **120**. 320, 1921 ; **145**. 88, 1925 ; **147**. 135, 1925 ; W. Herz, *ib.*, **170**. 237, 1928 ; S. Motylewsky, *ib.*, **38**. 410, 1904 ; F. Schuster, *ib.*, **146**. 299, 1925 ; W. Biltz, *ib.*, **115**. 241, 1921 ; W. Biltz and K. Jeep, *ib.*, **162**. 32, 1927 ; H. Braune and W. Tiedje, *ib.*, **152**. 39, 1926 ; P. Walden, *ib.*, **25**. 220, 1900 ; **29**. 377, 1902 ; *Zeit. phys. Chem.*, **43**. 437, 1903 ; L. Rotinjanz and W. Suchodsky, *ib.*, **87**. 635, 1914 ; S. Tolloczko, *ib.*, **30**. 705, 1899 ; *Bull. Acad. Cracovie*, 1, 1901 ; K. Frycz and S. Tolloczko, *Festschr. Univ. Lemberg*, 1. 1, 1912 ; S. Tolloczko and M. Meyer, *Kosmos*, **35**. 641, 1910 ; *Radziszewsky's Festband*, 641, 1910 ; F. M. Raoult, *Zeit. phys. Chem.*, **2**. 371, 1888 ; *Compt. Rend.*, **103**. 1125, 1886 ; E. van Aubel, *Bull. Acad. Belg.*, (5), **7**. 469, 1922 ; L. von Pebal and H. Jahn, *Wied. Ann.*, **27**. 584, 1886 ; L. Graetz, *ib.*, **40**. 18, 1890 ; H. Rose, *Pogg. Ann.*, **55**. 551, 1842 ; G. N. Guam and J. A. Wilkinson, *Proc. Iowa Acad.*, **32**. 324, 1925 ; H. Becquerel, *Ann. Chim. Phys.*, (5), **12**. 34, 1877 ; A. Guntz, *ib.*, (6), **3**. 53, 1884 ; J. B. A. Dumas, *ib.*, (3), **55**. 175, 1859 ; L. Kahlenberg and A. T. Lincoln, *Journ. phys. Chem.*, **3**. 26, 1899 ; A. T. Lincoln, *ib.*, **3**. 464, 1899 ; H. Schlundt, *ib.*, **5**. 503, 1901 ; M. Prud'homme, *Journ. Chim. Phys.*, **21**. 243, 1924 ; F. M. Jäger, *Zeit. anorg. Chem.*, **101**. 1, 1917 ; O. Gosmann, *Zeit. Physik*, **22**. 273, 1924 ; G. Bruni and A. Manuelli, *Zeit. Elektrochem.*, **11**. 554, 1905 ; C. G. Maier, *Vapor Pressures of the Common Metallic Chlorides and a Static Method for High Temperatures*, Washington, 1925 ; E. Mitscherlich, *Journ. prakt. Chem.*, (1), **19**. 455, 1840 ; J. Davy, *Phil. Trans.*, **102**. 169, 1812 ; O. Masson, *Phil. Mag.*, (5), **30**. 412, 1890 ; J. A. Groshans, *ib.*, (5), **20**. 197, 1885 ; *Ber.*, **19**. 974, 1886 ; G. Hänsel, *Wiss. Siemens Konz.*, **4**. 111, 1925 ; H. Henstock, *Chem. News*, **126**. 337, 1923 ; J. D. Sullivan, *Heavy Liquids for Mineralogical Analysis*, Washington, 1927.

³ J. P. Cooke, *Proc. Amer. Acad.*, **13**. 1, 72, 1878 ; *Amer. Journ. Science*, (3), **19**. 469, 1880 ; *Chem. News*, **44**. 221, 233, 245, 255, 1880 ; W. D. Bancroft and H. B. Weiser, *Journ. Phys. Chem.*, **18**. 213, 1914 ; W. P. Dexter, *Pogg. Ann.*, **100**. 568, 1857 ; R. Weber, *ib.*, **125**. 87, 1865 ; H. Rose, *ib.*, **3**. 445, 1824 ; **105**. 571, 1858 ; R. Brandes, *Schweigger's Journ.*, **51**. 437, 1827 ; A. Sabaneeff, *Zeit. Chem.*, (2), **7**. 204, 1871 ; E. Baudrimont, *Journ. Pharm. Chim.*, (3), **29**. 436, 1856 ; *Compt. Rend.*, **42**. 863, 1856 ; H. le Chatelier, *ib.*, **100**. 737, 1885 ; **102**. 1388, 1886 ; H. E. Causse, *ib.*, **113**. 1042, 1892 ; A. Ditte, *Ann. Chim. Phys.*, (5), **22**. 557, 1881 ; *Compt. Rend.*, **79**. 959, 1874 ; R. Engel, *ib.*, **106**. 1797, 1888 ; J. M. van Bemmelen, P. A. Meerburg. and U. H. Noodt, *Zeit. anorg. Chem.*, **33**. 272, 1803 ; W. Biltz and K. Jeep, *ib.*, **162**. 32, 1927 ; W. Biltz and E. Meinecke, *ib.*, **131**. 1, 1923 ; F. A. Gooch and H. W. Grener, *Amer. Journ. Science*, (3), **42**. 213, 1891 ; M. Berthelot, *Ann. Chim. Phys.*, (6), **10**. 133, 1886 ; H. Moissan, *ib.*, (6), **24**. 257, 1891 ; G. Watson, *Journ. Soc. Chem. Ind.*, **5**. 590, 1886 ; *Chem. News*, **58**. 297, 1888 ; M. Schleier, *Kritische Studien über die Trennung von Zinn und Antimon*, München, 1892 ; H. von Wartenberg, *Zeit. Elektrochem.*, **33**. 146, 1927 ; E. Fischer, *Liebig's Ann.*, **208**. 189, 1881 ; C. Lea and J. K. Wood, *Journ. Chem. Soc.*, **123**. 259, 1923 ; J. von Liebig, *Handwörterbuch der reinen und angewandten Chemie*, Braunschweig, **1**. 414, 1837 ; F. Hufschmidt, *Ber.*, **17**. 2245, 1884 ; L. Duparc and L. Ramadier, *Helvetica Chim. Acta*, **5**. 552, 1922 ; F. Feigl and O. Schummer, *Zeit. anal. Chem.*, **64**. 249, 1924 ; T. Karantassis, *Compt. Rend.*, **182**. 699, 1926 ; K. H. Butler and D. McIntosh, *Trans. Roy. Soc. Canada*, (3), **21**. 19, 1927.

⁴ H. A. von Vogel, *Schweigger's Journ.*, **21**. 70, 1817 ; A. Naumann, *Ber.*, **37**. 4332, 1904 ; G. Vortmann and C. Padberg, *ib.*, **22**. 2644, 1889 ; H. L. Snape, *Chem. News*, **74**. 27, 1896 ; H. Friedrich, *Monatsh.*, **14**. 519, 1893 ; F. Clausnizer, *Liebig's Ann.*, **196**. 295, 1879 ; H. Rose, *Pogg. Ann.*, **105**. 570, 1850 ; P. Walden, *Zeit. anorg. Chem.*, **25**. 217, 1900 ; W. Biltz and H. Keunecke, *ib.*, **147**. 171, 1925 ; G. N. Guam and J. A. Wilkinson, *Proc. Iowa Acad.*, **32**. 324, 1925 ; *Journ. Amer. Chem. Soc.*, **47**. 989, 1925 ; A. W. Ralston and J. A. Wilkinson, *ib.*, **50**. 258, 1928 ; F. Feigl and O. Schummer, *Zeit. anal. Chem.*, **64**. 249, 1924.

⁵ G. Gore, *Proc. Roy. Soc.*, **20**. 441, 1872 ; **21**. 140, 1873 ; P. Grouvelle, *Ann. Chim. Phys.*, (2), **17**. 37, 1821 ; J. Persoz, *ib.*, (2), **44**. 315, 1830 ; H. Rose, *Pogg. Ann.*, **24**. 165, 1832 ; **42**. 532, 1837 ; *Sur les combinaisons du bromine de bore avec les composés halogénés du phosphore, de l'arsenic et de l'antimoine*, Paris, 1899 ; *Compt. Rend.*, **132**. 204, 1901 ; P. P. Déherain, *ib.*, **52**. 734, 1861] ; V. Thomas, *ib.*, **120**. 1115, 1895 ; **123**. 51, 1896 ; T. Karantassis, *ib.*, **182**. 699, 1391, 1926 ; A. Besson, *ib.*, **108**. 1012, 1889 ; J. Nicklès, *ib.*, **52**. 396, 1861 ; A. Naumann, *Ber.*, **37**. 3801, 4332, 1904 ; **43**. 320, 1910 ; **47**. 1369, 1914 ; A. Rosenheim and W. Stellmann, *ib.*, **34**. 3383, 1901 ; H. Köhler, *ib.*, **13**. 875, 1880 ; W. Smith, *ib.*, **12**. 1420, 1879 ; W. Smith and G. W. Davis, *Journ. Chem. Soc.*, **41**. 411, 1882 ; O. C. M. Davis, *ib.*, **89**. 1577, 1906 ; H. A. von Vogel, *Schweigger's Journ.*, **21**. 70, 1817 ; R. Godefroy, *Zeit. anal. Chem.*, **16**. 244, 1877 ; C. Vincent, *ib.*, **19**. 479, 1880 ; Lassar Cohn, *Arbeitsmethoden für organischchemische Laboratorien*, Leipzig, **2**. 252, 1923 ; London, 190, 1895 ; R. Mahn, *Jena. Zeit.*, (1), **5**. 160, 1869 ; G. Bruni and A. Manuelli, *Zeit. Elektrochem.*, **11**. 554, 1905 ; A. Sabaneeff, *Zeit. Chem.*, (2), **7**. 205, 1871 ; P. Walden, *Zeit. anorg. Chem.*, **25**. 211, 1900 ; **29**. 374, 1902 ; J. P. Claësson, *Bull. Soc. Chim.*, (2), **25**. 183, 1876 ; M. Centnerszwer, *Journ. Russ. Phys. Chem. Soc.*, **33**. 545, 1901 ; *Bull. Soc.*

Chim., (3), 28. 405, 1901 ; J. P. Cooke, *Proc. Amer. Acad.*, 13. 1, 72, 1878 ; *Amer. Journ. Soc.*, (3), 19. 469, 1880 ; *Chem. News*, 44. 221, 233, 245, 1880 ; E. R. Schneider, *Journ. prakt. Chem.*, (2), 18. 402, 1878 ; (2), 21. 131, 1880 ; (2), 31. 420, 1885 ; *Ueber das Atomgewichte des Antimons*, Berlin, 1880 ; L. Schäffer, *Liebig's Ann.*, 152. 135, 1869 ; *Ber.*, 1. 135, 1868 ; F. Swarts, *Bull. Acad. Belg.*, (3), 29. 874, 1895 ; *Zeit. anorg. Chem.*, 12. 71, 1896 ; L. Belladen and R. Astengo, *Atti Accad. Lincei*, (5), 32. i, 491, 1923 ; W. Eidmann, *Ein Beitrag zur Erkenntnis des Verhaltens chemischer Verbindungen in nichtwässrigen Lösungen*, Giessen, 1899 ; L. Vanino and F. Mussgnug, *Ber.*, 50. 21, 1917 ; G. Grüttner and M. Wiernik, *ib.*, 48. 1473, 1749, 1915 ; A. Michaelis and A. Günther, *ib.*, 44. 2316, 1911 ; J. Hasenbäumer, *ib.*, 31. 3910, 1898 ; F. Ephraim and S. Weinberg, *ib.*, 42. 4447, 1909 ; H. Gall and H. Mengdehl, *ib.*, 60. B, 86, 1927 ; H. Rheinboldt and R. Wasserfuhr, *ib.*, 60. B, 732, 1927 ; G. T. Morgan and F. M. G. Micklethwait, *Journ. Chem. Soc.*, 99. 2286, 1911 ; P. May, *ib.*, 99. 1383, 1911 ; 101. 1033, 1037, 1912 ; E. Vanstone, *ib.*, 105. 1491, 1914 ; 127. 550, 1925 ; W. H. Gray, *ib.*, 129. 3174, 1926 ; B. N. Menschutkin, *Izvista Polyt. St. Petersburg*, 13. 277, 411, 1910 ; *Journ. Russ. Phys. Chem. Soc.*, 43. 1275, 1303, 1329, 1783, 1805, 1911 ; 44. 1108, 1128, 1929, 1939, 1912 ; 45. 1710, 1913 ; *Journ. Chim. Phys.*, 9. 314, 1911 ; 10. 598, 612, 1912 ; A. M. Wasilieff, *Journ. Russ. Phys. Chem. Soc.*, 49. 428, 1917 ; L. Barthe and A. Minet, *Compt. Rend.*, 148. 1609, 1909 ; V. Auger and M. Billy, *ib.*, 139. 597, 1904 ; L. Kahlenberg and J. V. Steinle, *Trans. Amer. Electrochem. Soc.*, 44. 493, 1923 ; N. S. Kurnakoff, *Zeit. anorg. Chem.*, 135. 81, 1924 ; F. Feigl and O. Schummer, *Zeit. anal. Chem.*, 64. 249, 1924 ; F. Oberhauser, *Ber.*, 60. B, 1434, 1927 ; S. Hakomori, *Science Rep. Tohoku Univ.*, 16. 841, 1927 ; O. Ruff, *Ber.*, 34. 1749, 1901 ; J. Tarible, *Compt. Rend.*, 116. 1521, 1893 ; 132. 204. 1901.

⁶ K. Seubert and A. Schmidt, *Liebig's Ann.*, 267. 237, 1892 ; F. Kessler, *Zeit. anal. Chem.*, 18. 1, 1879 ; A. Levallois, *Compt. Rend.*, 96. 1666, 1883 ; F. Ducelliez, *ib.*, 147. 1048, 1908 ; E. Vigouroux, *ib.*, 147. 976, 1908 ; A. C. Vournasos, *Zeit. anorg. Chem.*, 81. 364, 1913 ; E. Masing, *Russ. Pharm. Journ.*, 28. 757, 1889 ; V. A. Jacquelain, *Ann. Chim. Phys.*, (2), 66. 123, 1837 ; A. Mazzucchelli and A. Vercillo, *Atti Accad. Lincei*, (6), 1. i, 233, 1925.

⁷ C. F. Rammelsberg, *Handbuch der Mineralchemie*, Leipzig, 1. 284, 1881 ; P. P. Déherain, *Compt. Rend.*, 52. 734, 1861 ; A. B. Poggiale, *ib.*, 20. 1180, 1845 ; K. Seidel, *Ueber Salze des Antimonstrichlorids mit Chlorkalium und einige analoge Derivate mit organischen Säuren*, Erlangen, 1904 ; A. Ferratini, *Gazz. Chim. Ital.*, 42. i, 138, 1912 ; T. H. Behrens, *Zeit. anal. Chem.*, 30. 163, 1891 ; V. A. Jacquelain, *Ann. Chim. Phys.*, (2), 66. 123, 1837 ; E. H. Duclaux, *Anal. Assoc. Quim. Argentina*, 9. 215, 1921 ; C. Setterberg, *Oefvers. Akad. Förh. Stockholm.* 6, 1882 ; *Chem. News*, 46. 249, 1882 ; E. Jordis, *Ber.*, 36. 2539, 1903 ; F. Ephraim, *ib.*, 36. 1821, 1903 ; F. Godeffroy, *Russ. Pharm. Journ.*, 14. 35, 1875 ; *Ber.*, 7. 375, 1874 ; 8. 11, 1875 ; W. Muthmann, *ib.*, 26. 1425, 1893 ; J. Kendall, E. D. Crittenden, and H. K. Miller, *Journ. Amer. Chem. Soc.*, 45. 963, 1923 ; O. Bosek, *Journ. Chem. Soc.*, 67. 516, 1895 ; S. Miyake, *Mem. Coll. Eng. Kyushu Univ.*, 3. 187, 1925 ; J. von Liebig, *Handwörterbuch der reinen und angewandten Chemie*, Braunschweig, 1. 414, 1837 ; C. H. Herty, *Amer. Chem. Journ.*, 16. 495, 1894 ; I. Remsen and A. P. Saunders, *ib.*, 14. 152, 1892 ; R. Benedikt, *Proc. Amer. Acad.*, 20. 9, 212, 1894 ; *Zeit. anorg. Chem.*, 8. 224, 1894 ; H. L. Wells and H. W. Foote, *Amer. Journ. Science*, (4), 3. 461, 1897 ; H. L. Wells and F. J. Metzger, *Amer. Chem. Journ.*, 26. 268, 1901 ; *Amer. Journ. Science*, (4), 11. 455, 1901 ; H. J. Wheeler, *ib.*, (3), 46. 269, 1893 ; *Zeit. anorg. Chem.*, 5. 253, 1893 ; S. Miyake, *Journ. Japan. Chem. Ind.*, 27. 735, 1924 ; *Mem. Coll. Eng. Kyushu Univ.*, 3. 187, 1925.

⁸ P. Lohmann, *Pharm. Ztg.*, 36. 757, 1891 ; G. Franceschi, *L'Orosi*, 13. 397, 1890 ; *Boll. Chim. Farm.*, 29. 317, 1890 ; D. Vitali, *ib.*, 44. 49, 1905.

⁹ F. Ephraim, *Ber.*, 36. 1821, 1903 ; F. Ephraim and P. Barteczko, *Zeit. anorg. Chem.*, 61. 238, 1909 ; J. Kendall, E. D. Crittenden, and H. K. Miller, *Journ. Amer. Chem. Soc.*, 45. 963, 1923.

§ 18. The Higher Antimony Chlorides

According to H. Rose,[1] when hydrated antimony tetroxide is dissolved in conc. hydrochloric acid, the pale yellow soln. gives a white precipitate when treated with a small proportion of water, but with more water no precipitation occurs ; hydrogen sulphide precipitates antimony tetrasulphide from the soln. (*q.v.*). If this be correct, it might be inferred that the soln. contained Sb_2Cl_8, or **antimony tetrachloride**, $SbCl_4$; but it has not been possible to isolate such a compound, although many complex salts are known which probably contain this compound. F. Ephraim and S. A. Weinberg found that on adding solid ammonium chloride to a fused mixture of antimony tri- and penta-chlorides, the liquid becomes black, and solidifies on cooling to a violet mass, which slowly loses its colour at the ordinary temp., ultimately becoming white. The dark metastable salt is best obtained by pouring the hot mixture into chloroform ; it then remains for some hours without change. A. H. W. Aten's observations on the f.p. of mixtures of antimony tri- and penta-

chlorides, Fig. 43, show no evidence of the formation of the tetrachloride. Similarly
with W. Biltz and K. Jeep's observations, Fig. 36. According to R. F. Weinland
and H. Schmid, and F. Ephraim and S. A. Weinberg, a state of equilibrium ensues
when antimony tri- and penta-chlorides are mixed in hydrochloric acid soln.:
$SbCl_3 + SbCl_5 \rightleftharpoons 2SbCl_4$. The dark brown colour of the soln.
is supposed to be due to the presence of the chloride of
quadrivalent antimony. The amount of tetrachloride increases as the temp. is raised, or the conc. of the hydrochloric
acid is augmented. F. Ephraim and S. A. Weinberg were
able to prepare **ammonium hexachlorohypoantimonate,**
$(NH_4)_2SbCl_6$, and **potassium hexachlorohypoantimonate,**
$2KCl.SbCl_4$, only in isomorphous mixture with tin or platinum—e.g. $(NH_4)_2(Sb,Pt)Cl_6$; $(NH_4)_2(Sb,Sn)Cl_6$; $K_2(Sb,Pt)Cl_6$;
and $K_2(Sb,Sn)Cl_6$. O. Bosek found that when a soln. of
antimony in hydrochloric acid and potassium chlorate
was evaporated in vacuo, crystals of potassium pentachloroantimonate were produced—*vide supra*—there were also formed transparent, deliquescent, monoclinic,
lemon-yellow crystals of **potassium henachlorodihypoantimonate,** $3KCl.2SbCl_4$.
He added :

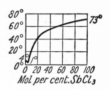

Fig. 43.—Freezing-
point Curve of the
System : $SbCl_3$–
$SbCl_5$.

> Repeated attempts were made to obtain this substance again by mixing antimony
> trichloride, pentachloride, and potassium chloride in different proportions and evaporating
> the hydrochloric soln. of these constituents in a vacuum, but the crystals could not be
> obtained again ; it is uncertain, therefore, whether they are the double compound of the
> new antimony tetrachloride, $SbCl_4$, or a mixture of double salts of the trichloride and
> pentachloride.

R. F. Weinland and H. Schmid prepared **rubidium hexachlorohypoantimonate,**
$2RbCl.SbCl_4$, by adding rubidium chloride to a hydrochloric acid soln. of equimolar
proportions of antimony tri- and penta-chlorides in hot conc. hydrochloric acid.
The black, microcrystalline powder is composed of octahedra. Their splinters are
reddish-violet in transmitted light. The salt is decomposed by water. If the soln.
of the two antimony chlorides, just indicated, is treated with rubidium chloride at
ordinary temp., a complex salt **rubidium octodecachlorodiantimonitohypoanti-
monate,** $Rb_2SbCl_6.2Rb_3SbCl_6$, separates in brown, transparent, hexagonal plates.
By working with ammonium chloride, **ammonium henachloroantimonitohypoanti-
monate,** $(NH_4)SbCl_5.(NH_4)_3SbCl_6$, was obtained in brown, hexagonal plates.
C. Setterberg obtained black, transparent prisms of **cæsium hexachlorohypoantimonate,** $2CsCl.SbCl_4$, by boiling a conc. hydrochloric acid soln. of antimony tri-
and penta-chlorides with an excess of cæsium chloride. H. L. Wells and
F. J. Metzger said that the crystals are octahedra, and the powder in thin layers is
dark blue. The dark colour of these compounds may mean that the products
are not direct derivatives of the tetroxide. The crystals are said to be isomorphous
with cæsium hexachloroplumbate. E. H. Duclaux also made this salt. C. Setterberg found that the salt is not decomposed by conc. hydrochloric acid ; but is converted into cæsium enneachlorodiantimonate by the dil. acid. According to
F. Ephraim and P. Barteczko, thallous chloride dissolves in molten antimony
pentachloride, chlorine is evolved, and a dark violet solid **thallous pentachloro-
hypoantimonate,** $TlCl.SbCl_4$, is formed ; and by passing chlorine into a soln. of
thallous chloride in antimony trichloride, a black felted mass of **thallosic trideca-
chlorodihypoantimonate,** $TlCl_3.2TlCl.2SbCl_4$, is formed. R. F. Weinland and
H. Schmid found that a conc. hydrochloric acid soln. of ammonium chloride,
quadrivalent antimony, and tin tetrachloride furnishes **ammonium hexachloro-
stannatohypoantimonate,** $(NH_4)_2(Sb,Sn)Cl_6$, in dark violet crystals ; and similarly,
by using potassium chloride in place of the ammonium salt, **potassium hexachloro-
stannatohypoantimonate,** $K_2(Sb,Sn)Cl_6$, is formed. If platinum tetrachloride
be used in place of tin tetrachloride, **ammonium hexachloroplatinatohypoantimonate,** $(NH_4)_2(Sb,Pt)Cl_4$, is formed in transparent, brownish-violet to opaque

black crystals; and also **potassium hexachloroplatinatohypoantimonate**, $K_2(Sb,Pt)Cl_6$, appears as a dark violet powder. F. Ephraim and S. A. Weinberg found that **ammonium ferric heptacosichlorotrihypoantimonate**, a ferric ammonium antimony chloride, $9NH_4Cl,2FeCl_3,3SbCl_4$, is obtained by mixing the chlorides in conc. hydrochloric acid and forms black octahedra. It may be regarded as $3(NH_4)_2SbCl_6+3NH_4Cl,2FeCl_3$. Pyridine salts were also prepared.

H. Rose [2] said that **antimony pentachloride**, $SbCl_5$, not the trichloride, is produced when antimony burns in chlorine gas; and J. von Liebig obtained the pentachloride by the action of chlorine on the trichloride—*vide* Fig. 37. H. Rose obtained very little pentachloride when a soln. of hydrated antimony pentoxide in hydrochloric acid is distilled. R. Anschütz and P. N. Evans prepared the pentachloride by saturating antimony trichloride with chlorine, and distilling the product under reduced press.

Antimony pentachloride is a colourless, mobile, or pale-yellow liquid which, according to E. Moles,[3] acquires an orange tint if chlorine is present. Analyses by H. Rose, and R. Anschütz and P. N. Evans, are in agreement with the formula $SbCl_5$. S. Sugden discussed the electronic structure—*vide* phosphorus penta-chloride. M. Nothomb measured the **vapour density** at various temp. between 180° and 386°, and found that decomposition into antimony trichloride and chlorine occurs in a way quite analogous to phosphorus pentachloride. R. Anschütz and P. N. Evans found that the vapour density, at about 218° and 55 mm. press., is 10·03, which corresponds with the theoretical value 10·27. The vapour is probably partially dissociated at these temp., and it is supposed that equilibrium was not attained owing to the short duration of the experiment. A. Haagen gave 2·346 for the **specific gravity** of the liquid at 20°; W. Herz gave 2·346; O. Ruff and W. Plato, 2·340 at 22·7°; and E. Moles, 2·3356 at 20°/4°. F. Kammerer found that the liquid freezes at −20°, forming a mass of acicular crystals with the **melting point** −6°. The sample was probably contaminated with chlorine because E. Moles found the m.p. to be 3°; and W. Biltz and K. Jeep, 3·5°. H. Braune and W. Tiedje found the **vapour pressure**, p mm., to be:

p	55·1°	72·1°	84·1°	93°	106·2°	111·7°	117·5°
	7·1	16·5	28·8	43·7	76·7	95·2	119·2

R. Anschütz and P. N. Evans found that the **boiling point** is 68° at 14 mm.; 79° at 22 mm.; 102°–103° at 68 mm.; and 143°–144° at 70 mm. The **dissociation** is very small when the liquid is boiled under reduced press., but H. Rose found that when heated at ordinary press., the compound is dissociated into the trichloride and chlorine, and very little pentachloride distils over unchanged. R. Anschütz and P. N. Evans said that dissociation becomes appreciable between 140°–150°; chlorine can be observed between 160°–170°; and there is a lively evolution of chlorine between 180°–190°. The dissociation was studied by M. Nothomb—*vide supra*—he gave for the equilibrium constant $K_p=a^2/(1-a^2)$, where $a=(p_0-p)/p$, and p_0 mm. denotes the total press., and p mm. the press. of the undecomposed pentachloride $K_p=2·22$ at 293° and 3·38 at 356°; and H. Braune and W. Tiedje, $\log K_p=0·548$ at 119° and 3·161 at 266°, or $\log K_p=9·740-3570T^{-1}$. P. Fireman and E. G. Portner said that dissociation can be detected even at ordinary temp. because solid potassium or ammonium iodide is coloured brown in consequence of the separation of iodine by the free chlorine. E. Moles found the **heat of fusion** to be 8·17 cals.; and W. Herz gave 8·18 cals. per gram. E. Moles found the **freezing-point constant** to be 18·5. H. Braune and W. Tiedje found the **heat of vaporization** to be 11,050 cals. at 67°. J. Thomsen gave for the **heat of formation** : $SbCl_{3solid}+Cl_{2gas}=SbCl_{5liquid}+13·8$ Cals.; since the heat of formation of the trichloride is 91·4 Cals., the heat of formation of the pentachloride from its elements is $Sb_{solid}+5Cl_{gas}=SbCl_{5liquid}+104·8$ Cals. Hence, 30·5 Cals. per atom are evolved with the fixing of the first three atoms of chlorine, and 6·7 Cals. per atom with the fourth and fifth atoms. H. Braune and

W. Tiedje gave for $SbCl_{3gas}+Cl_{2gas}=SbCl_{5gas}+17$ Cals. at 200°. H. Becquerel found the **index of refraction** of the pentachloride for Na-light is 1·5910 ; and the **electromagnetic rotatory power,** 1·656. C. R. Crymble measured the **absorption spectrum** of the pentachloride. W. Herz gave 238×10^{12} for the **vibration frequency.** H. Buff, and L. Bleekrode found the **electric conductivity** is very small, and P. Walden regarded the salt as a non-conductor, but found that when dissolved in liquid sulphur dioxide at 0° the eq. conductivities in 11·3, 46·0, and 224·0 litres are respectively 0·212, 0·737, and 27·29. The dissolved pentachloride is not ionized. H. Schlundt found the **dielectric constant** to be 3·58 at 21·5°.

Antimony pentachloride fumes in air and has a sharp acid odour ; it is very hygroscopic and rapidly attracts moisture from the air, forming a crystalline hydrate. These hydrates are produced by a small proportion of **water,** but a large proportion yields hydrates of antimony pentoxide (*q.v.*). R. Anschütz and P. N. Evans [4] prepared **monohydrated antimony pentachloride,** $SbCl_5.H_2O$, as a yellow crystalline mass, by slowly adding the calculated quantity of water to the well-cooled pentachloride ; or by cooling a mixture of the calculated quantity of water with a chloroform soln. of the pentachloride. No hydrogen chloride is given off. It can be crystallized from its soln. in chloroform. The yellowish-white plates melt between 87° and 92° ; and when heated to 105° at 20 mm. press., antimony pentachloride distils over ; the last fraction contains some trichloride, and a waxy mass remains. H. Daubrawa's antimony trichloride is probably this hydrate, which when heated under ordinary press., gives off chlorine but not water. The monohydrate deliquesces in air, forming a clear liquid which yields acicular crystals when evaporated over sulphuric acid. The compound is hydrolyzed by water, forming hydrated pentoxide ; conc. soln. of sodium carbonate precipitate antimony trioxide. The monohydrate is soluble in alcohol, and in chloroform. When the alcoholic soln. is evaporated, hydrogen chloride is evolved, and there remains a viscid yellow mass which with water forms a white precipitate, and alcohol. When the monohydrate is heated with chloroform in a closed tube, or in an open vessel on a water-bath, the reaction is symbolized : $SbCl_5.H_2O+CHCl_3$ $=COCl_2+3HCl+SbCl_3$; and carbonyl chloride is also formed when the mono-hydrate is heated in carbon tetrachloride. H. Rose, and R. Weber obtained **tetrahydrated antimony pentachloride,** $SbCl_5.4H_2O$, by mixing the pentachloride with as little water as is necessary for its soln., and evaporating the liquid over sulphuric acid ; or, according to R. Anschütz and P. N. Evans, by adding the calculated quantity of water to a well-cooled soln. of the pentachloride in twice its vol. of chloroform, and keeping the liquid in vacuo for crystallization. The mass of colourless, transparent, rhombic crystals gradually become opaque in dry air ; they deliquesce in air without becoming turbid ; water hydrolyzes the com-pound, forming the hydrated pentoxide, but the tetrahydrate can be obtained by crystallization from its soln. in a small proportion of water. The tetrahydrate is insoluble in chloroform. H. B. Kosmann made some observations on these hydrates.

E. Beckmann found that antimony pentachloride is insoluble in liquid **chlorine ;** W. Biltz and K. Jeep found that antimony pentachloride can react with chlorine, forming **antimony enneachloride,** $SbCl_5.2Cl_2$. E. Beckmann found that antimony pentachloride dissolves in conc. **hydrochloric acid,** forming chloroantimonic acids— *vide infra.* R. Engel reported crystals of *antimony pentachloropentahydrochloride,* $SbCl_5.5HCl.10H_2O$, by passing a current of hydrogen chloride through an aq. soln. of tetrahydrated antimony pentachloride, and cooling the soln. to 0°. The crystals are said to be stable in air. R. F. Weinland and H. Schmid could not verify these statements. O. Ruff found that **bromine** does not react with antimony pentachloride, but it does react with **iodine.** The main results are symbolized by the three equations : (i) $SbCl_5+2I=SbCl_3+2ICl$; (ii) $2SbCl_5+2I=SbCl_5+2ICl$ $+SbCl_3$; (iii) $3SbCl_5+4I=SbCl_5,3ICl+2SbCl_3+ICl$. Equation (i) represents the reaction which takes place when less than 1·5 per cent. of iodine is dissolved in the antimony pentachloride. Some iodine trichloride, antimony tri-iodide, and possibly a chloro-iodide of quinquevalent antimony are formed in addition, but no evidence can be adduced of the formation of a compound, $SbCl_5I$, analogous to SbF_5I. E. Moles found the mol. wt. of iodine, and of the iodine chlorides from their effect on the f.p. of antimony trichloride. E. Moles found that antimony pentachloride and **potassium iodide** form iodine monochloride; while **sulphur, selenium,** and **tellurium** furnish double compounds of their tetrachlorides with antimony pentachloride. S. Cloëz, and A. Bertrand and E. Finot observed that with **hydrogen sulphide,** antimony sulphotrichloride is formed—*vide supra*, reactions of antimony. W. Biltz and H. Krunecke found antimony pentachloride is thiohydrolyzed by dry liquid hydrogen sulphide. H. Rose, O. Ruff and W. Plato, O. Ruff and G. Fischer, and R. Weber obtained a complex $SbCl_5.SCl_4$ with **sulphur tetrachloride** ; R. Weber, $SbCl_5.SeCl_4$ with **selenium tetrachloride** ; and $SbCl_5SeOCl_2$ with **selenium oxydichloride.** The reduction of antimony pentachloride in hydrochloric acid soln. by means of **sulphur dioxide** or by **sulphites** was examined by G. von Knorre, B. Brauner, and A. Jolles. H. Friedrich observed that hot and cold **sulphuric acid** reacts with the pentachloride. F. Clausnizer found that equimolar parts of antimony pentachloride and **chlorosulphonic acid** form a greenish-yellow liquid which, when gently heated, gives off chlorine, hydrogen chloride, and sulphur dioxide and becomes brown ; at 160°, a white crystalline mass is formed which is hydrolyzed by water. If equimolar parts of chlorosulphonic acid and antimony pentachloride be heated in a sealed tube on the water-bath, no decomposition occurs ; nor does any appreciable reaction occur if the mixture be exposed to sunlight for a month.

H. Rose found that **ammonia** is strongly absorbed by antimony pentachloride, forming a brown substance which when warmed becomes colourless without any other perceptible change ; and it then sublimes. J. Persoz's analysis agrees with antimony hexamminopentachloride, $SbCl_5.6NH_3$, and J. Persoz represented the action of water : $SbCl_5.6NH_3+3H_2O=NH_4SbO_3+5NH_4Cl$. A. Rosenheim and F. Jacobsohn obtained a white crystalline powder by the action of liquid ammonia on monohydrated antimony pentachloride, but no definite formula could be assigned to the product. P. P. Déherain found that when ammonia is passed into a cold soln. of antimony pentachloride, and the red substance is heated in a retort, ammonium octchloroantimonate sublimes, and crystalline needles of **antimony triamminopentachloride,** $SbCl_5.3NH_3$, are formed. Hydrochloric acid converts it into the ammonium octchloroantimonate. There is simultaneously produced volatile **antimony tetramminopentachloride,** $SbCl_5.4NH_3$, which is converted by hydrochloric acid into ammonium enneachloroantimonate. A. Besson found that antimony pentachloride unites with **nitric oxide,** forming yellow crystals of **antimony heminitrosylpentachloride,** $2SbCl_5.NO$. It forms good crystals when heated for some hours in a sealed tube at 100° ; it is decomposed by water. With **nitrogen peroxide,** A. Besson obtained **antimony dinitroxyltrispentachloride,** $3SbCl_5.2NO$, which after heating in a sealed tube at 100° for some time furnished yellow crystals which are decomposed by water. R. Weber found that when the vapour from **aqua regia** is passed into antimony pentachloride a yellow, hygroscopic powder of **antimony chloronitrosylpentachloride,** $SbCl_5.NOCl$, is formed. It is decomposed by water. J. J. Sudborough found that **nitrosyl chloride** reacts with antimony pentachloride, forming lemon-yellow crystals of **antimony hemipentachloronitrosylpentachloride,** $2SbCl_5.5NOCl$. It is decomposed by water. W. J. van Heteren heated it in a sealed tube at 180° without decomposition. H. Rose found that antimony pentachloride absorbs **phosphine** with the evolution of a little hydrogen chloride, forming a red solid which, with water, and aq. ammonia, gives off phosphine. R. Mahn did not obtain this compound, and he represented the reaction : $PH_3+4SbCl_5=4SbCl_3+PCl_5+3HCl$. P. Fireman found that, in an open vessel, the pentachloride reacts explosively with **phosphonium iodide,** forming iodine, etc. ; and in a sealed tube so arranged that the substances only come

ANTIMONY 483

in contact when heated, the reaction can be represented : $3PH_4I+3SbCl_5=SbI_3$ $+2SbCl_3+9HCl+2P+PH_3$. R. Weber, and A. W. Cronander obtained **antimony phosphorus decachloride,** $PCl_5.SbCl_5$, by heating a mixture of **phosphorus pentachloride** and antimony pentachloride, and by the action of an excess of phosphorus pentachloride on antimony trichloride ; and H. Köhler, by the action of a mol of **phosphorus trichloride** on 2 mols of antimony pentachloride dissolved in chloroform. The yellow crystals of the complex decachloride, when heated, volatilize without melting ; and they are decomposed by water. T. Karantassis also made the complex **phosphorus diantimony pentadecachloride,** $PCl_5.2SbCl_5$. R. Weber found that with **phosphoryl chloride,** a white, deliquescent, crystalline mass of **antimony phosphoryl octochloride,** $SbCl_5.PCl_3$, is formed. T. Karantassis observed that **phosphorus triiodide** reacts by double decomposition with antimony pentachloride, but the reverse action does not occur. C. von Uslar found that **phosphoric acid** has no action on a hydrochloric acid soln. of antimony pentachloride.

J. Tarible represented the reaction with **boron tribromide :** $3SbCl_5+5BBr_3$ $=5BCl_3+3SbBr_3+3Br_2+91$ cals. When antimony chloride is mixed with a half-molar proportion of **carbon disulphide,** A. W. Hofmann observed that in a short time a vigorous reaction occurs : $2SbCl_5+CS_2=CCl_4+2SbCl_3+2S$; A. Bertrand and E. Finot said that if the mixture be cooled before the vigorous reaction occurs, crystals of antimony sulphotrichloride are formed : $2SbCl_5+CS_2=2SbSCl_3+CCl_4$; and when warmed, these decompose : $2SbSCl_3=2SbCl_3+2S$. According to A. Husemann, if the vapour of carbon disulphide be passed through a red-hot tube—vide 6. 39, 42—and then over antimony pentachloride, carbon tetrachloride and sulphur monochloride are formed. As emphasized by A. W. Hofmann, antimony pentachloride is a good chlorinating agent for **organic compounds.** Lassar Cohn has discussed this subject. H. Müller chlorinated benzene, and arsenic acid ; R. Anschütz and P. N. Evans, oxalic acid. Antimony pentachloride also reacts with many organic compounds, e.g., R. F. Weinland and H. Schmid, and A. Rosenheim and co-workers prepared compounds with pyridine ; L. Klein, with hydrogen cyanide and cyanogen chloride ; W. C. Williams, with acetylene, alcohols, and ethers ; A. Rosenheim and co-workers, with aldehydes, ketones, organic acids, acid amides, and chlorides, acid anhydrides, oxy-acids, and nitrobenzene, but not with quinoline, phenols, and hydrocarbons. K. Steiner and co-workers, T. Diehl, A. Zetter, and V. Merz and W. Weith studied the effect of antimony pentachloride on anthraquinone, fluorenone, phenanthrene, phenanthraquinone, xanthone, acridone, methylacridone, benzophenone, benzoic acid, benzoyl chloride, and benzoylbenzoic acid ; S. Hilpert and L. Wolf, on benzene, naphthalene, phenanthrene, carbazole, anthraquinone, fluorene, diphenyl methane, and triphenyl methane ; and P. Pfeifer, ethyl oxalate. T. S. Thomsen studied compounds of the pentachloride with many alkaloids—quinine, cinchonine, cinchonidine, morphine, codeine, strychnine, cocaine, caffeine, and nicotine. Summaries of the organic compounds of antimony will be found in G. T. Morgan's *Organic Compounds of Antimony* (London, 1918) ; and W. G. Christiansen's *Organic Derivatives of Antimony* (New York, 1925). R. Mahn found that **silane** reduces the pentachloride to trichloride, forming silicon tetrachloride.

A. C. Vournasos observed that antimony pentachloride, in boiling toluene soln., reacts like the trichloride towards **potassium.** The action of **metals,** and of **alkali hydroxides and carbonates** on hydrochloric acid soln. of antimony pentachloride, has been previously discussed. L. Wolf studied the reducing action of **mercury** on the pentachloride. The retarding action of the presence of tartaric acid on the precipitation by alkali hydroxides and carbonates was observed by H. Rose, and C. A. Winkler ; of aq. ammonia, and potassium cyanide, by C. A. Winkler ; and of magnesium sulphate and ammonia, by E. Lesser. The retarding action of oxalic acid on the precipitation by water, and aq. ammonia was observed by C. Luckow. The reducing action of **stannous chloride** was discussed by A. Streng, F. Weil, and F. Jean ; F. Kessler found that the soln. is not reduced by **ferrous salts**; and H. N. Warren, that **potassium ferrocyanide** has no action.

Chloroantimonic acids and chloroantimonates.—A number of complex salts formed by the union of metal chlorides with antimony pentachloride have been prepared. R. F. Weinland and co-workers [5] consider them to be salts of a series of hypothetical complex chloroantimonic acids analogous with the hypothetical antimonic acids.

Orthoantimonic acid, H_3SbO_4
Pyroantimonic acid, $H_4Sb_2O_7$
Metantimonic acid, $HSbO_3$

Orthochloroantimonic acid, H_3SbCl_8
Pyrochloroantimonic acid, H_2SbCl_7
Metachloroantimonic acid, $HSbCl_6$

There are also some organic derivatives of pyridine, quinoline, and dimethylaniline which can be referred to more complex acids—e.g. to $H_6Sb_4O_{13}$, or $4H_3SbO_8.6HCl$. A. Rosenheim and W. Stellmann also prepared a quinoline salt, $H_3Sb_2Cl_{13}.3C_9H_7N$. According to P. Pfeifer, this hypothesis of the constitution of these acids means that the chlorine and antimony are all contained in the negative radicle, and that the positive radicle is free from chlorine. He thinks that this does not explain the constitution of the chromium salts—*vide infra*. Neither **orthochloroantimonic acid**, H_3SbCl_8, nor **pyrochloroantimonic acid**, H_2SbCl_7, is known in the free state, although ferric and chromic salts can be referred to the former, and magnesium, and quinoline salts to the latter. R. F. Weinland and H. Schmid prepared **meta-chloroantimonic acid**, $HSbCl_6.4\frac{1}{2}H_2O$, by dissolving antimony trioxide in twice its weight of conc. hydrochloric acid; saturating the soln. with chlorine; concentrating the liquid on the water-bath; saturating the soln. with hydrogen chloride; and allowing the soln. to crystallize over sulphuric acid at a temp. not exceeding 0°. The greenish-yellow, prismatic crystals are very hygroscopic, but gradually effloresce over sulphuric acid. The compound forms clear soln. with water, alcohol, acetone, and acetic acid; the aq. soln. deposits hydrated antimony pentoxide after standing some time, but it remains clear if 10 per cent. of hydrochloric acid is present; nitric acid also retards the precipitation. The soln. in organic solvents remains clear even when boiled. Addition products are formed with ammonia, pyridine, and quinoline. White, four-sided, pyramidal crystals of **diamminometachloroantimonic acid**, $HSbCl_6.2NH_3$, are formed by treating a soln. of the acid with an excess of ammonia. The aq. soln. in water is opalescent and feebly acid; the acid is soluble in alcohol. The salts with pyridine were $HSbCl_6.C_2H_5N$, and $HSbCl_6.2C_5H_5N$; and with quinoline, $HSbCl_6.C_9H_7N$, and $HSbCl_6.2C_9H_7N$. Alkali hydroxides and carbonates precipitate hydrated antimony pentoxide. It is inferred that two ions are produced in aq. soln. because the mol. wt. deduced from the f.p. is about half that required for $HSbCl_6.4\frac{1}{2}H_2O$. A soln. of silver nitrate does not immediately give a precipitate with the acid. This is taken to mean that the ions are $H^·$ and $SbCl_6'$.

P. Fireman heated theoretical proportions of ammonium chloride and antimony pentachloride in a sealed tube at 230°–250° for 12 hrs. and obtained a compact mass of **ammonium metachloroantimonate**, $NH_4Cl.SbCl_5$, which when heated to 350° decomposes: $3NH_4SbCl_6=3SbCl_3+8HCl+NH_4Cl+N_2$. R. F. Weinland and C. Feige obtained the monohydrate from a soln. of the two chlorides in dil. hydrochloric acid evaporated over sulphuric acid. R. F. Weinland and F. Schlegelmilch at first thought the salt was constituted $NH_4SbCl_6.NH_4SbCl_5(OH)$. The rhombic crystals have the axial ratios $a:b:c=0.8909:1:0.7748$. P. P. Déherain also reported red, hexagonal plates of **ammonium octochloroantimonate**, $3NH_4Cl.SbCl_5$, or orthochloroantimonate, $(NH_4)_3SbCl_8$, by the action of hydrochloric acid on antimony triamminopentachloride, and reddish cubes or octahedra of **ammonium enneachloroantimonate**, $4NH_4Cl.SbCl_5$, by the action of hydrochloric acid on the tetramminopentachloride, or from a soln. of ammonium chloride and antimony pentachloride. A. Gutbier and W. Haussmann prepared salts with pyridine, and quinoline; and F. Ephraim and S. Weinberg, salts with methyl- and ethyl-ammonium.

R. F. Weinland and C. Feige obtained rectangular, four-sided, hygroscopic plates of **lithium metachloroantimonate**, $LiSbCl_6.4H_2O$; but did not succeed in making **sodium metachloroantimonate**. They made **potassium metachloroantimonate**, $KSbCl_6.H_2O$, which R. F. Weinland and F. Schlegelmilch represented by the formula $KSbCl_6.KSbCl_5(OH)$. The rhombic crystals, isomorphous with the ammonium salt, were shown by R. F. Weinland and C. Feige to have the axial ratios $a : b : c = 0.8889 : 1 : 0.7794$. The crystals gradually become moist in air ; and effloresce when dried over sulphuric acid or calcium chloride ; and R. F. Weinland and H. Schmid found that they behave towards silver nitrate like the free acid. The rhombic crystals of **rubidium metachloroantimonate**, $RbSbCl_6$, were found by R. F. Weinland and C. Feige to have the axial ratios $a : b : c = 0.6719 : 1 : 0.8136$. The corresponding **cæsium metachloroantimonate**, $CsSbCl_6$, was obtained by C. Setterberg, and H. L. Wells and F. J. Metzger by crystallization from a soln. of the component salts. E. H. Duclaux also made this salt. The salt is decomposed by water.

According to R. F. Weinland and H. Schmid, sky-blue prisms of **copper pentamminometachloroantimonate**, $Cu(SbCl_6)_2$, are obtained from a mixture of the acid and a cupric salt, and not too great an excess of ammonia. The crystals become green by the loss of ammonia, but the blue colour is restored in ammonia. An ultramarine salt with pyridine in place of ammonia was also prepared. Golden-yellow, hexagonal plates of **silver diamminometachloroantimonate**, $AgSbCl_6.2NH_3$, were obtained ; they gradually become white and finally violet ; the salt is decomposed by water. A pyridine salt was also prepared. L. Lindet found that antimony pentachloride dissolves auric chloride without forming **gold chloroantimonate**. R. F. Weinland and C. Feige prepared long, hygroscopic needles of **calcium metachloroantimonate**, $Ca(SbCl_6)_2.9H_2O$, and R. F. Weinland and F. Schlegelmilch previously assigned the formula $SbCl_5.SbCl_4(OH).CaCl_2.9H_2O$ to a similar product. R. F. Weinland and C. Feige obtained no **strontium chloroantimonate**, or **barium chloroantimonate**, but they prepared **beryllium metachloroantimonate**, $Be(SbCl_6)_2.10H_2O$, in small, yellow, hygroscopic needles ; greenish-yellow, hygroscopic triclinic plates of **magnesium pyrochloroantimonate**, $Mg(SbCl_7).10H_2O$, or $[(Cl)Mg(H_4O_2)_5]SbCl_6$, were obtained with the axial ratios $a : b : c = 0.714 : 1 : 2.595$, and $a = 100° 22'$, $\beta = 88° 3'$, and $\gamma = 91° 16'$. R. F. Weinland and H. Schmid found that silver nitrate precipitated from the soln. about one-fourth the chlorine. They also prepared **zinc tetramminometachloroantimonate**, $Zn(SbCl_6)_2.4NH_3$, from an ammoniacal soln. of the acid, and a zinc salt. It appears as a white, crystalline powder ; and a pale yellow crystalline powder of **cadmium heptamminometachloroantimonate**, $Cd(SbCl_6)_2.7NH_3$, has also been reported. No **mercury chloroantimonate** was obtained.

R. F. Weinland and C. Feige prepared **aluminium metachloroantimonate**, $Al(SbCl_6)_3.15H_2O$, in yellowish-green, hygroscopic needles. F. Ephraim and P. Barteczko obtained a yellow **thallous metachloroantimonate**, $TlSbCl_6$, by the action of thallous chloride on fused antimony pentachloride. The product decomposes very rapidly into the violet chlorohypoantimonate (*q.v.*). R. F. Weinland and C. Feige obtained **chromium metachloroantimonate**, $Cr(SbCl_6)_3.13H_2O$, in violet-grey, hygroscopic needles. The cold soln. in hydrochloric acid is bluish-violet, and green when hot. They also prepared **chromium orthochloroantimonate**, $CrSbCl_8.10H_2O$, in green, hygroscopic plates. The soln. in dil. hydrochloric acid is green, and when the soln. is mixed with tartaric acid, silver nitrate precipitates the whole of the chlorine after some time. P. Pfeifer also prepared the chromium salts, and objects to the view that $CrCl_3.SbCl_5.10H_2O$ is a derivative of an ortho-acid. The soln. obtained with each of the chromium salts by removing the antimony with hydrogen sulphide are not the same. In the one case a violet soln., and in the other, a green soln. is formed. These soln. are identical with those of the compounds $[Cr_2(OH_2)_6]Cl_3$ and $[Cr(OH_2)_4Cl_2]Cl,2H_2O$. The salts of R. E. Weinland and C. Feige should be formulated thus : $[SbCl_6]_3[Cr(OH_2)_6],7H_2O$

(violet), and $[SbCl_6][Cr(OH_2)_4Cl_2],6H_2O$ (green). In the violet salt, the chlorine atoms are in the negative radicle, but in the green salt they are divided between both radicles. P. Pfeifer also believed that the majority of the salts containing quinquevalent antimony can be referred to the co-ordination type $M'[SbCl_6]$. P. Pfeifer prepared **chromium dichlorodiethylenediaminoantimony pentachloride**, $[Cr(C_4H_8N_2H_2)Cl_2]SbCl_5$, by the action of the pentachloride on the violet cis-compound $[Cr(C_4H_8N_2H_2)Cl_2]Cl$; and from the trans-compound $[Co(C_4H_8N_2H_2)Cl_2]Cl$, he obtained **cobalt dichlorodiethylenediaminoantimony pentachloride**, $[Co(C_4H_8N_2H_2)Cl_2]SbCl_5$. The antimony was removed by hydrogen sulphide and from the respective filtrates derivatives containing two atoms of chlorine were obtained. This shows that the constitution is that just indicated, and agrees with the assumption that the chromium salt is constituted $[Cr(H_2O)_4Cl_2]SbCl_5$. No **manganese chloroantimonate** was obtained by R. F. Weinland and co-workers. R. F. Weinland and C. Feige prepared **ferric orthochloroantimonate**, $FeSbCl_8.8H_2O$, or $[(Cl_2)Fe(H_4O_2)_4]SbCl_6$, in yellow, hygroscopic, four-sided, tetragonal tablets with the axial ratio $a:c=1:1·0112$. P. Pfeifer represented the iron salts by $Fe[SbCl_8].8H_2O$, and $[SbCl_6][Fe(H_2O)_4Cl_2]4H_2O$. No **cobalt chloroantimonate** was obtained; but R. F. Weinland and H. Schmid obtained a pale green, crystalline powder of **nickel hexamminometachloroantimonate**, $Ni(SbCl_6)_2.6NH_3$.

H. L. Wells [6] described the deeply coloured **cæsium dodecachloroantimonito-antimonate**, $Cs_4Sb\cdots Sb^{IV}Cl_{12}$, and argued that in general complex salts containing the same metal in different states of valency are highly coloured, and he suggests that there is a constant exchange of electrons between the atoms of different valency and that this activity of electrons affects the passage of light, producing colours or opacity.

REFERENCES.

[1] H. Rose, *Pogg. Ann.*, 3. 41, 1824; O. Bosek, *Journ. Chem. Soc.*, 67. 516, 1895; H. L. Wells and F. J. Metzger, *Amer. Chem. Journ.*, 26. 268, 1901; R. F. Weinland and H. Schmid, *Ber.*, 38. 1080, 1905; H. Schmid, *Ueber chlorierte Antimoniate und die Metachlorantimonsäure sowie über Halogendoppelsalze des vierwertigen Antimons*, Wurzburg, 1905; A. H. W. Aten, *Zeit. phys. Chem.*, 68. 41, 1910; W. Biltz and K. Jeep, *Zeit. anorg. Chem.*, 162. 32, 1927; S. A. Weinberg, *Ueber Doppelhalogenide des Antimons mit besonderer Berücksichtigung der tetravalenten Stufe*, Bern, 1910; F. Ephraim and S. A. Weinberg, *Ber.*, 42. 4447, 1909; F. Ephraim and P. Barteczko, *Zeit. anorg. Chem.*, 61. 238, 1909; C. Setterberg, *Oefvers. Akad. Förh. Stockholm*, 6, 1882; *Chem. News*, 46. 249, 1882; E. H. Duclaux, *Anal. Asoc. Quim. Argentina*, 9. 215, 1921.
[2] H. Rose, *Pogg. Ann.*, 3. 443, 1824; 105. 571, 1858; J. von Liebig, *Handwörterbuch der reinen und angewandten Chemie*, Braunschweig, 1. 414, 1837; R. Anschütz and P. N. Evans, *Ber.*, 19. 1994, 1886; *Liebig's Ann.*, 253. 95, 1889.
[3] H. Rose, *Pogg. Ann.*, 3. 443, 1824; A. Haagen, *ib.*, 131. 122, 1867; *Zeit. Chem.*, (2), 4. 97, 1869; F. Kammerer, *Ber.*, 8. 507, 1875; O. Ruff and W. Plato, *ib.*, 37. 679, 1904; R. Anschütz and P. N. Evans, *ib.*, 19. 1994. 1886; *Liebig's Ann.*, 253. 95, 1889; H. Buff, *ib.*, 110. 267, 1859; P. Fireman and E. G. Portner, *Journ. Phys. Chem.*, 8. 500, 1904; A. Schlundt, *ib.*, 5. 503, 1901; M. Nothomb, *Bull. Acad. Belg.*, 551, 1900; H. Becquerel, *Ann. Chim. Phys.*, (5), 12. 34, 1877; L. Bleekrode, *Proc. Roy. Soc.*, 25. 322, 1877; *Wied. Ann.*, 3. 179, 1878; *Phil. Mag.*, (5), 5. 375, 439, 1878; P. Walden, *Zeit. anorg. Chem.*, 25. 219, 1900; *Zeit. phys. Chem.*, 43. 435, 1903; C. R. Crymble, *Proc. Chem. Soc.*, 30. 179, 1909; E. Moles, *Ann. Fis. Quim.*, 12. 214, 1914; S. Sugden, *Journ. Chem. Soc.*, 1173, 1927; *Zeit. phys. Chem.*, 90. 87, 1915; W. Biltz and K. Jeep, *Zeit. anorg. Chem.*, 162. 32, 1927; J. Thomsen, *Ber.*, 14. 40, 1883; H. Braune and W. Tiedje, *Zeit. anorg. Chem.*, 152. 39, 1926; W. Herz, *ib.*, 170. 237, 1928.
[4] H. Friedrich, *Monatsh.*, 14. 519, 1893; H. Daubrawa, *Liebig's Ann.*, 186. 118, 1876; H. Rose, *Pogg. Ann.*, 3. 41, 1824; 24. 165, 1831; 42. 532, 1837; F. Kessler, *ib.*, 95. 204, 1855; R. Weber, *ib.*, 125. 78, 328, 1865; A. Streng, *ib.*, 94. 493, 1855; F. Clausnizer, *Liebig's Ann.*, 196. 295, 1879; A. W. Hofmann, *ib.*, 115. 264, 1861; A. Husemann, *ib.*, 117. 229, 1861; R. Anschütz and P. N. Evans, *ib.*, 239. 293, 1887; 253. 103, 1889; L. Klein, *ib.*, 74. 86, 1850; W. C. Williams, *Ber.*, 9. 1135, 1875; O. Ruff, *Ber.*, 42. 4021, 1909; 48. 2068, 1915; O. Ruff and W. Plato, *ib.*, 34. 1749, 1901; O. Ruff and G. Fischer, *ib.*, 37. 4515, 1904; T. Diehl, *ib.*, 11. 173, 1878; A. Zetter, *ib.*, 11. 164, 1878; V. Merz and W. Weith, *ib.*, 16. 2869, 1883; S. Hilpert and L. Wolf, *ib.*, 46. 2218, 1913; A. Rosenheim and W. Stellmann, *ib.*, 34. 3377; 1901; 35. 1115, 1902; A. Rosenheim, W. Loewenstamm, and L. Singer, *ib.*, 36. 1833, 1903; A. Rosenheim and W. Levy, *ib.*, 37. 3662, 1904; A. Rosenheim and F. Jacobsohn, *Zeit. anorg. Chem.*, 50. 307, 1906; P. Pfeifer, *ib.*, 36. 349, 1903; W. J. van Heteren, *ib.*, 22. 273.

1900; **r. F. Weinland** and **H. Schmid**, *ib.*, **44.** 62, 1905: **K. Steiner.** *Monatsh.*, **36**
825, 1915; **A. Erkert** and **K. Steiner**, *ib.*, **36.** 175, 269, 1915; **T. S. Thomsen**, *Overs.
Danske Selsk.*, **41**, 1911; **A. Jolles**, *Zeit. anªew. Chem.*, **1.** 261, 1882; **G. von Knorre**,
ib., **1.** 155, 1888; **L. Wolf**, *Reduktion von Haloªenphosphor.* Berlin, 1915; **R. Mahn**, *Jena
Zeit.*, **5.** 159, 248, 1869; **H. N. Warren**, *Chem. News.* **37.** 124, 1888; **P. Fireman**,
Amer. Chem. Journ., **30.** 118, 1903; **A. Bertrand** and **E. Finot**, *Bull. Soc. Chim.*, (2), **34.** 201,
1880; **H. Müller**, *Journ. Chem. Soc.*, **15.** 41, 1862; **J. J. Sudborough**, *ib.*, **59.** 661,
1891; **B. Brauner**, *ib.*, **67.** 542, 1895: **L. Lindet**, *Compt. Rend.*, **101.** 1494, 1885; **T. Karantassis**,
ib., **182.** 699, 1391, 1926; **P. P. Déherain**, *ib.*, **52.** 734, 1861; **A. Besson**, *ib.*, **108.** 1012, 1889;
R. Engel, *ib.*, **106.** 1799, 1888; **J. Tarible**, *ib.*, **132.** 204, 1901; *Sur les combinaisons du bromure
de bore avec les composés haloªénés du phosphore, de l'arsenic et de l'antimoine*, Paris, 1899;
E. Moles, *Ann. Fis. Quim.*, **12.** 214. 1914; **J. Persoz**, *Ann. Chim. Phys.*, (2), **44.** 322, 1830;
S. Cloëz, *ib.*, (3), **30.** 374, 1850: **E. Beckmann**, *Zeit. anorg. Chem.*, **51.** 99, 1906; **A. C. Vournasos**,
ib., **81.** 364, 1913; **R. F. Weinland** and **H. Schmid**, *ib.*, **44.** 37, 1905; **W. Biltz** and **H. Krunecke**,
ib., **147.** 171, 1925; **W. Biltz** and **K. Jeep**, *ib.*, **162.** 32, 1927; **H. B. Kosmann**. *Chem. Ztg.*.
11. 1058, 1887; **H. Köhler**, *Ber.*, **13.** 875, 1880; **Lassar Cohn**, *Arbeitsmethoden für organisch
chemische Laboratorien*, Leipzig, **2.** 276, 1923; London, 196, 1895; **A. W. Cronander**, *Oefvers.
Akad. Stockholm*, **27.** 57, 1870; *Ber.*, **6.** 1466, 1873; *Bull. Soc. Chim.*, (2), **19.** 499, 1873; **F. Jean**,
ib., (3), **9.** 256, 1893; **C. von Uslar**, *Zeit. anal. Chem.*, **34.** 406, 1895; **F. Weil**, *ib.*, **17.** 438, 1878:
C. Luckow, *ib.*, **26.** 14, 1887; **C. A. Winkler**, *ib.*, **14.** 156, 1875; **E. Lesser**, *ib.*, **27.** 218, 1888;
Ueber einige Trennungs- und Bestimmungs-Methoden des Arsens, des Antimons und des Zinns,
Berlin, 1886.
⁵ **R. F. Weinland** and **C. Feige**, *Ber.*, **36.** 244, 1903; **F. Ephraim** and **S. Weinberg**, *ib.*, **42.**
4447, 1909; **A. Rosenheim** and **W. Stellmann**, *ib.*, **34.** 3378, 1901; **R. F. Weinland** and
F. Schlegelmilch, *ib.*, **34.** 2633, 1901; **F. Schlegelmilch**, *Ueber Doppelsalze des Antimonpenta-
chlorids*, Leipzig, 1902; **H. Schmid**, *Ueber chlorierte Antimoniate und die Metachlorantimonsäure,
sowie über Halogendoppelsalze des vierwertigen Antimons*, Würzburg, 1905; **R. F. Weinland** and
H. Schmid, *Ber.*, **38.** 1080, 1905; *Zeit. anorg. Chem.*, **44.** 37, 1905; **F. Ephraim** and **P. Barteczko**,
ib., **61.** 238, 1909; **A. Gutbier** and **W. Haussmann**, *ib.*, **128.** 173, 1923; **P. Pfeifer**, *ib.*, **36.** 349,
1903; **P. Pfeifer** and **M. Tapuach**, *ib.*, **49.** 437, 1906; **P. Fireman**, *Journ. Amer. Chem. Soc.*,
26. 741, 1904; **P. P. Déherain**, *Compt. Rend.*, **52.** 734, 1861; **L. Lindet**, *ib.*, **101.** 1494, 1885;
H. L. Wells and **F. J. Metzger**, *Amer. Journ. Science*, (4), **11.** 455, 1901; **C. Setterberg**, *Oefvers.
Akad. Förh. Stockholm*, **6**, 1882; *Chem. News*, **46.** 249, 1882; **E. H. Duclaux**, *Anal. Asoc. Quim.
Argentina*, **9.** 215, 1921.
⁶ **H. L. Wells**, *Amer. Journ. Science*, (5), **3.** 417, 1922.

§ 19. Antimony Bromides

A. J. Balard[1] obtained antimony bromide by the direct union of antimony
(*q.v.*) and bromine. For the preparation of **antimony tribromide,** $SbBr_3$,
G. S. Sérullas introduced into a retort containing bromine, powdered dry antimony
in small portions at a time, agitating the retort after each admixture, and when
combustion had ceased, the bromide was distilled from the excess of antimony.
The neck of the retort was kept hot to prevent its being blocked by the sublimate.
J. Nicklès added an excess of powdered antimony to a cooled soln. of bromine in
twice its weight of carbon disulphide, and evaporated the liquid for crystallization.
J. P. Cooke used a similar process distilling off first the solvent, and then the
tribromide; the product can be purified by recrystallization from carbon disulphide, or by the sublimation in a current of carbon dioxide. **A. Raynaud** covered
a layer of finely-powdered antimony in a flat-bottomed flask with a layer of dry
ether, and slowly added five parts of bromine; the mixture was heated with a reflux
condenser for 3 hrs. Crystals of *antimony ethyl oxypentabromide*, $SbBr_5(C_2H_5)_2O$,
were formed. When the crystals are allowed to stand under a bell-jar for some
weeks, or over sulphuric acid, they lose bromine and ether, and form antimony
tribromide. The crystals lose ether above 55°, forming *antimony pentabromide*,
$SbBr_5$, and this loses bromine at 78°–88°. **R. W. E. MacIvor** obtained the tribromide by heating an intimate mixture of antimony sulphate and dry potassium
bromide: $Sb_2(SO_4)_3 + 6KBr = 3K_2SO_4 + 2SbBr_3$. **G. Oddo** and **U. Giachery**
prepared the tribromide by distillation from a stoichiometrical mixture of arsenic
trioxide, sulphur, and halogen; and **A. C. Vournasos**, by the action of acetic
acid, antimony trioxide, and potassium bromide at 100°.

Analyses by **G. S. Sérullas, R. W. E. MacIvor,** and **J. P. Cooke** agree with the formula $SbBr_3$; and the **vapour density** observed by C. P. Worcester, 12·57, is in agreement with the value 12·43 calculated for SbBr. The colourless, acicular **crystals** obtained by sublimation, and the tabular crystals obtained from the soln. in carbon disulphide were found by J. P. Cooke to belong to the rhombic system and to have the axial ratios $a : b : c = 0.817 : 1 : 0.869$; C. B. Slawson gave 0·7808 : 1 : 1·1645. J. Nicklès also made some observations on the crystals. J. P. Cooke, and W. Herz gave 4·148 for the **specific gravity** at 23°; H. Kopp gave for sp. gr. of the molten tribromide 3·641 at 90°; and R. W. E. MacIvor, 3·473 at 96°. F. Ephraim calculated that a 12·5 per cent. contraction occurs in the formation of the tribromide. J. D. Sullivan discussed its use as a heavy liquid for mineralogical analyses. S. Motylewsky found the drop-weight to be 67 when that of water at 0° is 100. W. Biltz studied the **molecular volume.** I. I. Saslowsky calculated a 1·14 per cent. contraction in the formation of this compound from its elements. F. Schuster calculated for the **internal pressure,** 2013 atm. L. von Pebal and H. Jahn gave 0·0709 for the **specific heat** between 33° and 0°; 0·0613 between 0° and −21°; and 0·0640 between −21° and −80°. G. S. Sérullas, and W. Biltz and K. Jeep found the **melting point** to be 94°; E. K. Rideal, 94·2°; H. Kopp, N. A. Puschin and S. Löwy, and R. W. E. MacIvor, 90°; J. Kendall and co-workers, 96·6°; and J. P. Cooke, and G. B. Bernardis, 93°. The molten compound, added H. Kopp, is brown. S. Tolloczko found the **freezing-point constant** to be 267; and this subject was examined by F. Garelli and V. Bassani. W. Finkelstein found that the lowering of the f.p. of bromine shows that complexes are formed; the soln. is also an electrical conductor—*vide* arsenic tribromide. S. Tolloczko and M. Meyer, and W. Herz gave 9·76 cals. for the latent **heat of fusion** per gram, or 3·51 Cals. per mol. E. K. Rideal obtained for the mol. **heat of vaporization** 3·5 Cals. G. S. Sérullas found the **boiling point** to be 270°; H. Kopp, 275·4°; R. W. E. MacIvor, 283°; J. P. Cooke, and L. Rotinjanz and W. Suchodsky, 280°; and R. Anschütz and H. Weyer, 275° at 760 mm., and 143° at 11 mm. L. Rotinjanz and W. Suchodsky gave 631·5° for the **critical temperature,** and they gave 0·613 for the ratio T_m/T_c; M. Prud'homme, and E. van Aubel found the relation between the m.p., b.p., and the critical temp. to be normal. A. Guntz found the **heat of formation** to be $Sb_{solid} + 3Br_{gas} = SbBr_{3solid} + 76.9$ Cals. For the electrolysis of soln. of the tribromide, *vide supra,* explosive antimony. W. Herz gave 2.03×10^{12} for the **vibration frequency.** W. A. Isbekoff studied the **decomposition voltage** of the tribromide, and W. Finkelstein found that in ethyl acetate soln., and in nitrobenzene soln., the decomposition voltage is 0·63 volt.

When antimony tribromide is freshly prepared, J. P. Cooke found it to be colourless. It is hygroscopic, and G. S. Sérullas observed that it is decomposed by **water** with the separation of oxybromide; but, added J. P. Cooke, the oxybromide is not precipitated if tartaric acid be present. When the carbon disulphide soln. is exposed to **air** and light, an oxybromide is formed (*q.v.*). W. Biltz and K. Jeep measured the f.p. curve of mixtures of bromine and antimony tribromide. The results are summarized in Fig. 44. P. Walden found the tribromide is soluble in **sulphur monochloride.** C. Löwig found that the tribromide is decomposed by **sulphuric acid.** G. Gore found that antimony bromide is soluble in liquid **ammonia.** V. Thomas observed no reaction when **nitric oxide** is passed into a chloroform soln. of the tribromide, but with **nitrogen peroxide,** white antimony nitratobispentoxide, $2Sb_2O_5.N_2O_5$, is formed. C. Löwig showed that **nitric acid** has no action in the cold, but when heated bromine is evolved, and antimony nitrate is formed. W. Ramsay and R. W. E. MacIvor obtained antimony phosphide (*q.v.*) by the action of **phosphorus** on a chloroform soln. of the tribromide. P. Walden showed that the tribromide is freely soluble in **phosphorus trichloride and tribromide.** J. W. Retgers

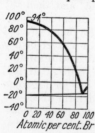

FIG. 44.—Freezing-point Curves of the System : $SbBr_3$–Br_2.

found thao antimony tribromide is dissolved by a warm soln. of **arsenic tribromide,** forming a mixture which melts at 47° and has a sp. gr. 3·685. N. A. Puschin and S. Löwy's f.p. curve for mixtures of antimony and arsenic tribromides, Fig. 45, shows that no compound is formed—only a series of solid soln. J. Tarible observed no reaction when antimony tribromide dissolves in **boron tribromide.** J. P. Cooke found that hot absolute **alcohol** converts the tribromide into the oxybromide. According to J. Nicklès, the tribromide is soluble in **carbon disulphide;** and with **ether,** the soln. separates into two layers, the lower viscid layer is a compound with ether. F. Oberhauser studied the reaction with **cyanogen bromide.** A. Naumann found the tribromide is soluble in **acetone.** B. N. Menschutkin measured the solubility of the tribromide in a number of organic liquids. Expressing the results in mols of tribromide per 100 mols of solvent, he found for **benzene :**

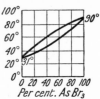

FIG. 45. — Freezing-point Curve of Mixtures of Antimony and Arsenic Tribromides.

	5·6°	25°	45°	65°	85°	94°
SbBr₃ •	0	4·3	8·6	17·1	84·9	100

chlorobenzene :

	−45·2	−30°	0°	30°	60°	94°
SbBr₃ •	0	3·2	7·2	15·4	37·6	100

bromobenzene :

	−31°	−15°	5°	35°	65°	94°
SbBr₃ •	0	6·9	13·4	22·7	52·6	100

iodobenzene :

	−28·6°	−20°	0°	40°	70°	94°
SbBr₃ •	0	13·5	4·0	43·7	67·0	100

paradichlorobenzene :

	54·5°	48·5°	55°	75°	90°	94°
SbBr₃ •	0	12·8	18·7	45·6	91·9	100

paradibromobenzene :

	88°	65°	70°	80°	90°	94
SbBr₃ •	0	52·0	59·1	74·4	91·8	100

nitrobenzene :

	6°	−17°	5°	25°	75°	94°
SbBr₃ •	0	(31·9)	35·3	42·8	74·9	100

metadinitrobenzene :

	90°	60°	47·5°	60°	75°	94°
SbBr₃ •	0	44·3	54·4	62·2	76·0	100

toluene :

	−93°	−30°	−1°	34°	60°	94°
SbBr₃ •	0	5·2	22·4	(54·0)	62·3	100

ethylbenzene :

	−93°	−20°	0°	20°	50°	94°
SbBr₃ •	0	2·3	6·4	19·5	51·6	100

propylbenzene :

	−80°	−30°	0°	30°	60°	94°
SbBr₃ •	0·4	5·5	25·8	34·1	51·5	100

isoamylbenzene :

	−70°	−20°	0°	30°	60°	94°
SbBr₃ •	1·9	13·4	18·2	25·9	43·3	100

N. A. Puschin and S. Löwy measured the f.p. curves of binary mixtures of antimony tribromide with resorcin, phenol, aniline chloride, α-naphthol, and ethyl-urethane. E. Kordes discussed the eutectic with triphenylmethane. J. A. Hayes prepared a compound with **pyridine.** Antimony tribromide reacts with a number of other **organic compounds.** Thus, B. N. Menschutkin obtained compounds with the chlorotoluenes, nitrotoluenes, benzaldehyde, benzonitrile, substituted benzenes, xylenes, toluenes, aniline, etc. E. Vanstone studied the action of the tribromide on a number of aromatic compounds ; and F. Ephraim and S. Weinberg, on methylamine. For the action of antimony tribromide on organic halides, *vide infra,* antimony triiodide. N. S. Kurnakoff studied the viscosity and f.p. of mixtures of antimony tribromide and triphenylmethane, benzophenone, and acetophenone. W. A. Isbekoff found that the tribromide is soluble in **aluminium bromide.**

A number of compounds with other bromides have been prepared ; and R. W. Atkinson made some mixed halides—*vide infra.* R. M. Caven prepared pale yellow hexagonal plates of **ammonium hexadecabromotriantimonite,** $7NH_4Br.3SbBr_3$, by adding an excess of glacial acetic acid to a conc. aq. soln. of the two halides and the halogen acid. He also obtained **ammonium enneabromodiantimonite,** $3NH_4Br.2SbBr_3$, in yellow prisms. C. H. Herty prepared yellow rhombic crystals with the composition : $23KBr.10SbBr_3.27H_2O$; which H. J. Wheeler would represent $7KBr.3SbBr_3.nH_2O$—**potassium hexadecabromo-triantimonite.** The salt was obtained by evaporating at 35° a soln. containing a mol of antimony tribromide and 3 mols of potassium bromide. F. Ephraim regarded it as $2KBr.SbBr_3$. H. J. Wheeler prepared yellow plates or prisms of **rubidium enneabromodiantimonite,** $3RbBr.2SbBr_3$, in a similar way. The hexagonal crystals have the axial ratio $a : c = 1 : 1.207$. By using a soln. with over six molecular proportions of the alkali bromide in hydrobromic acid, he obtained yellow, six-sided, pseudohexagonal crystals of **rubidium hexadecabromotriantimonite,** $7RbBr.3SbBr_3$, or $23RbBr.10SbBr_3$. F. Ephraim regarded it as $2RbBr.SbBr_3$. R. Benedikt obtained colourless plates of **calcium penta-bromoantimonite,** $CaBr_2.SbBr_3.8H_2O$. by the method used for the chloro-salt. The compound dissociates at ordinary temp. ; similarly also with **magnesium pentabromoantimonite,** $MgBr_2.SbBr_3.8H_2O$. J. Kendall and co-workers observed that there is evidence of the formation of **aluminium hexabromoantimonite,** $AlBr_3.SbBr_3$, on the f.p. curve of mixtures of the components, Fig. 46. R. F. Weinland and C. Feige[2] obtained **vanadium heptabromoantimonite,** $SbBr_3.VBr_4.7H_2O$, from a soln. of the component salts. The black, pointed, hygroscopic prisms are decomposed by water.

FIG. 46.—Freezing-point Curve of the Mixtures: $AlBr_3$–$SbBr_3$.

A compound—**antimony tetrabromide,** $SbBr_4$—corresponding with the tetrachloride has not been prepared, but R. F. Weinland and C. Feige obtained **rubidium hexabromohypoantimonate,** $2RbBr.SbBr_4$, from a soln. of 4 mols of antimony tribromide and one mol of rubidium bromide in conc. hydrobromic acid. The small, black, six-sided plates lose bromine slowly. H. L. Wells and F. J. Metzger prepared **cæsium hexabromohypoantimonate,** $2CsBr.SbBr_4$, by a method similar to that employed for the corresponding chloride. F. Ephraim and S. Weinberg prepared **ammonium hexabromohypoantimonate,** $(NH_4)_2SbBr_6$, by adding the requisite quantity of bromine, followed by ammonium bromide, to a soln. of antimony tribromide in conc. hydrobromic acid ; it forms black octahedra, stable in air. The free acid was obtained in a state of doubtful purity.

M. Berthelot and P. Petit[3] passed stibine into a soln. of potassium bromide containing free bromine, and acidified with hydrochloric acid ; under these conditions it was stated that **antimony pentabromide,** $SbBr_5$, is formed : $SbH_3 + 4Br_2 = SbBr_5 + 3HBr$; they also said that the pentabromide is formed when antimony tribromide is dissolved in a hydrochloric acid soln. of potassium bromide. The pentabromide has not been isolated ; but it exists in soln. E. Beckmann showed that the mol. wt. in boiling bromine is normal. As in the case of the pentachloride, a number of complex salts, and **bromoantimonic acids** have been prepared by R. F. Weinland and C. Feige. Of these acids, only the hydrated **metabromoantimonic acid**, $HSbBr_6.3H_2O$, is known in the free state. It crystallizes readily from a conc. hydrobromic acid soln. of bromine and antimony tribromide confined in vacuo over sulphuric acid. The black, six-sided, hydroscopic plates rapidly lose bromine when exposed to air, but are more stable in an atm. of bromine. The acid is decomposed by water.

A series of metabromoantimonates as well as a number of derivatives of more complex acids have been prepared. The meta-salts were prepared by R. F. Weinland and C. Feige by dissolving the metal bromide in a soln. of antimony tribromide in fuming hydrobromic acid of sp. gr. 1·49, and adding a large excess of bromine. The soln. is then evaporated over sulphuric acid. Six-sided, black crystals of **ammonium metabromoantimonate**, $NH_4SbBr_6.H_2O$, were so obtained ; and also black, square, hygroscopic tablets of **lithium metabromoantimonate**, $LiSbBr_6.4H_2O$; and stout, six-sided, black tablets of **potassium metabromoantimonate**, $KSbBr_6H_2O$. When cæsium bromide is treated in a similar way, **cæsium tridecabromodiantimonate**, $3CsBr.2SbBr_5.2H_2O$, was obtained as a black, microcrystalline powder consisting of six-sided, red, transparent plates, which rapidly lose bromine on exposure to air. In a similar way, it was found that **beryllium enneadecabromotriantimonate**, $2BeBr_2.3SbBr_5.18H_2O$, furnishes black, glistening prisms which are hygroscopic and very unstable ; **aluminium henitricontabromopentantimonate**, $2AlBr_3.5SbBr_5.24H_2O$, in black, glistening, stout prisms which are less hygroscopic than the beryllium salt ; **ferric metabromoantimonate**, $Fe(SbBr_6)_3.14H_2O$, forms black, irregular, six-sided tablets which are very hygroscopic ; and **nickel metabromoantimonate**, $Ni(SbBr_6)_2.12H_2O$, forms black, glistening, irregular, six-sided tablets. Some complexes of metabromoantimonic acid and pyridine have been made by A. Rosenheim and W. Stellmann ; and A. Raynaud obtained a compound with ether, $SbBr_5.(C_2H_5)_2O$.

REFERENCES.

[1] E. K. Rideal, *Phil. Mag.*, (6), **42**. 156, 1921 ; A. J. Balard, *Ann. Chim. Phys.*, (2), **32**. 337, 1826 ; G. S. Sérullas, *ib.*, (2), **38**. 322, 1828 ; *Journ. Pharm. Chim.*, (2), **14**. 19, 1828 ; J. Nicklès, *ib.*, (3), **41**. 145, 1862 ; *Compt. Rend.*, **52**. 396, 1861 ; J. Tarible, *ib.*, **132**. 204, 1901 ; *Sur les combinaisons du bromure de bore avec les composés halogénés du phosphore, de l'arsenic et de l'antimoine*, Paris, 1899 ; C. P. Worcester, *Proc. Amer. Acad.*, **18**. 61, 1883 ; J. P. Cooke, *ib.*, **13**. 1, 72, 1877 ; *Amer. Journ. Science*, (3), **19**. 469, 1880 ; *Chem. News*, **44**. 221, 233, 245, 255, 1880 ; A. Raynaud, *Bull. Soc. Chim.*, (4), **27**. 411, 1920 ; A. Guntz, *Compt. Rend.*, **101**. 161, 1885 ; L. Lindet, *ib.*, **101**. 1494, 1885 ; V. Thomas, *ib.*, **120**. 1115, 1895 ; A. C. Vournasos, *ib.*, **166**. 526, 1918 ; R. Anschütz and H. Weyer, *Liebig's Ann.*, **261**. 297, 1891 ; H. Kopp, *ib.*, **95**. 352, 1855 ; R. W. Atkinson, *Journ. Chem. Soc.*, **43**. 289, 1883 ; E. Vanstone, *ib.*, **105**. 1491, 1914 ; L. von Pebal and H. Jahn, *Wied. Ann.*, **27**. 584, 1886 ; J. D. Sullivan, *Heavy Liquids for Mineralogical Analyses*, Washington, 1927 ; G. Oddo and U. Giachery, *Gazz. Chim. Ital.*, **53**. i, 56, 1923 ; S. Tolloczko, *Bull. Acad. Cracovie*, 1, 1901 ; S. Tolloczko and M. Meyer, *Kosmos*, **35**. 641, 1910 ; *Radziszewsky's Festband*, 641, 1910 ; F. Garelli and V. Bassani, *Atti Accad. Lincei*, (5), **10**. i, 255, 1901 ; G. B. Bernardis, *ib.*, (5), **21**. ii, 438, 1912 ; J. W. Retgers, *Zeit. phys. Chem.*, **11**. 339, 1893 ; L. Rotinjanz and W. Suchodsky, *ib.*, **87**. 635, 1914 ; C. Löwig, *Repert. Pharm.*, **29**. 266, 1829 ; *Das Brom und seine chemischen Verhältnisse*, Heidelberg, 1829 ; F. Ephraim, *Helvetica Chim. Acta*, **7**. 298, 1924 ; J. A. Hayes, *Journ. Amer. Chem. Soc.*, **24**. 360, 1902 ; C. B. Slawson, *Amer. Min.*, **7**. 173, 1922 ; E. Cohen and T. Strengers, *Chem. Weekbl.*, **2**. 251, 1905 ; E. van Aubel, *Bull. Acad. Belg.*, (5), **7**. 469, 1921 ; R. W. E. MacIvor, *Chem. News*, **29**. 179, 1874 ; W. Ramsay and R. W. E. MacIvor, *Ber.*, **6**. 1362, 1873 ; A. Naumann, *ib.*, **37**. 4328, 1904 ; B. N. Menschutkin, *Journ. Russ. Phys. Chem. Soc.*, **43**. 1275, 1303, 1329, 1785, 1805, 1911 ; **44**. 1108, 1929, 1939, 1912 ; **45**. 1710, 1913 ; **46**. 259, 1914 ; *Journ. Chim. Phys.*, **10**. 598, 612, 1912 ; *Izvista Polyt. St. Petersburg*, **13**. 277, 411, 1910 ; R. M. Caven, *Proc. Chem. Soc.*, **21**. 187, 1905 ; C. H. Herty, *Amer. Chem. Journ.*, **16**. 490, 1894 ; H. J. Wheeler, *Amer. Journ. Science*, (3), **46**. 269, 1893 ; R. Benedikt, *Proc. Amer. Acad.*, **30**. 9, 212, 1894 ; *Zeit. anorg. Chem.*, **8**. 234, 1894 ; W. Biltz and K. Jeep, *ib.*, **162**. 32, 1917 ; F. Ephraim and S. Weinberg, *Ber.*, **42**. 4447, 1909 ; F. Ephraim, *ib.*, **36**. 1815, 1903 ; G. Gore, *Proc. Roy. Soc.*, **20**. 441, 1872 ; **21**. 140, 1873 ; P. Walden, *Zeit. anorg. Chem.*, **25**. 211, 1900 ; W. A. Isbekoff,

Zeit. phys. Chem., **116**. 304, 1925 : Zeit. anorg. Chem., **84**. 27, 1913 ; S. Motylewsky, ib., **38**. 410, 1904 ; F. Schuster, ib., **146**. 299, 1925 ; W. Biltz, ib., **115**. 241, 1921 ; N. S. Kurnakoff, ib., **135**. 81, 1924 ; I. I. Saslowsky, ib., **146**. 315, 1925 ; N. A. Puschin and S. Löwy, ib., **150**. 167, 1926 ; W. Finkelstein, ib., **105**. 10, 1923 : **115**. 303, 1925 ; J. Kendall, E. D. Crittenden, and H. E. Miller, Journ. Amer. Chem. Soc., **45**. 963, 1923 ; M. Prud'homme, Journ. Chim. Phys., **21**. 243, 1924 ; F. Oberhauser, Ber., **60**. B, 1434, 1927 ; E. Kordes, Zeit. anorg. Chem., **167**. 97, 1927 ; W. Herz, ib., **170**. 237, 1928.
  [2] R. F. Weinland and C. Feige, Ber., **36**. 244, 1903 ; H. L. Wells and F. J. Metzger, Amer. Chem. Journ., **26**. 268, 1901 ; F. Ephraim and S. Weinberg, Ber., **42**. 4447, 1909.
  [3] M. Berthelot and P. Petit, Ann. Chim. Phys., (6), **18**. 67, 1889 ; Compt. Rend., **108**. 546, 1889 ; E. Beckmann, Zeit. phys. Chem., **46**. 853, 1903 ; R. F. Weinland and C. Feige, Ber., **36**. 256, 1903 ; A. Rosenheim and W. Stellmann, ib., **34**. 3377, 1901 ; A. Raynaud, Bull. Soc. Chim., (4), **27**. 411, 1920.

§ 20. The Antimony Iodides

R. Brandes [1] found that iodine unites with antimony at ordinary temp., forming **antimony triiodide** SbI_3 ; and if large quantities are used, an explosion may occur. When powdered antimony is added to iodine, the first portions render the iodine fluid ; after that the antimony is gradually added until the liquid is saturated. The product is heated in a retort so that the triiodide can be separated from the excess of antimony by distillation. This mode of preparation was also employed by G. S. Sérullas, and J. B. Berthemot. F. M. Jäger and H. J. Doornbosch showed

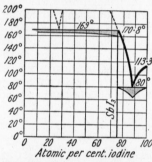

that the f.p. curves of iodine and antimony, Fig. 47, show that the triiodide is the only compound formed. There is no evidence of antimony tetraiodide, SbI_4, or of the pentaiodide. Antimony triiodide, Fig. 47, melts sharply at 170·8° ; it is not appreciably miscible with antimony, but forms two liquid layers with the horizontal branch at 169°. The eutectic with iodine occurs at 80° with 88·2 atm. per cent. of iodine. E. Quercigh made similar observations ; the eutectic at 80° is near the composition of that required for the pentaiodide.

FIG. 47.—Freezing-point Curves of Antimony and Iodine.

Antimony triiodide was prepared by J. Nicklès by warming antimony with a conc. soln. of iodine in carbon disulphide until the colour due to the iodine has vanished ; on evaporating the greyish-yellow liquid, the iodide separates out in red plates. A. Perrier and M. le Brument triturated a mixture of alcohol and antimony with twice its weight of iodine, and sublimed the product ; E. R. Schneider heated 6 gram-atoms of iodine with a mol of antimony trisulphide—the product is contaminated with some sulphoiodide ; R. W. E. MacIvor made the triiodide by heating a mixture of potassium iodide and antimony sulphate ; A. Naumann, by adding potassium iodide to a soln. of antimony trichloride in acetone ; A. C. Vournasos, by heating to 100° a mixture of antimony trioxide and potassium bromide with an excess of acetic acid ; and G. Oddo and U. Giachery, by heating a stoichiometrical mixture of antimony trioxide and sulphur with the halogen. J. P. Cooke purified the triiodide by recrystallization from carbon disulphide ; or better, by sublimation at 180°–200° in a current of carbon dioxide.

Analyses of the salt by R. Brandes, E. R. Schneider, and J. P. Cooke are in agreement with the formula SbI_3. The **vapour density,** 17·59, observed by C. P. Worcester is in agreement with the value 17·29 calculated for SbI_3. P. Walden calculated the mol. wt. from the effect on the f.p. of arsenic tribromide, and obtained three times the normal value ; and E. Beckmann found the value to be abnormal when the triiodide is dissolved in boiling arsenic trichloride, phosphorus trichloride, and in antimony trichloride. R. W. E. MacIvor observed that when a bar of the melted triiodide is cast in a mould, it forms a dull, reddish, semi-metallic mass with a radiated fracture and bright metallic lustre. According to J. P. Cooke, the **crystals** of antimony triiodide are trimorphous. (i) The ordinary form of the salt is *trigonal*. The warm sat. soln. in carbon disulphide deposits it as tabular, ruby-red or reddish-brown hexagonal plates ; and it is also formed in thin plates when the salt is sublimed above 114°. G. B. Negri's measurements did not agree with those of J. P. Cooke. The sp. gr. is 4·848 at 24°. The birefringence is very strong and negative. (ii) The *rhombic* form of the triiodide appears in greenish-yellow plates with angles 60° and 80°. It is obtained by sub-liming the salt at about 100°. It is transformed into the trigonal form at 114°, not at 112°. The rhombic crystals are isomorphous with those of antimony tri-bromide and trichloride. The birefringence is negative. The optic axial angle $2E=36°$. (iii) The *monoclinic* form of the triiodide is produced by crystallization from soln. containing free iodine, while most of the crystals obtained by the evapora-tion of the carbon disulphide soln. are trigonal, a small proportion are monoclinic. The monoclinic prisms or plates are greenish-yellow or lemon-yellow. The dark brown crystals contain free iodine. The axial ratios are $a : b : c=1·6408 : 1 : 0·6682$, and $\beta=109°\ 44'$. The (001)-cleavage is distinct. The sp. gr. is 4·768 at 22°. The monoclinic crystals slowly pass into the trigonal form at 125° ; and crystals con-taminated with iodine pass into the trigonal form on the water-bath. P. W. Bridg-man examined the effect of press. up to 12,000 kgrms. per sq. cm. and at 20° to 12°, but observed no abrupt change in vol. corresponding with a transition point. E. Cohen and H. R. Bruins were likewise unable to detect any signs of a transition temp. at 114°, and said that the effect was *ganz zufällige*. Antimony triiodide prepared by sublimation is said to be a metastable system which may remain unchanged for long periods of time, but the change to the stable system is greatly hastened by traces of the solvent as well as by ether, ethyl acetate, etc.

A. C. Vournasos alleged that in addition to the three forms of antimony triiodide re-ported by J. P. Cooke, yet a fourth form is obtained by cooling a hot sat. soln. of the red iodide in glycerol. It is thus obtained as an amorphous, yellow powder, m.p. 172°, at which temp. it steadily passes into the red variety, forming hexagonal crystals. This metastable, amorphous form may also be obtained from the red form by warming it on a water-bath with fifteen times its weight of acetic acid and a little potassium acetate. The soln. on cooling deposits the yellow amorphous iodide. It may also be prepared from antimony trioxide and potassium iodide by heating them at 100° with an excess of anhydrous acetic acid.

The stable form of antimony triiodide being the trigonal crystals, the following properties, unless otherwise stated, refer to that variety. C. H. D. Bödeker gave 5·01 for the **specific gravity** at ordinary temp., and H. G. F. Schröder, 4·676 at ordinary temp. referred to water at 0°. J. P. Cooke gave 4·848 at 24° for the trigonal, and 4·768 at 22° for the monoclinic crystals. F. Ephraim calculated that a 13·1 per cent. contraction occurs in the formation of the triiodide. W. Biltz studied the mol. vol. S. Motylewsky found the drop-weight to be 68 when that of water at 0° is 100. G. S. Sérullas said that the crystals melt to a garnet-red liquid, and J. P. Cooke gave 167° for the **melting point ;** R. W. E. MacIvor, 164·4° ; E. Quercigh, and G. B. Bernardis, 165° ; and F. M. Jäger and H. J. Doornbosch, 170·8°, Fig. 41. P. W. Bridgman found the m.p. to be 163° at atm. press., and 200·8° at a press. of 1160 kgrms. per sq. cm., and the change of vol. was 0·0240 c.c. per gram. The crystals of the triiodide were found by J. B. Berthemot to volatilize a little above the m.p. ; and J. P. Cooke found that the volatilization is perceptible at 100°. Volatilization is rapid and complete at 180°–200° in a current of carbon dioxide. T. Carnelley and W. C. Williams gave 414° to 427° for the **boiling point ;** J. P. Cooke, between 400·4° and 400·9° at 758·5° ; and L. Rotinjanz and W. Suchodsky, 401°. The vapour is orange-red, and, according to R. W. E. Mac-Ivor, the violet tinge is due to a trace of iodine. L. Rotinjanz and W. Suchodsky gave 828° for the **critical temperature,** and they found the ratio T_m/T_c to be quite normal 0·614. A. Guntz gave for the **heat of formation :** $Sb_{solid}+3I_{gas}=SbI_{3solid}$ $+45·4$ Cals. The mol. **electrical conductivity,** μ, in arsenic tribromide was found by P. Walden to be 0·104 for a mol in 100 litres of solvent at 33°. J. W. Williams and R. J. Allgeier studied the dielectric constant of benzene soln. of antimony iodide. Antimony triiodide was found by R. W. E. MacIvor to suffer no change when distilled in a current of **hydrogen.** J. P. Cooke found that all three modifications rapidly become opaque when exposed to **air** at ordinary temp. owing to the formation of a film of oxyiodide and the escape of iodine. R. W. E. MacIvor found that when the vapour comes in contact with air, an oxyiodide is immediately formed and violet iodine-vapour appears. If the vapour be in contact with **oxygen,** R. W. E. MacIvor said that it burns, forming antimony trioxide. J. P. Cooke found that soln. of the salt in carbon disulphide also furnish the oxyiodide (*q.v.*) when exposed to air and light. G. S. Sérullas observed that **water** decomposes the triiodide with the separation of yellow oxyiodide, and the formation of a red soln. of antimony triiodide in hydriodic acid. L. A. Buchner also studied the action of water on the triiodide. E. Beckmann found that liquid **chlorine** forms an insoluble product ; and R. W. E. MacIvor, that gaseous chlorine forms antimony triiodide and iodine chloride ; with molten **iodine monochloride,** antimony trichloride and free iodine are produced ; and with **bromine,** antimony tribromide and bromine chloride are formed. R. Brandes, and R. W. E. MacIvor showed that cold, fuming **hydrochloric acid** forms a yellow liquid from which water precipitates white oxyiodide ; the boiling conc. acid soon converts all the triiodide into trichloride. R. W. E. MacIvor found **hydriodic acid** dissolves the triiodide, forming a yellow liquid. V. Auger mixed carbon disulphide soln. of antimony triiodide and **sulphur** and obtained yellow prisms of **antimony tetracosisulphoiodide,** $SbI_3.3S_8$, with the m.p. 117°. J. P. Cooke said that when the carbon disulphide soln. is exposed to air and light, an oxyiodide is formed—*vide infra*. L. Ouvrard found that **hydrogen sulphide** converts the triiodide into a sulphoiodide. P. Walden said that the triiodide is soluble in **sulphur monochloride,** in **thionyl chloride,** and in **sulphuryl chloride.** R. W. E. MacIvor said that contrary to the statement of R. Brandes, cold **sulphuric acid**—$H_2SO_4.12H_2O$—has little or no action on antimony triiodide, but the application of a gentle heat produces iodine and antimony sulphate.

R. Brandes found that aq. **ammonia** converts the triiodide into a yellowish-white powder. G. Gore found that the triiodide reacts with liquid ammonia. V. Thomas showed that **nitrogen peroxide** acts on an ethereal soln. of the triiodide forming antimony nitratobispentoxide. According to R. W. E. MacIvor, **nitric acid** of sp. gr. 1·4–1·5 immediately decomposes the triiodide producing nitrous vapours, free iodine, and antimony oxide ; while nitric acid of sp. gr. 1·2 does not act at first, but in a short time heat is developed and the triiodide is decomposed. E. Beckmann found the triiodide to be soluble in **phosphorus trichloride,** and P. Walden, in **phosphorus tribromide** as well as the trichloride ; in **phosphoryl**

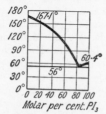

FIG. 48.—Freezing-point Curves of Mixtures SbI_3–PI_3.

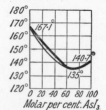

FIG. 49.—Freezing-point Curves of Mixtures SbI_3–AsI_3.

chloride ; and in **arsenic trichloride.** T. Karantassis studied the reaction with **phosphorus pentachloride** (*q.v.*). Antimony triiodide and **phosphorus triiodide** were found by F. M. Jäger and H. J. Doornbosch to furnish the f.p. curve, Fig. 48. The fusion curve is the typical V-shape with a eutectic at 56° ; the f.p. curve with **arsenic triiodide,** Fig. 49, shows that a continuous series of solid soln. is formed

with the solidus and liquidus curves melting at a minimum temp. of about 135°.
E. Quercigh also found the triiodides of arsenic and antimony give a similar curve
with a minimum at 128°. His study of the ternary system AsI_3–SbI_3–I_2 is
summarized in Fig. 50. J. W. Retgers found that antimony triiodide can
dissolve much arsenic triiodide, and the m.p. falls
31° while the sp. gr. of the mixture is 3·801 ; and
by mixing this product with a soln. of arsenic
triiodide in methylene iodide, a heavy liquid of sp.
gr. 3·7 at 20° can be prepared. P. Walden, and
J. W. Retgers found that antimony triiodide also
dissolves in warm **arsenic tribromide**, forming a
dark wine-red liquid which soon becomes opaque,
the sp. gr. of the sat. soln. is 3·72 at 40° ; it
solidifies at 37°. A. M. Wasiléeff studied the
eutectic phenomenon with arsenic and antimony
triiodides.

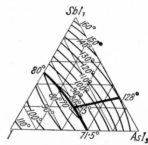

FIG. 50. — Freezing-point
Curves of the Ternary
System : AsI_3–SbI_3–I_2.

J. Tarible found that antimony triiodide dissolves in **boron tribromide**. R. W. E. MacIvor
found that antimony triiodide is not decomposed
when vaporized in **carbon dioxide**. A. C. Vournasos obtained some complex iodo-
cyanides by heating antimony triiodide with **mercuric or cuprous cyanide** in dry
xylene—e.g. $Hg[SbI_3Cy_2]$; $Hg_3[Sb_2I_6Cy_6]$; and $Cu_6[Sb_2I_6Cy_6]$. E. R. Schneider,
and J. P. Cooke found that antimony triiodide is slightly soluble in cold **carbon disulphide**, but freely soluble at a higher temp. The soln. is yellow. J. W. Retgers
found that 100 parts of **methylene iodide** dissolve 11·3 parts of antimony triiodide
at 12°, forming a soln. of sp. gr. 3·453 at 12° ; more is dissolved at a higher temp.,
and the salt crystallizes out again on cooling. The colour of the soln. is very dark
red. R. W. E. MacIvor said that antimony triiodide is nearly insoluble in **chloroform**, and that it does not dissolve in **carbon tetrachloride** or in **turpentine**.
J. P. Cooke found it to be insoluble in **petroleum** ; and R. W. E. MacIvor obtained
a yellow soln. with **benzene**, J. W. Retgers, a red one. On cooling, the boiling soln.
of the triiodide in benzene deposits red, tabular crystals of triiodide similar to those
deposited from the carbon disulphide soln. A. Naumann observed that the
triiodide is soluble in **acetone**. According to R. W. E. MacIvor, when the
triiodide is heated with **carbon hexachloride** to 250°, the triiodide dissolves
in the molten hexachloride, forming a dark brown soln., and on cooling a
lemon-yellow mass is first formed which, on further cooling, quickly changes
to a red crystalline mass—no carbon hexiodide is formed. According to
J. Nicklès, antimony triiodide is insoluble in **alcohol**, even when heated in
a sealed tube at 100° there is no change ; similar results were obtained with
ether. G. S. Sérullas observed that 80 per cent. alcohol partially hydrolyzes the
triiodide, forming an oxyiodide. According to J. P. Cooke, and R. W. E. MacIvor,
absolute ethyl alcohol partially dissolves the triiodide, forming a brown soln. but
the greater portion is converted into the yellow oxyiodide ; R. W. E. MacIvor
also found that anhydrous ether also partially decomposes the triiodide, forming a
yellow oxyiodide, and a dark brown soln. containing undecomposed triiodide.
J. P. Cooke said that a soln. of **tartaric acid** dissolves the triiodide without the
separation of oxyiodide. A number of compounds of antimony triiodide with
organic compounds have been prepared : F. Ephraim and S. Weinberg studied the
formation of compounds with alkylamines ; G. J. Burrows and E. E. Turner,
compounds with the ternary and halogenoarsines. R. Brix, and B. Köhnlein
showed that in the interchange of halogen with the antimony trihalides and organic
halides, antimony unites by preference with iodine rather than with bromine or
chlorine, and with bromine rather than with chlorine. A. M. Wasilieff studied
the systems : antimony trichloride with α-nitronaphthalene. and with β-chloro-
naphthalene.

J. Nicklès, and E. R. Schneider found that antimony triiodide is completely decomposed by a soln. of an **alkali hydroxide** with the separation of antimony trioxide ; similarly also with soln. of an **alkali carbonate.** The triiodide forms double salts with the **metal iodides ;** and they were prepared by L. Schäffer, and A. Welkow, by dissolving the triiodide in a conc. soln. of the metal iodide, and evaporating the liquid at ordinary temp. ; and by J. Nicklès, by treating the metal with a soln. of iodine in alcohol. The black crystals are decomposed by heat with the escape of antimony triiodide ; water decomposes the salts with the separation of oxyiodide, but water sat. with the metal iodide does not decompose the salts ; conc. sulphuric acid separates the iodine ; carbon disulphide extracts the antimony triiodide from the salts ; acetic, and hydrochloric acids dissolve the salts, forming yellow soln.—if tartaric acid be present, the soln. is colourless. L. Schäffer reported scarlet-red, four-sided prisms of *ammonium pentadecaiododotetrantimonite*, $3NH_4I.4SbI_3.9H_2O$, which are possibly the same as the red, tetragonal prisms of **ammonium metaiodoantimonite**, $NH_4SbI_4.2H_2O$, prepared by J. Nicklès, by the action of iodine on antimony in a sat. soln. of ammonium chloride ; R. M. Caven reported rectangular, four-sided, dark brown plates of **ammonium enneaiodo-diantimonite**, $3NH_4I.2SbI_3.3H_2O$, and L. Schäffer obtained a similar salt in red, tetragonal plates easily soluble in alcohol. L. Schäffer also obtained black, four-sided prisms of **ammonium heptaiodoantimonite**, $4NH_4I.SbI_3.3H_2O$; pale orange-red, four-sided prisms of **sodium enneaiodododiantimonite**, $3NaI.2SbI_3.12H_2O$; dark brown, four-sided plates of **potassium enneaiodododiantimonite**, $3KI.2SbI_3.3H_2O$; and L. Nicklès, red prisms of **potassium tetraiodoantimonite**, $KI.SbI.nH_2O$. H. J. Wheeler prepared **rubidium enneaiodododiantimonite**, $3RbI.2SbI_3$, in deep red, trigonal crystals isomorphous with the corresponding chloride and bromide. The axial ratio is $a : c = 1 : 1.230$, and $a = 89° 46'$; while H. L. Wells and F. J. Metzger obtained brick-red, octahedra, and yellow hexagonal plates of **cæsium enneaiodo-diantimonite**, $3CsI.2SbI_3$. The octahedra were produced from a mixed soln. of the component salts in conc. hydriodic acid ; and the hexagonal plates by using a less conc. soln. of hydriodic acid L. Schäffer prepared dark orange-red, rhombic prisms of **barium pentaiodoantimonite**, $BaI_2.SbI_3.9H_2O$; A. Welkow obtained prismatic crystals of **beryllium iodoantimonite** which were not analyzed because they could not be separated from the mother-liquor without decomposition ; similar results were obtained with **aluminium iodoantimonite**. A. M. Wasiléeff found that with mixtures of stannic iodide and antimony triiodide there is a eutectic at 127° with $SnI_4 : SbI_3 = 1 : 0.8728$. A. Mosnier added lead iodide to a boiling sat. soln. of antimony triiodide in fuming hydriodic acid, and on cooling found that black octahedra of **lead enneaiodoantimonite**, $Pb_3SbI_9.12H_2O$, were formed. The salt is decomposed by water, and alcohol ; and its heat of soln. in 40 parts of water at 15° is −8.5 Cals. ; when heated to 45° it is dehydrated, and the heat of soln. is then +20.6 Cals. The heat of formation is $(SbI_3,3PbI_2) = 21.4$ Cals.

The reported existence of **antimony pentaiodide,** SbI_5, is very doubtful. V. van der Espt [2] stated that he obtained the pentaiodide by heating the elements together in the required proportions, but R. W. E. MacIvor could not confirm this. There is no sign of the formation of such a compound on the f.p. curves of F. M. Jäger and H. J. Doornbosch, and R. Quercigh, Fig. 47. J. H. Pendleton reported that he had made the pentaiodide by fusing antimony with an excess of iodine in an atm. of an inert gas in a sealed tube, and the mixture was kept well fused for an hour or two ; the tube was then heated at 130° in a sulphuric acid-bath, one end which was cooled with water serving to collect the surplus iodine which distils off. The residue is a dark-brown crystalline mass, decomposable by water or long exposure to moist air. It melts at 78°–79°, but is very unstable, readily undergoing decomposition when exposed to even a moderate increase of temp. Analytical results correspond " pretty closely to the formula SbI_5." R. W. E. MacIvor said that the supposed pentaiodide of J. H. Pendleton dissolved in hot carbon disulphide, yielding a soln. possessing the characteristic colour imparted to that liquid by free iodine, and which, on cooling, deposited crystals of the triiodide melting at 165°. By means of chloroform, in which the triiodide is only slightly soluble, it is possible completely to dissolve out the free iodine from the substance and obtain pure triiodide. On being decomposed by water the material yielded yellow oxyiodide, hydriodic acid, and much free iodine—a result to be expected from such a mixture. R. Hanslian determined the mol. wt. from the f.p. of soln. in iodine.

REFERENCES.

[1] R. Brandes, *Arch. Pharm.*, (2), **14**. 135, 1838; (2), **17**. 283, 1839; **21**. 319, 1840; A. Perrier and M. le Brument, *Bull. Gén. Thérapeutique*, **62**. 164, 1862; *Répert. Chim. Pure Appl.*, **4**. 254, 1862; E. R. Schneider, *Pogg. Ann.*, **109**. 610, 1860; L. Schäffer, *Liebig's Ann.*, **152**. 134, 1869; G. S. Sérullas, *Journ. Pharm. Chim.*, (2), **14**. 19, 1828; J. B. Berthemot, *ib.*, (2), **14**. 615, 1828; J. Nicklès, *ib.*, (3), **40**. 277, 1860; (3), **41**. 147, 1862; *Compt. Rend.*, **48**. 837, 1859; **50**. 872, 1860; **51**. 1097, 1860; A. Guntz, *ib.*, **101**. 161, 1885; T. Karantassis, *ib.*, **182**. 699, 1391, 1926; V. Thomas, *ib.*, **120**. 1117, 1895; L. Ouvrard, *ib.*, **117**. 108, 1893; V. Auger, *ib.*, **146**. 477, 1908; J. Tarible, *ib.*, **132**. 204, 1901; *Sur les combinaisons du bromure de bore avec les composés halogénés du phosphore, de l'arsenic et de l'antimoine*, Paris, 1899; C. P. Worcester, *Proc. Amer. Acad.*, **18**. 61, 1883; J. P. Cooke, *ib.*, **13**. 1, 72, 1877; *Amer. Journ. Science*, (3), **19**. 469, 1880; *Chem. News*, **44**. 221, 233, 245, 255, 1880; R. W. E. MacIvor, *ib.*, **29**. 255, 1874; **32**. 232, 1875; *Journ. Chem. Soc.*, **29**. 328, 1876; T. Carnelley and W. C. Williams, *ib.*, **33**. 281, 1878; R. M. Caven, *Proc. Chem. Soc.*, **21**. 187, 1905; A. Naumann, *Ber.*, **37**. 4333, 1904; A. Welkow, *ib.*, **7**. 804, 1874; L. Rotinjanz and W. Suchodsky, *Zeit. phys. Chem.*, **87**. 635, 1914; J. W. Retgers, *ib.*, **11**. 340, 1893; *Zeit. anorg. Chem.*, **3**. 344, 1893; E. Beckmann, *ib.*, **51**. 99, 1906; P. Walden, *ib.*, **25**. 211, 1900; **29**. 377, 1902; S. Motylewsky, *ib.*, **38**. 410, 1904; F. M. Jäger and H. J. Doornbosch, *ib.*, **75**. 261, 1912; H. J. Doornbosch, *Proc. Acad. Amsterdam*, **14**. 623, 1911; G. B. Bernardis, *Atti Accad. Lincei*, (5), **21**. ii, 438, 1912; E. Quercigh, *ib.*, (5), **21**. i, 786, 1912; *Atti Ist. Veneto*, **70**. ii, 667, 1912; G. Oddo and U. Giachery, *Gazz. Chim. Ital.*, **53**. i, 56, 1923; C. H. D. Bödeker, *Die Beziehungen zwischen Dichte und Zusammensetzung bei festen und liquiden Stoffen*, Leipzig, 1860; H. G. F. Schröder, *Dichtigkeitsmessungen*, Heidelberg, 1873; G. B. Negri, *Riv. Min. Crist. Ital.*, **9**. 43, 1891; H. L. Wheeler, *Zeit. anorg. Chem.*, **5**. 253, 1893; *Amer. Journ. Science*, (4), **3**. 461, 1897; H. L. Wells and F. J. Metzger, *ib.*, (4), **11**. 455, 1901; P. W. Bridgman, *Phys. Rev.*, (2), **6**. 31, 1915; E. Cohen and H. R. Bruins, *Zeit. Phys. Chem.*, **94**. 465, 1920; A. C. Vournasos, *Compt. Rend.*, **166**. 526, 1918; **170**. 1256, 1920; A. M. Wasiléeff, *Journ. Russ. Phys. Chem. Soc.*, **44**. 1076, 1912; F. Ephraim and S. Weinberg, *Ber.*, **42**. 4447, 1909; G. J. Burrows and E. E. Turner, *Journ. Chem. Soc.*, **119**. 1448, 1921; L. A. Buchner, *Anz. Gel. München*, **20**. 846, 1845; G. Gore, *Proc. Roy. Soc.*, **20**. 441, 1872; **21**. 140, 1873; E. Quercigh, *Atti Accad. Lincei*, (5), **21**. i, 786, 1912; A. Mosnier, *Ann. Chim. Phys.*, (7), **12**. 421, 1925; A. M. Wasiléeff, *Journ. Russ. Phys. Chem. Soc.*, **49**. 88, 428, 1917; F. Ephraim, *Helvetica Chim. Acta*, **7**. 298, 1924; W. Biltz, *Zeit. anorg. Chem.*, **115**. 241, 1921; J. W. Williams and R. J. Allgeier, *Journ. Amer. Chem. Soc.*, **49**. 2416, 1927; B. Köhnlein, *Ueber den Austausch von Chlor, Brom, und Jod zwischen anorganischen und organischen Halogenverbindungen*, Karlsruhe, 1883; R. Brix, *Ueber den Austausch von Chlor, Brom, und Jod zwischen anorganischen und organischen Verbindungen*, Tübingen, 1882.

[2] F. M. Jäger and H. J. Doornbosch, *Zeit. anorg. Chem.*, **75**. 261, 1912; H. J. Doornbosch, *Proc. Acad. Amsterdam*, **14**. 623, 1911; R. W. E. MacIvor, *Journ. Chem. Soc.*, **29**. 328, 1876; *Chem. News*, **29**. 129, 1874; **32**. 232, 1875; **86**. 223, 1902; J. H. Pendleton, *ib.*, **48**. 97, 1883; V. van der Espt, *Arch. Pharm.*, (2), **117**. 115, 1864; *Journ. Pharm. Chim.*, (3), **45**. 554, 1864; R. Quercigh, *Atti Accad. Lincei*, (5), **21** i, 791, 1912; *Atti Ist. Veneto*, **70**. ii, 667, 1912; R. Hanslian, *Molekulargewichtsbestimmungen in gefrierendem und siedendem Jod*, Werda i Th., 43, 1910.

§ 21. Antimony Oxyhalides

F. A. Flückiger [1] found that **antimony oxyfluoride** is produced as a white precipitate by evaporating a soln. of antimony trifluoride in water without adding hydrofluoric acid; and when hydrofluoric acid is treated with an excess of antimony trioxide. The analysis can be represented $Sb_8O_7F_{10}$. J. C. G. de Marignac obtained a gummy mass by evaporating in vacuo a soln. of antimony pentoxide in hydrofluoric acid, and when heated it gives an oxyfluoride. A definite antimony **oxytrifluoride** has not been isolated, but some complex salts have been reported. Thus, J. C. G. de Marignac obtained small, deliquescent, hexagonal prisms of **sodium antimonyl tetrafluoride**, $NaF.SbOF_3.H_2O$, by concentrating a soln. of antimony pentoxide and sodium carbonate in an excess of hydrofluoric acid. The salt can be crystallized from water without decomposition.   H. L. Wells and F. J. Metzger reported acicular crystals of **cæsium antimony hydroxytetrafluoride**, $CsF.SbF(OH)$, to be formed by cooling a warm, conc. soln. of antimony pentafluoride and cæsium fluoride in conc. hydrofluoric acid.

In the sixteenth century, the supposed medical virtues of the white powder obtained by the action of water on *butyrum antimonii* were described by Paracelsus in his *Archidoxies*.   Because at that time butter of antimony was prepared from mercuric chloride and antimony sulphide, Paracelsus seems to have assumed that the white powder contained the principle of mercury, and he called it *mercurius vitæ*.   He invested this medicament with wondrous powers of rejuvenescence :

Youth and its powers do not fail on account of old age, but these exist equally in the old as in the young.   The corruption, however, which grows up with youth is so strengthened that it takes away the powers, whence old age is recognized. . . . The *mercurius vitæ* separates corruption. . . . So powerful is it in man, that, after the corruption shall have been separated from him, the quintessence is again excited, and lives as in youth. . . . The aged life then recovers most effectually its powers as they were before . . ., and corruption cannot demonstrate old age. . . . *Mercurius vitæ* restores the defective and lost powers so that in old women the menses and the blood flow naturally as in young ones ; for it brings back aged women to the same perfection of nature as the younger ones.

Basil Valentine [2] also observed the precipitation of a white powder when antimony trichloride is treated with water.   J. C. Barchusen and H. Boerhaave retained Paracelsus' term *mercurius vitæ* for the white powder.   Towards the end of the seventeenth century, Vittorio Algarotto described the *mercurius vitæ* as a medicament and named it *pulvis angelicus* ; but it afterwards came to be called *pulvis Algaroti—powder of Algaroth*.   J. R. Glauber called it *flores antimonii vomitivi albi*.   J. C. Barchusen explained the formation of the powder by assuming that the water extracted the acid from the antimony trichloride, because, when the water is evaporated, the acid is recovered as *spiritus salis resuscitatus*.   He added that the powder contains no mercury ; and the term *mercurius vitæ* is a misnomer. This explanation was accepted by H. Boerhaave.

The hydrolysis of antimony trichloride has been discussed in connection with the chemical action of water on antimony trichloride.   It is there shown that J. M. van Bemmelen and co-workers [3] believed that the solid phase *antimony oxytetrachloride*, $SbCl_3.SbOCl$, was stable within the limits indicated in Fig. 36. C. Lea and J. K. Wood were unable to confirm the existence of this oxychloride. J. P. Cooke obtained a crystalline product as a result of the action of an acidic soln. of antimony trichloride, and C. Lea and J. K. Wood represent its formula $Sb_4O_3(OH)_5Cl$—*antimony trioxypentahydroxychloride*—and they also observed acicular crystals of *antimony trioxytrihydroxytrichloride*, $Sb_4O_3(OH)_3Cl_3$.   These products are considered to be metastable compounds representing more or less transitory halting stages in the passage to the stable oxychlorides $SbOCl$, and $Sb_4O_5Cl_2$.   The arresting of the incomplete reaction at different stages accounts for the differences in the composition of the products by different investigators at a time when analysis was the main test available.   Thus, E. R. Schneider, and A. Sabanejeff reported Sb_8OCl_{22}, or $SbOCl.7SbCl_3$; J. P. Cooke, and A. Sabanejeff, $Sb_8O_{11}Cl_2$; and W. C. Williams, $10Sb_4O_5Cl_2.SbCl_3$—*vide infra*.   The mineral, found by A. Frenzel in cavities in the native antimony of Borneo, and named *sarawakite*, occurs in minute crystals " probably tetragonal." It is colourless, or wine-yellow, or greenish-yellow.   It is supposed to be an oxychloride of antimony.

E. M. Péligot showed that **antimony oxychloride, or antimonyl chloride,** $SbOCl$, is produced by the action of cold water on antimony trichloride.   A. Sabanejeff allowed a mixture of ten parts of antimony trichloride and seven parts of water to stand for some days to allow the oxychloride to crystallize ; he then washed the dry crystals with ether to remove the adherent antimony trichloride.   The conditions of equilibrium are illustrated by Fig. 35.   J. M. van Bemmelen showed that this oxychloride is formed at ordinary temp. when a mol of antimony trichloride is

treated with 45 mols of water—*i.e.* about four parts of water to one part of trichloride
by weight. If much more than this amount of water is used, the pentoxydichloride
is formed, and if less, some oxychloride remains in soln. If the amorphous
precipitate first obtained be allowed to stand for some time in contact with its
mother-liquor it becomes crystalline provided the liquor be not too dilute.
L. Schäffer prepared this salt by heating to 160° a mixture of equimolar parts of
antimony trichloride and ethyl alcohol in a sealed tube : $SbCl_3 + C_2H_5OH = C_2H_5Cl$
$+ SbOCl + HCl$; if 3 mols of alcohol be employed, the pentoxydichloride is formed.
The analyses of the amorphous white powder or white crystals by E. M. Péligot,
L. Schäffer, A. Sabanejeff, and J. P. Cooke agree with the formula SbOCl. The
mol. wt. is unknown ; it is sometimes represented as $Sb_4O_4Cl_4$ by analogy with the
pentoxydichloride, $Sb_4O_5Cl_2$, and the trioxide, Sb_4O_6 :

$$Cl—Sb.O.Sb—Cl \qquad Cl—Sb.O.Sb \qquad Sb.O.Sb$$
$$\overset{..}{O} \quad \overset{..}{O} \qquad \qquad \overset{..}{O} \quad \overset{..}{O}\overset{..}{O} \qquad \overset{..}{O}\overset{..}{O} \quad \overset{..}{O}\overset{..}{O}$$
$$Cl—Sb.O.Sb—Cl \qquad Cl—Sb.O.Sb \qquad Sb.O.Sb$$
$$Sb_4O_4Cl_4 \qquad\qquad Sb_4O_5Cl_2 \qquad\qquad Sb_4O_6$$

J. P. Cooke found that the crystals belong to the monoclinic system having the
axial ratios $a : b : c = 0.8934 : 1 : 0.7577$, and $\beta = 103°\ 29'$. A. Guntz gave for the
heat of formation : $Sb_{solid} + O_{gas} + Cl_{gas} = SbOCl_{solid} + 89.7$ Cals. L. Schäffer,
A. Sabanejeff, and J. P. Cooke showed that when heated, this oxychloride gives off
antimony trichloride, forming the pentoxydichloride. The evolution of the trichloride begins at about 170° and ceases at about 280° when the composition is
$Sb_4O_5Cl_2$. At a higher temp., it decomposes into antimony trioxide and trichloride.
Hot water decomposes antimony oxychloride into the pentoxydichloride. G. Gore
said that the oxychloride is insoluble in liquid ammonia. Antimony oxychloride
is insoluble in alcohol and ether (L. Schäffer) ; but it is soluble in carbon disulphide,
chloroform, benzene, and in tartaric and hydrochloric acids (A. Sabanejeff) ;
G. Mazzaron found that antimony oxychloride gives chlorine not chromyl chloride
when treated with sulphuric acid and potassium dichromate.

By treating antimony trichloride with 5 to 50 times its weight of cold water,
A. Sabanejeff obtained **antimony pentoxydichloride,** $Sb_4O_5Cl_2$. This oxychloride
is commonly considered to be powder of Algaroth. If more water is used, the
product contains less chlorine. If the amorphous solid be allowed to stand in its
mother-liquid it gradually becomes crystalline- The dried product is freed from
adhering antimony trichloride by washing. An analogous method was used by
F. J. Malaguti, and J. F. W. Johnston. The conditions of equilibrium were studied
by J. M. van Bemmelen—Fig. 33—C. Lea and J. K. Wood, and H. le Chatelier—
vide the action of water on antimony trichloride. E. M. Péligot found that boiling
water in not too great an excess furnishes the same product ; and A. Sabanejeff
said that 30 times the weight of cold water gives the same product as 3 times the
weight of water at 60°–70°. C. W. E. MacIvor used hot water for the precipitation.
C. W. Scheele obtained powder of Algaroth by heating a mixture of antimony oxide
(one part), sodium chloride (3·5 parts), sulphuric acid (2·5 parts), and water (2 parts)
for 12 hrs. nearly at the b.p. ; diluting the soln. with water until precipitation begins ;
and adding more water to the filtered liquid. C. F. Bucholz used a similar process.
Conc. hydrochloric acid can be used in place of sodium chloride and sulphuric acid.
J. von Liebig mixed finely powdered antimony sulphide with boiling conc. hydrochloric acid ; added water until a precipitate appears which carries down any
sulphide present in the liquid ; and treated the filtered liquid with more water.
J. P. Cooke mixed a soln. of 2 grms. of antimony in 30 c.c. of hydrochloric acid and
5 grms. of tartaric acid and precipitated the oxychloride by water, and allowed it
to crystallize by standing for some time. Soln. with 7 to 20 grms. of tartaric acid
may be diluted to a litre without turbidity, the oxychloride is precipitated by boiling
the soln. V. Merz and W. Weith obtained crystals of an oxychloride, which was

not analyzed, by heating antimony trichloride with 10 times its weight of water, in a sealed tube at 200° 250°. L. Schäffer obtained this oxychloride by heating in a sealed tube at 140°–150°, a mol of antimony trichloride with 3 mols of alcohol : $4SbCl_3+5C_2H_5OH=Sb_4O_5Cl_2+5C_2H_5Cl+5HCl$.   J. P. Cooke also used this process. According to E. R. Schneider, and W. C. Williams, boiling antimony trichloride can dissolve about 0·067 part of its weight of antimony trioxide, and the soln. deposits a crystalline mass, Sb_8OCl_{22}, which when treated with alcohol forms the pentoxydichloride.

Analyses of the product by E. M. Péligot, R. W. E. MacIvor, A. Duflos, E. R. Schneider, J. P. Cooke, J. M. van Bemmelen and co-workers, L. Schäffer, and A. Sabanejeff agree more or less closely with the formula $Sb_4O_5Cl_2$.   J. F. W. Johnston's analyses indicated a little more chlorine—probably owing to inadequate washing—and he represented the formula $2SbCl_3.9Sb_2O_3$; P. Grouvelle, R. Phillips, and C. F. Bucholz obtained too little chlorine—possibly owing to too much washing. W. C. Williams obtained a product $10Sb_4O_5Cl_2.SbCl_3$ by the action of boiling water on antimony trichloride.   The white powder may be amorphous, or it may consist of tabular or prismatic crystals.   According to J. P. Cooke, the monoclinic prisms have the axial ratios $a : b : c = 1·234 : 1 : 3·081$, and $\beta = 121°\ 2'$; and the crystals obtained from a soln. of tartaric acid at ordinary temp. have a sp. gr. 5·014.   T. Bergman, and A. Sabanejeff found that the compound could be melted without decomposition, but at a higher temp., antimony trichloride is evolved.   J. P. Cooke said that the decomposition begins at 320°, and is completed at a red-heat.   M. Lapschin and M. Tichanowitsch observed that it is not decomposed by an electric current at about 500 volts.   A. Sabanejeff said that cold water has very little action, but N. E. Henry, A. Duflos, and F. J. Malaguti observed that it loses its chlorine in contact with hot water.   H. Debray obtained prismatic crystals of antimony trioxide by heating the oxychloride in a sealed tube at 150° ; L. Schäffer said that hydrochloric acid dissolves the oxychloride ; P. Grouvelle, that when heated with sulphur, black antimony trisulphide is formed ; C. F. Bucholz, that sulphuric acid converts it into antimony sulphate ; and nitric acid, into antimony nitrate ; A. Sabanejeff, that it is insoluble in alcohol and ether ; L. Schäffer, that it is soluble in a soln. of tartaric acid ; and T. H. Behrens, that oxalic acid converts it into antimonyl oxalate.   The oxychloride is converted by alkali-lye into antimony trioxide.

R. Benedikt prepared **potassium antimonyl pentachloroantimonate**, $2KCl.SbCl_3.SbOCl$, from a cold soln. of the components without adding hydrochloric acid.   The monoclinic prisms are stable in air ; they are freely soluble in hydrochloric acid, tartaric acid, and in hot acetic acid ; when crystallized from hydrochloric acid, some hexagonal potassium pentachloroantimonite is formed ; and the hot acetic acid soln. on cooling, deposits some antimony oxychloride.   The salt is insoluble in a cold or hot soln. of potassium chloride ; carbon disulphide, alcohol, and ligroin.   When heated in a current of carbon disulphide, it leaves a residue of potassium chloride and antimony trioxide.

The oxychlorides so far discussed are supposed to contain tervalent antimony. H. Daubrawa's monohydrated antimony pentachloride (*q.v.*) has been regarded as *antimony oxytrichloride*, $SbOCl_3$; but such a compound has not been made.   M. Lapschin and M. Tichanowitsch said that it is a bad electrical conductor.   W. C. Williams heated a mol of hydrated antimony pentoxide with 3 mols of antimony pentachloride in a sealed tube at 140°, and obtained two products : (i) **Antimony oxytridecachloride**, Sb_3OCl_{13}, appears in white crystals which melt at 85°, and decompose when heated, giving off chlorine and antimony trichloride, leaving antimony pentoxide as a residue.   The compound deliquesces in air, and is decomposed by water. It is soluble in tartaric acid ; and insoluble in carbon disulphide. (ii) **Antimony tetroxyheptachloride**, $Sb_3O_4Cl_7$, which appears in small yellow crystals which melt at 97·5°.

The mineral **ochrolite** was found by G. Flink [4] in the Harstig mine at Pajsberg, Sweden, and it was named in allusion to its bright sulphur-yellow colour—ὤχρος, bright yellow ; λίθος, a stone. The analysis corresponds with $Pb_4Sb_2O_7.2PbCl_2$, or **lead antimony heptoxytetrachloride**, $Pb_4Sb_2O_7Cl_4$, or $Pb_{13}Sb_4O_{15}Cl_8$. The small, thick, tabular, rhombic crystals have the axial ratios $a : b : c = 0.90502 : 1 : 2.01375$. The mineral **nadorite** comes from Djebel-Nador, Constantine, Algiers, and it was described by M. Flajolot. A. Russell described a specimen from Cornwall. Nadorite is smoky-brown or brownish-yellow ; and analyses reported by F. Pisani, M. Flajolot, and M. Braun agree with the formula $PbSb_2O_4.PbCl_2$, or, as P. Groth puts it, $SbO_2(PbCl)$; *i.e.* **lead antimonyl oxychloride**, $Cl.Pb.O.SbO$, a derivative of $HO.SbO$.

$$\begin{array}{l} (PbCl)\!-\!O\!-\!Pb\!-\!SbO\!-\!O\!-\!Pb \\ (PbCl)\!-\!O\!-\!Pb\!-\!SbO\!-\!O\!-\!Pb \end{array}\!\!>\!\!O\!<\!\!\begin{array}{l} PbCl \\ PbCl \end{array}$$

G. Cesaro obtained a similar product by fusing a mixture of a gram of lead oxide and 0·778 grm. $SbOCl$. G. Cesaro gave for the axial ratios of the tabular or prismatic, rhombic crystals of nadorite : $a : b : c = 0.7490 : 1 : 1.0310$. Twinning occurs about the (011)-plane ; the (100)-cleavage is perfect. The optic axial angle is 145° ; the optical character is negative ; the dispersion is strong ; the sp. gr. is 7·02 ; and the hardness is 3·5–4·0.

Two **oxybromides** containing tervalent antimony have been reported, and they are analogous with the two stable oxychlorides. J. P. Cooke found that **antimony oxybromide**, or **antimonyl bromide**, $SbOBr$, or $Sb_4O_4Br_4$, separates out when a soln. of antimony tribromide in carbon disulphide is exposed to air and sunlight. The brown oxychloride is contaminated with decomposition products of the carbon disulphide, otherwise it would be white. The decomposition by heat takes place in two stages as in the case of the corresponding oxyiodide—antimony trioxide being the end-product ; and the pentoxydibromide is formed as an intermediate product. J. P. Cooke prepared **antimony pentoxydibromide**, $Sb_4O_5Br_2$, by heating a mixture of absolute alcohol and antimony tribromide in a sealed tube at 160°. A decrease in the proportion of alcohol does not lead to the formation of the oxybromide as in the corresponding case with the trichloride. The same compound is produced when the tribromide is hydrolyzed by cold water. R. W. E. MacIvor removed the adherent tribromide by washing the product with carbon disulphide. G. S. Sérullas said that by repeatedly washing the product with water, all the bromine can be removed. The white powder is either amorphous or crystalline, and, according to J. P. Cooke, the crystals are monoclinic. R. W. E. MacIvor said that at 300°, the compound decomposes into antimony tribromide and trioxide. G. S. Sérullas said that the oxybromide retains water very tenaciously, and is all expelled only when the tribromide is given off. G. Gore found that antimony oxybromide is slightly soluble in liquid ammonia.

Only **oxyiodides** of tervalent antimony are known. J. P. Cooke prepared **antimony oxyiodide**, or **antimonyl iodide**, $SbOI$, or $Sb_4O_4I_4$, by exposing to air and light a soln. of antimony triiodide in carbon disulphide. The soln. is simultaneously discoloured owing to the liberation of some free iodine. The blue and violet rays are the most acute ; the red and yellow rays have very little activity. The light from burning magnesium is also active. The amorphous yellow or yellowish-brown powder begins to liberate antimony triiodide at 150°, and at 200°, the evolution ceases ; the residue then suffers no further decomposition until a temp. of 350° is attained when its composition corresponds with **antimony pentoxydiiodide**, $Sb_4O_5I_2$. Some of this same iodide is formed along with the oxyiodide, $SbOI$. The pentoxydiiodide produced by the action of absolute alcohol on antimony triiodide has a variable composition. The pentoxydiiodide is also produced as a golden-yellow powder when a soln. of antimony triiodide in hydriodic acid is poured into water. G. S. Sérullas, and J. B. Berthemot found that the composition of the product obtained by the hydrolysis of the triiodide varies with the proportion of water employed, the temp., and the amount of washing to which it is subjected ; a protracted washing may remove all or nearly all the iodine. The product holds water very tenaciously so that the compound has begun to give off antimony triiodide at the temp. at which all the water is expelled. The water in which the iodide decomposes acquires a red colour, being a soln. of antimony triiodide in hydriodic acid. The analyses of R. W. E. MacIvor, J. P. Cooke, and H. Halle agree closely with the assigned formula. J. P. Cooke found that the yellowish-brown pentoxydiiodide may be amorphous, or in colourless monoclinic crystals; it is stable up to 350°, and at a dull red-heat, antimony triiodide is evolved, leaving a residue of cubic and prismatic antimony trioxide. The crystals of the pentoxydiiodide appear in the partially decomposed compound. H. Halle observed very little change in weight between 105° and 250°—then, 0·3622 grm. at 105° became 0·3596 grm. at 250°. R. W. E. MacIvor, and R. Brandes said that the pentoxydiiodide slowly dissolves in a soln. of tartaric acid; and J. B. Berthemot, that zinc or iron precipitates antimony from boiling water in which the pulverulent oxyiodide is suspended; tin acts similarly but more slowly. Alkali and alkaline earth hydroxides decompose the oxyiodide with the separation of antimony trioxide. A. C. Vournasos said that in the hydrolysis of antimony triiodide by water, there are indications of the intermediate formation of an unstable complex acid, $H_2(SbOI_3)$—*hydroantimonyloxytriiodic acid*. Thus, when equimolar proportions of antimony triiodide and mercuric cyanide are warmed in moist amyl alcohol on a water-bath for 4–6 hrs., **mercury antimonyl oxytriiodide**, $Hg(SbOI_3)$, m.p. 78°, is produced. The salt can be recrystallized from cold, dil. hydrochloric acid, but is decomposed by conc. acids, and by alkali-lye. Copper acetate under similar conditions furnishes **copper antimonyl triiodide**, $Cu(SbOI_3)$.

P. Gruhl melted potassium iodide with antimony trioxide; and, when the mass had cooled, separated the upper, greyish-green layer of potassium iodide from the lower, amber-yellow layer. The composition of the product corresponds with **potassium oxydi-iodo-hexadecantimonite**, $2KI.K_2O.8Sb_2O_3$. It is insoluble in, and not attacked by cold or hot water; acids and alkali-lyes do not act on the product; aqua regia decomposes it slowly; and tartaric acid dissolves it gradually.

REFERENCES.

[1] F. A. Flückiger, *Pogg. Ann.*, **87**. 249, 1852; *Liebig's Ann.*, **84**. 248, 1851; *Ann. Chim. Phys.*, (3), **39**. 495, 1853; J. C. G. de Marignac, *ib.*, (4), **10**. 371, 1867; *Bull. Soc. Chim.*, (1), **8**. 323, 1867; *Liebig's Ann.*, **145**. 239, 1868; *Bibl. Univ. Genève*, **28**. 13, 1867; H. L. Wells and F. J. Metzger, *Amer. Journ. Science*, (4), **11**. 453, 1901.

[2] J. C. Barchusen, *Pyrosophia*, Lugduni Batavorum, 222, 1698; H. Boerhaave, *Elementa chemiæ*, Lugduni Batavorum, **2**. 521, 1732; V. Algarotto, *Compendio della natura, virtu e modo d'usare una polve quint'essenza d'oro medicinale*, Verona, 1667; J. R. Glauber, *Novis furnis philosophius*, Amstelodami, 1648; London, 1689; Basil Valentine, *Triumphwagen Antimonii*, Nürnberg, 1676.

[3] J. M. van Bemmelen, P. A. Meerburg, and U. H. Noodt, *Zeit. anorg. Chem.*, **33**. 272, 1903; G. S. Sérullas, *Journ. Pharm. Chim.*, (2), **14**. 19, 1823; J. B. Berthemot, *ib.*, (2), **14**. 615, 1828; C. Lea and J. K. Wood, *Journ. Chem. Soc.*, **125**. 259, 1924; R. Brandes, *Arch. Pharm.*, (2), **17**. 238, 1839; J. P. Cooke, *Proc. Amer. Acad.*, **13**. 1, 72, 1878; *Amer. Journ. Science*, (3), **19**. 469, 1880; *Chem. News*, **44**. 221, 233, 245, 255, 1880; P. Grouvelle, *Ann. Chim. Phys.*, (2), **17**. 37, 1821; A. Guntz, *ib.*, (6), **3**. 57, 1884; E. M. Péligot, *ib.*, (3), **20**. 283, 1847; F. J. Malaguti, *ib.*, (2), **59**. 220, 1835; A. Duflos, *Schweigger's Journ.*, **67**. 268, 1833; H. le Chatelier, *Compt. Rend.*, **100**. 737, 1885; **102**. 1388, 1886; H. Debray, *ib.*, **58**. 1209, 1864; A. C. Vournasos, *ib.*, **170**, 1256, 1920; A. Sabanejeff, *Zeit. Chem.*, (2), **7**. 204, 1871; J. F. W. Johnston, *B.A. Rep.*, 587, 1834; *Edin. Phil. Journ.*, **18**. 40, 1835; *Phil. Mag.*, (3), **7**. 332, 1835; C. F. Bucholz, *Taschenbuch Scheidekünstler*, **27**. 18, 1806; W. C. Williams, *Proc. Manchester Lit. Phil. Soc.*, **11**. 3, 1871; *Mem. Manchester Lit. Phil. Soc.*, **5**. 61, 1876; *Chem. News*, **24**. 225, 1871; R. W. E. MacIvor, *ib.*, **32**. 229, 1875; *Journ. Chem. Soc.*, **29**. 328, 1874; E. R. Schneider, *Pogg. Ann.*, **108**. 411, 1859; L. Schäffer, *Liebig's Ann.*, **152**. 314, 1869; H. Daubrawa, *ib.*, **186**. 118, 1877; V. Merz and W. Weith, *Ber.*, **13**. 210, 1880; R. Anschütz and P. N. Evans, *ib.*, **19**. 1994, 1886; *Liebig's Ann.*, **239**. 287, 1887; J. von Liebig, *Handwörterbuch der reinen und angewandten Chemie*, Braunschweig, **1**. 414, 1837; T. H. Behrens, *Zeit. anal. Chem.*, **30**. 163, 1891; N. E. Henry, *Journ. Pharm. Chim.*, (2), **12**. 79, 1826; M. Lapschin and M. Tichanowitsch, *Bull. Acad. St. Petersburg*, (3), **4**. 81, 1862; *Phil. Mag.*, (4), **22**. 308, 1861; A. Frenzel, *Tschermak's Mitt.*, (1), **7**. 300, 1877; P. Grunl, *Verbindungen des Arsen- und Antimontrioxydes mit den Halogeniden mehrwertiger Metalle*, München, 1897; H. Halle, *Ueber Antimon und Arsen*, München, 1893; R. Benedikt, *Proc. Amer. Acad.*, **22**. 212, 1894; G. Mazzaron, *Atti Ist. Venezia*, (7), **7**. 1124, 1896; R. Phillips, *Phil. Mag.*, **8**. 406, 1830; *Journ. Roy. Inst.*, **1**. 387, 1831; T. Bergman, *De antimonialibus sulphuratis*, Upsala, 1782; M. Lapschine and M. Tichanowitsch, *Bull. Acad. St. Petersburg*, (3), **4**. 81, 1862; C. W. Scheele, *Svenska Acad. Handl.*, **40**. 1, 1778; G. Gore, *Proc. Roy. Soc.*, **20**. 441, 1872; **21**. 140, 1873.

[4] G. Flink, *Oefvers. Akad. Stockholm*, **46**. 5, 1880; G. Cesaro, *Compt. Rend.*, **71**. 319, 1870; *Bull. Soc. Min.*, **11**. 44, 1888; A. des Cloizeaux, *ib.*, **5**. 122, 1882; *Compt. Rend.*, **73**. 81, 1871;

F. Pisani, *ib.*, **71.** 319, 1870 ; M. Flajolot, *ib.*, **71.** 237, 406, 1870 ; *Zeit. deut. geol. Ges.*, **24.** 47, 1872 ; M. Braun, *ib.*, **24.** 42, 1872 ; P. Groth, *Tabellarische Uebersicht der Mineralien*, Braunschweig, 70, 1889 ; W. T. Schaller, *Bull. U.S. geol. Sur.*, 610 (108), 1916 ; A. Russell, *Min. Mag.*, **21.** 272, 1927 ; J. P. Cooke, *Proc. Amer. Acad.*, **13.** 1, 72, 1878 ; R. W. E. MacIvor, *Chem. News*, **32.** 229, 1875 ; *Journ. Chem. Soc.*, **29.** 328, 1874 ; G. S. Sérullas, *Journ. Pharm. Chim.*, (2), **14.** 19, 1823 ; G. Gore, *Proc. Roy. Soc.*, **20.** 441, 1872 ; **21.** 140, 1873 ; J. B. Berthemot, *Journ. Pharm. Chim.*, (2), **14.** 615, 1828 ; H. Halle, *Ueber Antimon und Arsen*, München, 1893 ; P. Gruhl, *Verbindungen des Arsen- und Antimontrioxydes mit den Halogeniden mehrwertiger Metalle*, München, 1897.

§ 22. The Mixed Antimony Halides

Mixed halides of tervalent antimony have not been prepared. G. B. Bernardis [1] examined the f.p. curves of antimony trichloride and tribromide, Fig. 51 ; of antimony tribromide and triiodide, Fig. 52 ; and of antimony trichloride and

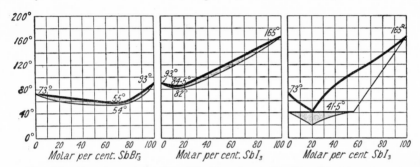

Fig. 51.—Freezing-point Curves of the Binary System : $SbCl_3$–$SbBr_3$.

Fig. 52.—Freezing-point Curves of the Binary System : $SbBr_3$–SbI_3.

Fig. 53.—Freezing-point Curves of the Binary System : $SbCl_3$–SbI_3.

triiodide. Antimony tribromide forms mixed crystals in all proportions with the trichloride and the triiodide with minima respectively at 54° and 82° ; but with the trichloride and triiodide there is a limit with the triiodide up to a conc. of about 45 per cent. $SbCl_3$. The eutectic at 41·5° has 82 per cent. $SbCl_3$.

A number of mixed halides of quinquevalent antimony have been prepared. F. Swarts [2] reported **antimony difluotrichloride,** SbF_2Cl_3, by the action of antimony trifluoride on antimony pentachloride, in the presence of an excess of chlorine :
$2SbF_3+SbCl_5+2Cl_2=3SbF_2Cl_3$. The crystals
are white or pale yellow. The vapour
density up to 200° and 760 mm. press. is
normal ; but at 360°, dissociation is complete.
The compound melts to a colourless liquid at
55°. The difluotrichloride mixes with water
with the development of a little heat. The
compound attacks glass slowly ; it reacts vigorously with ether, benzene, chloroform, and carbon
tetrachloride ; it carbonizes paper ; and with
ammonia forms **antimony triamminodifluotri-
chloride,** $SbF_2Cl_3.2NH_3$.

O. Ruff examined the f.p. curve of mixtures
of antimony pentachloride and pentafluoride,
and obtained evidence of the existence of six compounds. No signs of the existence of $3SbF_5.2SbCl_5$
appeared on the fusion curve, Fig. 54. The region
of stability of **antimony pentadecafluopentachloride,** $3SbF_5.SbCl_5$, is shown in the
diagram. It is primarily deposited from the vapour in a good vacuum. The region

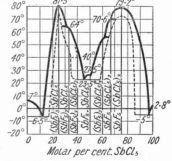

Fig. 54.—Freezing-point Curve of the Binary Mixture : SbF_5–$SbCl_5$.

of stability of **antimony decafluopentachloride,** $2SbF_5.SbCl_5$, is shown in the diagram ; the compound was obtained by extracting with liquid chlorine the solid obtained from fusions with 60 to 66·7 molar per cent. of the pentafluoride. Mol. wt. determinations in sulphuryl chloride soln. are normal with 10 per cent. soln., but in less conc. soln., the compound is dissociated. Its sp. gr. is 3·08 at 20°/0° ; and the mol. vol. 236. **Antimony pentafluopentachloride,** $SbF_5.SbCl_5$, can be isolated from the fusions in the region indicated in the diagram ; the same thing applies to **antimony decafluopentadecachloride,** $2SbF_5.3SbCl_5$. The mol. wt. in sulphuryl chloride is about one-third the theoretical value, even in conc. soln. The sp. gr. is 2·79 at 20°/0° ; and the mol. vol. 473. The crystalline form of **antimony pentafluodecachloride,** $SbF_5.2SbCl_5$, is different from that of either of its immediate neighbours. The sp. gr. is 2·82 at 20°/0° ; and the mol. vol. is 287. It is possible to isolate **antimony pentafluopentadecachloride,** $SbF_5.3SbCl_5$, from the fusions ; and it is primarily deposited from the vapour in a good vacuum. The mol. wt. in sulphuryl chloride soln. is about one-third the normal value, even in conc. soln. The sp. gr. is 2·73 at 20°/0° ; and the mol. vol. is 406. On fusion, all the compounds are dissociated to a great extent ; and there is a considerable decrease in vol. when they are formed from their constituents. The chemical behaviour of these compounds, except in so far as their behaviour towards bromine and a mixture of arsenic trifluoride and bromine is concerned, is similar to what one would expect from a mixture of antimony pentachloride and antimony pentafluoride in the given proportions. When bromine is mixed with twice its weight of $3SbF_5,SbCl_5$, or $2SbF_5,SbCl_5$, there is a slight development of heat, and some of the compound dissolves in the bromine ; on mixing with $2SbF_5,3SbCl_5$, $SbF_5,2SbCl_5$, or $SbF_5,3SbCl_5$, however, there is a considerable absorption of heat, and the mixture becomes liquid. The mixture of arsenic trifluoride and bromine does not give arsenic pentafluoride with any of the above compounds. In the formation of these compounds, the negative affinity of the antimony pentafluoride mol. is considered to lie between those of elementary fluorine and chlorine, whereas the affinity of the antimony pentachloride mol. is more negative than that of the iodine mol., and about as strong as that of the bromine mol. In the light of Werner's theory, the maximum co-ordination number of the antimony pentahalogenides is 8.

O. Ruff obtained **antimony pentafluobromide,** SbF_5Br, by the union of bromine with antimony pentafluoride at ordinary temp. The product is a dark brown, viscid mass. The vap. press. shows that the bromine is probably combined with the pentafluoride ; any bromine in excess can be removed by warming it in a current of carbon dioxide ; there is a slight dissociation of the warm pentafluobromide, and this is complete near the m.p. of antimony pentafluoride. O. Ruff also found that iodine reacts with antimony pentafluoride with the development of heat, and the formation either of a bluish-green liquid or of a dark brown or bluish-green solid, according to the proportion of pentafluoride employed. When iodine is heated to 160°–220° with an excess of the pentafluoride, **antimony decafluoiodide,** $(SbF_5)_2I$, is formed as a dark bluish-green crystalline mass which melts at 110°–115°, and does not lose iodine at 240°. When heated for a long time in a current of carbon dioxide, practically no iodine is given off, but antimony pentafluoride distils over. Water decomposes the decafluoiodide with a hissing noise, and the separation of iodine. If antimony pentafluoride be mixed with an **excess** of iodine, and the temp. be raised above the b.p. of iodine, **antimony pentafluoiodide,** SbF_5I, is obtained when the excess of iodine is volatilized. The dark brown compound is decomposed above 260° with the evolution of iodine ; its m.p. is a little below 80°. It is decomposed by water more slowly than is the case with antimony decafluoiodide.

According to R. W. Atkinson, tetragonal crystals of **potassium trichlorotribromantimonite,** $K_3SbCl_3Br_3,1\frac{1}{2}H_2O$, crystallize from a soln. of a mol of antimony trichloride and 3 mols of potassium bromide, or from a soln. of a mol of antimony tribromide and 3 mols of potassium chloride. If a theory of molecular compounds be true, then by mixing one eq. of antimony trichloride with 3 eq. of potassium bromide, and also one eq. of antimony tribromide with 3 eq. of potassium chloride, two different isomeric salts should be obtained, $viz.$ $SbCl_3.3BKr$, and $SbBr_3.3KCl$. R. W. Atkinson found the two products are identical, and hence inferred that in the act of soln. the elements must be so distributed that the same compound is obtained from whichever pair of salts a start is made. The formula of the stable salt is supposed to be:

$$Sb\begin{cases} Br=Cl—K \\ Br=Cl—K \\ Br=Cl—K \end{cases} \quad \text{rather than} \quad Sb\begin{cases} Cl=Br—K \\ Cl=Br—K \\ Cl=Br—K \end{cases}$$

because the affinity of chlorine for potassium is greater than that of bromine for antimony, and this is thought to explain why R. W. Atkinson could prepare but one compound by the action of potassium chloride on antimony tribromide or of potassium bromide on antimony trichloride. C. H. Herty said that these substances are in all probability not true individuals, but isomorphous mixtures of the double chloride and double bromide. This view is in harmony with the observation that, after heating the supposed substance, $SbCl_3,Br_3K_3,1\frac{1}{2}H_2O$, until a constant weight is obtained, the residue contains an appreciable quantity of antimony, and that therefore the determination of the halogens in it by R. W. Atkinson affords no satisfactory evidence of the nature of the substance. According to R. W. Atkinson, the salt effloresces over calcium chloride, and loses its water readily when the temp. is raised a little. When heated to 100°, the salt darkens in colour, and at a higher temp., 200°–300°, it loses equimolar parts of antimony trichloride and tribromide, and the residue is free from antimony. The salt deliquesces in air; and the yellow aq. soln., when sat., has a sp. gr. 1·9, and contains 120·5 grms. of salt per 100 c.c. The hydrochloric acid soln. of the salt quickly deposits crystals of potassium chloride. R. W. Atkinson also obtained pale yellow, octahedral crystals of **potassium trichlorobromoantimonite**, $KBrSbCl_3.H_2O$, from a soln. of 2 mols of antimony trichloride, and 3 mols of potassium bromide; and pale yellow rhombic crystals of **potassium hexachlorotribromodiantimonite**, $3KBr.2SbCl_3.2H_2O$, from a soln. containing rather a less proportion of antimony trichloride than that employed in preparing the trichlorotribromantimonite. C. H. Herty regards both salts as solid soln., not chemical individuals. A. C. Vournasos prepared the stable mixed halides **potassium tribromotriiodoantimonite**, $K_3[SbI_3Br_3]$, as well as **sodium triiodotricyanidoantimonite**, $Na_3[SbI_3Cy_3]$.

G. B. Bernardis' f.p. curve of mixtures of antimony trichloride and triiodide is shown in Fig. 53. O. Ruff measured the f.p. curves of mixtures of iodine monochloride and antimony pentachloride; and the results are summarized in Fig. 55. The compounds, **antimony heptachlorodiiodide**, $SbCl_5.2ICl$, and **antimony octochlorotriiodide**, $SbCl_5.3ICl$, may be isolated by sublimation from a mixture of antimony pentachloride (10 grms.) and iodine (4·3 or 8·6 grms.) under 15 mm. press., from a bath at 30°–35°. They form bluish-black crystals, stout prisms or needles, m.p. 62°–63°, which fume in the air, and dissolve readily in carbon tetrachloride or chloroform, but sparingly in antimony pentachloride. In the soln. they are strongly dissociated. A. C. Vournasos obtained a complex acid—**hydroantimonatobromotriiodic acid**, $HSbI_3Br$—by the action of dry gaseous hydrogen bromide on antimony triiodide in a non-aq. medium such as glacial acetic acid. It cannot be isolated in a solid state by the evaporation of the acetic acid soln., as, owing to dissociation, only a residue of the triiodide remains. The salts of this acid are,

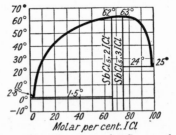

Fig. 55.—Freezing-point Curves of Mixtures of Antimony Pentachloride and Iodine Monochloride.

however, obtained in crystalline form by triturating and finally warming equi-molecular proportions of antimony triiodide and a bromide with a suitable non-aq. medium, acetic acid, xylene, etc. The compounds form coloured crystals, which are rapidly decomposed by water or ethyl alcohol, giving antimonious oxide, hydriodic acid, and the metallic bromide. **Sodium antimonatotriiodobromide,** $SbBrI_3Na$, prepared in xylene, forms small, orange-yellow crystals. **Potassium antimonatotriiodobromide,** $SbBrI_3K$, is similar in colour, but the **ammonium antimonatotriiodobromide,** NH_4SbI_3Br, and **lithium antimonatotriiodobromide,** $LiSbI_3Br$, are reddish-yellow. **Zinc antimonatotriiodobromide,** $ZnSbI_3Br_2$, forms brown, tabular crystals, which are fairly stable and only slowly decomposed by water.

REFERENCES.

[1] G. B. Bernardis, *Atti Accad. Lincei*, (5), **21**. ii, 438, 1912.
[2] F. Swarts, *Bull. Acad. Belg.*, (3), **29**. 874, 1895; C. H. Herty, *Amer. Chem. Journ.*, **15**. 81, 1893; **16**. 490, 1894; R. W. Atkinson, *Journ. Chem. Soc.*, **43**. 289, 1883; O. Ruff, *Ber.*, **39**. 4310, 1906; **42**. 4021, 1909; **48**. 2069, 1915; A. C. Vournasos, *Compt. Rend.*, **175**. 164, 1922; *Zeit. anorg. Chem.*, **150**. 147, 1926.

§ 23. Antimony Sulphides

The affinity of antimony for sulphur was discussed by K. Jellinek and J. Zakow-sky.[1] M. Faraday suggested the possibility of the existence of *antimony subsulphide,* or **antimony disulphide,** Sb_2S_2—analogous to realgar, As_2S_2—but J. J. Berzelius could find no evidence in support of this assumption. B. Unger found that by treating antimony trisulphide with a soln. of sodium hydroxide or sulphide with the exclusion of air, he obtained a mixture of sulphantimonite and sulphantimonate and antimonate. The oxidation product is ascribed to the reduction of the antimony trisulphide to disulphide, but he was unable to isolate the disulphide—acids precipitate the trisulphide from the soln.—and the existence of the disulphide as a chemical individual has not been confirmed.

J. J. Berzelius showed that molten antimony trisulphide can dissolve antimony, which separates out on cooling. H. Pélabon found that fused mixtures of antimony and antimony trisulphide form one or two liquid phases according to the ratio, R, of the antimony sulphide to the total mass of the mixture. When R is less than 0·015, the liquid is homogeneous, and consists of soln. of the trisulphide in antimony, the solidification temps. of which decrease, as R increases, from 632°, the f.p. of antimony to 615°, that of a sat. soln. of antimony trisulphide in antimony. For values of R between 0·015 and 0·25, the liquid product of fusion con-sists of two phases, of which the less dense is a soln. of antimony in the trisulphide, and the more dense a soln. of the trisulphide in antimony; the solidification temps., 515° and 615°, of these two liquids remain sensibly the same for all values of R between the limits stated above. Finally, when R is greater than 0·25, the fused mixture is a homogeneous soln. of antimony in the trisulphide, and the solidi-fication temp. increases with R from 515° to 555°, the f.p. of the trisulphide. These immis-cible soln. are represented by the curves on the right of Fig. 56. P. Chrétien and

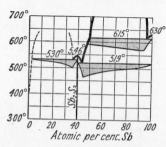

FIG. 56.—Freezing-point Curves of Antimony and Sulphur.

J. M. Guinchant said that the formation of the two liquid phases with fused mixtures of antimony and antimony trisulphide is conditioned by the lower sp. gr. and the higher coeff. of expansion of the trisulphide. The sp. gr. of the soln. of antimony in the trisulphide, and of trisulphide in antimony are:

	13°	643°	698°	1116°	1156°
Trisulphide layer . .	4·63	3·85	—	3·82	—
Antimony layer . .	6·75	—	6·55	—	6·45

and the percentage composition of the soln. of antimony in the trisulphide at different temp. is:

	539°	640°	702°	750°	825°	960°	1036°	1108°	1130°	1180°
Antimony .	11·28	14·34	16·00	17·96	19·01	20·6	210	21·8	21·3	21·1

They represented that the quantity, w, of antimony dissolved per 100 grams of the mixture at $\theta°$ by $w = 20·33 + 0·0333(\theta - 810)$ for temp. below 810°, and $w = 20·33 + 3·003(\theta - 810)$ for temp. above 810°. F. M. Jäger and H. S. van Klooster fused mixtures of antimony and sulphur, and observed only one maximum on the f.p. curve at 546°—Fig. 55. The eutectics are at 530° and 519° respectively with 61·3 and 55 at. per cent. of sulphur. On both sides of these limits two liquid layers are formed—at 530° for mixtures of sulphur and antimony trisulphide, and at 615° for mixtures of antimony and its trisulphide. There are no signs of the existence of either antimony disulphide or antimony pentasulphide on the f.p. curve. The failure of the f.p. curves to indicate the existence of the pentasulphide shows the indecisive character of this negative evidence as an *experimentum crucis* in establishing the individuality of a supposed compound.

The history of **antimony trisulphide**, Sb_2S_3, is intimately associated with the history of antimony (*q.v.*). The miners' term for grey mineral sulphide was *Spiessglas* or *Spiessglanz—le verre d'antimoine, antimony glass*, or *antimony glance*—and this term was employed by Basil Valentine,[2] and G. Agricola. After antimony itself had been separated from the *antimonium sulphure mineralisatum*, the mineral came to be called—by J. G. Wallerius, L. A. Emmerling, and A. G. Werner—*graues Spiessglanzerz*, and elemental antimony *Spiessglas*. Basil Valentine, and J. Kunckel knew that the mineral contained sulphur ; H. Boerhaave regarded it as a metal sulphide ; and, towards the end of the eighteenth century, T. Bergman analyzed the mineral. In allusion to the crystalline form, F. Mohs called the mineral *prismatoidal antimony glance*, a term abbreviated by C. C. von Leonhard to *Antimonglanz ;* and by W. Haidinger, to *antimonite*. F. S. Beudant designated it *stibine*, a term altered by J. D. Dana to **stibnite.**

In addition to the analyses made by T. Bergman, analyses of the natural or artificial trisulphide were later on reported by R. Brandes, J. Davy, and J. L. Proust; and still later by A. d'Achiardi, J. J. Berzelius, H. Credner, I. Domeyko, K. Friedrich, M. Garot, F. M. Jäger, W. Koort, J. Loczka, E. Luzzatto, W. van der Marck, M. M. P. Muir, E. Müller, G. de Angelis d'Ossat, E. Priwoznik, C. F. Rammelsberg, E. Reichardt, F. Sandberger, E. R. Schneider, O. Stutzer, T. Thomsor, A. R. C. Selwyn and G. H. F. Ulrich, L. N. Vauquelin, C. E. Waite, H. W. F. Wackenroder, W. Witting, and V. Zani. These all agree with the formula Sb_2S_3. Similar results were obtained in the analyses of the amorphous sulphide by J. P. Cooke, L. F. Nilson, E. R. Schneider, and P. Chrétien and J. M. Guinchant. The presence of arsenic was noted as early as 1617 by A. Libavius, and A. Sala.

Basil Valentine[3] obtained red antimony trisulphide by subliming the spiessglance with Armenian salt (ammonium chloride and sulphide) ; and J. R. Glauber, and N. Lemery alluded to the dissolution of spiessglance in alkaline soln. and its reprecipitation as a red sulphide. According to N. Lemery, a Carthusian monk, Frère Simon, first emphasized the medicinal properties of the red sulphide which was called *poudre des Chartreux, pulvis Carthusianorum,* or *Carthusian powder ;* and also *alkermes minerale,* or **mineral kermes**—in allusion to the resemblance of the colour to that called *kermes,* or *vegetable kermes,* derived from the *coccus ilicis*.

In 1720, this medical preparation was so much esteemed that the French government bought S. de la Ligerie's recipe for its preparation. This involved boiling spiessglance with a soln. of potassium carbonate ; the red powder separated from the cooling liquor. G. F. Stabel, and E. P. Meuder used potash-lye in a similar way. C. J. Geoffroy fused the spiessglance with alkali carbonate, and boiled the product with water. Many other methods of preparation were devised. C. J. Geoffroy considered mineral kermes to be a compound of alkali with antimony sulphide, and P. J. Macquer also considered the alkali to be an essential constituent, but this A. Baumé denied. It was then considered to be *oxyde d'antimoine sulfuré rouge.* This is not very different from the ideas of T. Bergman, and C. L. Berthollet, and A. F. de Fourcroy. In 1821, J. J. Berzelius showed that mineral kermes is hydrated antimony trisulphide ; and soon afterwards, H. Rose, and J. N. von Fuchs showed that it differs from spiessglance only in its state of aggregation. Later, confirmatory analyses were made by E. Matieu-Plessy, J. Akerman, N. Teclu, and H. Baubigny. L. Gmelin has given a detailed account of mineral kermes. According to J. Bougault, kermes mineral owes its therapeutic action to the antimony oxide formed by the acids of the stomach on the contained antimony trisulphide and sodium pyroantimonate.

The preparation of antimony trisulphide.—The extraction of antimony trisulphide as *antimonium crudum* has been indicated in a special section. The crystals of antimony trisulphide occurring in the preparation of crude antimony have been described by J. A. Krenner,[4] C. C. von Leonhard, C. W. C. Fuchs, and P. P. Heberdey. The preparation of crystalline antimony trisulphide is comparatively easy. The black sulphide can be made by the direct union of the two elements ; when melted together, the combination is attended by a feeble incandescence. The region of stability is indicated in Fig. 51. J. von Liebig made the trisulphide by gradually adding to a red-hot crucible a mixture of 13 parts of antimony and 5 parts of sulphur, and fusing the mixture. W. Spring found that union occurs when an intimate mixture of the two elements is strongly compressed ; C. Geitner, when a mixture is heated with water to 200° in a sealed tube ; C. Geitner, and J. Uhl, when antimony is heated with gaseous or an aq. soln. of sulphur dioxide ; and, according to C. Heumann and P. Köchlin, presumably, when sulphuryl chloride is passed over heated antimony—some antimony trichloride is formed at the same time.

P. Jannasch and W. Remmler made the crystalline sulphide by melting antimony trioxide with an excess of sulphur—the reaction is hastened if a trace of iodine be present. B. Unger obtained it by heating a mixture of an antimonate with an excess of sulphur ; J. Durocher, and H. Arctowsky, by the action of hydrogen sulphide on the vapour of antimony trichloride, or, according to A. Carnot, on other antimony compounds ; J. T. Norton, by heating a mixture of antimony chloride and sodium thiosulphate in a sealed tube at 140°-200° ; and E. Weinschenk, by heating potassium antimonyl tartrate with an aq. or tartaric acid soln. of ammonium thiocyanate, or by heating it with potassium thiocyanate. N. H. Warren said that at a low temp. the amorphous sulphide is formed, and at a higher temp., the crystalline sulphide. According to H. Rose, and T. Paul, crystalline antimony trisulphide is formed when antimony pentasulphide is heated to 200°-300° in a current of carbon dioxide. B. Brauner said that the pentasulphide forms the trisulphide in the presence of a soln. of hydrogen sulphide in dil. hydrochloric acid exposed to sunlight ; and the trisulphide, by the action of hydrogen sulphide on the pentasulphide suspended in dil. hydrochloric acid at 98°, or in the presence of chromium trichloride. H. de Sénarmont obtained the crystalline trisulphide by heating the pentasulphide in a soln. of sodium hydrocarbonate in a sealed tube at 250°. G. Tocco showed that alternating current electrolysis of sodium thiosulphate soln. with antimony electrodes yields the sulphides and thio-salts of this metal in proportions varying with the conditions. The proportion of the sulphide reaches 100 per cent. when a 20 per cent. thiosulphate soln. is electrolyzed at 50°–60° with a current density of 51 amps. per sq. dm. As a rule, the formation of sulphides is favoured by a high current density, limited by the value at which mechanical disintegration of the electrode begins, by a high concentration of the thiosulphate, and by a temp. of about 50°. The addition of alkali sulphide or carbonate hinders the formation of sulphide and enhances that of sulpho-salt. The current efficiency is 0·669 per cent.—*vide infra*, sodium sulphantimonite.

Amorphous antimony trisulphide was reported by J. N. von Fuchs, and H. Rose to be formed by rapidly cooling the molten compound—say by cooling the sulphide, melted in a narrow, thin-walled, glass tube, by ice-cold water. The shorter the time of fusion, and the longer the time of cooling, the greater the proportion of crystalline sulphide associated with the amorphous. A. Ditte obtained the black, crystalline sulphide by pouring the molten sulphide into cold water. H. Rose said that if a rapid current of carbon dioxide be passed over the molten trisulphide, a red sublimate of amorphous sulphide is formed a little distance away. P. Chrétien and J. M. Guinchant passed a current of nitrogen over artificial antimony trisulphide at 850°, and cooled the tube in the immediate vicinity by cold water. The sublimed trisulphide is amorphous, any excess sulphur can be removed by carbon disulphide at the b.p., and then in a sealed tube at 110°. J. von Liebig obtained the amorphous trisulphide by adding a dil. soln. of a strong acid to a soln. of an alkali or alkaline earth sulphantimonite. The amorphous trisulphide is formed when the so-called kermes (*q.v.*) is treated with tartaric or acetic acid. L. Brunet obtained the impure sulphide by the action of the sulphur dioxide fumes from roasting furnaces on sulphantimonites of the alkalies or alkaline earths. G. Vortmann obtained the amorphous trisulphide by the action of sodium thiosulphate on a soln. of an antimonious salt : $2SbCl_3 + 9Na_2S_2O_3 = Sb_2S_3 + 3Na_2S_4O_6 + 3Na_2SO_3 + 6NaCl$; a trace of sulphuric acid is formed at the same time. The colour—orange to dark red— of the product depends on the temp. and on the conc. of the soln. The amorphous trisulphide is also formed when stibine (*q.v.*) acts on sulphur or hydrogen sulphide.

O. Bosek found that the trisulphide, along with some pentasulphide, is formed when hydrogen sulphide acts slowly on a warm, hydrochloric acid soln. of antimony pentoxide, so that the long-continued passage of the gas favours the formation of the trisulphide. So does low acid conc., and a temp. not exceeding say 95°. L. M. Currie obtained similar results. As indicated in connection with some analytical reactions of antimony, antimony trisulphide is formed when hydrogen sulphide is passed into a soln. of an antimonious salt. H. Rose passed hydrogen sulphide through a soln. of antimony chloride and tartaric acid in hydrochloric acid, until the warm soln. is sat. The precipitate was washed with warm water. A. Duflos said that the soln. is not completely decomposed if the tartaric acid be omitted owing to the formation of a sulphochloride which is not all decomposed under these conditions ; and, added J. P. Cooke, for a soln. of 2 grms. of antimony in 30 c.c. of conc. hydrochloric acid, 15 grms. of tartaric acid are necessary to prevent the formation of the sulphochloride. F. Schmidt said that if the precipitation is made from potassium antimonyl tartrate, the tartrate can be removed from the precipitate by washing with water containing potassium carbonate. R. Finkener precipitated the sulphide from an ammoniacal soln. of antimony trichloride and tartaric acid. S. P. Sharples added that when the precipitation is made from boiling soln., the trisulphide is granular and easily washed.

According to L. A. Youtz, antimony trisulphide precipitated from a soln. containing free hydrochloric acid is never pure, but is always contaminated with more or less relatively volatile antimony oxychloride, which cannot be removed even by redissolving the precipitate in ammonium sulphide and reprecipitating with acetic acid. Antimony trisulphide precipitated from a soln. free from chlorides does not suffer loss on prolonged heating at 250° in a current of carbon dioxide

TABLE III.—THE SOLUBILITY OF ANTIMONY TRISULPHIDE IN HYDROCHLORIC ACID.

Conc. of free acid per cent. HCl	100 grms. of solution contain in grms.			100 c.c. of supernatant gas
	SbCl$_3$	HCl	H$_2$S	
21·44	0·308	21·372	0·023	0·014
20·5	0·250	20·460	0·014	0·009
19·5	0·183	19·420	0·009	0·005
18·4	0·122	18·36	0·005	0·002
17·4	0·074	17·41	0·002	trace
16·4	0·031	16·39	trace	trace
15·5	0·012	15·49	trace	trace
14·5	0·005	14·50	trace	trace
1·0	trace	1·00	trace	trace

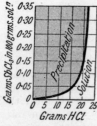

FIG. 57.—Solubility of Antimony Trisulphide in Hydrochloric Acid.

As previously indicated, the formation of antimony trisulphide, by the action of hydrogen sulphide on a hydrochloric acid soln. of antimony trichloride, is a reversible one, $2SbCl_3 + 3H_2S \rightleftharpoons Sb_2S_3 + 6HCl$. J. Lang found that when an excess of antimony trisulphide is allowed to remain in contact with hydrochloric acid of different conc. for 4 months, at 15°–18°, the amounts of antimony trichloride passing into soln. are those indicated in Table III. Fig. 57 depicts the amount of antimony which escapes precipitation as trisulphide in the presence of hydrochloric acid of different concentrations. On the other hand, when a soln. of antimony trichloride in hydrochloric acid, is treated with 0·250 grm. of hydrogen sulphide per 100 parts of liquid at 20°–24° :

Initial	SbCl$_3$	.	0·004	0·047	0·609	1·230	1·940	3·220 grms.
	HCl	.	18·362	20·458	22·046	22·660	22·905	23·203 „
Final	HCl	.	18·4	20·5	22·2	23·0	23·4	24·0 „

at 53° the results were :

Initial	SbCl$_3$	.	0·006	0·278	3·350	11·276	21·550 grms.
	HCl	.	16·870	19·077	20·480	20·760	19·088 „
Final	HCl	.	16·9	19·2	21·2	23·4	26·1 „

and at 97° :

Initial	SbCl$_3$	.	trace	0·102	4·602	8·220 grms.
	HCl	.	8·850	9·031	10·890	11·151 „
Final	HCl	.	8·86	9·04	11·42	12·2 „

J. Lang found that hydrochloric acid of all concentrations acts on antimony trisulphide. In the presence of an excess of the trisulphide, the action continues until the conc. of the hydrochloric acid diminishes to a certain point, this point depending on the proportion of hydrogen sulphide present in the soln. The equilibrium will then be disturbed if the press. on the hydrogen sulphide over the soln. be increased ; this causes a reversal of the reaction, which is shown by the separation of antimony trisulphide. On the other hand, if the hydrogen sulphide be removed from the soln. as it is formed, the action of the hydrochloric acid will continue until all the antimony trisulphide is dissolved. M. Berthelot, and A. Ditte discussed the phenomena from the point of view of the principle of maximum work.

H. Rose converted the red amorphous sulphide into the black crystalline form by heating it to 200° in a current of an indifferent gas. If the temp. be 180°–190°, the red amorphous form reappears on cooling. J. P. Cooke said that at 210°–220°, the conversion of red amorphous sulphide into the black crystalline form starts in one place, and extends throughout the whole mass ; and the black amorphous sulphide becomes crystalline at 265° in vacuo. G. Tammann made some observations on this subject. V. Zani found that the orange-red precipitate changes into the greyish-black form at about 217°, and heat is evolved during the change. Stibnite differs from the greyish-black form only in sp. gr. A. Mourlot found the transformation occurs when the amorphous sulphide is melted ; W. Spring, when it is subjected to great pressures ; A. Carnot, when it is heated in a current of hydrogen sulphide ; E. Schürmann, when it is heated in a sealed tube with water vapour at 200° ; and H. de Sénarmont, when it is heated with water at 200°, or a soln. of sodium hydrocarbonate or potassium sulphide. H. Rose observed that no transformation occurs in water at 100°. The transformation was also found by J. L. Proust, H. Rose, and A. Ditte to occur when the amorphous sulphide is treated with dil. acids, particularly hydrochloric acid. J. Lang said that the change occurs slowly in the presence of hydrochloric acid, and this the more rapidly, the more conc. the acid. For example, at 15°–16°, the transformation occupies the following periods in hydrochloric acid of the concentration named :

| HCl | . | . | . | 20–23 | 18 | 16 | 15 | 14 | 13 | 1 per cent. |
| Time for transformation | . | | | 8 | 13 | 21 | 26 | 33 | 40 | 150 days. |

H. Rose said that the boiling acid, of such a concentration, dissolves only a little sulphide, converting amorphous antimony trisulphide in 15–120 mins. into the crystalline sulphide—the precipitated sulphide rather more quickly than that prepared in the dry way. Hydrobromic acid was found by A. Ditte to act like hydrochloric acid. A. Ditte, and H. Rose also showed that sulphuric acid affects the conversion more slowly than does hydrochloric acid. Tartaric acid, and acids which have not the power to dissolve the trisulphide, were found by H. Rose to have no perceptible action on the transformation. S. Wilson and C. R. McCrosky observed no appreciable transformation during two months' action of $7N$-H_3PO_4, $7N$-H_2SO_4, glacial and normal acetic acid, and a sat. soln. of hydrochloric acid in ether—at 18°–22°. With $12N$-HCl, $7N$-HCl, and N-HCl, they found the times necessary for complete transformation were respectively 0·5 day, one day, and 10·5 days. The action was attributed to a dissolution of the red variety and a reprecipitation as the less soluble black variety. With 20 per cent. aq. hydrochloric acid, complete conversion at 26·5° required forty-four hrs. ; at 30°, twenty-nine hrs. ; 35°, sixteen hrs. ; 40°, nine hrs. ; 68·5°, sixty-two mins. ; and 75°, thirty-two mins. A 20 per cent. soln. of hydrobromic acid gave no change after 20 hrs. at 75°. F. de Bacho found that there is no material difference in the loss in weight when the red trisulphide is heated in carbon dioxide at temp. from 150° to 300°, the change to the black modification taking place at 212°, whilst in a current of hydrogen sulphide the change occurs at 207°. By adding ammonium chloride to the red sulphide, the temp. of the change in carbon dioxide is lowered (for example, to 170°), whilst the presence of antimony chloride reduces the temp. still further. Thus in the case of a mixture of equal parts of antimony trisulphide and trichloride, the black coloration appeared at 125°. Metallic silver also has a favourable influence on the transformation. The action of ammonium chloride in boiling soln. also promotes the formation of the black sulphide to an extent depending on the conc. of the soln., whilst the rapidity of the transformation stands in relationship to the degree of hydrolysis of the ammonium chloride and consequent acidity of the soln. The presence of antimony trichloride facilitates this conversion, which is accelerated by the presence of hydrochloric acid, antimony trisulphide, and potassium nitrate at high concentrations. Conc. soln. of electrolytes, such as sodium chloride, ammonium sulphate, or potassium nitrate alone have no effect on the transformation, which is therefore not merely the result of molecular condensation. The conversion always takes place when the conditions permit of immediate contact between the red antimony trisulphide and antimony trichloride, whether added as such or formed in the soln. It is probable that the following reaction takes place : $2Sb_2S_3 + 2SbCl_3 \rightarrow 6Sb + 3S_2Cl_2$. It is also probable that the trace of free antimony thus formed, or that produced by dissociation of the red trisulphide when heated, forms in the colloidal condition a solid soln. with the antimony trisulphide. C. A. Mitchell saturated with hydrogen sulphide a soln. of antimony trioxide in dil. hydrochloric acid, and passed carbon dioxide through the boiling hot liquid to obtain the crystalline trisulphide.

The physical properties of antimony trisulphide.—Amorphous antimony trisulphide has various colours ; it may appear dark lead-grey or reddish-brown, and in thin layers hyacinth-red (J. N. von Fuchs) without showing under the microscope any sign of crystalline structure (H. Rose,[5] and N. Teclu). It may be violet (P. Chrétien and J. M. Guinchant) ; dark red, fiery red, rose, carmine-red, orange-red (B. Unger, N. Teclu, J. Lang, and E. Kopp). As shown by J. Akerman, and M. Pettenkofer, the colour depends on the mode of preparation. The different colours are probably related with the size of the grain as in the analogous case of ferric oxide noted by L. Wöhler and C. Condrea. V. Zani found that the compositions of orange-red precipitated sulphide ; of the greyish-black sulphide obtained by heating the orange-red sulphide ; and of stibnite—all correspond with Sb_2S_3. L. M. Currie showed that the amorphous trisulphide is yellow if in a fine state of subdivision ; if the grain size is larger, the colour is crimson. Maroon colours are mixtures of the yellow-and-black crystalline sulphide. Yellow trisulphide can be obtained by electrical disintegration. Pigments precipitated in the presence of sulphides or hydrosulphides darken through varying shades of yellow, brown, and black. The difference between brown and maroon pigments is due to an adsorbed film of hydrogen sulphide on the former which prevents the growth of the particles. F. Kirchhof suggested that the colour of red antimony sulphide may be due to the closed ring structure :

$$Sb\!\!\left\langle\begin{smallmatrix}S\\[2pt]S\\[2pt]S\end{smallmatrix}\right\rangle\!\!Sb$$

Antimonium crudum, and the crystalline antimony trisulphide prepared by melting the constituent elements together, form dark grey masses with a metallic appearance. The artificial crystals may appear as greyish-black needles. The mineral *mine d'antimoine grise ou sulfureuse* was shown by J. B. L. Romé de l'Isle to have crystals belonging to the rhombic system. The mineral occurs in lead-grey, steel-grey masses, in coarse or fine granules, and sometimes as an impalpable grey powder. The crystals under ordinary conditions are opaque, but O. Mügge found that in sunlight very thin plates were transparent and coloured yellowish-red or deep red, and P. Drude found the transmitted light has a greater wave-length than the Li-light. The crystals commonly occur in confused aggregates or radiating groups of acicular crystals. A few measurements were reported by R. J. Haüy, J. J. Bernhardi, and F. Mohs. The subject was examined in some detail by J. A. Krenner in his monograph : *Crystallographische Studien uber den Antimonit*. E. S. Dana gave for the axial ratios of the rhombic crystals $a : b : c = 0.99257 : 1 : 1.01788$. The prismatic crystals often have acute terminations, and the vertical planes may be striated or deeply furrowed longitudinally. The crystals may also be curved, bent in knee-shaped forms, or twisted about an axial plane. The twinning or trilling of the crystals was described by J. A. Krenner, H. Schneiderhöhn, and H. Buttgenbach. The cleavage on the (010)-face is perfect, and that face is often bent transversely and striated. The (100)- and (110)-cleavages are imperfect. O. Mügge also detected cleavages on the (001)- and (101)-faces. The gliding plane, and the percussion figures were studied by O. Mügge, G. Seligmann, M. Kuhara, F. B. Peck, and A. S. Eakle ; and the corrosion figures by H. Schneiderhöhn. Observations on the crystals were also reported by A. Schrauf, P. Gravino, P. Groth, E. Quercigh, M. de Angelis, W. Koort, T. Haege, H. von Foullon, A. Schmidt,

O. Neff, **A. Lévy, E.** Rethwisch, **V.** Goldschmidt, H. Hessenberg, E. Artini, J. R. Blum, A. Sadebeck, and L. Bombicci. H. Schneiderhöhn studied the microstructure of polished surfaces etched with potash-lye. J. A. Krenner said that the crystals are isomorphous with those of bismuthinite, and guanajuatite. F. Rinne also discussed its isomorphism with antimony trioxide. The **X-radiogram** of stibnite was examined by H. Haga and F. M. Jäger, and P. F. Kerr. C. Gottfried found that the edge of the elementary rhomb has sides $a=11\cdot39$ A., $b=11\cdot48$ A., and $c=3\cdot89$ A.; each elementary cell has 4 mols. of Sb_2S_3; and the calculated axial ratios are $a:b:c=0\cdot992:1:0\cdot338$. Similar results were obtained by Z. Ooe.

The so-called amorphous antimony trisulphide was found by H. Rose [6] to retain $0\cdot2$–$0\cdot6$ per cent. of water when dried over sulphuric acid, or at $100°$, and this is driven off at $200°$ as the amorphous passes into the grey sulphide. Confirmatory observations were made by G. C. Wittstein, and W. P. Dexter. According to A. Ditte, the precipitated trisulphide retains water eq. to $Sb_2S_3.2H_2O$ when dried over sulphuric acid in vacuo for many days. J. P. Cooke said that some of the loss that occurs when the trisulphide is heated is due to the volatilization of adsorbed antimony trichloride. J. P. Cooke, L. F. Nilson, J. Akerman, and E. Matheu-Plessy found that the precipitate dried at $100°$ is free from water. V. Zani said that the losses in weight obtained by heating the orange-red precipitated sulphide to $100°$, are not due to the loss of water, but to secondary reactions involving the absorption of oxygen, the loss of sulphur dioxide, and the eventual production of antimony.

The **specific gravity** of the amorphous trisulphide prepared by fusion was found by J. N. von Fuchs to be $4\cdot15$; and that of a sample not all amorphous was found by H. Rose to be $4\cdot467$. P. Chrétien and J. M. Guinchant gave $4\cdot278$ for the sp. gr. of the violet form at $0°$; $4\cdot120$ for that of the red form at $0°$; V. Zani, $4\cdot1205$, for the orange-red, precipitated sulphide; J. P. Cooke, $4\cdot323$ at $23°$ for the red form dried at $180°$; H. Rose, $4\cdot421$ at $16°$ for the precipitated trisulphide dried at $200°$; and V. Zani, $4\cdot2906$ for the greyish-black form obtained by heating the orange-red trisulphide. The sp. gr. of the crystalline trisulphide prepared from its elements was found by H. Rose to be $4\cdot614$ at $16°$ when in lumps, and $4\cdot641$ when powdered; A. Ditte gave $4\cdot89$; E. Quercigh, $4\cdot651$; P. Chrétien and J. M. Guinchant, $4\cdot659$ at $0°$; $4\cdot63$ at $13°$; $3\cdot84$ at $643°$; and $3\cdot82$ at $1116°$. The expansion during fusion amounts to about 17 per cent. For the crystalline trisulphide obtained by heating the amorphous form, C. J. B. Karsten gave $4\cdot752$; H. Rose, $4\cdot753$–$4\cdot806$ at $16°$; J. P. Cooke, $4\cdot29$ at $27°$; and P. Chrétien and J. M. Guinchant, $4\cdot652$ at $0°$. For the crystalline trisulphide obtained by heating the amorphous form in dil. hydrochloric acid, H. Rose gave $4\cdot670$ at $16°$; and A. Ditte, $5\cdot01$. For the crystalline form derived from the pentasulphide, H. Rose gave $4\cdot57$. The high values reported by A. Ditte, and C. J. B. Karsten were attributed by P. Chrétien and J. M. Guinchant to the use of an impure sulphide. For the sp. gr. of stibnite, F. W. Clarke gave $4\cdot52$–$4\cdot75$; H. Schröder, $4\cdot624$; V. Zani, $4\cdot6353$; and F. E. Neumann, $4\cdot603$. F. de Bacho found a gradual increase in sp. gr. on heating the red trisulphide, but no sudden rise occurred in passing from the red to the black form. The **hardness** of the mineral is $2\cdot0$–$2\cdot5$. E. Madelung and R. Fuchs gave for the **compressibility,** $1\cdot94\times10^{12}$ dynes per sq. cm.

H. de Sénarmont measured the relative values of the **thermal conductivities** in the directions of the axes, and found for the ratio $c:b=1\cdot8$, for $c:a=1\cdot4$, and for $a:b=1\cdot3$; and for the isothermal ellipsoid in the directions $c:a:b$ $=1\cdot8:1\cdot3:1\cdot4$. F. B. Peck also made observations on this subject. F. E. Neuman gave for the **specific heat** of stibnite, $0\cdot0877$–$0\cdot0907$; H. V. Regnault, $0\cdot08403$ for the artificial crystals; and A. de la Rive and F. Marcet, $0\cdot1286$. A. S. Russell gave for the crystalline sulphide prepared from the fused elements $0\cdot0850$ from $4\cdot0°$ to $45\cdot7°$; $0\cdot0800$, from $0°$ to $-73\cdot2°$; and $0\cdot0627$, from $-83\cdot2°$ to $-188\cdot4°$. P. Chrétien and J. M. Guinchant gave $0\cdot0816$ for the mean sp. ht. between $20°$ and

500° ; 0·220 for the sp. ht. of the solid at 500°, and 0·263 for the sp. ht. of the liquid at 582°. N. Teclu observed that when the amorphous trisulphide is heated to 100° it becomes brown or grey, but the original colour returns on cooling. As indicated above, at temp. not far from 200°, the orange-red trisulphide becomes permanently greyish-black. R. Cusack found the **melting point** of stibnite to be between 513° and 523° ; L. H. Borgström, 546°–551° ; and for artificial trisulphide, H. Pélabon gave 550° ; Y. Takahashi, 494° ; E. Quercigh, 548° ; K. Konno, 549° ; P. Chrétien and J. M. Guinchant, 540° ; and F. M. Jäger and H. S. van Klooster, 546°—vide Fig. 50. K. Friedrich said that stibnite from Ichinokawa, Japan, does not decrepitate when heated ; if the fine-grained material is heated in oxygen, it sinters together at 370° ; in a current of air, at 440° ; and at 510°, the whole mass melts. A lump of the stibnite began to melt at 540°. F. Krafft and L. Merz observed that when the trisulphide is heated in vacuo at 530°, it distils with great rapidity, and it can thus be quantitatively separated from bismuthinite, which distils at 740°. If air be excluded, antimony trisulphide can be distilled without decomposition. C. Zengelis showed that antimony trisulphide can vaporize at ordinary temp. J. Joly gave 380° for the sublimation temp. of stibnite. P. Chrétien and J. M. Guinchant gave 1180° for the **boiling point.** H. Pélabon found the **freezing-point constant** to be 788°–797° ; and he found the latent **heat of fusion** to be 17·5 Cals., when the calculated value is 16·7 Cals. According to A. Mourlot, by raising the temp. of stibnite high enough for a few minutes in an electric arc furnace it can be completely decomposed into antimony, etc. P. Chrétien and J. M. Guinchant said that the trisulphide is usually dissociated at 600°. P. Chrétien and J. M. Guinchant found the **heat of formation** of antimony trisulphide from octahedral sulphur and antimony to be (2Sb,3S)=38·2 Cals. for the black variety, 33·9 Cals. for the violet ; and for the moist orange-red, 34·0 Cals., and for the dried, 32·6 Cals. They therefore gave for the **heat of transformation :** violet to black, 4·3 Cals. ; dry, precipitated, orange-red to black, 5·6 Cals. ; and moist, precipitated, orange-red to black, 4·2 Cals. K. Jellinek and J. Zakowsky calculated for the mol. ht. of formation, 31·3 Cals. M. Berthelot measured the **heat of solution** of the amorphous orange-red sulphide in a soln. of sodium sulphide at 12°, and found it to be 666 cals., when that of the crystalline form is 631 cals. ; the **heat of crystallization,** within the limits of experimental error, is therefore 35 cals.

P. Drude found the **indices of refraction,** μ, and μ_2, for sodium light to be 5·17 and 4·49 ; and for the **coefficients of absorption,** k, and k_2, he gave 0·143 and 0·177. E. C. Müller found for the light of wave-length λ :

λ		C-ray	610$\mu\mu$	D-ray	E-ray	510$\mu\mu$	F-ray	460$\mu\mu$	G-ray
μ_1	•	4·69	4·87	5·12	5·47	5·48	5·53	5·17	4·65
μ_2	•	0·0537	0·104	0·124	0·234	0·305	0·404	0·531	0·681
k_1	•	4·47	4·26	4·37	4·52	4·51	4·49	4·41	4·28
k_2	•	0·120	0·177	0·187	0·252	0·286	0·344	0·413	0·485
$\mu_1-\mu_2$	•	0·22	0·61	0·75	0·95	0·97	1·04	0·76	0·37

A. Hutchinson obtained the indices of refraction $a=3·194$, $\beta=4·046$, and $\gamma=4·303$. Stibnite has the highest known index of refraction and **birefringence,** $\mu_1-\mu_2$. K. Asagoe and N. Kumagai studied the reflecting power ; W. W. Coblentz and C. W. Hughes, the ultra-violet reflecting power ; W. W. Coblentz, and I. B. Crandall, the ultra-red reflecting power ; and I. B. Crandall, and E. P. T. Tyndall, the optical properties of stibnite. A. de Gramont examined the **spark spectrum** of stibnite. C. Doelter found that **radium rays** make stibnite rather more violet-grey, and somewhat darker ; the amorphous form is not crystallized by exposure to these rays. O. Stelling studied the **X-ray absorption spectrum** for the K-series. The mineral does not phosphoresce in the **cathode rays** ; and the sol is browned but not precipitated by **ultra-violet rays.** A. Hutchinson found the mineral is **diathermal** in that it is not opaque to **ultra-red rays.** If the plane of the symmetry of a crystal coincides with the plane of oscillation of the nicol's prism, no heat is transmitted through the crystal, but when the plane of symmetry is rotated 45°, a maximum transmission is obtained. E. T. Wherry classed stibnite as a poor **radiodetector.** W. W. Coblentz studied the **photoelectric effect** with stibnite. and found that the passage of an alternating current has no permanent effect on the photoelectric sensitivity. J. O. Perrine observed no ultra-violet fluorescence when stibnite is exposed to X-rays for 5 hrs. The maximum effect occurs at 0.77μ. H. F. Vieweg studied the frictional electricity.

According to H. Rose, amorphous antimony trisulphide is a very bad **electrical conductor ;** and F. Beijerinck said that the crystalline mineral is a very bad conductor at 240°. C. Doelter, G. Cesaro, and H. Bäckström and K. Angström obtained similar results. J. Königsberger and K. Schilling, and F. M. Jäger found rhombic antimony sulphide is a very bad conductor of electricity in darkness at room temp. while the sulphide which has been fused is a good conductor. The sp. resistance of the rhombic native crystals is about 10^8 ohms at ordinary temp., but this decreases with a rise of temp. F. M. Jäger found the **electrical resistance** of a centimetre rod of Japanese stibnite to be 500×10^6 to $20,000 \times 10^6$ ohms. C. Tubandt and M. Haedicke found that antimony trisulphide is an insulator below its m.p. The electrical conductivity of crystals of stibnite is photosensitive since it is very much augmented by exposure to light. The effect is not due to a rise of temp. With white-light, the conductivity was raised 200–210 per cent. ; in red-light, 194–205 per cent. ; in yellow-light, 150–153 per cent. ; in green-light, 116–118 per cent. ; and in blue-light, 175–176 per cent. The green rays for which the index of refraction and birefringence attain their greatest value, have least effect on the electrical conductivity. When the mineral is finely powdered, the effect is suppressed, showing that the effect is due to the microscopic structure of the mineral. This property of stibnite is important ; light sensitive cells can be obtained with a much larger potential difference than with selenium, and the recovery of the cell occupies less time. The subject was also investigated by B. Glatzel, T. W. Case, and C. Ries. J. Olie and H. R. Kruyt found that impure stibnite was not photoelectric. Artificial stibnite prepared by heating the constituents in vacuo at 600° is photosensitive ; and the maximum sensitiveness, corresponding with that of Japanese stibnite, is attained with a mixture equivalent to Sb_2S_3. The rapid change in the photoelectric sensitiveness when the mixture deviates slightly from Sb_2S_3, is probably due to the formation of mixed crystals. Small quantities of impurities are of considerable importance—even impurities derived from the glass in which the sulphur is heated have an effect. For the electrical conductivity of mixtures of antimony and antimony trisulphide, *vide supra*, antimony. Unlike F. M. Jäger, J. Olie and H. R. Kruyt found that the stibnite can be melted and solidified without appreciably changing the effect. The conductivity of a surface of stibnite strewn with lycopodium shows that the favoured zone is elliptical. This subject was studied by H. de Sénarmont, and E. Jannettaz. K. Fischbeck found that there is a 60 per cent. reduction of powdered antimony trisulphide on a platinum electrode in contact with 2 per cent. sulphuric acid. E. E. Fairbanks found the **dielectric constant** is less than 81.

The chemical properties of antimony trisulphide.—H. Rose,[7] and P. Berthier showed that when antimony trisulphide is heated to near its m.p., it is reduced to the metal by **hydrogen ;** E. R. Schneider observed no reduction at 320°, but found that it occurred near 360°, and at this temp., antimony is transformed into the trisulphide by hydrogen sulphide. The equilibrium conditions in the reaction $Sb_2S_3 + 3H_2 \rightleftharpoons 2Sb + 3H_2S$ were studied by H. Pélabon—*vide supra*, antimony. H. Pélabon gave for the ratio v_{H_2S}/v_{H_2}, 0·754 at 440° ; 0·945 at 510° ; 1·07 at 555° ; 1·27 at 610° ; and 1·32 at 625° ; and K. Jellinek and J. Zakowsky calculated for the vap. press., p, of the sulphur at 440°, $\log p = -6.93$; at 515°, -5.88 ; at 565°, -5.58 ; and at 610°, -4.92. When the trisulphide is heated in air, the crystalline form burns with a blue flame, before it melts, forming sulphur dioxide and a mixture of the tri- and tetra-oxides (*q.v.*) ; J. von Liebig said that the amorphous form glows when brought in contact with a red-hot substance. L. A. Buchner found that powdered, black antimony trisulphide slowly oxidizes when exposed to air ; a soln. of potassium tartrate will extract the trioxide from the exposed trisulphide. W. Haidinger observed the passage of stibnite to valentinite, and antimony ochre ; while A. S. Eakle reported the formation of sénarmontite, sulphur, and gypsum ; H. Laspeyres observed pseudomorphs of antimony ochre after stibnite ; and J. R. Blum reported pseudomorphs of several other minerals after stibnite. P. L. Geiger and L. Hesse said that when the moist, amorphous sulphide is exposed to air it is gradually converted into the trioxide ; while E. Pollacci said that antimony sulphide oxidizes rapidly in moist air. F. Carmichael observed 0·07 per cent. oxidation occurred by exposing the powdered mineral to the action of aerated water for 13 days. P. Jannasch found that stibnite is readily decomposed when heated in **oxygen**. According to W. R. Schoeller, antimony is produced when stibnite is heated alone in a current of air, and subsequently at 950° in a current of carbon dioxide. K. Friedrich found that the oxidation of antimony trisulphide : $2Sb_2S_3 + 9O_2 = 2Sb_2O_3 + 6SO_2$, begins at about 290° with a grain-size of 0·10 mm., and at 340°, with a grain-size 0·20 mm. H. Saito found that oxidation begins at about 290°, and above 500°, the oxidation of the trioxide : $Sb_2O_3 + \frac{1}{2}O_2 = Sb_2O_4$, begins ; it is rapid at 520°, and ceases at 560°. A. Mailfert said that **ozone** transforms stibnite into antimony sulphate. E. H. Riesenfeld and W. Haase found that a colloidal soln. of the trisulphide is oxidized by ozone to antimonic acid. G. Tammann and H. Bredemeier studied the surface oxidation of antimony sulphide. O. Weigel inferred from his conductivity measurements that a litre of **water** dissolves $5·2 \times 10^{-6}$ mol of the precipitated trisulphide per litre at 18°. A. Ditte said that the formula of the precipitated, amorphous trisulphide when dried in vacuo over sulphuric acid is $Sb_2S_3.2H_2O$, but this is probably a chance result, since there is no evidence of the formation of definite *hydrates of antimony trisulphide ;* E. M. Plessy gave $Sb_2S_3.H_2O$. As shown by P. L. Geiger and L. Hesse, and by A. Vogel, boiling water slowly decomposes the precipitated trisulphide, forming hydrogen sulphide and a little antimony trioxide which passes into soln. P. de Clermont and J. Frommel said that the freshly precipitated sulphide is more readily decomposed than that which has been dried at 125°. By boiling the trisulphide with water under reduced press., decomposition can be observed at 95°. E. Lesser, M. Rousseau, W. Elbers also observed the reaction with hot water. According to J. Lang, stibnite is also readily decomposed by boiling water, and a little soluble sulphantimonite is formed by the action of alkali dissolved from the glass. C. Doelter showed that powdered stibnite reacts with water when the mixture is heated in a sealed tube for some weeks. The presence of carbon dioxide, or of sodium or hydrogen sulphide, accelerates the reaction. H. V. Regnault found that when steam is passed over red-hot antimony trisulphide, hydrogen sulphide and sublimed antimony oxysulphide are formed. L. J. Thénard found that **hydrogen dioxide** converts antimony trisulphide into sulphate, and, added L. Zambelli and E. Luzzato, if the dioxide be in excess, at 40°, antimony pentoxide is formed. J. Clark observed that an ammoniacal soln. of hydrogen dioxide converts the trisulphide completely into ammonium metantimonite ; and F. Raschig, T. Poleck, and W. Hampe, that **sodium dioxide** converts the trisulphide into sodium metantimonite.

H. Moissan [8] found that, at ordinary temp., **fluorine** converts antimony trisulphide into the trifluoride, and the reaction is accompanied by a blue flame. H. Rose observed that **chlorine** does not act on the powdered crystalline trisulphide in the cold, but when heated, antimony trichloride is formed. P. Jannasch and W. Remmler showed that the trisulphide is completely decomposed by **bromine ;** and, in the presence of water, E. H. Bartley said that hydrated antimony pentoxide is formed. J. Lemberg found that a soln. of bromine in potash-lye converts the trisulphide into soluble potassium antimonate. H. C. Bolton found that **iodine** in the presence of water completely decomposes stibnite. H. Rose, C. Tookey, and L. L. de Koninck and A. Lecrenier observed that when a current of **hydrogen chloride** is passed over the heated trisulphide, hydrogen sulphide and antimony trichloride are formed ; and J. Kelley and E. F. Smith also noticed that antimony trisulphide is completely volatilized when heated in a current of hydrogen chloride or **hydrogen bromide.** Conc. **hydrochloric acid** was found by H. Rose to act similarly. H. N. Warren found that the native sulphide is more quickly attacked than the precipitated sulphide. W. R. Lang and C. M. Carson found that the trisulphide is soluble in a mixture of 50 parts of water and 18 parts of hydrochloric acid, of sp. gr. 1·16, even when completely saturated with hydrogen sulphide. Consequently, hydrogen sulphide does not precipitate antimony trisulphide from conc. hydrochloric acid soln.—*vide supra*, Fig. 54. The work of J. Lang, M. Berthelot, and A. Ditte on this subject has been previously discussed ; and the application of the reaction for the analytical separation of antimony trisulphide from the less soluble arsenic trisulphide has been discussed by F. Field, E. Lesser, M. Schleier, L. Loviton, H. Köhler, A. Stromeyer, F. Neher, etc.—*vide* arsenic trichloride. E. R. Schneider observed that amorphous trisulphide becomes crystalline in the presence of **hydrobromic acid**—*vide supra* for the conversion of amorphous into the crystalline trisulphide. According to R. Böttger, a mixture of **potassium chlorate** and antimony trisulphide is explosive, and it can be detonated by the electric spark.

The relations between antimony trisulphide and **sulphur** are indicated in Fig. 56. S. E. Linder and H. Picton [9] thought that colloidal antimony trisulphide is united with **hydrogen sulphide,** and M. Berthelot added that if a soln. of an antimony compound is added in very small drops with continual agitation to a sat. soln. of hydrogen sulphide, the precipitate which forms is redissolved. This fact points to the formation of a hydrosulphide or unstable *hydrosulphantimonious acid,* which, however, can exist only in contact with water in presence of a large excess of hydrogen sulphide. A. Baudrimont, and H. Feigel found that sulphur monochloride dissolves antimony trisulphide, forming sulphur and antimony trichloride. A. E. Becquerel, and A. V. L. Verneuil found that antimony trisulphide modifies the phosphorescence of **calcium and strontium sulphides.** According to H. Prinz, the reaction with heated **thionyl chloride** can be represented : $6SOCl_2 + 2Sb_2S_3$ $= 4SbCl_3 + 9S + 3SO_2$, and O. Ruff showed that antimony trisulphide is dissolved by **sulphuryl chloride,** forming antimony trichloride with the separation of sulphur, but in the presence of aluminium chloride, sulphur dichloride is produced. P. Berthier said that an aq. soln. of **sulphur dioxide** is without action on the trisulphide, but A. Gueront found that a little amorphous trisulphide is dissolved with the separation of sulphur, and the formation of hydrogen sulphide. R. Bunsen found that a boiling soln. of **potassium hydrosulphite** and sulphur dioxide completely dissolves the trisulphide, but L. F. Nilson said that in one experiment 71 per cent. remained undissolved ; arsenic trisulphide, however, was completely soluble under the same conditions. Antimony trisulphide remains quite undissolved in the presence of a large quantity of thiosulphate formed by boiling its soln. in potassium sulphide, after adding excess of sulphurous acid, but the thiosulphate precipitates a large quantity of arsenic trisulphide. If the proportion of thiosulphate is lessened, so as to ensure complete soln. of the arsenic, then antimony is also dissolved. According to H. Rose, boiling conc. **sulphuric acid** slowly dissolves the trisulphide producing a soln. of antimony sulphate, and sulphur dioxide gas, and a fused mass of sulphur. C. Hensgen obtained the sulphate in this way. H. Rose found that dil. sulphuric acid converts the amorphous into the crystalline trisulphide—*vide supra.* M. Websky found that when the trisulphide is fused with **potassium hydrosulphate,** a basic sulphate remains suspended in the fused mass ; it is insoluble in water. If the fusion be continued for a long time, a clear liquid is obtained and potassium **pyroantimonite,** soluble in water, is produced, as well as a little antimonate.

According to G. Gore,[10] red, orange, and black antimony trisulphides are insoluble in liquid **ammonia,** and E. G. Franklin and C. A. Kraus also confirmed the observation with the black trisulphide. M. Carot found that 0·005 part of crystalline antimony trisulphide dissolves in 100 parts of aq. ammonia, forming a yellow soln. from which hydrochloric acid separates a red precipitate ; 0·167 part of the amorphous sulphide is dissolved by aq. ammonia. L. Garnier also found that amorphous, freshly precipitated trisulphide is readily soluble in aq. ammonia, and H. Capitaine observed that when the soln. stands exposed to air, the trisulphide is again precipitated. P. de Clermont observed that a boiling soln. of **ammonium chloride** converts the trisulphide into antimony trichloride and ammonium sulphide. F. Ephraim found that when **sodamide** is heated with the trisulphide a vigorous reaction occurs, and antimony and sodium sulphantimonite are produced. H. Rose, and R. Bunsen found that conc. **nitric acid** transforms the trisulphide partly into sulphate and partly with nitrate with the separation of sulphur ; with fuming nitric acid of sp. gr. 1·52, on a water-bath, sulphuric acid and antimony pentoxide are formed. A hot mixture of dil. sulphuric and nitric acids gradually produces a mixture of antimony sulphate and sulphur ; a mixture of hydrochloric and nitric acids forms antimony trichloride and sulphur ; aqua regia forms hydrated antimonic acid ; and similarly also with a mixture of hydrochloric acid and potassium chlorate. C. R. Fresenius found that when the trisulphide is heated with a mixture of ammonium chloride and nitrate (5 : 1), the trisulphide is completely transformed into trichloride. A mixture of **potassium nitrate** and antimony trisulphide detonates at a red-heat yielding potassium sulphantimonate and antimony nitrate. H. Rose observed that when the trisulphide is heated with **phosphine,** hydrogen sulphide and a mixture of phosphorus and antimony are formed. E. Baudrimont found that **phosphorus chlorides** react with the trisulphide, forming antimony trichloride and phosphorus sulphide as well as some antimony sulphophosphide. For the behaviour of the trisulphide with **antimony,** vide supra, Fig. 56. H. Pélabon studied the effect of antimony on the trisulphide in an atm. of hydrogen. For the action of **antimony trioxide,** and of **antimony tetroxide,** vide supra. W. R. Schoeller showed that at 965°, a mixture of trisulphide and trioxide (1 : 2) furnishes antimony. J. Fiedler showed that a mixture of the sulphide and oxide loses oxygen in sunlight. E. R. Schneider observed the formation of antimony sulphochloride when the trisulphide is heated with **antimony trichloride,** and likewise sulphoiodide with **antimony triiodide.** 100 parts of the trichloride dissolve 6·67–7·14 parts of the trisulphide.

O. Materne [11] observed that antimony trisulphide, unlike arsenic trisulphide. is only slightly soluble in a hot two per cent. soln. of **borax,** and rather more soluble in a cold soln. L. Kahlenberg and W. J. Trautmann found that **silicon,** at comparatively low temp., does not act on antimony trisulphide, but at very high temp. a reaction occurs.

P. Berthier found that antimony trisulphide is quickly reduced by **carbon** to antimony, forming carbon disulphide when it is heated with carbon ; and A. P. Hermandez, discussing the possibility of reducing the proportion of reducing agent for a given yield, represented the reaction with carbon in the presence of potassium nitrate : $Sb_2S_3 + 8KNO_3 + 6C = 2Sb + 3K_2SO_4 + K_2CO_3 + 4CO_2 + CO + 4N_2$. F. Göbel found that the trisulphide is partly reduced when it is heated in a current of **carbon monoxide.** N. D. Costeanu observed no chemical action with **carbon dioxide** at temp. up to 1100°. H. C. Bolton found that the trisulphide is insoluble in **formic and acetic acids.** A. C. Vournasos observed that at 400° **sodium formate** reduces antimony trisulphide to antimony and hydrogen sulphide. According to F. W. Clarke, the amorphous sulphide is decomposed when boiled for a long time with **oxalic acid,** and the antimony which is dissolved is precipitated from the soln. by hydrogen sulphide, while the soln. of stannic sulphide is not precipitated in the presence of an excess of oxalic acid. Hence the two sulphides can be separated by the reaction. The analytical process was discussed by F. W. Clarke, E. P. Dewey, A. Carnot, J. Clark, and E. Lesser. H. C. Bolton also observed that antimony trisulphide is soluble in a hot soln. of oxalic acid ; and H. C. Bolton, and H. Gordon, in a hot soln. of **tartaric acid.** H. Rose said that the trisulphide is only slightly attacked when boiled with a soln. of tartaric acid or potassium tartrate. H. C. Bolton found that the trisulphide is soluble in cold or hot soln. of **citric acid,** and that it is very easily soluble in citric or oxalic acid in the presence of potassium nitrate, nitrite, or chlorate. The trisulphide is slightly soluble in **malic, benzoic, picric, and pyrogallic acids.** According to J. von Liebig, antimony trisulphide is reduced to antimony when fused with **potassium cyanide,** and potassium thiocyanate is produced. H. Rose also showed that some antimony trisulphide escapes reduction owing to the formation of a sulphantimonite. If the mixture be heated in a current of hydrogen, C. R. Fresenius observed the formation of an antimony mirror, but not so with a current of carbon dioxide. A. Levol reduced the trisulphide by heating it with **potassium ferrocyanide.** R. Zsigmondy found that glass is coloured yellow by antimony trisulphide.

When antimony trisulphide is heated to redness in the presence of many **metals**—sodium, potassium, copper, tin, iron, etc.—antimony is formed. This unites with the excess of metal, forming an antimonide (*q.v.*), and the metal sulphide unites with the antimony trisulphide, forming a sulphantimonite. According to G. Marchal,[12] the displacement of antimony from antimonious sulphide (stibnite) by copper always resulted in the formation of cuprous sulphide whatever the proportion of copper employed. The reaction, scarcely perceptible at 500°, occurs readily at 600°–700°, and at that temp. is complete in about 8 hrs., the antimony volatilizing whilst almost pure cuprous sulphide remains. When insufficient copper is used for the complete formation of cuprous sulphide, no cupric sulphide is formed, but instead the compound $3Cu_2S,Sb_2S_3$, which is only slowly decomposed above 700°, antimony sulphide subliming without decomposition, leaving finally a residue of cuprous sulphide only. C. Pertusi found that when antimony trisulphide is suspended in water and mixed with five times its weight of powdered magnesium, it reacts like arsenic trisulphide (*q.v.*). N. Parravano and P. Agostini studied the action of aluminium. Many **metal oxides** mixed with carbon act similarly because the carbon reduces the oxide to the metal. R. Bunsen found that **mercuric oxide** transforms the trisulphide into antimony pentoxide. J. J. Berzelius found that when an excess of **alkali hydroxide or carbonate** is heated with antimony trisulphide, antimony pentoxide and an alkali sulphide are formed ; the antimony pentoxide forms either an oxysulphantimonate or an antimonate with the undecomposed alkali and the trisulphide, while the alkali sulphide forms a sulphantimonite. The reaction with an excess of carbonate is symbolized : $5Sb_2S_3+7K_2CO_3=7CO_2+3K_4Sb_2S_5+K_2Sb_4O_7$; and with an excess of trisulphide, $4Sb_2S_3+3K_2CO_3=6KSbS_2+Sb_2O_3+3CO_2$. Some antimony may be produced by the reaction : $2K_2Sb_4O_7=2Sb+3Sb_2O_4+2K_2O$; or, according to H. Rose, by the reaction : $5K_4Sb_2S_5=4Sb+6K_3SbS_4+K_2S$. J. von Liebig found that the amorphous trisulphide dissolves in cold alkali-lye, forming potassium antimonite and sulphantimonite ; and, according to B. Unger, some sulphantimonate is formed at the same time. When the crystalline trisulphide is boiled with alkali-lye, the alkali sulphide and antimony oxide first produced are converted into antimonites and sulphantimonites. The pyrosulphantimonite can dissolve more trisulphide $K_4Sb_2S_5+Sb_2S_3=4KSbS_2$; but when the soln. is cooled, the pyrosulphantimonite is reformed, and the trisulphide is deposited as *mineral kermes*. O. Materne observed that a boiling soln. containing 5 per cent. Na_2CO_3 dissolves antimony trisulphide, but deposits it as orange-brown trisulphide on cooling. Acids, or ammonium chloride, precipitate the orange trisulphide from the soln., but the last trace is deposited only in the presence of hydrogen sulphide. A. Terreil said that a soln. of potassium carbonate does not act on antimony trisulphide ; and that fused potassium carbonate furnishes more mineral kermes than sodium carbonate. J. Lemberg said that a hot or cold soln. containing $KOH : 4H_2O$ covers stibnite with a red mixture of antimony trioxide and trisulphide. In etching stibnite with alkali-lye, H. Schneiderhöhn found that the (001)-face is the most quickly attacked, the (100)-face less quickly ; and the (010)-face is attacked the most slowly. H. Weppen said that soln. of the **alkaline earth hydroxides** form sulphantimonites when boiled with antimony trisulphide ; and A. Terreil found that while a soln. of calcium hydroxide reacts with antimony trisulphide, a soln. of strontium or barium hydroxide has no action. J. Lemberg said that baryta-water colours the surface of stibnite with a red mixture of antimony trioxide and trisulphide.

E. Schürmann found that a soln. of **copper sulphate** decomposes the trisulphide completely ; soln. of **zinc and cadmium sulphates,** and of **stannous chloride** have no action ; and a soln. of **mercuric chloride** completely decomposes the trisulphide. A. Vogel noticed that **mercurous chloride** gradually forms antimony trichloride and mercuric sulphide ; and P. L. Geither said that with freshly precipitated mercurous chloride and antimony trisulphide, moist or dry, the decomposition is rapid. At 100°, mercuric chloride is blackened by the dry trisulphide. A. Lindner found that a conc., feebly acidic soln. of **ferric chloride** completely decomposes antimony trisulphide with the separation of sulphur.

Colloidal antimony trisulphide.—According to H. O. Schulze,[13] colloidal antimony trisulphide is probably the primary product of the action of hydrogen sulphide on antimonious salts ; and the crystalline trisulphide is produced by the action of acids or salts on the amorphous variety. Assuming that the amorphous antimony trisulphide, previously described, is really non-crystalline, in modern terminology it would be called a **hydrogel of antimony trisulphide.** As in the corresponding case of arsenic trisulphide, colloidal soln. or the **hydrosol** of antimony trisulphide can be obtained by the action of hydrogen sulphide on a dil. soln. of antimonious salts. Thus, H. Capitaine saturated with hydrogen sulphide an aq. soln. of antimony trioxide. The small solubility of the trioxide in water renders it possible to obtain only a **very** dil. colloidal soln. by this means, but, added H. O. Schulze, a more conc. soln. can be obtained by repeating the addition of more trioxide, and hydrogen sulphide a number of times. H. O. Schulze treated soln. containing not more than 0·5 per cent. of potassium antimonyl tartrate with hydrogen sulphide ; soln. containing 1·6–1·7 per cent. of the salt are completely precipitated by hydrogen sulphide. He also obtained the colloidal soln. by passing hydrogen sulphide into a soln. of antimony trioxide (4·4 grms. per litre) and tartaric acid (12·9 grms. per litre). H. Picton poured the aq. soln. of antimony trioxide into hydrogen sulphide-water, and removed the excess of hydrogen sulphide by a current of air. According to A. Ditte, if a few drops of a soln. of potassium sulphide be added to water holding amorphous antimony trisulphide in suspension, a brownish-red gelatinous mass is formed which forms a yellow soln. with potash-lye. The soln. is coloured dark red by water, and it soon congeals to an orange-red or brownish-red jelly. If the water containing the trisulphide in suspension be treated with enough potassium sulphide to dissolve most of the antimony trisulphide, and the liquid be then diluted with 10–12 vols. of water, the soln. is coloured red, and it quickly congeals. A. Ditte showed that potassium sulphide can transform antimony trisulphide into a colloid, which subsequently produces complex sulphides (q.v.). S. Ghosh and N. R. Dhar found that antimony sulphide and its complex salts are peptized to the colloidal form by alkali-lye, yellow ammonium sulphide, and sodium arsenite. M. S. Wolvekamp obtained colloidal soln. with the trisulphide associated with a protein. F. V. von Hahn made the trisulphide by cathode charging, and by the arc process ; and S. Utzino, and H. Neugebauer, by extremely fine grinding. The soln. with particles in the finest state of subdivision are not the most stable.

According to H. O. Schulze, the antimony is present in colloidal soln. wholly as trisulphide. S. E. Linder and H. Picton thought that the trisulphide is actually united to some hydrogen sulphide. The colour of the colloidal soln. depends on the state of subdivision of the colloid. It may vary from red to yellow. If the liquid be contained in a litre flask, a soln. with 0·0025 per cent. of Sb_2S_3 appears raspberry-red ; with 0·00166 per cent., to 0·0010 per cent. yellowish-red ; 0·0001 per cent. wine-yellow ; 0·0000 per cent. light wine-yellow ; and one with 0·00001 per cent. Sb_2S_3 can be recognized only in thick layers. W. Biltz and W. Geibel has described the ultra-microscopic appearance of the soln. The clear dil. soln. shows intensely coloured, minute spheres of light. A dil. colloidal soln. of the trisulphide appears slightly fluorescent. H. Zsigmondy and C. Carius discussed the grain-size of the hydrosol. H. Picton said that the soln. keeps well, but has a tendency to deposit small quantities of the trisulphide. It is not coagulated by boiling. In a beam of light concentrated by a lens—Tyndall's effect—the track of the beam was marked by a beautiful, soft, red glow, the light of which, on examination with a Nicol's prism, was found to be completely polarized. The soln., therefore, has no true fluorescence, but consists of excessively minute particles in suspension. The most dil. soln. gave similar results. On dialyzing the colloidal soln. prepared from the tartrate, the liquid appeared to become more strongly fluorescent as dialysis proceeded, and in about 10 days, the particles in suspension were of microscopic dimensions. On further dialysis, by which means all the tartrate present was eliminated, the antimony began to precipitate, and in the course of a few weeks was completely thrown down. This is interesting, as showing the progress of a gradual condensation occurring among the minute particles. There was no sudden or irregular change, but, apparently, a regular increase of size among all the particles, forcibly reminiscent of molecular condensation. The presence of the tartrate thus hinders the precipitation of the colloid. The dialyzed soln., said H. O. Schulze, is tasteless, and dries to a brown film resembling lacquer, and containing water. N. R. Dhar and A. C. Chatterji studied the adsorption of sols and ions by antimony sulphide. H. O. Schulze found that a colloidal soln. of antimony trisulphide is less readily converted spontaneously into the insoluble form than is colloidal arsenic trisulphide. No sign of diffusion of the colloidal antimony trisulphide was observed by H. Picton, the trisulphide in suspension was separated by filtration through porous earthenware ; the soln. passed through well-washed filter-paper. The liquid gave a continuous spectrum. R. Wintgen found that the refractive index and sp. gr. are linear functions of the conc. of the soln. N. Lubavin, and A. Sabanéeff found that when the frozen soln. is thawed, the trisulphide is coagulated. H. Picton observed no temp. change during the coagulation of the soln. S. S. Bhatnagar and co-workers studied the action of light. A. Sabanéeff observed no perceptible lowering of the f.p. of water by the colloidal trisulphide. H. O. Schulze found that the maximum dilutions of soln. of acids and salts which cause the precipitation of antimony trisulphide are as follow :

HCl, 1 : 270 ; H_2SO_4, 1 : 140 ; $H_2C_2O_4$, 1 : 45 ; K_2SO_4, 1 : 65 ; $(NH_4)_2SO_4$, 1 : 130 ; $MgSO_4$, 1 : 1720 ; $MnSO_4$, 1 : 2060 ; NaCl, 1 : 135 ; $BaCl_2$, 1 : 2050 ; $MgCl_2$, 1 : 5800 ; $CoCl_2$, 1 : 2500 ; KNO_3, 1·75 ; $FeCl_3$, 1 : 2500 ; $Ba(NO_3)_2$, 1 : 1250 ; $K_2Al_2(SO_4)_4$, 1 : 35,000 ; $(NH_4)_2Fe_2(SO_4)_4$, 1 : 800 ; $K_2Cr_2(SO_4)_4$, 1 : 40,000 ; $KSbOC_4H_4O_6$, 1 : 18.

A few drops of a conc. soln. of tartaric acid with a conc. colloidal soln. of antimony trisulphide give a clear mixture, which then becomes turbid, particularly when warmed. Cane sugar, boric acid, and glacial acetic acid behave like tartaric acid. No precipitation occurs when to the hot or cold soln. is added carbon dioxide, arsenic trioxide, alcohol, chloral hydrate, or salicylic acid—vide colloidal arsenic trioxide. The subject was studied by K. C. Sen and co-workers, Wo. Ostwald, S. Ghosh and N. R. Dhar, A. Ivanitzkaja and L. Orlova, L. Schiloff, and S. Wosnessensky. S. S. Bhatnagar and co-workers studied the effect of the size of the colloidal particles on the coagulation by salts ; adsorbed sucrose, glucose, or gelatin loses its optical activity, and this is taken to agree with a chemical explanation of the mechanism of protective action with colloids ; K. Jablczynsk and co-workers studied the velocity of coagulation of the sol. P. B. Ganguly and N. R. Dhar found the colloid is coagulated by exposure to tropical sunlight.

N. R. Dhar and A. C. Chatterji did not succeed in making antimony trisulphide coagulate rhythmically. M. Prasad and co-workers studied the adsorption of sugars by antimony sulphide ; and S. S. Bhatnager and co-workers, the protective action of soaps, and the photochemical reaction with gold and silver sols.

REFERENCES.

[1] H. Pélabon, *Ann. Chim. Phys.*, (8), **17**. 526, 1909 ; *Compt. Rend.*, **138**. 277, 1904 ; **140**. 1389, 1905 ; P. Chrétien and J. M. Guinchant, *ib.*, **142**. 708, 1906 ; **138**. 1269, 1904 ; **139**. 288, 1904 ; M. Faraday, *Phil. Trans.*, **124**. 77, 1834 ; J. J. Berzelius. *Pogg. Ann.*, **37**. 163, 1836 ; F. M. Jäger and H. S. van Klooster, *Zeit. anorg. Chem.*, **78**. 245, 1912 ; K. Jellinek and J. Zakowsky, *ib.*, **142**. 1, 1925 ; J. Zakowsky, *Ueber die Affinität der Metalle zum Schwefel*, Danzig, 1904 ; B. Unger, *Arch. Pharm.*, (2), **147**. 199, 1871 ; '2), **148**. 2, 1871.

[2] Basil Valentine, *Triumphwagen antimonii*, Nürnberg, 1676 ; H. Boerhaave, *Elementa chemicæ*, Lugduni Batavorum, 1732 ; L. J. Thénard, *Ann. Chim. Phys.*, (1), **32**. 257, 1799 ; T. Bergman, *De antimonialibus sulphuratis*, Upsala, 1782 ; G. Agricola, *Bermannus sive de re metallica*, Basileæ, 1546 ; *De re metallica*, Basileæ, 1556 ; A. G. Werner, *Letztes Mineralsystem*, Freiberg, 23, 1817 ; J. G. Wallerius, *Mineralogia*, Stockholm, 307, 1750 ; L. A. Emmerling, *Lehrbuch der Mineralogie*, Giessen, **2**. 468, 1796 ; J. Kunckel, *Vollständiges Laboratorium Chymicum*, Hamburg, 432, 1722 ; F. Mohs, *Grundriss der Mineralogie*, Dresden, **2**. 582, 1824 ; W. Haidinger, *Handbuch der bestimmenden Mineralogie*, Wien, 568, 1845 ; F. S. Beudant, *Traité élémentaire de minéralogie*, Paris, **2**. 421, 1832 ; J. D. Dana, *A System of Mineralogy*, New York, 33, 1855 ; C. C. von Leonhard, *Handbuch der Oryktognosie*, Heidelberg, 152, 1821 ; W. Koort, *Beitrage zur Kenntnis der Antimonglanzes*, Berlin, 1884 ; C. F. Rammelsberg, *Handwörterbuch des chemischen Theils der Mineralogie*, Berlin, **4**. 87, 1849 ; *Handbuch der Mineralchemie*, Leipzig, 81, 1875 ; E. R. Schneider, *Pogg. Ann.*, **98**. 302, 1856 ; E. Müller, *Verh. Ver. Rheinl. Bonn.*, 56, 1860 ; *Arch. Pharm.*, (2), **103**. 6, 1860 ; W. von der Marck, *ib.*, (2), **86**. 6, 1856 ; E. Reichardt, *ib.*, (2), **91**. 136, 145, 1857 ; *Dingler's Journ.*, **169**. 281, 1863 ; H Credner, *Neues Jahrb. Min.*, 741, 1874 ; M. M. P. Muir, *Chem. News*, **24**. 163, 1871 ; *Phil. Mag.*, (4), **42**. 237, 1871 ; A. R. C. Selwyn and G. H. F. Ulrich, *Notes on Physical Geography, Geology and Mineralogy of Victoria*, Melbourne, **60**, 1866 ; T. Thomson, *Ann. Phil.*, **4**. 97, 1814 ; A. d'Achiardi, *Mineralogia della Toscana*, Pisa, **2**. 311, 1873 ; L. Zambelli and E. Luzzatto, *Atti 1st. Veneto*, (6), **4**. 395, 1886 ; J. Loczka, *Zeit. Kryst.*, **20**. 317, 1892 ; *Ber. Math. Nat. Ungarn*, **8**. 99, 1891 ; J. Davy, *Phil. Trans.*, **112**. 196, 1812 ; J. L. Proust, *Journ. Phys.*, **55**. 325, 1802 ; R. Brandes, *Trommsdorff's Journ.*, **3**. 252, 1819 ; C. E. Waite, *Eng. Min. Journ.*, **31**. 146, 1881 ; W. Witting, *Nordamer. Monatsber.*, **3**. 486, 1852 ; J. J. Berzelius, *Pogg. Ann.*, **37**. 163, 1836 ; A. Libavius, *De natura metallorum*, Francofurti, 1600 ; A. Sala, *Anatomia antimonii*, Francofurti, 1617 ; L. N. Vauquelin, *Ann. Chim. Phys.*, (1), **34**. 136, 1800 ; P. Chrétien and J. M. Guinchant, *Compt. Rend.*, **138**. 1269, 1904 ; **139**. 51, 288, 1904 ; **142**. 708, 1906 ; L. F. Nilson, *Oefvers. Akad. Stockholm*, 5, 1877 ; *Zeit. anal. Chem.*, **16**. 417, 1877 ; H. W. F. Wackenroder, *Arch. Pharm.*, (2), **71**. 257, 1852 ; M. Garot, *Journ. Pharm. Chim.*, (3), **83**. 843 ; E. Priwoznik, *Mittheilungen aus dem Laboratorium des General-Probirantes*, Wien, 1886 ; *Berg. Hütt. Jahrb.*, **35**. 1, 1886 ; F. Sandberger, *Neues Jahrb. Min.*, i, 99, 1890 ; J. P. Cooke, *Amer. Journ. Science*, (3), **19**. 469, 1880 ; *Proc. Amer. Acad.*, **13**. 1, 72, 1877 ; *Chem. News*, **44**. 221, 233, 245, 255, 1880 ; P. Jannasch, *Journ. prakt. Chem.*, (2), **41**. 566, 1890 ; O. Stutzer, *Zeit. prakt. Geol.*, **15**. 219, 1907 ; I. Domeyko, *Elementos de mineralojia*, Santiago, 271, 1879 ; F. M. Jäger, *Proc. Acad. Amsterdam*, **15**. 809, 1907 ; K. Friedrich, *Met.*, **6**. 177, 1909 ; G. de Angelis d'Ossat, *Atti Accad. Lincei*, (5), **11**. 548, 1902 ; *Rassegna Min.*, **15**. 11, 1901 ; V. Zani, *Bull. Acad. Belg.*, 1169, 1909 ; E. Luzzato, *Atti 1st. Veneto*, (6), **4**. 1005, 1886.

[3] Basil Valentine, *Triumphwagen antimonii*, Nürnberg, 1676 ; London, 1893 ; J. R. Glauber, *Novi furni philosophici*, Amstelodami, 1648 ; Frère Simon in N. Lemery, *Cours de chimie*, Paris, 1675 ; *Traité sur l'antimoine*, Paris, 1707 ; S. de la Ligerie, *Mém. Acad.*, 417, 1720 ; G. F. Stabel, *Chymia dogmatico-experimentalis*, Halse Magdeburgæ, 1728 ; E. P. Meuder, *Analysis antimonii*, Paris, 1738 ; P. J. Macquer, *Dictionnaire de chymie*, Paris, **2**. 469, 1778 ; A. Baumé, *Chymie expérimentale et raisonnée*, Paris, 1773 ; T. Bergman, *De antimonialibus sulphuratis*, Upsala, 1782 ; C. L. Berthollet, *Journ. Phys.*, **46**. 436, 1798 ; *Ann. Chim. Phys.*, (1), **25**. 233, 1798 ; J. J. Berzelius, *Schweigger's Journ.*, **34**. 58, 1822 ; *Pogg. Ann.*, **20**. 365, 1830 ; **37**. 163, 1836 ; E. Kopp, *Bull. Soc. Mulhouse*, **29**. 379, 1859 ; E. Mathieu-Plessy, *ib.*, **26**. 297, 1854 ; L. F. Nilson, *Zeit. anal. Chem.*, **16**. 424, 1877 ; *Oefvers. Akad. Stockholm*, 5, 1877 ; J. Akerman, *Oefvers. Akad. Förh. Stockholm*, 235, 1861 ; *Journ. prakt. Chem.*, (1), **86**. 57, 1862 ; R. Böttger, *ib.*, (1), **70**. 437, 1857 ; E. Mitscherlich, *ib.*, (1), **19**. 51, 1830 ; H. Baubigny, *Compt. Rend.*, **119**. 687, 1894 ; A. Carnot, *ib.*, **103**. 258, 1888 ; A. Terreil, *ib.*, **77**. 1500, 1873 ; *Bull. Soc. Chim.*, (2), **25**. 98, 1876 ; *Journ. Pharm. Chim.*, (4), **19**. 131, 1874 ; C. Himly, *Liebig's Ann.*, **43**. 150, 1842 ; H. Vohl, *ib.*, **96**. 240, 1855 ; E. Lenssen, *ib.*, **114**. 118, 1860 ; F. J. Otto, *ib.*, **26**. 88, 1838 ; J. H. Long, *Journ. Amer. Chem. Soc.*, **18**. 342, 1896 ; M. Pettenkofer and B. Unger, *Dingler's Journ.*, **113**, 215, 1849 ; N. Teclu, *ib.*, **236**. 336, 1880 ; T. Rieckher, *Neues Jahrb. Pharm.*, **6**. 260, 1856 ; A. Strohl, *Journ. Pharm. Chim.*, (3), **16**. 11, 1849 ; J. Bougault, *ib.*, (6), **18**. 509, 547. 1903 ; *Compt. Rend.*, **137**. 497, 1903 ; R. Wagner, *Wagner's Jahresb.*, 235, 1858 ; 331, 1862 ; G. Vort-

mann, *Monatsh.*, **7**. 421, 1886 ; A. L. Orlowsky, *Zeit. anal. Chem.*, **22**. 358, 1883 ; L. Gmelin, *Handbook of Chemistry*, London, **4**. 340, 1850 ; E. Lesser, *Ueber einige Trennungs und Bestimmungs-Methoden Arsens, des Antimons und des Zinns*, Berlin, 1886 ; R. Brandes, *Ann. Pharm. Chim.*, (2), **17**. 416, 1831 ; *Brandes' Arch.*, **37**. 257, 1831 ; *Schweigger's Journ.*, **62**. 209, 1831 ; A. Vogel, *ib.*, **33**. 291, 1822 ; H. Weppen, *Ber.*, **8**. 523, 1875 ; L. A. Buchner, *Journ. Pharm. Chim.*, (2), **16**. 51, 1830 ; *Repert. Pharm.*, **13**. 169, 203, 1822 ; P. L. Geiger, *ib.*, **9**. 274, 1829 ; *Mag. Pharm.*, **29**. 229, 1830 ; J. von Liebig, *ib.*, **35**. 120, 1831 ; *Liebig's Ann.*, **7**. 194, 545, 1833 ; F. C. Bucholz, *Berlin. Jahrb. Pharm.*, **29**. 26, 1839 ; **32**. 199, 1831 ; A. Duflos, *Brandes' Arch.*, **31**. 94, 1829 ; **36**. 278, 1831 ; *Schweigger's Journ.*, **62**. 210, 1831 ; **67**. 269, 1833 ; *Kastner's Arch.*, **19**. 61, 289, 1830 ; F. Jahn, *Brandes' Arch.*, **22**. 43, 1827 ; M. Cluzel, *Ann. Chim. Phys.*, (1), **63**. 155, 1807 ; J. L. Gay Lussac, *ib.*, (1), **42**. 87, 1829 ; A. F. de Fourcroy, *Mém. Soc. Médicines Paris*, 248, 1781 ; *Crell's Ann.*, i, 423, 1788 ; P. J. Robiquet, *Journ. Pharm. Chim.*, (2), **9**. 326, 1823 ; *Ann. Chim. Phys.*, (1), **81**. 317, 1812 ; L. J. Thénard, *ib.*, (1), **32**. 257, 1800 ; G. Cavezzali, *ib.*, (1), **42**. 177, 1802 ; J. G. Bremser, *ib.*, (1), **23**. 79, 1797 ; J. F. A. Goettling, *ib.*, (1), **23**. 79, 1797 ; *Taschenbuch Scheidekünstler*, **18**. 30, 1797 ; C. J. Geoffroy, *Mém. Acad.*, 162, 1745 ; 593, 1734 ; 94, 1735 ; P. J. Hensmans, *Ann. Gen. Science Phys.*, **7**. 382, 1820 ; *Taschenbuch Scheidekünstler*, **43**. 184, 1822 ; O. Henry, *Journ. Pharm. Chim.*, (2), **14**. 545, 1828 ; C. P. Kosman, *ib.*, (3), **18**. 321, 1850 ; T. Derouen, *ib.*, (3), **15**. 5, 17, 1849 ; L. Thorel, *ib.*, (3), **17**. 185, 191, 1850 ; A. Jossart, *Journ. Pharm. d'Anvers*, **36**. 81, 1880 ; *Journ. Pharm. Chim.*, (5), **2**. 47, 1880 ; V. Roussel, *ib.*, (5), **14**. 557, 1886 ; C. Méhu, *ib.*, (4), **8**. 99, 1868 ; E. Soubeiran, *ib.*, (2), **27**. 294, 1841 ; J. Bougault, *ib.*, (6), **18**. 509, 547, 1903 ; M. Wahren, *ib.*, (1), **1**. 127, 1809 ; A. Fabroni, *ib.*, (2), **10**. 451, 1824 ; F. Musculus, *ib.*, (2), **22**. 241, 1836 ; T. Thomson, *Ann. Phil.*, **4**. 171, 1814 ; R. Phillips, *ib.*, **25**. 378, 1825 ; *Phil. Mag.*, (1), **65**. 396, 1825 ; E. Pollacci, *Boll. Chim. Farm.*, **45**. 401, 1906 ; H. Rose, *Liebig's Ann.*, **75**. 244, 1869 ; *Pogg. Ann.*, **17**. 324, 1829 ; **28**. 481, 1833 ; **47**. 323, 1839 ; J. N. von Fuchs, *ib.*, **31**. 578, 1834 ; J. C. C. Schrader, *Gehlen's Journ.*, **3**. 159, 1807 ; J. B. Trommsdorff. *Ann. Chim. Phys.*, (1), **34**. 132, 1800 ; *Trommsdorff's Journ.*, **8**. 128, 1824 ; J. S. F. Pagenstecher, *ib.*, **3**. 389, 1819 ; *Repert. Pharm.*, **14**. 194, 545, 1822 ; B. Unger, *Arch. Pharm.*, (2), **145**. 15, 1871 ; F. Feist, *ib.*, (2), **240**. 241, 1902 ; J. T. Norton, *Amer. Journ. Science*, (4), **12**. 115, 1901.

[4] C. Geitner, *Liebig's Ann.*, **129**. 359, 1864 ; E. Schürmann, *ib.*, **249**. 336, 1889 ; J. von Liebig, *ib.*, **7**. 1, 1833 ; **31**. 57, 1859 ; *Mag. Pharm.*, **35**. 120, 1833 ; W. Spring, *Zeit. phys. Chem.*, **18**. 556, 1895 ; *Ber.*, **16**. 999, 1883 ; C. Heumann and P. Köchlin, *ib.*, **16**. 1625, 1883 ; P. Jannasch and W. Remmler, *ib.*, **26**. 1425, 1893 ; J. Uhl, *ib.*, **23**. 2154, 1890 ; J. Lang, *ib.*, **18**. 2716, 1885 ; G. Vortmann, *ib.*, **22**. 2311, 1889 ; L. Brunet, *German Pat.*, *D.R.P.* 172410, 1906 ; J. Durocher, *Compt. Rend.*, **32**. 823, 1851 ; A. Carnot, *ib.*, **89**. 169, 1879 ; A. Ditte, *ib.*, **102**. 212, 1886 ; P. Chrétien and J. M. Guinchant, *ib.*, **139**. 51, 1904 ; A. Mourlot, *ib.*, **123**. 54, 1896 ; *Ann. Chim. Phys.*, (7), **17**. 510, 1899 ; H. Arctowsky, *Zeit. anorg. Chem.*, **8**. 220, 1895 ; E. Weinschenk, *Zeit. Kryst.*, **17**. 499, 1890 ; H. N. Warren, *Chem. News*, **66**. 187, 1893 ; C. A. Mitchell, *ib.*, **67**. 291, 1893 ; H. Rose, *Pogg. Ann.*, **89**. 131, 1853 ; J. N. von Fuchs, *ib.*, **31**. 578, 1834 ; *Schweigger's Journ.*, **67**. 418, 1833 ; *Edin. Phil. Journ.*, **18**. 263, 1835 ; H. de Sénarmont, *Compt. Rend.*, **32**. 409, 1851 ; *Ann. Chim. Phys.*, (3), **32**. 129, 1851 ; M. Berthelot, *ib.*, (6), **10**. 139, 1886 ; J. L. Proust, *Journ. Phys.*, **55**. 325, 1802 ; T. Paul, *Zeit. anal. Chem.*, **31**. 539, 1892 ; B. Brauner; *Journ. Chem. Soc.*, **67**. 527, 1895 ; O. Bosek, *ib.*, **67**. 524, 1895 ; J. A. Krenner, *Sitzber. Akad. Wien*, **51**. 481, 1865 ; P. P. Heberdey, *ib.*, **104**. 256, 1895 ; B. Unger, *Arch. Pharm.*, (2), **147**. 193, 1871 ; C. W. C. Fuchs, *Die künstlich dargestellten Mineralien nach Roses System geordnet*, Haarlem, 51, 1872 ; C. C. von Leonhard, *Hüttenerzeugnisse und andere künstliche Mineralien als Stützpunkte geologische Hypothesen*, Stuttgart, 340, 1858 ; F. Fouqué and A. Michel-Lévy, *Synthèse des minéraux et des roches*, Paris, 318, 1882 ; R. Finkener, *Journ. Soc. Chem. Ind.*, **8**. 733, 1889 ; W. R. Lang and C. M. Carson, *ib.*, **21**. 1018, 1902 ; A. Duflos, *Arch. Pharm.*, (2), **31**. 94, 1829 ; (2), **36**. 278, 1831 ; *Schweigger's Journ.*, **62**. 210, 1830 ; **67**. 269, 1833 ; *Kastner's Arch.*, **1**. 56, 289, 1830 ; S. P. Sharples, *Chem. News*, **22**. 190, 1871 ; *Amer. Journ. Science*, (2), **50**. 248, 1870 ; J. P. Cooke, *ib.*, (3), **19**. 469, 1880 ; *Proc. Amer. Acad.*, **13**. 1, 72, 1877 ; *Chem. News*, **44**. 221, 233, 245, 255, 1880 ; F. Schmidt, *Mag. Pharm.*, **13**. 65, 1826 ; G. Tammann, *Krystallisieren und Schmelzen*, Leipzig, 59, 1903 ; V. Zani, *Bull. Acad. Belg.*, 1169, 1909 ; S. Wilson and C. R. McCrosky, *Journ. Amer. Chem. Soc.*, **43**. 2178, 1921 ; L. A. Youtz, *ib.*, **30**. 975, 1908 ; F. de Bacho, *Annali Chem. Appl.*, **12**. 143, 1919 ; G. Tocco, *Gazz. Chim. Ital.*, **54**. i, 23, 1924 ; L. M. Currie, *Journ. Phys. Chem.*, **30**. 205, 1926 ; J. T. Norton, *Amer. Journ. Science*, (4), **12**. 115, 1901.

[5] J. A. Krenner, *Sitzber. Akad. Wien*, **51**. 72, 1865 : *Földt. Kögl.*, **13**. 2, 1883 ; A. Schrauf, *Atlas der Krystallformen des Mineralreiches*, Wien, 1877 ; W. Koort, *Beiträge zur Kenntnis des Antimonglanzes*, Berlin, 1884 ; P. Groth, *Die Mineraliensammlung der Universität Strassburg*, Strassburg, 22, 1878 ; *Zeit. Kryst.*, **11**. 159, 1886 ; G. Seligmann, *Neues Jahrb. Min.*, i, 135, 1880 ; O. Mügge, *ib.*, ii, 19, 1883 ; i, 55, 1884 ; i, 77, 1897 ; i, 79, 1889 ; T. Haege, *Die Mineralien des Siegerlandes und der abgrenzenden Bizerke*, Siegen, 31, 1887 ; H. von Foullon, *Verh. geol. Reichsanst. Wien*, 171, 1892 ; F. Ephraim, *Helvetica Chim. Acta*, **7**. 298, 1924 ; A. Schmidt, *Zeit. Kryst.*, **29**. 195, 1898 ; F. B. Peck, *ib.*, **27**. 299, 1896 ; A. S. Eakle, *ib.*, **24**. 587, 1895 ; E. Rethwisch, *ib.*, **12**. 78, 1886 ; *Beiträge zur mineralogischen und chemischen Kenntnis des Rothgültigerzes*, Göttingen, 1885 ; A. Lévy, *Description d'une collection des minéraux formée par M. Henri Heuland*, Londres, **3**. 312, 1837 ; F. Hessenberg, *Mineralogische Notizen*, Frankfurt, **1**. 30, 1856 ; E. Artini, *Atti Accad. Lincei*, (5), **3**. 416, 1894 ; J. R. Blum, *Die Pseudomorphosen*

2 M

530

530   INORGANIC AND THEORETICAL CHEMISTRY

des Mineralreiches, Stuttgart, 171, 1843; 91, 1847; 168, 1863; L. M. Currie, Journ. Phys. Chem., 30. 205, 1926 : V. Zani, Bull. Acad. Belg., 1169, 1909; P. Drude, Wied. Ann., 34. 483, 1888; A. Sadebeck, Zeit. deut. geol. Ges., 24. 792, 1872; F. Rinne, ib., 42. 62, 1890; H. Buttgenbach, Ann. Soc. Geol. Belg., 23. 3, 1897; E. S. Dana, Amer. Journ. Science, (3), 26. 218, 1883; L. Bombicci, Atti 1st. Bologna, 7. 129, 1886; Atti Soc. Toscana, 8. 129, 1886; N. Teclu, Dingler's Journ., 236. 336, 1880; M. Pettenkofer, ib., 113. 215, 1849; P. F. Kerr, Econ. Geol., 19. 1, 1924; V. Goldschmidt, Index der Krystallformen der Mineralien, Berlin, 1. 221, 1886; A. Lacroix, Minéralogie de la France et de ses colonies, Paris, 2. 449, 1897; B. Unger, Arch. Pharm., (2), 148. 11, 1871; E. Kopp, Bull. Soc. Mulhouse, 29. 120, 379, 1859; P. Chrétien and J. M. Guinchant, Compt. Rend., 138. 1269, 1904; 139. 97, 1904; 142. 708, 1906; J. Akerman, Oefvers. Akad. Förh. Stockholm, 235, 1861; Journ. prakt. Chem., (1), 86. 57, 1862; L. Wöhler and C. Condrea, Zeit. angew. Chem., 21. 481, 1908; F. Mohs, Grundriss der Mineralogie, Dresden, 2. 582, 1824; J. J. Bernhardi, Leonhard's Taschenbuch, 3. 86, 1809; R. J. Haüy, Traité de minéralogie, Paris, 4. 266, 1801; J. B. L. Romé de l'Isle, Cristallographie, Paris, 3. 49, 1783; H. Haga and F. M. Jäger. Versl. Akad. Amsterdam, 24. 1612, 1916; H. Schneiderhöhn, Anleitung zur mikroskopischen Bestimmung und Untersuchung von Erzen und Aufbereitungsprodukte besonders im auffallenden Licht, Berlin, 151, 1922; C. Gottfried, Zeit. Kryst., 65. 428, 1927; A. Hutchinson, Centr. Min., 333, 1903; Zeit. Kryst., 43. 464, 1907; F. de Bacho, Annali Chim. Appl., 12. 143, 1919; F. Kirchof, Zeit. anorg. Chem., 112. 67, 1920; M. Kuhara, Mem. Coll. Eng. Kyoto Univ., 2. 71, 1918; O. Neff, Beitr. Kryst. Min., 1. 107, 1916; 2. 47, 1923; Z. Ooe, Journ. Geol. Scc. Tokyo, 33. 187, 1926; Japanese Journ. Geol. Geogr., 4. 21, 1927; J. N. von Fuchs, Pogg. Ann., 31. 578, 1834; H. Rose, ib., 89. 123, 1853; N. Teclu, Dingler's Journ., 236, 336, 1880; E. C. Kopp, Bull. Soc. Mulhouse, 30. 379, 1859; J. Lang, Ber., 18. 2714, 1885; E. Quercigh, Atti Accad. Lincei, (5), 32. ii, 411, 1923; M. de Angelis, ib., (5), 32. ii, 30, 1923; P. Gravino, ib., (6), 3. i, 210, 1926.

⁶ H. Rose, Pogg. Ann., 89. 123, 1853; J. N. von Fuchs, ib., 31. 578, 1834; F. E. Neumann, ib., 23. 1, 1831; W. P. Dexter, Zeit. anal. Chem., 9. 264, 1870; G. C. Wittstein, ib., 9. 267, 1870; L. F. Nilson, ib., 16. 418. 1877; Oefvers. Akad. Stockholm, 5, 1877; H. Bäckström and K. Angström, ib., 533, 1888; 10. 545, 1891; J. Akerman, ib., 235, 1861; Journ. prakt. Chem., (1), 86. 57, 1862; Y. Takahashi, Mem. Coll. Science Kyoto, 4. 47, 1919; E. Mathieu-Plessy, Bull. Soc. Mulhouse, 26. 297. 1855; E. Kopp, ib., 30. 379, 1859; A. Ditte, Compt. Rend., 102. 214, 1886; A. Mourlot, ib., 123. 55, 1896; Ann. Chim. Phys., (7), 17. 510, 1889; E. Quercigh, Atti Accad. Lincei, (5), 32. ii, 411, 1924; N. Teclu, Dingler's Journ., 236. 336, 1880; J. P. Cocke, Amer. Journ. Science, (3), 19. 469, 1880; Proc. Amer. Acad., 13. 1, 72, 1877; Chem. News, 44. 221, 233, 245, 255, 1880; A. de la Rive and F. Marcet, Bibl. Univ. Genève, 28. 360, 1840; Ann. Chim. Phys., (3), 2. 121, 1841; H. de Sénarmont, ib., (3), 32. 129, 1851; Compt. Rend., 32. 409, 1851; P. Chrétien and J. M. Guinchant, Compt. Rend., 138. 1269, 1904; 139. 288, 1904; 142. 708, 1906; H. Pélabon, ib., 137. 920, 1903; 138. 277, 1904; 140. 1387, 1905: Ann. Chim. Phys., (3), 17. 526, 1909; H. V. Regnault, ib., (3), 1. 129, 1841; M. Berthelot, ib., (6), 10. 136, 1887; Compt. Rend., 139. 97, 1904; E. Jannettaz, ib., 116. 317, 1893; A. Strohl, Journ. Pharm. Chim., (3), 16. 11, 1849; C. J. B. Karsten, Schweigger's Journ., 65. 395, 1832; F. M. Jäger, Proc. Acad. Amsterdam, 14. 89, 799, 1906; 15. 809, 1907; J. Olie and H. R. Kruyt, ib., 14. 740, 1912; F. M. Jäger and H. S. van Klooster, Zeit. anorg. Chem., 78. 246, 1912; C. Doelter, Sitzber. Akad. Wien, 109. 49. 1910; Das Radium und die Farben, Dresden, 18. 95, 1910; G. Cesaro, Bull. Acad. Belg., 115, 1904: V. Zani, ib., 1169, 1909; F. Beijerinck, Neues Jahrb. Min. B.B., 11. 423, 1897; E. C. Müller, ib., 17. 187, 1903; A. S. Russell, Phys. Zeit., 13. 59, 1912; J. Joly, Phil. Mag., (6), 27. 1, 1914; F. B. Peck, Zeit. Kryst., 27. 318, 1897; A. Hutchinson, Centr. Min., 333, 1903; B. Glatzel, Verh. deut. phys. Ges., 14. 607, 1912; C. Ries, Ann. Physik, (4), 36. 1055, 1911; J. Königsberger and K. Schilling, ib., (4), 32. 179, 1910; E. Madelung and R. Fuchs, ib., (4), 65. 289, 1921; H. Schröder, Ber., 7. 898, 1874; F. Krafft and L. Merz, ib., 40. 4777, 1907; L. Merz, Ueber das Verhalten der Elemente und Verbindungen der Schwefelgruppe im Vacuum, Heidelberg, 1905; F. W. Clarke, A Table of Specific Gravity for Solids and Liquids, London, 59, 1888; P. Drude, Wied. Ann., 34. 483, 1888; Zeit. Kryst., 18. 644, 1891; R. Cusack, Proc. Roy. Irish Acad., (3), 4. 399, 1897; L. H. Borgström, Oefvers. Finska Vet. Soc. Förh., 57. 24, 1915; K. Friedrich, Met., 6. 177, 1909; A. de Gramont, Bull. Soc. Min., 18. 310, 1895; H. F. Vieweg, Journ. Phys. Chem., 30. 865, 1926; K. Asagoe and N. Kumagai, Mem. Coll. Kyoto, 9. 439, 1926; E. T. Wherry, Amer. Min., 10. 28, 1925; F. de Bacho, Annali Chim. Appl., 12. 143, 1919; E. Quercigh, Atti Accad. Lincei., (5), 21. i, 415, 1912; K. Jellinek and J. Zakowsky, Zeit. anorg. Chem., 142. 1, 1925; E. P. T. Tyndall, Phys. Rev., (2), 21. 162. 1923; C. Zengelis, Zeit. phys. Chem., 50. 219, 1904; O. Stelling, ib., 117. 180, 1925; W. W. Coblentz, Various Photoelectrical Investigations, Washington, 1922; Positive and Negative Photoelectric Properties of Molybdenite and Several other Substances, Washington, 1920; Supplementary Investigations of infra-red Spectra, Washington, 1908; W. W. Coblentz and C. W. Hughes, Ultraviolet Reflecting Power of Some Metals and Sulphides, Washington, 1924; K. Fischbeck, Zeit. anorg. Chem., 148. 97, 1925; K. Konno, Mem. Coll. Science Kyoto, 4. 51, 1919; E. E. Fairbanks, Econ. Geol., 21. 399, 1926; T. W. Case, Phys. Rev., (2), 9. 305, 1917; J. O. Perrine, ib., (2), 22. 48, 1923; I. B. Crandall, ib., (2), 2. 343, 1913; C. Tubandt and M. Haedicke, Zeit. anorg. Chem., 160. 297, 1927.

⁷ H. Rose, Ann. Phil., 10. 416, 1825; Phil. Mag., 67. 124, 1826; Pogg. Ann., 3. 441, 1824; W. Haidinger, ib., 11. 178, 1827; E. R. Schneider, ib., 98. 296. 1856: E. M. Plessy. Bull. Soc.

Mulhouse, **26**. 297, 1855 ; H. Pélabon, *Amer. Chem. Phys.*, (8), **17**. 526, 1909 ; *Compt. Rend.*, **137**. 920, 1903 ; **138**. 277, 1904 ; **139**. 911, 1900 ; **140**. 1389, 1905 ; *Ann. Chim. Phys.*, (8), **17**. 526, 1909 ; *Journ. Chim. Phys.*, **2**. 334, 1904 ; C. Doelter, *Tschermak's Mitt.*, (2), **11**. 319, 1890 ; *Monatsh.* **11**. 149, 1890 ; H. Saito, *Science Rep. Tohoku Univ.*, **16**. 37, 1927 ; K. Friedrich, *Met.*, **7**. 323, 1910 ; P. de Clermont and J. Frommel, *Compt. Rend.*, **86**. 828, 1878 ; **87**. 330, 332, 1879 ; *Ann. Chim. Phys.*, (5), **18**. 189, 1879 ; H. V. Regnault, *ib.*, (2), **62**. 383, 1836 ; L. J. Thénard, *ib.*, (1), **32**. 257, 1800 ; P. Berthier, *ib.*, (2), **22**. 239, 1823 ; (2), **25**. 379, 1824 ; W. R. Schoeller, *Journ. Soc. Chem. Ind.*, **34**. 6, 1915 ; M. Rousseau, *Compt. Rend.*, **17**. 1173, 1843 ; *Journ. Pharm. Chim.*, (4), **5**. 57, 1844 ; L. A. Buchner, *Repert. Pharm.*, **13**. 169, 203, 1822 ; *Journ. Pharm. Chim.*, (2), **16**. 51, 1830 ; O. Weigel, *Nachr. Gött.*, 1, 1906 ; *Zeit. Phys. Chem.*, **58**. 293, 1907 ; J. Clark, *Journ. Chem. Soc.*, **61**. 424, 1892 ; *Chem. News*, **67**. 249, 1893 ; W. Hampe, *Chem. Ztg.*, **18**. 1899, 1895 ; W. Elbers, *ib.*, **12**. 355, 1888 ; J. R. Blum, *Die Pseudomorphosen des Mineralreiche*, Stuttgart, 91, 1847 ; 67, 1852 ; E. Pollacci, *Boll. Chim. Farm.*, **47**. 363, 1908 ; P. L. Geiger and L. Hesse, *Liebig's Ann.*, **7**. 19, 1833 ; J. von Liebig, *Handwörterbuch der reinen und angewandten Chemie*, Braunschweig, **1**. 414, 1837 ; P. Jannasch, *Zeit. anorg. Chem.*, **6**. 303, 1894 ; K. Jellinek and J. Zakowsky, *Ueber die Affinität der Metalle zum Schwefel*, Danzig, 1924 ; *Zeit. anorg. Chem.*, **142**. 1, 1925 ; G. Tammann and H. Bredemeier, *ib.*, **136**. 337, 1924 ; E. H. Riesenfeld and W. Haase, *ib.*, **147**. 188, 1925 ; H. Laspeyres, *Zeit. Kryst.*, **9**. 186, 1884 ; **A**. S. Eakle, *ib.*, **24**. 581, 1895 ; L. Zambelli and E. Luzzato, *Ann. Chim. Farm.*, (4), **3**. 229, 1886 ; J. Lang, *Ber.*, **18**. 2715, 1885 ; T. Poleck, *ib.*, **27**. 1051, 1894 ; F. Raschig, *ib.*, **18**. 2743, 1885 ; E. Lesser, *Ueber einige Trennungs- und Bestimmungs-Methoden des Arsens, des Antimons und des Zinns*, Berlin, 1886 ; A. Vogel, *Journ. Chim. Pharm.*, (2), **8**. 128, 1822 ; A. Mailfert, *Compt. Rend.*, **94**. 1186, 1882 ; A. Ditte, *ib.*, **102**. 169, 1886 ; F. Carmichael, *Univ. Toronto Geol. Studies*, 29, 1926.

⁸ H. Moissan, *Ann. Chim. Phys.*, (6), **24**. 262. 1891 ; M. Berthelot, *ib.*, (6), **10**. 139, 1886 ; H. Rose, *Pogg. Ann.*, **3**. 441, 1824 ; *Phil. Mag.*, **67**. 124, 1826 ; *Ann. Phil.*, **10**. 416, 1825 ; E. R. Schneider, *ib.*, **99**. 470, 1856 ; **109**. 610, 1860 ; **110**. 150, 1860 ; C. Tookey, *Journ. Chem. Soc.*, **15**. 462, 1862 ; L. L. de Koninck and A. Lecrenier, *Zeit. anal. Chem.*, **27**. 462, 1888 ; A. Stromeyer, *ib.*, **9**. 264, 1870 ; H. Köhler, *ib.*, **29**. 192, 1890 ; F. Neher, *ib.*, **32**. 50, 1893 ; R. Böttger, *Jahresb. Phys. Ver. Frankfurt*, 26, 1869 ; L. Loviton, *Journ. Pharm. Chim.*, (5), **17**. 361, 1888 ; M. Schleier, *Kritische Studien über die Trennung von Zinn und Antimon*, München, 1892 ; F. Field, *Chem. News*, **3**. 114, 1861 ; H. N. Warren, *ib.*, **65**. 232, 1892 ; H. C. Bolton, *ib.*, **38**. 168, 1878 ; *Ann. New York Acad.*, **1**. 153, 1879 ; E. Lesser, *Ueber einige Trennungs- und Bestimmungs-Methoden des Arsens, des Antimons und des Zinns*, Berlin, 1886 ; H. Feigel, *Verhalten von Schwermetallverbindungen gegen Polysulfide und Chlorschwefel*, Erlangen, 1905 ; W. R. Lang and C. M. Carson, *Journ. Soc. Chem. Ind.*, **21**. 1018, 1902 ; J. Lang, *Ber.*, **18**. 2714, 1885 ; A. Ditte, *Compt. Rend.*, **102**. 212, 1886 ; E. Baudrimont, *ib.*, **64**. 369, 1867 ; E. H. Bartley, *Amer. Chemist*, **5**. 436, 1875 ; P. Jannasch and W. Remmler, *Ber.*, **26**. 1422, 1893 ; J. Lemberg, *Zeit. deut. geol. Ges.*, **46**. 792, 1894 ; J. Kelley and E. F. Smith, *Journ. Amer. Chem. Soc.*, **18**. 1096, 1896 ; E. F. Smith, *ib.*, **20**. 289, 1898.

⁹ H. Prinz, *Liebig's Ann.*, **223**. 364, 1884 ; R. Bunsen, *ib.*, **106**. 8, 1858 ; **192**. 305, 1878 ; O. Ruff, *Ber.*, **34**. 1752, 1901 ; P. Berthier, *Ann. Chim. Phys.*, (2), **22**. 239, 1823 ; M. Berthelot, *ib.*, (6), **10**. 132, 1886 ; *Compt. Rend.*, **102**. 22, 1886 ; A. Gueront, *ib.*, **75**. 1276, 1872 ; A. E. Becquerel, *ib.*, **107**. 895, 1888 ; A. V. L. Verneuil, *ib.*, **103**. 600, 1886 ; L. F. Nilson, *Oefvers. Akad. Stockholm*, 5, 1877 ; 9, 1878 ; *Zeit. anal. Chem.*, **16**. 419, 1877 ; **18**. 165, 1879 ; M. Websky, *ib.*, **11**. 124, 1872 ; H. B. North and C. B. Conover, *Journ. Amer. Chem. Soc.*, **37**. 2486, 1915 ; *Amer. Journ. Science*, (4), **40**. 640, 1915 ; H. Rose, *Pogg. Ann.*, **3**. 441, 1824 ; *Ann. Phil.*, **10**. 416, 1875 ; *Phil. Mag.*, **67**. 124, 1826 ; C. Hensgen, *Rec. Trav. Chim. Pays-Bas*, **4**. 401, 1885 ; S. E. Linder and H. Picton, *Journ. Chem. Soc.*, **61**. 133, 1892 ; J. Milbauer and J. Tucek, *Chem. Ztg.*, **50**. 323, 1926.

¹⁰ E. C. Franklin and C. A. Kraus, *Amer. Chem. Journ.*, **20**. 820, 1898 ; G. Gore, *Proc. Roy. Soc.*, **20**. 441, 1872 ; **21**. 140, 1873 ; M. Carot, *Journ. Pharm. Chim.*, (4), **3**. 118, 1843 ; L. Garnier, *Journ. Chim. Pharm.*, (5), **28**. 97, 1893 ; H. Capitaine, *ib.*, (3), **25**. 516, 1839 ; P. de Clermont, *Compt. Rend.*, **88**. 972, 1879 ; H. Pélabon, *ib.*, **136**. 812, 1903 ; R. Bunsen, *Liebig's Ann.*, **106**. 3, 1858 ; W. R. Schoeller, *Journ. Soc. Chem. Ind.*, **34**. 6, 1915 ; H. Rose, *Ann. Phil.*, **10**. 416, 1825 ; *Phil. Mag.*, **67**. 124, 1826 ; *Pogg. Ann.*, **3**. 441, 1824 ; **20**. 336, 1830 ; E. R. Schneider, *ib.*, **98**. 296, 1856 ; **108**. 407, 1859 ; C. R. Fresenius, *Zeit. anal. Chem.*, **25**. 200, 1826 ; F. Ephraim, *Zeit. anorg. Chem.*, **44**. 195, 1905 ; E. Baudrimont, *Ann. Chim. Phys.*, (4), **2**. 12, 1864 ; J. Fiedler, *De lucis effectibus chemicis in corpora anorganica*, Vratislaviæ, 1835.

¹¹ P. Berthier, *Ann. Chim. Phys.*, (2), **22**. 239, 1823 ; A. Levol, *ib.*, (3), **46**. 471, 1856 ; F. Göbel, *Bull. Soc. Nat. Moscou*, **9**. 312, 1836 ; *Journ. prakt. Chem.*, (1), **6**. 386, 1835 ; J. von Liebig, *Handwörterbuch der reinen und angewandten Chemie*, Braunschweig, **1**. 414, 1837 ; J. Clark, *Journ. Chem. Soc.*, **61**. 424, 1892 ; *Chem. News*, **65**. 213, 1892 ; F. W. Clarke, *ib.*, **21**. 124, 1870 ; H. C. Bolton, *ib.*, **37**. 14, 86, 99, 1878 ; *Ann. New York Acad.*, **1**. 1, 1879 ; **2**. 1, 1882 ; C. R. Fresenius, *Anleitung zur qualitativen chemischen Analysen*, Braunschweig, 314, 1919 ; H. Rose, *Pogg. Ann.*, **89**. 140, 1853 ; **90**. 204, 1853 ; R. Zsigmondy, *Dingler's Journ.*, **273**. 29, 1889 ; A. Carnot, *Compt. Rend.*, **103**. 258, 1888 ; N. D. Costeanu, *Étude de l'action de gas carbonique sur les sulfures métalliques*, Paris, 1914 ; E. Lesser, *Ueber einige Trennungs- und Bestimmungs-Methoden des Arsens, des Antimons und des Zinns*, Berlin, 1886 ; F. P. Dewey, *Amer. Chem. Journ.*, **1**. 244, 1879 ; O. Materne, *Bull. Soc. Chim. Belg.*, **20**. 46, 1906 ; A. P. Hermandez, *Anal. Soc. Quim. Argentina*, **6**. 306, 1918 ; A. C. Vournasos, *Ber.*, **43**. 2264,

1910; H. Gordon, *Ueber die Komplexität verschiedener Metalltartrationen und die Löslichkeit verschiedener Metalldioxyde und Sulfide*, Danzig, 1924; L. Kahlenberg and W. J. Trautmann, *Trans. Amer. Electrochem. Soc.*, 39. 377, 1921.

¹² R. Bunsen, *Liebig's Ann.*, 106. 4, 1858; E. Schürmann, *ib.*, 249. 341, 1889; J. J. Berzelius, *Schweigger's Journ.*, 34. 58, 1822; Pogg. *Ann.*, 20. 365, 1830; 37. 163, 1836; H. Rose, *ib.*, 3. 441, 1824; *Ann. Phil.*, 10. 416, 1825; *Phil. Mag.*, 67. 124, 1826; J. von Liebig, *Liebig's Ann.*, 7. 1, 1833; 19. 24, 1836; 22. 58, 1837; *Handwörterbuch der reinen und angewandten Chemie*, Braunschweig, 1. 414, 1837; O. Materne, *Bull. Soc. Chim. Belg.*, 20. 46, 1906; A. Terreil, *Bull. Soc. Chim.*, (1), 4. 2, 1865; (2), 25. 98, 1876; *Compt. Rend.*, 77. 1500, 1873; *Journ. Pharm. Chim.*, (4), 19. 131, 1874; H. Weppen, *Ber.*, 8. 525, 1875; C. Pertusi, *Ann. Chim. Anal.*, 20. 229, 1915; G. Marchal, *Bull. Soc. Chim.*, (4), 33. 597, 1923; J. Lemberg, *Zeit. deut. geol. Ges.*, 46. 792, 1894; A. Lindner, *Zeit. Chem.*, (2), 5. 442, 1869; A. Vogel, *Schweigger's Journ.*, 33. 291, 1822; H. Schneiderhöhn, *Anleitung zur mikroskopischen Bestimmung und Untersuchungen von Erzen und Aufbereitungsprodukte besonders im auffallenden Licht*, Berlin, 151, 1922; P. L. Geiger, *Mag. Pharm.*, 29. 240, 1830; B. Unger, *Arch. Pharm.*, (2), 114. 147, 1863; (3), 7. 193, 1875; N. Parravano and P. Agostini, *Gazz. Chim. Ital.*, 49. i, 103, 1919.

¹³ H. O. Schulze, *Journ. prakt. Chem.*, (2), 27. 320, 1883; K. Jablczynsky and A. P. Jedrzejevska, *Bull. Soc. Chim.*, (4), 37. 608, 1925; *Rocz. Chem.*, 5. 173, 1925; K. Jablczynsky and H. L. Zienkovska, *ib.*, 5. 178, 1925; H. Capitaine, *Journ. Pharm. Chim.*, (3), 25. 516, 1839; F. V. von Hahn, *Zeit. Koll.*, 36. 277, 1925; Wo. Ostwald, *ib.*, 40. 201, 1926; M. Prasad, D. L. Shrivastava, and R. S. Gupta, *ib.*, 37. 101, 1925; S. Wosnessensky, *ib.*, 33. 32, 1923; H. Picton, *Journ. Chem. Soc.*, 61. 137, 1892; S. E. Linder and H. Picton, *ib.*, 61. 133, 1892; S. Utzino, *Koll. Zeit.*, 32. 149, 1923; R. Wintgen, *Koll. Beihefte*, 7. 251, 1915; A. Ditte, *Compt. Rend.*, 102. 169, 1886; N. Schiloff, *Zeit. phys. Chem.*, 100. 425, 1922; M. S. Wolvekamp, *Brit. Pat. No.* 197061, 1922; W. Biltz and W. Geibel, *Nachr. Gött.*, 141, 1906; W. Biltz, *ib.*, 1, 1904; *Ber.*, 37. 1095, 1904; A. Ivanitzkaja and L. Orlova, *Koll. Beihefte*, 18. 1, 1923; S. Utzino, *Koll. Zeit.*, 32. 149, 1923; *Japan. Journ. Chem.*, 2. 21, 1923; N. Lubavin, *Journ. Russ. Phys. Chem. Soc.*, 21. 397, 1889; A. Sabanéeff, *ib.*, 21. 515, 1889; 22. 102, 1890; S. S. Bhatnagar, M. Prasad, and D. C. Bahl, *Journ. Indian Chem. Soc.*, 2. 11, 1925; N. R. Dhar, *ib.*, 4. 173, 1927; S. S. Bhatnagar, N. A. Yajnik and V. D. Zadov, *ib.*, 4. 209, 1927; K. K. Mathur and D. L. Shrivastava, *Journ. Phys. Chem.*, 28. 387, 1924; S. S. Bhatnagar, N. A. Yajnik, and V. D. Zadov, *Journ. Indian Chem. Soc.*, 4. 209, 1927; S. S. Bhatnagar and D. L. Shrivastava, *Journ. Phys. Chem.*, 28. 730, 1924; S. S. Bhatnagar, K. K. Mathur, and D. L. Shrivastava, *ib.*, 28. 392, 1924; K. C. Sen, P. B. Ganguly, and N. R. Dhar, *ib.*, 28. 313, 1924; P. B. Ganguly and N. R. Dhar, *ib.*, 31. 16, 1922; S. Ghosh and N. R. Dhar, *Journ. Phys. Chem.*, 30. 628, 1926; 31. 187, 449, 1927; *Koll. Zeit.*, 39. 346, 1926; 41. 229, 1927; *Zeit. anorg. Chem.*, 152. 408, 1926; *Koll. Zeit.*, 29. 435, 658, 1925; *Zeit. Koll.*, 36. 129, 1925; N. R. Dhar and A. C. Chatterji, *ib.*, 37. 26, 1925; *Zeit. anorg. Chem.*, 159. 186, 1927; H. Neugebauer, *Koll. Zeit.*, 43. 65, 1927; R. Zsigmondy and C. Carins, *Ber.*, 60. B, 1047, 1927.

§ 24. The Sulphoantimonites

Antimony trisulphide can play the part of an acid anhydride, forming a series of complex salts with the basic sulphides, and the products can be regarded as derivatives of a series of hypothetical **sulphoantimonious acids**, which, by analogy with the corresponding sulpharsenious acids (*q.v.*), can be tabulated :

Orthosulphoantimonious acid	H_3SbS_3
Metasulphoantimonious acid	$HSbS_2$
Pyrosulphoantimonious acid	$H_4Sb_2S_5$
Orthosulphotetrantimonious acid (*i.e.* $H_{12}Sb_4S_{12}$ less $3H_2S$)	$H_6Sb_4S_9$
Metasulphotetrantimonious acid (*i.e.* $H_{12}Sb_4S_{12}$ less $5H_2S$)	$H_2Sb_4S_7$
Orthosulphoctoantimonious acid (*i.e.* $H_{24}Sb_8S_{24}$ less $7H_2S$)	$H_{10}Sb_8S_{17}$
Metasulphoctoantimonious acid (*i.e.* $H_{24}Sb_8S_{24}$ less $11H_2S$)	$H_2Sb_8S_{13}$

Some of the acids furnish basic salts, some of which can be regarded as combinations of orthosulphoantimonites with nM_2S. Some mineral sulphoantimonites belong to this family—*e.g.*, silver, cuprous, mercurous, lead, and ferrous sulphoantimonites. Arsenic replaces antimony isomorphously in many of these minerals. J. J. Berzelius [1] made the sulphoantimonites by fusing together the component sulphides ; by treating antimony trisulphide with a soluble sulphide ; and by treating a soluble sulphoantimonite with a salt of the heavy metals. Modifications of the process were employed by A. Ditte, I. Pouget, V. Stanek, and B. Unger. H. Sommerlad obtained the salts by melting together antimony trisulphide and the chlorides of copper, silver or lead. B. Unger obtained some sulphoantimonites by the action of the hydroxides of the alkalies or alkaline earths, or of the alkali carbonates on antimony trisulphide ; and M. Berthelot, by the action of alkali sulphides on antimony trisulphide. A. Duflos reduced antimonates to antimonites by means of antimony.

The alkali sulphoantimonites are yellow, red, or brown ; they melt easily, and without decomposition if air be excluded. The sulphoantimonites of the heavy metals are usually black and rarely red. The artificial salts are usually amorphous. Some of the heavy metal salts give off antimony trisulphide when heated out of contact with air. When the sulphoantimonites are heated in air, sulphur dioxide, and the metal oxides are formed. The alkali salts are hygroscopic, and some are decomposed by the absorbed moisture. The heavy metal salts are stable in air. The alkali and alkaline earth salts are usually soluble in water—they are not decomposed by water if alkali sulphides be present in excess. The aq. soln. are usually brown. The aq. soln. may be decomposed by the carbon dioxide of the air with the separation of antimony trisulphide ; and they may be oxidized to sulph-antimonates. The salts are decomposed by acids as well as by carbon dioxide, and oxalic and acetic acids. Many of these salts are decomposed by nitric acid with the formation of sulphur and antimony oxide. W. Hampe decomposed some of the native sulphoantimonites with a mixture of nitric and tartaric acids ; and H. C. Bolton, with a mixture of citric acid with potassium nitrate, nitrite, or chlorate. H. Rose, and T. Poleck oxidized the sulphoantimonites with chlorine ; P. Jannasch and T. Poleck, with bromine ; H. C. Bolton, with iodine and water ; T. Poleck, with sodium dioxide ; R. Bunsen, C. Doelter, and A. Terreil, with soln. of alkali sulphides ; and E. F. Smith, by electrolyzing a molten mixture of the sulpho-antimonite and potassium hydroxide. I. Pouget found that the sulphoantimonites reduce cupric salts to cuprous salts, and mercurous salts to mercury. The reduction of cupric oxide to cuprous sulphide and the formation of sulphoantimonates was studied by E. Berglund, C. Serons, K. Heumann, and H. Rose.

G. Kohl treated an excess of antimony trisulphide with a boiling soln. of ammonium hydrosulphide ; and added alcohol to the soln. The pale yellow mass of rhombohedral crystals is precipitated. G. Kohl supposed the salt to be a sulphoanti-monite ; V. Stanek, a sulphoantimonate. If alcohol be added to a soln. of a mol of antimony trisulphide and a conc. soln. of 3 mols of ammonium sulphide, I. Pouget found that a white, crystalline precipitate of **ammonium orthosulphoantimonite,** $(NH_4)_3SbS_3$, is formed. It is less stable than the corresponding salts of the alkalies. It is soluble in water, and the soln. loses ammonium sulphide on exposure to air. If the soln. be crystallized without the addition of alcohol, **ammonium meta-sulphoantimonite,** $NH_4SbS_2.2H_2O$, is formed. V. Stanek obtained the same salt by treating pulverulent stibnite with a freshly prepared soln. of ammonium sulphide. Small yellow crystals are soon formed. In 12 hrs., the crystals are drained from the mother-liquor, washed with water, then with alcohol and ether, and dried between bibulous paper. The yellow, four-sided needles or plates are fluorescent ; they become brownish-red on exposure to air ; they are insoluble in water ; they lose 22·13 per cent. in weight at 105°, forming, according to V. Stanek, and I. Pouget, **ammonium metasulphotetrantimonite,** $(NH_4)_2Sb_4S_7$. V. Stanek also made this salt by heating a mixture of antimony trisulphide and ammonium hydrosulphide in a sealed tube at 150° ; and also by heating ammonium orthosulphoantimonate and antimony pentasulphide in a sealed tube : $Sb_2S_5+2(NH_4)_3SbS_4=2(NH_4)_2S_3+(NH_4)_2Sb_4S_7$. I. Pouget treated a mol of antimony trisulphide with 3 mols of a dil. soln. of 3 mols of ammonium sulphide (0·15 mol of the salt per litre). The yellow, acicular crystals are stable in air ; they are not decomposed at 200°, but break down at a higher temp. They are insoluble in boiling water.

I. Pouget did not succeed in making *lithium pyrosulphoantimonite*, $Li_4Sb_2S_5$ and *lithium metasulphoantimonite*, $LiSbS_2$; but he obtained **lithium orthosulphoanti-monite,** $Li_3SbS_3.3H_2O$, by evaporating a soln. containing 3 mols of lithium sulphide and one mol of antimony trisulphide. The small, white, deliquescent crystals are freely soluble in water. The properties of the salt are like those of the other alkali orthosulphoantimonites. If a hot soln. of lithium sulphide be sat. with antimony trisulphide, a dark red, gelatinous precipitate of **lithium metasulpho-tetrantimonite,** $Li_2Sb_4S_7.3H_2O$, is formed ; it could not be crystallized.

G. Kohl obtained a liver-brown mass by melting a mixture of a mol of antimony trisulphide, 9 mols of sodium sulphide, and 0·20–0·25 gram-atom of antimony. When the aq. extract were evaporated, deliquescent prisms of an impure sodium sulphoantimonite were formed. P. Berthier melted 15 parts of antimony trisulphide and 10 parts of anhydrous sodium sulphate in a closed carbon crucible at a white-heat. Along with a little reduced antimony there is produced a reddish-brown mass which deliquesces in air, and with water furnishes a brown soln. and a precipitate of antimony trisulphide. J. J. Berzelius, B. Unger, and C. Doelter obtained impure sulphoantimonites by dissolving antimony trisulphide in soln. of sodium sulphide. C. Tocco prepared sodium sulphoantimonite by the electrolysis of soln. of sodium thiosulphate—*vide supra,* antimony trisulphide. The proportion of the sulphide reaches 100 per cent. when a 20 per cent. sodium thiosulphate soln. is electrolyzed at 50°–60°, with a current density of 51 amps. per sq. dm. As a rule the formation of sulphides is favoured by a high current density, limited by the value at which mechanical disintegration of the electrode begins, by a high conc. of the thiosulphate, and by a temp. of about 50°. The addition of alkali sulphide or carbonate hinders the formation of sulphide and enhances that of sulpho-salt. The current efficiency is 9·41 per cent. I. Pouget prepared **sodium orthosulphoantimonite,** $Na_3SbS_3.9H_2O$, by concentrating in an atm. of hydrogen a soln. of a mol of antimony trisulphide and 3 mols of sodium sulphide. The pale yellow, acicular crystals lose all their water when heated in a current of hydrogen at 150°, and furnish a red powder. The salt retains its water in vacuo over sulphuric acid, and both the solid and aq. soln. are readily oxidized to sulphoantimonate. According to M. Berthelot, the heat of formation is $SbCl_3+3Na_2S_{soln.}=Na_3SbS_3+3NaCl+62$ to 69 Cals., according to the conc. of the soln. of sodium sulphide. Most of the heat is developed with the first two mols of sodium sulphide, the third mol develops only 2·26 Cals. When a mol of sodium orthosulphoantimonite is treated with 3 mols of hydrochloric acid 18·12–18·59 Cals. are evolved. E. Giebe and A. Schiebe studied the piezoelectric properties of the crystals. I. Pouget obtained **potassium orthosulphoantimonite,** K_3SbS_3, in a similar way. The small white crystals are dried on a porous tile in vacuo. The crystals are very deliquescent ; they are soluble in water ; and readily oxidize in air. I. Pouget, and A. Ditte made **potassium pyrosulphoantimonite,** $K_4Sb_2S_7$, by evaporating in the cold a conc. soln. of antimony trisulphide and potassium sulphide (2 mols). The soln. behaves like that of the metasulpho-antimonite. J. J. Berzelius obtained a product with the same composition, but mixed with some antimonite by fusing antimony trisulphide with potassium carbonate. A. Ditte made **potassium metasulphoantimonite,** $KSbS_2$, in red, transparent crystals by melting a mixture of antimony trisulphide, potassium carbonate, and sulphur, and allowing a soln. of the product, in a small proportion of water, to crystallize. I. Pouget obtained this salt by the method employed for the sodium salt ; J. J. Berzelius obtained this salt in dark brown crystals resembling graphite, and contaminated with some antimonite, by fusing a mixture of 6 parts of antimony trisulphide and 3 parts of potassium carbonate ; and W. Müller, by heating potassium metantimonite in a current of carbon disulphide. I. Pouget said the small red crystals are unchanged in air ; they are insoluble in cold water ; and decomposed by hot water. If the mother-liquor remaining after the separation of the sulphoantimonate from a partially oxidized soln. of orthosulphoantimonite be evaporated, it furnishes crystals of **sodium orthosulphotetrantimonite,** $Na_6Sb_4S_9$. I. Pouget evaporated a soln. of a mol of antimony trisulphide and 2 mols of sodium sulphide, and obtained a mixture of **sodium metasulphoantimonite,** $NaSbS_2$ and orthosulphoantimonite. The former salt separates as the first crop of crystals.

B. Unger made the same salt by adding alcohol to a soln. of antimony trisulphide in an excess of sodium sulphide; washing away the excess of sodium sulphide by alcohol; and evaporating an aq. soln. of the product on a water-bath when pale yellow crystals of sodium orthosulphoantimonite, and dark brown metasulphoantimonite are formed. According to I. Pouget, if a dil. soln. of a mol of antimony trisulphide and 2 mols of sodium sulphide be evaporated in vacuo, besides yellow, tetrahedral crystals of orthosulphoantimonate, there are produced small red crystals of **sodium metasulphotetrantimonite,** $Na_2Sb_4S_7.2H_2O$, which can be purified by levigation. A hot sat. soln. of antimony trisulphide in one of sodium sulphide deposits a brown gelatinous precipitate, and the mother-liquor contains the metasulphotetrantimonite; and when a soln. of a mol of antimony trisulphide and 2 mols of sodium sulphide is treated with much water, a red gelatinous precipitate of the metasulphotetrantimonite is formed. A. Ditte prepared **potassium metasulphotetrantimonite,** $K_2Sb_4S_7.3H_2O$, by evaporating a soln. of antimony trisulphide in a less conc. soln. of potassium sulphide than that used for the metasulphoantimonite; and I. Pouget, by diluting a conc. soln. or cooling a hot sat. soln. of the pyrosulphoantimonite. The small, pale red, prismatic crystals, or red amorphous powder are superficially discoloured by light. If a soln. of sodium orthosulphoantimonite be treated with hydrogen sulphide, I. Pouget found that a red precipitate of **sodium hydrometasulphotetrantimonite,** $NaHSb_4S_7.2H_2O$, is formed. This should be washed in an atm. of hydrogen sulphide and dried on a porous tile. It furnishes a garnet-red powder. I. Pouget obtained **potassium hydrometasulphotetrantimonite,** $KHSb_4S_7$, in a similar manner.

According to H. Pélabon,[2] the m.p. of antimony trisulphide is lowered from 555° to 498°, by the addition of 4 mols of cuprous sulphide to one mol of antimony trisulphide, and any further additions of cuprous sulphide raise the m.p. The 2 : 1 mixture has two m.p., and these are indications of the formation of a compound $2Cu_2S.3Sb_2S_3$. N. Parravano and P. de Cesaris examined the f.p. curve of mixtures of cuprous and antimonious sulphides more closely, and the results are represented in Fig. 58. Two maxima appear on the curve; the one at 542° corresponds with cuprous metasulphoantimonite, $Cu_2S.Sb_2S_3$, or $CuSbS_2$; and the other at 607° corresponds with cuprous orthosulphoantimonite, $3Cu_2S.Sb_2S_3$, or Cu_3SbS_3. There are two arrests in the f.p. curve of the ortho-salt, one at 607° and the other at the eutectic temp. The more the mixtures differ in composition from the eutectics the lower are the temp. at which the eutectic arrests occur. This is attributed to the low thermal conductivity of the fused masses. M. Chikashige and Y. Yamanchi considered that the first maximum occurs at 520°, corresponding with $4Cu_2S.5Sb_2S_3$,

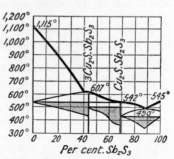

FIG. 58.—Freezing-point Curves of the Binary Mixtures: Sb_2S_3–Cu_2S.

and the second at 571°, corresponding with the orthosulphoantimonite. They place the eutectics at 463° with 7 per cent. Cu_2S; at 514°, with 37 per cent. Cu_2S; and 571°, with 68 per cent. of Cu_2S. No solid soln. are formed. W. Guertler and K. L. Meissner showed that sulphur cannot exist in equilibrium with copper antimonide and that a reaction occurs with the formation of cuprous sulphide: $2Cu_3Sb+S=2Cu_2Sb+Cu_2S$; $Cu_2Sb+S=Cu_2S+Sb$. Cuprous sulphide melted with either antimony or the antimonides yields stable mixtures, but no ternary compounds are formed. Copper and antimony trisulphides react according to the equations: $12Cu+Sb_2S_3=3Cu_2S+2Cu_3Sb$; $10Cu+Sb_2S_3=3Cu_2S+2Cu_2Sb$; $6Cu+Sb_2S_3=3Cu_2S+2Sb$. The rectangle Cu–Sb–Sb_2S_3–Cu_2S is subdivided into six triangles by the five quasi-binary intersections, Cu_2S–Cu_3Sb; Cu_2S–Cu_2Sb; Cu_2S–Sb; Cu_3SbS_3–Sb; and $CuSbS_2$–Sb. Two independent mixture gaps occur

in the system, which are probably dependent on similar gaps in the binary systems $Cu-Cu_2S$ and $Sb-Sb_2S_3$. For **tetrahedrite**, see tennantite—8. 51, 31.
The mineral **stylotypite** was named by F. von Kobell; he obtained it from Copiapo, Chili. It was named in allusion to its columnar form—from $\sigma\tau\hat{\upsilon}\lambda o\varsigma$, column; and $\tau\acute{\upsilon}\pi o\varsigma$, form. Analyses by F. von Kobell, and S. Stevanovic correspond approximately with $(Cu_2,Ag_2,Fe,Zn)_3\{(As,Sb,Bi)S_3\}_2$; and E. T. Wherry and W. F. Foshag represent the idealized mineral as **cuprous orthosulphoantimonite**, Cu_3SbS_3. N. Parravano and P. de Cesaris obtained the compound by fusing its component sulphides in an atm. of hydrogen—Fig. 57. H. Sommerlad synthesized it by melting a mol of antimony trisulphide with 3 mols of either cuprous chloride or cuprous sulphide; and I. Pouget, by the action of water on potassium cuprous orthosulphoantimonite. F. von Kobell supposed the crystals of the iron-black mineral belong to the rhombic system, and to exhibit cruciform twinning. S. Stevanovic showed that the crystals are more probably monoclinic with the axial ratios $a : b : c = 1\cdot9202 : 1 : 1\cdot0355$, and $\beta = c$. 90°. P. Groth, and S. Stevanovic supposed the mineral to be isomorphous with xanthoconite, and pyrostilpnite. The sp. gr. ranges from F. von Kobell's 4·79 to S. Stevanovic's 5·18, and J. J. Saslawsky made some calculations on the contraction which occurs in the formation of the compound from its elements. H. Sommerlad gave 5·13–5·182 for the artificial orthosulphoantimonite. The hardness of the mineral is 3. The m.p. by N. Parravano and P. de Cesaris is 607°; and by M. Chikashige and Y. Yamanchi, 571°. The mineral is soluble in nitric acid; and **potash-lye extracts antimony trisulphide**.

W. T. Page described a fahlerz from Colorado which appears to be related to stylotypite ; and A. Raimondi, a plumbiferous mineral from Cinquimarca, which is also related to stylotypite when due allowance is made for admixed quartz. A. Raimondi called *dürfeldtite*—after R. Dürfeldt. S. Stevenovic said that similar remarks can be made respecting a mineral from Joachimsthal which he called *falkenhaynite*—after J. Falkenhayn. F. Sandberger supposed falkenhaynite to be related to amonite or tetrahedrite. The antimonial varieties of fahlerz, represented in the limiting case by *tetrahedrite*, have been discussed in connection with tennantite, the limiting case at the arsenical end of the series.

J. C. L. Zincken discovered a mineral at Wolfsberg, Harz, which he called *Kupferantimonglanz*. The crystals were examined by G. Rose, they were analyzed by H. Rose, and the resemblance to zinckenite and miargyrite was noted. J. J. N. Huot called it *rosite;* E. F. Glocker, **chalcostibite**, or rather *Chalkostibit;* and J. Nicol, *wolfsbergite*. E. Cumenge described a mineral from Guejar, Andalusia, which he called *guejarite*, and to which he ascribed the formula $Cu_2Sb_4S_7$. These crystals were examined by C. Friedel. L. J. Spencer showed that guejarite and chalcostibite are probably the same mineral species, and this was confirmed by S. L. Penfield, and A. Frenzel. Analyses were made by H. Rose, T. Richter, P. N. Tschirwinsky, E. Cumenge, and A. Frenzel ; the results agree with the formula $Cu_2S.Sb_3S_3$, or **cuprous metasulphoantimonite**, $CuSbS_2$—or possibly with $4Cu_2S.5Sb_2S_3$. H. Sommerlad obtained this salt by heating a mixture of 3 mols of cuprous chloride, and 2 mols of antimony trisulphide. The reaction begins at about 130°, and proceeds slowly at 300°. It was also made by H. Sommerlad, and N. Parravano and P. de Cesaris, by melting together the constituent sulphides. The lead-grey or iron-grey mineral occurs granular, massive, and in small aggregated prisms belonging to the rhombic system, with the axial ratios, according to S. L. Penfield, $a : b : c = 0\cdot5312 : 1 : 0\cdot63955$. L. J. Spencer described the twinning of the crystals. The cleavage on the (001)-face is perfect, and that on the (100)- and (010)-faces imperfect. The crystals were examined by G. Rose, P. Groth, H. Laspeyres, L. J. Spencer, G. A. Kenngott, and P. N. Tschirwinsky. L. J. Spencer discussed the isomorphous zinckenite, etc. For the isomorphous family of which chalcostibite is a member, *vide infra*, zinckenite. The sp. gr. of the mineral given by J. C. L. Zincken was 4·748; and S. L. Penfield gave 4·959. H. Sommerlad found for the artificial compound a sp. gr. 4·885–4·979. The hardness is 3–4. N. Parravano and P. de Cesaris found the m.p. to be 542°, Fig. 58; and M. Chikashige and Y. Yamanchi, about 520°. A. de Gramont examined the spark spectrum. T. W. Case found chalcostibite is a poor conductor, and light has no measurable effect. The mineral is decomposed by nitric acid with the separation of sulphur ; aq. ammonia has no action ; and soln. of the alkali hydroxides or sulphides extract antimony trisulphide.

According to C. F. Rammelsberg, when cupric sulphoantimonate is heated in a retort, **cuprous orthosulphotetrantimonite,** $Cu_6Sb_4S_9$, or $3Cu_2S.2Sb_2S_3$, is formed ; and H. Sommerlad found that by melting 6 mols of cuprous chloride and 7 mols of antimony trisulphide in a retort chemical action begins at about 180°, and at 300°, **cuprous metasulphotetrantimonite,** $Cu_2Sb_4S_7$, is formed as a grey mass with a scaly fracture and sp. gr. 4·814. It resembles the metasulphoantimonite in its chemical reactions. The mineral *guejarite* was at first thought to have this composition, but was later shown to be chalcostibite (*q.v.*).

According to I. Pouget, if a dil. soln. of potassium orthosulphoantimonite be treated with sufficient cupric salt, a black precipitate of **cupric orthosulphoanti-monite,** $Cu_3(SbS_3)_2$, is formed ; and if a conc. soln. of the potassium salt is used, a black precipitate of **potassium cuprous orthosulphoantimonite,** KCu_2SbS_3, is formed. The black precipitate gradually becomes yellow and crystalline. It should be dried in an atm. of hydrogen. If the precipitate be dried below 100°, it is trihydrated, $KCu_2SbS_3.3H_2O$, and anhydrous if dried over that temp. Water decomposes it, forming cuprous orthosulphoantimonite.

The m.p. curves of mixtures of silver and antimonious sulphides were examined by H. Pélabon,[3] who found two maxima corresponding with $Ag_2S.Sb_2S_3$, and $3Ag_2S.Sb_2S_3$; and three eutectics at 438°, 440°, and 454°, corresponding respectively with 17·5, 52·7, and 79 per cent. of silver sulphide. P. Chrétien and J. M. Guinchant found that 4·936, 10·34, 15·1, and 20·6 grms. of silver sulphide in 100 grms. of antimony trisulphide lowered the m.p. respectively 18°, 35°, 53°, and 78°. F. M. Jäger and H. S. van Klooster's observations are summarized in Fig. 59. The f.p. curve has two maxima, corresponding with $3Ag_2S,Sb_2S_3$ and Ag_2S,Sb_2S_3 respectively. The first of these, identical with the mineral pyrargyrite, has m.p. 483°. The second maximum corresponds with miargyrite, m.p. 509°. Eutectic points occur at 81, 64·5, and 28·2 mol. per cent. Ag_2S, and 463°, 455°, and 449°

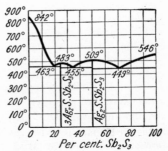

FIG. 59.—Freezing-point Curves of the Binary System : Ag_2S–Sb_2S_3.

respectively. The minerals bolivianite, stephanite, pyrostilpnite, polybasite, and polyargyrite can only have been formed from soln., as they are not represented in the equilibrium diagram. K. Konno found one maximum corresponding with $Ag_2S.Sb_2S_3$ and two eutectics—at 462° and 22 per cent. Ag_2S, and 464° and 72 per cent. Ag_2S. This compound does not form solid soln. with either component.

The history of the mineral **pyrargyrite** has been indicated in connection with proustite. Some early analyses were reported in connection with proustite ; and later analyses have been reported by C. G. A. von Weissenbach, J. Loczka, C. Castro, P. A. von Bonsdorff, R. Böttger. T. Petersen, F. Field, A. Streng, I. Domeyko, F. Wöhler, E. Rethwisch, H. A. Miers, and H. Traube. The results show that the idealized mineral is **silver orthosulphoantimonite,** Ag_3SbS_3. The antimony is replaced by more or less arsenic, and finally merges into proustite, Ag_3AsS_3. Indeed, F. M. Jäger and N. S. van Klooster found that proustite and pyrargyrite form an unbroken series of solid soln. The f.p. curve, Fig. 60, has a flat minimum at 473·5°. Silver orthosulphoantimonite was obtained by J. Margottet by heating a mixture of silver, antimony, and sulphur ; by C. F. Rammelsberg, by heating silver sulpho antimonite in a retort ; by J. Fournet, F. Wöhler, and F. M. Jäger and H. S. van

Klooster, by heating a mixture of the component sulphides in stoichiometrical proportions—Fig. 59 ; by H. Sommerlad, by heating a mixture of silver chloride and antimony trisulphide in the proportions : $3AgCl+Sb_2S_3=Ag_3SbS_3+SbCl_3$—

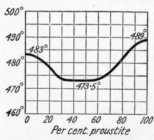

FIG. 60.—Melting-point Curve of Mixtures of Ag_3AsS_3 and Ag_3SbS_3.

the reaction begins at 140°, but the temp. is raised to distil off the trichloride—F. Ducatte, and J. Rondet always found the product contaminated with halides ; H. de Sénarmont, by heating a mixture of silver sulphate, and sodium sulphoantimonite and hydrocarbonate to 275°, or by heating a mixture of silver sulphoantimonate and sodium hydrocarbonate to 325° ; J. Durocher, by heating a mixture of silver and antimonious chlorides in a current of hydrogen sulphide—C. Doelter said that miargyrite is formed at low temp., and pyrargyrite at high ones. C. Doelter obtained this salt by the action of hydrogen sulphide on a soln. of silver chloride and potassium antimonate, or on a mixture of silver chloride, antimony trioxide, and sodium carbonate in a sealed tube for a long time between 80° and 150° ; by I. Pouget, as a black, amorphous precipitate, by adding silver nitrate to an excess of a dil. soln. of potassium orthosulphoantimonite 0·1 mol per litre—if the silver nitrate be in excess, the black precipitate is a mixture of several silver sulphoantimonites ; and F. M. Jäger and H. S. van Klooster, by heating for 50 hrs. a mixture of antimony trichloride, silver sulphide, a conc. soln. of sodium sulphide, and sodium hydrocarbonate. All the trichloride is transformed into pyrargyrite, but without the sodium hydrocarbonate some antimony sulphide remains in soln. The compound is not produced in acidic soln.

The **colour** of the artificial products is usually dark red and the material is crystalline ; the mineral may be black, dark grey, or deep red. Pyrargyrite may be massive and compact ; or it may occur in prismatic and hemimorphic **crystals** belonging to the trigonal system. H. A. Miers gave for the axial ratio of the trigonal pyramid $a:c=1:0.7880$. For a monoclinic form, *vide infra*, pyrostilpnite. The **twinning** of the crystals of pyrargyrite is common about the (11$\bar{2}$0)- and (10$\bar{1}$4)-planes ; less common about the (10$\bar{1}$1)-plane ; and rare about the (01$\bar{1}$2)-plane. The **cleavage** on the (10$\bar{1}$1)-face is distinct, and that on the (01$\bar{1}$2)-face imperfect. The crystals were also examined by M. J. Schuster, H. Traube, V. Goldschmidt, O. Mügge, C. Busz, E. Rethwisch, W. Haidinger, R. J. Haüy, F. Mohs, A. Lévy, Q. Sella, O. Luedecke, A. Frenzel, F. Sandberger, M. Fenoglio, and E. A. Schenck. H. Schneiderhöhn examined polished sections of the mineral ; and L. G. Raviez, the etching of polished surfaces with potash-lye. For the **specific gravity** of pyrargyrite, R. Böttger gave 5·89 ; T. Petersen, 5·90 ; A. Streng, 5·68 ; E. Rethwisch, 5·716–5·871 ; H. A. Miers, 5·77–5·86 ; H. Traube, 5·76 ; and J. Loczko, 5·852. The sp. gr. of the artificial product by H. Sommerlad is 5·49–5·76 ; and F. M. Jäger and H. S. van Klooster, 5·75–5·79. The **hardness** is 2–3. O. Mügge examined the effect of **pressure** on the crystals. H. Fizeau found the coeff. of **thermal expansion** to be 0.0_691 at 40° when parallel to the chief axis, and 0.0_42012 at 40° when vertical thereto. A. Sella gave for the **specific heat**, 0·0755. F. M. Jäger and H. S. van Klooster found the **melting point** to be 483°—Fig. 59. A. des Cloizeaux reported the **indices of refraction** to be $\omega=3.084$, and $\epsilon=2.881$ at 19° for Li-light. The **birefringence** is strong and negative. W. W. Coblentz and J. F. Eckford studied the photoelectric sensitivity. At 22° there is a wide, unsymmetrical maximum in the ultra-violet with a weak, ill-defined maximum in the region of 0·63. It also differs from that of the constituent sulphides, but resembles that of proustite (silver arsenic sulphide). At −165°, pyrargyrite reacts electrically to all wave-lengths from the extreme ultra-violet to 1·5, but the greatest reaction is localized in the band at 0·63. A. de Gramont examined the **spark spectrum,** and said that its **electrical conductivity** is smaller than that of argentite or dyscrasite. C. Tubandt and M. Haedicke found that the pure salt is an insulator. M. von Laue, T. W. Case, and E. Giebe and A. Scheibe studied the piezoelectric properties of the crystals; and P. H. Geiger, the **photoelectric effect.** H. E. McKinstry found that the surface of the mineral is roughened by exposure to the light of an electric arc. E. E. Fairbanks found the **dielectric constant** to be less than 81.

Pyrargyrite is decomposed by **hydrochloric acid** with the separation of sulphur and antimony trioxide; it is also decomposed by **nitric acid;** it is soluble in a mixture of tartaric and nitric acids, and is decomposed by **chlorine;** it is blackened by a warm soln. of **alkali hydroxide,** and L. G. Raviez found that a hot soln. of **alkali carbonate** extracts a trace of antimony trisulphide, while a hot dil. soln. of **alkali sulphide** dissolves out the antimony trisulphide, and leaves black silver sulphide behind. C. A. Burghardt found that when melted with **ammonium nitrate,** and extracted with water, it yields a soln. of silver sulphate, and a residue of mixed antimony tri- and penta-oxides. H. B. North and C. B. Conover observed that the mineral is attacked by **thionyl chloride** at 150°. The weathering of pyrargyrite has been studied by W. Maucher, and A. Hofmann and F. Slavik; the transformation of the mineral into argentite and silver, by the leaching out of the antimony trisulphide, has been frequently observed—by J. R. Blum, A. Breithaupt, etc.

A. Breithaupt [4] described monoclinic crystals of a rare mineral from Kurprinz, near Freiberg, which he called *Feuerblende;* it contained silver and antimonious sulphides. J. D. Dana translated A. Breithaupt's term into *fire blende,* or **pyrostilpnite**—from $\pi\tilde{v}\rho$, fire; and $\sigma\tau\iota\lambda\pi\nu\acute{o}s$, shining; M. Adam called it *pyrochrolite;* and A. Breithaupt later called it *pyrochrotite.* The analysis reported by O. Luedecke showed that the mineral, like pyrargyrite, is silver orthosulphoantimonite, Ag_3SbS_3. G. Cesaro wrote the formula $(Ag_2S_2)(SbS_2)_2$. C. Doelter synthesized crystals of this mineral along with those of pyrargyrite. G. A. Kenngott supposed the hyacinth-red, slender, prismatic, or tabular crystals are rhombic; but A. Breithaupt, F. A. Roemer, W. H. Miller, and A. Streng showed that they are monoclinic, and O. Luedecke gave for the axial ratios $a : b : c = 0.35465 : 1 : 0.17819$, and $\beta = 90°$. H. A. Miers calculated the values for another orientation of the crystals and gave $a : b : c = 1.9465 : 1 : 1.0973$, and $\beta = 90°$ for pyrostilpnite; and $1.9187 : 1 : 1.0152$, and $\beta = 88° \ 47'$ for xanthoconite, Ag_3AsS_4, so that the two minerals are isomorphous. Twinning occurs about the (100)-plane; the (010)-cleavage is perfect. W. H. Miller gave 4.3 for the sp. gr., but this value is probably too small. J. J. Saslawsky calculated the contraction which occurs when the mineral is formed from its elements. The hardness is over 2. The general chemical properties are like those of pyrargyrite.

F. Mohs [5] described *hemiprismatic ruby blende* as a mineral obtained from Bräunsdorf, Freiberg; H. Rose called it **miargyrite**—from $\mu\epsilon\acute{\iota}\omega\nu$, less; and $\mathring{a}\rho\gamma\upsilon\rho os$, silver—in allusion to its containing less silver than kindred ores. A. Breithaupt called a sample from Clausthal, *hypargyrite;* and W. Haidinger, a sample from Felsöbanya, *kenngotite.* Analyses were reported by H. Rose, R. Helmhacker, I. Domeyko, L. Sipöcz, A. Weisbach, J. Rumpf, L. J. Spencer, and H. Sommerlad. C. F. Rammelsberg calculated the formula $Ag_2S.Sb_2S_3$, or **silver metasulphoantimonite,** $AgSbS_2$, *i.e.* S=Sb—ASg—*vide* arsenomiargyrite. H. Sommerlad made this salt by melting together a mixture of silver chloride and antimony trisulphide: $3AgCl + 2Sb_2S_3 = 3AgSbS_2 + SbCl_3$; and C. Doelter, a mixture of silver chloride, and antimony trichloride and trioxide in a current of hydrogen sulphide. If the temp. exceeds 300°, some pyrargyrite is formed. F. M. Jäger and H. S. van Klooster obtained it by melting together the constituent sulphides—Fig. 59. C. Doelter, and C. Vrba discussed the formation of the mineral in nature.

The iron-grey or steel-grey mineral in thin splinters appears blood-red. It occurs massive, and also in thick tabular or prismatic crystals. Some of the flakes may show striations. According to W. J. Lewis, the crystals are monoclinic, with the axial ratios $a:b:c=2.99449:1:2.90951$ and $\beta=81°\ 22'\ 35''$. The (010)· cleavage shows in traces. Observations on the crystals were also made by C. F. Naumann, P. Groth, G. vom Rath, A. Weisbach, W. H. Miller, O. Mügge, E. V. Shannon, and A. S. Eakle. L. J. Spencer compared monoclinic miargyrite, $AgSbS_2$, with monoclinic andorite, $PbAg(SbS_2)_3$; and with monoclinic zinckenite, $Pb(SbS_2)_2$; and V. Goldschmidt, L. Tokody, and A. S. Eakle discussed the possible isomorphism of miargyrite and lorandite. L. Sipöcz gave 6·06 for the sp. gr.; J. Rumpf, 5·08; L. J. Spencer, 5·20; and G. A. Kenngott, 6·06 for a variety containing lead. For the artificial compound C. Doelter gave 5·28; H. Sommerlad, 5·20; and F. M. Jäger and H. S. van Klooster, 5·36. J. J. Saslawsky studied the contraction which occurs during the formation of the mineral. The hardness is 2·0–2·5. G. vom Rath, and O. Mügge discussed the effect of press. H. Pélabon gave 503° for the m.p.; and F. M. Jäger and H. S. van Klooster, 507°—vide Fig. 59. H. E. McKinstry observed that the mineral is not changed when it is exposed to the light of an electric arc. T. W. Case observed the resistance to be less than a megohm, and insolation has no perceptible influence; and C. Tubandt and M. Haedicke, that the pure salt is an insulator. E. E. Fairbanks gave 81 for the dielectric constant (water 81). The mineral is decomposed by nitric acid with the separation of sulphur and antimony oxide.

An iron-black or blackish-grey silver sulphoantimonite occurs at Wolfach, Baden, in cubic crystals which are usually in the form of distorted and indistinct octahedra. T. Petersen [6] called it **polyargyrite**—from πολύς, many; and ἄργυρος, silver—in allusion to the high proportion of silver present. T. Petersen's analysis corresponds with $12Ag_2S.Sb_2S_3$, or **silver enneasulphodiorthosulphoantimonite**, $9Ag_2S.2Ag_3SbS_3$. G. Cesaro supposed that silver formed a bivalent radicle Ag_2, or $-Ag.Ag-$, and copper, Cu_2, or $-Cu.Cu-$. He represented the constitution of polyargyrite $S=Sb-S(Ag_2-S)_{12}-Sb=S$. H. Sommerlad obtained it by melting the components together in stoichiometrical proportions; but he did not obtain it by heating silver chloride with antimony trisulphide. T. Petersen gave 6·974 for the sp. gr. of the mineral, and H. Sommerlad, 6·50 for the artificial product. J. J. Saslawsky calculated the contraction which occurs during the formation of the compound. The hardness is 2–3. The chemical properties are like those of pyrargyrite. H. E. McKinstry found that the mineral is not altered by exposure to the light of an electric arc. F. Sandberger discussed its formation in nature. There is no sign of it in the f.p. curve, Fig. 59.

In 1546, G. Agricola [7] referred to a black silver ore, *argentum rude nigrum ;* and a couple of centuries later, J. G. Wallerius described a *Schwarzerz* or *Schwarzgulden ;* I. S. R. I. Eques a Born, *argentum mineralisatum nigrum fragile,* or the *Roschgewachs* of the Hungarian miners; M. H. Klaproth, and A. G. Werner, *Sprödglaserz—brittle silver ore ;* C. C. von Leonhard, *Schwarzgultigerz ;* R. Jameson, and F. Mohs, *prismatischer Melanglanz ;* E. F. Glocker, *melanargyrite ;* R. J. Haüy, *argent noir,* or *argent antimoiné sulfuré noir ;* F. S. Beudant, *psaturose*—from ψαθυρός or ψαδαρός, fragile; and W. Haidinger, **stephanite**—after Stephan von Oerterreich. A. Breithaupt, and C. F. Naumann showed that F. Mohs' prismatic melanoglance covers only a part of the brittle silver ore of A. G. Werner; the other part is hexagonal, and A. Breithaupt called it *Eugenglanz*—from εὐγενής, rare. H. Rose called the form **polybasite**—from πολύς, many; and βάσις, base—in allusion to the many metallic bases present.

Analyses of polybasite were reported by M. H. Klaproth, H. Rose, C. A. Joy, F. Tonner, G. A. Kenngott, W. J. Taylor, I. Domeyko, F. A. Genth, G. T. Prior, and H. Ungemach. The complexity of the mineral makes the formula somewhat speculative. H. Rose gave $9Ag_2S.Sb_2S_3$, or rather $9(Cu,Ag)_2S(Sb,As)_2S_3$, *i.e.* in the limiting case, **silver trisulpho-orthosulphoantimonite**, $3Ag_2S Ag_3SbS_3$. C. F. Rammelsberg, and F. R. van Horn, however, gave this formula, $8Ag_2S.Sb_2S_3$, or rather $Ag_{16}Sb_2S_{11}$; G. Boländer found the ratio $R_2S:R_2S_3$ varied from 7·22 : 1 to 10 : 1, and he considered the mineral to be a mixture of $R_2S.As_2S_3$ with a preponderating proportion of $7R_2S.Sb_2S_3$. S. L. Penfield gave Ag_9SbS_6 analogous with the formula Ag_9AsS_6 for pearcite; and G. Cesaro, $9Ag_2S.Sb_2S_3$, or $S=Sb-S-(Ag_2S)_9-Sb=S-vide$ *supra*, pyrostilpnite. The subject was also discussed by E. H. Kraus and J. P. Goldsberry, and W. F. Foshag. H. Sommerlad obtained polybasite—free from copper—by heating a mixture of silver chloride and antimony trisulphide in the molar proportions 1 : 24·5. The product was extracted with a soln. of sodium thiosulphate to remove silver chloride, and the dried residue melted in a current of hydrogen sulphide. There is no sign of the compound on the f.p. curve, Fig. 59. Polybasite is an iron-black mineral which in thin splinters appears cherry-red. J. L. C. Schröder van der Kolk wrote on this subject. While H. and G. Rose considered that the tabular prisms with bevelled edges belong to the hexagonal, A. des Cloizeaux showed that it is rhombic, and probably isomorphous with stephanite. This was supported by H. A. Miers, who gave for the axial ratios $a : b : c=0.5793 : 1 : 0.91305$, and S. L. Penfield showed that it is more probably monoclinic with the axial ratios $a : b : c=1.7309 : 1 : 1.5796$, and $\beta=90° 0'$. The twinning is supposed to be like that of mica; the (001)-cleavage is imperfect. A. des Cloizeaux gave for the optical axial angle $2E=88° 15'$, for white light. For the sp. gr., H. Rose gave 6·214; C. A. Joy, and F. A. Genth, 6·009; G. A. Kenngott, 6·03; and G. T. Prior, 6·33. For the artificial mineral, H. Sommerlad gave 6·352. J. J. Saslawsky estimated the contraction which occurs during the formation of polybasite from its constituents. The hardness is 2–3. J. Joly found that sublimation occurs at 430°. A. de Gramont examined the spark spectrum. H. E. McKinstry observed that the surface of the mineral is roughened by exposure to the light of an electric arc. T. W. Case found that polybasite has a resistance less than a megohm, and light decreases the resistance. E. E. Fairbanks found the dielectric constant of polybasite to be less than 81, and of stephanite, greater than 81. O. Mügge made some observations on the weathering of polybasite.

Analyses of stephanite were made in the early days by R. Brandes, B. Kerl, and H. Rose, and later ones have been reported by A. Frenzel, C. Vrba, J. D. Dana, I. Domeyko, G. T. Prior, W. E. Ford, and T. L. Walker. C. F. Rammelsberg calculated the formula $5Ag_2S.Sb_2S_3$, or $Ag_2S.Ag_3SbS_3$, **silver orthosulphoantimonite.** G. T. Prior, and P. Groth and K. Mieleitner used C. F. Rammelsberg's formula. R. F. Weinland regarded stephanite as a complex salt $[SbS_4]Ag_5$; and G. Cesaro gave $S=Sb-S-(Ag_2-S)_5-Sb-S$. W. F. Foshag also discussed this subject. C. Doelter made the mineral by heating silver chloride and antimony trioxide in the molar proportions 10 : 1 with a soln. of sodium carbonate in an atm. of hydrogen sulphide, in a sealed tube at 80°–150° for some weeks. H. Sommerlad heated silver chloride and antimony trisulphide in the molar proportion 15 : 4 at 200°. L. G. Ravicz obtained a product with a composition between that of polybasite and that of stephanite, by adding an excess of silver sulphate to a soln. of antimony trisulphide and alkali sulphide. No sign of stephanite appears on the f.p. diagram, Fig. 59. The iron-black mineral occurs massive, and disseminated; it also occurs in short prisms or in elongated, and tabular forms. The crystals of stephanite were at first supposed by J. F. von der Null to be hexagonal, but W. Haidinger, and F. Mohs showed that the crystals belong to the rhombic system. F. H. Schröder gave for the axial ratios $a : b : c=0.62911 : 1 : 0.68526$, and C. Vrba, $0.629129 : 1 : 0.685135$. The hemimorphism of the crystals was established by O. Luedecke, H. A. Miers, and G. d'Achiardi. It shows itself by a want of symmetry in the striations on the —(110)-face parallel to the edge (110) : (371). Oft-repeated twinning occurs about the —(110)-plane giving a pseudo-hexagonal form to the crystals; twinning also occurs about the (130)-, (110)-, or (010)-plane. The crystals were also examined by V. R. von Zepharovich, A. Reuss, J. F. Slavik, V. Nejdl, E. Artini, G. vom Rath, C. Morton, L. J. Spencer, A. Frenzel, P. Groth, W. J. Lewis, F. Sandberger. H. Rose gave for the sp. gr., 6·275; B. Kerl, 6·15; A. Frenzel, 6·28; C. Vrba, 6·271; and G. T. Prior, 6·24–6·26. H. Sommerlad gave 6·173 for the artificial crystals. J. J. Saslawsky estimated the contraction which occurs during the formation of the mineral from its components. The hardness is 2–3. A. de Gramont examined the spark spectrum. T. W. Case said that the resistance is less than a megohm, and it is lessened by insolation. P. H. Geiger studied the photoelectric effect. The weathering of stephanite was studied by V. R. von Zepharovich, A. Reuss, E. Döll, and J. R. Blum.

A. Breithaupt [8] described an *antimonial silver sulphide* occurring as a leaden-grey mineral from Bolivia, and he called it *bolivian*, *i.e.* **bolivianite**. The tufts of acicular prisms resemble stibnite. The composition approaches $Ag_2S.6Sb_2S_3$. The sp. gr. is 4·820–4·828, and the hardness 2·5. Further details are wanting.

According to I. Pouget,[9] when a conc. soln. of potassium orthosulphoantimonite is treated with silver nitrate, the black precipitate rapidly becomes yellow and crystalline owing to the formation of **potassium silver orthosulphoantimonite**, KAg_2SbS_3; and in a similar manner, **sodium silver orthosulphoantimonite**, $NaAg_2SbS_3$; **lithium silver orthosulphoantimonite**, $LiAg_2SbS_3$; and **ammonium silver orthosulphoantimonite**, $NH_4Ag_2SbS_3$, are formed. All these salts are yellow, and decomposed into silver orthosulphoantimonite when treated with water. I. Pouget obtained a brown precipitate of **gold sulphoantimonite** on adding a soln. of gold chloride to a conc. soln. of potassium sulphoantimonite. The precipitate dissolves when the liquid is agitated. When heated, the liquid deposits gold.

J. S. F. Pagenstecher [10] heated to a high temp. a mixture of antimony trisulphide, barium sulphate, and carbon, and obtained a reddish-brown, sintered mass of indefinite composition. With hot water, a yellow powder separates out. I. Pouget was unable to prepare *calcium orthosulphantimonite*, $Ca_3(SbO_3)_2$, he obtained **strontium orthosulphoantimonite**, $Sr_3(SbS_3)_2.10H_2O$, from a hot soln. of a mol of antimony trisulphide and 3 mols of strontium hydrosulphide. The brown liquid, on cooling, furnishes white scales. He obtained **barium orthosulphoantimonite**, $Ba_3(SbS_3)_2.8H_2O$, in a similar way. These salts are deliquescent, and are decomposed by water, forming orthosulphotetrantimonite. The salts are oxidized by air; and dissolve in a soln. of the alkaline earth sulphide. I. Pouget prepared **calcium pyrosulphoantimonite**, $Ca_2Sb_2S_5.15H_2O$, by evaporating in vacuo, in an atm. of hydrogen, a hot soln. of antimony trisulphide and calcium sulphide. The colourless, triclinic crystals dissolve in water without decomposition; they readily oxidize in air; and when dry become black on exposure to light. If the soln. be evaporated by heat, small red crystals of **calcium hydroxymetasulphoantimonite**, $HO.Ca.SbS_2$, are formed. They are insoluble in water, dissolve without residue in conc. hydrochloric acid; and when heated to redness in a current of hydrogen sulphide they lose water and hydrogen sulphide. The mother-liquor, remaining after the separation of this salt, yields the pyrosulphoantimonite. I. Pouget said that if strontium sulphide be used instead of the hydrosulphide employed in the preparation of strontium orthosulphoantimonite, or if the mother-liquor from that salt be evaporated in vacuo, **strontium pyrosulphoantimonite**, $Sr_2Sb_2S_5.15H_2O$, is formed in small, yellow, triclinic crystals which easily change to a brown colour. The salt is soluble in water without decomposition, but it easily oxidizes, forming pyrosulphoantimonite. If in the preparation of barium orthosulphoantimonite the barium sulphide be not in excess, greyish-green crystals of **barium pyrosulphoantimonite**, $Ba_2Sb_2S_5.8H_2O$, are formed. The crystals become yellow on exposure to air. The salt is almost insoluble in a soln. of barium sulphide. The mother-liquor furnishes crystals of the orthosulphoantimonite. If a soln. of barium orthosulphotetrantimonite be boiled for a long time with much water, amorphous, brown **barium metasulphoantimonite**, $Ba(SbS_2)_2.4\frac{1}{2}H_2O$, is produced. A salt of the composition $Ba_5Sb_4S_{11}.16H_2O$ is formed when an excess of barium sulphide is employed in the method used for the preparation of the pyrosulphoantimonite. The product may be a basic salt: $Ba_3Sb_4S_9.2BaS.16H_2O$—**barium disulphorthosulphotetrantimonite**; or a mixture of $Ba_3(SbS_3)_2.8H_2O$ and $Ba_2Sb_2S_5.8H_2O$; if it be treated with much water, yellowish-green **barium orthosulphotetrantimonite**, $Ba_3Sb_4S_9.10H_2O$, is formed. It dries to a brown, amorphous mass.

I. Pouget prepared **zinc orthosulphoantimonite**, $Zn_3(SbS_3)_2$, **by** adding a salt of zinc to a dil. soln. of potassium orthosulphoantimonite; with a conc. soln., crystalline **potassium zinc orthosulphoantimonite**, $KZnSbS_3$, is formed. I. Pouget also prepared **cadmium orthosulphoantimonite**, $Cd_3(SbS_3)_2$, in a similar way.

According to H. Pélabon,[11] the f.p. curve for mixtures of antimony and mercuric sulphides consists of two simple branches melting at a eutectic point at 455°. The eutectic mixture contains 34 per cent. of mercuric sulphide. On account of the volatilization of the mercuric sulphide, it was not possible to study the behaviour of mixtures containing more than 68 per cent. of it. The mol. lowering of the f.p. was calculated to be 788 for mercuric sulphide, and 797 for cuprous sulphide. I. Pouget found that the precipitates with both mercurous and mercuric salts in dil. or conc. soln. of potassium sulphoantimonite are rapidly reduced. M. Barcena described a lead-grey mineral which he called **livingstonite**—after D. Livingstone—and obtained from Huitzuco, Mexico. F. Sandberger, A. Hilger, and W. T. Page also described specimens from other localities. Analyses by M. Barcena, F. P. Venable, and W. T. Page correspond with $HgS.2Sb_2S_3$, or, in harmony with the views of P. Groth, with **mercuric metasulphotetrantimonite**, $HgSb_4S_7$. P. Groth and K. Mieleitner gave this formula with the possibility that it might be a mercurous salt, $Hg_2S.4Sb_2S_3$, or $Hg_2Sb_8S_{13}$. L. Baker called it an acid sulphoantimonite, $HgS.2Sb_2S_3$, but represented it graphically with quinquevalent antimony. G. Cesaro represented it graphically with tervalent antimony :

$$Hg \Big\langle \begin{matrix} S-Sb-S-Sb=S \\ \ddot{S} \\ S-Sb-S-Sb=S \end{matrix}$$

E. T. Wherry and W. F. Foshag used L. Baker's formula, but were doubtful about its homogeneity. W. M. Davy and C. M. Farnham made some observations on the mineral. He obtained a crystalline mass of a similar composition by melting a mixture of mercuric sulphide and antimony trisulphide in an atm. of carbon dioxide. H. Sommerlad obtained only mixtures of mercuric sulphide and antimony trisulphide by heating mercurous or mercuric chloride and antimony trisulphide at 100°–150°. Livingstonite occurs either massive, or in groups of slender, prismatic crystals. The sp. gr. is 4·81, and the hardness, 2. J. J. Saslawsky calculated the contraction which occurs during the formation of the mineral from its components. The mineral was found by J. Joly to sublime at 440°. J. Joly gave 430° for the sublimation temp. E. S. Lassen found the mineral is pleochroic ; that its double refraction is strong ; and its optical character positive.

According to L. F. Hawley [12] thallous sulphide forms mixed precipitates or solid soln. with either antimony trisulphide or antimony pentasulphide analogous to those with arsenic trisulphide ; but not **thallous sulphoantimonite** or sulphoantimonate. The two series of solid soln., respectively with antimony tri- and pentasulphides, are so much alike that they are described in the same words. Each series is homogeneous and complete. These solid soln. vary in colour from black when high in thallous sulphide through red to orange when high in the antimony sulphide. Dil. acids readily dissolve some of the thallous sulphide, the solid soln. becoming richer in the antimony sulphides and hence more resistant towards acids, so that only warm conc. acids will completely remove the thallium sulphide. In the same way dil. alkaline sulphides partially dissolve the antimony sulphides, but only hot conc. alkaline sulphides will completely remove the antimony sulphides. These solid soln. are stable in the air except when high in thallous sulphide ; then they are readily oxidized especially when not completely dry. Most of these solid soln. of intermediate composition if heated to about 100° in the air or even in the soln. in which they are prepared sinter and become black and vitreous without change in composition.

N. Parravano and P. de Cesaris [13] investigated the m.p. of the stannous sulphide and antimony trisulphide system in an atm. of nitrogen. The results are summarized in Fig. 61 ; there is probably formed **stannous metasulphoantimonite,** $SnS.Sb_2S_3$, or $Sn(SbS_2)_2$. Antimony trisulphide does not furnish solid soln., or does so with only small conc. of stannous sulphide ; but the stannous sulphide forms solid soln. with up to 15 per cent. of antimony trisulphide. W. Guertler,[14] and H. Schack made a partial study of the ternary system Pb–Sb–S. K. Wagemann investigated the f.p. curve of lead sulphide and antimony trisulphide, and

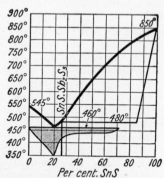

FIG. 61.—Freezing-point Curves of the Binary System : $SnS–Sb_2S_3$.

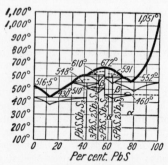

FIG. 62.—Freezing-point Curves of the Binary System : $PbS–Sb_2S_3$.

found only one compound, $2PbS.Sb_2S_3$, with a eutectic between lead pyrosulphoantimonite and the antimony trisulphide. Solid soln. were formed. F. M. Jäger and H. S. van Klooster examined the curve in more detail, and found breaks corresponding with $5PbS.4Sb_2S_3$ at 609°, and $2PbS.Sb_2S_3$ at 570°. The latter compound has a transition temp. at 523°. D. Iitsuka, Fig. 62, observed (i) a maximum at 672° corresponding with $2PbS.Sb_2S_3$; (ii) the formation of a compound $3PbS.2Sb_2S_3$ at 610° with a transition temp. at 510° ; (iii) the formation of $PbS.Sb_2S_3$; and (iv) the formation of $5PbS.2Sb_2S_3$ at 590° and a transition temp. at 468°.

C. L. Boulanger described a *plomb antimonié sulfuré* which he obtained from Molières, France. J. F. L. Hausmann called it **boulangerite.** A. Breithaupt obtained a variety from Nerchinsk, Siberia, which he called *embrithite*—from ἐμβριθής, heavy—and another variety from the same locality which he called *plumbostib*, or *plumbostibite*. Analyses were reported by C. L. Boulanger, M. C. J. Thaulow, J. F. L. Hausmann, W. Brüel, L. G. Eakins, V. R. von Zepharovich, E. Bechi, R. W. Helmhacker, F. A. Genth, G. vom Rath, M. Websky, A. Frenzel, T. Haege, C. Guillemain, E. V. Shannon, H. Sjögren, and H. Sommerlad. The formulæ calculated by C. F. Rammelsberg from the analyses were $5PbS.Sb_2S_3$, $3PbS.Sb_2S_3$, and $10PbS.3Sb_2S_3$. E. V. Shannon gave $5PbS.Sb_2S_3$, and $7PbS.3Sb_2S_3$. Most of the older analyses correspond with $5PbS.2Sb_2S_3$, or *lead henasulphotetrantimonite*, $Pb_5Sb_4S_{11}$, and some of the more recent analyses with $3PbS.Sb_2S_3$, or $Pb_3Sb_2S_6$, **lead orthosulphoantimonite.** Some of the minerals analyzed by M. Websky, and E. V. Shannon approximate to $Pb_3(SbS_3)_2$, and were called *epiboulangerite*. M. Websky represented epiboulangerite as $12PbS.Sb_2S_3.Sb_2S_5$, or $Pb_3(SbS_3)_2.3Pb_3(SbS_4)_2$, *lead orthosulphodiantimonohexantimonate*. Idealized boulangerite has not been definitely recognized ; it is most commonly regarded as boulangerite, $Pb_5Sb_4S_{11}$, or as epiboulangerite, $Pb_3(SbS_3)_2$, and, according to C. Guillemain, contaminated with more or less lead sulphide ; and epiboulangerite has not been accepted as a definite mineral species. C. F. Rammelsberg prepared what he regarded as boulangerite by heating to redness lead orthosulphoantimonate out of contact with air ; H. Sommerlad, by treating a soln. of sodium orthosulphoantimonate with lead acetate, washing and drying at 100° the reddish-brown precipitate, and heating the product a little in a covered crucible ; H. Sommerlad, by melting 3 mols of lead chloride into two of antimony trisulphide and repeating the treatment with more trisulphide—F. L. Ducatte, and J. Rondet do not consider that this process gives the desired product. I. Pouget obtained lead orthosulphoanti-monite by adding a lead salt soln. to a dil. soln. of potassium orthosulphoantimonite —if a conc. soln. be used, a potassium lead orthosulphoantimonite is formed. There is no sign of the ortho-salt on F. M. Jäger and H. S. van Klooster's or D. Iitsuka's f.p. curves, Fig. 62 ; but D. Iitsuka observed that the compound $5PbS.2Sb_2S_3$, which he regards as artificial boulangerite, is formed by the action of plumosite on lead sulphide at 590°. This compound exists in two modifications with a transi-tion temp. at 468°, and it forms a eutectic with 78 per cent. of lead sulphide at 557°. W. Guertler and H. Schack said that antimony trisulphide forms a eutectic with 10 per cent. of lead sulphide, which melts at 485°. There is a region of immiscibility in the series between 52 and 68 per cent. of lead sulphide. In the system Pb–Sb–S, two ternary compounds can exist in the molten state, $3PbS.Sb_2S_3$ and $2PbS.3Sb_2S_3$. The former corresponds with boulangerite. F. Zambonini made observations on the formation of the Pb–Sb–S minerals in nature.

Boulangerite is described as a lead-grey mineral which occurs granular and compact, and also in plumose masses with a crystalline fracture. J. L. C. Schröder van der Kolk made some observations on the colour. H. Sjögren showed that the rhombic, bipyramidal crystals have these axial ratios $a : b : c = 0.5527 : 1 : 0.7478$, and are isomorphous with diaphorite, $(Pb,Ag)_5Sb_4S_{11}$. W. Brüel gave 5.690 for the sp. gr. ; C. F. Rammelsberg, 5.831 ; V. R. von Zepharovich, 5.690–6.08 ; R. W. Helmhacker, 5.520 ; G. vom Rath, 5.935 ; F. Zambonini, 6.01 ; M. Websky, 5.835–6.309 ; A. Frenzel, 6.120–6.320 ; H. Sjögren, 6.185 at 16.5° ; and E. V. Shannon, 6.274–6.407. H. Sommerlad's artificial preparations had a sp. gr. between 5.860 and 5.907. H. Sommerlad gave 5.871 for the sp. gr. of the synthetic product. J. J. Saslawsky made some observations on the contraction which occurs during the formation of the mineral from its components. The hardness is 2–3. W. W. Coblentz studied the photoelectric sensitivity of a mineral approxi-mating Pb_3SbS_3. T. W. Case found that boulangerite and epiboulangerite are poor conductors, but in light the former conducts better than in darkness, while light has no effect on the latter. E. E. Fairbanks gave 36 for the dielectric constant (water 81). S. B. Christy found the potential of the mineral in N-KCy to be -0.50 volt, and in $0.1N$- to $0.01N$-soln., -0.55 volt. M. C. J. Thaulow showed that the mineral is decomposed but not all dissolved by nitric acid ; and is soluble in hydrochloric acid with the development of hydrogen sulphide. A. Terreil said that boulangerite is not decomposed by a 10 per cent. soln. of sodium sulphide.

E. V. Shannon found a mineral which he called *mullanite*, near Mullan, Idaho, and also accompanying epiboulangerite in the Iron Mountain, Montana. Mullanite is indistinguish-able from epiboulangerite except that the latter gives a greyish-black streak, the former, a brownish-black streak. The mineral occurs in fine, matted, wool-like masses of dark grey fibres, and as a compact, steel-grey, fibrous material. The needles are usually flattened and are deeply striated longitudinally ; they are terminated by the basal plane, and are probably orthorhombic $(a : b = 1 : 0.835)$ with the three pinacoidal cleavages, The thinner fibres are very flexible, whilst the thicker ones are quite brittle. The sp. gr. is between 6.274 and 6.407. Analyses correspond with $5PbS.2Sb_2S_3$, as in some forms of boulangerite, and E. V. Shannon withdrew mullanite as a special name.

Several lead sulphoantimonites occur as minerals which are more basic than the ortho-salt. L. F. Navarro [15] reported a lead-grey mineral from some Spanish lead mines which he called *quirogite*—after F. Quiroga. The analysis corresponds with $23PbS.3Sb_2S_3$, but, according to A. Schrauf, it may be only an impure galena. The tetragonal crystals have the axial ratio $a : c = 1 : 1.286$; the sp. gr. is 7.22 ; and the hardness 3.

L. F. Svanberg [16] obtained from the silver mines at Sala, Sweden, a mineral which he named **geocronite**, or rather *geokronite*, from γῆ, earth, and Κρόνος, Saturn—the alchemists' name for lead. The mineral also contained some arsenic. C. Sauvage obtained from Meredo, Spain, a variety free from arsenic, and J. F. L. Hausmann called it *schulzite*—after W. Schulz. J. Apjohn obtained from Kilbricken, Ireland, a mineral which was called **kilbrickenite**. J. D. Dana suggested that this mineral is the same as geocronite, and this hypothesis was established by G. T. Prior, D. Forbes, F. A. Genth, C. H. T. Kerndt, and V. Goldschmidt. Analyses were reported by L. F. Svanberg, C. Guillemain, G. Nauckhoff, J. Apjohn, G. T. Prior, C. Sauvage, C. H. T. Kerndt, and G. d'Achiardi. The analysis by L. F. Svanberg corresponds with **lead octosulphodiantimonite**, $5PbS.(Sb,As)_2S_3$; J. Apjohn's analysis of kilbrickenite, with $6PbS.Sb_2S_3$. C. F. Rammelsberg gave as the best representative value, $5PbS.Sb_2S_3$, or $Pb_5(Sb,As)_2S_8$. This is virtually in agreement with G. d'Achiardi's and C. Guillemain's results ; and with G. T. Prior's observations on kilbrickenite and geocronite. H. Sommerlad obtained a grey, crystalline mass of the same composition by melting the constituent sulphides in an atm. of hydrogen sulphide. The light lead-grey mineral usually occurs massive, granular, or earthy ; crystals are rare. C. H. T. Kerndt gave for the axial ratios of the rhombic crystals $a : b : c = 0.5805 : 1 : 0.5028$; and G. d'Achiardi, $0.6145 : 1 : 0.6797$. G. d'Achiardi considered the mineral to be isomorphous with stephanite. The crystals of geocronite were also examined by V. Goldschmidt, A. d'Achiardi, G. d'Achiardi, P. Groth, G. T. Prior, and R. H. Solly. The cleavage on the (110)-face is distinct ; that on the (211)-face is not so clear. J. Apjohn gave 6.407 for the sp. gr. ; C. Sauvage, 6.430 ; C. H. T. Kerndt, 6.470 ; L. F. Svanberg, 6.434 ; G. Nauckhoff, 6.260 ; and G. T. Prior, 6.450. For the artificial crystals H. Sommerlad gave 6.447–6.657. P. E. W. Oeberg found the sp. ht. to be 0.0659. J. Joly gave 430°–440° for the sublimation temp.

Another related mineral from Bottino, Tuscany, was called, by E. Bechi,[17] **meneghinite**—after G. Meneghini. Analyses were made by O. Sella, E. Bechi, G. vom Rath, A. Martini and A. Funaro, J. A. Krenner, A. Frenzel, B. J. Harrington, and G. Flink. C. F. Rammelsberg represented the results by the formula $4PbS.Sb_2S_3$, **lead disulphopyrosulphoantimonite**, $(Pb.S.Pb)_2Sb_2S_5$—*vide* jordanite. H. Sommerlad prepared the substance by melting a mixture of the constituent sulphides in an atm. of hydrogen sulphide. J. L. C. Schröder van der Kolk studied the colour of the mineral. The mineral occurs in dark lead-grey, fibrous, and compact masses, and in slender prismatic crystals which are vertically striated. H. A. Miers gave for the axial ratios of the rhombic crystals $a : b : c = 0.52891 : 1 : 0.36317$. The (100)-cleavage is perfect but interrupted, the (001)-cleavage is indistinct. Both H. A. Miers and C. Hintze emphasized the crystallographic relationship between jordanite, $Pb_4As_2S_7$, and meneghinite, $Pb_4Sb_2S_7$; the monoclinic prisms of the latter have the axial ratios $a : b : c = 0.4845 : 1 : 0.265$, and $\beta = 80° 33'$; and the rhombic pyramids of the former $0.5289 : 1 : 0.3632$. E. Bechi gave for the sp. gr. 6.373 ; A. Frenzel, 6.360 ; J. A. Krenner, 6.4316 ; B. J. Harrington, 6.33 ; and G. Flink, 6.430. H. Sommerlad gave 6.296 for the artificial crystals. J. J. Saslawsky calculated the contraction in the formation of the mineral from its constituents. The hardness is 2–3. According to D. Iitsuka, **lead orthosulphotetrantimonite**, $Pb_3Sb_4S_9$, appears on the f.p. curve of lead and antimonious sulphides, as being formed at 610° ; and there are two modifications with a transition temp. at 510°.

The *mineræ antimonii plumosæ*, plumose antimonial ores, *les mines d'antimoine aux plumes*, or the *Federerze* of the old mineralogists—A. G. Werner,[18] L. A. Emmerling, R. J. Haüy. and J. G. Wallerius—were usually antimonial sulphides. H. Rose, V. R. von Zepharovich, and E. Kaiser showed that stibnite alone may occur in capillary (hair-like) crystals characteristic of the plumose minerals. According to L. J. Spencer, these minerals include varieties of stibnite, zinckenite, jamesonite, plumosite, boulangerite, and meneghinite. W. Haidinger called the feathery ore **plumosite** ; E. F. Glocker, *plumite* ; R. Jameson, *axotomous antimony glance* ; and A. Breithaupt. axotomous *Chalybinglanz*, or *Stahlantimonglanz*. W. Haidinger applied the term **jamesonite**—after R. Jameson—to a variety obtained by F. Mohs from Cornwall in 1820, and whose composition was represented by H. Rose by the formula $3PbS.2Sb_2S_3$, while the plumose ore from Wolfsberg, previously regarded as stibnite, had the composition $2PbS.Sb_2S_3$. D. Iitsuka obtained a substance of this composition which he regarded as artificial jamesonite—*vide infra*, plumosite. H. Rose's view was confirmed later by C. F. Rammelsberg, who observed that a compact mineral from the same locality had the same composition, and he called it **heteromorphite**—from ἕτερος, different; and μορφή, form. Jamesonite and heteromorphite were considered to be distinct mineral species until, in 1860, C. F. Rammelsberg united them as jamesonite, $2PbS.Sb_2S_3$; and H. Rose's formula $3PbS.2Sb_2S_3$ was supposed to have represented jamesonite contaminated with stibnite. F. Pisani obtained a feathery ore with a composition $7PbS.4Sb_2S_3$, which he assumed to be crystalline heteromorphite. These crystals were regarded as plagionite by F. Sandberger, E. Kaiser, and L. J. Spencer, but L. J. Spencer later stated that F. Pisani was justified in applying the term heteromorphite to this mineral, and that C. F. Rammelsberg's heteromorphite was probably the same mineral.

Analyses of heteromorphite were reported by H. Rose, E. Bechi, M. Sénez, P. Berthier, C. Guillemain, and L. J. Spencer. The results calculated by C. F. Rammelsberg agree with $2PbS.Sb_2S_3$, and those by F. Zambonini approximate to this value, but, according to L. J. Spencer, they are better represented by the formula $11PbS.6Sb_2S_3$, the $9PbS.5Sb_2S_3$ given by C. F. Rammelsberg for a sample from Wolfsberg, or the $7PbS.4Sb_2S_3$ given by F. Pisani, *i.e.* **lead enneadecasulph-octoantimonite,** $Pb_7Sb_8S_{19}$. According to L. J. Spencer, the monoclinic crystals have the axial ratios, and the angle β between those of plagionite and semseyite. For the relations between these two minerals, *vide infra*. The sp. gr. given by F. Pisani ranges from 5·60 to 5·73. The hardness is 2 to 3. T. W. Case found that jamesonite has a resistance greater than an ohm, and it becomes less in light.

J. C. L. Zincken reported a variety of Spiessglance from Wolfsberg which G. Rose named **plagionite**—from πλάγιος, oblique—in allusion to the unusual oblique crystallization. It has also been called *rosenite*. Analyses were reported by H. Rose, J. Kudernatsch, C. F. Rammelsberg, F. Zambonini, and L. J. Spencer. The formula derived from C. F. Rammelsberg's result is $5PbS.4Sb_2S_3$; that from H. Rose's, $9PbS.7Sb_2S_3$: and that from J. Kudernatsch's, $4PbS.3Sb_2S_3$. L. J. Spencer adopts the formula $9PbS.7Sb_2S_3$ or $5PbS.4Sb_2S_3$—*i.e.* **lead heptadecasulphoctoantimonite,** $Pb_5Sb_8S_{17}$. L. J. Spencer, and F. Zambonini discussed the relations between plagionite, heteromorphite, and semseyite—*vide infra*. H. Sommerlad prepared $5PbS.4Sb_2S_3$ by heating a mixture of lead chloride and antimony trisulphide; and by fusing together a mixture of the component sulphides. F. L. Ducatte, and J. Rondet doubt the chemical individuality of the former product; and F. M. Jäger and H. S. van Klooster obtained it from the constituent sulphides at about 570°— *vide* Fig. 62. There is a transformation temp. at 523° above which α-*plagionite*, and below which β-*plagionite* are formed. There is no marked evidence of the formation of sold soln. The mineral occurs in dark grey, granular, or compact masses, or in thick plates or short prisms in druses and geodes. O. Luedecke gave for the axial ratios of the monoclinic crystals, $a:b:c=1·1331:1:0·4228$, and $\beta=72° 49·5'$; L. J. Spencer, $1·1363:1:0·8410$, and $\beta=72° 28'$; G. Rose, $1·1363:1:0·4205$, and $\beta=72° 28'$; and F. Zambonini $1·1305:1:1·6844$, and $\beta=72° 45'$. The (111)-cleavage is nearly perfect. J. L. C. Schröder van der Kolk made observations on the colour. H. Rose gave 5·400 for the sp. gr.; L. J. Spencer, 5·500; and F. Zambonini, 5·600. H. Sommerlad gave 5·474-5·500 for the artificial crystals, and F. M. Jäger and H. S. van Klooster, 5·47 at 15°/15°. J. J. Saslawsky calculated the contraction during the formation of the mineral from its constituents. The hardness is 2·5. T. W. Case observed that the mineral is non-conducting, and that light has no appreciable effect.

J. A. Krenner [19] reported a grey, opaque mineral occurring at Felsöbanya,

Hungary, which he called **semseyite**—after A. von Semsey. The analysis reported by J. A. Krenner agrees with $21PbS.10Sb_2S_3$, or, according to L. Sipöcz, with $9PbS.4Sb_2S_3$; J. Loczko gave $13PbS : 6Sb_2S_3$; and G. T. Prior and L. J. Spencer's analyses agreed with $21PbS.10Sb_2S_3$, or $9PbS.4Sb_2S_3$, *i.e.* **lead hemicosisulphoctoantimonite**, $Pb_9Sb_8S_{21}$. F. Zambonini gave $5PbS.2Sb_2S_3$, in agreement with mullanite; but sp. gr. are different. The mineral occurs in small tabular, monoclinic tablets which, according to J. A. Krenner, have the axial ratios $a : b : c = 1.4424 : 1 : 1.0515$, and $\beta = 71° 4'$. The (111)-cleavage is perfect. The sp. gr. is 5.952 ; G. T. Prior and L. J. Spencer gave 5.820–5.920. T. W. Case said that semseyite shows no change in its electrical resistance when exposed to light.

F. Zambonini supposes that solid soln. are formed with the end-numbers : plagionite, $5PbS.4Sb_2S_3$, and semseyite, $5PbS.2Sb_2S_3$, but L. J. Spencer showed that this is improbable since the various analyses fall into these well-marked groups, and not into a continuous series between the two end-members. These three groups are represented by plagionite, heteromorphite, and semseyite. There is no evidence that the crystals enclose galena. The most probable hypothesis is that these three minerals form a morphotropic series analogous to that which occurs with the humite group of silicates, for in both these cases the crystals of members of each group are so similar in appearance that they cannot be distinguished by mere inspection, and the only essential difference between them is in the greater length of the vertical axis, which varies regularly with the chemical composition, while the parameters $a : b$ remain practically constant. Although the crystals of heteromorphite could not be accurately measured, it can be said that the three minerals, plagionite, heteromorphite, and semseyite, are very similar in appearance and physical characters, and the monoclinic crystals are the same in habit, striations, and the pyramidal cleavage (111) ; they differ in the specific gravity, percentage chemical composition, and in the length of the vertical crystallographic axis c.

	$a : b : c$	β	Formula.	Sp. gr.
Plagionite . .	$1.1361 : 1 : 0.8410$	$72° 28'$	$5PbS.4Sb_2S_3$	5.5
Heteromorphite .	. . . . .		$7PbS.4Sb_2S_3$	5.7
Semseyite . .	$1.1442 : 1 : 1.1051$	$71° 4'$	$9PbS.4Sb_2S_3$	5.9

V. C. Butureanu, and L. J. Spencer represent these minerals by the structural formation in which each bivalent Pb atom can be represented by a bivalent $Pb.S.Pb$-group :

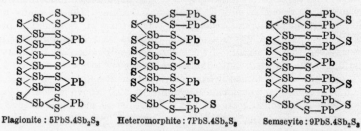

Plagionite : $5PbS.4Sb_2S_3$ Heteromorphite : $7PbS.4Sb_2S_3$ Semseyite : $9PbS.4Sb_2S_3$

The flexible feather ore called by W. Haidinger plumosite, mentioned above, is now considered to be best represented as **lead pyrosulphoantimonite**, $2PbS.Sb_2S_3$, or $Pb_2Sb_2S_5$. This is in agreement with analyses reported by C. F. Rammelsberg, B. S. Burton, O. Luedecke, and C. Guillemain. L. J. Spencer supposed that J. Loczka's analyses of plumosite were really made on specimens of jamesonite. H. Sommerlad prepared the compound by heating a mixture of the component sulphides at a high temp., and F. M. Jäger and H. S. van Klooster by fusing the component sulphides in a current of hydrogen sulphide. The conditions of equilibrium are shown in D. Iitsuka's diagram, Fig. 62. K. Wagemann made the pyrosulphoantimonite in a similar manner. The crystals are probably rhombic. C. F. Rammelsberg gave 5.697 for the sp. gr. of plumosite ; B. S. Burton, 6.030 ;

and for the artificial crystals, H. Sommerlad gave 5·750–5·832 ; and F. M. Jäger and H. S. van Klooster, 5·62 at 15°/15°. D. Iitsuka gave 672° for the m.p.

J. C. L. Zincken [20] described a mineral which he obtained from Wolfsberg, Harz, and which was called by G. Rose, **zinckenite.** Analyses were reported by H. Rose, B. Kerl, C. Guillemain, H. A. Hilger, W. F. Hillebrand, P. Groth, F. Gonnard, F. Sandberger, A. Stelzner, and P. P. Pillipenko. According to C. F. Rammelsberg, and C. Guillemain, the results are best summarized by the formula $PbS.Sb_2S_3$, *i.e.* **lead metasulphoantimonite,** $Pb(SbS_2)_2$. F. Wöhler, and J. Fournet prepared it by fusing together the constituent sulphides ; and H. Sommerlad, by melting lead chloride with antimony trisulphide : $3PbCl_2 + 4Sb_2S_3 = 3Pb(SbS_2)_2 + 2SbCl_3$; and by melting the component sulphides in an atm. of hydrogen sulphide. F. M. Jäger and H. S. van Klooster could not make it by this process, but D. Iitsuka observed that this compound is formed by the interaction of $3PbS.2Sb_2S_3$ with antimony trisulphide below 546°—Fig. 62. The mineral occurs in steel-grey, fibrous or columnar masses, and in crystals which are rarely distinct. The rhombic crystals were found by G. Rose to have the axial ratios $a : b : c = 0·5575 : 1 : 0·6353$. The crystals sometimes appear in hexagonal forms through twinning ; the lateral faces may be longitudinally striated. L. J. Spencer described crystals free from twinning, and studied the isomorphism with wolfs-bergite, etc. The cleavage is not distinct. The crystals were also described by G. A. Kenngott, O. Luedecke, E. S. von Fedoroff, E. Schulze, and V. Goldschmidt. L. J. Spencer showed that zinckenite, sartorite, emplectite, and chalcostibite, form a group of isomorphous minerals with the corresponding parameters :

							$a : b : c$
Zinckenite, $Pb(SbS_2)_2$	.	.	.	.	.	.	$0·5575 : 1 : 0·6353$
Sartorite, $Pb(AsS_2)_2$	.	.	.	.	.	.	$0·5389 : 1 : 0·6188$
Emplectite, $CuBiS_2$	.	.	.	.	.	.	$0·5430 : 1 : 0·6256$
Chalcostibite, $CuSbS_2$	.	.	.	.	.	.	$0·5242 : 1 : 0·6376$

The colour of zinckenite was discussed by J. L. C. Schröder van der Kolk. W. F. Hillebrand gave 5·21 for the sp. gr. of the mineral ; W. F. Petterd, 5·16 ; and G. Rose, 5·303–5·310. H. Sommerlad gave 5·280–5·320 for the sp. gr. of the artificial crystals ; and J. Fournet, and F. Wöhler, 5·30–5·35. J. J. Saslawsky calculated the contraction which occurs in the formation of zinckenite from its constituent sulphides. The hardness is 3·0–3·5. J. Joly found that when zinckenite is heated, sublimation occurs at about 460°. A. de Gramont examined the spark spectrum. T. W. Case observed that the resistance is less than a megohm, and insolation has no perceptible effect. J. Fournet said that when the compound is boiled with hydrochloric acid it is decomposed ; and with nitric acid, or aqua regia, a white residue containing lead and antimony oxides is formed ; while H. Sommerlad found that with a mixture of nitric and tartaric acids, lead sulphate is precipitated. The compound is also decomposed by soln. of alkali hydroxides or sulphides. When heated in hydrogen gas, F. Wöhler found that hydrogen sulphide is given off, and lead and antimony are formed.

S. G. Gordon [21] described a mineral from Oruro, Bolivia, and he called it keeleyite—after F. J. Keeley. Its composition, allowing for impurities, approximates **lead hena-sulphohexantimonite,** $2PbS.3Sb_2S_3$, corresponding with *rezbanyite.* It is very like zincken-ite. It occurs in dark grey radiating aggregates of acicular crystals—possibly rhombic. The sp. gr. is 5·21, and hardness 2. E. T. Wherry regarded keeleyite as a variety of zinc-kenite, but not so E. V. Shannon and M. N. Short.

I. Pouget [22] prepared **potassium lead orthosulphoantimonite,** $KPbSbS_3$, by adding a lead salt to a conc. soln. of potassium orthosulphoantimonite. The precipitate was rapidly washed by suction, pressed between bibulous paper, and dried in hydrogen. The chestnut-brown crystals are decomposed by water into soluble potassium and insoluble lead orthosulphoantimonites.

P. Rashleigh [23] described an ore of antimony from Endellion, Cornwall, which J. L. Bournon found to be a triple sulphuret of lead, antimony, and copper.

F. X. M. Zippe named it *endellione*, which was altered to *endellionite*; D. L. G. Karsten, *Spiessglanzbleierz*; A. Breithaupt, *Tripelglanz*, or *Antimonkupferglanz*; F. Mohs, *prismatischer Spiesglasglanz*, or *prismatoidischer Kupferglanz*; W. Haidinger, *wölchite*; F. Mohs and F. X. M. Zippe, *Dystomglanz*; J. F. L. Hausmann, *Bleifahlerz*; P. Groth, *Antimonbleikupferblende*; A. G. Werner, *Schwarzspiessglanzerz*, and *Rädelerz—wheel ore*; and R. Jameson, **bournonite**—after T. L. Bournon. Analyses were reported by F. Babanek, C. Bromeis, I. Domeyko, P. A. Dufrénoy, F. Field, A. Frenzel, C. Guillemain, C. Hatchett, R. W. Helmhacker, C. Hidegh, P. Jannasch, B. Kerl, M. H. Klaproth, C. Kuhlemann, A. Lacroix, D. Lovisato, O. Luedecke, W. Meissner, A. W. F. Petterd, C. F. Rammelsberg, H. Rose, W. T. Schaller, A. von Schrötter, Z. Sipöcz, J. Smithson, P. Termier, H. Traube, G. Tschermak, F. G. Wait, and V. R. von Zepharovich. A variety with 5·47–28·64 per cent. of nickel and cobalt was described by C. F. Rammelsberg and J. C. L. Zincken as *Nickel-bournonite*; and as *bournonite-nickel glance*, by O. Luedecke. L. Sipöcz observed that part of the antimony in bournonite may be replaced by arsenic. C. F. Rammelsberg represented the composition of bournonite as **copper lead orthosulphoantimonite**, $2PbS.Cu_2S.Sb_2S_3$, or $CuPbSbS_3$, and this is in agreement with the observations of C. Guillemain, and W. F. Foshag. C. Doelter heated a mixture of the chlorides or oxides of copper, lead, and antimony at a temp. below redness in a current of hydrogen sulphide and obtained a mass of homogeneous crystals of bournonite; he also obtained the crystals by heating the mixed chlorides with a soln. of sodium sulphide. B. von Cotta found crystals of a copper lead sulphoantimonite as a furnace product. A. Stelzner also found that crystals of jamesonite often contain copper.

Bournonite occurs in dark steel-grey, lead-grey, or iron-black compact or granular masses; and in plates or short prisms. The colour was studied by J. C. L. Schröder van der Kolk. The crystals are often aggregated in a parallel position. The prism faces may be vertically and the macrodomes horizontally striated. Twinning about the (110)-plane may be oft repeated so as to furnish cruciform or wheel-shaped crystals, or twin lamellæ. The cleavage on the (010)-face is imperfect; and less marked on the (010)- and (001)-faces. W. H. Miller gave for the axial ratios of the rhombic crystals $a : b : c = 0.93797 : 1 : 0.89686$. Observations on the crystals were made by H. A. Miers, G. Rose, F. Zirkel, V. Goldschmidt, O. Luedecke, F. B. Peck, N. von Kokscharoff, A. Schrauf, T. Haege, G. vom Rath, A. Frenzel, H. Traube, F. Babanek, G. Szellemy, V. R. von Zepharovich, F. Hessenberg, A. Schmidt, A. Lacroix, G. Benko, R. P. Greg and W. G. Lettsom, F. Gonnard, P. Groth, P. Termier, I. Domeyko, G. T. Prior and L. J. Spencer, A. d'Achiardi, and W. P. Jervis. The optical anisotropy of the crystals was examined by J. Königsberger. H. Schneiderhöhn examined polished surfaces of the crystals etched with nitric or hydrochloric acid, aqua regia, soln. of potassium hydroxide, permanganate, or cyanide, ferric chloride, or alkaline hydrogen dioxide. C. Guillemann gave 5·736–5·855 for the sp. gr.; C. Bromeis, 5·70–5·79; C. F. Rammelsberg, 5·82–5·86; V. R. von Zepharovich, 5·585–5·700; A. Breithaupt, 5·83; and P. Termier, 5·78. C. Doelter gave for the artificial crystals, 5·719. C. F. Rammelsberg and J. C. L. Zincken found 5·592 for the sp. gr. of nickel-bournonite, and O. Luedecke, 5·635–5·706. The hardness is 2–3. F. B. Peck measured the elliptical heat conductivity curve of the crystal. A. Sella gave 0·0730 for the sp. ht. A. de Gramont studied the spark spectrum, and found the mineral has a feeble electrical conductivity. P. H. Geiger studied the photoelectric effect; and W. W. Coblentz and J. F. Eckford, the photoelectric sensitivity. Bournonite has a high spectrophoto-electrical sensitivity from the extreme violet to 1μ in the ultra-red with two wide, ill-defined maxima in the region of 0.55μ and 0.95μ, its reaction being entirely different from that of the constituent sulphides. The intrinsic intensity is greatly increased with fall of temp., the maxima shifting towards the short wave-lengths. T. W. Case said that the mineral has a resistance greater than a megohm, and that light has a marked effect in reducing the resistance.

Bournonite is decomposed by nitric acid forming a blue soln., and a residue of sulphur, antimony oxide, and lead sulphate. C. A. Burghardt observed that when bournonite is heated with ammonium nitrate, it forms a greenish-yellow mass, which gives a blue soln. with water, and a residue of lead sulphate and antimony oxides. C. Doelter found that 100 parts of water dissolve 0·03 part of bournonite ; and more is dissolved when the powdered mineral is heated with water in a sealed tube at 80°. C. Doelter also found that a soln. of sodium sulphide can dissolve about 0·1 per cent. of bournonite. The mineral is affected by water less than pyrite, zinc blende, or galena. The composition of soln. and residues were determined. The weathering of bournonite was studied by G. Tschermak, J. R. Blum, E. Döll, and G. Sillem.

H. Buttgenbach **²⁴** described a fine-grained, lead-grey mineral from the Slata mine, Tunis ; the analyses corresponded with $9Cu_2S.5PbS.7Sb_2S_3$. It was called **berthonite**— after M. Berthon ; and it is related to jamesonite. Its sp. gr. was 5·49, and its hardness 4-5.

J. A. Krenner [25] described a mineral from Felsöbanya, Hungary, which he called **andorite**—after Andor von Semsey—and which approximated in composition $Pb_2Ag_2Sb_6S_{12}$; soon afterwards, W. C. Brögger,[26] and R. Pöhlmann described a mineral from Oruro, Bolivia, which he called *sundtite*—after L. Sundt—and which approximated $(Ag_2,Cu_2,Fe)Sb_2S_6$; and about the same time, A. Stelzner obtained from Oruro, Bolivia, a related mineral which he called *webnerite*—after A. Webner. According to G. T. Prior and L. J. Spencer, these three minerals are identical, and therefore the term andorite is retained for all. L. J. Spencer gave for the best representative formula $(Pb,Ag_2)S.Sb_2S_3$, *i.e.* **lead silver metasulphoantimonite,** $(Pb,Ag_2)(SbS_2)_2$; W. F. Foshag, $Ag_2S.2PbS.3Sb_2S_3$; and E. V. Shannon, $PbAgSb_3S_6$. The mineral occurs in dark grey compact masses or crystal aggregates. The tabular or prismatic crystals belong to the rhombic system ; W. C. Brögger gave for the axial ratios $a : b : c = 0.6771 : 1 : 0.6458$; with a different orientation, J. A. Krenner, $0.97756 : 1 : 0.86996$; and L. J. Spencer, $0.9846 : 1 : 0.6584$. J. A. Krenner found that the (010)-cleavage is good. L. J. Spencer said that although andorite is rhombic, it bears no crystallographic relationship with the rhombic zinckenite, $(PbSb_2S_4)$, and the few analyses all agree with the formula $PbAgSb_3S_6$. The mineral is therefore a double salt, and is not an isomorphous member of the zinckenite group as represented by the formula $(Pb,Ag_2)Sb_2S_4$. J. A. Krenner gave 5·341 for the sp. gr. ; W. C. Brögger, 5·50 ; R. Pöhlmann, 5·377 ; and G. T. Prior and L. J. Spencer, 5·33–5·35. The hardness is 3. J. Joly gave 510° for the sublimation temp. H. E. McKinstry observed that the mineral is not changed by exposure to the light from an electric arc. J. A. Krenner and J. Loczka found an argentiferous lead ore at Kisbanya, Hungary, and they called it **fizelyite.** Its composition approximates **lead silver sulphoctoantimonite,** $5PbS.Ag_2S.4Sb_2S_3$. It is dark grey, and brittle, with a hardness of 2. T. W. Case said that the mineral is a non-conductor, and that insolation has no appreciable effect.

The *argentum antimonio sulphurato mineralisatum* of A. Cronstedt, the *dunkles Weissgültigerz* of M. H. Klaproth, and the *mine d'antimoine grise tenant argent* of Himmelsfürst, Freiberg, were probably the *Schilfglaserz* described by J. C. Freiesleben, and named *Basitomglanz* by A. Breithaupt ; *donacargyrite*— from δόναξ, a reed—by E. J. Chapman ; and **freieslebenite,** by W. Haidinger. The crystals were represented as rhombic by W. Phillips, A. Breithaupt, and J. F. L. Hausmann ; and monoclinic by W. H. Miller. V. R. von Zepharovich showed that there are both rhombic and monoclinic forms—the latter he called freieslebenite, and the former, **diaphorite**—from διαφορά, difference—in allusion to its resemblance to and difference from freieslebenite. A. Damour also described a mineral from Mexico which he called *brongniardtite*—after A. Brongniardt. C. F. Rammelsberg regarded it as a variety of Schilfglaserz, and G. T. Prior and L. J. Spencer, as a variety of diaphorite.

Analyses of freieslebenite were reported by F. Wöhler, L. de la Escosura, N. y Garza, C. Vrba, L. G. Eakins, and I. Domeyko. The results are not easily represented by a single formula. C. F. Rammelsberg gave several formulæ, the latest was $R_2Sb_2S_5.R_3(SbS_3)_2$; $5RS.2Sb_2S_3$; W. S. von Waltershausen, and C. F. Naumann used $3PbS.Sb_2S_3.2AgS.Sb_2S_3$; G. Tschermak, $Ag_3Pb_2Sb_3S_8$: G. Rose, $3(Pb,Ag)S.Sb_2S_3$. J. D. Dana's latest formula was $5RS.2Sb_2S_3$; and this is considered by L. J. Spencer to be the best—silver lead henasulpho-tetrantimonite, $5(Pb,Ag_2)S.2Sb_2S_3$. W. F. Foshag gave $3Ag_2S.4PbS.3Sb_2S_3$ for diaphorite, and freieslebenite; and $Ag_2S.PbS.Sb_2S_3$ for brongniardtite. The mineral occurs in pale grey, inclining to silver-white, or dark grey, prismatic crystals with the prismatic planes vertically striated. W. H. Miller gave for the axial ratios of the monoclinic crystals $a:b:c=0.58714:1:0.92768$, and $\beta=87°\ 46'$, and L. J. Spencer, $0.9786:1:0.9277$, and $\beta=87°\ 46'$. The crystals were also examined by A. Frenzel, A. Breithaupt, J. F. L. Hausmann, V. Goldschmidt, V. R. von Zepharovich, A. Lévy, C. Vrba, L. F. Navarro, and H. Bücking. J. C. Freiesleben gave 6.108–6.114 for the sp. gr.; F. Wöhler, 6.194; L. de la Escosura, 6.01–6.02; C. Vrba, 7.035–6.051; and L. J. Spencer gave 6.3 for the best representative value. The hardness is 2.0–2.5.

Analyses of diaphorite were reported by A. E. Reuss, R. W. Helmhacker, G. A. Kenngott, and C. Vrba. L. J. Spencer said that the best representative formula is near that of freieslebenite, and is probably intermediate between those of freieslebenite and andorite. Thus brongniardtite is represented by $2(Pb,Ag_2)S.Sb_2S_3$. The steel-grey prismatic crystals may have faces vertically striated. The rhombic crystals were found by V. R. von Zepharovich to have the axial ratios $0.49194:1:0.73447$; and by L. J. Spencer, $0.9839:1:0.7345$. Twinning may occur about the (120)- and (122)-planes. A. E. Reuss gave 6.23 for the sp. gr.; R. W. Helmhacker, 5.731; V. R. von Zepharovich, 5.885–5.919; C. Vrba, 6.038–6.044; and L. J. Spencer, 6.9. The hardness is 2–3. A. de Gramont studied the spark spectrum. T. W. Case observed that freieslebenite has a resistance greater then a megohm, and that light has no perceptible influence. According to L. J. Spencer, the minerals andorite, diaphorite, and freieslebenite are strikingly similar in appearance, and between them there is the same kind of morphotropic relation as that existing between plagionite, heteromorphite, and semseyite, since in diaphorite the vertical axis c and sp. gr. fall between those of andorite and freieslebenite, it is to be expected that they should also be intermediate in composition:

	$a:b:c$	Sp. gr.	
Andorite	$0.9846:1:0.6584$	5.35	$(Pb,Ag_2)S.Sb_2S_3$
Diaphorite	$0.9839:1:0.7345$	5.9	—
Freieslebenite	$0.9786:1:0.9277$	6.3	$5(Pb,Ag_2)S.2Sb_2S_3$

I. Pouget [27] treated a conc. soln. of potassium orthosulphoantimonite with a lead salt, and on standing a short time, crystals of potassium lead orthosulphoantimonite, $KPbSbS_3$, were formed. The salt is decomposed by water into its component sulphides. V. Rosicky and J. Sterba-Boehm described a black mineral from Himmelsfürst, Freiberg, which they called ultrabasite—in allusion to the extremely basic composition. The analysis corresponds with $11Ag_2S.28PbS.3GeS_2.2Sb_2S_3$. Assuming the silver sulphide and part of the lead sulphide are admixtures, the mineral can be regarded as lead germanium sulphoantimonite. P. Groth regarded it as being a compound of lead orthosulphogermanate, Pb_2GeS_4, lead orthosulpho-antimonite, and silver and lead sulphides. Morphologically but not chemically, it is related with teallite, for the rhombic crystals of teallite have the axial ratios $a:b:c=0.93:1:1.31$; and those of ultrabasite, $0.988:1:0.462$. The sp. gr. is 6.026, and the hardness 5. A. Frenzel obtained from Poopo, Bolivia, a massive dark grey mineral which he called cylindrite—or rather kylindrit—in allusion to its occurrence in cylindrical forms which separate under press. into distinct shells or folia which like graphite are difficult to pulverize. A. Frenzel analyzed the mineral and represented his results by the formula $6PbS.Sb_2S_3.6SnS$, **lead sulpho-stannitantimonite**, or $3PbS.Sb_2S_3+3(PbS.2SnS_2)$; G. T. Prior represented his analysis by $3PbSnS_2.SnFeSb_2S_3$; and P. Groth regarded it as a salt of sulpho-stannous acid $Hs-Sn\equiv S_3\equiv Sn-5H$. C. Winkler found that it contained germanium. The sp. gr. is 5·42 ; and the hardness between 2 and 3. W. W. Coblentz and H. Kohler found that cylindrite is photoelectrically sensitive for spectral radiations of the highest intensity. The mineral is not attacked by cold acid ; it is gradually dissolved by hot hydrochloric acid ; and hot nitric acid decomposes it with the separation of sulphur, and oxides of tin and antimony. The mineral is related to plumbostannite ; and to **franckeite**—named after C. and E. Francke—by A. Stelzner, who obtained it at Animas, Bolivia, where it is locally known as *llicteria*. The mineral occurs massive with an imperfect radiated and foliated structure, and in part as reniform aggregates of a dark grey or black colour. Analyses reported by A. Stelzner corresponded with $5PbS.2SnS_2.SbS_3$, or $Pb_5Sn_2Sb_2S_{12}$; G. T. Prior gave formulæ ranging from 2·5 to $3PbSnS_2.Pb_2FeSb_2S_3$. G. Lincio found 0·10 per cent. of germanium to be present. The hardness is between 2 and 3 ; and the sp. gr. 5·88–5·92. It behaves like cylindrite towards acids. Another related mineral **plumbostannite** was obtained by A. Raimondi from Mohs, Peru. C. Hintze assigned to it the formula $(Fe,Zn)_2Pb_2Sn_2Sb_2S_{11}$, and this formula is used by P. Groth. It is an amorphous, granular, grey mineral with a sp. gr. 4·5, and hardness 2. A. de Gramont examined the spark spectrum. The mineral was also found by C. Ochsenius along with franckeite ; and A. Stelzner regards it as an admixture of franckeite and pyrite.

H. Pélabon [28] said that the f.p. curve of mixtures of bismuth monosulphide and antimony trisulphide has three straight lines inclined at angles which corresponds to *bismuth orthosulphoantimonite*, $3BiS.Sb_2S_3$, or $Bi_3(SbS_3)_2$; and *bismuth metasulphoctoantimonite*, $BiS_4Sb_2S_3$, or $BiSb_4S_{13}$. This is probably all wrong because the tri-sulphides of these elements were found by Y. Takahashi to form a complete series of mixed crystals. At the m.p., bismuth trisulphide is dissociated to the extent of about 1·5 per cent.

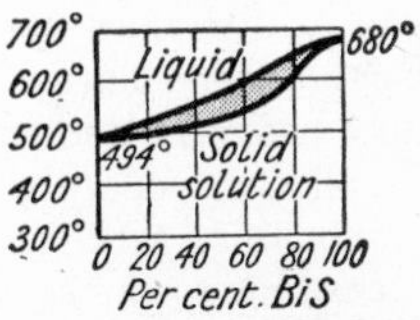

I. Pouget [29] prepared **manganese orthosulphoantimonite**, $Mn_3(SbS_3)_2$, by adding a manganese salt soln. to a soln. of a mol of potassium orthosulphoantimonite in 10 litres of water ; and also by treating the potassium manganese salt with water. The product is a dirty rose colour, and readily oxidized in air. If a conc. soln. of the potassium salt is used, the precipitate rapidly forms crystalline **potassium manganese orthosulphoantimonite**, $KMnSbS_3$, which is decomposed by water as just indicated. I. Pouget also obtained **ferrous orthosulpho-antimonite**, $Fe_3(SbS_3)_2$, by the action of a ferrous salt on a dil. soln. of potassium orthosulphoantimonite ; with conc. soln., an impure *potassium ferrous orthosulpho-antimonite*, $KFeSbS_3$, is formed.

Fig. 63.—Freezing-point Curves of the System : Sb_2S_3–BiS.

P. Berthier [30] observed a mineral occurring at Chazelle, Pay-de-Dôme, which corresponded with an impure ferrous metasulphoantimonite, and he named it *haidingerite*. This term, however, having been previously employed by E. Turner for a native arsenate, was replaced by W. Haidinger by **berthierite**. P. Groth called it *Eisenantimonglanz*. For the three varieties obtained by P. Berthier, N. G. Nordenskjöld introduced the names *anglarite*, $FeS.Sb_2S_3$; *chazellite*, $3FeS.2Sb_2S_3$; and *martocirite*, $3FeS.4Sb_2S_3$. Analyses were reported by C. F. Rammelsberg, C. von Hauer, A. Hofmann, J. von Pettko, and P. Berthier. J. Loczka found that some varieties of berthierite are contaminated with stibnite. In agreement with the observations of J. D. Dana, F. L. Stillwell found that the best representative formula is $Fe(SbS_2)_2$, or **ferrous metasulphoantimonite.** P. Berthier obtained a product of the same composition by fusing together the correct proportions of the constituent sulphides ; and he added that the two sulphides form solid soln. in all proportions. The mineral occurs in dark grey or brown, plumose, fibrous, or granular masses, and in elongated, prismatic crystals with a rather indistinct longitudinal cleavage. J. L. C. Schröder van der Kolk made observations on the colour. J. von Pettko gave 4·043 for the sp. gr.; A. Breithaupt, 4·03–4·042; A. Hofmann, 3·89–3·91; and C. F. de Landero, 4·062. The hardness is 2–3. H. Fischer found some varieties fuse readily, others with difficulty. A. de Gramont examined the spark spectrum. Berthierite dissolves readily in hydrochloric acid, giving off hydrogen sulphide.

W. Skey described a mineral from Richmond Hill, New Zealand; and he accordingly called it **richmondite**. The black mineral may occur massive, and crystalline. It is represented as a **cuprous lead ferrous enneasulphodiantimonite**, $(Pb,Cu_2Ag_2,Zn,Fe)_6Sb_2S_9$. The sp. gr. is 4·317; and the hardness 4·5. The mineral comuccite from St. Georges, Sardinia, has the composition $18PbS.7FeS.15Sb_2S_3$. It was described by P. Comucci. Its sp. gr. is 5·65; and it is probably a member of the plagionite group of solid soln. The history of the mineral *jamesonite* has been previously discussed. Analyses of jamesonite were reported by J. Antipoff, F. Boricky, F. P. Dunnington, F. A. Genth, C. Guillemain, W. Haidinger, J. Loczka, V. Novarese, A. Pichler, A. Raimondi, C. F. Rammelsberg, G. vom Rath, H. Rose, F. von Schaffgotsch, E. V. Shannon, L. J. Spencer, A. Stelzner, and C. E. Wait. For many years jamesonite was represented by the formula $2PbS.Sb_2S_3$, but, according to L. J. Spencer, it is best to reserve this formula for plumosite, and to represent the analyses made in material with characteristic and well-defined physical properties—*e.g.* basal cleavage—by the formula $7(Pb_{0·8}Fe_{0·2})S.4Sb_2S_3$; while J. Loczka, and W. T. Schaller represented jamesonite by the formula $4PbS.FeS.3Sb_2S_3$ **lead ferrous tetradecasulphohexantimonite**, V. Novarese agreed that the iron of jamesonite is not to be regarded as an impurity, and added that the mineral may be regarded as a mixture of boulangerite and berthierite. There is no evidence in favour of this assumption. The mineral may occur in compact and fibrous masses coloured dark lead-grey, or steel-grey; usually, however, it occurs in acicular crystals, which, according to F. Slavik, are monoclinic, with axial ratios $a : b : c = 0·8316 : 1 : 0·4260$, and $\beta = 91° 24·5'$; and, according to S. Stevanovic, $0·9223 : 1 : 0·5218$. The crystals show basal cleavage. J. L. C. Schröder van der Kolk made some observations on the colour. H. Rose gave for the sp. gr. 5·560; F. von Schaffgotsch, 5·616; W. Haidinger, 5·601; C. F. Rammelsberg, 5·700; A. Stelzner, 5·540; F. A. Genth, 6·467; A. Pilcher, 5·20; and L. J. Spencer, 5·480. J. J. Saslawsky calculated the contraction occurring during the formation of the mineral from its components. The hardness is 2·5. W. W. Coblentz and H. Kohler found that jamesonite is photoelectrically sensitive for spectral radiation of the highest intensities. E. E. Fairbanks found the dielectric constant is less than 81. H. C. Bolton observed that the mineral is feebly attacked by a boiling soln. of citric acid. Jamesonite may be weathered to antimony ochre. W. Maucher, and J. R. Blum made some observations on the weathering of the mineral. E. V. Shannon [31] described a kind of *silver-jamesonite* occurring in Owyhee County, U.S.A. It was called **owyheeite**; and the analysis corresponds with $(Ag,Cu)_2S.5(Pb,Fe)S.3Sb_2S_3$; or, according to E. T. Wherry and W. F. Foshag, $2Ag_2.S.8PbS.5Sb_2S_3$; W. F. Foshag gave $Ag_2S.5PbS.3Sb_2S_3$.

L. G. Eakins [32] described the occurrence at the Domingo mine, Colorado, of a mineral which he called *warrenite*—after E. R. Warren—and P. Groth *domingite* It appears as an aggregate of acicular crystals, forming matted, wool-like masses, locally called mineral wool. Its composition approximates $3PbS.2Sb_2S_3$. W. T. Schaller said that the crystals may be both brittle and flexible. H. Sommerlad obtained what he regarded as artificial warrenite, of sp. gr. 5·632, by melting a mixture of lead chloride and antimony trisulphide; and of sp. gr. 5·602, by melting together a mixture of lead and antimonious sulphides; and D. Iitsuka observed that **lead orthosulphotetrantimonite**, $Pb_3Sb_4S_9$, is formed below 610°, and that it has a transition point from the a- to the β-forms at 510°. He regards the a-form as artificial warrenite. L. J. Spencer showed that warrenite is probably identical with jamesonite; and W. T. Schaller that it is probably a mixture of jamesonite and zinckenite in the proportions 2 : 3. G. Lehmann described what he called *Zundererz*, or *Bergzunderz—tinder ore*—occurring at Andreasburg and Clausthal, Harz. It is a soft, dirty-red mineral resembling tinder. It has been likened to kermesite, but, according to A. Bornträger, B. Rösing, and O. Luedecke, it is an impure jamesonite or feather ore. B. Rösing represented the tinder ore from Clausthal as *lead sulphodiantimonotetrantimonate*, $Pb_4Sb_6S_{17}$, or $4PbS.Sb_2S_3.2Sb_2S_5$. The *Bleischimmer* analyzed by C. H. Pfaff, and J. Antipoff, was called by J. J. N. Huot *pfaffite*. It is possibly a mixture of galena and antimony ochre.

W. Guertler and H. Schack [33] found that molybdenum dissolves in fused antimony trisulphide with the separation of an eq. amount of antimony, forming what appears to be **molybdenum sulphoantimonite**. W. Guertler studied the ternary system Mo–Sb–S, but obtained no *molybdenum sulphoantimonite*.

I. Pouget prepared **cobalt orthosulphoantimonite**, $Co_3(SbS_3)_2$, by the action of a cobalt salt on a dil. soln. of potassium orthosulphoantimonite; if conc. soln. be used, **potassium cobalt orthosulphoantimonite**, $KCoSbS_3$, is formed. Cobalt orthosulphoantimonite is very easily oxidized. By a similar process, I. Pouget prepared **nickel orthosulphoantimonite**, $Ni_3(SbS_3)_2$; and **potassium nickel ortho-sulphoantimonite**, $KNiSbS_3$.

W. Guertler and H. Schack [34] made a partial study of the ternary system Ni–Sb–S. J. C. Ullmann described a mineral occurring on the Jungfrau, at Gosenbach, Westphalia, and named it *Nickelspiessglaserz ;* J. F. L. Hausmann called it *Nickelspiessglanzerz*. Many analogous terms were also employed by other writers, until J. Fröbel applied to it the term **ullmannite**—after J. C. Ullmann. Analyses were reported by J. C. Ullmann, M. H. Klaproth, J. F. John, J. F. L. Hausmann, H. Rose, H. Laspeyres, T. Haege, C. F. Rammelsberg, V. R. von Zepharovich, P. Jannasch, F. Ullik, M. von Lill, and S. Traverso. The results fit the formula NiSbS—**nickel sulphoantimonide**—fairly well. The antimony may be replaced in part by arsenic, and, in the extreme case may approximate to gersdorffite, NiAsS. Thus, V. R. von Zepharovich's mineral *corynite*, Ni(As,Sb)S—from κορύνη, a club—is a *nickel sulphoarsenoantimonide*, occurring in silver-white or steel-grey, cubic crystals at Olsa, Carinthia, has 13·45 per cent. of arsenic and 37·85 per cent. of antimony. W. Guertler made a partial study of the ternary system : Ni–Sb–S. There are four binary compounds, Ni_5Sb_2, NiSb, Ni_3S_2, and NiS, that melt unchanged, and one ternary compound, NiSbS, whose zone of stability is indicated in Fig. 64. There are indications of a ternary eutectic consisting of NiS and NiSbS. N. S. Kurnakoff and Y. Posternak melted a mixture of barium chloride with 10 per cent. of sodium chloride, in a graphite

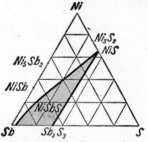

FIG. 64.—The Ternary System : Ni–Sb–S.

crucible; added nickel antimonide; raised the temp. to 200°, and added antimony trisulphide. On slowly cooling the mass, small cubes and dodecahedra were formed.

Ullmannite is steel-grey or silver-white ; it occurs in masses with a granular structure or in cubic crystals which, according to C. Klein, may be pyritohedral; according to N. S. Kurnakoff and Y. Posternak, dodecahedral; or, according to V. R. von Zepharovich, tetrahedral. The cubic cleavage is perfect. The crystals were examined by A. Breithaupt, K. Mieleitner, G. Rose, E. F. Glocker, M. Hörnes, G. A. Kenngott, H. A. Miers, A. Russell, and J. Rumpf. M. L. Huggins studied the electronic and lattice structures. L. S. Ramsdell's X-radiograms corresponded with a structure like that of pyrite with the Sb-atoms occupying alternate positions with the S-atoms. The Sb-atoms occupy the same relative positions on the diagonals of the small cubes as do the S-atoms of pyrite, but with the Sb-atoms a little closer and the S-atoms a little farther from the vacant corners of the small cubes than do the S-atoms of pyrite. The length of the side of the unit cube is 5·91 A. For the sp. gr. J. C. Ullmann gave 6·333–6·833 ; A. Breithaupt, 6·281–6·331 ; P. Jannasch, 6·625–6·883 ; V. R. von Zepharovich, 6·72 ; N. S. Kurnakoff and Y. Posternak, 6·62 at 20° ; and M. von Lill, 6·63 ; the best representative value is 6·72. The hardness is about 5. H. Fizeau gave $0·0_41112$ for the coeff. of linear expansion. J. Joly found sublimation occurs at 185°–285°. N. S. Kurnakoff and Y. Posternak said that it melts at 758° without decomposition. A. de Gramont examined the spark spectrum of ullmannite and corynite ; and F. Beijerinck found the electrical conductivity is good—better than that of pyrite ; T. W. Case said that the corynite is a poor conductor, but the resistance of ullmannite is less than a megohm ; and that insolation has no measurable effect in either case. E. T. Wherry found the crystals of ullmannite to be poor radio-detectors. The mineral is soluble in warm nitric acid with the separation of sulphur and antimony oxide ; it dissolves in aqua regia with the separation of sulphur ; and is but little attacked by hydrochloric acid. E. F. Smith found that the mineral is attacked by sulphur monochloride, and that decomposition is complete at about 180°.

E. F. Pittman [35] described **cobalt nickel sulphoantimonide,** approximating CoNiSbS, which occurs at Willyama, New South Wales—hence the name **willyamite.** It occurs in tin-white or steel-grey masses or cubic crystals. The cubic cleavage is perfect. M. L. Huggins studied the electronic and lattice structures. The hardness is 5·5 ; and the sp. gr. 6·87. F. Sandberger described a mineral from Wolfach, Baden, and he called it **wolfachite.** Its composition approximates to **nickel bissulphoarsenoantimonide,** $Ni(Sb,As,S)_2$. It occurs in silver-white or tin-white columnar, or radiating aggregates of rhombic crystals. M. L. Huggins studied the electronic and lattice structures. F. Sandberger, and T. Petersen found the sp. gr. to be 6·372 ; and the hardness, 4–5·3. F. Beijerinck said that wolfachite is a good electrical conductor.

REFERENCES.

[1] I. Pouget, *Recherches sur les sulfo- et les selenio-antimonites,* Paris, 1899 : *Ann. Chim. Phys.,* (7), **18.** 524, 1899 ; *Compt. Rend.,* **124.** 103, 1897 ; **126.** 1145, 1896 ; **129.** 103, 1899 ; A. Ditte, *ib.,* **102.** 168, 212, 1886 ; A. Terreil, *ib.,* **69.** 1360, 1870 ; A. Duflos, *Schweigger's Journ.,* **62.** 210, 1831 ; **67.** 269, 1833 ; J. J. Berzelius, *ib.,* **34.** 58, 1822 ; *Pogg. Ann.,* **20.** 365, 1830 ; **37.** 163, 1836 ; C. F. Rammelsberg, *ib.,* **52.** 204, 1841 ; W. Müller, *ib.,* **127.** 413, 1866 ; B. Unger, *Arch. Pharm.,* (2), **147.** 203, 1871 ; (2), **148.** 8, 1871 ; V. Stanek, *Zeit. anorg. Chem.,* **17.** 118, 1898 ; H. Sommerlad, *ib.,* **18.** 420, 1898 ; M. Berthelot, *Ann. Chim. Phys.,* (6), **10.** 133, 1887 ; P. Berthier, *ib.,* (2), **22.** 239, 1823 ; (2), **25.** 379, 1824 ; H. C. Bolton, *Ann. New York Acad.,* **1.** 1, 153, 1879 ; **2.** 1, 1882 ; *Chem. News,* **36.** 249, 260, 1877 ; **37.** 14, 24, 65, 86, 98, 1878 ; **38.** 168, 1878 ; W. Hampe, *Zeit. anal. Chem.,* **31.** 320, 1892 ; P. Jannasch, *ib.,* **33.** 214, 1894 ; *Journ. prakt. Chem.,* (2), **40.** 230, 1889 ; H. Rose, *Ausführliches Handbuch der analytischen Chemie,* Braunschweig, 1867 ; C. Doelter, *Monatsh.,* **11.** 150, 1890 ; E. Berglund, *Ber.,* **17.** 95, 1884 ; T. Poleck, *ib.,* **27.** 1052, 1894 ; E. F. Smith, *ib.,* **23.** 2276, 1890 ; R. Bunsen, *Liebig's Ann.,* **106.** 4, 1858 ; K. Heumann, *ib.,* **173.** 33, 1874 ; C. Serons, *Gazz. Chim. Ital.,* **24.** ii, 274, 1894 ; C. Tocco, *ib.,* **54.** i, 23, 1924 ; G. Kohl, *Arch. Pharm.,* (2), **17.** 267, 1839 ; E. Giebe and A. Schiebe, *Zeit. Physik,* **33.** 760, 1925.

[2] N. Parravano and P. de Cesaris, *Atti Accad. Lincei,* (5), **21.** i, 798, 1912 ; *Gazz. Chim. Ital.,* **42.** ii, 189, 1912 ; H. Pélabon, *Compt. Rend.,* **140.** 1389, 1905 ; H. Ungemash, *ib.,* **169.** 918, 1919 ; F. von Kobell, *Ber. Akad. München,* **1.** 163, 1865 ; S. Stevanovic, *Zeit. Kryst.,* **37.** 237, 1903 ; J. J. Saslawsky, *ib.,* **59.** 205, 1924 ; A. Kretschmer, *ib.,* **48.** 502, 1910 ; A. Frenzel, *ib.,* **28.** 602, 1897 ; H. Laspeyres, *ib.,* **19.** 428, 1891 ; P. Groth, *Tabellarische Uebersicht der Mineralien,* Braunschweig, 35, 1898 ; E. T. Wherry and W. F. Foshag, *Journ. Washington Acad.,* **11.** 1, 1921 ; M. Chikashige and Y. Yamanchi, *Mem. Coll. Science Kyoto,* **1.** 341, 1916 ; H. Sommerlad, *Zeit. anorg. Chem.,* **18.** 430, 1898 ; I. Pouget, *Recherches sur les sulfo- et les selenio-antimonites,* Paris, 1899 ; *Ann. Chim. Phys.,* (7), **18.** 524, 1899 ; *Compt. Rend.,* **124.** 103, 1897 ; **126.** 1145, 1896 ; **129.** 103, 1899 ; C. F. Rammelsberg, *Pogg. Ann.,* **52.** 226, 1841 ; H. Rose, *ib.,* **35.** 357, 1835 ; J. C. L. Zincken, *ib.,* **35.** 357, 1835 ; G. Rose, *ib.,* **35.** 361, 1835 ; W. T. Page, *Chem. News,* **46.** 215, 1882 ; J. D. Dana, *A System of Mineralogy,* New York, 130, 1892 ; J. J. N. Huot, *Manuel de minéralogie,* Paris, **1.** 197, 1841 ; E. F. Glocker, *Generum et specierum mineralium secundum*

ordines naturales digestorum synopsis, Halle, 32, 1847 ; J. Nicol, Manual of Mineralogy, Edin-
burgh, 484, 1849 ; L. J. Spencer, Min. Mag., 11. 1, 190, 1897 ; P. N. Tschirwinsky, Tschermak's
Mitt., (2), 35. 17, 1922 ; A. Raimondi, Minéraux de Pérou, Paris, 125, 1878 ; R. Scharizer,
Jahresb. geol. Reichsanst. Wien, 40. 433, 1890 ; T. Richter, Berg. Hütt. Ztg., 16. 220, 1857 ;
E. Cumenge, Bull. Soc. Min., 2. 202, 1879 ; A. de Gramont, ib., 18. 321, 1895 ; C. Friedel, ib., 2.
204, 1879 ; S. L. Penfield, Amer. Journ. Science, (4), 4. 27, 1897 ; G. A. Kenngott, Sitzber. Akad.
Wien, 16. 161, 1855 ; T. W. Case, Phys. Rev., (2), 9. 305, 1917 ; F. Sandberger, Untersuchungen
über Erggänges, Wiesbaden, 297, 1885 ; W. Guertler and K. L. Meissner, Metall Erz, 18. 410, 1921.
    3 H. Pélabon, Compt. Rend., 136. 1450, 1903 ; P. Chrétien and J. M. Guinchant, ib., 138.
1270, 1904 ; H. Fizeau, 66. 1005, 1072, 1868 ; C. G. A. von Weissenbach, Journ. tech. ökon.
Chem., 10. 210, 1831 ; F. M. Jäger, Versl. Akad. Amsterdam, 20. 497, 1911 ; F. M. Jäger and
H. S. van Klooster, Zeit. anorg. Chem., 78. 252, 1912 ; H. Sommerlad, ib., 15. 173, 1897 ; 18.
423, 1898 ; H. Schneiderhöhn, Anleitung zur mikroskopischen Bestimmung und Untersuchungen von
Erzen und Aufbereitungsprodukte besonders im auffallenden Licht, Berlin, 236, 1922 ; C. F. Ram-
melsberg, Pogg. Ann., 52. 218, 1841 ; R. Böttger, ib., 55. 117, 1842 ; K. Konno, Mem. Coll.
Science Kyoto, 4. 51, 1920 ; P. A. von Bonsdorff, Akad. Handl. Stockholm, 338, 1821 ; Ann.
Phil., 8. 29, 1824 ; F. Wöhler, Liebig's Ann., 27. 157, 1838 ; F. Field, Journ. Chem. Soc., 12. 12,
1859 ; T. Petersen, Journ. prakt. Chem., (1), 106. 143, 1869 ; Neues Jahrb. Min., 480, 1869 ;
A. Streng, ib., 916, 1878 ; I. Domeyko, ib., 380, 1879 ; H. Traube, ib., i, 287, 1890 ; L. G. Raviez,
Econ. Geol., 10. 368, 1915 ; Neues Jahrb. Min., ii, 144, 1922 ; O. Mügge, ib., ii, 81, 1897 ; Centr.
Min., 37, 1920 ; E. Rethwisch, Neues Jahrb. Min. B.B., 4. 89, 1886 ; Zur mineralogischen und
chemischen Kenntnis des Rothgültigerzes, Göttingen, 1885 ; H. A. Miers, Min. Mag., 8. 94, 1888 ;
C. A. Burghardt, ib., 9. 231, 1891 ; J. Loczka, Ann. Hist. Nat. Mus. Hungar, 9. 320, 1911 ; Zeit.
Kryst., 54. 185, 1915 ; C. Doelter, ib., 11. 40, 1886 ; Allgemeine chemische Mineralogie, Leipzig,
152, 1890 ; P. Niggli, Zeit. Kryst., 56. 14, 185, 1921 ; A. Sella, ib., 22. 180, 1894 ; Gött. Nachr.,
311, 1891 ; Q. Sella, Nuovo Cimento, (1), 3. 287, 1856 ; (1), 4. 93, 1856 ; I. Pouget, Recherches
sur les sulfo- et les selenio-antimonites, Paris, 1899 ; Ann. Chim. Phys., (7), 18. 524, 1899 ; Compt.
Rend., 124. 103. 1897 ; 126. 1145, 1896 ; 129. 103, 1899 ; M. Fenoglio, Atti Accad. Torino, 61.
357, 1926 ; J. Rondet, Action des sels halogénés du plomb et de l'argent sur le sulfure d'antimoine,
Paris, 1904 ; F. Ducatte, Essai de reproduction artificielle par voie sèche de quelques minéraux
naturels du bismuth. (Sur les dérivés halogénés des sulfobismuthites), Paris, 1902 ; J. Durocher,
Compt. Rend., 32. 825, 1851 ; J. Margottet, Recherches sur les sulfures, les seleniures et les tellurures
métalliques, Paris, 1879 ; Compt. Rend., 85. 1142, 1877 ; H. de Sénarmont, ib., 32. 409, 1851 ;
J. Fournet, Ann. Mines, (3), 4. 3, 1833 ; W. Maucher, Die Bildungsreihe der Mineralien als
Unterlage für die Einteilung der Erzlagerstätten, Freiberg, 1914 ; A. Hofmann and F. Slavik,
Rozpravy Tescheck. Akad., 19. 27, 1910 ; A. de Gramont, Bull. Soc. Min., 18. 329, 1895 ; A. des
Cloizeaux, Nouvelles recherches sur les propriétés optiques des cristaux, Paris, 521, 1867 ;
W. W. Coblentz and J. F. Eckford, Bur. Standards Scient, Paper, 451, 1922 ; E. A. Schenck,
Ueber die elliptische Polarisation des Lichtes bei Reflexion an Krystalloberflächen, Strassburg, 1882 ;
Wied. Ann., 15. 177, 1882 ; Zeit. Kryst., 10. 283, 1885 ; M. J. Schuster, ib., 12. 117, 1886 ; C. Busz,
ib., 20. 557, 1892 ; W. Haidinger, Edin. Journ. Science, 1. 326, 1824 ; V. Goldschmidt, Index der
Krystallformen der Mineralien, Berlin, 3. 59, 1888 ; E. F. Glocker, Handbuch der Mineralogie,
Nürnberg, 905, 1839 ; F. Sandberger, Untersuchungen über Erzgänge, Wiesbaden, 297, 1885 ;
Neues Jahrb. Min., 309, 1869 ; O. Luedecke, Die Minerale des Harzes, Berlin, 141, 1896 ;
R. J. Hauy, Traité de minéralogie, Paris, 3. 406, 1801 ; F. Mohs, Grundriss der Mineralogie,
Dresden, 2. 601, 1824 ; A. Lévy, Description d'une collection de minéraux formée par M. Henri
Heuland, Londres, 2. 344, 1838 ; C. J. Selb, Denks. Ges. Aertze Naturf. Schwabens, 1. 311, 1817 ;
Leonhard's Taschenbuch, 11. ii, 404, 1817 ; A. Frenzel, Mineralogisches Lexikon für das Königreich
Sachsen, Leipzig, 246, 1864 ; J. R. Blum, Die Pseudomorphosen des Mineralreichs, Stuttgart, 21,
1893 ; A. Breithaupt, Die Poragenesis der Mineralien, Freiberg, 152, 1849 ; Berg. Hütt. Ztg., (2),
401, 1853 ; E. Giebe and A. Scheibe, Zeit. Physik, 33. 760, 1925 ; P. H. Geiger, Phys. Rev., (2),
22. 461, 1923 ; C. Castro, Bol. Min. Mexico, 7. 275, 1919 ; E. E. Fairbanks, Econ. Geol., 21. 399.
1926 ; H. B. North and C. B. Conover, Amer. Journ. Science, (4), 40. 640, 1915 ; T. W. Case,
Phys. Rev., (2), 9. 305, 1927 ; M. von Laue, Zeit. Kryst., 63. 312, 1926 ; C. Tubandt and
M. Haedicke, Zeit. anorg. Chem., 160. 297, 1927 ; H. E. McKinstry, Econ. Geol., 22. 669, 1927.
    4 A. Breithaupt, Vollständiges Charakteristik des Mineralsystem, Dresden, 285, 333, 1832 ;
in A. Frenzel, Mineralogisches Lexikon für das Königreich Sachsen, Leipzig, 252, 1874 ;
O. Luedecke, Die Minerale des Harzes, Berlin, 133, 1896 ; Zeit. Kryst., 6. 570, 1882 ; J. D. Dana,
A System of Mineralogy, New York, 543, 1850 ; 93, 1868 ; W. H. Miller, Introduction to
Mineralogy, London, 217, 1852 ; G. A. Kenngott, Mineralogisch Untersuchungen, Breslau, 29,
1849 ; M. Adam, Tableau minéralogique, Paris, 60, 1869 ; F. A. Roemer, Neues Jahrb. Min., 312,
1848 ; A. Streng, ib., 917, 1878 ; i, 60, 1886 ; G. Cesaro, Bull. Soc. Min., 38. 38, 1915 ; J. J. Saslawsky, Zeit. Kryst., 59. 204, 1924 ; C. Doelter, ib., 11. 40, 1886 ; Allgemeine chemische Mineralogie, Leipzig, 152, 1890 ; H. A. Miers, Min. Mag., 10. 214, 1894.
    5 F. Mohs, Grundriss der Mineralogie, Dresden, 2. 606, 1824 ; A. Breithaupt, Vollständiges
Charakteristik des Mineralsystems, Dresden, 286, 333, 1832 ; H. Rose, Pogg. Ann., 15. 469,
1826 ; G. A. Kenngott, ib., 98. 165, 1856 ; Uebersichte der Resultate mineralogischer Forschungen,
Leipzig, 172, 1857 ; W. Haidinger, Sitzber. Akad. Wien, 22. 236, 1856 ; R. Helmhacker, Berg.
Hütt. Ztg., 13. 380, 1864 ; W. H. Miller, Introduction to Mineralogy, London, 214, 1852 ;
W. J. Lewis, Proc. Cambridge Phil. Soc., 4. 365, 1883 ; V. Goldschmidt, Index des Krystallformen

der Mineralien, Berlin, 2. 386, 1890 ; P. Groth, Die Mineraliensammlung der Universität Strass-
burg, Strassburg, 58, 1878 ; C. Tubandt and M. Haedicke, Zeit. anorg. Chem., 160. 297, 1927 :
L. Sipöcz, Tschermak's Mitt., (1), 7. 215, 1877 ; J. Rumpf, ib., (2), 4. 186, 1882 ; I. Domeyko,
Elementos de mineralojia, Santiago, 385, 1879 ; A. Weisbach, Neues Jahrb. Min., ii, 109, 1880 ;
O. Mügge, ib., i, 100, 1898 ; C. F. Rammelsberg, Handbuch der Mineralchemie, Leipzig, 41, 1895 :
L. J. Spencer, Min. Mag., 14. 308, 1907 ; C. Doelter, Allgemeine chemische Mineralogie, Leipzig,
152, 247, 1890 ; Zeit. Kryst., 11. 40, 1886 ; V. Goldschmidt, ib., 30. 291, 1898 ; A. S. Eakle, ib.,
31. 215, 1899 ; G. vom Rath, ib., 8. 38, 1884 ; J. J. Saslawsky, Proc. Russ. Polyt. Inst., 1. 61,
1919 ; Zeit. Kryst., 59. 209, 1924 ; C. Vrba, ib., 5. 429, 1881 ; H. Sommerlad, Zeit. anorg. Chem.,
15. 177, 1897 ; 18. 422, 1898 ; F. M. Jäger and H. S. van Klooster, ib., 78. 254, 1912 ; T. W. Case,
Phys. Rev., (2), 9. 305, 1917 ; H. Pélabon, Compt. Rend., 136. 1450, 1903 ; C. F. Naumann.
Pogg. Ann., 17. 142, 1829 ; A. Weisbach, ib., 125. 441, 1865 ; Zeit. Kryst., 2. 55, 1877 ; L. Tokody,
ib., 59. 83, 250, 1924 ; E. E. Fairbanks, Econ. Geol., 21. 399, 1926 ; E. V. Shannon, Amer. Min.,
13. 18, 1928 ; H. E. McKinstry, Econ. Geol., 22. 669, 1927.
    [6] T. Petersen, Pogg. Ann., 137. 386, 1869 ; H. Sommerlad, Zeit. anorg. Chem., 18. 424, 1898 :
J. J. Saslawsky, Zeit. Kryst., 59. 205, 1924 ; F. Sandberger, Neues Jahrb. Min., 310, 1869 ;
G. Cesaro, Bull. Soc. Min., 38. 53, 1915 ; H. E. McKinstry, Econ. Geol., 22. 669, 1927.
    [7] G. Agricola, Interpretatio germanica vocum rei metallicæ, Basileæ, 362, 1546 ; J. G. Wal-
lerius, Mineralogia, Stockholm, 313, 1747 ; A. G. Werner, Berg. Journ., 1. 369, 1789 ; C. C. von
Leonhard, Handbuch der Orktognosie, Heidelberg, 202, 1821 ; F. Mohs, Grundriss der Mineralogie,
Dresden, 2. 587, 1824 ; R. J. Haüy, Traité de minéralogie, Paris, 3. 416, 1801 ; C. F. Naumann,
Elemente der Mineralogy, Leipzig, 583, 1828 ; M. H. Klaproth, Beiträge zur chemischen Kenntnis
der Mineralkörper, Berlin, 1. 162, 1795 ; Crell's Chem. Ann., 2. 14, 1787 ; F. S. Beudant, Traité
élémentaire de minéralogie, Paris, 1832 ; W. Haidinger, Handbuch der bestimmenden Mineralogie,
Wien, 472, 570, 1845 ; I. S. R. I. Eques a Born, Lythophylacium Bornianum, Prague, 1. 81, 1772 ;
R. Jameson, A System of Mineralogy, Edinburgh, 287, 1804 ; A. Breithaupt, Vollständige Charak-
teristik des Mineralsystems, Dresden, 266, 1832 ; Schweigger's Journ., 55. 296, 1829 ; R. Brandes,
ib., 22. 344, 1818 ; H. Rose, Pogg. Ann., 15. 573, 1829 ; G. Rose, ib., 28. 158, 1833 ;
F. H. Schröder, ib., 95. 257, 1855 ; Berg. Hütt. Ztg., 13. 233, 241, 249, 1854 ; C. F. Rammelsberg,
Handbuch des Mineralchemie, Leipzig, 194, 1853 ; 122, 1875 ; 52, 1895 ; E. E. Fairbanks,
Econ. Geol., 21. 399, 1926 ; G. Bodländer, Neues Jahrb. Min., i, 99, 1895 ; F. Tonner, ib., 716,
1860 ; Lotos, 7. 85, 1859 ; 10. 88, 1860 ; E. H. Kraus and J. P. Goldsberry, Neues Jahrb. Min.,
ii, 140, 1914 ; A. Frenzel, ib., 788, 1873 ; C. A. Joy, Miscellaneous Chemical Researches, Göttingen,
21, 1853 ; F. A. Genth, Proc. Amer. Phil. Soc., 23. 39, 1886 ; W. J. Taylor, Proc. Acad. Philadelphia, 306, 1859 ; I. Domeyko, Elementos de mineralojia, Santiago, 391, 1879 ; G. T. Prior,
Min. Mag., 9. 14, 1890 ; H. A. Miers, ib., 8. 204, 1889 ; L. J. Spencer, ib., 11. 1897 ; H. Sommerlad, Zeit. anorg. Chem., 18. 424, 1898 ; S. L. Penfield, Amer. Journ. Science, (4), 2. 24, 1896 ;
F. R. van Horn, ib., (4), 32. 40, 1911 ; W. F. Foshag, ib., (5), 1. 444, 1921 ; W. E. Ford, ib., (4),
25. 244, 1908 ; C. Doelter, Allgemeine chemische Mineralogie, Leipzig, 152, 1890 ; G. A. Kenngott,
Uebersichte der Resultate mineralogischer Forschungen, Leipzig, 119, 1861 ; E. F. Glocker, Handbuch der Mineralogie, Nürnberg, 417, 1831 ; P. Groth, Die Mineraliensammlung der Universität
Strassburg, Strassburg, 70, 1878 ; P. Groth and K. Mieleitner, Mineralogische Tabellen, München,
28, 1921 ; H. Ungemach, Bull. Soc. Min., 33. 375, 1910 ; A. de Gramont, ib., 18. 323, 1895 ;
G. Cesaro, ib., 38. 53, 1915 ; J. L. C. Schröder van der Kolk, Centr. Min., 71, 1901 ; J. J. Saslawsky, Zeit. Kryst., 59. 205, 1924 ; O. Mügge, ib., 41. 631, 1905 ; C. Vrba, Ber. Böhm. Ges. Wiss.,
66, 1886 ; Zeit. Kryst., 5. 435, 1881 ; C. Morton, ib., 9. 239, 1884 ; G. vom Rath, ib., 10. 173,
1885 ; A. des Cloizeaux, Nouvelles recherches sur les propriétés optiques des cristaux, Paris, 85,
1867 ; J. D. Dana, A System of Mineralogy, New York, 1025, 1893 ; T. L. Walker, Geol. Studies
Toronto Univ., 12, 1921 ; L. G. Ravicz, Econ. Geol., 10. 368, 1915 ; E. Döll, Verh. geol. Reichsanst. Wien, 222, 1897 ; Tschermak's Mitt., (2), 4. 87, 1874 ; B. Kerl, Berg. Hütt. Ztg., 12. 17,
1853 ; R. F. Weinland, in P. Niggli, Lehrbuch der Mineralogie, Berlin, 365, 1920 ; W. J. Lewis,
Proc. Cambridge Phil. Soc., 4. 365, 1883 ; A. E. Reuss, Sitzber. Akad. Wien, 10. 44, 1853 ; 22.
129, 1856 ; 47. 13, 1863 ; J. F. von der Null, Mineralienkabinet, Wien, 3. 160, 1804 ; G. d'Achiardi,
Atti Soc. Toscana, 18. 12, 1901 ; V. R. von Zepharovich, Mineralogisches Lexikon für die Kaiser-
thum Oesterreich, Wien, 434, 1859 ; 309, 1873 ; 239, 1893 ; O. Luedecke, Die Minerale des
Harzes, Berlin, 171, 1896 ; A. Frenzel, Mineralogisches Lexikon für das Königreich Sächsen,
Leipzig, 307, 1874 ; J. Joly, Phil. Mag., (6), 27. 1, 1914 ; Chem. News, 107. 241, 1913 ; E. Artini,
Giorn. Min. Crist. Ital., 2. 241, 1891 ; F. Sandberger, Untersuchungen über Erzgänge, Wies-
baden, 300, 1885 ; Neues Jahrb. Min., 312, 1869 ; F. Slavik, Ber. Böhm. Ges. Wiss., 16, 1901 ;
V. Nejdl, ib., 6, 1895 ; J. R. Blum, Die Pseudomorphosen des Mineralreichs, Stuttgart, 25, 1863 ;
P. H. Geiger, Phys. Rev., (2), 22. 461, 1923 ; T. W. Case, ib., (2), 9. 305, 1917 ; H. E. McKinstry,
Econ. Geol., 22. 669, 1927 ; G. A. Kenngott, Mineralogisch Untersuchungen, Breslau, 29, 1849.
    [8] A. Breithaupt, Berg. Hütt. Ztg., 25. 188, 1866 ; Mineralogische Studien, Leipzig, 110, 1866.
    [9] I. Pouget, Recherches sur les sulfo- et les selenio-antimonites, Paris, 1899 ; Ann. Chim. Phys.
(7), 18. 524, 1899 ; Compt. Rend., 124. 103, 1897 ; 126. 1145, 1898 ; 129. 103, 1899.
    [10] J. S. F. Pagenstecher, Repert. Pharm., 14. 212, 1822 ; I. Pouget, Recherches sur les sulfi
et les selenio-antimonites, Paris, 1899 ; Ann. Chim. Phys., (7), 18. 524, 1899 ; Compt. Rend., 124.
103, 1897 ; 126. 1145, 1896 ; 129. 103, 1899.
    [11] M. Barcena, Naturaleza, 3. 35, 172, 1874 ; Amer. Journ. Science, (3), 8. 145, 1874 ; (3),
9. 64, 1874 ; H. Pélabon, Compt. Rend., 140. 1389, 1905 ; W. T. Page, Chem. News, 42. 195,

1880; F. P. Venable, *ib.*, 40. 186, 1879; L. Baker, *ib.*, 42. 196, 1880; J. Joly, *Phil. Mag.*, (6), 25. 856, 1913; P. Groth, *Tabellarische Uebersicht der Mineralien*, Braunschweig, 32, 1898; P. Groth, *Zeit. Kryst.*, 6. 97, 1892; P. Groth and K. Mieleitner, *Mineralogische Tabellen*, 23, 1921; E. T. Wherry and W. F. Foshag, *Journ. Washington Acad.*, 11. 1, 1921; J. J. Saslawsky. *Zeit. Kryst.*, 59. 204, 1924; E. S. Lassen, *Bull. U.S. Geol. Soc.*, 679, 1921; W. M. Davy and C. M. Farnham, *Microscopic Examination of Ore Minerals*, New York, 111, 1920; G. Cesaro, *Bull. Soc. Min.*, 38. 41, 1915; I. Pouget, *Recherches sur les sulfo- et les selenio-antimonites*, Paris, 1899; *Ann. Chim. Phys.*, (7), 18. 524, 1899; *Compt. Rend.*, 124. 103, 1897; 126. 1145, 1896; 129. 103, 1899; J. Joly, *Phil. Mag.*, (6), 27. 1, 1914; *Chem. News*, 107. 241, 1913; F. Sandberger, *Neues Jahrb. Min.*, 874, 1875; 281, 1876; A. Hilger, *ib.*, 630, 1879; H. Sommerlad, *Zeit. anorg. Chem.*, 18. 447, 1898.

[12] L. F. Hawley, *Journ. Amer. Chem. Soc.*, 29. 1011, 1907.

[13] N. Parravano and P. de Cesaris, *Atti Accad. Lincei*, (5), 21. i, 535, 1912.

[14] K. Wagemann, *Met.*, 9. 518, 1912; *Metall. Erz.* 17. 403, 1920; W. Guertler, *ib.*, 22. 199, 1925; F. M. Jäger and H. S. van Klooster, *Proc. Aead. Amsterdam*, 20. 510, 1911; *Zeit. anorg. Chem.*, 78. 260, 1912; H. Sommerlad, *ib.*, 18. 439, 1898; D. Iitsuka, *Metn. Coll. Science Kyoto*, 4. 61, 1920; C. L. Boulanger, *Ann. Mines*, (3), 7. 575, 1835; M. C. J. Thaulow, *Pogg. Ann.*, 41. 216, 1837; J. F. L. Hausmann, *ib.*, 46. 281, 1839; G. vom Rath, *Ber. Niederrh. Ges. Bonn.*, 28, 1869; *Pogg. Ann.*, 136. 431, 1869; W. Brüel, *ib.*, 48. 550, 1839; C. F. Rammelsberg, *ib.*, 41. 493, 1839; 52. 223, 1841; 68. 509, 1846; *Handbuch der Mineralchemie*, Leipzig, 74, 1860; 97, 1875; 41, 1895; P. Groth, *Tabellarische Uebersicht der Mineralien*, Braunschweig, 18, 1874; 35, 1898; C. Guillemain, *Beiträge zur Kenntnis der natürlichen Sulfosalze*, Breslau, 1898; T. Haege. *Die Mineralien des Siegerlandes und der abgrenzenden Bezirke*, Siegen, 34, 1887; F. A. Genth, *Amer. Journ. Science*, (2), 45. 320, 1868; L. G. Eakins, *ib.*, (3), 36. 450, 1888; E. Bechi, *ib.*, (2), 14. 60, 1852; *Rapp. Espos. Firenze*, 1, 1850; W. Guertler and H. Schack, *Metall. Erz*, 20. 361, 426, 1923; T. W. Case, *Phys. Rev.*, (2), 9. 305, 1917; A. Frenzel, *Journ. prakt. Chem.*, (2), 2. 360, 1870; A. Breithaupt, *ib.*, (1), 10. 442, 1837; A. d'Achiardi, *Mineralogia della Toscana*, Pisa, 2. 338, 1873; M. Websky, *Zeit. deut. geol. Ges.*, 21. 751, 1869; V. R. von Zepharovich, *Sitzber. Akad. Wien.* 56. 32, 1869; H. Schack, *Metall. Erz*, 20. 426, 1923; R. W. Helmhacker, *Berg. Hütt. Jahrb.*, 13. 377, 1863; H. Sjögren, *Geol. För. Förh. Stockholm*, 19. 153, 1897; J. L. C. Schröder van der Kolk, *Centr. Min.*, 79, 1901; F. Zambonini, *Riv. Min. Crist. Ital.*, 41. 338, 1912; W. W. Coblentz, *Bur. Standards Scient. Paper*, 18. 585, 1922; I. Pouget, *Recherches sur les sulfo- et les selenio-antimonites*, Paris, 1899; *Ann. Chim. Phys.*, (7), 18. 524, 1899; *Compt. Rend.*, 124. 103, 1897; 126. 1145, 1896; 129. 103, 1899; E. V. Shannon, *Proc. Nat. Hist. Museum*, 58. 589, 1921; *Amer. Journ. Science*, (4), 45. 66, 1918; (5), 1. 423, 1921; *Amer. Min.*, 2. 131, 1917; *Journ. Washington Acad.*, 15. 195, 1925; J. Rondet, *Action des sels halogénés du plomb et de l'argent sur le sulfure d'antimoine*, Paris, 1904; J. J. Saslawsky, *Zeit. Kryst.*, 59. 209, 1924; F. L. Ducatte, *Essai de reproduction artificielle par voie sèche de quelques minéraux naturels du bismuth (Sur les dérivés halogénés des sulfobismuthites)*, Paris, 1902; A. Terreil, *Bull. Soc. Min.*, 13. 115, 1870; S. B. Christy, *Amer. Chem. Journ.*, 27. 362, 1902; E. E. Fairbanks, *Econ. Geol.*, 21. 399, 1926.

[15] L. F. Navarro, *Anal. Soc. Espan. Hist. Nat.*, 24. 96, 1895; *Bull. Soc. Min.*, 20. 163, 1897; A. Schrauf, *Zeit. Kryst.*, 28. 202, 1897.

[16] L. F. Svanberg, *Oefvers. Akad. Handl. Stockholm*, 184, 1839; 64, 1848; *Pogg. Ann.*, 51. 535, 1840; C. Guillemain, *Beiträge zur Kenntnis der natürlichen Sulfosalze*, Breslau, 35, 1898; G. T. Prior, *Min. Mag.*, 13. 187, 1902; R. H. Solly, *ib.*, 12. 290, 1900; G. d'Achiardi, *Atti Soc. Toscana*, 18. 1, 1901; A. d'Achiardi, *Mineralogia della Toscana*, Pisa, 2. 351, 1873; C. H. T. Kerndt, *Pogg. Ann.*, 45. 302, 1845; C. Sauvage, *Ann. Mines*, (3), 17. 525, 1840; J. Apjohn, *Trans. Roy. Irish. Acad.*, 1. 469, 1841; V. Goldschmidt, *Index der Krystallformen der Mineralien*, Berlin, 2. 78, 1890; C. F. Rammelsberg, *Handbuch der Mineralchemie*, Leipzig, 117, 1875; J. D. Dana, *A System of Mineralogy*, New York, 494, 1850; 105, 1868; J. F. L. Hausmann, *Handbuch der Mineralogie*, Göttingen, 166, 1847; P. Groth, *Tabellarische Uebersicht der Mineralien*, Braunschweig, 29, 1882; G. Nauckhoff, *Geol. För. Förh. Stockholm*, 1. 88, 1872; *Bull. Soc. Min.*, 18. 179, 1872; F. A. Genth, *Amer. Journ. Science*, (2), 19. 9, 1855; D. Forbes, *Phil. Mag.*, (4), 29. 9, 1865; P. E. W. Oeberg, *Oefvers. Akad. Förh.*, 8, 1885; *Zeit. Kryst.*, 14. 622, 1888; J. J. Saslawsky, *ib.*, 59. 203, 1924; H. Sommerlad, *Zeit. anorg. Chem.*, 18. 435, 1898; J. Joly, *Phil. Mag.*, (6), 21. 1, 1914.

[17] E. Bechi, *Amer. Journ. Science*, (2), 14. 60, 1852; *Cont. Atti Georg.*, 30. 84, 1852; A. Martini and A. Funaro, *Atti Soc. Toscana*, 2. 116, 1876; G. vom Rath, *Pogg. Ann.*, 132. 377, 1867; A. Frenzel, *ib.*, 141. 443, 1870; *Mineralogisches Lexikon für das Königreich Sachsen*, Leipzig, 203, 1874; A. d'Achiardi, *Mineralogia della Toscana*, Pisa, 2. 345, 1873; J. A. Krenner, *Földt. Közl.*, 13. 362, 1883; H. A. Miers, *Min. Mag.*, 5. 325, 1883; A. Schmidt, *ib.*, 8. 613, 1884; C. Hintze, *ib.*, 9. 294, 1884; H. Sommerlad, *Zeit. anorg. Chem.*, 18. 440, 1898; G. Flink, *Ark. Kemi Min.*, 3. 35, 1910; J. J. Saslawsky, *Zeit. Kryst.*, 59. 204, 1924; C. F. Rammelsberg, *Handbuch der Mineralchemie*, Leipzig, 104, 1875; J. L. C. Schröder van der Kolk, *Centr. Min.*, 79, 1908; B. J. Harrington, *Trans. Roy. Soc. Canada*, 1. 79, 1883; O. Sella, *Gazz. uff. Regno d'Italia*, 10, 1862; D. Iitsuka, *Mem. Coll. Science Kyoto*, 4. 61, 1920.

[18] A. G. Werner, *Letzes Mineralsystem*, Freiberg, 23, 1817; J. G. Wallerius, *Mineralogia*, Stockholm, 309, 1750; L. A. Emmerling, *Lehrbuch der Mineralogie*, Giessen, 2. 468, 1796; W. Haidinger, *Handbuch der Bestimmenden Mineralogie*, Wien, 569, 1845; *Treatise on Mineralogy*,

Edinburgh, **1**. 451, 1825 ; *Ber. Naturf. Berlin*, **1**. 63, 1847 ; E. F. Glocker, *Generum et specierum mineralium secundum ordines naturales digestorum synopsis*, Halle, 30, 1847 ; F. Mohs, *Grundriss der Mineralogie*, Dresden, 2. 586, 1824 ; A. Breithaupt, *Vollständige Charakteristik des Mineralsystems*, Dresden, 271, 1832 ; F. von Kobell, *Charakteristik des Mineralien*, Nürnberg, 2. 175. 1831 ; R. J. Haüy, *Traite de Minéralogie*, Paris, 4. 266, 1801 ; C. F. Rammelsberg, *Handbuch der Mineralchemie*, Leipzig, 70, 1006, 1860 ; 92, 1875 ; *Pogg. Ann.*, **77**. 241, 1849 ; J. Kudernatsch, *ib.*, 37. 588, 1836 ; J. C. L. Zincken, *ib.*, 22. 492, 1831 ; R. Jameson, *Manual of Mineralogy*, Edinburgh, 285, 1821 ; G. Lehmann, *Mém. Acad. Berlin*, 20, 1758 ; H. Rose, *Pogg. Ann.*, **8**. 99, 1826 ; **15**. 471, 1829 ; **28**. 482, 1833 ; **77**. 240, 1849 ; G. Rose, *ib.*, **28**. 421, 1831 ; F. von Schaffgotsch, *ib.*, **38**. 403, 1836 ; F. Sandberger, *Neues Jahrb. Min.*, ii, 94, 1883 ; E. Kaiser, *Zeit. Kryst.*, **27**. 49, 1898 ; J. J. Saslawsky, *ib.*, **59**. 204, 1924 ; C. Doelter, *ib.*, **11**. 40, 1885 ; V. Novarese, *ib.*, **40**. 293, 1905 ; *Boll. Com. Geol. Ital.*, **23**. 319, 1902 ; E. V. Shannon, *Amer. Min.*, **10**. 194, 1925 ; L. J. Spencer, *Min. Mag.*, **11**. 195, 1897 ; **12**. 57, 1899 ; **14**. 303, 1907 ; F. Pisani, *Compt. Rend.*, **83**. 747, 1847 ; J. L. C. Schröder van der Kolk, *Centr. Min.*, 79, 1901 ; F. Slavik, *ib.*, 8, 1914 ; A. Hofmann and F. Slavik, *Abh. Böhm. Akad.*, 27, 1910 ; *Bull. Acad. Cracovie*, 21, 1913 ; S. Stevanovic, *Ann. Géol. Balken*, **7**. 1, 1922 ; F. Boricky, *Sitzber. Akad. Wien*, 56. 37, 1867 ; A. Stelzner, *Tschermak's Mitt.*, (1), **3**. 248, 1873 ; A. Richler, *ib.*, (1), **7**. 355, 1877 ; F. P. Dunnington, *Proc. Amer. Assoc.*, 184, 1877 ; E. E. Fairbanks, *Econ. Geol.*, **21**. 399, 1926 ; V. R. von Zepharovich, *Mineralogisches Lexikon für das Kaiserthum Oesterreich*, Wien, 156, 1873 ; J. R. Blum. *Die Pseudomorphosen des Mineralreichs*, Stuttgart, 14, 1852 ; 168, 1863 ; W. Maucher, *Die Bildungsreihe des Mineralien als Unterlage für die Einteilung der Erzlagerstätten*, Freiberg, 1914 ; V. C. Butureanu, *Bull. Soc. Bucarest*, **6**. 179, 1897 ; G. vom Rath, *Ber. Niederrh. Ges. Bonn*, 80, 1879 ; P. Groth, *Tabellarische Uebersicht der Mineralien*, Braunschweig, 30, 1889 ; A. Raimondi, *Minéraux du Pérou*, Paris, 166, 192, 1878 ; F. A. Genth, *Amer. Chem. Journ.*, **1**. 325, 1879 ; C. E. Wait, *Trans. Amer. Inst. Min. Eng.*, **8**. 51, 1880 ; J. Loczka, *Ann. Miss. Nat. Hungar.*, **6**. 586, 1908 ; W. T. Schaller, *Bull. U.S. Geol. Sur.*, 490, 1911 ; *Zeit. Kryst.*, **48**. 563, 1911 ; E. V. Shannon, *Amer. Min.*, **10**. 194, 1925 ; B. S. Burton, *Amer. Journ. Science*, (2), **45**. 36, 1868 ; L. G. Eakins, *ib.*, (3), **36**. 450, 1888 ; E. Bechi, *ib.*, (2), **14**. 60, 1852 ; *Cont. Atti Georg.*, **30**. 84, 1852 ; C. Guillemain, *Beiträge zur Kenntnis der natürlichen Sulfosalze*, Breslau, 1887 ; K. Wagemann, *Met.*, **9**. 518, 1912 ; *Metall. Erz*, **17**. 403, 1920 ; F. L. Ducatte, *Essai de reproduction artificielle par voie sèche de quelques minéraux naturels du bismuth (Sur les dérivés halogénés des sulfobismuthites)*, Paris, 1902 ; J. Rondet, *Action des sels halogénés du plomb et de l'argent sur le sulfure d'antimoine*, Paris, 1904 ; H. Sommerlad, *Zeit. anorg. Chem.*, **18**. 438, 1898 ; F. M. Jäger and H. S. van Klooster, *ib.*, **78**. 259, 1912 ; F. Zambonini, *Riv. Min. Crist. Ital.*, **41**. 338, 1912 ; O. Luedecke, *Die Minerale des Harzes*, Berlin, 127, 1874 ; *Neues Jahrb. Min.*, ii, 117, 1883 ; A. Bornträger, *Journ. prakt. Chem.*, (1), **36**. 40, 1845 ; M. Sénez, *Ann. Mines*, (3), **18**. 535, 1840 ; P. Berthier, *ib.*, (3), **15**. 634, 1839 ; J. Antipoff, *Journ. Russ. Min. Soc.*, **28**. 275, 1891 ; C. H. Pfaff, *Schweigger's Journ.*, **27**. 1, 1819 ; H. C. Bolton, *Ber.*, **13**. 733, 1880 ; B. Rösing, *Zeit. deut. geol. Ges.*, **21**. 747, 1869 ; 30. 527, 1878 ; D. Iitsuka, *Mem. Coll. Science Kyoto*, **4**. 61, 1910 ; T. W. Case, *Phys. Rev.*, (2), **9**. 305, 1917.

[19] J. A. Krenner, *Magyar. Akad. Ertes.*, **15**. 111, 1881 ; *Unger. Rev.*, 367, 1881 ; *Zeit. Kryst.*, **8**. 532, 1883 ; G. T. Prior and L. J. Spencer, *Min. Mag.*, **12**. 60, 1898 ; **14**. 308, 1907 ; F. Zambonini, *Riv. Min. Crist. Ital.*, **41**. 338, 1912 ; J. Loczka, *Math. Termes etud. Ertesito*, 42. 6, 1924 ; L. Sipöcz, *Tschermak's Mitt.*, (2), **7**. 261, 1884 ; *Zeit. Kryst.*, **11**. 216, 1885 ; T. W. Case, *Phys. Rev.*, (2), **9**. 305, 1917 ; V. C. Butureanu, *Bull. Soc. Bucarest*, **6**. 179, 1897 ; L. J. Spencer, *Min. Mag.*, **11**. 195, 1897 ; **12**. 57, 1899 ; **14**. 303, 1907 ; W. Haidinger, *Handbuch der Bestimmenden Mineralojie*, Wien, 569, 1845 ; *Treatise on Mineralogy*, Edinburgh, **1**. 451, 1825 ; *Ber. Naturf. Berlin*, **1**. 63, 1847 ; C. F. Rammelsberg, *Handbuch der Mineralchemie*, Leipzig, 70, 1006, 1860 ; 92, 1875 ; *Pogg. Ann.*, **77**. 241, 1849 ; B. S. Burton, *Amer. Journ. Science*, (2), **45**. 36, 1868 ; O. Luedecke, *Die Minerale des Harzes*, Berlin, 127, 1874 ; *Nenes Jahrb. Min.*, ii, 117, 1883 ; C. Guillemain, *Beiträge zur Kenntnis der natürlichen Sulfosalze*, Breslau, 1887 ; L. J. Spencer, *Min. Mag.*, **11**. 195, 1897 ; **12**. 57, 1899 ; **14**. 303, 1907 ; H. Sommerlad, *Zeit. anorg. Chem.*, **18**. 438, 1898 ; F. M. Jäger and H. S. van Klooster, **78**. 259, 1912 ; D. Iitsuka, *Mem. Coll. Science Kyoto*, **4**. 61, 1910 ; K. Wagemann, *Met.*, **9**. 518, 1912.

[20] J. C. L. Zincken, *Der östliche Harz, mineralogisch und bergmannisch betrachtet*, Braunschweig, 130, 1825 ; G. Rose, *Pogg. Ann.*, 7. 91, 1826 ; H. Rose, *ib.*, **8**. 199, 1826 ; F. Wöhler, **46**. 1839 ; B. Kerl, *Berg. Hütt. Ztg.*, 12. 20, 1853 ; H. A. Hilger, *Liebig's Ann.*, **185**. 205, 1877 ; F. Sandberger, *Neues Jahrb. Min.*, 514, 1876 ; W. F. Hillebrand, *Proc. Colorado Scient. Soc.*, **1**. 121, 1884 ; A. Stelzner, *Zeit. Kryst.*, **24**. 126, 1895 ; J. J. Saslawsky, *ib.*, **59**. 206, 1924 ; P. Groth, *ib.*, **1**. 415, 1877 ; E. S. von Fedoroff, *ib.*, **53**. 362, 1919 ; C. Guillemain, *Beiträge zur Kenntnis der natürlichen sulfosalze*, Breslau, 14, 1898 ; V. Goldschmidt, *Index der Krystallformen der Mineralien*, Berlin, **3**. 332, 1891 ; E. Schulze, *Lithia Hercynica*, Leipzig, 1895 ; P. P. Pillipenko, *Bull. Imp. Tomsk. Univ.*, 63, 1915 ; C. F. Rammelsberg, *Handbuch der Mineralchemie*, Leipzig, 86, 1875 ; A. de Gramont, *Bull. Soc. Min.*, 18. 312, 1895 ; F. Gonnard, *ib.*, 5. 49, 90, 1882 ; W. F. Petterd, *Proc. Roy. Soc. Tasmania*, 62, 1897 ; J. L. C. Schröder van der Kolk, *Centr. Min.*, 79, 1901 ; J. Fournet, *Ann. Chim. Phys.*, (2), **56**. 412, 1834 ; H. Sommerlad, *Zeit. anorg. Chem.*, **18**. 436, 1898 ; F. M. Jäger and H. S. van Klooster, *ib.*, **78**. 260, 1912 ; J. Joly, *Chem. News*, **107**. 241, 1913 ; *Phil. Mag.*, (6), 27. 1, 1914 ; G. A. Kenngott, *Sitzber. Akad. Wien*, **9**. 557, 1852 ; L. J. Spencer, *Min. Mag.*, **11**. 189, 1897 ; O. Luedecke, *Die Minerale des Harzes*, Berlin, 123, 1896 ; D. Iitsuka, *Mem. Coll. Science Kyoto*, **4**. 61, 1920 ; T. W. Case, *Phys. Rev.*, (2), **9**. 305, 1917.

[21] S. G. Gordon, *Proc. Acad. Philadelphia*, **94**. 101, 1922; E. T. Wherry, *Amer. Min.*, **13**. 1928; E. V. Shannon and M. N. Short, *ib.*, **12**. 405, 1927. [22] I. Pouget, *Recherches sur les sulfo- et les selenio-antimonites*, Paris, 1899; *Ann. Chim. Phys.*, (7), **18**. 524, 1899; *Compt. Rend.*, **124**. 103, 1897; **126**. 1145, 1896; **129**. 103, 1899. [23] P. Rashleigh, *Specimens of British Minerals*, London, **1**. 34, 1797; J. L. Bournon, *Catalogue de la collection minéralogique particulière du roi*, 409, 1813; *Phil. Trans.*, **94**. 30, 1804; C. Hatchett, *ib.*, **94**. 63, 1804; J. Smithson, *ib.*, **98**. 55, 1808; R. Jameson, *A System of Mineralogy*, Edinburgh, **2**. 579, 1805; M. H. Klaproth, *Beiträge zur chemischen Kenntniss der Mineralkörper*, Berlin, **4**. 83, 1807; D. L. G. Karsten, *Mineralogische Tabellen*, Berlin, 68, 1808; A. G. Werner, *Letztes Mineralsystem*, Freiberg, 23, 57, 1817; A. Breithaupt, *Berg. Hütt. Ztg.*, **11**. 67, 1852; *Vollständige Charakteristik des Mineralsystems*, Dresden, 125, 1823; *Mineralogische Studien*, Leipzig, 111, 1866; F. Mohs, *Grundriss der Mineralogy*, Dresden, **2**. 560, 1824; *Charakteristik des Mineralsystems*, Dresden, 1821; F. Mohs and F. X. M. Zippe, *Aufangsgründe der Naturgeschichte der Mineralreichs*, Wien, 1839; F. X. M. Zippe, *Lehrbuch der Mineralogie*, Wien, 213, 1859; R. J. Haüy, *Tableau comparatif des résultats de la cristallographie et de l'analyse chimique relativement à la classification des minéraux*, Paris, 80, 245, 1809; *Traité de minéralogie*, Paris, **4**. 295, 1822; W. Haidinger, *Handbuch der bestimmenden Mineralogie*, Wien, 564, 1845; J. F. L. Hausmann, *Handbuch der Mineralogie*, Göttingen, 172, 1813; P. Groth, *Zeit. Kryst.*, **31**. 82, 1899; *Tabellarische Uebersicht der Mineralien*, Braunschweig, 18, 83, 1874; *Die Mineraliensammlung der Universität Strassburg*, Strassburg, 61, 1878; V. Goldschmidt, *Index der Krystallformen der Mineralien*, Berlin, **1**. 330, 1886; C. F. Rammelsberg, *Handbuch der Mineralchemie*, Leipzig, 80, 1860; C. F. Rammelsberg and J. C. L. Zincken, *Pogg. Ann.*, **77**. 251, 1849; H. Rose, *ib.*, **15**. 573, 1829; G. Rose, *ib.*, **76**. 291, 1849; C. Bromeis, *ib.*, **74**. 251, 1848; F. Zirkel, *Sitzber. Akad. Wien*, **45**. 431, 1862; G. Tschermak, *ib.*, 53, 518, 1866; H. A. Miers, *Min. Mag.*, **6**. 59, 1885; C. A. Burghardt, *ib.*, **9**. 227, 1891; G. T. Prior and L. J. Spencer, *ib.*, **11**. 22, 1895; O. Luedecke, *Die Minerale des Harzes*, Berlin, 157, 1896; H. Traube, *Die Minerale des Schlesiens*, Breslau, 39, 1888; A. Lacroix, *Minéralogie de la France et de ses colonies*, Paris, **2**. 701, 1897; C. Guillemain, *Beiträge zur Kenntnis der natürlichen Sulfosalze*, Breslau, 1887; B. Kerl, *Zeit. Ges. Naturwiss.*, **3**. 592, 1854; C. Kuhlemann, *ib.*, **8**. 500, 1856; R. P. Greg and W. G. Lettsom, *Manual of the Mineralogy of Great Britain and Ireland*, London, 304, 1858; B. von Cotta, *Gangstudien oder Beiträge zur Kenntniss der Erzgänge*, Freiberg, 2, 1851; W. H. Miller, *Introduction to Mineralogy*, London, 201, 1852; T. Haege, *Die Mineralien des Siegerlandes und der abgrenzenden Bezirke*, 41, 1887; A. d'Achiardi, *Mineralogia della Toscana*, Pisa, **2**. 336, 1873; W. P. Jervis, *I Tesori sotterranei dell'Italia*, Turin, **1**. 51, 73, 105, 118, 1873; G. Szellemy, *Zeit. prakt. Geol.*, **3**. 20, 1895; P. H. Geiger, *Phys. Rev.*, (2), **22**. 461, 1923; I. Domeyko, *Elementos de mineralojia*, Santiago, 235, 1879; A. Frenzel, *Mineralogisches Lexikon für das Königsreich Sachsen*, Leipzig, 47, 1874; *Zeit. Kryst.*, **28**. 608, 1897; F. Hessenberg, *Mineralogische Notizen*, Frankfurt, **5**. 36, 1863; A. Schrauf, *Atlas der Krystallformen des Mineralreiches*, Wien, 37, 1877; V. R. von Zepharovich, *Mineralogisches Lexikon für das Kaiserthum Oesterreich*, Wien, 70, 1859; 68, 1873; 46, 1893; *Sitzber. Akad. Wien*, **51**. 110, 1865; N. von Kokscharoff, *Materialen zur Mineralogie Russlands*, St. Petersburg, **8**. 123, 1883; R. W. Helmhacker, *Berg. Hütt. Jahrb.*, **13**. 377, 1864; A. Stelzner, *Tschermak's Mitt.*, (1), **3**. 240, 1873; F. Babanek, *ib.*, (1), **2**. 30, 1872; (1), **5**. 86, 1875; (2), **6**. 86, 1855; C. Doelter, *ib.*, (2), **11**. 323, 1890; *Zeit. Kryst.*, **11**. 39, 1886; *Anz. Akad. Wien*, **37**. 101, 1900; F. Field, *Journ. Prakt. Chem.*, (12), **40**. 232, 1889; W. Meissner, *Schweigger's Journ.*, **26**. 79, 1819; H. F. Foshag, *Amer. Journ. Science*, (5), **1**. 444, 1921; C. Hidegh, *Zeit. Kryst.*, **8**. 534, 1883; L. Sipöcz, *Tschermak's Mitt.*, (2), **7**. 283, 292, 1882; *Zeit. Kryst.*, **11**. 218, 1886; G. Benko, *Orvos Termeszettadomanyi Ertesito*, **14**. ii, 163, 1889; *Zeit. Kryst.*, **19**. 199, 1891; F. B. Peck, *ib.*, **27**. 320, 1897; G. vom Rath, *ib.*, **1**. 162, 1877; A. Schmidt, *ib.*, **20**. 153, 1892; *Term. Füz.*, **14**. 208, 1891; E. Döll, *Verh. geol. Reichsanst. Wien*, 144, 1874; P. A. Dufrénoy, *Ann. Mines*, (3), **10**. 371, 1836; D. Lovisato, *Atti Accad. Lincei*, (5), **11**. ii, 357, 1903; F. G. Wait, *Chem. News*, **28**. 271, 1873; W. T. Page, *ib.*, **44**. 190, 203, 1881; A. von Schrötter, *Baumgartner's Zeit. Phys.*, **8**. 284, 1830; W. W. Coblentz and J. F. Eckford, *Bur. Standards Scient. Paper*, 451, 1922; P. Termier, *Bull. Soc. Min.*, **20**. 102, 1897; F. Gonnard, *ib.*, **20**. 317, 1897; A. de Gramont, *ib.*, **18**. 316, 1895; *Compt. Rend.*, **118**. 748, 1894; **119**. 70, 1894; W. T. Schaller, *Bull. U.S. Geol. Sur.*, 262, 1895; A. W. F. Petterd, *Proc. Roy. Soc. Tasmania*, 51, 1901; J. R. Blum, *Die Pseudomorphosen des Mineralreichs*, Stuttgart, **2**. 14, 1852; G. Sillem, *Neues Jahrb. Min.*, 523, 1852; J. C. L. Schröder van der Kolk, *Centr. Min.*, 79, 1901; J. Königsberger, *ib.*, 565, 597, 1908; A. Sella, *Gött. Nachr.*, 311, 1891; *Zeit. Kryst.*, **22**. 180, 1894; H. Schneiderhöhn, *Anleitung zur mikroskopischen Bestimmung und Untersuchungen von Erzen und Aufbereitungs produkte besonders im auffallenden Licht*, Berlin, 234, 1922; T. W. Case, *Phys. Rev.*, (2), **9**. 305, 1917. [24] H. Buttgenbach, *Ann. Soc. Géol. Belg.*, **46**. 212, 1923. [25] J. A. Krenner and J. Loczka, *Math. Term. Tud. Ertesite*, **42**. 18, 1926; J. A. Krenner, *ib.*, **11**. 119, 1893; *Zeit. Kryst.*, **23**. 497, 1894; T. W. Case, *Phys. Rev.*, (2), **9**. 305, 1917; H. E. McKinstry, *Econ. Geol.*, **22**. 669, 1927. [26] J. A. Krenner, *Math. Term. Tud. Ertesito*, **11**. 119, 1893; *Zeit. Kryst.*, **23**. 497, 1894; R. Pöhlmann, *ib.*, **24**. 124, 1895; C. Vrba, *ib.*, **2**. 160, 1878; H. Bücking, *ib.*, **2**. 425, 1878; A. Stelzner, *ib.*, **24**. 125, 1895; *Zeit. deut. geol. Ges.*, **49**. 128, 1897; W. C. Brögger, *Forh. Vid. Selsk. Christiania*, 18, 1892; *Zeit. Kryst.*, **21**. 193, 1893; G. T. Prior and L. J. Spencer, *Min. Mag.*, **11**. 292, 1887; **12**. 11, 1898; L. J. Spencer, *ib.*, **14**. 308, 1907; *Amer. Journ.*

Science, (4), **6**. 316, 1898; L. G. Eakins, *ib.*, (3), **36**. 452, 1888; A. Cronstedt, *Mineralogie*, Stockholm, 1758; H. E. McKinstry *Econ. Geol.*, **22**. 669, 1927; J. B. L. Romé de l'Isle, *Cristallographie*, Paris, 35, 1773; **3**. 54, 1783; J. C. Freiesleben, *Geognostische Arbeiten*, Freiberg, **6**. 97, 1817; E. J. Chapman, *Practical Mineralogy*, London, 128, 1843; A. Breithaupt, *Vollständige Charakteristik des Mineralsystem*, Dresden, 267, 1832; *Die Paragenesis der Mineralien*, Freiberg, 152, 251, 1849; *Mineralogische Studien*, Leipzig, 112, 1866; *Berg. Hütt. Ztg.*, **13**. 9, 1854; W. Haidinger, *Handbuch der bestimmenden Mineralogie*, Wien, 569, 1845; W. Phillips, *An Elementary Introduction to the Knowledge of Mineralogy*, London, 291, 1823; W. H. Miller, *Introduction to Mineralogy*, London, 208, 1852; A. Lévy, *Description d'une collection de minéraux formée par M. Henri Heuland*, Londres, **2**. 367, 1838; J. F. L. Hausmann, *Gött. Gel. Anz.*, 1505, 1838; *Neues Jahrb. Min.*, 85, 1839; *Pogg. Ann.*, **46**. 146, 1839; *Handbuch der Mineralogie*, Göttingen, 182, 1847; V. R. von Zepharovich, *Sitzber. Akad. Wien*, **63**. 147, 1871; *Mineralogisches Lexikon für das Kaiserthum Oesterreich*, Wien, 108, 1873; C. F. Rammelsberg, *Handbuch der Mineralchemie*, Leipzig, 133, 1843; 106, 1847; 94, 1875; 39, 1895; W. S. von Waltershausen, *Pogg. Ann.*, **94**. 130, 1855; F. Wöhler, *ib.*, **46**. 153, 1839; *Gött. Gel. Anz.*, 1505, 1838; G. Rose, *Das krystallochemischen Mineralsystem*, Leipzig, 59, 1852; J. Joly, *Phil. Mag.*, (6), **27**. 1, 1914; *Chem. News*, **107**. 241, 1913; I. Domeyko, *Elementos de mineralojia*, Santiago, 397, 1879; L. de la Escosura, *Ann. Mines*, (5), **8**. 495, 1855; A. Damour, *ib.*, (4), **16**. 227, 1849; (5), **6**. 146, 1854; N. y Garza, *Rev. Minera*, **6**. 358, 1855; L. F. Navarro, *Act. Soc. Espan. Hist. Nat.*, **4**. 12, 1895; A. E. Reuss, *Lotos*, **9**. 51, 1859; V. Goldschmidt, *Index des Krystallformen der Mineralien*, Berlin, **2**. 60, 1890; A. Frenzel, *Mineralogisches Lexikon für das Königreich Sachsen*, Leipzig, 117, 1874; J. D. Dana, *A System of Mineralogy*, New York, 541, 1850; 93, 1868; 125, 1892; H. Sjögren, *Geol. För. Förh. Stockholm*, **19**. 153, 1897; F. Babanek, *Tschermak's Mitt.*, (1), **2**. 32, 1872; R. W. Helmhacker, *Berg. Hütt. Jahrb.*, **13**. 379, 1864; G. A. Kenngott, *Uebersichte der Resultate mineralogischer Forschungen*, Leipzig, 294, 1865; M. H. Klaproth, *Beiträge zur chemischen Kenntnis der Mineralkörper*, Berlin, **1**. 173, 1795; J. A. Krenner and J. Loczka, *Math. Term. Tud. Ertesite*, **42**. 18, 1926; C. F. Naumann, *Elemente der Mineralogie*, Leipzig, 515, 1868; G. Tschermak, *Lehrbuch der Mineralogie*, Wien, 370, 1897; A. de Gramont, *Bull. Soc. Min.*, **18**. 322, 1895; E. V. Shannon, *Proc. U.S. Nat. Museum*, **60**. 16, 1922; *Amer. Min.*, **6**. 82, 1921; W. F. Foshag, *Amer. Journ. Science*, (5), **1**. 444, 1921; T. W. Case, *Phys. Rev.*, (2), **9**. 305, 1917.

    [27] V. Rosicky and J. Sterba-Boehm, *Rozpr. Ceske Akad. Prag*, **25**. 45, 1916; *Zeit. Kryst.*, **55**. 430, 1916; P. Groth and K. Mieleitner, *Mineralogische Tabellen*, München, 29, 1921; I. Pouget, *Recherches sur les sulfo- et les selenio-antimonites*, Paris, 1899; *Amer. Chim. Phys.*, (7), **18**. 524, 1899; *Compt. Rend.*, **124**. 103, 1897; **126**. 1145, 1896; **129**. 103, 1899; A. Frenzel, *Neues Jahrb. Min.*, ii, 125, 1893; A. Stelzner, *ib.*, ii, 120, 1893; C. Winkler, *ib.*, ii, 120, 1893; G. T. Prior, *Min. Mag.*, **14**. 21, 1904; W. W. Coblentz and H. Kohler, *Bull. Bur. Standards*, **15**. 231, 1919; P. Groth, *Tabellarische Uebersicht der Mineralien*, Braunschweig, 40, 1898; A. de Gramont, *Bull. Soc. Min.*, **18**. 340, 1895; C. Hintze, *Zeit. Kryst.*, **6**. 632, 1881; G. Lincio, *Centr. Min.*, 142, 1904; C. Ochsenius, *Zeit. deut. geol. Ges.*, **49**. 673, 1897; A. Raimondi, *Minéraux du Pérou*, Paris, 187, 1878.

    [28] H. Pélabon, *Compt. Rend.*, **137**. 920, 1903; Y. Takahashi, *Mem. Coll. Science Kyoto*, **4**. 47, 1920; W. Guertler, *Metall Erz*, **22**. 199, 1925.

    [29] I. Pouget, *Recherches sur les sulfo- et les selenio-antimonites*, Paris, 1899; *Amer. Chim. Phys.*, (7), **18**. 524, 1899; *Compt. Rend.*, **124**. 103, 1897; **126**. 1145, 1896; **129**. 103, 1899.

    [30] N. G. Nordenskjöld, *Ueber des atomistisch-chemische Mineralsystem und des Examinationssystem der Mineralien*, Helsingfors, 1852; P. Berthier, *Ann. Chim. Phys.*, (2), **35**. 351, 1827; *Ann. Mines*, (3), **3**. 49, 1833; E. Turner, *Edin. Journ. Science*, **3**. 308, 1825; W. Haidinger, *ib.*, **7**. 353, 1827; *Pogg. Ann.*, **11**. 478, 1827; P. Groth, *Tabellarische Uebersicht der Mineralien*, Braunschweig, 16, 80, 1874; C. F. de Landero, *Sinopsis mineralogica o catalogo descriptivo de los minerales*, Mexico, 59, 1888; J. L. C. Schröder van der Kolk, *Centr. Min.*, 78, 1901; J. D. Dana, *A System of Mineralogy*, New York, 115, 1892; C. F. Rammelsberg, *Handbuch der Mineralchemie*, Leipzig, 988, 1860; *Pogg. Ann.*, **40**. 153, 1837; *Zeit. deut. geol. Ges.*, **18**. 244, 1866; C. von Hauer, *Jahrb. geol. Reichsanst. Wien*, **4**. 635, 1853; J. von Pettko, *Ber. Mitt. Freund. Wiss. Wien*, **1**. 62, 1847; A. Hofmann, *Zeit. Kryst.*, **31**. 527, 1899; H. Fischer, *ib.*, **4**. 362, 1880; J. Loczka, *Chem. Ztg.*, **25**. 438, 1901; A. de Gramont, *Bull. Soc. Min.*, **18**. 326, 1895; A. Breithaupt, *Journ. prakt. Chem.*, (1), **4**. 279, 1835; W. Skey, *Trans. N.Z. Inst.*, **9**. 556, 1877; P. Comucci, *Atti Accad. Lincei*, (5), **25**. ii, 111, 1916; F. L. Stillwell, *Min. Mag.*, **21**. 83, 1926; J. Antipoff, *Journ. Russ. Min. Soc.*, **28**. 275, 1891; F. P. Dunnington, *Proc. Amer. Assoc.*, 184, 1877; F. Boricky, *Sitzber. Akad. Wien*, **56**. 37, 1867; F. A. Genth, *Journ. Amer. Chem. Soc.*, **1**. 325, 1879; C. Guillemain, *Beiträge zur Kenntnis der natürlichen Sulfosalze*, Breslau, 1887; V. Novarese, *Ann. Mus. Nat. Hunger.* **40**. 293, 1905; *Boll. Com. Geol. Ital.*, **23**. 319, 1902; *Zeit. Kryst.*, **40**. 293, 1905; A. Pichler, *Trans. Amer. Inst. Min. Eng.*, (1), **7**. 355, 1877; C. E. Wait. *ib.*, **8**. 51, 1880; A. Raimondi, *Minéraux du Pérou*, Paris, 116, 192, 1878; G. vom Rath, *Ber. Niederrh. Ges. Bonn.*, 80, 1879; H. Rose, *Pogg. Ann.*, **8**. 99, 1826; **15**. 471, 1829; **28**. 422, 1833; **77**. 240, 1849; F. von Schaffgotsch, *Ber.*, **38**. 403, 1836; A. Stelzner, *Tschermak's Mitt.*, (1), **3**. 248, 1873; E. V. Shannon, *Amer. Min.*, **10**. 194, 1925; L. J. Spencer, *Min. Mag.*, **11**. 195, 1897; **12**. 57, 1899; W. T. Schaller, *Bull. U.S. Geol. Sur.*, 490, 1911; *Zeit. Kryst.*, **48**. 563, 1911; J. J. Saslawsky, *Zeit. Kryst.*, **59**. 204, 1924; W. W. Coblentz and H. Kohler, *Bull. Bur. Standards*, **15**. 231, 1919; W. Maucher, *Die Bildungsreihe des Mineralien*

als Unterlage für die Einteilung der Erzlagerstätten, Freiberg, 1914; **J. R.** Blum, *Die Pseudo-morphosen des Mineralreichs*, Stuttgart, 14, 1852; 168, 1863; **E. E.** Fairbanks, *Econ. Geol.*, 21. 399, 1926; **H. C.** Bolton, *Chem. News*, 37. 14, 86, 99, 1878; *Ann. New York Acad.*, 1. 1. 1879; 2. 1, 1882.
[31] **E. V.** Shannon, *Proc. U.S. Nat. Mus.*, 58. 601, 1920; *Amer. Min.*, 6. 68, 1921; **E. T.** Wherry and **W. F.** Foshag, *Journ. Washington Acad.*, 11. 1, 1921; **W. F.** Foshag, *Amer. Journ. Science*, (5), 1. 444, 1921.
[32] **C. H.** Pfaff, *Schweigger's Journ.*, 27. 1, 1819; **J.** Antipoff, *Journ. Russ. Min. Soc.*, 28. 275, 1891; **J. J. N.** Huot, *Manuel de minéralogie*, Paris, 1. 192, 1841; **J.** Antipoff, *Journ. Russ. Min. Soc.*, 28. 275, 1891; **C.** Guillemain, *Beiträge zur Kenntnis der natürlichen Sulfosalze*, Breslau, 1887; **H.** Rose, *Pogg. Ann.*, 8. 99, 1826; 15. 471, 1829; 28. 422, 1833; 77. 240, 1849; **F.** von Schaffgotsch, *ib.*, 38. 403, 1836; **W.** Haidinger, *Handbuch der bestimmenden Mineralogie*, Wien, 569, 1845; *Treatise on Mineralogy*, Edinburgh, 1. 451, 1825; *Ber. Naturf. Berlin*, 1. 63, 1847; **C. F.** Rammelsberg, *Handbuch der Mineralchemie*, Leipzig, 70, 1006, 1860; 92, 1875; *Pogg. Ann.*, 77. 241, 1849; **F.** Boricky, *Sitzber. Akad. Wien*, 56. 37, 1867; **A.** Stelzner, *Tschermak's Mitt.*, (1), 3. 248, 1873; **G.** vom Rath, *Ber. Niederrh. Ges. Bonn.*, 80, 1879; **F. P.** Dunnington, *Proc. Amer. Assoc.*, 184, 1877; **A.** Raimondi, *Minéraux du Pérou*, Paris, 166, 192, 1878; **F. A.** Genth, *Journ. Amer. Chem. Soc.*, 1. 325, 1879; **J.** Loczka, *Ann. Mus. Nat. Hunger.*, 6. 586, 1908; **V.** Novarese, *ib.*, 40. 293, 1905; *Boll. Com. Geol. Ital.*, 23. 319, 1902; *Zeit. Kryst.*, 40. 293, 1905; **L. J.** Spencer, *Min. Mag.*, 11. 195, 1897; 12. 57, 1899; 14. 308, 1907; **C. E.** Wait, *Trans. Amer. Inst. Min. Eng.*, 8. 51, 1880; **A.** Pichler, *ib.*, (1), 7. 355, 1877; **W. T.** Schaller, *Bull. U.S. Geol. Sur.*, 490, 1911; *Zeit. Kryst.*, 48. 563, 1911; **F.** Slavik, *Centr. Min.*, 8, 1914; **S.** Stevanovic, *Ann. Geol. Balkan.*, 7. 1, 1922; **J. L. C.** Schröder van der Kolk, *Centr. Min.*, 79, 1901; **H. C.** Bolton, *Ber.*, 13. 733, 1880; **F.** von Schaffgotsch, *ib.*, 38. 403, 1836; **J. J.** Saslawsky, *Zeit. Kryst.*, 59. 204, 1924; **J. R.** Blum, *Die Pseudomorphosen des Mineralreichs*, Stuttgart, 14, 1852; 168, 1863; **W.** Maucher, *Die Bildungsreihe des Mineralien als Unterlage für die Einteilung der Erzlagerstätten*, Freiberg, 1914; **L. G.** Eakins, *Amer. Journ. Science*, (3), 36. 450, 1888; **P.** Groth, *Tabellarische Uebersicht der Mineralien*, Braunschweig, 30, 1889; **G.** Lehmann, *Mém. Acad. Berlin*, 20, 1758; **H.** Sommerlad, *Zeit. anorg. Chem.*, 18. 438, 1898; **A.** Bornträger, *Journ. prakt. Chem.*, (1), 36. 40, 1845; **B.** Rösing, *Zeit. deut. geol. Ges.*, 21. 747, 1869; 30. 527, 1878; **O.** Luedecke, *Die Minerale des Harzes*, Berlin, 127, 1874; *Neues Jahrb. Min.*, ii, 117, 1883; **W. W.** Coblentz and **H.** Kohler, *Bull. Bur. Standards*, 15. 231, 1919; **W. W.** Coblentz, *ib.*, 18. 283, 1922; **E. V.** Shannon, *Amer. Min.*, 10. 194, 1925; **D.** Iitsuka, *Mem. Coll. Science Kyoto*, 4. 61, 1910.
[33] **I.** Pouget, *Recherches sur les sulfo- et les selenio-antimonites*, Paris, 1899; *Amer. Chim. Phys.*, (7), 18. 524, 1899; *Compt. Rend.*, 124. 103, 1897; 126. 1145, 1896; 129. 103, 1899; **H.** Schack and **W.** Guertler, *Metall Erz*, 20. 361, 426, 1923.
[34] **J. C.** Ullmann, *Systematischtabellarische Uebersicht der mineralogisch-einfachen Fossilien*, Cassel, 379, 1814; **J.** Fröbel, *Grundzüge eines Systems der Krystallologie*, Zürich, 1843; **J. F. L.** Hausmann, *Handbuch der Mineralogie*, Göttingen, 192, 1813; **W.** Haidinger, *Handbuch der bestimmenden Mineralogie*, Wien, 561, 1845; **E. F.** Glocker, *Handbuch der Mineralogie*, Nürnberg, 443, 1831; **A.** Breithaupt, *Vollständige Charakteristik des Mineralsystems*, Dresden, 249, 1823; *Schweigger's Journ.*, 68. 445, 1833; 69. 94, 1833; *Journ. prakt. Chem.*, (1), 6. 263, 1835; **H.** Schack, *Metall Erz.*, 20. 162, 1923; **W.** Guertler, *ib.*, 22. 199, 1925; **W.** Guertler and **H.** Schack, *ib.*, 20. 162, 361, 426, 1923; **T. W.** Case, *Phys. Rev.*, (2), 9. 305, 1907; **M. H.** Klaproth, *Mag. Ges. Nat. Freund. Berlin*, 6. 71, 1814; *Beiträge zur chemischen Kenntniss der Mineralien*, Berlin, 6. 329, 1815; **J. F.** John, *Schweigger's Journ.*, 12. 238, 1814; **H.** Rose, *Pogg. Ann.*, 15. 588, 1829; **G.** Rose, *ib.*, 13. 167, 1828; **E. T.** Wherry, *Amer. Min.*, 10. 28, 1925; **G. A.** Kenngott, *Uebersichte der Resultate mineralogischer Forschungen*, Wien, 231, 1852; **M.** Hörnes, *Uebersichtlich Darstellung des Mohs'chen Mineralsystems*, Wien, 107, 1847; *Neues Jahrb. Min.*, 783, 1846; **C.** Klein, *ib.*, i, 180, 1883; ii, 170, 1887; **P.** Jannasch, *ib.*, i, 186, 1883; ii, 171, 1887; **S.** Traverso, *ib.*, ii, 220, 1899; **V. R.** von Zepharovich, *Mineralogisches Lexikon für das Kaiserthum Oesterreich*, Wien. 3. 256, 1893; *Sitzber. Akad. Wien*, 51. 117, 1865; 60. 809, 1869; **J.** Rumpf, *ib.*, 61. 7, 1870; **F.** Ullik, *ib.*, 61. 7, 1870; **H.** Laspeyres, *Zeit. Kryst.*, 19. 10, 424, 1891; 25. 598, 1896; *Ber. Niederrh. Ges. Bonn*, 67, 1887; *Ber. Nat. Hist. Ver. Rheinl.*, 215, 1893; **K.** Mieleitner, *Zeit. Kryst.*, 56. 105, 1921; **T.** Haege, *Die Mineralien des Siegerlandes und der abgrenzenden Bezirke*, Siegen, 28, 1887; **J.** Joly, *Phil. Mag.*, (6), 27. 1, 1914; *Chem. News*, 107. 241, 1913; **C. F.** Rammelsberg, *Handbuch der Mineralchemie*, Leipzig, 41. 1875; 24, 1895; *Pogg. Ann.*, 64. 189, 1845; **M.** von Lill, *Verh. geol. Reichsanst. Wien*, 132, 1871; **H. A.** Miers, *Min. Mag.*, 9. 212, 1891; **L. S.** Ramsdell, *Amer. Min.*, 10. 67, 281, 1925; **A.** de Gramont, *Bull. Soc. Min.*, 18. 337, 1895; **F.** Beijerinck, *Neues Jahrb. Min. B.B.*, 11. 436, 1897; **H.** Fizeau, *Compt. Rend.*, 66. 1005, 1072, 1868; **E. F.** Smith, *Journ. Amer. Chem. Soc.*, 20. 289, 1898; **M. L.** Huggins, *ib.*, 44. 1841, 1922; **A.** Russell, *Min. Mag.*, 21. 383, 1927; **N. S.** Kurnakoff and **Y.** Posternak, *Ann. Anal. Phys. Chim.*, 3. 484, 1926.
[35] **E. F.** Pittman, *Proc. Roy. Soc. New South Wales*, 27. 366, 1893; **F.** Beijerinck, *Neues Jahrb. Min. B.B.*, 11. 436, 1897; **F.** Sandberger, *Neues Jahrb. Min.*, 313, 1869; *Untersuchungen über Erzgäuge*, Wiesbaden, 307, 1885; **T.** Petersen, *Pogg. Ann.*, 139. 397, 1869; **M. L.** Huggins, *Journ. Amer. Chem. Soc.*, 44. 1841, 1922.

§ 25. The Higher Sulphides of Antimony

According to J. J. Berzelius,[1] and H. Rose, when hydrogen sulphide is passed through a soln. of antimony trioxide, or potassium antimonite in hydrochloric acid, **antimony tetrasulphide**, Sb_2S_4, is formed ; and M. Websky used a tartaric acid soln. of fused antimony trisulphide and potassium hydrosulphate. J. J. Berzelius obtained it by adding an acid to a soln. of antimony tetroxide in potassium hydrosulphide. J. J. Berzelius said that when the yellowish-red powder is heated, it loses sulphur, forming grey antimony trisulphide ; and when treated with hydrochloric acid, it gives off hydrogen sulphide and forms antimony trichloride with the deposition of sulphur. H. Capitaine found that it produces a yellow soln. when treated with aq. ammonia.

O. Bosek reported that the tetrasulphide is formed as a red, crystalline powder when a soln. of potassium henachlorohypoantimonate is treated with hydrogen sulphide ; and by the action of hydrogen sulphide on a hydrochloric acid soln. of antimony trioxide oxidized with potassium dichromate. T. Wilm reported it to be formed by treating antimony pentasulphide with carbon disulphide ; and B. Brauner, by adding insufficient hydrogen sulphide for precipitating the antimony from a soln. of potassium metantimonate, adding ammonium chloride, and extracting the orange-red precipitate with carbon disulphide. There is nothing here proving that the alleged tetrasulphide is a chemical individual ; it may be a mixture of the tri- and penta-sulphides. F. Kirchhof takes the contrary view and holds that while the tetrasulphide has a real existence, the pentasulphide *existiert überhaupt nicht*. According to F. Kirchhof, the latter possibility is disproved in the case of the tetrasulphide obtained by the action of dil. hydrochloric or sulphuric acid on the so-called zinc **orthosulphoantimonate**, $Zn_3(SbS_4)_2 : Zn_3Sb_2S_8 + 6HCl = Sb_2S_5 + 3ZnCl_2 + 3H_2S$, for the product, after drying at 100°, contains no free sulphur removable by extraction with carbon disulphide, and the analysis agrees with Sb_2S_4. The tetrasulphide is also formed in the reaction $Na_3SbS_4 + SbCl_3 = Sb_2S_4 + 3NaCl$. The alleged orthosulphoantimonate is said to be a compound of tervalent, not quinquevalent antimony ; either

$$Zn<^S_S>Sb\text{—}S\text{—}Zn\text{—}S\text{—}S\text{—}Sb<^S_S>Zn ; \quad \text{or} \quad Sb{\Large\langle}\genfrac{}{}{0pt}{}{^{S.S.Zn.S.S}{S\text{—}Zn\text{—}S}}{\;S\text{—}Zn\text{—}S\;}{\Large\rangle}Sb$$

He assumes that the tetrasulphide is constituted with ter- or quinque-valent antimony :

$$\begin{matrix} S=Sb=S \\ S=Sb=S \end{matrix} \qquad Sb{\Large\langle}\genfrac{}{}{0pt}{}{S.S}{\;S\;}{S}{\Large\rangle}Sb \qquad \genfrac{}{}{0pt}{}{S}{S}{\Large\rangle}Sb\text{—}S\text{—}Sb\text{—}S$$

but added that it is *unwahrscheinlich* that quinquevalent antimony is present because of the formation of hydrogen disulphide from two mols. of sodium orthosulphoantimonate. The closed ring structure is supposed to account for the colour. This subject was discussed by L. M. Currie. For the action of heat, *vide infra*, the pentasulphide.

Basil Valentine [2] frequently speaks of a red antimony sulphide which, in some cases, may have been **antimony pentasulphide**, Sb_2S_5, and, in other cases, the red trisulphide. In 1603, J. Quercetanus, and M. Ettmüller obtained a golden sulphide —*sulphur auratum*—by adding an acid to a soln. of antimony trisulphide and alkali sulphide. R. J. Glauber also obtained a similar product which he called *panacea antimonialis*, or *sulphur purgans universale* in allusion to its medicinal properties. This substance received many other names from the alchemists—*e.g. Saffran Spiessglanz, liver of spiesglance, golden antimony sulphide, sulphur antimonii auratum*, etc. The name *golden antimony sulphide* originally referred to a mixture of antimony sulphides, but it is now applied indiscriminately to the tri- or penta-sulphide or to a mixture of both. Manufacturers of the golden sulphide for use in the rubber industry try to obtain as large a proportion of the pentasulphide as possible. The commercial golden sulphides vary in colour from a golden yellow to a deep orange, and in composition, from nearly pure trisulphide to one containing a relatively high proportion of the pentasulphide. The use of the golden sulphide is almost entirely confined to the rubber industry for producing the familiar orange-red colour. In the process of vulcanization, the colour is maintained in the presence of sulphur—except in the presence of certain impurities. Some *antimony vermilions*, prepared by J. H. Long by the interaction of sodium thiosulphate and antimony trichloride, consist of the trisulphide either alone or mixed with some oxide.

J. J. Berzelius,[3] and H. Rose prepared antimony pentasulphide by the action of hydrogen sulphide on hydrated antimony pentoxide suspended in water, or on a hydrochloric acid, or tartaric acid soln. of the pentoxide. Some trisulphide is usually formed at the same time. H. Rose, O. Bosek, B. Brauner, G. C. Wittstein, R. Bunsen, A. Classen and co-workers, T. Wilm, O. Klenker, J. Thiel, and F. Neher have made observations on this subject—*vide supra*, antimony trisulphide, and also the analytical reactions of antimony. According to O. Klenker, the precipitate obtained on passing a stream of hydrogen sulphide into a moderately conc. alkaline soln. of a quinquevalent compound of antimony consists of a mixture of antimony trisulphide and sulphur (pure antimony trisulphide remaining on extraction with carbon disulphide). Neutral or acid soln. give a precipitate composed of a mixture of the two sulphides and free sulphur, the largest proportion of pentasulphide being formed from a soln. containing 12 per cent. of free hydrochloric acid. As the quantity of free acid further increases, the proportion of pentasulphide formed decreases until from a soln. containing 27 per cent. of free hydrochloric acid, none is precipitated. The analyses of L. J. Thénard, P. L. Geiger, and L. A. Buchner showed that the dried precipitate obtained by the action of the gas on a soln. of the pentachloride, gives off water when heated. H. Rose said that the precipitate can be thoroughly dried at 100°, while G. C. Wittstein said that the precipitate dried at that temp. still retains less than one per cent. of water; R. Bunsen said that the drying is complete at 110°; and O. Bosek, at 105°–107°. The analyses of T. Wilm, G. C. Wittstein, R. Bunsen, O. Bosek, J. J. Berzelius, H. Rose, and L. M. Currie, correspond with the formula Sb_2S_5. The golden sulphide may contain, as A. Short and F. H. Sharpe, and F. Kirchhof suggest, no sulphide higher than the tetrasulphide; or, as O. Klenker, and D. F. Twiss suggest, it may be a solid soln. or mixture of the tri- and penta-sulphides. L. Prunier said that the pentasulphide is formed by fusing antimony trisulphide with the necessary amount of sulphur—but this conclusion does not agree with the results indicated in Fig. 56.

When a soln. of alkali or alkaline earth sulphoantimonate is treated with a strong acid, the resulting precipitate has the composition of the pentasulphide. K. Schlippe, A. Sartorius, N. E. Wilson, F. Jahn, and W. Artus treated a sulphoantimonate with sulphuric acid, and M. Bertsch and M. Harmsen, with a soln. of antimony trichloride. L. M. Currie found that the product obtained by treating a sulphoantimonate with an acid is a mixture of sulphur, and a solid soln. of sulphur and antimony tetrasulphide. The upper limiting composition of this solid soln. corresponds with $Sb_2S_{4\cdot 66}$. Various old recipes for preparing the golden sulphide are mainly concerned with the preliminary formation of a soln. of the sulphoantimonate from antimony trisulphide. Thus, E. Mitscherlich, J. F. A. Göttling, and J. F. Westrumb boiled the trisulphide with a mixture of alkali-lye and sulphur; E. Mitscherlich, F. Musculus, and G. Abesser used alkali carbonate and lime-water; and A. Duflos obtained the sulphoantimonate by the action of a soln. of alkali polysulphide on powdered antimony. In another group of processes, the soln. of alkali sulphoantimonite is obtained by dissolving the crude alkali sulphoantimonite prepared in the dry way. Thus, C. F. Bucholz, P. L. Geiger, and J. B. Trommsdorff heated antimony trisulphide with a mixture of alkali sulphate and charcoal; W. A. Lampadius, and J. B. Trommsdorff used a mixture of the trisulphide with barium sulphate and charcoal; E. Mitscherlich, J. J. Berzelius, G. W. Mullen, J. C. Wieglieb, J. F. Westrumb, A. L. Stark, and W. S. C. Hirsching, a mixture of alkali carbonate, etc., antimony trisulphide, and sulphur. According to T. Wilm, if the precipitate of the colloidal pentasulphide be washed, until the sodium sulphate is removed, it is deflocculated and passes through the filter-paper. A. Grein, therefore, recommended washing the precipitate with a mixture of alcohol and water (1 : 4) until the filtrate is no longer acid, and no longer contains sulphates or chlorides.

T. Wilm said that the precipitate may contain a little more sulphur than corresponds with the pentasulphide, owing to the decomposition of some hydrogen sulphide. O. Klenker found that the pentasulphide is readily converted into the black trisulphide at 150° in an air-bath, and at 230° oxidation occurs. Organic solvents boiling below 100° have no effect on antimony pentasulphide. Boiling alcohol, benzene, and chloroform extract as much sulphur from the pentasulphide as carbon disulphide does, but in the latter case less time is required for the extraction. Boiling oil of turpentine causes a partial decomposition of the pentasulphide. The precipitate formed on acidifying sodium sulphoantimonate consists of a mixture of sulphur, and antimony tri- and penta-sulphides. F. Kirchhof found that analyses of the purest golden antimony sulphide contain about 8 per cent. of free sulphur which can be extracted with acetone or carbon disulphide, and that the residue has the composition Sb_2S_4. He therefore maintained that antimony pentasulphide does not exist ; and that the alleged pentasulphide is really a mixture of the tetrasulphide (q.v.), and 8 per cent. of sulphur. The varieties of commercial *sulphur auratum* containing less than 8 per cent. of free sulphur extractable by solvents have probably been obtained by the reaction : $Na_3SbS_4+SbCl_3=3NaCl+Sb_2S_4$.

F. V. von Hahn prepared fairly stable **colloidal solutions** of antimony pentasulphide by the hydrolysis of alkali antimony thiosulphate : $2Na_3Sb(S_2O_3)_3 = Sb_2S_5+3Na_2SO_4+3SO_2+S$. A 0·5 per cent. soln. of sodium antimony thiosulphate is kept until it commences to turn yellow and to show a definite Tyndall cone ; it is then placed in a dialyzer and washed with warm distilled water. After several hours' dialysis, the soln. has taken on a deep red colour. The main point to be observed in the preparation is the rapid removal of the alkali sulphate. In the presence of sodium chloride the sol cannot be prepared, nor can a sol having a greater molecular conc. than 0·4 be obtained. Sols of one-tenth this conc. are stable for a few hours only. The sols prepared from the sodium salt are more stable than those prepared from either lithium or potassium antimony thiosulphate. M. E. Wolvekamp obtained colloidal soln. with the pentasulphide associated with protein.

Antimony pentasulphide appears as a dark brown, yellowish-brown, or a fiery orange-red powder, with a feeble smell, and sweetish taste. T. Wilm said that when triturated the powder is electrified. H. Rose, L. Heffter, and T. Paul found that when the pentasulphide is heated to 120°, it loses one per cent. of sulphur ; at 150°, about 2 per cent. ; and at 170°, it gradually forms grey antimony trisulphide. This change occurs rapidly in a current of carbon dioxide at 200°–230°. O. Klenker noticed that there is an appreciable decomposition of the pentasulphide at 85°–90°, and the subject was discussed by F. de Bacho, V. Zani, and D. W. Luff and B. D. Porritt, while L. M. Currie showed that the main reaction which occurs when the pentasulphide is heated to about 110° is : $Sb_2S_5=Sb_2S_4+S$; and $Sb_2S_4=Sb_2S_3+S$ between 110° and 150° ; while above 150°, the reaction in air is largely oxidation, and in the absence of air sublimation of sulphur, and a change in the physical properties of the trisulphide. O. Stelling studied the X-ray absorption spectrum with the K-series. R. Robl observed no fluorescence when the pentasulphide is exposed to ultraviolet light. L. Heffter observed that the pentasulphide is reduced when heated in **hydrogen.** T. Wilm found that when dried at 100°–110° for some hours exposed to **air,** it is partially oxidized and loses weight appreciably owing to the volatilization of the oxide. O. Bosek said that it can be dried at 105°–107°, and R. Bunsen, at 110°, without decomposition. A. Classen observed a blackening of the pentasulphide at 110°, and this was attributed by B. Unger to the presence of a trace of oxide. E. Pollacci, F. J. Otto, and F. Jahn found that the moist pentasulphide rapidly oxidizes in air, but only slowly if the pentasulphide be dry. The resulting antimony trioxide can be extracted with tartaric acid. A. Vogel observed that when heated in air, it burns with a visible flame. An ammoniacal soln. of **hydrogen dioxide** was found by A. C. Classen and O. Bauer to oxidize the pentasulphide incompletely.

J. S. F. Pagenstecher showed that the pentasulphide is decolorized and decomposed by an aq. soln. of **chlorine** ; and P. L. Geiger, that conc. **hydrochloric acid** at ordinary temp. colours the pentasulphide grey owing to the formation of the grey trisulphide, and the separation of sulphur. J. M. Scherer showed that hydrochloric acid of sp. gr. 1·12 dissolves the pentasulphide with the separation of sulphur ; and A. Classen and O. Bauer's observations agreed with : $Sb_2S_5 + 6HCl = 2SbCl_3 + 3H_2S + 2S$, although G. O. Wittstein obtained less sulphur than corresponded with this equation. The conversion of the pentasulphide into trisulphide by exposure to light while suspended in dil. hydrochloric acid containing hydrogen sulphide was observed by B. Brauner, and a similar conversion by heating the pentasulphide in dil. hydrochloric acid alone or in the presence of chromic acid was observed by O. Bosek, and B. Brauner. O. Ruff found that **sulphuryl chloride** transforms the pentasulphide into pentachloride.

According to P. L. Geiger, 100 parts of cold, dil. aq. **ammonia** dissolve 2 parts of antimony pentasulphide leaving only a slight residue which dissolves as the liquid is warmed. If the proportion of sulphur is too small, kermes is left undissolved, and if too great, sulphur. Sometimes a little antimony trioxide remains undissolved. When the yellow ammoniacal soln. is treated with acids, the pentasulphide is again precipitated without the evolution of hydrogen sulphide. When the ammoniacal soln. is boiled, H. Capitaine observed that a mixture of sulphur and antimony trisulphide is precipitated, but precipitation does not occur with potassium hydrocarbonate. C. F. Rammelsberg said that the ammoniacal soln. contains ammonium sulphoantimonate. J. S. F. Pagenstecher, and T. Wilm observed that the pentasulphide is decomposed by **nitric acid.** E. Mitscherlich found that a boiling soln. of **carbon disulphide** extracts two gram-atoms of sulphur leaving behind a mol of antimony trisulphide. T. Wilm said that the amount of sulphur extracted from the pentasulphide depends on the mode of preparation, thus the pentasulphide obtained from sodium sulphoantimonate yielded 6–8 per cent. of sulphur, while that made from hydrogen sulphide and antimony pentachloride gave up about 14 per cent. of sulphur—the calculated amount for one gram-atom is 8 per cent., and for 2 gram-atoms, 16 per cent. F. Kirchhof's observations are indicated above. C. F. Rammelsberg extracted 2 per cent. of sulphur from the pentasulphide obtained from hydrogen sulphide and antimonic acid by boiling 15 minutes ; A. Classen extracted 9·63 per cent. of sulphur from the pentasulphide obtained from sodium sulphoantimonate ; and B. Unger, never more than 5·7 per cent. In these cases, the pentasulphide treated by the solvent may have originally contained free sulphur. C. O. Weber stated that boiling carbon disulphide decomposes the pentasulphide, but, added W. Esch and F. Balla, this occurs only when impure carbon disulphide is employed. R. Ditmar said that if the extraction with carbon disulphide is of long duration, some pentasulphide may be decomposed ; A. van Rossem and P. Dekker attributed the partial decomposition of the pentasulphide to the action of this solvent. A. Hutin also said that the cold solvent has no action on the pentasulphide, but the boiling solvent decomposes the pentasulphide to tetrasulphide and sulphur. There is no suggestion that the boiling carbon disulphide acts chemically, and the decomposition is considered to be due to the thermal decomposition of the pentasulphide. If so, then solvents of sulphur with a higher b.p.—*e.g.* benzene, or acetone, as recommended by C. O. Weber, and

A. Hutin—should give a worse result than that attributed to carbon disulphide. A. Dubosc, indeed, stated that there is little likelihood of the pentasulphide decomposing at the b.p. of carbon disulphide, but at 130°–135°, the pentasulphide is reduced to the trisulphide. B. D. W. Luff and B. D. Porritt found that purified carbon disulphide does not decompose the pentasulphide at the boiling temp. This is in agreement with the observation of O. Klenker, who showed that the pentasulphide is not decomposed by boiling carbon disulphide ; but there is a slow separation of sulphur at 85°–90°. Consequently, boiling water may cause the liberation of sulphur ; but the pure pentasulphide is not appreciably affected by organic solvents boiling below 85° ; and E. Mitscherlich found boiling turpentine extracts sulphur. L. M. Currie, for instance, found that cold carbon disulphide, chloroform, carbon tetrachloride, benzene and toluene have practically no effect on the pure pentasulphide ; at their b.p., there is rather more action—particularly with carbon disulphide, for boiling acetone has less effect and yet its b.p. is higher. A. C. Vournasos observed that at 400° antimony trisulphide is reduced by **sodium formate** to antimony and hydrogen sulphide. H. Rose found that the pentasulphide is reduced by fused **potassium cyanide,** forming a little sulphoantimonite—*vide supra,* antimony trisulphide.

P. L. Geiger said that a cold aq. soln. of alkali hydroxide completely dissolves antimony pentasulphide ; and F. Jahn added that the soln. in potash-lye is at first transparent, but furnishes a crystalline precipitate of potassium antimonate if allowed to stand overnight. E. Mitscherlich, C. F. Rammelsberg, and W. Feit and C. Kubierschky represented the reaction : $4Sb_2S_5 + 18NaOH = 5Na_3SbS_4 + 3NaSbO_3 + 9H_2O$, and the sodium metantimonate is precipitated. According to C. F. Rammelsberg, the filtrate from the soln. in potash-lye gives a brown precipitate of sulphoantimonate when treated with acids ; and when treated with acids it gives off hydrogen sulphide and deposits antimony pentasulphide. A cold soln. of **potassium carbonate** does not sensibly affect antimony pentasulphide, but, on boiling, carbon dioxide is evolved and the liquor behaves like the soln. in potash-lye. A soln. of **barium or strontium hydroxide** behaves like potash-lye, but a greater proportion of antimonate is precipitated. When immersed in an aq. soln. of **silver nitrate,** the pentasulphide is coloured brown, and on boiling, it is blackened ; a similar result is obtained with a soln. of **copper sulphate.** H. Schiff said that **stannous chloride** is without action ; and with **mercurous chloride** the action resembles that with antimony trisulphide (*q.v.*).

REFERENCES.

¹ J. J. Berzelius, *Schweigger's Journ.*, 34. 58, 1822 ; *Pogg. Ann.*, 20. 365, 1830 ; 37. 163, 1836 ; H. Rose, *ib.*, 3. 441, 1824 ; *Ann. Phil.*, 10. 416, 1825 ; *Phil. Mag.*, 67. 124, 1826 ; M. Websky, *Zeit. Anal. Chem.*, 11. 124, 1872 ; T. Wilm, *ib.*, 30. 438, 1891 ; H. Capitaine, *Journ. Pharm. Chim.*, (3), 25. 516, 1839 ; O. Bosek, *Journ. Chem. Soc.*, 67. 516, 1895 ; B. Brauner, *ib.*, 67. 540, 1895 ; F. Kirchhof, *Zeit. anorg. Chem.*, 112. 67, 1920 ; 114. 266, 1920 ; L. M. Currie, *Journ. Phys. Chem.*, 30. 205, 1926.

² Basil Valentine, *Triumphwagen antimonii,* Nürnberg, 1676 ; London, 1893 ; J. Quercetanus, *Pharmacopœa restituta,* Parisiis, 1607 ; J. R. Glauber, *Pharmacopœa spagyrica,* Amstelodami, 1654 ; M. Ettmüller, *Nouvelle chimie raisonée,* Lyon, 187, 1693 ; J. H. Long, *Journ. Amer. Chem. Soc.,* 18. 342, 1896.

³ J. J. Berzelius, *Schweigger's Journ.*, 34. 58, 1822 ; *Pogg. Ann.*, 20. 365, 1830 ; 37. 163, 1836 ; H. Rose, *Ann. Phil.*, 10. 416, 1825 ; *Phil. Mag.,* 67. 124, 1826 ; *Pogg. Ann.*, 3. 441, 1824 ; 89. 141, 1853 ; 4C. 207, 1853 ; L. Heffter, *ib.*, 86. 421, 1852 ; C. F. Rammelsberg, *ib.*, 52. 213, 1841 ; A. Vogel, *Schweigger's Journ.*, 33. 291, 1822 ; R. Grein, *Pharm. Ztg.*, 49. 126, 1904 ; A. Sartorius, *Apoth. Ztg.*, 23. 342, 1908 ; L. Prunier, *Journ. Pharm. Chim.*, (6), 3. 289, 1896 ; F. Musculus, *ib.*, (2), 22. 241, 1837 ; H. Capitaine, (3), 25. 516, 1839 ; L. A. Buchner, *ib.*, (2), 16. 51, 1830 ; *Repert. Pharm.*, 13. 202, 1822 ; C. Ludwig, *Arch. Pharm.*, (2), 144. 107, 1858 ; B. Unger, *ib.*, (2), 147. 196, 1871 ; E. Mitscherlich, *Journ. prakt. Chem.*, (1), 19. 458, 1840 ; O. Klenker, *ib.*, (2), 59. 150, 353, 1899 ; W. Artus, *ib.*, (1), 27. 381, 1842 ; *Mag. Pharm.*, (2), 22. 43, 1828 ; G. Abesser, *Repert. Pharm.*, 9. 274, 1820 ; P. L. Geiger, *ib.*, 9. 251, 1829 ; *Mag. Pharm.*, 29. 241, 1830 ; F. Jahn, *ib.*, (2), 22. 43, 1827 ; A. Duflos, *ib.*, (2), 29. 94, 1839 ; (2), 31. 94, 1831 ; F. Kirchhof, *Zeit. anorg. Chem.*, 112. 67, 1920 ; 114. 266, 1920 ; C. F. Bucholz, *Berlin Jahrb.*

Pharm., **29**. 26, 1822 ; M. Bertsch and M. Harmsen, *German Pat.*, *D.R.P.* **94**124, 1896 ; *Zeit. angew. Chem.*, **70**. 641, 1897 ; Anon., *Chem. Ztg.*, **45**. 747, 1921 ; J. B. Trommsdorff, *Tromms. dorff's Journ.*, **1**. 33, 1794 ; **8**. 128, 1824 ; J. S. F. Pagenstecher, *ib.*, **3**. 391, 1819 ; K. Schlippe, *Schweigger's Journ.*, **33**. 320, 1821 ; J. C. Wieglieb, in R. A. Vogel, *Lehrsatze der Chemie*, Weimar, 600, 1775 ; J. F. Westrumb, *Kleine physikalisch-chemische Abhandlungen*, Hannover, **4**. 329, 1793 ; J. F. A. Göttling, *Ann. Chim. Phys.*, (1), **23**. 79, 1797 ; W. S. C. Hirsching, in A. F. von Delius, *Frankische Sammulung*, Nürnberg, 1761 ; T. Wilm, *Zeit. anal. Chem.*, **30**. 444, 1891 ; T. Paul, *ib.*, **31**. 533, 1892 ; J. M. Scherer, *ib.*, **3**. 206, 1864 ; G. C. Wittstein, *Pharm. Viertelj.*, **18**. 533, 1869 ; A. Classen, *Ber.*, **16**. 1071, 1883 ; A. Classen and O. Bauer, *ib.*, **16**. 1067, 1883 ; O. Ruff, *ib.*, **34**. 1752, 1901 ; W. Feit and C. Kubierschky, *ib.*, **21**. 1660, 1888 ; J. H. Long, *Journ. Amer. Chem. Soc.*, **18**. 342, 1896 ; R. Bunsen, *Liebig's Ann.*, **192**. 317, 1878 ; F. J. Otto, *ib.*, **26**. 88, 1838 ; H. Schiff, *ib.*, **120**. 59, 1861 ; J. Thiel, *ib.*, **263**, 371, 1891 ; A. Dubosc, *Le Caoutchouc et la guttaperche*, 8886, 8958, 1916 ; O. Bosek, *Journ. Chem. Soc.*, **67**. 515, 1895 ; B. Brauner, *ib.*, **67**. 527, 1895 ; F. de Bacho, *Ann. Chim. Applicata*, **12**. 143, 1919 ; E. Pollacci, *Boll. Chim. Farm.*, **45**. 401, 1906 ; **47**. 363, 1908 ; V. Zani, *Bull. Acad. Belg.*, 1169, 1909 ; L. J. Thénard, *Ann. Chim. Phys.*, (1), **32**. 257, 1800 ; W. A. Lampadius, *Schweigger's Journ.*, **5**. 9, 1812 ; F. V. von Hahn, *Koll. Zeit.*, **31**. 200, 1922 ; O. Stelling, *Zeit. Phys. Chem.*, **117**. 180, 1925 ; R. Robl, *Zeit. angew. Chem.*, **39**. 608, 1926 ; N. E. Wilson, *Canadian Pat. No.* 252563, 1924 ; M. E. Wolvekamp, *Brit. Pat. No.* 197061, 1922 ; A. L. Stark, *U.S. Pat. No.* 1414836, 1922 ; G. W. Mullen, *ib.*, 1498564, 1924 ; A. C. Vournasos, *Ber.*, **43**. 2264, 1910 ; A. Short and F. H. Sharpe, *Journ. Soc. Chem. Ind.*, **41**. 109, 1922 ; D. F. Twiss, *ib.*, **41**. 171, 1922 ; B. D. W. Luff and B. D. Porritt, *ib.*, **40**. 275, T, 1921 ; L. M. Currie, *Journ. Phys. Chem.*, **30**. 205, 1926 ; A. van Rossem and P. Dekker, *Indiarubber Journ.*, **60**. 905, 1920 ; R. Ditmar, *ib.*, **34**. 373, 1907 ; *Gummi Ztg.*, **21**. 497, 1907 ; C. O. Weber, *ib.*, **17**. 181, 1902 ; *Chemistry of Indiarubber*, London, 186, 1906 ; W. Esch and F. Balla, *Chem. Ztg.*, **28**. 595, 1904 ; A. Hutin, *Ann. Chim. Anal.*, **21**. 32, 1916 ; F. Neher, *Zeit. anal. Chem.*, **32**. 45, 1893.

§ 26. The Sulphoantimonates

Antimony pentasulphide reacts with metal sulphides, forming a series of **sulpho-antimonates,** analogous to the sulpharsenates (*q.v.*). Many of these salts occur in nature. K. Schlippe,[1] E. Donath, F. Becker, H. Rose, and C. F. Rammelsberg obtained them by fusing together the component sulphides ; C. F. Rammelsberg, and V. Stanek, by dissolving the pentasulphide, or a mixture of the trisulphide and sulphur in soln. of the alkali or alkaline earth sulphides or hydrosulphide—even at a boiling temp. no more is dissolved than corresponds with the formation of the orthosulphoantimonate ; C. F. Rammelsberg, by the action of the pentasulphide on soln. of the hydroxides or carbonates ; by the action of hydrogen sulphide on soln. of the antimonates ; and by double decomposition between the alkali sulpho-antimonates and salts of the heavy metals—in some cases the sulphoantimonate is decomposed by the acid formed during the reaction.

The sulphoantimonates of the alkalies and alkaline earths are colourless or yellow; and those of the heavy metals are yellow, orange, brown, or black. The sulphoanti-monates of the alkalies can be heated in the absence of air without decomposition, but those of the heavy metals form sulphur and the trisulphide (*q.v.*). When the aq. soln. of the alkali and alkaline earth sulphoantimonates are allowed to stand in air, antimony trisulphide is precipitated, and carbonate and thiosulphate are formed ; acids, even carbonic acid, decompose soln. of the sulphoantimonates, separating antimony pentasulphide ; the soln. gave no precipitate with the alkali carbonates. A. Duflos found that the salts are decomposed by nitric acid, aqua regia, and potash-lye ; they are insoluble in alcohol ; and when boiled with pow-dered antimony they are reduced to sulphoantimonites. L. Storch found that cupric, cadmium, mercuric, and ferrous sulphides dissolve in soln. of the alkali sulphoantimonates. H. Rose said that fused potassium cyanide does not reduce the salts to antimony ; and W. Feit and C. Kubierschky, that the aq. soln. is desulphurized by lead hydroxide, forming the antimonate.

V. Stanek[2] prepared **ammonium orthosulphoantimonate,** $(NH_4)_3SbS_4$, by dissolving powdered antimonite and flowers of sulphur in red ammonium sulphide and recrystallizing the product from colourless ammonium sulphide. The salt crystallizes in pale yellow prisms, which, after the removal of the mother-liquor, quickly decompose and become brown, and are easily soluble in water ; it is decomposed by dil. acids, with the formation of antimony pentasulphide and hydrogen sulphide, and when heated in carbon dioxide yields ammonium sulphide, sulphur, and antimony trisulphide. When heated with antimony pentasulphide in a sealed tube at 150°, it is converted into **ammonium metasulphotetrantimonate,** $(NH_4)_2Sb_4S_7$. It is obtained crystalline as the *tetrahydrate* $(NH_4)_3SbS_4 4H_2O$, in

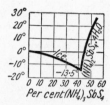

FIG. 65.—The Solubility of Ammonium Orthosulphoantimonate.

aggregates of colourless needles by saturating colourless ammonium sulphide with antimony pentasulphide, adding an equal quantity of ammonium sulphide and then alcohol until a precipitate commences to form ; the filtered soln. is then covered with a layer of alcohol and allowed to stand. A. D. Donk also obtained the tetrahydrate from aq. soln., in ethyl alcohol and water, and in aq. ammonia. The solubility is shown in Fig. 65. A. D. Donk also examined the ternary system : $(NH_4)_3SbS_4-NH_4OH-H_2O$.

A. Brinkmann boiled sulphur with a soln. of lithium orthosulphoantimonite—obtained from a soln. of antimony trisulphide and lithium hydrosulphide—and obtained yellow prisms of *enneahydrated* lithium orthosulphoantimonate, $Li_3SbS_4.9H_2O$, which, when heated, lose water and fuse, forming a brown mass which is soluble in water. The salt becomes covered with a reddish film on exposure to moist air. A. D. Donk's solubility curve is shown in Fig. 66. A. D. Donk obtained crystals of the *decahydrate*, $Li_3SbS_4.10H_2O$, from aqueous-alcoholic soln. ;

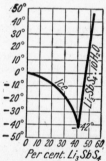

FIG. 66.—Solubility Curve of Lithium Orthosulphoantimonate.

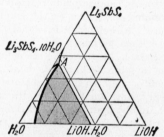

FIG. 67.—The Ternary System : $Li_3SbS_4-LiOH-H_2O$ at 30°.

and from mixtures of lithium sulphoantimonate and hydroxide at 30°. The equilibrium conditions in the presence of lithium hydroxide at 30° are illustrated by the diagram, Fig. 67, for the ternary system : $Li_3SbS_4-LiOH-H_2O$. At A, Fig. 67, there are two solid phases, $LiOH.H_2O$ and $Li_3SbS_4.10H_2O$.

In 1821, K. Schlippe[3] prepared *enneahydrated* **sodium orthosulphoantimonate,** $Na_3SbS_4.9H_2O$—which came to be called *Schlippe's salt*—by fusing a mixture of antimony trisulphide, dry sodium sulphate, and charcoal in the proportions 4 : 8 : 2. The cold mass was boiled with water and one part of sulphur. When the filtrate is allowed to stand, it deposits crystals of the salt, and the mother-liquor is thus almost freed from antimony. A. Duflos added that some antimony may be produced during the transformation of the sulphoantimonite into sulphoantimonate. Modifications of the process were described by G. Kohl, J. S. F. Pagenstecher, P. L. Geiger, B. Unger, E. van den Corput, C. Jansen, and J. Kirchner. A. Duflos made the sulphoantimonate by fusing a mixture of sodium sulphate with about six times its weight of carbon, and digesting the boiling cold mass with sodium sulphide for half an hour with six parts of water, 18 of antimony trisulphide, and 3 of sulphide. The filtered soln. deposits about 36 parts of sodium orthosulphoantimonate. Modifications of the process were made by F. C. Buchholz, and F. Jahn. E. Mitscherlich, J. von Liebig, and C. Frederking boiled a mixture of antimony trisulphide, sulphur, sodium carbonate and lime-water for a couple of hours, filtered, and crystallized. According to A. Sartorius, in the usual method of preparing sodium orthosulphoantimonate, by boiling antimony trisulphide and sulphur with soda-lye for $1\frac{1}{2}$ to 2 hrs., theoretically sodium sulphoantimonate and sodium metantimonate should be formed. If, however, the process is stopped after one-quarter of an hour's boiling, it is found that scarcely any of the antimony trisulphide has been acted on, the reaction that takes place being expressed by $6NaOH+4S=2Na_2S+Na_2S_2O_3+3H_2O$. To avoid this formation of thiosulphate, the mixture of antimony trisulphide and sulphur is added to the boiling sodium hydroxide soln., in small portions at a time. Under these conditions, the reaction proceeds according to the following equation : $4(Sb_2S_3+2S)+18NaOH=5Na_3SbS_4+3NaSbO_3+9H_2O$, and in a shorter time a larger yield of sodium orthosulphoantimonate of a better quality is obtained. In another process, J. von Liebig saturated a soln. of sodium sulphoantimonite with antimony trisulphide and sulphur. L. Prunier melted a mixture of antimony trisulphide and sulphur, and digested the cold mass with a soln. of sodium sulphide. I. Pouget found that a soln. of the sulphoantimonite forms the sulphoantimonate when it is oxidized by exposure to air. B. Unger also prepared the sulphoantimonate by warming at 60°–80° a conc. soln. of sodium sulphide with finely divided antimony, while exposed to air. F. Kirchhof melted a mixture of antimony pentasulphide and twice its weight of sodium sulphide with about one

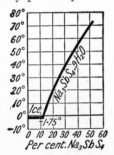

FIG. 68.—Solubility of Sodium Orthosulphoantimonate.

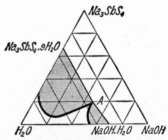

FIG. 69.—The Ternary System : Na_3SbS_4–$NaOH$–H_2O at 30°.

per cent. of sulphur. The cold mass was dissolved in hot water, filtered, and cooled for crystallization. A. D. Donk's solubility curve is shown in Fig. 68. A. D. Donk also obtained the enneahydrate from aq. soln. at 0° and 30°, as well as from soln. in alcohol and water, and from soln. in dil. soda-lye at 30°. The equilibrium diagram for the system Na_3SbS_4–$NaOH$–H_2O at 30° is shown in Fig. 69. At A, there are two solid phases, $NaOH.H_2O$ and $Na_3SbS_4.9H_2O$.

Analyses of the salt made by A. Duflos agreed with $Na_4Sb_2O_7.8H_2O$; and that made by J. von Liebig with $NaSbS_3.6H_2O$; but the analyses by C. F. Rammelsberg, A. D. Donk, B. Unger, and I. Pouget, correspond with $Na_3SbS_4.9H_2O$, or, in the case of K. Schlippe, with $Na_3SbS_4.10H_2O$. F. Kirchhof regards the so-called sulphoantimonates as salts, not of quinquevalent antimony $S=Sb\equiv(SNa)_3$, but as derivatives of compounds of the type $M_m(SbS_4)_n$, in which, when $m=n$, and M represents Sb, the tetrasulphide is formed. The sodium salt

$$Sb{\Large\langle}\begin{smallmatrix}S.S\\S\\S\end{smallmatrix}{\Large\rangle}Sb$$

then becomes $NaS-S-Sb=(SNa)_2$, and the zinc salt :

$$Zn{<}\begin{smallmatrix}S\\S\end{smallmatrix}{>}Sb-S.S.Zn.S.S-Sb{<}\begin{smallmatrix}S\\S\end{smallmatrix}{>}Zn\ ;\quad or\quad Sb{\Large\langle}\begin{smallmatrix}S.S.Zn.S.S\\S-Zn-S\\S-Zn-S\end{smallmatrix}{\Large\rangle}Sb$$

Zinc orthosulphoantimonate, $Zn_3(SbS_4)_2$.

The colour of the antimony tetrasulphide, and of the sulphoantimonates of the heavy metals, is attributed to the presence of closed ring systems, in the structure of these compounds; the sodium salt, $NaS.S.Sb : (18Na)_2$, having no closed ring, is colourless. F. Kirchhof also represents the formation of the sodium salt from sulphur, antimony trisulphide, and sodium sulphide by the equations : (i) $2Na_2S+S_2=2Na_2S_2$; (ii) $Sb_2S_3+2Na_2S_2=Na_4Sb_2S_7$; and (iii) $Na_4Sb_2S_7 +Na_2S=2Na_3SbS_4$. The sodium orthosulphoantimonate, and sodium pyrosulphoantimonate, $Na_4Sb_2S_7$, then have the respective graphic formulæ :

$$Sb\!\!\begin{array}{l} S.SNa \\ \leftarrow SNa \\ SNa \end{array} \qquad \begin{array}{l} NaS.S \\ NaS \end{array}\!\!>\!\!Sb.S.Sb\!\!<\!\!\begin{array}{l} S.SNa \\ SNa \end{array}$$

R. Robl observed no fluorescence occurs when the dehydrated salt, Na_3SbS_4, is exposed to ultra-violet light. M. von Laue studied piezoelectric properties of the crystals of enneahydrated sodium orthosulphoantimonate. The methods of C. F. Rammelsberg, J. von Liebig, P. L. Geiger, and I. Pouget, indicated in connection with sodium orthosulphoantimonate, were also employed for the potassium salt, but the soln. required more concentration by evaporation for crystallization. The analyses of C. F. Rammelsberg, and I. Pouget correspond with the formula for *hemienneahydrated* **potassium orthosulphoantimonate**, $K_3SbS_4.4\frac{1}{2}H_2O$. A. D. Donk obtained the *trihydrate*, $K_3SbS_4.3H_2O$; and the *pentahydrate*, $K_3SbS_4.5H_2O$, from

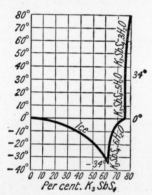

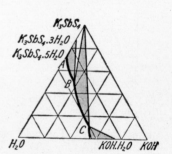

Fig. 70.—The Solubility Curves of Potassium Orthosulphoantimonate.

Fig. 71.—The Ternary System : K_3SbS_4–KOH–H_2O at 30°.

a soln. in water, in a mixture of ethyl, alcohol, and water, and in dil. potash-lye ; the *hexahydrate*, $K_3SbS_4.6H_2O$, from aq. soln. at 30° ; the *enneahydrate*, $K_3SbS_4.9H_2O$, from a soln. in methyl alcohol and water at 15° ; and the solubility curve is shown in Fig. 70. There is no sign of the hemienneahydrate. The equilibrium diagram with the ternary system, K_3SbS_4–KOH–H_2O, at 30° is shown in Fig. 71, where the solid phases are the anhydrous salt, the tri- and penta-hydrates, and $KOH.H_2O$. These are the two hydrates as solid phases in equilibrium at the transition point A ; the trihydrate and the anhydrous salt at B ; and the anhydrous salt and $KOH.H_2O$ at C.

C. F. Rammelsberg, and H. Marbach described enneahydrated sodium orthosulphoantimonate as a pale yellow, almost colourless solid, having cubic, hemihedral crystals, which show circular polarization when solid, but when melted in their water of crystallization or dissolved in water, they do not polarize light. P. L. Geiger, and C. F. Rammelsberg said that the crystals of hemienneahydrated potassium orthosulphoantimonate are colourless or pale yellow, hygroscopic crystals, or radiating masses of crystals. H. G. F. Schröder gave 1·806 for the sp. gr. of the enneahydrated sodium salt, and C. Soret, 1·839. C. F. Rammelsberg found that the crystals of the hemienneahydrated potassium salt melt in their water of crystallization, give off water, and form a brown mass; the enneahydrated sodium salt behaves similarly, forming a greyish-white mass which, in air, forms a voluminous white powder; when the salt is heated in the absence of air, it melts without decomposition to a liver-brown mass, which dissolves in water except for a little antimony trisulphide. When heated in vacuo, I. Pouget found very little sulphur is given off at the softening temp. of hard glass. A. Classen, and G. Vortmann studied the electrolysis of aq. soln. of the salt.

H. Rose observed that water but not sulphur is given off when the salt is heated in hydrogen. K. Schlippe found that when heated in air the salt quickly reddens after the water has passed off; it then blackens, and the liberated sulphur catches fire. C. F. Rammelsberg said that when the salt is exposed to air, it attracts carbon dioxide, and slowly acquires a brown film of antimony trisulphide, while sodium carbonate and thiosulphate are formed. 100 parts of water dissolve 34·5 parts of the salt; A. Duflos said that 100 parts of cold water dissolve 25 parts of salt, and hot water dissolves an equal weight of salt. J. von Liebig said that when a conc. soln. is exposed to air, it deposits antimony pentasulphide, and forms a soln. of sodium carbonate and thiosulphate. The decomposition is effected by the carbon dioxide, for when the air is freed from that gas, and is passed through a conc. soln., no change can be observed; while H. Rose observed that if carbon dioxide be passed through the soln., antimony pentasulphide, etc., are formed. Ammoniacal hydrogen dioxide was found by F. Raschig to convert the salt into sodium metantimonate. The aq. soln. is decomposed by acids—even by those so feeble as carbonic acid—antimony pentasulphide is precipitated, and hydrogen sulphide is formed. Boiling hydrochloric acid dissolves the salt with the separation of sulphur. A soln. of the salt is decomposed when it is boiled for a few hours with sulphur. According to B. Unger, if a soln. of sodium orthosulphoantimonate be mixed with much sodium thiosulphate, it furnishes yellowish-green, pyramidal crystals, probably belonging to the rhombic system; their composition corresponds with sodium thiosulphatosulphoantimonate, $Na_2S_2O_3.Na_3SbS_4.20H_2O$; they melt when heated and lose their water; some is lost over sulphuric acid; they are soluble in water, but decompose into their constituents on concentrating the soln. A. Duflos found that the boiling aq. soln. is converted by powdered antimony into the sulpho-antimonite, and on cooling deposits some antimony trisulphide; the boiling aq. soln. also dissolves hydrated antimony pentoxide, and on cooling, it deposits a mixture of antimony pentoxide and trisulphide; with an excess of the hydrated antimony pentoxide, some sodium antimonate as well as antimony pentoxide and trisulphide are precipitated. A boiling soln. of the salt also dissolves antimony trisulphide and gives it up again on cooling; C. F. Rammelsberg said that antimony pentasulphide is not dissolved by the boiling soln.; and that the salt is not dissolved by alcohol, even when largely diluted with water. R. Palm found that aq. soln. of the salt give coloured precipitates with many salts of the alkaloids. C. F. Rammelsberg found that a soln. of potassium antimonyl tartrate gives an orange precipitate, $2Sb_2O_3.Sb_2S_3.Sb_2S_5$, with sodium orthosulphoantimonate. H. Rose found that an alkali carbonate does not give a brownish-red precipitate with a soln. of sodium orthosulphoantimonate as it does with sodium orthosulphoantimonite. C. F. Rammelsberg studied the action of this salt on metal salt soln.

A. Stelzner[4] described a mineral from the Sierra de Famatina, Argentina, and he called it famatinite. It also occurs in the Cerro de Pasco, Peru. It may occur massive and reniform, and it is grey more or less tinged copper-red in colour. Analyses were made by M. W. Siewert, A. Frenzel, S. Stevanovic, and F. L. Ransome. A. Stelzner represented it by the formula $4(3Cu_2S.Sb_2S_3)(3Cu_2S.As_2S_3)$, that is, $Cu_3(Sb,As)S_3$; C. F. Rammelsberg, $4CuS.Cu_2S.Sb_2S_3$; A. Frenzel, $3Cu_2S.Sb_2S_3$; S. Stevanovic, $Cu_3(As,Sb)S_4$; and P. Groth and K. Mieleitner, cuprous sulphoanti-monate, Cu_3SbS_4. F. Klockmann investigated the famatinite of the Sierra de Famatina, and also the mineral luzonite, Cu_3AsS_4, from the same locality; he suggested that both minerals **are** isomorphous, and unlike enargite, Cu_3AsS_4, in form, although famatinite and enargite are considered by G. vom Rath to be isomorphous. If famatinite is isomorphous with luzonite, H. W. Witt said that it is monoclinic, and if isomorphous with enargite, rhombic. The sp. gr. is 4·5–4·6, or, according to J. J. Saslawsky, 4·57, and the contraction constant in its formation from its elements is 0·93. A. de Gramont studied the spark spectrum; and E. T. Wherry said that it is a fair radio-detector.

C. F. Rammelsberg [5] prepared **cupric orthosulphoantimonate**, $Cu_3(SbS_4)_2$, by adding cupric sulphate to an excess of a soln. of the sodium salt. When heated in a retort, a fused residue of cuprous sulphoantimonite is formed. If an excess of the copper salt is used in the precipitate, and the liquids are mixed cold, a precipitate with a variable composition is formed, but on boiling the mixture, the precipitate is converted into $8CuS.Sb_2O_5$, which when treated with potash-lye leaves a residue of copper sulphide. When the oxysulphide is heated to redness in a retort, it furnishes a basic cuprous sulphoantimonite: $3Cu_8Sb_2S_8O_5=2Cu_{12}Sb_2S_9+Sb_2O_3+6SO_2$. C. F. Rammelsberg prepared **silver orthosulphoantimonate**, Ag_3SbS_4, by boiling antimony pentasulphide with an excess of a soln. of silver nitrate whereby the product is first brown and then black: $8Sb_2S_5+15Ag_2O=10Ag_3SbS_4+3Sb_2O_5$; it is also made by adding silver nitrate soln. to an excess of a soln. of sodium orthosulphoantimonate. The precipitate dried at 130°, when heated in a retort gives off sulphur, and forms artificial red silver ore. Potash-lye converts it into silver sulphide. If in its preparation the sodium orthosulphoantimonate be dropped into an excess of silver nitrate soln. and boiled, the black precipitate may be a mixture or an oxysulphide, $Ag_{16}Sb_2S_8O_5$, which when boiled with potash-lye yields silver sulphide. It is decomposed when heated.

The so-called calx *antimonii cum sulphure Hofmanii*, or the *calcaria sulphurato-stibiata*, of the alchemists is produced by igniting a mixture of antimony trisulphide, sulphur, and calcium oxide or carbonate (oyster shells) out of contact with air as recommended by J. G. Bremser, and C. F. Bucholz. The product is probably a mixture of **calciumorthosulphoantimonate**, and sulphate; or of calcium sulphoantimonate and antimonate. When boiled with a large proportion of water it partly dissolves, forming an impure soln. of calcium sulphoantimonate, which was called, once upon a time, *solutio calcia antimonii cum sulphure*. J. S. F. Pagenstecher also obtained an impure soln. of calcium orthosulphoantimonate by boiling a mixture of antimony trisulphide and lime-water; and C. F. Rammelsberg, by boiling antimony pentasulphide and calcium sulphide with water. The yellow soln. does not deposit any crystals, and deposits an oily liquid when treated with alcohol. C. F. Rammelsberg obtained a similar result in the attempt to prepare **strontium orthosulphoantimonate**, but I. Pouget obtained **strontium pyrosulphoantimonate**, $Sr_2Sb_2S_7.11H_2O$, in white, needle-like crystals by oxidizing a soln. of the pyrosulphoantimonite in air. C. F. Rammelsberg obtained **barium orthosulphoantimonate**, $Ba_3(SbS_4)_2.6H_2O$, by dissolving antimony pentasulphide in a soln. of barium sulphide, evaporating the filtrate to a small volume, and adding alcohol. In the absence of alcohol, the crystallization proceeds with difficulty. The same compound is formed along with barium antimonate when antimony pentasulphide is dissolved in baryta-water. It is also formed by igniting a mixture of barium sulphate, charcoal, antimony trisulphide and sulphur, and extracting the mass with water. J. S. F. Pagenstecher seems to have obtained the salt by boiling antimony trisulphide with a soln. of barium sulphide. According to C. F. Rammelsberg, the salt appears in stellate masses of white needles which when heated leave a brown mass without fusing. When exposed to air, the salt becomes brown from the separation of antimony pentasulphide.

C. F. Rammelsberg prepared **magnesium orthosulphoantimonate**, $Mg_3(SbS_4)_2$, as an orange-red substance, which could not be crystallized, by treating antimony pentasulphide with a soln. of magnesium hydrosulphide, and adding alcohol to the yellow liquid. He also dropped a soln. of zinc sulphate into an excess of a soln.

of sodium sulphoantimonate, and obtained a deep orange-yellow precipitate of **zinc oxysulphoantimonate**, $Zn_3(SbS_4)_2.ZnO$, which dissolves in the boiling liquid, and passes through the filter-paper in a colloidal form on washing. If the zinc sulphate soln. be in excess, and the liquid be boiled for a short time, a deep orange-yellow precipitate is formed, which, when washed and dried, forms a brownish-red mass with a shining fracture. It is decomposed when ignited in a retort; it dissolves in boiling hydrochloric acid; it dissolves in potash-lye with the separation of zinc sulphide, and the formation of a yellow soln. from which acids precipitate antimony pentasulphide with a slight evolution of hydrogen sulphide. F. Kirchhof mixed 25 grms. of sodium orthosulphoantimonate with 10·5 grms. of zinc chloride, and water. The chrome-yellow precipitate was allowed to stand for some time when it became crystalline. It was thoroughly washed in boiling water, dried at 80°; ground to powder, and then dried at 100°. It changes colour when heated to 160°, and decomposes at 200°. It yields about 6 per cent. of sulphur when extracted about 4 hrs. with carbon disulphide, or 10 hrs. with acetone. The analyses then correspond with **zinc orthosulphoantimonate**, $Zn_3(SbS_4)_2$. For F. Kirchhof's observations on the constitution of this salt, *vide supra*. By working as in the case of the zincsalt, C. F. Rammelsberg obtained **cadmium sulphoantimonate** as a light orange-yellow precipitate when the sodium sulphoantimonate is in excess, and a darker coloured precipitate if the cadmium sulphate be in excess. It becomes reddish-brown if allowed to stand in its mother-liquor for some time. C. F. Rammelsberg obtained **mercurous orthosulphoantimonate**, Hg_3SbS_4, as a black precipitate by adding a mercurous salt, in any proportion, to a soln. of sodium orthosulphoanti-monate, and **mercuric orthosulphoantimonate**, $Hg_3(SbS_4)_2$, as a dark yellow precipitate, by adding mercuric chloride to an excess of the sodium salt.

Some observations on **thallium sulphoantimonate** have been made in connection with the sulphoantimonites. L. F. Hawley [6] could obtain only solid soln. of the component sulphides. B. Jezek found a mineral associated with the realgar and orpiment at Allchar, Macedonia; and he called it **vrbaite**—after C. Vrba. The analyses by F. Krehlik correspond with **thallium pentasulphodiarsenoanti-monate**, $Tl_2S.2As_2S_3.Sb_2S_3$, $TlAs_2SbS_5$, or $Tl.S.Sb(S—As=S)_2$. E. T. Wherry and W. F. Foshag represent it as a member of the group $Tl_2S.3(As,Sb)_2S_3$. The dark red to greyish-black crystals are tabular or pyramidal in habit; they occur in groups; and belong to the rhombic system, having the axial ratios $a:b:c=0.5659:1:0.4836$. The (010)-cleavage is good. The sp. gr. ranges from 5·271 to 5·333; and the hardness is 3·5. The mineral is soluble in aqua regia, and nitric acid; and if warmed sulphur separates from the soln. It is soluble in conc. sulphuric acid; but not in hydrochloric acid. It is partly decomposed by alkali-lye.

According to C. F. Rammelsberg,[7] stannous chloride gives a dark brown precipitate of **stannous sulphoantimonate** with a soln. of sodium orthosulphoanti-monate. When a soln. of lead acetate is gradually added, with constant agitation, to an excess of a soln. of sodium orthosulphoantimonate, C. F. Rammelsberg, and F. Kirchhof observed that a dark brown precipitate of **lead orthosulphoantimonate**, $Pb_3(SbS_4)_2$, is formed which when heated out of contact with air forms ortho-sulphoantimonite. Boiling potash-lye decomposes it leaving a residue of lead sulphide. If the lead acetate soln. be in excess, and the mixture boiled for some time, the precipitate is probably a mixture of lead sulphide and antimony pentoxide, $8PbS+Sb_2O_5$. C. F. Rammelsberg found that a soln. of ammonium uranyl chloride gives a yellowish-brown precipitate of **uranyl sulphoantimonate** with a soln. of sodium orthosulphoantimonate. He also obtained a reddish-brown precipitate of **manganese sulphoantimonate** by adding a soln. of manganese sulphate to one of sodium orthosulphoantimonate. It readily oxidizes during the washing and drying. Similarly with ferrous sulphate, a black precipitate of **ferrous sulphoantimonate** was formed which turns rusty-yellow on exposure to air; ferric salts likewise yield **ferric sulphoantimonate** as a black precipitate.

but if the ferric salt is in excess, a yellowish-brown precipitate containing sulphur and antimony pentasulphide is formed. When an excess of a cobalt salt is added to a soln. of sodium orthosulphoantimonate, a black precipitate of **cobalt sulphoantimonate** is formed which gradually oxidizes in air, and is decomposed by hot hydrochloric acid. Nickel salts under similar conditions furnish **nickel sulphoantimonate**, which resembles the cobalt salt in its general properties.

REFERENCES.

[1] K. Schlippe, *Schweigger's Journ.*, 33. 320, 1821 ; E. Donath, *Zeit. anal. Chem.*, 19. 23, 1880 ; F. Becker, *ib.*, 17. 185, 1878 ; C. F. Rammelsberg, *Pogg. Ann.*, 52. 213, 1841 ; H. Rose, *ib.*, 3. 441, 1824 ; 89. 141, 1853 ; 90. 207, 1853 ; *Ann. Phil.*, 10. 416, 1825 ; *Phil. Mag.*, 67. 124, 1826 ; V. Stanek, *Zeit. anorg. Chem.*, 17. 122, 1898 ; A. Duflos, *Brandes' Arch.*, (2), 31. 94, 1830 ; (2), 36. 278, 1831 ; *Kastner's Arch.*, 1. 289, 353, 1830 ; W. Feit and C. Kubierschky, *Ber.*, 21. 1661, 1888 ; L. Storch, *ib.*, 16. 2015, 1883.

[2] A. Brinkmann, *Beiträge zur Kenntniss der Lithiumverbindungen*, Göttingen, 1892 ; A. D. Donk, *Chem. Weekbl.*, 5. 529, 629, 1908 ; V. Stanek, *Zeit. anorg. Chem.*, 17. 122, 1898.

[3] K. Schlippe, *Schweigger's Journ.*, 33. 321, 1821 ; A. Duflos, *Kastner's Arch.*, 1. 56, 289, 1830 ; *Brandes Arch.*, (2), 31. 94, 1831 ; F. Jahn, *ib.*, (2), 22. 43, 1827 ; F. C. Bucholz, *ib.*, (2), 33. 1, 1830 ; C. Frederking, *ib.*, (2), 28. 64, 1829 ; G. Kohl, *ib.*, (1), 17. 259, 1826 ; J. von Liebig, *Handwörterbuch der reinen und angewandten Chemie*, Braunschweig, 1. 433, 1837 ; *Liebig's Ann.*, 7. 13, 1833 ; E. Mitscherlich, *Pogg. Ann.*, 49. 413, 1840 ; H. Marbach, *ib.*, 99. 460, 1856 ; 52. 196, 1841 ; *Handbuch der krystallographisch-physikalischen Chemie*, Leipzig, 1. 607, 1881 ; B. Unger, *Arch. Pharm.*, (2), 147. 192, 1871 ; (2), 148. 1, 1871 ; J. S. F. Pagenstecher, *Repert. Pharm.*, 14. 112, 1822 ; L. Prunier, *Journ. Pharm. Chim.*, (6), 3. 289, 1896 ; J. Kirchner, *Liebig's Ann.*, 31. 341, 1839 ; H. Schiff, *ib.*, 114. 202, 1860 ; I. Pouget, *Recherches sur les sulfo- et les selenio-antimonites*, Paris, 1899 ; *Amer. Chim. Phys.*, (7), 18. 524, 1899 ; *Compt. Rend.*, 124. 103, 1897 ; 126. 1145, 1896 ; 129. 103, 1899 ; H. G. F. Schröder, *Dichtigkeitsmessungen*, Heidelberg, 1873 ; C. Soret, *Arch. Sciences Genève*, (3), 16. 468, 1886 ; F. Raschig, *Ber.*, 18. 2745, 1885 ; O. Pavel, *ib.*, 15. 2603, 1882 ; A. Classen, *ib.*, 19. 323, 1886 ; G. Vortmann, *ib.*, 24. 2762, 1891 ; R. Palm, *Zeit. anal. Chem.*, 22. 224, 1883 ; P. L. Geiger, *Mag. Pharm.*, 29. 236, 1830 ; *Repert. Pharm.*, 9. 251, 1829 ; L. W. MacCay, *Amer. Chem. Journ.*, 17. 770, 1896 ; R. F. Weinland and A. Gutmann, *Zeit. anorg. Chem.*, 17. 414, 1898 ; F. Kirchhof, *ib.*, 112. 67, 1920 ; 114. 266, 1920 ; A. Sartorius, *Apoth. Ztg.*, 23. 342, 1908 ; A. D. Donk, *Chem. Weekbl.*, 5. 529, 629, 1908 ; C. Janssen, *Journ. prakt. Chem.*, (1), 33. 336, 1844 ; E. van den Corput, *Chem. Gaz.*, 6. 268, 1848 ; *Repert. Pharm.*, 4. 281, 1848 ; C. F. Rammelsberg, *Pogg. Ann.*, 52. 213, 1841 ; H. Rose, *ib.*. 3. 441, 1824 ; 89. 141, 1853 ; 90. 207, 1853 ; *Ann. Phil.*, 10. 416, 1825 ; *Phil. Mag.*, 67. 124, 1826 ; M. von Laue, *Zeit. Kryst.*, 63. 312, 1926 ; R. Robl, *Zeit. angew. Chem.*, 39. 608, 1926.

[4] A. Stelzner, *Tschermak's Mitt.*, (1), 3. 242, 1873 ; M. W. Siewert, *ib.*, (1), 3. 243, 1873 ; E. T. Wherry, *Amer. Min.*, 10. 30, 1925 ; C. F. Rammelsberg, *Handbuch der Mineralchemie*, Leipzig, 1. 83, 1886 ; P. Groth and K. Mieleitner, *Mineralogische Tabellen*, München, 28, 1921 ; A. de Gramont, *Bull. Soc. Min.*, 18. 319, 1895 ; *Analyse spectrale directe des minéraux*, Paris, 1895 ; J. J. Saslawsky, *Zeit. Kryst.*, 59. 203, 1924 ; F. Klockmann, *ib.*, 19. 275, 1891 ; S. Stevanovic, *ib.*, 37. 240, 1903 ; H. W. Witt, *Amer. Journ. Science*, (4), 44. 469, 1917 ; A. Frenzel, *Neues Jahrb. Min.*, 679, 1895 ; *Tschermak's Mitt.*, (1), 4. 279, 1874 ; F. L. Ransome, *Bull. U.S. Geol. Sur.*, 66, 1900 ; G. vom Rath, *Ber. Niederrh. Ges. Bonn.*, 148, 1878.

[5] J. G. Bremser, *Trommsdorff's Journ.*, 4. 152, 1797 ; C. F. Bucholz, *Berlin. Jahrb. Pharm.*, 29. 26, 1822 ; J. S. F. Pagenstecher, *Repert. Pharm.*, 14. 217, 1822 ; I. Pouget, *Recherches sur les sulfo- et les selenio-antimonites*, Paris, 1899 ; *Amer. Chim. Phys.*, (7), 18. 524, 1899 ; *Compt. Rend.*, 124. 103, 1897 ; 126. 1145, 1896 ; 129. 103, 1899 ; C. F. Rammelsberg, *Pogg. Ann.*, 52. 193, 1841 ; F. Kirchhof, *Zeit. anorg. Chem.*, 112. 67, 1920.

[6] B. Jezek, *Bull. Bohm. Acad.*, 21, 1912 ; *Zeit. Kryst.*, 51. 365, 1913 ; F. Krehlik, *ib.*, 51. 379, 1912 ; E. T. Wherry and W. F. Foshag, *Journ. Washington Acad.*, 11. 1, 1921 ; L. F. Hawley, *Journ. Amer. Chem. Soc.*, 29. 1011, 1907.

[7] C. F. Rammelsberg, *Pogg. Ann.*, 52. 223, 1841 ; F. Kirchhof, *Zeit. anorg. Chem.*, 112. 67, 1920.

§ 27. Antimony Oxysulphides

H. Rose [1] found that fused antimony trioxide and trisulphide mix together in all proportions, forming oxysulphides which are to be regarded as mixtures of isomorphous crystals ; but E. Quercigh observed that although the fused compounds are miscible in all proportions, the formation of solid soln. in the binary system, Sb_2S_3–Sb_2O_3, is really very limited, Fig. 72. There is an antimony oxypenta-sulphide, Sb_4OS_5, or $5Sb_2S_3.Sb_2O_3$, formed which does not melt unchanged, **but** decomposes at 520° into crystals of antimony trisulphide and a liquid phase. Solid soln. of antimony trioxide, and oxypentasulphide exist between the conc. 0–18 per cent. Sb_2S_3 and 16·66–23 per cent. Sb_2O_3. The eutectic at 489°, and 33·33 per cent. Sb_2O_3 has the composition of the mineral kermesite, which cannot therefore be obtained from fused mixtures of its components.

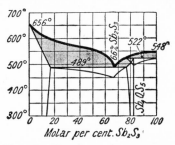

Fig. 72.—Freezing-point Curve of Antimony Trisulphide and Trioxide.

The product obtained by fusing mixtures of antimony trioxide and trisulphide is the *Spiessglanzglas*, *antimony glass*, or *vitrum antimonii* of the alchemists. According to H. Rose, if the molten mixture is rapidly cooled, a glassy mass is produced. The product is redder, the larger the proportion of the trioxide ; and darker, the more trisulphide present. If the molten mixture is cooled slowly, it forms a black, crystalline mass ; and when the molten mixture is dropped into cold water, the portion near the surface may be glassy and red, while the core is black and crystalline. The glassy product is a non-conductor of electricity ; the crystalline is a poorer conductor than the crystalline trisulphide. A. Werner made *antimony glass* by rapidly fusing in a fireclay crucible a mixture of *antimony-ash*—i.e. the trisulphide roasted without fusion in a reverberatory furnace—with about one-twentieth of its weight of antimony trisulphide until its molten surface becomes bright like a mirror. It is then poured on to a marble slab or polished copper plate. With antimony-ash and antimony trisulphide in the proportions 100 : 3·35, the product is a reddish-yellow, transparent glass ; 100 : 5·28, yellowish-red ; and 100 : 6·69, hyacinth-red. J. L. Proust, and E. Soubeiran obtained analogous products. The so-called *Spiessglanz-safran*, or *antimonial saffron*, *crocus antimonii*, or *crocus metallorum*, was described by M. Ettmüller. It was prepared by J. L. Proust by melting a mixture of antimony pentoxide and 25 per cent. of the trisulphide, or a mixture of antimony trior penta-oxide with the proper proportion of sulphur. J. J. Berzelius recommended mixing freshly precipitated trisulphide with antimony pentachloride in acid soln., and adding water until the hydrated pentoxide begins to separate. The *regulus antimonii medicinalis*, or *rubinus antimonii*, of the alchemists is an antimony trisulphide containing very little trioxide. It is black when *en masse*, and dark red when powdered. It was made by fusing a mixture of potassium carbonate with five times its weight of antimony trisulphide, and rejecting the upper stratum of potassium sulphoantimonite from the cold mass. The Miniere e fonderie d'antimonio prepared a chocolate-brown oxysulphide by roasting antimony sulphide ores.

O. Schumann [2] obtained **antimony oxypentasulphide**, Sb_4OS_5, or $5Sb_2S_3.Sb_2O_3$, by passing a current of dry hydrogen sulphide over antimony pentoxide. At ordinary temp., the oxide is coloured yellow, but at a higher temp., sulphur and water are evolved and the black oxypentasulphide appears. E. Quercigh showed the limits of stability of this compound when prepared from mixtures of the trioxide and trisulphide, as well as the solid soln. which it forms when an excess of either component is present. It decomposes at 522° into trisulphide and a liquid—vide Fig. 72.

In 1747, J. G. Wallerius described a native antimonial earth whose red colour was attributed to the presence of arsenic. The mineral was also mentioned by A. Cronstedt, and I. S. R. I. Eques a Born, and J. B. L. Romé de l'Isle called it *antimonium plumosum ;* B. G. Sage, *mine d'antimoine en plumes ;* A. G. Werner, L. A. Emmerling, M. H. Klaproth, *Rothspiessglaserz* or *Rothspiessglanzerz ;* and R. J. Haüy, *antimoine oxydé sulphuré*. J. F. L. Hausmann united tinder ore and this red antimonial earth under the name *Spiessglanzblende ;* and C. C. von Leonhard, *Antimonblende*, or *antimony blende*. F. S. Beudant called it *kermès ;* E. J. Chapman, **kermesite**—possibly from a Persian word, *qurmizq*, crimson—E. F. Glocker, *pyrantimonite*, and also *pyrostibite*. Analyses of the mineral were reported by M. H. Klaproth, H. Rose, and H. Baubigny. The results agree with the empirical formula, $2Sb_2S_3.Sb_2O_3$, or Sb_2OS_2, or $Sb_4O_2S_4$, **antimony dioxytetrasulphide**. H. V. Regnault obtained this compound, as an orange-red mass, by heating antimony trisulphide in a current of steam ; O. Schumann, as a black powder, by the action of dry hydrogen sulphide on antimony trioxide ; R. Schneider, as a reddish-brown powder, by boiling antimony sulphoiodide with zinc oxide and water ; and H. Rose, by fusing together a mixture of the components—antimony trioxide and trisulphide. There is no evidence of the formation of this compound on the f.p. curve of the components—Fig. 72. According to H. Baubigny, and N. Teclu, the oxysulphide reported by R. Wagner, A. Carnot,, and A. Strohl, to be formed by the action of sodium thiosulphate on antimonious salt soln.—e.g. antimony trichloride—is only impure antimony trisulphide.

Kermesite usually occurs in tufts of capillary crystals of a cherry-red colour, belonging to the rhombic or monoclinic system. F. Mohs called the mineral prismatic *Purpurblende*, and considered the crystals to be monoclinic ; G. A. Kenngott came to the same conclusion. P. Pjatnitzky found the axial ratios of the crystals to be $a : b : c = 3.9650 : 1 : 0.8535$, and $\beta = 90°$. The (100)-cleavage is perfect ; and the (101)-cleavage imperfect. The crystals were also examined by V. Goldschmidt ; and the colour by J. L. C. Schröder van der Kolk. Pseudomorphs after the antimony sulphide ores, particularly stibnite, have been observed by J. R. Blum, V. R. von Zepharovich, etc. P. Pjatnitzky said that the indices of refraction are large ; and the birefringence small. The pleochroism is feeble. The sp. gr. of the mineral given by P. Pjatnitzky is 4·5–4·6 ; A. Breithaupt gave 4·493. The hardness is between 1 and 2. L. H. Borgström gave 517° for the m.p. ; and J. Joly said that a sublimate appears at 430°. F. Beijerinck found the mineral to be a non-conductor of electricity ; T. W. Case also said that kermesite is a non-conductor, and that its resistance is not appreciably affected by light. H. Rose said that this compound melts easily—*vide* Fig. 72—that it forms a black glass when heated in a current of carbon dioxide ; and that it is reduced when heated in a current of hydrogen. The compound was found by H. Baubigny to be attacked by hot hydrochloric acid, and by potash-lye. It is not dissolved by a 7 per cent. soln. of tartaric acid.

According to C. F. Rammelsberg, when a soln. of potassium antimonyl tartrate is treated with sodium orthosulphoantimonate, an orange-red precipitate of *antimonyl sulphoantimonate*, $(SbO)_3SbS_4$, or **antimony trioxytetrasulphide**, $Sb_4O_3S_4$, is formed. This compound melts when heated, forming a very dark red mass ; the red powder dissolves in hot hydrochloric acid ; and it is reduced to metal when heated in hydrogen. With potash-lye, a yellow residue is formed. F. J. Faktor boiled aq. soln. of potassium antimonyl tartrate and sodium thiosulphate, prepared in the cold, and obtained a fiery-red precipitate, which, when washed with water, alcohol, and carbon disulphide, and dried at 100°, has the composition, **antimony dioxysulphide**, SbO_2S. When this product is suspended in water, at ordinary temp. or at 80°, and treated with hydrogen sulphide, no change in colour or composition was observed. It is, however, darkened by exposure to sunlight. If a soln. of potassium antimonyl tartrate and sodium thiosulphate is prepared with boiling water, and boiled, F. J. Faktor said that the dark brown precipitate is **antimony tetroxysulphide**, Sb_2O_4S, or **antimony pentoxysulphide**, Sb_2O_5S.

J. J. Berzelius [3] obtained an antimony oxysulphide, by igniting a mixture of antimony trisulphide with about one part of potassium carbonate or nitrate, and extracting the product with hot water. It was formerly regarded as an *antimonial crocus or saffron with potash*. It was also made by boiling the grey trisulphide with potash-lye, or by digesting the red trisulphide in the cold lye. The product fuses to a yellowish glass. When the crocus is digested with dil. hydrochloric acid, potassium antimonite passes into soln. The crocus was also prepared by J. von Liebig, and B. Unger. According to C. F. Rammelsberg, if antimony pentasulphide be treated with a conc. soln. of potash-lye, potassium trihydrotriantimonate separates out (*q.v.*), and when the clear liquid is evaporated, **potassium hydrodioxydisulphoantimonite**, $K_2HSbO_2S_2.2H_2O$, is formed. L. W. McCay made it by allowing a cold soln. of potassium hydroxide to act on antimony pentasulphide for 24 hrs. H. Schiff employed an analogous process. If sodium thiosulphate be

eated with a conc. soln. of sodium antimonite, sodium pyroantimonate, sulphantimonate, and sulphite are formed ; potassium salts under similar conditions yield
potassium antimonate and sulphoantimonate. If action with the potassium
alts takes place in the cold, antimony trisulphide is precipitated, and the
mother-liquor, on evaporation, gives crystals of what is probably the hydro-
dioxydisulphoantimonate. The same salt was produced by the action of
potassium hydroxide and sulphur on antimony trioxide : $Sb_2O_3+5KOH+2S$
$=K_2HSbO_2S_2+KH_2SbO_4+2KOH$; and also by the action of potassium hydroxide
nd polysulphide on antimony trioxide : $3Sb_2O_3+18KOH+2K_2S_4=3K_2HSbO_2S_2$
$+3KH_2SbO_4+2K_2S+9KOH$. C. F. Rammelsberg also made it by boiling antimony
risulphide with a soln. of potassium carbonate and calcium oxide. The salt
urnishes pale yellow clusters of radiating needles ; which, when dried over sulphuric
acid out of contact with air, were found by H. Schiff to become dark yellow ; and
n moist air L. W. McCay observed that the salt becomes red or crimson without
deliquescing. C. F. Rammelsberg said that the salt deliquesces in air, and acquires
a brown film ; and that it does not lose its water below 100°. L. W. McCay
observed that the salt loses its water of crystallization at 150°, but a temp. of 250°
is necessary for the expulsion of the combined water. C. F. Rammelsberg found
hat the salt melts to a reddish-brown liquid, which, on cooling, forms a yellow
solid. Cold water dissolves the salt with the partial separation of potassium
antimonate ; hot water dissolves it completely. The salt is decomposed by acids,
forming potassium trihydrotriantimonate, antimonic acid, antimony pentasulphide, and some hydrogen sulphide ; but L. W. McCay represented the
reaction : $8H_3SbO_2S_2=Sb_2S_5+2Sb_2S_3+5S+H_3SbO_4+H_3SbO_3+9H_2O$. He said
that aq. soln. of the salt react with alkaline earth salts, forming white precipitates
which become crystalline ; with silver salts, a black precipitate ; with copper and
lead salts, red precipitates which gradually turn black. C. F. Rammelsberg said
that with barium chloride, the hot aq. soln. gives barium antimonate ; and the
filtrate yields antimony pentasulphide when treated with acids.

C. F. Rammelsberg could not prepare analogous sodium, calcium, or barium salts.
H. Schiff's, and W. Feit and C. Kubierschky's attempts were also nugatory. When
antimony pentasulphide is treated with soda-lye, the orthosulphoantimonate and
metantimonate are produced ; and similar products are obtained when antimonyl
chloride is treated with sodium sulphide ; or sulphoantimonyl chloride with soda-lye.
Lead hydroxide desulphurizes sodium orthosulphoantimonate ; and a boiling soln.
of sodium sulphide and metantimonate gives the orthosulphoantimonate. For a
possible *copper pentoxyoctosulphodiantimonate*, $8CuS.Sb_2O_5$, but more probably a
mixture *vide* copper sulphoantimonate ; similarly with *silver pentoxyoctosulphodiantimonate*, $8Ag_2S.Sb_2O_5$.

REFERENCES

[1] H. Rose, *Pogg. Ann.*, **89**. 316, 1853 ; J. J. Berzelius, *ib.*, **20**. 365, 1830 ; **37**. 163, 1836;
Schweigger's Journ., **34**. 58, 1822 ; J. L. Proust, *Journ. Phys.*, **55**. 325, 1802 ; A. Werner, *Journ.
prakt. Chem.*, (1), **12**. 53, 1837 ; *Liebig's Ann.*, **27**. 89, 1838 ; Miniere e fonderie d'antimonio,
German Pat., *D.R.P.* 160110, 1905 ; E. Soubeiran, *Journ. Pharm. Chim.*, (3), **10**. 528, 1824 ;
E. Quercigh, *Atti Accad. Lincei*, (5), **21**. i, 415, 1912 ; M. Ettmüller, *Nouvelle chimie raisonée*,
Lyon, 187, 1693.
[2] O. Schumann, *Liebig's Ann.*, **187**. 312, 1877 ; H. V. Regnault, *Ann. Chim. Phys.*, (2),
62. 383, 1836 ; P. Pjatnitzky, *Zeit. Kryst.*, **20**. 422, 1892 ; H. Rose, *Pogg. Ann.*, **3**. 452, 1824 ;
89. 318, 1853 ; R. Schneider, *ib.*, **110**. 151, 1860 ; C. F. Rammelsberg, *ib.*, **52**. 236, 1841 ;
119. 737, 1894 ; F. J. Faktor, *Pharm. Post*, **33**. 233, 1900 ;
E. Quercigh, *Atti Accad. Lincei*, (5), **21**. i, 415, 1912 ; A. Cronstedt, *Mineralogie*, Stockholm, 203, 1758 ; J. G. Wallerius, *Mineralogia*, Stockholm, 239, 1747 : B. G. Sage, *Élémens de
minéralogie docimastique*, Paris, 2. 251, 1779 ; L. A. Emmerling, *Lehrbuch der Mineralogie*, Giessen,
477, 1796 ; R. J. Haüy, *Traité de minéralogie*, Paris, **4**. 276, 1801 ; M. H. Klaproth, *Beiträje
zur chemischen Kenntniss der Mineralkorper*, Berlin, **3**. 180, 1802 ; J. F. L. Hausmann, *Handbuch
der Mineralogie*, Göttingen, 225, 1813 ; C. C. von Leonhard, *Handbuch der Oryktognosie*, Heidelberg, 157, 1821 ; E. F. Glocker, *Handbuch der Mineralogie*, Nürnberg, 392, 1831 ; *Generum et*

specierum mineralium secundum ordines naturales digestorum synopsis, Halle, 16, 1847 ; E. J. Chapman, *Practical Mineralogy*, London, 61, 1843 ; F. S. Beudant, *Traité élémentaire de minéralogie*, Paris, 2. 617, 1832 ; I. S. R. I. Eques a Born, *Lithophylacium Bornianum*, Prag, 1. 137, 1772 ; J. B. L. Rome de l'Isle, *Cristallographie*, Paris, 3. 56, 1783 ; R. Jameson, *A System of Mineralogy*, Edinburgh, 3. 421, 1820 ; A. Breithaupt, *Die Paragenesis der Mineralien*, Freiberg, 152, 1849 ; V. Goldschmidt, *Krystallographische Winkeltabellen*, Berlin, 389, 1897 ; G. A. Kenngott, *Mineralogische Untersuchungen*, Breslau, 1. 1, 1849 ; F. Mohs, *Grundriss der Mineralogy*, Dresden, 2. 598, 1824 ; V. R. von Zepharovich, *Mineralogisches Lexikon für das Kaiserthum Oesterreich*, 327, 1859 ; 248, 1873 ; 17, 1893 ; J. R. Blum, *Die Pseudomorphosen der Mineralreichs*, Stuttgart, 173, 1843 ; 168, 1863 ; J. Roth, *Allgemeine und chemische Geologie*, Berlin, 1. 262, 1879 ; R. Wagner, *Wagner's Jahresb.*, 4. 235, 1858 ; 8. 331, 1862 : A. Carnot, *Compt. Rend.*. 103. 258, 1888 ; N. Teclu, *Dingler's Journ.*, 236. 336, 1880 ; A. Strohl, *Journ. Pharm. Chim.*, (3), 16. 11, 1848 ; J. L. C. Schroder van der Kolk, *Centr. Min.*, 79, 1901 ; F. Beijerinck, *Neues Jahrb. Min. B.B.*, 11. 442, 1897 ; A. G. Werner, *Letztes Mineralsystem*, Freiberg, 23, 57, 1817 ; L. H. Borgström, *Oefvers. Finksa Vet. Soc. Förh.*, 57. 24, 1915 ; J. Joly, *Phil. Mag.*, (6), 27. 1, 1914 ; *Chem. News*, 107. 241, 1913 ; T. W. Case, *Phys. Rev.*, (2), 9. 305, 1917.

[3] J. J. Berzelius, *Schweigger's Journ.*, 34. 58, 1822 ; *Pogg. Ann.*, 20. 365, 1830 ; 37. 163, 1836 ; C. F. Rammelsberg, *ib.*, 52. 199, 1841 ; J. von Liebig, *Handwörterbuch der reinen und angewandten Chemie*, Braunschweig, 1. 434, 1837 ; R. F. Weinland and A. Gutmann, *Zeit. anorg. Chem.*, 17. 414, 1898 ; B. Unger, *Arch. Pharm.*, (2), 147. 192, 1871 ; (2), 148. 1, 1871 ; H. Schiff, *Liebig's Ann.*, 114. 202, 1860 ; L. W. McCay, *Amer. Chem. Journ.*, 17. 770, 1896 ; W. Feit and C. Kubierschky, *Ber.*, 21. 1661, 1888.

§ 28. Antimony Sulphates

Like arsenic trioxide, antimony trioxide behaves as a base towards the stronger acids. According to J. J. Berzelius,[1] antimony trioxide is sparingly soluble in sulphuric acid. R. Brandes, and W. P. Dexter obtained crystals of normal **antimony sulphate,** $Sb_2(SO_4)_3$, by cooling a hot soln. of antimony trioxide in hot sulphuric acid. A similar product was obtained by C. Schultz-Sellack, and C. Hensgen. S. Metzl washed the crystals with xylene to remove the sulphuric acid. According to R. H. Adie, if the acid employed has the composition $H_2SO_4.H_2O$, normal antimony sulphate is formed, but if a more dil. acid is used, basic salts are formed. W. P. Dexter also heated antimony trioxide or antimony chloride with sulphuric acid, and distilled off the excess acid. C. Hensgen found that if antimony trisulphide be heated with conc. sulphuric acid until sulphuric acid fumes are no longer evolved, the normal sulphate is produced. S. Metzl added that sulphuric acid transforms antimony trisulphide into sulphate at 300°, and the product is contaminated with acid and a basic salt. If alkali or magnesium sulphate be present, the reaction is facilitated so that even with a dil. acid at 130°, the reaction may be represented : $Sb_2S_3 + 12H_2SO_4 = Sb_2(SO_4)_3 + 12SO_2 + 12H_2O$. Antimonial sulphide ores can be used as the source of the antimony . The analyses of R. Brandes, W. P. Dexter, C. Schultz-Sellack, C. Hensgen, R. H. Adie, and S. Metzl are in agreement with the empirical formula $Sb_2(SO_4)_3$.

W. P. Dexter described the crystals as four-sided prisms, the other workers as acicular crystals, or as a crystalline powder. S. Metzl gave 3·6216 for the sp. gr. at 4°. C. Hensgen, and C. Schultz-Sellack found that the crystals are stable in dry air, but in moist air, they deliquesce rapidly taking up, according to C. Hensgen, 3 mols of water, or, according to S. Metzl, 2·5 mols. C. Hensgen said that only part of the absorbed water is removed by drying the product over sulphuric acid, but crystals separate from the liquor after some time. When the normal sulphate is treated with a small proportion of water, heat is developed and a solid mass is produced ; with more water, the mass dissolves, and the soln. forms a crystalline mass when evaporated in vacuo over sulphuric acid. W. Ipatieff and co-workers observed that antimony sulphate is reduced by hydrogen under press. to form antimony sulphide. The normal sulphate is partly hydrolyzed by water furnishing various basic sulphates (*q.v.*), and, according to R. Brandes, and C. Hensgen, the hydrolysis may be completed with hot water. R. H. Adie found that absolute alcohol also converts it into a basic salt. According to J. L. Gay Lussac, C. Schultz-Sellack, and A. Bussy, when the sulphate is heated, it gives off sulphur trioxide and dioxide and oxygen; C. F. Bucholz observed that some antimony trioxide sublimes; and S. Metzl found that if heated slowly, sulphur trioxide is given off, and the residue contains both trioxide and tetroxide. R. Robl observed no fluorescence when the sulphate is exposed to ultra-violet light. J. A. Arfvedson found that when heated in hydrogen, antimony, and antimony trioxide and trisulphide are formed. C. Hensgen found that up to 5·2 mols of hydrogen chloride are absorbed with some avidity, and the fused mass solidifies on cooling, forming, possibly, chlorosulphates. F. Ephraim obtained a complex of antimony sulphate and hydrogen chloride. A. B. Prescott observed no change when a gram of the sulphate is evaporated on a water-bath to dryness with 3·5 c.c. of hydrochloric acid of sp. gr. 1·153.

C. Schultz-Sellack found that a soln. of antimony trioxide in fuming sulphuric acid furnishes **antimony tetrasulphate**, or **antimony tetrasulphatotrioxide**, $Sb_2O_3.4SO_3$, or $Sb_2(SO_3)(SO_4)_3$, in small crystals; and E. Péligot obtained the same salt from a soln. of antimonyl chloride in conc. sulphuric acid. According to R. H. Adie, when the trioxide is treated with fuming sulphuric acid, $2H_2SO_4.SO_3$, it forms a hard cake which dissolves when heated, and on cooling furnishes fine needles which rapidly deliquesce in moist air. They are decomposed by water. R. H. Adie found that when a mixture of antimony and sulphur trioxides is heated in a sealed tube, the composition of the product depends on the proportion of sulphur trioxide present, and on the temp. At 120°, the product had 55·87–61·55 per cent. SO_3; at 160°, 73·55 per cent.; and at 180°, 74·56 per cent. The value calculated for $Sb_2O_3.8SO_3$ is 68·98 per cent., and for $Sb_2O_3.10SO_3$, 73·52 per cent. The formation of the compound with the highest proportion of sulphur trioxide requires a temp. of 160°; and would appear to be $Sb_2O_3.9SO_3$, but, since the corresponding arsenic compound can be completely freed from the excess of sulphur trioxide, and is probably $As_2O_3.8SO_3$, it is best to assume that the compound formed is **antimony octosulphatotrioxide**, or **antimony octosulphate**, $Sb_2O_3.8SO_3$.

A number of basic sulphates can be obtained by the hydrolysis of antimony sulphates. R. H. Adie said that alcohol furnishes $Sb_2O_3.2SO_3$; cold water, $2Sb_2O_3.SO_3$; and hot water, $7Sb_2O_3.2SO_3$. There are many doubts which, if any, of the reported basic sulphates are chemical individuals. Arsenic sulphate is hydrolyzed by cold water to form arsenic trioxide. The basic antimony sulphates are also produced by the action of acid more dilute than $H_2SO_4.H_2O$ on antimony trioxide. Thus, while H_2SO_4 forms with arsenic trioxide $As_2O_3.2SO_3$, this acid as well as $H_2SO_4.H_2O$, with antimony trioxide, furnishes normal antimony sulphate; $H_2SO_4.2H_2O$ yields $Sb_2O_3.2SO_3.H_2O$; and $H_2SO_4.4H_2O$ gives $Sb_2O_3.3H_2O$. After comparing the arsenic and antimony sulphates, R. H. Adie added that antimony trioxide with sulphuric and weaker acids forms a different order of sulphates from As_2O_3, while it resembles it in forming acidic sulphates when subjected to the action of stronger acids. The characteristic group salt $Sb_2(SO_4)_3$, which is produced by the former, is replaced by the basic $As_2O(SO_4)_2$ in the latter case. The limits of existence both as regards dilution and temp., are much narrower for the arsenic than for the antimony salt. The practically complete formation of $Sb_2(SO_4)_3$ in one crystallization also contrasts with the formation of $As_2O(SO_4)_2$ only by repeated crystallization. Arsenic trioxide does not form any basic sulphates containing water, whilst the oxide of the more metallic antimony does form hydrated sulphates in acids weaker than $H_2SO_4.H_2O$. This acid is the limit of existence of $Sb_2(SO_4)_3$ in soln. and of any arsenic sulphates whatever. In contrast to the case of the arsenic compounds, one cannot remove all the SO_3 from the antimony sulphates by water. The stability of the latter in dil. acids far exceeds that of the former. M. Websky made a basic sulphate by the action of antimony or its trisulphide on molten potassium hydrosulphate. W. P. Dexter said that all the sulphates are soluble in hydrochloric acid, and if tartaric acid be present, the soln. can be diluted with water. The soln. are decomposed by alkali hydroxides or carbonates yielding antimony trioxide.

S. Metzl said that *antimony heptitasulphatotrioxide*, $7Sb_2O_3.SO_3$, is produced by boiling the normal sulphate with 14 times its weight of water, and allowing the mixture to stand at rest for 24 hrs. According to R. H. Adie, if normal antimony sulphate be treated with boiling water until the washings are free from sulphuric acid, *antimony diheptitasulphatotrioxide*, $7Sb_2O_3.2SO_3.3H_2O$, is formed as a white powder. Both R. Brandes, and C. Hensgen said that by repeatedly treating the normal sulphate with hot water, antimony trioxide and sulphuric acid are formed. Hence the two products just indicated are probably mixtures of antimony trioxide with one of the other basic sulphates.

According to R. Brandes, R. H. Adie, and W. P. Dexter, when the normal sulphate, or, according to E. Péligot, when the tetrasulphate is decomposed by cold water, **antimony hemisulphatotrioxide**, $2Sb_2O_3.SO_3.7H_2O$, is produced. C. Hensgen gave $5Sb_2O_3.2SO_3.7H_2O$ for the composition of the product obtained in this way. R. H. Adie supposes that this compound is a sulphate of meta-tetrantimonic acid, $H_2Sb_4O_7$. R. Brandes obtained the same compound by treating the normal sulphate with twice its weight of water, and so much sulphuric acid as is necessary for dissolution; and then adding water to precipitate the white powder. The product contains a variable proportion of water dependent on the mode of drying; and the temp. of the water employed for the hydrolysis. That prepared by water at 18° and dried in air had 4 mols. of water; that prepared by water at 6°, and air-dried, 2–3 mols.; that prepared by water at 6° and dried by press. between porous tiles, 16 mols. of water. W. P. Dexter said that the powder becomes crystalline if allowed to stand in contact with the mother-liquor, and it then contains one mol. of water. R. H. Adie said that all the water is expelled at 100°; and W. P. Dexter, at 240°. R. Brandes found that the salt is completely hydrolyzed by boiling water.

S. Metzl found that if the normal sulphate be decomposed by ten times its weight of cold water, **antimonyl sulphate**, $(SbO)_2SO_4$, is produced; R. Brandes obtained it as a white powder by the action of alcohol on antimony disulphatotrioxide; and W. P. Dexter, by the action of boiling sulphuric acid of sp. gr. 1·554, or $H_2SO_4.6H_2O$, on antimony trioxide—the second crop of crystals contains $(SbO)_2SO_4.H_2O$; the first crop contains four-sided prisms with the composition $3Sb_2O_3.5SO_3.2H_2O$, or $(SbO)_2SO_4.4(SbOH)SO_4$.

According to R. H. Adie, **antimony disulphatotrioxide**, $Sb_2O_3.2SO_3$, or $SO_4 : Sb.O.Sb : SO_4$, is formed from a soln. of antimony trioxide in boiling sulphuric acid of the composition $H_2SO_4.2$ to $4H_2O$; on cooling the *monohydrate* separates, as a white powder, which, if left in contact with its mother-liquor, crystallizes as the *trihydrate*. W. P. Dexter made the compound by the prolonged boiling of antimony trioxide with sulphuric acid dil. with its own vol. of water; by S. Metzl, and R. H. Adie, by the action of absolute alcohol at 18° on the normal sulphate; and by E. Péligot, by the action of fuming sulphuric acid on antimonyl chloride. The product loses all its water at 100°, and decomposes at about 250°. It is scarcely affected by cold water, but is hydrolyzed by hot water, it is slowly dissolved by hot dil. sulphuric acid. G. Karl considered that the *les anhydrides mixtes—cf.* arsenic—are represented by :

$$Sb_2O_3.SO_3 \qquad Sb_2O_3.2SO_3 \qquad Sb_2O_3.3SO_3 \qquad Sb_2O_3.4SO_3 \qquad Sb_2O_3.8SO_3$$

A. Gutmann obtained crystal plates of **ammonium antimony sulphate**, $(NH_4)_2SO_4.Sb_2(SO_4)_3$, by cooling a boiling soln. of 5–6 grms. of ammonium sulphate in 15 grms. of sulphuric acid, and about as much antimony trioxide as the soln. will dissolve, about half a gram. The salt is dried by press. between warm porous tiles. S. Metzl said that the exact proportioning of the components is not necessary. The sp. gr. of the crystals is 3·0948 at 4°. The salt is slowly dissolved by water, and the aq. or alcoholic soln. behaves like a mixture of the components. A. Gutmann prepared **sodium antimony sulphate**, $Na_2SO_4.Sb_2(SO_4)_3$, in an analogous way, using 5 grms. of sodium sulphate, 20 of conc. sulphuric acid, and 10 of antimony trioxide. S. Metzl gave 3·2298 for the sp. gr. at 4°. The salt resembles that of ammonium. A. Gutmann prepared the analogous **potassium antimony sulphate,** $K_2SO_4.Sb_2(SO_4)_3$, using one part of potassium sulphate, 3 parts of sulphuric acid, and about half a part of antimony trioxide. S. Metzl showed that these proportions need not be strictly observed, and he gave 3·3396 for the sp. gr. at 4°. A. Gutmann said that it forms with water a basic sulphate. E. Péligot obtained another complex sulphate which N. Svensson formulates $\{6K_2SO_4.Sb_2(SO_4)_3\}2KHSO_4.2H_2O$, or **potassium antimony henasulphate,** $7K_2O.Sb_2O_3.11SO_3.3H_2O$. E. Péligot obtained it from a boiling soln. of antimony tetrasulphate and potassium sulphate ; and N. Svensson, by boiling with a soln. of potassium hydrosulphate the cold cake obtained by melting a mixture of potassium hydrosulphate and antimony oxychloride or trioxide. The salt is decomposed by water. H. Kühl prepared **silver antimony sulphate,** $Ag_2SO_4.Sb_2(SO_4)_3$, in colourless, cubic, doubly refracting crystals, by concentrating a soln. of antimony sulphate and an excess of silver sulphate in conc. sulphuric acid. Slender needles of **calcium antimony sulphate,** $CaSO_4.Sb_2(SO_4)_3.6H_2O$, were obtained by mixing a soln. of 3 grms. of antimony trioxide in 150 c.c. of conc. sulphuric acid, and 4 grms. of dihydrated calcium sulphate in about 80 c.c. of sulphuric acid. The soln. is conc. until crystals begin to form, and then cooled. The corresponding **strontium antimony sulphate,** $SrSO_4.Sb_2(SO_4)_3.6H_2O$; and **barium antimony sulphate,** $BaSO_4.Sb_2(SO_4)_3.6H_2O$, were obtained in a similar way.

REFERENCES.

[1] R. Brandes, *Arch. Pharm.*, (2), **21**. 156, 1827 ; G. Karl, *Sur quelques anhydrides mixtes de l'acide sulfurique*, Genève, 1908 ; R. H. Adie, *Journ. Chem. Soc.*, **57**. 540, 1890 ; C. Hensgen, *Rec. Trav. Chim. Pays-Bas*, **4**. 401, 1885 ; E. Péligot, *Ann. Chim. Phys.*, (3), **20**. 283, 1847 ; J. L. Gay Lussac, *ib.*, (2), **42**. 87, 1829 ; *Journ. Mines*, **22**. 325, 1807 ; *Nicholson's Journ.*, **33**. 44, 1812 ; W. P. Dexter, *Amer. Journ. Science*, (2), **46**. 78, 1868 ; *Journ. Prakt. Chem.*, (1). **106**. 134, 1869 ; C. Schultz-Sellack, *Ber.*, **4**. 13, 109, 1871 ; F. Ephraim, *ib.*, **59**. B, 790, 1926 ; S. Metzl, *German Pat.*, *D.R.P.* 161776, 1904 ; *Zeit. anorg. Chem.*, **48**. 146, 1906 ; H. Kühl, *ib.*, **54**. 256, 1907 ; J. A. Arfvedson, *Pogg. Ann.*, **1**. 74, 1824 ; *Ann. Phil.*, **7**. 329, 1824 ; A. Gutmann, *Arch. Pharm.*, **236**. 477, 1898 ; *Antimonalkalimetallsulfate*, Munchen, 1897 ; N. Svensson, *Lund Acta Univ.*, **4**. 5, 1867 ; J. J. Berzelius, *Schweigger's Journ.*, **6**. 144, 1812 ; **22**. 69, 1818 ; A. B. Prescott, *Chem. News*, **36**. 179, 1877 ; C. F. Bucholz, *Berlin Jahrb. Pharm.*, **29**. 26, 1822 ; A. Bussy, *Journ. Pharm. Chim.*, (2), **10**. 202, 368, 1824 ; M. Websky, *Zeit. anal. Chem.*, **11**. 124, 1872 ; R. Robl, *Zeit. angew. Chem.*, **39**. 608, 1926 ; W. Ipatieff, *Ber.*, **59**. B, 1412, 1926 ; W. Ipatieff and W. Nikolaieff, *Journ. Russ. Phys. Chem. Soc.*, **58**. 664, 686, 692, 698, 1926.

§ 29. Antimony Sulphohalides or Halogenosulphides

Complex salts with ammonium sulphate and antimony trifluoride have been mentioned in connection with the latter salts, and $SbCl_5.SCl_4$ is mentioned in connection with antimony pentachloride. According to J. F. W. Johnston,[1] the trisulphide precipitated when hydrogen sulphide is passed into a soln. of antimony trichloride, contains some chloride which cannot be removed by washing ; and when the precipitate is heated, some antimony trichloride volatilizes. E. G. Beckett assumed that in precipitating antimony sulphide from hydrochloric acid soln. of the trichloride by hydrogen sulphide in the ordinary course of analysis, a series of **antimony chlorosulphides,** as well as the normal hydrosulphide, may be formed :

$$HS{-}Sb{<}^{HS}_{HS} \qquad Cl{-}Sb{<}^{HS}_{HS} \qquad HS{-}Sb{<}^{Cl}_{Cl} \qquad Cl{-}Sb{<}^{Cl}_{Cl}$$

| Antimony trihydrosulphide. | Antimony monochloro-dihydrosulphide. | Antimony dichloro-hydrosulphide. | Antimony trichloride. |

M. Berthelot studied the heat of formation of the sulphochlorides. L. Ouvrard treated antimony trichloride, not quite at its m.p., with dry hydrogen sulphide, and obtained small crystals of **antimony pentasulphodichloride,** $Sb_4S_5Cl_2$, as soon as the evolution of hydrogen chloride had ceased ; but, by stopping the operation before that stage is reached, **antimony sulphochloride,** SbSCl, or $Sb_4S_4Cl_4$, was obtained in reddish-brown crystals, insoluble in carbon disulphide, but decomposed by acids. If the temp. of the reaction be increased, antimony trisulphide is the end-product. H. J. Taverne obtained the pentasulphodichloride by passing dry hydrogen sulphide into a soln. of antimony trichloride in dry carbon disulphide or tetra-chloride, or in a mixture of these solvents, when there is formed a white precipitate, which is converted by a little water into antimony trisulphide. On continued passage of hydrogen sulphide, the colour of the white compound changes to yellow, yellowish-red, orange, and finally dark red. The end product is crystalline, and has the formula $Sb_4S_5Cl_2$. It probably results from replacement of one S-atom in two mols of antimony trisulphide by two Cl-atoms. The light orange, crystalline, intermediate product, **antimony hexasulphotrichloride,** $Sb_5S_6Cl_3$, has also been isolated. According to R. Schneider, 100 parts of boiling antimony trichloride dissolve 6·67 parts of antimony trisulphide, and on cooling a mass of yellow, rhombic crystals of **antimony sulphodocosichloride,** Sb_8SCl_{22}, or $SbSCl.SbCl_3$, is produced. This compound decomposes when heated, giving off antimony trichloride and forming the trisulphide. It deliquesces in air, producing a clear liquid, which later becomes turbid. The salt is hydrolyzed by water, and with absolute alcohol passes into a yellow amorphous powder, **antimony henasulphodichloride,** $Sb_8S_{11}Cl_2$. It is decomposed, when heated, with the evolution of antimony trichloride ; it is decomposed at ordinary temp. by dil. hydrochloric acid, forming antimony tri-sulphide ; the conc. acid produces hydrogen sulphide. By treating antimony pentachloride with dry hydrogen sulphide, S. Cloez obtained a crystalline mass of **antimony sulphotrichloride,** $SbSCl_3$; A. Bertrand and E. Finot obtained it by the action of carbon disulphide on cold antimony pentachloride. The white crystalline mass is fusible, and is decomposed by heat into sulphur and antimony trichloride. It is stable in dry air, but deliquesces in moist air. It is decomposed by water into oxychloride, SbOCl, and sulphur ; and by tartaric acid with the separation of antimony trisulphide, and trioxide.

L. Ouvrard prepared **antimony sulphobromide,** SbSBr, by the action of dry hydrogen sulphide on molten antimony tribromide. It forms small crystals insoluble in carbon disulphide.

J. F. W. Johnston obtained no satisfactory evidence of the formation of a sulphiodide by the action of a hydrogen sulphide on a dil. soln. of antimony triiodide in hydrochloric acid. O. Henry and M. Carot heated a mixture of equal parts of iodine and antimony trisulphide, and obtained what was regarded as **antimony trisulphohexaiodide,** $Sb_2S_3I_6$, in blood-red needles or plates, which melt at a lower temp. than the triiodide, and sublime without decomposition. The compound decomposes when heated in air ; when treated with water ; conc. acids ; or alkali-lye. R. Schneider found that antimony trisulphide dissolved a molten triiodide, and when the cold product is treated with hydrochloric acid, **antimony sulphoiodide,** SbSI, or $Sb_4S_4I_4$, remains. L. Ouvrard obtained it from a molten mixture of equal parts of antimony trisulphide and iodine—R. Schneider obtained a very small yield by this process. L. Ouvrard obtained the sulphiodide by passing hydrogen sulphide over antimony triiodide at 150°. R. Schneider said that the dark brown, acicular crystals resemble those of kermesite ; they are not decomposed by hot or cold water ; nor by dil. acids. Conc. hydrochloric acid decomposes the compound with the evolution of hydrogen sulphide ; and nitric acid, with the separation of sulphur and iodine ; a soln. of alkali hydroxide or carbonate furnishes iodine and sulphoantimonite ; and with zinc oxide and water, antimony oxydisulphide, Sb_2OS_2, is formed. L. Ouvrard heated a mixture of 5 gram-atoms of iodine with a mol of antimony trisulphide in an evacuated tube, and obtained a sublimate of antimony triiodide, crystals of **antimony sulphotriiodide,** $SbSI_3$, and unchanged trisulphide. The compound is soluble in carbon disulphide, and when protected from air can be recrystallized unchanged. It is decomposed by moist air into antimony triiodide and sulphur. V. Auger prepared **antimony tetracosisulphoiodide,** $SbI_3.3S_8$, in long, bright yellow prisms of m.p. 117°, by mixing carbon disulphide soln. of the two constituents.

P. Gruhl found that it is not possible to prepare halogenized antimonites analogous to the halogenized arsenites because of the low solubility of antimony trioxide in soln. of the alkali iodides. By melting a mixture of potassium iodide and antimony trioxide, he obtained **potassium oxyiodoantimonite,** $K_4Sb_{16}O_{25}I_2$, or $8Sb_2O_3.K_2O.2KI$, as an amber-yellow crystalline mass. It is insoluble in cold or hot water; acids and alkali-lye do not act on it; aqua regia decomposes it slowly; and tartaric acid dissolves it gradually.

REFERENCES.

[1] R. Schneider, *Pogg. Ann.*, **108.** 407, 1858; **109.** 610, 1860; **110.** 150, 1860; L. Ouvrard, *Ann. Chim. Phys.*, (7), **2.** 212, 1894; *Compt. Rend.*, **116.** 1517, 1893; **117.** 108, 1893; V. Auger, *ib.*, **146.** 477, 1908; J. F. W. Johnston, *Edin. Phil. Journ.*, **18.** 43, 1835; *B.A. Rep.*, 587, 1834; *Phil. Mag.*, (3), **7.** 332, 1835; E. G. Beckett, *Beitrag zur Bestimmung des Antimons*, Zürich, 1909; *Chem. News*, **102.** 101, 1911; S. Cloez, *Ann. Chim. Phys.*, (3), **30.** 374, 1850; M. Berthelot, *ib.*, (4), **10.** 130, 1886; A. Bertrand and E. Finot, *Bull. Soc. Chim.*, (2), **33.** 1252, 1880; P. Gruhl, *Verbindungen des Arsen- und Antimontrioxydes mit den Halogeniden mehrwertiger Metalle*, München, 1897; O. Henry and M. Carot, *Journ. Pharm. Chim.*, (2), **10.** 511, 1824; H. J. Taverne, *Chem. Weckbl.*, **5.** 19, 1908.

§ 30. Antimony Nitrates and Phosphates

No *antimony carbonate* has been prepared. A. Naumann [1] reported that **antimony nitrate,** $Sb(NO_3)_3$, is obtained along with silver chloride, by adding silver nitrate to a soln. of antimony trichloride in acetone. In aq. soln. the nitrate is hydrolyzed. As shown by J. J. Berzelius, and H. Rose, neither antimony trioxide nor the pentoxide is soluble in nitric acid. C. F. Bucholz, and J. J. Berzelius treated antimony or an antimony oxide with nitric acid, and obtained a basic nitrate as a white powder. E. Péligot dissolved antimony oxide in cold fuming nitric acid, and on adding water obtained crystals of **antimonyl nitrate,** $2Sb_2O_3N_2O_5$, or $(SbO)_4N_2O_7$, with a nacreous lustre. J. B. Senderens also obtained it as a grey powder on reducing $0.5N$-$AgNO_3$ with antimony. The grey powder burns like tinder. J. J. Berzelius said that water decomposes the salt, forming nitric acid. By passing nitrogen peroxide into a soln. of antimony tribromide in chloroform, or of antimony triiodide in ether. V. Thomas obtained a white, crystalline precipitate of **antimony nitrate bispentoxide,** $2Sb_2O_5.N_2O_5$. It is not decomposed by water; but when heated it gives antimony pentoxide or tetroxide.

According to C. F. Wenzel,[2] aq. phosphoric acid dissolves a little antimony trioxide, and on evaporation a dark green mass is obtained which fuses to a glass when heated. R. Brandes obtained small crystals of **antimony phosphate,** $2Sb_2O_3.3P_2O_5,4SbPO_4.P_2O_5.nH_2O$, which, with cold water, form antimonyl pyrophosphate, $2Sb_2O_3.P_2O_5$, or $(SbO)_4P_2O_7$; and with hot water, a more basic salt $(SbO)_8P_2O_9$. These statements all want revision. H. Rose found that sodium hydrophosphate gives a white incomplete precipitation with antimony salts, and A. Brand that sodium or ammonium pyrophosphate also gives a white precipitate soluble in excess. According to A. Schwarzenberg, when antimony trioxide is boiled with a soln. of sodium pyrophosphate, and the soln. evaporated over sulphuric acid, a cauliflower-like mass is obtained, which, when treated with water, leaves the greater part of the antimony trioxide undissolved.

E. Glatzel's work on *antimony orthosulphophosphate*, $SbPS_4$, is discussed in connection with the thiophosphates—8 50, 39. Complex salts with antimony pentachloride and phosphorus pentachloride, and phosphoryl chloride have been mentioned in connection with phosphorus pentachloride.

REFERENCES.

¹ A. Naumann, *Ber.*, **37**. 4333, 1904 ; E. Péligot, *Ann. Chim. Phys.*, (3), **20**. 283, 1847 ; J. B. Senderens, *Bull. Soc. Chim.*, (3), **15**. 218, 1896 ; C. F. Bucholz, *Taschenbuch Scheidekünstler*, **27**. 89, 1806 ; J. J. Berzelius, *Schweigger's Journ.*, **6**. 144, 1812 ; **22**. 69, 1818 ; V. Thomas, *Compt. Rend.*, **120**. 1116, 1895 ; H. Rose, *Pogg. Ann.*, **9**. 45, 1826.
² H. Rose, *Pogg. Ann.*, **9**. 45, 1826 ; A. Brand, *Zeit. anal. Chem.*, **28**. 599, 1889 ; R. Brandes, *Schweigger's Journ.*, **62**. 201, 1831 ; C. F. Wenzel, *Lehre von der Verwandschaft des Körper*, Dresden, 1777 ; A. Schwarzenberg, *Journ. prakt. Chem.*, (1), **46**. 247, 1849 ; *Untersuchungen über die pyrophosphorsauren Salzen*, Göttingen, 1847 ; *Liebig's Ann.*, **65**. 2, 1848 ; E. Glatzel, *Ber.*, **24**. 3886, 1891 ; *Zeit. anorg. Chem.*, **4**. 219, 1893.

CHAPTER LIII

BISMUTH

§ 1. The History of Bismuth

It is sometimes stated that bismuth was probably known to the ancients, but was confused with lead and tin. Even as late as the seventeenth century, Basil Valentine [1] could write in his *Letztes Testamentum* (Hambourg, 1777) :

Antimony is the bastard of lead, and bismuth is marcassite, the bastard of tin. . . . Antimony comes between tin and lead, while bismuth or magnesia comes between tin and iron.

The term *marcasite* was used by Albertus Magnus, in his thirteenth-century *De rebus metallicis et mineralibus* (Rouen, 1476), and by A. Libavius in his fourteenth-century *Alchymia* (Francofurti, 1595), for a variety of different minerals. It is therefore unlikely, as G. Hoffmann has shown, that bismuth was known to the Orientals under the name *markaschite*, or marcasite. Towards the end of the sixteenth century, G. Agricola referred to *bisemutum* or *plumbum cinereum* as a specific metal different from lead and from tin ; A. Libavius said that the regulus of bismuth does not differ from that of antimony ; and it was sometimes called *antimonium femininum* or *female antimony*. M. Ettmüller, about the end of the seventeenth century, regarded bismuth as a kind of lead, for he said : Three kinds of lead are known : (i) ordinary lead, (ii) tin, and (iii) bismuth ; and added that the third approaches more nearly to silver. This seems to have been an untested hypothesis because for at least a century longer bismuth was confused with other metals. Thus, G. Agricola said that bismuth was also called *testum argenti*, since it was supposed to be silver which nature had not perfected. N. Lemery did not consider bismuth to be a specific metal. He said :

Bismuth is a sulphureous marcasite found in tin mines. Many believe that bismuth is an imperfect tin which partakes of a good store of arsenic. . . . It is more probably a regulus of tin prepared artificially in England in imitation of a rare natural bismuth. . . . The pores of bismuth are disposed in another manner than those of tin because the menstruum which dissolves tin cannot entirely dissolve bismuth.

Similar views were held by M. Poli, C. F. du Fay, and J. H. G. von Justi. J. Hellot did not accept N. Lemery's opinion that bismuth can be made by melting arsenic and tin with potassium tartrate and nitrate ; and he prepared a button of *véritable bismuth* from a cobaltiferous bismuth ore. In 1739, J. H. Pott observed the action of many reagents on bismuth ; and in 1753, C. J. Geoffroy showed that bismuth is a specific metal which has many analogies with lead. The reactions of bismuth were studied by J. d'Arcet, B. G. Sage, B. Pelletier, T. Bergman, L. B. G. de Morveau, L. E. Pouchet, R. J. Haüy, L. Clouet, C. Hatchett, W. Lewis, W. A. Lampadius, C. L. Cadet de Gassicourt, J. Davy, P. Lagerhjelm, L. J. Chaudet, G. S. Sérullas, etc.

The origin of the word *bismuth* has not been clearly established. F. von Kobell [2] accepted the opinion that the word comes from the Arabian *wiss majaht*—in allusion to its melting as easily as storax, but S. Fraenkel could not accept this. According to C. Hintze, M. de Lazarde connects it with the Persian word *sipedak* or *isfidaz*, meaning white ; and G. Hoffmann, and M. Ruland connect the word with *Bleiweiss* —white-lead. J. Matthesius, and E. O. von Lippmann consider that the word is of German origin, for *wismat* is a German miner's term, *wis mat* meaning *weisse masse, i.e.* a white mass or a white metal. The *w* passes into *b* when latinized.

REFERENCES.

[1] G. Hoffmann, *Neues Jahrb. Min.*, 291, 1878 ; G. Agricola, *De natura fossilium*, Basileæ, 337, 1558 ; *De ortu et causis subterraneorum*, Basileæ, 1558 ; *Bermannus sive de re metallica*, Basileæ, 439, 1558 ; M. Ruland, *Lexicon alchemiæ*, Francofurti, 1612 ; A. Libavius, *De natura metallorum*, Francofurti, 1600 ; M. Ettmüller, *Nouvelle chimie raisonée*, Lyon, 187, 1693 ; N. Lemery, *Cours de chymie*, Paris, 1675 ; *Dictionaire universel des drozues simples*, Paris, 1698 ; *Mém. Acad.*, 329, 1707 ; J. H. G. von Justi, *Neue Wahrheiten zum Vortheil der Naturkunde*, Leipzig, 1754 ; J. H. Pott, *Observationum et animadversionum chymicurum de wismuths*, Berolini, 1739 ; T. Bergman, *De minerarum docimasia Lumida*, Upsala, 1780 ; J. Hellot, *Mém. Acad.*, 231, 1737 ; C. J. Geoffroy, *ib.*, 296, 1753 ; B. G. Sage, *ib.*, 99, 1780 ; C. F. du Fay, *ib.*, 31, 1727 ; M. Poli, *ib.*, 40, 1713 ; J. d'Arcet, *Journ. Méd. Chim.*, 43. 552, 1775 ; Basil Valentine, *Offenbahrung des verborgenen Handgriffe*, Erfurth, 29, 1624 ; W. A. Lampadius, *Handbuch der chemischen Analyse der Mineralkörper*, Freiburg, 1801 ; B. Pelletier, *Ann. Chim. Phys.*, (1), 13. 121, 1792 ; L. B. G. de Morveau, *ib.*, (1), 30. 185, 1797 ; L. E. Pouchet, *ib.*, (1), 27. 99, 1798 ; L. Clouet, *ib.*, (1), 34. 208, 1800 ; G. S. Sérullas, *ib.*, (2), 38. 318, 1828 ; L. J. Chaudet, *ib.*, (2), 5. 142, 1817 ; (2), 8. 113, 1818 ; (2), 9. 397, 1818 ; P. Lagerhjelm, *ib.*, (1), 94. 161, 1818 ; *Acad. Handl. Stockholm*, 34. 219, 1813 ; J. Davy, *Phil. Trans.*, 102. 169, 1812 ; C. Hatchett, *ib.*, 93. 26, 1803 ; C. L. Cadet de Gassicourt, *Journ. Pharm. Chim.*, (1), 1. 46, 1809 ; R. J. Haüy, *Journ. Mines*, 5. 582, 1797 ; W. Lewis, *Commercium Philosophico-Technicum*, London, 509, 573, 1754.
[2] C. Hintze, *Handbuch der Mineralogie*, Leipzig, 1. i, 123, 1904 ; F. von Kobell, *Geschichte der Mineralogie*, München, 604, 1864 ; E. O. von Lippmann, *Entstehung und Ausbreitung der Alchemie*, Berlin, 642, 1919 ; S. Fraenkel in C. Hintze, *Handbuch der Mineralogie*, Leipzig, 1. 123, 1904 ; M. Ruland, *Lexicon alchemie*, Francofurti, 1612 ; G. Hoffmann, *Neues Jahrb. Min.*, 291, 1878 ; J. Matthesius, *Sarepta oder Berg-Postell*, Nürnberg, 395, 1562.

§ 2. The Occurrence of Bismuth

Bismuth is a common element, but it is neither abundantly nor widely diffused in nature. F. W. Clarke and H. S. Washington [1] estimated that the igneous rocks of the earth's crust contained $n \times 10^{-7}$ per cent. of bismuth, and J. H. L. Vogt, $n \times 10^{-8}$ per cent. According to H. Rowland,[2] and M. N. Saha, the spectral lines of bismuth have not been detected in sunlight; although J. N. Lockyer, and C. C. Hutchins and E. S. Holden attributed to bismuth some of the lines in the solar spectrum. The bismuth lines in the spectra of meteorites were examined by J. N. Lockyer.

Elemental bismuth occurs in veins in gneiss and other crystalline rocks, and in clay slate. It usually accompanies various ores of silver, cobalt, lead, zinc, and tin. It may also be associated with gold and silver. G. Agricola [3] referred to the deposits of bismuth in Saxony and Bohemia ; and J. Hellot, to those in Cornwall. Native bismuth probably results from the reduction of other ores of the metal, although the Bolivian deposit may be primary. The bismuth is intergrown with cassiterite, and wolframite may also be present. The following analyses of native bismuth were reported respectively by H. Sjögren, D. Forbes, F. A. Genth, P. T. Cleve and C. H. J. von Feilitzen, and V. I. Vernadsky and A. E. Fersman :

	Bi	Te	As	Pb	Sb	Fe	S	SO₂
Nordmark	63	—	—	28·65	—	2·46	5·18	—
Illampu, Bolivia	94·46	5·09	0·38	—	—	—	0·07	—
Pic, Bolivia	99·91	0·04	—	—	—	trace	—	—
Fahlun	91–95	—	—	—	—	—	—	—
Transbalkans	79·45	—	—	—	0·35	—	18·61	0·19

The occurrence of native bismuth in Cornwall was described by R. Hörnes, J. H. Collins, and R. P. Greg and W. G. Lettsom ; in Devonshire, by G. A. Kenngott ; and in Cumberland, and Stirlingshire by R. P. Greg and W. G. Lettsom. The German and Czechoslovakian deposits—Schneeberg, Annaberg, Johangeorgenstadt, Altenburg, Reuss,

Württemberg, Wittichen, Bieber, Hartz, Silesia, Bohemia—were described by A. Frenzel, P. Groth, F. Sandberger, L. Fletcher, G. Leonhard, W. von Gümbel, M. Websky, V. R. von Zepharovich, and C. Zimmermann ; those in Hungary, by V R. von Zepharovich ; in Steiermark, by V. R. von Zepharovich, and E. Hatle ; in Carinthia, by V. R. von Zepharovich, and A. Brunlechner ; in Salzburg, by V. R. von Zepharovich, and E. Fugger ; in Switzerland, by C. Heusler, and M. Ossent ; in France, by G. Leonhard, and A. Carnot ; in Norway, by G. Leonhard ; in Sweden, by A. Erdmann, H. Sjögren, L. J. Igelström, G. Leonhard, and P. T. Cleve and C. H. J. von Feilitzen ; in Russia, by M. von Tscheffkin, and N. von Kokscharoff ; in Canada, by G. C. Hoffmann ; in Connecticut, South Carolina, and Colorado, by J. D. Dana, G. F. Kunz, and H. J. Burkart ; in Mexico, by H. J. Burkart, and C. F. de Landero ; in Bolivia and Chili, by I. Domeyko, G. Rose, D. Forbes, F. A. Genth, and A. Arzruni ; in Tasmania, by G. vom Rath, and H. von Foullon ; in Victoria, by C. H. F. Ulrich ; in New South Wales, and Queensland, by A. Liversidge ; in South Australia, by A. L. Sack ; and in South-West Africa, by G. Gürich.

Native bismuth is perhaps the most important ore mineral. The bismuth minerals rarely occur alone, and are nearly always associated with other ores. The bismuth deposits are grouped in these classes : (i) The *bismuth-tin deposits* in which the bismuth is associated with tin and copper, with tungsten and molybdenum as accessories—*e.g.* the Bolivian deposits, and those at Chili, Peru, Argentina, Queensland, New South Wales, Tasmania, France, and Cornwall. (ii) The *bismuth-cobalt deposits* have the bismuth associated with cobalt and uranium —*e.g.*, the deposits in Saxony. (iii) The *bismuth-gold deposits—e.g.*, Queensland, New South Wales, Norway, and United States.

The bismuth minerals include : **Bismithides.**—*Chilenite*, or bismuth-silver, Ag_5Bi or Ag_6Bi ; *matildite*—a bismuth-silver alloy ; *maldonite*, bismuth-gold, Au_2Bi. **Sulphides, selenides, or tellurides.**—*Bismuthinite* (sometimes *bismuthite*) Bi_2S_3 ; *guanajuatite*, or *frenzelite*, $Bi_2(Se,S)_3$; *alaskaite*, a galeno-bismuthinite ; *silaonite*—a mixture of guanajuatite, bismuthinite, and bismuth ; *tapalpite*, a silver bismuth sulphotelluride ; *tellurobismuth*, Bi_2Te_3 ; *tetradymite*, Bi_2Te_2S ; *joseite*, $Bi_3Te(S,Se)$; *grünlingite*, Bi_4S_3Te ; and *wehrlite*, Bi_3Te_2, or $AgBi_7Te_7$. **Sulpharsenide, and sulphantimonides.**—*Callilite*, $(Ni,Co,Fe)(Sb,Ad,Bi)S$; *bismutosmaltite*, $Co(As,Bi)_3$; *alloclase*, $Co(As,Bi)_2$; *hauchecornite*, $(Ni,Co,Fe)_7(S,Bi,Sb,As)_8$; and *saynite*, a mixture of polydymite, Ni_4S_5, and bismuthinite. **Sulphobismuthites.**—*Chiviatite*, $Pb_3Bi_4S_{11}$; *cuprobismutite*, $Cu_6Bi_8S_{15}$; *rezbanyite*, and *dognacskaite*, $Pb_4Bi_{10}S_{19}$; *plenargyrite*, and *matildite*, $AgBiS_2$; *emplectite*, $Cu_2Bi_2S_4$; *galenobismutite*, $PbBi_2S_4$; *bismutoplagionite*, $Pb_5Bi_8S_{17}$; *alaskaite*, $(Pb,Ag_2,Cu_2)Bi_2S_4$; *selenobismutite*, $PbBi_2(S,Se)_4$; *klaprothite*, $Cu_6Bi_4S_9$; *schirmerite*, $(Ag_2,Pb)_3Bi_4S_9$; *kobellite*, $Pb_2(Bi,Sb)_2S_5$; *cosalite* or *bjelkite*, $Pb_2Bi_2S_5$; *schapbachite*, $(Pb,Ag_2)_2Bi_2S_5$; *wittichenite*, Cu_3BiS_3 ; *tapalpite*, $Ag_3Bi(S,Te)_3$; *aikainite*, or *needle-ore*, or *patrinite*, $Cu_2Pb_2Bi_2S_6$; *lillianite*, $Pb_3Bi_2S_6$; *beegerite*, $Pb_6Bi_2S_9$; and *jahlerz*, in which some of the antimony is replaced by bismuth, **Oxides, and oxidized ores.** —*Bismite* or *bismuth ochre* is a yellow earth approximating in some cases to Bi_2O_3 ; *tanzite* is a mixture of bismuth ochre with other substances ; and *bolivite*, a mixture of bismuth ochre and bismuthinite. Amongst other oxidized ores are *carelinite*, Bi_4O_3S ; *atelesite*, $(BiO)_3.Bi(OH)_2(AsO_4)$; *montanite*, $\{Bi(OH)_2\}_2TeO_4$; *arsenobismite*, $2Bi_2O_3.As_2O_5.2H_2O$; *rhagite*, $Bi(BiO)_9(AsO_4)_4.8H_2O$; *pucherite*, $BiVO_4$; *mixite*, $BiCu_{10}(AsO_4)_6(OH)_8.7H_2O$; *walpurgite*, $Bi_{10}(VO_2)_3As_4O_{28}$; *uranosphärite*, $(BiO)_2U_2O_7.3H_2O$; *eulytite* and *agricolite*, $Bi_4(SiO_4)_3$; *bismutoferrite*, $Bi_2Fe_4Si_4O_{27}$ (probably a mixture) ; *bismuthspar, bismuthite*, or *bismutosphaerite*, $(BiO)_2CO_3$; and *daubréeite*, $BiOCl$.

It will be observed that of the three related amphoteric elements, arsenic, antimony, and bismuth, the acidic property is dominant in arsenic ; and the basic property is dominant in bismuth ; while in antimony, the acidic property is rather more pronounced than the basic quality. Most of the minerals just enumerated are not of common occurrence. Bismuth and its sulphide, bismuthinite, are the principal ores ; and bismuth ochre or bismite is the commonest oxidation product. The geographical distribution of the bismuth ores is illustrated by the map, Fig. 1.

Europe.—In *Britain*,[4] small, unimportant deposits occur in Cornwall, and Cumberland ; and also at Alva, Stirlingshire. Formerly a small amount of bismuth was produced in England. In *Germany*,[5] Saxony for a long time had the world monopoly in the production of bismuth, but the output in recent years has been small. The ores are found mainly at Schneeberg, Johangeorgenstadt, Schwarzenberg, Altenberg, Annaberg, and Zinnwald in Saxony. Ores also occur near Nassau, at Wittschen, and at Schutzbach. There is a small deposit in *France* at Meymac, Corrèze ; Pay-les-Vignes ; and at Framont, Vosges. In *Spain*,[6] a small amount of bismuth ore is also produced in the Conquista district of Cordoba.

Some veins of bismuth occur in the Val d'Anniviers, Switzerland. In *Austria*, fahlbands occur at Schladming, Styria, where they are known as *Brandes* on account of the brown, weathered zone they form at the surface. Native bismuth also occurs in the Lölling-Hüttenberg district of Carinthia. In *Czechoslovakia*, bismuth ores occur at Joachimstal, Bohemia. In *Yugo-Slavia*,[7] there are bismuth deposits at Gradiste, Aldinats, Algin Dol, and Jasikova. In *Rumania*, bismuth ore is found at Cziklova, and at Rezbanaya. In *Russia*, bismuth-gold occurs at Schil-Isset, Urals. Small amounts occur in the cobalt ores of Scandinavia. In *Norway*, bismuth is associated with gold ores at Svartdal ; and with copper near Drammen. The bismuth mines are at Kjennar. In *Sweden*, bismuth is found at Fahen, and in some of the deposits of the cobalt fahlbands.

Asia.—Bismuth ores occur in Lower *Burma*.[8] Small quantities have been found in the *Dutch East Indies* [9]—near Lake Toba ; Banca ; Western Borneo ; and Western Celebes. In *China*,[10] some bismuth ochre has been produced in the Kiangsi Province ; but the districts of Wong Yuen, Yuigte, Pao Au, Shiang Shau, and Chin Chow have deposits of bismutite and bismuth ochre, which are worked from the surface, and furnish over 5 per cent. of the world's production. In *Japan*,[11] there are scattered occurrences of bismuth ore which may be associated with ores of tungsten and molybdenum, and with gold, silver, or copper. The chief occurrences are at Nishizawa in Shimotsuke ; Nakanosawa in Yechigo ; Ikuno in Tajima ; Imooka, and Hade in Mimasaka ; Tomikuni in Tamba ; and Kamioka in Hida. In *Korea*,[12] there are deposits in the Hwang Hai Province. In *Siberia*,[13] bismuth ore occurs between Olovyana and Berezoff, and also in the Zabaykalye region.

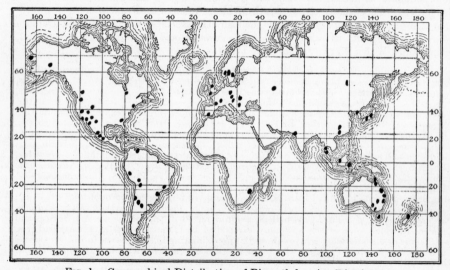

FIG. 1.—Geographical Distribution of Bismuth-bearing Districts.

Africa.—Bismuth ore is distributed in Northern *Rhodesia*,[14] particularly in the Kaomba field of the Luana Valley. Ores have also been found in the Lomagundi, Umtali, and Victoria districts of Southern Rhodesia. In the *Transvaal*, bismuth is associated with the gold ores of the Sabi and Lydenberg districts.

North America.—In *Canada*,[15] bismuthinite is associated with the gold-silver-copper ores of Rossland, British Columbia ; and native bismuth is associated with the ores of the Cobalt District, South Lorrain, Otter Township, Shining Tree, and Port Arthur, Lake Superior. Bismuth ores are found in many parts of the *United States* ; [16] but the metal is produced only as a by-product in the smelting of lead, copper, gold, and silver ores. Thus some is recovered from the flue-dust of the copper smelters ; and some from the slimes in the electrolytic refining of lead. Bismuth minerals occur in Alaska—Eva Creek, Cherley Creek, and Fairbanks ; in Yuma Co., Arizona ; in Rincon, and Nevada City, California ; in Leadville, Colorado ; Trumbull, Connecticut ; at Dahlonega, and Ashbury, Georgia ; at Cooper, Maine ; at Elkhorn, Montana ; in the goldfield district, Nevada ; at Eagle, New Mexico ; in the Chesterfield district, South Carolina ; Garfield, Utah ; near Loon Lake, Washington ; and in the Jelm mountains of Wyoming. Bismuth minerals occur in several parts of *Mexico* [17]—in the States of Guanajuato, Jalisco, Queretaro, Sinaloa, Sonora, and Zacatecas.

South America.—A small amount of bismuth ore is produced in *Argentina*,[18] from the provinces of La Rioja, and Sierra de San Luis. *Bolivia* [19] is the principal producer of bismuth ores in the world, and it could easily supply all the world's demands. The ores are always associated with tin ; they occur in the departments of Potosi, and La Paz on the Cordillera Real, or the eastern branch of the Andes. In *Brazil*,[20] native bismuth and bismuth ochre occur in the gold mines of Minas Geraes ; in the State of Rio Grande do Sul ; and at Brijões and St. Antonio du Jesus in Bahia. In *Chili*, native bismuth and bismuth ores occur near Juan Godoy and San Antonio, Atacania. In *Peru*,[21] there is an important mine in the Department of Junin. Deposits of bismuth minerals occur near Tocuyo, *Venezuela*.

Australasia.—Native bismuth occurs in the Owen gold-field, *New Zealand*.[22] In *Australia*,[23] native bismuth and bismuth minerals occur with those of tin, tungsten, and molybdenum. In *New South Wales*, bismuth deposits occur in the districts of New England, Cobar, and Whipstick ; in Queensland in the Eastern districts, particularly Cook, and Burnett—and comprising the districts of Kennedy, and Port Curtis, Moreton, Burke, Darling Downs, Leichardt, and Wide Bay ; in *Victoria*, bismuth and bismuth ores occur at Linton, and Maldon ; in *Tasmania*, in the Middlesex district, and at Dundas, South Heemiskirk, Mount Ramsay, Mount Lyell, and King Island ; in *South Australia*, there is an important deposit in the Onkaparinga Hundred ; and in *Western Australia*, at Melville.

In 1909, Australia produced 19·2 metric tons of bismuth ; Spain, 76·5 ; and Peru, 30·3. In 1911, Australia produced 18 metric tons ; Bolivia, 550 ; Spain, 51 ; and Peru, 24·4. Incomplete returns are indicated in Table I. The average price in

TABLE I.—THE WORLD'S PRODUCTION OF BISMUTH OR BISMUTH ORE.

—	1918.	1919.	1924.	1926.
Argentina (ore) . . .	28	—	222	—
Australia (ore and metal) .	52·20	21·33	305	165
,, (concentrate) .	120·87	143·99	—	—
Bolivia (ore and metal) .	360·50	263·28	39£	—
,, (concentrate) . .	129·57	110·80	7855	7379
Canada	—	—	—	58
China (ore)	—	86·36	—	—
Germany (concentrate) .	300·00	197·0	100	—
India (metal) . . .	0·25 (1917)	—	—	—
Japan (metal) . . .	0·44	0·73	583	—
,, (ore)	1·23	0·88	—	—
Peru	—	—	—	—
Rhodesia (ore) . . .	—	1·22	—	48
Spain (ore)	33·50	75·00	2460	—
South Africa. . . .	—	0·30	—	—
United States . . .	—	145·00	—	—

London was 7s. 6d. per lb. in 1892 ; 3s. in 1895 ; 5s. in 1897 ; 7s. 6d. in 1900 ; 10s. in 1904 and in 1914 ; 11s. in 1917 ; 12s. 6d. in 1919 ; 9s. in 1922 ; and 8s. 6d. in 1924. According to R. Allen,[24] refined bismuth is usually put on the market in 25-lb. bars, which are packed in wooden boxes, holding 150 lb., with wooden wedges between the bars, the minimum wholesale lot being 500 lb. There are no standard specifications, but the refined metal must be 99·9 per cent. pure. When used for making medicines the metal must be absolutely free from arsenic ; for alloy-making the freedom from arsenic is not so important.

Bismuth occurs as an accessory constituent in many minerals. Antimony and bismuth are not so commonly associated as is the case with arsenic and bismuth. K. A. Hofmann [25] found bismuth in *bröggerite ;* and W. F. Hillebrand, in *uraninite ;* but F. Soddy observed none in Singalese *thorite.* C. M. Kersten, A. Frenzel, and A. Carnot found bismuth associated with arsenic or arsenical *pyrites ;* T. Petersen, with *arsenical nickel ;* H. Laspeyres, and C. F. Rammelsberg, with *smaltite ;* C. Winkler, with *trögerite ;* H. Laspeyres, with *corneyite ;* A. Piutti and E. Stoppani, with *pyrites ;* H. Ramage, with the flue-dust from South Yorkshire *coals ;* G. T. Lindroth, with *scheelite ;* F. Field and F. A. Abel, with *copper ores ;* and H. N. Warren, and W. N. Hartley and H. Ramage, with *iron ores.* In consequence of the association of bismuth with many of metal ores, bismuth is sometimes found associated with metals—*e.g.* copper, iron, tin, and lead. F. Field said that bismuth is contained in all copper coinage—from the Bactrian coins, 181 B.C., to our own—in all cupreous ores except the carbonates, and in nearly all specimens of commercial copper.

Traces of bismuth have been reported in some spring waters, or in the ochreous deposits from the same. Thus, A. and G. de Negri [26] found traces in the water of Casteggio, Cremona; and T. Poleck, in the water of Flinsberg, Silesia. H. A. L. Wiggers found a trace of bismuth in the ochreous deposit from the spring-water of Driburg, but R. Fresenius did not confirm this. T. Poleck found 0·003 per cent. Bi_2O_3 in the ochreous deposit of the spring-water of Flinsberg, Silesia, and E. Reichardt, the same amount of bismuth trioxide in the deposit from the spring-water at Liebenstein, Thuringia.

REFERENCES.

[1] F. W. Clarke and H. S. Washington, *The Composition of the Earth's Crust*, Washington, 1924; *Proc. Nat. Acad. Sciences*, 8. 108, 1922; J. H. L. Vogt, *Zeit. prakt. Geol.*, 6. 225, 314, 377, 413, 1898; 7. 10, 274, 1899.

[2] H. Rowland, *Amer. Journ. Science*, (3), 41. 243, 1891; *Johns Hopkins Univ. Circulars*, 85, 1891; *Chem. News*, 63. 133, 1891; J. N. Lockyer, *Proc. Roy. Soc.*, 27. 279, 1877; 43. 117, 1887; C. C. Hutchins and E. S. Holden, *Phil. Mag.*, (5), 24. 325, 1887; M. N. Saha, *ib.*, (6), 40. 808, 1920.

[3] G. Agricola, *De natura fossilium*, Basileæ, 337, 1558; *Bermannus sive de re metallica*, Basileæ, 439, 1558; J. Hellot, *Mém. Acad.*, 231, 1737; G. A. Kenngott, *Uebersichte der Resultate mineralogischer Forschungen*, Leipzig, 111, 1861; R. P. Greg and W. G. Lettsom, *Manual of the Mineralogy of Great Britain and Ireland*, London, 377, 1858; J. H. Collins, *A Handbook to the Mineralogy of Cornwall and Devon*, London, 15, 1876; A. Frenzel, *Tschermak's Mitt.*, (2), 16. 523, 1897; *Mineralogisches Lexikon für das Königreich Sachsen*, Leipzig, 341, 1874; G. Leonhard, *Handwörterbuch der topographischen Mineralogie*, Heidelberg, 526, 1843; *Die Mineralien Badens nach ihrem Vorkommen*, Stuttgart, 44, 1876; F. Sandberger, *Uebersicht der Mineralien Unter-frankens und Aschaffenburg*, 3, 1890; *Untersuchungen über Erzgäuge*, Wiesbaden, 1882; *Neues Jahrb. Min.*, 419, 1868; M. von Tscheffkin, *Isis*, 434, 1837; *Neues Jahrb. Min.*, 59, 1838; H. J. Burkart, *ib.*, 32, 310, 1874; G. Gürich, *ib.*, i, 104, 1890; A. L. Sack, *ib.*, 333, 1852; L. Fletcher, *Phil. Mag.*, (5), 9. 195, 1880; D. Forbes, *ib.*, (4), 29. 4, 1865; V. R. von Zepharovich, *Mineralogisches Lexikon für das Kaiserthum Oesterreich*, Wien, 472, 1859; 343, 1873; W. von Gümbel, *Geognostische Beschreibung des Königreichs Bayern*, Gotha, 3. 303, 404, 426, 1879; E. Fugger, *Die Mineralien des Herzoathumes Salzburg*, Salzburg, 2, 1878; A. Brunlechner, *Die Minerale des Herzogthumes Kärnten*, Klagenfurt, 102, 1884; P. Groth, *Die Mineraliensammlung der Universitat Strassburg*, Strassburg, 10, 1878; C. Zimmerman, *Das Harzgebirge*, Darmstadt, 208, 1834; M. Websky, *Zeit. deut. geol. Ges.*, 5. 406, 1853; C. Heusler, *ib.*, 28. 238, 1870; A. Carnot, *Compt. Rend.*, 78. 171, 1874; 79. 302, 477, 1874; *Bull. Soc. Chim.*, (2), 20. 487, 1873; (2), 21. 113. 1874; H. Sjögren, *Geol. För. Förh. Stockholm*, 4. 106, 1878; L. J. Igelström, *ib.*, 7. 106, 1884; A. Erdmann, *Lärobok i Mineralogien*, Stockholm, 171, 1853; I. Domeyko, *Elementos de mineralojia*, Santiago, 296, 1879; *Compt. Rend.*, 85. 977, 1877; *Ann. Mines*, (7), 18. 538, 1881; N. von Kokscharoff, *Materialen zur Mineralogie Russlands*, St. Petersburg, 6. 235, 1874; C. F. de Landero, *Sinopsis mineralogica o catalogo descriptivo de los minerales*, Mexico, 65, 1888; C. H. F. Ulrich, *Contributions to the Mineralogy of Victoria*, Melbourne, 50, 1866; 5, 1870; G. C. Hoffmann, *List of Minerals Occurring in Canada*, Ottawa, 76, 1890; *Trans. Roy. Soc. Canada*, 7. 65, 1890; A. Liversidge, *The Minerals of New South Wales*, Sydney, 1882; E. Hatle, *Die Minerale Steiermarke*, Graz, 4, 1885; M. Ossent, *Zeit. Kryst.*, 9. 563, 1884; A. Arzruni, *ib.*, 9. 75, 1884; R. Hörnes, *Sitzber. Akad. Wien*, 1. 624, 1848; P. T. Cleve and C. H. J. von Feilitzen, *Oefvers. Akad. Stockholm*, 159, 1861; *Journ. prakt. Chem.*, (1), 86. 384, 1862; V. I. Vernadsky and A. E. Fersman, *Bull. Acad. St. Petersburg*, (6), 4. 487, 1910; F. A. Genth, *Amer. Journ. Science*, (2), 27. 247, 1859; G. F. Kunz, *ib.*, (4), 16. 398, 1903; G. vom Rath, *Ber. Niederrh. Ges. Bonn.*, 63, 1877; 81, 1879; H. von Foullon, *Verh. geol. Reichsanst. Wien*, 144, 1884; G. Rose, *Abhand. Akad. Berlin*, 90, 1849; *Pogg. Ann.*, 77. 144, 1849; K. Meileitner, *Edelerden Erze*, 3. 61, 74, 1922; S. P. de Rubies and F. G. Esteban, *Anal. Soc. Fis. Quim.*, 19. 347, 1921; J. D. Dana, *A System of Mineralogy*, New York, 1892.

[4] W. J. Harwood, *Trans. Roy. Geol. Soc. Cornwall*, 5. 12, 129, 1843; H. T. de la Bache, *Report on the Geology of Cornwall, Devon, and West Somerset*, London, 1839; J. H. Collins, *Observations on the West of England Mining Region*, London, 1912; H. Dewey, *Copper Ores of Cornwall and Devon*, London, 1923; *Tungsten and Manganese Ores*, London, 1923.

[5] R. Beck, *Ore Deposits*, New York, 1905; J. A. Phillips and H. Louis, *A Treatise on Ore Deposits*, London, 1896; H. H. Thomas and D. A. MacAlister, *The Geology of Ore Deposits*, London, 1909; V. C. Heikes, *Min. Resources U.S. Geol. Sur.*, i, 137, 1921.

[6] S. P. de Rubies and F. G. Esteban, *Anal. Fis. Quim.*, 19. 347, 1921; S. P. de Rubies, *ib.*, 18. 335, 1920.

[7] D. A. Wray, *The Geology and Mineral Resources of the Serb-Croat-Slovene State*, London, 1921.
[8] A. M. Heron, *Rec. Geol. Sur. India*, 53. i, 81, 1921; J. C. Brown, *Bull. Indian Ind. and Labour*, 6, 1921.
[9] Anon., *Iron Coal Trade Rev.*, 108. 173, 1924.
[10] V. C. Heikes, *Min. Resources U.S. Geol. Sur.*, i, 67, 1920.
[11] Anon., *Mining in Japan, Past and Present*, Tokyo, 110, 1909.
[12] D. F. Higgins, *Econ. Geol.*, 13. 1, 1918.
[13] V. C. Heikes, *Min. Resources U.S. Geol. Sur.*, i, 21, 1922.
[14] Anon., *Bull. Imp. Inst.*, 22. 342, 1922; *South African Min. Eng. Journ.*, 1425, 1921; F. P. Mennell, *South African Journ. Ind.*, 1308, 1918; T. G. Trevor, *ib.*, 379, 1924; A. E. V. Zealley *South Rhodesian Geol. Sur.*, 2, 1918; *Proc. Rhodesia Science Assoc.*, 16. 17, 1827.
[15] W. Lindgren, *Mineral Deposits*, New York, 1919; W. G. Miller, *Rep. Ontario Bur. Mines*, 19, 1913.
[16] T. Chaplin, *Bull. U.S. Geol. Sur.*, 592, 1914; F. A. Moffit. *ib.*, 533, 1913; H. D. McCaskey, *ib.*, 666, 1919; J. B. Mertie, *ib.*, 662, 1918; R. M. Overbeck, *ib.*, 662, 1918; J. B. Umpleby, *Mem. Resources U.S. Geol. Sur.*, i, 29, 1917; F. L. Ransome, *Prof. Paper U.S. Geol. Sur.*, 66, 1909; C. P. Linville, *Min. Ind.*, 31. 77, 1922; D. C. Davies, *Metalliferous Mines and Mining*, London, 1901.
[17] Anon., *Bull. Pan-Amer. Union*, 282, 1920.
[18] J. B. Miller and J. T. Singewald, *Mineral Deposits of South America*, New York, 1919.
[19] G. A. Easley, *Eng. Min. Journ.*, 117. 123, 1924.
[20] A. T. Ward, *Min. Ind.*, 30. 70, 1921; A. J. de Socisa Carneiro, *Riquezas Mineras de Estado da Bahia*, 1908.
[21] J. E. Singewald and B. J. Miller, *Eng. Min. Journ.*, 102. 583, 1916.
[22] J. Park, *The Geology of New Zealand*, Christchurch, 1910; E. B. Dow, *Proc. Australasian Inst. Min. Mat.*, 58. 29, 1925.
[23] F. E. Pittman, *Ann. Rep. N.S.W. Geol. Survey*, 1901; J. E. Carne and E. C. Andrews, *ib.*, 152, 1918; J. E. Carne, *Min. Resources N.S.W. Geol. Sur.*, 15, 1911; J. A. Watt, *ib.*, 4. 1898; C. L. Ball, *Pub. Queensland Geol. Sur.*, 248, 1915; B. Dunstan, *Queensland Min. Journ.*, 18. 17, 1917; H. Y. L. Broun, *Record South Australia Dept. Mines*, 1908; L. Hills, *Rep. Tasmania Geol. Sur. Dept. Mines*, 1, 1916; W. H. Twelvetrees, *Bull. Tasmania Geol. Sur. Dept. Mines*, 14, 1913; L. L. Waterhouse, *Min. Resources Tasmania Geol. Sur.*, 1, 1916; W. C. W. Pierce, *Trans. Inst. Min. Met.*, 21. 239, 1912; C. M. Harris, *ib.*, 29. 3, 1919; P. G. Tait, *Min. Eng. Rev.*, 435, 1913.
[24] Anon., *Bismuth, Mineral Resources Bureau*, London, 1920; R. Allen, *Bismuth*, London, 1925; H. M. Brush, *Eng. Min. Journ.*, 115. 272, 1923; L. H. Quin, *Metal Handbook and Statistics*, London, 1925; Anon., *Bull. Imp. Inst.*, 10. 628, 1912; J. B. Umpleby, *Mineral Resources United States*, Washington, i, 501, 1918.
[25] C. M. Kersten, *Schweigger's Journ.*, 53. 377, 1828; A. Carnot, *Compt. Rend.*, 79. 479, 1874; F. Field and F. A. Abel, *Journ. Chem. Soc.*, 16. 304, 1861; *Chem. News*, 7. 164, 1863; F. Field, *ib.*, 36. 261, 1877; H. N. Warren, *ib.*, 58. 27, 1888; A. Piutti and E. Stoppani, *Gazz. Chim. Ital.*, 35. ii, 29, 1905; H. Laspeyres, *Zeit. Kryst.*, 19. 8, 1891; A. Frenzel, *Neues Jahrb. Min.*, 677, 1874; T. Petersen, *Pogg. Ann.*, 134. 82, 1868: C. Winkler, *Journ. prakt. Chem.*, (2), 7. 6, 1873; C. F. Rammelsberg, *Handbuch der Mineralchemie*, Leipzig, 46, 1875; W. N. Hartley and H. Ramage, *Journ. Chem. Soc.*, 71. 533, 1897; W. F. Hillebrand, *Bull. U.S. Geol. Sur.*, 299, 1903; K. A. Hofmann, *Ber.*, 34. 914, 1901; F. Soddy, *Nature*, 94. 615, 1915; H. Ramage, *ib.*, 119. 783, 1927; G. T. Lindroth, *Geol. För. Förh. Stockholm*, 44. 110, 1922; 46. 168, 1924.
[26] E. Reichardt, *Arch. Pharm.*, (2), 98. 257, 1850; H. A. L. Wiggers, *ib.*, (2), 102. 215, 1860; A. and G. de Negri, *Gazz. Chim. Ital.*, 8. 120, 1878; R. Fresenius, *Journ. prakt. Chem.*, (1), 98. 325, 1866; T. Poleck, *Ber.*, 12. 1902, 1879.

§ 3. The Extraction of Bismuth

Bismuth ores are usually associated with other minerals; and the ore requires concentrating before the bismuth is extracted. The ore is first milled in a stamp-battery, and then undergoes a system of water concentration. In the case of an ore containing, say, quartz gangue, native bismuth, bismuthinite, bismite, molybdenite, and wolframite, the water classification furnishes concentrates which are dried, and screened to three products. The over-size is re-ground. The three products are passed through magnetic concentrators, and the resulting products are a bismuth concentrate, a tungsten concentrate, and a tungsten-iron concentrate. The magnetic concentration of the bismuth ores in Tasmania was described by W. E. Hitchcock and J. R. Pound.[1] The tailings from the slime tables are passed on to the flotation plant. They contain the bulk of the molybdenite which is classified by differential treatment with kerosene liquor as described by W. H. Bowater.

Bismuth can be extracted from its ores by dry or wet processes. These operations have been discussed by C. F. Plattner,[2] C. Winkler, and C. Schnabel. When the ores contain bismuth in the form of metal, it can be separated by a *process of liquation*. The bismuth melts at a relatively low temp., 270°. When the ore is heated to the m.p. of bismuth in inclined, cylindrical, cast-iron retorts, the molten bismuth separates from the gangue, trickles down the retort, and is tapped at the lower end. The process was formerly used at Saxony. The objection to the process is that it is very wasteful, since from 5 to 33 per cent. bismuth may escape extraction and remain in the residues. In the *fusion or smelting process*, the whole of the ore is melted with a suitable flux. The gangue separates as a slag, and floats on the surface of the metal. On account of the volatility of the bismuth and its oxide, the smelting has to be conducted at a relatively low temp. The fluxes employed are soda-ash with 10–30 per cent. of lime, and hæmatite. In some cases pyrolusite replaces the hæmatite so as to give a slag with a smaller sp. gr. Fluorspar can also be employed to make the slag fluid. All depends on the nature of the gangue to be slagged. Shaft furnaces are not used for the work because of the severe corrosive action of bismuth on the lining of the furnace. On a small scale, the smelting is effected in crucibles made of fireclay or of fireclay fortified with 10–20 per cent. plumbago. The crucibles are heated in the ordinary wind furnace. On a large scale, the smelting is effected in a reverberating furnace built on an iron pan because of the rapid penetration of the brickwork by the bismuth.

The fusion process allows the addition of desulphurizing or of reducing agents to ores so as simultaneously to extract the bismuth from the bismuth sulphides or oxides which may be associated with metallic bismuth. Ores containing a high proportion of sulphide are often roasted ; and coal, or iron, or both, may be used as the reducing agent. Sulphide ores can be directly reduced by fusion with iron ; or the roasted ore is reduced with carbon. The direct reduction process resembles the extraction of lead by the precipitation process. During the roasting, the chemical processes resemble those which occur during the extraction of lead from galena by roasting and reduction. A certain quantity of sulphate is formed during the roasting of bismuth sulphide, and the sulphate is only incompletely decomposed by raising the temp. of the charge, but it is reduced in the fusion. The arsenic and antimony are converted into trioxides during the roasting, and are partly volatilized and partly converted into arsenates and antimonates. The latter are decomposed by coal, coke, or charcoal added towards the end of the roasting, and much of the arsenic and antimony volatilized. Any bismuth oxide volatilized is caught in condensers attached to the flues. A. Valenciennes[3] described the treatment of some Bolivian ores containing 22·80–30·05 per cent. Bi ; 10·20–16·90 per cent. Fe ; 9·50–12·15 per cent. Cu ; and 16·90–19·50 per cent. S. He said :

The powdered mineral was roasted for 24 hrs. in a reverberatory furnace. The oxidized mass was then mixed with 3 per cent. of carbon, and a flux of lime, carbonate of soda, and fluorspar, and placed in another reverberatory furnace having a basin-shaped bed. For two hrs. a reducing flame was made to play over the mass, which was frequently stirred ; the heat was then urged to whiteness, and in two hrs., the whole being quite fused, the furnace was tapped at the side, and the fused mass collected in a cast-iron receiver lined with clay, in which it was allowed to become quite cold. Three layers were found in the receiver, the lowest being metallic bismuth, the next a matte of sulphides of bismuth and copper, and the uppermost a slag containing all the iron. The bismuth contained 2 per cent. of antimony and lead, and 2 per cent. of copper, with traces of silver. The antimony was removed by fusion with nitre, the other metals being separated by the wet process. The matte contained 5 per cent. to 8 per cent. of bismuth, and was treated exactly as above, whereby all but 1 per cent. of bismuth was removed, which was recovered by the wet process.

Oxidized ores are rarely available for smelting. They can be reduced by carbon in crucibles or reverberatory furnaces. The oxycarbonate ore at Meymac was formerly treated by a wet process described by A. Carnot. A. Valenciennes thus described the process for an oxidized ore containing tungsten :

The bismuth was extracted by treating the powdered mineral with hydrochloric acid ; the acid decanted and partially neutralized with sodium carbonate, was then turned into a large quantity of water ; and the precipitated bismuth oxychloride collected and washed, was p'aced in contact with metallic iron. The bismuth so reduced was dried and fused with an alkaline flux. It still retained traces of lead and silver. The residues, insoluble in hydrochloric acid, were dried and calcined with sodium nitrate. This on extraction with boiling water gave sodium tungstate.

The oxide is dissolved by hydrochloric acid more cheaply than by nitric acid. W. Mrazek proposed sulphuric acid as a solvent for bismuth in agentiferous lead ; V. de Luynes, nitric acid for lead-bismuth alloys ; C. Rössler, sulphuric acid. Aqua regia or hot conc. sulphuric acid may be necessary to dissolve the metal or alloy. F. F. G. Eulert proposed a salt soln. and nitric and sulphuric acid as solvent, and ferric chloride has also been proposed. Once in soln., the bismuth can be precipitated as metal by iron—the metals lead, zinc, tin, .cadmium, copper, or manganese also precipitate the bismuth. The bismuth can also be precipitated as a basic salt by diluting the chloride with water. The precipitated oxychloride is reduced by fusion with lime and charcoal ; or by treating the moist oxychloride with iron or zinc along with some slaked or caustic lime to remove the acid. Precipitated bismuth is fused in graphite or iron crucibles with an alkaline flux if necessary. J. W. Kynaston recovered bismuth from cupriferous flue-dust by treatment with hydrochloric acid, precipitation with calcium carbonate ; and reduction with carbon under molten sodium chloride. Guggenheim Bros. obtained bismuth from ores, etc., by volatilization as sulphide when heated in the vapour of sulphur, hydrogen sulphide, or carbon disulphide at 800°–900°. W. Buddëus reduced the ore with silicon or silicides.

Bismuth is generally obtained from metallurgical products—mattes and alloys —by wet processes. In special cases, mattes can be treated for bismuth by roasting followed by smelting with carbon. When a lead-bismuth alloy is submitted to an oxidizing fusion, the lead is first oxidized, and the bismuth commences to oxidize only when the greater proportion of lead has been removed. If the alloy be cupelled the cupel first removes the litharge, then litharge containing bismuth oxide, and last, if the oxidation be stopped at the right moment, bismuth is produced. The bismuth is ground fine, and digested with hydrochloric acid, when the bismuth and a little lead are dissolved as chlorides. The soln. is neutralized with sodium carbonate, and the bismuth precipitated as oxychloride by water. The washed oxychloride is reduced to bismuth as previously indicated. W. Borchers proposed to extract bismuth from lead by an electrolytic process. The alloy is fused with molten alkali chlorides through which is passed an electric current. The lead is dissolved as chloride, and deposited as metal at the cathode or at the bottom of the cathode compartment, while, with a suitable current density, the bismuth and silver remain undissolved, and collect at the bottom of the anode compartment. The results are less satisfactory than smelting processes. The electrodeposition of bismuth was discussed by A. Engelenburg, and J. Lukas and A. Jilek.

The crude bismuth obtained by these processes may contain lead, copper, arsenic, antimony, sulphur, tellurium, iron, cobalt, nickel, thallium, etc. Johnson, Matthey, and Co.[4] gave the following as typical analyses of South America crude bismuth metal :

Bi	Pb	Sn	Sb and As	Cu	Ag	Au
96·0	3·5	0·2	0·2	0·1	—	—
84·800	4·925	0·725	5·525	3·450	0·3005	0·0045

The former had 34 ozs. of silver per ton, and the latter had traces of iron and sulphur, and 0·270 per cent. of oxygen and loss. This composition of bismuth was discussed by R. Schneider, V. Sill, H. Thürach, C. Ekin, N. G. O. Coad, F. A. Genth, D. Forbes, A. Classen, E. Matthey, and G. Brownen. E. A. Smith found from 0·0003 to 0·0110 per cent. of gold, and 0·0705 to 0·3319 per cent. of silver in various samples of bismuth. Impure bismuth is not suited for many of the purposes fo* which bismuth is employed. Bismuth intended for the pharmaceutical preparations must be freed from arsenic and tellurium. The so-called pure commercial bismuth on the market should be freed from copper, tellurium, antimony, lead, and contain not more than 2 parts per million of arsenic. The silver content varies from 3 to 10 ozs. per ton.

The purification of bismuth by the dry methods is less effective, but cheaper, than by wet processes. In the cases when a number of foreign elements are present, the dry method cannot be completed in one operation. The dry process of refining bismuth may involve a liquation of the nickel, or remelting the metal with fluxes of various kinds. C. Méhu removed arsenic by heating the bismuth above its m.p. so as to expose a large surface to air; sulphur is also removed as sulphur dioxide. The residue is remelted with soda and charcoal and tartar or dry soap, and again heated in air. E. Matthey said that all the arsenic can be eliminated from the well-stirred alloy heated above its m.p.—say, to 395°-513°—in air—no loss of bismuth was observed; and antimony can likewise be removed by prolonged fusion and constant stirring. The arsenic volatilizes as oxide, the arsenic oxide separates as an oily film. H. Thürach removed arsenic and iron by fusing the bismuth with potassium chlorate mixed with 2-5 per cent. of sodium hydroxide. G. A. Quesneville removed the arsenic by melting the bismuth with nitre and common salt—some iron and lead are removed at the same time. W. Borchers also removed arsenic and antimony by melting the metal with nitre and sodium hydroxide taking care to avoid overheating; he used a mixture of sodium hydroxide and sulphur when a considerable proportion of antimony is present. H. Tamm removed arsenic by fusing the metal with iron in the presence of a flux, say borax, and removing the compound of iron and arsenic as a scum. Much bismuth is lost by volatilization. G. Werther removed arsenic by fusing the bismuth with one-eighth of its weight of sodium hydroxide, and one-sixty-fourth of its weight of sulphur. E. Matthey said that antimony can be completely removed by melting in clay crucibles the bismuth with bismuth oxide in an amount equal to 2·5-3 times the weight of the antimony to be removed. The reaction is $2Sb+Bi_2O_3=Sb_2O_3+2Bi$. The antimony oxide mixed with some bismuth oxide rises to the surface as a scum. E. Matthey removed copper by fusing the bismuth with small proportions of sodium sulphide, and skimming off the scoria, which contains all the copper. The temp. is low and there is very little loss of bismuth by volatilization. According to H. Tamm, copper can be removed by projecting a mixture of potassium cyanide and sulphur (8 : 3) on to molten bismuth. The potassium thiocyanate which is formed with the evolution of heat causes the copper to form sulphide which separates as a scum; any bismuth sulphide formed is reduced to metal. Lead, antimony, and arsenic are removed at the same time. E. Matthey said that copper is removed as sulphide by melting the bismuth with bismuth sulphide, which is in turn reduced to bismuth. To remove lead, W. Borchers recommended fusing the metal in cast-iron pots for 3 hrs. with a mixture of bismuth oxychloride, sodium and potassium chlorides, and sodium hydroxide. Gold and silver can be removed by the aid of zinc, and the zinc is removed by oxidation in air as recommended by W. Mrazek.

The wet processes usually furnish bismuth of a higher degree of purity than the dry processes; and are employed only when the salts are required for medicinal purposes, or for use in the laboratory. According to H. Thürach, silver is not all precipitated from a soln. of bismuth nitrate by adding hydrochloric acid; and R. Schneider said that traces of silver follow the precipitate of the basic nitrate. According to H. Rose, H. Thürach, and A. Classen, the lead cannot be all removed by repeatedly precipitating the bismuth as basic nitrate; nor by repeatedly precipitating the bismuth as oxychloride. W. B. Herapath dissolved the metal in nitric acid; precipitated the basic nitrate with water; boiled the residue with alkali-lye to remove arsenic or lead; redissolved the washed oxide in nitric acid; and again precipitated the basic nitrate with water. E. C. Deschamps dissolved bismuth in nitric acid, so that tin or tin oxide remained in the residue. When the soln. is treated with ammonia, bismuth hydroxide is precipitated leaving copper and silver in soln. The precipitate was boiled with potash-lye to dissolve lead and arsenic. The precipitate was then dissolved in nitric acid, and the basic nitrate precipitated by water. R. Schneider dissolved the bismuth in nitric acid at 75°-90° when the arsenic separates out as bismuth arsenate accompanied by some basic nitrate. If cold acid is used, sparingly soluble bismuth arsenite is formed. The filtered soln. is evaporated for crystals of bismuth nitrate which are quite free from arsenic. J. Löwe treated an acid soln. of the metal with ammonia, and washed the precipitate with ammonia-water. The residue was dissolved in a mixture of 8 per cent. soda-lye mixed with one-twelfth its vol. of glycerol. The filtrate from the insoluble iron and nickel hydroxides was boiled with glucose to precipitate the bismuth. The washed precipitate, often fused with carbon in a covered crucible, contained no arsenic. W. Hampe melted the bismuth with a mixture of sodium carbonate and sulphur ; dissolved the well-washed sulphide in nitric acid ; precipitated the basic nitrate by water ; again dissolved in nitric acid, and precipitated the oxide by ammonia. The dried oxide was reduced to metal by heating it in a current of hydrogen. G. W. Kahlbaum and co-workers, and F. Krafft and co-workers, purified the metal by distillation in vacuo. Other observations on the wet process of extraction, or the purification of bismuth, were made by J. J. Berzelius and P. Lagerhjelm, R. Böttger, H. M. Forstner, J. L. Smith, C. Winkler, P. L. Haskisson, E. Rupp, E. R. Darling, and W. Spring. A. Yamada and co-workers dissolved the crushed ore in 5-20 per cent. sulphuric or hydrochloric acid—preferably the former ; precipitated the bismuth by adding iron ; and washed the precipitate with acid, and water, and dried in inert or reducing gases or in vacuo. The product was put in paraffin and heated to 300°-500° to expel impurities—arsenic or molybdenum—and the molten bismuth poured into a mould.

According to A. Classen, the bismuth obtained by repeated precipitation as oxychloride still contains lead ; but it is possible to obtain the metal spectroscopically pure by electrolysis. The purified salt can be deposited from a nitric acid soln. so that lead and bismuth peroxides are deposited on the anode, and crystalline bismuth on the cathode. The bismuth is washed with alcohol, melted under 98 per cent. potassium cyanide, cast in a mould, and when cold, washed with water and polished. B. Zakorsky and co-workers proposed to refine bismuth commercially by using the impure metal, cast into plates, as anode, and a carbon, purified bismuth, or platinum cathode in the electrolysis of dil. nitric acid with a current density of 3 amps. per sq. dm. The purified bismuth which collects on the cathode is washed with dil. nitric acid, dried, melted, and cast into ingots. If the electrolyte becomes too rich in lead, the bismuth in soln. can be precipitated by lead ; and the lead nitrate recovered from the liquor. In refining lead electrolytically, the anode mud contains bismuth, lead, and silver. F. Förster and E. Scwabe said that the mixture can be separated electrolytically by using a soln. of bismuth fluosilicated as electrolyte. The lead passes into soln., the silver remains undissolved. The potentials of lead and silver in soln. of their fluosilicates containing an eq. per litre are $+0.144$ and -0.295 volt respectively. Soln. containing as little as 26 grms. of bismuth per litre give perfect deposits with 0.004 amp. per sq. cm. More conc. soln., and higher temp. allow higher current densities to be used.

According to F. Mylius and P. Groschuff, in the further purification of commercially " pure " bismuth, by precipitation as oxide and sulphide the amorphous precipitates retain other metals tenaciously. The electrolytic method of separation also fails. The basic salts form amorphous precipitates, and the best method of separation is found to be the crystallization of the normal nitrate from conc. nitric acid. This is also suitable for the purification of bismuth. The nitrate, if already of fair purity, is dissolved in half its weight of 8 per cent. nitric acid, and mixed with an equal weight of the conc. acid. The crystals, which separate on cooling to 0° or $-10°$, are washed with a little ice-cold nitric acid. All impurities are thus conc. in the mother-liquor   The nitrate is converted into oxide by heat, and the oxide is then reduced by fusion with potassium cyanide. A further purification, if necessary, is effected by melting the metal under paraffin and removing the first (purest) crystals by means of a glass spoon.

According to P. Thibault,[5] when bismuth mellitate, $Bi_2C_{12}O_{12}$, is heated under reduced press. in closed tubes, decomposition begins at about 350°, carbon dioxide is evolved, and *pyrophoric bismuth*—a mixture of carbonaceous matter with finely divided bismuth—is formed. It inflames spontaneously when thrown into air, forming bismuth trioxide. L. Vanino and A. Menzel obtained pyrophoric bismuth by reducing a mixed precipitate of aluminium and bismuth hydroxide by heating to 170°–210° in hydrogen. F. Hérard reported *amorphous bismuth* to be formed by heating ordinary bismuth to bright redness in a current of nitrogen—hydrogen and carbon dioxide do not give the same result. The product contains 99·6 per cent. of bismuth and 0·4 per cent. of oxygen. The presence of oxide explains the high m.p., 410°, but not the low sp. gr. 9·483. The amorphous bismuth is more readily attacked by reagents than the ordinary form—*e.g.* it dissolves almost instantly in nitric acid. E. Cohen and J. Olie said that this form of bismuth can be obtained only by the use of imperfectly purified nitrogen, and that it really consists of the ordinary metal, in a finely divided state, mixed with more or less bismuth trioxide.

G. F. Taylor[6] described the manufacture of thin filaments of bismuth; and J. A. Becker and L. F. Curtiss, F. K. Richtmyer and L. F. Curtiss, and B. Pogany examined the properties of these films of bismuth; and H. Kahler, the structure. V. Kohlschütter and J. L. Tüscher obtained highly dispersed bismuth trioxide by volatilization in the electric arc. T. Goldschmidt and V. Kohlschütter condensed the vapour either by a drop in temp., or oxidation in a blast; and L. Gurwitsch obtained highly dispersed bismuth by shaking bismuth shot in a liquid. C. Paal and L. di Pol found sodium protalbinate to be an effective protective agent; and they obtained a hydrosol by the addition of bismuth nitrate dissolved in aq. glycerol to an aq. soln. of sodium protalbinate or lysalbinate containing sodium hydroxide; after being centrifuged, the soln. are dialyzed against water and subsequently evaporated in vacuo at 50°, and finally over conc. sulphuric acid. They also obtained colloidal bismuth by reducing commercial *bismon*—*i.e.* colloidal bismuth hydroxide—by formaldehyde. The reduction of a dil. aq. soln. of a bismuth salt with an organic substance furnishes a **colloidal solution of bismuth.** For example, L. Vanino dissolved 2 grms. of bismuth tartrate in a soln. of tartaric acid and potassium hydroxide, and made it up to about 600 c.c., and obtained a clear brown liquid when the soln. was treated with 1·5 grms. of stannous chloride dissolved in dil. alkali-lye. Nearly all the bismuth remains in suspension as a **hydrosol.** The sol behaves like the hydrosol of gold towards the electric current and is deposited on the. anode. If the bismuth be salted out, only part of it again forms a hydrosol. R Schneider assumed that the suspensoid is bismuth suboxide, but L. Vanino and F. Treubert hold that it is elemental bismuth. According to A. Lottermoser, when bismuth nitrate (2 mols) is dissolved in water containing a little nitric acid, and a soln. of ammonium citrate is added until the resulting precipitate dissolves, the soln. made alkaline with ammonia, added to a soln. of stannous chloride (3 mols) prepared in a similar manner, and the mixture quickly heated, colloidal bismuth is deposited in the form of a very fine, black precipitate of the **hydrogel.** This will dissolve in water, but is re-precipitated on addition of a soln. of any salt, or of an acid. It is transformed into the insoluble form of the metal by continued boiling of its soln., or by a large excess of stannous salts. L. Kalle and Co. mixed a dialyzed soln. of egg-albumen in soda-lye, with a glycerol soln. of bismuth nitrate, and after dialysis, evaporated the soln. to dryness in vacuo below 60°. The product is *bismuth colloidale.* A. Gutbier and G. Hofmeier obtained an unstable colloidal form of bismuth by the action of hypophosphorous acid on bismuth oxychloride. When a dil. soln. of hydrazine hydrate is added to a hot soln. of ammoniacal copper sulphate, a copper hydrosol is obtained from which copper gradually separates. In the presence of gum arabic, this hydrosol is more stable. A. Gutbier and co-workers also used titanous chloride as reducing agent, and they studied the action of the protective colloids—agar-agar, tubera salep, and gum arabic. They obtained colloidal soln. by the action of sodium thiosulphate on bismuth nitrate in the presence of the protective colloid. According to A. Kuhn and H. Pirsch, bismuth sols containing 3·5 mgrms. per c.c. may be prepared by the reduction of bismuth tartrate soln. with sodium hyposulphite in weakly alkaline soln. This shows an improvement on the methods which with stannic acid as a protective colloid give sols containing 1·5 mgrms. per c.c. A. Gutbier used hæmoglobin as protective colloid in preparing the colloid by reducing soln. of bismuth salts with sodium hyposulphate, or with formaldehyde. E. Fouard prepared colloidal bismuth by electrolyzing a soln. of a salt of the metal containing a pure organic colloid (albumin, starch, or gelatin) with a current of a few milliampères. At the cathode, the metal ions are neutralized by the repelled negatively-charged colloid micelles. A colloidal organo-metallic complex is thus formed. The anode is separated by immersion in a collodion cell rendered semi-permeable by precipitated copper ferrocyanide. The cathode should be a bad conductor so as to reduce the frequency with which formation of the complex occurs on the cathode. T. Svedberg prepared **organosols** by the electrical spluttering of bismuth electrodes dipping in say ethyl ether, or isobutyl alcohol— **8.** 23, 10. According to E. F. Burton, some of the particles of the electrically prepared bismuth sol are positively charged, presumably in consequence of the formation of hydroxide.

REFERENCES.

¹ W. E. Hitchcock and J. R. Pound, *Proc. Australasian Inst. Min. Eng.*, **35.** 33, 1920; W. H. Bowater, *Proc. Australian Inst. Min. Met.*, **40.** 259, 1921.

² C. Winkler in A. W. Hofmann, *Berichte über die Entwickelung der chemischen Industrie*, Braunschweig, **2.** 953, 1875; C. Schnabel, *Handbuch der Metallhüttenkunde*, Berlin, **2.** 361, 1893; London, **2.** 444, 1907; C. F. Plattner, *Verbindungen über allgemeine Hüttenkunde*, Freiberg, 23, 1860; Anon., *Berg. Hütt. Ztg.*, **31.** 79, 1876; P. Lemay, *La chimie du bismuth*, Paris, 1925; E. Ferray, *Bismuth—ses composés, son dosage*, Evreux, 1871.

³ A. Valenciennes, *Ann. Chim. Phys.*, (4), **31.** 397, 1874; *Bull. Soc. Chim.*, (2), **21.** 426, 1874; A. Carnot, *ib.*, (2), **21.** 113, 1874; *Compt. Rend.*, **78.** 172, 1874; F. F. G. Eulert, *German Pat.*, *D.R.P.* 130963, 1900; *Rev. Prod. Chim.*, **4.** 164, 1901; J. Ronald, *Min. Ind.*, **8.** 57, 1898; *Brit. Pat. No.* 16622, 1898; W. Mrazek, *Oesterr. Zeit. Berg. Hütt.*, **22.** 319, 327, 1874; *Berg. Hütt. Ztg.*, **33.** 413, 1874; C. Rössler, *ib.*, **48.** 388, 1889; *Chem. Ztg.*, **20.** 105, 1896; J. W. Kynaston, *Journ. Soc. Chem. Ind.*, **12.** 932, 1893; W. Borchers, *Jahrb. Elektrochem.*, **1.** 168, 1895; *Elektrometallurgie*, Leipzig, 481, 1903; *Zeit. Elektrotech.*, **1.** 13, 1894; Guggenhein. Bros., *Brit. Pat. No.* 235157, 1924; A. Engelenburg, *Elektro-analytische Methoden zur Bestimmung von Metallen aus salzsaurer Lösung*, Aachen, 1921; V. de Luynes, *Dingler's Journ.*, **167.** 289, 1863; *Bull. Soc. Enc. Nat. Ind.*, (2), **9.** 649, 1862; W. Buddëus, *Brit. Pat. No.* 264834, 1927; J. Lukas and A. Jilek, *Chem. Listy*, 21. 541, 1927.

⁴ E. A. Smith, *Journ. Soc. Chem. Ind.*, **12.** 315, 1893; *Journ. Chem. Soc.*, **65.** 624, 1894; E. Matthey, *Chem. News*, 56. 241, 1887; *ib.* 30, 1891; **67.** 63, 1893; *Proc. Roy. Soc.*, **49.** 78, 1891; **52.** 467, 1893—I am indebted to Messrs. Johnson, Matthey, and Co. for the analyses of crude bismuth given in the text. R. Schneider, *Pogg. Ann.*, **96.** 494, 1855; *Journ. prakt. Chem.*, (2), **20.** 418, 1880; (2), **23.** 75, 298, 1881; (2), **44.** 23, 1891; (2), **50.** 461, 1894; G. Werther, *ib.*, (1), **55.** 227, 1852; C. Winkler, *ib.*, (2), **23.** 298, 1881; A. Classen, *ib.*, (2), **44.** 411, 1891; *Ber.*, 23. 938, 1890; **26.** 941, 1890; H. Thürach, *Journ. prakt. Chem.*, (2), **14.** 309, 1877; G. A. Quesneville, *Journ. Pharm. Chim.*, (2), **16.** 554, 1830; *Schweigger's Journ.*, **60.** 378, 1830; H. M. Forstner, *German Pat.*, *D.R.P.* 395893, 1920; W. B. Herapath, *Pharm. Journ.*, (2), **4.** 302, 1863; P. L. Haskisson, *ib.*, (3), **15.** 668, 1885; C. Ekin, *ib.*, (3), **3.** 381, 1873; (3), **6.** 501, 1876; N. G. O. Coad, *ib.*, (3), **6.** 384, 1876; M. Knörtzer, *Bull. Soc. Chim.*, (3), **9.** 465, 1893; C. Méhu, *Ann. Pharm.*, 23, 1873; *Dingler's Journ.*, **211.** 187, 1874; L. Löwe, *Zeit. anal. Chem.*, **22.** 498, 1883; V. Sill, *Berg. Hütt. Ztg.*, **23.** 323, 1864; F. A. Genth, *Amer. Journ. Science*, (2), **27.** 247, 1859; D. Forbes, *Phil. Mag.*, (4), **29.** 1, 1885; G. Brownen, *Pharm. Journ.*, (2), **6.** 561, 1876; *Arch. Pharm.*, (3), **10.** 265, 1877; E. Rupp, *ib.*, **241.** 435, 1903; J. J. Berzelius and P. Lagerhjelm, *Schweigger's Journ.*, **17.** 416, 1816; W. Spring, *Ann. Chim. Phys.*, (5), **7.** 194, 1876; R. Böttger, *Chem. Centr.*, (3), **5.** 371, 1874; H. Tamm, *Chem. News*, 25. 85, 1872; W. Borchers, *Elektrometallurgie*, Leipzig, 328, 1895; 481, 1903; W. Mrazek, *Berg. Hütt. Ztg.*, 33. 413, 1874; *Oesterr. Zeit. Berg. Hütt.*, **22.** 319, 327, 1874; E. C. Deschamps, *Repert. Pharm.*, (2), **8.** 193, 1880; W. Hampe, *Chem. Ztg.*, **15.** 410, 1892; H. Rose, *Pogg. Ann.*, **110.** 411, 1860; J. L. Smith, *Bull. Soc. Chim.*, (2), **27.** 329, 1877; G. W. Kahlbaum, K. Roth, and P. Siedler, *Zeit.*

anorg. Chem., 29. 177, 292, 1902 ; F. Mylius and E. Groschuff, *ib.*, 96. 237, 1916 ; F. Krafft, *Ber.*, 36. 1704, 1903 ; F. Krafft and L. Bergfeld, *ib.*, 38. 257, 1905 ; E. R. Darling, *Met. Chem. Engg.*, 24. 1108, 1921 ; B. Zakorsky, F. Hurter, and J. Brock, *Brit. Pat. No.* 22251, 1895 ; F. Förster and E. Schwabe, *Zeit. Elektrochem.*, 16. 279, 1910 ; A. Yamada, T. Miyazaki, and K. Hiede, *Japan. Pat. No.* 39626, 1921.

⁵ P. Thibault, *Bull. Soc. Chim.*, (3), 31. 135, 1904 ; F. Hérard, *Compt. Rend.*, 108. 293, 1889 ; E. Cohen and J. Olie, *Zeit. phys. Chem.*, 61. 596, 1908 ; L. Vanino and A. Menzel, *Zeit. anorg. Chem.*, 149. 18, 1915.

⁶ L. Vanino, *Pharm. Centrh.*, 40. 276, 1899 ; L. Vanino and F. Treubert, *Ber.*, 31. 1113, 2267, 1898 ; 32. 1072, 1899 ; T. Svedberg, *ib.*, 38. 3618, 1905 ; 39. 1711, 1906 ; A. Kuhn and H. Pirsch, *Koll. Beichefte*, 21. 78, 1925 ; R. Schneider, *Pogg. Ann.*, 88. 45, 1853 ; *Journ. prakt. Chem.*, (2), 58. 562, 1898 ; A. Lottermoser, *ib.*, (2), 59. 489, 1899 ; *Ueber anorganische Colloide*, Stuttgart, 1901 ; E. F. Burton, *Phil. Mag.*, (6), 11. 425, 1906 ; A. Gutbier and G. Hofmeier, *Zeit. anorg. Chem.*, 44. 225, 1905 ; A. Gutbier, *ib.*, 151. 153, 1926 ; A. Gutbier, B. Ottenstein, and F. Allam, *ib.*, 164. 287, 1927 ; A. Gutbier, T. Kautter, and R. Gentner, *ib.*, 149. 167, 1925 ; A. Gutbier and T. Kautter, *ib.*, 146. 166, 1925 ; A. Gutbier and H. Weithase, *ib.*, 169. 264, 1928 ; L. Kalle and Co., *Pharm. Ztg.*, 48. 94, 1903 ; E. Fouard, *Compt. Rend.*, 184. 328, 1927 ; V. Kohlschütter and J. L. Tüscher, *Zeit. Elektrochem.*, 27. 225, 1921 ; T. Goldschmidt and V. Kohlschütter, *Brit. Pat. No.* 189706, 1922 ; G. F. Taylor, *Phys. Rev.*, (2), 23. 655, 1924 ; F. K. Richtmyer and L. F. Curtiss, *Phys. Rev.*, (2), 15. 465, 1920 ; J. A. Becker and L. F. Curtiss, *ib.*, (2), 15. 457, 1920 ; H. Kahler, *ib.*, (2), 18. 210, 1921 ; C. Paal and L. di Pol, *Ber.*, 59. B, 874, 877, 1926 ; B. Pogany, *Ann. Physik*, (4), 64. 196, 1921 ; L. Gurwitsch, *Koll. Zeit.*, 33. 321, 1923.

§ 4. The Physical Properties of Bismuth

Bismuth metal is tin-white with a reddish tinge and a high lustre. F. Hérard [1] said that the vapour in a current of nitrogen is green ; and W. L. Dudley, greenish-blue. A. W. Wright found that these films are also greyish-blue. J. C. Poggendorff also obtained films coloured yellow, red, violet, blue, and green. G. A. Quesneville obtained it as a mass of **crystals** by melting the commercial metal in a crucible, adding nitre from time to time, and stirring, until a portion of the fused metal taken out and exposed to the air no longer assumes an indigo-blue and afterwards a violet or rose colour which disappears on cooling, but rather assumes a green or golden-yellow tint which is retained on cooling. The fused metal is then poured into a heated pot which is covered so as to prevent the surface from solidifying before the other part. If the metal be cooled too slowly, it forms layers, and not fine crystals. As soon as the mass is half solidified, the crust formed on the surface is pierced with a hot coal, and the still liquid portion poured out. A. Nies obtained crystals by suspending pieces of iron in a bath of molten metal and allowing it to cool. It is difficult to obtain crystals in the wet way. N. W. Fischer, J. Löwe, C. W. C. Fuchs, and J. Barlot obtained a black crystalline powder by the action of zinc or iron on a soln. of bismuth nitrate. N. A. Puschin obtained crystals from the soln. in mercury. P. P. Heberdey observed acicular crystals of bismuth in the slag from a smelting furnace at Przibran, Bohemia.

The early observers reported that bismuth crystallizes in cubes and octahedra, but G. Rose showed that the crystals are trigonal, and have the axial ratio $a : c$ $= 1 : 1.3036$. Observations were also made by W. Haidinger, C. W. Zenger, F. Stolba, J. Barlot, H. C. H. Carpenter, and F. Wöhler. The **cleavage** on the (0091)-face is perfect ; while that on the (02$\bar{2}$1)-face is not so good. M. L. Huggins studied the relation between the cleavage and the electronic structure. O. Mügge studied the **percussion figures** ; and A. Johnsen, the **gliding planes**. The **X-radiograms** were found by A. Johnsen to agree with the assumption that the molecule is diatomic, with atomic centres 3×10^{-8} cm. apart. This is in agreement with the fact, observed by H. Biltz and V. Meyer, that bismuth dissolved in a large proportion of lead is diatomic, and that the vap. density of bismuth between 1600° and 1700° lies between 10.125 and 11.983 when the value calculated for Bi is 7.2, and for Bi_2, 14.4. R. W. James found that the edge of unit rhomb of bismuth is 3.28×10^{-8} cm., and the closest approach between two atomic centres is 3.11×10^{-8}. A. Ogg calculated 6.52×10^{-8} for the length of the bismuth rhombs. **W. P. Davey** gave $a=4·539$ A., and $c/a=2·606$ A. O. Hassel and H. Mark represented the atoms arranged on two interpenetrating face-centred rhombohedra ; and L. W. McKeehan represented the lattice as a simple rhombohedron with a set of rhombohedral axes mutually inclined at 57° 16'. The atoms are not uniformly placed along the trigonal axis. The data were collected by P. P. Ewald and C. Hermann. The results with arsenic, antimony, and bismuth are :

	As	Sb	Bi
Edge a of the face-centred rhomb . .	5·60 A.	6·20 A.	6·56 A.
Angle a	84° 36'	86° 58'	87° 34'
Short atomic distances . .	2·51 A.	2·87 A.	3·11 A.
Long atomic distances . . .	3·15 A.	3·37 A.	3·47 A.

H. Kahler examined the structure of thin films. M. L. Huggins, and J. Barlot studied the lattice and electronic structure. H. Kahler found that thin films obtained by spluttering have a crystalline structure. Polished surfaces of the metal were examined by W. Campbell, and W. Herold. F. Stöber, J. A. M. van Liempt, and I. V. Obreimoff and L. V. Shubnikoff described the preparation of large crystals, and E. von Gomperz, the properties of single crystals drawn into wires ; while G. Tammann and H. Bredemeier observed the vol. of the channels opening out on the surface of the metal. E. Bekier measured the velocity of crystallization. The analogies between the phosphorus-bismuth family of elements were discussed by P. Möller, G. Linck and H. Jung, etc.—*vide* arsenic.

Among the early records of the **specific gravity** of bismuth, P. von Muschen broek [2] gave 9·67 ; T. Bergman, 9·861 ; J. Dalton, 9·8 ; M. J. Brisson, 9·822 ; G. Leonhard, 9·800 ; L. J. Thénard, and J. J. Berzelius, 9·8827 ; W. Herapath, 9·831 ; C. J. B. Karsten, 9·6542 ; H. G. F. Schröder, 9·713 ; A. Matthiessen and M. Holzmann, 9·823 at 12° ; G. Quincke, 9·819 at 0° ; E. Grüneisen, 9·78 ; and F. L. Perrot, 9·848–9·887. R. F. Marchand and T. Scheerer gave 9·799 for the sp. gr. of the purified metal, at 19° ; 9·783 for the commercial metal ; and 9·556 for the compressed metal ; C. J. St. C. Deville, 9·935 for the crystals ; and 9·677 for the metal which had been rapidly cooled from the fused state. For native bismuth, D. Forbes gave 9·77–9·98 ; and P. T. Cleve and C. H. J. Feilitzen, 9·1. A. Classen gave 9·7474 for the sp. gr. of the highly purified metal ; J. F. Spencer and M. E. John, 9·23 at 20° ; H. G. Dorsey, 9·84 at 20° for cast bismuth ; R. von Dallwitz-Wegner, 9·80 ; and G. W. Kahlbaum, 9·78143 at 20°/4° for the metal distilled in vacuo. I. I. Saslawsky gave 9·806 for the sp. gr. at room temp., and 21·3 for the at. vol. C. del Fresno studied this subject. T. M. Lowry and R. G. Parker gave 9·8093 for the sp. gr. of bismuth *en masse*, and 9·7798 when in the form of filings. G. Quincke gave 9·819 for the sp. gr. at 0°, and 9·709 for the sp. gr. of the molten metal ; L. Playfair and J. P. Joule gave 9·798 for the molten metal ; and H. Siedentopf, 10·004. W. C. Roberts-Austen and T. Wrightson gave 9·82 for the sp. gr. at ordinary temp., and 10·039 for that of the molten metal ; while G. Vicentini and D. Omodei gave 9·787 for the sp. gr. at 0°, 9·673 for the sp. gr. of the solid at 270·9°, and 10·004 for the liquid at 270·9°. L. L. Bircumshaw gave 10·03 at 300° ; 9·91 at 400° ; 9·66 at 600° ; 9·40 at 802° ; and 9·20 at 962°. K. Bornemann and P. Siebe measured the sp. vol. at different temp. F. Nies and A. Winkelmann gave 1·0310–1·0497 for the ratio of the sp. gr. of bismuth in the liquid and solid states. R. Böttger observed that a glass tube can be broken by the expansion of the contained bismuth during solidification. J. Johnston and L. H. Adams gave 0·00342 c.c. per gram for the expansion which occurs on melting ; K. Bornemann and P. Siebe found a 3 per cent. contraction and A. Hess a 3·5 per cent. expansion, and H. Endo, 3·32 per cent. K. Töpler found the expansion to be 3·27 per cent. Observations were also made by W. C. Roberts-Austen and T. Wrightson. C. Lüdeking showed that the maximum density is attained some degrees above the m.p.—between 268° and 270°—for in rising to that temp. from the m.p., there is a 3 per cent. contraction. C. J. St.

C. Deville gave 9·935 for the sp. gr. of bismuth before fusion, and 9·677 after fusion ; but T. Murray was unable to detect the slightest expansion at or after the moment of solidification.   The metal attains a maximum density just above its f.p., and it decreases in density until its f.p. is attained, after which it contracts uniformly. T. R. Hogness gave 10·00 for the sp. gr. of the liquid at 320° ; 9·95 at 365° ; 9·88 at 426° ; and 9·82 at 472° ; or, the sp. gr., D, at $\theta°$ is $D=10\cdot07-0\cdot00125(\theta-269)$. M. Plüss gave 9·999 for the sp. gr. of the liquid at 283° ; 9·981 at 330° ; 9·973 at 350° ; 9·968 at 361° ; and 9·967 at 365° ; R. Arpi, 9·75 at 528° ; 9·82 at 452° ; 9·89 at 390° ; 9·91 at 366° ; 9·94 at 335° ; and 9·99 at 280° : but F. Sauerwald and K. Töpler, 9·430 at 600° ; 9·810 at 451° ; and 9·984 at 304°.   According to W. Spring, the sp. gr. is increased by compression until the pores are closed, and thereafter, compression makes very little difference.   Thus, the sp. gr. of a sample at 13·5° before compression was 9·804 ; after 3 weeks' compression at 20,000 atm., the sp. gr. at 15°, rose to 9·856 ; and after a second compression, the sp. gr. at 15° was 9·863.   He also found that the sp. gr. fell from 9·783 to 9·779 by compression at 50,000 kgrms. per sq. cm. ; to 9·655 by compression at 75,000 kgrms. ; and to 9·556 by compression at 100,00 kgrms. per sq. cm.   The sp. gr. was also reduced a little by torsion.   J. Johnston and L. H. Adams found that the sp. gr. of these cylinders after compression at 15,000 atm. were 9·8012, 9·7886, and 9·8001, and after annealing for 2 hrs. at 340°, respectively 9·8028, 9·7898, and 9·7971.   A wire which had been considerably deformed had a sp. gr. 9·7692–9·7693, and 9·7767–9·7768 after annealing for 2 hrs. at 230°.   T. M. Lowry and R. G. Parker noticed an expansion on annealing.   These data do not agree with the assumption of W. Spring, and G. T. Beilby that by deformation a part of the metal passes into the amorphous state, although it fits in with the assumption that there are enantiotropic forms of bismuth.   O. Faust and G. Tammann hold that the hardening during the deformation is not due to the formation of a harder crystalline form, or to a change to the amorphous condition, but rather to a diminution in the size of the crystallites of which the metal is composed, owing to the formation of systems of sliding surfaces.   M. Polanyi studied the changes in structure produced in bismuth **by** cold-work.   A. Ludwig found that when molten bismuth is subjected to a press. of 8000–17,000 atm. during cooling, the sp. gr. of the solid did not differ from that of ordinary bismuth ; the crystalline structure was different, for the texture was very finely crystalline, resembling that of fine-grained iron.   When the press. was 3000 atm. the piston sprang back with an audible shock corresponding with the expansion on solidification.   W. L. Bragg calculated 1·48 A. for the **atomic radius ;** M. L. Huggins, 2·6 A. ; V. M. Goldschmidt, 1·82 A.; and E. N. Gapon, 1·88 A.   H. G. Grimm made observations on the ionic radius.   H. H. Potter found no difference between the **gravitational accelerations** of bismuth and brass ; H. A. Wilson examined the relation between the mass and weight of bismuth ; and G. F. Brush found that bismuth falls slightly faster than zinc under conditions where the time of descent would be the same if equal masses represented equal weights.

H. Biltz and V. Meyer found the **vapour density** of bismuth to be 10·125— 11·983 between 1600° and 1700°.   The value calculated for the molecule Bi is 7·2, and for Bi_2, 14·4.   A. Johnsen said that the mol. wt. of the vapour between 1600° and 1700° corresponds with Bi and Bi_2.   According to H. von Wartenberg, the **molecular weight** of bismuth corresponds with monatomic molecules at 2070°. C. T. Heycock and F. H. Neville found that the lowering of the f.p. of bismuth dissolved in cadmium or tin agrees with a monatomic mol ; and with lead as solvent, with a diatomic mol ; and G. McP. Smith, with mercury as solvent, found the results agree with a monatomic mol ; and I. Traube found that the properties of bismuth are in general agreement with a monatomic mol.   A. Jouniaux obtained the average mol. wt. 245 over the range from the m.p. to the b.p. A. Johnsen said that the molecule in the rhombohedral crystals is diatomic ; dissolved in lead, diatomic ; and dissolved in mercury or cadmium, monatomic. W. R. Fielding discussed the polymerization of bismuth.

According to G. Linck, **allotropic forms** of bismuth analogous to the three forms of antimony and arsenic have not been discussed, although he assumed that anisotropic and isotropic forms remain to be discovered. F. L. Perrot noticed that the thermoelectric force of cast bismuth changes spontaneously with time. According to E. Cohen, and A. L. T. Moesveld, bismuth exists in two allotropic forms with a transition temp. at 75° and 760 mm.; and the transition of the α-**bismuth**, stable below this temp., into the β-**bismuth** stable above this temp., is accompanied by an increase in vol. The β-variety can exist in a metastable state below the transition temp. E. Cohen showed that the transition temp. varies with the previous history of the metal. Finely-divided bismuth which has been in contact with a 10 per cent. soln. of potassium chloride for 12 hrs. diminishes in vol. at 70°, although the same sample of metal, before treatment with the salt soln., showed no change in vol. at this temp. J. Würschmidt observed anomalies in the changes in volume with bismuth amalgams near 75°; and he said that the sp. gr. of bismuth *en masse* is 9·80, and in powder, 9·70. This is taken to mean that during the comminution, the material passes from one allotropic form to another. J. Johnston and L. H. Adams said that the sp. gr. of most substances is variable owing to the lack of homogeneity, and that, in consequence, slight changes of sp. gr., whether produced by compression or other means, cannot be regarded as satisfactory evidence of a transformation or chemical reaction. E. Jänecke [3] observed a break at 112° in the press.-temp. curve of bismuth. This is assumed to correspond with an allotropic transformation.

The **hardness** of native bismuth on Mohs' scale is 2·0–2·5; R. J. Rydberg gave 2·5. C. A. Edwards and A. M. Herbert gave 14·0 for Brinell's hardness. P. Ludwig gave for hardness by the press. of a sphere for 300 seconds at 17°, 8·90; at 55°, 6·85; at 108°, 4·55; at 160°, 2·96; at 227°, 1·69; and at 263°, 1·16; and when the load is exerted for 15 seconds, at 17°, 12·2; at 54°, 9·55; at 156°, 4·66; at 181°, 3·60; at 252°, 2·01; and at 262°, 1·65. K. Houda and R. Yamada studied the abrasive hardness. M. Georgieff and E. Schmid found that the breaking strain of bismuth crystals by a force perpendicular to the plane of splitting is 324 grms. per sq. mm. It is independent of temp. between −80° and +20°. The plastic deformation begins at a definite critical tension which diminishes with rising temp. up to 200°, and then remains about constant until the m.p. is reached. Whether a crystal is ductile or brittle depends on its orientation in the bismuth wire. E. Grüneisen found the **elastic modulus** or **Young's modulus** of cast bismuth of sp. gr. 9·78 to be 3250 kgrms. per sq. mm., and for the **transverse modulus,** 3390 kgrms. per sq. mm. F. A. Schulze, and W. Voigt found 3200 kgrms. per sq. mm. for the elastic modulus; 1240–1372 kgrms. per sq. mm. for the **torsion modulus**; and **Poisson's ratio,** 0·33. E. von Gomperz found the elastic limit is lower with wires of single crystals than in wires of crystal aggregates. B. MacNutt and A. Concilio measured the load at which a noise is heard in the stressed metal. P. W. Bridgman found $2·29 \times 10^{11}$ and $2·45 \times 10^{11}$ for Young's modulus in c.g.s. units for bismuth wires, and if the compressibility be $2·8 \times 10^{-12}$ c.g.s.units, Poissan's ratio becomes 0·39. W. Voigt, and F. A. Schulze gave for the **compressibility,** $0·3 \times 10^{-5}$ kgrm. per sq. cm. P. W. Bridgman measured the elastic constants of single crystals of bismuth; and he also found the initial compressibility of extruded bismuth to be $31·8 \times 10^{-7}$ at 30°, and $\delta v/v_0 = -(35·35 - 28·0 \times 10^{-5} p) p \times 10^{-7}$; and at 75°, $\delta v/v_0 = -(35·94 - 28·7 \times 10^{-5} p) p \times 10^{-7}$; and for a cast cylinder the initial value at 30° was $25·6 \times 10^{-7}$ at 30°, and $\delta v/v_0 = -(22·02 - 9·0 \times 10^{-5} p) p \times 10^{-7}$; and at 75°, $\delta v/v_0 = -(22·11 - 9·0 \times 10^{-5} p) p \times 10^{-7}$. He also found the cubic compressibility of single crystals over the range $p = 12,000$ kgrms. per sq. cm. to be $29·17 \times 10^{-7} p - 22·43 \times 10^{-12} p^2$ at 30°, and $29·89 \times 10^{-7} p - 31·13 \times 10^{-12} p^2$ at 75°. P. W. Bridgman gave for the compressibility, β, for samples of cast and extruded bismuth at 30° respectively $\beta = 0·0_5 2202$ and $0·0_5 3535$; $\delta\beta/\beta\delta p = 0·0_5 82$ and $0·0_4 158$; and $-\delta a/a\delta p = 0·0_5 50$ and $0·0_4 33$. T. W. Richards gave $3·0 \times 10^{-6}$ for the average compressibility at 20° between 100 and 500 megabars. **L. H. Adams** and co-workers obtained 3.00×10^{-6} per megabar at zero press. and 2.57×10^{-6} at 10,000 kgrms. per sq. cm. press. They also gave for the change in volume $\delta v = 0.9 \times 10^{-4 + 2.923} \times 10^{-6}(p - p_0) - 2.38 \times 10^{-11}(p - p_0)^2$. L. H. Adams gave for $\delta \beta = -0.47$. E. Jänecke found a break at about $112°$ in the press.-temp. curve of bismuth. J. H. Hildebrand and co-workers measured the **internal pressure** of bismuth. N. S. Kurnakoff and S. F. Schamtschuschny gave for the plasticity or **pressure of flow**, 21·0 kgrms. per sq. mm. with a piece of metal of diameter 8·66 mm. M. Georgieff and E. Schmid, O. Hasse and E. Schmid also measured the flow of the metal under press. D. C. Stockbarger prepared wires by the extrusion process. H. Siedentopf found the **surface tension** of bismuth at its m.p. to be 43·78 mgrms. per mm., and the temp. coeff. was 0·000233; the **specific cohesion**, $a^2 = 8.755$ per sq. mm.; and the temp. coeff. 0·000117; and the mol. **surface energy**, 0·50. W. Hagemann gave $\sigma = 300$ dynes per cm. for the surface tension; H. Siedentopf, 430 dynes per cm.; G. Quincke gave $\sigma = 464.9$ dynes per cm.; and $a^2 = 9.76$ per sq. mm.; and T. R. Hogness gave 375 dynes per cm. at $320°$; 371 at $365°$; 367 at $426°$; and 365 at $472°$. F. Sauerwald and G. Drath found at $583°$, $\sigma = 353.9$ dynes per cm.; at $770°$, $\sigma = 344.0$ dynes per cm.; and at $779°$, $\sigma = 343.9$ dynes per cm. The temp. coeff. is $\delta\sigma/aT = 0.060$. L. L. Bircumshaw gave 388 dynes per cm. at $300°$; $380°$ at $400°$; 367 at $600°$; 353 at $802°$; and 340 at $962°$; and for the sp. cohesion, a^2 per sq. cm., 0·0779 at $300°$; 0·0782 at $400°$; 0·0775 at $600°$; 0·0767 at $802°$; and 0·0754 at $962°$. For the temp. coeff. of the surface tension, L. L. Bircumshaw gave -0.27; and for the surface energy, 3176 ergs per sq. cm. at $300°$; 3224 at $400°$; 3279 at $600°$; 3332 at $802°$; and 3359 at $962°$. Observations were also made by Y. Matuyama. R. von Dallwitz-Wegner found the **cohesion pressure** to be 112,535 atm. at $0°$, and 90,372 atm. at $100°$. C. E. Fawsitt found the **viscosity** of bismuth at $360°$ to be 0·0167; M. Plüss gave 0·01620 at $283°$; 0·01609 at $288°$; 0·01525 at $330°$; 0·01494 at $350°$; 0·01473 at $355°$; 0·014685 at $361°$; 0·01455 at $365°$; R. Arpi, 0·0146 at $280°$; 0·0131 at $355°$; 0·0130 at $366°$; 0·0122 at $390°$; 0·0119 at $452°$; and 0·0114 at $528°$; and F. Sauerwald and K. Töpler, 0·00996 at $600°$; 0·01280 at $451°$; and 0·01662 at $304°$. Observations were made by G. Subrahmaniam. W. B. Hardy measured the static **friction** between bismuth and lubricants. The **diffusion** of bismuth in mercury was studied by W. J. Humphreys, and R. Kremann and A. Hrasovic, and of gold in bismuth by W. C. Roberts-Austen. J. Groh measured the rate of diffusion or the rate of exchange of the bismuth in bismuth-amalgam (0·627 grm. Bi per 10 c.c. of mercury) with the bismuth in a soln. of bismuth nitrate and found that in 39, 23, and 14 hrs., respectively with 20 c.c. of a $0.25M$-soln., 23 c.c. of a $0.4M$-soln., and 20 c.c. of a $4M$-soln., the bismuth is exchanged at the respective rates of 0.2×10^{-6}, 0.36×10^{-6}, and 4.7×10^{-6} grm. per sq. cm. of amalgam per sec.

According to H. Kopp,[4] the coeff. of **thermal expansion**—cubical—between $12°$ and $41°$ is 0·000040; and A. Matthiessen found the vol., v, at $\theta°$, to be $v = v_0(1 + 0.0_4 3502\theta + 0.0_7 4466\theta^2)$, when v_0 is the vol. at $0°$. F. Sauerwald and K. Töpler gave 0·00012 for the coeff. of cubical expansion at $300°$. G. Vicentini and G. Omodei gave for the coeff. of expansion of (linear) of bismuth at about $270°$, 0·04132, and for the mean coeff. of cubical expansion of molten bismuth between $271°$ and $300°$; A. Hess gave $0.0_3 264$ for the liquid and $0.0_3 148$ for the solid; and C. Lüdeking, $0.0_4 4425$ for the interval $270°-303°$. For the coeff. of linear expansion, A. Matthiessen gave $0.0_4 1316$ between $0°$ and $100°$; H. G. Dorsey gave for the coeff. of thermal expansion, a, of cast bismuth of sp. gr. 9·84:

	$-170°$	$-150°$	$-140°$	$-110°$	$-90°$	$-50°$	$-10°$	$10°$
a	$1.0_4 1129$	$0.0_4 1136$	$0.0_4 1196$	$0.0_4 1201$	$0.0_4 1230$	$0.0_4 1287$	$0.0_4 1311$	$0.0_4 1280$

W. Voigt gave $0.0_4 1575$, and for the length, l, at θ, $l = l_0(1 + 0.0_4 1367\theta + 0.0_7 520\theta^2)$, where l_0 is the length at $0°$. For the linear expansion of the crystals per degree H. Fizeau gave $0.0_4 1621$ at $40°$ and $0.0_4 1642$ at $50°$ when parallel to the chief **axis**;

0.0_41208 at $40°$ and 0.0_41239 at $50°$, when perpendicular to the chief axis; and for the average value, 0.0_41346 at $49°$, and 0.0_41374 at $50°$. E. Grüneisen gave for the coeff. of linear expansion, 0.0_41297 between $-140°$ and $17°$, and 0.0_41345 between $17°$ and $100°$; and G. Vicentini and D. Omodei, 0.0_4132 at $270°$. R. von Dall-witz-Wegner gave for the coeff. of cubical expansion, 0.0_4351 at $0°$ and 0.0_4439 at $100°$. J. K. Roberts found that the thermal expansion of crystals of metallic bismuth parallel and perpendicular to the vertical axis, by comparison with that of crystalline quartz, are practically constant from ordinary temp. up to $240°$. Bismuth melts at about $270°$. The constant expansion coefficients over this range are perpendicular to the axis, 12.0×10^{-6}; parallel to the axis, 16.2×10^{-6}; mean, 13.4×10^{-6}. The bending over of the length-temp., curve as the m.p. is approached indicates dissocia-tion of the atoms in the solid. P. W. Bridgman found the linear expansion of single crystals of bismuth at room temp. to be 13.96×10^{-6} parallel and 10.36×10^{-6} perpendicular to the axis. S. Lussana gave 0.0_41574 for the coeff. of linear ex-pansion between $8°$ and $180°$ at 1 atm. press.; 0.0_41294 at 1000 atm. press.; and 0.0_41146 at 2000 atm. press. E. Grüneisen discussed the relation between the thermal expansion, compressibility, and at. vol.; and A. Schrauf, the relation between the coeff. of expansion and crystallographic axes.

G. Wiedemann and R. Franz,[5] and A. von Ettingshausen and W. Nernst found bismuth a bad conductor. The former showed that if the conductivity of silver be 100, that of bismuth is 1·8. L. Lorenz gave for the **heat conductivity** in absolute units 0·0177 at $0°$ and 0·0164 at $100°$; W. Jäger and H. Diesselhorst, 0·0194 at $18°$, and 0·0161 at $100°$; and E. Giebe, 0·0558 at $-186°$, 0·0252 at $-79°$, and 0·0192 at $18°$. G. Gehlhoff and F. Neumeier found for electrolytic bismuth, cast, 0·0623 at $-190°$; 0·0257 at $-77°$; 0·0244 at $0°$; and 0·0231 at $100°$. For the pressed powder, 0·0498 at $-190°$; 0·0194 at $0°$; and 0·0121 at $100°$. L. Lorenz gave for the temp. coeff. of the conductivity $a = -0.0_37343$, and W. Jäger and H. Diesselhorst, -0.0_2197. S. Konno interpolated the following values for the thermal conductivity, k, from his observations:

	$0°$	$100°$	$200°$	$300°$	$400°$	$500°$	$600°$	$700°$
k .	0·020	0·018	0·017	0·041*	0·037*	0·037*	0·037*	0·037*

The values marked with an asterisk refer to the liquid. If k_a be the thermal conductivity in the direction of the chief axis, and k_y, that in the direction of the base, the square root of the ratio $k_a : k_y$ was found by F. L. Perrot to be 1·170; by L. Lownds, 1·19; and by F. M. Jäger, 1·22. This subject was discussed by E. Jannetaz, C. Cailler, and F. T. Trouton. G. W. C. Kaye and J. K. Roberts found the thermal conductivity of bismuth, in C.G.S. units, at $18°$, is 0·0159 when parallel to the trigonal axis; 0·0221, when perpendicular to that axis; and the ratio of these two conductivities is 1·39. For the effect of a magnetic field on the thermal conductivity, *vide infra*, electrical conductivity. H. Kronauer found the so-called temperature conductivity in absolute units to be 0·037 at 2·8°; W. Jäger and H. Diesselhorst, 0·0679 at $18°$; and 0·0546 at $100°$ with the temp. coeff. -0.0023; and E. Giebe, 0·0655 at $18°$; 0·0847 at $-79°$; and 0·1884 at $-186°$. P. W. Bridgman found that the effect of press. on the thermal conductivity is to reduce the conductivity 37·8 per cent. per 12,000 kgrms. per sq. cm. The press. coeff. is -0.0_431, which is negative and numerically high. He also measured the thermal conductivity of single crystals.

The **specific heat** was found by H. V. Regnault[6] to be 0·03084 between $15°$ and $98°$; E. Bède gave 0·02979 between $9°$ and $102°$, or for temp. up to about $200°$, $c = 0.0269 + 0.000020$; and for commercial bismuth 0·02889 between $13°$ and $106°$; 0·03036 between $15°$ and $175°$; and 0·03085 between $13°$ and $205°$. H. Kopp gave 0·0292 and 0·0318; G. W. Kahlbaum, 0·0305; L. Lorenz, 0·03013 at $0°$; 0·03066 at $50°$; 0·03090 at $75°$; and 0·03116 at $100°$. F. A. Waterman gave 0·03055; O. Richter, 0·029928 between $0°$ and $108°$; and W. Jäger and H. Diesselhorst, 0·0292 at $18°$, and 0·0303 at $100°$. E. Giebe gave 0·0303 at $18°$, 0·0296 at $79°$, and

0·0284 at —186°, or 0·0295 between 18° and —186°; A. Classen, 0·0318 between 21·7° and 61·6°; A. Levi, 0·03080 between 22° and 99°; A. Magnus, 0·300 at 17° to 100°; and 0·0307 at 16° to 248°; P. Schübel, 0·0299 at 18° to 100°; and 0·0305 at 18° to 200°; and S. Umino gave :

Sp. ht.	75°	150°	200°	300°	400°	500°	600°
	0·0296	0·0332	0·0360	0·0373	0·0373	0·0373	0·0373

H. Schimpf gave 0·03031 for the sp. ht. between 17° and 100°; 0·02854 between 17° and —79°; and 0·02752 between 17° and —190°; and for the value at 0°, he gave 0·0291. R. Ewald gave 0·0251 at —135°; 0·0279 at —38°; and 0·0295 at 28°; T. W. Richards and F. G. Jackson gave 0·0284 between 18·7° and —188·5°. J. Dewar gave 0·0218 at —223°. N. Stücker gave for the sp. ht., c, at θ, between 60° and 125°, $c=0·0302+0·000054(\theta-60)$; and between 60° and 225°, $c=0·0302+0·000101(\theta-60)$; between 125° and 175°, $c=0·0338+0·000162(\theta-12)$, and between 125° and 225°, $c=0·0338+0·000192(\theta-125)+0·0000006(\theta-125)^2$. At 60° the sp. ht. is thus 0·03024; at 125°, 0·03375; at 175°, 0·04185; and at 220°, 0·04695. H. John represented the mean sp. ht. between 22° and $\theta°$, by $c=0·02956327+0·0_5304501124(\theta-22)-0·0_611519898(\theta-22)^2+0·0_945607(\theta-22)^3$; and for the true sp. ht. at $\theta°$, $c=0·02956327+0·0_5609(\theta-22)-0·0_63456(\theta-22)^2+0·0_818243(\theta-22)^3$. This subject was discussed by W. Voigt, L. Schüz, J. H. Awbery and E. Griffiths, E. Horn, and K. Schulz. I. Iitaka gave 0·0338 at 271° for the solid, and 0·0356 at 291° for the liquid; and C. C. Person gave 0·0363 for the sp. ht. of the liquid at 280°–380°. N. Stücker gave 0·03024 for the true sp. ht. at 60°; 0·03375 at 125°; 0·04185 at 175°; and 0·04695 at 225°. For the mean sp. ht. between 60° and 225°, $c=0·0302+0·000101(\theta-60°)$. For the **atomic heat** at 0°, H. Schimpf gave 6·38, and T. W. Richards and F. G. Jackson, 5·91; and at —223°, J. Dewar gave 4·54. G. N. Lewis gave $C_p=6·3$, and $C_v=6·2$ at 20°; and E. D. Eastman and co-workers examined the effect of temp. on the relation C_p-C_v.

J. Dalton [7] gave 249° for the **melting point** of bismuth. These results refer to the impure metal; and the results of A. Ermann, 265°; L. B. G. de Morveau, 246°; J. Crichton, 249°; F. Rudberg, 264°–268·3°; C. C. Person, 266·8°–270·5°; and A. D. van Riemsdyk, 268·3°, represent metals of a higher degree of purity. Later results with bismuth supposed to be purified gave W. Guertler and M. von Pirani 270°; L. I. Dana and P. D. Foote, 271°; G. Vicentini, 268·3°; J. H. Awbery and E. Griffiths, 269°; A. Classen, 264°; C. T. Heycock and F. H. Neville, 267·54°; H. Siedentopf, 264°; H. L. Callendar, 269·2°; B. G. Eggink, 271·5°; H. S. van Klooster, 272°; F. Mylius and E. Groschuff, 271°±0·15°; and J. Johnston and L. H. Adams, 270·95°±0·05. The f.p. of the metal given by C. Lüdeking is 260°–261°; G. Grube, and R. S. Williams, 268°; W. R. Mott, 268°; G. J. Petrenko, D. P. Smith, K. Hüttner and G. Tammann, and H. G. Mathewson, 273°. The effect of press. is to lower the m.p. of bismuth as is the case with water. According to G. Tammann, the effect of a press. p kgrms. per sq. cm., is to lower the m.p. $a\theta=-0·00386(p-1)$; while J. Johnston and L. H. Adams found that the m.p. is lowered by 3·56° per 1000 atm. press.; and that at

p .	1	500	1000	1550	2010 atm.
M.p. .	270·7°	767·71°	265·67°	264·04°	262·18°

J. Johnston represented the press., p atm., in atm. necessary to melt the substance at a temp. $\theta°$ by $p=95·1QD \log (T_m/\theta)$, where Q denotes the heat of fusion per gram, 12·5 cals.; and T_m, the absolute temp. of the m.p. Hence at 27°, $p=3000$ atm. Some relations between the m.p. and other physical constants were discussed by H. Crompton, P. W. Robertson, N. F. Deerr, and R. de Forcrand. H. Carlsohn said that the m.p. of bismuth compounds does not follow the addition rule. A. D. van Riemsdyk said that at a clear red-heat, the volatilization of bismuth is very small. J. Mensching and V. Meyer observed that at 1450°, volatilization is appreciable, and H. Biltz and V. Meyer said that volatilization occurs between 1600° and 1700°. According to C. Barus, the **vapour pressure** at 1199° is 32 mm.; and at 1211°, 86 mm. O. Ruff and B. Bergdahl gave 126 mm. at 1290°; 300 mm. at 1385°; 406 mm. at 1410°; and 657 mm. at 1490°; while J. N. Greenwood gave for the vap. press., p mm., at

	1200°	1310°	1420°	1740°	1950°	2060°
p .	102	25·7	760°	$6·3 \times 760°$	$11·7 \times 760$	$16·5 \times 760$

From these results, J. A. M. van Liempt gave $\log_{10} p = 5·50 - 9786T^{-1}$; and for the sublimation curve $\log_{10} p = 6·54 - 10360T^{-1}$. J. Johnston gave $\log p = -9010T^{-1} + 8·12$. T. Carnelley and W. C. Williams observed that the **boiling point** lies between 1090° and 1450°. T. Carnelley and W. C. Williams found 1390°–1450°, when H. F. Wiebe's relation furnished 1580°. W. R. Mott gave 1420°; J. N. Greenwood, 1420°; C. Barus, 1450°; J. A. M. van Liempt, 1506° at 760 mm.; and O. Ruff and B. Bergdahl, 1490° at 760 mm. E. Demarçay said that considerable vaporization occurs in vacuo at 292°; and A. Schuller distilled the metal in vacuo and observed that at dull redness the vapour condensed into drops. F. Krafft said that the b.p., in the vacuum of the cathode light, is 1050°; and F. Krafft and L. Bergfeld gave 1000°; F. Krafft and P. Lehmann gave for the b.p. at 50 mm. press. 993°; at 90 mm., 1002°; and at 140 mm., 1009°. J. Johnston gave 540° for the b.p. at 10^{-3} mm.; 620° at 10^{-2} mm.; 720° at 0·1 mm.; 84$\cup$° at 1 mm.; 990° at 10 mm.; 113$\cup$° at 50 mm.; 12$\cup\cup$° at 100 mm.; and 1440° at 760 mm. W. Herz found that the constant c in the equation $\theta_1/\theta_2 = T_1/T_2 + c(\theta_1 - T_1)$ varies from $-0·0004273$ to $+0·0005562$, where θ_1 and θ_2 denote the b.p. of two liquids at a definite press., and T_1 and T_2, the b.p. at another press. Some relations of the transition temp. were studied by R. Lorenz and W. Herz. W. G. Duffield made estimates of the **rate of vaporization** of liquid bismuth.

C. C. Person found the **heat of fusion** at 266·8° to be 12·6 cals. per gram, or 2·6 Cals. per gram-atom; F. Wüst and co-workers, 10·23 cals.; P. W. Robertson, 12·64 cals.; I. Iitaka, 12·24 cals.; S. Umino, 14·10 cals.; W. Herz, 12·2 cals.; J. H. Awbery and E. Griffiths, 13·0 cals. per gram; and D. Mazotto, and J. Johnston and L. H. Adams, obtained similar results. J. Tate gave 188·6 cals. per gram at 920° for the **heat of vaporization**; J. Johnston, 41·3 Cals.; and J. A. M. van Liempt gave 44·8 Cals. per gram-atom, and for **Trouton's constant**, 25·19. F. A. Henglein discussed the heat of vaporization. This subject was also investigated by R. de Forcrand, E. van Aubel, and A. Wehnelt and C. Musceleanu. C. M. Guldberg estimated the **critical temperature** to be 4600°. G. Tammann and E. Ohler found the at. **heat of solution** of bismuth in gold-amalgam to be -3730 cals., which is nearly the same as in mercury-2730 cals. M. Kawakami studied the heat developed on mixing bismuth with some other metals. E. Kordes gave 4·65 (cals.) for the **entropy**; and B. Bruzs gave 15·2 entropy units at 25°, and 19·4 at the m.p.

S. Haughton[8] gave 1·17 for the **index of refraction** of bismuth for the C-line; G. Quincke gave 1·824 for the C-line; 1·315 for the D-line; 1·155 for the E-line; 1·079 for the F-line; and 0·9671 for the G-line; A. Kundt gave 2·61 for red-light, and 2·13 for blue-light; P. Drude, 2·07 for red-light, and 1·90 for the D-ray; G. Horn, 1·841 for C-line; 1·670 for D-line; 1·563 for E-line; 1·466 for F-line; and 1·385 for G-line; and P. A. Ross gave 1·78 for red-light, 1·92–1·98 for yellow-light, and 2·20–2·30 for blue-light. The coefficient of absorption of bismuth for the C-line was found by S. Haughton to be $k = 2·5$; G. Quincke gave 2·119 for the C-line; 2·605 for the D-line; 2·679 for the E-line; 2·656 for the F-line; and 2·651 for the G-line; P. Drude gave 1·9 for red-light, and 1·93 for D-line; G. Horn gave 2·493 for C-line; 2·492 for D-line; 2·459 for E-line; 2·418 for F-line; and 2·640 for G-line. W. Meyer found for the index of refraction, μ, and the coeff. of absorption, k, for light of wave-length λ in $\mu\mu$:

λ	.	.	.	441·3	467·8	508	589·3	668
μ	.	.	.	1·38	1·47	1·55	1·78	1·96
k	.	.	.	2·26	2·42	2·54	2·80	3·09

E. Hagen and H. Rubens, P. Drude, G. Quincke, and W. Meyer obtained values for the **reflecting power,** R, of bismuth :

λ	.	.	431	508	630	668	3000	7000	11,000	14,000
R	.	.	58·5	52·2	66·9	57·2	71·7	79·5	83·2	81·6

H. Buisson, and C. W. Heaps observed no change in the emissivity of bismuth when its electrical resistance is increased by a magnetic field. The optical constants were also studied by A. K. Aster, and L. H. Rowse. F. E. Dix and L. H. Rowse measured the index of refraction, μ ; the extinction coeff., k ; and the reflecting power, R, for single crystals with light travelling parallel to the optic axis for wave-lengths 670$\mu\mu$ to 350$\mu\mu$. The reflecting power is nearly constant at 70 per cent. ; while both the index of refraction and extinction coeff. have a maximum at 460$\mu\mu$, which is taken to represent the photoelectric threshold of a cleavage surface. J. H. Gladstone gave 0·154 for the **specific refraction,** and 32·0 for the **atom-refraction** of bismuth ; E. van Aubel gave 39·2. According to M. Hurion, a beam of light passing through a hole bored in a bismuth plate is deflected when the bismuth is in a magnetic field. S. Procopiu studied the **electro-optical effect,** and the **magneto-optical effect** with powdered bismuth suspended in toluene ; and B. Pogany, with thin films of bismuth. O. Wiedeburg investigated the radiation of heat by bismuth. C. W. Heaps found that the emissivity of bismuth at 100° was not affected by a magnetic field of 4900 gauss—probably on account of the absence of magnetic resistance in the surface layers of metal.

J. Piccard and E. Thomas [9] discussed the colour of bismuth ions. R. Bunsen [10] said that bismuth changes the colourless gas-flame blue. According to R. Böttger, the **flame spectrum** of bismuth chloride in the colourless gas flame shows lines in the red and blue. There are bands due to the oxide. The flame-spectrum is not studied for spectral analysis ; it was examined by A. Gouy, J. N. Lockyer, and C. de Watteville ; the spectrum with the oxy-coal gas flame, or oxy-hydrogen flame was examined by O. Vogel, W. N. Hartley, and J. Meunier. The **spark spectrum** was observed more or less qualitatively by C. Wheatstone, A. Masson, D. Alter, and T. R. Robinson. The first measurements were made by W. Huggins, and since then numerous observations have been made—notably by W. A. Miller, R. Thalén,

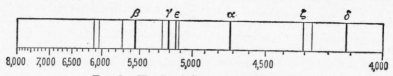

FIG. 2.—The Spark Spectrum of Bismuth.

L. de Boisbaudran, M. C. W. Buffam and H. J. C. Ireton, R. Capron, G. Cianician, J. Parry and A. E. Tucker, E. O. Hulburt, W. N. Hartley and co-workers, A. de Gramont, E. Demarçay, A. Schuster and co-workers, F. Exner and E. Haschek, O. Lohse, L. and E. Bloch, J. Hartmann, A. Hagenbach and H. Konen, W. Schwetz, R. J. Lang, S. R. Milner, T. Royds, J. M. Eder and E. Valenta, A. Mitscherlich, H. Rausch von Traubenberg, J. H. Pollock, G. A. Hemsalech, E. Diacon, B. Reismann, and J. Offermann. The principal lines in the visible spectrum are illustrated by Fig. 2. There are the two weak lines, 6129 and 6048, in the orange-yellow ; the weak yellow line, 5717 ; the green lines, 5552(β), 5271, 5209(γ), 5144(ϵ), and 5124 ; the blue line, 4724(α) ; the indigo-blue lines, 4302(ζ) and 4259 ; and the violet line, 4118. F. Brasack was able to detect 0·000166 mgrm. of bismuth by means of the

spark spectrum. *Les raies ultimes* were examined by A. de Gramont, and
W. N. Hartley and H. W. Moss; the spark spectrum in aq. soln. of salts by
E. O. Hulburt; the spectral analysis of bismuth-lead alloys by E. Schweitzer;
and the spectral detection of bismuth in gold, by A. Reis. G. Balasse observed
the continuous emission spectrum produced by an electrodeless discharge. The
arc spectrum was examined by R. Capron, J. C. McLennan and co-workers,
T. Royds, M. Kimura, B. E. Moore, A. Sellerio, H. Kayser and C. Runge,
J. Hartmann, F. Exner and E. Haschek, A. Hagenbach and H. Konen, J. Stark
and R. Küch, W. Schwetz, J. M. Eder and E. Valenta, F. M. Walters, G. R. Toshniwal, and J. Offermann. The intermittent arc spectrum was observed by
M. Kimura. The **ultra-red spectrum** was examined by H. Becquerel, H. M. Randall, H. Lehmann, V. P. Lubovich and E. M. Pearen, and F. M. Walters; and
the **ultra-violet spectrum,** by W. A. Miller, G. D. Liveing and J. Dewar,
R. J. Lang, L. and E. Bloch, V. Schumann, and J. M. Eder. The **absorption
spectrum** was studied by J. N. Lockyer and co-workers, W. Grotrian, A. L. Narayan and K. R. Rao, R. Mecke, M. Kimura, R. V. Zumstein, W. Friederichs,
J. C. McLennan and A. B. McLay, H. Sponer, J. J. Dobbie and J. J. Fox, and
J. G. Frayne and A. W. Smith. A. L. Narayan and K. R. Rao found that the
fluorescence of the vapour of bismuth, excited by radiations from 6000 A. to 3500 A.,
consisted of a banded spectrum in the orange-yellow; when excited by the ultra-
violet rays from a bismuth arc, the fluorescence became bluish in colour and had
lines at 4722 A. and 3068 A. J. C. McLennan and co-workers studied the
fluorescence spectrum of bismuth vapour. Bismuth salts are colourless, according
to J. Formanek. The soln. show no absorption effect after treatment with alkanna.
C. R. Crymble found an absorption band, with a head at 2852, as the ultra-violet
spectrum of bismuth chloride soln. (1 : 1000). He also compared the absorption
spectra of the family group—P, As, Sb, and Bi. The absorption spectrum was
studied by K. Schäfer and F. Hein, and A. E. Ruark and co-workers. A. L. Narayan
and K. R. Rao found that bismuth vapour at 1300° yields an absorption spectrum
composed of a very great number of bands shading off towards the red, and presenting
a fine structure, they extend from 6500 to 4500 A. The vapour emits an orange-
yellow fluorescence, the spectrum of which contains 24 bands from 6600 to 5050 A.
A. Terenin, and K. R. Rao studied the resonance and fluorescence spectra of
bismuth vapour. The effect of *pressure* on the spectral lines was examined by
W. J. Humphreys; and the effect of a *magnetic field,* or the **Zeeman effect,** by
J. E. Purvis, P. A. van der Harst, H. Luneland, S. Goudsmit and E. Back, and
C. Wali-Mohammed; and the influence of an *electric field*—the **Stark effect** by
H. Nagaoka and Y. Sugiura. The *self-induction* effect was examined by G. A. Hem-
salech, E. Néculcéa, and D. Huber; the *dispersion,* by O. von Baeyer, and
H. Geisler; and the *enhanced lines,* by J. N. Lockyer, M. Miyanishi, and J. Stein-
hausen. The *structure of the lines* and the **series spectrum** were investigated by
A. Ditte, H. Kayser and C. Runge, G. Joos, J. C. McLennan and A. B. McLay,
S. Goudsmit and E. Back, E. Gehrcke and O. von Baeyer, A. E. Ruark and
R. L. Chenault, C. Wali-Mohammed, V. Thorsen, H. Nagaoka and T. Mishima,
L. Aronberg, and K. Schäfer and F. Hein. H. Nagaoka and Y. Sugiura pointed
out a number of frequency differences in a few bismuth lines, but, according to
A. E. Ruark and R. L. Chenault, some of these are spurious, and C. Runge said
that the connection between the satellites of mercury 2536, and bismuth 4722,
and the isotopes of these elements described by H. Nagaoka and co-workers is a
mere chance effect. E. T. Wherry found that the crystals are poor **radio-
detectors.**

The *K*-series of the **X-ray spectrum** was examined by W. Duane [11] and
co-workers, J. M. Cork and co-workers, E. Friman, H. R. Robinson and
A. M. Cassie, G. Réchou, and M. Siegbahn and E. Jönsson; the *L*-series was
found by H. Hirata, D. Coster, M. de Broglie, H. R. Robinson, E. Friman,
C. E. Eddy and L. H. Turner, K. Lang, W. Duane and R. A. Patterson, S. J. M. Allen,

and M. Siegbahn to have the lines a_2a, 1·1533; a_1a, 1·14115; $\beta_1\beta$, 0·94930; $\beta_2\gamma$, 0·95293; $\gamma_1\delta$, 0·83708; $l\epsilon$, 1·31295; η, 1·057; $\beta_5\zeta$, 0·9223; $\gamma_2\theta$, 0·7929; β_4v, 0·9754; $\beta_3\phi$, 0·9357; $\gamma_3\chi$, 0·7874; and $\gamma_4\psi$, 0·761. J. C. Karcher, E. Hjalmer, W. Stenström, G. Wentzel, D. Coster, and M. Siegbahn gave for the M-series, a, 5·124; β_1, 4·915; β_3, 4·604; γ_1, 4·534; γ_2, 3·932; γ_3, 3840; a', 3·916; a, 3·9014; β, 3·7083; γ, 3·4714; δ, 2·943; ϵ, 2·813; M, 5·124; M_2, 3·326; and M_3, 2·873. V. Dolejsek gave for the N-series, $N_7P_1=13·040$, and $N_7P_2=13·140$ for the N-series, N_7P_1, 13·040; and K_7P_2, 13·140. J. C. Chapman [12] found that the **X-rays** have a fluorescent effect. H. Whiddington observed the effect of X-rays on the ejection of high-speed electrons from bismuth (oxide). A. L. Foley observed no definite change occurs when bismuth is exposed for a long time to X-rays. S. J. M. Allen studied the absorption of X-rays by bismuth; and T. E. Aurén found the absorption coeff. to be 677 when that of hydrogen is unity. J. Stark and G. Wendt observed that the surface perpendicular to the crystals is attacked by **canal rays** three times as fast as the basal-surface. A. E. Ruark and co-workers gave 8·0 volts for the **ionizing potential,** and 1·9, 3·9, and 5·7 volts for the inelastic collision potential of bismuth. G. Shearer examined the emission of electrons from bismuth exposed to X-rays. K. H. Kingdon gave 8 volts for the **ionizing potential** of bismuth vapour; and G. Riccardi, 8·48 volts. B. Rosen discussed this subject. J. E. P. Wagstaff gave $1·63\times10^{12}$ for the **vibration frequency;** and W. Herz, $1·62\times10^{12}$. W. P. Jorissen and J. A. Vollgraff thought that the proportion of thallium spectroscopically perceptible in bismuth was increased by exposing the metal to **cathode rays.** M. Kimura and G. Nakamura found the cathode ray spectrum closely resembled the spark spectrum. L. Meitner showed that the a-**ray** activity of bismuth from Joachimsthal pitchblende residues is due to ionium, and not to a new element as supposed by K. Fajans and E. Towara. A. G. Shenstone concluded that the passage of an electric current through a plate of bismuth augmented the **photoelectric effect;** but F. Horton attributed the result to the evolution of gases owing to the warming of the apparatus by the current. T. J. Parmley found the photoelectric threshold of single crystals lies between 2804 A. and 2894 A. B. Gudden [13] and R. Pohl, R. Hamer, R. S. Bartlett, and M. Hake studied the photoelectric effect with submicroscopic particles of bismuth; F. Gross, the effect with films of bismuth; and A. T. Waterman, the effect of temp. on the emission of electrons. The **radioactivity** of bismuth—*vide* polonium—was examined by F. Giesel, W. Marckwald, etc. The effect of bismuth compounds on the **luminescence** of calcium sulphide, etc., was studied by A. Forster, L. de Boisbaudran, H. Becquerel, A. Verneuil, V. Klatt and P. Lenard, etc. H. Kopfermann found that the fluorescence of bismuth vapours at 950° gave the spectral lines 4722·72 A. and 3067·81 A. The glowing of bismuth wires was shown by W. B. Pietenpol and H. A. Miley to be due to a film of oxide. The optical resonance of bismuth was measured by G. Mie. E. Adinolfi found that **X-rays** have an effect on the arrangement of bismuth during solidification, varying in nature with the hardness of the rays. H. R. Robinson, and R. Whiddington studied the liberation of electrons by X-rays from bismuth oxide; S. J. M. Allen, R. A. Houstoun and N. Ahmad, the absorption of X-rays; and A. L. Foley, the effect of exposure to X-rays, or to ultra-violet light on the spectrum.

P. E. Shaw and C. S. Jex [14] found that bismuth does not show a negative charge by frictional electricity with glass. The **electrical conductivity** of bismuth is good. K. F. Herzfeld, and A. Günther-Schulze studied the metallic conduction of bismuth. L. Lorenz gave 9290 mhos at 0° and 6300 mhos at 100°; E. van Aubel, at 0°, 9200 mhos for hard bismuth and 9260 mhos for soft bismuth; F. A. Schulze, 8300 mhos at room temp.; W. Jäger and H. Diesselhorst, 8400 mhos at 18°, and 6240 mhos at 100°; E. Giebe, 8610 mhos at 18°, 11,960 mhos at −79°, and 24,520 mhos at −186°; and J. A. Fleming and J. Dewar, 7500 mhos at 60°, 8840 mhos at 19°, 11,970 mhos at −58·6°, and 24,570 mhos at $-187 \cdot 5°$. The **electrical resistance,** the reciprocal of the conductivity, is $0 \cdot 000088$ when at 19°, according to J. Dewar and J. A. Fleming; E. Giebe gave $0 \cdot 000086$ ohm at 18° : W. Jäger and H. Diesselhorst, $0 \cdot 000084$ ohm at 18° ; and A. Werner, $0 \cdot 000083$ ohm at 22°. P. Lenard gave $0 \cdot 000092$ ohm at 155° for pressed wire, and $0 \cdot 000087$ ohm at 230°. For the effect of *temperature* on the resistance, R_0, between 0° and 100°, E. van Aubel gave $R = R_0(1 + 0 \cdot 04429\theta)$ for soft bismuth, and $R = R_0(1 + 0 \cdot 00422\theta)$ for hard bismuth ; for the same range of temp., W. Jäger and H. Diesselhorst gave for the temp. cœff., $0 \cdot 0045$; P. Lenard, $0 \cdot 00458$; F. Streintz, $0 \cdot 0045$; L. Holborn, $0 \cdot 00446$; and G. Vicentini and D. Omodei, from 0° to 271°, $R = R_0(1 + 0 \cdot 0011760\theta + 0 \cdot 0_5 5532\theta^2 + 0 \cdot 0_7 1289\theta^3)$. W. E. Williams made observations on this subject. P. Lenard and J. L. Howard gave the high value $0 \cdot 0052$. Whilst P. Lenard, and E. van Aubel said that the temp. cœff. is constant between 0° and 100°, the latter observed $0 \cdot 00412$ between 0° and $19 \cdot 5°$ and $0 \cdot 00450$ between 0° and $99 \cdot 7°$. W. Tuijn and H. K. Onnes found that the metal is not supraconducting at $1 \cdot 24°$ K. P. W. Bridgman gave a negative cœff., $-0 \cdot 00039$, between 0° and 100° for an impure sample, while for electrolytic bismuth, of a high degree of purity, he found the average cœff. was $0 \cdot 00438$ from 0° to 100°, and $0 \cdot 00381$ at 0°—*vide infra*. He also found the sp. resistance of single crystals to be $13 \cdot 8 \times 10^{-6}$ ohms parallel and $10 \cdot 9 \times 10^{-6}$ ohms when perpendicular to the chief axis. R. S. Bartlett found the resistance of a thin film of bismuth exposed to ultra-violet light was reduced to $0 \cdot 0014$ at 0° to nearly zero at $-185°$. For the ratio of the electrical conductivities taken vertical and parallel to the axes of the crystals, C. Matteucci gave $1 \cdot 6$, and E. von Everdingen, $1 \cdot 68$. According to A. Matthiessen and M. von Bose, when a bismuth wire has been heated for a long time at 100°, its conductivity increases so that if the conductivity measured at 0° be $1 \cdot 2517$, the conductivity at 0° after heating for a day at 100° is $1 \cdot 4494$, a longer heating made very little difference to the result. This is taken to support E. Cohen and A. T. L. Moesveld's view as to the allotropy of bismuth—*vide supra*.

The various observations on electrical conductivity were reviewed by A. Schulze. E. F. Northrup and V. A. Suydam's measurements of the electrical resistance of bismuth over a range of temp. covering the fusion of the metal, are :

	17·5°	100°	200°	300°	400°	600°	750°
R . .	120·00	156·50	214·50	128·90	134·20	145·25	153·55

The data are plotted in Fig. 3. Y. Matsuyama gave $126 \cdot 7 \times 10^{-6}$ ohm for the sp. resistance of molten bismuth. G. Vassura gave 3640 mhos for the solid at 271°, and 7810 mhos for the liquid at the same temp.

L. de la Rive gave 7370 mhos for the liquid at 358°, and 6220 at 860°. H. Tsutsumi found that the electrical resistance of metals usually increases during fusion, but with bismuth and antimony the contrary is true. The ratio of the resistance of the liquid to that of the solid is $0 \cdot 43$. H. Perlitz studied the relation between the crystal lattice and the change of resistance on fusion. This phenomenon is attributed to a transformation of the molecules during fusion as exemplified by the abnormally high heat of fusion of bismuth. While the sp. resistance of the metals in the liquid and solid states at the m.p. approximates 2, the ratio for antimony and bismuth is roughly $0 \cdot 5$—actually, $0 \cdot 43$ for bismuth. G. Bretano, and P. W. Bridgman found the effect of *pressure* on antimony and bismuth, and the latter showed that, unlike the result with most metals, the effect is large and positive. Expressing the press. p, in kilograms per sq. cm., and the resistance, R, relative to unity at 0° :

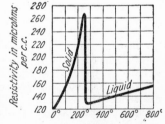

FIG. 3.—The Effect of Temperature on the Resistance of Bismuth.

p		0	2,000	4,000	6,000	8,000	10,000	12,000
R $\begin{cases} 0° \\ 25° \\ 50° \\ 75° \end{cases}$		1·0000	1·0336	1·0726	1·1163	1·1638	1·2143	1·2672
		1·0969	1·1333	1·1748	1·2204	1·2698	1·3225	1·3779
		1·1996	1·2389	1·2830	1·3316	1·3841	1·4498	1·4980
		1·3115	1·3540	1·4013	1·4527	1·5078	1·5664	1·6279

and for the press. coeff. with 0, 6000, and 12,000 kgrms. press. per sq. cm., he found respectively at 0°, $0 \cdot 0_4 153$, $0 \cdot 0_4 195$, and $0 \cdot 0_4 212$—average $0 \cdot 0_4 2027$; at 25°, $0 \cdot 0_4 155$, $0 \cdot 0_4 198$, and $0 \cdot 0_4 202$—average $0 \cdot 0_4 2142$; at 50°, $0 \cdot 0_4 155$, $0 \cdot 0_4 192$, and $0 \cdot 0_4 199$—average $0 \cdot 0_4 2076$; and at 75°, $0 \cdot 0_4 154$, $0 \cdot 0_4 185$, and $0 \cdot 0_4 194$—average $0 \cdot 0_4 2023$. W. E. Williams obtained $0 \cdot 0_4 191$ for the press. coeff. between 0 and 300 kgrms. per sq. cm., at 0°. P. W. Bridgman summarized his observations by saying that the average press. coeff. is positive, increasing in numerical value with increasing press., and decreasing with increasing temp. ; the instantaneous coeff. at zero press. is nearly independent of the temp., but at higher press., it decreases at the higher temp. This means that as the press. increases, the temp. coeff. of the resistance decreases. He also found that taking the electrical resistance of liquid bismuth at 271° as unity, the resistance at

p		0	2,000	4,000	6,000	8,000	10,000	12,000
R $\begin{cases} 275° \\ 260° \\ 240° \end{cases}$		1·0019	0·9789	0·9584	0·9400	—	—	—
		—	—	0·9520	0·9336	0·9167	—	—
		—	—	—	0·9253	0·9088	0·8931	0·0783

The press. coeff. of the resistance of the liquid is negative like normal metals so that the positive coeff. with the solid is an effect of the crystalline structure. The press. coeff. is little affected by temp., and the temp. coeff. is little affected by press. within the observed ranges. The initial press. coeff. for the sp. resistance is $-0 \cdot 0_4 132$; and the temp. coeff. 0·00048. This is about five times less than for a normal solid at the same temp. At a press. of 7000 kgrms. per sq. cm., the resistance of the liquid is approximately 45 per cent. of that of the solid— E. F. Northrup and R. G. Sherwood observed 43 per cent. E. D. Williamson gave 1·2672 for the ratio of the resistance at 12,000 kgrms. per sq. cm. press. to the resistance at 1 kgrm. per sq. cm. E. Zavattiero, and P. W. Bridgman found that *tension* decreased the electrical resistance of all samples of bismuth. The effect is comparatively large with a range of tension of 100 grms., the tension coeff. was $-0 \cdot 0_4 292$; with less pure samples, the tension coeff. was $-0 \cdot 0_4 520$ at 0°, and $0 \cdot 0_4 427$ at 31·1°. Beyond the elastic limit the electrical resistance increases with tension as in the case of other metals. A. Schulze found that bismuth has a higher resistance for alternating than for direct currents ; but that the metal is electrically anisotropic. The resistance of thin films is disproportionately high. This subject was also studied by E. H. Hall, and P. Kapitza. L. Tiere and V. Ricca studied the resistance of bismuth solidified in a *magnetic field*. G. W. Schneider studied the resistance in a longitudinal magnetic field. According to R. Paillot, the electrical resistance of a spiral of bismuth wire is considerably diminished when the latter is placed in the neighbourhood of *radium radiations*. A wire of resistance $15 \cdot 103 \times 10^{-4}$ ohms was placed 0·5 mm. distant from 0·03 grm. of radium bromide (activity=500,000) ; in these circumstances, the resistance of the bismuth spiral was reduced considerably. The action of the radium salt is instantaneous, and remains constant as long as the distance from the wire is unaltered.

A. E. Malinovsky obtained negative results in an attempt to find if the random motion of the conductivity electrons is affected by the self-induction of the metal. The relation between the thermal and electrical conductivities was examined by A. Eucken and O. Neumann [15]—*vide* antimony. L. Lownds found that while the ratio of the thermal conductivities of bismuth perpendicular and parallel to the chief axis is 1·42, this ratio becomes 1·80 when the bismuth is in a *magnetic field* with $H=4980$ C.G.S. units. The corresponding values for the electrical conductivities are respectively 1·78 and 1·87. A. Righi, however, found that the ratio of the thermal conductivity inside and outside a magnetic field is very nearly the same as the ratio of corresponding values for the electrical conductivity. In the former case the ratio was 0·878, and in the latter, 0·886. A. Leduc obtained similar results; but A. von Ettingshausen said that the decrease in the thermal conductivity in a magnetic field is less than is the case with the electrical conductivity, being in the one case 4 per cent. and in the other 28 per cent. L. Lownds found that the sp. resistance of bismuth parallel and vertical to the principal axis is respectively 269,000 and 151,000 at 0°; 379,000 and 135,000 at −79°; and 243,000 and 86,000 at −186°. At 255°, −79°, and −186°, the percentage increase in the electrical resistance, parallel to the chief axis, is respectively 5·0, 22·5, and 33·5 for $H=2120$ C.G.S. units; 9·2, 37·7, and 44·2 for $H=3120$; 12·1, 43·1, and 47·4 for $H=3500$, and 19·8, 62·1, and 56·5 for $H=4980$. At 14°, −79°, and −186°, vertical to the chief axis, the percentages increases are respectively 3·9, 9·6, and 6·1 for $H=2120$; 7·3, 14·2, and 9·7 for $H=3120$; 8·6, 15·7, and 10·6 for $H=3500$; and 14·3, 21·5, and 11·4 for $H=4980$. According to C. Carpini, the variation of the electrical resistance of bismuth in both feeble and strong magnetic fields is a hyperbolic function of the strength of field, and it is also a sine function of the angle made by the coil of bismuth with the lines of force. No hysteresis phenomena were observed on changing the strength of field. When an alternating current is employed, the change of resistance is far smaller than with the corresponding direct current. The curves appear to depend in a very complicated manner on the amplitude and period of the alternating current. C. W. Heaps, and P. Lenard found that for small transverse fields, the relation between the resistance R and the strength H of the field is $dR/R=12000\times10^{-12}H^2$; and for longitudinal fields, $dR/R=3200\times10^{-12}h^2$. F. A. Ward found that the decrease in the thermal conductivity of bismuth is 3·22 per cent. in a transverse magnetic field of 5370 C.G.S. units, and 5 per cent. in a field of 6260 C.G.S. units. The subject was also examined by E. von Everdingen, J. Dewar and J. A. Fleming, P. Lenard, L. F. Curtiss, F. A. Ward, G. C. Trabaschi, P. le Rossi, G. W. Schneider, G. Berndt, E. J. Williams, F. P. König, F. C. Blake, R. Geipel, and R. Seidler. The periodic relation between the electrical conductivities was studied by Z. A. Epstein; E. Horn, and C. Drucker, the relation between the sp. ht. and the temp. coeff. of the resistance; and the theory of electronic conduction, by A. T. Waterman. G. A. Rogers studied the effect of X-rays on the resistance of thin films of bismuth, but observed no perceptible change. P. Fischer found cylinders from compressed mixtures of bismuth and 50 per cent. cupric oxide are non-conducting.

If an electric current flows between two points, P and Q, in a thin metal plate, the lines of flow diverge on passing from P and converge at Q, while the equipotential lines are everywhere at right angles to the current. If the plate be in a magnetic field, with its plane at right angles to the field, the lines of flow and the equipotential lines are distorted so that looking along the lines of force, the system of lines is deformed as if twisted to the right (positive) with zinc, antimony, tellurium, and iron, and to the left (negative) with gold, bismuth, and nickel. This is the so-called **Hall effect.** It is very large with bismuth and tellurium. This subject was studied by A. von Ettingshausen and W. Nernst,[16] E. von Everdingen, L. Lownds, L. Tieri and E. Persico, G. Polvani, P. la Rossi, E. H. Hall, C. W. Heaps, P. H. Craig, F. Klaiber, W. van B. Roberts, O. M. Carbino, D. Goldhammer, A. Righi, G. P. Grimaldi, and P. Senepa. L. J. Neuman measured the influence of the crystalline texture on the Hall effect; and T. F. Hargitt, the Hall effect in spluttered films. H. Rausch von Traubenberg found that the rotation effect decreases with temp. so that the fall is rapid at first, then slow up to about 260°, and thereafter rapid up to the m.p.; and E. Adinolfi showed that the Hall effect varies linearly with the strength of the magnetic field, and exponentially with the temp. P. W. Bridgman investigated the relation between the four transverse electro- and thermo-magnetic effects. According to G. P. Grimaldi, if two bismuth plates be dipped in the same soln., and one only be in a strong magnetic field, a feeble current flows from the magnetized to the unmagnetized bismuth. G. Polvani observed a lag with respect to the magnetic field of the Hall effect in bismuth. J. Beattie, G. C. Trabacchi, and C. W. Heaps studied the relation between the thermoelectric power and the Hall effect with bismuth.

According to A. L. Hughes,[17] bismuth free from air is electronegative to platinum, but in air, the contact difference of potential increases so that the metal becomes more electropositive, reaches a maximum, and then decreases to a stationary value. R. D. Kleeman and W. Frederickson found that bismuth assumes a positive charge in distilled water ; and R. Saxon noted that when a piece of bismuth is placed between, but without touching, two electrodes immersed in water, and a current passed between the electrodes, the surface of the metal remains bright on the cathode side, and is oxidized on the anode side. R. Saxon observed a grey oxide forms on the anode when water is electrolyzed with bismuth electrodes. According to A. Classen, in the electrolysis of a nitric acid soln. of bismuth, at first some bismuth peroxide deposits on the anode, but this gradually disappears, and elemental bismuth is deposited on the cathode. The reaction has been employed in quantitative analysis by E. F. Smith and co-workers, O. Steen, D. Balachowsky, K. Wimmenauer, O. Brunck, A. Hollard and L. Bertiaux, H. J. S. Sand, F. F. Exner, S. C. Schmucker, L. G. Kollock, F. Rüdorff, T. Moore, C. Luckow, L. Schucht, A. Brand, A. Jilek and J. Lukas, A. Fischer and R. J. Boddaert, S. Eliasberg, J. Wieland, H. Kammerer, etc. B. Neumann gave for the absolute electrode potential of bismuth in normal soln. of the sulphate, -0.490 volt ; in normal chloride, -0.315 volt ; and in normal nitrate, -0.500 volt. D. F. Smith measured the e.m.f. of cells of the type $H_2 \mid HClO_4 \mid HClO_4 + BiOClO_4 \mid Bi$, and calculated for the electrode potential $Bi \mid BiO^\cdot + H^\cdot$, -0.314 volt, and E. H. Swift, -0.318 volt ; while the latter obtained for $Bi \mid Bi(OH)^{\cdot\cdot} + H^\cdot$, -0.310 volt, and the former -0.298 volt. F. H. Smith gave for the electrode potential of bismuth against a normal soln. of hydrogen chloride in the presence of solid oxychloride 0.022–0.090 volt against the calomel electrode ; and A. A. Noyes and M. Chow gave for the specific potential of the $Bi \mid BOCl$-electrode, -0.1635 volt at $15°$; -0.1599 volt at $25°$; and -0.1563 volt at $35°$. J. Tafel studied the over-voltage, and polarization effects of a bismuth cathode in $2N$-H_2SO_4 at $12°$. The initial potential with the $Hg_2SO_4 \mid Hg$-electrode was 1.640 volts, and in 20 mins., about 1.670 volts, and thereafter a drop to the initial value when it remains constant. The over-voltage is about one volt. W. Isbekoff studied the decomposition voltages of a number of metal bromides, and hence deduced the electrochemical series : Al, Zn, Cd, Ag, Hg, Sb, Bi. F. W. Bergstrom found in liquid ammonia soln. the order Pb, Bi, Sn, Sb, As, P, Te, Se, S, I. M. Bose found that the anodic decomposition curve of bismuth nitrate soln. exhibits a decomposition point with about 1.86 volts, a bright yellow oxide is produced at higher voltages, and ozonized oxygen is evolved in considerable quantity from the surface of the oxide. N. W. Taylor studied the activity of bismuth in binary liquid metals. A. Thiel and W. Hammerschmidt found the over-voltage in $2N$-H_2SO_4 at $25°$ to be 0.388 volt. E. Newberry observed a white thick coating is formed in acidic soln., but a slight bronze film in alkaline soln. A. Günther-Schulze studied the cathodic spluttering of bismuth. T. Andrews, and G. C. Schmidt studied the passivity of the metal. A. Günther-Schulze and W. Winter found that bismuth exhibits the electrolytic valve action in nearly all electrolytes. The effect is due to the formation of a layer of oxide on the surface of the anode. C. Bellia utilized the Hall effect to obtain the rectification of alternating to direct current. The electrolytic solution pressure of bismuth is 2.4×10^{-27}. K. Elbs and H. Thümmel found that an anode of bismuth dissolves in soln. of sodium chloride or hydrochloric acid entirely in the tervalent form. V. Bayerle found the normal deposition potential is 0 volts (calomel electrode), and in acidic soln. the deposition proceeds reversibly ; while in alkaline soln., the action resembles metallic deposition from zincates or plumbates in accord with the metallic nature of bismuth, and in contrast with arsenic and antimony. The solubility product $[Bi^{\cdots}][OH']^3$ is $4\cdot3\times10^{-31}$. The **anodic corrosion** of bismuth in nitric acid, and soln. of sodium nitrate, was studied by E. B. R. Prideaux and H. W. Hewis. With 10 per cent. soln. of sodium nitrate and a current density of 12·5 amps. per sq. dm., there was an average of 4·6 volts ; the current efficiency was 100 per cent., and 1·76 kilowatt-hours were consumed per kilogram of bismuth dissolved. The product was a white oxynitrate. A negligibly small amount of bismuth remained in soln. With sat. soln. of sodium nitrate, the oxynitrate was formed as a loose precipitate, but three-fourths of the bismuth remained in soln. and was precipitated by water. G. Grube and F. Schweigardt found that, like antimony, bismuth dissolves anodically in soln. of potassium or sodium hydroxide in the tervalent form. A gram of bismuth can be dissolved in a litre of the conc. alkali-lye, forming the bismuthite. The anode then becomes passive and covered with the higher oxide. F. Paneth found that the ratio of cathodic to anodic dissolution of bismuth (thorium-C) in dil. soln. of potassium hydroxide is $1:1\cdot2$ and $1:3\cdot0$ for 0·0004N- and 0·001N-soln. respectively.

According to J. Svanberg,[18] rods cut parallel to the chief axis are more negative, and those cut perpendicular to that axis are more positive in the thermoelectrical series than rods cut in any other direction. There is a marked **thermoelectric force** between rods cut in each of these two directions. Rods cut in other directions are negative towards rods cut perpendicular to the chief axis, and positive with rods cut parallel to the chief axis. This subject was examined by R. Franz, H. Zahn, H. Pélabon, C. W. Heaps, C. Matteucci, and A. Matthiessen. E. Wagner obtained at 300 kgrms. press. between 0° and 100°, 707×10^{-12} volts per degree per kgrm. P. W. Bridgman measured the thermoelectric power of single crystals. According to P. W. Bridgman, the thermal e.m.f. E in volts $\times16^{-6}$, of couples composed of uncompressed and of metal compressed by a press. p kgrms. per sq. cm., when the cold junctions were at 0°, are :

p	2,000	4,000	6,000	8,000	10,000	12,000
10°	11	21	38	54	74	93
20°	21	42	73	106	145	183
E 40°	42	87	141	205	281	364
60°	64	134	218	308	416	539
80°	85	185	302	425	560	710

The effect is large and positive, increasing regularly with press. and temp. up to 710×10^{-6} volts at 100° and 12,000 kgrms. per sq. cm. press. E. Siegel found the effect of press. on the thermal e.m.f. of molten bismuth is very much smaller than with solid bismuth. P. H. Dowling found the contact potential between solid and liquid bismuth to be of the order of −0·020 volt. T. Todesco obtained a thermoelectric effect with two specimens of single crystals of bismuth, the crystals in contact were asymmetrically oriented ; T. Terada and T. Tsutui, with single crystals of bismuth with *cadmium ;* and R. W. Boydston, with *constantan.* A. Matthiessen found the thermoelectric power of the *lead-bismuth* thermo-couple, with commercial pressed bismuth wire, to be −97·0 microvolts at 20° ; with pure pressed bismuth wire, −89·0 microvolts ; with crystalline bismuth parallel with the chief axis, −65·0 microvolts ; and perpendicular to that axis, −45·0 microvolts. P. W. Bridgman gave for the effect with the lead-bismuth couple, $E=(-74\cdot42\theta+0\cdot0160\theta^2)\times10^{-6}$ volts. F. L. Perrot found that the thermal effect of a *copper-bismuth* couple, with the bismuth parallel and perpendicular to the (0001)-face, is :

	30°	50°	70°	95°
Bi parallel to (0001)	0·00190	0·00396	0·00610	0·00899 volt.
Bi perpendicular to (0001)	0·00084	0·00185	0·00299	0·00417 „

Different values were obtained using prisms cast from the molten metal, and E. Cohen and T. Moesveld attributed this to the presence of different proportions of α- and β-bismuth. L. Lownds gave for the thermal e.m.f., E millivolts, of the copper-bismuth couple when the two junctions were at $\theta°$, and $\theta°_2$,

$E=18\cdot32(\theta_1\ \theta_2)+0\cdot2988(\theta_1{}^2-\theta_2{}^2)$ when the bismuth is taken perpendicular to the chief axis, and $E=130\cdot2(\theta_1-\theta_2)+0\cdot3504(\theta_1{}^2-\theta_2{}^2)$ when taken parallel to that axis. P. W. Bridgman made observations on this subject. W. B. Burnie noticed the very great drop in the thermoelectric force of this couple when the bismuth melts. W. W. Coblentz gave 80 millivolts per degree for the thermal e.m.f. of a *silver-bismuth* couple; and K. Bädeker, 100 millivolts per degree between 20° and 22° for the *antimony-bismuth* couple. J. Dewar and J. A. Fleming gave for the *platinum-bismuth* couple, at 100° when the cold junction is at 0°, $-7\cdot25$ millivolts; W. Jäger and H. Diesselhorst, $-6\cdot52$ millivolts; E. Wagner, $-7\cdot39$ millivolts; E. Rudolfi, $-6\cdot31$ millivolts; and G. Borelius and A. E. Lindh, $-5\cdot2$ millivolts when taken perpendicular, and $7\cdot7$ millivolts when taken parallel to the chief axis of bismuth. H. Pélabon studied the effect of temp. on the thermoelectric power of bismuth. G. Spadavecchia, and G. P. Grimaldi observed that a strong magnetic field lessens the thermoelectric power of bismuth. C. R. Darling and R. H. Rinaldi found marked breaks in the e m.f.-temp. curves of the alloys of bismuth which expand on solidification, but not when there is contraction. T. Todesco examined the effect of light on the thermoelectric current.

F. P. le Roux found that when an electric current flows from the copper through a copper-bismuth couple to the bismuth, $25\cdot8$ cals. are produced per ampère-hour with bismuth containing 10 per cent. of antimony, and $19\cdot1$ cals. with purified bismuth—the **Peltier effect.** Expressing the Peltier effect in millivolts, F. P. le Roux gave $22\cdot3$; E. Edlund, $17\cdot7$; and A. E. Caswell, $16\cdot1$. P. W. Bridgman gave for the Peltier effect, P volts with the lead-bismuth couple $P=(-74\cdot2+0\cdot0320\theta)\theta+273)\times10^{-6}$ volt; and with a couple of bismuth uncompressed and compressed at p kgrms. per sq. cm., the Peltier effect, p in joules per coulomb $\times10^6$:

p			2,000	4,000	6,000	8,000	10,000	12,000
	0°	• •	289	574	1070	1530	2080	2580
	20°	• •	311	644	1020	1490	2050	2670
P	40°	• •	332	720	1090	1530	2070	2760
	60°	• •	353	800	1330	1790	2309	2860
	80°	• •	374	950	1580	2180	2600	2960

The Peltier effect is thus positive and, in general, it increases with rising press. and temp., but at the middle of the range passes through a flat minimum with rising temp. The **Thompson effect** in joules per coulomb per degree $\times10^8$, using the same couple is zero at 2000 kgrms. per sq. cm. press.; at 4000 kgrms. press., it is negative; and at higher press. it is initially negative, rising to positive values:

p			2,000	4,000	6,000	8,000	10,000	12,000
	0°	• •	0	0	$+1150$	-1150	-125C	-520
	20°	• •	0	117	-290	-500	-760	-470
σ	40°	• •	0	250	$+500$	$+250$	-160	-440
	60°	• •	0	430	$+800$	$+1000$	$+530$	-370
	80°	• •	0	600	$+460$	$+1660$	$+1270$	-280

Also, M. O'Day measured the Thompson effect with bismuth. In Table VI, **9**. 51, 5, N. C. Little has compared the thermomagnetic effect and the galvanomagnetic effect of bismuth, antimony, and arsenic. W. B. Nottingham [19] studied the characteristic curves of the bismuth arc; and E. Blechschmidt, T. Baum, and A. Günther-Schulze, the cathodic spluttering of bismuth.

In 1778, A. Brugman, [20] and in 1827, M. le Baillif, observed that bismuth is repelled by a magnet. M. Faraday showed that bismuth is strongly diamagnetic, so that if a metal rod cut parallel to the chief axis be suspended so that it is free to rotate in a horizontal axis, between the poles of an electromagnet, it will rotate in a direction so that the chief axis makes an angle ϕ with the lines of force. This subject was studied by J. Tyndall, H. Knoblauch, and G. W. Hankel. T. Collodi found that the Corbino effect decreases rapidly with rise of temp. and reaches a minimum at the m.p., and thereafter remains constant. W. W. Jaques found the magnetization coeff. to be -12554×10^{-12} when parallel to the principal axis, and -14323×10^{-12} when vertical thereto. A. Leduc allowed small spherical glass bulbs of 2 cms. diameter to be filled with molten bismuth, and the metal to solidify, whilst the bulbs were under the influence of a strong magnetic field. If the crystalline spheres of bismuth are then suspended freely in the same magnetic field, they take up the same orientation as that which they had at the moment of solidification of the metal. If the magnetic field is cut off and the bulbs are made to rotate about the axis of suspension, the motion is at once stopped when the magnetic field is established, and the bulbs are found to be orientated as at the time of crystallization. J. Dewar and J. A. Fleming gave for the **magnetic susceptibility** at 15°, -14×10^{-6} vol. units and at $-182°$, -16×10^{-6} vol. units. A. von Ettinghausen gave for the susceptibility at ordinary temp., -14×10^{-6} vol. units; L. Lombardi, -13×10^{-6} vol. units; and A. P. Wills, -12×10^{-6} vol. units. P. Curie obtained at 20°, $-1·4 \times 10^{-6}$ mass units, at 273°, $-1·0 \times 10^{-6}$ and at 273°–405°, $-0·04 \times 10^{-6}$ mass units. K. Honda gave at 18°, $-1·4 \times 10^{-6}$ mass units; at 260°, $-1·0 \times 10^{-6}$ mass units; and at 270° for the molten metal, $-0·01 \times 10^{-6}$ mass units. G. Meslin gave $-1·39 \times 10^{-6}$ mass units for the crystalline, and $-1·42 \times 10^{-6}$ mass units for the cast metal. H. Isnardi and R. Gans gave $-1·346 \times 10^{-6}$ mass units for field of strength $H=1029$ to 13,680 gauss. C. Nusbaum studied the effect with single crystals; and found $1·13 \times 10^{-6}$ dyne cm. when parallel to the principal axis, and $1·32 \times 10^{-6}$ when vertical thereto; H. K. Onnes and A. Perrier, and M. Owen, the effect of low temp. on the susceptibility, and found that between $-170°$ and 268°, the higher the temp. the lower the value of the magnetic susceptibility. S. Meyer gave $-5·25 \times 10^{-6}$ for the magnetization number of powdered bismuth, and P. Pascal gave -406×10^{-7} for the atomic susceptibility of tervalent bismuth, and -698×10^{-7} for that of quinquevalent bismuth. J. Forrest studied the parallel and transverse components of magnetization of bismuth crystals. W. Gerlach studied the atomic susceptibility of bismuth vapour; J. A. Becker and L. F. Curtiss, and F. K. Richtmyer, the magnetic properties of thin films. J. F. Spencer and M. E. John measured the magnetic susceptibility of bismuth-tin alloys, finding for bismuth alone $-1·24 \times 10^{-6}$ mass units. E. H. Williams found compounds of bismuth with an odd mol. number are paramagnetic, and those with an even mol. number are diamagnetic. M. Pierucci measured the effect of abrupt variations of temp. on the diamagnetic properties of bismuth; and P. Ehrenfest tried to explain the high magnetic susceptibility of bismuth by an electronic structure in which electrons have orbits crystallographically defined and enclosing several atomic nuclei.

REFERENCES.

[1] G. A. Quesneville, *Journ. Pharm. Chim.*, (2), **16**. 554, 1830; *Schweigger's Journ.*, **60**. 378, 1830; F. Stöber, *Zeit. Kryst.*, **61**. 299, 1925; A. Nies, *Ber. Oberrh. Geol. Ver.*, **52**, 1896; G. Rose *Abhand. Akad. Berlin*, **90**, 1849; *Pogg. Ann.*, **77**. 148, 1849; J. C. Poggendorff, *ib.*, **74**, 1848; J. Barlot, *Ann. Chim. Phys.*, (10), **6**. 135, 1926; W. L. Dudley, *Amer. Chem. Journ.*, **14**. 185, 1892; *Chem. News*, **66**. 163, 1892; A. W. Wright, *Amer. Journ. Science*, (3), **13**. 49, 1877; (3), **14**. 169, 1877; W. Haidinger, *Sitzber. Akad. Wien*, **1**. 624, 1848; C. W. Zenger, *ib.*, **44**. 311, 1861; P. P. Heberdey, *ib.*, **104**. 254, 1895; F. Stolba, *Journ. prakt. Chem.*, (1), **96**. 183, 1865; F. Wöhler, *ib.*, (1), **60**. 58, 1846; *Liebig's Ann.*, **85**. 253, 1853; C. W. C. Fuchs, *Die künstlich dargestellten Mineralien nach Roses System geordnet*, Haarlem, **26**, 1872; N. A. Puschin, *Zeit. anorg. Chem.*, **36**. 243, 1903; O. Mügge, *Neues Jahrb. Min.*, i, 183, 1886; N. W. Fischer, *Pogg. Ann.*, **8**. 497, 1826; F. Hérard, *Compt. Rend.*, **108**. 293, 1889; E. von Gomperz, *Zeit. Physik*, **8**. 184, 1922; W. Herold in C. Doelter, *Handbuch der Mineralchemie*, Leipzig, **3**. i, 812, 1918; A. Johnsen, *Centr. Min.*, 385, 1916; J. Löwe, *Zeit. anal. Chem.*, **22**. 498, 1883; P. W. James, *Phil. Mag.*, (6), **42**. 193, 1921; W. P. Davey, *Phys. Rev.*, (2), **23**. 292, 1924; (2), **25**. 753, 1925; H. Kahler, *ib.*, (2), **18**. 210, 1921; E. Bekier, *Zeit. anorg. Chem.*, **78**. 178, 1912; G. Tammann and H. Bredemeier, *ib.*, **142**. 54, 1925; G. Linck and H. Jung, *ib.*, **147**, 291, 1925; *Trans. Phys. Lab. Leningrad*, **100**. 21, 1925; H. Kahler, *Phys. Rev.*, (2), **17**. 230, 1921; P. W. James and N. Tunstall, *Phil. Mag.*, (6), **40**. 233, 1920; P. W. James, *ib.*, (6), **42**. 193, 1921; A. Ogg, *ib.*, (6), **42**. 163, 1921; L. W. McKeehan, *Journ. Franklin Inst.*, **195**. 59, 1922; O. Hassel and H. Mark, *Zeit. Physik*, **23**. 269, 1924; P. Möller, *Ueber den roten Phosphor und die eutropische Reihe Phosphor, Arsen, Antimon, Wismut*, Langensala, 1907; M. L. Huggins,

Journ. Amer. Chem. Soc., **44**. 1841, 1922 ; *Phys. Rev.*, (2), **19**, 369, 1922 ; *Amer. Journ. Science*, (5), **5**. 303, 1922 ; J. A. M. van Liempt, *Tech. Publ. Amer. Inst. Min. Eng.*, 15, 1927; H. C. H. Carpenter, *Metal Ind.*, **32**. 405, 1928 ; H. Biltz and V. Meyer, *Ber.*, **22**. 726, 1889; P. P. Ewald and C. Hermann, *Zeit. Kryst.*, **65**. Suppl., 27, 1927; W. Campbell, *Met.*, **4**. 329, 1907 ; *Journ. Franklin Inst.*, **154**. 1, 131, 201, 1902 ; I. V. Obriemoff and L. V. Shubnikoff, *Trans. Phys. Lab. Leningrad*, **100**. 21, 1925.

[2] J. Dalton, *A New System of Chemical Philosophy*, Manchester, **2**. 263, 1810 ; C. J. St. C. Deville, *Compt. Rend.*, **40**. 769, 1855 ; *Phil. Mag.*, (4), **11**. 144, 1856 ; L. L. Bircumshaw, *ib.*, (7), **3**. 1286, 1927 ; A. Ludwig, *Journ. Amer. Chem. Soc.*, **31**. 1130, 1909 ; L. Perrot, *Arch. Sciences Genève*, (4), **18**. 260, 1904 ; A. Classen, *Ber.*, **23**. 945, 1890 ; H. Biltz and V. Meyer, *ib.*, **22**. 726, 1889 ; I. Traube, *ib.*, **31**. 1562, 1898 ; W. Spring, *ib.*, **16**. 2724, 1883 ; *Journ. Chim. Phys.*, **1**. 593, 1903 ; T. Bergman, *De minerarum docimasia humide*, Upsala, 1780 ; G. W. Kahlbaum, K. Roth, and P. Siedler, *Zeit. anorg. Chem.*, **29**. 177, 1902 ; A. Johnsen, *Centr. Min.*, 385, 1916 ; J. Johnston and L. H. Adams, *ib.*, **76**. 295, 1912 ; *Amer. Journ. Science*, (4), **31**. 501, 1911 ; *Journ. Amer. Chem. Soc.*, **34**. 563, 1912 ; T. R. Hogness, *ib.*, **43**. 1621, 1921 ; G. McP. Smith, *ib.*, **36**. 123, 1906 ; P. T. Cleve and C. H. J. Feilitzen, *Journ. prakt. Chem.*, (1), **86**. 384, 1862 ; *Oefvers. Akad.*, 159, 1861 ; F. Nies and A. Winkelmann, *Sitzber. Akad. München*, 43, 1881 ; *Wied. Ann.*. **13**. 64, 1881 ; C. Lüdeking, *ib.*, **34**. 21, 1888 ; M. Teopler, *ib.*, **53**. 343, 1894 ; H. Siedentopf, *ib.*, **61**. 239, 1897 ; *Ueber Capillaritätsconstanten geschmolzener Metalle*, Göttingen, 1897 ; R. Arpi, *Internat. Zeit. Metallog.*, **5**. 142, 1914 ; G. T. Beilby, *Phil. Mag.*, (6), **8**. 258, 1904 ; W. L. Bragg, *ib.*, (6), **40**. 169, 1920 ; W. C. Roberts-Austen and T. Wrightson, *ib.*, (5), **11**. 295, 1881 ; (5), **13**. 360, 1882 ; (5), **40**. 295, 1881 ; *Proc. Phys. Soc.*, **4**. 195, 1881 ; **5**. 97, 1884 ; *B.A. Rep.*, 543, 1880 ; *Nature*, **24**. 470, 1881 ; G. Vicentini and D. Omodei, *Atti Accad. Torino*, **23**. 38, 1888 ; T. Murray, *Journ. Inst. Metals*, **2**. 134, 1909 ; O. Faust and G. Tammann, *Zeit. anorg. Chem.*, **75**. 108, 1911 ; G. Linck, *ib.*, **56**. 399, 1908 ; H. von Wartenberg, *ib.*, **56**. 320, 1908 ; R. F. Marchand and T. Scheerer, *Journ. prakt. Chem.*, (1), **27**. 209, 1842 ; R. Böttger, *Dingler's Journ.*, **212**. 441, 1874 ; H. G. Dorsey, *Phys. Rev.*, (1), **25**. 88, 1907 ; M. J. Brisson, *Pesanteur spécifique des corps*, Paris, 1787 ; J. F. Spencer and M. E. John, *Proc. Roy. Soc.*, **116**. A, 61, 1927 ; E. N. Gapon, *Zeit. Physik*, **44**. 535, 1927 ; L. Playfair and J. P. Joule, *Mem. Chem. Soc.*, **3**. 75, 1848 ; T. M. Lowry and R. G. Parker, *Journ. Chem. Soc.*, **107**. 1005, 1915 ; G. Quincke, *Pogg. Ann.*, **135**. 642, 1808 ; H. G. F. Schröder, *ib.*, **107**. 113, 1859 ; P van Muschenbroek, *Phil. Trans.*, **33**. 370, 1726 ; G. Leonhard, *Handwörterbuch der topographischen Mineralogie*, Heidelberg, 526, 1843 ; L. J. Thénard, *Traité de chimie*, Paris, **1**. 355, 1824 ; A. Matthiessen and M. Holzmann, *Pogg. Ann.*, **110**. 21, 1860 ; *Phil. Trans.*, **150**. 35, 1860 ; *Chem. News*, **2**. 217, 1860 ; W. Herapath, *Phil. Mag.*, (1), **64**. 321, 1834 ; D. Forbes, *ib.*, (4), **29**. 4, 1865 ; C. J. B. Karsten, *Schweigger's Journ.*, **65**. 394, 1832 ; J. J. Berzelius, *ib.*, **7**. 70, 1814 ; *Gilbert's Ann.*, **40**. 286, 1812 ; E. Cohen, *Proc. Acad. Amsterdam*, **17**. 1236, 1915 ; E. Cohen and A. L. T. Moesveld, *Chem. Weekbl.*, **10**. 656, 1913 ; *Zeit. phys. Chem.*, **85**. 419, 1913 ; *Versl. Akad. Amsterdam*. **28**. 762, 1920 ; J. Würschmidt, *Elster and Geitel's Festschrift*, 326, 1915 ; *Ber. deut. phys. Ges.*, **15**. 1027, 1913 ; **16**. 799, 1914 ; A. Hess, *ib.*, **3**. 403, 1906 ; E. Grüneisen, *Zeit. Instok.*, **27**. 38, 1908 ; *Ann. Physik*, (4), **22**. 801, 1907 ; C. T. Heycock and F. H. Neville, *Journ. Chem. Soc.*, **61**. 888, 1892 ; M. Plüss, *Zur Kenntnis der Viskosiät und Dichte geschmolzener Metalle und Legierungen*, Basel, 20, 1915 ; A. Jouniaux, *Bull. Soc. Chim.*, (4), **35**. 696, 1924 ; A. Vosmaer, *Chem. Engg.*, **13**. 535, 1915 ; W. R. Fielding, *Chem. News*, **123**. 1, 1921 ; K. Bornemann and P. Siebe, *Zeit. Metallkunde*, **14**. 329, 1922 ; F. L. Perrot, *Arch. Sciences Genève*, (4), **6**. 105, 229, 1898 ; (4), **7**. 149, 1899 ; *Compt. Rend.*, **126**. 1194, 1898 ; H. Endo, *Science Rep. Tohoku Univ.*, **13**. 193, 1924 ; *Journ. Inst. Metals*, **30**. 121, 1923 ; H. H. Potter, *Proc. Roy. Soc.*, **104**. A, 588, 1923 ; M. Polanyi, *Zeit. Physik*, **17**. 42, 1923 ; H. A. Wilson, *Phys. Rev.*, (2), **20**. 75, 1922 ; M. L. Huggins, *ib.*, (2), **28**. 1086, 1926 ; G. F. Brush, *Proc. Amer. Phil. Soc.*. **60**. 43, 1921 ; **61**. 167, 1922 ; H. G. Grimm, *Zeit. phys. Chem.*, **122**. 177, 1926 ; I. I. Saslawsky, *Zeit. anorg. Chem.*, **145**. 315, 1925 ; C. del Fresno, *ib.*, **152**. 25, 1926 ; F. Sauerwald and K. Töpler, *ib.*, **157**. 117, 1926 ; P. P. Ewald and C. Hermann, *Zeit. Kryst.*, **65**. Suppl., 27, 1927 ; R. von Dallwitz-Wegner, *Zeit. Elektrochem.*, **33**. 42, 1927 ; V. M. Goldschmidt, *Zeit. phys. Chem.*, **133**. 397, 1928.

[3] R. J. Rydberg, *Zeit. phys. Chem.*, **33**. 353, 1900 ; L. Ludwik, *ib.*, **91**. 232, 1916 ; *Zeit. anorg. Chem.*, **94**. 161, 1915 ; G. Quincke, *Pogg. Ann.*, **135**. 621, 1868 ; R. Arpi, *Internat. Zeit. Metallog.*, **5**. 142, 1914 ; E. Grüneisen, *Zeit. Instrk.*, **27**. 38, 1908 ; *Ann. Physik*, (4), **22**. 801, 1907 ; B. MacNutt and A. Concilio, *Phys. Rev.*, (2), **20**. 95, 1922 ; C. A. Edwards and A. M. Herbert, *Metal Ind.*, **18**. 221, 1921 ; *Journ. Inst. Metals*, **25**. 175, 1921 ; T. W. Richards, *Zeit. Elektrochem.*, **13**. 519, 1907 ; *Journ. Amer. Chem. Soc.*, **37**. 1643, 1915 ; J. Johnston, *ib.*, **34**. 788, 1912 ; T. R. Hogness, *ib.*, **43**. 1621, 1921 ; J. H. Hildebrand, T. R. Hogness, and N. W. Taylor, *ib.*, **45**. 3828, 1925 ; L. H. Adams, E. D. Williamson, and J. Johnston, *ib.*, **41**. 1, 1919 ; L. H. Adams, *Journ. Washington Acad.*, **17**. 529, 1927 ; R. Kremann and A. Hrasovec, *Monatsh.*, **46**. 409, 1925 ; F. A. Schulze, *Sitzber. Ges. Marburg*, 80, 94, 1903 ; *Ann. Physik*, (4), **13**. 583, 1904 ; (4), **14**. 384, 1904 ; W. Voigt, *Wied. Ann.*, **48**. 674, 1893 ; E. Jänecke, *Zeit. phys. Chem.*, **90**. 324, 1915 ; W. B. Hardy, *Phil. Mag.*, (6), **40**. 201, 1920 ; N. S. Kurnakoff and S. F. Schemtschuschny, M. Georgieff and E. Schmid, *Zeit. Physik*, **36**. 759, 1926 ; *Journ. Russ. Phys. Chem. Soc.*, **45**. 1004, 1912 ; *Zeit. anorg. Chem.*, **64**. 149, 1909 ; W. B. Hardy, *Phil. Mag.*, (6), **40**. 201, 1920 ; L. L. Bircumshaw, *ib.*, (7), **3**. 1286, 1927 ; W. Hagemann, *Ueber die Oberflachenspannung geschmolzener Metalle*, Freiberg, 1914 ; G. Quincke, *Pogg. Ann.*, **138**. 141, 1869 ; H. Siedentopf,

Ueber Capillaritätsconstanten geschmolzener Metalle, Göttingen, 1897; *Wied. Ann.,* **61**. 258, 1897; P. W. Bridgman, *Proc. Amer. Acad.,* **57**. 50, 1922; **58**. 166, 1923; **60**. 364, 1925; *Proc. Nat. Acad.,* **10**. 411, 1924; J. Groh, *Zeit. phys. Chem.,* **128**. 449, 1927; O. Hasse and E. Schmid, *Zeit. Physik,* **33**. 413, 1925; C. E. Fawsitt, *Journ. Chem. Soc.,* **93**. 1299, 1908; *Proc. Roy. Soc.,* **80**. A, 290, 1908; M. Plüss, *Zur Kenntnis der Viskosität und Dichte geschmolzener Metalle und Legierungen,* Basel, 20, 1915; W. J. Humphreys, *Journ. Chem. Soc.,* **69**. 243, 1896; F. Sauerwald and K. Töpler, *Zeit. anorg. Chem.,* **157**. 117, 1926; F. Sauerwald and G. Drath, *ib.,* **154**. 79, 1926; W. C. Roberts-Austen, *Phil. Trans.,* **187**. 383, 1896; *Proc. Roy. Soc.,* **59**. 281, 1896; **67**. 101, 1900; *Chem. News,* **74**. 289, 1896; K. Houda and R. Yamada, *Science Rep. Tokohu Univ.,* **14**. 63, 1925; E. von Gomperz, *Zeit. Physik,* **8**. 184, 1922; M. Georgieff and E. Schmid, *ib.,* **36**. 759, 1926; D. C. Stockbarger, *Publ. Mass. Inst. Tech.,* ii, 47, 1927; R. von Dallwitz-Wegner, *Zeit. Elektrochem.,* **33**. 42, 1927; G. Subrahmaniam, *Nature,* **120**. 770, 1927; M. Matuyama, *Science Rep. Tohoku Univ.,* **16**. 555, 1927.

[4] H. Kopp, *Pogg. Ann.,* **86**. 156, 1852; A. Matthiessen, *ib.,* **130**. 50, 1867; *Phil. Trans.,* **156**. 361, 1866; *Proc. Roy. Soc.,* **15**. 220, 1867; *Phil. Mag.,* (4), **32**. 472, 1866; G. Vicentini and D. Omodei, *Atti Accad. Torino,* **23**. 38, 1888; J. K. Roberts, *Proc. Roy. Soc.,* **106**. A, 385, 1924; *Nature,* **113**. 275, 1924; A. Hess, *Ber. deut. phys. Ges.,* **3**. 403, 1906; F. Sauerwald and K. Töpler, *Zeit. anorg. Chem.,* **157**. 117, 1926; H. G. Dorsey, *Phys. Rev.,* (1), **25**. 88, 1907; (1), **27**. 1, 1908; H. Fizeau, *Compt. Rend.,* **68**. 1125, 1 869; S. Lussana, *Nuovo Cimento,* (5), **19**. 182, 1910; C. Lüdeking, *Wied. Ann.,* **34**. 21, 1881; W. Voigt, *ib.,* **49**. 697, 1893; E. Grüneisen, *Zeit. Instrk.,* **27**. 38, 1907; *Ann. Physik,* (4), **26**. 293, 1908; P. W. Bridgman, *Proc. Nat. Acad.,* **10**. 411, 1924; A. Schrauf, *Zeit. Kryst.,* **12**. 375, 1887; R. von Dallwitz-Wegner, *Zeit. Elektrochem.,* **33**. 42, 1927.

[5] L. Lorenz, *Ved. Selsk. Skr. Kopenhagen,* (6), **11**. 37, 1886; *Wied. Ann.,* **13**. 422, 582, 1881; A. von Ettingshausen and W. Nernst, *Sitzber. Akad. Berlin,* **94**. 560, 1886; G. Wiedemann and R. Franz, *Pogg. Ann.,* **89**. 497, 1853; G. W. C. Kaye and J. K. Roberts, *Proc. Roy. Soc.,* **104**. A, 98, 1923; S. Konno, *Science Rep. Univ. Tohoku,* **8**. 169, 1919; *Phil. Mag.,* (6), **542**, 1920; F. L. Perrot, *Compt. Rend.,* **136**. 1246, 1903; *Arch. Sciences Genève,* (4), **18**. 260, 445, 1904; C. Cailler, *ib.,* (4), **18**. 457, 1904; F. M. Jäger, *ib.,* (4), **22**. 240, 1907; W. Jäger and H. Diesselhorst, *Abh. Phys. Tech. Reichsanst.,* **3**. 269, 1900; A. Eucken and O. Neumann, *Zeit. phys. Chem.,* **111**. 431, 1924; E. Jannetaz, *Bull. Soc. Min.,* **15**. 136, 1892; *Compt. Rend.,* **114**. 1352, 1892; G. Gehlhoff and F. Neumeier, *Verh. deut. phys. Ges.,* **15**. 876, 1069, 1913; E. Giebe, *ib.,* **5**. 60, 1903; *Ueber die Bestimmung des Wärmeleitvermögens bei tiefen Temperaturen,* Berlin, 1903; L. Lownds, *Ann. Physik,* (4), **9**. 677, 1902; F. T. Trouton, *Proc. Roy. Soc. Dublin,* **8**. 691, 1898; H. Kronauer, *Viertelj. Nat. Ges. Zürich,* **25**. 257, 1880; P. W. Bridgman, *Proc. Amer. Acad.,* **57**. 114, 1922; *Proc. Nat. Acad.,* **11**. 608, 1925; *Phys. Rev.,* (2), **18**. 115, 1921.

[6] H. V. Regnault, *Ann. Chim. Phys.,* (2), **73**. 1, 1840; C. C. Person, *ib.,* (3), **21**. 295, 1847; P. L. Dulong and A. T. Petit, *ib.,* (2), **7**. 113, 1818; (2), **10**. 395, 1819; E. Bède, *Mém. Courron. Acad.,* **27**. 1, 1856; E. Giebe, *Verh. deut. phys. Ges.,* **5**. 60. 1903; *Ueber die Bestimmung des Wärmelectvermögens bei tiefen Temperaturen,* Berlin, 1903; H. Kopp, *Liebig's Ann.,* **3**. 289, 1865; A. Classen, *Ber.,* **23**. 939, 1890; J. H. Awbery and E. Griffiths, *Proc. Phys. Soc.,* **38**. 378, 1926; F. A. Waterman, *Phys. Rev.,* (1), **4**. 161, 1896; W. Jäger and H. Diesselhorst, *Abh. Phys. Tech. Reichsanst.,* **3**. 269, 1900; R. Ewald, *Ann. Physik,* (4), **44**. 1213, 1914; A. Magnus, *ib.,* (4), **31**. 597, 1910; *Eine Prüfung der Grundhypothese der Nernstschen Wärmetheorems,* Tübingen, 1910; F. Wüst, A. Meuthen, and R. Durrer, *Ver. deut. Ind. Forsch.,* 204, 1918; E. D. Eastman, A. M. Williams, and T. F. Young, *Journ. Amer. Chem. Soc.,* **46**. 1184, 1924; G. N. Lewis, *ib.,* **29**. 1165, 1907; N. Stücker, *Sitzber. Akad. Wien,* **114**. 657, 1905; G. W. Kahlbaum, K. Roth, and P. Siedler, *Zeit. anorg. Chem.,* **29**. 177, 1902; H. John, *Viertelj. Nat. Ges. Zürich,* **53**. 186, 1908; *Die Abhängigkeit der spezifischen Wärme des festen Antimons und des festen Wismuts von der Temperatur,* Zürich, 1908; O. Richter, *Untersuchungen der spezifischen Wärme von Legierungen und ihrer Beziehung zur kinetischen Theorie der Elektronen und Atome,* Marburg, 1908; A. Levi, *Atti Ist. Veneto,* (2), **68**. 47, 345, 1909; H. Schimpf, *Zeit. phys. Chem.,* **71**. 257, 1910; T. W. Richards and F. G. Jackson, *ib.,* **70**. 414, 1910; K. Schulz, *Fortsch. Min.,* **3**. 291, 1913; J. Dewar, *Proc. Roy. Soc.,* **89**. 158, 1912; O. Wiedeburg, *Wied. Ann.,* **66**. 92, 1898; L. Lorenz, *Ved. Selsk. Skr. Kopenhagen,* (6), **2**. 37, 1886; *Wied. Ann.,* **13**. 422, 1891; L. Schüz, *ib.,* **46**. 177, 1892; W. Voigt, *ib.,* **49**. 709, 1893; P. Schübel, *Zeit. anorg. Chem.,* **87**. 81, 1914; I. Iitaka, *Science Rep. Tohoku Univ.,* **8**. 99, 1919; S. Umino, *ib.,* **15**. 597, 1926; E. Horn, *Ueber die Abhängigkeit der wahren spezifischen Wärmen der Metalle Nickel, Wismut und Zink von der Temperatur, Wärmebehandlung und Zusammensetzung,* Weida i. Th., 1927.

[7] J. Crichton, *Phil. Mag.,* **15**. 147, 1803; **16**. 48, 1903; J. Dalton, *A New System of Chemical Philosophy,* Manchester, **2**. 263, 1810; A. Ermann, *Pogg. Ann.,* **20**. 283, 1830; F. Rudberg, *ib.,* **71**. 460, 1847; C. C. Person, *Compt. Rend.,* **33**. 162, 1847; *Ann. Chim. Phys.,* (3), **24**. 129, 1848; L. B. G. de Morveau, *Mém. l'Inst.,* **12**. ii, 89, 1811; A. D. van Riemsdyk, *Arch. Néerl.,* (1), **3**. 347, 1868; *Chem. News,* **20**. 32, 1869; J. H. Awbery and E. Griffiths, *Proc. Phys. Soc.,* **38**. 378, 1926; G. Vicentini, *Atti Accad. Torino,* **22**. 28, 1886; A. Classen, *Ber.,* **23**. 945, 1890; H. F. Wiebe, *ib.,* **12**. 788, 1879; F. Krafft, *ib.,* **36**. 1705, 1903; F. Krafft and P. Lehmann, *ib.,* **38**. 453, 1905; F. Krafft and L. Bergfeld, *ib.,* **38**. 257, 1905; H. Biltz and V. Meyer, *ib.,* **22**. 726, 1889; J. Mensching and V. Meyer, *Liebig's Ann.,* **240**. 325, 1887; C. T. Heycock and F. H. Neville, *Journ. Chem. Soc.,* **65**. 69, 1894; T. Carnelley and W. C. Williams, *ib.,* **35**. 563, 1879; H. Siedentopf, *Ueber Capillaritätsconstanten geschmolzener Metalle,* Göttingen, 1897;

Wied. Ann., **61**. 239, 1897 ; H. L. Callendar, *Phil. Mag.*, (5), **48**. 541, 1899 ; W. G. Duffield, *ib.*, (6), **45**. 641, 1104, 1923 ; T. Carnelley and W. C. Williams, *Journ. Chem. Soc.*, **35**. 563, 1879 ; P. W. Robertson, *ib.*, **81**. 1233, 1902 ; H. Crompton, *ib.*, **67**. 315, 1895 ; **71**. 925, 1897 ; N. F. Deerr, *Proc. Chem. Soc.*, **11**. 125, 1895 ; *Chem. News.*, **76**. 234, 1897 ; R. de Forcrand, *Compt. Rend.*, **132**. 878, 1901 ; J. Tate, *Die experimentelle Bestimmung der Verdampfungswärme einiger Metalle*, Berlin, 1914 ; W. Guertler and M. von Pirani, *Zeit. Metallkunde*, **11**. 1, 1911 ; L. I. Dana and P. D. Foote, *Trans. Faraday Soc.*, **15**. 186, 1920 ; F. A. Henglein, *Zeit. Elektrochem.*, **26**. 431, 1920 ; F. Wüst, A. Meuthen, and U. R. Durrer, *Ver. deut. Ing. Forsch.*, 204, 1918 ; *Zeit. Instrkd.*, **39**. 204, 1919 ; B. Bruzs, *Journ. Phys. Chem.*, **31**. 681, 1927 ; I. Iitaka, *Science Rep. Tohoku Univ.*, **8**. 99, 1910 ; S. Umino, *ib.*, **15**. 597, 1926 ; B. G. Eggink, *Zeit. phys. Chem.*, **64**. 492, 1908 ; C. M. Guldberg, *ib.*, **1**. 234, 1887 ; J. Johnston and L. H. Adams, *Amer. Journ. Science*, (4), **31**. 506, 1911 ; J. Johnston, *Journ. Ind. Eng. Chem.*, **9**. 873, 1917 ; *Journ. Amer. Chem. Soc.*, **34**. 788, 1912 ; C. Barus, *ib.*, (3), **48**. 332, 1894 ; *Phil. Mag.*, (5), **29**. 150, 1890 ; *Bull. U.S. Geol. Sur.*, **54**, 1889 ; D. Mazotto, *Mem. 1st. Lombardo*, **16**. 1, 1891 ; H. Carlsohn, *Ber.*, **59**. B, 1916, 1926 ; G. Tammann, *Zeit. anorg. Chem.*, **40**. 54, 1904 ; K. Hüttner and G. Tammann, *ib.*, **44**. 131, 1905 ; G. Tammann and E. Ohler, *ib.*, **135**. 118, 1924 ; G. H. Mathewson, *ib.*, **50**. 188, 1906 ; G. J. Petrenko, *ib.*, **50**. 133, 1906 ; G. Grube, *ib.*, **49**. 84, 1906 ; E. Kordes, *ib.*, **160**. 68, 1927 ; R. Lorenz and W. Herz, *ib.*, **135**. 372, 1924 ; F. Mylius and E. Groschuff, *ib.*, **96**. 261, 1916 ; J. A. M. van Liempt, *ib.*, **114**. 105, 1920 ; D. P. Smith, *ib.*, **56**. 109, 1908 ; R. S. Williams, *ib.*, **55**. 1, 1907 ; O. Ruff and B. Bergdahl, *ib.*, **106**. 89, 1919 ; M. Chikashige, *ib.*, **51**. 328, 1907 ; H. S. van Klooster, *ib.*, **80**. 104, 1913 ; C. Lüdeking, *Wied. Ann.*, **34**. 21, 1881 ; A. Schuller, *ib.*, **18**. 321, 1883 ; O. Wiedeburg, *ib.*, **66**. 92, 1898 ; J. N. Greenwood, *Proc. Roy. Soc.*, **82**. A, 396, 1909 ; **83**. A, 483, 1910 ; *Zeit. Elektrochem.*, **18**. 319, 1912 ; *Zeit. phys. Chem.*, **76**. 484, 1911 ; E. Demarçay, *Compt. Rend.*, **95**. 183, 1882 ; R. de Forcrand, *ib.*, **156**. 1648, 1912 ; E. van Aubel, *ib.*, **156**. 456, 1912 ; A. Wehnelt and C. Musceleanu, *Ber. deut. phys. Ges.*, **14**. 1032, 1912 ; W. Herz, *Zeit. Elektrochem.*, **25**. 45, 1919 ; *Zeit. anorg. Chem.*, **170**. 237, 1928 ; M. Kawakami, *ib.*, **167**. 345, 1927 ; W. R. Mott, *Trans. Amer. Elektrochem. Soc.*, **34**. 255, 1918.

[8] S. Haughton, *Phil. Trans.*, **153**. 87, 1863 ; W. Voigt, *Wied. Ann.*, **23**. 104, 1884 ; A. Kundt, *ib.*, **34**. 469, 1888 ; P. Drude, *ib.*, **39**. 481, 1890 ; O. Wiedeburg, *ib.*, **66**. 92, 1898 ; G. Horn, *Neues Jahrb. Min. B.B.*, **12**. 335, 1899 ; P. A. Ross, *Phys. Rev.*, (1), **33**. 549, 1911 ; A. K. Aster, *ib.*, (2), **20**. 349, 1922 ; L. H. Rowse, *ib.*, (2), **27**. 247, 1926 ; C. W. Heaps, *ib.*, (2), **27**. 764, 1926 ; W. Meyer, *Ann. Physik*, (4), **31**. 1017, 1910 ; E. Hagen and H. Rubens, *ib.*, (4), **1**. 352, 1900 ; (4), **8**. 1, 1902 ; (4), **11**. 873, 1903 ; B. Pogany, *ib.*, (4), **64**. 196, 1921 ; M. Hurion, *Compt. Rend.*, **98**. 1257, 1884 ; H. Buisson, *ib.*, **126**. 462, 1898 ; J. H. Gladstone, *Proc. Roy. Soc.*, **23**. 101, 1870 ; **60**. 140, 1896 ; E. van Aubel, *Zeit. phys. Chem.*, **30**. 566, 1899 ; G. Quincke, *Pogg. Ann. Jubelbd.*, 336, 1874 ; S. Procopiu, *Compt. Rend.*, **174**. 1170, 1922 ; F. E. Dix and L. H. Rowse, *Journ. Amer. Opt. Soc.*, **14**. 304, 1927 ; L. H. Rowse, *Phys. Rev.*, (2). **27**. 247, 1926.

[9] J. Piccard and E. Thomas, *Helvetica Chim. Acta*, **6**. 1040, 1923.

[10] C. Wheatstone, *Phil. Mag.*, (3), **7**. 299, 1835 ; T. Royds, *ib.*, (6), **19**. 285, 1910 ; *Phil. Trans.*, **208**. A, 333, 1908 ; *Proc. Roy. Soc.*, **107**. A, 360, 1925 ; J. H. Pollock, *Proc. Roy. Soc. Dublin*, (2), **13**. 202, 1912 ; A. Masson, *Ann. Chim. Phys.*, (3), **31**. 295, 1851 ; E. Diacon, *ib.*, (4), **6**. 5, 1865 ; H. Luneland, *Ann. Physik*, (4), **34**. 505, 1911 ; H. Lehmann, *ib.*, (4), **39**. 53, 1912 ; D. Alter, *Amer. Journ. Science*, (2), **18**. 55, 1854 ; F. R. Robinson, *Phil. Trans.*, **152**. 939, 1862 ; W. A. Miller, *ib.*, **152**. 861, 1862 ; W. Huggins, *ib.*, **154**. 139, 1864 ; G. D. Liveing and J. Dewar, *ib.*, **174**. 187, 1883 ; C. de Watteville, *ib.*, **204**. A, 139, 1904 ; *Spectres de flammes*, Paris, 1804 ; R. Böttger, *Journ. prakt. Chem.*, (1), **65**. 392, 1862 ; F. Brasack, *Abhand. Nat. Ges. Halle*, **9**. 1, 1864 ; A. Mitscherlich, *Pogg. Ann.*, **121**. 459, 1864 ; R. Bunsen, *Liebig's Ann.*, **138**. 277, 1866 ; R. Thalén, *Om Spectralanalys*, Upsala, 1866 ; *Nova Acta Soc. Upsala*, (3), **6**. 9, 1868 ; *Ann. Chim. Phys.*, (4), **18**. 235, 1869 ; A. Ditte, *Compt. Rend.*, **73**. 738, 1871 ; A. Gouy, *ib.*, **85**. 439, 1877 ; H. Becquerel, *ib.*, **99**. 374, 1884 ; L. de Boisbaudran, *ib.*, **73**. 943, 1871 ; *Spectres luminaux*, Paris, 1874 ; E. Demarçay, *Spectres électriques*, Paris, 1895 ; P. A. van der Harst, *Proc. Acad. Amsterdam*, **22**. 300, 1920 ; *Arch. Neerl.*, (3), **9**. 1, 1925 ; R. Capron, *Photographed Spectra*, London, 1877 ; G. Ciamician, *Sitzber. Akad. Wien*, **76**. 499, 1877 ; F. Exner and E. Haschek, *ib.*, **106**. 337, 1897 ; *Tabellen der Funkenspectra*, Wien, 1902 ; *Tabellen der Bogenspectren*, Wien, 1904 ; *Die Spektren der Elemente bei normalen Druck*, Leipzig, 1911–1912 ; A. E. Ruark, F. L. Mohler, P. D. Foote, and R. L. Chenault, *Nature*, 112. 831, 1923 ; *Phys. Rev.*, (2), **23**. 770, 1924 ; *Journ. Franklin Inst.*, **198**. 541, 1924 ; *The Spectra and Critical Potentials of the Fifth Group Elements*, Washington, 1924 ; A. E. Ruark and R. L. Chenault, *Phil. Mag.*, (6), **50**. 937, 1925 ; M. Kimura, *Science Papers Japan. Inst. Phys. Chem. Research*, **3**. 71, 1925 ; A. L. Narayan and K. R. Rao, *Proc. Roy. Soc.*, **107**. A, 762, 1925 ; *Proc. Phys. Soc.*, **38**. 321, 1926 ; *Nature*, **114**. 645, 1924 ; *Phil. Mag.*, (6), **50**. 645, 1925 ; E. O. Hulburt, *Phys. Rev.*, (2), **24**. 129, 1924 ; (2), **25**. 888, 1925 ; D. Cater, *ib.*, (2), **12**. 20, 1922 ; W. Duane and R. A. Patterson, *ib.*, (2), **19**. 542, 1922 ; J. M. Cork and B. R. Stephenson, *ib.*, (2), **27**. 103, 138, 1926 ; R. V. Zumstein, *ib.*, (2), **27**. 562, 1926 ; J. N. Lockyer, *Proc. Roy. Soc.*, **22**. 371, 1874 ; **27**. 279, 1877 ; **43**. 117, 1887 ; **65**. 451, 1899 ; J. N. Lockyer and W. C. Roberts-Austen, *ib.*, **23**. 344, 1875 ; J. C. McLennan, J. F. T. Young, and H. J. C. Ireton, *ib.*, **98**. A, 95, 1920 ; J. J. Dobbie and J. J. Fox, *ib.*, **98**. A, 147, 1920 ; K. R. Rao, *ib.*, **107**. A, 760, 1925 ; J. Parry and A. E. Tucker, *Engg.*, **27**. 127, 429, 1879 ; **28**. 141, 1879 ; W. N. Hartley and H. W. Moss, *Proc. Roy. Soc.*, **87**. A, 38, 1912 ; W. N. Hartley, *Trans. Roy. Soc. Dublin*, (2), **1**. 231, 1883 ; *Phil. Trans.*, **175**. 49, 1884 ; **185**. 161, 1894 ; W. N. Hartley and W. E. Adney, *ib.*, **175**. 63, 1884 ; S. R. Milrer, *ib.*, **209**. A, 71,

1908 ; R. J. Lang, *ib.*, **224.** A, 371, 1924 ; A. Schuster and G. A. Hemsalech, *ib.*, **193.** 189, 1899 ; A. Schuster, *B.A. Rep.*, 557, 1897 ; G. A. Hemsalech, *Journ. Phys.*, (3), **8.** 652, 1899 ; *Compt. Rend.*, **154.** 872, 1912 ; J. Meunier, *ib.*, **152.** 1760, 1911 ; V. Schumann, *Phot. Rund.*, **41.** 71, 1890 ; A. Sellerio, *Nuovo Cimento*, (6), **25.** 69, 1923 ; O. Vogel, *Zeit. anorg. Chem.*, **5.** 42, 1894 ; K. Schäfer and F. Hein, *ib.*, **100.** 249, 1917 ; H. Kayser and C. Runge, *Sitzber. Akad. Berlin*, **3,** 1893 ; *Wied. Ann.*, **52.** 93, 1894 ; C. Runge, *Nature*, **113.** 781, 1924 ; A. de Gramont, *Analyse directe spectrale des minéraux*, Paris, 1895 ; *Compt. Rend.*, **118.** 591, 1894 ; **144.** 1101, 1879 ; **170.** 31, 1920 ; L. and E. Bloch, *ib.*, **158.** 1416, 1914 ; **170.** 320, 1920 ; **171.** 709, 1920 ; **178.** 472, 1924 ; *Journ. Phys. Rad.*, **2.** 229, 1921 ; G. Réchou, *Compt. Rend.*, **180.** 1107, 1925 ; M. de Broglie, *ib.*, **170.** 585, 1920 ; B. E. Moore, *Astrophys. Journ.*, **54.** 191, 1921 ; W. Duane and R. A. Patterson, *Proc. Nat. Acad.*, **8.** 85, 1922 ; W. Duane, H. Fricke, and W. Stenström, *ib.*, **6.** 607, 1920 ; A. Terenin, *Zeit. Physik*, **31.** 26, 1925 ; V. Thorsen, *ib.*, **40.** 642, 1926 ; O. Lohse, *Publ. Astrophys. Obs. Potsdam*, **12.** 109, 1902 ; J. Hartmann, *Sitzber. Akad. Berlin*, 234, 1903 ; C. R. Crymble, *Proc. Chem. Soc.*, **30.** 179, 1914 ; A. Hagenbach and H. Konen, *Atlas der Emissionsspectra*, Jena, 1905 ; J. Steinhausen, *Ueber " enhanced lines,"* Bonn, 1904 ; *Zeit. wiss. Photochem.*, **3.** 45, 1905 ; H. Geisler, *ib.*, **7.** 89, 1909 ; *Zur. anomalen Dispersion des Lichtes in Metalldämpfen*, Bonn, 1909 ; E. Gehrcke and O. von Baeyer, *Ann. Physik*, (4), **20.** 269, 1906 ; O. von Baeyer, *Verh. deut. phys. Ges.*, **10.** 733, 1908 ; J. Stark and R. Küch, *Phys. Zeit.*, **6.** 438, 1905 ; H. Rausch von Traubenberg, *ib.*, **11.** 105, 1910 ; G. Joos, *ib.*, **26.** 380, 1925 ; E. Néculcéa, *Recherches théoriques et expérimentales sur la constitution des spectres ultraviolettes d'étincelles oscillantes*, Paris, 1906 ; J. E. Purvis, *Proc. Cambridge Phil. Soc.*, **14.** 216, 1907 ; W. Schwetz, *Die Spectren des Wismuths*, Bonn, 1908 ; H. Nagaoka and Y. Sugiura, *Science Papers Japan. Inst. Phys. Chem.*, **2.** 139, 1924 ; H. Nagaoka, D. Nukiyama, and T. Futagami, *Proc. Acad. Tokyo*, **3.** 392, 398. 403, 409, 415, 1927 ; W. Grotrian, *Zeit. Physik*, **18.** 169, 1923 ; E. Hjalmer, *ib.*, **15.** 65, 1923 ; V. Thorsen, *ib.*, **40.** 642, 1926 ; R. Mecke, *ib.*, **22.** 390, 1927 ; S. Goudsmit and E. Back, *ib.*, **43.** 321, 1927 ; **47.** 174, 1928 ; V. Dolezsek, *ib.*, **10.** 129, 1922 ; **21.** 111, 1924 ; *Nature*, **109.** 582, 1922 ; M. Kimura, *Japan. Journ. Phys.*, **3.** 217, 1924 ; M. Kimura and G. Nakamura, *ib.*, **3.** 29, 51, 1924 ; H. Nagaoka, Y. Sugiura, and T. Mishima, *Nature*, **113.** 459, 1924 ; H. Nagaoka and T. Mishima, *Proc. Imp. Acad. Tokyo*, **4.** 249, 1926 ; H. Robinson, *Phil. Mag.*, (6), **104.** A, 455, 1923 ; A. E. Ruark and R. L. Chenault, *Phil. Mag.*, (6), **50.** 937, 1925 ; J. G. Frayne and A. W. Smith, *ib.*, (7), **1.** 732, 1926 ; H. Sponer, *Naturwiss.*, **12.** 619, 1924 ; K. Lang, *Ann. Physik*, (6), **75.** 439, 1924 ; M. C. W. Buffam and H. J. C. Ireton, *Trans. Roy. Soc. Canada*, (3), **19.** 113, 1925 ; J. C. McLennan and A. B. McLay, *ib.*, (3), **19.** 89, 1925 ; J. C. McLennan, I. Walerstein, and H. G. Smith, *Phil. Mag.*, (7), **3.** 390, 1927 ; J. C. McLennan and A. B. McLay, *ib.*, (7), **4.** 407, 1927 ; W. Friederichs, *Ueber Absorptionsspektra von Dämpfen*, Bonn, 1905 ; *Astrophys. Journ.*, **53.** 339, 1921 ; L. Aronberg, *ib.*, **47.** 102, 1918 ; H. M. Randall, *ib.*, **34.** 1, 1911 ; W. J. Humphreys, *ib.*, **6.** 169, 1897 ; F. M. Walters, *Wave-length Measurements in Arc Spectra photographed in the Yellow, Red, and Infra-red*, Washington, 1921 ; E. Schweitzer, *Zeit. anorg. Chem.*, **164.** 127, 1927 ; J. Offermann, *Das Bogen- und Funkenspectren des Wismut*, Bonn, 1920 ; H. Bracchetti, *Ueber die kathodische Herstellung von Metallspiegeln*, Münster, 1919 ; B. Reismann, *Die Unterschiede der Polspektra verschiedener Elemente im Geisslerrohr*, Münster, 1913 ; *Zeit. wiss. Photochem.*, **13.** 269, 1913 ; J. M. Eder and E. Valenta, *Atlas typischer Spektren*, Wien, 1911 ; *Sitzber. Akad. Wien*, **118.** 511, 1077, 1909 ; **119.** 519, 1910 ; J. M. Eder, *ib.*, **122.** 607, 1913 ; D. Huber, *Einfluss der Selbstinduktion auf die Spektren von Metallen und besonders von Liegierungen*, Freiburg, 1909 ; C. Wali-Mohammed, *Untersuchungen über Struktur und magnetische Zerlegung feiner Spektrallinien von Vakuumlichtbogen*, Göttingen, 1912 ; *Astrophys. Journ.*, **39.** 185, 1914 ; J. Formanek, *Die qualitative Spektralanalyse anorganischer und organischer Körper*, Berlin, 159, 1905 ; K. Schäfer and F. Hein, *Zeit. anorg. Chem.*, **100.** 249, 1917 ; E. T. Wherry, *Amer. Min.*, **10.** 28, 1925 ; V. P. Lubovich and E. M. Pearen, *Trans. Roy. Soc. Canada*, (3), **16.** 195. 1922 : B. Rosen, *Naturwiss.*, **14.** 978, 1926 ; A. Reis, *ib.*, **14.** 1118, 1926 ; G. R. Toshniwal, *Phil. Mag.*, (7), **4.** 774, 1927 ; M. Miyanishi, *Mem. Coll. Kyoto*, **10.** 263, 1927 ; G. Balasse, *Compt. Rend.*, **186.** 310, 1928.

    [11] M. de Broglie, *Compt. Rend.*, **163.** 81, 1916 ; **169.** 962, 1919 ; B. Rosen, *Naturwiss.*, **14.** 978, 1926 ; H. Hirata, *Proc. Roy. Soc.*, **105.** A, 40, 1924 ; H. R. Robinson, *ib.*, **104.** A, 455, 1923 ; H. R. Robinson and A. M. Cassie, *ib.*, **113.** A, 282, 1926 ; C. E. Eddy and L. H. Turner, *ib.*, **114.** A, 615, 1927 ; E. Friman, *Die Hochfrequenzspektra der Elemente*, Lund, 1916 ; *Zeit. Physik*, **29.** 813, 1926 ; M. Siegbahn and E. Friman, *Phys. Zeit.*, **17.** 17, 1916 ; *Phil. Mag.*, (6), **32.** 39, 1916 ; *Ann. Physik*, (4), **49.** 616, 1916 ; M. Siegbahn, *Jahrb. Rad. Elektron.*, **13.** 296, 1916 ; M. Siegbahn and E. Jönsson, *Phys. Zeit.*, **20.** 254, 1919 ; F. Wagner, *ib.*, **18.** 405, 432, 460, 488, 1917 ; J. C. Karcher, *ib.*, **15.** 285, 1920 ; W. Stenström, *Experimentelle Untersuchungen der Röntgenspektren*, Lund, 1919 ; *Ann. Physik*, (4), **57.** 347, 1918 ; W. Duane and R. A. Patterson, *Proc. Nat. Acad.*, **6.** 509, 1920 ; W. Duane, H. Fricke, and W. Stenström, *ib.*, **6.** 607, 1920 ; L. D. Webster, *ib.*, **6.** 26, 1920 ; D. Coster, *Zeit. Physik*, **4.** 178, 1921 ; **6.** 185, 1921 ; *Compt. Rend.*, **172.** 1176, 1921 ; **173.** 77, 1921 ; *Phys. Rev.*, (2), **18.** 218, 1921 ; *Phil. Mag.*, (6), **43.** 1070, 1923 ; T. E. Aurén, *ib.*, (6), **33.** 471, 1917 ; G. Wentzel, *Naturwiss.*, **10.** 369, 1922 ; V. Dolejsek, *Zeit. Physik*, **10.** 129, 1922 ; E. Friman, *ib.*, **39.** 813, 1926 ; S. J. M. Allen, *Phys. Rev.*, (2), **27.** 266, 1926 ; J. M. Cork and B. R. Stephenson, *ib.*, (2), **27.** 103, 138, 1926 ; J. E. Mack and J. M. Cork, *ib.*, (2), **30.** 741, 1927 ; A. E. Ruark, F. L. Mohler, R. D. Foote, and R. L. Chenault, *Nature*, **112.** 831, 1923 ; *Phys. Rev.*, (2), **23.** 770, 1924 ;

Journ. Franklin Inst., **198**. 541, 1924 ; *The Spectra and Critical Potentials of the Fifth Group Elements*, Washington, 1924 ; A. E. Ruark and B. L. Chenault, *Phil. Mag.*, (6), **50**. 937, 1925 ; G. Réchou, *Compt. Rend.*, **180**. 1107, 1925 ; E. Hjalmer, *Zeit. Physik*, **15**. 65, 1923.
[12] J. C. Chapman, *Proc. Roy. Soc.*, **86**. A, 439, 1911 ; J. Stark and G. Wendt, *Ann. Physik*, (4), **38**. 921, 1913 ; W. P. Jorissen and J. A. Vollgraff, *Chem. Weekbl.*, **12**. 741, 1915 ; L. Meitner, *Phys. Zeit.*, **16**. 4, 1915 ; K. Fajans and E. Towara, *Naturwiss.*, **2**. 685, 1914 : F. Giesel, *Ber.*, **35**. 3608, 1902 ; **36**. 728, 2368, 1903 ; W. Marckwald, *ib.*, **35**. 4239, 1902 ; **36**. 2662, 1903 ; H. Whiddington, *Phil. Mag.*, (6), **43**. 1116, 1923 : G. Shearer, *ib.*, (6), **44**, 793, 1922 ; J. E. P. Wagstaff, *ib.*, (6), **47**. 84, 1924 ; E. Adinolfi, *Atti Accad. Lincei*, (6), **1**. i, 382, 1925 ; K. H. Kingdon, *Phys. Rev.*, (2), **23**. 778, 1924 ; S. J. M. Allen, *ib.*, (2), **27**. 266, 1926 ; T. J. Parmley, *ib.*, (2), **29**. 902, 1927 ; (2), **30**. 656, 1927 ; W. Herz, *Zeit. anorg. Chem.*, **170**. 237, 1928 ; G. Piccardi, *Atti Accad. Lincei*, (6), **6**. 305, 428, 1927 ; A. L. Foley, *Proc. Indiana Acad.*, **34**. 185, 1925 ; T. E. Aurén, *Phil. Mag.*, (6), **33**. 471, 1917 ; A. E. Ruark, F. L. Mohler, R. D. Foote, and R. L. Chenault, *Nature*, **112**. 831, 1923 ; *Phys. Rev.*, (2), **23**. 770, 1924 ; *Journ. Franklin Inst.*, **198**. 541, 1924 ; *The Spectra and Critical Potentials of the Fifth Group Elements*, Washington, 1924 ; A. E. Ruark and B. L. Chenault, *Phil. Mag.*, (6), **50**. 937, 1925 ; B. Rosen, *Naturwiss.*, **14**. 978, 1926 ; F. Horton, *Phil. Mag.*, (6), **42**. 279, 1921 ; A. G. Shenstone, *ib.*, (6), **41**. 916, 1921 ; M. Kimura and G. Nakamura, *Japan. Journ. Phys.*, **3**. 29, 51, 1924.
[13] A. Forster, *Pogg. Ann.*, **133**. 94, 228, 1864 ; L. de Boisbaudran, *Compt. Rend.*, **103**. 629, 1064, 1886 ; **104**. 478, 1680, 1887 ; **105**. 45, 206, 1887 ; H. Becquerel, *ib.*, **103**. 1098, 1886 ; **107**. 892, 1888 ; A. Verneuil, *ib.*, **103**. 600, 1886 ; R. Whiddington, *Phil. Mag.*, (6), **43**. 1116, 1922 ; R. A. Houstoun, *ib.*, (7), **2**. 512, 1926 ; E. Adinolfi, *Atti Accad. Lincei*, (6), **1**. 382, 1925 ; V. Klatt and P. Lenard, *Wied. Ann.*, **38**. 90, 1889 ; N. Ahmad, *Proc. Roy. Soc.*, **105**. A, 509, 1924 ; A. L. Foley, *Proc. Indiana Acad.*, **34**. 185, 1925 ; H. Kopfermann, *Zeit. Physik*, **21**. 316, 1924 ; G. Mie, *ib.*, **15**. 56, 1923 ; **18**. 105, 1923 ; B. Gudden and R. Pohl, *ib.*, **3**. 98, 1920 ; H. R. Robinson, *Proc. Roy. Soc.*, **104**. A, 455, 1923 ; M. Hake, *Zeit. Physik*, **15**. 110, 1923 ; F. Gross, *ib.*, **31**. 637, 1925 ; A. T. Waterman, *Phys. Rev.*, (2), **24**. 366, 1924 ; S. J. M. Allen, *ib.*, (2), **23**. 291, 1924 ; R. Hamer, *Journ. Amer. Orst. Soc.*, **9**. 251, 1924 ; F. Horton, *Phil. Mag.*, (6), **42**. 279, 1921 ; A. G. Shenstone, *ib.*, (6), **41**. 916, 1921 ; R. S. Bartlett, *Phys. Rev.*, (2), **26**. 247, 1925 ; W. B. Pietenpol and H. A. Miley, *ib.*, (2), **30**. 697, 1927 ; F. Giesel, *Ber.*, **35**. 3608, 1902 ; **36**. 728, 2368, 1903 ; W. Marckwald, *ib.*, **35**. 4239, 1902 ; **36**. 2662, 1903.
[14] A. Eucken, *Zeit. Metallkunde*, **18**. 182, 1926 ; A. Matthiessen and M. von Bose, *Pogg. Ann.*, **115**. 352, 1862 ; *Proc. Roy. Soc.*, **11**. 516, 1862 ; *Phil. Trans.*, **152**. 1, 1862 ; F. Horton, *Phil. Mag.*, (6), **11**. 505, 1906 ; H. Perlitz, *ib.*, (7), **2**. 1148, 1926 ; J. Dewar and J. A. Fleming, *Proc. Roy. Soc.*, **60**. 72, 1896 ; E. Giebe, *Ueber die Bestimmung des Warmeleitvedmögens bei tiefen Temperaturen*, Berlin, 1903 ; *Verh. deut. phys. Ges.*, **5**. 60, 1903 ; Z. A. Epstein, *Zeit. Physik*, **32**. 620, 1925 ; L. Lorenz, *Wied Ann.*, **13**. 422, 582, 1881 ; P. Lenard, *ib.*, **39**. 619, 1890 ; P. Lenard and J. L. Howard, *Elektrotech. Zeit.*, **9**. 340, 1880 ; W. E. Williams, *Phil. Mag.*, (6), **13**. 635, 1907 ; E. J. Williams, *ib.*, (6), **50**. 27, 1925 ; E. Zavattiero, *Rend. Accad. Lincei*, (5), **29**. i, 48, 1920 ; P. Fischer, *Zeit. Elektrochem.*, **33**. 172, 1927 ; A. Günther-Schulze, *ib.*, **33**. 360, 1927 ; A. E. Malinovsky, *Zeit. Physik*, **42**. 319, 1927 ; E. D. Williamson, *Journ. Franklin Inst.*, **193**, 191, 1922 ; G. Vicentini and D. Omodei, *Atti Accad. Torino*, **20**. 869, 1884 ; **25**. 30, 1890 ; W. Jäger and H. Diesselhorst, *Abhand. Phys. Tech. Reichsanst.*, **3**. 269, 1900 ; E. F. Northrup and V. A. Suydam, *Journ. Franklin Inst.*, **175**. 153, 1912 ; E. F. Northrup and R. G. Sherwood, *ib.*, **182**, 477, 1916 ; G. Vassura, *Nuovo Cimento*, (3), **31**. 25, 1892 ; P. le Rossi, *ib.*, (6), **2**. 337, 1911 ; (6), **18**. 26, 39, 1919 ; A. Schulze, *Ann. Physik*, (4), **9**. 555, 1902 ; *Zeit. Metallkunde*, **15**. 158, 1923 ; **16**. 48, 1924 ; L. de la Rive, *Arch. Sciences Genève*, (2), **17**. 105, 1863 ; *Compt. Rend.*, **56**. 588, 1863 ; **57**. 698, 1863 ; C. Matteucci, *Ann. Chim. Phys.*, (3), **43**. 467, 1855 ; *Compt. Rend.*, **40**. 541, 913, 1855 ; **42**. 1133, 1856 ; E. van Aubel, *ib.*, **108**. 1102, 1889 ; *Journ. Phys.*, (3), **2**. 407, 1893 ; *Phil. Mag.*, (5), **28**. 332, 1889 ; P. W. Bridgman, *Proc. Amer. Acad.*, **52**. 624, 1917 ; **56**. 114, 1921 ; **57**. 50, 1922 ; *Proc. Nat. Acad.*, **10**, 411, 1924 ; *Phys. Rev.*, (2), **19**. 114, 1922 ; K. F. Herzfeld, *ib.*, (2), **29**. 703, 1927 ; H. Tsutsumi, *Science Rep, Tohoku Univ.*, (i), **7**. 93, 1918 ; A. Werner, *Phys. Zeit.*, **17**. 346, 1916 ; L. Holborn, *Zeit. Physik*, **8**. 58, 1921 ; *Ann. Physik*, (4), **59**. 14, 1919 ; E. von Everdingen, *Versl. Akad. Amsterdam*, **8**. 218, 380, 1900 ; **9**. 181, 448, 1900 ; *Phys. Zeit.*, **2**. 585, 1901 ; E. Cohen and A. T. L. Moesveld, *Zeit. phys. Chem.*, **85**. 419, 1913 ; *Chem. Weekbl.*, **10**. 656, 1913 ; R. Paillot, *Compt. Rend.*, **138**. 189, 1904 ; F. Streintz, *Zeit. Elektrochem.*, **11**. 273, 1905 ; R. S. Bartlett, *Phil. Mag.*, (7), **5**. 848, 1928 ; *Phys. Rev.*, (2), **26**. 247, 1925 ; L. F. Curtiss, *ib.*, (2), **17**. 235, 1921 ; E. H. Hall, *ib.*, (2), **28**. 392, 1926 ; A. T. Waterman, *ib.*, (2), **22**. 259, 1923 ; G. Bretano, *Ann. Physik*, (4), **46** 941, 1915 ; G. Berndt, *ib.*, (4), **23**. 805, 1907 ; Y. Matsuyama, *Kinzoku no Kenku*, **3**. 254, 1926 ; *Science Rep. Tohoku Univ.*, **16**. 447, 1927 ; P. E. Shaw and C. S. Jex, *Proc. Roy. Soc.*, **118**. A, 97, 1928 ; P. Kapitza, *ib.*, **119**. A, 358, 387, 401, 1928 ; W. Tuijn and H. K. Onnes, *Arch. Néerl.*, (3), **10**. 5, 1927 ; L. Tiere and V. Ruca, *Nuovo Cimento*, (7), **4**. 248, 1927 ; G. W. Schneider, *Phys. Rev.*, (2), **31**. 251, 1928.
[15] C. Carpini, *Nuovo Cimento*, (5), **8**. 171, 1904 ; F. A. Ward, *Phil. Mag.*, (6), **48**. 971, 1924 ; C. W. Heaps, *ib.*, (6), **24**. 815. 1912 ; E. von Everdingen, *Versl. Akad. Amsterdam*, **8**. 218, 380, 1900 ; **9**. 181, 448, 1900 ; *Phys. Zeit.*, **2**. 585, 1901 ; *Arch. Néerl.*, (2), **4**. 511, 1901 ; A. von Ettinghausen, *Anz. Akad. Wien*, **24**. 234, 237, 1887 ; *Sitzber. Akad. Wien*, **94**. 808, 1886 ; *Wied. Ann.*, **31**. 737, 1887 ; P. Lenard, *ib.* **39**. 669, 1890 ; A. Righi, *Compt. Rend.*, **105**. 168, 1887 ; *Atti Accad. Lincei*, (4), **3**. ii, 6, 1887 ; (4), **4**. 433, 1888 ; *Gazz. Chim. Ital.*, **17**. 358, 1887 ;

G. C. Trabaschi, *Atti Accad. Lincei*, (5), **24**. 1053, 1915 ; A. Leduc, *Compt. Rend.*, **104**. 1783, 1887 ; J. Dewar and J. A. Fleming, *Proc. Roy. Soc.*, **60**. 72, 425, 1897 ; A. Eucken and O. Neumann, *Zeit. phys. Chem.*, **111**. 431, 1924 ; P. Lenard, *Wied. Ann.*, **39**. 619, 1890 ; L. Lownds, *Ann. Physik*, (6), **9**. 677, 1902 ; R. Seidler, *ib.*, (4), **32**. 337, 1910 ; R. Geipel, *ib.*, (4), **38**. 149, 1912 ; F. C. Blake, *ib.*, (4), **28**. 449, 1900 ; F. P. König, *Phys. Rev.*, (1), **25**. 921, 1908 ; A. E. Malinovsky, *Zeit. Physik*, **42**. 319, 1927 ; C. Drucker, *Zeit. phys. Chem.*, **130**. 673, 1927 ; E. Horn, *Ueber die Abhängigkeit der wahren spezifischen Wärmen der Metalle Nickel, Wismut, und Zink von der Temperatur, Wärmebehandlung, und Zusammensetzung*, Weida i. Thür., 1927 ; G. W. Schneider, *Phys. Rev.*, (2), **31**. 149, 251, 1928 ; L. F. Curtiss, *ib.*, (2), **17**. 235, 1921 ; P. le Rossi, *Nuovo Cimento*, (6), **2**. 337, 1911 ; (6), **18**. 26, 39, 1919 ; G. Berndt, *Ann. Physik*, (4), **23**. 805, 1907 ; E. J. Williams, *Phil. Mag.*, (6), **50**. 27, 1925 ; Z. A. Epstein, *Zeit. Physik*, **32**. 620, 1925 ; A. T. Waterman, *Phys. Rev.*, (2), **22**. 259, 1923 ; P. Fischer, *Zeit. Elektrochem.*, **33**. 172, 1927.

¹⁶ L. Tieri and E. Persico, *Atti Accad. Lincei*, (5), **30**. ii, 464, 1921 ; E. H. Hall, *Amer. Journ. Science*, (3), **20**. 52, 161, 1880 ; (3), **19**. 117, 1885 ; (3), **36**. 131, 277, 1888 ; *Proc. Nat. Acad.*, **6**. 613, 1920 ; **7**. 98, 1921 ; *Phil. Mag.*, (5), **10**. 136, 1880 ; (5), **12**. 157, 1881 ; (5), **15**. 341, 1883 ; *Amer. Journ. Math.*, **2**. 287, 1879 ; J. Beattie, *Proc. Roy. Soc. Edin.*, **21**. 146, 1896 ; C. W. Heaps, *Phil. Mag.*, (6), **50**. 1001, 1925 ; *Phys. Rev.*, (2), **30**. 61, 1927 ; G. C. Trabacchi, *Atti Accad. Lincei*, (5), **28**. ii, 137, 276, 1919 ; *Nuovo Cimento*, (6), **9**. 95, 1915 ; (6), **16**. 197. 1918 ; G. Polvani, *ib.*, (7), **3**. 184, 1926 ; P. la Rossi, *ib.*, (6), **18**. 26, 39, 1919 ; T. Collodi, *ib.*, (6), **19**. 163, 1920 ; W. van B. Roberts, *Phys. Rev.*, (2), **24**. 532, 1924 ; C. W. Heaps, *ib.*, (2), **27**. 252, 1926 ; (2), **29**. 332, 1927 ; (2), **30**. 61, 1927 ; (2), **31**. 313, 648, 1928 ; P. H. Craig, *ib.*, (2), **31**. 713, 1928 ; T. F. Hargitt, *ib.*, (2), **28**. 1034, 1926 ; L. J. Neuman, *ib.*, (2), **27**, 643, 1926 ; P. H. Craig, *ib.*, (2), **27**. 772, 814, 1926 ; N. C. Little, *ib.*, (2), **28**. 418, 1926 ; A. von Ettinghausen and W. Nernst, *Sitzber. Akad. Wien*, **94**. 560, 1886 ; E. von Everdingen, *Versl. Akad. Amsterdam*, **7**. 484, 535, 1899 ; **8**. 218, 380, 1900 ; **9**. 181, 1900 ; L. Lownds, *Ann. Physik*, (4), **6**. 146, 1901 ; (4), **9**. 677, 1902 ; G. P. Grimaldi, *Atti Accad. Lincei*, (4), **6**. 37, 1889 ; P. Senepa, *ib.*, (5), **21**. ii, 53, 1912 ; A. Righi, *ib.*, (3), **7**. 262, 1883 ; (3), **8**. 331, 1884 ; E. Adinolfi, *ib.*, (5), **33**. i, 500, 1924 ; O. M. Carbino, *ib.*, (5), **20**. i, 342, 1911 ; (5), **28**. i, 49, 1920 ; *Nuovo. Cimento*, (6), **16**. 185, 1918 ; *Phys. Zeit.*, **12**. 561, 1911 ; D. Goldhammer, *Wied. Ann.*, **31**. 370,; 1877 ; H. Rausch von Traubenberg, *Ann. Physik*, (4), **17**. 78, 1905 ; P. W. Bridgman, *Phys., Rev.*, (2), **24**. 444, 1924 ; F. Klaiber, *Zeit. Physik*, **43**. 66, 1927.

¹⁷ D. Balachowsky, *Compt. Rend.*, **131**. 179, 1900 ; A. Hollard and L. Bertiaux, *ib.*, **139**. 366, 1904 ; R. Saxon, *Chem. News*, **132**. 170, 1926 ; G. Grube and F. Schweigardt, *Zeit. Elektrochem.*, **29**. 257, 1923 ; H. J. S. Sand, *Journ. Chem. Soc.*, **91**. 373, 1907 ; E. Newberry, *ib.*, **109**. 1066, 1916 ; *Proc. Roy. Soc.*, **114**. A, 103, 1927 ; H. Kammerer, *Journ. Amer. Chem. Soc.*, **25**. 83, 1903 ; A. L. Hughes, *Phil. Mag.*, (6), **28**. 337, 1914 ; O. Brunck, *Ber.*, **35**. 1871, 1902 ; A. Classen, *ib.*, **14**. 1626, 1881 ; J. Wieland, *ib.*, **17**. 1612, 1884 ; S. Eliasberg, *ib.*, **19**. 326, 1888 ; G. Vortmann, *ib.*, **24**. 2749, 1891 ; A. Jilek and J. Lukas, *Chem. Listy*, **21**. 49, 1927 ; H. W. Thomas and E. F. Smith, *Amer. Chem. Journ.*, **5**. 114, 1883 ; F. F. Smith and E. B. Knerr, *ib.*, **8**. 206, 1886 ; E. F. Smith and L. H. Frankel, *ib.*, **12**. 428, 1891 ; F. F. Smith and J. C. Saltar, *Zeit. anorg. Chem.*, **3**. 414, 1893 ; *Journ. Amer. Chem. Soc.*, **15**. 28, 101, 1894 ; L. G. Kollock, *ib.*, **21**. 925, 1899 ; L. G. Kollock and E. F. Smith, *ib.*, **27**. 1539, 1905 ; E. F. Exner, *ib.*, **25**. 901, 1903 ; S. C. Schmucker, *ib.*, **15**. 203, 1893 ; *Zeit. anorg. Chem.*, **5**. 199, 1894 ; A. Thiel and W. Hammer-schmidt, *ib.*, **132**. 15, 1923 ; E. F. Smith and J. B. Moyer, *ib.*, **4**. 96, 270, 1893 ; M. Bose, *ib.*, **44**. 237, 1905 ; K. Wimmenauer, *ib.*, **27**. 1, 1901 ; T. Andrews, *B.A. Rep.*, 69, 1838 ; (3), **11**. 554, 1837 ; *Phil. Mag.*, (3), **12**. 305, 1858 ; K. Elbs and H. Thümmel, *Zeit. Elektrochem.*, **10**. 364, 1904 ; A. Fischer and R. J. Boddaert, *ib.*, **10**. 947, 1904 ; F. Paneth, *ib.*, **31**. 572, 1925 ; J. Tafel, *Zeit. phys. Chem.*, **50**. 704, 1905 ; B. Neumann, *ib.*, **14**. 218, 1894 ; V. Bayerle, *Rec. Trav. Chim. Pays-Bas*, **44**. 514, 1925 ; C. Luckow, *Zeit. anal. Chem.*, **19**. 16, 1880 ; A. Brand, *ib.*, **28**. 596, 1889 ; L. Schucht, *ib.*, **22**. 492, 1883 ; G. C. Schmidt, *Zeit. phys. Chem.*, **106**. 105, 1923 ; T. Moore, *Chem. News*, **53**. 209, 1886 ; R. Saxon, *ib.*, **132**. 170, 1926 ; F. Rüdorff, *Zeit. angew. Chem.*, **5**. 199, 1892 ; E. B. R. Prideaux and H. W. Hewis, *Journ. Soc. Chem. Ind.*, **41**. 167, 1922 ; W. Winter, *Phys. Zeit.*, **14**. 824, 1913 ; A. Günther-Schulze, *Ann. Physik*, (4), **24**. 43, 1907 ; (4), **65**. 223, 1921 ; *Zeit. Physik*, **36**. 563, 1926 ; D. F. Smith, *Journ. Amer. Chem. Soc.*, **45**. 360, 1923 ; E. H. Swift, *ib.*, **45**. 371, 1923 ; N. W. Taylor, *ib.*, **45**. 2865, 1923 ; F. H. Smith, *The Potential of the Bismuth Electrode*, Boston, 1915 ; A. A. Noyes and M. Chow, *Journ. Amer. Chem. Soc.*, **40**. 739, 1918 ; W. Isbekoff, *Zeit. phys. Chem.*, **116**. 304, 1925 ; C. W. Heaps, *Phys. Rev.*, (2), **27**. 252, 1926 ; R. D. Kleeman and W. Frederickson, *ib.*, (2), **19**. 409, 1923 ; C. Bellia, *Nuovo Cimento*, (7), **2**. 321, 1925 ; O. Steen, *Zeit. angew. Chem.*, **7**. 530, 1895 ; F. W. Bergstrom, *Journ. Amer. Chem. Soc.*, **47**. 1503, 1925.

¹⁸ R. Franz, *Pogg. Ann.*, **83**. 374, 1851 ; **85**. 388, 1852 ; A. Matthiessen, *ib.*, **103**. 402, 1853 ; *Phil. Trans.*, **148**. 369, 383, 1858 ; *Phil. Mag.*, (4), **16**. 219, 1858 ; E. Edlund, *Pogg. Ann.*, **140**. 435, 1870 ; **143**. 404, 1834, 1871 ; *Oefvers. Akad. Stockholm*, **27**. 3, 1870 ; *Akad. Handl. Stockholm*, **9**. 14, 1870 ; *Phil. Mag.*, (4), **41**. 18, 1871 ; (4), **43**. 81, 213, 264, 1872 ; J. Svanberg, *Pogg. Ann. Ergbd.*, **3**. 153, 1853 ; *Compt. Rend.*, **31**. 250, 1850 ; F. L. Perrot, *ib.*, **126**. 1194, 1898 ; *Arch. Sciences Genève*, (4), **6**. 105, 229, 1898 ; (4), **7**. 149, 1899 ; J. Beckenkamp, *Zeit. Kryst.*, **32**. 540, 1900 ; **37**. 521, 1903 ; C. Matteucci, *Ann. Chim. Phys.*, (3), **43**. 470, 1855 ; F. P. le Roux, *ib.*, (4), **10**. 201, 1867 ; E. Cohen and T. Moesveld, *Zeit. phys. Chem.*, **85**. 427, 1913 ; L. Lownds, *Ann. Physik*, (4), **6**. 146, 1901 ; E. Wagner, *ib.*, (4), **27**. 955, 1908 ; K. Bädeker, *ib.*, (4), **22**. 749,

1907; E. Siegel, *ib.*, (4), **38**. 588, 1913; G. Borelius and A. E. Lindh, *ib.*, (4), **51**. 607, 1916; E. Wagner, *ib.*, (4), **27**. 955, 1908; H. Zahn, *ib.*, (4), **14**. 886, 1904; W. W. Coblentz, *Journ. Franklin Inst.*, **172**. 559, 1911: G. P. Grimaldi, *Atti Accad. Lincei*, (3), **3**. 1, 1887; T. Todesco, *ib.*, (6), **4**. 94, 1927; (6), **5**. 377, 434, 1927; T. Terada and T. Tsutui, *Proc. Acad. Tokyo*, **3**. 132, 1927; T. Terada, S. Tanaka and S. Kusaba, *ib.*, **3**. 200, 1927; G. Spadavecchia, *Nuovo Cimento*, (4), **9**. 432, 1898; (4), **10**. 161, 1899; C. Bellia, *ib.*, (7), **2**. 321, 1925; J. Dewar and J. A. Fleming, *Phil. Mag.*, (5), **40**. 95, 1895; E. H. Hall, *Proc. Nat. Acad.*, **6**. 613, 1920; W. Jäger and H. Diesselhorst, *Abhand. Phys. Tech. Reichsanst.*, **3**. 269, 1900; P. W. Bridgman, *Proc. Amer. Acad.*, **53**. 269, 1918; **61**. 101, 1926; *Proc. Nat. Acad.*, **11**. 608, 1925; E. Rudolfi, *Zeit. anorg. Chem.*, **67**. 65, 1910; A. E. Caswell, *Phys. Rev.*, (1), **33**. 379, 1911; R. D. Kleeman and W. Frederickson, *ib.*, (2), **19**. 409, 1923; M. O'Day, *ib.*, (2), **27**. 643, 1926; R. W. Boydston, *ib.*, (2), **30**. 911, 1927; P. H. Dowling, *ib.*, (2), **31**. 245, 1928; C. W. Heaps, *ib.*, (2), **27**. 252, 1926; W. B. Burnie, *Phil. Mag.*, (5), **43**. 397, 1897; C. R. Darling and R. H. Rinaldi, *Proc. Phys. Soc.*, **36**. 281, 1924; F. W. Bergstrom, *Journ. Amer. Chem. Soc.*, **47**. 1503, 1925; H. Pélabon, *Ann. Physique*, (9), **13**. 169, 1920; *Compt. Rend.*, **176**. 1305, 1923.

[19] W. B. Nottingham, *Phys. Rev.*, (2), **27**. 806, 1926; (2), **28**. 764, 1926; A. Günther-Schulze, *Zeit. Physik*, **36**. 563, 1926; T. Baum, *ib.*, **40**. 686, 1927; E. Blechschmidt, *Ann. Physik*, (4), **81**. 999, 1926.

[20] M. Faraday, *Phil. Trans.*, **136**. 21, 41, 1846; **139**. 1, 1849; A. Brugman, *Magnetismus seu de affinitatibus magneticis observationes magneticæ*, Lugduni Batavorum, 1778; M. le Baillif, *Bull. Univ.*, **7**. 37, 1827; **8**. 87, 91, 94, 1827; J. Tyndall, *Phil. Mag.*, (4), **2**. 174, 1851; G. W. Hankel, *Ber. Sächs. Ges. Wiss.*, **99**, 1851; A. Leduc, *Compt. Rend.*, **140**. 1022, 1905; P. Curie, *Journ. Phys.*, (3), **4**. 197, 1895; *Compt. Rend.*, **115**. 1292, 1892; **116**. 136, 1893; P. Pascal, *ib.*, **174**. 1698, 1922; W. W. Jaques and H. A. Rowland, *Amer. Journ. Sciences*, (3), **18**. 360, 1879; P. Ehrenfest, *Physica*, **5**. 388, 1925; E. van Aubel, *Journ. Phys.*, (3), **2**. 407, 1893; T. Collodi, *Nuovo Cimento*, (6), **19**. i, 163, 1920; M. Pierucci, *ib.*, (6), **34**. 45, 1922; J. Forrest, *Trans. Roy. Soc. Edin.*, **54**. 601, 1927; J. F. Spencer and M. E. John, *Proc. Roy. Soc.*, **116**. A, 61, 1927; S. Meyer, *Monatsh.*, **20**. 369, 1899; J. Dewar and J. A. Fleming, *Proc. Roy. Soc.*, **60**. 283, 1896; **63**. 311, 1898; A. von Ettinghausen, *Sitzber. Akad. Wien*, **96**. 777, 1887; *Wied. Ann.*, **17**. 272, 1882; K. Honda, *Science Rep. Tohoku Univ.*, **1**. 1, 1912; *Ann. Physik*, (4), **32**. 1027, 1910; M. Owen, *ib.*, (4), **37**. 657, 1912; H. Isnardi and R. Gans, *ib.*, (4), **61**. 585, 1920; W. Gerlach, *ib.*, (4), **75**. 163, 1925; W. Gerlach and A. C. Cilliers, *Zeit. Physik*, **26**. 106, 1924; L. Lombardi, *Mem. Accad. Torino*, (2), **47**. 1, 1897; A. P. Wills, *Phil. Mag.*, (5), **45**. 432, 1898; *Phys. Rev.*, (1), **20**. 188, 1905; C. Nusbaum, *ib.*, (2), **29**. 270, 905, 1927; J. A. Becker and L. F. Curtiss, *ib.*, (2), **15**. 457, 1920; F. K. Richtmyer, *ib.*, (2), **15**. 465, 1920; E. H. Williams, *ib.*, (2), **28**. 167, 1920; G. Meslin, *Ann. Chim. Phys.*, (8), **7**. 145, 1906; H. K. Onnes and A. Perrier, *Proc. Acad. Amsterdam*, **20**. 75, 1911; H. Knoblauch, *Sitzber. Akad. Berlin*, 271, 1851; *Pogg. Ann.*, **83**. 289, 1851.

§ 5. The Chemical Properties of Bismuth

H. von Wartenberg [1] observed no sign of a combination between heated bismuth and **argon**, nor did F. Fischer and co-workers obtain any evidence of chemical action when bismuth is sparked beneath liquid argon. W. Ramsay and J. N. Collie observed no reaction with **helium** at a red-heat. F. H. Newman studied the adsorption of **hydrogen** in discharge tubes. There is no sign of interaction when hydrogen is passed over heated bismuth, and, according to F. Paneth, M. Matthies and E. Schmidt-Hebbel, no identifiable quantity of bismuth hydride formed when activated hydrogen is passed over bismuth powder. According to R. L. Richland, if water be electrolyzed with a bismuth cathode, this metal is blackened, and covered with black dendrites once thought to be a **bismuth hydride**. F. Meurer believed that a hydride is produced when zinc acts on dil. hydrochloric or sulphuric acid containing a bismuth salt in soln., but J. Schlossberger and C. R. Fresenius were unable to confirm this. Organic derivatives of a bismuthine, BiH_3, are known with the hydrogen atoms replaced by methyl, ethyl, phenyl, and other radicles. E. J. Weeks and J. G. F. Druce failed to make a bismuth hydride analogous to that of arsenic, but they obtained **bismuth dihydride**, Bi_2H_2, as a grey flocculent precipitate by adding bismuth chloride to a mixture of zinc and conc. hydrochloric acid; and by reducing a bismuth salt with aluminium and potassium hydroxide. The dihydride deposits bismuth when heated, and is rapidly oxidized by fused potassium nitrate. A. C. Vournasos reported an unstable hydride to be formed by treating alkali bismuthide with hydrogen at 350°, and digesting the product with water. L. Vanino and E. Zumbusch reported the following unsuccessful attempts to make bismuth hydride : Hydrogen passed over alloys of lead, tin, and bismuth, or of one of these three metals with cadmium, heated to their m.p. Aluminium, zinc, iron, cadmium, or lead added to an acid or neutral soln. of a bismuth compound. Bismuth-magnesium or bismuth-zinc alloys placed in dil. acid. Calcium hydride mixed with bismuth compounds moistened with water or aq. soln. of bismuth chloride. Hydrogen passed over mixtures of bismuth or bismuth oxide with platinum black, nickel-asbestos, or reduced nickel. Palladium sat. with hydrogen placed in a soln. of bismuth sulphate, or an electric current passed through a cell containing bismuth sulphate in soln., and having an anode of palladium sat. with hydrogen and a cathode of platinum or a cathode of bismuth and anode of platinum. Activated aluminium when allowed to remain in bismuth-mannitol soln. or with a mixture of bismuth and bismuth oxide, or in soln. of bismuth salts in alcohol. Hypophosphorous acid added to bismuth sulphate or to bismuth nitrate in soln. gave only a precipitate of metallic bismuth. The presence of bismuth hindered the preparation of copper hydride by this method. P. Sachs also obtained negative results with sodium formate and bismuth. F. Paneth reported that a gaseous bismuth hydride can be formed and that it is comparatively stable at ordinary temp., but it is decomposed at an elevated temp. The gas can be condensed by cooling in liquid air. He said :

Bismuth hydride is obtained by dissolving an alloy of magnesium with thorium-C or radium-C in 0·2N-hydrochloric or sulphuric acid. The alloy is prepared by exposing magnesium foil to the radiations of a radiothorium preparation contained in a glass capsule covered with silk paper, which is impermeable to thorium-X; shortly after its removal, in consequence of the rapid decay of thorium emanation and thorium-A, the deposit consists entirely of thorium-B and thorium-C. The alloy is placed in a weighing bottle connected with an electroscope in such a manner that a regular current of nitrogen can be sent through the apparatus. After the determination of the natural leak of the electroscope, 0·2N-hydrochloric acid is dropped on to the alloy; the electroscope soon indicates an activity, which becomes feebler after a few minutes. The results of this and similar experiments show that when magnesium superficially alloyed with bismuth and lead is dissolved in dil. hydrochloric acid, a small fraction of the bismuth is converted into such a state that it can be carried by a gas current through a cotton wool filter, and that a similar reaction does not occur with lead. The observed effects are actually due to a volatile compound of bismuth, and not to the liberation of thorium-C, to the selective action of the filter, or to the relatively greater volatility of thorium-C chloride.

F. Paneth and E. Winternitz obtained the hydride from a bismuth-magnesium alloy prepared by heating equal weights of powdered bismuth and magnesium (as free from silicon as possible) in an iron crucible in a rapid stream of dry hydrogen. The alloy is dissolved in approximately 4N-hydrochloric or sulphuric acid (or in some cases nitric acid). Bismuth hydride is thus obtained in sufficient quantity to permit its detection either by the formation of a mirror or by luminescence tests. The bismuth mirror is obtained in the usual Marsh's apparatus, and very closely resembles the antimony mirror. As generally obtained, it consists of a strong brown ring in front of and a fainter ring behind the heated spot. The former deposit appears to be frequently burnt into the glass and to be unsuitable for further experiments. This drawback can be overcome by placing a pierced clay disk on the tube and allowing the flame to play against this, and also by increasing the velocity of the gas current. Attempts to estimate the yield of bismuth hydride by weighing the bismuth mirrors show that about 5×10^{-5} of the bismuth used is converted into the hydride, or that the yield is only about one-twentieth of that obtained from thorium-C. The absorption of bismuth hydride by various reagents has been examined ; the most suitable for this purpose appears to be 0·4N-silver nitrate soln. Water absorbs the gas to some degree, and 4N-sulphuric acid to about the same extent. 0·5N-sodium carbonate soln. and N-potassium hydroxide soln. are more active, whilst the gas is also absorbed by desiccating agents, such as calcium chloride or soda-lime. It is completely decomposed by concentrated sulphuric acid. An aq. soln. of hydrogen sulphide is no more efficient than pure water.

F. Paneth and co-workers found that small quantities of the hydride are produced when bismuth electrodes are used in the preparation of active hydrogen and are so arranged that the bases are rapidly removed from the zone of the discharge. According to E. J. Weeks and J. G. F. Druce, when bismuth dihydride is heated in vacuo, it furnishes **bismuthine** or **bismuth trihydride,** BiH_3, thus : $3Bi_2H_2$ $=4Bi+2BiH_3$; and the same product is obtained by reducing the dihydride with hot hydrogen : $2Bi_2H_2+H_2=2Bi+2BiH_3$. The gas burns with a steel-grey flame producing thin clouds of bismuth oxide. It gives a precipitate of silver tritabismuthide with silver nitrate. W. Strecker and W. Daniel were unable to verify these results.

When bismuth is heated in **air,** until it boils, it burns with a faint, bluish-white flame, and the fumes of bismuth trioxide so formed condense as *flowers of bismuth,* or *flores bismuthi,* on cold surfaces. According to P. A. von Bonsdorff,[2] T. Thomson, and W. Heintz, bismuth at ordinary temp. does not oxidize in dry or moist air, but if heated in air, it acquires a thin film ; if the film be skimmed from the molten metal as it is formed, the dark brown product is the so-called *bismuth ash,* which may be a mixture of metal and trioxide, or it may contain a suboxide (*q.v.*). Bismuth precipitated by zinc was found by W. Heintz to be rapidly oxidized in air at 200°–220° ; and a mixture of bismuth and aluminium hydroxides co-precipitated, and reduced by hydrogen at 170°–210° is spontaneously inflammable at ordinary temp. C. F. Schönbein found that **ozone** slowly oxidizes bismuth to the pentoxide. P. A. von Bonsdorff showed that if bismuth be partially covered with **water,** and exposed to air freed from carbon dioxide, hydrated bismuth oxide is first formed, and afterwards crystals of the yellow oxide are produced. If the air is not freed from carbon dioxide, white scales of bismuth carbonate are produced, and the surface of the metal acquires first a reddish-brown, and then a blue film. H. V. Regnault found that bismuth at a red-heat slowly decomposes water, forming bismuth trioxide. L. J. Thénard found that **hydrogen dioxide** is slowly decomposed by powdered bismuth, which itself suffers no appreciable change —C. F. Schönbein said that a brown oxide is formed—a mixture or compound of bismuth tri- and penta-oxides. W. R. Dunstan observed a well-marked reaction for hydrogen dioxide when the metal is shaken up with dil. sulphuric acid and air.

H. Moissan[3] found that bismuth is only superficially attacked by **fluorine** at a red-heat. J. Davy, and R. Weber found that finely-divided bismuth unites with **chlorine,** forming the trichloride ; but, according to R. Weber, P. P. Dehérain, W. Heintz, and R. Schneider, if the chlorine is brought closely in contact with the bismuth, the dichloride or both the di- and tri-chlorides are formed. J. Thomsen said that finely-divided bismuth may or may not inflame when projected into chlorine gas, and V. Thomas and P. Dupais found that chlorine at its b.p. has no action on bismuth. R. Cowper said that thoroughly dried chlorine attacks bismuth only at the surface. Bismuth was found by C. Willgerodt and A. G. Page to be a very poor catalyst in the chlorination of organic compounds. R. Weber, G. S. Sérullas, and M. M. P. Muir found that when bismuth is heated in the vapour of **bromine,** yellow bismuth tribromide, and grey dibromide may be formed. W. Heintz, R. Schneider, and R. Weber observed that **iodine** unites directly with heated bismuth, forming the triiodide. Dry **hydrogen chloride** was found by W. Heintz to attack red-hot bismuth to a small extent, forming traces of the trichloride. W. Heintz, and G. Gore observed no reaction between liquid hydrogen chloride and bismuth. A. Ditte and R. Metzner showed that if air be excluded, hydrogen chloride, and **hydrochloric acid** have no action on bismuth, but if oxygen be present in the acid, an amount of bismuth is dissolved eq. to the oxygen in soln. —no hydrogen is developed : $4Bi+3O_2+12HCl=4BiCl_3+6H_2O$. R. Schneider also noted the solvent action of aerated hydrochloric acid on bismuth. C. F. Schönbein observed that aq. soln. of **hypochlorites** act slowly on bismuth, forming the higher oxide ; W. S. Hendrixson, that **chloric acid** oxidizes bismuth slowly, and only a small proportion passes into soln.; and M. M. P. Muir, that **perchloric acid** forms bismuthyl perchlorate.

D. Lagerhjelm,[4] and R. Schneider observed that when bismuth is melted with **sulphur** in the absence of air, bismuth trisulphide is formed (*q.v.*), and, according to W. Spring, union occurs when the powdered elements are highly compressed. L. Moser and E. Neusser said that **hydrogen sulphide** converts heated bismuth completely into sulphide. N. Domanicky found that **sulphur monochloride** in the presence of ether forms bismuth chloride. J. Uhl, and H. Schiff observed that bismuth suffers no change when heated in a current of **sulphur dioxide,** and C. Geitner, that when heated with an aq. soln. of sulphur dioxide in a sealed tube at 200°, bismuth trisulphide is formed. Dil. **sulphuric acid** is without action on bismuth, but when warmed with the conc. acid bismuth sulphate and sulphur dioxide are formed. R. H. Adie found that when bismuth is heated with sulphuric acid, sulphur dioxide appears at about 90°, but no hydrogen sulphide. According to M. Websky, when heated with **potassium hydrosulphate,** below the m.p. of the metal, bismuth sulphate is formed; but at a higher temp., a basic sulphate is produced. M. G. Levi and co-workers observed the formation of a basic sulphate by the action of a soln. of **alkali persulphate.** J. J. Berzelius, and F. Rössler observed that when bismuth is fused with **selenium,** a selenide is formed, and J. J. Berzelius said that bismuth and **tellurium** are completely miscible in the fused state. E. B. Hutchins found that hot conc. soln. of **telluric acid** attack bismuth.

P. Vigier [5] observed no evidence of the direct union of **nitrogen** and bismuth— *vide supra,* F. Hérard, amorphous bismuth. F. H. Newman studied the adsorption of nitrogen in discharge tubes. According to G. Gore, liquefied **ammonia** does not dissolve the metal; and the gas, or the aq. soln., has no action on bismuth. C. A. Kraus observed complex-ion formation with bismuth in ammonia soln. E. Müller and H. Barck found that bismuth decomposes **nitric oxide** at 400°, forming bismuth trioxide. J. J. Berzelius found that at ordinary temp., **nitric acid** is transformed into the nitrate ; if fuming nitric acid be poured over powdered bismuth, the metal becomes red-hot; and J. L. Proust added that an explosion occurs when nitric acid is added to molten bismuth. N. A. E. Millon showed that the presence of nitrous acid is necessary for the nitric acid to attack the bismuth. Bismuth assumes the **passive state** in nitric acid of sp. gr. 1·54. According to T. Andrews :

Bismuth in nitric acid of sp. gr. 1·4, was rapidly acted upon, but this action immediately ceased when the bar was touched by platinum. On removing the platinum from the liquor, the bismuth will sometimes begin again to dissolve ; at other times, its surface will become covered with a black crust, which is soon removed by the acid ; but the metal, though now exhibiting a beautifully polished surface, is no longer acted upon by the acid, or, at least, is dissolved only with extreme slowness. Thus, a slip of metal, which, in its ordinary state, will require only a few seconds to complete its soln., will, when thus slightly modified, resist for many hours the action of the same acid.

According to C. Montemartini, the action of nitric acid of 27·5 or 70 per cent. HNO_3 yields with bismuth no ammonia, nitrogen, or nitrous oxide. More nitric oxide is obtained with the dil. than with the conc. acid, and it is produced by the secondary reaction. With the 27·5 per cent. acid, no nitrogen peroxide is produced, but with the 70 per cent. acid, this gas is the main product. C. C. Palit and N. R. Dhar observed only a slight action, and no nitrous acid was formed when 13 or 26 per cent. nitric acid acted on bismuth for 3 hrs. at ordinary temp. A. Quartaroli studied the period of induction ; and found that nitric acid freed from nitrous acid by urea does not attack bismuth. J. H. Stansbie found that when bismuth is treated with nitric acid of sp. gr. 1·2 at 65° in an atm. of hydrogen, nitric oxide, nitrogen peroxide, and nitrogen are evolved, and nitrous acid accumulates in the soln.—probably as nitrite. The reaction closely resembles those with copper and silver under similar conditions (*q.v.*). G. Tammann found that cold work makes the metal less noble, and it dissolves more quickly in acid. N. R. Dhar said that when nitric acid acts on bismuth, only nitrous and hyponitrous acids are formed, and not hydroxylamine, hydrazine, or ammonia, which require the hydrogenation of nitric acid. Aqua regia readily dissolves bismuth, forming the trichloride. According to J. J. Sudborough, **nitrosyl chloride** acts on bismuth at ordinary temp., forming the trichloride, which in turn forms a complex salt with the excess of nitrosyl chloride. F. W. Bergstrom found that **potassium amide** reacts slowly with bismuth. B. Pelletier, and C. M. Marx, found that bismuth takes up very little **phosphorus** when the two elements are heated together. A. Michaelis observed that when bismuth is heated with **phosphorus trichloride** in a sealed tube some bismuth trichloride and phosphorus are formed. C. Braun said that when bismuth is heated to redness with **metaphosphoric acid,** some bismuth is projected away as fine rain, and some bismuth phosphate is formed. Both **arsenic** and **antimony** mix in all proportions in the molten state—*vide* arsenides and antimonides. Bismuth was found by W. Finkelstein to precipitate arsenic from a soln. of **arsenic trichloride** in nitrobenzene ; and A. Mazzucchelli and A. Vercillo observed no alloy is formed by the action of bismuth on **antimony trichloride.** F. E. Brown and J. E. Snyder found that **vanadium oxytrichloride** has no action on bismuth. H. Giebelhausen found that amorphous **boron** is scarcely wetted by molten bismuth. H. Moissan found that **carbon** does not dissolve in molten bismuth. W. Fränkel studied the action of bismuth on **carbon dioxide** : $Bi_2O_3 + 3CO \rightleftharpoons 3CO_2 + 2Bi$, and found that at 400°, 500°, and 600°, equilibrium is attained respectively in 16, 5, and $2\frac{1}{2}$ hrs. Y. Shibata and H. Kaneko studied the oxidizing action of the colloidal metal on pyrogallol soln. C. B. Gates found that 0·5 c.c. of **oleic acid** dissolves 0·0091 grm. of bismuth in 6 days. A. Korczynsky studied the catalytic action of bismuth in the halogenization of hydrocarbons. E. Vigouroux said that **silicon** dissolves in molten bismuth, but is rejected as the metal solidifies without forming a silicide.

The action of bismuth on the **metals** is discussed in a separate section ; and for the fusible alloys, *vide* tin, and lead. W. Guertler [6] discussed the affinity of bismuth for some of the metals. K. Jellinek and J. Wolff studied the equilibrium of bismuth with chlorides of sodium, potassium, calcium, and barium. A. Joannis found that a soln. of **sodium** in liquid ammonia forms sodium tritabismuthide. According to M. Kohn, bismuth reduces soln. of **copper salts** to the cuprous state : $Bi + 3CuCl_2 = BiCl_3 + 3CuCl$; while alkaline soln. of cupric salts are reduced to copper. N. W. Fischer, and J. B. Senderens observed that bismuth incompletely precipitates copper from a boiling soln. of cupric nitrate, and with a soln. of cupric chloride, cuprous chloride, and bismuth oxychloride are formed. H. Rose found that bismuth decomposes **silver hydroxide ;** and N. W. Fischer observed that an alcoholic soln. of **silver nitrate** deposits silver. He also noticed that bismuth completely precipitates the gold from a soln. of **gold chloride** in a few hours. R. Boyle observed that when bismuth is heated with an excess of **mercuric chloride,** bismuth trichloride is formed, but if stoichiometrical proportions are used, both **mercurous chloride** and mercuric chloride furnish bismuth dichloride.

The physiological action of bismuth.—Soluble bismuth compounds are toxic. L. F. Meyer,[7] and W. Steinfeld observed that when bismuth salts are injected subcutaneously into mammals or birds, or if large doses are given them through the mouth, effects as severe as those due to antimony may be produced. Death follows in 24–48 hrs., and the fatal issue is preceded by convulsions. After death, the organs are blackened—presumably by hydrogen sulphide in the parenchyma— but the small intestine and stomach are healthy unless sulphur compounds have been eaten. P. Dalché mentioned symptoms of poisoning in cases where wounds have been treated with bismuth preparations. The symptoms resembled mercurial poisoning. Bismuth leaves the rectum as sulphide and colours the fæces black ; it may cause a purplish line on the gums ; and the breath may have a garlic odour due to the contamination of bismuth with tellurium. Bismuth is slowly absorbed and excreted chiefly in the urine, and it may be found in the liver, kidney, spleen, and nervous system. **P. Lemay** and **L. Jaloustre** found comparatively large amounts in the brains of two individuals to whom bismuth hydroxide had been administered. Bismuth salts are dusted on sores as protectives and mild astringents. The salts are also used in relieving gastric pains ; and as astringents in diarrhœa. The oxynitrate, carbonate, and salicylate are used medicinally. G. Fuchs studied the effect of bismuth salts on the secretion of mucus, and C. Levaditi and co-workers, on trypanosomiases and spirilloses. The physiological action of bismuth was studied by C. S. Lenard.

Some reactions of bismuth of analytical importance.—Bismuth salts are nearly all hydrolyzed by **water,** forming compounds containing the univalent radicle *bismuthyl,* BiO ; thus, bismuth trichloride forms the oxychloride BiOCl, which, unlike the corresponding antimony oxychloride, is insoluble in tartaric acid. The soln. of bismuth salts do not give a precipitate with **hydrochloric acid ;** and **hydrogen sulphide** precipitates brown bismuth trisulphide from neutral or dil. acidic soln. ; the precipitate is insoluble in cold dil. mineral acids and alkali sulphide soln., but soluble in hot, dil. nitric acid, and boiling, conc. hydrochloric acid. The precipitate from alkaline soln., or that produced by **alkaline sulphides** is soluble in an excess of the alkali sulphide. Cold acidic soln. are partially precipitated by **ammonium thioacetate,** and completely when the soln. is boiling. Bismuth trisulphide is also precipitated when a soln. of a bismuth salt is treated with **sodium thiosulphate.** When cold soln. of bismuth are treated with **potassium hydroxide,** white bismuth hydroxide, $Bi(OH)_3$, is precipitated ; this becomes yellow on boiling owing to the formation of bismuthyl hydroxide, BiO(OH). Bismuth hydroxide is soluble in boiling, conc. alkali-lye, but on cooling part is reprecipitated, and all is precipitated by dilution. Both hydroxides are insoluble in the cold in an excess of the precipitant, and are readily soluble in acids. Water containing the hydroxides in suspension gave a yellow or brown precipitate of metabismuth acid, $HBiO_3$, when treated with oxidizing agents like chlorine, bromine, hypochlorites, or hydrogen **dioxide.** Aq. **ammonia** precipitated a white basic salt from soln. of bismuth **salts.** According to F. Jackson,[8] the sensitiveness of the reactions with ammonia and with alkali-lye is 1 : 8000. Soln. of **alkali carbonate** also precipitate basic carbonates from soln. of bismuth salts. F. Jackson said that the sensitiveness of the reaction is 1 : 32000. The hydrated oxide was found by J. von Liebig to be completely precipitated, even in the cold, by calcium carbonate ; H. Demarçay added that barium, strontium, and magnesium carbonates act in an analogous way. Black bismuth triiodide is precipitated by **potassium iodide,** and the precipitate is soluble in excess, forming a yellow or orange soln. of $KBiI_4$. According to F. B. Stone, the yellow colour with potassium iodide is a soln. of a bismuth salt feebly acidified with sulphuric acid, is perceptible with a dilution 1 : 1,000,000. A soln. of **sodium phosphate** gives a white, granular precipitate of $BiPO_4$, insoluble in dil. nitric acid, and sparingly soluble in conc. hydrochloric acid. With **potassium cyanide,** the whole precipitate of the cyanide is instantly hydrolyzed to $Bi(OH)_3$; **potassium thiocyanate** precipitates bismuth monosulphide ; **potassium ferrocyanide** gives a white precipitate soluble in hydrochloric acid ; **potassium ferricyanide,** a yellow precipitate soluble in hydrochloric acid ; and **potassium cobalticyanide,** a white precipitate. With **potassium dichromate or chromate,** yellow bismuthyl chromate is precipitated, soluble in mineral acids, and insoluble in alkali-lye. F. Jackson said that the sensitiveness of the chromate reaction is 1 : 4000. An alkaline soln. of stannous chloride, *i.e.* an **alkali stannite,** was shown by L. Vanino and F. Treubert to give a black precipitate of bismuth. If too much alkali-lye be present, metallic tin, or black stannous oxide may be precipitated. M. M. P. Muir said that with tartaric acid soln. of stannous oxide and of bismuth oxide, one part of bismuth can be detected in 210,000 parts of soln. Dil. **sulphuric acid** gives no precipitate with a dil. soln. of bismuth nitrate ; H. Herzog [9] found that a boiling neutral soln. gives a precipitate of basic acetate ; M. M. P. Muir, that **sodium acetate** gives a white precipitate soluble in an excess of acetic acid ; H. Rose, and R. Schneider, that **oxalic acid** gives a white precipitate, and **ammonium acetate,** a white precipitate soluble in excess ; and C. Reichard, that a conc. soln. of **brucine** gives an intense red coloration.

The metallic precipitation of bismuth.—N. W. Fischer [10] said that **copper** has no action on bismuth salt soln., but V. A. Jacquelain said that copper precipitates bismuth slowly and incompletely, and H. Reinsch added that a soln. of bismuth nitrate in 500 parts of dil. hydrochloric acid immediately forms a grey film on copper. The effect is obtained with soln. even more dilute. R. Schneider said that bismuth dissolves in a boiling soln. of cupric chloride—the soln. is decolorized, presumably owing to the formation of cuprous chloride. A. Commaille, and F. J. Faktor observed that **magnesium** precipitates bismuth from soln. of its salts, but K. Seubert and A. Schmidt said that precipitation is not complete in hydrochloric acid soln. N. W. Fischer said that **zinc and cadmium** precipitate bismuth rapidly and completely with the evolution of some gas, and a rise of temp. After the free acid has been neutralized, a basic salt of bismuth is precipitated, but this is also slowly reduced to the metal. K. Seubert and A. Schmidt found that the precipitation by zinc is not complete in hydrochloric acid soln. N. W. Fischer said that the precipitation by **lead** is incomplete, ceases after a time, and no gas is evolved ; A. Patera found the action with lead is incomplete in the presence of nitric acid ; and C. Ullgren, in acetic acid soln. O. Prelinger observed that **manganese** precipitates bismuth from soln. of its salts. N. W. Fischer said that **arsenic,** and **antimony** do not do so. The precipitation of bismuth by **iron** was found by N. W. Fischer to be rapid and complete, without the evolution of gas. J. Clark, J. G. Gallety and G. C. **Henderson,** and A. T. Starting also said that the precipitation with iron is complete. H. Cousin discussed the precipitation of bismuth by an alkaline soln. of dextrose.

The uses of bismuth.[11]—Metallic bismuth is largely employed in the preparation of fusible alloys—*vide* tin, 7. 46, 5—used in automatic sprinklers and other apparatus for the prevention of fires ; electric fuses ; safety plugs in boilers ; in dentistry for making dies for plaster casts ; for special solders ; as crystals in the detectors of radiophone receiving apparatus ; etc. A. Lassieur [12] gave the following *fusible alloys :* with Sn : Pb : Bi : Cd=2 : 4 : 7·5 : 1·5, m.p. 75°–76° ; 19 : 33·1 : 33·6 : 14·3, m.p. 94°–95° ; 2 : 4 : 10 : 1·5, m.p. 74°–75° ; 4 : 4 : 7·5 : 1·5, m.p. 75° ; 2 : 2 : 7·5 : 1·5, soft at 75°, molten at 80° ; 1 : 2 : 4 : 1, m.p. 74°–75° ; and 2 : 4 : 5 : 2, pasty at 77°, molten at 80°. Some of these alloys melt in hot water. The increased resistance of bismuth in a magnetic field is utilized in making instruments for determining the strength of magnetic fields. Bismuth salts—chiefly the oxycarbonate, or oxynitrate, oxysalicylate, oxygallate, oxylactate—are used medicinally for indigestion ; they are used in surgery dressings for wounds—some mixtures have trade names as *dermatol, airol, iodogallicine,* etc. An insoluble bismuth salt given with a meal distributes itself in the alimentary canal and allows an X-ray photograph to be taken which shows the digestive tract in clear outline. The oxychloride, and oxynitrate were formerly used as a cosmetic for toilet purposes, but have given way to the cheaper zinc oxide. Bismuth oxide has been used as a constituent of certain optical glasses ; in making enamels for cast-iron ; in porcelain painting and enamelling ; bismuth antimonate is used in making certain yellow colours ; the oxychloride and oxynitrate have been used as white pigments in painting—blanc d'espagne, and blanc de perle ; bismuth along with gold appears in some recipes for gilding porcelain ; and the oxynitrate, ground with an essential oil, is used in imparting an iridescent surface—mother-of-pearl lustre—to pottery. Some inflammable materials—*e.g.* tar, creosote, asphalt, and oils used for waterproofing cloth, wood, and paper—are rendered much less inflammable by admixture with 5–20 per cent. of bismuth chloride with or without a solvent like amyl acetate, etc.

REFERENCES.

[1] **F. H. Newman**, *Proc. Phys. Soc.*, **33**. 73, 1921; R. L. Richland, *Schweigger's Journ.*, **15**. 417, 1815; W. Ramsay and J. N. Collie, *Proc. Roy. Soc.*, **60**. 53, 1896; F. Fischer and F. Schrötter, *Ber.*, **43**. 1442, 1454, 1910; F. Fischer and G. Iliovici, *ib.*, **41**. 4449, 1908; H. von Wartenberg, *Zeit. anorg. Chem.*, **56**. 320, 1907; W. Strecker and W. Daniel, *Ber.*, **59**. A, 1691, 1926; F. Meurer, *Arch. Pharm.*, (2), **36**. 33, 1843; E. Zumbusch, *Ueber Wismut*, München, 1911; L. Vanino and E. Zumbusch, *Ber.*, 249, 483, 1911; F. Paneth, *Ber.*, **51**. 1704, 1918; *Zeit. Elektrochem.*, **24**. 298, 1918; F. Paneth and E. Winternitz, *Ber.*, **51**. 1704, 1728, 1918; F. Paneth, A. Johannsen, and M. Matthies, *ib.*, **55**. B, 769, 1922; F. Paneth and E. Rabinovitsch, *ib.*, **58**. B, 1138, 1925; F. Paneth, M. Matthies and E. Schmidt-Hebbel, *ib.*, **55**. B, 775, 1922; P. Sachs, *Ueber Wismuthwasserstoff*, München, 1913; A. C. Vournasos, *Compt. Rend.*, **152**. 714, 1911; J. Schlossberger and C. R. Fresenius, *Liebig's Ann.*, **51**. 418, 1844; E. J. Weeks and J. G. F. Druce, *Chem. News*, **129**. 31, 1924; **133**. 243, 1926,; *Journ. Chem. Soc.*, **127**. 1799, 1925; *Nature*, **116**. 710, 1925.

[2] T. Thomson, *Proc. Glasgow Phil. Soc.*, **1**. 4, 1842; W. Heintz, *Liebig's Ann.*, **52**. 252, 1844; *Pogg. Ann.*, **63**. 58, 1844; P. A. von Bonsdorff, *ib.*, **41**. 305, 1837; **42**. 325, 1837; H. V. Regnault, *Ann. Chim. Phys.*, (2), **62**. 363, 1836; L. J. Thénard, *ib.*, (2), **9**. 441, 1818; (2), **10**. 114, 335, 1819; (2), **11**. 85, 1819; *Traité de chimie*, Paris, **2**. 66, 1824; J. Löwe, *Zeit. anal. Chem.*, **22**. 502, 1883; C. F. Schönbein, *Journ. prakt. Chem.*, (1), **93**. 59, 1864; L. Vanino and A. Menzel, *Zeit. anorg. Chem.*, **149**. 18, 1925; W. R. Dunstan, H. A. D. Jowett, and E. Goulding, *Journ. Chem. Soc.*, **87**. 1548, 1905.

[3] H. Moissan, *Ann. Chim. Phys.*, (6), **24**. 247, 1891; P. P. Dehérain, *Bull. Soc. Chim.*, (1), **3**. 51, 1861; (1), **4**. 22, 1862; *Compt. Rend.*, **52**. 734, 1861; **54**. 724, 1862; **55**. 807, 1862; V. Thomas and P. Dupais, *ib.*, **143**. 272, 1906; A. Ditte and R. Metzner, *ib.*, **115**. 1303, 1892; *Ann. Chim. Phys.*, (6), **29**. 389, 1893; G. S. Sérullas, *ib.*, (2), **38**. 323, 1828; M. M. P. Muir, *Chem. News*, **33**. 15, 1876; *Journ. Chem. Soc.*, **29**. 144, 1876; R. Cowper, *ib.*, **43**. 153, 1883; R. Schneider, *Journ. prakt. Chem.*, (2), **50**. 463, 1894; *Pogg. Ann.*, **96**. 130, 1855; **97**. 482, 1856; R. Weber, *ib.*, **107**. 598, 1859; W. Heintz, *ib.*, **63**. 59, 1844; *Liebig's Ann.*, **52**. 252, 1844; J. Thomsen, *Ber.*, **16**. 40, 1883; C. Willgerodt, *Journ. prakt. Chem.*, (2), **34**. 285, 1887; (2), **35**. 391, 1887; C. F. Schönbein, *ib.*, (1), **93**. 59, 1864; A. G. Page, *Liebig's Ann.*, **225**. 199, 1884; W. S. Hendrixson, *Journ. Amer. Chem. Soc.*, **26**. 747, 1904; J. Davy, *Phil. Trans.*, **102**. 169, 1812; G. Gore, *Phil. Mag.*, (4), **29**. 546, 1865.

[4] D. Lagerhjelm, *Akad. Handl. Stockholm*, **34**. 219, 1813; *Schweigger's Journ.*, **17**. 416, 1816; W. Spring, *Ber.*, **16**. 1001, 1883; J. Uhl, *ib.*, **23**. 2154, 1890; R. H. Adie, *Proc. Chem. Soc.*, **15**. 133, 1899; *Chem. News*, **79**. 261, 1899; H. Schiff, *Liebig's Ann.*, **117**. 95, 1861; C. Geitner, *ib.*, **129**. 354, 1864; L. Moser and E. Neusser, *Chem. Ztg.*, **47**. 541, 1923; M. Websky, *Zeit. anal. Chem.*, **11**. 127, 1872; E. B. Hutchins, *Journ. Amer. Chem. Soc.*, **27**. 1157, 1905; R. Schneider, *Pogg. Ann.*, **91**. 404, 1854; **97**. 480, 1856; *Journ. prakt. Chem.*, (2), **60**. 524, 1900; F. Rössler, *Zeit. anorg. Chem.*, **9**. 74, 1895; J. J. Berzelius, *Schweigger's Journ.*, **6**. 311, 1812; **34**. 78, 1823; M. G. Levi, E. Migliorini, and G. Ercolini, *Gazz. Chim. Ital.*, **38**. i, 598, 1908; N. Domanicky, *Russ. Phys. Chem. Soc.*, **48**. 1724, 1916.

[5] F. H. Newman, *Proc. Phys. Soc.*, **33**. 73, 1921; G. Gore, *Proc. Roy. Soc.*, **21**. 140, 1873; P. Vigier, *Bull. Soc. Chim.*, (1), **3**. 5, 1861; *Chem. News*, **3**. 273, 1861; O. E. A. Hjelt, *Journ. prakt. Chem.*, (1), **90**. 261, 1863; A. Michaelis, *ib.*, (2), **4**. 454, 1871; C. Montemartini, *Gazz. Chim. Ital.*, **22**. 384, 1892; A. Quartaroli, *ib.*, **53**. i, 345, 1923; N. A. E. Millon, *Compt. Rend.*, **14**. 905, 1842; F. Hérard, *ib.*, **108**. 293, 1889; F. E. Brown and J. E. Snyder, *Journ. Amer. Chem. Soc.*, **47**. 2671, 1925; C. A. Kraus, *ib.*, **44**. 1216, 1922; J. J. Berzelius, *Gilbert's Ann.*, **40**. 286, 1812; *Schweigger's Journ.*, **7**. 70, 1814; C. M. Marx, *ib.*, **58**. 471, 1830; J. L. Proust, *Journ. Phys.*, **59**. 321, 1804; T. Andrews, *B.A. Rep.*, 69, 1838; *Phil. Mag.*, (3), **11**. 554, 1837; (2), **12**. 305, 1838; J. J. Sudborough, *Journ. Chem. Soc.*, **59**. 662, 1891; B. Pelletier, *Ann. Chim. Phys.*, (1), **13**. 130, 1792; E. Vigouroux, *ib.*, (7), **12**. 153, 1897; *Compt. Rend.*, **123**. 115, 1896; H. Moissan, *ib.*, **122**. 1462, 1896; N. Domanicky, *Journ. Russ. Phys. Chem. Soc.*, **48**. 1724, 1916; C. Braun, *Zeit. Chem.*, (2), **2**. 282, 1866; J. H. Stansbie, *Journ. Soc. Chem. Ind.*, **27**. 365, 1908; C. B. Gates, *Journ. Phys. Chem.*, **15**. 143, 1911; N. R. Dhar, *ib.*, **29**. 142, 1925; **309**, 1923; H. Giebelhausen, *Zeit. anorg. Chem.*, **91**. 251, 1915; E. Müller and H. Barck, *ib.*, **129**. 309, 1923; W. Finkelstein, *Zeit. phys. Chem.*, **115**. 303, 1925; W. Fränkel, *Festschrift zur Jahrhundertfeier des physikalischen Vereins, Frankfurt a. M.*, 136, 1924; A. Mazzucchelli and A. Vercillo, *Atti Accad. Lincei*, (6), **1**. 233, 1925; A. Korczynsky, *Bull. Soc. Chim.*, (4), **29**. 283, 1921; G. Tammann, *Gött. Nahr.*, 351, 1918; F. W. Bergstrom, *Journ. Phys. Chem.*, **30**. 15, 1926; C. C. Palit and N. R. Dhar, *ib.*, **30**. 1125, 1926; Y. Shibata and H. Kaneko, *Journ. Japan. Chem. Soc.*, **45**. 155, 1924.

[6] M. Kohn, *Monatsh.*, **42**. 83, 1921; J. B. Senderens, *Bull. Soc. Chim.*, (3), **15**. 218, 1896; (3), **17**. 271, 1897; A. Joannis, *Compt. Rend.*, **113**. 795, 1891; **114**. 585, 1892; N. W. Fischer, *Pogg. Ann.*, **8**. 492, 1826; *Verhältniss der Chemischen Verwandtschyft zur galvanischen Elektrizität in Versuchen Largestellt*, Berlin, 1830; R. Schneider, *Pogg. Ann.*, **93**. 312, 1896; R. Boyle, *Experiments and considerations touching colours*, 1663; W. Guertler, *Metall Erz*, **22**. 199, 1925; K. Jellinek and J. Wolff, *Zeit. anorg. Chem.*, **146**. 329, 1925; H. Rose, *Sitzber. Akad. Berlin*, **245**, 1857.

[7] L. F. Meyer, *Rossbach's Pharm. Unters.*, **3**. 23, 1882; W. Steinfeld, *Arch. Exp. Path.*, **20**.

40, 1856; *Ueber die Wirkung des Wismuts auf den thierischen Organismus*, Dorpat, 1884;
C. S. Lenard, *Journ. Pharm. Exp. Thereup.*, 28. 81, 89, 109, 121, 1926; P. Dalché, *Brit. Med.
Journ.*, i, 749, 1887; *Ann. Hyg. Publ.*, 16. 358, 1886; P. Lemay and L. Jaloustre, *Compt. Rend.
Soc. Biol.*, 88. 474, 1923; G. Fuchs, *Verh. deut. Naturf. Aerzte*, 2. 90, 1902; C. Levaditi and
S. Nicolan, *Ann. Inst. Pasteur*, 38 179, 1924; C. Levaditi, *Journ. State Med.*, 32. 62, 1924; *Compt.
Rend.*, 176. 1189, 1923.
    [8] F. Jackson, *Journ. Amer. Chem. Soc.*, 25. 992, 1903; L. Vanino and F. Treubert, *Ber.*, 31.
1113, 1898; J. von Liebig, *Mag. Pharm.*, 35. 114, 1831; H. Demarçay, *Ann. Chim. Phys.*, (2),
55. 398, 1833; *Liebig's Ann.*, 11. 240, 1834; F. B. Stone, *Journ. Soc. Chem. Ind.*, 6. 416, 1887;
M. M. P. Muir, *Journ. Chem. Soc.*, 32. 45, 1877.
    [9] H. Herzog, *Chem. News*, 58. 129, 1888; M. M. P. Muir, *Journ. Chem. Soc.*, 31. 658, 1877;
R. Schneider, *Pogg. Ann.*, 88. 54, 1853; H. Rose, *ib.*, 90. 199, 1853; C. Reichard, *Chem. Ztg.*,
28. 1024, 1904.
    [10] N. W. Fischer, *Das Verhältniss der chemischen Verwandtschaft zur galvanischen Electricität
in Versuchen dargestellt*, Berlin, 1830; *Pogg. Ann.*, 8. 497, 1826; R. Schneider, *ib.*, 93. 312, 1854;
K. Seubert and A. Schmidt, *Liebig's Ann.*, 267. 238, 1892; J. G. Gallety and G. C. Henderson,
Analyst, 34. 389, 1909; O. Steen, *Zeit. angew. Chem.*, 8. 531, 1895; H. Reinsch, *Journ. prakt.
Chem.*, (2), 24. 248, 1841; A. T. Starting, *Arch. Pharm.*, (3), 7. 10, 1875; F. J. Faktor, *Pharm.
Post*, 38. 153, 1904; H. Cousin, *Journ. Pharm. Chim.*, (7), 28. 170, 1923; O. Prelinger, *Monatsh.*,
14. 369, 1893; A. Patera, *Zeit. anal. Chem.*, 5. 226, 1866; C. Ullgren, *Liebig's Ann.*, 40. 269,
1848; V. A. Jacquelain, *Ann. Chim. Phys.*, (2), 66. 113, 1837; A. Commaille, *Compt. Rend.*, 63.
556. 1866; *Bull. Chim. Soc.*, (2), 6. 257, 1866; J. Clark, *Journ. Soc. Chem. Ind.*, 19. 26, 1900.
    [11] A. Arent, *Brit. Pat. No.* 146099, 1920; J. Grünwald, *The Raw Materials for the Enamelling
Industry*, London, 1914; J. C. Brown, *Bull. Indian Ind. and Labour*, 6, 1921.
    [12] A. Lassieur, *Bull. Recherches Ind. Inventions*, 31. 304, 1922.

§ 6. The Atomic Weight and Valency of Bismuth

According to J. Dalton,[1] 1810, the atomic weight of bismuth is 68.   J. J. Berzelius at first supposed that ordinary bismuth oxide is analogous to lead oxide, and
he assigned to both the same formula, RO_2—this made the at. wt. of bismuth 284
(oxygen 16); and in 1826, he represented the formula RO, which made the at. wt.
of bismuth 142 (oxygen 16). In 1817, J. J. G. Meinecke represented the eq. wt. of
bismuth as 72; L. Gmelin gave 71; C. G. Bischof, T. Thomson, and C. M. Despretz,
72.   In 1826, L. J. Thénard, gave 213 for the at. wt. of bismuth; then followed
P. T. Meissner, O. B. Kühn with 71; and P. F. Cauchy with 142.   P. L. Dulong
and A. T. Petit's observation in 1869 on the sp. ht. correspond with the at. wt.
213 (oxygen 16); but J. J. Berzelius did not accept this value.   A. E. Arppe,
A. Stromeyer, W. Heintz, and W. Wiluéef showed that the formula of the ordinary
oxide is probably Bi_2O_3, and that of the higher oxide Bi_2O_5, and the at. wt. of bismuth approximating 212·86 (oxygen 16) was then generally accepted.   This is in
agreement with the vapour densities of the volatile compounds of bismuth; with
the sp. ht. rule, the isomorphous rule, and the periodic table.

Usually, bismuth acts as a tervalent element, and its halides are typified by
$BiCl_3$.   A. Marquerdt prepared bismuth trimethide, $Bi(CH_3)_3$, and triethide,
$Bi(C_2H_5)_3$; and A. Michaelis and A. Marquerdt, the triphenylide, $Bi(C_6H_5)_3$.   Bismuth trimethide yields the trichloride with hydrochloric acid; and the triethide,
with iodine yields $Bi(C_2H_5)_2I$, and with mercuric chloride, $Bi(C_2H_5)Cl_2$.
E. B. Hutchins and V. Lenher were unable to make bismuth pentachloride, $BiCl_5$;
but O. Ruff and co-workers obtained evidence of the formation of the pentafluoride,
BiF_5, by the action of fluorine on the trifluoride at $-80°$.   In bismuth oxytrifluoride,
$BiOF_3$, the bismuth is probably quinquevalent, as is also the case with bismuth
pentoxide, Bi_2O_5.   The quinquevalency of bismuth is supported by the existence
of the complexes $Bi(OH_3)_3Br_2$, $Bi(C_6H_5)_3Br_2$, and $Bi(C_6H_5)_3Cl_2$ prepared by
A. Michaelis, and A. Gillmeister.   The evidence for bivalent bismuth turns on the
existence of bismuth monoxide, and of the dihalides (*q.v.*).   E. Neusser doubted
the existence of bivalent bismuth.

D. Lagerhjelm calculated the at. wt. of bismuth to be 210·9–212·9 from the ratio
$2Bi : B_2O_3$; R. Schneider, 208·00–208·04; L. Birckenbach, 208·05; A. Classen,
208·90; and J. Löwe, 207·83, from the same ratio; J. C. G. de Marignac obtained
208·6 from the ratio $Bi_2O_3 : 2Bi$. D. Lagerhjelm obtained 215·2 from the ratio
$2Bi : Bi_2S_3$; and 212·4 from the ratio $2Bi : Bi_2(SO_4)_3$; R. I. Janssen, 208·07, from

the same ratio. J. C. G. de Marignac obtained 208·16 and B. Kuzma 208 0 from the ratio $Bi_2O_3 : Bi_2(SO_4)_3$. G. H. Bailey obtained 208·9 from an analysis of the sulphate. J. B. A. Dumas calculated 210·89 from the ratio $BiCl_3 : 3Ag$; and H. Mehler, 208·05 from the ratio $BiBr_3 : 3AgBr(Ag, 107·934)$. In 1907, B. Brauner gave 208·0 for the best representive value, and in 1910, F. W. Clarke gave 208·062. G. D. Hinrichs favoured the whole number. R. H. Adie attributed the difference between the high and the low results to the presence of silicon, and he obtained 208·8 for the at. wt. Since then, W. O. de Coninck and P. Gérard obtained 208·50 from the ratio $BiCl_3 : Bi$; O. Hönigschmid and L. Birckenbach, 209·024 from the ratio $BiCl_3 : 3AgCl$, and 209·026 from the ratio $BiCl_3 : 3Ag$, and they favour the round value 209·00. They criticize A. Classen and O. Ney's value 208·9967, calculated from the ratio $2Bi(C_6H_5)_3 : Bi_2O_3$; in confirmation thereof, A. Classen and G. Strauch gave for the same ratio 208·989.

The **atomic number** of bismuth is 83. F. W. Aston [2] found that bismuth has no **isotopes**, being a simple element of at. mass 209. H. Müller obtained negative evidence of **atomic disintegration** when bismuth is exposed to intense α-radiation. G. Kirsch and H. Pettersson investigated the action of the α-particle on the atoms of bismuth. W. F. Jorissen and J. A. Vollgraff attempted to transform bismuth into thallium by the cathode rays, but without success. Bismuth commonly contains a trace of thallium which can be detected spectroscopically. A. Holmes and R. W. Lawson discussed bismuth as a possible end-product in the radioactive thorium compounds. K. A. Hofmann found bismuth in two samples of bröggerite, but F. Soddy found none in Singalese thorite. The **electronic structure**, according to N. Bohr's scheme, is (2) (4, 4) (6, 6, 6) (8, 8, 8, 8) (6, 6, 6) (4, 1). The electronic structure was discussed by C. D. Niven, R. N. Ghosh, M. L. Huggins, E. C. Stoner, H. G. Grimm and A. Sommerfield, G. Runge, and H. Nagaoka and co-workers. H. Collins has made some speculations on this subject.

REFERENCES.

[1] J. Dalton, *A New System of Chemical Philosophy*, Manchester, 2. 263, 1810; J. J. G. Meinecke, *Die Chemische Messkunst*, Halle, 1817; L. Gmelin, *Handbuch der theoretischen Chemie*, Frankfurt a. M., 1827; B. Brauner in R. Abegg, *Handbuch der anorganischen Chemie*, Leipzig, 3. iii, 628, 1907; B. Kuzma, *ib.*, 3. iii, 635, 1907; F. W. Clarke, *A Recalculation of the Atomic Weights*, Washington, 328, 1910; C. G. Bischof, *Lehrbuch der Stöchiometrie*, Erlangen, 1819; L. J. Thénard, *Traité de chimie élémentaire, théorique et prátique*, Paris, 1826; P. F. Cauchy, *Principes generaux de chimie inorganique*, Bruxelles, 1838; O. B. Kühn, *Lehrbuch der Stöchiometrie*, Leipzig, 1857; P. T. Meissner, *Chemische Equivalenten oder Atomlehre*, Wien, 1838; C. M. Despretz, *Élémens de chimie théorique et prátique*, Paris, 1826; W. O. de Coninck and P. Gérard, *Compt. Rend.*, 162. 252, 1916; O. Hönigschmid and L. Birckenbach, *Sitzber. Akad. München*, 83, 1920; *Zeit. Elektrochem.*, 26. 403, 1920; *Ber.*, 54. B, 1873, 1921; O. Ney, *Ueber das Atomgewich des Wismuts*, Aachen, 1920; A. Classen and O. Ney, *Ber.*, 53. B, 2267, 1920; A. Gillmeister, *ib.*, 30. 2843, 1897; A. Michaelis, *ib.*, 20. 52, 1887; A. Marquerdt, *ib.*, 20. 1516, 1887; 21. 2035, 1888; A. Michaelis and A. Marquerdt, *Liebig's Ann.*, 251. 324, 1889; E. B. Hutchins and V. Lenher, *Journ. Amer. Chem. Soc.*, 29. 31, 1907; O. Ruff, M. Knoch, and J. Zedner, *Zeit. anorg. Chem.*, 57. 220, 1908; E. Neusser, *ib.*, 135. 313, 1924; J. J. Berzelius, *Lehrbuch der Chemie*, Dresden, 3. 1216, 1845; A. Stromeyer, *Pogg. Ann.*, 26. 548, 1832; R. Schneider, *ib.*, 82. 303, 1851; 107. 626, 1859; *Journ. prakt. Chem.*, (2), 30. 240, 1884; (2), 42. 133, 1890; (2), 44. 23, 1891; (2), 50. 461, 1894; A. Classen, *ib.*, (2), 43. 133, 1891; *Ber.*, 23. 938, 1890; A. Classen and G. Strauch, *Zeit. anorg. Chem.*, 141. 82, 1924; A. E. Arppe, *Pogg. Ann.*, 64. 237, 1845; *Dissertatio de jodeto bismutico*, Helsingfors, 1843; *Akad. Handl. Stockholm*, 133, 1842; D. Lagerhjelm, *ib.*, 219, 1813; *Ann. Phil.*, 4. 358, 1814; *Schweigger's Journ.*, 17. 416, 1816; W. Heintz, *Pogg. Ann.*, 43. 55, 1844; *Liebig's Ann.*, 52. 252, 1844; G. D. Hinrichs, *Monit. Scient.*, (4), 20. 169, 1906; T. Thomson, *Proc. Glasgow Phil. Soc.*, 1. 4, 1842; *A System of Chemistry*, Edinburgh, 1822; W. Wiluéef, *Dissertation on the Atomic Weight of Bismuth*, St. Petersburg, 1849; J. B. A. Dumas, *Ann. Chim. Phys.*, (3), 55. 176, 1869; J. C. G. de Marignac, *ib.*, (6), 1. 289, 1884; P. L. Dulong and A. T. Petit, *ib.*, (2), 7. 113, 1818; (2), 10. 395, 1819; J. Löwe, *Zeit. anal. Chem.*, 22. 498, 1883; G. H. Bailey, *Journ. Chem. Soc.*, 51. 676, 1887; R. H. Adie, *Proc. Cambridge Phil. Soc.*, 12. 240, 1903; L. Birckenbach, *Ueber das Atomgewichts des Wismuths*, Erlangen, 1905; A. Gutbier and L. Birckenbach, *Zeit. Elektrochem.*, 11. 831, 1903; *Journ. prakt. Chem.*, (2), 47. 457, 1908; A. Gutbier and H. Mehler, *ib.*, (2), 78. 409. 1908; H. Mehler, *Ueber das Atomgewicht des Wismuts*, Erlangen, 1905; *Sitzber. Phys. Med. Soc. Erlangen*, 37. 343, 1905; R. L. Janssen, *Ueber das Atomgewicht des Wismuts*, Erlangen, 1906; A. Gutbier and R. L. Janssen, *Journ. prakt. Chem.*, (2), 78. 420, 1908.

² F. W. Aston, *Journ. Franklin Inst.*, **199**. 260, 1925 ; *Phil. Mag.*, (6), **49**. 1197, 1925 ; *Nature*, **114**. 717, 1924 ; G. Runge, *ib.*, **113**. 781, 1924 ; H. Nagaoka, Y. Sugiura and T. Mishima, *ib.*, **113**. 532, 567, 1924 ; H. Nagaoka, *ib.*, **114**. 245, 1924 ; F. Soddy, *Nature*, **94**. 615, 1915 ; N. Bohr, *ib.*, **112**. Suppl., 1923 ; K. A. Hofmann, *Ber.*, **34**. 914, 1901 ; H. G. Grimm and A. Sommerfield, *Zeit. Physik*, **36**. 36, 1926 ; G. Kirsch and H. Pettersson, *Sitzber. Akad. Wien*, **134**. 491, 1925 ; *Atomzertrümmerung*, Leipzig, 104, 1926 ; M. L. Huggins, *Journ. phys. Chem.*, **26**. 601, 1922 ; W. P. Jorissen and J. A. Vollgraff, *Zeit. phys. Chem.*, **90**. 557, 1915 ; A. Holmes and R. W. Lawson, *Phil. Mag.*, (6), **29**. 677, 1915 ; E. C. Stoner, *ib.*, (6), **48**. 732, 1924 ; C. D. Niven, *ib.*, (7), **3**. 1314, 1927 ; H. Collins, *Chem. News*, **129**. 1, 1924 ; H. Müller, *Sitzber. Akad. Wien*, **135**. 563, 1926 ; R. N. Ghosh, *Journ. Indian Chem. Soc.*, **4**. 423, 1927.

§ 7. The Bismuthides

J. L. Gay Lussac and L. J. Thénard,[1] C. M. Marx, and H. Caron obtained alloys of sodium and bismuth by melting together a mixture of the two elements. The combination starts below the m.p. of bismuth and is attended by vivid combustion. G. S. Sérullas made the alloy by heating a mixture of bismuth and charred soap. A. Joannis, and P. Lebeau obtained an alloy approximating Na₃Bi by the action of sodammonium on bismuth. C. A. Kraus and H. F. Kurtz observed that by reducing soln. of bismuth salts in liquid ammonia by sodium, alloys are formed. C. T. Heycock and F. H. Neville found that the lowering of the f.p. of bismuth by sodium agrees with the assumption that the sodium is monatomic. N. S. Kurnakoff found that an alloy with 75 per cent. of bismuth, Na₃Bi, has a m.p. of 720°. E. Kordes studied the eutectic mixtures. C. T. Heycock and F. H. Neville, and C. H. Matthiesson measured the f.p. of the alloys and the curve, Fig. 4, has a

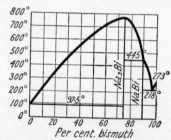

FIG. 4.—Freezing-point Curves of Sodium-Bismuth Alloys.

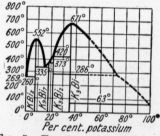

FIG. 5.—Freezing-point Curves of Potassium-Bismuth Alloys.

maximum at 775° and 75 at. per cent. of bismuth corresponding with **sodium tritabismuthide,** Na₃Bi A Joannis obtained the tritabismuthide by the action of a soln. of sodium in liquid ammonia on the metal. F. Paneth and co-workers observed the formation of no bismuth hydride when the alloy is treated with acid. The tritabismuthide is bluish-violet in colour, brittle, and rapidly oxidizes in moist air. There is a eutectic in the curve at 218° and 22 at. per cent. of sodium ; and a break in the curve at 445° and 47 at. per cent. of sodium. This corresponds with **sodium monobismuthide,** NaBi. This substance is brittle. Both compounds are about as hard as bismuth. R. Kremann and co-workers measured the electrode potential of sodium-bismuth alloys in a pyridine soln. of sodium iodide or in an aq. soln. of sodium sulphate with alloys having less than 5 per cent. of sodium against a bismuth electrode. Concordant results were not obtained, but with alloys having 10 to 80 at. per cent. of bismuth, the e.m.f. was constant at about 1·6 or 1·7 volts. J. L. Gay Lussac and L. J. Thénard, and C. M. Marx prepared alloys of potassium and bismuth, by melting a mixture of the two elements. Union is attended by incandescence. L. N. Vauquelin made an alloy by heating a mixture of bismuth and potassium tartrate covered with lamp-black ; and G. S. Sérullas, by heating a mixture of bismuth with half its weight of carbonized potassium tartrate, and about half per cent. of nitre. C. Méhu also studied these alloys ; and E. Kordes, the eutectic mixtures. D. P. Smith measured the f.p. of the potassium-bismuth alloys, and the results are illustrated by Fig. 5. **The metals in the fused state** are miscible in all proportions. The f.p. curve has a maximum at 540° and 35 at. per cent. of potassium corresponding with **potassium dibismuthide**, KBi_2 ; and a maximum at 671° and 75 at. per cent. of potassium corresponding with **potassium tritabismuthide**, K_3Bi. This compound has a transition temp. at 280°. The break in the f.p. curve at 420° indicates the formation of **potassium tritadibismuthide**, K_3Bi_2. There are two eutectics at 260° and 3 at. per cent., and at 335° and 50 at. per cent. of potassium respectively. The tritadibismuthide reacts with the fused mass near 373°, forming what is probably *potassium heptaennitabismuthide*, K_9Bi_7. N. Parravano thinks that this compound is more likely to be **potassium monobismuthide**, KBi, because it results from a peritectic reaction, and the duration of the reaction cannot furnish an absolute criterion of the composition. R. Kremann and co-workers measured the electrode potential of potassium-bismuth alloys in a pyridine soln. of potassium chloride against bismuth. The e.m.f. showed two sharp steps corresponding with K_3Bi at 1·6 volts, and KBi_2 at about 0·80 volt. T. Seebeck studied the thermoelectric properties of the alloys. G. Bredig and F. Haber made colloidal soln. of sodium and potassium bismuthides by the submerged arc process.

C. M. Marx [2] made *copper-bismuth alloys* by fusing mixtures of the elements ; E. Vigouroux obtained pale yellow lamellæ of the alloy as a by-product in the preparation of copper silicide. H. Gautier and R. Gosselin said that the f.p. curve shows a maximum corresponding with *copper monobismuthide*, $CuBi$. Alloys were made by R. H. Thurston, C. R. A. Wright, A. Gibb, and W. Hampe ; the microstructure was studied by M. Merle, and J. E. Stead ; and the hardness by A. Mallock. The f.p. curve has been measured by H. Gautier, A. H. Hiorns, K. Jeriomin, W. C. Roberts-Austen, C. T. Heycock and F. H. Neville, E. A. Lewis, K. L. Meissner, and A. Portevin. The results are shown in Fig. 20, **3. 21, 6**. There are no compounds, and no solid soln. F. C. Calvert and R. Johnson studied the sp. gr. of the copper-bismuth alloys ; F. C. Calvert and R. Johnson, the electrical conductivity ; T. Seebeck, and A. Battelli, the thermoelectric properties. The general properties of the alloys, and the effect of bismuth on the mechanical properties of copper—C. M. Marx, E. A. Lewis, A. Portevin, D. Hanson and G. W. Ford, C. J. B. Karsten, F. C. Calvert and R. Johnson, W. C. Roberts-Austen, M. Knoerzer, C. T. Heycock and F. H. Neville, J. Arnold and J. Jefferson, F. Johnson, H. N. Lawrie, N. Parravano, P. Jolibois and P. Thomas, etc.—are described **3. 21, 6**. E. Matthey observed that copper can be removed from an alloy with a low proportion of bismuth by fusion with bismuth sulphide, and from one with a high proportion of bismuth, by fusion with sodium sulphide. J. H. Stansbie measured the rate of dissolution of the copper-bismuth alloys in nitric acid.

The *silver-bismuth alloys* have been discussed in connection with silver—**3. 22, 7**. No definite compounds are formed. Alloys were made by P. Berthier,[3] C. R. A. Wright, C. W. Kayser, A. Matthiessen, R. Schneider, and C. M. Marx. The mutual solubility of the elements was studied by W. Alexejeff. The sp. gr., by P. von Muschenbrock, A. Matthiessen and M. Holzmann, and E. Maey ; the hardness, elongation, and tensile strength, by L. Jordan and co-workers ; D. H. Andrews and J. Johnston, the solubility of silver in bismuth ; the mixture rule, J. Dejmek ; the diffusion by W. C. Roberts-Austen ; the f.p. curves, by C. T. Heycock and F. H. Neville, and C. I. Petrenko ; the electrical conductivity, by A. Matthiessen, and R. Kremann and K. Bayer ; the thermoelectric properties, by A. Battelli ; the e.m.f. by W. N. Lacey, A. P. Laurie, and H. le Chatelier. I. Domeyko [4] described naturally occurring *silver bismuthide*, in Corpinpo, Chile. He called the mineral *aleacion de plata con bismuto*, and J. D. Dana, **chilenite**. Analyses by I. Domeyko, and D. Forbes correspond with $Ag_{10}Bi$ to $Ag_{12}Bi$. It occurs in silver-white amorphous grains, which soon acquire a yellow tarnish. The mineral is soluble in nitric acid. H. E. McKinstry observed no action when the mineral is exposed to the light of an electric arc. The *bismuth-gold alloys* were discussed in connection with gold—**3. 23, 6**. No compounds are formed.

The alloys were prepared by C. Hatchett,[5] A. Matthiessen, and F. Rössler. No compounds are formed. T. Andrews, F. Osmond and W. C. Roberts-Austen, L. Nowack, and M. Merle, studied the microstructure ; J. Arnold and J. Jefferson, the effect of bismuth on the properties of gold ; W. C. Roberts-Austen, the diffusion ; A. Matthiessen, and E. Maey, the sp. gr. of the alloys ; C. T. Heycock and F. H. Neville, and R. Vogel, the f.p. curve ; A. Matthiessen, the electrical conductivity ; A. P. Laurie, and H. le Chatelier, the e.m.f. F. Rössler found the alloy to be insoluble in a mixture of equal parts of nitric and tartaric acids. C. U. Shepard [6] mentioned *bismuthic gold* occurring in North Carolina ; and he called it **bismuthaurite.** It was not mentioned by F. A. Genth. It is thought that bismuthaurite was an artificial product. The *black gold* of the Australian miners occurs in Maldon, Victoria, and G. H. F. Ulrich [7] called it **maldonite.** Analyses reported by G. H. F. Ulrich, and R. W. E. MacIvor correspond with *gold hemibismuthide*, Au_2Bi. The colour is silver-white with a pink tinge ; the sp. gr. 8·2–9·7 ; and the hardness 1–2. W. Vernadsky made some observations on the mineral.

H. Caron [8] melted a sodium-bismuth alloy with barium chloride and obtained an alloy of bismuth with 28 per cent. of barium free from sodium. The crystalline *barium-bismuth alloy* loses only a little weight when heated in a carbon crucible. It oxidizes rapidly in air, and if it contains more than 5 per cent. of barium, it is

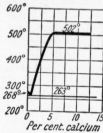

FIG. 6.—The Freezing Point of Alloys of Calcium and Bismuth.

decomposed by water with the evolution of hydrogen, and the separation of bismuth. He obtained a *bismuth-calcium alloy* in a similar manner. L. Donsky could prepare alloys with only up to 10 per cent. of calcium. The f.p. of bismuth is lowered about 5° by the addition of calcium ; and the eutectic contains less than one per cent. The f.p. curve, Fig. 6, rises from the eutectic to 502°, with 4·5 per cent. of calcium, and then runs horizontally as far as it could be followed. Acicular crystals of a **calcium bismuthide** are formed, but the formula could not be determined. P. Kremann and co-workers examined the e.m.f. of the Ca–Bi-alloys. The compound is decomposed rapidly in moist air, and even in vacuo over sulphuric acid. O. Ruff and H. Hartmann studied the velocity of absorption of nitrogen by the alloys at 400°–520°.

J. Parkinsom [9] made alloys with magnesium. E. Kordes studied the eutectic mixtures. The f.p. curve of magnesium-bismuth alloys was examined by C. T. Heycock and F. H. Neville. G. Grube's curve is shown in Fig. 5, of **4.** 29, 5. The curve consists of three branches. There is a well-defined maximum at 710° and 85·09 per cent. of bismuth corresponding with the steel-grey, brittle **magnesium ditritabismuthide,** Mg_3Bi_2, which is slowly oxidized in moist air. The compound is practically insoluble in bismuth. There is a eutectic at 552° and 65 per cent. of bismuth. No mixed crystals are formed. The *zinc-bismuth alloys,* and the *cadmium-bismuth alloys* have been previously discussed—*vide* Figs. 21 and 22 of **4.** 30, 6. D. H. Andrews and J. Johnston studied the solubility of bismuth in cadmium ; M. Kawakami, the heat of admixture ; and E. Kordes, the eutectic mixtures. G. J. Petrenko and A. S. Fedoroff observed that the amount of each metal in solid soln. with the other cannot exceed 0·1 per cent. The eutectic has 40 per cent. bismuth. K. Houda and T. Ishigaki studied this subject ; P. Fischer, and N. W. Taylor, the e.m.f. ; A. W. Smith, and M. Naumann, the electrical conductivity ; M. Naumann, the thermoelectric force ; R. Kremann and A. Tröster, the electrolysis of these alloys ; C. di Capua and M. Arnone, and M. Naumann, the hardness ; C. H. Mathewson and W. M. Scott, the ternary system, Zn–Cd–Bi ; D. H. Andrews and J. Johnston the ternary system, Sn–Cd–Bi. No compounds have been observed. *Mercury-bismuth alloys,* or *bismuth amalgams,* have been prepared, though V. Rothmund,[10] and A. Gouy found the solubility of bismuth in mercury to be very small. J. Groh measured that rate of dissolution of bismuth **in** mercury. R. Büttger obtained an amalgam by the action of sodium amalgam on bismuth nitrate; and G. Vortmann electrolyzed a soln. obtained by dissolving bismuth trioxide and mercuric chloride in hydrochloric **acid**, and adding potassium iodide until the precipitate has all dissolved; or **an** alcoholic hydrochloric acid soln. of bismuth and mercuric chlorides; a soln. of the two nitrates in nitric and tartaric acids; and an ammoniacal soln. of the two chlorides. The f.p. of soln. of bismuth in mercury were determined by C. T. Heycock and F. H. Neville, and G. Tammann. N. A. Puschin's observations are summarized in Fig. 7. G. Tammann, G. McP. Smith, E. Kordes, N. A. Puschin, K. Bornemann, and D. Mazzotto made observations on this subject, and failed to establish the existence of any definite compound, or solid soln. Hence, P. I. Bachmetjeff and J. V. Washaroff's $Hg_{28}Bi$, shown by a maximum on the sp. ht. curve, is probably not a chemical individual; and a similar remark applies to J. H. Croockewit's $HgBi_2$, obtained by pouring molten bismuth into warm mercury, and squeezing out the excess of mercury through chamois-leather.

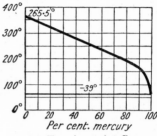

FIG. 7.—Freezing-point Curve of Mercury-Bismuth Alloys.

Amalgams were also made by C. M. Marx, V. Merz and W. Weith, J. Regnauld, J. Schumann. A. Battelli found that amalgams with more mercury than Hg : Bi$=9 : 1$ are liquid; those with less mercury than Hg : Bi$=2 : 1$ are solid; the solid amalgams are very brittle. D. H. Andrews and J. Johnston measured the solubility of bismuth in mercury; H. Feninger, the viscosity; F. C. Calvert and R. Johnson gave 11·208 for the sp. gr. of Hg : Bi; 10·693 for Hg : Bi$_2$; 10·474 for Hg : Bi$_4$; 10·350 for Hg : Bi$_4$; and 10·240 for **Hg** : Bi$_5$. G. Vicentini and C. Cattaneo measured the contraction coeff. G. Tammann and W. Jander, and J. Würschmidt found anomalies in the change of vol. with temp. indicating a transition point between the allotropic forms of bismuth at 75°. The change is attended by a considerable contraction. W. J. Humphreys studied the diffusion; C. Cattaneo, the thermal expansion; P. I. Backmetjeff and J. V. Washaroff, the sp. ht.; and W. Ramsay, and E. D. Eastman and J. H. Hildebrand made some observations on the vap. press. The electrical conductivity or the electrical resistance was measured by A. Matthiessen, A. Matthiessen and C. Vogt, H. Feninger, A. Lohr, C. Michaelis, E. Lassen, G. Vicentini and C. Cattaneo, C. L. Weber, and A. Battelli; E. J. Williams, the change in the electrical resistance of the amalgam when placed in a magnetic field; T. Seebeck, and W. Rollmann, the thermoelectric process; V. Rothmund, R. Sabine, N. A. Puschin, A. Oberbeck and J. Edler, and G. Gore measured the electrode potential of the amalgams; and R. Kremann and A. Kapaun, the electrolysis of the amalgams. The amalgams are stable in air, but H. Lucas found that mercury with one eight-thousandth part of bismuth forms a black powder when shaken in air; and G. S. Sérullas said that water and potassium-amalgam will reveal as a black powder, one part of bismuth in 1,200,000 parts of mercury. V. Merz and W. Weith said that the mercury is all expelled by heating the amalgam to the temp. of boiling sulphur, mercury, or diphenylamine. C. F. Schöbein found that hydrogen dioxide is formed when the amalgam is shaken with water or dil. sulphuric acid. K. Someya found that bismuth amalgam reduces ferric to ferrous **salts**; quinquevalent to quadrivalent vanadium; stannic to stannous salts; cupric to cuprous salts; and titanic to titanous salts. K. Someya found that bismuth amalgam reduces vanadates to hypovanadates; ferric to ferrous salts; titanic to titanous salts; and molybdic acid to quinquevalent molybdenum. A. S. Russell and D. C. Evans studied the reducing efficiency of amalgams of bismuth on ferric sulphate, potassium permanganate, and uranyl sulphate, and expressed the results in terms of the overvoltages.

According to C. R. A. Wright,[11] *aluminium-bismuth alloys* separate into two layers —the lower layer is a soln. of about 0·28 per cent. aluminium in bismuth ; and the upper one a soln. of about 2·02 per cent. bismuth in aluminium. C. and A. Tissier, and E. Self prepared alloys of the two elements. A. G. C. Gwyer also found that the reciprocal solubility of these two elements is small. The f.p. curve is shown in Fig. 8. The sat. soln. of bismuth in aluminium contains about 0·5 at. per cent. of the former metal and solidifies at 652°, about 5° below the m.p. of aluminium. At the same temp., the layer rich in bismuth contains about 8 at. per cent. of aluminium, but the solubility diminishes with decrease of temp., and is practically zero at the m.p. of bismuth. The two metals show no sign of chemical combination, even on heating for some time at 1200°. W. Campbell and J. Mathews studied the micro-structure ; C. T. Heycock and F. H. Neville, the f.p. of the alloys ; and H. Schirmeister, the tensile strength and elongation. H. Pécheux found that the alloys with

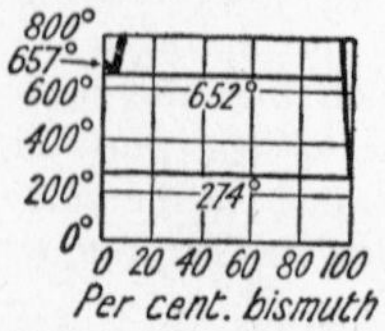

Fig. 8.—Freezing-point Curve of Alloys of Aluminium and Bismuth.

Aluminium	75	85	88	94 per cent.
Specific gravity (20°)	2·857	2·79	2·776	2·74
Melting point	719°–720°	674°–680°	663°–664°	650°–655°

The alloys are stable in moist and dry air ; but they are attacked readily by conc. acids, or dil. or conc. alkali-lye. The powdered alloy decomposes water especially in the presence of copper sulphate. C. R. A. Wright studied the ternary systems, Bi–Al–Sb ; Bi–Al–Sn ; and Bi–Al–Ag.

E. Carstanjen,[12] and E. J. Chapman found that thallium forms alloys with bismuth. N. S. Kurnakoff and N. A. Puschin, and C. T. Heycock and F. H. Neville studied the f.p. of alloys of these two elements, and M. Chikashigé's results are summarized in Fig. 4 of **5. 36, 4.** The f.p. curve has three maxima. The one at 211·7° and 37 per cent. of thallium corresponds with **thallium pentatritabismuthide,** Tl_3Bi_5. This maximum was not observed by C. T. Heycock and F. H. Neville. The pentatritabismuthide forms a series of mixed crystals with 35·5–38·5 per cent. of thallium, and another series with 66·3–88·75 per cent. of thallium. There is a transition point at 90° indicating that the mixed crystals react to form **thallium tritabismuthide,** Tl_3Bi. The pentatritabismuthide is soft, and difficult to polish; the freshly cut surface is light grey, but rapidly becomes yellow. The compound is oxidized by long contact with air. The alloys in the region of the maxima of 303·5° and 88·7 per cent. of thallium, and at 302° and 99·2 per cent. of thallium behave as mixed crystals and not as chemical compounds. The three eutectics are at 197° and 20 per cent., 186° and 53 per cent., and 297° and 93 per cent. of thallium respectively. W. Guertler and A. Schulze measured the electrical conductivity of the alloys; and W. Jenge, the electrode potential. The observations of R. Kremann and A. Lobinger on the e.m.f. of cells with these alloys as one electrode agreed with the existence of the trita- and the pentatrita-bismuthides ; but N. S. Kurnakoff and co-workers observed no evidence of the latter in their study of the f.p. of these alloys. D. Omodei studied the thermal expansion of these alloys ; and E. van Aubel, the thermoelectric properties. The electrical con-

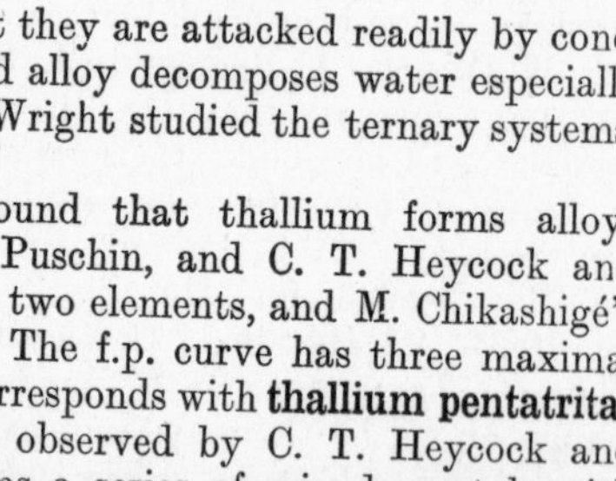

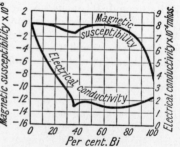

Fig. 9.—Properties of Thallium-Bismuth Alloys.

ductivities by A. E. Whitford, and the magnetic susceptibilities by C. E. Medenhall and W. E. Lent are illustrated by Fig. 9. R. Vogel's observations[13] on **cerium tritabismuthide,** Ce_3Bi, formed at about 1400° ; **cerium tritetritabismuthide,** Ce_4Bi_3, m.p. 1630° ; **cerium monobismuthide,** $CeBi$, formed at 1525° ;

and **cerium dibismuthide,** $CeBi_2$, formed at 882° are indicated in connection with cerium—**5**. 38, 10.

The *silicon-bismuth alloys* are discussed in connection with bismuth silicides —**6**. 40, 12 ; the *tin-bismuth alloys,* in connection with tin—**7**. 46, 5 ; and the *lead-bismuth alloys,* in connection with lead—**7**. 47, 5. No *tin bismuthides* or *lead bismuthides* have been isolated. R. S. Williams [14] found that *chromium and bismuth* are immiscible in the fused state so that the f.p. curves appear as in Fig. 10. No compounds are formed. S. Hilpert and T. Dieckmann examined the magnetic properties of the alloys. C. Sargent prepared a *molybdenum-bismuth alloy* and a *tungsten-bismuth alloy* in the electric furnace. J. J. and F. de Elhuyar also made bismuth-tungsten alloys. Observations on the *manganese-bismuth alloys* were made by E. Bekier, N. Parravano and U. Perret, and P. Siebe. The two metals are not completely miscible. The f.p. diagram is shown in Fig. 11. When more than 23 per cent. of manganese has been determined by the cooling curve method, the two metals are not completely miscible. When more than 23 per cent. of manganese is present, two layers are formed, the upper consisting of practically pure manganese, whilst the lower is a 23 per cent. soln. of manganese

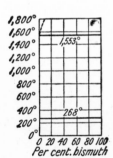

FIG. 10.—Freezing-point Curves of Chromium-Bismuth Alloys.

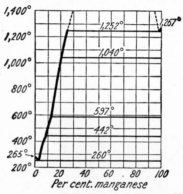

FIG. 11.—Freezing-point Curve of Manganese-Bismuth Alloys.

in bismuth. Five arrest points were found, corresponding with five crystalline phases. The eutectic horizontal is at 259°, and the other four horizontals, corresponding with the arrest points, are at 442°, 1043°, and 1252°. The last represents a eutectic containing at most 0·5 per cent. bismuth, which lowers the m.p. of manganese 13°. From alloys containing up to 0·5 per cent. of manganese, pure bismuth first separates ; with 0·5–9 per cent. of manganese, the first compound separates ; from 9 per cent. to 11 per cent. a second compound, and from 11 per cent. to 20 per cent., a third. The nature of the compounds has not been determined. Between 23 per cent. and 99·5 per cent. of manganese there is a complete gap. The hardness of the alloys increases with the manganese content. They are ferromagnetic, and this property is peculiar to the first compound, crystallizing from alloys containing between 0·5 per cent. and 9 per cent. of manganese. E. Wedekind and T. Veit prepared **manganese bismuthide**, MnBi, by the interaction of manganese thermite and bismuth. It forms octahedral and eight-sided columnar crystals which are strongly magnetic ; it is very sensitive towards acids, with the exception of conc. hydrochloric acid, which reacts very slowly and may be used for its purification. The same compound was also obtained, but with difficulty, by the direct fusion of the components in an atm. of hydrogen S. Hilpert and T. Dieckmann prepared the same compound by heating manganese amalgam with the necessary amount of bismuth in an atm. of hydrogen, and then distilling off the mercury. The grey substance burns in air giving non-magnetic products ; it is soluble in nitric acid and in hot hydrochloric acid. The magnetic bismuthide loses its magnetic properties **at** 360° and regains them at 380° on cooling. P. Martin studied the magneto-optical effect with manganese bismuthide.

E. Isaac and G. Tammann [15] studied the *iron-bismuth alloy*, and found that iron is not miscible with bismuth in the solid or fused state, and no compounds are formed. The f.p. curves thus appear as in Fig. 12.

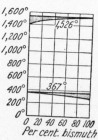

FIG. 12.— Freezing-point Curve of Iron-Bismuth Alloys.

C. J. B. Karsten said that he could prepare iron with only 0·081 per cent. of bismuth. C. M. Marx could not obtain an alloy of the two metals although J. F. Henkel reported a brittle alloy with 25 per cent. of iron ; and C. E. Gellert made observations on the sp. gr. of these alloys. · S. Hilpert and T. Dieckmann examined the magnetic properties of the alloys. K. Lewkonja studied the *cobalt-bismuth alloys* and found that the two elements are partially miscible in the liquid state—the limits of miscibility being 6 and 93 per cent. of cobalt—Fig. 13. G. Voss examined the *nickel-bismuth alloys* and found that the two elements are completely miscible in the fused state. The f.p. curve, Fig. 14, consists of three branches without maxima or minima. There is one series of mixed crystals with up to 0·5 per cent. of bismuth. At 638°, the sat. solid soln. reacts with the fused mass containing 32 per cent. of nickel to form **nickel monobismuthide,** NiBi ; and this, in turn, reacts with the fused mass containing 11 per cent. of nickel to form **nickel tribismuthide,** NiBi₃. These compounds could not be prepared in a pure state. The transition temp. of magnetic to non-magnetic nickel is lowered 20° by the addition of sufficient bismuth to form the sat. solid soln., and then remains constant at 325° up to a composition of 32 per cent. nickel, beyond which the alloys are no longer magnetic. F. Rössler made some nickel-bismuth alloys. G. Tammann

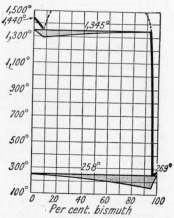

FIG. 13.—Freezing-point Curve of Cobalt-Bismuth Alloys.

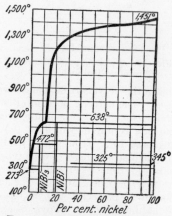

FIG. 14.—Freezing-point Curves of Nickel-Bismuth Alloys.

and K. Dahl studied the brittleness of the NiBi- and the NiBi₃-alloys. W. Meissner partially studied the ternary system : Bi–Cu–Ni.

A. F. Gehlen [16] said that *platinum-bismuth alloys* can be readily obtained of a bluish-grey colour, brittle, and readily fusible. They were also made by C. Barus, J. Murray, R. W. Fox, and C. Winkler. C. T. Heycock and F. H. Neville found that the f.p. of platinum is lowered 2·09° and 2·16° respectively by the addition of 0·206 and 0·939 at. per cent. of bismuth. The f.p. curve was surmised by W. Guertler to be similar to that of platinum and lead. C. Barus found the sp. resistance of an alloy of sp. gr. 21·33 at 0° to be 15·83 with the temp. coeff. of 0·0₇21 between 0°

and 100°. R. W. Fox found that when calcined in air, most of the bismuth is oxidized to the trioxide. A. B. von der Ropp, and C. Winkler examined the solvent action of nitric acid on these alloys. According to F. Rössler, **platinum dibismuthide**, PtBi$_2$, is formed when 10 grms. of platinum and 400 grms. of bismuth are fused together under glass in a coke furnace. The product is slowly cooled and washed with dil. nitric acid. The dark grey plates are slightly attacked by nitric acid. R. Chenevix [17] prepared a grey-coloured *palladium-bismuth alloy* with a sp. gr. 12·587. F. Rössler found the alloy to be insoluble in a mixture of nitric and tartaric acids. T. Graham said that it absorbs no hydrogen. C. T. Heycock and F. H. Neville studied the effect of bismuth on the f.p. of palladium. W. H. Wollaston made a *rhodium-bismuth alloy* soluble in nitric acid. F. Rössler found the alloy to be insoluble in a mixture of nitric and tartaric acids.

REFERENCES.

[1] J. L. Gay Lussac and L. J. Thénard, *Recherches physicochimiques*, Paris, 1. 219, 1811 ; T. Seebeck, *Sitzber. Akad. Berlin*, 265, 1823 ; *Pogg. Ann.*, 6. 148, 1826 ; C. M. Marx, *Schweigger's Journ.*, 58. 462, 1830 ; G. S. Sérullas, *Journ. Phys.*, 91. 123, 170, 1820 ; *Ann. Chim. Phys.*, (2), 21. 200, 1822 ; L. N. Vauquelin, *ib.*, (2), 7. 32, 1817 ; *Mém. Mus. Nat. Hist.*, 4. 248, 1818 ; C. Méhu, *Ann. Pharm.*, 23, 1873 ; *Dingler's Journ.*, 211. 187, 1874 ; D. P. Smith, *Zcit. anorg. Chem.*, 56. 125, 1907 ; C. H. Mathewson, *ib.*, 50. 187, 1906 ; N. S. Kurnakoff, *ib.*, 23. 457, 1900 ; E. Kordes, *ib.*, 154. 97, 1926 ; P. Lebeau, *Bull. Soc. Chim.*, (3), 23. 250, 1900 ; *Compt. Rend.*, 130. 502, 1906 ; A. Joannis, *ib.*, 113. 795, 1891 ; 114. 587, 1892 ; H. Caron, *ib.*, 48. 440, 1859 ; C. T. Heycock and F. H. Neville, *Journ. Chem. Soc.*, 55. 668, 1889 ; 61. 888, 1892 ; *Chem. News*, 62. 280, 1890 ; N. Parravano, *Gazz. Chim. Ital.*, 45. i, 485, 1915 ; R. Kremann, J. Fritsch, and R. Liebl, *Zeit. Metallkunde*, 13. 66, 1921 ; G. Bredig and F. Haber, *Ber.*, 31. 2741, 1898 ; F. Paneth, A. Johannsen, and M. Matthies, *ib.*, 55. B, 769, 1922 ; C. A. Kraus and H. F. Kurtz, *Journ. Amer. Chem. Soc.*, 47. 43, 1925.

[2] C. M. Marx, *Schweigger's Journ.*, 58. 470, 1830 ; M. Knoerzer, *Bull. Soc. Chim.*, (3), 9. 731, 1893 ; E. Vigouroux, *ib.*, (3), 35. 1238, 1907 ; *Compt. Rend.*, 132. 87, 1906 ; K. Jeriomin, *Zeit. anorg. Chem.*, 55. 412, 1907 ; G. Tammann, *ib.*, 49. 117, 1906 ; A. Portevin, *Rev. Mét.*, 4. 1078, 1907 ; H. Gautier and R. Gosselin, *Bull. Soc. Enc. Nat. Ind.*, (5), 1. 1309, 1896 ; H. Gautier, *ib.*, (5), 1. 1293, 1896 ; *Contribution à l'étude des alliages*, Paris, 110, 1901 ; E. A. Lewis, *Engg.*, 76. 753, 1903 ; J. Arnold and J. Jefferson, *ib.*, 61, 176, 1896 ; W. Hampe, *Zeit. Berg. Hütt. Sal.*, 22. 122, 1874 ; F. C. Calvert and R. Johnson, *Phil. Mag.*, (4), 18. 354, 541, 1859 ; *B.A. Rep.*, 66, 1859 ; C. J. B. Karsten, *System der Metallurgie*, Berlin, 5. 246, 263, 1831 ; C. T. Heycock and F. H. Neville, *Phil. Trans.*, 189. A, 25, 1897 ; *Journ. Chem. Soc.*, 61. 911, 1892 ; *Chem. News*, 62. 280, 1890 ; J. H. Stansbie, *Journ. Soc. Chem. Ind.*, 25. 45, 1075, 1906 ; A. H. Hiorns, *ib.*, 25. 616, 1906 ; J. E. Stead, *ib.*, 16. 200, 1897 ; C. R. A. Wright, *ib.*, 13. 1014, 1894 ; E. Matthey, *Chem. News*, 56. 241, 1887 ; 63. 30, 1891 ; *Proc. Roy. Soc.*, 43. 172, 1887 ; 49. 78, 1891 ; W. C. Roberts-Austen, *Report Alloys Research Committee*, London, 2. 121, 1893 ; *Proc. Inst. Mech. Eng.*, 102, 1893 ; 238, 1895 ; A. Battelli, *Atti Ist. Veneto.* (6), 5. 1137, 1887 ; M. Merle, *Monit. Scient.*, (4), 9. 35, 1895 ; R. H. Thurston, *The Materials of Engineering*, New York, 1884 ; A. Gibb, *Proc. Inst. Mech. Eng.*, 254, 1895 ; W. Hampe, *Zeit. Berg. Hütt. Sal.*, 21. 218, 1873 ; 22. 93, 1874 ; 24. 6, 1876 ; T. Seebeck, *Sitzber. Akad. Berlin*, 265, 1823 ; *Pogg. Ann.*, 6. 148, 1826 ; W. Spring, *Bull. Acad. Belg.*, (3), 28. 23, 1894 ; *Zeit. phys. Chem.*, 15. 65, 1894 ; H. N. Lawrie, *Trans. Amer. Inst. Min. Eng.*, 40. 604, 1909 ; N. Parravano, *Internat. Zeit. Metallog.*, 1. 89, 1911 ; F. Johnson, *Journ. Inst. Metals*, 8. 192, 1912 ; D. Hanson and G. W. Ford, *ib.*, 37. 169, 1927 ; P. Jolibois and P. Thomas, *Rev. Mét.*, 10. 1264, 1913 ; K. L. Meissner, *Zeit. Metallkunde*, 14. 173, 1922 ; G. Sachs, *ib.*, 17. 85, 1925 ; A. Mallock, *Nature*, 119. 669, 1927.

[3] W. Alexejeff, *Journ. Russ. Phys. Chem. Soc.*, 17. 282, 1885 ; A. Battelli, *Atti Ist. Veneto*, (6), 5. 1137, 1887 ; C. T. Heycock and F. H. Neville, *Chem. News*, 62. 280, 1891 ; *Journ. Chem. Soc.*, 61. 888, 1892 ; *Phil. Trans.*, 189. A, 25, 1897 ; A. Matthiessen, *ib.*, 150. 161, 177, 1860 ; *Pogg. Ann.*, 110. 21, 190, 1860 ; *B.A. Rep.*, 37, 1863 ; L. Jordan, L. H. Grenall, and H. K. Herschman, *Trans. Amer. Inst. Min. Met. Eng.*, . , 1927 ; A. Matthiessen and M. Holzmann, *Pogg. Ann.*, 110. 21, 1860 ; *Phil. Trans.*, 150. 85, 1860 ; P. von Muschenbrock, *ib.*, 33. 370, 1726 ; C. W. Kayser, *Ber.*, 2. 309, 1869 ; D. H. Andrews and J. Johnston, *Journ. Inst. Metals*, 32. 385, 1924 ; A. P. Laurie, *Journ. Chem. Soc.*, 65. 1031, 1894 ; H. le Chatelier, *Bull. Soc. Enc. Nat. Ind.*, (4), 10. 192, 1895 ; C. Marx, *Schweigger's Journ.*, 58. 454, 1830 ; W. C. Roberts-Austen, *B.A. Rep.*, 402, 464, 1883 ; C. R. A. Wright, *Journ. Soc. Chem. Ind.*, 13. 1014, 1894 ; P. Berthier, *Traité des essais par la voie sèche*, Liége, 2. 681, 1847 ; R. Schneider, *Sitzber. Akad. Berlin*, 495, 1855 ; G. I. Petrenko, *Zeit. anorg. Chem.*, 50. 133, 1906 ; E. Maey, *Zeit. phys. Chem.*, 38. 295, 1901 ; W. N. Lacey, *Chem. Ztg.*, 36. 1146, 1912 ; J. Dejmek, *Phys. Zeit.*, 28. 409, 1927 ; R. Kremann and K. Bayer, *Monatsh.*, 46. 649, 1927.

[4] I. Domeyko, *Elementos de mineralogia*, Santiago, 356, 1879 ; *Ann. Mines*, (4), 6. 165, 1844 ;

(6), 5. 456, 1864 ; D. Forbes, *Phil. Mag.*, (4), 25. 103, 1863 ; J. D. Dana, *A System of Mineralogy,* New York, 187, 1845 ; 45, 1893 ; H. E. McKinstry, *Econ. Geol.*, 22. 669, 1927.
  ⁵ C. Hatchett, *Phil. Trans.*, 93. 43, 1803 ; A. Matthiessen, *ib.*, 150. 161, 177, 1860 ; *Pogg. Ann.*, 110. 21, 190, 1860 ; *B.A. Rep.*, 37, 1863 ; E. Maey, *Zeit. phys. Chem.*, 38. 292, 1901 ; R. Vogel, *Zeit. anorg. Chem.*, 50. 147, 1906 ; F. Rössler, *ib.*, 9. 31, 1895 ; *Synthese einiger Erzmineralien und analoger Metallverbindungen durch Auflösen und Kristallisierenlassen derselben in geschmolzen Metallen*, Berlin, 1895 ; T. Andrews, *Engg.*, 66. 411, 541, 733, 1898 ; J. Arnold and J. Jefferson, *ib.*, 61. 176, 1896 ; F. Osmond, *ib.*, 66. 756, 1898 ; F. Osmond and W. C. Roberts-Austen, *B.A. Rep.*, 464, 1883 ; *Proc. Inst. Mech. Eng.*, 543, 1891 ; *Phil. Trans.*, 179. 339, 1888 ; 187. A. 417, 1896 ; *Bull. Soc. Eng. Nat. Ind.*, (5), 1. 1136, 1896 ; *Contribution à l'étude des alliages*, Paris, 71, 1901 ; C. T. Heycock and F. H. Neville, *Chem. News*, 62. 280, 1890 ; *Journ. Chem. Soc.*, 61. 888, 1892 ; A. P. Laurie, *ib.*, 65. 1031, 1894 ; H. le Chatelier, *Bull. Soc. Enc. Nat. Ind.*, (4), 10. 192, 1895 ; M. Merle, *Monit. Scient.*, (4), 9. 35, 1895 ; L. Nowack, *Zeit. Metallkunde*, 19. 238, 1927 ; W. C. Roberts-Austen, *B.A. Rep.*, 402, 464, 1883.
  ⁶ C. U. Shepard, *Amer. Journ. Science*, (2), 4. 280, 1847 ; (2), 24. 112, 281, 1857 ; F. A. Genth, *The Mineral Resources of North Carolina*, Philadelphia, 1871.
  ⁷ G. H. F. Ulrich, *Contribution to the Mineralogy of Victoria*, Melbourne, 41, 1866 ; 4, 1870 ; G. vom Rath, *Ber Niederrh. Ges. Bonn*, 73, 1877 ; R. W. E. Maclvor, *Chem. News*, 55. 191, 1887 ; W. Vernadsky, *Centr. Min.*, 760, 1912 ; *Bull. Acad.*, St. Petersburg, (6), 1. 27, 1907.
  ⁸ H. Caron, *Compt. Rend.*, 48. 440, 1859 ; L. Donsky, *Zeit. anorg. Chem.*, 57. 185, 1908 ; O. Ruff and H. Hartmann, *ib.*, 121. 167, 1922 ; R. Kremann, H. Wostal, and H. Schöpfer, *Forsch. Arb. Metallkunde*, 5, 1922.
  ⁹ G. Grube, *Zeit. anorg. Chem.*, 49. 72, 1906 ; C. T. Heycock and F. H. Neville, *Journ. Chem. Soc.*, 61. 888, 1892 ; J. Parkinson, *ib.*, 20. 117, 1867 ; C. di Capua and M. Arnone, *Atti Acad. Lincei*, (5), 33. i, 28, 1924 ; V. Fischer, *Zeit. tech. Phys.*, 6. 146, 1925 ; G. J. Petrenko and A. S. Fedoroff, *Internat. Zeit. Metallog.*, 6. 212, 1914 ; C. H. Mathewson and W. M. Scott, *ib.*, 5. 1, 1913 ; N. F. Taylor, *Journ. Amer. Chem. Soc.*, 45. 2875, 1923 ; A. W. Smith, *Phys. Rev.*, (2), 23. 307, 1924 ; P. Fischer, *Zeit. anorg. Chem.*, 109. 80, 1919 ; E. Kordes, *ib.*, 134. 97, 1926 ; K. Houda and T. Ishigaki, *Science Rep. Tohoku Univ.*, 14. 219, 1925 ; R. Kremann and A. Tröster, *Monatsh.*, 47. 285, 1926 ; R. Kremann, *ib.*, 47. 295, 1926 ; D. H. Andrews and J. Johnston, *Journ. Inst. Metals*, 32. 385, 1924 ; M. Naumann, *Studien über die Zinn-Wismub-Legierung*, Leipzig, 1927 ; M. Kawakami, *Zeit. anorg. Chem.*, 167. 345, 1927 ; *Science Rep. Tohoku Univ.*, 16. 915, 1927.
  ¹⁰ R. Böttger, *Journ. prakt. Chem.*, (i), 3. 278, 1834 ; (1), 12. 350, 1837 ; G. Vortmann, *Ber*, 24. 2760, 1891 ; E. de Souza, *ib.*, 9. 1050, 1876 ; V. Merz and W. Weith, *ib.*, 14. 1441, 1881 ; P. I. Bachmetjeff and J. V. Washaroff, *Journ. Russ. Phys. Chem. Soc.*, 25. 115, 219, 237, 1893 ; N. A. Puschin, *ib.*, 34. 635, 856, 1902 ; *Zeit. anorg. Chem.*, 36. 229, 1903 ; V. Rothmund, *Zeit. phys. Chem.*, 15. 17, 1894 ; G. Tammann, *ib.*, 3. 444, 1889 ; C. M. Marx, *Schweigger's Journ.*, 58. 454, 1830 ; A. Gouy, *Journ. Phys.*, (3), 4. 320, 1895 ; G. McP. Smith, *Amer. Chem. Journ.*, 36. 135, 1906 ; J. H. Croockewit, *Specimen chemicum de conjunctionibus chemicis metallorum*, Amsterdam, 1848 ; *Liebig's Ann.*, 68. 289, 1848 ; *Journ. prakt. Chem.*, (1), 45. 87, 1848 ; C. Michaelis, *Ueber die elektrische Leitungsfähigkeit verunreinigten Quecksilbers und die Methoden zur Reinigung desselben*, Berlin, 1883 ; J. Schumann, *Untersuchungen von Amalgamen*, Leipzig, 1891 ; *Wied. Ann.*, 43. 112, 1891 ; C. L. Weber, *ib.*, 23. 472, 1884 ; 31. 243, 1887 ; C. T. Heycock and F. H. Neville, *Chem. News*, 62. 280, 1890 ; *Journ. Chem. Soc.*, 61. 888, 1892 ; A. S. Russell and D. C. Evans, *ib.*, 127. 2221, 1925 ; W. Ramsay, *ib.*, 55. 533 1889 ; W. J. Humphreys, *ib.*, 69. 243, 1896 ; K. Bornemann, *Met.*, 7. 109, 1910 ; D. Mazzotto, *Atti Ist. Veneto*, (7), 4. 1311, 1527, 1893 ; G. Vicentini and C. Cattaneo, *Atti Accad. Lincei*, (4), 7. ii, 95, 1891 ; (5), 1. i, 343, 1892 ; C. Cattaneo, *ib.*, (4), 7. 88, 1891 ; A. Battelli, *ib.*, (4), 3. 37, 1887 ; (4), 4. 206, 1887 ; F. C. Calvert and R. Johnson, *Phil. Mag.*, (4), 18. 354, 541, 1859 ; *B.A. Rep.*, 66, 1859 ; C. F. Schönbein, *Pogg. Ann.*, 112. 445, 1861 ; W. Rollmann, *ib.*, 83. 77, 1851 ; 84. 275, 1851 ; 89. 90, 1853 ; T. Seebeck, *ib.*, 6. 148, 1826 ; *Sitzber. Akad. Berlin*, 265, 1823 ; A. Matthiessen, *Phil. Mag.*, (4), 22. 195, 1861 ; *Pogg. Ann.*, 114. 310, 1861 ; A. Matthiessen and C. Vogt, *ib.*, 116. 373, 1862 ; *Phil. Mag.*, (4), 23. 171, 1862 ; (4), 24. 32, 1862 ; E. J. Williams, *ib.*, (6), 50. 27, 1925 ; R. Sabine, *ib.*, (4), 23. 457, 1862 ; E. Lassen, *Ann. Physik*, (4), 1. 128, 1900 ; G. Gore, *Chem. News*, 61. 40, 1890 ; G. S. Sérullas, *Ann. Chim. Phys.*, (2), 34. 192, 1827 ; H. Lucas, *Trommsdorff's Journ.*, 10. 195, 1825 ; D. H. Andrews and J. Johnston, *Journ. Inst. Metals*, 32. 385, 1924 ; J. Würschmidt, *Ber. deut. phys. Ges.*, 15. 1027, 1913 ; 16. 799, 1914 ; A. Oberbeck and J. Edler, *Wied. Ann.*, 42. 209, 1891 ; J. Regnauld, *Compt. Rend.*, 52. 533, 1861 ; J. Schumann, *Untersuchungen von Amalgamen*, Erlangen, 1891 ; *Wied. Ann.*, 43. 101, 1891 ; E. D. Eastman and J. H. Hildebrand, *Journ. Amer. Chem. Soc.*, 36. 2020, 1914 ; A. Lohr, *Ueber Widerstandsänderungen von Amalgamen und einigen leichtschmelzbaren Legierungen mit der Temperatur und der Zeit*, Erlangen, 1914 ; H. Feninger, *Die Elektrische Leitfähigkeit und innere Reibung Verdünnter Amalgame*, Freiburg i Br., 1914 ; K. Someya, *Zeit. anorg. Chem.*, 138. 291, 1924 ; 152. 368, 382, 386, 391, 1926 ; 160. 404, 1927 ; G. Tammann and W. Jander, *ib.*, 124. 105, 1922 ; R. Kremann and K. Kapaun, *ib.*, 140. 183, 1924 ; E. Kordes, *ib.*, 154. 97, 1926 : 167. 97, 1927 ; J. Groh, *Zeit. phys. Chem.*, 128. 449, 1927.
  ¹¹ C. R. A. Wright, *Proc. Roy. Soc.*, 52. 19, 530, 1892 ; 55. 130, 1894 ; *Journ. Soc. Chem. Ind.*, 11. 492, 1892 ; 13. 1014, 1894 ; C. T. Heycock and F. H. Neville, *Journ. Chem. Soc.*, 61. 888, 1892 ; H. Pécheux, *Compt. Rend.*, 138. 1501, 1904 ; 140. 1535, 1905 ; 143. 397, 1906 ;

C. and A. Tissier, *ib.*, **43**. 885, 1856 ; A. G. C. Gwyer, *Zeit. anorg. Chem.*, **49**. 316, 1906 ; E. Self, *Journ. Franklin Inst.*, **123**. 209, 313, 388, 1887 ; W. Campbell, *ib.*, **154**. 1, 131, 201, 1902 ; W. Campbell and J. Mathews, *Journ. Amer. Chem. Soc.*, **24**. 253, 1902 ; H. Schirmeister, *Beiträge zur Kenntnis der binären Aluminiumlegierungen hinsichtlich ihrer technischen Ergenschaften*, Dusseldorf, 1914 ; *Stahl Eisen*, **35**. 649, 873, 966, 1915.

¹² E. Carstanjen, *Journ. prakt. Chem.*, (1), **102**. 65, 1867 ; E. J. Chapman, *Phil. Mag.*, (5), **2**. 397, 1876 ; M. Chikashigé, *Zeit. anorg. Chem.*, **51**. 330, 1906 ; W. Jenge, *ib.*, **118**. 105, 1921 ; D. Omodei, *Atti Accad. Fisiocritici Sienna*, (4), **2**. 15, 1890 ; R. Kremann and A. Lobinger, *Zeit. Metallkunde*, **12**. 246, 1920 ; N. S. Kurnakoff and N. A. Puschin, *Zeit. anorg. Chem.*, **30**. 86, 1902 ; *Journ. Russ. Phys. Chem. Soc.*, **33**. 565, 1902 ; N. S. Kurnakoff, S. F. Schemtschusny. and V. Tararin, *ib.*, **45**. 300, 1913 ; *Zeit. anorg. Chem.*, **83**. 200, 1913 ; C. T. Heycock and F. H. Neville, *Journ. Chem. Soc.*, **61**. 888, 1892 ; **65**. 31, 65, 1894 ; *Chem. News*, **62**. 280, 1890 ; W. Guertler and A. Schulze, *Zeit. phys. Chem.*, **106**. 1, 1923 ; E. van Aubel, *Bull. Acad. Belg.*, (5), **12**. 559, 1926 ; A. E. Whitford, *Phys. Rev.*, (1), **35**. 144, 1912 ; C. E. Mendenhall and W. E. Lent, *ib.*, (1), **32**. 415, 1911.

¹³ R. Vogel, *Zeit. anorg. Chem.*, **84**. 323, 1913.

¹⁴ R. S. Williams, *Zeit. anorg. Chem.*, **55**. 1, 1907 ; C. Sargent, *Journ. Amer. Chem. Soc.*, **22**. 783, 1900 ; E. Bekier, *Internat. Zeit. Metallog.*, **7**. 83, 1915 ; P. Siebe, *Zeit. anorg. Chem.*, **108**. 161, 1919 ; T. Dieckmann, *Ueber einige Mono- und Bi-arsenide des Eisens, Mangans, und Chrome, über ihre chemischen und magnetischen Eigenschaften, sowie über die magnetischen Eigenschaften einiger Mangan-Wismuth Legierungen*, Berlin, 1911 ; S. Hilpert and T. Dieckmann, *Ber.*, **44**. 2831, 1911 ; E. Wedekind and T. Veit, *ib.*, **44**. 2663, 1911 ; N. Parravano and U. Perret, *Gazz. Chim. Ital.*, **45**. i, 390, 1915 ; P. Martin, *Ann. Physik*, (4), **39**. 625, 1912 ; J. J. and F. de Elhuyar, *Análisis quimico del volfram y exámen de un nuevo metal que entra en su composicion*, Bascongada, 1783 ; *A Chemical Examination of Wolfram and Examination of a New Metal which enters into its Composition*, London, 1785 ; *Chemische Zerkliederung des Wolframs*, Halle, 1786 ; *Mém. Acad. Toulouse*, **2**. 141, 1784.

¹⁵ E. Isaac and G. Tammann, *Zeit. anorg. Chem.*, **55**. 58, 1907 ; K. Lewkonja, *ib.*, **59**. 293, 1908 ; G. Voss, *ib.*, **57**. 34, 1908 ; H. Rössler, *ib.*, **9**. 31, 1895 ; G. Tammann and K. Dahl, *ib.*, **123**. 104, 1923 ; W. Meissner, *Metall Erz*, **22**. 243, 1925 ; S. Hilpert and T. Dieckmann, *Ber.*, **44**. 2831, 1911 ; T. Dieckmann, *Ueber einige Mono- und Bi-arsenide des Eisens, Mangans, und Chrome, über ihre chemischen und magnetischen Eigenschaften, sowie über die magnetischen Eigenschaften einiger Mangan Wismuth Legierungen*, Berlin, 1911 ; C. J. B. Karsten, *System der Mineralogie*, Berlin, **4**. 33 1831 ; J. F. Henkel, *Pyritologia oder Kiess-Historie*, Leipzig, 414, 1725 ; C. E. Gellert, *Comment Acad. Petrop.*, **13**. 393, 1751 ; C. M. Marx, *Schweigger's Journ.*, **58**. 471, 1830 ; F. Rössler, *Zeit. anorg. Chem.*, **9**. 77, 1895.

¹⁶ A. F. Gehlen, *Schweigger's Journ.*, **20**. 353, 1817 ; J. Murray, *Edin. Phil. Journ.*, **4**. 202, 1821 ; *Journ. Franklin Inst.*, **1**. 316, 1826 ; C. Winkler, *Zeit. anal. Chem.*, **13**. 375, 1874 ; W. Guertler, *Metallographie*, Berlin, **1**. 622, 1912 ; C. T. Heycock and F. H. Neville, *Journ. Chem. Soc.*, **61**. 911, 1892 ; *Chem. News*, **62**. 280, 1890 ; C. Barus, *Amer. Journ. Science*, (3), £6. 434, 1888 ; R. W. Fox, *Ann. Phil.*, **13**. 467, 1819 ; A. B. von der Ropp, *Eine Untersuchungen über die Oxydation des Platins durch Salpetersäure*, Berlin, 1900 ; F. Rössler, *Zeit. anorg. Chem.*, **9**. 77, 1895 ; *Synthese einiger Erzmineralien und analoger Metallverbindungen durch Auflösen und Kristallisierenlassen derselben in geschmolzenen Metallen*, Berlin, 1895.

¹⁷ R. Chenevix, *Phil. Trans.*, **93**. 4, 1903 ; T. Graham, *ib.*, **156**. 399, 1866 ; W. H. Wollaston, *ib.*, **94**. 419, 1804 ; F. Rössler, *Zeit. anorg. Chem.*, **9**. 31, 1895 ; *Synthese einiger Erzmineralien und analoger Metallverbindungen durch Auflösen und Kristallisierenlassen derselben in geschmolzenen Metallen*, Berlin, 1895 ; *Chem. Ztg.*, **24**. 733, 1900 ; C. T. Heycock and F. H. Neville, *Chem. News*, **62**. 280, 1890 ; *Journ. Chem. Soc.*, **61**. 888, 1892.

§ 8. Bismuth Monoxide, and Trioxide

The brownish-grey film of oxide which can be skimmed from molten bismuth was considered by T. Thomson to be a suboxide ; so also did W. Heintz believe that the bismuth precipitated by zinc absorbs rather more oxygen than corresponds with the formula BiO. It is probable that in these cases a mixture of bismuth trioxide and bismuth is involved. S. M. Tanatar heated the basic oxalate, $Bi_2O(C_2O_4)_2$, in a current of dry carbon dioxide and obtained a product with the ultimate composition, *bismuth suboxide, or hemioxide*, Bi_2O. Its sp. gr. at 19° is 8·356 ; and the supposed compound gives the same chemical reactions as bismuth monoxide. This fact, and the heat of dissolution in acids, agrees with the assumption that the hemioxide is a mixture of the monoxide and metal.

Another oxide, also referred to as a suboxide, is regarded as **bismuth monoxide,** BiO, from the analyses of R. Schneider, and H. Schiff. It was made by A. Vogel by heating bismuth trioxide or the basic nitrate with stannous chloride. It forms a black powder, which, after washing and drying, glows with a yellowish-green light when heated, forming the trioxide. It turns yellow in air at ordinary temp., and is soluble in hydrochloric acid. J. J. Berzelius, and A. E. Arppe said that A. Vogel's suboxide always contains some tin which cannot be removed by washing. H. Schiff obtained this oxide by the action of a soln. of an alkali stannite on bismuth trioxide or hydroxide; R. Bunsen treated a neutral or feebly alkaline soln. of bismuth tartrate with a neutral or feebly alkaline soln. of stannous chloride and tartaric acid. R. Schneider, F. Hartl, and M. M. P. Muir prepared the oxide by an analogous process—pouring a soln. of bismuth trichloride into a soln. of alkali stannite. R. Schneider recommended pouring slowly, with constant stirring, a soln. of bismuth trioxide in nitric acid into an excess of dil. potash-lye, washing the precipitated bismuth hydroxide, and suspending it in a capacious flask containing a 2 per cent. soln. of potassium hydroxide. A freshly prepared soln. of stannous chloride was slowly added to the flask, which was then completely filled with air-free water, tightly closed, and the contents well shaken. The product is a light homogeneous black powder which, on exposure to air, forms ordinary bismuth hydroxide. A. Jaworososky warmed a gram of bismuth oxynitrate with a soln. of 3 grms. of ferrous sulphate, 4 of sodium antimonate, 5 of sodium hydroxide, and 40 of water, and obtained the monoxide as a dark brown powder. E. Zumbusch employed a similar process.

L. Vanino and F. Treubert maintained that bismuth monoxide is never formed by the action of stannous chloride on bismuth trichloride in alkaline soln. If the bismuth trichloride is in excess, the precipitate consists of a mixture of metallic bismuth with metahydroxide or the oxychloride. Three mol. proportions of stannous chloride suffice to reduce completely bismuth trioxide, Bi_2O_3, to metallic bismuth. A. Lottermoser also held that the reaction progresses : $Bi_2O_3+3SnO=3SnO_2+2Bi$. R. Schneider replied that L. Vanino and F. Treubert did not keep the bismuth soln. always in excess, but added the latter gradually to the soln. of the stannous salt. Under these conditions, the bismuth salt is completely reduced to the metal. W. Herz and A. Guttmann confirmed R. Schneider's observation that the reaction progresses $Bi_2O_3+SnO=SnO_2+2BiO$; and showed that the product is identical with that obtained by S. M. Tanatar by heating the oxalate, $(BiO)_2C_2O_4$, in a current of carbon dioxide : $(BiO)_2C_2O_4=2BiO+2CO_2$. W. Herz and A. Guttmann found that in an evacuated tube, the decomposition of the oxalate begins at 18° and 15 mm. press., and is completed at 245°–250°. If the temp. be too high, the oxalate furnishes a mixture of bismuth and its trioxide, not the monoxide. M. M. P. Muir said that the monoxide is formed when bismuth trioxide is heated to 265° in a current of hydrogen; C. F. Schlagdenhauffen and C. Pagel obtained a similar result with carbon monoxide at 400°. F. J. Brislee observed a break in the reduction curve of bismuth by carbon monoxide at 300° trioxide at different intervals of time.

Time in hours	0	3	4·5	6	9	12	15
Weight of oxide	3·00	2·934	2·920	2·890	2·868	2·850	2·831

R. Schneider reduced potassium bismuth sulphate with hydrogen and obtained the monoxide above 300°; below that temp., only water and sulphuric acid are given off. The brownish monoxide is mixed with some trisulphide. A. Hilger and P. A. von Scherpenberg said that the monoxide is probably formed by the action of warm potassium cyanide on bismuth hydroxide.

J. J. Berzelius said that a suboxide is formed when bismuth is heated with microcosmic salt on charcoal in the reducing flame of the blowpipe. The clear glass becomes black on cooling. J. L. Proust, and H. Davy believe that J. J. Berzelius' oxide is a mixture of bismuth and bismuth trioxide. A. E. Arppe's attempt to make the suboxide by reducing an alkaline soln. of bismuth trioxide with glucose gives according to R. Schneider, and J. Löwe, a precipitate of bismuth ; W. Heintz reduced bismuth phosphate in hydrogen, and obtained bismuth phosphide ; and R. Schneider obtained but a small yield of bismuth monoxide by heating potassium bismuth tartrate and similar compounds in a current of hydrogen.

R. Schneider said that the dark grey or black powder appears more or less crystalline under the microscope, and gives no metallic streak on polished steel. When prepared by the wet process, and kept in vacuo, or at 100°, it contains about one per cent. of water—$8BiO.H_2O$; but, according to W. Herz and A. Guttmann, when heated in a current of carbon dioxide, it is free from water, has a pale grey colour, and is somewhat hygroscopic. The sp. gr. of the monoxide, prepared by the wet process, is 7·88–7·90 at room temp. ; 7·24–7·28 when dried over sulphuric acid ; and 7·55–7·60 when quite dehydrated. S. M. Tanatar gave 7·153–7·201 for the sp. gr. at 19° of the product obtained by the dry process. These results do not agree with the assumption that the monoxide is a mechanical mixture of bismuth and its trioxide ; and W. Herz and A. Guttmann obtained 8·9 for the sp. gr. of a mixture of colloidal bismuth and bismuth trioxide. S. M. Tanatar's observations on the heat of soln. of the monoxide in acids agree with the chemical individuality of the monoxide ; the heat of formation of 3 mols of the monoxide from a mol of bismuth trioxide and a gram-atom of bismuth is 11·814 Cals. If the monoxide be heated above the m.p. of bismuth in carbon dioxide, W. Herz and A. Guttmann, and S. M. Tanatar found that it decomposes into a mixture of bismuth and its trioxide. R. Schneider said that when dried in vacuo, the monoxide is only slightly oxidized by exposure to air ; while M. M. P. Muir, and S. M. Tanatar said that it is stable in dry air, but in moist air, R. Schneider, and H. Schiff noticed that it quickly acquires a film of ordinary bismuth hydroxide, and, added M. M. P. Muir, heat is at the same time evolved. If the oxide has been dried, and afterwards moistened, oxidation occurs only slowly. When heated in air, oxidation occurs without glowing—but A. Vogel, R. Schneider, and S. M. Tanatar observed a glow. The monoxide prepared from the oxalate oxidizes only slowly when heated in air. M. M. P. Muir found that oxidation in air begins at 180°, and proceeds slowly up to 220°, when it is not completed ; in oxygen, oxidation begins at 140°, and is completed at 240° ; hydrogen reduces it at 300°–310° ; and carbon monoxide at 250°. R. Schneider, and S. M. Tanatar found that the monoxide slowly decomposes under cold and rapidly under boiling water ; and under hot dil. acids, forming bismuth and bismuth salts : $3BiO+6HCl=2BiCl_3+3H_2O+Bi$. D. L. Hammick found that when heated in sulphur dioxide, it gives a reddish-brown sublimate (as does bismuth trioxide to a much less extent), which blackens on heating, contains oxygen, and may be bismuth monoxide, a lower oxide, free bismuth, or a mixture. The ultimate product is $4Bi_2O_3.3SO_3$, and no sulphide or free sulphur is formed, but a trace of sulphur trioxide is produced. Some evidence of the volatilization of the monoxide in sulphur dioxide was obtained. S. M. Tanatar found that the monoxide reduces Fehling's soln., and a soln. of potassium permanganate. M. M. P. Muir also found that alkaline permanganate oxidizes the monoxide to tetra- and penta-oxides ; and a soln. of bromine in alkali-lye oxidizes it to the trioxide and then to the pentoxide. Bismuth monoxide appears to be a feeble base in that it forms a corresponding sulphide, and also halides. R. Schneider, and M. M. P. Muir showed that bismuth separates out when the monoxide is boiled with a conc. aq. soln. of potassium hydroxide, or with an alkaline soln. of tartaric acid or glycerol.

E. Neusser doubted if the alleged monoxide really exists as a chemical individual. Metallic bismuth can be extracted from the substance by shaking with mercury. When heated for 16–18 hours in dry hydrogen sulphide, the suboxide behaves as a mixture of metal trioxide, and hydroxide, each of which is attacked by the gas at a different rate. The presence of hydroxide explains the variable composition of the suboxide and also the low density (7·16 at 22° when freshly prepared) compared with that calculated for a mixture of bismuth metal and trioxide. He was unable to accept S. M. Tanatar's observations on the thermochemistry of the monoxide since he found that the heat of the reaction with hydrochloric acid, the solubility in aq. soln. of sodium hydroxide, and the sp. magnetic susceptibility are indistinguishable from those of a mixture of a mol of the trioxide and a gram-atom of the metal. He therefore concluded that *there is no satisfactory proof of the existence of bivalent bismuth, and that the so-called compounds of bivalent bismuth are only mixtures of the metal and the trioxide.*

According to G. Agricola,[2] yellow bismuth oxide—**bismuth trioxide,** Bi_2O_3, or *bismuthous oxide*—was used as a pigment in the Middle Ages. The impure trioxide occurs in nature as the mineral *bismuth ochre.* J. G. Wallerius called the yellow pulverulent earth *ochra wismuthi ;* J. B. L. Romé de l'Isle, *mine de bismuth calciforme ;* L. A. Emmerling, *Wismuthokker ;* and J. D. Dana, **bismite.**

As indicated in connection with bismuth, the trioxide is produced when bismuth is heated in air, then, when the molten metal is continuously stirred in air, it forms a yellowish-brown powder of the trioxide ; and when bismuth is heated to its b.p. in air it forms *flowers of bismuth* or *flores bismuthi* as a lemon-yellow, flocculent powder. The trioxide is also formed when the monoxide is heated in air. The most convenient process is to heat the basic nitrate in air until it no longer loses weight. This method was used by D. Lagerhjelm,[3] R. Schneider, F. Chemnitius, and A. Classen. A similar result is obtained by heating the carbonate or sulphate. V. A. Jacquelain, and A. E. Nordenskjöld fused the hydroxide with an excess of potassium hydroxide and obtained crystals of bismuth trioxide. L. Vanino and E. Zumbusch obtained the hydroxide by dissolving bismuth nitrate (20 grms.) in water (100 c.c.) containing mannitol (7·5 grms.), adding 50 c.c. of ice-cold potassium hydroxide soln. (22 grms. in 100 c.c. of water), and finally dil. sulphuric acid until the mixture was only slightly alkaline. E. R. Darling fused the metal with sodium nitrate and passed chlorine into the fused mass. P. A. von Bonsdorff covered bismuth with water exposed to air freed from carbon dioxide, and obtained first the hydroxide and then yellow crystals of the trioxide. E. B. R. Prideaux and H. W. Hewis obtained the oxide by the corrosion of bismuth anodes in an anolyte of a sat. soln. of sodium nitrate. From one-fourth to one-half the bismuth is precipitated as oxynitrate, and the remainder in soln. is precipitated as bismuth hydroxide by running the anodic liquor into an equal vol. of $\frac{1}{2}N$-NaOH diluted about five times ; the precipitate is washed by decantation. With a 10 per cent. soln. of sodium nitrate as anodic liquor, the amount of bismuth remaining in soln. is negligible, and the precipitate consists of oxynitrate with about 30 per cent. of bismuth trioxide. The current density used was 12·5 amp. per sq. dcm., and an average of 4·6 volts. Crystals were also obtained by A. Stromeyer, and E. Frémy, by boiling the hydroxide with alkali-lye ; and M. M. P. Muir and A. Hutchinson, by boiling for 15 mins. in soln. of $2\frac{1}{2}$–3 parts of potassium cyanide with a soln. of one part of bismuth trioxide in the smallest amount of nitric acid, and repeated by treating the product with boiling potash-lye.

Analyses of bismuth-ochre, by W. A. Lampadius, A. Stelzner, G. A. Suckow, A. Carnot, and W. T. Schaller and F. L. Ransome agree with the assumption that it is an impure bismuth trioxide ; but W. T. Schaller does not consider that the evidence is at all satisfactory, and he showed that the bismuth ochres—native bismite—are more probably impure bismuth hydroxides, $Bi_2O_3.3H_2O$, or $Bi(OH)_3$. Those from San Diego Co., California, were described by C. F. Kunz, and W. T. Schaller. According to A. F. Rogers, the crystals of bismite agree with those of artificial bismuth trioxide, but W. T. Schaller and F. L. Ransome could not confirm this statement. Analyses of artificial bismuth trioxide by J. Davy, T. Thomson, D. Lagerhjelm, M. H. Klaproth, C. F. Bucholz, L. J. Proust, L. B. G. de Morveau, J. Löwe, J. C. G. de Marignac, A. Classen, and R. Schneider agree with the formula Bi_2O_3. The **colour** of bismuth ochre—probably bismuth hydroxide, *vide infra*—is greyish-white, straw-yellow, or greenish-yellow ; the artificial product is pale lemon-yellow, and, according to R. Schneider, when heated it becomes first orange-yellow and then reddish-brown. The mineral occurs massive with a conchoidal or earthy fracture ; and also as a pulverulent earth. Bismuth trioxide is dimorphous. The greyish-black **crystals** obtained by M. M. P. Muir and A. Hutchinson were small tetrahedra belonging to the cubic system ; those prepared by A. E. Nordenskjöld were rhombic with the axial ratios $a : b : c = 0.8166 : 1.0649$.

V. M. Goldschmidt described solid soln. of yttrium and bismuth oxides. W. Guertler observed that when melted bismuth trioxide is allowed to cool, the mass glows after crystallization has commenced. The cooling curve, Fig. 15, shows a break at 820°, then falls to 688°, rises to 704°, and then falls rapidly to the ordinary temp. Hence 704° represents the **transition temperature** of the II-modification to the ordinary or III-modification. This is confirmed by the heating curve, Fig. 15. The II-modification cannot be obtained at ordinary temp. Another form, the I-modification, is produced by heating bismuth trioxide in a porcelain crucible. It melts at a higher temp. than the II-form, and it is more stable, for it dissolves less readily in dil. nitric or sulphuric acid. L. Moser also said that bismuth trioxide exists in several modifications ; R. Lorenz and W. Herz made some observations on this subject.

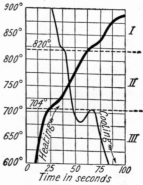

FIG. 15.—Heating and Cooling Curves of Bismuth Trioxide.

The **specific gravity** of bismuth trioxide which has been obtained by fusing the basic nitrate was found by A. Classen to be 9·044 ; P. F. G. Boullay, 8·968 ; by H. G. F. Schröder, 8·855–8·868 at 4°. W. Herapath gave 8·21 ; C. J. B. Karsten, 8·173 ; and L. Playfair and J. P. Joule, 8·079 ; A. le Royer and J. B. A. Dumas gave 8·45 for the glassy trioxide, and M. M. P. Muir and A. Hutchinson gave 8·37 for the rhombic form, and 8·828 for the cubic form. W. Guertler gave 8·20 for the sp. gr. of the II-form, and 8·55 for the III-form. D. Balareff studied the mol. vol. O. Hauser and W. Steger gave for the **specific heat** of bismuth trioxide 0·0568 at 20°–100° ; 0·0598 at 20°–204° ; 0·0604 at 20°–312° ; 0·0616 at 20°–414° ; and 0·0623 at 20°–503°. J. N. von Fuchs, and F. W. Schmidt said that the trioxide melts to an amber-yellow liquid, which, on cooling, forms a crystalline mass. T. Carnelley and J. Walker gave for the **melting point,** a temp. between 655° and 710°. W. Hempel said that **volatilization** of the trioxide occurs at a very high temp. as when it is heated by the gas-blowpipe flame. According to G. H. Bailey, if the temp. of bismuth sulphate be high enough to ensure complete decomposition, some bismuth oxide is lost by volatilization. J. Joly found that no volatilization occurs except at a very high temp. ; and A. A. Read observed no change in the composition of bismuth trioxide when heated to 1750° in an oxidizing atmosphere. E. L. Nichols and D. T. Wilber sublimed the oxide in an electric arc. W. R. Mott calculated 900° for the **boiling point.** A. Ditte and R. Metzner gave for the **heat of formation** of bismuth trioxide $(2Bi,3O)=137\cdot8$ Cals., and W. G. Mixter, 136 Cals. C. Renz found that bismuth trioxide is **photosensitive,** for, when exposed to light in the presence of glycerol, benzaldehyde, or tartaric acid dissolved in alcohol, it becomes grey and ultimately black. Reduction to a lower oxide or the metal occurs. A. Kundt gave 1·91 for the **index of refraction** of bismuth trioxide for white light. E. L. Nichols and D. T. Wilber observed no flame luminescence with the oxide. J. O. Perrine observed no ultra-violet fluorescence with bismuth oxide. A. Karl found that the oxide is triboluminescent. H. R. Robinson and A. M. Cassie studied the line spectra of secondary and tertiary X-rays produced by primary K-rays. F. Beijerinck found that the **electrical conductivity** of bismuth trioxide in compact masses is zero ; but at elevated temp., it is a conductor. F. Horton measured the effect of temp. on the electrical resistance in ohms, and the electrical conductivity in mhos of bismuth oxide melted and cast into slabs :

	225°	315°	376°	487°	535°	645°
Ohms	8×10^7	255×10^4	259,000	15,300	7,150	2,050
Mhos	$4\cdot27\times10^{-9}$	$1\cdot34\times10^{-7}$	$1\cdot32\times10^{-6}$	$2\cdot23\times10^{-5}$	$4\cdot77\times10^{-5}$	$1\cdot66\times10^{-4}$

The electrolysis of the oxide can be detected at 200°. T. W. Case found that

light has no appreciable influence on the non-conductivity of bismuth trioxide.
J. Dewar and J. A. Fleming found the **dielectric constant** was only slightly changed
by cooling the oxide to $-185°$. The **magnetic susceptibilities** of bismuth trioxide
and hydroxide given by K. Honda, and G. Meslin are -0.188×10^{-6}, and
-0.129×10^{-6} respectively; and by S. Meyer, -0.150×10^{-6}, and -0.103×10^{-6}
respectively.

A. K. Sanyal and N. R. Dhar found that the hydrated oxide is discoloured by
exposure to tropical sunlight for 20 hrs. R. Schneider observed that when bismuth
trioxide is heated in **hydrogen** it is reduced to metal; as J. C. G. de Marignac
also observed, the reduction proceeds with difficulty and at a temp. at which
some of the oxide is volatilized; and M. M. P. Muir said that at $300°$, less oxygen
is given off than corresponds with the formation of the monoxide. E. S. Meunier
found that when heated in air in contact with alkali a bismuthate is formed.
A. Mailfert said that **ozone** transforms the trioxide into pentoxide, and if alkalies
be present, the alkali bismuthate is formed. Various other oxidizing agents
—e.g. chlorine-water, and bromine-water—in the presence of alkali transform the
trioxide into the tetroxide, or pentoxide; and T. Poleck obtained bismuth
pentoxide by the action of **sodium dioxide.** For the action of **water,** vide infra.
M. M. P. Muir found that when heated in **chlorine,** bismuth trichloride and a little
oxychloride, $Bi_3O_2Cl_3$, are formed; with **bromine** vapour, the oxybromide,
$Bi_{11}O_{13}Br_7$, and a little tribromide are produced. J. L. Gay Lussac found that
iodine transforms the trioxide into triiodide. The equilibrium between the halogen
acids—**hydrochloric and hydriodic acids**—was studied by M. M. P. Muir. W. Jacobs
studied the action of hydrochloric acid. E. A. Atkinson found that **hydrobromic
acid** converts heated bismuth trioxide into tribromide. When the trioxide is
heated with **sulphur,** some trisulphide is formed, and when heated in a current of
hydrogen sulphide, O. Schumann said that the sulphide, Bi_4S_3, is produced (q.v.).
L. Moser and E. Neusser said that the reaction is not complete. D. L. Hammick
observed that when heated in **sulphur dioxide,** bismuth trioxide yields first a black
powder, which contains sulphate and gives bismuth on treatment with hydrochloric
acid; it is a mixture of a bismuth sulphate with either bismuth monoxide, free
bismuth, or both oxide and bismuth. The ultimate product is $4Bi_2O_3.3SO_3$;
and no sulphide or free sulphur is formed, and only a trace of sulphur trioxide.
G. Oddo and E. Serra found that **sulphur chloride** converts the heated trioxide
into trichloride. Hydrated bismuth trioxide readily transforms a number of
metal **sulphides** into oxides—e.g. arsenic trisulphide. G. Gore said that bismuth
trioxide, or rather the hydroxide, is insoluble in liquid **ammonia.** M. M. P. Muir
showed that when heated with ammonia the trioxide is reduced to the metal, and,
added A. Gutbier and L. Birckenbach, particularly if silver and quartz-sand be
present. A similar result occurs with **ammonium chloride;** and R. H. Brett
said that the freshly precipitated hydroxide is soluble in a soln. of ammonium
chloride, but not in one of **ammonium nitrate.** A. Michaelis observed that when the
trioxide is heated with **phosphorus trichloride** in a sealed tube, at $160°$, bismuth
phosphate, and phosphoryl and bismuthyl chlorides are formed. W. R. Schoeller
found that **bismuth trisulphide** readily reacts with the trioxide at $965°$—either in
a current of carbon dioxide, or below molten sodium chloride in a crucible. Sulphur
dioxide is evolved at a comparatively low temp., and globules of bismuth are
formed. The yield of bismuth is 90 per cent., and a little basic bismuth sulphate
is formed. The trioxide is readily reduced to the metal by **carbon,** and
M. M. P. Muir found that the reduction with **carbon monoxide** begins at $200°$;
F. Schlagdenhauffen and C. Pagel found that dry bismuth trioxide is not altered
by carbon monoxide at $230°$, but at $400°$ is reduced to the monoxide without forming
the metal—vide bismuth. R. H. Purcell found that by the intensive drying of
carbon monoxide, the temp. of reduction was increased from $175°$ to $430°$.
F. J. Brislee also studied the reaction—vide bismuth suboxide. W Müller
observed that the trioxide is slowly but completely reduced by **methane.**

H. Rose found that fused **potassium cyanide** reduces the trioxide to metal; J. Milbauer, that molten **potassium thiocyanate** furnishes microcrystalline bismuth trisulphide and potassium metasulphobismuthate; and J. N. Pring, that **aluminium carbide** reduces it to metal. N. Tarugi, and H. Moissan observed that **calcium carbide** reduces the trioxide to bismuth free from calcium. W. Eidmann found that the trioxide is insoluble in **acetone.** Combinations with **organic compounds** have been obtained. Thus, P. Thibault prepared complexes with gallic acid; and L. Lévy observed coloured products with morphine, codeïne, and other alkaloids. J. Spiller found that bismuth hydroxide is not precipitated in the presence of **sodium nitrate.** L. Kahlenberg and W. J. Trautmann observed a slow reaction when the trioxide is heated with **silicon.** W. Hempel showed that the molten trioxide decomposes **silicates;** and G. Rauter, that at 270°–280° in a sealed tube with **silicon tetrachloride** part of the trioxide is decomposed, forming silica and bismuth trichloride. F. Kuwa examined the colouring effect on glass.

J. L. Gay Lussac and L. J. Thénard observed that **potassium** reduces the heated trioxide to the metal. The reaction is accompanied by incandescence. Similar results were obtained with **sodium.** A. Stavenhagen and E. Schuchard observed that when the trioxide is heated with powdered **aluminium,** the reduction occurs with explosive violence. F. W. Schmidt found that the trioxide is reduced to black bismuth monoxide by **alkali stannites.** This reaction has been previously indicated; if an excess of reducing agent is used, bismuth itself is formed. M. M. P. Muir said that **potassium permanganate** in alkaline soln. oxidizes the trioxide slowly; and conversely, R. Schneider observed that manganese oxide is converted by bismuth tetroxide and nitric acid into permanganate. J. Knox found that when bismuth trioxide is shaken for 2–3 weeks with soln. of **sodium hydroxide,** colourless soln. are obtained free from opalescence. The amount of trioxide dissolved is proportional to the conc. of the alkali-lye; thus, 100 c.c. of soln. with 1·0, 2·0, and 3·0 mols of sodium hydroxide per litre, dissolved respectively 0·0013, 0·0026, and 0·0049 grm. of bismuth trioxide. According to L. Moser, freshly precipitated bismuth hydroxide is practically insoluble in soln. of sodium hydroxide up to N-NaOH at 20°; slightly soluble in soln. up to $4N$-NaOH; and markedly so in more conc. soln. At 100°, the solubility is greater, but still small in dil. soln. Thus, for the solubility of freshly precipitated bismuth hydroxide (grams of Bi per litre) a soln. of sodium hydroxide (grams per litre), L. Moser gave:

NaOH .	400	320	240	200	160	120	80	40	20
Bi { 20°	0·16	0·11	0·11	0·10	0·08	0·07	0·04	trace	0
Bi { 100°	1·70	1·20	—	0·50	0·50	—	0·35	0·20	0·15

J. Knox obtained similar results with soln. of **potassium hydroxide.** Expressing conc. as before, L. Moser gave:

KOH .	560	448	336	280	224	168	112	56	28
Bi { 20°	0·14	0·11	0·11	0·10	0·08	0·06	0·03	trace	0
Bi { 100°	1·65	1·20	—	0·50	0·50	—	0·3	0·02	0·15

Hence, bismuth trioxide behaves as a weak base, but, in agreement with its more electropositive character, its basic character is weaker than the corresponding oxides of antimony and arsenic. Bismuthyl hydroxide, BiO.OH, or $Bi_2O_3.H_2O$, is a weak base. According to M. Lebaigue, when hydrated bismuth trioxide is boiled for a quarter of an hour with certain **metal salt** soln., the hydroxides are precipitated— *e.g.* from soln. of aluminium, chromic, or ferric salts—soln. of cupric, zinc, lead, manganese, ferrous, cobalt, or nickel salts. He therefore proposed to employ the process for the separation of metals in analyses, but J. Alog showed that the precipitation of the metals just indicated is complete only under certain conditions, and that other metals are partially precipitated either as oxides or basic salts. E. Laborde and co-workers found that radioactive compounds of radium, mesothorium, or thorium, precipitated with bismuth oxide, enhance its catalytic activity. J. A. Hedvall and N. von Zweigbergk studied the action of **barium**

dioxide on bismuth trioxide ; and F. de Carli found that bismuth trioxide reacts when heated with barium oxide, but not with the oxides of calcium, lead, zinc, or cadmium.

N. R. Dhar and S. Gosh found that bismuth hydroxide is peptized by alkalilye along with starch, glycerol, sugar, etc. According to W. Biltz, if a soln. of bismuth nitrate be diluted with water as long as no precipitation occurs, and the soln. dialyzed, a **colloidal solution** of bismuth trioxide is formed. C. Paal and L. di Pol found sodium protalbate to be an effective protective agent in the preparation of the colloidal soln.—*vide supra*, colloidal bismuth. L. Hugounenq and J. Loiseleur found that bismuth oxide is peptized by glycogen in the cold. Commercial colloidal bismuth hydroxide has the commercial name *bismon*. A. Kuhn and H. Pirsch studied the peptization of bismuth hydroxide with sucrose, mannitol, glycerol, and lactose—*vide infra*, bismuth sulphide. Kalle and Co. also obtained **organosols** of the trioxide—*vide supra*, colloidal bismuth. Bismuth trioxide is considered to be insoluble in water, and M. M. P. Muir and co-workers said that it does not pass into the hydrated oxide when exposed to moist air, or confined under water. G. Almkvist said that a litre of water at 20° dissolves 1·44 mgrms. of bismuthyl hydroxide, BiO.OH. T. Carnelley and J. Walker found that when a soln. of the normal nitrate is precipitated by ammonia in the cold, and the product dried in air, the composition approximates to that of normal **bismuth hydroxide,** $Bi(OH)_3$, or *trihydrated bismuth trioxide*, $Bi_2O_3.3H_2O$, or *orthobismuthous acid*, H_3BO_3. M. M. P. Muir and D. Carnegie recommended dissolving bismuth nitrate in the smallest possible quantity of dil. nitric acid, pouring the soln. into an excess of conc. aq. ammonia, and washing the precipitate first with water, then with a dil. soln. of sodium carbonate, and finally with water. L. Moser said that the best way to make the normal hydroxide free from basic salts is to run a glycerol soln. of a bismuth salt into sodium hydroxide and immediately to neutralize the whole excess of alkali with dil. nitric or acetic acid. If sulphuric acid is used, as recommended by P. Thibault, some basic sulphate is formed. The precipitate after washing with a little alcohol, and drying in air, has the composition $Bi(OH)_3$. It readily absorbs carbon dioxide from air. The loss of water over sulphuric acid is quite continuous, no arrest occurs at BiO.OH. R. Lorenz found bismuth forms a film of hydroxide when made the anode in the electrolysis of aq. soln. of alkali chlorides, nitrates, or sulphates. T. Carnelley and J. Walker observed that the white powder loses water quite regularly on a rising temp., up to 415°, when the composition approximates $B_2O_3.H_2O$; at 400°, all the water is expelled. M. M. P. Muir and co-workers said that all the water is driven off at 100°. J. Thomsen gave for the heat of formation : $2Bi+3O_{gas}+3H_2O_{liq.}=2Bi(OH)_3$ $+2\times68\cdot9$. R. Robl observed no perceptible fluorescence with the metabismuthous acid, $HBiO_2$, exposed to ultra-violet light. G. Almkvist gave 1·44 mgrm. per litre for the solubility of BiO(OH) in water.

According to W. T. Schaller the bismuth ochres—bismite—are grey, yellow, or green, pulverulent masses which under the microscope appear to be homogeneous and amorphous, but not transparent. The composition corresponds with more or less impure bismuth hydroxide, $Bi(OH)_3$, not the trioxide, Bi_2O_3. The combined water is not given off at 210°, but it is expelled on ignition at a red-heat. F. L. Ransome, and W. T. Schaller described some Nevada bismite as occurring in pearly scales which are probably trigonal.

According to M. M. P. Muir, if a soln. of bismuth pentoxide in hydrochloric acid be treated with sulphur dioxide, and then with potash-lye, and the precipitate exposed under water to sunlight, there is formed a yellowish-white powder, which, when dried over sulphuric acid, in vacuo, has the composition of *dihydrated bismuth trioxide*, $Bi_2O_3.2H_2O$, or *pyrobismuthous acid*, $H_4Bi_2O_5$. T. Carnelley and J. Walker observed no evidence of the formation of this compound on the heating curve of the normal hydroxide. According to A. E. Arppe, if a soln. of bismuth nitrate be poured into potash-lye, and the mixture heated for a time, the precipitate, after washing with water and drying at 100°, has the composition of *monohydrated bismuth trioxide*, $Bi_2O_3.H_2O$; *metabismuthous acid*, $HBiO_2$; or *bismuthyl hydroxide*, BiO.OH. These products represent different stages in the drying of colloidal hydrated bismuth trioxide. If the temp. of the alkaline liquor be over 70°, the yellow trioxide is formed. A. Stromeyer, and J. Löwe said that if the trichloride be used, some oxychloride is precipitated as well. E. B. R. Prideaux and H. W. Hewis obtained the hydrated oxide by pouring a soln. of bismuth nitrate into dil. alkalilye ; and E. Moles and R. Portillo, by precipitating an acetic soln. of bismuth nitrate with conc. ammonia. H Meerwein observed no complex formation with alcohol. P. Thibault said that the hydroxide, bismuth oxide, prepared by the addition of an alkali to a soln. of bismuth nitrate or chloride, always contains some basic nitrate or chloride. It may, however, be obtained free from these compounds by taking advantage of the fact that bismuth oxide is soluble in a soln. of potassium hydroxide which contains glycerol. Bismuth nitrate is intimately mixed with glycerol, water is added until the salt is entirely dissolved, and then potassium hydroxide until the precipitated oxide is redissolved. If dil. sulphuric acid is then added, a precipitate of bismuth oxide is produced, which is entirely free from any combined acid, and after drying in air, or in a vacuum over sulphuric acid, or at 100°–105°, has the composition $Bi_2O_3.H_2O$. E. Zumbusch prepared the hydroxide by this process. H. Schiff said that this oxide is produced when moist bismuth monoxide is exposed to air, while M. M. P. Muir found that the dihydrated oxide is so formed. T. Carnelley and J. Walker observed a small break in the heating curve, near 415°, corresponding with the formation of the monohydrate. A. K. Sanyal and N. R. Dhar found that the hydroxide is blackened after 20 hrs.' exposure to tropical sunlight.

L. Belladen[4] studied the f.p. curve of mixtures of lead monoxide and bismuth trioxide. The results are summarized in Fig. 16 ; they show the existence of an unstable **lead metaoctobismuthite,** $PbO.4Bi_2O_3$, or $PbBi_8O_{13}$, melting with decomposition at 695° ; **lead mesohexabismuthite,** $Pb_2Bi_6O_{11}$, or $2PbO.3Bi_2O_3$, melting at 686° ; and **lead pyrobismuthite,** $2PbO.Bi_2O_3$, or $Pb_2Bi_2O_5$, melting at 625°.

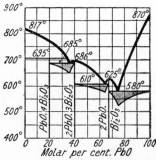

FIG. 16.—Freezing-point Curve of Mixtures, $PbO–Bi_2O_3$.

C. W. Balke and E. F. Smith[5] obtained what they regarded as **ammonium bismuthotungstate,** $3(NH_4)_2O.2Bi_2O_3.11WO_3.10H_2O$, from a soln. of bismuth hydroxide in a boiling soln. of ammonium paratungstate. The yellow oil, when dried, forms a yellow, transparent, vitreous mass. The corresponding **potassium bismuthotungstate,** $3K_2O.2Bi_2O_3.11WO_3.15H_2O$, is an oil which dries to a pale yellow, transparent, vitreous mass ; and **strontium bismuthotungstate,** $3SrO.2Bi_2O_3.11WO_3.11H_2O$, is an oil which solidifies to a wax-like mass ; and when dried at 100°, it furnishes a hard yellow, vitreous mass, insoluble in water.

REFERENCES.

[1] T. Thomson, *Proc. Glasgow Phil. Soc.*, **1**. 4, 1842 ; W. Heintz, *Liebig's Ann.*, **52**. 252, 1844 ; *Pogg. Ann.*, **63**. 58, 1844 ; A. E. Arppe, *ib.*, **64**. 237, 1845 ; *Dissertatio de jodato bismutico*, Helsingfors, 1843 ; *Akad. Handl. Stockholm*, 133, 1842 ; S. M. Tanatar, *Zeit. anorg. Chem.*, **27**. 304, 437, 1901 ; E. Neusser, *ib.*, **135**. 313, 1924 ; **138**. 180, 1924 ; W. Herz and A. Guttmann, *ib.*, **53**. 63, 1907 ; *Zeit. anal. Chem.*, **54**. 103, 413, 1915 ; J. J. Berzelius, *Lehrbuch der Chemie*, Dresden, **2**. 574, 1826 ; *Gilbert's Ann.*, **40**. 286, 1812 ; *Schweigger's Journ.*, **7**. 70, 1814 ; A. Vogel, *Kastner's Arch.*, **23**. 68, 1832 ; H. Schiff, *Liebig's Ann.*, **119**. 331, 1861 ; R. Bunsen, *ib.*, **138**. 277, 1866 ; F. Hartl, *Beiträge zur Chemie des Goldes und des Wismuts*, München, 1906 ; L. Vanino and F. Hartl, *Journ. prakt. Chem.*, (2), **74**. 142, 1906 ; M. M. P. Muir, *Journ. Chem. Soc.*, **32**. 128, 1877 ; **39**. 28, 1881 ; F. J. Brislee, *ib.*, **93**. 154, 1908 ; D. L. Hammick, *ib.*, **111**. 379, 1917 ; C. F. Schlagdenhauffen and C. Pagel, *Compt. Rend.*, **128**. 309, 1899 ; R. Schneider, *Pogg. Ann.*,

88. 45, 1853; *Journ. prakt. Chem.*, (2), 58. 562, 1898; (2), 60. 524, 1898; A. Jaworososky, *Russ. Journ. Pharm.*, 35. 359, 1896; E. Zumbusch, *Ueber Wismut*, München, 1911; L. Vanino and E. Zumbusch, *Arch. Pharm.*, 248. 665, 1910; L. Vanino and F. Treubert, *Ber.*, 31. 113, 2267, 1898; 32. 1072, 1899; *Zeit. anal. Chem.*, 53. 564, 1914; 54. 255, 1915; J. Löwe, *Zeit. anal. Chem.*, 22. 498, 1883; A. Lottermoser, *Ueber anorganische Colloide*, Stuttgart, 1901; A. Hilger and P. A. von Scherpenberg, *Mett. Erlanger Pharm. Inst.*, 2. 4, 7, 1889; J. L. Proust, *Journ. Phys.*, 59. 328, 1804; H. Davy, *The Elements of Chemical Philosophy*, London, 406, 1812.

² G. Agricola, *Bermannus sive de re metallica*, Basileæ, 1558; J. G. Wallerius, *Mineralogia*, Paris, 2. 209, 1753; J. B. L. Romé de l'Isle, *Cristallographie*, Paris, 3. 113, 1783; L. A. Emmerling, *Lehrbuch der Mineralogie*, Giessen, 2. 400, 1796; J. D. Dana, *A System of Mineralogy*, New York, 185, 1868.

³ D. Lagerhjelm, *Akad. Handl. Stockholm.*, 34. 219, 1813; *Ann. Phil.*, 4. 358, 1814; *Schweiger's Journ.*, 17. 416, 1816; A. E. Arppe, *Pogg. Ann.*, 64. 237, 1845; *Dissertatio de jodeto bismuthico*, Helsingfors, 1843; *Akad. Handl. Stockholm*, 133, 1842; A. Classen, *Journ. prakt. Chem.*, (2), 43. 133, 1891; *Ber.*, 23. 938, 1890; V. A. Jacquelain, *Ann. Chim. Phys.*, (2), 64. 113, 1837; A. E. Nordenskjöld, *Oefvers. Akad. Stockholm*, 17. 447, 1860; *Pogg. Ann.*, 114. 622, 1861; A. Stromeyer, *ib.*, 26. 549, 1832; E. Moles and R. Portillo, *Anal. Fis. Quim.*, 21. 401, 1923; 22. 187, 1924; M. M. P. Muir and A. Hutchinson, *Journ. Chem. Soc.*, 55. 143, 1889; M. M. P. Muir, G. B. Hoffmeister, and C. E. Robbs, *Chem. News*, 42. 242, 1880; *Journ. Chem. Soc.*, 39. 24, 1881; M. M. P. Muir and D. Carnegie, *ib.*, 51. 79, 1887; M. M. P. Muir, *ib.*, 31. 28, 647, 1877; 35. 335, 1879; 39. 28, 1891; T. Carnelley and J. Walker, *ib.*, 53. 86, 1888; J. N. Pring, *ib.*, 87. 1520, 1905; F. J. Brislee, *ib.*, 93. 154, 1908; J. Knox, *ib.*, 95. 1760, 1909; G. H. Bailey, *ib.*, 51. 680, 1887; A. A. Read, *ib.*, 65. 313, 1894; D. L. Hammick, *ib.*, 111. 379, 1917; P. Thibault, *Journ. Chim. Pharm.*, (6), 12. 559, 1900; *Bull. Soc. Chim.*, (3), 29. 680, 1903; J. Alog, *ib.*, (3), 27. 136, 1902; W. Guertler, *Zeit. anorg. Chem.*, 37. 222, 1903; O. Hauser and W. Steger, *ib.*, 80. 1, 1913; J. Milbauer, *ib.*, 42. 433, 1905; G. Almkvist, *ib.*, 103. 240, 1918; L. Moser, *ib.*, 61. 379, 1909; A. K. Sanyal and N. R. Dhar, *ib.*, 128. 212, 1923; N. R. Dhar and S. Ghosh, *ib.*, 152. 409, 1926; R. Lorenz and W. Herz, *ib.*, 135. 374, 1924; J. Löwe, *Zeit. anal. Chem.*, 22. 498, 1883; W. Hempel, *ib.*, 20. 496, 1881; A. Michaelis, *Journ. prakt. Chem.*, (2), 4. 454, 1871; D. Balareff, *ib.*, (2), 102. 283, 1921; R. Schneider, *ib.*, (2), 23. 86, 1881; (2), 30. 240, 1884; (2), 42. 133, 1890; (2), 44. 23, 1891; (2), 50. 461, 1892; *Pogg. Ann.*, 82. 303, 1851; W. Müller, *ib.*, 122. 145, 1864; H. Rose, *ib.*, 90. 199, 1853; J. C. G. de Marignac, *Ann. Chim. Phys.*, (6), 1. 289, 1884; H. R. Robinson and A. M. Cassie, *Proc. Roy. Soc.*, 113. A, 282, 1926; O. Schumann, *Liebig's Ann.*, 187. 313, 1877; G. Rauter, *ib.*, 270. 251, 1892; H. Schiff, *ib.*, 119. 335, 1861; R. Robl, *Zeit. angew. Chem.*, 39. 608, 1926; W. R. Schoeller, *Journ. Soc. Chem. Ind.*, 34. 6, 1915; J. N. von Fuchs, *Schweiger's Journ.*, 67. 429, 1833; C. J. B. Karsten, *ib.*, 65. 320, 394, 1832; F. W. Schmidt, *Ber.*, 27. 236, 1894; T. Poleck, *ib.*, 27. 1051, 1894; J. Thomsen, *ib.*, 16. 42, 1883; W. Biltz, *ib.*, 35. 4431, 1902; A. Mailfert, *Compt. Rend.*, 93. 863, 1882; A. Carnot, *ib.*, 79. 478, 1874; E. Laborde, J. Bressolles, and L. Jaloustre, *ib.*, 183. 354, 1926; L. Lévy, *ib.*, 103. 1196, 1886; H. Moissan, *ib.*, 114. 617, 1892; 125. 839, 1897; F. Schlagdenhauffen and C. Pagel, *ib.*, 128. 309, 1899; A. Ditte and R. Metzner, *ib.*, 115. 1303, 1892; E. Frémy, *Journ. Pharm. Chim.*, (3), 3. 30, 1843; *Ann. Chim. Phys.*, (3), 12. 493, 1844; *Compt. Rend.*, 15. 1108, 1842; E. S. Meunier, *ib.*, 60. 557, 1252, 1863; J. L. Gay Lussac, *Ann. Phys. Chim.*, (1), 91. 56, 1814; J. L. Gay Lussac and L. J. Thénard, *Recherches physicochimiques*, Paris, 1. 261, 1811; L. Schneider, *Monatsh.*, 8. 242, 1888; A. Gutbier and L. Birckenbach, *Zeit. Elektrochem.*, 11. 831, 1905; *Journ. prakt. Chem.*, (2), 47. 457, 1908; L. Birckenbach, *Ueber das Atomgewichte des Wismuths*, Erlangen, 1905; W. M. Mott, *Trans. Amer. Electrochem. Soc.*, 34. 255, 1918; L. Kahlenberg and W. J. Trautmann, *ib.*, 39. 377, 1921; A. le Royer and J. B. A. Dumas, *Journ. Pharm. Chim.*, (2), 92. 408, 1821; M. Lebaigue, *ib.*, (3), 39. 51, 1861; *Chem. News*, 3. 147, 1861; H. G. F. Schröder, *Dichtigkeitsmessungen*, Heidelberg, 1873; *Wied. Ann.*, 11. 997, 1880; W. G. Mixter, *Amer. Journ. Science*, (4), 28. 103, 1908; C. F. Kunz, *ib.*, (4), 16. 398, 1903; F. L. Ransome, *Prof. Paper U.S. Geol. Sur.*, 66. 121, 1909; W. T. Schaller and F. L. Ransome, *Amer. Journ. Science*, (4), 29. 173, 1910; W. T. Schaller, *Journ. Amer. Chem. Soc.*, 33. 162, 1911; *Science*, (2), 19. 266, 1904; *Bull. U.S. Geol. Sur.*, 490, 1911; A. Kundt, *Sitzber. Akad. Berlin*, 255, 1888; A. K. Sanyal and N. R. Dhar, *Zeit. anorg. Chem.*, 128. 212, 1923; J. Davy, *Phil. Trans.*, 102. 169, 1812; R. Lorenz, *Zeit. anorg. Chem.*, 12. 436, 1896; J. A. Hedvall and N. von Zweigbergk, *ib.*, 108. 119, 1919; T. Thomson, *Proc. Glasgow Phil. Soc.*, 1. 4, 1842; L. B. G. de Morveau, *Ann. Chim. Phys.*, (1), 69. 261, 1809; P. F. G. Boullay, *ib.*, (2), 43. 266, 1830; J. L. Proust, *Journ. Phys.*, 59. 328, 1804; M. H. Klaproth, *Beiträge zur chemischen Kenntniss der Mineralkörper*, Berlin, 2. 294, 1797; C. F. Bucholz, *Grundriss der Pharmezie mit vorzirglecher Hinsicht auf die pharmazeutische Chemie*, Erfert, 368, 1819; F. Horton, *Phil. Mag.*, (6), 11. 505, 1906; C. Paal and L. di Pol, *Ber.*, 59. 3, 874, 877. 1926; G. A. Suckow, *Dir Verwitterung im Mineralreiche*, Leipzig, 14, 1848; J. Joly, *Phil. Mag.*, (6), 27. 1, 1914; *Chem. News*, 107. 241, 1913; W. A. Lampadius, *Handbuch der Chemischen Analyse der Mineralkörper*, Freyberg, 288, 1801; A. Stelzner, *Zeit. deut. geol. Ges.*, 49. 134, 1897; P. A. von Bonsdorff, *Pogg. Ann.*, 41. 305, 1837; F. Beijerinck, *Neues Jahrb. Min. B.B.*, 11. 442, 1897; W. Herapath, *Phil. Mag.*, (1), 64. 321, 1824; R. H. Brett, *ib.*, (3), 10. 98, 335, 1837; L. Playfair and J. P. Joule, *Mem. Chem. Soc.*, 3. 57, 1848; Kalle and Co., *German Pat.*, *D.R.P.* 164663, 1905; 172683, 1906; *Pharm. Centrh.*, 44. 552, 1903; E. A. Atkinson, *Journ. Amer. Chem. Soc.*, 20. 797, 1898; T. W. Case, *Phys. Rev.*, (2), 9. 305, 1917; C. Renz, *Helvetica Chim. Acta.*, 4. 961, 1921; K. Faux,

Journ. Japan. Cer. Soc., **32**. 18, 1924 ; G. Oddo and E. Serra, *Gazz. Chim. Ital.*, **29. ii**, 355, 1899 ; L. Moser and E. Neusser, *Chem. Ztg.*, **47**. 541, 1923 ; V. M. Goldschmidt, *Skrift. Norske Akad.*, **7**, 1925 ; N. Tarugi, *ib.*, **29**. i, 509, 1899 ; E. R. Darling, *U.S. Pat. No.* 1354806, 1920 ; A. Kuhn and H. Pirsch, *Koll. Zeit.*, **36**. 310, 1925 ; *Koll. Chem. Berhefte*, **21**. 78, 1925 ; A. Stavenhegen and E. Schuchard, *Ber.*, **53**, 909, 1902 ; E. L. Nichols and D. T. Wilber, *Phys. Rev.*, (2), **17**. 707, 1921 ; J. O. Perrine, *ib.*, (2), **22**. 48, 1923 ; G. Gore, *Proc. Roy. Soc.*, **21**. 140, 1873 ; F. de Carli, *Atti Accad. Lincei*, (6), **1**. 533, 1925 ; W. Jacobs, *Chem. Weekbl.*, **14**. 208, 1917 ; L Hugounenq and J. Loiseleur, *Compt. Rend.*, **182**. 851, 1926 ; A. Karl, *ib.*, **146**. 1104, 1908 ; E. Zumbusch, *Ueber Wismut*, München, 1911 ; L. Vanino and E. Zumbusch, *Arch. Pharm.*, **248**. 665, 1910 ; A. F. Rogers, *School Mines Quart.*, **31**. 208, 1910 ; J. Spiller, *Journ. Chem. Soc.*, **10**. 110, 1858 ; *Chem. News*, **8**. 280, 1863 ; **19**. 166, 1869 ; E. B. R. Prideaux and H. W. Hewis, *Journ. Soc. Chem. Ind.*, **41**. 167, T, 1922 ; K. Honda, *Ann. Physik*, (4), **32**. 1027, 1910 ; *Science Rep. Tohoku Univ.*, **1**. 1, 1912 ; **2**. 25, 1913 ; **3**. 139, 223, 1914 ; **4**. 215, 1915 ; S. Meyer, *Wied. Ann.*, **67**. 707, 1899 ; **68**. 325, 1899 ; **69**. 236, 1899 ; *Ann. Physik*, (4), **1**. 664, 1900 ; *Sitzber. Akad. Wien*, **106**. 595, 1899 ; **108**. 171, 1899 ; G. Meslin, *Ann. Chim. Phys.*, (8), **7**. 145, 1906 ; F. Chemnitius, *Pharm. Centr.*, **68**. 513, 1927 ; H. Meerwein, *Liebig's Ann.*, **455**. 227, 1927 ; G. Almkvist, *Zeit. anorg. Chem.*, **103**. 240, 1908 ; J. Dewar and J. A. Fleming, *Proc. Roy. Soc.*, **61**. 368, 1897 ; R. H. Peircell, *Journ. Chem. Soc.*, 1207, 1928 ; T. W. Case, *Phys. Rev.*, (2), **9**. 305, 1917 ; W. Eidmann, *Ein Beitrag zur Kenntnis des Verhaltens chemischer Verbindungen in nichtwässerigen Lösungen*, Giessen, 1899 ; F. Kuwa, *Journ. Japan. Cer. Soc.*, **32**. 5, 1924.
⁴ L. Belladen, *Gazz. Chim. Ital.*, **52**. ii, 160, 1922.
⁵ C. W. Balke and E. F. Smith, *Journ. Amer. Chem. Soc.*, **25**. 1229, 1903.

§ 9. The Higher Oxides of Bismuth

In 1818, C. F. Bucholz and R. Brandes [1] showed that when bismuth trioxide is heated with an excess of an alkali hydroxide in air, the trioxide takes up oxygen, forming what was called *bismuth peroxide*. Subsequent workers were not agreed as to the composition of the oxide remaining after the alkali had been washed away. The end-product of the oxidation is probably **bismuth pentoxide**, Bi_2O_5, but various intermediate stages of the oxidation have been regarded as definite compounds— Bi_4O_7 of M. M. P. Muir, and G. André ; Bi_4O_8—or $(Bi_2O_4)_2$ or $(BiO_2)_4$—Bi_4O_9 of A. Stromeyer, C. Hoffmann, and A. E. Arppe as well as G. André's $Bi_{10}O_{23}.6H_2O$; and Bi_4O_{10}—or Bi_2O_5. J. Lorch was unable to wash out all the alkali, and he therefore supposed the product of the operation to be an alkali bismuthate. Later observations, however, have shown that the only stable oxides concerned in the oxidation of the trioxide are **bismuth tetroxide**, Bi_2O_4, *bismuth dioxide*, BiO_2, and bismuth pentoxide.

The formation of bismuth tetroxide.—C. F. Schönbein obtained the tetroxide by oxidizing bismuth with ozone ; and A. Mailfert, by oxidizing bismuth trioxide with ozone. M. M. P. Muir oxidized bismuth monoxide with potassium permanganate and obtained a mixture of tetra- and penta-oxides. C. F. Bucholz and R. Brandes, V. A. Jacquelain, and E. Frémy obtained the tetroxide by melting the trioxide with an excess of alkali hydroxide while exposed to air ; and E. Frémy, and L. Schneider added potassium chlorate as oxidizing agent. I. Meschtschersky heated the trioxide with barium, calcium, or magnesium oxide mixed with potassium chlorate or nitrate ; and R. Böttger fused the basic nitrate with the alkali hydroxide. In a number of modes of formation of the tetroxide, bismuth trioxide, the dioxide, oxychloride, or oxynitrate is suspended in alkalilye and treated with an oxidizing agent—*e.g.*, the processes of G. André, A. E. Arppe, C. Deichler, A. Gutbier and R. Bünz, W. Heintz, A. Hilger and P. A. von Scherpenberg, C. Hoffmann, V. A. Jacquelain, J. Lorch, and M. M. P. Muir. C. Schrader used chlorine or bromine ; C. Deichler, and A. Gutbier and R. Bünz, used electrolytic chlorine developed in the presence of the alkali hydroxide ; A. E. Arppe, R. Brandes, V. A. Jacquelain, E. Rupp and G. Schaumann, H. Schiff, C. Schrader, and A. Stromeyer boiled the liquor with hypochlorites— C. Schrader said that the oxidation does not occur at ordinary temp. ; C. Deichler, A. Gutbier and R. Bünz, and E. Rupp and G. Schaumann used potassium persulphate ; J. Lorch used chlorine and sodium dioxide jointly ; and L. Vanino

and O. Hauser, and A. Gutbier and R. Bünz, potassium ferricyanide.
K. Hasebroek, E. Rupp and G. Schaumann, L. Moser, L. Vanino and O. Hauser,
A. Gutbier and R. Bünz, J. Hanus and O. Kallauner, and P. Jannasch oxidized
bismuth salt soln. with an ammoniacal soln. of hydrogen dioxide, and obtained a
yellow or orange precipitate, but, added J. Lorch, the yield is very small.   J. Hanus
and O. Kallauner used sodium dioxide for the oxidation.   An acid soln. of bismuth
trioxide was found by C. F. Schönbein to be more or less oxidized by hydrogen
dioxide ; J. Lorch, and T. Polcck said that sodium dioxide alone has only a slight
oxidizing action on bismuth hydroxide or basic nitrate ; and similarly also when
sodium dioxide is fused with the trioxide.   C. Deichler observed no effect with
barium dioxide.   The tetroxide was found by W. Wernicke, C. Luckow, J. Lorch,
L. Schucht, A. Hollard, M. Bose, A. Classen, and C. Deichler to be deposited on the
anode during the electrolysis of neutral or alkaline soln. of a bismuth salt with a
feeble current.   A. Gutbier and co-workers obtained a light brown amorphous
powder containing 97·93 per cent. Bi_2O_3 and about 2 per cent. of active oxygen.
C. E. Corfield and E. Woodward obtained bismuth tetroxide by the action of
nitric acid on sodium bismuthate.   The dihydrate could not be reduced to the
monohydrate without simultaneous decomposition—*vide infra*, the preparation of
bismuth pentoxide.   C. H. D. Bödeker found that the oxidized product is obtained by
the action of a soln. of potassium cyanide on bismuth nitrate ; W. Foster, by heating
bismuth ferrocyanide with sodium hypobromite ; and by M. M. P. Muir, by the
action of chlorine or bromine on a soln. of bismuth ferricyanide.   M. M. P. Muir
and co-workers' directions for preparing bismuth tetroxide are :

Bismuth trioxide is suspended in a large excess of potash-lye of about 1·35 sp. gr. ;
the potash-lye is kept nearly boiling, and chlorine is passed in until the precipitate is
homogeneous, and of a dark chocolate-red colour ; the precipitate is washed free from
potash-lye with hot water, kept in contact with dil. nitric acid (about 1 acid to 20 water)
for 12–16 hrs. until the colour of the solid has changed to brownish-yellow, washed free
from acid, boiled for about an hour with a strong soln. of sodium, or calcium, hypochlorite (preferably the former), till a perfectly homogeneous yellow-brown, heavy powder
is produced, which settles readily.   This is washed with hot water till free from chlorine and
alkali.   When dried at 100° or over sulphuric acid, the composition approximates
$Bi_2O_4.2H_2O$; and when dried at 180°–200° for two or three hours, Bi_2O_4.   The prolonged
digestion with nitric acid serves to dissolve any bismuth trioxide which may have escaped
oxidation, and also to deoxidize the bismuth pentoxide which has been formed ; subsequent
treatment with the alkaline hypochlorite appears to convert any traces of bismuth trioxide
yet present into bismuth tetroxide.

C. Deichler recommended alkali-lye of sp. gr. 1·05–1·35, and at a temp. of 95°–100°.
According to A. Gutbier and R. Bünz, the results obtained by the action of chlorine
on bismuth hydroxide suspended in hot, conc. alkali-lye, and the product treated
with conc. nitric acid to remove the lower oxide, are greatly influenced by the nature
and conc. of the alkali-lye.   The best results with chlorine were obtained by the
action with a large excess of conc. potash-lye of sp. gr. 1·4.   No product of uniform
composition could be isolated ; and the same remarks apply to the oxidation with
potassium persulphate ; and ferricyanide as oxidizing agents.   R. R. L. Worsley
and P. W. Robertson obtained a mixture of $Bi_2O_4.2H_2O$ and of $Bi_2O_5.H_2O$ by the
action of chlorine on the trioxide suspended in boiling alkali-lye ; and a mixture of
Bi_2O_4 and $Bi_2O_4.H_2O$ with a trace of Bi_2O_6 by the action of ammonium persulphate
or potassium ferricyanide on the trioxide suspended in boiling alkali-lye.

The properties of bismuth tetroxide.—Bismuth tetroxide may appear as a
dark brown, yellowish-brown, or orange-yellow powder.   The products obtained
by the action of chlorine, ammonium persulphate, or potassium ferricyanide on dil.
alkali-lye are brown or purplish-black anhydrous tetroxides, but the yellow dihydrate,
$Bi_2O_4.2H_2O$, mixed with the hydrated pentoxide, is produced by the action of
chlorine on conc. alkali-lye.   It is only sparingly soluble in boiling nitric acid of
sp. gr. 1·4, and the hydrated pentoxide is dissolved.   The yellow dihydrate loses
water and oxygen at 100°.   Analyses reported by A. E. Arppe, W. Heintz,

C. Schrader, M. M. P. Muir, and C. Deichler agree with the formula Bi_2O_4 ; and when prepared by wet processes, and dried at 100° or over sulphuric acid, M. M. P. Muir, W. Wernicke, and C. Schrader gave $Bi_2O_4.2H_2O$, while L. Vanino and O. Hauser gave $Bi_2O_4.H_2O$. M. M. P. Muir gave 5·60 for the sp. gr. of the anhydrous tetroxide at 20°, and 5·80 for the dihydrate—W. Wernicke gave 5·57. When the tetroxide is heated in **hydrogen** at 265°, M. M. P. Muir obtained the monoxide, and in a current of **carbon monoxide** at 245°–250° it forms the trioxide. When heated in **air** or **oxygen** at 300°, yellow trioxide is formed. M. M. P. Muir said that the dihydrate loses a mol. of water at 110°, and the remainder at 180°–200°—L. Vanino and O. Hauser said 160°–170°, and C. Schrader, 150°. R. R. L. Worsley and P. W. Robertson said that the tetroxide decomposes at 160°. The dehydrated tetroxide is brown, and, according to M. M. P. Muir, takes up a mol. of water on exposure to ordinary air, and rather more than 2 mols. in moist air ; when kept under water, it gradually forms ordinary bismuth hydroxide. C. F. Schönbein found that it decomposes **hydrogen dioxide** and forms a peroxide. L. Vanino and O. Hauser observed that when heated with the **oxyacids**, the hydrated tetroxide dissolves, forming bismuthous salts, and oxygen is given off ; cold dil. **sulphuric acid** does not decompose it ; and cold, dil. **nitric acid** attacks it slowly. The cold, conc. acids readily attack the tetroxide ; and no trace of hydrogen dioxide is formed by the action of cold, conc. sulphuric acid. Conc. **hydrochloric acid** decomposes it at −15° with the evolution of chlorine, but without forming a chloride of quadrivalent bismuth. **Sulphurous acid** reduces the tetroxide, forming normal bismuth sulphate slowly in the cold, rapidly when heated. M. M. P. Muir, and C. Schrader said that the orange-yellow, hydrated tetroxide is scarcely attacked by dil. nitric acid, but L. Schneider found that most of it is dissolved by nitric acid of sp. gr. 1·2, leaving a dark brown residue which is mainly Bi_2O_4—ozonized oxygen is given off. Aq. **ammonia** has no action on the tetroxide. G. Tammann studied the reducing action of the tetroxide on silver nitrate in light. L. Schneider observed that **manganous salts** in nitric acid soln. are oxidized at ordinary temp. to permanganates. M. M. P. Muir found that the tetroxide is insoluble in a conc. soln. of **potassium hydroxide** ; L. Vanino and O. Hauser added that the hydrated tetroxide has a feeble acidic character in that when digested with hot alkali-lye, some alkali is taken up by the tetroxide, and this is not removed by washing ; they supposed that definite *hypobismuthates* could be formed which form the hydrated tetroxide when treated with dil. nitric acid. A. Gutbier and R. Bünz do not agree that hypobismuthates are formed. R. R. L. Worsley and P. W. Robertson said that an unstable per-salt is formed when the tetroxide dissolves in conc. alkali-lye.

The preparation of bismuth pentoxide.—M. M. P. Muir and D. Carnegie showed that **hydrated bismuth pentoxide,** $Bi_2O_5.H_2O$, or **metabismuthic acid,** $HBiO_3$, is the final product of the reaction between chlorine and bismuth hydroxide or oxychloride suspended in a large excess of a very conc. soln. of potassium hydroxide, when washed for a long time with water nearly boiling. M. M. P. Muir recommended the following mode of preparation :

Bismuth trioxid. is suspended in a large excess of very conc. potash-lye of sp. gr. 1·37–1·38. The liquid is kept near.y boiling, and chlorine is passed in until the precipitate is quite homogeneous, and of a dark-red colour ; the precipitate is then washed with hot water, until free from potash, and then with co'd water, until every trace of chloride is removed ; if any chloride is allowed to remain it is decomposed by the nitric acid subsequently added with formation of hydrochloric acid, which acts on the bismuthic oxide. The product is then boiled for a very few minutes with conc. nitric acid (whereby any remaining bismuth tetroxide or hypobismuthic oxide is removed) until all is distinctly scarlet, washed repeatedly and quickly with boiling dil. nitric acid, each quantity of acid being more dil. than the preceding, and finally the acid is comp'etely removed by washing with cold water ; the scarlet precipitate is then dried at 125° for three or four hours.

The composition of the product is $HBiO_3$, and when dried at 120° it forms reddish-brown bismuth pentoxide, Bi_2O_5. W. Heintz, and C. Deichler used a similar process ; and the latter obtained the monohydrate mixed with a little dihydrate. C. E. Corfield and E. Woodward were unable to prepare bismuthic acid or bismuth pentoxide by decomposing sodium bismuthate with nitric acid—bismuth tetroxide was always produced. A. Gutbier and R. Bünz were unable to prepare *ein einheitlich zusammengesetztes Produkt,* or to isolate *eine wohldefinierte chemische Verbindung* by the oxidation of the bismuth trioxide suspended in potash-lye. A. E. Arppe used only a moderate excess of the conc. alkali-lye, but M. M. P. Muir, and C. Schrader were then unable to prepare the hydrated pentoxide. R. R. L. Worsley and P. W. Robertson said that the product is a mixture of $Bi_2O_5.H_2O$ and $Bi_2O_4.2H_2O$, which cannot be separated. That obtained by oxidizing the trioxide suspended in dil. alkali-lye gives a mixture of $Bi_2O_5.H_2O$ and $Bi_2O_4.H_2O$, which can be separated by the solvent action of hot nitric acid of sp. gr. 1·2. A brown variety is produced by the action of glacial acetic acid on commercial sodium bismuthate. C. Hoffmann reported that potassium bismuthates united with different proportions of bismuth tri- or penta-oxide are the solid products first deposited. M. M. P. Muir was unable to confirm this, but he noted the extreme slowness with which the alkali is removed from the precipitate, and that hot water continues to dissolve out alkali after cold water has ceased to affect the product. According to C. Deichler, impure bismuth pentoxide can be prepared by an electrolytic process :

Bismuth trioxide (10 gms.) is mixed with potassium hydroxide (150 grms. of sp. gr. 1·42-1·45) and potassium chloride (15 grms.), and the soln. electrolyzed in a platinum dish, using the dish as anode and a platinum plate as cathode, the latter being protected by a porous diaphragm in order to prevent the deposition of bismuth. A current density of 2–3 ampères per sq. cm. is employed, and the temp. is kept just below that of the b.p. of the soln. Potassium bismuthate is deposited as a dense red precipitate which adheres firmly to the dish and is easily washed with water, the excess of bismuth trioxide remaining in suspension. When the potassium bismuthate is treated for a short time with hot conc. nitric acid and then washed with water, a mixture of bismuthic acid and the hydrate $Bi_2O_4.2H_2O$ is obtained containing 95 per cent. of bismuthic acid. If dil. nitric acid is employed, a large quantity of $Bi_2O_4.2H_2O$ is formed, and by the prolonged action of nitric acid of sp. gr. 1·3, the tetroxide dihydrate, $Bi_2O_4.2H_2O$, is obtained as an orange-yellow powder. The same compound is also obtained by the action of warm acetic acid on bismuthic acid.

The properties of bismuth pentoxide and bismuthic acid.—The wet methods for preparing the pentoxide furnish a scarlet-red powder which, according to the analyses of A. E. Arppe, and M. M. P. Muir, has the composition $Bi_2O_5.H_2O$, or HBO_3, and the sp. gr. 5·75 at 20° ; and it forms the anhydride at 120°. The analyses of the pentoxide by A. E. Arppe, W. Heintz, M. M. P. Muir, and A. Hilger and P. A. von Scherpenberg agree with the formula Bi_2O_5. The dark red powder was found by M. M. P. Muir to have a sp. gr. 5·10 at 20°. C. del Fresno studied the mol vol. E. Friederich gave $1·2 \times 10^8$ ohms per sq. mm. for the resistance of the pentoxide. A. Stromeyer said that the pentoxide gives off oxygen at the temp. of boiling mercury, forming the yellow trioxide ; the pentoxide is reduced to the trioxide by **hydrogen** at a lower temp. than that at which the pentoxide is reduced when heated alone. At a red-heat, hydrogen reduces the oxide to metal. According to M. M. P. Muir, when the pentoxide is heated in hydrogen it is reduced to the tetroxide at 215° ; and to the trioxide at 255°. W. Fränkel and co-workers studied the reduction of bismuth pentoxide by **carbon monoxide,** at 400°, 500°, and 600°. With carbon monoxide, the reduction begins at 75°. When heated in **air** or **oxygen,** at 250°, the pentoxide passes into the tetroxide, but even when heated alone, the evolution of oxygen begins at 150° ; at 300°, in air or oxygen, yellow bismuth trioxide is formed. When kept in moist air, or under water, the pentoxide passes into a lower oxide. R. R. L. Worsley and P. W. Robertson said that the anhydrous pentoxide is incapable of existence because when the hydrate is left in vacuo (one mm. press.), over phosphorus pentoxide, it darkens in colour, and slowly loses oxygen and water. The decomposition is rapid at 100°. When heated in a current of **chlorine,** bismuth trichloride and oxychloride, $Bi_3O_2Cl_3$, are formed ; and with the vapour of **bromine,**

bismuth tribromide and an oxybromide, $Bi_{11}O_{13}Br_7$, are produced. R. F. Weinland and O. Lauenstein found that when bismuthic acid is treated with 40 per cent. **hydrofluoric acid** at ordinary temp., a violent reaction occurs with the formation of bismuth trifluoride, and the evolution of ozonized oxygen; at a low temp., a pentafluoride seems to be formed. A. Stromeyer said that **hydrochloric acid** dissolves the pentoxide with the formation of chlorine; and with **hydriodic acid,** iodine and bismuth triiodide are formed. The pentoxide is converted into the trisulphide (q.v.) when treated with **hydrogen sulphide,** or with alkali sulphide; and A. Hilger and P. A. von Scherpenberg observed that the reaction with **hydrogen selenide** occurs with incandescence, and an oxyselenide is formed. A. Stromeyer found that **sulphurous acid**—not gaseous **sulphur dioxide**—slowly transforms the pentoxide into the ordinary sulphate; and a similar product is obtained by the action of **sulphuric acid,** but with the evolution of oxygen. C. Hoffmann found that dil. sulphuric acid converts the pentoxide into tetroxide. M. M. P. Muir said that the pentoxide is scarcely affected by dil. **nitric acid,** but conc. nitric acid transforms it into the hydrated tetroxide and subsequently into a soln. of bismuth nitrate as observed by A. Stromeyer. With phosphoric acid, oxygen is given off. When a mixture of the pentoxide with **carbon,** sugar, or other organic substance, is set on fire by a red-hot coal, it smoulders away like tinder without deflagration. A soln. of **oxalic, tartaric, citric, or acetic acid** does not act on the pentoxide even when boiling; but if sulphuric acid be present, dissolution occurs with violent effervescence. C. Hoffmann said that oxalic acid transforms the pentoxide at ordinary temp., forming bismuth oxalate and oxygen. H. Schiff said that an alcoholic soln. of oxalic acid or **sugar** does not reduce the pentoxide; but an alkaline soln. of sugar, when warmed, reduces it to the yellow trioxide and then to the metal. Tincture of **guaiacum** is coloured blue by the pentoxide; a soln. of **stannous chloride** reduces the pentoxide to the yellow trioxide which then reacts as previously indicated. G. Rauter represented the reaction with **silicon tetrachloride** in a sealed tube at $370°$-$380°$: $Bi_2O_5+SiCl_4=Bi_2O_3+SiO_2+2Cl_2$; and $2Bi_2O_3+3SiCl_4=4BiCl_3+3SiO_2$. B. Diethelm and F. Förster, and E. Zinth and A. Rauch, studied the electrometric titration of bismuth salts with **titanous chloride.**

According to R. R. L. Worsley and P. W. Robertson, **bismuth hexoxide,** Bi_2O_6, or BiO_3, is produced in small quantities by the action of ammonium persulphate or potassium ferricyanide on bismuth trioxide suspended in a boiling conc. soln. of alkali hydroxide, together with bismuth tetroxide (Bi_2O_4, or $Bi_2O_4.H_2O$), from which it can be separated by continuous extraction with warm nitric acid of sp. gr. 1·2. It may also be prepared by the oxidation of the tetroxide and subsequent treatment of the product with nitric acid. Bismuth hexoxide is pale brown and contains no water. At the ordinary temp. it loses oxygen slowly, darkening in colour.

The alkali bismuthates.—A. Stromeyer said that aq. soln. of **alkali hydroxides** have no action on the pentoxide. M. M. P. Muir said that a hot, conc. soln. of potassium hydroxide, which solidifies on cooling, dissolves 0·01 grm. of bismuthic acid per gram of hydroxide, and when diluted, the tetroxide is deposited as a reddish or yellowish powder. The existence of no definite bismuthate could be demonstrated, although **potassium bismuthate** probably exists in the presence of an excess of potassium hydroxide; these compounds are decomposed when the excess of potassium hydroxide is removed by washing. C. F. Bucholz and R. Brandes, V. A. Jacquelain, and A. Stromeyer assumed that an alkali bismuthate is formed when a mixture of bismuth trioxide and potassium hydroxide is fused while exposed to air. C. Hoffmann reported that potassium metabismuthate, associated with bismuth pentoxide or tetroxide, is deposited when chlorine is passed into boiling potash-lye with bismuth hydroxide in suspension. He said that with alkali-lye of sp. gr. 1·08, the product is $2KBiO_3.4Bi_2O_5.Bi_2O_3$, and when chlorinated three times, $2KBiO_3 5B_2O_5$; with lye of sp. gr. 1·128, $2KBiO_3.5Bi_2O_5$; and with lye of sp. gr. 1·539, $KBiO_3.Bi_2O_5$, if bismuth hydroxide is used, and

$4Bi_2O_3.6Bi_2O_5$, if the trioxide is used; if the latter product be washed with cold water, the product is $KBiO_3.Bi_2O_3$. M. M. P. Muir said that the products of successive experiments have a different composition, although the experimental conditions are as nearly the same as is practicable. G. André reported the bismuthate, $KBiO_3.HBiO_3$, but J. Lorch could not confirm this; nor could M. M. P. Muir or J. Lorch confirm C. Hoffmann's results. As indicated above, C. Deichler reported potassium bismuthate to be formed electrolytically, but A. Gutbier and R. Bünz could not obtain a homogeneous process by this means. J. Lorch also reported **sodium bismuthate** to be formed by the alkali-chlorine process; and C. Deichler, by the electrolytic process, but A. Gutbier and R. Bünz were unable to make definite bismuthates by this means. It therefore follows that alkali bismuthates probably exist in conc. soln. of alkali-lye, but are too readily hydrolyzed to enable them to be isolated in the ordinary way. According to J. Aloy and P. Frébault, potassium and sodium metabismuthates in an impure state can be prepared by slowly adding a soln. of bismuth nitrate in nitric acid to a conc. soln. of the alkali hydroxide, through which a current of chlorine was passed. The precipitate formed, when washed with water, gradually decomposed. When chlorine was replaced by hydrogen dioxide, anhydrous crystalline products were obtained, varying in colour, with the conc. of the alkali, from deep yellow to chocolate-brown. It is probable that these products consisted of the acid, H_3BiO_4, in which one or more atoms of hydrogen were replaced by bismuthyl, BiO, and the remainder by the alkali metal, thus : $BiO_4(BiO)_3$, $BiO_4K(BiO)_2$, or $BiO_4K_2(BiO)$. O. Ruff obtained sodium bismuthate by treating bismuth oxytrifluoride with soda-lye; and by adding, drop by drop, a soln. of bismuth pentoxide—60 per cent. hydrochloric acid at $0°$ into N-NaOH, also at $0°$. The yellow precipitate, rapidly washed and partially dried on a porous plate, contained 95–98 per cent. of its bismuth in the quinquevalent form, and 1 mol. of sodium hydroxide. On further washing, sodium bismuthate loses alkali and darkens in colour; it does not lose much oxygen, even on heating to boiling, when excess of alkali is present. From this bismuthate by treating with ice-cold 15 per cent. nitric acid to neutral reaction and washing rapidly by decantation, a reddish-brown precipitate containing up to 93 per cent. of bismuth pentoxide is obtained. On treating the fresh pentoxide with 15 per cent. sodium hydroxide, it slowly changes to yellow bismuthate. Hence, in opposition to the belief of A. Gutbier and R. Bünz, the higher oxide of bismuth has acidic properties. According to A. Gutbier and H. Micheler, two different bismuthic oxides are here in question. W. D. Collins and co-workers discussed the testing of the purity of the commercial salt.

REFERENCES

[1] C. F. Bucholz and R. Brandes, *Schweigger's Journ.*, **22.** 23, 1818; R. Brandes, *ib.*, **69.** 158, 1858; A. Stromeyer, *Pogg. Ann.*, **26.** 533, 1832; W. Wernicke, *ib.*, **141.** 117, 1870; *Journ. prakt. Chem.*, (1), **110.** 419, 1870; W. D. Collins, H. V. Farr, J. Rosin, G. C. Spencer, and E. Wichers, *Journ. Ind. Eng. Chem.*, **19.** 645, 1927; C. del Fresno, *Anal. Fis. Quim.*, **24.** 107, 1926; W. Heintz, *Liebig's Ann.*, **52.** 252, 1844; *Pogg. Ann.*, **63.** 61, 559, 1844; A. E. Arppe, *ib.*, **64.** 237, 1845; *Dissertatio de jodato bismuthico*, Helsingfors, 1843; *Akad. Handl. Stockholm*, 133, 1842; C. H. D. Bödeker, *Liebig's Ann.*, **123.** 61, 1862; C. Hoffmann, *ib.*, **223,** 110, 1884; H. Schiff, *ib.*, **119.** 342, 1861; G. Rauter, *ib.*, **270.** 251, 1892; C. Schrader, *ib.*, **121.** 204, 1862; *Ueber die höheren Oxydationsstufen des Wismuths*, Gottingen, 1861; C. F. Schönbein, *Journ. prakt. Chem.*, (1), **93.** 59, 1864; R. Böttger, *ib.*, (1), **73.** 494, 1858; G. André, *Compt. Rend.*, **113.** 860, 1891; **114.** 352, 1892; E. Frémy, *ib.*, **15.** 1108, 1842; *Journ. Pharm. Chim.*, (3), **3.** 30, 1843; *Ann. Chim. Phys.*, (3), **12.** 493, 1844; V. A. Jacquelain, *ib.*, (2), **66.** 113, 1837; A. Hollard, *Bull. Soc. Chim.*, (3), **29.** 151, 1903; *Compt. Rend.*, **136.** 229, 1903; A. Mailfert, *ib.*, **94.** 863, 1882; K. Hasebroek, *Ber.*, **20.** 213, 1887; T. Poleck, *ib.*, **27.** 1051, 1899; W. Foster, *ib.*, **12.** 846, 1879, C. Reichard, *ib.*, **30.** 1913; 1897; *Chem. News*, **39.** 131, 1879; P. Jannasch, *Ber.*, **26.** 1499, 2908, 1893; **27.** 2227, 1894; **28.** 994, 1408, 1895; *Zeit. anorg. Chem.*, **8.** 302, 1895; L. Vanino and O. Hauser, *ib.*, **39.** 381, 1904; J. Hanus and O. Kallauner, *ib.*, **70.** 232, 1911; C. Deichler, *ib.*, **20.** 81, 1899; A. Gutbier, E. Birchenbach, and R. Bünz, *Sitzber. Phys. Med. Soc. Erlangen*, **39.** 172, 1908; A. Gutbier and R. Bünz, *ib.*, **40.** 90, 1909; *Ber.*, **48.** 162, 294, 1906; **49.** 432, 1906; **50.** 210, 1906; **52.** 124, 1907; A. Gutbier and H. Micheler, *ib.*, **59.** 143,

1908 ; L. Moser, *ib.*, **50.** 33, 1906 ; M. Bose, *ib.*, **44.** 237, 1905 ; R. F. Weinland and O. Lauenstein, *ib.*, **20.** 46, 1899 ; O. Ruff, *ib.*, **57.** 220, 1908 ; E. Rupp and G. Schaumann, *Zeit. anal. Chem.*, **42.** 732, 1903 ; L. Schneider, *Monatsh.*, **8.** 242, 1888 ; A. Hilger and P. A. von Scherpenberg, *Mitt. Erlangen. Pharm. Inst.*, **2.** 4, 7, 1889 ; I. Meschtschersky, *Bull. Soc. Chem.*, (2), **39.** 507, 1883 ; L. Schucht, *Ber. Hütt. Ztg.*, **39.** 121, 1880 ; *Chem. News*, **41.** 280, 1880 ; J. Lorch, *Ueber Wismuthsäure und Natriummetabismuthat*, München, 1893 ; M. M. P. Muir, *Chem. News*, **35.** 122, 1877 ; **43.** 289, 1881 ; **44.** 236, 1887 ; *Journ. Chem. Soc.*, **29.** 149, 1876 ; **31.** 29, 647, 1877 ; **32.** 132, 1877 ; M. M. P. Muir and D. Carnegie, *ib.*, **51.** 77, 1887 ; M. M. P. Muir, G. B. Hoffmeister, and C. E. Robbs, *ib.*, **39.** 21, 1881 ; *Chem. News*, **42.** 242, 1880 ; C. Luckow, *Dingler's Journ.*, **177.** 231, 1865 ; P. Thibault, *Journ. Pharm. Chem.*, (6), **12.** 559, 1900 ; R. R. L. Worsley and P. W. Robertson, *Journ. Chem. Soc.*, **117.** 63, 1920 ; J. Aloy and P. Frébault, *Bull. Soc. Chim.*, (3), **35.** 396, 1906 ; C. E. Corfield and E. Woodward, *Pharm. Journ.*, (4), **57.** 80, 1923 ; K. Friederich, *Zeit. Physik*, **31.** 813, 1925 ; B. Diethelm and F. Förster, *Zeit. phys. Chem.*, **62.** 138, 1908 ; E. Zinth and A. Rauch, *Zeit. anorg. Chem.*, **139.** 397, 1924 ; G. Tammann, *ib.*, **114.** 151, 1920 ; W. Fränkel and W. Snipschsky, *ib.*, **125.** 235, 1922 ; *Festschrift zur Jahrhundertfeier des physikalischen Vereins*, Frankfurt a. M., 136, 1924.

§ 10. The Bismuth Fluorides

H. Moissan [1] found that bismuth is attacked only superficially by fluorine. J. J. Berzelius obtained a white powder, which has been assumed to be **bismuth trifluoride,** BiF, by evaporating a soln. of the trioxide in hydrofluoric acid. It is probably an oxyfluoride. M. M. P. Muir and co-workers heated bismuth trioxide with aq. hydrofluoric acid, replacing the acid as it evaporated ; when action had ceased, the clear liquor when evaporated on a water-bath, furnished a deliquescent, greyish-white crystalline mass with a composition $BiF_3.3HF$, or bismuth trihydrotrifluoride. If the product be heated until fumes of hydrofluoric acid are no longer evolved, a grey, crystalline powder, bismuth trifluoride, BiF_3, is formed. The crystalline residue remaining after the reaction with hydrofluoric acid and bismuth trioxide had the composition $BiOF.2HF$, and when strongly heated in a covered platinum crucible for an hour, it furnished bismuth trifluoride. M. M. P. Muir and B. S. Gott also made the trifluoride by adding a conc. soln. of potassium fluoride to a soln. of bismuth nitrate containing as little nitric acid as possible, washing the product first with cold and then with hot water, and drying at 100°. H. B. Fullerton, and G. Gore also prepared the trifluoride as a grey crystalline powder of sp. gr. 5·32. It can be fused without decomposition. According to M. M. P. Muir, bismuth trifluoride is more stable towards water, and heat than any of the other bismuth halides. W. Herz and A. Bulla said that bismuth trifluoride is not hydrolyzed by cold or boiling water. A. C. Vournasos prepared complexes with pyridine, and quinoline. It is quite insoluble in, and is unacted on by water, is decomposed and dissolved by hot hydrochloric, sulphuric, or nitric acid, and is scarcely altered or volatilized by heating in an open platinum basin at a full redheat. The trihydrotrifluoride is slowly decomposed by cold, more quickly by hot water, with formation of $BiOF.2HF$. If a little free hydrofluoric acid be present in the wash-water a considerable amount of bismuth goes into soln. It does not form *bismuth fluosulphide* when melted with sulphur.

H. von Helmolt prepared **ammonium tetrafluobismuthite,** NH_4BiF_4, or $NH_4F.BiF_3$, by cooling a sat. soln. of freshly precipitated bismuth hydroxide in a hot conc. soln. of ammonium fluoride. The white powder consists of tabular monoclinic or rhombic crystals. It is decomposed by water with the precipitation of bismuthyl fluoride, and the dissolution of a little bismuth. It is soluble in hot dil. acids. The corresponding *potassium fluobismuthite* could not be prepared by H. von Helmolt either by evaporation, or by adding alcohol to a mixed soln. of the two fluorides.

According to R. F. Weinland and O. Lauenstein, when bismuth pentoxide is treated with 40 per cent. hydrofluoric acid at −10°, a very unstable **bismuth pentafluoride,** BiF_5, is formed, which cannot be isolated ; the soln. has strong oxidizing properties, liberates iodine from potassium iodide, or chlorine from hydrochloric acid; converts alcohol into aldehyde, and rapidly destroys organic substances. With traces of manganese salts, the soln. gives a violet-red coloration; when concentrated in vacuo, it yields bismuth trifluoride, and when it is extracted with ether or poured into a large quantity of cold water, the theoretical quantity of bismuthic acid is precipitated. Potassium bismuthate behaves in a similar manner when treated with hydrofluoric acid. O. Ruff said that there is evidence of the formation of traces of the pentafluoride by the action of fluorine on bismuth trichloride at −80°. Evidence of the formation of an unstable *potassium fluobismuthate* was obtained by R. F. Weinland and O. Lauenstein.

REFERENCES.

[1] H. Moissan, *Ann. Chim. Phys.*, (6), **24**. 247, 1891; M. M. P. Muir and B. S. Gott, *Journ. Chem. Soc.*, **39**. 33, 1881; **53**. 137, 1887; M. M. P. Muir, G. B. Hoffmeister, and C. E. Robbs, *ib.*, **39**. 33, 1881; R. F. Weinland and O. Lauenstein, *Zeit. anorg. Chem.*, **20**. 46, 1899; O. Ruff, *ib.*, **57**. 220, 1908; W. Herz and A. Bulla, *ib.*, **61**. 387, 1909; A. C. Vournasos, *ib.*, **150**. 143, 1926; H. von Helmolt, *ib.*, **3**. 143, 1893; *Ueber einige Doppelfluoride*, Berlin, 1892; H. B. Fullerton, *Amer. Journ. Science*, (3), **14**. 282, 1877; G. Gore, *Proc. Roy. Soc.*, **21**. 140, 1873; J. J. Berzelius, *Gilbert's Ann.*, **40**. 286, 1812; *Schweigger's Journ.*, **7**. 70, 1814.

§ 11. The Bismuth Chlorides

In addition to the ordinary *bismuth trichloride*, $BiCl_3$, *bismuth dichloride*, $BiCl_2$, or Bi_2Cl_4, has been reported by a number of workers. The *bismuth pentachloride*, $BiCl_5$, has not been prepared. The well-defined quinquevalency shown by arsenic and antimony in their oxides and halides has stimulated the quest for similar relations with bismuth. Although quinquevalent bismuth forms an oxide, this element does not exhibit a higher valency than three in its fluorides. M. M. P. Muir [1] tried to prepare it by the action of chlorine on molten bismuth trichloride, and by heating bismuthyl chloride with charcoal in a stream of chlorine, but without success; nor did he succeed in making a mixed pentahalide. E. B. Hutchins and V. Lenher's attempts were also nugatory. They tried the action of chlorine on bismuth trichloride at the temp. of liquid air; the action of chlorine on a hydrochloric acid soln. of the trichloride at −10°; the action of bismuth trichloride on the cæsium pentahalides; and the saturation of a hydrochloric acid soln. of bismuth pentoxide at −10°, in the presence of ammonium chloride furnishes only the trichloride, $2NH_4Cl.BiCl_3$. G. Rauter also failed to obtain the pentachloride by the action of carbon tetrachloride on bismuth pentoxide.

According to R. Weber,[2] and P. P. Dehérain, chlorine acts slowly on bismuth at ordinary temp., forming a brown, oily liquid—bismuth dichloride, $BiCl_2$. W. Heintz obtained a violet trichloride by passing chlorine over molten bismuth. This was probably a mixture of the tri- and di-chlorides. W. Heintz tried to make it by heating bismuth and bismuth trichloride, but at no temp. did he find evidence of the formation of the dichloride; on the other hand, R. Weber said that in a sealed tube, a reaction begins at the m.p. of the trichloride, and by maintaining this temp. for a long time, obtained some brown dichloride. W. Herz and A. Guttmann examined the f.p. curve of mixtures of bismuth and bismuth trichloride, and found a maximum at 163° corresponding with the formation of the dichloride. B. G. Eggink observed no sign of the dichloride on his fusion curve of bismuth and chlorine, but he said that *bismuth monochloride*, $BiCl$, is formed. It melts at 320°, forming two liquid phases; there is also an endothermal compound, *bismuth tetrachloride*, $BiCl_4$, partially dissociated on fusion. He observed no sign of the dichloride on the f.p. curve. L. Marino and R. Becarelli found that when mixtures of bismuth with 5–85 per cent. of bismuth trichloride are fused in sealed tubes, two layers are obtained above 320°—the upper one being black, the lower one white with a metallic lustre. Lowering the temp. from 320° results in the formation of (i) a crystalline product melting over the range 270°–320°, and at about 240° two

other products are formed, one melting about 270°, and the other between 270°
and 320°; and (ii) the other stratum furnishes a eutectic Bi–BiCl₃, melting at about
180°. Thus, there is no evidence of the formation of a subchloride, the fused
mixtures of bismuth and its trichloride yielding, over a certain interval of concentration, a series of solid soln., α-crystals—which undergo transformation, accompanied by marked development of heat, into β-crystals with m.p. points higher in all
cases than those of bismuth and its trichloride. After complete fusion the β-crystals
yield, on cooling, α-crystals of the different composition in presence of two liquid
layers which reproduce the same phenomena. B. G. Eggink's curve is given in
Fig. 18; it shows the probable formation of **bismuth tetrachloride**, BiCl₄, melting

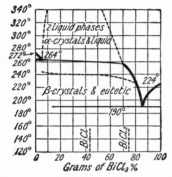

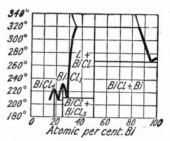

FIG. 17.—Equilibrium Diagram of
the System : Bi–BiCl₃.

FIG. 18.—Equilibrium Diagram
of the System : Bi–Cl₂.

at 225°. W. Heintz, and R. Schneider sublimed bismuth trichloride in hydrogen
without the occurrence of any appreciable change, but M. M. P. Muir said that if
the trichloride be heated in a current of dry hydrogen it melts, and quickly changes
colour, producing black bismuth dichloride, which, on raising the temp., is quickly
decomposed, yielding a white crystalline sublimate of the trichloride, and a black
residue of metallic bismuth. R. Schneider added that if a complex salt of bismuth
trichloride, say ammonium chlorobismuthite, be heated to about 300° in a current
of hydrogen, ammonia and hydrogen chloride are evolved, and a purple-red mass
is produced which is a mixture of ammonium chloride, and of bismuth di- and
tri-chlorides. By regulating the temp., the proportion of trichloride can be made
very small, but the ammonium salt cannot be removed. R. Weber said
that bismuth trichloride can be reduced to the dichloride by warming it with
mercurous chloride, or with phosphorus, silver, zinc, mercury, or tin, but not with
gold or platinum. The dichloride is also formed by heating an intimate mixture
of bismuth and mercuric or mercurous chlorides in stoichiometrical proportions.
A. Michaelis also obtained the dichloride mixed with bismuth phosphate and oxychloride by the action of heat on a mixture of phosphorus trichloride and bismuth
trioxide.

Analyses of the dark brown crystalline mass by P. P. Dehérain, R. Weber, and
R. Schneider agree with the formula BiCl₂. The product obtained by slowly cooling
the molten dichloride may show acicular crystals when broken. W. Herz and
A. Guttmann gave 4·85–4·88 for the sp. gr. of the black, needle-like crystals—this
is lower than the value for a corresponding mixture of bismuth and its trichloride.
The dichloride is readily fused ; W. Herz and A. Guttmann gave 163° for the m.p.;
and R. Schneider, V. Thomas, R. Weber, and M. M. P. Muir said that it decomposes
at about 300° into the trichloride and bismuth. The dichloride is very hygroscopic,
and is decomposed by water into bismuth oxychloride. P. P. Dehérain said that
dry chlorine converts the di- into the tri-chloride ; and that there is simultaneously
formed *bismuth tritaoctochloride*, Bi₃Cl₈—but this statement has not been confirmed;

the product is probably a mixture of the di- and tri-chlorides. B. G. Eggink found no sign of it on the f.p. curve of bismuth and chlorine. The dichloride is decomposed by mineral acids, forming a salt of tervalent bismuth, and bismuth. P. P. Dehérain said that the dichloride forms no compound with ammonia; and R. Weber that it is decomposed by a soln. of ammonium chloride. V. Thomas found that nitrogen peroxide converts it into bismuthyl chloride. R. Weber found that the dichloride can dissolve a little bismuth. A conc. soln. of potassium hydroxide was found by R. Schneider to convert the dichloride into dark grey bismuth monoxide which passes rapidly into yellow trioxide. It has not been decided whether the bismuth dichloride forms a double salt. According to R. Schneider, the product obtained by the action of hydrogen on ammonium chloro-bismuthite may be $NH_4Cl.BiCl_2$, *ammonium trichlorohypobismuthate.*

R. Boyle,[3] and M. Poli prepared **bismuth trichloride,** $BiCl_3$; they obtained it by sublimation from a mixture of bismuth and mercuric chloride. As indicated in connection with the action of chlorine on bismuth, J. Davy [4] obtained the trichloride by the direct union of the elements. W. Heintz, R. Weber, and M. M. P. Muir obtained the trichloride by heating bismuth in a current of chlorine, and subliming the product in a current of carbon dioxide. The trichloride was obtained by M. M. P. Muir by the action of chlorine on heated bismuth tri- or penta-oxide, or, according to M. M. P. Muir and E. M. Eagles, in the trisulphide at a red-heat—W. Remmler said at the temp. of boiling sulphur—if the temp. is too low, some chlorosulphide is formed. A. Michaelis observed that a little trichloride is formed by heating in a sealed tube a mixture of phosphorus trichloride and bismuth ; and G. Rauter, a mixture of silicon tetrachloride and bismuth tri- or penta-oxide. G. Oddo and E. Serra prepared it by passing the vapour of sulphur monochloride over heated bismuth trioxide ; and G. Oddo and U. Giachery, by passing chlorine through a heated mixture of the trioxide and sulphur. The trichloride can also be prepared by evaporating a soln. of bismuth in aqua regia, or bismuth oxide or sulphide in conc. hydrochloric acid, and subliming the product in a current of carbon dioxide. F. M. Jäger purified the salt by sublimation in a current of dry hydrogen chloride. W. L. Miller and F. B. Kenrick illustrated the reversibility of the reaction $BiCl_3 + H_2O = BiOCl + 2HCl$ by the following lecture-table experiment :

Forty grms. of commercial bismuth nitrate and 40 c.c. of hydrochloric acid (sp. gr. 1·175) are rubbed together in a mortar and filtered from a trace of residue which may remain undissolved ; 5 c.c. of the bismuth soln. to 50 c.c. of water in a reaction cylinder the reaction goes → ; add 5 c.c. of hydrochloric acid (sp. gr. 1·175) ← ; 75 c.c. of water → ; 5 c.c. of acid ← ; 200 c.c. of water → ; 10 c.c. of acid ← ; 500 c.c. of water → ; added acid from the reagent bottle ←. The acid and water may be added from burettes.

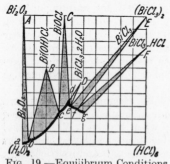

Fig. 19.—Equilibrium Conditions in the Ternary System : Bi_2O_3–HCl–H_2O at 30°.

W. Jacobs examined the ternary system Bi_2O_3–HCl–H_2O at 30°, and the results are illustrated by the graph of the quaternary system of components : $2BiCl_3 + 3H_2O \rightleftharpoons Bi_2O_3 + 6HCl$, shown in Fig. 19, when the four components are represented as eq. mols Bi_2Cl_6, H_6O_3, Bi_2O_3, and H_6Cl_6. The curve *ab* represents the solubility with *bismuth oxide* as the solid phase : *bc*, with the solid phase *hydrated bismuthyl chloride,* $BiOCl.H_2O$; *cd*, with *bismuthyl chloride,* $BiOCl$; *de*, with *dihydrated bismuth trichloride,* $BiCl_3.2H_2O$; *ef*, with *bismuth trichloride,* $BiCl_3$; and *fg*, with *bismuth hydrotetrachloride,* $BiCl_3.HCl$. The areas *abA*, *bcB*, etc., refer to supersaturated soln. A. A. Noyes and co-workers, K. Jellinek and W. Kühn, and A. Mutscheller made some observations on this subject. G. Waris observed only one oxychloride in the ternary system Bi_2O_3–HCl–H_2O at 25°. The following data are expressed in percentages :

Solution$\begin{cases} Bi_2O_3 \\ HCl \end{cases}$ . . $\begin{array}{cccccccc} 0{\cdot}60 & 2{\cdot}60 & 11{\cdot}44 & 23{\cdot}75 & 50{\cdot}74 & 58{\cdot}72 & 58{\cdot}59 \\ 2{\cdot}50 & 4{\cdot}22 & 10{\cdot}68 & 17{\cdot}56 & 30{\cdot}23 & 33{\cdot}67 & 35{\cdot}14 \end{array}$

Solid phases   BiOCl   BiCl₃

A. Mutscheller concluded that in acid soln., the basic salts are ionized to form a
univalent $Bi(OH)_2$-ion ; and in alkaline soln., a tervalent Bi····-ion.
R. Weber [5] said that the trichloride can be obtained as a snow-white mass,
which M. M. P. Muir obtained by sublimation in fine crystals. If some dichloride
is present, the compound is coloured brown or grey. Analyses reported by J. Davy,
W. Heintz, and J. B. A. Dumas agree with the formula $BiCl_3$. V. A. Jacquelain
found that the vapour density is 11·35 in agreement with 10·98 calculated for
$BiCl_3$. L. Rügheimer found the **vapour density** at 490° to be normal.
C. H. D. Bödeker gave 4·56 for the **specific gravity** at 11°. R. Lorenz and W. Herz
gave 4·75 at ordinary temp. and 3·910 at the m.p. A. Voigt and W. Biltz found
the sp. gr. of molten bismuth trichloride varies from 3·87 at 250° to 3·64 at 350°,
or $D=3{\cdot}87{-}0{\cdot}0023(\theta{-}250)$. W. Biltz studied the **molecular volume ;** R. Lorenz
and W. Herz gave 315·4 for the mol. vol. I. I. Saslowsky calculated a 0·99 per
cent. contraction in the formation of this compound from its elements. F. M. Jäger
found the sp. gr. at different temp. referred to water at 4° ; the **surface tension** θ
dynes per cm. ; the **specific cohesion,** a^2 in sq. mm. ; and the molar **surface energy,**
E ergs per sq. cm., to be :

	271°	304°	331°	353°	382°
θ . . .	61·2	61·8	58·1	55·3	52·0
E . . .	1254·4	1187·0	1126·6	1084·3	1032·4
a^2 . . .	3·54	3·58	3·22	3·11	2·98
Sp. gr. . . .	3·811	3·735	3·682	3·621	3·554

He represented the sp. gr. of the liquid at $\theta°$ by $D=3{\cdot}860{-}0{\cdot}00232(\theta{-}250)$.
S. Motylewsky found the drop-weight of bismuth trichloride to be 85 when that of
water is 100. R. Lorenz and W. Herz studied some relations of the surface tensions
of the family of halides. M. M. P. Muir gave 225°–230° for the **melting point ;**
G. Scarpa, 224° ; and R. Lorenz and W. Herz, 232·5°. The last-named also gave
0·000545 for the coeff. of **thermal expansion.** T. Carnelley and W. C. Williams
gave 427°–439° for the **boiling point ;** V. Meyer and A. Krause, 435°–441° ;
C. G. Maier, 442·2° ; V. Meyer and F. Freyer, and L. Rügheimer, 447° ; R. Anschütz
and H. Weyer, 264° at 11 mm. C. G. Maier gave for the **vapour pressure,** p mm. :

	94·1°	139·3°	212·3°	287·3°	371·4°	403·2°	434·0°	439·0°	445·1°°	468·8°
p .	19·8	24·5	36·7	56·0	238·0	408·4	701·7	755·5	831·5	1235·6

V. A. Jacquelain observed that the trichloride can be sublimed in a current of
carbon dioxide without decomposition. C. G. Maier also gave 18·3 Cals. for the
heat of vaporization per mol. E. Liesegang found that the trichloride is
sensitive to light, and paper soaked in the soln. becomes brown when exposed to
light, but it becomes colourless again when kept in darkness. C. R. Crymble,
and A. K. Macbeth and N. I. Maxwell measured the absorption spectrum of bismuth
trichloride. K. Schäfer and F. Hein compared the absorption spectra of bismuth
trichloride dissolved in aq. hydrochloric acid, ether, and ethyl acetate ; and
assumed that absorption complexes, $[BiCl_3(Cl)(OH)]H$, or $[BiCl_3(H_2O)Cl_2]H_2$, are
formed. A. K. Macbeth and N. I. Maxwell studied this subject. N. P. Peskoff
found bismuth hydroxide sensitized organic substances affected by X-rays.
A. A. Noyes and co-workers explained the conductivity of hydrochloric acid soln.
of bismuth oxide on the assumption that with conc. acid, the complex *hydropentachlorobismuthous acid*, H_2BiCl_5, and with a less conc. acid *hydrotetrachlorobismuthous acid*, $HBiCl_4$, are formed—*vide infra*. G. Hänsel found that the electrolysis of bismuth chloride in soln. of hydrochloric acid or of sodium chloride is not
satisfactory. M. Escher observed the absorption of polonium by bismuth hydroxide.
L. Rügheimer and E. Rudolfi measured the effect of some salts—sodium, barium,
strontium, manganese, cobalt, and copper chlorides—on the b.p. of bismuth

trichloride, and inferred that their mol. wts. are nearly normal. A. Ditte and R. Metzner represented the heat of formation by $2Bi+6HCl+3O=2BiCl_3.3H_2O +242.2$ Cals.; and J. Thomsen, $(Bi,3Cl)=24.6$ Cals. A. Voigt and W. Biltz gave 0.0442 mho for the sp. electrical conductivity of the molten chloride at $260°$; 0.481 at $295°$; 0.506 at $315°$; 0.533 at $335°$; and 0.255 at $350°$; while W. Biltz and W. Klemm gave for the eq. conductivity $\lambda=10.2+0.047(\theta-250)$.

The effect of **hydrogen** on bismuth trichloride has been discussed in connection with the dichloride. V. A. Jacquelain observed that when heated to the vaporization temp., in **air,** bismuth oxychloride is formed. The salt deliquesces in air. **Water** or steam was found by R. W. E. MacIvor, V. Merz and W. Weith, W. Heintz, and V. A. Jacquelain to decompose the trichloride with the formation of the oxychloride, and W. Oswald found the result is in accord with the mass law—*confer* Fig. 19. W. Herz and A. Bulla showed that the equilibrium conditions agree with the relation $[BiCl_3]/[HCl]^2$, a constant, over a wide range of dilution; and R. Dubrisay obtained an analogous result at $18°$, $80°$, and $85°$. The curves are continuous, and indicate a decrease in the hydrolysis as the temp. rises in harmony with the rule for exothermal reactions. Only one oxychloride, BiOCl, is formed. W. Heintz, A. E. Arppe, and W. Jacobs prepared the *dihydrate*, $BiCl_3.2H_2O$—*vide* Fig. 19. T. Karantassis studied the interchange of halogens—chlorine, bromine, and iodine. As indicated in connection with the higher chlorides of bismuth— *vide supra*—M. M. P. Muir showed that **chlorine** has no action on the trichloride; and **bromine** does not form an addition product. R. Engel observed that if a soln. of bismuth trichloride be sat. with **hydrogen chloride** at $20°$, acicular crystals of **bismuth hydroheptachloride,** $2BiCl_3.HCl.3H_2O$, are formed. They are stable at ordinary temp. W. Jacobs obtained the anhydrous bismuth hydrotetrachloride, $BiCl_3.HCl$—Fig. 18—not R. Engel's salt. A. Ditte also reported that he prepared **bismuth trihydrohexachloride,** $BiCl_3.3HCl$, in prismatic crystals, by evaporating a hydrochloric acid soln. of bismuth trichloride; but W. Jacobs did not confirm this. A. E. Arppe examined these compounds. W. Eidmann, and H. E. Causse added that the presence of conc. **hydrochloric acid** or of **alkali chlorides** hinders the precipitation of the bismuthyl chloride. W. Herz and A. Bulla found that alkali chlorides increase the solubility of bismuth trichloride; bromides have a greater and acids a less influence than chlorides in reducing the hydrolysis. Sodium sulphate has no appreciable effect. According to G. Vortmann and C. Padberg, an acidic soln. of bismuth trichloride is not altered when boiled with **sulphur.** According to M. M. P. Muir and E. M. Eagles, and J. Durocher, when the trichloride is heated with sulphur, or in a current of **hydrogen sulphide,** it forms bismuth sulphochloride; at a red-heat, however, bismuth trisulphide is formed. U. Antony and G. Magri found that 100 c.c. of liquid hydrogen sulphide dissolves 0.08 grm. of the trichloride, forming a colourless soln.; and G. N. Quam showed that bismuth chlorosulphide, BiSCl, is formed. G. N. Quam and J. A. Wilkinson also observed that liquid hydrogen sulphide forms an insoluble compound with bismuth trichloride. M. M. P. Muir found that if the trichloride is heated to the volatilization temp., in a current of **sulphur dioxide,** a great part of the salt sublimes unchanged, and a small proportion of the oxychloride, $Bi_3O_2Cl_3$, is formed; no reaction occurs when the trichloride is heated with **sulphur monochloride.** A. Vogel found that conc. **sulphuric acid** converts the trichloride into sulphate.

According to G. Gore, liquid **ammonia** dissolves the trichloride, and J. Persoz found that when exposed to ammonia the absorption of the gas is accompanied by a small rise of temp.; and, added P. P. Dehérain, three ammines are formed: (i) **bismuth amminobistrichloride,** $2BiCl_3.NH_3$, is a red stable compound which melts when heated, and crystallizes on cooling; it is sensitive towards moisture, and is decomposed by hydrochloric acid, forming $NH_4Cl.2BiCl_3$; (ii) **bismuth diammino-trichloride,** $BiCl_3.2NH_3$, is a dirty-green substance which forms $2NH_4Cl.BiCl_3$ when treated with hydrochloric acid; and (iii) **bismuth triamminotrichloride,** $BiCl_3.3NH_3$, a colourless substance which can be volatilized unchanged in ammonia gas, and which forms $3NH_4Cl.BiCl_3$, when treated with hydrochloric acid. J. Hanus and A. Jilek showed that when a soln. of a bismuth salt is boiled with **hydrazine hydrate,** bismuth is quantitatively precipitated. A. Besson, and V. Thomas obtained **bismuth nitrosyltrichloride,** $BiCl_3.NO$, by the action of **nitric oxide ;** the complex salt is very hygroscopic and can be melted without decomposition. J. J. Sudborough found that **nitrosyl chloride** reacts vigorously with bismuth trichloride ; and from the resulting liquid, **bismuth nitrosyltetrachloride,** $BiCl_3.NOCl$, is separated as a deliquescent orange-yellow powder which is decomposed by water. H. Rheinboldt and R. Wasserfuhr found that it melts at $115°-120°$. A. Besson, and V. Thomas obtained **bismuth nitroxyltrichloride,** $BiCl_3.NO_2$, by exposing bismuth trichloride to **nitrogen peroxide** for 10 hrs. at ordinary temp. The yellow product loses no nitrogen peroxide in vacuo ; it is stable in dry air, but is decomposed in moist air, and water transforms it into bismuthyl chloride. S. Schlesinger observed that **nitric acid** converts the trichloride into nitrate. As indicated in connection with the dichloride, R. Weber, and L. Rosenstein found that bismuth trichloride is reduced by **phosphorus.** A. Cavazzi, G. Vortmann and C. Padberg, and P. Kulisch studied the action of **phosphine,** and obtained a bismuth phosphide associated with some oxygen and chlorine. T. Karantassis found that **phosphorus triiodide** reacts by double decomposition with bismuth trichloride, but the reverse reaction does not occur. E. Glatzel found that **phosphorus pentasulphide** converts the trichloride into sulphophosphate ; F. E. Brown and J. E. Snyder observed no reaction with **vanadium oxytrichloride.** As indicated above, **carbon dioxide** has no action on the heated trichloride. The trichloride is soluble in **alcohol,** and in **ether.** W. Eidmann found that the trichloride is soluble in **methylal,** and in **acetone ;** A. Naumann and P. Schulz, that 100 grms. of acetone dissolve 17·89 grms. of the trichloride, forming a soln. of sp. gr. 0·9194 at $18°/4°$; the pale yellow liquid gradually turns brown. and behaves towards ammonia, potassium iodide, silver nitrate, and hydrogen sulphide like an aq. soln. of the salt. Bismuth trichloride dissolves in many **hydrocarbons** at appropriate temp., and can be recovered by crystallization as the soln. cools ; at higher temp. the trichloride is reduced to dichloride, and bismuth trichloride thus serves as a feeble chlorinating agent. V. Thomas also observed that it can also serve as a condensation agent. L. Vanino and co-workers, C. Montemartini, H. Schiff, etc., studied its reactions with **organic compounds.** F. Challenger and co-workers, F. Hartl, L. Vanino and O. Hauser, A. Gutbier and M. Müller, and H. Schiff studied the organic derivatives of bismuth ; and L. Vanino and F. Hartl, the compounds with organic bases. G. Bruni and A. Manuelli studied the hydrolysis of bismuth trichloride in a soln. of **formamide.** A. C. Vournasos prepared complexes with organic amines, pyridine, and quinoline. A. Naumann observed that the trichloride is soluble in **benzonitrile, methyl acetate,** and at 18°, 100 parts of **ethyl acetate** dissolve 1·66 parts of bismuth trichloride and the soln. has a sp. gr. 0·9106 at $18°/4°$. H. Cousin found that when the soln. is boiled with **dextrose** in excess, bismuth is quantitatively precipitated. J. P. Wibaut and co-workers studied bismuth trichloride as a catalyst in the addition of hydrogen chloride or bromide to ethylene and propylene.

A. C. Vournasos observed the reduction of a toluene soln. of bismuth halide by **potassium.** R. Weber observed the reducing action of **silver, zinc, mercury,** and tin on the trichloride—*vide supra*—**gold** and **platinum** are without action, although F. M. Jäger noted that platinum is attacked by the liquid towards 400°. F. Winkler studied the action of **bismuth** on the trichloride. K. Seubert and A. Schmidt observed that the vapour of the trichloride is reduced by **magnesium** to bismuth and its dichloride. R. Weber found that the trichloride is reduced when heated with **mercuric chloride ;** and J. Volhard that when heated with **mercuric oxide** bismuth trioxide is formed. M. M. P. Muir found that bismuth trichloride is not attacked when heated with **chromyl chloride ;** and E. Zintl and G. Rienäcker studied the electrometric titration of bismuth salts with **chromous chloride.**

Bismuth trichloride forms complex salts with the alkali and ammonium chlorides. A. A. Noyes and co-workers examined the electrical conductivity of soln. of bismuth trichloride and the solubility of bismuth oxychloride in hydrochloric acid, and explained the results on the assumption that **hydrotetrachlorobismuthous acid,** $HBiCl_4$—cf. $BiCl_3.HCl$, Fig. 19—and **hydropentachlorobismuthous acid,** H_2BiCl_4, are formed in soln. K. Schäfer and F. Hein obtained $HBiCl_4.2(C_2H_5)_2O$ as a viscid oil by passing dry hydrogen chloride into an ethereal soln. of bismuth trichloride. A. Gutbier and M. Müller prepared a number of chloro-derivatives of organic bases. P. P. Dehérain obtained colourless, deliquescent needles of **ammonium hepta-chlorodibismuthite,** $NH_4Cl.2BiO_3$, by the action of hydrochloric acid on bismuth hemiamminohexachloride ; and from bismuth diamminotrichloride he similarly obtained six-sided plates of **ammonium pentachlorobismuthite,** $2NH_4BiCl_5$; C. F. Rammelsberg obtained it as a *hemipentahydrate* by evaporating, at ordinary temp., a soln. containing equimolar parts of bismuth trichloride, and ammonium chloride ; and V. A. Jacquelain from a soln. of a mol of bismuth trichloride and 2 mols of the ammonium salt. C. F. Rammelsberg said that the hydrated salt forms colourless rhombic prisms isomorphous with the corresponding bromide, and with the corresponding potassium salt. V. A. Jacquelain said that the anhydrous salt forms six-sided prisms. C. F. Rammelsberg obtained from the mother-liquor in the preparation of the preceding salt, tabular trigonal crystals of *ammonium henachlorodibismuthite,* $5NH_4Cl.2BiCl_3$, with the axial ratios $a : c = 1 : 1.9728$. P. Groth regards the salt as the pentachlorobismuthite. P. P. Dehérain obtained tabular, rhombic crystals of **ammonium hexachlorobismuthite,** $3NH_4Cl.BiCl_3$, by the action of hydrochloric acid on bismuth triamminotrichloride ; and A. E. Arppe, by crystallization from a soln. of a mol of bismuth trichloride and six mols of ammonium chloride. A. Ferratini found that when an alcoholic soln. of the trichloride is boiled with an excess of hydrazine hydrochloride, it forms **hydrazine hexachlorobismuthite,** $BiCl_3.3N_2H_5Cl$.

V. A. Jacquelain [6] obtained deliquescent plates of trihydrated **sodium penta-chlorobismuthite,** $Na_2BiCl_5.3H_2O$, by crystallization from an aq. soln. of a mol of bismuth trichloride with 3 mols of water ; A. E. Arppe prepared six-sided prisms of the *monohydrate* from a hydrochloric acid soln. of 2 mols of bismuth trioxide and 3 mols of sodium chloride. J. Aloy and A. Frébault prepared **potassium penta-chlorobismuthite,** K_2BiCl_5, by passing a current of chlorine and bismuth trichloride vapour over potassium chloride at a red-heat. The amber-yellow, crystalline mass is deliquescent, but is more stable than bismuth trichloride. It is hydrolyzed by water, forming bismuthyl chloride. The evaporation of the hydrochloric acid soln. furnishes the *hemipentahydrate,* $K_2BiCl_5.2\frac{1}{2}H_2O$. C. F. Rammelsberg obtained the hydrate by crystallization from an aq. soln. of the component salts in the molar ratio $BiCl_3 : KCl = 1 : 1$; V. A. Jacquelain from a soln. with this ratio $1 : 2$; C. P. Brigham, $1 : 3$; and A. E. Arppe, $4 : 3$. According to C. F. Rammelsberg, the colourless plates are rhombic bipyramids with the axial ratios $a : b : c = 0.6873 : 1 : 7.7979$. The salt is stable in air ; it loses no water in the desiccator, but gives off all its water of crystallization at $100°$. As indicated above, it is hydrolyzed by water ; and crystallizes unchanged from conc. hydrochloric acid. C. P. Brigham showed that **potassium tetrachlorobismuthite,** $KBiCl_4.H_2O$, is formed when a hot, hydrochloric acid soln. of 5 mols of bismuth oxide and 4 mols of potassium chloride is evaporated until on cooling radiating masses of fibrous crystals separate out on cooling. The salt loses half its water of crystallization over calcium chloride, and the remainder at $105°$. The salt begins to decompose at $140°$. It can be recrystallized from a conc. soln. of bismuth trichloride ; when crystallized from hydrochloric acid, it forms $K_2BiCl_5.2\frac{1}{2}H_2O$; when treated with conc. sulphuric acid, it forms $KBi(SO_4)_2$. By a similar process, C. P. Brigham prepared **rubidium tetrachlorobismuthite,** $RbBiCl_4.H_2O$, in colourless needles. P. P. Dehérain obtained six-sided plates of **sodium hexachlorobismuthite,** Na_3BiCl_6, by crystallization from a soln. with stoichiometrical proportions of the component salts. A. E. Arppe reported that rhombic plates of **potassium hexachlorobismuthite,** K_3BiCl_6, crystallize from a hydrochloric acid soln. of a mol of bismuth trichloride and 2 mols of potassium chloride, but C. F. Rammelsberg, and C. P. Brigham obtained the pentachlorobismuthite under these conditions. P. P. Dehérain said that rhombic plates of **ammonium potassium hexachlorobismuthite,** $(NH_4)_2KBiCl_5$, are produced from a soln. of the component salts. C. P. Brigham prepared **rubidium hexachlorobismuthite,** Rb_3BiCl_6, as a crystalline precipitate by slowly adding a hydrochloric acid soln. of bismuth chloride to a conc. soln. of rubidium chloride in dil. hydrochloric acid. T. H. Behrens also prepared the salt. R. Godeffroy reported $6RbCl.BiCl_3$ to be formed by this process, but C. P. Brigham showed that this product was probably a mixture ; similar remarks apply to R. Godeffroy's $6CsCl.BiCl_3$. C. P. Brigham prepared transparent plates of **cæsium hexachlorobismuthite,** $3CsCl.BiCl_3$, and T. H. Behrens obtained a similar salt. C. P. Brigham obtained **rubidium hexadecachlorotribismuthite,** $7RbCl.3BiCl_3$—possibly $23RbCl.10BiCl_3$—analogous to the antimony compound, by crystallization from a dil. hydrochloric acid soln. of a mol of bismuth trioxide and 2 mols of rubidium chloride. It can be recrystallized from a soln. of bismuth trichloride ; but by crystallization from a soln. in hydrochloric acid, rubidium hexachlorobismuthite is formed. If a hydrochloric acid soln. of bismuth trichloride be added to a soln. of cæsium chloride in dil. hydrochloric acid, a crystalline precipitate which is a mixture of the colourless plates of the hexachlorobismuthite, and yellow pyramids of **cæsium enneachlorodibismuthite,** $3CsCl.2BiCl_3$, are formed. The latter salt is decomposed by water, but can be crystallized unchanged from its soln. in hydrochloric acid. E. H. Duclaux examined the cæsium salt as an aid to the microdetection of bismuth.

G. Hermann's measurements of the f.p. of mixtures of cuprous and bismuth chlorides give a simple **V**-curve, Fig. 20, with no evidence of the formation of a

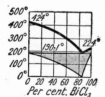

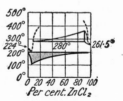

FIG. 20.—Freezing-point Curve of Mixtures : CuCl–BiCl₃.

FIG. 21.—Freezing-point Curve of Mixtures : ZnCl₂–BiCl₃.

cuprous chlorobismuthite. R. F. Weinland and co-workers described a series of salts of an imaginary *pentachlorobismuthous acid,* $H_2[BiCl_5]$, represented by **calcium pentachlorobismuthite,** $CaBiCl_5.7H_2O$, in tabular crystals ; **strontium pentachlorobismuthite,** $SrBiCl_5.H_2O$, in rectangular, four-sided plates, and **barium pentachlorobismuthite,** $BaBiCl_5.4H_2O$, in rhombic plates. Another series referred to *tetrachlorobismuthous acid,* $HBiCl_4$, was represented by colourless needles of **calcium tetrachlorobismuthite,** $Ca(BiCl_4)_2.7H_2O$; stout needles of **strontium tetrachlorobismuthite,** $Sr(BiCl_4)_2.7H_2O$; and slender needles of **barium tetrachlorobismuthite,** $Ba(BiCl_4)_2.5H_2O$. Yet a third series corresponding with *heptachlorodibismuthous acid,* HBi_2Cl_7, is represented by **strontium heptachlorodibismuthite,** $Sr(Bi_2Cl_7)_2.12H_2O$. Other representatives of these acids have been made : **magnesium pentachlorobismuthite,** $MgBiCl_5.8H_2O$, in stout, rectangular plates ; and **magnesium heptachlorodibismuthite,** $Mg(Bi_2Cl_7)_2.16H_2O$, in six-sided leaflets. G. Hermann's observations on the f.p. of mixtures of zinc and bismuth chlorides are summarized in Fig. 21. The two salts are only partially miscible in the liquid state, but solid soln. are formed to a limited extent, but no *zinc chlorobismuthite* is formed.

J. Nicklès obtained a complex salt with thallium by adding a soln. of potassium thallium chloride to one of a bismuth salt. G. Scarpa studied the f.p. curve of the system $TlCl–BiCl_3$. The results are summarized in Fig. 22. There is a eutectic at 360° and 12·5 molar per cent. of bismuth trichloride, and a maximum at 413° corresponding with **thallium hexachlorobismuthite**, $3TlCl.BiCl_3$. F. Ephraim and

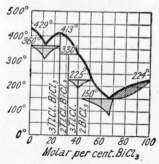

FIG. 22.—Freezing-point Curves of the Binary System : TlCl–BiCl₃.

P. Barteczko prepared thin, colourless plates of this compound in a hydrochloric acid soln. of its components ; if an excess of bismuth trichloride be used, **thallium enneachlorobismuthite**, $6TlCl.BiCl_3$, is formed. G. Scarpa observed a break in the f.p. curve at 330° and about 40 molar per cent. of the trichloride corresponding with the formation of **thallium pentachlorobismuthite**, $2TlCl.BiCl_3$; and another break at 225° and about 52 molar per cent. of bismuth trichloride corresponding with **thallium enneachlorodibismuthite**, $3TlCl.2BiCl_3$. There is a eutectic at 150° and 67 molar per cent. of the trichloride ; with more trichloride, mixed crystals are formed. G. Hermann's observations on the f.p. of mixtures of lead and bismuth chlorides are summarized in Fig. 23. There is a break at 323·5° corresponding with the formation of lead chlorobismuthite of unknown composition. Resuming the observations of R. F. Weinland and co-workers, A. C. Vournasos studied the complex chloro- and chlorofluoammines. Flesh-coloured, six-sided plates of **manganese heptachlorodibismuthite**, $Mn(Bi_2Cl_7)_2.12H_2O$; faintly yellowish-red plates of **ferrous heptachlorodibismuthite**, $Fe(Bi_2Cl)_7.12H_2O$, were obtained by the same process. G. Hermann's observations on the f.p. curve of ferric and bismuth chlorides are summarized in Fig. 24. There is a simple V-curve with no indication

FIG. 23.—Freezing-point Curve of Mixtures : PbCl₂–BiCl₃.

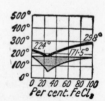

FIG. 24.—Freezing-point Curve of Mixtures : FeCl₃–BiCl₃.

of a *ferric chlorobismuthite.* R. F. Weinland and co-workers prepared prisms of **cobalt pentachlorobismuthite**, $CoBiCl_5.6H_2O$; green needles of **nickel pentachlorobismuthite**, $NiBiCl_5.6H_2O$; **cobalt heptachlorodibismuthite**, $Co(Bi_2Cl_7)_2.12H_2O$, in red, six-sided plates ; and **nickel heptachlorodibismuthite**, $Ni(Bi_2Cl_7)_2.12H_2O$, in pale green, six-sided plates. These salts were obtained by dissolving bismuth chloride in the smallest possible quantity of conc. hydrochloric acid, and treating the soln. with the carbonate, hydroxide, or chloride of the bivalent metal. The heptachlorobismuthites are produced from the sat. soln. of the metal hydroxide or carbonate in the soln. of bismuth trichloride ; the tetrachlorobismuthites from soln. with the molar ratio of bismuth trichloride to that of the bivalent metal chloride is as 5 : 2 or 5 : 1 ; and the heptachlorodibismuthites when this ratio is 10 : 1.

REFERENCES.

[1] M. M. P. Muir, *Journ. Chem. Soc.*, 29. 146, 1876 ; 32. 138, 1877 ; A. Gutbier, *Zeit. anorg. Chem.*, 48. 162, 298, 1906 ; 49. 432, 1906 ; 50. 210, 1906 ; E. B. Hutchins and V. Lenher, *Journ. Amer. Chem. Soc.*, 29. 31, 1907 ; G. Rauter, *Liebig's Ann.*, 270. 251, 1892.
[2] P. P. Dehérain, *Bull. Soc. Chim.*, (1), 3. 51, 1861 ; (1), 4. 22, 1862 ; *Compt. Rend.*, 52. 734, 1861 ; 54. 724, 1862 ; 55. 807, 1862 ; V. Thomas, *ib.,* 122. 1060, 1896 ; *Ann. Chim. Phys.*,

(7), **13**. 145, 1898 ; A. Michaelis, *Journ. prakt. Chem.*, (2), **4**. 454, 1871 ; R. Schneider, *Pogg. Ann.*, 96. 130, 496, 1855 ; R. Weber, *ib.*, **107**. 596, 1859 ; W. Heintz, *ib.*, **63**. 59, 1843 ; M. M. P. Muir, *Journ. Chem. Soc.*, **29**. 144, 1876 ; L. Marino and R. Becarelli, *Atti Accad. Lincei*, (5), **24**. ii, 625, 1915 ; (5), **25**. i, 105, 171, 221, 326, 1916 ; W. Herz and A. Guttmann, *Zeit. anorg. Chem.*, **56**. 422, 1908 ; B. G. Eggink, *Zeit. phys. Chem.*, **64**. 449, 1908.

³ R. Boyle, *Experiments and Considerations touching Colours*, London, 1664 ; M. Poli, *Mém. Acad.*, 40, 1713.

⁴ W. Jacobs, *Chem. Weekbl.*, **14**. 208, 1917 ; G. Oddo and E. Serra, *Gazz. Chim. Ital.*, **29**. ii, 355, 1899 ; G. Oddo and U. Giachery, *ib.*, **53**. i, 56, 1923 ; A. Mutscheller, *Met. Chem. Engg.*, **16**. 594, 1917 ; A. Michaelis, *Journ. prakt. Chem.*, (2), **4**. 454, 1871 ; W. L. Miller and F. B. Kenrick, *Journ. Amer. Chem. Soc.*, **22**. 291, 1900 ; W. Remmler, *Ber.*, **24**. 3554, 1891 ; G. Waris, *Journ. Indian Chem. Soc.*, **1**. 307, 1924 ; G. Rauter, *Liebig's Ann.*, **270**. 251, 1892 ; R. Weber, *Pogg. Ann.*, **107**. 596, 1859 ; W. Heintz, *ib.*, **63**. 59, 1844 ; R. Schneider, *ib.*, **96**. 130, 1855 ; M. M. P. Muir and E. M. Eagles, *Journ. Chem. Soc.*, **67**. 90, 1895 ; M. M. P. Muir, *ib.*, **33**. 193, 1878 ; **39**. 36, 1881 ; A. A. Noyes, F. W. Hall, and J. A. Beattie, *Journ. Amer. Chem. Soc.*, **39**. 1526, 1917 ; K. Jellinek and W. Kühn, *Zeit. phys. Chem.*, **105**. 337, 1923 ; J. Davy, *Phil. Trans.*, **102**. 169, 1812 ; F. M. Jäger, *Zeit. anorg. Chem.*, **101**. 175, 1917.

⁵ C. G. Maier, *Vapour Pressures of the Common Metallic Chlorides*, Washington, 45, 1925 ; J. B. A. Dumas, *Ann. Chim. Phys.*, (3), **55**. 176, 1859 ; J. Persoz, *ib.*, (2), **44**. 315, 1830 ; V. A. Jacquelain, *ib.*, (2), **66**. 113, 1837 ; J. Durocher, *Compt. Rend.*, **32**. 823, 1851 ; H. E. Causse, *ib.*, **112**. 1220, 1891 ; **113**. 547, 1891 ; A. Ditte, *ib.*, **91**. 986, 1880 ; A. Ditte and R. Metzner, *ib.*, **115**. 1303, 1892 ; *Ann. Chim. Phys.*, (6), **29**. 389, 1893 ; R. Engel, *Bull. Soc. Chim.*, (3), **1**. 695, 1889 ; *Compt. Rend.*, **106**. 1797, 1888 ; V. Thomas, *ib.*, **121**. 129, 1895 ; **122**. 611, 1896 ; A. Besson, *ib.*, **108**. 1012, 1889 ; R. Dubrisay, *ib.*, **148**. 830, 1909 ; T. Karantassis, *ib.*, **182**. 699, 1391, 1926 ; F. Winkler, *Das Atomgewicht des Antimons. Neubestimmung durch Ueberführung des Metalls in Antimon-Tetroxyd*, München, 1917 ; L. Rosenstein, *Journ. Amer. Chem. Soc.*, **42**. 883, 1920 ; J. Hanus and A. Jilek, *Chem. Listy*, **18**. 8, 1924 ; P. Groth, *Chemische Krystallographie*, **1**. 429, 1906 ; C. F. Rammelsberg, *Handbuch der krystallographischen Chemie*, Berlin, 215, 1855 ; *Pogg. Ann.*, **106**. 146, 1859 ; W. Herz and A. Bulla, *Zeit. anorg. Chem.*, **61**. 387, 1909 ; **63**. 59, 282, 1909 ; K. Schäfer and F. Hein, *ib.*, **100**. 249, 1917 ; A. Gutbier and M. Müller, *ib.*, **128**. 137, 1923 ; R. Lorenz and W. Herz, *ib.*, **120**. 320, 1921 ; **145**. 89, 1925 ; **147**. 135, 1925 ; S. Motylewsky, *ib.*, **38**. 410, 1904 ; A. Voigt and W. Biltz, *ib.*, **133**. 277, 1924 ; W. Biltz, *ib.*, **115**. 241, 1921 ; **133**. 304, 1924 ; I. I. Saslowsky, *ib.*, **146**. 315, 1925 ; F. Challenger and J. F. Wilkinson, *Journ. Chem. Soc.*, **121**. 91, 1922 ; F. Challenger and C. F. Allpress, *ib.*, **107**. 21, 1915 ; **119**. 913, 1921 ; F. Challenger, *ib.*, **105**. 2210, 1916 ; **109**. 250, 1916 ; F. Challenger and A. E. Goddard, *ib.*, **117**. 762, 1920 ; F. Challenger and L. R. Ridgway, *ib.*, **121**. 104, 1922 ; C. R. Crymble, *Proc. Chem. Soc.*, **30**. 179, 1914 ; A. K. Macbeth and N. I. Maxwell, *Journ. Chem. Soc.*, **123**. 370, 1923 ; G. Bruni and A. Manuelli, *Zeit. Elektrochem.*, **11**. 554, 1905 ; A. A. Noyes, F. W. Hall, and J. A. Beattie, *Journ. Amer. Chem. Soc.*, **39**. 25, 26, 1917 ; F. E. Brown and J. E. Synder, *ib.*, **47**. 2671, 1925 ; H. Schiff, *Untersuchungen über metallhältige Anilinderivate*, Berlin, 1864 ; *Ber.*, **34**. 805, 1901 ; H. Cousin, *Journ. Pharm. Chim.*, (7), **28**. 179, 1923 ; A. K. Macbeth and N. I. Maxwell, *Journ. Chem. Soc.*, **123**. 370, 1923 ; N. P. Peskoff, *Bull. Inst. Polyt. Ivanovo-Zoznesesk*, **17**. 119, 1923 ; G. Hänsel, *Wiss. Siemens Konz.*, **4**. 111, 1925 ; M. Escher, *Compt. Rend.*, **177**. 172, 1923 ; T. Karantassis, *ib.*, **182**. 699, 1926 ; J. P. Wibaut, J. J. Diekmann, and A. J. Rutgers, *Proc. Acad. Amsterdam*, **27**. 671, 1924 ; A. Gutbier, *Zeit. anorg. Chem.*, **128**. 137, 1923 ; A. C. Vournasos, *ib.*, **81**. 364, 1913 ; **159**. 147, 1926 ; M. M. P. Muir, *Journ. Chem. Soc.*, **29**. 144, 1876 ; **33**. 193, 1878 ; **39**. 36, 1881 ; M. M. P. Muir and E. M. Eagles, *ib.*, **67**. 90, 1895 : T. Carnelley and W. C. Williams, *ib.*, **33**. 281, 1878 ; J. J. Sudborough, *ib.*, **59**. 655, 1891 ; E. F. Smith and P. Heyl, *Zeit. anorg. Chem.*, 7. 87, 1894 ; W. Biltz and W. Klemm, *ib.*, **152**. 267, 1926 ; E. Glatzel, *ib.*, **4**. 186, 1893 ; F. M. Jäger, *ib.*, **101**. 175, 1917 ; E. Zintl and G. Rienäcker, *ib.*, **161**. 374, 385, 1927 ; V. Meyer and F. Freyer, *ib.*, **2**. 4, 1892 ; V. Meyer and A. Krause, *Liebig's Ann.*, **264**. 124, 1891 ; R. Anschütz and H. Weyer, *ib.*, **261**. 297, 1891 ; K. Seubert and A. Schmidt, *ib.*, **267**. 238, 1892 ; J. Davy, *Phil. Trans.*, **102**. 169, 1812 ; W. Heintz, *Journ. prakt. Chem.*, (1), **45**. 102, 1848 ; *Pogg. Ann.*, **63**. 59, 1844 ; R. Weber, *ib.*, **107**. 596, 1859 ; R. Schneider, *ib.*, **93**. 464, 1854 ; **96**. 132, 1855 ; A. E. Arppe, *ib.*, **64**. 237, 1845 ; *Dissertatio de jodato bismuthico*, Helsingfors, 1843 ; *Akad. Handl. Stockholm*, 133, 1842 ; F. Hartl, *Arch. Pharm.*, **244**. 216, 1906 ; U. Antony and G. Magri, *Gazz. Chim. Ital.*, **35**. i, 206, 1905 ; A. Cavazzi, *ib.*, **14**. 219, 1884 ; C. Montemartini, *ib.*, **30**. ii, 493, 1900 ; **32**. ii, 178, 1902 ; A. Ferratini, *ib.*, **42**. i, 138, 1912 ; A. Naumann and P. Schulz, *Ber.*, **37**. 4331, 1904 ; A. Naumann, *ib.*, **42**. 3790, 1909 ; **43**. 314, 320, 1910 ; **47**. 1369, 1914 ; G. Vortmann and C. Padberg, *ib.*, **22**. 2642, 1889 ; H. Rheinboldt and R. Wasserfuhr, *ib.*, **60**. B, 732, 1927 ; L. Rügheimer, *ib.*, **36**. 3030, 1903 ; L. Rügheimer and E. Rudolfi, *Liebig's Ann.*, **339**. 349, 1905 ; P. Kulisch, *ib.*, **231**. 349, 1885 ; J. Volhard, *ib.*, **198**. 331, 1879 ; V. Merz and W. Weith, *Ber.*, **13**. 210, 1880 ; G. Vortmann and C. Padberg, *ib.*, **22**. 2642, 1889 ; H. Schiff, *ib.*, **34**. 804, 1901 ; J. Thomson, *ib.*, **16**. 39, 1883 ; L. Vanino and O. Hauser, *ib.*, **33**. 2271, 1900 ; **34**. 416, 1901 ; **35**. 663, 1902 ; **36**. 3682, 1903 ; L. Vanino and F. Hartl, *Arch. Pharm.*, **244**. 216, 1906 ; W. Jacobs, *Chem. Weekbl.*, **14**. 208, 1917 ; E. Liesegang, *Phot. Arch.*, **34**. 177, 1893 ; W. Ostwald, *Journ. prakt. Chem.*, (2), **12**. 264, 1875 ; W. Eidmann, *Ein Beitrag zur Erkenntnis des Verhaltens chemischer Verbindungen in nichtwässerigen Lösungen*, Giessen, 1899 ; C. H. D. Bödeker, *Die Beziehungen zwischen Dichte und Zusammensetzung bei festen und liquiden Stoffen*, Leipzig, 1860 ;

G. Gore, *Proc. Roy. Soc.*, 21. 140, 1873; R. W. E. MacIvor, *Chem. News*, 32. 229, 1875;
S. Schlesinger, *Repert. Pharm.*, (2), 35. 74, 1844; A. Vogel, *Kastner's Arch.*, 23. 68, 1832;
P. P. Dehérain, *Bull. Soc. Chim.*, (1), 3. 51, 1861; (1), 4. 22, 1862; *Compt. Rend.*, 52. 734,
1861; 54. 724, 1862; 55. 807, 1862; G. Scarpa, *Atti Accad. Lincei*, (5), 21. ii, 719, 1912;
G. N. Quam and J. A. Wilkinson, *Proc. Iowa Acad.*, 32. 324, 1925; *Journ. Amer. Chem. Soc.*,
47. 990, 1925; G. N. Quam, *ib.*, 47. 103, 1925.
    [6] A. E. Arppe, *Dissertatio de jodato bismutico*, Helsingfors, 1843; *Akad. Handl. Stockholm*,
133, 1842; *Pogg. Ann.*, 64. 237, 1845; C. F. Rammelsberg, *ib.*, 106. 145, 1854; *Handbuch
der krystallographischen Chemie*, Berlin, 215, 1855; V. A. Jacquelain, *Ann. Chim. Phys.*,
(2), 46. 113, 1838; I. Remsen, *Amer. Chem. Journ.*, 14. 81, 1892; C. P. Brigham, *ib.*, 14.
81, 164, 1892; J. Aloy and A. Frébault, *Bull. Soc. Chim.*, (3), 35. 397, 1906; P. P. Dehérain, *ib.*,
(1), 3. 51, 1861; (1), 4. 22, 1862; *Compt. Rend.*, 52. 734, 1861; 54. 724, 1862; 55. 807, 18(2;
T. H. Behrens, *Zeit. anal. Chem.*, 30. 162, 1891; E. H. Duclaux, *Mikrochemie*, 2. 108, 19:4;
Anal. Asoc. Quim. Argentina, 9. 215, 1921; R. Godeffroy, *Ber.*, 8. 9, 1875; R. F. Weinland,
A. Alber, and J. Schweiger, *Arch. Pharm.*, 254. 521, 1916; G. Scarpa, *Atti Accad. Lincei*, (5), 21.
ii, 719, 1912; F. Ephraim and P. Barteczko, *Zeit. anorg. Chem.*, 61. 238, 1909; J. Nicklès, *Journ.
Pharm. Chim.*, (4), 1. 27, 1865; (4), 2. 218, 1865; G. Hermann, *Zeit. anorg. Chem.*, 71. 257, 1911;
A. C. Vournasos, *ib.*, 150. 147, 1926.

§ 12. The Bismuth Bromides

According to R. Weber,[1] when 2 mols of bismuth trichloride are melted together
with a gram-atom of bismuth, and cooled, a brown mass of needle-like crystals is
obtained which is probably **bismuth dibromide**, $BiBr_2$. G. S. Sérullas' description
of bismuth dibromide as a steel-grey mass makes it probable that his product was
contaminated with the tribromide. M. M. P. Muir also observed that in the preparation of the tribromide by the action of bromine on bismuth, the dibromide may be
formed in dark grey crystals which are very difficult to separate from the tribromide.
W. Herz and A. Gutmann gave 5·9 for the sp. gr. of the black leaflets, and 198° for
the m.p. R. Weber said that the dibromide is decomposed by water, and by
hydrochloric acid with the separation of bismuth. B. G. Eggink observed no sign
of the dichloride on the f.p. curve of bismuth and bromine; but he observed the
formation of *bismuth monobromide*, BiBr, melting at 287°, forming two liquid phases.
L. Marino and R. Becarelli found that when the mixtures of bismuth with 5 to 85
per cent. of bismuth tribromide are fused in

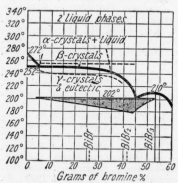

sealed tubes, two layers are obtained above
320°—the upper one being black, the lower one
white. Lowering the temp. from 320° results
in the formation of (i) a crystalline product
melting over the range 270°–305°, and at about
240° this is transformed into a product melting at about 260° and one at 270°–305°; and
(ii), the other stratum furnishes the eutectic
Bi–BiBr₃, melting at about 202°. Hence, the
solidification of the fused mixtures lying within
definite limits of concentration yields two
layers, the upper one consisting of black,
acicular crystals and the lower one of a mass

Fig. 25.—Portion of Equilibrium
Diagram of the System : Bi–BiBr₃.

of crystals with metallic lustre, m.p. 230°–270°,
and covered with a black skin; the lower
crystals are sensitive to light, and soon
lose their brilliancy and become iridescent and then greyish-blue. The black
upper layer does not consist of a single compound, but is separable into a
highly hygroscopic black mass and a crystalline network melting over a range of
temp. above 270°. From all the upper layers formed in the different mixtures of
bismuth and its tribromide at 200°, there drops in greater or less quantity, according
to the composition of the mixture, a black hygroscopic substance. For each of these
strata there remains a crystalline network which melts between about 270° and 300°–

305°, and is regarded as a series of mixed crystals, which undergo transformation into a β-form and then into a γ-form with pronounced development of heat. The m.p. of the γ-crystals is always above those of bismuth and bismuth tribromide, and on fusion and cooling they yield α-crystals of different composition, together with two liquid strata which reproduce this series of changes. At 153°, bismuth tribromide undergoes transformation into the solid form. There is no evidence of the formation of a sub-bromide. B. G. Eggink studied the system and interpreted his results on the assumption that a sub-bromide is formed.

Bromine does not unite so vigorously with bismuth as it does with antimony, and G. S. Sérullas [2] said that **bismuth tribromide,** $BiBr_3$, is formed. If the bismuth be in excess, R. Weber, and M. M. P. Muir showed that some dibromide is formed. R. Weber obtained the tribromide by heating bismuth in the vapour of bromine ; V. Meyer and A. Krause, by introducing finely powdered bismuth into bromine, distilling off the tribromide after it has stood for a few days ; and purifying the product by repeated distillation ; J. Nicklès, by adding powdered bismuth to a mixture of equal parts of bromine and ether, filtering the liquid after it had stood for some time, and evaporating in vacuo ; M. M. P. Muir, by heating the oxide in a current of bromine vapour—the oxybromide, $Br_{11}O_{13}Br_7$, is formed as a by-product ; P. Jannasch, by strongly heating the trisulphide in a current of bromine vapour ; G. Oddo and U. Giachery, by heating a mixture of stoichiometrical proportions of bismuth oxide and sulphur in a current of bromine ; and A. C. Vournasos, by heating to 100° a mixture of bismuth trioxide and potassium bromide with acetic acid.

Bismuth tribromide furnishes an orange-yellow, crystalline mass, or, when slowly sublimed, golden-yellow crystals. M. M. P. Muir's analysis corresponds with $BiBr_3$. C. H. D. Bödeker gave 5·604 for the **specific gravity** of the crystals ; and M. M. P. Muir, 5·4 at 20°. R. Lorenz and W. Herz gave 5·604 for the sp. gr. at ordinary temp., and 4·682 at the b.p. W. Biltz studied the **molecular volume ;** R. Lorenz and W. Biltz gave 448·8 for the mol. vol. I. I. Saslawsky calculated a 0·01 per cent. contraction in the formation of this compound from its elements. F. M. Jäger gave the following values for the sp. gr. of the liquid, referred to water at 4° ; the **surface tension,** σ dynes per cm. ; the **specific cohesion,** a^2 sq. mm. ; and the molar **surface energy,** E ergs per sq. cm. :

	250°	281°	299°	320°	346°	370°	389°	417°	442°
Sp. gr.	4·598	4·525	4·471	4·416	4·348	4·286	4·237	4·164	4·099
σ	66·5	63·6	61·6	59·5	56·7	53·8	52·0	48·9	46·2
E	1407·6	1360·6	328·4	293·8	1245·7	1191·3	1162·3	1105·8	1055·8
a^2	2·95	2·88	2·81	2·74	2·66	2·58	2·50	2·40	2·30

The sp. gr., D, at $\theta°$ was represented by $4·598—0·0026(\theta—250)$. S. Motylewsky gave 78 for the drop-weight of the tribromide when that of water is 100. R. Lorenz and W. Herz studied some relations of the surface tensions of the family of halides. R. Lorenz and W. Herz gave 0·000375 for the coeff. of thermal expansion. R. Weber said that the tribromide melts to a red liquid ; and F. M. Jäger, to a yellow liquid. G. S. Sérullas gave 200° for the **melting point ;** R. W. E. MacIvor, 198°-202° ; J. Kendall and co-workers, 220·4° ; M. M. P. Muir, 210°-215° ; R. Lorenz and W. Herz, 217·5° ; F. M. Jäger, 215° ; T. Carnelley and W. C. Williams found the **boiling point** to be 454°-498° ; V. Meyer and A. Krause, 453° ; and R. Anschütz and H. Weyer, 278° at 11 mm. press. V. Meyer and A. Krause said that the vapour is deep red, very like that of sulphur ; and it can be heated in a glass vessel for an hour without decomposition. K. Schäfer and F. Hein measured the **absorption spectrum** of soln. of bismuth tribromide in hydrobromic acid and in ether, and inferred that the absorbing complex in the aq. soln. is a simple bromobismuthous acid. W. A. Isbekoff measured the **decomposition voltage** of bismuth tribromide dissolved in aluminium bromide ; and W. Finkelstein found that in nitrobenzene soln., the decomposition voltage is 0·60 volt.

M. M. P. Muir said that the tribromide can be distilled in **hydrogen** without change ; and when heated in **air,** the oxybromide, $Bi_8O_{15}Br_6$, is formed, while

V. Thomas said that very little oxidation occurs, for only a little BiOBr is formed.
G. S. Sérullas, and M. M. P. Muir found that the tribromide attracts moisture from
air, and is decomposed by **water** with the separation of bismuthyl bromide.
A. K. Sanyal and N. R. Dhar found that bismuth bromide is decomposed by
exposure to tropical sunlight. W. Herz and A. Bulla observed that the tribromide
behaves like the trichloride ($q.v.$) towards water, and only one oxybromide, BiOBr, is
formed ; the hydrolysis is very little affected by a rise of temp. from 25° to 50°.
J. Aloy and A. Frébault found that when the tribromide is dissolved to saturation by
conc. **hydrobromic acid,** and cooled to −10°, **hydropentabromobismuthous acid,**
$H_2BiBr_5.4H_2O$, or $BiBr_3.2HBr.4H_2O$, is formed. The yellow, deliquescent needles
lose hydrogen bromide when exposed to air. According to M. M. P. Muir, only a
little sulphobromide is formed when bismuth tribromide is heated with **sulphur**
and, according to M. M. P. Muir and E. M. Eagles, the same compound is produced
by the action of **hydrogen sulphide** at a suitable temp.—but at a higher temp.,
bismuth trisulphide is formed. The tribromide is not changed by heating it in a
current of **sulphur dioxide.** According to M. M. P. Muir, when the tribromide is
warmed in a current of dry **ammonia,** it melts, and a yellow vapour is given off which
condenses in the cold part of the tube as **bismuth triamminotribromide,** $BiBr_3.3NH_3$,
as a straw-yellow, amorphous powder which attracts moisture from the air, is
decomposed by water, forming an oxybromide ; and with hydrochloric acid it forms
$3NH_4Cl.BiBr_3.H_2O$. If bismuth tribromide be melted in ammonia gas, the olive-
green residue is **bismuth diamminotribromide,** $BiBr_3.2NH_3$. It deliquesces in air :
is decomposed by water ; and forms $3NH_4Cl.BiBr_3.3H_2O$ when treated with hydrochloric acid. If molten bismuth tribromide be heated in ammonia until no more
vapour is given off at a red-heat, the product is **bismuth hemipentamminotri-**
bromide, $2BiBr_3.5NH_3$. It is also formed by heating one of the oxybromides in a
current of ammonia. The greyish-green sublimate decomposes when heated in air
giving off the tribromide, and leaving an oxybromide as residue. It is not decomposed by water, and is freely soluble in dil. acids , with hydrochloric acid, it forms
$5NH_4Cl.2BiBr_3.H_2O$. R. Weber said that the tribromide dissolves with decomposition in **nitric acid,** and V. Thomas, that at ordinary temp. **nitrogen peroxide**
transforms it into bismuthyl oxide. A. Cavazzi and D. Tivoli observed that
phosphine in an ethereal soln. of bismuth tribromide, yields $P(BiBr_2)_3HBr$,
phosphorus tribismuthodibromide hydrobromide. J. W. Retgers said that bismuth
tribromide readily dissolves in **arsenic tribromide ;** and S. Tolloczko, that when
bismuth tribromide is added to antimony tribromide, the f.p. is raised. J. Nicklès
said that the tribromide is freely soluble in **ether,** and forms a crystalline complex.
R. Brix studied the action of bismuth tribromide on ethyl iodide, and on ethyl
monochloracetate. A. C. Vournasos prepared complexes with organic amines,
pyridine, and quinoline. W. A. Isbekoff said that bismuth tribromide is soluble
in **aluminium tribromide.**

K. Schäfer and F. Hein showed that a bromobismuthous acid is probably formed
in soln. of hydrobromic acid ; and they isolated ethereal compounds of **hydropenta-**
bromobismuthous acid, $H_2BiBr_5.4(C_2H_5)_2O$, and $H_2BiBr_5.10(C_2H_5)_2O$. J. Aloy
and P. Frébault prepared this acid—*vide supra.* Complex salts of bismuth tribromide with ammonium and alkali bromides have been prepared in yellow crystals
which are decomposed by water. Thus, J. Nicklès obtained yellow, rhombic
needles of **ammonium tetrabromobismuthite,** $NH_4BiBr_4.H_2O$, by the action of
bromine and alcohol on bismuth in the presence of ammonium bromide. The salt
is soluble in alcohol. He also obtained **ammonium pentabromobismuthite,**
$(NH_4)_2BiBr_5.2\frac{1}{2}H_2O$, by heating in a sealed tube a mixture of bismuth tribromide,
ammonium bromide, alcohol, and a little ammonium acetate. The greenish-yellow,
rhombic crystals were found by C. F. Rammelsberg to be isomorphous with those
of the corresponding chloride, and the potassium salt. J. Nicklès reported
$2NH_4BrBi(Br,Cl)_3.2\frac{1}{2}H_2O$, in mixed isomorphous crystals. The water of crystallization is all expelled at 100° ; the salt is decomposed by heat, and by water,

J. Aloy and **A. Frébault** prepared **potassium pentabromobismuthite,** K_2BiBr_5, by the method employed for the corresponding chloride, namely, by passing bromine vapour with the aid of carbon dioxide over molten bismuth and the tribromide passed over potassium bromide at a red-heat. The product is cooled in a current of carbon dioxide. The amber-yellow, crystalline mass becomes dark-yellow and then brownish-red when heated; it melts at about 600° without giving off vapours. It is decomposed by water.

Some mixed salts have been reported. Thus, M. M. P. Muir obtained yellow crystals of **ammonium dichlorotribromobismuthite,** $2NH_4Cl.BiBr_3.3H_2O$, by the action of hydrochloric acid on bismuth diamminotribromide; by similarly treating the hemipentamminotribromide he obtained ammonium pentachlorohexabromobismuthite, $5NH_4Cl.2BiBr_3.H_2O$; while the triamminotribromide yields **ammonium trichlorotribromobismuthite,** $3NH_4Cl.BiBr_3.H_2O$, in pale yellow, deliquescent plates. E. Field obtained the same salt from a soln. of equimolar parts of bismuth trichloride and ammonium bromide, or of ammonium chloride and bismuth tribromide. E. Field obtained what was regarded as **potassium pentachlorobromobismuthite,** $K_2BiBrCl_4$, by crystallization from a soln. of equimolar parts of bismuth trichloride and potassium bromide; a soln. of equimolar parts of bismuth tribromide and potassium chloride furnishes **potassium chlorotetrabromide,** $K_2BiClBr_4$. R.W. Atkinson said that **potassium trichlorodibromide,** $K_2BiCl_3Br_2.1\frac{1}{2}H_2O$, separates in yellow prisms from a soln. of bismuth tribromide in a sat. soln. of potassium chloride. J. Kendall and co-workers found that the f.p. curve of mixtures with aluminium bromide, Fig. 27, showed the existence of **aluminium hexabromobismuthite,** $AlBr_3.BiBr_3$. C. Canneri and G. Perina prepared **thallous pentabromobismuthite,** Tl_2BiBr_5, by adding potassium bromide to a soln. of bismuth carbonate in nitric acid. It forms lustrous, lemon-yellow, hexagonal lamellæ, and is rapidly hydrolyzed in neutral aq. soln. to thallous

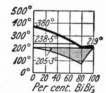

Fig. 26.—Freezing-point Curve of Lead and Bismuth Bromides.

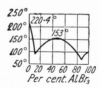

Fig. 27.—Freezing-point Curve of Mixtures : $AlBr_3$–$BiBr_3$.

bromide, bismuth oxybromide, and bromine. G. Hermann measured the f.p. of mixtures of lead and bismuth bromides; the results are summarized in Fig. 26. There is a break at 238·5°, corresponding with the formation of **lead bromobismuthite** of unknown composition. A. C. Vournasos studied the complex mixed halogenoammines.

REFERENCES.

¹ R. Weber, *Pogg. Ann.*, **107**. 600, 1859 ; M. M. P. Muir, *Journ. Chem. Soc.*, **29**. 145, 1876 ; G. S. Sérullas, *Ann. Chim. Phys.*, (2), **38**. 323, 1828 ; B. G. Eggink, *Zeit. phys. Chem.*, **64**. 449, 1908 ; L. Marino and R. Becarelli, *Atti Accad. Lincei*, (5), **24**. ii, 625, 1915 ; (5), **25**. i, 105, 171, 221, 326, 1916 ; W. Herz and A. Gutmann, *Zeit. anorg. Chem.*, **64**. 449, 1908.

² M. M. P. Muir and E. M. Eagles, *Journ. Chem. Soc.*, **67**. 90, 1895 ; M. M. P. Muir, *ib.*, **29**. 145, 1876 ; **39**. 37, 1881 ; T. Carnelley and W. C. Williams, *ib.*, **33**. 231, 1878 ; J. Nicklès, *Mém. Acad. Nancy*, 454, 1859 ; 1, 351, 354, 1860 ; *Journ. Pharm. Chim.*, (3), **39**. 33, 247, 423, 1861 ; (3), **40**. 191, 1861 ; (3), **41**. 146, 1859 ; *Compt. Rend.*, **48**. 837, 1859 ; **51**. 1097, 1862 ; **52**. 396, 1861 ; V. Thomas, *ib.*, **122**. 1060, 1896 ; H. Dubrisay, *ib.*, **148**. 830, 1909 ; A. C. Vournasos, *ib.*, **166**. 526, 1918 ; *Zeit. anorg. Chem.*, **150**. 147, 1926 ; J. Aloy and A. Frébault, *Bull. Soc. Chim.*, (3), **35**. 396, 1906 ; R. W. E. MacIvor, *Chem. News*, **30**. 190, 1874 ; E. Field, *ib.*, **67**. 157, 1893 ; *Journ. Chem. Soc.*, **63**. 540, 1893 ; R. W. Atkinson, *ib.*, **43**. 289, 1883 ; R. Weber, *Pogg. Ann.*, **107**. 600, 1859 ; C. F. Rammelsberg, *ib.*, **106**. 146, 1859 ; G. S. Sérullas, *Ann. Chim. Phys.*, (2), **38**. 323, 1828 ; R. Anschütz and H. Weyer, *Liebig's Ann.*, **261**. 297, 1891 ; V. Meyer and A. Krause,

2 κ

ib., **264**. 124, 1891 ; R. Brix, *ib.*, **225**. 146, 1884 ; J. W. Retgers, *Zeit. phys. Chem.*, **11**. 340, 1893 ;
W. Finkelstein, *ib.*, **115**. 303, 1925 ; P. Jannasch, *Ber.*, **24**. 3746, 1891 ; *Zeit. anorg. Chem.*, **9**.
194, 1895 ; R. Lorenz and W. Herz, *ib.*, **120**. 320, 1921 ; **145**. 88, 1925 ; **147**. 135, 1925 ;
G. Hermann, *ib.*, **71**. 257. 1911 ; K. Schäfer and F. Hein, *ib.*, **100**. 249, 1917 ; S. Motylewsky,
ib., **38**. 410, 1904 ; A. K. Sanyal and N. R. Dhar, *ib.*, **128**. 212, 1923 ; W. Biltz, *ib.*, **115**. 241,
1921 ; I. I. Saslawsky, *ib.*, **146**. 315, 1925 ; F. M. Jäger, *ib.*, **101**. 175, 1917 ; W. Herz and
A. Bulla, *ib.*, **61**. 387, 1909 ; **63**. 59, 282, 1909 ; W. A. Isbekoff, *ib.*, **84**. 27, 1913 ; *Zeit.
phys. Chem.*, **116**. 304, 1925 ; C. H. D. Bödeker, *Die Beziehungen zwischen Dichte und Zusammensetzung bei festen und liquiden Stoffen*, Leipzig, 1860 ; G. Oddo and U. Giachery, *Gazz. Chim.
Ital.*, **53**. i, 56, 1923 ; A. Cavazzi and D. Tivoli, *ib.*, **21**. ii, 306, 1891 ; C. Canneri and G. Perina,
ib., **52**. i, 241, 1922 ; S. Tolloczko, *Bull. Acad. Cracovie*, **1**, 1901 ; J. Kendall, E. D. Crittenden,
and H. K. Miller, *Journ. Amer. Chem. Soc.*, **45**. 963, 1923.

§ 13. The Bismuth Iodides

According to R. Weber,[1] bismuth triiodide readily dissolves bismuth, and when
the cold mass is treated with hydrochloric acid, bismuth remains as a fine black
powder ; if the iodide is fused with an excess of bismuth, a part of the dissolved
metal separates out on cooling, and the regulus contains 55·8 per cent. of bismuth
—bismuth triiodide has 35·4 per cent., and the diiodide, 45·1 per cent. It is uncertain whether an intermediate **bismuth diiodide**, BiI_2, is formed. A change of
colour analogous to that obtained with bismuth trichloride or tribromide does not
occur. L. Marino and R. Becarelli examined the f.p. of mixtures of bismuth

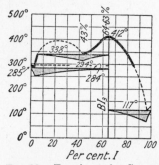

and iodine, and their results are summarized in
Fig. 28. There is here no evidence of the formation
of any iodide other than the triiodide. The eutectic
of bismuth and bismuth triiodide lies at 284°.
When mixtures containing 5–43 per cent. of iodine
are cooled, two layers are formed, of which the
upper contains excess of bismuth triiodide, and the
lower excess of bismuth. At 340°, the upper layer
begins to deposit solid bismuth triiodide, and as an
invariant system is thus formed, this crystallization
continues until all the upper has solidified ; during
this process the upper layer contains 66·5 per
cent. of bismuth triiodide, and the lower 7·73 per
cent. Mixtures with 43–64·63 per cent. of iodine
deposit bismuth triiodide, until the temp. 340°

Fig. 28.—Freezing-point Curves
of the Binary System: Bi–I.

is reached ; two layers are then formed as before. After the upper layer has
crystallized, the temp. falls until the eutectic 284° is reached, but there is
a thermal effect at 294°, possibly due to a transformation product of bismuth.
Mixtures containing more than 64·63 per cent. of iodine deposit bismuth triiodide,
and show a eutectic at 117°, but mixtures with more than 90 per cent. of iodine
could not be investigated, owing to the breakage of the tubes by the press. of the
iodine vapour. H. S. van Klooster also examined the f.p. curve, and said that there
is a reaction between the triiodide and the matrix, indicating the formation of
bismuth monoiodide, BiI ; there was no evidence of the formation of a diiodide.
On the other hand, W. Herz and A. Guttmann said that they obtained crystals
of bismuth diiodide by heating the triiodide with the calculated amount of bismuth ;
and H. G. Denham obtained the diiodide by distilling methyl iodide over lead
suboxide below 262°. The reaction vessel contained a non-volatile, brick-red
powder—bismuthyl iodide—and a bright-red sublimate of bismuth diiodide.

H. G. Denham said that bismuth diiodide is a volatile substance which crystallizes in red, rhombic needles, which, according to W. Herz and A. Guttmann, have
a sp. gr. of 6·5, and decompose below their m.p. H. G. Denham found that in aq.
soln., the diiodide gives stronger reactions for bismuth and iodine than the oxyiodide ;
it dissolves freely in potassium iodide soln., giving soln. of the colour of dichromate

soln. It speedily reduces aq. soln. of iodine and acid permanganate, and is decomposed at 400° into bismuth triiodide and bismuth. The distillate of excess methyl iodide from the preparation of the above compounds was yellow in colour, but on exposure to air it became colourless, and a white solid which turned yellow on keeping separated. This white compound is probably *bismuth dimethide*, and is insoluble in alcohol ; it is a strong reducing agent, and on oxidation is converted into *bismuth dimethoxide*, $Bi(OCH_3)_2$.

J. B. Berthemot prepared what was probably impure **bismuth triiodide,** BiI_3, by heating bismuth in iodine vapour. J. Nicklès employed a similar process ; R. Weber, by adding strongly heated bismuth to iodine vapour ; and W. Heintz, R. Schneider, and M. M. P. Muir and co-workers, by heating an intimate mixture of iodine and bismuth in an atm. of hydrogen or carbon dioxide. C. F. Rammelsberg added potassium iodide to an acetic acid soln. of a bismuth salt—with nitric acid soln., A. E. Arppe said that the precipitate is contaminated with nitrate ; and M. M. P. Muir and B. S. Gott, with iodine. Both obtained it pure by precipitating its soln. in conc. hydriodic acid with cold water. The reaction was studied by F. B. Stone, and J. C. Thresh ; A. C. Vournasos, by heating to 100° a mixture of bismuth trioxide and potassium iodide with acetic acid ; M. M. P. Muir, and C. F. Rammelsberg obtained bismuth triiodide by the action of conc. hydriodic acid on bismuth trioxide or oxyiodide at ordinary temp. ; and of hydrochloric acid on bismuth oxyiodide ; R. Schneider, and M. M. P. Muir and E. M. Eagles, by sublimation from a mixture of iodine and bismuth trisulphide—bismuth sulphoiodide remains in the residue ; G. Oddo and U. Giachery, by heating a mixture of the trioxide and sulphur in the vapour of iodine ; V. Auger, by the action of ethyl iodide on bismuth trichloride when ethyl chloride is formed as a by-product ; and L. Birckenbach, by saturating a soln. of stannous chloride, sat. with hydrogen chloride with iodine, then adding a hydrochloric acid soln. of bismuth trioxide or oxychloride, then drying the crystals first on porous tiles and afterwards in vacuo over calcium chloride ; and subliming the crystals in a current of hydrogen or carbon dioxide.

J. Nicklès described the sublimed triiodide as consisting of six-sided, probably hexagonal crystals isomorphous with antimony triiodide ; and R. Schneider, as crystalline plates with a metallic lustre. G. E. Linck said that the crystals belong to the hexagonal system. W. Heintz said the colour is dark green ; J. Nicklès, black ; and R. Schneider, greyish-black ; J. W. Retgers said that when crystallized from methylene iodide, the hexagonal plates have a dark brownish-violet colour. C. H. D. Bödeker gave 5·65 for the **specific gravity** of the sublimed triiodide at 10° ; F. W. Clarke, 5·9225 at 16°, and 5·88 at 17·5° ; and M. M. P. Muir, 5·64 at 20° for the precipitated iodide. W. Biltz studied the mol. vol. T. Carnelley and W. C. Williams found the **melting point** to be 439° ; H. S. van Klooster, 408° ; and L. Marino and R. Becarelli, 412°. R. Schneider, and W. Heintz said that at a higher temp., the triiodide sublimes, and yields a reddish-brown vapour.

Analyses, reported by C. F. Rammelsberg, W. Heintz, R. Schneider, M. M. P. Muir, A. E. Arppe, and L. Birckenbach agree with the formula BiI_3. E. Rimini and F. Olivari found the effect of the triiodide on the b.p. of fenchone agrees with the same formula. R. Hanslian measured its effect on the b.p. of iodine and found it dissociated into atoms. According to W. Heintz, R. Schneider, R. Weber, and M. M. P. Muir, bismuth triiodide can be sublimed in **hydrogen** or carbon dioxide without decomposition ; and R. Schneider, M. Berthelot, and J. Nicklès said that when heated in **air,** most of it sublimes unchanged, but a small part is oxidized to the oxyiodide—V. Thomas said that the non-volatilized residue is bismuth trioxide. R. Schneider said that the sublimed iodide is scarcely attacked by cold **water,** and M. M. P. Muir found that the precipitated iodide is rather more quickly attacked ; hot water was found by W. Heintz, R. Schneider, and R. Weber to transform it into the oxyiodide. W. Herz and A. Bulla found that the triiodide is hydrolyzed by water so slowly at 25° and 50° that measurements of the speed of the reaction could not be made. According to R. Dubrisay, the addition of water to soln. of bismuth triiodide gives a black precipitate which turns brick-red when the conc. of the bismuth in the liquid phase falls below 0·002 gram-atoms per litre. This shows that probably two oxyiodides are formed. According to R. Schneider, **hydrochloric acid** dissolves the triiodide, forming a brown soln., without perceptible decomposition ; while A. E. Arppe found that by evaporating, over sulphuric acid, a soln. of the triiodide in conc. **hydriodic acid,** rhombic pyramids of **bismuth hydro-tetraiodide,** $BiI_3.HI.3H_2O$, are formed ; the product fumes in dry air ; is decomposed by water, forming bismuthyl iodide ; and it dissolves in a soln. of potassium iodide. According to M. M. P. Muir and E. M. Eagles, when the triiodide is heated with **sulphur** it does not behave like the trichloride and tribromide and form sulphoiodide—both elements sublime separately ; nor is the triiodide altered when it is strongly heated in **hydrogen sulphide.** E. C. Franklin and C. A. Kraus found the triiodide to be slightly soluble in liquid **ammonia.** When the triiodide is warmed in a current of dry ammonia, it forms a brick-red mass of **bismuth triamminotri-iodide,** $BiI_3.3NH_3$, from which water extracts ammonium iodide. W. Heintz said that **nitric acid** decomposes the triiodide with the separation of iodine ; V. Thomas, that **nitrogen peroxide** transforms it at ordinary temp. into the trioxide, not the oxyiodide ; while M. M. P. Muir reported that the nitrous vapours obtained from a mixture of nitric acid and starch form a little oxyiodide. H. Moissan said that the triiodide is readily reduced by heated **boron.** M. M. P. Muir and B. S. Gott found that 100 parts of **alcohol** at 20° dissolve about 3·5 parts of the triiodide ; J. Nicklès reported it to be insoluble in ethyl alcohol, **amyl alcohol, ether,** and **carbon disulphide ;** J. W. Retgers, that it is soluble in **benzene, toluene,** and **xylene ;** that 100 parts of **methylene iodide** at 12° dissolve 0·15 part of the triiodide, forming a wine-red soln.—the solubility increases only a little as the temp. is raised and that it dissolves readily in warm arsenic triiodide. A. Naumann found bismuth triiodide to be soluble in **methyl acetate,** and in **acetone.** P. Planés said that the presence of **glycerol** hinders the decomposition of the triiodide by water. S. Delépine, K. Kraut, H. Ley, and A. B. Prescott studied the reactions with various **organic compounds.** G. Dragendorff, and E. Léger used a soln. of bismuth triiodide in potassium iodide as a reagent for **alkaloids.** A. C. Vournasos prepared complex salts with organic amines, pyridine, and quinoline. According to R. Schneider, bismuth triiodide is decomposed at ordinary temp. by the **alkali hydroxides** with the separation of bismuth trioxide, and iodate ; **alkali carbonates** act similarly but more slowly ; **alkali sulphides** quickly form bismuth trisulphide ; and when heated with an excess of **mercuric oxide** it forms bismuth trioxide, and with **mercuric sulphide,** bismuth trisulphide. F. Winkler studied the action of **bismuth** on the triiodide.

Bismuth triiodide forms a series of complex compounds with the ammonium and the metal iodides. The products usually form red or brownish-red crystals which are decomposed by water, forming bismuthyl iodide ; and are soluble in ethyl acetate. Thus, J. Nicklès obtained **ammonium tetraiodobismuthite,** $NH_4BiI_4.H_2O$, by the action of iodine on bismuth in a conc. soln. of ammonium chloride—the complex chloride simultaneously formed remains in soln. He also obtained it by the action of iodine on bismuth in alcohol in the presence of ammonium iodide. The black, needle-like crystals belong to the rhombic system. Isomorphous mixed crystals with the antimony salt were also obtained, $NH_4(Bi,Sb)I_4.2H_2O$. E. M. Bartholomew and G. J. Burrows obtained a *phenyl-dimethylarsine tetraiodobismuthite,* $[As(C_6H_5)(CH_3)_2H]BiI_4$; W. Linau prepared **ammonium heptaiodobismuthite,** $(NH_4)_4BiI_7.3H_2O$, by slowly evaporating a sat. soln. of bismuth triiodide in a conc. soln. of ammonium iodide. The dark reddish-brown, hygroscopic crystals are isomorphous with the corresponding iodoantimonite. E. M. Bartholomew and G. J. Burrows isolated the *hexaiodo-bismuthites* of aniline, dimethylaniline, phenyldimethylarsine, etc. These are all crystalline compounds which can be recrystallized from conc. hydrochloric acid without change. They may all be regarded as derivatives of bismuthous iodide.

The **anilinium**, **pyridinium**, **dimethylanilinium**, and p-toluidinium salts are all derivatives of hexa-iodo bismuthous acid, $H_3(BiI_6)$, whilst phenyl dimethyl arsonium tetra-iodobismuthite is a derivative of the acid $H(BiI_4)$.

C. Astre obtained black, acicular, **r**hombic crystals of **potassium heptaiododibismuthite**, $KI.2BiI_3$, from a soln. of iodine and bismuth in one of potassium chloride. J. Nicklès had previously reported the product to be **potassium tetraiodobismuthite**, $KI.BiI_3.H_2O$; and he also reported **sodium tetraiodobismuthite**, $NaI.BiI_3.H_2O$, to be formed by the action of iodine on bismuth and a sat. soln. of sodium chloride. The dark brown, prismatic crystals were found by C. F. Rammelsberg to belong to the monoclinic system and to have the axial ratios $a:b:c = 0.864:1:0.717$, and $\beta = 102°\ 21'$. The crystals effloresce in dry air. They form isomorphous mixed crystals with the corresponding iodoantimonite, $Na(Bi,Sb)I_4.H_2O$. W. Linau prepared **sodium enneaiododibismuthite**, $3NaI.2BiI_3.12H_2O$, in small, garnet-red, rectangular prisms from a sat. soln. of bismuth triiodide in a conc. soln. of sodium iodide. The crystals are probably isomorphous with the corresponding iodoantimonite. A. C. Vournasos prepared **potassium hexaiodobismuthite**, $K_3[BiI_6]$, and **sodium hexaiodobismuthite**, $Na_3[BiI_6]$. C. Astre obtained quadratic prisms of **potassium enneaiododibismuthite**, $3KI.2BiI_3.2H_2O$, by allowing a mixture of iodine (1·5 mols), potassium iodide (2 mols), an excess of bismuth, and 50 c.c. of water to stand for 2 months with frequent shaking, and crystallizing the product from ethyl acetate. A. E. Arppe obtained rhombic plates of a similar salt by evaporating a soln. of potassium iodide and bismuth triiodide. H. L. Wells made **cæsium enneaiododibismuthite**, $3CsI.2BiI_3$, in crystals sparingly soluble in water. C. Astre reported **potassium pentaiodobismuthite**, $2KI.BiI_3$, to be formed from a soln. of a mol of bismuth triiodide and 3 mols of potassium iodide in ethyl acetate. P. P. Dehérain obtained six-sided plates of **sodium hexachlorobismuthite**, $3NaCl.BiCl_3$, from a soln. of the component salts, and C. Astre, **potassium hexachlorobismuthite**, $3KCl.BiCl_3$, by rubbing up a mol of bismuth nitrate with 4 mols of potassium iodide and 50 c.c. of water, evaporating to dryness; and extracting the complex salt with ethyl acetate. A. E. Arppe prepared small black crystals of **potassium heptabismuthite hemihydriodide**, $4KI.BiI_3.\frac{1}{2}HI$, by concentrating a mixed soln. of potassium iodide and bismuth triiodide in hydriodic acid. When warmed, **potassium heptaiodobismuthite**, $4KI.BiI_3$, is formed.

W. Linau prepared **calcium pentaiodobismuthite**, $CaI_2.BiI_3.9H_2O$, was prepared by evaporating a warm soln. of calcium iodide with bismuth triiodide. The red, rhombic prisms are probably isomorphous with the corresponding antimonite. The salt loses its water of crystallization at 150°. He also made **barium pentaiodobismuthite**, $BiI_2.BiI_3.9H_2O$, in a similar way, and found that it had similar properties. A. Welkoff made **beryllium iodobismuthite** by a process analogous to that used for the corresponding antimonite. W. Linau prepared **magnesium octoiododibismuthite**, $MgI_2.2BiI_3.12H_2O$, by the method used for the barium salt; it forms garnet-red, rectangular prisms which lose their water of crystallization at 175°. Similarly with **zinc octoiododibismuthite**, $ZnBi_2I_8.12H_2O$, which forms garnet-red, hygroscopic, rectangular prisms which lose their water at 100°. He also obtained crystals of *zinc bromoiodobismuthite* from a soln. of bismuth triiodide, and zinc bromide. W. Linau could not make *cadmium iodobismuthite* analogous to the zinc salt. A. Welkoff made **aluminium iodobismuthite**, analogous to the corresponding antimonite. G. Canneri and G. Perina obtained **thallous pentaiodobismuthite**, Tl_2BiI_5, in red, hexagonal plates, by adding potassium iodide to an acidic soln. containing thallium and bismuth. The salt resembles the corresponding bromide; and, in consequence of its low solubility in water, *viz.* 1 in 20,000, its formation can be used for the detection and estimation of bismuth. A. Mosnier showed that when a boiling sat. soln. of bismuth triiodide in fuming hydriodic acid is mixed with lead iodide and cooled, small red, needle-like crystals of **lead enneaiodobismuthite**, $Pb_3BiI_9.12H_2O$, are formed. They are decomposed by water and alcohol.   The heat of soln. in 40 parts of water at 15° is $-17 \cdot 2$ Cals. ; when heated to 45° the salt becomes anhydrous.   The heat of soln. is then $+16 \cdot 6$ Cals. ; and the heat of formation $(BiI_3,3PbI_2)=13 \cdot 8$ Cals.   F. Ephraim and P. Mosimann prepared cobaltibismuth hexamminoiodide, $[Co(NH_3)_6]I_3 \cdot BiI_3$, in dark   red   pointed   crystals ;   cobaltibismuth   chloropentamminoiodide, $[Co(NH_3)_5Cl]I_3 2BiI_3$, as a red microcrystalline powder ; cobaltibismuth dinitroxyltetramminoiodide, $[Co(NH_3)_4(NO_3)_2]I_3 \cdot BiI_3$, hexagonal rods—flaveo salt—or as a microcrystalline powder of the croceo-salt ; and cobaltibismuth carbonatotetramminoiodide, $[Co(NH_3)_4CO_3]I \cdot BiI_3$, in reddish-yellow grains by adding the bismuth iodide dissolved in an excess of potassium iodide to a soln. of the necessary amine.   A. C. Vournasos studied the complex mixed amines.

REFERENCES.

[1] L. Marino and R. Becarelli, *Atti Accad. Lincei*, (5), **21**. ii, 695, 1912; E. Rimini and F. Olivari, *ib.*, (5), **16**. i, 665, 1907; R. Weber, *Pogg. Ann.*, **107**. 600, 1869 ; W. Heintz, *ib.*, **63**. 75, 1844 ; C. F. Rammelsberg, *Handbuch der krystallographischphysikalischen Chemie*, Berlin, **1**. 308, 1881 ; *Pogg. Ann.*. **48**. 166, 1839 ; E. R. Schneider, *ib.*, **99**. 470, 1856 ; *Journ. prakt. Chem.*, (1), **79**. 421, 1860 ; (2), **50**. 463, 1894 ; H. S. van Klooster, *Zeit. anorg. Chem.*, **80**. 104, 1913 ; W. Herz and A. Guttmann, *ib.*, **56**. 422, 1908 ; W. Herz and A. Bulla, *ib.*, **61**. 387, 1909 ; **63**. 59, 1909 ; W. Biltz, *ib.*, **115**. 241, 1921 ; J. W. Retgers, *ib.*, **3**. 345, 1893 ; *Zeit. phys. Chem.*, **11**. 340, 1893 ; H. G. Denham, *Journ. Amer. Chem. Soc.*, **43**. 2367, 1921 ; A. B. Prescott, *ib.*, **20**. 96, 1898 ; A. E. Arppe, *Akad. Handl. Stockholm*, 133, 1842 ; *Dissertatio de jodato bismuthico*, Helsingfors, 1843 ; *Pogg. Ann.*, **64**. 237, 1845 ; W. Linau, *ib.*, **11**. 242, 1860 ; G. Oddo and U. Giachery, *Gazz. Chim. Ital.*, **53**. i, 56, 1923 ; G. Canneri and G. Perina, *ib.*, **52**. i, 241, 1922 ; M. M. P. Muir, *Journ. Chem. Soc.*, **33**. 200, 1878 ; M. M. P. Muir, G. B. Hoffmeister, and C. E. Robbs, *ib.*, **39**. 33, 1881 ; M. M. P. Muir and B. S. Gott, *ib.*, **53**. 137, 1888 ; M. M. P. Muir and E. M. Eagles, *ib.*, **67**. 90, 1895 ; T. Carnelley and W. C. Williams, *ib.*, **37**. 125, 1880 ; F. B. Stone, *Journ. Soc. Chem. Ind.*, **6**. 416, 1887 ; F. Field, *Chem. News*, **36**. 261, 1877 ; J. C. Thresh, *Pharm. Journ.*, (3), **10**. 641, 1880 ; J. B. Berthemot, *Journ. Pharm. Chim.*, (2), **14**. 616, 1848 ; P. Planés, *ib.*, (6), **18**. 385, 1903 ; J. Nicklès, *ib.*, (3), **40**. 324, 1861 ; (3), **41**. 148, 1860 ; *Compt. Rend.*, **50**. 872, 1860 ; V. Auger, *ib.*, **139**. 671, 1904 ; R. Dubrisay, *ib.*, **149**. 451, 1909 ; C. Astre, *ib.*, **110**. 525, 1137, 1890 ; M. Berthelot, *ib.*, **86**. 628, 1878 ; H. Moissan, *ib.*, **114**. 617, 1892 ; V. Thomas, *ib.*, **123**. 1060, 1896 ; A. C. Vournasos, *Zeit. anorg. Chem.*, **150**. 147, 1926 ; *Compt. Rend.*, **166**. 526, 1918 ; P. P. Dehérain, *ib.*, **52**. 734, 1861 ; **54**. 724, 1862 ; **55**. 807, 1862 ; *Bull. Soc. Chim.*, (1), **3**. 51, 1861 ; (1), **4**. 22, 1862 ; E. Léger, *ib.*, (2), **50**. 91, 1888 ; S. Delépine, *ib.*, (3), **13**. 351, 1895 ; E. C. Franklin and C. A. Kraus, *Amer. Chem. Journ.*, **20**. 827, 1898 ; C. H. D. Bödeker, *Die Beziehungen zwischen Dichte und zusammensetzung bei festen und liquiden Stoffen*, Leipzig, 1860 ; *Liebig's Ann.*, **123**. 61, 1862 ; F. W. Clarke, *Amer. Journ. Science*, (3), **14**. 281, 1877 ; H. L. Wells, *ib.*, (4), **3**. 464, 1897 ; G. E. Linck, *Ber.*, **40**. 1405, 1907 ; L. Birckenbach, *ib.*, **40**. 1404, 1907 ; A. Naumann, *ib.*, **37**. 4328, 1904 ; **42**. 3792, 1909 ; A. Welkoff, *ib.*, **7**. 804, 1874 ; H. Ley, *Liebig's Ann.*, **278**. 57, 1894 ; K. Kraut, *ib.*, **210**. 310. 1881 ; G. Dragendorff, *Russ. Journ. Pharm.*, **5**. 85, 1866 ; **6**. 663, 1867 ; A. Mosnier, *Ann. Chim. Phys.*, (7), **12**. 421, 1897 ; F. Winkler, *Das Atomgewicht des Antimons. Neubestimmung durch Ueberführung des Metalls in Antimon-Tetroxyd*, München, 1917; F. Ephraim and P. Mosimann, *Ber.*, **54**. B, 396, 1921 ; R. Hanslian, *Molekulargewichtsbestimmungen in gefrierenden und siedenden Jod*, Werda i. Th., 46, 1910 ; E. M. Bartholomew and G. J. Burrows, *Proc. Roy. Soc. New South Wales*, **60**. 208, 1926.

§ 14. The Oxyhalides of Bismuth

M. M. P. Muir [1] and co-workers found that by repeated treatment of bismuth trihydrotrifluoride or of a soln. of bismuth hydroxide in hydrofluoric acid with boiling water, there is formed bismuthyl fluoride, or bismuth oxyfluoride, $BiOF$.   It is also produced by adding freshly precipitated bismuth hydroxide to hot hydrofluoric acid, until the acid reaction disappears, washing the precipitate with hot water, drying at 100°, and feebly calcining the product.   The heavy, white, non-hygroscopic powder has a sp. gr. 7·5 at 20° ; it is stable at a dull red-heat but decomposed at a higher temp.   When bismuth hydroxide is digested with hydrofluoric acid, part dissolves and part remains as insoluble bismuthyl dihydrotrifluoride, or bismuth oxydihydrotrifluoride, $BiOF.2HF$.   This is washed with cold water and dried at 100°—if washed with hot water, bismuthyl fluoride is formed.   The oxydihydrotrifluoride is also obtained by the action of cold water on bismuth trihydrotrifluoride. When the white powder is strongly calcined, it forms bismuth trifluoride.

According to R. F. Weinland and O. Lauenstein, the product obtained by the action of conc. hydrofluoric acid on metabismuthic acid at $-10°$ gives a reddish-brown soln. and powder, which decomposes at ordinary temp. with a brisk evolution of ozonized oxygen; the mixture acquires a pale yellow colour and furnishes no quinquevalent bismuth. It is supposed that an unstable quinquevalent compound of bismuth with oxygen in fluorine is formed analogous with, say, potassium fluoroarsenate, $KAsOF_4$, or with arsenic oxyfluoride, $AsOF_3$. O. Ruff also found that when bismuthic acid is added to conc. hydrofluoric acid, the colourless unstable soln. which is formed consists mainly of **bismuth oxytrifluoride**, $BiOF_3$. When the soln. is evaporated in vacuo, the oxytrifluoride is partially decomposed; and on adding a molar proportion of potassium fluoride before evaporation, a compound or mixture with the composition $Bi_3OF_7.3KF$ is obtained in small, yellow crystals; and with three molar proportions, **potassium oxyhexafluoride**, $BiOF_3.3KF$, is formed in colourless, prismatic crystals, which become yellow, and decompose rapidly in moist air. A. C. Vournasos prepared **potassium tribromotriiodo-bismuthite**, $K_3[BiBr_3I_3]$, and **potassium tricyanidotriiodobismuthite**, $K_3[BiI_3Cy_3]$.

According to A. E. Arppe,[2] C. F. Bucholz, W. Heintz, R. Phillips, H. Rose, and E. Ruge, when bismuth trichloride is decomposed by cold or hot water—say by treatment of a hydrochloric acid soln. of the trichloride with water—or when a soln. of bismuth nitrate is treated with an alkali chloride, **bismuthyl chloride**, or **bismuth oxychloride**, $BiOCl$, is formed. H. Rose said that if sulphur or phosphoric acid be present the precipitate will be contaminated with bismuth sulphate or phosphate respectively. A. de Schulten obtained crystals of the oxychloride by dissolving 3 grms. of bismuth trioxide in 300 c.c. of hydrochloric acid of sp. gr. 1·05; adding 2·5 litres of boiling water; and the filtered soln., on cooling, deposits colourless, quadratic crystals. V. A. Jacquelain obtained it by heating the trichloride in steam, and removing the unchanged trichloride by heating it to a higher temp. According to V. A. Jacquelain, and V. Thomas, it is also produced in small quantities when the trichloride is sublimed in air; or, according to W. Heintz, in hydrogen containing some air. According to W. Herz and A. Bulla, the oxychloride is also obtained by treating a soln. of bismuth hydroxide with an alkali chloride, $BiO.OH + KCl \rightleftharpoons BiOCl + KOH$, the equilibrium constant is 0·082. M. M. P. Muir made it by treating bismuth trioxide with dil. hydrochloric acid. E. Lebaigue obtained micaceous plates by heating bismuth sulphate with sodium chloride, and leaching out the soluble salts with water.

Analyses by A. E. Arppe, W. Heintz, V. A. Jacquelain, H. Rose, E. Ruge, and V. Thomas agree with the formula $BiOCl$. C. Haushofer described the oxychloride as a snow-white, amorphous powder; A. de Schulten, as forming colourless, transparent, quadratic crystals. E. Ruge said that when dried in air at 100°–125°, it retains what is eq. to one-sixth of a mol of water which is lost only at 300°; and W. Heintz, that it is anhydrous when dried at 100°; A. E. Arppe, when dried at 125°; and W. Herz, when dried in vacuo. A. de Schulten said the sp. gr. is 7·717 at 15°, and the mol. vol. 33·7; M. M. P. Muir gave 7·2 at 20° for the sp. gr. of the precipitated oxychloride. P. Grouvelle, and V. A. Jacquelain found that the oxychloride melts at a red-heat without decomposition; and E. Ruge added that there is but an insignificant volatilization of bismuth trichloride when the oxychloride is strongly heated, but A. E. Arppe observed that the proportion of chlorine is reduced when the oxychloride is strongly calcined. A. de Schulten, and V. Thomas confirmed this. J. Thomsen gave for the heat of formation $(Bi,O,Cl,H_2O) = 88·41$ Cals.; $(BiCl_3,H_2O,Aq.) = 7·83$ Cals.; and $\{Bi(OH)_3,HClaq.\} = 14·18$ Cals. A. K. Sanyal and N. R. Dhar found that bismuth oxychloride is decomposed by exposure to tropical sunlight for a few hours. R. Robl observed no fluorescence when the salt is exposed to ultra-violet light. A. A. Noyes and co-workers found that the electrical conductivity of hydrochloric acid is diminished by the addition of bismuth chloride. The observed diminution can be most satis-factorily interpreted on the assumption that hydropentachlorobismuthic acid is formed. Measurements of the solubility of bismuth oxychloride in hydrochloric acid soln. of varying conc. at 25° afford support for this hypothesis in the case of the more conc. soln., whilst for the less conc. acid soln. the solubility data suggest that the predominant complex acid has the formula $HBiCl_4$.

H. Rose found that when the oxychloride is reduced in **hydrogen** a little bismuth trichloride is volatilized ; and that it is sparingly soluble in **water**. E. Ruge said that when treated with boiling water, no more basic chloride is produced. V. A. Jacquelain found that at a dull red-heat, **chlorine** transforms the oxychloride into the trichloride, with the liberation of some oxygen. It dissolves in **hydro-chloric acid,** and this subject was studied by A. A. Noyes and co-workers—*vide supra*, Fig. 19. M. M. P. Muir observed that **hydriodic acid** transforms its oxy-chloride into the trichloride and triiodide, while it is not changed by a soln. of **potassium iodide.** C. F. Bucholz said that when freshly precipitated it dissolved in a soln. of **potassium chloride,** but when dried, it is insoluble in that menstruum ; L. Moser and E. Neusser said that the oxychloride is completely converted into sulphide when heated in **hydrogen sulphide.** V. A. Jacquelain found that when heated with **sulphuric acid** it is transformed into bismuth sulphate ; and that on evaporation of the soln. in **nitric acid,** the oxychloride remains unchanged. H. Rose found that molten **potassium cyanide** reduces the oxychloride to metal. A. Stromeyer, and V. A. Jacquelain said that the trioxide is not attacked by a boiling dil. soln. of **potassium hydroxide** ; R. Warington found that a little decom-position occurs ; and with the hot, conc. lye, the oxychloride is completely decom-posed to grey bismuth trioxide which, according to R. Phillips, becomes yellow when fused. According to W. Herz and G. Muhs, at 30°, when equilibrium : $BiOCl + KOH \rightleftharpoons BiO.OH + KCl$, is attained, there must be some secondary reactions because the results do not agree with $[KOH] = K[KCl]$. The oxychloride becomes greyish-yellow when treated with alkali-lye, and it is inferred that there are several distinct hydroxides. As indicated above, W. Herz and A. Bulla obtained 0·082 for the constant. E. F. Smith and P. Heyl found that when calcined with **mercuric oxide,** the oxychloride is completely transformed into the oxide.

Several other oxychlorides have been reported. V. Merz and W. Weith obtained one by heating bismuth trichloride with ten times its weight of water in a sealed tube. A yellowish or greyish-white, amorphous, compact earth, or fibrous mineral found by I. Domeyko in Cerro de Tazna, Bolivia, was named **daubréeite**—after A. Daubrée. Its composition corresponds with hydrated bismuth, $Bi_5O_6Cl_3.3H_2O$. The sp. gr. is 6·4–6 5, and the hardness 2·0–2·5. P. P. Dehérain heated bismuth dichloride in air and obtained a crystalline mass approximating *bismuth trioxydichloride*, $Bi_2O_3Cl_2$. M. M. P. Muir reported *bismuth dioxytrichloride*, $Bi_3O_2Cl_3$, to be formed as an orange-yellow, crystalline powder, by slowly subliming bismuth trichloride in air, or in sulphur dioxide ; by heating bismuth trioxide or pentoxide in chlorine ; or by passing nitric acid vapours over molten bismuth trichloride. V. Thomas made this oxychloride by the action of nitrogen peroxide on bismuth trichloride. The dioxytrichloride may be impure BiOCl.

M. M. P. Muir obtained **bismuthyl bromide,** or **bismuth oxybromide,** BiOBr, by treating with water solid bismuth tribromide, or a soln. of that salt in hydro-bromic acid ; and probably by heating the trioxide with the tribromide. R. Dubri-say found that the variation of the proportions of bismuth and bromine in the liquid, when the tribromide is diluted with water, follows a regular curve showing that only one oxybromide is formed. The effect of temp. between 15° and 95° on the degree of hydrolysis is not appreciable. A. de Schulten obtained bismuthyl bromide by dissolving 3 grms. of bismuth trioxide in 50 c.c. of hydrobromic acid of sp. gr. 1·38, and adding 1500–1600 c.c. of hot water to the boiling liquid. When the clear filtrate cools, it deposits the oxybromide in crystals which are washed with water to remove the adherent acid. The salt occurs as a snow-white amorphous powder, or in colourless, transparent crystals. A. de Schulten gave 8·082 for the sp. gr. of the crystals at 15°, and M. M. P. Muir, 6·7 for the amorphous powder at 20°. M. M. P. Muir said that the oxybromide can be heated to redness without decomposition ; while A. de Schulten found that it melts at a bright red-heat. and some tribromide is volatilized. W. Herz said that when exposed to light it is darkened, and this more readily in a closed than in an open vessel. M. M. P. Muir said that the oxybromide is insoluble in water, and soluble in dil. hydrobromic acid ; and when heated in a current of ammonia, a part is reduced to bismuth, and a little sublimes as the hemipentamminotribromide. W. Herz and G. Muhs observed the equilibrium conditions of the reaction with a soln. of potassium hydroxide : $BiOBr + KOH \rightleftharpoons BiO.OH + KBr$, and W. Herz and A. Bulla gave 0·57 for the equilibrium constant.

M. M. P. Muir reported *bismuth tridecaoxyheptabromide*, $Bi_{11}O_{13}Br_7$, to be formed by heating bismuth tri- or penta-oxide in a current of bromine. Some bismuth tribromide is formed at the same time. The white, amorphous powder is not changed in air ; it becomes darker in colour when heated ; and it is insoluble in hot or cold water, but soluble in nitric or hydrochloric acid. M. M. P. Muir obtained *bismuth pentadecaoxyhexabromide*, $Bi_8O_{15}Br_6$, by the action of nitric acid fumes on the molten tribromide ; and by subliming the tribromide in the presence of air. V. Thomas said that bismuthyl bromide is the product of these reactions. M. M. P. Muir described the pentadecoxyhexabromide as a greyish-yellow, crystalline powder which when heated in hydrogen is reduced to the metal ; and with carbon forms bismuth tribromide. It is soluble in water ; and in mineral acids ; and it behaves towards ammonia like bismuthyl bromide.

H. G. Denham[3] reported bismuth suboxyiodide, $BiI_2.3BiO$, to be formed as a by-product in the preparation of bismuth diiodide (*q.v.*). It appears as a non-volatile, brick-red substance which is stable in dry air. It commences to decompose at 350°. A sat. soln. gives a faint darkening with hydrogen sulphide ; and a faint turbidity with silver nitrate. It is decomposed into the metal and a soluble ter-valent bismuth salt by sulphuric, hydrochloric, and acetic acids. It is insoluble in alcohol, and in aq. soln. of potassium iodide ; and it reduces acidic soln. of potassium permanganate.

J. B. Berthemot[4] prepared **bismuthyl iodide, or bismuth oxyiodide,** BiOI, by boiling bismuth triiodide with water ; M. M. P. Muir, by pouring a hydriodic acid soln. of the triiodide in hot water ; and A. de Schulten, by dissolving 0·250 grm. of bismuth trioxide in 40 c.c. of hydriodic acid, of sp. gr. 1·2, and mixing the liquid with 6 litres of cold water. The liquid is warmed on the water-bath and crystals of the oxyiodide are formed. These are washed with water. The great excess of hydriodic acid is necessary to prevent the evaporation of bismuth triiodide. E. R. Schneider observed that the oxyiodide is formed when the triiodide is heated in air. This product is the *bismutum oxyjodatum* of pharmaceutical chemistry. Its preparation for this purpose was described by C. Astre, B. Fischer, F. W. Fletcher and H. P. Cooper, C. Greene, G. Greuel, J. Jaillet, O. Kaspar, and C. Mayr and co-workers. The pharmaceutical product can be obtained by treating a cold or hot, dil. nitric acid soln. with potassium iodide—with or without acetic acid—and also by the action of potassium iodide on bismuth oxynitrate. R. Dubrisay obtained indications of the formation of a brick-red oxyiodide, BiOI, and of a black *bis-muthyl trihydropentaiodide*, $2BiOI.3HI.H_2O$, or $Bi_2O_3.5HI$, in the hydrolysis of bismuth triiodide (*q.v.*).

W. Heintz, and A. E. Arppe described the oxyiodide as a brick-red powder, which, according to B. Fischer, consists of cubic crystals. A. de Schulten obtained copper-red, quadratic crystals, and E. R. Schneider, rhombic plates. A. de Schulten gave 7·922 for the sp. gr. at 15°, and 44·4 for the mol. vol. He also said that the salt melts at a red-heat with decomposition. The oxyiodide is stable in air, and in the absence of air, it can be sublimed without decomposition, but when strongly heated in air, E. R. Schneider observed that it is converted into the trioxide—but, added A. E. Arppe, all the iodine cannot be expelled by roasting. Boiling water was found by A. E. Arppe, and E. R. Schneider to have only a slight action on the salt ; M. M. P. Muir, and B. Fischer found that dil. mineral acids convert it into the triiodide ; E. R. Schneider, and B. Fischer observed that conc. hydrochloric acid dissolves it, forming a yellow soln. ; while conc. sulphuric or nitric acid decomposes it with the separation of iodine, and acetic acid is without action. J. B. Berthemot found that the oxyiodide is decomposed when boiled with water and zinc or iron : and that hot dil. soln. of alkali hydroxides or carbonates, or lime-water, or baryta-water have only a slight action ; but conc. alkali-lye forms bismuth trioxide. According to W. Heintz, the decomposition is incomplete. C. F. Rammelsberg reported the oxyiodide $Bi_{11}O_{13}I_3$; and T. R. Blyth, $Bi_{14}O_{15}I_{12}$, and $Bi_{17}O_{27}I_3$ to be formed by the action of alkali-lye on the oxyiodide. M. M. P. Muir found that a soln. of potassium chloride has no action on the oxyiodide ; while E. R. Schneider showed that a mixture of alkali-lye and ammonium sulphide transforms the oxyiodide into trisulphide. M. M. P. Muir and E. M. Eagles found hydrogen sulphide to be without action.

A. C. Vournasos [5] prepared **ammonium chloroiodobismuthite,** $NH_4[BiCl_3I]$, in transparent needles, by the action of bismuth halide on ammonium iodide in an organic solvent ; **hydrazine chloroacetatobismuthite,** $N_2H_4[BiI_3CH_3COOH]$, was obtained in colourless prisms in an analogous way.

REFERENCES.

[1] M. M. P. Muir, G. B. Hoffmeister, and C. F. Robbs, *Journ. Chem. Soc.,* **39**. 33, 1881 ; M. M. P. Muir, *ib.,* **53**. 137, 1888 ; R. F. Weinland and O. Lauenstein, *Zeit. anorg. Chem.,* **20**. 46, 1899 ; O. Ruff, *ib.,* **57**. 220, 1908 ; A. C. Vournasos, *ib.,* **150**. 147, 1926.
[2] R. Phillips, *Phil. Mag.,* **8**. 456, 1830 ; R. Warington, *ib.,* **9**. 30, 1831 ; C. F. Bucholz, *Trommsdorff's Journ.,* **5**. 81, 1798 ; A. Mutscheller, *Met. Chem. Engg.,* **16**. 594, 1917 ; W. Heintz, *Pogg. Ann.,* **63**. 72, 1844 ; H. Rose, *Pogg. Ann.,* **110**. 425, 1860 ; A. Stromeyer, *ib.,* **26**. 549, 1832 ; A. E. Arppe, *ib.,* **64**. 246, 1845 ; *Dissertatio de jodato bismuthico,* Helsingfors, 1843 ; *Akad. Handl. Stockholm,* 133, 1842 ; A. de Schulten, *Bull. Soc. Chim.,* (3), **23**. 156, 1900 ; P. P. Dehérain, *ib.,* (1), **3**. 51, 1861 ; (1), **4**. 22, 1862 ; *Compt. Rend.,* **52**. 734, 1861 ; **54**. 724, 1862 ; **55**. 807, 1862 ; V. Thomas, *ib.,* **122**. 611, 1896 ; R. Dubrisay, *ib.,* **148**. 830, 1909 ; **149**. 122, 451, 1909 ; E. Ruge, *Journ. prakt. Chem.,* (1), **96**. 133, 1865 ; M. M. P. Muir, *Journ. Chem. Soc.,* **32**. 133, 1877 ; **33**. 193, 1878 ; **39**. 36, 1881 ; E. Lebaigue, *Journ. Pharm. Chim.,* (3), **39**. 108, 1860 ; L. Moser and E. Neusser, *Chem. Ztg.,* **47**. 541, 1923 ; J. Thomsen, *Thermochemische Untersuchungen,* Leipzig, **4**. 338, 1886 ; *Ber.,* **16**. 39, 1883 ; W. Merz and W. Weith, *ib.,* **13**. 210, 1880 ; W. Herz, *Zeit. anorg. Chem.,* **36**. 346, 1903 ; W. Herz and A. Bulla, *ib.,* **63**. 282, 1909 ; W. Herz and G. Muhs, *ib.,* **39**. 115, 1904 ; E. F. Smith and P. Heyl, *ib.,* **7**. 87, 1894 ; A. K. Sanyal and N. R. Dhar, *ib.,* **128**. 212, 1923 ; A. A. Noyes, F. W. Hall, and J. A. Beattie, *Journ. Amer. Chem. Soc.,* **39**. 2526, 1917 ; E. Ruge, *Journ. prakt. Chem.,* (1), **96**. 133, 1865 ; V. A. Jacquelain, *Ann. Chim. Phys.,* (2), **66**. 113, 1837 ; P. Grouvelle, (2), **17**. 37, 1821 ; (2), **19**. 137, 1821 ; I. Domeyko, *Elementos de mineralojia,* Santiago, 297, 1879 ; *Compt. Rend.,* **82**. 922, 1876 ; C. Haushofer, *Ueber einige mikroskopisch-chemische Reaktionen,* München, 139, 1886 ; E. C. Franklin and C. A. Kraus, *Amer. Chem. Journ.,* **20**. 827, 1898 ; A. A. Noyes, F. W. Hall, and J. A. Beattie, *Journ. Amer. Chem. Soc.,* **39**. 2526, 1917 ; R. Robl, *Zeit. angew. Chem.,* **39**. 608, 1926.
[3] H. G. Denham, *Journ. Amer. Chem. Soc.,* **43**. 2367, 1921.
[4] M. M. P. Muir, *Journ. Chem. Soc.,* **33**. 201, 1878 ; **41**. 4, 1882 ; M. M. P. Muir and E. M. Eagles, *ib.,* **67**. 90, 1895 ; A. de Schulten, *Bull. Soc. Chim.,* (3), **23**. 156, 1900 ; R. Dubrisay, *Compt. Rend.,* **149**. 451, 1909 ; E. R. Schneider, *Sitzber. Akad. Berlin,* 59, 1860 ; *Journ. prakt. Chem.,* (1), **79**. 424, 1860 ; J. B. Berthemot, *Journ. Pharm. Chim.,* (2), **14**. 616, 1828 ; C. Astre, *ib.,* (5), **22**. 195, 1890 ; O. Kaspar, *Schweiz. Wochschr. Pharm.,* **25**. 213, 257, 1887 ; C. Greene, *Amer. Journ. Pharm.,* **61**. 161, 1880 ; C. Mayr, *Amer. Journ. Pharm.,* **58**. 590, 1886 ; F. Moerk, *ib.,* **59**. 117, 273, 1887 ; E. Reynolds, *Medical News,* **49**. 393, 1886 ; *Arch. Pharm.,* (3), **25**. 416, 592, 1887 ; G. Greuel, *ib.,* (3), **25**. 437, 1887 ; J. Jaillet, *ib.,* (3), **19**. 395, 1881 ; *Répert. Pharm.,* **9**. 272, 1881 ; F. W. Fletcher and H. P. Cooper, *Pharm. Journ.,* (3), **13**. 250, 1882 ; W. Heintz, *Pogg. Ann.,* **63**. 72, 1844 ; C. F. Rammelsberg, *ib.,* **44**. 568, 1838 ; A. E. Arppe, *ib.,* **64**. 246, 1845 ; *Dissertatio de jodato bismuthico,* Helsingfors, 1843 ; *Akad. Handl. Stockholm,* 133, 1842 ; B. Fischer, *Die neuen Arzneimittel,* 25, 1893 ; *Pharm. Ztg.,* **32**. 504, 1887 ; T. R. Blyth, *Chem. News,* **74**. 200, 1896.
[5] A. C. Vournasos, *Compt. Rend.,* **176**. 1555, 1923.

§ 15. The Bismuth Sulphides

The affinity of bismuth for sulphur was discussed by K. Jellinek and J Zakowsky.[1] E. R. Schneider reported **bismuth disulphide,** Bi_2S_2, or *bismuth* *subsulphide*, to be formed by the action of hydrogen sulphide on bismuth dioxide. This was confirmed by W. Herz and A. Guttmann, but they both gave up the idea that bismuth disulphide is so formed. E. R. Schneider also made the disulphide by dissolving 8 parts of bismuth tartrate in the necessary amount of potash-lye, diluting the soln. with air-free water to 1500 c.c., adding an alkaline soln. of 2 parts of stannous chloride and passing hydrogen sulphide through the liquid. The bismuth disulphide is precipitated, the tin remains in soln. as a sulpho-salt. The product is washed with hot dil. potash-lye, finally with water, and then dried in a steam-oven. L. Vanino and F. Treubert said that the product is really a mixture of bismuth and bismuth trisulphide, though E. R. Schneider contested this. C. Hoffmann made the disulphide by heating bismuth trioxide with an aq. soln. of potassium cyanide and thiocyanate.

According to D. Lagerhjelm, and G. Werther, bismuth trisulphide and bismuth are mutually soluble in all proportions ; and, on cooling the fused mass, the disulphide crystallizes out first, carrying with it all the nickel and copper contained as impurities in the bismuth. If a 10 : 3-mixture of bismuth and sulphur be fused in a crucible, and the operation on the product repeated three times with fresh sulphur, and the product quickly cooled, there is formed a radiating mass with a nest of crystals of the disulphide in the interior. This was confirmed by W. Heintz, and E. R. Schneider. Nevertheless, E. R. Schneider said that the crystals are to be regarded as bismuth trisulphide mixed mechanically with bismuth, because when treated with hydrochloric acid, bismuth remains undissolved—but this *probus* is not a good one. E. R. Schneider said that if all the bismuth is to be transformed into sulphide, the mixture must be re-fused a number of times at as low a temp. as possible. This agrees with G. Rose's observation that these crystals are the same as those of the trisulphide. H. Pélabon made some observations on the fusibility of mixtures of bismuth and sulphur ; and the subject was investigated by A. H. W. Aten. The results show that

Sulphur	0	0·9	4·2	17·2	28·8	40·7	46·9	52·4 at. per cent.
F.p. {Start	277°	318°	452°	535°	602°	656°	702°	760°
F.p. {End	277°	271°	272°	263°	267°	270°	—	—

There is nothing here to show the existence of bismuth disulphide, although H. Pélabon believed that such a compound is formed. A. H. W. Aten represented what he believed to be the general form of the equilibrium diagram by Fig. 29. Here, A and B represent respectively the b.p. and m.p. of bismuth ; and C and D, those of sulphur. AH, KC, AI, and LC are boiling curves, the first two belonging to the liquid, and the last two, to the vapour ; HE and KF are solubility curves of the trisulphide ; BE, that for bismuth, and DF, that for sulphur. IL represents the vapour curve of the solid trioxide. The region $AILC$ represents homogeneous vapour ; $AHEB$ and $KCDF$, homogeneous liquids ; AHI, and KLC, liquids in contact with vapour ; $HMOE$, and $KFPN$, soln. in contact with the solid trisulphide ; BEQ, soln. in contact with solid bismuth, and DRF, soln. in contact with solid sulphur ; below QEO, the solid trisulphide is in contact with solid bismuth, and below PFR, in contact with solid sulphur.

According to E. R. Schneider, bismuth disulphide appears as a dark grey powder. W. Herz and A. Guttmann gave 7·6–7·8 for the sp. gr. ; G. Werther, 7·29 ; and L. Playfair and J. P. Joule, 7·466. E. R. Schneider said that bismuth disulphide decomposes into bismuth and the trisulphide when heated to redness in an atm.

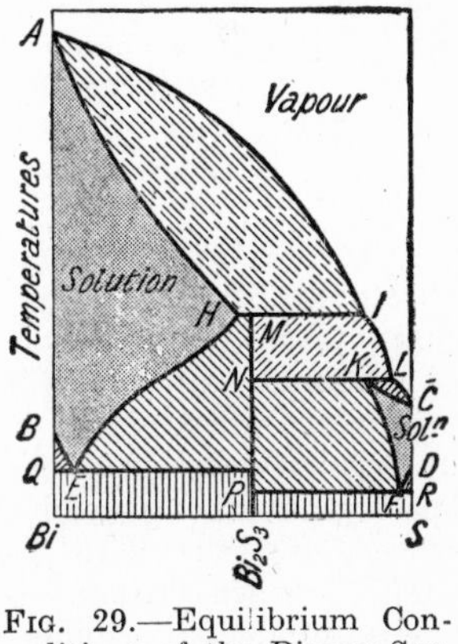

FIG. 29.—Equilibrium Conditions of the Binary System : Bi–S (Diagrammatic).

of carbon dioxide ; and if heated very strongly most of the sulphur can be driven off. When fused in hydrogen, the disulphide is reduced to metal ; H.Pélabon studied the reaction with hydrogen. The disulphide is fairly stable in air, but, according to W. Herz and A. Guttmann, when heated in air it forms sulphur dioxide ; and when heated in steam, H. V. Regnault observed that some bismuth is formed. E. R. Schneider said that acids decompose the disulphide with the separation of bismuth : $3Bi_2S_2+12HCl=2Bi+4BiCl_3+6H_2S$; and if the liquid is boiled in air, the excess of hydrochloric slowly dissolves the bismuth. H. Pélabon studied the fusibility of silver and antimonious sulphides with the alleged disulphide. He said that there is a maximum with the Ag_2S-BiS curve at 750° corresponding with *silver sulphohypobismuthite*, $Ag_2S.4BiS$; and with the Sb_2S_3-BiS curve there are singularities at 632° corresponding with *bismuthous orthosulphoantimonite*, $3BiS.Sb_2S_3$. or $Bi_3(SbS_3)_2$; and at 591° corresponding with *bismuthous metasulphoctoantimonite*, $BiS.4Sb_2S_3$, or $BiSb_8S_{13}$.

Attempts to make *bismuth pentasulphide*, Bi_2S_5, have not been successful. M. M. P. Muir,[2] A. Hilger and P. A. von Scherpenberg tried passing hydrogen sulphide into water or a dil. soln. of potassium hydroxide or boiling benzene holding bismuth pentoxide in suspension ; and by heating potassium polysulphide with the pentoxide—sulphobismuthites or oxysulphides are formed. The trisulphide is not changed by melting with sulphur, potassium carbonate, and carbon.

J. G. Wallerius [3] described a *galena wismuthi* which he supposed contained bismuth, cobalt, and arsenic ; and it was considered by J. B. L. Romé de l'Isle to be *mine de bismuth sulphureuse*. A. Cronstedt also made an analogous term. It was called *bismuth glance*, or rather *Wismuthglanz*, by A. G. Werner, and L. A. Emmerling ; *sulphurated bismuth* by R. Kirwan ; *sulphuret of bismuth* by W. Phillips ; *bismutolamprite* by E. F. Glocker ; *bismuthin* by F. S. Beudant ; and **bismuthinite** by J. D. Dana. The form *bismuthite* also occurs in literature—*e.g.* by P. Groth—but this term has also been applied to the carbonate. An early analysis by B. G. Sage,[4] in 1782, was rather a bad one ; later analyses reported by H. Rose, A. Bianchi, A. Carnot, A. Wehrle, A. von Hubert, V. R. von Zepharovich, R. Warington, C. F. Rammelsberg, T. Scheerer, F. A. Genth, D. Forbes, I. Domeyko, W. H. Melville, and G. C. Hoffmann agree with the formula for **bismuth trisulphide,** Bi_2S_3. Confirmatory analyses of the artificial product were made by F. Rössler,[5] D. Lagerhjelm, J. Davy, and H. Rose. K. Jellinek and J. Zakowsky studied the affinity of bismuth for sulphur in forming the trisulphide.

Bismuth trisulphide is prepared by fusing a mixture of the elements as indicated in connection with the disulphide. As shown by E. R. Schneider, the fusion should be repeated many times to ensure the complete dissolution of the bismuth. It was made in this way by E. R. Schneider, F. Rössler, H. Pélabon, A. H. W. Aten, C. M. Marx, etc. W. Spring reported that he had made it by compressing an intimate mixture of powders of the constituent elements. It is not easy to make the trisulphide of a high degree of purity from its elements, but it is easily obtained by precipitation by the action of hydrogen sulphide, or of an alkali sulphide on a soln. of a bismuth salt. H. Rose observed that if soln. of bismuth nitrate are used, the precipitate will probably contain some free sulphur ; with hydrochloric acid soln., no sulphochloride has been observed. S. Ramachandran showed that bismuth trisulphide is not precipitated from soln. when the conc. of the hydrochloric acid exceeds one part of the conc. acid to 3 parts of water ; nor is the precipitation complete when the conc. of the acid exceeds 1 : 5. Conversely, the trisulphide is almost completely soluble in acid of conc. 1 : 3 at 30°. The first sign of the evolution of hydrogen sulphide with an acid diluted 1 : 1 is at about 30° ; 1 : 3, at 38° ; 1 : 4, at 50° ; 1 : 5, at 65° ; 1 : 7, at 75° ; 1 : 10, at 80° ; and with the 1 : 16-acid, at 85°. H. Müller and L. Kürthy found the retarding action of urine on the precipitation gradually diminishes with time owing to the formation of complexes. J. Durocher, H. de Sénarmont, and W. W. Mather obtained a crystalline trisulphide by the action of the vapour of bismuth trichloride on hydrogen sulphide.

M. M. P. Muir and E. M. Eagles strongly heated bismuth trichloride ut tribromide, and A. Carnot, bismuthyl chloride, in hydrogen sulphide. Bismuth trisulphide was made by F. Faktor by the action of sodium thiosulphate on a neutral soln. of a bismuth salt—J. T. Norton worked with the mixture in sealed tubes at 140°–200° ; by N. Tarugi, by the action of thioacetic acid on a nitric acid soln. of bismuth nitrate ; by E. R. Schneider, by heating bismuth triiodide with mercuric sulphide in a current of dioxide ; and by J. Milbauer, by melting bismuth trioxide with potassium thiocyanate—if the temp. be too high, potassium sulphobismuthite is formed.

O. Schumann said that if bismuth trioxide is heated in a current of hydrogen sulphide, bismuth *tritetritasulphide*, Bi_4S_3, is formed—but this statement lacks confirmation. M. Mayençon observed needles of bismuth trisulphide along with lead sulphide as a sublimate or incrustation from gob-fires in the coal pits of St. Étienne. C. Winssinger obtained a **colloidal solution** of bismuth trisulphide by passing hydrogen sulphide into a very dil. soln. of bismuth nitrate acidified with acetic acid, and removing the extraneous acids and salts by dialysis. The reddish-brown liquid can be heated to the b.p. without decomposition. P. B. Gangully and N. R. Dhar found that the sol is coagulated by exposure to tropical sunlight. According to A. Kuhn and H. Pirsch, bismuth sulphide sols are stable only in the presence of protective colloids. With 1 per cent. of gum arabic a sol containing 10 mgrms. per c.c. may be obtained. By mixing bismuth sulphide, sulphiodide, or hydroxide with wool fat, subsequent intensive pulverization of the mixture at the temp. of liquid air, and dissolution of the product in sesamé oil, fairly stable sols result containing 12–16 mgrms. of bismuth per c.c. for 15–20 per cent. of protective colloid By G. Bredig's method—3. 23, 10—stable sols of the metal may be prepared containing 8 mgrms. per c.c. with 5 per cent. of wool fat and 0·6 mgrm. per c.c. with 1 per cent. of caoutchouc-ether sol. By T. Svedberg's protected arc method—3. 23, 10—met.. sols cannot be obtained in water even with a protective colloid, but in sesamé oil with t least 5 per cent. of wool fat stable sols containing 6 mgrms. per c.c. are formed.

The mineral bismuthinite usually occurs in grey or tin-white masses with a foliated or fibrous structure ; it also occurs in acicular **crystals.** The artificial compound is greyish or brownish-black ; and H. de Sénarmont obtained the tri-sulphide in crystals by heating it with soln. of potassium sulphide in a sealed tube at 200°. H. Rose, and W. Phillips showed that the natural and artificial crystals belong to the rhombic system ; and P. Groth found the axial ratios to be $a : b : c$ =0·96794 : 1 : 0·98498 ; E. Quercigh gave 0·985 : 1 : 1·004. The **cleavage** on the (010)-face is perfect, and that on the (100)- and (110)-faces, imperfect. Measurements were also made by A. Bianchi, and G. Lugaro. A. Russell studied the **twinning** of the crystals ; and O. Mügge, the **gliding planes.** H. de Sénarmont, F. Rinne, and P. Groth regarded the crystals as isomorphous with those of antimony trisulphide. P. F. Kerr studied the **X-radiogram.** C. J. B. Karsten gave 7·0001 for the **specific gravity** of bismuth trisulphide which had been obtained by precipitation and fusion ; F. W. Clarke gave 7·00–7·81 ; C. J. B. Karsten, 7·0001 ; A. Wehrle, 7·807 ; W. Herapath, 7·591 at 14·5° ; and for the native sulphide, D. Forbes gave 7·16 ; A. Bianchi gave 6·55 ; A. Weisbach, 6·643 ; V. R. von Zepharovich, 5·73 ; W. H. Melville, 6·624 ; F. A. Genth, 6·306 ; and G. C. Hoffmann, 6·781. The **hardness** is 2. E. Madelung and R. Fuchs found the **compressibility** to be $0·42 \times 10^{12}$ dynes per sq. cm. C. M. Marx said that the trisulphide melts at a higher temp. than bismuth, and the liquid expands in a marked degree on solidification. H. Pélabon gave 685° for the **melting point ;** and L. H. Borgström, 718°. Y. Takahashi gave 680°, and found that at the m.p. about 1·5 per cent. is dissociated into bismuth and sulphur. J. Joly found that a sublimation occurs at 400°–600° ; E. R. Schneider, that it very slowly sublimes undecomposed at a high temp. in a current of carbon dioxide ; and L. Merz observed that **sublimation** begins at about 300° in the vacuum of the cathode light.

C. M. Marx said that after the trisulphide has been heated and re-heated a number of times, globules of bismuth separate from the molten mass; and E. R. Schneider observed that if heated to whiteness in a current of carbon dioxide for a long time, the sulphur is completely or almost completely volatilized; while A. Mourlot found that the trisulphide is completely desulphurized when heated a short time in the electric arc-furnaces. K. Jellinek and J. Zakowsky calculated the mol. **heat of formation** to be 39·8 Cals. W. W. Coblentz and H. Kohler found that bismuth trisulphide exhibits a **photoelectric effect** when exposed to radiations from 0·6μ in the visible spectrum to 3μ in the ultra-red. The sensitiveness is increased at low temp. At $-166°$ there are maxima at 0·64μ and 1·08μ. B. Aulenkamp also studied this subject. E. T. Wherry found that the crystals are poor **radio-detectors.** A. de Gramont examined the **spark spectrum** of the mineral; and O. Stelling, the **X-ray absorption spectrum**—K-series. A. Karl said that the sulphide is triboluminescent. F. Beijerinck said that its **electrical conductivity** is good, and is about 4 times greater when vertical to the chief axis than when parallel thereto. T. W. Case found the electrical resistance to be greater than a megohm, and to be lessened by exposure to light. O. Weigel found the conductivity of the sat. aq. soln. to be 0·527$\times 10^{-6}$ mho at 18°. A. Schrauf and E. S. Dana found that the **thermoelectric effect** in contact with copper is negative.

According to H. Rose,[6] bismuth trisulphide is slowly reduced when heated in a current of **hydrogen.** H. Pélabon studied the balanced reaction: $Bi_2S_3 + 3H_2 \rightleftharpoons 3H_2S + 2Bi$. L. Moser and E. Neusser said that the decomposition of bismuth sulphide in a neutral atm. begins at 300°, forming bismuth and sulphur. K. Jellinek and J. Zakowsky found for the ratio v_{H_2S}/v_{H_2}, 2·59 at 515°; 3·85 at 630°. They calculated for the vap. press. of the sulphur at 440°, log $p = -6·27$; and at 515°, $-5·10$. H. Rose found that the trisulphide is stable in **air,** and can be heated to 100° without changing in weight. C. R. Fresenius observed a slow oxidation. H. Rose said that it loses 0·13 per cent. in weight at 200°, and more as the temp. rises, reaching 0·54 per cent. at dull redness; it can then be kept at this temp. without any further loss. This result may be due to the presence of free sulphur or to moisture. The effect of still higher temp. is indicated above. A. Mailfert observed that **ozone** converts bismuth trisulphide into sulphate. O. Weigel said that the solubility of the trisulphide in **water** is 0·35$\times 10^{-6}$ mol. per litre at 18°. H. V. Regnault said that at a red-heat, steam forms bismuth trioxide and hydrogen sulphide together with a little bismuth. The **halogens** form chloro-, bromo-, and iodo-sulphides (q.v.). Thus, M. M. P. Muir and E. M. Eagles represented the reaction with chlorine at dull redness: $Bi_2S_3 + 3Cl_2 = BiSCl + BiCl_3 + S_2Cl_2$; at a higher temp., bismuth trichloride is formed. Dil. **hydrochloric acid** has no action on the trisulphide, but the hot conc. acid forms the soluble trichloride and hydrogen sulphide—vide supra, the preparation of the trisulphide. F. von Kobell showed that when the trisulphide is fused with **potassium iodide,** it forms a bright red deposit of bismuth iodide. H. Picton and S. E. Linder observed that bismuth trisulphide forms no compound with **hydrogen sulphide,** and in this respect differs from the corresponding sulphide of arsenic, and antimony. H. Feigel found that bismuth trisulphide and a benzene soln. of **sulphur monochloride** form a thiophenol complex, and also some bismuth trichloride. A. Guerout found that the tri- sulphide is slightly soluble in **sulphurous acid,** but C. R. Fresenius observed that it is insoluble in an aq. soln. of **sodium sulphite;** and it is insoluble in a soln. of **sodium thiosulphate.** J. Milbauer and J. Tucek found that when **sulphur dioxide** is passed over heated bismuth trisulphide the sulphate and sulphur are formed. When the trisulphide is heated with conc. **sulphuric acid,** it furnishes sulphur dioxide; and it is attacked by dil. **nitric acid** with the separation of sulphur. N. R. Dhar found that the action of nitric acid on bismuth gives only nitrous acid and hyponitrous acid and not hydroxylamine, hydrazine, or ammonia, which are formed by the hydrogenation of nitric acid. Bismuth can take only oxygen away from nitric acid and cannot add hydrogen to it. The corrosion of this metal, therefore, takes place by direct formation of an oxide. Nitrogen is formed by decomposition of hyponitrous acid and nitric oxide from the deccmposition of nitrous acid. G. Gore found that the trisulphide is insoluble in liquid **ammonia**. P. de Clermont found that a boiling soln. of **ammonium chloride** is without action on the trisulphide. H. Rose observed that when heated in a current of **phosphine**, the trisulphide is reduced to bismuth with the formation of phosphorus and hydrogen sulphide. J. J. Berzelius noted that when heated with **carbon,** the trisulphide is reduced to metal; H. Rose that it is slowly reduced by molten **potassium cyanide.** According to N. D. Costeanu, bismuth trisulphide is not affected chemically when heated to 1000° in an atm. of **carbon dioxide** although the sulphide is dissociated. T. Rosenbladt said that the trisulphide is insoluble in a soln. of **potassium thiocarbonate.** C. Hoffmann found that an aq. soln. of potassium cyanide is without action; and F. W. Schmidt, that when evaporated to dryness with an ammoniacal soln. of **mercuric cyanide,** and the residue heated, a mixture of bismuth and its trioxide is formed. F. Paneth and W. Thimann examined the adsorption of aniline dyes by bismuth trisulphide.

L. Kahlenberg and W. J. Trautmann observed no reaction with **silicon** at relatively low temp., but at very high temp. there is a rapid reaction. N. Parravano and P. Agostini studied the action of aluminium. Dil. soln. of **alkali hydroxides** are without action. W. R. Schoeller found that **bismuth trioxide** and trisulphide react at a comparatively low temp. in a current of carbon dioxide. A little basic sulphate is produced. Dil. aq. soln. of **alkali sulphides** are without action; but T. Stillmann, and G. C. Stone found that the sulphide is slightly soluble in soln. of alkali sulphides. When the trisulphide is treated with a conc. soln. of the alkali sulphides, or fused with the solid, sulphobismuthites are formed; and J. Knox found that, at 25°, soln. with 0·5, 1·0, and 1·5 mols of sodium sulphide per litre dissolve respectively 0·0040, 0·0238, and 0·1023 grm. of bismuth trisulphide per 100 c.c.; soln. with 0·5, 1·0, and 1·25 mols of potassium sulphide per litre dissolve respectively 0·0042, 0·0337, and 0·0639 grm. of bismuth trisulphide per 100 c.c.; soln. with a mol of sodium hydroxide and 0·5 and 1·0 mol of sodium trisulphide per litre dissolve respectively 0·0185 and 0·0838 grm. of the trisulphide per litre; while soln. with 0·5 mol K₂S and 1·0 mol KOH, 1·0 mol K₂S and 1·0 mol KOH, and 1·25 mol K₂S and 1·25 mol KOH per litre dissolve respectively 0·0240, 0·1230, and 0·2354 grm. of bismuth trisulphide per litre. The trisulphide is insoluble in 2N-**ammonium sulphide.** A. Hilger and P. A. von Scherpenberg found that the trisulphide is insoluble in a soln. of the **alkali polysulphides.** J. Knox said that 0·090 grm. of bismuth trisulphide dissolves in 100 c.c. of N-Na₂S. H. de Sénarmont observed that a little is dissolved by a soln. of **sodium hydrocarbonate** in a sealed tube at 200°. F. Raschig found that when bismuth trisulphide is boiled with an aq. soln. of **cupric chloride,** cupric sulphide, and bismuth trichloride or oxychloride are formed; with **cuprous chloride,** cuprous sulphide is formed. E. Schürmann found that with a soln. of **copper sulphate,** bismuth sulphate and cupric sulphide are formed, while **cadmium, lead, and antimony salts** are without action. J. B. Cammerer represented the reaction with **ferric chloride :** $Bi_2S_3 + 6FeCl_3$ $= 2BiCl_3 + 3S + 6FeCl_2$; and J. Hanus, with **ferric sulphate :** $Bi_2S_3 + 3Fe_2(SO_4)_3$ $= Bi_2(SO_4)_3 + 6FeSO_4 + 3S$, and by titrating the resulting ferrous sulphate, it is possible to determine the bismuth concerned in the reaction.

REFERENCES

¹ G. Werther, *Journ. prakt. Chem.*, (1), **27**. 65, 1842 ; E. R. Schneider, *ib.*, (2), **60**. 524, 1900 ; *Pogg. Ann.*, **91**. 404, 1854 ; G. Rose, *ib.*, **91**. 401, 1854 ; W. Heintz, *ib.*, **63**. 57, 1844 ; D. Lagerhjelm, *Schweigger's Journ.*, **17**. 416, 1816 ; *Akad. Handl. Stockholm*, 219, 1873 ; *Ann. Phil.*, **4**. 358, 1814 ; W. Herz and A. Guttmann, *Zeit. anorg. Chem.*, **53**. 71, 1907 ; **56**. 422, 1908 ; A. H. W. Aten, *ib.*, **47**. 386, 1905 ; K. Jellinek and J. Zakowsky, *ib.*, **142**. 1, 1925 ; J. Zakowsky, *Ueber die Affinität der Metalle zum Schwefel*, Danzig, 1904 : C. Hoffmann, *Liebig's Ann.*, **223**. 134, 1884 ; H. Pélabon, *Compt. Rend.*, **132**. 78, 1901 ; **137**. 648, 920, 1903 ; *Journ. Chim. Phys.,*

2. 321, 1904 ; L. Vanino and F. Treubert, *Ber.*, **32.** 1078, 1899 ; L. Playfair and J. P. Joule, *Mem. Chem. Soc.*, **3.** 57, 1846 ; H. V. Regnault, *Ann. Chim. Phys.*, (2), **62.** 382, 1836.

² A. Hilger and P. A. von Scherpenberg, *Mitt. Erlangen Pharm. Inst.*, **2.** 4, **7,** 1889 ; M. M. P. Muir, *Journ. Chem. Soc.*, **33.** 199, 1878.

³ J. G. Wallerius, *Mineralogia*, Stockholm, 315, 1750 ; A. G. Werner, *Letztes Mineralsystem*, Freiberg, 1817 ; A. Cronstedt, *Mineralogie*, Stockholm, 193, 1758 ; F. S. Beudant, *Traité élé-mentaire de minéralogie*, Paris, **2.** 418, 1832 ; J. B. L. Romé de l'Isle, *Cristallographie*, Paris, **3.** 116, 1783 ; R. Kirwan, *Elements of Mineralogy*, London, **2.** 266, 1794 ; W. Phillips, *Introduction to Mineralogy*, London, 203, 1819 ; J. D. Dana, *A System of Mineralogy*, New York, 30, 1868 ; E. F. Glocker, *Generum et specierum mineralium secundum ordines naturales digestorum synopsis*, Halle, 27, 1847 ; P. Groth, *Tabellarische Uebersicht der Mineralien*, Braunschweig, 17, 1898 ; L. A. Emmerling, *Lehrbuch der Mineralogie*, Giessen, **2.** 438, 1796.

⁴ B. G. Sage, *Mém. Acad.*, 307, 1782 ; H. Rose, *Gilbert's Ann.*, **72.** 192, 1822 ; T. Scheerer, *Pogg. Ann.*, **65.** 299, 1845 ; C. F. Rammelsberg, *Handbuch der Mineralchemie*, Leipzig, 261, 1853 ; 81, 1875 ; F. A. Genth, *Amer. Journ. Science*, (2), **23.** 415, 1857 ; (3), **41.** 402, 1891 ; G. C. Hoffmann, *Ann. Rep. Geol. Sur. Canada*, **6.** 19, 1893 ; W. H. Melville, *Bull. U.S. Geol. Sur.*, 90, 1892 ; I. Domeyko, *Elementos de mineralojia*, Santiago, 302, 1879 ; A. Wehrle, *Zeit. phys. Math. Wien*, **10.** 385, 1832 ; A. von Hubert, *Ber. Freund. Naturwiss. Wien*, **3.** 401, 1848 ; V. R. von Zepharovich, *Mineralogisches Lexikon für das Kaiserthum Oesterreich*, Wien, 58, 1873 ; R. Warington, *Phil. Mag.*, (2), **9.** 29, 1831 ; D. Forbes, *ib.*, (4), **29.** 4, 1865 ; A. Carnot, *Compt. Rend.*, **79.** 303, 1874 ; A. Bianchi, *Atti Accad. Lincei*, (5), **33.** ii, 254, 1924.

⁵ P. B. Gangully and N. R. Dhar, *Koll. Zeit.*, **31.** 16, 1922 ; A. Russell, *Min. Mag.*, **20.** 302, 1924 ; L. H. Borgström, *Oefvers. Finston Vet. Soc. Förh.*, **57.** 24, 1915 ; M. Mayençon, *Compt. Rend.*, **92.** 854, 1881 ; J. Durocher, *ib.*, **32.** 823, 1851 ; A. Carnot, *ib.*, **89.** 169, 1879 ; A. Ditte, *ib.*, **120.** 186, 1895 ; H. Pélabon, *ib.*, **132.** 78, 1901 ; **137.** 648, 920, 1903 ; A. Mourlot, *ib.*, **124.** 768, 1897 ; F. Rössler, *Synthese einiger Erzmineralien und analoger Metallverbindungen durch Auflösen und Kristallisierenlassen derselben in geschmolzenen Metallen*, Berlin, 1895 ; *Zeit. anorg. Chem.*, **9.** 44, 1895 ; A. H. W. Aten, *ib.*, **47.** 386, 1905 ; J. Milbauer, *ib.*, **42.** 441, 1905 ; H. Müller and L. Kürthy, *Biochem. Zeit.*, **147.** 385, 1924 ; W. Phillips, *Phil. Mag.*, **2.** 181, 1827 ; D. Forbes, *ib.*, (4), **29.** 4, 1865 ; W. Herapath, *ib.*, (1), **64.** 322, 1824 ; F. Faktor, *Pharm. Post.*, **33.** 301, 1900 ; J. Davy, *Phil. Trans.*, **102.** 169, 1812 ; P. F. Kerr, *Econ. Geol.*, **19.** 1, 1924 ; N. Tarugi, *Gazz. Chim. Ital.*, **27.** i, 316, 1897 ; F. Rinne, *Zeit. deut. geol. Ges.*, **62.** 62, 1890 ; O. Stelling, *Zeit. phys. Chem.*, **117.** 180, 1925 ; B. Aulenkamp, *Zeit. Physik*, **18.** 70, 1923 ; O. Schumann, *Liebig's Ann.*, **187.** 313, 1877 ; Y. Takahashi, *Mem. Coll. Science Kyoto*, **4.** 47, 1919 ; E. R. Schneider, *Journ. prakt. Chem.*, (2), **50.** 464, 1894 ; *Pogg. Ann.*, **91.** 420, 1854 ; H. Rose, *ib.*, **91.** 408, 1854 ; A. Weisbach, *ib.*, **128.** 440, 1866 ; A. Bianchi, *Atti Accad. Lincei*, (5), **33.** ii, 254, 1924 ; E. Quercigh, *ib.*, (6), **1.** 33, 1925 ; M. M. P. Muir and E. M. Eagles, *Journ. Chem. Soc.*, **67.** 90, 1895 ; S. Ramachandran, *Chem. News*, **131.** 135, 294, 386, 1925 ; K. Jellinek and J. Zakowsky, *Zeit. anorg. Chem.*, **142.** 1, 1925 ; P. Groth, *Zeit. Kryst.*, **5.** 252, 1880 ; W. W. Coblentz and H. Kohler, *Bull. Bur. Standards*, **15.** 231, 1919 ; H. Rose, *Pogg. Ann.*, 20. 336, 1830 ; D. Lagerhjelm, *Schweigger's Journ.*, **17.** 416, 1816 ; *Akad. Handl. Stockholm*, 219, 1813 ; *Ann. Phil.*, **4.** 358, 1814 ; E. T. Wherry, *Amer. Min.*, **10.** 28, 1925 ; C. Winssinger, *Bull. Acad. Belg.*, (3), **15.** 403, 1888 ; W. Spring, *Ber.*, **16.** 1001, 1883 ; *Zeit. phys. Chem.*, **17.** 556, 1895 ; O. Weigel, *ib.*, **58.** 293, 1907 ; H. de Sénarmont, *Ann. Chim. Phys.*, (3), **32.** 129, 1851 ; *Compt. Rend.*, **32.** 409, 1851 ; A. Karl, *ib.*, **146.** 1104, 1908 ; F. W. Clarke, *Constants of Nature*, Washington, 63, 1873 ; W. W. Mather, *ib.*, (1), **24.** 189, 1833 ; J. T. Norton, *ib.*, (4), **12.** 115, 1901 ; *Zeit. anorg. Chem.*, **28.** 225, 1901 ; C. J. B. Karsten, *Schweigger's Journ.*, **65.** 394, 1832 ; A. Wehrle, *ib.*, **59.** 483, 1830 ; C. M. Marx, *ib.*, **58.** 472, 1830 ; **59.** 114, 1830 ; A. de Gramont, *Bull. Soc. Min.*, **18.** 260, 1895 ; A. Schrauf and E. S. Dana, *Sitzber. Akad. Wien*, **69.** 148, 1874 ; O. Mügge, *Neues Jahrb. Min.*, ii, 19, 1883 ; i, 81, 1898 ; F. Beijerinck, *Neues Jahrb. Min. B.B.*, **11.** 424, 1897 ; N. R. Dhar, *Journ. Phys. Chem.*, **29.** 142, 1925 ; F. A. Genth, *Amer. Journ. Science*, (2), **23.** 415, 1857 ; (3), **41.** 402, 1891 ; G. C. Hoffmann, *Ann. Rep. Geol. Sur. Canada*, **6.** 19, 1893 ; W. H. Melville, *Bull. U.S. Geol. Sur.*, 90, 1892 ; V. R. von Zepharovich, *Mineralogisches Lexikon für das Kaiserthum Oesterreich*, Wien, 58, 1873 ; N. D. Costeanu, *Étude de l'action du gaz carbonique sur les sulfures minéraux*, Paris, 1914 ; *Chem. News*, **107.** 241, 1913 ; J. Joly, *Phil. Mag.*, (6), **27.** 1, 1914 ; H. Feigel, *Verhalten von Schwermetallverbindungen gegen Polysulfide und Chlorschwefel*, Erlangen, 1905 ; K. Jellinek and J. Zakowsky, *Zeit. anorg. Chem.*, **142.** 1, 1925 ; J. Zakowsky, *Ueber die Affinität der Metalle zum Schwefel*, Danzig, 1924 ; A. Kuhn and H. Pirsch, *Koll. Berhefte*, **21.** 78, 1925 ; J. Milbauer and J. Tucek, *Chem. Ztg.*, **50.** 323, 1926 ; L. Merz, *Ueber das Verhalten der Elemente und Verbindungen der Schwefelgruppe im Vakuum*, Heidelberg, 1905 ; G. Lugaro, *Atti Accad. Lincei*, (6), **3.** i, 416, 1926 ; L. Kahlenberg and W. J. Trautmann, *Trans. Amer. Electrochem. Soc.*, **39.** 377, 1921 ; T. W. Case, *Phys. Rev.*, (2), **9.** 305, 1917.

⁶ H. Rose, *Pogg. Ann.*, **20.** 336, 1830 ; **91.** 104, 1854 ; **110.** 136, 1860 ; E. R. Schneider, *ib.*, **91.** 420, 1854 ; C. R. Fresenius, *Anleitung zur quantitativen chemischen Analyse*, Braunschweig, **2.** 811, 1877 ; C. M. Marx, *Schweigger's Journ.*, **58.** 472, 1830 ; **59.** 114, 1830 ; A. Mourlot, *Compt. Rend.*, **124.** 768, 1897 ; A. Guerout, *ib.*, **75.** 1276, 1872 ; P. de Clermont, *ib.*, **88.** 973, 1879 ; A. Mailfert, *ib.*, **94.** 1186, 1882 ; H. Pélabon, *ib.*, **132.** 78, 1901 ; *Bull. Soc. Chim.*, (3), **25.** 149, 1901 ; C. Hoffmann, *Liebig's Ann.*, **233.** 134, 1884 ; E. Schürmann, *ib.*, **249.** 331, 1888 ; F. Raschig, *ib.*, **228.** 18, 1885 ; H. de Sénarmont, *Ann. Chim. Phys.*, (3), **32.** 129, 1851 ;

fl. V. Regnault, *ib.*, (2), **62**. 382, 1836 ; M. M. P. Muir and E. M. Eagles, *Journ. Chem. Soc.*, **67**. 90, 1895 ; N. Parravana and P. Agostini, *Gazz. Chim. Ital.*, **49**. i, 103, 1919 ; T. Stillman, *Journ. Amer. Chem. Soc.*, **18**. 683, 1896 ; G. C. Stone, *ib.*, **18**. 1091, 1896 ; L. Moser and E. Neusser, *Chem. Ztg.*, **47**. 541, 1923 ; *ib.*, **50**. 323, 1926 ; A. Hilger and P. A. von Scherpenberg, *Mitt. Erlangen Pharm. Inst.*, **2**. 4, 7, 1889 ; T. Rosenbladt, *Zeit. anal. Chem.*, **26**. 15, 1887 ; J. B. Cammerer, *Berg. Hütt. Ztg.*, **50**. 295, 1891 ; W. R. Schoeller, *Journ. Soc. Chem. Ind.*, **34**. 6, 1915 ; J. Hanus, *Zeit. anorg. Chem.*, **17**. 111, 1898 ; K. Jellinek and J. Zakowsky, *ib.*, **142**. 1, 1925 ; F. W. Schmidt, *Ber.*, **27**. 235, 1894 ; F. Paneth and W. Thimann, *ib.*, **57**. 1215, 1924 ; O. Weigel, *Zeit. phys. Chem.*, **58**. 293, 1907 ; G. Gore, *Proc. Roy. Soc.*, **21**. 140, 1873 ; F. von Kobell, *Sitzber. Bayr. Akad.*, **1**. 167, 1871 ; *Neues Jahrb. Min.*, 938, 1871 ; *Journ. prakt. Chem.*, (1), **111**. 469, 1871 ; H. Picton and S. E. Linder, *Journ. Chem. Soc.*, **61**. 132, 1892 ; J. Knox, *ib.*, **95**. 1760, 1909 ; L. Kahlenberg and W. J. Trautmann, *Trans. Amer. Eletrochem. Soc.*, **39**. 377, 1921 ; H. Feigel, *Verhalten von Schwermetallverbindungen gegen Polysulfide und Chlorschwefel*, Erlangen, 1905 ; N. R. Dhar, *Journ. Phys. Chem.*, **29**. 142, 1925 ; N. D. Costenau, *Étude de l'action du gaz carbonique sur les sulfures minéraux*, Paris, 1914 ; *Chem. News*, **107**. 241, 1913 ; J. J. Berzelius, *Lehrbuch der Chemie*, Dresden, **2**. i, 261, 1826 ; J. Milbauer and J. Tucek, *Chem. Ztg.*, **50**. 323, 1926.

§ 16. Complex Bismuth Sulphides ; Sulphobismuthites

Metal sulphides unite with bismuth sulphide, forming **sulphobismuthites ;** those of copper, silver, and lead occur in minerals. As in the case of the sulpharsenates and sulphantimonites, the sulphobismuthites have been referred to complex sulphobismuthous acids. Thus, there are representatives of

Orthosulphobismuthous acid	.	.	.	.	.	.	.	H_3BiS_3
Metasulphobismuthous acid	.	.	.	.	.	.	.	$HBiS_2$
Orthosulphotetrabismuthous acid	.	.	.	.	.	.	.	$H_6Bi_4S_9$
Metasulphotetrabismuthous acid	.	.	.	.	.	.	.	$H_3Bi_4S_7$

The preparation of these salts is indicated below.

E. R. Schneider [1] prepared **potassium metasulphobismuthite,** $KBiS_2$, by fusing a mixture of one part of bismuth with six parts each of sulphur, and potassium carbonate, and washing the matters soluble in water from the cold product. A. Hilger and P. A. von Scherpenberg used a similar process, and they also melted together a mixture of bismuth trioxide and potassium polysulphide and washed away the soluble matters as before. J. Milbauer made the salt by fusing at a high temp. of mixture of potassium thiocyanate and bismuth trioxide ; if the heating is not sufficient, bismuth trisulphide is formed. According to E. R. Schneider, the salt forms needle-like crystals which are stable in air ; and they can be heated out of contact with air without decomposition, but if heated in air, potassium and bismuth sulphates are formed. When heated in hydrogen, a mixture of potassium sulphide and bismuth is formed, while hydrogen sulphide is given off. The salt is insoluble in water. The salt is soluble in hydrochloric acid with the evolution of hydrogen sulphide. E. R. Schneider made **sodium metasulphobismuthite,** $NaBiS_2$, by a method similar to that employed for the potassium salt. The sodium salt is more easily decomposed by hydrogen than the potassium salt.

A. Ditte found that amorphous, precipitated bismuth trisulphide dissolves readily in a cold soln. of potassium sulphide, in a proportion increasing with the quantity of alkali sulphide present, and forms a red soln. If an excess of bismuth trisulphide is added and the liquid is heated, a further quantity dissolves, and, when the soln. is sufficiently conc. and is allowed to cool, it deposits very brilliant, transparent, highly refractive, reddish-yellow rhombohedra, of **basic potassium sulphobismuthite,** $Bi_2S_3.4K_2S+4H_2O$. The crystals effloresce in dry air, and in moist air become covered with a black film of bismuth trisulphide. They are immediately decomposed by water with separation of bismuth trisulphide, and a similar decomposition takes place on adding a small quantity of water to their mother-liquor. If the amorphous trisulphide is placed in a soln. of potassium sulphide just sufficiently conc. to form a small quantity of the double salt, and if the liquid is heated in such a way that the temp. is not uniform, the double sulphide will form in the cooler parts and be decomposed in the hotter parts, and the bismuth tri-sulphide will separate in a crystalline form, not readily attacked by the alkali sulphide. In this way, the whole of the bismuth trisulphide may become crystalline. According to A. Ditte, bismuth trisulphide is only slightly soluble in cold sat. soln. of sodium sulphide, and, although on heating the soln., and allowing it to con-centrate at the same time, the solubility increases sufficiently to produce a small quantity of double salt, and thus convert the bismuth trisulphide into the crystalline form, the liquid does not deposit the double sulphide.

W. Guertler,[2] and W. Meissner made a study of the ternary system : Cu–Bi–S. C. J. Selb described a mineral from Wittichen, Baden, which he called *Kupferwis-mutherz ;* C. C. von Leonhard called it *Wismuthkupfererz ; F.* von Kobell, *wittichite ;* and G. A. Kenngott, **wittichenite.** Analyses reported by M. H. Klaproth, J. Stauffacher, C. Weltzien, E. Tobler, E. R. Schneider, A. Hilger, T. Petersen, and F. Sandberger indicate that the mineral is **cuprous orthosulphobismuthite,** Cu_3BiS_3. This same salt was prepared by E. R. Schneider by boiling a soln. of cupric oxide in conc. hydrochloric acid with bismuth in an atm. of carbon dioxide until the green colour became yellow, and potash-lye gave a voluminous yellow precipitate ; the yellow soln. was mixed with tartaric acid, and treated with hydrogen sulphide. The precipitate was filtered, washed, and dried, and melted at a red-heat. Wittichenite occurs in steel-grey or tin-white, coarse or granular masses ; it may also be disseminated in small masses, or occur as an aggregate of imperfect prisms. According to A. Breithaupt, the rhombic crystals are isomorphous with those of bournonite—but P. Groth considers this doubtful. The sp. gr. ranges from 4·3 to 4·5—A. Hilger gave 4·3. E. R. Schneider gave 5·9 for the sp. gr. of the arti-ficial salt which had been fused. J. J. Saslawsky estimated the contraction which occurs when the mineral is formed from its component sulphides. The hardness is 2-3. Wittichenite is decomposed by nitric acid with the separation of sulphur ; and dissolves in hydrochloric acid with the evolution of hydrogen sulphide.

C. J. Selb [3] described a copper bismuth sulphide ore from Tannenbaum, Saxony, and it was called *Kupferwismuthglanz* by E. R. Schneider ; **emplectite**—from ἔμπλεκτος, entwined or interwoven—in allusion to its intimate association with quartz—by G. A. Kenngott ; *tannenite,* by J. D. Dana ; and *hemichalcite*—from ἡμί, half ; χαλκός, copper, in allusion to its containing half the proportion of copper in wittichenite—by F. von Kobell. Analyses reported by E. R. Schneider, T. Petersen, W. F. Hillebrand, F. R. Daw, J. A. Krenner, I. Domeyko, and C. Guille-main are in agreement with the formula $Cu_2S.Bi_2S_3$, or **copper metasulpho-bismuthite,** $CuBiS_2$. E. H. Kraus and J. P. Goldsberry represent emplectite as a member of a series represented by the general formula $M'_nR_2S_{\frac{1}{2}n+3}$, where R denotes tervalent bismuth, antimony, or arsenic. The salt was prepared by E. R. Schneider by melting together the correct proportions of chalcocite, Cu_2S, and artificial bismuth trisulphide ; by triturating potassium metasulphobismuthite, in the absence of air, with an ammoniacal soln. of cuprous oxide in hydrochloric acid, and shaking the mixture in a closed vessel frequently for 8–10 days. The soln. is decolorized, and is then mixed with a freshly prepared soln. of hydrogen sulphide in dil. hydrochloric acid (1 : 10), and melted at a red-heat out of contact with air. Sodium metasulphobismuthite gives a very poor yield ; the reaction is slower with more conc. acid, and with more dil. acid, basic chlorides are formed. F. Rössler obtained this salt as a regulus by fusing together the component elements. Before fusion, the salt appears as a black powder ; and after fusion, as a greyish-white or tin-white mass with a radiating, crystalline structure. J. L. C. Schröder van der Kolk made some observations on the colour of the mineral. Emplectite occurs in grey or tin-white thin striated prisms which belong to the rhombic system, and, according to A. Weisbach, have the axial ratios $a : b : c = 0.5430 : 1 : 0.6256$. The cleavage on the (100)-face is perfect—that on the (010)-face is less clear, and that on the (506)-face is distinct. The crystals were also examined by H. Dauber, V. Goldschmidt, and P. Groth. L. J. Spencer discussed the isomorphism of emplectite with zinckenite, etc. E. R. Schneider gave 6·10 at 15° for the artificial product; and for the mineral, A. Weisbach gave 5·18. The sp. gr. of emplectite ranges between 6·23 and 6·52 ; and J. J. Saslawsky estimated the contraction which occurs when the mineral is formed from its constituents. The hardness is 2. J. Joly gave 400°–600° as the temp. at which a sublimation occurs. T. W. Case found that the high resistance of emplectite is not affected appreciably by light. E. R. Schneider said that his product loses three-fourths of its sulphur when heated in hydrogen, and a mixture of cuprous sulphides and bismuth remains. The mineral is decomposed by nitric acid with the separation of sulphur.

T. Petersen and F. Sandberger [4] found a mineral which they named **klaprothite** —after M. H. Klaproth ; but since lazulite was named klaprothite by F. S. Beudant in 1824, G. J. Brush suggested that the term be altered to *klaprotholite*. Klaprothite occurs with other bismuth minerals near Wittichen, Baden ; and in a few other localities. Analyses by E. R. Schneider, and T. Petersen agree with the formula $3Cu_2S.2Bi_2S_3$, or **cuprous orthosulphotetrabismuthite,** $Cu_6Bi_4S_9$. E. H. Kraus and J. P. Goldsberry regarded this mineral as a member of a series including rathite, warrenite, and schirmerite, represented by the general formula $M'_nR_4S_{\frac{1}{2}n+6}$, where R denotes arsenic, antimony, or bismuth. The colour is steel-grey tarnishing to brass-yellow ; the furrowed, prismatic crystals belong to the rhombic system with $a:b:c=0.74:1:-$. The cleavage on the (100)-face is distinct ; and twinning occurs about the (110)-plane. The sp. gr. given by T. Petersen is 4·6, and the hardness 2·5. J. J. Saslawsky estimated the contraction which occurs when the mineral is formed from its constituents. It dissolves in nitric and hydrochloric acids. F. Sandberger discussed the products obtained by the weathering of klaprothite. A mineral from Dognacska, Hungary, was called by J. A. Krenner, **dognacskaite.** Analyses reported by J. A. Krenner,[5] and F. Neugebauer agree with $Cu_2S.2Bi_2S_3$, or **cuprous metasulphotetrabismuthite,** $Cu_2Bi_4S_7$. A. Otto thought that it is the same as wittichenite, but F. Neugebauer regards it as a distinct mineral species. Its sp. gr. is 6·79.

O. Grosspietsch [6] described **an** Alpine mineral from the magnesite of Eichberg, and he called it **eichbergite.** It is iron-grey with an irregular fracture. The analysis agrees with $(Cu,Fe)_2S.3(Bi,Sb)_2S_3$, or **cuprous metasulphotrisantimonitobismuthite,** $Cu.Sb_3Bi_3S_5$. Its sp. gr. is 5·36 ; and its hardness, 6. A mineral occurring in the quartz gangue of the Missouri mine, Colorado, was regarded by W. H. Hillebrand [7] as a sulphobismuthite of copper and silver. J. D. Dana called it **cuprobismuthite.** Analyses by W. F. Hillebrand agree with the formula $3(Cu_2,Ag_2,Pb)S.4Bi_2S_3$, and it is usually represented as $3Cu_6S.4Bi_2S_3$, or **cuprous mesosulphoctobismuthite,** $Cu_6Bi_8S_{15}$. If occurs in dark-bluish compact masses, or in groups of slender, prismatic crystals striated longitudinally. The sp. gr. is 6·31–6·38. It is soluble in acids.

C. F. Rammelsberg [8] described a *Silberwismuthglanz* from the Matilde mine near Morococha, Peru. P. y Rico named it *peruvite ;* A. d'Achiardi, **matildite ;** M. F. Heddle, *morocochite ;* and F. A. Genth, *argentobismuthinite.* Analyses reported by C. F. Rammelsberg, F. A. Genth, T. Wada, T. L. Walker, E. R. Schneider, and F. Rössler agree with the formula $Ag_2S.Bi_2S_3$, or **silver metasulphobismuthite,** $AgBiS_2$. In some cases, a little silver is replaced by lead. F. Sandberger described a non-black mineral from Schapbach, Baden, which he called plenargyrite. The analysis approximated to that of matildite. E. R. Schneider found that when finely powdered bismuth trisulphide is shaken with a feebly ammoniacal, one per cent. soln. of silver nitrate, practically no change occurs, a mere trace only of silver being thrown down as sulphide ; but if the silver nitrate soln. be neutral, the silver will be precipitated as sulphide and the bismuth converted into basic nitrate. One grm. of finely powdered potassium metasulphobismuthite is put into a flask (60 c.c.) together with 25–30 c.c. of air-free water and a soln. of 0·550 grm. of silver nitrate to which ammonia has been added until the brown precipitate just redissolves; the flask is then filled up with air-free water and continually shaken. After 12–24 hrs., the supernatant liquid is found to be free from silver ; it is then decanted, and the residue shaken with air-free water for two days, then filtered, washed with water and absolute alcohol, pressed between filter-paper, and dried at 100°. Artificial silver-bismuth-glance was also prepared by fusing silver sulphide and bismuth trisulphide together in mol. proportion. F. Rössler prepared steel-grey octahedra by melting a mixture of 20 grms. of bismuth and 2 grms. of silver sulphide, and washing the cold product with cold nitric acid of sp. gr. 1·1. Matildite occurs in slender, prismatic, grey crystals, and also in compact masses. E. R. Schneider described silver metasulphobismuthite as a dark-grey powder; if crystals of bismuth sulphide are employed instead of powder in the above prescription, the resulting glance is crystalline and of the same form as the bismuth sulphide. It fuses without decomposition; the fused mass is light-grey and of metallic lustre; its fracture shows a homogeneous, leafy, crystalline structure; it is brittle, but not easily powdered. The powder is grey; its hardness is about 3·5; its sp. gr. at 15° is 6·96, that of the mineral being 6·92 (C. F. Rammelsberg). J. J. Saslawsky calculated the contraction which occurs when matildite is formed from its constituents. Cold nitric acid and hydrochloric acid do not attack it, but both acids decompose it when hot.

The mineral **aramayoite**—named after F. A. Aramayo—was discovered by M. Roberts in a silver-tin mine at Chocaya, Potosi, Bolivia, and described by L. J. Spencer. The analysis corresponds with **silver sulphoantimoniobismuthite**, $Ag(Sb,Bi)S_2$; E. Kittl gave $Ag(Sb,As,Bi)S_2$. The colour is iron-black with a brilliant metallic lustre on the perfect cleavage. It shows an irregular and confused aggregate of bright cleavage surfaces with striated areas at the edges, like "books" of mica. These cleavage flakes are pliable but not elastic. The crystals appear as if they were tetragonal with perfect basal (001)-cleavage, and good cleavages in the (001–100)-, (001–110)-zones. K. Yardley gave for the axial ratios of the triclinic crystals $a : b : c = 0\cdot9972 : 1 : 0\cdot9886$, and $a = 86° 55', \beta = 90° 53'$, and $\gamma = 93° 18'$. The X-radiogram corresponds with a triclinic cell with the dimensions $a = 5\cdot672$ A., $b = 5\cdot688$ A., and $c = 5\cdot623$ A. According to L. J. Spencer, when the mineral is powdered in a mortar it breaks up into short fibres which have a tendency to clog together. The sp. gr. is 5·602; the hardness, 2·5. The cleavage flakes are quite opaque. G. A. König [9] described what he called *auro-bismuthinite* as a mineral with the composition $(Ag_2Au,Bi)_5S_6$.

The **lead sulphobismuthite**, $PbS.Bi_2S_3$, or $Pb(BiS_2)_2$, found on Vulcano, Lipari Islands, in the deeper parts of the fumaroles, at a temp. of 560°–615°, occurs in lead-grey, flattened crystals which F. Zambonini and co-workers [10] say are probably rhombic. They called the mineral **cannizzarite**—after S. Cannizzaro. This may be the same mineral as chiviatite—*vide infra*. A mineral from the Baltic Lode in Colorado was described by G. A. König, and called **beegerite**—after H. Beeger. Analyses reported by G. A. König, and F. A. Genth correspond with $6PbS.Bi_2S_3$, or $6(Pb,Ag_2)S.Bi_2S_3$, or **lead tristulphorthosulphobismuthite**, $3PbS.Pb_3(BiS_3)_2$. R. F. Weinland regarded it as containing mixed tetra- and penta-sulphobismuthous acid anions, $[(BiS_3)(BiS_4)]Pb_6$. E. H. Kraus and J. P. Goldsberry regarded it as a member of the series:

Bismuthinite, Bi_2S_3	Galenabismuthinite, $Pb(BiS_2)_2$	Cosalite, $Pb_2Bi_2S_5$	Lilianite, $Pb_3(BiS_3)_2$	Beegerite, $Pb_6Bi_2S_9$	Galena, PbS
6·5	6·88–7·14	6·39–6·75	6·7	7·273	7·45

E. T. Wherry and W. F. Foshag questioned whether beegerite is homogeneous and a mineralogical individual. The colour of the mineral is light or dark grey; it occurs indistinctly crystalline—probably cubic. The cleavage is cubic. The sp. gr. given by G. A. König is 7·273, and when silver is present the sp. gr. may fall to 6·565. J. J. Saslawsky calculated the contraction which occurs when the mineral is formed from its constituents. A. de Gramont examined the spark spectrum. E. T. Wherry found the crystals to be fair radio-detectors. Beegerite is soluble in conc. hydrochloric acid. According to F. Ducatte,[11] the methods of synthesis employed by H. Sommerlad for the sulpharsenites and sulphantimonites are inapplicable because the chlorine cannot be removed from the products.

H. F. and H. A. Keller [12] obtained crystals of a mineral from the mines of the Lilian Mining Co., Leadville, Colorado, and they called it **lilianite**. It has also been found at Hoena, Sweden. Analyses reported by H. F. and H. A. Keller, C. F. Rammelsberg, G. Lindström, T. L. Walker and E. Thomson, and G. Flink agree with the formula $3(Pb,Ag_2)S.Bi_2S_3$, or $3PbS(Bi,So)_2S_3$, or **lead orthosulphobismuthite**, $Pb_3(BiS_3)_2$. The steel-grey mineral occurs massive and crystalline. The mineral is probably rhombic with the axial ratios $a:b:c=0.8002:1:0.5435$. The cleavage on the (100)-face is very distinct, that on the (010)-face less so. T. L. Walker and E. Thomson consider it to be a definite species. C. F. Rammelsberg gave 6·145 for the sp. gr.; T. L. Walker and E. Thomson, 7·090; and G. Flink, 7·40. The hardness is 2–3. J. Setterberg described a mineral from Hoena, Sweden, which he called **kobellite**—after F. von Kobell. Analyses were reported by J. Setterberg, C. F. Rammelsberg, H. F. Keller, and G. Flink. The analyses of J. Setterberg, and H. F. Keller agree with $2PbS(Bi,Sb)_2S_3$, and the others with $3PbS.(Bi,Sb)_2S_3$. G. Rose gave $3(4PbS.FeS).(4Bi_2S_3.Sb_2S_3)$. P. Groth and K. Mieleitner gave $Pb_3\{(Sb,Bi)S_3\}_2$. There is therefore some confusion of this mineral with lilianite. The lead-grey or steel-grey mineral occurs massive—granular, and radiated and fibrous like stibnite. The hardness is 2·5–3·0; and the sp. gr. 6·29–6·32. J. J. Saslawsky estimated the contraction which occurs when the mineral is formed from its component sulphides. J. Joly found bismuth oxide sublimes when the mineral is heated to a high temp. in air. T. W. Case said that the resistance is greater than a megohm, and is not affected appreciably by light. E. T. Wherry found the crystals to be poor radio-detectors.

F. Mohs [13] described what he called *Nadelerz—needle ore*—from Berezoff, Urals. E. J. Chapman called it **aikinite**; W. Haidinger, *patrinite*—after E. L. M. Patrin; J. Nicol, *aciculite*; and E. F. Glocker, *belonite*—from βελόνη, a needle. Analyses reported by C. Guillemain, G. Lindström, J. F. John, H. Frick, E. J. Chapman, and R. Hermann agree with C. F. Rammelsberg's formula $CuPbBiS_3$, or **cuprous lead orthosulphobismuthite**. Analogous formulæ were given by E. T. Wherry and W. F. Foshag, W. F. Foshag, C. Guillemain, and P. Groth and K. Mieleitner. E. H. Kraus and J. P. Goldsberry represented aikinite as a member of a series with the general formula $M'_nRS_{\frac{1}{2}n+3}$, where R denotes As, Sb, or Bi—*e.g.* bournonite, and seligmannite. M. Hörner observed the isomorphism of the crystals with those of bournonite. The dark, lead-grey mineral may occur massive, and also in embedded acicular crystals, longitudinally striated. According to H. A. Miers, the rhombic crystals have the axial ratios $a:b:c=0.9719:1:$ —. The sp. gr. is 6·1–6·8, and the hardness 2. J. Joly gave 420°–670° for the temp. at which sublimation occurs. A. de Gramont examined the spark spectrum. E. T. Wherry found the crystals are good radio-detectors. The mineral is decomposed by nitric acid with the separation of lead sulphate. The weathering of the mineral was noted by F. A. Genth, J. R. Blum, G. Sillem, G. Rose, C. C. Leonhard, and E. L. M. Patrin.

H. Sjögren [14] described a mineral from Nordmark, Sweden, which he called **galenobismuthite**. The analysis corresponded with $PbS.Bi_2S_3$, or **lead metasulphobismuthite**, $Pb(BiS_2)_2$. The colour varies from dark lead-grey to tin-white. The mineral occurs in compact masses, in foliated or radiated masses, or in columnar crystals with indistinct faces. E. V. Shannon described prismatic crystals of the mineral. The sp. gr. is 6·88, and the hardness 3–4. J. Joly gave 470°–560° for the temp. at which sublimation occurs. T. W. Case found that the mineral has a resistance less than a megohm, and is not affected by light. E. T. Wherry found galenobismuthite a poor radio-detector. G. A. König described an argentiferous variety from the Alaska mine, Colorado, and he called it **alaskaite**. It contained 3·26–8·74 per cent. of silver, and 3·46–5·11 per cent. of copper, making the mineral $(Pb,Ag_2,Cu_2)(Bi_2S_2)_2$. This agrees with the views of E. T. Wherry and W. F. Foshag, and E. H. Kraus and J. P. Goldsberry. P. Groth and K. Mieleitner gave $Pb(Ag,Cu)(BiS_2)_3$. It was also described by F. Ahlfeld. T. Liweh's analysis makes alaskaite resemble fahlerz ; H. W. Brown regarded it as a galena-bismuthinite. A. de Gramont studied the spark spectrum. The sp. gr. was 6·782–6·878. M. Weibull also described a seleniferous variety from Falun, Sweden, which contained 12·43–13·61 per cent. of selenium, replacing the sulphur. Its sp. gr. was 6·97–7·145. E. T. Wherry found the crystals are poor radio-detectors. T. L. Walker and E. Thomson have reported analyses of Fahlun galenobismuthite which make it like cosalite. W. F. Foshag gave $Ag_2PbBi_4S_8$.

The mineral cosalite from a silver mine at Cosala, Mexico, was described by F. A. Genth.[15] H. Sjögren, and A. E. Nordenskjöld obtained a similar mineral from the Bjelke mine, Nordmark, Sweden, and called it *bjelkite ;* and an impure form of the mineral from Rezbanya, Hungary, was called by R. Hermann. *rezbanyite.* Analyses were reported by F. A. Genth, R. Hermann, J. Loczka, A. Frenzel, H. Sjögren, E. le Neve Foster, W. F. Hillebrand, G. A. König, A. H. Low, H. Bancroft, T. L. Walker and E. Thomson, and G. Lindström. The results agree with the formula $2(Pb,Ag_3)S.BiS_3$, or with lead pyrosulphobismuthite, $Pb_2Bi_2S_5$. The lead-grey mineral usually occurs massive with an indistinct crystalline structure—fibrous or radiated. The rhombic crystals were found by G. Flink to have the axial ratios $a : b : c = 0.91874 : 1 : 1.4601$; and he said that the mineral is isomorphous with dufrenoysite and jamesonite. A. Frenzel gave 6·22–6·33 for the sp. gr. of rezbanyite ; H. Sjögren, 6·39–6·75 for bjelkite ; and for cosalite, G. A. König gave 6·782 ; and T. L. Walker, 6·55. J. J. Saslawsky calculated the contraction which occurs during the formation of cosalite from its constituent sulphides. The hardness is 2·5–3·0. J. Joly gave 720° for the temp. at which a sublimation occurs. T. W. Case found the resistance is less than a megohm, and is not affected appreciably by light. A. de Gramont examined the spark spectrum. Cosalite is slowly attacked by hydrochloric acid, and is decomposed by nitric acid with the formation of lead sulphate.

The *wismuthisches Silber* from Schapbach, Baden, was described by C. J. Selb,[16] and L. A. Emmerling, and called by C. C. von Leonhard, *Wismuthbleierz,* and by G. A. Kenngott, and F. Sandberger, schapbachite. Its analyses reported by M. H. Klaproth, and F. Sandberger agree with the formula $PbS.Ag_2S.Bi_2S_3$, or lead silver pyrosulphobismuthite, $PbAg_2Bi_2S_5$; this was confirmed by W. F. Foshag. It occurs in lead-grey masses and in minute, acicular crystals, probably rhombic. E. le Neve Foster described what he called lead silver *sulphobismutite,* as a mineral occurring at Chihuahua, Mexico, with the composition $2(Ag,Pb,Cu)S.Bi_2S_3$, or $Ag_4PbBi_5S_{13}$. It sp. gr. was 5·8, and its hardness 3–3·5.

The mineral rezbanyite, from Rezbanya, Hungary, has been regarded as an impure cosalite—*vide supra.* A. Frenzel's [17] analysis agrees with the formula $4PbS.5Bi_2S_3$, or $Pb_4Bi_{10}S_{19}$, while E. T. Wherry and W. F. Foshag represent it by the formula $2PbS.3Bi_2S_3$; and K. Johansson, by $3PbS.Cu_2S.5Bi_2S_3$. The sp. gr. is 6·09–6·38 ; and the hardness, 2·5–3·0. K. Johansson described lindströmite —named after G. Lindström—from the Gladhammar mine ; its composition corresponds with cuprous lead metasulphohexabismuthite, $2PbS.Cu_2S.3Bi_2S_3$. The crystals of the light blue mineral have a sp. gr. 7·01 ; and hardness 3·0–3·5 ; and gladite from the same locality, and having a composition corresponding with cuprous lead tetrerosulphodecabismuthite, $2PbS.Cu_2S.5Bi_2S_3$. The sp. gr. is 6·96, and the hardness 2–3.

F. Zambonini and co-workers [18] observed a crystalline mineral in the fumaroles of Vulcano, Lipari Islands, where the temp. is 550°–615°, and where the emission of acidic volcanic gases is greatest, and access of air is prevented. He called the mineral cannizzarite—after S. Cannizzaro. Its analysis corresponds with lead deuterosulphotetrabismuthite, $PbS.2Bi_2S_3$. The sp. gr. is 6·54 at 10°. The mineral is rhombic, and isogonal with bismuthinite and antimonite in the (001)·

zone. It is supposed to have been formed by the action of hydrogen on the chlorides of bismuth and lead. C. F. Rammelsberg described a mineral from Chiviato, Peru, which he called **chiviatite**. It occurs in foliated masses resembling bismuthinite. The analyses reported by C. F. Rammelsberg, and A. Raimondi agree with the formula $2PbS.3Bi_2S_3$, or *lead mesosulphohexabismuthite*, $Pb_2Bi_6S_{11}$. This formula was also given by G. Cesaro. On the other hand, E. T. Wherry and W. F. Foshag gave $PbS.2Bi_2S_3$, or **lead metasulphotetrabismuthite**, $PbBi_4S_7$. The sp. gr. given by C. F. Rammelsberg is 6·920, and J. J. Saslawsky calculated the contraction which occurs when it is formed from its component sulphides. E. T. Wherry found the crystals are fair radio-detectors. The composition of **benjaminite** described by E. V. Shannon, and obtained from the Round Mountain, Nevada, corresponds with **silver copper lead orthosulphotetrabismuthite**, $Pb_2(Cu,Ag)_2Bi_4S_9$. The grey mineral has a hardness 3·5, and it is soluble in hot nitric or hydrochloric acid. F. A. Genth [19] described a mineral from the Treasury lode, Colorado, and he named it **schirmerite**—after J. F. L. Schirmer. The analysis agrees with the formula $3(Ag_2,Pb)S.2Bi_2S_3$, or **silver lead orthosulphobismuthite**, $(Ag_2,Bi)_3Bi_4S_9$; W. F. Foshag gave $2Ag_2S.PbS.2Bi_2S_3$. It occurs in finely granular masses ; the colour is lead-grey ; and the sp. gr. 6·737. The schirmerite described by F. M. Endlich is a mixture of petzite and pyrite—*vide infra*, hammarite. A. de Gramont examined the spark spectrum. T. W. Case said that the mineral is a poor conductor, and light has no appreciable effect.

E. S. Simpson [20] described a mineral, found near Lake Goongardie, Western Australia, which he called **goongardite**. The analysis corresponds with $4PbS.Bi_2S_3$, and it is a **lead disulphopyrosulphobismuthite**, $Pb_4Bi_2S_7$,

$$S{<}^{Pb—S—Pb}_{>}S$$
$$S{>}^{Bi—S—Bi}{<}S$$

and this belongs to the jordanite group. The crystals are probably isomorphous with jordanite, and meneghinite. The sp. gr. is 7·29 ; the hardness, 3 ; and its m.p., 950°. Dil. nitric acid has very little action, but it is decomposed by the conc. acid forming lead sulphate. J. Krenner and J. Loczka reported *warthaite* as a steel-grey mineral occurring as radially fibrous bundles in the Hungarian limestones. The analysis corresponds with $4(Pb,Cu,Ag)S.Bi_2S_3$, that is, with $(Pb,Cu,Ag)_4Bi_2S_7$, so that it appears to be a variety of goongardite.

E. V. Shannon [21] described a lead-grey fibrous mineral occurring at Wickes, Montana. It is completely soluble in hot, conc. hydrochloric acid. The analysis agrees with $5PbS.4Bi_2S_3$, and it therefore forms a family group with liveingite, $5PbS.4As_2S_3$, and plagionite, $5PbS.4Sb_2S_3$—hence the name **bismutoplagionite**, or **lead heptadecasulphoctobismuthite**, $Pb_5Bi_8S_{17}$. K. Johansson reported a leaden grey **lead selenosulphohexabismuthite**, $5PbS.3Bi_2(S,Se)_3$, occurring in the Falun Mine, Sweden. He called it **wittite**—after T. Witt. The mineral has either rhombic or monoclinic symmetry as shown by the X-radiograms. The sp. gr. is 7·12 ; the hardness 2·0–2·5 ; and the cleavage is good. E. T. Wherry found the crystals are poor radio-detectors. K. Johansson found a steel-grey, reddish mineral in the Gladhammar mine of Kalmar, Sweden, and he called it **hammarite**. It occurs in short needles or prisms—possibly monoclinic. Its composition was represented by $5PbS.3Bi_2S_3$, or **lead sulphohexabismuthite** ; but since the mineral has 7·6 per cent. of copper, W. F. Foshag regarded it as $2PbS.Cu_2S.2Bi_2S_3$, the copper analogue of schirmerite. The sp. gr. is high, the hardness 3–4. K. Johansson obtained from the same locality lead-grey prismatic crystals of a mineral which he called **lindströmite**—after G. Lindström—and represented as **cuprous lead deuterosulphohexabismuthite**, $Cu_2S.PbS.3Bi_2S_3$. Its sp. gr. is 7·01, and hardness 3–3·5. Yet a third mineral called gladite appeared in lead-grey prismatic crystals with the sp. gr. 6·96, and hardness 2–3. Its composition approximated **cuprous lead triterosulphodecabismuthite**, $2PbS.Cu_2S.5Bi_2S_3$.

G A. König [22] described a mineral from Nacozari, Somora, Mexico, and he called it **stibiobismuthinite**. It occurs in long prismatic crystals with the cleavage and structure of bismuthinite. The analysis approximates $(Sb,Bi)_4S_7$. E. Quercigh suggested that it belongs to the type of mixed sulphides $(Bi,Sb)_2S_3$, prepared by C. Geitner.

G. Tschermak [23] described a mineral occurring at Orawitza, Hungary, and named it **alloclasite**, or rather *Alloclas*—from ἄλλος, another; κλάειν, to break, in allusion to its cleavage, which at that time was believed to differ from those of arsenopyrite and marcasite—*vide* smaltite. Analyses reported by G. Tschermak, A. von Hubert and A. Patera, and A. Frenzel were represented by C. F. Rammelsberg by the formula $Co_6As_{10}S_9$; by P. Groth, by $Co(As,Vi,S)$, or **cobalt ferrous sulphoarsenitobismuthite**, $(Co,Fe)(As,Bi)S$. A. Lacroix supposed the bismuthiferous arsenical pyrites of Meymac to be a variety of alloclasite. The mineral occurs in steel-grey aggregates or rarely in rhombic crystals with the axial ratios $a : b : c = 0.15 : 1 : 1.36$. The cleavage on the (110)-face is perfect, and that on the (001)-face is distinct. W. F. de Jong found the X-radiogram closely resembled that of glaucodolite. The sp. gr. is 6·6, and the hardness 4·5. J. Joly gave 440° as the temp. at which a sublimation occurs. It is soluble in nitric acid.

The *Nickelwismuthglanz* obtained by F. von Kobell [24] from Grüneau, was named *saynite;* A. Breithaupt called it *theophrastite;* and J. Nicol, **grünanite**. Analyses reported by F. von Kobell, and C. F. Rammelsberg correspond with $Bi_2S_3.12(Ni,Co,Fe)_2S_3$, or $Bi_2S_3.10R_2S_3$; M. L. Frankenheim gave $NiS(Ni,Bi)_2S_3$. H. Laspeyres considers it to be polydymite contaminated with bismuthinite. The steel-grey mineral furnishes cubic crystals with an octahedral cleavage. The sp. gr. is 5·13; and the hardness, 4·5. H. Laspeyres [25] described a mineral from Schönstein, Rhine provinces, and he called it **kallilite**—from a local name. The analysis corresponds with $NiBi_2.NiS_2$, or **nickel sulphobismuthite**, $NiBiS$. It is considered to be a variety of ullmanite. M. L. Huggins examined the electronic structure of kallilite. The sp. gr. is 7·011. R. Scheibe also described a nickel bismuth sulphide from Niederhöfels. G. Werther obtained a complex nickel sulphobismuthite, $Ni_5Bi_{24}S_2$, by melting nickel with 64 parts of bismuth, 8 parts of sodium carbonate, and one part of sulphur. The reddish crystals had a sp. gr. 9·15.

REFERENCES.

[1] E. R. Schneider, *Pogg. Ann.*, **136**. 464, 1869; **138**. 309, 1869; *Journ. prakt. Chem.*, (2), **40**. 564, 1869; A. Hilger and P. A. von Scherpenberg, *Mitt. Erlangen Pharm. Inst.*, **2**. 4, 7, 1889; F. Rössler, *Zeit. anorg. Chem.*, **9**. 47, 1895; J. Milbauer, *ib.*, **42**. 441, 1905; A. Ditte, *Compt. Rend.*, **120**. 186, 1895.

[2] W. Guertler, *Metall Erz*, **22**. 199, 1925; W. Meissner, *ib.*, **22**. 343, 1925; J. J. Saslawsky, *Zeit. Kryst.*, **59**. 206, 1924; P. Groth, *Tabellarische Uebersicht der Mineralien*, Braunschweig, **35**, 1898; C. J. Selb, *Ges. Aerzte Naturf. Schwaben*, **1**. 419, 1805; G. A. Kenngott, *Uebersichte der Resultate mineralogischer Forschungen*, Leipzig, **118**, 1855; J. Stauffacher, *Verh. Nat. Ges. Basel*, **29**. 198, 1918; M. H. Klaproth, *Beiträge zur chemischen Kenntniss der Mineralkörper*, Berlin, **4**. 91, 1807; C. C. von Leonhard, *Handbuch der Oryktognosie*, Heidelberg, **215**, 1821; F. Sandberger, *Untersuchungen über Erzgänge*, Ukisbaden, **386**, 1885; *Neues Jahrb. Min.*, **275**, 1865; **414**, 1868; A. Breithaupt, *Mineralogische Studien*, Leipzig, **111**, 1866; F. von Kobell, *Charakteristik der Mineralien*, Nürnberg, **127**, 1830; *Tafeln zur Bestimmung der Mineralien*, München, **13**, 1853; C. Weltzien, *Liebig's Ann.*, **91**. 232, 1854; E. Tobler, *ib.*, **96**. 307, 1855; A. Hilger, *Pogg. Ann.*, **125**. 144, 1865; E. R. Schneider, *Journ. prakt. Chem.*, (2), **40**. 565, 1889; *Pogg. Ann.*, **93**. 305, 472, 1854; **97**. 476, 1856; **127**. 308, 1866; T. Petersen, *ib.*, **136**. 501, 1869.

[3] C. J. Selb, *Leonhard's Taschenbuch Min.*, **11**. 441, 451, 1817; G. A. Kenngott, *Uebersichte der Resultate mineralogischer Forschungen*, Wien, **125**, 1853; F. von Kobell, *Geschichte der Mineralogie*, München, **600**, 1864; J. D. Dana, *A System of Mineralogy*, New York, **73**, 1854; E. R. Schneider, *Journ. prakt. Chem.*, (2), **40**. 51, 1895; *Pogg. Ann.*, **90**. 166, 1853; A. Weisbach, *ib.*, **128**. 436, 1866; H. Dauber, *ib.*, **92**. 241, 1854; F. Rössler, *Zeit. anorg. Chem.*, **9**. 51, 1895; L. J. Spencer, *Min. Mag.*, **11**. 1, 1896; W. F. Hillebrand, *Amer. Journ. Science*, (3), **27**. 355, 1884; E. H. Kraus and J. P. Goldsberry, *ib.*, (4), **37**. 539, 1914; I. Domeyko, *Ann. Mines*, (6), **5**. 459, 1864; J. Joly, *Phil. Mag.*, (6), **27**. 1, 1914; *Chem. News*, **107**. 241, 1913; F. R. Daw, *Chem. News*, **40**. 225, 1879; J. A. Krenner, *Földt. Közl.*, **14**. 519, 564, 1884; *Zeit. Kryst.*, **11**. 265, 1886;

J. J. Saslawsky, *ib.*, **59**. 203, 1924 ; T. Petersen, *Neues Jahrb. Min.*, 847, 1869 ; C. Guillemain, *ib.*, ii, 190, 1899 ; *Zeit. Kryst.*, **33**. 73, 1900 ; *Beiträge zur Kenntnis der natürlichen Sulfosalze,* Breslau, 1898 ; J. L. C. Schröder van der Kolk, *Centr. Min.*, 79, 1901 ; F. Sandberger, *Untersuchungen über Erzgänge*, Wiesbaden, 391, 1885 ; P. Groth, *Tabellarische Uebersicht der Mineralien,* Braunschweig, 33, 1898 ; V. Goldschmidt, *Index der Krystallformen der Mineralien*, Berlin, 1. 549, 1886 ; T. W. Case, *Phys. Rev.*, (2), **9**. 305, 1917.

⁴ T. Petersen and F. Sandberger, *Neues Jahrb. Min.*, 415, 1868 ; F. Sandberger, *Untersuchungen über Erzgänge*, Wiesbaden, 389, 1885 ; T. Petersen, *Neues Jahrb. Min.*, i, 263, 1881 ; *Pogg. Ann.*, **134**. 96, 1868 ; E. R. Schneider, *ib.*, **127**. 315, 1866 ; G. J. Brush in J. D. Dana, *A System of Mineralogy*, New York, 8, 1892 ; J. J. Saslawsky, *Zeit. Kryst.*, **59**. 204, 1924 ; E. H. Kraus and J. P. Goldsberry, *Amer. Journ. Science*, (4), **37**. 539, 1914 ; F. S. Beudant, *Traité élémentaire de minéralogie*, Paris, 464, 1824.

⁵ J. A. Krenner, *Zeit. Kryst.*, **11**. 265, 1886 ; *Földt. Közl.*, **14**. 564, 1884 ; A. Otto, *Tschermak's Mitt.*, (2), **24**. 117, 1905 ; F. Neugebauer, *ib.*, (2), **24**. 323, 1905.

⁶ O. Grosspietsch, *Centr. Min.*, 433, 1911.

⁷ J. D. Dana, *A System of Mineralogy*, New York, 110, 1892 ; W. F. Hillebrand, *Amer. Journ. Science*, (3), **27**. 355, 1884.

⁸ C. F. Rammelsberg, *Sitzber. Akad. Berlin*, 700, 1876 ; *Zeit. deut. geol. Ges.*, **29**. 80, 1877 ; P. y Rico, *Anal. Esc. de Minas Peru*, **3**. 62, 1883 ; A. d'Achiardi, *Metalli*, **1**. 136, 1883 ; M. F. Heddle, *Encyclopædia Britannica*, London, **16**. 394, 1883 ; F. A. Genth, *Proc. Amer. Phil. Soc.*, **23**. 35, 1885 ; M. Roberts, *Min. Mag.*, **21**. 157, 1926 ; K. Yardley, *ib.*, **21**. 163, 1926 ; L. J. Spencer, *ib.*, **21**. 156, 1926 ; E. Kittl, *Rev. Min. Bolivia*, 2. 53, 1927 ; E. R. Schneider, *Journ. prakt. Chem.*, (2), **41**. 414, 1890 ; F. Rössler, *Zeit. anorg. Chem.*, **9**. 48, 1893 ; *Synthese einiger Erzmineralien und analoger Metallverbindungen durch Auflösen und Kristallisierenlassen derselben in geschmolzenen Metallen*, Berlin, 1895 ; T. Wada, *The Minerals of Japan*, Tokyo, 1904 ; T. L. Walker, *Toronto Univ. Geol. Stua.*, 12, 1921 ; J. J. Saslawsky, *Zeit. Kryst.*, **59**. 204, 1924 ; F. Sandberger, *Untersuchungen über Erzgänge*, Wiesbaden, 96, 1882.

⁹ G. A. König, *Journ. Acad. Philadelphia*, **15**. 405, 1912.

¹⁰ G. A. König, *Journ. Amer. Chem. Soc.*, **2**. 379, 1881 ; *Proc. Amer. Phil. Soc.*, **22**. 212, 1885 ; F. A. Genth, *ib.*, **23**. 37, 1886 ; F. Zambonini, O. de Fiore and G. Carobbi, *Rend. Accad. Napoli*, (3), **31**. 24, 1925 ; F. A. Genth, *ib.*, **23**. 37, 1886 ; E. H. Kraus and J. P. Goldsberry, *Amer. Journ. Science*, (1), **37**. 539, 1914 ; R. F. Weinland in P. Niggli, *Lehrbuch der Mineralogie*, Berlin, 365, 1920 ; E. T. Wherry and W. F. Foshag, *Journ. Washington Acad.*, **11**. 1, 1921 ; J. J. Saslawsky, *Zeit. Kryst.*, **59**. 202, 1924 ; A. de Gramont, *Bull. Soc. Min.*, **18**. 265, 1893 ; E. T. Wherry, *Amer. Min.*, **10**. 29, 1925.

¹¹ H. Sommerlad, *Zeit. anorg. Chem.*, **4**. 435, 1898 ; F. Ducatte, *Essai de revroduction artificielle par voie sèche de quelques minéraux naturels du bismuth (Sur les dérivés halogénés des sulfobismuthites)*, Paris, 1902.

¹² H. F. and H. A. Keller, *Journ. Amer. Chem. Soc.*, **7**. 194, 1885 ; *Zeit. Kryst.*, **12**. 492, 1887 ; **13**. 590, 1888 ; H. F. Keller, *ib.*, **17**. 72, 1889 ; C. F. Rammelsberg, *Handbuch der Mineralchemie*, Leipzig, 100, 1875 ; *Sitzber. Akad. Berlin*, 237, 1862 ; *Journ. prakt. Chem.*, (1), **86**. 340, 1862 ; G. Lindström, *Geol. För. Förh. Stockholm*, **9**. 523, 1887 ; **11**. 171, 1889 ; G. Flink, *Arkiv Kemi Min.*, **3**. 35, 1910 ; **5**. 10, 1915 ; T. L. Walker and E. Thomson, *Univ. Toronto Geol. Stud.*, 12, 1921 ; P. Groth and K. Mieleitner, *Mineralogische Tabellen*, München, 27, 1921 ; P. Groth, *Tabellarisch Uebersicht der Mineralien*, Braunschweig, 30, 1887 ; J. Setterberg, *Akad. Handl. Stockholm*, 188, 1839 ; *Pogg. Ann.*, **55**. 635, 1842 ; G. Rose, *Das krystallochemischen Mineralsystem*, Leipzig, 23, 61, 1852 ; J. Joly, *Phil. Mag.*, (6), **27**. 1, 1914 ; *Chem. News*, **107**. 241, 1913 ; J. J. Saslawsky, *Zeit. Kryst.*, **59**. 204, 1924 ; E. T. Wherry, *Amer. Min.*, **10**. 29, 1925 ; H. W. Brown, *ib.*, **12**. 21, 1927 ; T. W. Case, *Phys. Rev.*, (2), **9**. 305, 1917.

¹³ F. Mohs, *Des Herrn J. F. Null Mineralienkabinet*, Wien, 3. 726, 1804 ; E. F. Glocker, *Generum et specierum mineralium secunum ordines naturales digestorum synopsis*, Halle, 27, 1847 ; W. Haidinger, *Handbuch der bestimmenden Mineralogie*, Wien, 568, 1845 ; J. Nicol, *Manual of Mineralogy*, London, 487, 1849 ; E. J. Chapman, *Practical Mineralogy*, London, 127, 1843 ; *Phil. Mag.*, (3), **31**. 541, 1847 ; J. F. John, *Gehlen's Journ.*, **5**. 227, 1808 ; *Chemische Untersuchungen*, Berlin, 2. 204, 1811 ; R. Hermann, *Bull. Soc. Moscow*, **31**. 537, 1858 ; *Journ. prakt. Chem.*, (1), **75**. 452, 1858 ; C. F. Rammelsberg, *Handbuch der Mineralchemie*, Leipzig, 85, 1847 ; 103, 1875 ; 43, 1895 ; G. Lindström, *Geol. För. Förh. Stockholm*, **9**. 523, 1887 ; H. A. Miers, *Min. Mag.*, **8**. 206, 1889 ; H. Frick, *Pogg. Ann.*, **31**. 529, 1834 ; M. Hörnes, *Ber. Mitt. Freund. Naturwiss. Wien*, 2. 254, 1847 ; E. L. M. Patrin, *Histoire naturelle des minéraux*, Paris, **4**. 182, 1786 ; C. C. Leonhard, *Handbuch der Oryktognosie*, Heidelberg. 215, 1821 ; C. Guillemain, *Beiträge zur Kenntnis der natürlichen Sulfosalze*, Breslau, 1898 ; *Neues Jahrb. Min.*, ii, 190, 1899 ; G. Sillem, *ib.*, 534, 1852 ; *Zeit. Kryst.*, **33**. 75, 1900 ; J. J. Saslawsky, *ib.*, **59**. 204, 1924 ; A. de Gramont, *Bull. Soc. Min.*, **18**. 265, 1895 ; P. Groth and K. Mieleitner, *Mineralogische Tabellen*, München, 27, 1921 ; E. H. Kraus and J. P. Goldsberry, *Amer. Journ. Science*, (4), **37**. 539, 1914 ; F. A. Genth, *ib.*, (2), **33**. 190, 1862 ; (2), **34**. 212, 1862 ; W. F. Foshag, *ib.*, (5), 1. 444, 1921 ; E. T. Wherry and W. F. Foshag, *Journ. Washington Acad.*, **11**. 1, 1920 ; **23**. 34, 1886 ; H. M. Sjögren, *Geol. För. Förh. Stockholm*, 2. 76, 1874 ; **4**. 109, 1878 ; M. Weibull, E. T. Wherry, *Amer. Min.*, **10**. 28, 1925 ; J. R. Blum, *Die Pseudomorphosen der Mineralreichs*, Stuttgart, 173, 1843 ; G. Rose, *Reise nach dem Ural, dem Altai, und dem Kaspischen Meere*, Berlin, **1**. 196, 1837 ; J. Joly, *Phil. Mag.*, (6), **27**. 1, 1914 ; *Chem. News*, **107**. 241, 1913.

698　　INORGANIC AND THEORETICAL CHEMISTRY

[14] G. A. König, Proc. Amer. Phil. Soc., 18. 472, 1881; 22. 211, 1885; F. A. Genth, ib., 23. 34, 1886; H. Sjögren, Geol. For. Forh. Stockholm, 2, 76, 1874; 4. 109, 1878; M. Weibull, ib., 7. 657, 1885; J. Joly, Phil. Mag., (6), 27. 1, 1917; Chem. News, 107. 241, 1913; T. W. Case, Phys. Rev., (2), 9. 305, 1917; P. Groth, Tabellarische Uebersicht der Mineralien, Braunschweig, 28, 1889; T. L. Walker and E. Thomson, Univ. Toronto Geol. Stud., 12, 1921; T. Liweh, Zeit. Kryst., 10. 488, 1885; E. V. Shannon, Journ. Washington Acad., 11. 298, 1921; P. Groth and K. Mieleitner, Mineralogische Tabellen, München, 1921; E. H. Kraus and J. P. Goldsberry, Amer. Journ. Science, (6), 37. 539, 1914; A. de Gramont, Bull. Soc. Min., 18. 171, 1895; W. F. Foshag, Amer. Journ. Science, (5), 1. 444, 1921; E. T. Wherry and W. F. Foshag, ib., 11. 1, 1921; E. T. Wherry, Amer. Min., 10. 28, 1925; H. W. Brown, ib.; 12. 21, 1927; F. Ahlfeld, Centr. Min., 388, 1926.

[15] G. A. König, Proc. Amer. Phil. Soc., 22. 20, 1885; F. A. Genth, ib., 23. 36, 1885; Amer. Journ. Science, (2), 45. 319, 1868; W. F. Hillebrand, ib., (3), 27. 344, 1884; A. Frenzel, Neues Jahrb. Min., 681, 1874; G. Lindström, Geol. För. Förh. Stockholm, 2. 178, 1874; 11. 171, 1889; H. Sjögren, ib., 4. 107, 1878; A. E. Nordenskjöld, ib., 4. 46, 1878; E. le Neve Foster, Proc. Colorado Scient. Soc., 1. 74, 1884; A. H. Low, 1. 111, 1884; R. Hermann, Bull. Acad. Moscow, 31. 533, 1858; Journ. prakt. Chem., (1), 75. 450, 1879; G. Flink, Akad. Handl. Stockholm, 12. 2, 1886; H. Bancroft, Bull. U.S. Geol. Sur., 430, 1910; J. Loczka, Math. Termes Tud. Ertesito, 42. 6, 1926; T. W. Case, Phys. Rev., (2), 9. 305, 1917; T. L. Walker, Univ. Toronto Geol. Stud., 11, 1921; T. L. Walker and E. Thomson, ib., 12, 1921; A. de Gramont, Bull. Soc. Min., 18. 264, 1895; A. Lacroix, Mineralogie de Madagascar, Paris, 1. 189, 1922; J. J. Saslawsky, Zeit. Kryst. 59. 203, 1924; J. Joly, Phil. Mag., (6), 27. 1924; Chem. News, 107. 241, 1913.

[16] C. J. Selb, Crell's Ann., 1. 10, 1793; F. Sandberger, Untersuchungen über Erzgänge, Wiesbaden, 90, 1882; Neues Jahrb. Min., 22, 1864; G. A. Kenngott, Das Mohs'sche Mineralsystem, Wien, 118, 1853; M. H. Klaproth, Beiträge zur chemischen Kenntniss der Mineralkörper, Berlin, 2. 297, 1797; L. A. Emmerling, Lehrbuch der Mineralogie, Giessen, 2. 203, 1796; C. C. von Leonhard, Handbuch der Oryktognosie, Heidelberg, 216, 1821; E. le Neve Foster, Proc. Colorado Scient. Soc., 1. 73, 1885; W. F. Foshag, Amer. Journ. Science, (5), 1. 444, 1921.

[17] A. Frenzel, Tschermak's Mitt., (2), 5. 175, 1883; E. T. Wherry and W. F. Foshag, Journ. Washington Acad., 11. 1, 1921; K. Johansson, Arch. Kemi Min. Geol., 9. 8, 1924.

[18] C. F. Rammelsberg, Handbuch der Mineralchemie, Leipzig, 120, 1875; 36, 1895; Pogg. Ann., 88. 320, 1853; G. Cesaro, Bull. Soc. Min., 38. 41, 1915; F. Zambonini, O. de Fiore, and G. Carobbi, Rend. Accad. Napoli, (3), 31. 24, 1925; E. V. Shannon, Proc. U.S. Nat. Museum, 65. 24, 1924; A. Raimondi, Minéraux du Pérou, Paris, 176, 1878; E. T. Wherry and W. F. Foshag, Journ. Washington Acad., 11. 1, 1920; J. J. Saslawsky, Zeit. Kryst., 59. 203, 1924; E. T. Wherry, Amer. Min., 10. 28, 1925.

[19] F. A. Genth, Proc. Amer. Phil. Soc., 14. 230, 1874; T. W. Case, Phys. Rev., (2), 9. 305, 1917; F. M. Endlich, Eng. Min. Journ., 18. 133, 1874; A. de Gramont, Bull. Soc. Min., 18. 265, 1895; W. F. Foshag, Amer. Journ. Science, (5), 1. 444, 1921.

[20] E. S. Simpson, Journ. Roy. Soc. West. Australia, 10. 65, 1924; J. Krenner and J. Loczka, Math. Termes Tud. Ertesito, 42. 4, 1926.

[21] K. Johansson, Ark. Kemi Min. Geol., 9. 8, 1924; Amer. Min., 10. 157, 1925; E. T. Wherry, ib., 10. 28, 1925; E. V. Shannon, Amer. Journ. Science, (4), 49. 166, 1920; W. F. Foshag, ib., (5), 1. 444, 1921.

[22] C. Geitner, Liebig's Ann., 129. 359, 1864; G. A. König, Journ. Acad. Philadelphia, 15. 405, 1912; E. Quercigh, Atti Accad. Lincei, (6), 4. ii, 68, 1926.

[23] C. F. Rammelsberg, Handbuch der Mineralchemie, Leipzig, 33, 1875; P. Groth, Tabellarische Uebersicht der Mineralien, Braunschweig, 24. 1898; A. Frenzel, Tschermak's Mitt., (2), 5. 220, 1880; G. Tschermak, Sitzber. Akad. Wien, 53. 220, 1866; A. Lacroix, Minéralogie de la France et de ses colonies, Paris, 2. 664, 1897; A. von Hubert and A. Patera, Neues Jahrb. Min., 325, 1848; J. Joly, Phil. Mag., (6), 27. 1, 1914; Chem. News, 107. 241, 1913; W. F. de Jong, Physica, 6. 325, 1926.

[24] F. von Kobell, Tafeln zur Bestimmung des Mineralien, München, 13, 1853; Grundzüge der Mineralogie, Nürnberg, 269, 1838; Journ. prakt. Chem., (1), 6. 332, 1835; (1), 8. 342, 1836; C. F. Rammelsberg, Handbuch der Mineralchemie, Leipzig, 164, 1849; 108, 1860; Verh. Nat. Ver. Reinl. Bonn, 184, 1850; A. Breithaupt, Die Paragenesis der Mineralien, Freiberg, 216, 1849; M. L. Frankenheim, Verh, Leop. Carol. Akad., 11. 494, 643, 1842; H. Laspeyres, Zeit. deut. geol. Ges., 27. 742, 1875; Journ. prakt. Chem., (2), 14. 397, 1876; J. Nicol, Manual of Mineralogy, London, 458, 1849.

[25] H. Laspeyres, Zeit. Kryst., 25. 592, 1896; G. Werther, Journ. prakt. Chem., (1), 55. 227, 1852; R. Scheibe, Zeit. deut. geol. Ges., 40. 611, 1889; L. M. Huggins, Journ. Amer. Chem. Soc., 44. 1840, 1922.

§ 17. Bismuth Sulphates, and Oxysulphides

According to A. Hilger and P. A. von Scherpenberg,[1] bismuth trioxysulphide, Bi_2O_3S, is formed with incandescence when bismuth pentoxide is treated with dry hydrogen sulphide, or by passing the gas into boiling benzene in which the finely-divided oxide is suspended. If the benzene is cold, the product does not contain so much sulphur. The greyish-black powder is stable in air, and it can be heated to 120° without change, but at a higher temp., sulphur dioxide and bismuth trioxide are formed ; it dissolves in hydrochloric acid, and is decomposed by water with the separation of sulphur.

R. Hermann [2] described a mineral from Altai, Russia, which he called **karelinite**— after M. Karelin. Its composition approximates Bi_4SO_3. It occurs in lead-grey masses, with a crystalline structure. The mineral is not homogeneous, and when treated with hydrochloric acid to remove the carbonates, etc., a metallic powder remains which is supposed to be the mineral karelinite. R. Hermann, and C. F. Rammelsberg consider that it is free from bismuth metal, but P. Groth doubted this. The sp. gr. is 6·60 ; and the hardness 2. When heated in air, it gives off sulphur dioxide, and forms a grey slag. It is reduced to bismuth when heated in hydrogen. R. Hermann obtained a complex oxysulphide, $Bi_2(S,O)_3$, or $Bi_{10}S_9O_6$, by heating a mixture of bismuth trioxide and sulphur so as to volatilize the excess of sulphur. The grey mass has a sp. gr. 6·31. It contains some bismuth. I. Domeyko described a *bismuth oxydisulphide*, approximating $Bi_4S_2O_3$, as a mineral from Chlorolque, Bolivia. It was called *bolivite*, and was said to be derived from the oxidation of bismuthinite. It is considered by P. Groth to be a mixture of bismuthinite and bismuth ochre.

The early workers prepared more or less impure bismuth sulphates, but the results are complicated by the tendency of the salt to hydrolyze in dil. soln., and to form acidic salts in conc.soln. D. Lagerhjelm [3] obtained normal **bismuth sulphate,** $Bi_2(SO_4)_3$, by evaporating bismuth trioxide with an excess of conc. sulphuric acid, and gently heating the residue until its weight was constant. G. H. Bailey, A. Classen, C. Hensgen, and J. G. C. de Marignac used this process; A. Gutbier and R. L. Janssen evaporated the nitrate with conc. sulphuric acid, and heated the product to constant weight at 380° ; and they also analyzed the salt and found it corresponded with the formula just indicated. The needle-like crystals obtained by C. Schultz-Sellack by evaporating a soln. of bismuth trioxide in conc. sulphuric acid was shown by A. Leist to have the composition $Bi_2(SO_4)_3.H_2SO_4.6H_2O$. Instead of starting from the trioxide, the trisulphide can be used. The crystals of the salt were said by G. Bodman to be isomorphous with the sulphates of lanthanum, didymium, and yttrium. L. de Boisbaudran noted that as in the case of the trioxide (*q.v.*), it stimulates the phosphorescence of alkaline earth sulphides. C. Hensgen said that the salt is very hygroscopic, and at ordinary temp. forms with water the *hemiheptahydrate*, $Bi_2(SO_4)_3.3\frac{1}{2}H_2O$; and when evaporated at 100°, the dihydrate, $Bi_2(SO_4)_3.2H_2O$, is formed, and it loses no water when kept over conc. sulphuric acid. The sulphate is slowly hydrolyzed by cold water, rapidly by hot water, forming dibismuthyl sulphate, $(BiO)_2SO_4$. According to G. H. Bailey, the normal sulphate can be heated to 405° without change ; but between 405° and 418° decomposition sets in, producing, according to W. Heintz, dibismuthyl sulphate. At a high enough temp. G. H. Bailey, and F. W. Schmidt found that all the combined sulphuric acid can be expelled. K. Schäfer and F. Hein examined the absorption spectrum in the ultra-violet of a soln. of bismuth sulphate in sulphuric acid. J. A. Arfvedson said that hydrogen reduces the sulphate to metal at a red-heat. E. Hensgen observed that when exposed to hydrogen chloride it becomes warm, and absorbs over 3 mols of the gas per mol of sulphate ; it dissolves in hydrochloric acid. A. B. Prescott found that 0·836 grm. remained undecomposed when a gram of the sulphate was evaporated on a water-bath to dryness with 3·5 c.c. of hydrochloric acid of sp. gr. 1·153. When heated in ammonia gas, W. R. E. Hodgkinson and C. C. Trench found that the sulphate is reduced to metal. The normal salt dissolves in nitric acid. G. Bodman found that bismuth sulphate forms complex salts with the ammonium and alkali sulphates ; and solid soln. with some rare earth sulphates.

A number of basic sulphates have been reported. Their composition depends on the temp. and conc. of the acid. F. B. Allan found that at 50°, acid bismuth sulphate, $Bi_2O_3.4SO_3$, is in equilibrium with sulphuric acid of more than 51·4 per cent. concentration ; $Bi_2O_3.2SO_3.2\frac{1}{2}H_2O$, with sulphuric acid between 51·4 and 5·4 per cent. ; and $Bi_2O_3.SO_3$, with sulphuric acid soln. below 5·4 per cent. The latter compound is not acted on by water at 50°. The other basic sulphates were not found in aq. soln. at 50°. According to R. H. Adie, with sulphuric acid between $H_2SO_4.6H_2O$ and $H_2SO_4.12H_2O$, the product has the composition $5Bi_2O_3.HSO_3.17H_2O$. This does not appear to be a chemical individual because F. B. Allan could not obtain the same result. R. H. Adie also reported that with an acid between $H_2SO_4.3H_2O$ and $H_2SO_4.5H_2O$, he obtained a product of **bismuth dihydrotetrasulphate,** $Bi_2(SO_4)_3.H_2SO_4.6H_2O$, or $Bi_2O_3.4SO_3.7H_2O$; and with an acid between $H_2SO_4.2H_2O$ and $H_2SO_4.H_2O$, he obtained a lower hydrate, $Bi_2O_3.4SO_3.3H_2O$, or $Bi(SO_4)_3.H_2SO_4.2H_2O$. A. Leist found that when bismuth trioxide is treated with dil. sulphuric acid (1 : 2 or 3), much oxide dissolves, but most remains as a basic salt ; if much hot sulphuric acid be used—100 grms. of acid to one gram of oxide—the basic sulphate dissolves, and when the filtered soln. is cooled, and evaporated until the fumes of the sulphuric acid appear, the same acid sulphate is formed. F. B. Allan said that the acid sulphate is in equilibrium with 51·4 per cent. sulphuric acid. The silky, needle-like crystals were found by R. H. Adie to form dibismuthyl sulphate at 170° ; and by A. Leist to form the basic salt $4Bi_2O_3.3SO_3.15H_2O$, as a white powder, when treated with water. D. L. Hammick found $4Bi_2O_3.3SO_3$ to be the ultimate product of the action of sulphur dioxide on bismuth mono- or tri-oxide.

$$SO_4{=}Bi.O.Bi{<}^O_O{>}Bi.O.Bi{<}^O_O{>}Bi.O.Bi{<}^O_{SO_4}{>}Bi.O.Bi{=}SO_4$$

M. Websky obtained a basic sulphate by melting bismuth with potassium hydrosulphate ; and F. Rössler, by warming to 60° a soln. of bismuth in boiling conc. sulphuric acid. N. Athanasesco heated a feebly acidic soln. of bismuth nitrate with an excess of sodium sulphate in a sealed tube at 250°, and obtained white, microscopic needles of the basic sulphate $3Bi_2O_3.2SO_3.2H_2O$, **bismuth heptoxydisulphate,** $Bi_6O_7(SO_4)_2.2H_2O$:

$$SO_4{=}Bi{>}^O{\ }^O{<}Bi{=}SO_4$$

W. Heintz prepared **bismuthyl sulphate,** $Bi_2O_3.SO_4$, or $(BiO)_2SO_4$, by evaporating to dryness a soln. of bismuth trioxide in sulphuric acid and heating the residue to redness ; it was also obtained by W. Heintz, W. Lüddecke, C. Hensgen, and E. Ruge, by heating the more acid sulphates under similar conditions ; by W. Lüddecke, by heating ammonium bismuth sulphate ; and by C. P. Brigham, by heating potassium bismuth sulphate, and washing the product with water. The sulphate prepared at the high temp. is an anhydrous white powder ; and that prepared at the lower temp. is dihydrated. F. B. Allan said that the white powder is not atracked by water ; it is soluble in nitric and hydrochloric acids; and when calcined, J. L. Gay Lussac said that it loses oxygen and sulphur dioxide. F. E. Brown and J. E. Snyder observed no reaction with bismuth sulphate and vanadium oxytrichloride.

According to W. Heintz, when conc. sulphuric acid is added to a soln. of bismuth nitrate in nitric acid, **bismuth hydroxysulphate,** $Bi_2O_3.2SO_3.3H_2O$, or $Bi(OH)SO_4.$ H_2O, crystallizes out. The crystals are separated from the mother-liquor by draining on porous tiles. E. Ruge employed this method. W. Lüddecke found that when ammonium bismuth sulphate is digested for a long time with acetic or dil. sulphuric acid, part dissolves, and the hydroxysulphate remains as a residue ; and A. Leist obtained it by evaporating a soln. of bismuth trioxide in hot, dil. sulphuric acid (1 : 2 or 3) ; according to F. B. Allan, the evaporation should proceed until a large

proportion of the sulphuric acid has volatilized. The prismatic or acicular crystals
are transformed by water into bismuthyl sulphate ; and W. Heintz found that the
hydroxysulphate forms a complex salt—**potassium bismuth hydroxydisulphate,**
$K_2SO_4.Bi(OH)SO_4$, or $K_2Bi(OH)(SO_4)_2$—with potassium sulphate. This is obtained
as a white precipitate by adding a soln. of potassium sulphate to a dil. soln. of
bismuth nitrate.

W. Lüddecke obtained **ammonium sulphatobismuthite,** $(NH_4)Bi(SO_4)_2.4H_2O$,
in six-sided plates by mixing a soln. of a mol of bismuth nitrate with 3 mols or more
of bismuth sulphate. The precipitate was drained on a porous tile. It is freely
soluble in nitric and hydrochloric acids, and less soluble in conc. sulphuric acid and
hot dil. acids. It is decomposed by water, forming bismuthyl sulphate ; and cold
acetic acid or dil. sulphuric acid converts it into bismuth hydroxysulphate. Microscopic, prismatic crystals of **sodium sulphatobismuthite,** $3Na_2SO_4.2Bi_2(SO_4)_3$, or
$Na_6Bi_4(SO_4)_9$, were obtained in a similar manner, and W. Heintz obtained **potassium
trisulphatobismuthite,** $K_3Bi(SO_4)_3$, as a white precipitate by adding an excess of
potassium sulphate or hydrosulphate to a conc. soln. of bismuth nitrate. If the
bismuth nitrate soln. be not conc., and the alkali sulphate not in great excess, the
precipitate has a variable composition. The precipitate is dried on a porous tile.
T. H. Behrens described hexagonal crystals which he obtained in a similar way.
C. P. Brigham obtained **potassium disulphatobismuthite,** $KBi(SO_4)_2$, by heating
the corresponding chloride with conc. sulphuric acid. The acicular or tabular
crystals are insoluble in cold water ; and with boiling water, they yield bismuthyl
sulphate. V. Caglioti and A. Stolfi observed the formation of only the one
compound **potassium trisulphatobismuthite,** $3K_2SO_4.Bi_2(SO_4)_3$, or $K_3Bi(SO_4)_3$, in
the ternary system $Bi_2(SO_4)_3-K_2SO_4-H_2O$ at 25°. It is stable in soln. containing 5·32 to 12·8 per cent. of K_2SO_4. Some evidence was obtained of the formation of a basic sulphate. G. Bodman, and V. Cuttica showed that *bismuth sulphate
and the sulphates of didymium, lanthanum, and yttrium,* are isomorphous and form a
series of solid soln.—*vide* the rare earths. R. F. Weinland and H. Kühl evaporated
a conc. sulphuric acid soln. of stannic acid and bismuth sulphate, and obtained
rhombic leaflets of **stannic bismuth hydroxytrisulphate,** $Bi(OH)Sn(SO_4)_3$.

F. Ephraim found that bismuth sulphate absorbs rather more than 4 vols. of
hydrogen chloride at atm. temp., forming **bismuth sulphatotetrahydrochloride,**
$Bi_2(SO_4)_3.4HCl$, stable up to 110° ; at 111°, **bismuth sulphatodihydrochloride,**
$Bi_2(SO_4)_3.2HCl$, is formed ; and at 154°, **bismuth sulphatohydrochloride,**
$Bi_2(SO_4)_3.HCl$.

REFERENCES.

[1] A. Hilger and P. A. von Scherpenberg, *Mitt. Erlangen Pharm. Inst.,* 2. 4, 7, 1889.
[2] R. Hermann, *Journ. prakt. Chem.,* (1), 75. 448, 1858 ; C. F. Rammelsberg, *Handbuch der
Mineralchemie,* Leipzig, 195, 1875 ; I. Domeyko, *Compt. Rend.,* 85. 977, 1877 ; *Elementos de
mineralojia,* Santiago, 304, 1879 ; P. Groth, *Tabellarische Uebersicht der Mineralien,* Braun-
schweig, 18, 49, 1898.
[3] W. Lüddecke. *Liebig's Ann.,* 140. 277, 1866 ; A. Leist, *ib.,* 160. 29, 1871 ; T. H. Behrens,
Zeit. anal. Chem., 30. 135, 163, 1891 ; M. Websky, *ib.,* 11. 127, 1872 ; C. P. Brigham, *Amer. Chem.
Journ.,* 14. 170, 1892 ; F. B. Allan, *ib.,* 27. 284, 1902 ; W. Heintz, *Pogg. Ann.,* 63. 82, 1844 ;
J. A. Arfvedson, *ib.,* 1. 74, 1824 ; *Acad. Handl. Stockholm,* 427, 1822 ; *Ann. Phil.,* 7. 329, 1824 ;
D. Lagerhjelm, *Schweigger's Journ.,* 17. 416, 1817 ; *Akad. Handl. Stockholm,* 34. 219, 1813 ;
G. Bodman, *Ber.,* 31. 1237, 1898 ; *Zeit. anorg. Chem.,* 27. 254, 1901 ; R. F. Weinland and H. Kühl,
ib., 54. 244, 1907 ; K. Schäfer and F. Hein, *ib.,* 100. 249, 1917 ; R. H. Adie, *Proc. Chem. Soc.,*
15. 226, 1899 ; D. L. Hammick, *Journ. Chem. Soc.,* 111. 379, 1917 ; A. B. Prescott, *Chem.
News,* 36. 179, 1877 ; N. Athanasesco, *Compt. Rend.,* 103. 271, 1886 ; L. de Boisbaudran, *ib.,*
103. 629, 1064, 1886 ; 104. 478, 1680, 1887 ; 45. 206, 1887 ; F. Rössler, *Chem. Ztg.,* 20. 105,
1896 ; C. Hensgen, *Rec. Trav. Chim. Pays-Bas,* 4. 409, 1885 ; E. Ruge, *Journ. prakt. Chem.,*
(1), 96. 138, 1865 ; A. Gutbier and R. L. Janssen, *ib.,* (2), 78. 421, 1908 ; A. Classen, *ib.,* (2),
43. 133, 1891 ; (2), 44. 411, 1891 ; *Ber.,* 23. 938, 1890 ; J. L. Gay Lussac, *Mém. Arcueil,* 1.
215, 1807 ; *Journ. Mines,* 22. 325, 1807 ; *Nicholson's Journ.,* 33. 44, 1812 ; J. C. G. de Marignac,
Ann. Chim. Phys., (6), 1. 294, 1884 ; *Arch. Sciences Genève,* (3), 10. 5, 1883 ; F. W. Schmidt,
Ber., 27. 236, 1894 ; C. Schultz-Sellack, *ib.,* 4. 13, 1871 ; F. Ephraim, *ib.,* 59. B, 790, 1926 ;
G. H. Bailey, *Journ. Chem. Soc.,* 51. 676, 1887 ; W. R. E. Hodgkinson and C. C. Trench, *Chem.*

News, **66**. 223, 1892 ; V. Cuttica, *Gazz. Chim. Ital.*, **53**. 761, 1923 ; F. E. Brown and J. E. Snyder, *Journ. Amer. Chem. Soc.*, **47**. 2671, 1925; V. Caglioti and A. Stolfi, *Atti Accad. Lincei*, (6), **5**. 896, 1927.

§ 18. The Bismuth Halogenosulphides, or Sulphohalides

M. M. P. Muir [1] observed no tendency on the part of bismuth trifluoride to form **a bismuth fluosulphide** when it is melted with sulphur ; but if bismuth trichloride be similarly treated, the dark red, crystalline product is **bismuth chlorosulphide,** BiSCl. M. M. P. Muir and E. M. Eagles exposed bismuth trichloride to the action of hydrogen sulphide at ordinary temp. or at a temp. not exceeding dull redness, and obtained the same chlorosulphide—at a higher temp., bismuth trisulphide is formed. They also obtained it by the action of chlorine on bismuth trisulphide at dull redness. G. N. Quam found that bismuth trichloride reacts with liquid hydrogen sulphide, forming this chlorosulphide. According to E. R. Schneider, when 8–10 grms. of ammonium pentachlorobismuthite are heated with one part of sulphur in a retort, and the fused mass when cold extracted with dil. hydrochloric acid, a small yield of the chlorosulphide is obtained ; similarly when the same salt is heated to 250°–300° in a stream of hydrogen sulphide and the product treated as before ; and also when the same salt is fused with bismuth trisulphide and the product treated as before—this process gives the best yield.

Bismuth sulphochloride appears in dark grey needles which in thin layers appear brick-red or dark cherry-red in transmitted light. When heated in hydrogen, some bismuth trichloride is given off, then hydrogen chloride and sulphide, and bismuth contaminated with a little sulphide and chloride remains ; and in air, some bismuth trichloride is volatilized, and at a higher temp., sulphur dioxide is formed—the residue is a mixture of bismuth oxychloride and basic sulphate. Boiling water does not decompose the sulphochloride ; dil. acids have no action at ordinary temp. ; and with conc. hydrochloric acid, hydrogen sulphide is evolved. When heated in hydrogen sulphide, at a red-heat, bismuth trisulphide is formed ; and in carbon dioxide, bismuth trichloride and trisulphide are formed. Conc. nitric acid decomposes the sulphochloride with the separation of sulphur. All the chloride is removed by a soln. of an alkali-hydroxide, forming black oxysulphide ; soln. of alkali carbonates act similarly, but more slowly.

M. M. P. Muir prepared **bismuth bromosulphide,** BiSBr, by the action of bromine vapour on bismuth trisulphide at a dull red-heat. The reaction begins at ordinary temp., and at too high a temp. it forms the trisulphide. Similar results were obtained by the action of hydrogen sulphide on bismuth tribromide. The greyish-red crystalline product is washed with hydrochloric acid. When heated in hydrogen sulphide, bismuth trisulphide is formed.

E. R. Schneider, and M. M. P. Muir and E. M. Eagles obtained **bismuth iodo-sulphide,** BiSI, by dissolving bismuth trisulphide in molten bismuth triiodide. The product contains the sulphoiodide mixed with an excess of iodine. It is purified by repeatedly washing it with dil. hydrochloric acid. E. R. Schneider obtained it by heating bismuth trisulphide with iodine, the bismuth triiodide formed as a by-product volatilizes ; W. Linau, by heating a mixture of iodine, sulphur, and bismuth trisulphide in a clay crucible for a long time ; and N. Tarugi, by the action of thioacetic acid on bismuth iodide, or potassium iodobismuthite : $BiI_3 + CH_3.COSH + H_2O = BiSI + CH_3COOH + 2HI$. The small, steel-grey, acicular crystals resemble bismuth glance. When heated out of contact with air, bismuth triiodide is given off, but the residue of bismuth trisulphide retains some iodine even when heated for a long time. Boiling water or a dil. mineral acid has no action ; it is decomposed by hot, conc. hydrochloric acid giving off hydrogen sulphide ; with nitric acid, sulphur, and iodine are separated ; aq. ammonia extracts the iodine, forming an oxysulphide ; a soln. of alkali hydroxide acts similarly ; and likewise also with a boiling mixture of zinc oxide and water. In the last case, the action is slow and incomplete. A. Kuhn and H. Pirsch found that bismuth sulphoiodide sols cannot be prepared without protective colloids. Sols containing 0·3 mg. of bismuth per c.c. with 0·59 per cent. of gum arabic, 1·6 mg. with 0·5 per cent. of hæmoglobin, and 0·3 mg. with 0·25 per cent. of gelatin may be obtained. The gum arabic sol is reversible—*vide supra*, bismuth trisulphide.

F. L. Ducatte [2] melted stoichiometrical proportions of bismuth sulphide and cuprous chloride in an atm. of carbon dioxide and obtained **cuprous chlorosulpho-bismuthite,** $2Cu_2S.Bi_2S_3.2BiSCl$, which may be a mixture of $BiSCl$ with cuprous and bismuth sulphides. The product has a sp. gr. 6·78 ; it is stable at ordinary temp., but decomposes when heated in air ; and is attacked by dil. acids with the liberation of hydrogen sulphide. It is insoluble in cold water, but is decomposed by boiling water, forming hydrochloric acid. F. L. Ducatte obtained in a similar manner **cuprous bromosulphobismuthite,** $2Cu_2S.Bi_2S_3.2BiSBr$, of sp. gr. 6·41 ; and **cuprous iodosulphobismuthite,** $2Cu_2S.Bi_2S_3.2BiSI$, of sp. gr. 6·50. The properties of these compounds are like those of the chloro-sulphobismuthite. He also pre-pared **lead chlorosulphobismuthite,** $PbS.Br_2S_3.2BiSCl$, by heating a mixture of equal parts of lead chloride and bismuth sulphide to the fusion point in a current of carbon dioxide. It is obtained in long crystals of sp. gr. 6·42, which are quite stable in the air and insoluble in water. It oxidizes at a red-heat and is decomposed by boiling water. With acid, it gives hydrogen sulphide. The corresponding **lead bromosulphobismuthite,** $PbS.Bi_2S_3.2BiSBr$, of sp. gr. 6·50 ; and **lead iodo-sulphobismuthite,** $PbS.Bi_2S_3.2BiSI$, of sp. gr. 6·59, are prepared similarly, and have analogous properties.

REFERENCES.

[1] G. N. Quam, *Journ. Amer. Chem. Soc.*, **47**. 103, 1925 ; A. Kuhn and H. Pirsch, *Koll. Bei-hefte*, **21**. 78, 1925 ; M. M. P. Muir, *Journ. Chem. Soc.*, **32**. 139, 1877 ; **39**. 33, 1881 ; M. M. P. Muir and E. M. Eagles, *ib.*, **67**. 90, 1895 ; E. R. Schneider, *Journ. prakt. Chem.*, (2), **79**. 422, 1860 ; *Pogg. Ann.*, **93**. 464, 1854 ; **110**. 147, 1860 ; W. Linau, *ib.*, **110**. 148, 1860 ; N. Tarugi, *Gazz. Chim. Ital.*, **27**. i, 316, 1897.

[2] F. L. Ducatte, *Essai de reproduction artificielle par voie sèche de quelques minéraux naturals du bismuth ; Sur les dérivés halogènes des sulphobismuthites*, Paris, 1902 ; *Compt. Rend.*, **134**. 1061, 1212, 1902.

§ 19. The Bismuth Carbonates

In 1817, A. G. Werner [1] referred to a mineral from Schneeberg, Saxony, which he called *Arsenikwismuth ;* and A. Weisbach showed that the mineral is probably a basic carbonate, which he called **bismutosphaerite.** Analyses reported by A. Frenzel, C. Winkler, E. S. Sperry, and H. L. Wells correspond with $2Bi_2O_3.Bi_2(CO_3)_3$, or **bismuthyl carbonate,** $(BiO)_2CO_3$. The compound was made by W. Heintz, and K. Seubert and M. Elten by adding an excess of an alkali carbonate to an excess of a soln. of bismuth nitrate ; and in order to free the precipitate from basic nitrate it should be heated for some time in contact with its mother-liquor. It is then washed with water and dried at 100°. It is difficult to remove the alkali nitrate, and carbonates adsorbed by the precipitate. L. Vanino recommended the following mode of preparation :

A little water is added to 18·2 grms. of mannitol and the whole triturated with 48·2 grms. of powdered bismuth nitrate, whereby a soln. is obtained. To 100 c.c. of this soln. at 0° are added 20·7 grms. of potassium carbonate dissolved in the minimum quantity of water ; when almost all the potassium carbonate has been added the bismuthyl carbonate separates as a fine, heavy powder. The precipitate is washed with water, alcohol, and ether, and dried in the air. Ammonium carbonate may be used instead of potassium carbonate. Bismuth metahydrate, dissolved in conc. hydrochloric acid, is not suitable for the preparation of bismuthyl carbonate.

J. Lefort said that if an alkali hydrocarbonate be used as precipitant, the *mono-hydrate,* $(BiO)_2CO_3.H_2O$, is formed. When the white powder is dried at 100°, or over sulphuric acid in vacuo, it retains from 0·5 to 1·0 mol of water which W. Heintz attributes to the presence of some bismuth hydroxide as impurity. A. J. Jones discussed the effect of concentration, and temp. on the density of the carbonate. While the artificial preparation is white, bismutosphaerite is coloured bright yellow to dark grey or brown, and it occurs in a spherical form with concentric, fibrous, radiated structures; and in pseudomorphs after bismuthinite. A. Frenzel gave for the sp. gr. of the mineral 7·59; C. Winkler, 7·30–7·64; and H. L. Wells, 6·83–7·42. The hardness is 3·0–3·5. R. Robl observed that the carbonate gives no fluorescence in ultra-violet light. When heated, bismuthyl carbonate loses carbon dioxide. C. R. Fresenius, and H. Rose said that the carbonate is insoluble in water, in an aq. soln. of carbon dioxide, and in potash-lye; but it is slightly soluble in a soln. of an alkali carbonate, and when the soln. is warmed, or treated with alkali hydroxide, the basic carbonate is again precipitated. R. H. Brett said that the freshly precipitated carbonate is readily soluble in a soln. of ammonium chloride. but not in one of ammonium nitrate. F. E. Brown and J. E. Snyder observed a reaction with the hydrated carbonate and vanadium oxytrichloride.

A. Breithaupt [2] described a *kohlensaures Wismuthoxyd* from Schneeberg, and called it **bismutite**. Analyses were reported by A. Liversidge, C. F. Rammelsberg, F. A. Genth, H. Louis, C. Winkler, A. Carnot, F. G. Cairns, W. Bodenbender, and K. Thaddéeff. C. F. Rammelsberg represented it by $2Bi_2(CO_3)_3.3Bi_2O_3.3H_6Bi_2O_6$; A. Carnot, by $Bi_2O_3(CO_2,H_2O).nBi_2O_3(HO,CO_2)$; A. Weisbach, by $Bi_6CO_{11}.H_2O$; F. G. Cairns, $Bi_2C_3O_9.2Bi_2H_2O_5$; K. Thaddéeff, $5Bi_2O_3.H_2O.CO_2$; and H. Louis, $Bi_2H_2CO_6$, or **bismuth oxydihydroxycarbonate**,

$$O<\frac{Bi}{Bi}<\begin{matrix}OH\\CO_2\\OH\end{matrix}$$

The difference in the composition of the specimens so far described shows that the composition is very doubtful. A related mineral, from Joachimsthal, was called *waltherite* by M. Adam, and described by J. F. Vogl, and E. Bertrand. W. Macgregor described another mineral bismuth carbonate from St. Agnes, Cornwall; W. H. Miller called it *agnesite;* and M. Adam, *gregorite*. T. Thomson's analysis said that it contained no carbonate, and only a trace of bismuth, while F. S. Beudant indicated that the assumption that the steatite-like mineral is a carbonate is based on *quelque grande erreur* in W. Macgregor's analysis. The mineral may be white, yellow, green, or grey, and it occurs as an amorphous incrustation, or earth. A. Breithaupt gave 6·84–6·90 for the sp. gr.; C. F. Rammelsberg, 7·67; A. Carnot, 6·94–7·26; C. Winkler, 6·12–6·27; H. Louis, 6·84; and F. A. Genth, 6·293–7·330. The hardness is 4·0–4·5.

REFERENCES.

[1] A. G. Werner, *Letztes Mineralsystem*, Freiberg, 56, 1817; A. Weisbach, *Jahrb. Berg. Hütt.*, 42, 1877; *Neues Jahrb. Min.*, 409, 1877; R. Robl, *Zeit. angew. Chem.*, 49. 608, 1926; F. E. Brown and J. E. Snyder, *Journ. Amer. Chem. Soc.*, 47. 1671, 1925; C. Winkler, *Journ. prakt. Chem.*, (2), 16. 91, 1878; *Neues Jahrb. Min.*, ii, 249, 1882; A. Frenzei, *ib.*, 801. 946, 1873; E. S. Sperry, *Amer. Journ. Science*, (3), 34. 271, 1887; H. L. Wells, *ib.*, (3), 34. 271, 1887; K. Seubert and M. Elten, *Zeit. anorg. Chem.*, 4. 76, 1893; L. Vanino, *Pharm. Centrh.*, 52. 761, 1911; W. Heintz, *Pogg. Ann.*, 63. 55, 559, 1844; H. Rose, *Ausführliches Handbuch der analytischen Chemie*, Leipzig, 1871; C. R. Fresenius, *Anleitung zur quantitativen chemischen Analyse*, Braunschweig, 1877; J. Lefort, *Compt. Rend.*, 27. 268, 1848; A. J. Jones, *Pharm. Journ.*, 143, 1925; *Chem. Trade Journ.*, 77. 239, 1925; F. Janzen, *Apoth. Ztg.*, 14. 79, 1899; R. H. Brett, *Phil. Mag.*, 10. 89, 335, 1837.

[2] A. Breithaupt, *Pogg. Ann.*, 53. 627, 1841; C. F. Rammelsberg, *ib.*, 76. 564, 1849; F. S. Beudant, *Traité élémentaire de minéralogie*, Paris, 2. 375, 1832; J. F. Vogl, *Gangverhältnisse im Mineralreichtum Joachimsthals*, Teplitz, Brüx, 1856; M. Barcena, *Rev. Cientif. Mexico*, 1. 8, 1879; S. Calderon, *Los minerales de Espana*, Madrid, 1910; F. A. Genth, *Amer. Journ. Science*, (3), 43. 184, 1892; F. G. Cairns, *ib.*, (3), 33. 284, 1887; A. Carnot, *Compt. Rend.*, 79. 302, 1874; C. Winkler, *Neues Jahrb. Min.*, ii, 112, 1880; A. Weisbach, *ib.*, ii, 112, 1880; W. H. Miller, *Introduction to Mineralogy*, London, 591, 1852. M. Adam, *Tableau minéralogique*, Paris, 27.

1869 ; W. Macgregor, in J. Sowerby, *British Mineralogy*, London, 1802 ; T. Thomson, *Outlines of Mineralogy, Geology, and Mineral Analysis*, London, **2**. 594, 1836 ; W. Bodenbender, *Zeit. prakt. Geol.*, **7**. 322, 1899 ; K. Thaddéeff, *Zeit. Kryst.*, **31**. 246, 1899 ; A. Arzruni, *ib.*, **31**. 238, 1899 ; H. Louis, *Min. Mag.*, **7**. 139, 1887 ; A. Liversidge, *Proc. Roy. Soc. New South Wales*, **14**. 181, 213, 1880 ; H. Bertrand, *Bull. Soc. Min.*, **4**. 58, 1881.

§ 20. The Bismuth Nitrates

When a soln. of bismuth or its oxide in hot nitric acid is allowed to crystallize at ordinary temp., **bismuth nitrate**, $Bi(NO_3)_3.5H_2O$, separates in clear, colourless, triclinic crystals. J. J. Berzelius,[1] T. Graham, J. H. Gladstone, W. Heintz, E. Ruge, A. Duflos, J. M. Ordway, G. M. Rutten, F. Chemnitius, A. de Schulten, P. Yvon, and L. Freundt prepared this salt. According to C. F. Rammelsberg, the crystals belong to the triclinic system, and have the axial ratios $a : b : c = 0.8053 : 1 : 0.6172$, and $\alpha = 90° 4'$, $\beta = 104° 26'$, and $\gamma = 79° 6'$. The cleavage is marked on the (100)-face. G. Bodman found that the crystals are isomorphous with those of the rare earth nitrates—lanthanum, didymium, and yttrium. L. Playfair and J. P. Joule gave 2·736 for the sp. gr. of the salt, and F. W. Clarke, 2·823 at 20°. B. Powell, and L. Ditscheiner measured the refractive indices of soln. of the salt; and the effect of the nitrate on the optical rotatory power of some organic substances was studied by H. Grossmann. W. D. Bancroft and H. B. Weiser found that with a cold surface in the colourless gas-flame charged with bismuth nitrate there is deposited a bright white, metallic mirror. According to A. Quartaroli, soln. of bismuth nitrate containing an excess of nitric acid are strongly hydrolyzed even in the presence of a considerable excess of nitric acid. This was shown by the electrical conductivity of the soln., and by the conc. of the H·-ions indicated by the catalysis of methyl acetate. The calculated ionization constant is 0·0230. Analyses by A. Duflos, J. J. Berzelius, T. Graham, W. Heintz, W. Lüddecke, and E. Ruge show that the salt crystallizing from the nitric acid soln. at ordinary temp. is the *pentahydrate*. The conditions of equilibrium are indicated in Fig. 30. G. M. Rutten said that the *dihydrate*, $Bi(NO_3)_3.2H_2O$, is formed by heating the pentahydrate to 75·5°. It appears as a solid phase in aq. soln. with 37·23 and 47·76 per cent. respectively of Bi_2O_3 and N_2O_5 at 72°; 36·74 and 47·91 per cent. respectively at 75°; and 39·75 and 45·16 per cent. respectively at 80°. According to E. Moles and E. Sellés, the *monohydrate*,

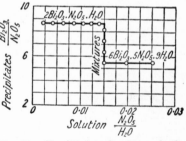

FIG. 30.—Equilibrium Conditions in the System : $Bi_2O_3–N_2O_5–H_2O$ at 21°.

$Bi(NO_3)_3.H_2O$, in nacreous, tabular crystals, is obtained when bismuth is dissolved in nitric acid at as low a temp. as possible, and the soln. evaporated at 60° to 70°. When heated in dry carbon dioxide, the anhydrous salt is formed. The *hemitrihydrate*, $Bi(NO_3)_3.1\frac{1}{2}H_2O$, was obtained by A. Ditte, and G. M. Rutten as a crystalline powder by heating the pentahydrate, or bismuth trioxide with water-free nitric acid. The hemitrihydrate rapidly attracts moisture from the air and passes into the pentahydrate. The conditions of equilibrium are indicated in Fig. 29. M. Picon said that in vacuo over phosphorus pentoxide, the normal nitrate loses 3·2 mols of water; and at 100°, the salt decomposes. This salt cannot be dehydrated by phosphorus pentoxide without decomposition. G. Bodman reported that the *hexahydrate*, $Bi(NO_3)_3.6H_2O$, occurs only when associated in solid soln. with the corresponding rare earth nitrates.

W. Heintz, and E. Ruge observed that when triturated in air dried by sulphuric acid and potassium hydroxide, at ordinary temp., water, nitric acid, and bismuth hydroxydinitrate is formed. Even at 30°, the salt loses nitric acid, but it has no definite m.p., and, according to G. M. Rutten, it forms hemihydrated bismuthyl nitrate at 75·5°, while at a higher temp. it passes into bismuth trioxide. T. Graham, and J. H. Gladstone also made some observations on this subject. K. Schäfer and F. Hein examined the absorption spectrum of nitric acid soln. of bismuth nitrate in the ultra-violet. E. Wrede studied bismuth nitrate, etc., as a target for indicating magnetic separation in a stream of hydrogen. A. Duflos said that when bismuth nitrate is treated with water, it forms dihydrated bismuthyl nitrate ; and when treated with a very large excess of water, the product contains $Bi : HNO_3$ in the proportion 1 : 12. U. Antony and G. Gigli found that when treated with increasing proportions of water, the quantity of bismuth passing into soln. becomes less and less, until, with 50,000 parts of water to one part of nitrate, no more bismuth can be detected in soln. Following the method indicated in connection with mercurous sulphate—Fig. 37, **4.** 31, 29—W. L. Miller and F. B. Kenrick represented the equilibrium conditions in the case of bismuth nitrate and water by Fig. 29. This shows the existence of the two basic nitrates with $Bi_2O_3 : N_2O_5 : H_2O=2 : 1 : 1$ and 6 : 5 : 9. When normal bismuth nitrate in nitric acid is poured into water at ordinary temp. the basic nitrate $BiO(NO_3).H_2O$ is formed if the precipitate be filtered from the mother-liquid. When the crystalline precipitate is left in contact with water, it begins to change into a more basic salt. The reaction is, however, so slow that no appreciable change is produced in a few hours. At 21°, the salt $Bi_{12}O_{13}(NO_3)_{10}.9H_2O$ is in equilibrium with nitric acid soln. from 0·03 to 0·32 normality, and the salt $BiO.NO_3$ with soln. from 0·425 to 0·7 normality. At 50°, the salt $Bi_4O_5(NO_3)_2.H_2O$ is in equilibrium with nitric acid soln. from 0·057 to 0·285 normality ; and the salt $Bi_{12}O_{13}(NO_3)_{10}.9H_2O$ with soln. from 0·285 to 0·466 normality. At 75°, the salt $Bi_4O_5(NO_3)_2.H_2O$ is in equilibrium with nitric acid soln. of 0·109 to 0·314 normality.

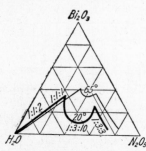

FIG. 31.—The Ternary System : Bi_2O_3–N_2O_5–H_2O at 20° and at 65°.

No signs of any basic nitrate other than these two just mentioned have been observed at 50°, although the transition of one form to another is so slow that mixtures not in equilibrium with the mother-liquid have been reported as if they were true chemical individuals. L. Vanino and F. Mussgnug showed that one of the chief difficulties in the preparation of bismuth compounds is due to the ready hydrolysis of bismuth salts except in acidic soln. ; and they added that this can be prevented by working with mixtures of say bismuth nitrate and mannitol (1 : 1) in aq. soln. G. M. Rutten studied the ternary system Bi_2O_3–N_2O_5–H_2O at different temp., and the results at 20° and 65° are summarized in Fig. 31. He found at 25°, the results indicated in Table II. J. S. Muspratt studied the action of sulphur dioxide on bismuth nitrate. E. C. Franklin and C. A. Kraus observed that the nitrate is soluble in liquid ammonia, and in the presence of ammonium nitrate.

A. Libavius, in his *De natura metallorum* (Francofurti, 1600), stated that a soln. of bismuth in nitric acid gives a white precipitate when treated with water, and in that respect it differs from a soln. of zinc in the same acid. A few years later, N. Lemery, in his *Cours de chymie* (Paris, 1681), and R. Boyle, in his *Reflections on the hypothesis of alkali and acidum* (London, 1675), made some observations on the subject. B. Hepner said that the first decomposition product of bismuth nitrate is $BiO.NO_3.H_2O$ which furnishes scaly crystals ; when this is exposed for 8 hrs. in a desiccator it furnishes $Bi_2O_3.N_2O_5.1·9H_2O$. No loss of nitric acid occurs when the water is given off. The compound $NO_3.BiO.(HO)_2Bi(NO_3)$ is obtained by heating equal parts of bismuth nitrate and water on the water-bath until the scaly crystals change, or by allowing the scaly crystals to stand in contact with a soln. of one part of bismuth nitrate and 11 parts of water ; or by the continued action of a soln. of

TABLE II.—SOLUBILITY OF BISMUTH TRIOXIDE IN NITRIC ACID AT 20°.

190 grms. liquid.		Solid Phase.
Grms. Bi$_2$O$_3$	Grms. N$_2$O$_5$	
0·321	0·963	Bi$_2$O$_3$.N$_2$O$_5$.2H$_2$O ; or Bi(OH)$_2$(NO$_3$)
3·54	4·68	
6·37	7·17	
14·85	13·31	
18·74	15·90	
23·50	19·29	Bi$_2$O$_3$.N$_2$O$_5$.H$_2$O ; or BiO(NO$_3$).½H$_2$O
28·11	21·64	
31·48	23·70	
32·93	24·83	Triple point
32·80	24·86	
32·67	24·70	
24·16	28·25	Bi$_2$O$_3$.3N$_2$O$_5$.10H$_2$O ; or Bi(NO$_3$)$_3$.5H$_2$O
11·19	49·38	
15·20	54·66	
20·76	53·74	
27·85	51·02	Triple point
8·58	68·28	Bi$_2$O$_3$.3N$_2$O$_5$.3H$_2$O ; or Bi(NO$_3$)$_3$.1½H$_2$O
4·05	74·90	

nitric acid with less than 6 per cent. N$_2$O$_5$. The crystals prepared in the wet way are monoclinic, and in the dry way, hexagonal plates. The final degradation produced by the action of water on bismuth nitrate, NO$_3$BiO.(HO)BiO, is obtained by digesting one part of bismuth nitrate with 24 parts of water on a water-bath, in 2-hour periods, rejecting the water at the end of each period. The product is an aggregate of hexagonal crystals. The *bismuticum subnitricum—bismuth subnitrate* —the *magisterium bismuthi—magistery of bismuth—basic bismuth nitrate, bismuth-white, pearl-white, blanc d'espagne—Spanish white*—and *white cosmetic* are pharmaceutical or trade names for the basic nitrate or mixture of basic nitrates obtained by adding water to bismuth nitrate. Several other white powders were also called Spanish white or pearl-white. G. Kassner said the grey colours developed by a preparation of bismuth nitrate in a year was due to the separation of tellurium impurity.

The composition of the white precipitate depends on the temp. and on the proportion of water employed. According to A. Ditte, and E. Ruge, the composition usually ranges between Bi(OH)(BiO$_2$)NO$_3$, and BiO(NO$_3$). According to G. M. Rutten, the pharmaceutical preparation cannot be BiO(NO$_3$).½H$_2$O because it is washed with hot water ; it may be 10Bi$_2$O$_3$.9N$_2$O$_5$.7H$_2$O, or 6Bi$_2$O$_3$.5N$_2$O$_5$.8H$_2$O, or a mixture of the two. If washed for a long time, its composition approximates (OH)(BiO)$_2$(NO$_3$). The preparation and properties of the pharmaceutical oxynitrate were discussed by A. Adriaansz, W. L. Baylor, A. Béchamp, C. Bouchet, L. A. Buchner, E. Busch, C. L. Cadet de Gassicourt, P. P. Carles, A. Carnot, A. Chapius and G. Linossier, A. Chevallier, C. E. Cornfield and G. R. A. Short, E. C. Deschamps, A. Duflos, F. P. Dulk, A. Glénard, A. Grandval, M. Grossmann, J. E. Herberger, M. Janssen, M. H. Klaproth, J. L. Lassaigne, J. Löwe, H. Reinsch, A. Riche, J. H. Salisbury, E. R. Schneider, A. T. Starting, H. Thoms, and A. Underhill. E. B. R. Prideaux and H. W. Hewis described an electrolytic process of preparation. The presence of lead as an impurity was noted by A. Carnot, A. Riche, G. Guérin, and A. Chapius and G. Linossier ; the presence of ammonium nitrate, by E. Luce, E. Crouzel ; and of tellurium, by J. O. Braithwaite, E. Isnard, A. Reissert, G. Brownen, and E. A. Letts. Some uses of the basic nitrate were discussed by E. C. Behrendt, C. Winkler, and U. Gayon and G. Dupetit. P. W. K. Böckmann concluded that at an acidity similar to that which prevails in the stomach, basic bismuth nitrate does not possess any neutralizing capacity. A. Böhme observed that the internal administration of the basic nitrate leads to the formation of nitrous acid which produces methæmoglobinura in men and animals. G. Gimel said that the basic nitrate is soluble in acidic liquids like musts, etc., and that it inhibits acetous fermentation.

According to G. M. Rutten, the basic salts : 5Bi$_2$O$_3$.4N$_2$O$_5$.9H$_2$O, reported by

E. Becker, and M. Janssen ; $4Bi_2O_3.3N_2O_5.9H_2O$, reported by **A.** Duflos, and J. E. Herberger ; and $5Bi_2O_3.3N_2O_5.6(or 8)H_2O$, reported by A. Laurent, B. Fischer, V. Thomas, H. A. L. Wiggers, J. H. Weibel, V. A. Jacquelain, E. Frémy, J. Löwe, R. Phillips, and C. Ullgren, are non-existent.   E. Isnard did not find arsenic in the commercial salt, but tellurium was present.   According to B. Hepner, the compound known as *magisterium bismuthi Duflos* :

$$\left[\begin{array}{c} NO_3.Bi \overset{O.}{\underset{OH}{\diagdown}} \overset{OH \cdots Bi}{\underset{OH \cdots Bi}{\diagup}} Bi \overset{O\ HO}{\underset{OH}{<}} Bi\ NO_3 \\ \end{array} \right] (NO_3)_2$$

is formed by mixing one part of bismuth nitrate with 24 parts of water, and dissolving this mixture in 120 parts of water ; or by heating one part of nitrate with 24 parts of water at 75° until the precipitate becomes crystalline ; or by allowing scaly crystals of $BiO.NO_3.H_2O$ to stand covered with water for a year when formed at ordinary temp., it furnishes large rhombic crystals, but at higher temp. the crystals are rectangular.   E. Moles and E. Sellés regarded the salt $[Bi(H_3NO_4)_2(H_2O)_2]NO_4$, as well as $BiNO_4$, and $BiNO_4.BiO.OH$ to be derivatives of orthonitric acid.   The co-ordination number of bismuth is taken as 4.

Bismuth nitrate was stated by L. V. Brugnatelli to detonate slightly and emit sparks when placed on red-hot coals ; and these effects are more marked when the crystals are rubbed with phosphorus.   W. D. Bancroft and H. B. Weiser observed that in the Bunsen flame, bismuth nitrate decomposes and a white metallic mirror is deposited on a cold surface.   Hydrogen dioxide with acid soln. of bismuth nitrate gives a yellow or orange precipitate on filtering into conc. ammonia.   The precipitate dissolves in conc. nitric acid and contains but traces of active oxygen.   It contains 95 per cent. Bi_2O_3, and is probably neither a peroxide nor a basic hydroxide. E. P. Alvarez found that when an almost neutral soln. of bismuth nitrate is treated with a soln. of potassium pernitrate, a white crystalline precipitate of what may be **bismuth pernitrate** is formed.   Dil. nitric acid dissolves the salt completely. A. Ditte said that this occurs with a soln. containing 83 grms. HNO_3 per litre, and when this soln. is diluted it becomes turbid ; it also deposits a basic salt when heated, and this re-dissolves on cooling.   The presence of acetic acid in the nitric acid soln. makes it hinder the precipitation of a basic salt by water.   B. Hepner and A. Likiernik, and L. Vanino and co-workers, observed a similar result in the presence of mannitol, dulcitol, or sorbitol.   S. von Laszcynsky found that 100 grms. of acetone at 0° dissolve 48·66 grms. of the nitrate, and at 19°, 41·70 grms. K. A. Hofmann and K. L. Gonder observed that a complex is formed with thiourea ; R. Weinland and H. Sperl, one with pyrocatechol ; and J. Pastureau, one with phenylhydrazine.   G. Urbain and H. Lacombe obtained complex salts with the nitrate of some bivalent metals—*vide infra*.

According to E. Ruge, if pentahydrated bismuth nitrate be kept for 2 or 3 months in dry air—over sulphuric acid and potassium hydroxide—it forms **bismuth hydroxydinitrate**, $Bi(OH)(NO_3)_2.\frac{1}{2}H_2O$.   The conditions of equilibrium are indicated in Fig. 29.   A similar product is obtained when the normal salt is heated for 18–19 days at 50°–78°, or until its weight during 12 hrs.' heating diminishes by only a milligram.   If dried to constant weight, bismuthyl nitrate is formed. G. M. Rutten obtained a product with a similar composition by heating penta-hydrated bismuth nitrate at 75·5°.   If normal bismuth nitrate be treated with cold water, the gelatinous precipitate soon forms scaly crystals, which are drained on porous tiles.   When dried in air, the composition is $Bi_2O_3.N_2O_5.2H_2O$, or **bismuth dihydroxynitrate**, $Bi(OH)_2(NO_3)$.   It was so prepared by F. B. Allan, E. Becker, C. F. Bucholz, W. Heintz, A. Laurent, M. Janssen, E. Ruge, G. M. Rutten, and P. Yvon.   A. Quartaroli showed that the formation of this salt does not occur directly from $Bi(NO_3)_3$, but probably through the intermediate formation of the hydroxydinitrate. A. Ditte said that the proportion of water ranges from 0·5 to 2 mols. A. de Schulten's salt, $5Bi_2O_3.5N_2O_5.9H_2O$, is also considered to be identical with this salt. The conditions of equilibrium are indicated in Fig. 29. According to E. Schmidt, the same salt is precipitated by water at 60°, but with warmer water, a more basic salt is deposited. P. Yvon found that the same salt is deposited when a soln. of bismuth nitrate is neutralized with alkaline earth carbonates. E. Ruge observed the formation of the same salt by the action of an excess of nitric acid on bismuth, or of a warm conc. soln. of bismuth nitrate on powdered bismuth. B. Fischer was unable to make a definite salt by the action of bismuth nitrate on the hydroxide. The snow-white, lustrous powder contains needles, prisms, or plates. A. des Cloizeaux found the crystals prepared by P. Yvon to be triclinic. A. de Schulten gave 4·928 for the sp. gr. W. Heintz, and E. Becker said that half the water of crystallization is lost at 100°–120°; J. H. Gladstone, that water and acid are lost at 260°; and at a red-heat, E. Ruge obtained the trioxide. G. M. Rutten found that when the salt $Bi_2O_3.N_2O_5.2H_2O$ was kept over sulphuric acid of different conc., and therefore of different vap. press. of water vapour, it retained the following amounts of water:

	9·5	8	6	5·2	2·9	0·8	0 mm.
Mols H_2O	1·91	1·86	1·83	1·83	1·78	1·67	0·75

M. Picon studied the dehydration of this salt—over phosphorus pentoxide it forms $BiO(NO_3).\frac{5}{12}H_2O$, and at 100°, it loses 3·64 per cent. of water. A. K. Sanyal and N. R. Dhar found bismuth oxynitrate is coloured by exposure to tropical sunlight for 35 hrs. According to E. Ruge, the salt is not sensitive to light; it dissolves slightly in water and a more basic salt separates out again; hot water converts it into bismuthyl hydroxynitrate; and A. Ditte showed that boiling water containing 4·5 grms. HNO_3 per litre is without action on the salt. H. Müller and L. Kürthy observed that in certain concentrations of glycine, bismuth nitrate undergoes considerable hydrolysis which is ascribed to the interaction of the amphoteric bismuthous acid with both positively (simple) and negatively (complex) charged bismuth ions. A. Vogel said that stannous chloride gradually colours it orange-yellow, and when heated, brown or black.

According to E. Ruge, T. Graham, and E. Becker, the basic nitrate corresponding with $Bi_2O_3.N_2O_5.H_2O$, or bismuthyl nitrate, $BiO(NO_3).\frac{1}{2}H_2O$, is formed when pentahydrated bismuth nitrate, or bismuth hydroxydinitrate, or dihydroxynitrate is heated to 78° until its weight is constant. P. Yvon heated bismuth nitrate to 120°, and J. H. Gladstone to 149°. G. M. Rutten said that bismuth nitrate begins to decompose at 155°; and P. Yvon said that the salt loses half its water at 120°. G. M. Rutten obtained bismuthyl nitrate by leaving bismuth dihydroxynitrate in contact with its mother-liquor or dil. nitric acid for some time, or by treating pentahydrated bismuth nitrate with an equal weight of water, and heating the mixture on a water-bath until it forms tabular crystals. B. Fischer made it by mixing alcoholic nitric acid, and a mixture of alcohol and bismuth hydroxide. G. M. Rutten, A. Butleroff, and F. B. Allan said that the hexagonal, prismatic crystals are probably monoclinic. They are not decomposed when washed with nitric acid containing 10 per cent. N_2O_5.

If bismuth nitrate be treated with hot or cold water until no more nitric acid is extracted, and the hydrolysis is completed, F. B. Allan, A. Butleroff, A. Ditte, W. Lüddecke, E. Ruge, G. M. Rutten, and P. Yvon said that a snow-white, microcrystalline powder, $2B_2O_3.N_2O_5.H_2O$, or bismuthyl hydroxynitrate, $(BiO)_2(NO_3)(OH)$, is formed. E. Ruge said that the crystals obtained with hot water belong to the cubic system. One mol. of water is retained at 100°; and the salt suffers no further change when boiled with water. The conditions of equilibrium are indicated in Fig. 29. F. B. Allan said that the salt is in equilibrium with 0·057N- to 0·285N-HNO_3 at 30°; with 0·109N- to 0·314N-HNO_3 at 75°. If heated in a sealed tube at 200°–205° with water, often renewed, G. Rousseau and G. Tite said that it finally passes into bismuth trioxide. If the mother-liquor remaining after the deposition of the scaly crystals of $Bi_2O_3.N_2O_5.2H_2O$, be allowed to stand a couple of days at ordinary temp., G. M. Rutten found that crystals of $6Bi_2O_3.5N_2O_5.8$(or 9)H_2O, or **bismuthyl hydroxypentanitrate,** $(BiO)_6(NO_3)_5(OH).3\frac{1}{2}$(or 4)$H_2O$, are formed. The crystals are probably rhombic. The salt is also formed when pentahydrated bismuth nitrate is heated with 24 times its weight of water until crystals begin to form. The conditions of equilibrium are indicated in Fig. 29.   F. B. Allan said that at 21° this salt is in equilibrium with $0.5N$- to $0.32N$-HNO_3; and at 50° with $0.285N$- to $0.446N$-HNO_3. Salts prepared by E. Becker, W. Heintz, M. Janssen, and E. Ruge are probably identical with this salt. K. H. Butler and D. McIntosh said that the nitrate is insoluble in liquid chlorine.

H. L. Wells and co-workers prepared **cæsium bismuth nitrate,** $2CsNO_3.Bi(NO_3)_3$, in long, colourless prisms from a soln. of the constituents. It melts at 102°. G. Urbain obtained **ammonium bismuth nitrate,** $2NH_4NO_3.Bi(NO_3)_3.4H_2O$, from a soln. of the component salts. A. C. Vournasos prepared white crystals of **methyl-amine nitratobismuthate,** $NH_3(CH_3)[Bi(NO_3)_4]$, in white crystals—vide 8. 49, 21. G. Urbain and H. Lacombe prepared a number of complex salts $3M''(NH_3)_2.2Bi(NO_3)_3.24H_2O$, where M stands for Mg, Zn, Mn, Co, or Ni. The salts are isomorphous with the complex nitrates of the rare earths; they effloresce in dry air, but deliquesce in moist air—the manganese salt being the most, and the nickel and magnesium salts least deliquescent; and the salts are all decomposed by water. It was not found possible to prepare *copper bismuth nitrate.* The colourless **magnesium bismuth nitrate** has a sp. gr. 2·32 at 16°/16°, and melts with decomposition at 71°. Colourless **zinc bismuth nitrate** has a sp. gr. 2·75 at 16°/16°, and melts with decomposition at 67·5°. The *cadmium bismuth nitrate* could not be made. Pale red **manganese bismuth nitrate** is the most unstable member of the series, and it does not exist in contact with the solid phase of either constituent; its sp. gr. is 2·42 at 16°/16°; and it melts without decomposition at 43°–44°. They could not make *ferrous bismuth nitrate.* Red **cobalt bismuth nitrate** has a sp. gr. 2·48 at 16°/16°, and melts without decomposition at 58°. Green **nickel bismuth nitrate** has a sp. gr. 2·51 at 16°/16°, and it melts with decomposition at 69°.

REFERENCES.

[1] L. Vanino and F. Hartl, *Journ. prakt. Chem.,* (2), **74.** 142, 1906 ; L. Vanino and O. Hauser, *Zeit. anorg. Chem.,* **28.** 210, 1901 ; G. M. Rutten, *ib.,* **30.** 34z, 1902 ; G. Bodman, *ib.,* **27.** 254, 1901 ; *Ber.,* **31.** 1237, 1898 ; A. Duflos, *Schweigger's Journ.,* **68.** 191, 1833 ; *Arch. Pharm.,* (2), **23.** 307, 1840 ; B. Fischer, *ib.,* (3), **32.** 460, 1894 ; M. Janssen, *Journ. Pharm. Chim.,* (3), **23.** 319, 1853 ; *Arch. Pharm.,* (2), **68.** 1, 129, 1851 ; (2), **77.** 241, 1854 ; (2), **78.** 1, 1854 ; E. Becker, *ib.,* (2), **55.** 1, 129, 1848 ; (2), **79.** 1, 1854 ; A. T. Starting, *ib.,* (3), **13.** 411, 1878 ; E. Busch, *ib.,* (3), **24.** 341, 1888 ; M. Grossmann, *ib.,* (3), **22.** 297, 1884 ; H. Grossmann, *Ber.,* **38.** 1711, 1905 ; *Zeit. Ver. Rübenzucker Ind.,* 650, 1058, 1905 ; A. Ditte, *Compt. Rend.,* **79.** 956, 1874 ; **84.** 1317, 1877 ; U. Gayon and G. Dupetit, *ib.,* **103.** 883, 1886 ; M. Picon, *ib.,* **181.** 516, 1925 ; G. Rousseau and G. Tite, *ib.,* **115.** 174, 1892 ; P. Yvon, *Bull. Soc. Chim.,* (2), **27.** 491, 1877 ; *Compt. Rend.,* **84.** 1161, 1877 ; A. C. Vournasos, *ib.,* **176.** 1555, 1923 ; A. de Cloizeaux, *ib.,* **84.** 1162, 1877 ; A. Carnot, *ib.,* **86.** 718, 1878 ; **87.** 208, 1878 ; A. Chapius and G. Linossier, *ib.,* **87.** 169, 1878 ; A. Riche, *ib.,* **86.** 1502, 1878 ; A. Ditte, *ib.,* **79.** 956, 1874 ; **84.** 1317, 1877 ; *Ann. Chim. Phys.,* (5), **18.** 320, 1879 ; A. de Schulten, *Bull. Soc. Chim.,* (3), **29.** 720, 1903 ; A. Vogel, *Kastner's Arch.,* **23.** 68, 1832 ; E. Ruge, *Journ. prakt. Chem.,* (1), **96.** 117, 1865 ; J. Löwe, *ib.,* (1), **74.** 341, 1858 ; E. R. Schneider, *ib.,* (2), **23.** 84, 1881 ; W. Lüddecke, *Liebig's Ann.,* **140.** 277, 1866 ; L. Schäffner, *ib.,* **51.** 172, 1844 ; C. Ullgren, *ib.,* **40.** 269, 1848 ; J. S. Muspratt, *ib.,* **50.** 286, 1844 ; *Journ. Chem. Soc.,* **1.** 45, 1849 ; W. Heintz, *Pogg. Ann.,* **63.** 83, 1844 ; *Journ. prakt. Chem.,* (1), **45.** 105, 1836 ; B. Powell, *Pogg. Ann.,* **69.** 110, 1846 ; E. Wrede, *Zeit. Physik,* **41.** 569, 1927 ; L. Freundt, *Chem. Gaz,* **2.** 128, 1844 ; G. Gimel, *Bull. Assoc. Chim. Enc. Dist.,* **31.** 138, 1913 ; F. P. Dulk, *Repert. Pharm.,* **33.** 1, 1844 ; J. E. Herberger, *ib.,* **55.** 289, 306, 1836 ; H. Reinsch, *ib.,* **64.** 206, 1838 ; G. C. Wittstein, *ib.,* **74.** 243, 1841 ; L. A. Buchner, *ib.,* **55.** 306, 1836 ; F. B. Allan, *Amer. Chem. Journ.,* **25.** 307, 1901 ; E. C. Franklin and C. A. Kraus, *ib.,* **20.** 827, 1988 ; C. F. Bucholz, *Trommsdorff's Journ.,* **5.** 81, 1798 ; J. J. Berzelius, *Gilbert's Ann.,* **40.** 286, 1812 ; *Schweigger's Journ.,* **7.** 70, 1814 ; J. H. Gladstone, *Mem. Chem. Soc.,* **3.** 480, 1848 ; L. Playfair and J. P. Joule, *ib.,* **2.** 401, 1845 ; T. Graham, *Phil. Trans.,* **127.** 47, 1837 ; P. W. K. Böckmann, *Arch. Exp. Path.*

BISMUTH

Pharm., **80.** 140, **1916**; A. Böhme, *ib.*, **57.** 447, 1907; P. Grouvelle, *Ann. Chim. Phys.*, (2), **19.**
141, 1821; A. Laurent, *ib.*, (3), **36.** 353, 1852; V. Thomas, *ib.*, (7), **13.** 145, 1898; J. H. Weibel,
Reaktionen einiger Metallsalzlösungen unter erhöhten Temperaturen und Drucken, Zürich, 1923;
H. Thoms, *Ber. deut. pharm. Ges.*, **8.** 119, 1898; A. K. Sanyal and N. R. Dhar, *Zeit. anorg. Chem.*,
128. 212, 1923; E. Crouzel, *Ann. Chim. Anal. Appl.*, **10.** 349, 1905; E. P. Alvarez, *ib.*, **11.** 401,
1906; E. B. R. Prideaux and H. W. Lewis, *Journ. Soc. Chem. Ind.*, **41.** 167, T, 1922;
E. C. Behrendt, *Ber.*, **36.** 3390. 1903; S. von Laszcynsky, *ib.*, **27.** 2287, 1894; K. A. Hofmann
and K. L. Gonder, *ib.*, **37.** 242, 1904; A. Chevallier, *Journ. Pharm. Chim.*, (2), **15.** 383, 1829;
C. L. Cadet de Gassicourt, *ib.*, (1), **1.** 46, 1809; E. Luce, *ib.*, (6), **30.** 310, 1924; G. Guérin, *ib.*,
(7), **10.** 22, 1914; E. Isnard, *ib.*, (6), **27.** 216, 1923; (7), **27.** 216, 1923; E. Frémy, *Ann.
Chim. Phys.*, (3), **12.** 361, 457, 1844; *Journ. Pharm. Chim.*, (3), **3.** 30, 1843; P. P. Carles, *ib.*,
(4), **28.** 397, 1878; J. L. Lassaigne, *ib.*, (3), **20.** 353, 1851; A. Béchamp, *ib.*, (3), **32.** 330, 1857;
M. Ménigaut, *ib.*, (2), **13.** 7, 1827; G. Urbain, *Journ. Chim. Phys.*, **4.** 105, 1906; G. Urbain and
H. Lacombe, *Chem. News*, **89.** 52, 1904; **137.** 568, 1903; **138.** 84, 1904; J. Pastureau, *ib.*, **127.** 485,
1898; U. Antony and G. Gigli, *Gazz. Chim. Ital.*, **28.** 245, 1898; A. Quartaroli, *ib.*, **43.** i, 97, 1913;
L. V. Brugnatelli, *Ann. Chim. Phys.*, (1), **27.** 72, 1798; V. A. Jacquelain, *ib.*, (2), **66.** 113, 1837;
F. W. Clarke, *Amer. Journ. Science*, (3), **14.** 281, 1877; J. M. Ordway, *ib.*, (2), **27.** 14, 1859;
E. C. Deschamps, *Répert. Pharm.*, (2), **8.** 193, 1880; L. Ditscheiner, *Sitzber. Akad. Wien*, **49.** 326,
1864; H. L. Wells, H. P. Beardsley, G. S. Jamieson, and F. J. Metzger, *Amer. Chem. Journ.*, **26.**
275, 1901; L. Vanino and F. Mussgnug, *Arch. Pharm.*, **251.** 261, 1919; C. F. Rammelsberg,
Handbuch der Mineralchemie, Leipzig, 366, 1881; K. Schäfer and F. Hein, *Zeit. anorg. Chem.*,
100. 249, 1917; R. Weinland and H. Sperl, *ib.*, **150.** 69, 1925; H. Müller and L. Kürthy, *Biochem.
Zeit.*, **147.** 385, 1924; M. H. Klaproth, *Beiträge zur chemische Kenntniss der Mineralkörper*,
Berlin, **1.** 256, 1795; C. E. Corfield and G. R. A. Short, *Pharm. Journ.*, (4), **59.** 80, 1923;
C. Winkler in A. W. Hofmann, *Bericht über die Entwicklung der chemischen Industrie*, Braun-
schweig, **2.** 953, 1875; A. Reissert, *Deut. Med. Ztg.*, 16, 1885; J. O. Braithwaite, *Chemist
Druggist*, **26.** 122, 1884; *Amer. Drugg.*, **13.** 88, 1884; G. Brownen, *Pharm. Journ.*, (3), **6.** 561, 1876;
E. A. Letts, *ib.*, (3), **9.** 405, 1878; R. Phillips, *ib.*, (1), **18.** 688, 1859; C. Bouchet, *Bull. Théra-
peut.*, **94.** 315, 1878; A. Grandval, *Union Méd. Scient. Reims*, **2.** 189, 1878; W. L. Miller and
F. B. Kenrick, *Journ. Amer. Chem. Soc.*, **22.** 291, 1900; *Trans. Roy. Soc. Canada*, (2), **7.** 35, 1901;
Journ. Phys. Chem., **7.** 259, 1903; W. D. Bancroft and H. B. Weiser, *ib.*, **18.** 213, 1914; B. Hepner,
Arch. Pharm., **264.** 65, 1926; B. Hepner and A. Likiernik, *ib.*, **264.** 46, 1926; H. A. L. Wiggers,
Jahresb. Pharm., (2), **2.** 105, 1851; A. Glénard, *Pharm. Centr.*, 366, 1865; A. Butleroff, *Journ.
Russ. Phys. Chem. Soc.*, **12.** 37, 1880; A. Adriaansz, *Arch. Néerl.*, (1), **3.** 186, 1868; *Journ. prakt.
Chem.*, (1), **105.** 320, 1868; W. L. Baylor, *Trans. Med. Soc. Virginia*, **2.** 413, 1879; J. H. Salis-
bury, *Chicago Med. Times*, **36.** 601, 1878; A. Underhill, *Cincinatti Lancet*, (2), **1.** 231, 1878;
E. Schmidt, *Ausführliches Lehrbuch der pharmazeutischen Chemie*, Braunschweig, 1919; E. Moles
and E. Sellés, *Anal. Fis. Quim.*, **25.** 453, 1927; G. Kassner, *Tschermah's Festschrift*, 80, 1926;
F. Chemnitius, *Pharm. Centr.*, **68.** 513, 1927; K. H. Butler and D. McIntosh, *Trans. Roy. Soc.
Canada*, (3), **21.** 19, 1927.

§ 21. The Bismuth Phosphates

According to C. F. Wenzel,[1] an aq. soln. of phosphoric acid forms with bismuth
hydroxide a white insoluble powder, and a soluble phosphate. According to
C. Montemartini and U. Egidi, the pharmaceutical preparation *bismuthum phosphori-
cum solubile* contains bismuth oxide, prepared by the addition of an alkali phosphate
to a soln. of bismuth nitrate or chloride, and always contains some basic nitrate
or chloride. It may, however, be obtained free from these compounds by taking
advantage of the fact that bismuth oxide is soluble in a soln. of potassium
hydroxide which contains glycerol. Bismuth nitrate is intimately mixed with
glycerol, water is added until the salt is entirely dissolved, and then potassium
hydroxide until the precipitated oxide is redissolved. If dil. sulphuric acid is then
added, a precipitate of bismuth oxide is produced, which is entirely free from any
combined acid, and after drying in air, or in a vacuum over sulphuric acid, or at
100°–105°, has the composition $Bi_2O_3.H_2O$.

According to C. Montemartini and U. Egidi, **bismuth orthophosphate, $BiPO_4$,**
is the only phosphate stable towards water which is obtainable from soln. of bismuth
salts by precipitation and subsequent washing. W. Heintz obtained this phosphate
by precipitating a soln. of bismuth nitrate with sodium hydrophosphate, and
washing the product with nitric acid of decreasing conc. G. Chancel said that the
composition of the precipitate is the same if an excess of either salt be present,
but the soln. should be free from hydrochloric or sulphuric acid; M. M. P. Muir

said that a varying conc. of nitric acid makes very little difference. A. de Schulten obtained microscopic crystals of the orthophosphate by heating on a water-bath a mixture of 15 grms. of pentahydrated bismuth nitrate, 7 grms. of hydrated sodium hydrophosphate, and conc. nitric acid, and adding water slowly drop by drop. L. Vanino and F. Hartl treated a soln. of bismuth nitrate and mannitol with phosphoric acid or a phosphate; and C. Braun fused metaphosphoric acid with bismuth. In both cases, bismuth orthophosphate was formed. L. S. T. Rügheimer and E. Rudolfi found the mol. wt. of bismuth orthophosphate in soln. in bismuth trichloride to be normal. C. Haushofer described the orthophosphate as a white crystalline powder containing spherical, stellar, or octahedral aggregates; and A. de Schulten said that the clear crystals are monoclinic prisms of sp. gr. 6·323 at 15°. G. Chancel, W. Heintz, M. M. P. Muir, and A. de Schulten said the phosphate is anhydrous; the product obtained by L. Vanino and F. Hartl was the *trihydrate*, $BiPO_4.3H_2O$. W. Heintz, and G. Chancel found that the phosphate is reduced when heated to redness in hydrogen; but not in carbon monoxide. R. M. Caven and A. Hill said that this phosphate is not hydrolyzed by water even when boiled for a long time; and C. Montemartini and U. Egidi added that it is relatively stable towards water, but suffers a little decomposition when the water is allowed to act for a long time. W. Heintz, M. M. P. Muir, and G. Chancel said that the phosphate is but sparingly soluble in water, and in dil. nitric acid, while boiling with dil. nitric acid does not alter the salt. L. Vanino and F. Hartl found that warming with potassium iodide does not change the phosphate, but hydrogen sulphide blackens it, forming the trisulphide; a boiling soln. of potassium hydroxide was found by R. M. Caven and A. Hill to decompose the phosphate easily and completely. R. H. Brett found the freshly precipitated phosphate to be readily soluble in a soln. of ammonium chloride. F. Paneth and W. Thimann studied the adsorption of aniline dyes by the phosphate.

According to A. Cavazzi, when a soln. of 10 grms. sodium hydrophosphate in 100 grms. of water and 55 c.c. of aq. ammonia is treated with a dil. ammoniacal soln. of 6 grms. of bismuth citrate, the basic salt, $4Bi_2O_3.P_2O_5$, or *bismuth enneaoxydiorthophosphate*, $3Bi_2O_3.2BiPO_4$, is precipitated; and conversely, if the soln. of the bismuth citrate be added to the soln. of the sodium hydrophosphate, the precipitated basic salt is mixed with citrate. The white powder is insoluble in water, and soluble in hydrochloric, nitric, and citric acids.

According to A. Schwarzenberg, a boiling soln. of sodium pyrophosphate readily dissolves bismuth trioxide; and A. Stromeyer obtained **bismuth pyrophosphate**, $Bi_4(P_2O_7)_3$, by adding sodium pyrophosphate to a soln. of bismuth nitrate; the same precipitate was obtained by G. Chancel when the bismuth salt is in excess. K. A. Wallroth obtained this phosphate by dissolving bismuth trioxide in molten microcosmic salt at a bright red-heat, and keeping the glass in a state of fusion until crystallization occurs. The cold mass is extracted first with water, and then with dil. hydrochloric acid. Hexagonal plates are formed which are decomposed by water. G. Chancel said that if the salt be boiled with an acid soln. of bismuth nitrate, it rapidly forms the orthophosphate; F. Passerini said that the salt is sparingly soluble in water, and acetic acid, and freely soluble in hydrochloric or nitric acid; A. Stromeyer, and A. Brand said that the salt is soluble in a soln. of sodium pyrophosphate, but F. Passerini found it to be insoluble in that menstruum, as well as in a soln. of ammonium citrate. C. Raspe made **alkali bismuth pyrophosphates** by melting bismuth trioxide with the secondary alkali phosphates. A. Rosenheim and T. Triantaphyllides found that **sodium bismuth pyrophosphate**, $Na(BiP_2O_7).3H_4O$, forms microscopic crystals.

J. Persoz obtained **bismuth metaphosphate** by mixing a nitric acid soln. of bismuth nitrate with metaphosphoric acid, and then adding ammonia. The white precipitate is insoluble in an excess of ammonia. When boiled with water, G. Chancel found that it slowly passes into the orthophosphate. According to T. Fleitmann, bismuth trioxide dissolves in molten phosphoric acid, forming a clear glass, which, when **slowly cooled**, forms crystals of **bismuth tetrametaphosphate,** $Bi_4(P_4O_{12})_3$. It is insoluble in water, and when treated with sodium sulphide, it forms sodium tetrametaphosphate.

E. Glatzel prepared **bismuth orthosulphophosphate**, $BiPS_4$, by heating bismuth trichloride with phosphorus pentasulphide. The dark grey crystalline mass furnishes a red powder. It burns with a pale flame when heated in air. It furnishes hydrogen sulphide when treated with hydrochloric acid; with conc. sulphuric acid it forms sulphur dioxide, but the dil. acid is without action; it is decomposed by aq. ammonia, by nitric acid, and by aqua regia with the separation of sulphur; it is insoluble in water, carbon disulphide, benzene, alcohol, ether, and acetic acid; and it is decomposed by aq. soln. of alkali hydroxides.

REFERENCES.

[1] G. Chancel, *Compt. Rend.*, **50**. 416, 1860; **51**. 882, 1860; C. Braun, *Zeit. Chem.*, (2), **2**. 282, 1866; R. H. Brett, *Phil. Mag.*, **10**. 98, 335, 1837; A. Stromeyer, *Pogg. Ann.*, **26**. 553, 1832; W. Heintz, *ib.*, **63**. 55, 559, 1844; T. Fleitmann, *ib.*, **78**. 233, 338, 1849; A. Brand, *Zeit. anal. Chem.*, **28**. 596, 1889; C. F. Wenzel, *Lehre von der Verwandschaft der Körper*, Dresden, 1777; J. Persoz, *Ann. Chim. Phys.*, (3), **20**. 315, 1847; C. Montemartini and U. Egidi, *Gazz. Chim. Ital.*, **30**. ii, 377, 421, 1900; A. Cavazzi, *ib.*, **14**. 289, 1884; A. Schwarzenberg, *Untersuchungen über der pyrophosphorsauren Salze*, Göttingen, 1847; *Liebig's Ann.*, **65**. 133, 1848; L. S. T. Rügheimer and E. Rudolfi, *ib.*, **339**. 349, 1905; C. Raspe, *German Pat.*, *D.R.P.* 78324, 1893; M. M. P. Muir, *Journ. Chem. Soc.*, **32**. 674, 1877; A. de Schulten, *Bull. Soc. Chim.*, (3), **29**. 723, 1903; K. A. Wallroth, *ib.*, (2), **39**. 316, 1883; *Oefvers. Akad. Stockholm*, **40**. 3, 1883; L. Vanino and F. Hartl, *Journ. prakt. Chem.*, (2), **74**. 151, 1906; C. Haushofer, *Ueber einige mikroskopisch-chemische Reaktionen*, München, **140**, 1885; R. M. Caven and A. Hill, *Journ. Soc. Chem. Ind.*, **16**. 29, 1897; F. Passerini, *Nuovo Cimento*, (1), **9**. 84, 1859; *Il Tempo*, 2. 443, 1858; F. Paneth and W. Thimann, *Ber.*, **57**. B, 1215, 1924; E. Glatzel, *Zeit. anorg. Chem.*, **4**. 211, 1893; A. Rosenheim and T. Triantaphyllides, *Ber.*, **48**. 582, 1915.

CHAPTER LIV

VANADIUM

§ 1. The History of Vanadium

IN a letter to *l'Academie des Sciences de Paris*, A. von Humbolt [1] announced the discovery of a new metal by A. M. del Rio in 1801. The element was found in a plumbiferous mineral from Zimapan, Mexico, and it was called *erythronium*— from ἐρυθρός, red—in allusion to the red colour furnished by its salts when treated with acids. Both A. M. del Rio, and H. V. Collet-Descotils examined the mineral and announced that erythronium was nothing but a basic lead chromate ; and the idea of a new element was abandoned. In 1830, N. G. Sefström described a new element which he found in the iron ores of Taberg, Sweden, and he observed that the properties of the iron prepared from these ores were peculiar, and he traced the anomaly to the presence of a new element. He suggested that it be named **vanadium**—from *Göttin Freya Vanadin*, a Scandinavian goddess. Immediately afterwards, F. Wöhler established the identity of A. M. del Rio's erythronium with N. G. Sefström's vanadium. Thus erythronium was rediscovered, but its baptismal name was disregarded. F. Wöhler came near to the re-discovery, for he said that he had found something strange in a lead ore from Zimapan, Mexico, before N. G. Sefström's announcement of the discovery of vanadium, but he put it on one side for future examination. As J. J. Berzelius expressed it :

In the far north, there lived a goddess Vanadin, as beautiful as she was gracious. One day there came a knock at the door. The goddess was in no hurry and thought, " They can knock again " ; but there came no further knocking, for he who knocked had passed on. The goddess wondered who it could be who cared so little to be let in and ran to the window, and recognized the departing one in the person of Wöhler. Some days afterwards some one else knocked repeatedly and loud. The goddess opened the door herself to Sefström, and vanadium was discovered.

In 1831, J. J. Berzelius [2] published a memoir : *Om vanadin och dess egenskaper*, describing some properties of the new element ; but he overlooked the fact that what he supposed to be the element was really vanadous oxide, VO, and the trichloride was an oxychloride, VOCl₃. This was established by the work of H.E. Roscoe. The relationship between phosphorus and vanadium was brought out by the work of C. F. Rammelsberg,[3] and J. Schabus. The monographs on vanadium include :

G. J. Rockwell, *Index to the Literature of Vanadium*—1801–1877, *Ann. New York Acad.*, **1.** 133, 1879 ; V. von Klecki, *Analytische Chemie des Vanadins*, Hamburg, 1894 ; W. Prandtl, *Die Literatur des Vanadins*—1804–1905, Hamburg, 1906 ; F. Ephraim, *Die Vanadin und seine Verbindungen*, Stuttgart, 1904 ; H. Brearley, *A Bibliography of Steelworks Analysis*, *Chem. News*, **83.** 163, 1901 ; P. Nicolardot, *Le vanadium*, Paris, 1905.

The element *vesbium*—named after an ancient name for Vesuvius—reported by E. Bechi,[4] and A. Scacchi in some crevices in the lava flows of the 1631 Vesuvian eruption, was shown by F. Zambonini, and L. de Luise to be probably impure vanadium oxide—*vide infra*, vesbine. Similar remarks apply to M. Websky's *idunium* found in a vanadium ore from Aquadita.

714

REFERENCES.

[1] A. von Humbolt, *Ann. Mus. Nat.*, **3.** 396, 1804 ; *Gehlen's Journ.*, **2.** 695, 1804 ; *Gilbert's Ann.*, **18.** 118, 1804 ; A. M. del Rio, *ib.*, **71.** 7, 1822 ; *Schweigger's Journ.*, **62.** 324, 1831 ; *Pogg. Ann.*, **22.** 2, 1831 ; *Ann. Ciencias Nat. Madrid*, **7.** 30, 1804 ; *Ann. Mines*, (1), **4.** 499, 1819 ; H. V. Collet-Descotils, *Ann. Chim. Phys.*, (1), **53.** 260, 1805 ; N. G. Sefström, *Acad. Handl. Stockholm*, 255, 1830 ; *Schweigger's Journ.*, **62.** 316, 1831 ; *Pogg. Ann.*, **21.** 43, 1831 ; *Ann. Chim. Phys.*, (2), **46.** 105, 1831 ; *Phil. Mag.*, (2), **10.** 151, 1831 ; F. Wöhler, *Schweigger's Journ.*, **62.** 124, 1831 ; *Pogg. Ann.*, **21.** 49, 1831 ; *Ann. Chim. Phys.*, (1), **46.** 111, 1831 ; J. J. Berzelius, *ib.*, (2), **45.** 332, 1830 ; *Phil. Mag.*, (2), **10.** 151, 157, 1831. [2] J. J. Berzelius, *Acad. Handl. Stockholm*, **1**, 1831 ; *Schweigger's Journ.*, **62.** 323, 1831 ; **63.** 26, 1821 ; *Pogg. Ann.*, **22.** 1, 1831 ; *Ann. Chim. Phys.*, (1), **47.** 337, 1831 ; *Phil. Mag.*, (2), **10.** 321, 1831 ; (2), **11.** 7, 1832 ; H. E. Roscoe, *Phil. Trans.*, **158.** 1, 1868 ; **159.** 679, 1869 ; **160.** 317, 1870 ; *Proc. Roy. Soc.*, **16.** 220, 1868 ; **18.** 37, 316, 1870 ; *Journ. Chem. Soc.*, **21.** 332, 1868 ; **23.** 344, 1870 ; **24.** 23, 1871 ; *Chem. News*, **17.** 135, 1868 ; **20.** 37, 1869 ; **21.** 183, 1870 ; *Phil. Mag.*, (4), **35.** 307, 1868 ; (4), **39.** 146, 1870 ; (4), **40.** 62, 1870. [3] C. F. Rammelsberg, *Sitzber. Akad. Berlin*, 153, 1856 ; *Journ. prakt. Chem.*, (1), **68.** 244, 1856 ; *Pogg. Ann.*, **98.** 249, 1856 ; J. Schabus, *ib.*, **100.** 297, 1857. [4] M. Websky, *Sitzber. Akad. Berlin*, 661, 1884 ; A. Scacchi, *Atti Accad. Napoli*, **8.** 10, 1879 ; E. Bechi, *Atti Accad. Lincei*, (3), **3.** 403, 1879 ; F. Zambonini, *Mineralogia Vesuviana*, Napoli, 315, 1910 ; F. Zambonini and G. Carobbi, *Amer. Min.*, **12.** 1, 1927 ; *Rend. Accad. Napoli*, (3), **32.** 124, 1927 ; L. de Luise, *Notize sulla eruzione Vesuviana del 1906*, Partici, 17, 1914.

§ 2. The Occurrence of Vanadium

Elemental vanadium does not occur in nature. Vanadium was once regarded as a scarce element, actually it is amongst one of the more abundant of the minor constituents of the earth's crust, for it is more abundantly distributed than nickel, nitrogen, copper, zinc, or lead. Estimates have been made by F. W. Clarke,[1] and J. H. L. Vogt. According to F. W. Clarke and H. S. Washington, vanadium constitutes 0·038 per cent. of the ten-mile crust—zirconium constitutes 0·048 per cent. and strontium, 0·032 per cent. J. H. L. Vogt gave 0·00n per cent. According to F. W. Clarke, the igneous rocks contain an average of 0·026 per cent. V_2O_3, or 0·041 per cent. of vanadium. Analyses of 235 samples of Mississippi delta silts showed 0·02 per cent. of V_2O_3 ; and 52 samples of marine clays, 0·03 per cent. of V_2O_3. W. Vernadsky gave 0·0034 for the percentage amount and 0·01 for the atomic proportion of antimony on the earth's crust.

J. N. Lockyer[2] showed that vanadium is probably contained in the sun. This was confirmed by H. A. Rowland, A. de Gramont, F. W. Dyson, W. M. Mitchell, W. S. Adams, G. E. Hale and co-workers, and C. C. Hutchins and E. L. Holden. The presence of vanadium in meteorites has been reported by R. Apjohn,[3] and B. Hasselberg. The last-named found vanadium in thirty-one stony meteorites which he examined, but not in meteoric iron, but he could not confirm J. N. Lockyer's report that vanadium occurs in the meteoric iron of Nejed, and Obernkirchen.

The occurrence of vanadium has been discussed by C. Czudnowicz,[4] D. T. Day, L. Dieulafait, I. Domeyko, C. R. Fletcher, A. A. Hayes, M. W. Iles, C. F. Rammelsberg, H. E. Roscoe, F. M. Turner, R. Wagner, etc. The vanadium minerals include :

Sulphide ores.—*Patronite*—a vanadium sulphide with the varieties rizopatronite, and vanadiferous asphaltite containing asphaltic carbon. *Bravoite* is an iron nickel sulphide containing vanadium. *Sulvanite* has the composition $V_2S_5.3Cu_2S$.

Oxidized ores.—*Alaite*, $V_2O_5.H_2O$; *ardennite* or *dewalquite*, a complex iron aluminium vanadate-silicate, $10(Mn,Mg,Ca,Fe)O.5(Al,Fe)_2O_3.5(V,As)_2O_5.10SiO_2.6H_2O$; *roscoelite*, vanadium-mica ; *pucherite*, $BiVO_4$; *deschenite*, and *eusynchite* varieties of lead vanadate ; *vanadinite*, $Pb_4(VO_4)_3.PbCl$—with the variety *endlichite* ; *descloizite*, $(Pb,Zn)_4V_2O_8(OH)_2$—with the varieties *cuprodescloizite*, *arœoxene*, *ramirite*, *tritochorite* ; *calciovolborthite*, $(Cu,Ca)_4V_2O_8(OH)_2$; *brackebuschite*, $(Pb,Fe,Mn)_3V_2O_8.H_2O$, *psittacinite* $(Pb,Cu)_4V_2O_8(OH)_2.H_2O$; *mottramite*, $(Cu,Pb)_5V_2O_{10}.2H_2O$; *eosite*, a lead vanadate ; and molybdate ; *chileite*, a lead copper vanadate ; *vanadiolite*, a siliceous lead vanadate ; *wicklowite*, a lead vanadate ; *volborthite*, $(Cu,Ca,Ba)_3V_2O_8(OH)_3.6H_2O$; *carnotite*, $(KO)_2.U_2O_3.V_2O_5.3H_2O$; *ferganite*, $U_3(VO_4)_2.6H_2O$; *turanite*, $5CuO.V_2O_5.2H_2O$; *hewettite*, and *metahewittite*—$CaH_2V_6O_{17}.8H_2O$—*pascoite*, $Ca_2V_6O_{17}.11H_2O$—and *fernandinite*,

$CaO.V_2O_4.5V_2O_5.14H_2O$; *tyuyamunite*, uranium calcium vanadate; *minasragrite* is vanadium sulphate; *fritscheite*, a vanadiferous autunite—it is coloured red by manganese *lawrowite* or *laffroffite*, a vanadiferous pyroxene; *vanadiferous augite*; *vanadiferous gummite*; *vanadium ochre*. G. P. Tschernik[5] studied the urano-vanadium ores of the Ferghan territory, Russia; and S. Kurbatoff, in Minusinsk.

Vanadium is very widely distributed on the earth's crust, but this fact is of little economic importance. The specialized deposits, where the element is sufficiently concentrated to enable it to be extracted for commercial purposes, were classified by L. de Launay[6] somewhat as follows : (i) Segrations from basic magmas—*e.g.* in association with ilmenites and titaniferous magnetites. (ii) In veins of hydrothermal origin—*e.g.* in association with uranium ores or gold tellurides. (iii) Sulphide ores associated with hydrocarbons—*e.g.* the patronite deposit of Minasrag and the asphaltites of Peru and Nevada. (iv) The oxidized upper levels of lead and copper lodes—*e.g.* the vanadium minerals—vanadinite, descloizite, chileite, etc. (v) Deposits in sedimentary rocks—*e.g.* the carnotites of Colorado and Utah ; the French bauxites and laterites ; the minette ores of Lorraine, etc. The geographical distribution is illustrated by the map, Fig. 1.

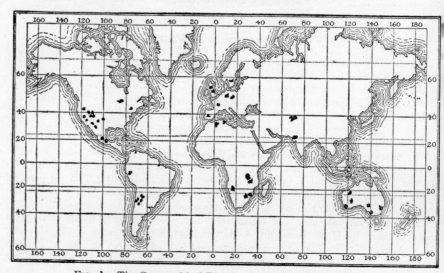

FIG. 1.—The Geographical Distribution of the Vanadium Ores.

Europe and Asia.—*In England*,[7] vanadiferous minerals occur at Mottram St. Andrew and Alderley Edge in Cheshire ; and associated with the lead-copper-cobalt deposits of Staffordshire and Shropshire. None of the deposits are of commercial value as sources of vanadium. In *Czechoslovakia*, vanadium is associated with the silver and other ores of Joachimsthal. In *Germany*,[8] vanadium has been found associated with the Kupferschiefer of Mansfield. In *Luxemberg*, and *France*,[9] vanadium is found in bauxites, shales, clays, and the minette iron ores. At Le Creusot, vanadium has been extracted commercially from the slags derived from the smelting of the volcanic ores of Mazenay, Saône-et-Loire. In *Spain*,[10] much of the world's supply was obtained from the vanadate ores of Santa Marta, Estremadura. In *Sweden*,[11] vanadium occurs in the titaniferous ores of Taberg, and in the ash of the coal in Billingen Skaraborg Län. In *Russia*,[12] vanadium ores have been reported from some parts of the Ural Mountains. Vanadium ores have been obtained from the Altai Mountains in the north of Russian *Turkestan*. One deposit is said to have been formerly worked by the Chinese for copper.

Africa.—In northern *Rhodesia*,[13] vanadium ores are found associated with the oxidized lead and zinc ores of the Broken Hill district ; some mottramite has been mined in the *Tanganyika Territory* ; and there are a number of workable deposits in the northern part of *South-West Africa* near a line running N.W. to S.E. between Uris and Berg Ankas. In the *Transvaal*, there are deposits at the Doornhock lead mine, Marico district ; at Kaffirskraal, near Ottoshoop ; and at Messina. Vanadate minerals occur in North Africa at Oran in *Algeria*, in *Tunis*, etc. There is a deposit at Ruwe in the *Congo Free State*.

America.—Vanadium ores occur in the *United States* [14] in the area comprising the states of Colorado and Utah ; and in the southern regions of the Rocky Mountain chain in the states of Arizona, and New Mexico. Some carnotite occurs near Mauch Chunk, Pennsylvania ; and vanadium ores have been reported from Baraga Co., Michigan ; Eastern Oregon ; Sangre de Cristo Range, Colorado ; San Benardine Co., California ; and Good Springs, Nevada. The asphaltites of Oklahoma and Arkansas are vanadiferous. There are numerous ores of the vanadate class associated with the deposits of lead ores in the northern and central portions of *Mexico*.[15] There is a small output of vanadium from *Argentina*.[16] It occurs in the provinces of Mendoza, San Luis, and Cordoba. Vanadium minerals have been reported from several places in the provinces of Coquimbo, *Chili*— Arqueros, and Mina Grande near Marqueza. There are deposits of vanadium in *Peru*.[17]

Australia.—Small quantities of vanadium have been reported in coal ashes, ironstones, etc., in the vicinity of Sydney, *New South Wales*.[18] Carnotite has been reported from Radium Hill, and Mount Painter ; vanadium ore has also been found in a few other localities—Leigh's Creek District, Booleroo Springs, and Apoinga—in *South Australia*. Vanadium is said to be of widespread occurrence in the greenstones, laterites, coal-ashes, and clays of *Western Australia*. Roscoelite occurs at Kalgoorlie, Niagara, Coolgardie, Menzies, and Pinyalling.

Up to the end of the nineteenth century, only a small amount of vanadium was used in commerce. A little of this was obtained from Joachimsthal, Bohemia, from the vanadiferous slags of the ironworks at Creusot, France, from Spain, and from Mexico. The discovery of the vanadium ores at Minasraga, Peru, in 1904, led to the commercial development of vanadium. These deposits are the main source of the world's supply, and this is supplemented by supplies from Colorado, and Utah. The following data are abridged from the monograph on *Vanadium Ores* by the Imperial Institute, London :

	1909	1912	1915	1918	1920	1922
Peru	392	684	804	371	1110	none
United States	—	300	569	250	462	100

where the concentrate is expressed in metric tons of metal. In 1912, Argentina produced 14, and Spain 199 metric tons of concentrate ; in 1913, 40 and 30 metric tons respectively; and in 1914, none. For 1926, Northern Rhodesia produced 171 long tons; South-West Africa Territory, 5058; and United States, 275 long tons. The price of ferrovanadium in 1909–10 was about $5.00 per pound of contained vanadium ; in 1915–16, about $2.50 ; in 1920, $6.00–$7.00 ; and in 1921, $5.00–$5.50.

The occurrence of vanadium in a number of minerals and rocks has been reported. Thus, C. Porlezza and A. Donati [19] found vanadium in the tufa of Fiuggi ; A. Donati found it in the 1916-eruption products of Stromboli ; G. Carobbi, in a boric acid fumarole on Vesuvius ; and L. Ricciardi found $0.0063-0.0081$ per cent. V_2O_3 in *lava* from Vesuvius and Etna ; and $0.0105-0.13$ per cent. in *basaltic rocks*. W. F. Hillebrand found up to 0.08 per cent. V_2O_3 in the more basic eruptive and metamorphic rocks, and vanadium was generally absent from rocks rich in silica. He supposed that *biotite, pyroxene*, and *amphibole* carry the vanadium, and he found $0.012-0.127$ per cent. of V_2O_3 in biotites and amphiboles. The vanadium is supposed to be present as V_2O_3, in isomorphous association with alumina and ferric oxide. This subject was discussed by J. H. L. Vogt. Vanadium was also found by E. Bechi to occur in many Italian rocks—basalt, *travertine, calcite*, and *sandstone*. T. Engelhardt observed up to 0.012 per cent. of V_2O_5 in some German basalts, and *dolerites*. V. Roussel found vanadium in some French basalts ; J. C. H. Mingaye, in some basalts of New South Wales ; and R. Apjohn, and E. Sonstadt, in some trap-rocks. W. F. Hillebrand found very small quantities of vanadium in a number of limestones, and sandstones ; and W. F. Hillebrand and F. L. Ransome observed that the binding agent of some Colorado sandstones—designated by C. Friedel and E. Cumenge, carnotite—is a cryptocrystalline potassium vanadatoaluminosilicate. The occurrence of vanadium in the *clays* of Gentilly has been observed by P. Beauvallet ; in the clays of Forges-les-Eaux, and Dreux, by A. Terreil ; in London clay $(0.02-0.06$ per cent. $V_2O_3)$, Sussex gault clay $(0.06-0.07$ per cent.$)$, and in a white

Belgian clay (0·03 per cent.), by T. L. Phipson ; in the Keuper clay of Bornholm, by G. Forchhammer ; the clay of Lindener Mark, by C. Huber ; in lignitic clays, by H. Seger, O. Kallauner and I. I. Hruda, and F. Stolba ; in the clays of New South Wales, by J. C. H. Mingaye. Nearly all British fireclays contain some vanadium. Naturally, also, vanadium occurs in goods made from titaniferous clays, and if such are under-fired, the vanadium is liable to work its way to the surface in wet weather, and it then produces a yellowish-green scum of alkali vanadate. This was observed by H. Seger, F. Stolba, and J. C. H. Mingaye.

Vanadium has been reported in many *iron ores* of the magnetite type ; and J. Walz found the largest proportion in the titaniferous ores. F. J. Pope obtained between 0·23 and 0·63 per cent. V_2O_5 in some titaniferous magnetites. Many secondary iron ores, like limonite (*q.v.*), contain vanadium. This was established by the observations of C. Bödeker, T. Bodemann, R. Böttger, F. W. Daw, I. Deck, H. St. C. Deville, J. Fritzsche, R. J. Hodges, L. l'Hôte, C. Kersten, A. Müller, T. L. Phipson, E. Riley, N. G. Sefström, R. von Seth, A. Schultz, C. M. Stillwell, L. F. Svanberg, and A. Terreil. As a consequence of the presence of vanadium in iron ores, vanadium has also been frequently found in *raw iron* as well as in the *slag* from blast furnaces—*e.g.*, by L. Blum, I. Deck, J. Fritzsche, C. Kersten, A. Müllers E. Riley, A. Schrötter, N. G. Sefström, R. von Seth, A. Terreil, and G. Witz and, F. Osmond. C. Kersten found vanadium to be present in the *copper schists* of Mansfield ; while H. E. Roscoe, P. Krusch, D. J. Planer, C. Czudnowicz, and H. Credner found the element present in other cupriferous ores. A. R. Alderman observed up to 0·84 per cent. V_2O_5 in some titaniferous ores of South Australia.

H. St. C. Deville, L. l'Hôte, and L. Dieulafait reported vanadium to be present in *bauxite* ; H. St. C. Deville, in *cerite* ; A. Breithaupt and F. W. Fritzsche, in *conichalcite* ; C. F. Rammelsberg, in *crednerite* ; H. St. C. Deville, in *cryolite* ; A. Jorissen, in *delvauxite* ; E. S. Larsen and W. F. Hunt, in *ægirite* ; A. E. Fersman, in *vanadiolaumontite* ; C. Bergmann, in *ehlite* ; C. Kersten, in *gummite* ; G. A. Koenig, in *garnet* ; L. F. Svanberg, in *hydrophite* ; F. Wöhler, C. F. Rammelsberg, and C. Czudnowicz, in a yellow *lead ore* ; W. F. Hillebrand, in *mica* ; I. Domeyko, N. von Kokscharoff, and W. P. Blake, in *mimetesite*, and in *pyromorphite* ; A. Patera, C. Kersten, C. von Hauer, L. l'Hôte, H. D. A. Ficinus, F. Wöhler, L. F. Svansberg, C. Giseke, and H. C. Bolton, in *pitchblende, uraninite*, and other *uranium ores* ; C. Huber, H. Laspeyres, and C. F. Rammelsberg, in *psilomelane* ; C. F. Naumann, in *pyrolusite* ; H. St. C. Deville, O. F. von der Pfordten, C. B. Hasselberg, and, W. B. Giles, in *rutile* ; C. Palache and E. V. Shannon, in *higginsite* ; G. A. Koenig, in *schorlomite* ; H. D. A. Ficinus, and A. Vogel, in *serpentine* ; E. F. Smith and F. F. Exner, in *woframite* ; J. L. Smith, C. F. Rammelsberg, and F. Wöhler, in *wulfenite* ; R. Klemm, in *zircon* ; and F. Zambonini, in *vesbine*.

Vanadium has been reported to occur in the ash or flue-dust of numerous *lignites* and *coals* by C. Baskerville, H. Ramage, A. Jorissen, J. Kyle, T. y Meca, J. C. H. Mingaye, and A. Mourlot ; and the occurrence of vanadium in Mexican *petroleum* was observed by J. E. Hackford, E. de Golyer ; in Egyptian oil, by W. A. Guthrie ; and in Persian petroleum, by A. E. Dunstan. The Standard Development Co. extracted vanadium from petroleum ash. According to E. S. Porter, the fact that vanadium is found in peat, lignite, and coal in small percentages, indicates that the vanadium was a constituent of the plant life from which these deposits originated ; and this view is supported by the presence of vanadium in the ashes of many plants. On the other hand, in the asphaltitic deposits of Peru, where comparatively high percentages of vanadium occur, it is probable that the element has been concentrated by some means other than the inspissation of petroleum (*vide infra*). A. A. Hayes, and G. Witz and F. Osmond found vanadium occurring in certain *natural waters*. A. A. Bado observed it in the subterranean waters of Bellville, Cordova, Argentine. E. Demarçay found vanadium in the ashes of some *plants*—*e.g.* horn-beam, poplar, vine, oak, silver fir, and Scotch fir. E. O. von Lippmann, and A. von Wachtfl found vanadium in beet vinasse, or in potassium hydroxide derived therefrom; E. F. Smith also found it in commercial potassium hydroxide; A. Baumgarten, T. E. Thorpe, A. Scheurer-Kestner, E. Donath, and H. L. Robinson found it in commercial sodium hydroxide; C. F. Rammelsberg, in the mother-liquors of a soda-works; A. Baumgarten, in alkali phosphate; H. C. Bolton, in uranium oxide.

The vanadium cycle in nature.—Water charged with atmospheric gases can dissolve vanadium in soluble alkali vanadates; if such water comes in contact with natural ores of lead—galena, anglesite, cerussite—lead vanadate will be formed, and such an ore is the chief natural source of vanadium. According to W. Lindgren,[20] during the process of the weathering of rocks and ores, a part of the vanadium passes into soln., and becomes concentrated in the limonite like phosphorus, but in smaller proportions. This is illustrated by the fact that bog-iron ores usually contain vanadium. Much of the vanadium is concentrated in sediments as shown by the wide distribution of vanadium in many sandstones. Vanadium also accumulates in silts and muds more than it does in the coarser sediments. This is illustrated by the common occurrence of vanadium in clays. It may be carried along with alumina in colloidal suspensions. Finally, a small proportion of vanadium is taken into soln. by surface waters, probably as calcium vanadate, and is carried to the sea. While vanadium has not been reported as a constituent of sea-water, it seems to be there, for it is absorbed from this source by holothurians and ascidians as a substitute for copper or phosphorus in their blood. After the death of the animal, the vanadium returns to the sea-water, or becomes buried in the sediments. It is not unlikely that vanadium is concentrated in sea-water by other animals.

W. Lindgren continued : " It is strongly suspected that plants use vanadium as a substitute for phosphorus. The ashes of plants, coals, and asphaltic substances in many localities contain vanadium. This element seems to have been gradually concentrated during the formation of asphaltum. Coaly substances may precipitate vanadium from meteoric waters, but it is more probable that vanadium formed part of the original organism from which asphaltum is derived. Bituminous shales often contain vanadium. The mesozoic sediments of Peru represented by black shales, contain 0·12–0·41 per cent. When sedimentary rocks containing vanadium are percolated by underground waters, at considerable depths, some of the element passes into soln. and is again precipitated as vanadium mica—roscoelite—or potassium uranium vanadate—carnotite. The ores are formed later than the beds, and are characterized by a very strange assortment of elements, among which, besides the two already mentioned, are copper, lead, silver, barium, chromium, nickel, molybdenum, and selenium. Igneous rocks are absent. Thus far no entirely satisfactory explanation of the mode of origin of these deposits has been formulated. Most of the elements just referred to are such as are known to be relatively concentrated in sediments. To sum up, it is believed that vanadium was first moderately conc. in fine sediments, and that a second conc. has been effected by biochemical processes followed by a third conc. by meteoric waters and representation at suitable places. It is held that the second conc. and perhaps the third resulted in finely disseminated ' patronite,' owing to the combination of vanadium with sulphur likewise of organic origin. Still later processes of alteration resulted in such minerals as carnotite and roscoelite." The formation of vanadium minerals in nature has been also discussed by L. Dieulafait, J. H. L. Vogt, F. B. Notestein, and A. Ditte.

REFERENCES.

1 F. W. Clarke and H. S. Washington, *The Composition of the Earth's Crust*, Washington, 1924; *Proc. Nat. Acad. Science*, 8. 108, 1922; J. H. L. Vogt, *Zeit. prakt. Geol.*, 6. 225, 314, 377, 413, 1898; 7. 10, 274, 1899; F. W. Clarke, *The Data of Geochemistry*, Washington, 29, 1924; W. Vernadsky, *Centr. Min.*, 758, 1912; *Essai de mineralogie descriptive*, St. Petersburg, 1. 121, 740, 1914; *Geochimie*, Paris, 16, 1924; A. E. Fersman, *Bull. Acad. St. Petersburg*, (6), 6. 367, 1912.

¹ J. N. Lockyer, *Proc. Roy. Soc.*, 27. 49, 279, 1878 ; C. C. Hutchins and E. L. Holden, *Phil. Mag.*, (5), 24. 325, 1887 ; H. A. Rowland, *Johns Hopkins Univ. Circ.*, 85, 1891 ; *Amer. Journ. Science*, (3), 41. 243, 1891 ; *Chem. News*, 63. 133, 1891 ; W. M. Mitchell, *Astrophys. Journ.*, 22. 4, 1905 ; W. S. Adams, *ib.*, 30. 86, 1909 ; G. E. Hale, W. S. Adams, and A. G. Gale, *ib.*, 24. 185, 1906 ; F. W. Dyson, *Phil. Trans.*, 206. A, 403, 1906 ; A. de Gramont, *Compt. Rend.*, 150. 37, 1910.
³ R. Apjohn, *Journ. Chem. Soc.*, 27. 104, 1874 ; B. Hasselberg, *Oefvers. Akad. Förh.*, 56. 131, 1899 ; J. N. Lockyer, *Phil. Trans.*, 185. 1023, 1894.
⁴ C. Czudnowicz, *Pogg. Ann.*, 120. 17, 1863 ; D. T. Day, *Ann. Rep. U.S. Geol. Sur.*, 21. 314, 1900 ; 23. 99, 1902 ; 24. 125, 1903 ; L. Dieulafait, *Rev. Scient.*, (3), 5. 613, 1883 ; C. R. Fletcher, *Berg. Hütt. Ztg.*, 46. 231, 1887 ; *Eng. Min. Journ.*, 43. 291, 1887 ; M. W. Iles, *Amer. Journ. Science*, (3), 23. 381, 1882 ; H. E. Roscoe, *Liebig's Ann. Suppl.*, 6. 77, 1868 ; *Phil. Trans.*, 158. 1, 1868 ; 160. 317, 1870 ; F. M. Turner, *Canadian Min. Journ.*, 36. 457, 1915 ; Anon., *Vanadium Ores*, London, 1924 ; R. Wagner, *Jahresb. Chem. Tech.*, 5. 134, 1859 ; C. F. Rammelsberg, *Sitzber. Akad. Berlin*, 53, 1864 ; 652, 1880 ; *Ber.*, 1. 158, 1868 ; I. Domeyko, *Ann. Mines*, (7), 19. 333, 1881 ; A. A. Hayes, *Proc. Amer. Assoc. Boston*, 10. 294, 1875 ; E. Prost, *Rev. Univ. Mines*, 10. 153, 1921 ; F. W. Clarke, *Bull. U.S. Geol. Sur.*, 330, 1908.
⁵ G. P. Tschernik, *Bull. Acad. Russ.*, 16. 505, 1922 ; S. Kurbatoff, *ib.*, 19. 315, 1925.
⁶ L. de Launay, *Traité de métallogénie-gites minéraux et metallifères*, Paris, 713, 1913 ; Anon., *Vanadium Ores*, London, 1924.
⁷ N. Collie, *Journ. Chem. Soc.*, 55. 91, 1889 ; H. S. Maskelyne and W. Flight, *ib.*, 25. 1053, 1872 ; R. P. Greg and W. G. Lettsom, *Manual of the Mineralogy of Great Britain and Ireland*, London, 409, 1838 ; G. C. Greenwell, *Proc. South Wales Inst. Eng.*, 4. 44, 1866 ; E. Hull and A. H. Green, *The Geology of the Country around Stockport, Macclesfield, Congleton, and Leek*, London, 39, 1866 ; E. Hull, *Geol. Mag.*, (1), 1. 65, 1864 ; G. V. Wilson, *The Lead, Zinc, Copper, and Nickel Ores of Scotland*, London, 16, 19, 1921 ; J. A. Phillips, *A Treatise on Ore Deposits*, London, 1896 ; L. Thompson, *Journ. Arts Sciences*, 16. 260, 1862.
⁸ W. Lindgren, *Econ. Geol.*, 6. 568, 1911 ; R. Schreiter, *Centr. Min.*, 214, 242, 1925.
⁹ G. Witz and F. Osmond, *Compt. Rend.*, 95. 42, 1882 ; L. von Blum. *Stahl Eisen*, 35. 14, 1915.
¹⁰ T. F. V. Curran, *Min. Ind.*, 19. 672, 1910 ; J. K. Smith, *Trans. Amer. Inst. Min. Eng.*, 38. 698, 1908.
¹¹ G. Nordenström, *Geol. För. Förh. Stockholm*, 4. 209, 1879 ; T. Nordström, *ib.*, 4. 267, 1879 ; Anon., *Min. Resources U.S. Geol. Sur.*, i, 959, 1917.
¹² H. Hess, *Bull. Acad. St. Petersburg*, (6), 4. 21, 1838 ; G. Rose, *Pogg. Ann.*, 29. 455, 1833 ; R. Hermann, *Bull. Soc. Moscow*, 42. 234, 1869 ; *Journ. prakt. Chem.*, (2), 1. 442, 1870 ; F. L. Hess, *Min. Resources U.S. Geol. Sur.*, i, 1031, 1912 ; N. von Kokscharoff, *Bull. Acad. St. Petersburg*, (7), 11. 78, 1867 ; *Materialien zur Mineralogie Russlands*, St. Petersburg, 4. 281, 1862 ; 5. 109, 1866 ; Z. S. Kolovrot-Tschervinsky, *Comm. Trav. Tech. Russ.*, 5. 108, 1921 ; S. M. Kurbatoff, *Bull. Acad. Russ.*, 19. 315, 1925.
¹³ G. D. Hubbard, *Eng. Min. Journ.*, 95. 1297, 1913 ; Anon., *Bull. Imp. Inst.*, 16. 466, 1918 ; *South African Min. and Eng. Journ.*, 107, 1920 ; P. A. Wagner and B. de C. Marchand, *ib.*, 280, 1920 ; *Trans. Geol. Soc. South Africa*, 23. 59, 1920 ; P. A. Wagner, *Mem. Union South Africa, Geol. Sur.*, 7. 89, 1916 ; *Journ. South African Ind.*, 2. 911, 1921 ; M. Ferguson and P. A. Wagner, *ib.*, 3. 1058, 1920 ; L. J. Spencer, *Min. Mag.*, 15. 1, 1908.
¹⁴ D. F. Hewitt, *Eng. Min. Journ.*, 115. 232, 1923 ; T. F. V. Curran, *ib.*, 96. 1123, 1165, 1913 ; B. Burwell, *ib.*, 110. 755, 1920 ; P. A. Larsh, *ib.*, 92. 118, 1911 ; 96. 1103, 1913 ; F. B. Notestein, *Econ. Geol.*, 13. 50, 1918 ; 9. 675, 1914 ; *Min. Resources U.S. Geol. Sur.*, i, 943, 1914 ; i, 956, 1917 ; *Bull. U.S. Geol. Sur.*, 530, 1911 ; W. F. Hillebrand and F. L. Ransome, *Amer. Journ. Science*, (4), 10. 120, 1900 ; *Bull. U.S. Geol. Sur.*, 262, 1905 ; J. M. Bontwell, *ib.*, 260, 1905 ; H. S. Gale, *ib.*, 315, 340, 1907 ; K. L. Kithil and J. A. Davis, *ib.*, 103, 1917 ; R. B. Moore and K. L. Kithil, *Bull. U.S. Bur. Mines*, 70, 1913 ; K. L. Kithil and J. A. Davis, *ib.*, 103, 1917 ; F. W. Horton, *ib.*, 111, 1916 ; H. Fleck and W. G. Haldane, *Rep. State Bur. Mines Colorado*, 47, 1906 ; E. T. Wherry, *Amer. Journ. Science*, (4), 33. 574, 1912 ; R. C. Wells, *ib.*, (4), 36. 636, 1913 ; J. Blake, *Proc. Californian Acad.*, 6. 150, 1875 ; *Amer. Journ. Science*, (3), 12. 31, 1876 ; F. A. Genth, *ib.*, (3), 12. 32, 1876 ; *Proc. Amer. Phil. Soc.*, 17. 119, 1878 ; R. C. Coffin, *Radium, Uranium, and Vanadium Deposits of Southwestern Colorado*, Denver, 1921 ; J. E. Teschemacker, *Amer. Journ. Science*, (2), 11. 233, 1851 ; J. L. Smith, *ib.*, (2), 19. 127, 1855 ; (2), 20. 245, 1855 ; M. A. Allen and G. M. Butler, *Bull. Univ. Arizona*, 115, 1921 ; S. Fischer, *Min. Ind.*, 23. 762, 1914 ; R. M. Keeney, *ib.*, 24. 707, 1915 ; G. W. McGhee, *Min. Eng. Journ.*, 41. 1088, 1914.
¹⁵ G. de Caballero, *Mem. Soc. Cient. Antono Alzate*, 20. 87, 1902 ; J. G. Aguilera, *Bol. Inst. geol. Mexico*, 11, 1898 ; T. F. V. Curran, *Eng. Min. Journ.*, 93. 1093, 1912 ; T. Kirby, *Min. Ind.*, 18. 696, 1909 ; H. Fleck, *Proc. Colorado Scient. Soc.*, 11. 103, 1916 ; B. Leatherbee, *Min. World*, 33. 799, 1910.
¹⁶ B. L. Miller and J. T. Singewald, *Mineral Deposits of South Africa*, New York, 1909 ; W. Bodenbinder, *Zeit. prakt. geol.*, 9. 51, 1901 ; E. Longobard and N. Gamus, *Anal. Soc. Cient. Argentina*, 283, 1911 ; M. Websky, *Sitzber. Akad. Berlin*, 799, 1880 ; *Bol. Acad. Cient. Cordoba*, 5. 441, 1883.
¹⁷ D. F. Hewitt, *Trans. Amer. Ind. Min. Eng.*, 40. 274, 1910 ; J. G. Baragwanath, *Eng.*

VANADIUM

721

in. Journ., 111. 778, 1921 ; J. T. Singewald and B. L. Miller, *ib.*, 102. 583, 1916 ; E. I. Duenas
ıd B. L. Miller, *Bol. Cuerpo Eng. Mines Peru*, 39, 1906 ; C. J. Stark, *Iron Trade Rev.*, 57.
▸1. 812, 1916.
    [18] P. Krusch, *Zeit. prakt. geol.*, 9. 215, 1901 ; H. Y. L. Brown, *Record. Dept. Mines South
ustralia*, 362, 1908 ; E. S. Simpson, *Bull. Geol. Sur. West Australia*, 59, 1914 ; L. K. Ward,
ev. Min. Operations, South Australia, 17, 1912 ; 19, 1913 ; 20, 1914.
    [19] L. Ricciardi, *Sulla diffusione del vanadio nel regniominerale e vegetable*, Roma, 1883 ;
nzz. Chim. Ital., 13. 259, 1883 ; *Atti Accad. Gioenia Catania*, (3), 17. 161, 1883 ; E. Bechi,
tti Accad. Lincei, (3), 3. 403, 1879 ; E. Sonstadt, *Chem. News*, 26. 214, 1874 ; R. Apjohn, *ib.*,
6. 183, 1872 ; R. J. Hodges, *Chem. News*, 26. 238, 1872 ; F. W. Daw, *ib.*, 76. 145, 1897 ; J. Kyle,
., 66. 211, 1892 ; H. L. Robinson, *ib.*, 70. 199, 1894 ; W. B. Giles, *ib.*, 76. 137, 1897 ; T. L. Phip-
ɔn, *ib.*, 7. 210, 1863 ; *Compt. Rend.*, 57. 152, 1863 ; T. Engelbach, *Liebig's Ann.*, 135. 123,
865 ; C. Huber, *ib.*, 130. 365, 1864 ; A. Müller, *Analysen der auf der Carlshütt. geschmolzen
isensteine, der dar aus gewonnen Eisen und der Schlacken*, Göttingen, 1852 ; *Journ. prakt. Chem.*,
), 57. 124, 1852 ; (1), 60. 63, 1853 ; *Liebig's Ann.*, 86. 127, 1853 ; *Journ. prakt. Chem.*, (1), 57.
24, 1852 ; H. Laspeyres, *ib.*, (2), 13. 26, 1876 ; A. Vogel, *ib.*, (1), 30. 474, 1843 ; H. D. A. Ficinus,
., (1), 26. 35, 1842 ; (1), 29. 491, 1843 ; R. Böttger, *ib.*, (1), 90. 33, 1863 ; *Jahresb. phys. Ver.
rankfurt a. M.*, 18, 1872 ; J. C. H. Mingaye, *Records Geol. Sur. New South Wales*, 7. 217, 1903 ;
ɔurn. Chem. Soc.*, 86. 420, 1904 ; T. E. Thorpe, *ib.*, 25. 1053, 1872 ; E. Riley, *ib.*, 17. 21, 1864 ;
hem. News, 8. 261, 277, 1863 ; E. F. Smith, *ib.*, 61. 20, 1890 ; *Journ. Franklin Inst.*, 128. 490,
889 ; V. Roussel, *Compt. Rend.*, 77. 1102, 1873 ; C. Friedel and E. Cumenge, *ib.*, 128. 522, 1899 ;
. Beauvallet, *ib.*, 49. 301, 1859 ; A. Terreil, *ib.*, 51. 94, 1860 ; 84. 497, 1877 ; L. Dieulafait,
>., 93. 804, 1881 ; A. Mourlot, *ib.*, 117. 546, 1893 ; H. E. Roscoe, *Phil. Trans.*, 158. 1, 1868 ;
roc. Roy. Soc., 16. 220. 1868 ; *Chem. News*, 17. 135, 1868 ; *Journ. Chem. Soc.*, 21. 322, 1868 ;
J. F. Hillebrand, *Journ. Amer. Chem. Soc.*, 20. 461, 1898 ; *Amer. Journ. Science*, (4), 6. 209,
898 ; E. S. Larsen and W. F. Hunt, *ib.*, (4), 36. 289, 1913 ; C. Porlezza and A. Donati, *Ann.
him. Applicata*, 16. 457, 1926 ; A. Donati, *ib.*, 16. 475, 1926 ; H. W. Turner, W. F. Hillebrand,
I. N. Stokes, and W. Valentine, *ib.*, (4), 7. 294, 1899 ; W. F. Hillebrand and F. L. Ransome,
>., (4), 10. 120, 1900 ; J. L. Smith, *ib.*, (2), 20. 245, 1855 ; J. H. L. Vogt, *Zeit. prakt. Geol.*,
. 325, 1898 ; 7. 274, 1899 ; P. Krusch, *ib.*, 27. 76, 1919 ; G. Forchhammer, *Oefvers. Vid.
elsk. Skr.*, 88, 1864 ; R. von Seth, *Jernkont. Ann.*, 108. 561, 1924 ; H. Seger, *Tonind. Ztg.*,
. 367, 423, 1877 ; O. Kallauner and I. I. Hruda, *Sprech.*, 55. 333, 345, 1922 ; F. Stolba,
Berg. Hütt. Ztg.*, 55. 325, 1896 ; T. y Meca, *ib.*, 53. 358, 1895 ; F. J. Pope, *ib.*, 58. 556, 1899 ;
rans. Amer. Inst. Min. Eng.*, 29. 372, 1899 ; J. Walz, *Amer. Chemist*, 6. 453, 1876 ;
. M. Stillwell, *ib.*, 7. 41, 1877 ; H. C. Bolton, *ib.*, 5. 363, 1875 ; A. Schultz, *Pharm. Centr.*,
1), 13. 372, 1842 ; N. G. Sefström, *Pogg. Ann.*, 21. 43, 1831 ; C. Czudnowicz, *ib.*, 120. 17,
863 ; T. Bodemann, *ib.*, 55. 633, 1842 ; C. Kersten, *Journ. prakt. Chem.*, (1), 29. 333, 1843 ;
ogg. Ann., 51. 539, 1840 ; 53. 385, 1841 ; 59. 121, 1843 ; A. Schrötter, *ib.*, 46. 311, 1839 ;
*. Wöhler, *ib.*, 54. 600, 1841 ; *Liebig's Ann.*, 102. 383, 1857 ; L. F. Svanberg, *Svenska Acad.
landl.*, 184, 1839 ; C. B. Hasselberg, *Bihang Svenska Akad. Handl.*, 22. 7, 1897 ; 23. 3, 1897 ;
efvers. Akad. Handl., 56. 131, 1899 ; I. Deck, *Chem. Gaz.*, 6. 298, 1848 ; J. Fritzsche, *Bull.
Acad. St. Petersburg*, (2), 9. 195, 1851 ; A. Breithaupt and F. W. Fritzsche, *Pogg. Ann.*, 77. 139,
849 ; L. Blum, *Stahl Eisen*, 20. 393, 1900 ; E. S. Porter, *Mining Met.*, 5. 133, 1924 ; C. Bödeker,
iebig's Ann.*, 94. 355, 1855 ; O. F. von der Pfordten, *ib.*, 237. 202, 1887 ; C. Giseke, *Arch. Pharm.
2), 69. 150, 1852 ; *Journ. prakt. Chem.*, (1), 55. 445, 1852 ; G. Witz and F. Osmond, *Bull. Soc.
him.*, (2), 45. 309, 1886 ; *Compt. Rend.*, 95. 42, 1882 ; E. Demarçay, *ib.*, 130. 91, 1900 ; H. St. C.
Deville, *ib.*, 49. 210, 1859 ; *Ann. Chim. Phys.*, (3), 61. 309, 1861 ; L. l'Hôte, *ib.*, (6), 22. 409,
891 ; C. von Hauer, *Sitzber. Akad. Wien*, 20. 37, 1856 ; 21. 333, 1856 ; C. F. Naumann, *Ele-
nente der Mineralogie*, Leipzig, 559, 1874 ; P. Krusch, *Zeit. prakt. Geol.*, 27. 76, 1919 ; C. Basker-
ille, *Journ. Amer. Chem. Soc.*, 21. 706, 1899 ; E. F. Smith and F. F. Exner, *ib.*, 24. 573, 1902;
A. Jorissen, *Bull. Acad. Belg.*, 178, 1905 ; *Am. Soc. Géol. Belg.*, 6. 39, 1879 ; F. Wöhler, *Liebig's
Inn.*, 102. 383, 1856 ; H. Ramage, *Nature*, 119. 783, 1927 ; A. von Wachtfl, *Repert. Anal.
:hem.*, 3. 170, 1883 ; E. de Golyer, *Econ. Geol.*, 19. 550, 1924 ; E. O. von Lippmann, *Ber.*, 21.
492, 1888 ; C. Palache and E. V. Shannon, *Amer. Min.*, 5. 155, 1920 ; A. A. Hayes, *Proc.
Imer. Acad. Boston*, 10. 298, 1875 ; A. E. Fersman, *Trav. Musée Geol. Min. Pierre le Grand,
2), 2. 311, 1922 ; F. Zambonini, *Amer. Min.*, 12. 1, 1927 ; A. R. Alderman, *Proc. Roy. Soc. S.
Iustralia*, 49. 88, 1925 ; D. J. Planer, *Neues Jahrb. Min.*, 220, 1850 ; C. Bergmann, *ib.*, 191,
858 ; H. Credner, *ib.*, 1, 1847 ; C. F. Rammelsberg, *Sitzber. Akad. Berlin*, 33, 681, 1864 ;
Iandbuch der Mineralchemie*, Leipzig, 179, 181, 1860 ; 2. 283, 1875 ; A. Baumgarten, *Ueber
las Vorkommen des Vanadins in dem Aetznatron des Handels*, Göttingen, 1865 ; A. Scheurer-
Kestner, *Bull. Soc. Chim.*, (2), 39. 412, 1863 ; J. E. Hackford, *Journ. Inst. Pet. Tech.*, 8. 193,
.923 ; A. E. Dunstan, *ib.*, 9. 235, 1923 ; W. A. Guthrie, 9. 212, 1923 ; E. Donath, *Dingler's
Journ.*, 235. 407, 1880 ; 240. 318, 1881 ; A. Patera, *ib.*, 141. 372, 1856 ; *Oesterr. Zeit. Berg.
Iütt.*, 4. 244, 1856 ; G. A. Koenig, *Proc. Acad. Philadelphia*, 36, 1876 ; The Standard Development Co., *U.S. Pat. No.* 1563061, 1925 ; I. Domeyko, *Ann. Mines*, (4), 14. 145, 1848 ;
A. A. Bado, *Bol. Acad. Nac. Ciencias Cordoba*, 23. 85, 1918 ; N. von Kokscharoff, *Materialien
ır Mineralogie Russlands*, St. Petersburg, 3. 42, 1858 ; W. P. Blake, *Min. Scient. Press.*, 43.
3, 1881 ; G. Carobbi, *Atti Accad. Lincei*, (6), 4. ii, 306, 1926 ; R. Klemm, *Centr. Min.*, 267.
927.
    [20] W. Lindgren, *Econ. Geol.*, 18. 430, 1923 ; B. F. Notestein, *ib.*, 13. 50, 1918 ; L. Dieulafait.
VOL. IX. 3 A

Rev. Scient., (3), 5. 613, 1883 ; J. H. L. Vogt, Zeit. prakt. Geol., 6. 325, 1898 ; 7. 274, 1899
A. Ditte, Compt. Rend., 138. 1303, 1904.

§ 3. The Extraction of Vanadium

Vanadium is extracted from the sulphide ores typified by patronite ; from th
silicates typified by roscoelite ; from uranium-vanadium ores typified by carnotite
and from vanadate ores typified by descloizite and volborthite.   It can also b
extracted from slags and other substances—clays, iron ores, etc.   Vanadium i
also produced as an alloy with iron—ferrovanadium.

The extraction of vanadium salts as ammonium vanadate, etc.—In the we
processes for the extraction of vanadic oxide from minerals opened up by nitric aci
the soln. is treated with aq. ammonia, and ammonium sulphide.   Lead sulphid
is precipitated, and the dark red filtrate gives a precipitate of vanadium sulphid
when treated with acids.   The sulphide is roasted in air, fused with potassiun
nitrate, and the aq. soln. of potassium vanadate is treated with ammonium chloride
and the ammonium vanadate crystallizes out.   J. F. W. Johnston [1] dissolve
vanadinite in nitric acid, precipitated the lead and arsenic by hydrogen sulphide
evaporated the filtrate to dryness ; and boiled the residue with a sat. soln. o
ammonium carbonate.   On cooling the liquid, he obtained crystals of ammoniun
vanadate which were purified by recrystallization.   F. Wöhler treated vanadinit
with fuming hydrochloric acid and alcohol ; evaporated the filtrate from lea
chloride with an excess of acid ; decomposed the product with an excess of sodiun
hydroxide ; oxidized the liquid with chlorine ; and precipitated ammoniun
vanadate by the addition of ammonium chloride.

A number of dry processes have been employed.   In L. l'Hôte's process, th
powdered mineral was mixed with four times its weight of lamp-black, made into ɛ
pasty mass with oil, heated, and then exposed at 300° to a current of chlorine
Vanadium oxychloride distils off at 210°, and is collected in a suitable receiver
H. Herrenschmidt fused a mixture of vanadinite with sodium carbonate to conver
all the vanadium into sodium vanadate by the oxidizing action of the air
H. P. Smith melted the vanadinite with potassium nitrate ; the aq. extract wa
warmed with steam, while iron plates were immersed in the liquid.   The mixed iror
and vanadium hydroxides were precipitated from the dark green liquid by mean
of soda-lye, and the washed precipitate used for the manufacture of ferro-vanadium
The sodium vanadate was washed out with boiling water and converted into vanadi
acid by treatment with sulphuric acid.

To extract vanadium from clays, slags, etc., the powdered product is opened uɪ
by fusion in air with potassium nitrate (F. Wöhler); sodium nitrate (G. Forch
hammer); a mixture of potassium nitrate and sodium hydroxide (R. Böttger); ɛ
mixture of potassium nitrate and sodium carbonate (N G. Sefström, J. J. Berzelius
F. Wöhler, C. Kersten, and A. Patera); sodium chloride and sulphuric aci
(H. T. Koenig); or a mixture of alkali and a sulphide (Electrometallurgica
Co.).   E. Classen treated powdered magnetite with sulphuric acid and drove of
the excess of acid by heat ; the residue was fused with six times its weight o
sodium carbonate alone or in admixture with potassium nitrate.   This treat
ment converts the vanadium into soluble alkali vanadate.   A. Wittig used ɛ
mixture of sulphuric acid and sulphurous acid or a sulphite.   N. G. Sefströn
thoroughly extracted the mass with boiling water, and neutralized the liquor witl
nitric acid free from nitrites to avoid reducing the vanadic acid.   The silica iɛ
removed by filtration.   If the silica has a red colour, it is freed from vanadium bɟ
digestion with ammonia and washing with water.   The filtrate is treated witl
lead nitrate or acetate.   The precipitated lead vanadate is washed ; and repeatedlɟ
agitated with conc. hydrochloric acid ; mixed with alcohol ; and heated for som
hours nearly to the b.p. of the alcohol.   The blue filtered liquid is evaporated t
dryness, dissolved in water, mixed with nitric acid, sat. with potassium carbonate

evaporated to dryness, and fused. The cold product is dissolved in the smallest possible quantity of water; and the vanadic acid precipitated as ammonium vanadate by the addition of solid ammonium chloride. The phosphoric acid is removed by washing this salt with a soln. of ammonium chloride, and then with alcohol. J. J. Berzelius said that silica is removed by treating the soln. in sulphuric acid with hydrofluoric acid, evaporating the mixture to dryness, etc. B. W. Gerland showed that it is easy to remove soda from the ammonium vanadate, but potash is retained very tenaciously. Modifications of the process for iron ores and slags were used by J. J. Berzelius, B. P. F. Kjellberg, K. B. Thews, J. A. Norblad, R. von Seth, H. Nagell, E. Petersen, G. Witz and F. Osmond, and L. Blum. F. L. Hahn and W. Franke heated at 250°–300° a vanadate under press. with carbon tetrachloride and extracted the product with acids. J. E. Conley described the extraction of vanadium from descloizite and vanadinite.

In Peru, patronite is mixed with the necessary fluxes and roasted in a reverberatory furnace. The heavy metals form a matte, and the vanadium and gangue pass into the slag. The slag is granulated in water, dried, and reduced to ferrovanadium in a blast furnace. In general, the vanadates are fused with sodium salts when the vanadium passes into the slag as sodium vanadate, while the lead, copper, or zinc separates as metals. The slag is crushed, mixed with sulphuric acid, and baked so as to form a dry cake. This is crushed, leached with boiling water, and the soln. of vanadium sulphate is evaporated. This is roasted and reduced to ferrovanadium by the thermite process. J. E. Conley described a process for the recovery of vanadium from lead vanadate, etc. The extraction of vanadium from iron slags was described by R. H. von Seth and G. Hult; from iron and copper slags, by J. Fritzsche, E. Riley, R. H. von Seth, and C. Kersten; from ferruginous and calcareous bauxites, by H. St. C. Deville, and E. E. Dutt; from tufa, lava, and granite, by C. Porlezza and A. Donati; from clays, by P. Beauvallet, H. St. C. Deville, H. A. Doermer, and G. Forchhammer; from ilmenite, by the Radium and Rare Earths Treatment Co.; from sandstone, by H. E. Roscoe; and from petroleum residues, by A. Oberle. B. D. Saklatwalla roasted roscoelite with salt and pyrites; leached the product with hot water; and added ferrous sulphate to the cold soln. to precipitate the vanadium as iron vanadate. B. P. F. Kjellberg described a process for recovering vanadium from titaniferous ores; and H. G. C. Fairbanks, for the purification of vanadates.

The extraction of vanadium from pitchblende, and carnotite was described by F. Wöhler, C. Giseke, W. F. Bleecker, J. E. Conley, C. von Hauer, A. Safarik, A. Patera, A. T. Elliott, K. B. Thews, K. B. Thews and F. J. Heinle, C. Lallemand, and J. Ohly. G. Gin decomposed carnotite by fusion with potassium hydrosulphate. After soln. in water, concentration, and cooling, the uranium and vanadium separate as the double potassium sulphate. On treatment with zinc the vanadium is reduced, and is then precipitated by neutralization with ammonia and addition of ammonium carbonate; the uranium is obtained on boiling the filtrate. Another method is based on heating to redness in the vapour of ferric chloride, when vanadyl chloride $VOCl_3$, which is readily volatile, is formed. B. D. Saklatwalla boiled the ore with dil. sulphuric acid (1 : 1), and added ammonium persulphate to the soln. After a prolonged boiling, vanadium separates as a red hydroxide, which forms the pentoxide when heated. H. Fleck and W. G. Haldane patented a method in which the crushed ore is agitated with 15–20 per cent. sulphuric acid, and the acidic soln. containing the uranium, vanadium, iron, and copper brought into contact with fresh ore until neutral, when some of the required constituents will be precipitated upon it as basic sulphates or carbonates; the enriched ore is then treated with fresh acid, and the neutral soln. clarified by filtration; powdered limestone added until the uranium, vanadium, and copper fractions just commence to separate; the soln. is then freed from calcium sulphate, and the required fraction completely precipitated by further treatment with limestone. The product (a complex mixture) may be dried, ignited, or else further purified by any of the known methods.

J. H. Haynes believed that no method employing sulphuric acid can be commercially successful. It is considered that the best method of separating the uranium and vanadium of carnotite is founded on the fact that both elements can be dissolved by a hot soln. of sodium carbonate as sodium uranium carbonate, $2Na_2CO_3.UO_2CO_2$, and sodium vanadate, $NaVO_4$, and thus separated from calcium and iron. The uranium is then precipitated as sodium uranate, $Na_2O.3UO_2$, with sodium hydroxide, and the vanadium subsequently separated from the filtrate as calcium vanadate or as ferrous vanadate. The metallurgy of the lead vanadates was discussed by W. Baughman. In the case of carnotite, the radium is first extracted, and the vanadium recovered as a by-product. In the process described by C. L. Parsons and co-workers :

The ore is first leached with conc. nitric acid heated to 100° by steam. The soln. is neutralized with sodium hydroxide, and treated with barium chloride and sulphuric acid to precipitate radium and barium sulphates. The precipitate settles in about 3 or 4 days. The clear liquor is decanted into tanks, and treated with an excess of a boiling soln. of sodium carbonate so as to precipitate iron, calcium, and most of the aluminium. The soln. containing sodium uranyl carbonate, and sodium vanadate is nearly neutralized with nitric acid and treated with sodium hydroxide so as to precipitate uranium as sodium uranate. The remaining soln. is treated with nitric acid and ferrous sulphate so as to precipitate the vanadium as iron vanadate. It is said that 90 per cent. of the radium, nearly all the uranium, and 50 per cent. of the vanadium, are recovered from the ore by this process. Summarizing the operations :

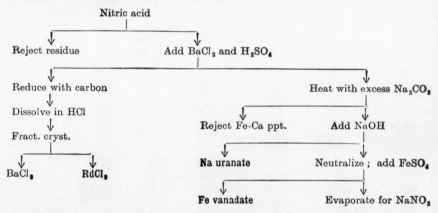

The isolation of vanadium metal.—In 1831, **J. J.** Berzelius [2] thought that he had isolated vanadium by heating vanadium oxytrichloride in ammonia gas, but A. Safarik, E. Uhrlaub, and H. E. Roscoe showed that the product was probably vanadium nitride ; and if the nitride be heated in hydrogen, H. E. Roscoe said that no metal is formed. The crystals obtained by A. Safarik by passing the vapour of vanadium oxytrichloride and hydrogen through a red-hot tube were shown by H. E. Roscoe to be a mixture of lower oxychlorides. The product obtained by J. J. Berzelius by heating vanadium pentoxide with potassium was found by H. E. Roscoe to be a mixture of oxides ; and he was unable to prepare the metal by heating white-hot vanadium trioxide alone or mixed with sodium in a current of hydrogen, by heating the trioxide mixed with magnesium in a graphite crucible ; or by passing the vapour of vanadium oxytrichloride over heated sodium. He also showed that the product obtained by J. F. W. Johnston by heating vanadium pentoxide with carbon was probably vanadium silicide ; with a mixture of vanadium trioxide and silicon-free carbon, a mixture of oxides is produced. M. A. Hunter and A. Jones obtained a metal of sp. gr. 5·97 by heating the anhydrous chloride with sodium in a steel bomb. H. von Wartenberg said that the trioxide at 2500° can be reduced to the metal by hydrogen at 5 atm. press. H. Moissan obtained a vanadium-aluminium alloy by heating vanadium pentoxide and aluminium ;

K. Hélouis obtained a mixture of oxides by reducing the pentoxide with aluminium ; and H. Kunzel and E. Wedekind, with calcium. H. Goldschmidt obtained a regulus which W. Hittorf found to be vanadium hemioxide ; and J. Koppel and A. Kaufmann were unable to make vanadium by the thermite process alone or in the presence of calcium fluoride, carbon, or calcium carbide. A. Wittig used the thermite process, but first heating to redness the vanadium compound with an ammonium salt before it is mixed with aluminium in the usual way.

H. E. Roscoe obtained vanadium by heating to redness vanadium di- or tri-chloride, contained in a platinum boat, in a current of hydrogen free from traces of oxygen, and after 40–80 hrs. raising the temp. to whiteness for a short time. The product contained 95·8 per cent. vanadium, and occluded hydrogen. The operation is difficult to carry out successfully, and H. E. Roscoe has given a full description of the experimental minutiæ. R. Edson and D. McIntosh made vanadium on a small scale by passing a current of hydrogen through vanadyl chloride past a glowing platinum wire filament heated electrically, a silver-grey coating of vanadium is deposited smoothly on the platinum. The metal was also obtained by H. E. Roscoe by reducing the solid chloride by sodium, at a red-heat in hydrogen. The product was separated from admixed trioxide by levigation, and after washing in water, contained 91·1 per cent. metal. W. Prandtl and H. Manz, and C. Setterberg obtained 98·7 per cent. vanadium by this process. M. Billy prepared what he regarded as pure vanadium by passing the vapour of the chloride over sodium hydride at about 400°. The sodium chloride is extracted by acid and water, and the metal dried at 100° in a current of carbon dioxide. Attempts to prepare vanadium by reducing the oxide with aluminium by H. Goldschmidt and C. Vautin's process, were failures in the hands of J. Koppel and A. Kaufmann, and gave only an impure metal in the hands of R. Vogel and G. Tammann. W. Muthmann reduced vanadium pentoxide by rare earth metals in the form of *mischmetal*. L. Weiss and O. Aichel recommended heating a mixture of 25 grms. of vanadium pentoxide, 49 grms. of mischmetal in a fireclay crucible lined wth magnesia, and ignited by a mixture of 40 parts of barium dioxide, 7 parts of potassium chlorate, and 10 parts of aluminium powder. The reaction proceeds very rapidly, and the regulus of 10 grms. is vanadium of a high degree of purity. H. Moissan heated a mixture of vanadium oxide with sugar charcoal for 2 mins. in an atm. of hydrogen in a carbon tube furnace, vanadium containing 4·4–5·3 per cent. of carbon was obtained—if the heating be too long continued, a carbide is formed. According to W. Prandtl and B. Bleyer, calcium reduces vanadium oxide vigorously, but owing to the absence of a fusible slag, the metal remains in isolated particles. A mixture of calcium (3 gram atoms) and aluminium (2 gram atoms) acts readily, and yields a fusible, crystalline slag and a homogeneous regulus. If large quantities are used, it is advisable to moderate the violence of the reaction by dil. with slag or previously prepared metal. According to O. Ruff and W. Martin, vanadium trioxide gives better results than the pentoxide on account of the greater fusibility of the latter which causes it to pass into the slag; on the other hand, W. Plandtl and H. Manz said that the better results are obtained with the pentoxide. A. S. Cachemaille heated to 800°–1000° a mixture of vanadium oxide with an excess of calcium and an alkali or alkaline earth halide in an iron bomb lined with lime. The cold product was washed with water, dil. acid, or alcohol. J. W. Marden and M. N. Rich recommended reducing vanadium pentoxide by a mixture of calcium and calcium carbide with a small piece of potassium or sodium on top of the charge placed in a bomb. The function of the alkali metal is to clean up any moisture present. The sealed bomb is heated to 900°–950°.

W. von Bolton prepared the metal by passing an electric current through thin rods of vanadium trioxide contained in a vacuum furnace. O. Ruff and W. Martin obtained vanadium by pressing a mixture of aluminium, vanadium trioxide, and 2 per cent. of carbon into a crucible lined with magnesia. The crucible is covered and heated to redness after adding a layer of ignition mixture. The product contains

95 per cent. of vanadium. Reduction with carbon in an arc gives a less pure product. Products containing from 95 to 97 per cent. of vanadium are obtained by moulding mixtures of the trioxide and carbon with starch into rods, sintering in an electric furnace at 1750°, and finally in an arc. The impurity consists of carbon or oxygen, according to the proportions employed. They also obtained vanadium by heating vanadium trioxide and carbide in a zirconia crucible at 1950°. W. Prandtl and H. Manz said that the presence of alkali in the aluminothermite process is harmful because of the passage of alkali vanadate into the slag. Attempts to remove oxygen from the product by adding the hydride, were not successful.

According to G. Gin, vanadium can be obtained by the electrolysis of fused calcium fluoride, to which some fluoride of iron is added. The anode consists of a mixture of vanadium trioxide and carbon; compressed and roasted in the way used in making anodes of carbon alone, the cathode is a bath of fused steel. In making alloys containing more than 25 per cent. of vanadium, a current density of 2 amps. per sq. cm. at the anode and 6 amps. per sq. cm. at the cathode is used; 11–12 volts are required. It is supposed that iron fluoride is electrolyzed, the fluorine liberated reacting with the anode, thus: $6F+V_2O_3+3C=2VF_3+3CO$, the vanadium fluoride dissolves in the fused calcium fluoride and is then itself electrolyzed. According to S. Cowper-Coles, vanadium can be obtained as a brilliant, metallic deposit by the electrolysis of a soln. of 1·75 parts of vanadium pentoxide, 2 parts of sodium hydroxide, 160 parts of water, and 32 parts of hydrochloric acid, using a current of 18–20 amps. per sq. ft., and an e.m.f. of 1·88 volts at the terminals of the electrolytic cell—the anode is of carbon, the cathode of platinum. C. Setterberg was unable to obtain the metal by the electrolysis of aq. soln. If a soln. of ammonium vanadate be electrolyzed, a reddish-brown mass containing nitrogen, oxygen and vanadium is deposited on the anode; and if a soln. of vanadium tetroxide in hydrochloric acid be electrolyzed in a compartment cell, the blue liquid becomes brown, and a black deposit of vanadium trioxide collects on the cathode, and flecks of vanadium pentoxide collect on the anode. The electrical conductivity of vanadyl chloride or vanadium tetrachloride is too small to enable it to be electrolyzed. P. Truchot found that vanadium is deposited as oxyhydrate when hot, slightly ammoniacal soln. of sodium vanadate are electrolyzed. R. E. Myers obtained a reduction but no deposition of vanadium by the electrolysis of an acidified soln. of sodium vanadate using a mercury cathode. It may be said that all attempts to obtain the metal vanadium from aq. soln. by electrolysis have failed. L. Schicht, and G. Gore obtained a reduction but no metal. Neither W. Borchers nor S. Fischer could succeed in verifying S. Cowper-Coles' statement. S. Fischer showed that the reduction is limited in most cases to the blue V_2O_4-stage, but at 90°, the reduction can go to the lavender V_2O_2-stage. Lead electrodes reduce the soln. to the green V_2O_3-stage at temp. below 9°, but above that temp. the lavender V_2O_2-stage appears. Carbon electrodes reduce the electrolyte to the sesquioxide form (V_2O_3), green colour. Platinum cathodes at temp. below 90° C. reduce the electrolyte to the blue vanadyl state only (V_2O_4), and the current density seemingly has no further effect. At temp. of 90° C. and above the lavender state (V_2O_2) is reached only when porous cells are used; otherwise not. The black deposit on platinum cathodes is not a vanadium compound.

The preparation of vanadium alloys.—The preparation of vanadium is so difficult that the metal of a high degree of purity has not been obtained. It is, however, comparatively easy to prepare alloys of vanadium with other metals. Thus, by reducing a mixture of the metal oxides with carbon in the electric furnace, H. Moissan [3] prepared **ferrovanadium,** and **cuprovanadium ;** and H. Herrenschmidt obtained ferrovanadium, cuprovanadium, **nickelovanadium,** and **cobaltovanadium** by heating in an electric furnace the precipitate obtained by mixing a soln. of sodium vanadate with, say, the requisite proportions of ferrous, cupric, or cobaltous sulphate and sodium carbonate, or by heating, say, a mixture of vanadium pentoxide and nickel oxide. F. R. Carpenter obtained ferrovanadium by heating a mixture of the vanadium ore with ferric oxide, dolomite, and a reducing agent at a high temp. An electric furnace, lined with magnesia, is charged with steel turnings; when those are melted, vanadium pentoxide is added, and this is followed by a mixture of silicon or ferrosilicon and lime. The pentoxide is reduced by the silicon : $2V_2O_5+5Si=4V+5SiO_2$, and the silica forms a slag with the lime. D. W. Berlin, and K. Nishida, also prepared these alloys; and R. Vogel and G. Tammann obtained them by the aluminothermite reduction of a mixture of ferric oxide and vanadium pentoxide. L. F. Vogt, and H. P. Smith reduced a mixture of vanadium and ferric oxides (*vide supra*) with charcoal and aluminium in an electric furnace, or treated the mixed oxides by the thermite process. G. Gin obtained vanadium alloys as indicated above. H. Moissan prepared **aluminovanadium** by melting fluorspar in the electric furnace, then dropping in aluminium, and finally adding a thermite mixture of vanadium pentoxide and aluminium shot. C. Matignon and E. Monnet obtained ferrovanadium by reducing a mixture of vanadium pentoxide and ferric oxide by aluminium ; and aluminovanadium by similarly reducing a mixture of vanadium pentoxide and alumina. Cuprovanadium is prepared by heating a mixture of vanadium pentoxide, copper oxide, and aluminium shot with lime, soda-ash, and fluorspar in a crucible lined with magnesite. J. J. Boericke prepared some alloys by the thermite process.

REFERENCES.

[1] J. F. W. Johnston, *Edin. Journ. Science*, (2), **5**. 166, 319, 1831 ; F. Wöhler, *Die Mineralanalyse in Beispielen*, Göttingen, 151, 1861 ; *Liebig's Ann.*, **41**. 345, 1842 ; **78**. 125, 1851 ; L. l'Hôte, *Compt. Rend.*, **101**. 1151, 1885 ; H. Herrenschmidt, *ib.*, **139**. 635, 862, 1904 ; G. Witz and F. Osmond, *ib.*, **95**. 42, 1882 ; *Chem. News*, **47**. 12, 1883 ; *Bull. Soc. Chim.*, (2), **28**. 49, 1882 ; P. Beauvallet, *Compt. Rend.*, **49**. 301, 1859 ; H. St. C. Deville, *ib.*, **49**. 210, 1859 ; *Ann. Chim. Phys.*, (3), **61**. 309, 1861 ; H. P. Smith, *Journ. Soc. Chem. Ind.*, **20**. 1183, 1901 ; C. Lallemand, *Ann. Mines*, (7), **17**. 326, 1880 ; J. Ohly, *Min. Scient. Press.*, **82**. 125, 1900 ; J. A. Norblad, *Acta Lund Univ.*, **2**. 1, 1874 ; *Bull. Soc. Chim.*, (2), **23**. 64, 1875 ; J. H. Haynes, *Mines Minerals*, **30**. 139, 1909 ; R. Böttger, *Jahresb. Phys. Ver. Frankfurt a. M.*, 18, 1872 ; H. Fleck and W. G. Haldane, *U.S. Pat. No.* 880645, 890584, 1908 ; N. G. Sefström, *Akad. Handl. Stockholm*, 255, 1830 ; *Schweigger's Journ.*, **62**. 316, 1831 ; *Pogg. Ann.*, **21**. 43, 1831 ; C. Kersten, *ib.*, **51**. 539, 1840 ; J. J. Berzelius, *ib.*, **22**. 1, 1831 ; *Schweigger's Journ.*, **62**. 323, 1831 ; **63**. 26, 1831 ; *Akad. Handl. Stockholm*, 1, 1831 ; A. Patera, *Dingler's Journ.*, **141**. 372, 1856 ; **231**. 556, 1879 ; *Oesterr. Zeit. Berg. Hütt.*, **4**. 242, 1856 ; *Amtlicher Bericht über die Wiener Weltausstellung in Jahre* 1873, Braunschweig, **3**. i, 841, 1875 ; E. Classen, *Amer. Chem. Journ.*, **8**. 437, 1886 ; G. Kunkle, *U.S. Pat. No.* 1554917, 1925 ; W. F. Bleecker, *ib.*, 1445660, 1923 ; B. W. Gerland, *Ber.*, **9**. 869, 1876 ; **10**. 1216, 1513, 1516, 2109, 1877 ; *Chem. News*, **34**. 2, 1876 ; **36**. 29, 271, 272, 1877 ; H. Nagell, *German Pat.*, *D.R.P.* 356225, 1918 ; E. Petersen, *Journ. prakt. Chem.*, (2), **40**. 44, 193, 271, 1889 ; *Chem. News*, **60**. 210, 1889 ; **61**. 61, 1890 ; L. Blum, *Chem. Ztg.*, **9**. 1407, 1885 ; G. Gin, *Trans. Amer. Electrochem. Soc.*, **16**. 393, 1909 ; *Elektrochem. Zeit.*, **13**. 119, 1906 ; C. Giseke, *Arch. Pharm.*, (2), **69**. 150, 1852 ; *Journ. prakt. Chem.*, (1), **55**. 445, 1852 ; R. H. von Seth, *Jernkon. Ann.*, **108**. 561, 1924 ; C. von Hauer, *Sitzber. Akad. Wien*, **20**. 37, 1856 ; **21**. 333, 1856 ; A. Safarik, *ib.*, **33**. 1, 1858 ; *Liebig's Ann.*, **109**. 84, 1859 ; *Journ. prakt. Chem.*, (1), **76**. 142, 1859 ; E. Riley, *Journ. Chem. Soc.*, **17**. 21, 1864 ; Anon., *Min. Eng. World*, **43**. 105, 1915 ; A. Wittig, *Brit. Pat. No.* 218981, 1923 ; 215737, 1924 ; H. Stevens, G. C. Norris, and W. N. Watson, *ib.*, 269779, 1926 ; C. L. Parsons, R. B. Moore, S. C. Lind, and O. C. Schaefer, *The Extraction and Recovery of Radium, Uranium, and Vanadium from Carnotite*, Washington, 30, 1915 ; H. E. Roscoe, *Phil. Trans.*, **158**. 1, 1868 ; *Proc. Roy. Soc.*, **16**. 220, 1868 ; *Chem. News*, **17**. 135, 1868 ; *Journ. Chem. Soc.*, **21**. 322, 1868 ; K. B. Thews and F. J. Heinle, *Journ. Ind. Eng. Chem.*, **15**. 1159, 1923 ; A. T. Elliott, *U.S. Pat. No.* 1471514, 1923 ; K. B. Thews, *Continental Chem. Met. Engg.*, **1**. 45, 1926 ; *U.S. Pat. No.* 1430864, 1922 ; 1495538, 1924 ; 1522040, 1526943, 1925 ; E. Laist, *ib.*, 1544911, 1925 ; F. F. Frick, *ib.*, 1596486, 1926 ; W. E. Stokes, *ib.*, 1482276, 1924 ; A. L. D. d'Adrian, *ib.*, 1434485, 1922 ; A. Oberle, *ib.*, 1570170, 1926 ; J. V. Dixon, *ib.*, 1522040, 1925 ; Electrometallurgical Co., *ib.*, 1513200, 1924 ; Stockholders Syndicate, *ib.*, 1604630, 1926 ; H. T. Koenig, *ib.*, 1654820, 1928 ; R. H. von Seth, *Brit. Pat. No.* 211111, 1924 ; *Eng. Min. Press*, **120**. 51, 1925 ; *Metall. Erz.* **22**. 219, 1925 ; W. Baughman, *Trans. Amer. Electrochem. Soc.*, **43**. 281, 1923 ; E. E. Dutt, *Brit. Pat. No.* 189700, 1922 ; C. Porlezza and A. Donati, *Atti Accad. Lincei*, (5), **33**. i, 232, 1924 ; J. E. Conley, *Metal Ind.*, **14**. 521, 1919 ; **16**. 296, 1920 ; *Chem. Met. Engg.*, **20**. 465, 514, 1919 ; H. A. Doermer, *ib.*, **31**. 429, 1924 ; B. P. F. Kjellberg, *French Pat. No.* 598315, 1925 ; *Brit. Pat. No.* 260661, 1925 ; *U.S. Pat. No.* 1583053, 1926 ; *Eng. Min. Journ.*, **123**. 521, 1927 ; B. D. Saklatwalla, *Trans. Amer. Electrochem. Soc.*, **36**. 341, 1920 ; *German Pat.*, *D.R.P.* 270346.

1914 ; Radium and Rare Earths Treatment Co., *Australian Pat. No.* 20300, 1924 ; R. H. Stevens, G. C. Norris, and W. N. Watson, *Brit. Pat. No.* 269779, 269780, 1926 ; R. von Seth and G. Hult, *Tek. Tid. Uppsala*, **57**. 20, 1927 ; J. E. Conley, *Chem. Met. Engg.*, **20**. 465, 514, 1919 ; H. G. C. Fairbanks, *Brit. Pat. No.* 287401, 1927 ; G. Forchhammer, *Oefvers. Vid. Selsk. Skr.*, 88, 1864 ; J. Fritzsche, *Bull. Acad. St. Petersburg*, (2), **9**. 195, 1851 ; F. L. Hahn and W. Franke.

² E. Uhrlaub, *Die Verbindungen einiger Metalle mit Stickstoff*, Göttingen, 22, 1859 ; *Pogg. Ann.*, **103**. 134, 1858 ; *Journ. prakt. Chem.*, (1), **73**. 378, 1858 ; A. Safarik, *Sitzber. Akad. Wien*, **33**. 5, 1858 ; J. J. Berzelius, *Pogg. Ann.*, **22**. 1, 1831 ; *Akad. Handl. Stockholm*, 1, 1831 ; H. E. Roscoe, *Phil. Trans.*, **158**. 1, 1868 : **159**. 679, 1869 ; **160**. 317, 1870 ; *Proc. Roy. Soc.*, **16**. 220, 1868 ; **18**. 37, 316, 1870 ; *Journ. Chem. Soc.*, **21**. 322, 1868 ; **23**. 344, 1870 ; **24**. 23, 1871 ; *Chem. News*, **17**. 135, 1868 ; **20**. 37, 1869 ; **21**. 183, 1870 ; *Phil. Mag.*, (4), **35**. 307, 1868 ; (4), **39**. 146, 1870 ; (4), **40**. 62, 1870 ; K. Hélouis, *Bull. Soc. Enc. Nat. Ind.*, (5), **1**. 904, 1896 ; H. Moissan, *Compt. Rend.*, **116**. 1225, 1893 ; **122**. 1297, 1896 ; M. Billy, *ib.*, **158**. 578,1914 ; A. Wittig, *Brit. Pat. No.* 215734, 1924 ; A. S. Cachemaille, *ib.*, 238663, 1924 ; O. Ruff and W. Martin, *Zeit. angew. Chem.*, **25**. 49, 1912 ; H. Goldschmidt, *ib.*, **11**. 321, 1898 ; *Zeit. Elektrochem.*, **4**. 494, 1898 ; G. Gin, *ib.*, **9**. 831, 1903 ; *German Pat.*, *D.R.P.* 154619, 1904 ; *Chem. News*, **88**. 38. 1903 ; *Elektrochem. Zeit.*, **13**. 119, 1906 ; H. von Wartenberg, J. Broy, and R. Reinicke, *Zeit. Elektrochem.*, **29**. 214, 1923 ; J. Koppel and A. Kaufmann, *Zeit. anorg. Chem.*, **45**. 352, 1905 ; W. Hittorf, *Phys. Zeit.*, **4**. 196, 1903 ; W. von Bolton, *Zeit. Elektrochem.*, **11**. 45, 1905 ; C. Setterberg, *Oefvers. Vet. Akad. Förh.*, **39**. 10, 1882 ; R. Edson and D. McIntosh, *Trans. Roy. Soc. Canada*, (3), **9**. 81, 1915 ; J. F. W. Johnston, *Edin. Journ. Science*, (2), **5**. 166, 319, 1831 ; W. Muthmann, *Chem. Ztg.*, **28**. 506, 1904 ; *Sitzber. Akad. München*, **34**. 201, 1904 ; J. W. Marden and M. N. Rich, *Journ. Ind. Eng. Chem.*, **19**. 786, 1927 ; J. W. Marden, *U.S. Pat. No.* 1646734, 1927 ; L. Weiss and O. Aichel, *Liebig's Ann.*, **337**. 380, 1904 ; S. Cowper-Coles, *Chem. News*, **79**. 147, 1899 ; *Trans. Inst. Min. Met.*, **7**. 198, 1899 ; P. Truchot, *Ann. Chim. Anal. Appl.*, **7**. 165, 1902 ; R. E. Myers, *Journ. Amer. Chem. Soc.*, **26**. 1124, 1904 ; A. Classen, *Ber.*, **14**. 2783, 1881 ; F. L. Nilson and O. Petersson, *Wied. Ann.*, **4**. 554, 1878 ; R. Vogel and G. Tammann, *Zeit. anorg. Chem.*, **58**. 73, 1908 ; **64**. 225, 1909 ; W. Prandtl and H. Manz, *ib.*, **79**. 209, 1912 ; **80**. 59, 1913 ; W. Prandtl and B. Bleyer, *ib.*, **64**. 217, 1909 ; *Ber.*, **43**. 2602, 1910 ; S. Fischer, *Trans. Amer. Electrochem. Soc.*, **30**. 175, 1916 ; M. A. Hunter and A. Jones, *ib.*, **44**. 23, 1923 ; L. Schicht, *Chem. News*, **41**. 280, 1880 ; **42**. 331, 1880 ; W. Borchers, *Elektrometallurgie*, Leipzig, 498, 1902 ; G. Gore, *Electrochemistry*, London, 101, 1906 ; H. Goldschmidt and C. Vautin, *Journ. Soc. Chem. Ind.*, **17**. 543, 1898 ; J. J. Boericke, *U.S. Pat. No.* 1562201, 1925 ; A. N. Erickson, *ib.*, 1515245, 1925 ; M. J. Udy, *ib.*, 1513200, 1925 ; H. Kunzel and E. Wedekind, *ib.*, 1088909, 1914 ; *Met. Chem. Engg.*, **21**. 260, 1914 ; J. A. Hedvall and N. von Zweigbergh, *Zeit. anorg. Chem.*, **108**. 119, 1919.

³ H. Moissan, *Compt. Rend.*, **122**. 1297, 1896 ; H. Herrenschmidt, *ib.*, **139**. 635, 1904 ; C. Matignon and E. Monnet, *ib.*, **134**. 542, 1902 ; E. K. Scott, *Eng.*, **136**. 636, 1923 ; F. R. Carpenter, *U.S. Pat. No.* 781808, 1905 ; J. J. Boericke, *ib.*, 1562201, 1925 ; H. P. Smith, *Journ. Soc. Chem. Ind.*, **20**. 1183, 1901 ; G. Gin, *Zeit. Elektrochem.*, **9**. 831, 1903 ; *German Pat.*, *D.R.P.* 154619, 1904 ; *Trans. Amer. Electrochem. Soc.*, **16**. 439, 1909 ; R. Vogel and G. Tammann, *Zeit. anorg. Chem.*, **58**. 73, 1908 ; **64**. 225, 1909 ; R. von Seth, *Jernkont. Ann.*, **108**. 561, 1924 ; L. F. Vogt, *U.S. Pat. No.* 1564156, 1925 ; B. D. Saklatwalla and A. N. Anderson, *ib.*, 1435742, 1922 ; D. W. Berlin, *Swedish Pat. No.* 58887, 1925 ; The Vanadium Corporation of America, *Brit. Pat. No.* 195688, 1921 ; K. Nishida, *Japan. Pat. No.* 42511, 1922.

§ 4. The Properties of Vanadium

Owing to the fact that most of the observations on the physical properties of vanadium have been made with the element containing more or less impurity, it is necessary to affix to the following record *cum grano impuritiæ*. H. E. Roscoe's [1] vanadium was described as a silver-white, crystalline powder ; C. Setterberg's, as a grey powder containing acicular crystals ; L. Weiss and O. Aichel's, as a regulus of hexagonal crystals. W. Prandtl and B. Bleyer described it as a steel-grey metal which can take a high polish. W. C. Brögger and G. Flink said that the crystals obtained by C. Setterberg often have an olive-green or a bluish-green film, and are combinations of the dodecahedron and cube, and the tabular crystals are often twinned. According to A. W. Hull, the **X-radiogram** of vanadium agrees with a body-centred cubic lattice. The side of unit cube is 3·04 A., and there are two atoms per unit cube. H. E. Roscoe gave 5·5 at 15° for the **specific gravity** of vanadium ; C. Setterberg, 5·866–5·875 at 15° ; W. Muthmann and co-workers, 6·025 at 15°/15° ; O. Ruff and W. Martin, 5·688 at 18·7° ; J. W. Marden and M. N. Rich, 6·0 at 22° for cold-worked wire ; and W. Prandtl and H. Manz found

luminothermic, 95 per cent. vanadium has a sp. gr. 5·987 at 20°, while that prepared from sodium and the chloride had a sp. gr. 5·819 at 20°. H. G. Grimm
made observations on the ionic radius. According to W. Prandtl and B. Bleyer,
vanadium is hard enough to scratch quartz ; and L. Weiss and O. Aichel say that
the **hardness** of vanadium exceeds that of any other metal, being very nearly 7 on
Mohs' scale ; J. R. Rydberg gave 6. Consequently, it is scratched neither by the
hardest steel, nor by quartz. W. Muthmann and co-workers gave 7·5 for the
hardness, and said that it is as brittle as glass. G. W. Bridgman found the
cubic **compressibility** calculated from the linear compressibility of a mass of
cubic crystals is, at 30°, $\delta v/v_0 = -6{\cdot}090 \times 10^{-7}p + 2{\cdot}58 \times 10^{-12}p^2$; and at 75°,
$v/v_0 = -6{\cdot}117 \times 10^{-7}p + 2{\cdot}55 \times 10^{-12}p^2$. J. Laissus discussed the **diffusion** of
vanadium in iron.

C. Setterberg gave 0·1259 for the **specific heat** and 6·46 for the **atomic heat** of
vanadium ; W. Muthmann and co-workers gave 0·124 ; H. Mache, 0·1153 from
0° to 100° ; J. W. Marden and M. N. Rich, 0·120 from 20° to 100° ; and C. Matignon
and E. Monnet calculated 0·1258 for the sp. ht. from the value for ferrovanadium,
and 0·1235 for the value for aluminovanadium. E. Donath and J. Mayrhofer
studied the relations between the at. ht., at. wt., and sp. gr. of vanadium and
some other elements. O. Ruff and W. Martin found that the presence of either
oxygen or carbon raises the **melting point** of vanadium, and by extrapolation
they found the m.p. of the pure metal to be 1715°. G. K. Burgess and R. G. Waltenberg gave 1720° ; W. von Bolton, 1680° ; and J. W. Marden and M. N. Rich,
1700° ; and W. R. Mott gave 1750° for the m.p., and calculated 3400° for the
boiling point. J. W. Marden and M. N. Rich found vanadium to be one of the
least volatile of metals at its m.p. A sample may be kept molten in a high vacuum
for a long time without appreciable blackening of the glass container. The **heat
of combustion** of a gram of metal to the pentoxide is 2456 cals. ; W. Muthmann
and co-workers gave 31·303 Cals. per equivalent ; W. G. Mixter found that (2V, 5O)
exceeds 441 Cals., and O. Ruff and L. Friedrich gave 437±7 Cals.

H. von Wartenberg[2] found 3·03 for the **index of refraction** of vanadium for
light of wave-length 0·579μ ; 0·351 for the **absorption coefficient ;** and 58 per cent.
for the **reflecting power.** W. W. Coblentz found that the reflecting power rises
gradually from 58 per cent. in the yellow to 92 per cent. at 9μ. In this respect
it resembles iron and chromium. He gave :

λ	0·5	0·6	0·8	1·0	2·0	4·0	7·0μ
R	57	58	60	61	69	79	88 per cent.

W. Biltz[3] discussed the relationship between the colour of vanadium and the
magnetic properties of the element—*vide* chromium. K. Someya stated that
the violet colour obtained by reducing ammonium vanadate soln. fades on dilution,
showing that the vanadous ions are probably colourless. The colour is restored
by conc. hydrochloric acid or potassium thiocyanate, showing that the colour is
due to non-ionized molecules or complex ions. The **spark spectrum** of vanadium
was examined by R. Thalén,[4] H. A. Rowland, J. Parry and A. E. Tucker,

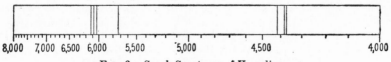

8,000 7,000 6,500 6,000   5,500   5,000   4,500   4,000

FIG. 2.—Spark Spectrum of Vanadium.

E. Demarçay, W. N. Hartley and H. W. Moss, O. Lohse, F. Exner and E. Haschek,
J. H. Pollock, C. E. Gissing, M. Eppley, A. de Gramont, A. Hagenbach and
H. Konen, A. M. Kilby, and J. M. Eder and E. Valenta. The more important
lines have wave-lengths 6120, 6090, 6040 A. in the orange-yellow ; 5726 A. in
the yellow ; 4407, 4384, and 4379 A. in the indigo-blue—Fig. 2. The **arc spectrum**

was examined by H. A. Rowland and C. N. Harrison, B. Hasselberg, A. Frerichs, M. Eppley, J. N. Lockyer and F. E. Baxandall, F. Exner and E. Haschek, A. S. King, W. F. Meggers, H. Shaw, A. M. Kilby, J. M. Eder and E. Valenta, and R. Rossi. C. C. Kiess and W. F. Meggers measured the red, and ultra-red lines exceeding 5500 A., and W. Ludwig the lines between 2207-4646 A. in the arc spectrum of vanadium. C. Porlezza and A. Donati discussed the detection and determination of vanadium in ores from the arc spectrum. The **band spectrum** was examined by H. Konen, E. Demarçay, J. M. Eder and E. Valenta, A. Hagenbach and H. Konen and F. Exner and E. Haschek; the *enhanced lines*, by J. N. Lockyer, and M. Kimura and G. Nakamura; the effect of *pressure*, by W. J. Humphreys, and R. Rossi; the effect of a strong *magnetic field*—the **Zeeman effect**—by J. E. Purvis, W. F. Meggers, and H. D. Babcock. C. C. Kiess and O. Laforte, A. S. King, and R. J. Lang examined the **ultra-violet spectrum**; and the influence of an *electric field*—the **Stark effect**—by H. Nagaoka and Y. Sugiura. G. A. Hemsalech excited the spectrum by thermoelectronic currents. The **series spectrum** was studied by M. A. Catalan, R. C. Gibbs and M. E. White, K. Bechert and M. A. Catalan, R. Frerichs, T. Okaya, K. Bechert and L. A. Sommer, R. J. Lang, O. Laporte, R. Mecke, H. N. Russell, S. Goudsmit, and W. F. Meggers. H. Gieseler and W. Grotrian measured the lines in the **absorption spectrum** of vanadium vapour at 2000°. H. Gieseler and W. Grotrian studied the absorption spectrum of the vapour of vanadium. According to J. Formanek, the greenish-blue aq. soln. of vanadium dichloride has an absorption spectrum with a band in the red; and the green alcoholic soln. absorbs the red and violet. If tincture of alkanna be present, the soln. becomes blue, and the absorption spectrum has bands at 6099 and 5643 with a feeble band at 5250. The position of the bands does not change when the soln. are allowed to stand some time. A trace of ammonia does not alter the absorption spectrum, but an excess of ammonia renders the liquid turbid and red; it then shows the absorption spectrum of alkanna.

The K-series in the **X-ray spectrum** was examined by V. Dolejsek,[5] A. Leide, D. Coster, M. Levi, M. J. Druyvesteyn, K. Chamberlain, H. Fricke, D. M. Bose, A. E. Lindh, B. B. Ray, G. Wentzel, O. Stelling, B. Walter, E. Hjalmar, N. Stensson, N. Seljakoff and co-workers, and M. Siegbahm. There are : a_2a', 2·50212 ; a,a, 2·49834 ; a_3a_4, 2·4846 ; β,β, 2·27968 ; and $\beta_2\gamma$, 2·26537. S. B. Hendricks and R. W. C. Wyckoff, R. Thoraeus, and D. Coster studied the L-series; and D. M. Bose the M-series and the N-series. K. H. Kingdon gave 7·69 volts for the **ionizing potential** of vanadium vapour; H. N. Russell gave 6·76 volts; and R. N. Ghosh, 6·5 volts. R. Robl observed no fluorescence when vanadium is exposed to ultra-violet light.

K. F. Herzfeld [6] studied the metallic conduction of vanadium. J. W. Marden and M. N. Rich gave 0·000026 ohm per c.c. for the sp. **electrical resistance** of cold-worked vanadium ; and for the effect of temp. from 20° to 150°, $R=R_0(1+0\cdot0028\theta)$. L. Marino found that the **electromotive force** of vanadium is not analogous to that of chromium, but is more related with the behaviour of phosphorus and arsenic. When an electrolyte, which has no action on vanadium at the ordinary temp., is electrolyzed with a vanadium anode, a complex vanadium anion is produced, the vanadium going into soln. as a quadrivalent ion. The loss of weight of the anode is always greater than that corresponding with the amount of silver separated in the voltameter ; this is attributed to the oxidation of some carbon to carbon dioxide. In alkaline soln., vanadium dissolves vanadate, independently of conc., temp., and current density. Potential measurements were made according to the scheme, V | MX | NaNO$_3$ | AgNO$_3$ | Ag, where X=Cl, Br, OH, and M=Na, K, Zn, Mg, etc. ; with the exception of the cases of sodium and potassium hydroxides, the e.m.f. was independent of the nature of the electrolyte. The e.m.f. of the combination V | MX | H$_2$CrO$_4$ | Pt was also determined. In no case did the vanadium become passive. G. C. Schmidt measured the electrode potential of vanadium in N-KCl. G. Tammann and J. Hinnüber studied the cell $V_n Hg \mid V_2(SO_4)_3, HgSO_4 \mid Hg$. A. Thiel and W. Hammerschmidt found the overvoltage in $2N$-H_2SO_4 at 25° to be 0·1352 volt. W. Muthmann and F. Fraunberger, and G. C. Schmidt examined the **passivity** of vanadium. They found that with purified vanadium in N-KOH, the potential at the beginning is −0·13 volt, and after ten minutes, it has attained the maximum value 0·737 volt. The passivity is shown when the metal is treated with oxidizing agents, or after anodic polarization. T. F. Rutter measured the **oxidation and reduction potentials** of vanadium salts, or the e.m.f. of the chains $V^{..} \rightarrow V^{...}$; of $V^{...} \rightarrow V^{....}$; and of $V^{....} \rightarrow V^{.....}$ from soln. containing di- and ter-valent vanadium salts, ter- and quadrivalent vanadium compounds, and quadri- and quinquevalent compounds in variable quantities. The soln. were referred to a mercurous sulphate electrode in 0·5N-H_2SO_4 of potential 0·679 volt.

He found for (1) $V^{..} \rightarrow V^{...}$, with 0·1$N$-$V^{II}$ salt and 0·5N-H_2SO_4 free from V^{III}-salt, a potential of 0·909 volt with 0·05N-V^{II}-salt, 0·05N-V^{III}-salt, and 0·5N-H_2SO_4, 0·889 volt ; 0·033N-V^{II}-salt, 0·066N-V^{III}-salt, and 0·5N-H_2SO_4, 0·881 volt ; 0·025N-V^{II}-salt, 0·075N-V^{III}-salt, and 0·5N-H_2SO_4, 0·875 volt ; and 0·1N-V^{III}-salt, and 0·5N-H_2SO_4, free from V^{II}-salt, 0·464 volt—the mercury electrode was positive. (2) For $V^{...} \rightarrow V^{....}$, with 0·1$N$-$V^{III}$-salt free from V^{II}- and V^{V}-salts, 0·462 volt ; with 0·075N-V^{III}-salt and 0·025N-V^{IV}-salt, 0·0397 volt ; with 0·05N-V^{III}-salt and 0·05N-V^{IV}-salt, 0·0373 volt ; with 0·025N-V^{III}-salt, and 0·075N-V^{IV}-salt, 0·363 volt ; and 0·1N-V^{IV}-salt free from V^{III}- and V^{V}-salts, 0·051 volt—the mercury electrode was positive. (3) For $V^{....} \rightarrow V^{.....}$, with 0·1$N$-$V^{IV}$-salt free from V^{III}- and V^{V}-salts, 0·051 volt—mercury electrode positive ; with 0·05N-V^{IV}-salt, and 0·05N-V^{V}-salt, 0·241 volt ; and 0·1N-V^{V}-salt, and 0·05N-H_2SO_4 free from V^{V}-salt, 0·462 volt—mercury electrode negative.

T. F. Rutter also found that vanadium of its own accord could form ions of the type $VO^{..}$ from $V^{....}$; VO_2^{II}, VO_3^{I}, and $V_6O_{17}^{IV}$. Also if the ratio of ($V^{II} . V^{III}$ =0·05 : 0·05) and ($V^{III} . V^{IV}$=0·05 : 0·05) existed, then the single potentials are respectively +0·21 and −0·30. This means that the tendency to form V^{II} to V^{III} is greater than the tendency to change H to H·, and the potential to change V^{III} to V^{IV} is greater than that to change Ag to Ag· : therefore, vanado-salts liberate hydrogen, and vanadi-salts liberate silver or copper of the soln. of copper sulphate used is concentrated and heat applied. Vanadyl salts are said to be very weak reducing agents, but they are quickly oxidized by permanganic acid, chromic acid, and hydrogen dioxide ; slowly by persulphates ; and only slightly by iodine and bromine. T. F. Rutter also established the fact that various oxides of vanadium immediately come to an equilibrium.

The electrolytic reduction of quadri- and quinque-valent vanadium salts was studied by A. Stahler and H. Wirthwein, A. Piccini and N. Brizzi, A. Bültemann, E. Renschler, R. Luther, W. F. Bleecker, L. Pissarjewsky, P. Truchot, R. E. Myers, and S. Fischer—*vide infra*, vanadium trioxide.

K. Honda [7] showed that the **magnetic susceptibility** of vanadium is $1 \cdot 5 \times 10^{-6}$ units at 18°, and $1 \cdot 8 \times 10^{-6}$ units at 1100° ; M. Owen gave $2 \cdot 4 \times 10^{-6}$ units at ordinary temp. P. Weiss and H. K. Onnes showed that the magnetic properties of vanadium are not intensified by cooling the element down to the temp. of solid hydrogen. W. Biltz associated the colour of unsaturated vanadium compounds with the magnetic power. E. Wedekind compared the magnetic susceptibility of vanadium compounds with those of the other elements. R. Dieterle investigated the magnetic susceptibility of the iron vanadium alloys ; and D. M. Bose and H. G. Bhar, I. Tamm, and P. Pascal, of vanadium salts. N. Perrakis found the paramagnetic susceptibility constant of quinquevalent vanadium to be $44 \cdot 0 \times 10^{-6}$ mass units. According to P. Pascal, when the chemical properties of a metal become masked by its entry into a complex ion or colloid, the magnetic properties are similarly affected and to the same degree. For example, vanadium pentoxide dissolves in conc. sulphuric acid to a red soln., which on dilution, becomes first yellow and then colourless. The pentoxide in the red soln. has the mol. magnetic susceptibility $-2 \times 85 \cdot 7 \times 10^{-5}$; in the yellow soln., $-2 \times 31 \cdot 5 \times 10^{-5}$; and in the colourless soln., $-2\times30\cdot2\times10^{-5}$. From these values, it is permissible to conclude that the strongly acid soln. contain red sulphovanadic compounds which dissociate on dilution. These complexes doubtless include $VO_2(SO_4)_3$; $V_2O_5.3H_2SO_4$; and $K_2O.4SO_3V_2O_5$.

F. Fischer and F. Schrötter [8] observed no reaction occurs when vanadium is sparked beneath liquid **argon**. H. E. Roscoe found that vanadium prepared by reducing the chloride in **hydrogen** contains some of that occluded gas. H. Huber and co-workers found that vanadium which has been heated in vacuo to 1100° readily absorbs hydrogen and the equilibrium is rapidly attained from either side. They measured the pv-curves between 300° and 800°; and observed no evidence of the ageing of the metal. According to W. Muthmann and co-workers, finely divided vanadium at 1300° unites with 16·1 per cent. of hydrogen, forming a stable **vanadium hydride** as a black powder which is not affected by water or by boiling hydrochloric acid, but is oxidized by nitric acid. W. Prandtl and H. Manz were unable to prepare a hydride by heating electrolytically disintegrated vanadium in hydrogen at 1000°. The sp. gr. is 5·30. The hydride was studied by A. Sieverts and A. Gotta. According to H. E. Roscoe, vanadium in the cold is not changed by moist or dry **air.** When warmed gently in air, it forms brown hemioxide, which when heated further passes into black trioxide, then to blue tetroxide, and finally to yellowish-red pentoxide. When vanadium is heated in **oxygen,** or strewn into a flame, it burns brilliantly with the emission of sparks. Vanadium can be repeatedly moistened with **water** and dried in vacuo without the slightest increase in weight. Vanadium containing occluded hydrogen is gradually oxidized in air; and the cold, powdered metal, prepared by the sodium reduction process, and dried by heating it to dull redness in vacuo or in hydrogen, may ignite like a pyrophorus when brought into air or oxygen. When vanadium is heated with an excess of dry **chlorine,** it forms the dark brown tetrachloride, but it is not attacked by **bromine** water. The powdered metal is not attacked by cold or hot, dil. or conc. **hydrochloric acid ;** it is slowly dissolved by **hydrofluoride acid** with the evolution of hydrogen, and the formation of a green soln. L. Marino found that the metal with 8·66 per cent. carbon is not attacked by the **halide acids.** Vanadic acid is produced by the action of **chloric, perchloric, and bromic acids** on vanadium. Sat. soln. of **potassium chlorate, bromate, iodate, and perchlorate** oxidize vanadium to vanadic acid : $6V+5KClO_3=5KCl+3V_2O_5$. N. Domanicky saw that **sulphur monochloride** in the presence of ether will probably form a higher chloride. H. E. Roscoe found that dil. **sulphuric acid,** or the cold conc. acid, is without action on vanadium, but the hot, conc. acid dissolves the metal, forming a greenish-yellow soln. L. Marino found vanadium to be soluble in hot sulphuric acid (2 : 1), and when the temp. is raised to 330°, vanadic acid is formed and some sulphur dioxide is set free. The metal is attacked by a warm soln. of **ammonium persulphate,** and the liquid becomes strongly acid owing to the formation of monopersulphuric and sulphuric acids. H. E. Roscoe found that when vanadium is heated in **nitrogen,** a bronze-coloured nitride is formed, and W. Muthmann and co-workers obtained the nitride by the direct union of the elements at a red-heat. I. I. Tschukoff studied this subject. H. E. Roscoe found that vanadium is converted into vanadium tetranitrate by **nitric acid** of sp. gr. 1·18, and vanadic acid is produced by nitric acid of sp. gr. greater than 1·35. According to H. E. Roscoe, nitric acid of any conc. attacks vanadium in the cold, forming brown fumes and a blue soln.; **aqua regia** attacks the metal very vigorously. M. Wunder and B. Janneret found that ferrovanadium is rapidly dissolved by **phosphoric acid** of sp. gr. 1·75. G. Tammann and K. Schönert found that **carbon** does not diffuse in vanadium at temp. up to 750°. H. W. Underwood, and O. Schmidt studied vanadium as a catalyst in the hydrogenation of organic substances. L. Marino found that vanadium remains unchanged in soln. of **alkali acetates, oxalates, sulphates,** etc. O. Schmidt discussed the catalysis hydrogenation of organic substances in the presence of vanadium salts.

H. Giebelhausen found that vanadium reacts with **silicon** to form silicides (*q.v.*). According to H. E. Roscoe, and L. Weiss and O. Aichel, when the metal is heated in **glass** or **porcelain** vessels, the silicate is attacked and vanadium silicide is formed. C. Setterberg also observed that the metal readily reacts with **silica** at an elevated temp. H. E. Roscoe found that neither hot nor cold soln. of **alkali hydroxides** attack vanadium, but, when exposed to air, molten alkalies, **sodium carbonate** or **potassium nitrate,** gradually oxidize the metal to a vanadate. L. Marino observed that a soln. of **mercuric chloride** is reduced by vanadium to mercurous chloride : **cupric chloride** is likewise reduced to cuprous chloride ; and **ferric chloride** to ferrous chloride. Vanadium also reduces soln. of **silver nitrate, gold chloride,** and of **platinum and iridium tetrachlorides.**

The **vanadides** of the metals have not been closely investigated. H. Giebelhausen [9] showed that *vanadium-copper alloys* form two immiscible liquids at 1800°. A sample with 92 per cent. vanadium freezes at 1084° ; and likewise also the end of the freezing of that metal with 2·8–21·0 per cent. of copper freezes at the same temp. The regulus consists of two layers, one vanadium and the other copper ; each layer carries only traces of the other element. The f.p. diagram assumes the form shown in Fig. 3. R. M. Keeney discussed these alloys. Similar results were obtained by H. Giebelhausen with *vanadium-silver alloys.* The two elements are immiscible at 1800°, and the alloy has two f.p., one corresponding with vanadium, the other with silver, Fig. 3, with the 1884°-line at 961°. Silver does not dissolve appreciably in vanadium or vanadium in silver. According to R. J. Dunn and O. F. Hudson, the critical point at about 460° in brass and alloys of copper and zinc, containing the β-phase, is only slightly affected by vanadium, for 1 per cent. raises it only about 10°. Vanadium is practically without influence on the resolution of the β-phase.

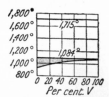

FIG. 3. — Freezing-point Curve of Vanadium-Copper Alloys.

R. Hohage and A. Grützner described some *vanadium-iron alloys.* When added to mild steels with 0·10–0·17 per cent. carbon, vanadium increased the yield-point and maximum strength, and reduced the elongation, reduction of area, and impact values, proportionally to its content, and exerted these effects to a greater degree as the quenching temp. was raised. With rising vanadium content, the critical cooling velocity was diminished and a tendency to air-hardening produced. E. Maurer said that there is only a slight increase in hardness of vanadium steels with a rise in the quenching temp. Additions of vanadium to a steel containing 0·74 per cent. of carbon reduce the specific resistance, but, in the absence of carbon, the resistance is increased. Vanadium steels, in which the ratio vanadium ; carbon is 5·17 or lower, have their specific resistance markedly raised by quenching at 950°, but not when the ratio is 6·20 or higher. This is in agreement with the formula, V_4C_3, for the carbide, which was confirmed by analysis. Vanadium carbide dissolves gradually with rise of temp. like cementite, the degree of solubility depending on the amount of vanadium already in the matrix. The coercive strength of 10 per cent. vanadium steel shows a 37 per cent. increase when carbon-free, and 80 per cent. increase with 1 per cent. carbon, when the steel is quenched at 1300°. This alteration in property is attributed to the passing into soln. of carbon according to the equation $V_4C_3 \rightleftharpoons 4V + 3C$ (dissolved). The decomposition of vanadium carbide at higher temp. (1400°) has no bearing on high-speed or tool steel as these are quenched at 1280° and 800° respectively. J. O. Arnold and A. A. Reid discussed these iron-vanadium alloys—*vide,* iron ; and G. Tammann and G. Siebel investigated their temper colours. Alloys containing more than 0·5 per cent. of vanadium contain hard, blue inclusions, possibly an oxide. G. Tammann and J. Hinnüber prepared an alloy with **mercury** by the electrolysis of vanadium sulphate, $V_2(SO_4)_3$; but the solubility of vanadium in mercury is too small for measurement. H. E. Roscoe found that vanadium attacks the

platinum vessels in which it is heated. J. Aloy and A. Valdiguié studied the catalytic action of vanadium in hydrogenations.

Some reactions of analytical interest.—If vanadium pentoxide or vanadic acid be boiled with conc. **hydrochloric acid,** chlorine is given off, and mixed chlorides or oxychlorides are formed. An acid soln. of a vanadium salt gives no precipitate with **hydrogen sulphide,** but soln. of vanadic acid are reduced to blue vanadic tetroxide. Many other reducing agents—sulphur dioxide, hydrobromic acid, oxalic and tartaric acids, and sugar—act similarly : $V_2O_5+SO_2=SO_3+V_2O_4$; others—e.g. hydriodic acid—reduce vanadic acid to green vanadium trioxide : $V_2O_5+4HI=2H_2O+2I_2+V_2O_3$—the iodine is removed by boiling; and **metals** —zinc, cadmium, and aluminium—reduce the vanadic acid to violet or lavender vanadium dioxide so that the soln. becomes blue, then green, and then violet. A soln. of vanadic acid is coloured brown by **ammonium sulphide** owing to the formation of sulpho-salts, and vanadium pentasulphide—soluble in alkalies, and alkali carbonates and sulphides—is precipitated on adding an acid. The precipitation is not complete. A cold acidic soln. of a vanadate gives with **ammonia** a yellow coloration until the soln. is neutral ; soln. of **alkali hydroxides** give a brown precipitate soluble in excess, forming a yellowish-green soln. If a piece of solid **ammonium chloride** be added to a soln. of an alkali vanadate, colourless ammonium vanadate is precipitated, and this is but sparingly soluble in a conc. soln. of ammonium chloride. When an acid soln. of a vanadate is treated with a few drops of **hydrogen dioxide,** and shaken, the soln. becomes reddish-brown—vide titanium salts—this reaction is very sensitive. When a neutral soln. of a vanadate is treated with **mercurous nitrate,** white mercurous vanadate is precipitated, and the precipitate is soluble in nitric acid ; **lead acetate** under similar conditions gives a yellow precipitate of lead vanadate, also soluble in nitric acid ; **barium chloride**— not strontium or calcium chloride—gives a yellow precipitate which soon becomes colourless when warmed ; **copper salts** give a bluish-yellow precipitate with metavanadates, and a green precipitate with orthovanadates. A soln. of vanadate containing acetate and free ammonia or acetic acid, gives a precipitate of ammonium uranyl vanadate when treated with a soln. of a **uranium salt ;** and a boiling soln. of a vanadate, mixed with ammonium chloride and ammonia, gives manganous vanadate when treated with **manganous chloride.** A soln. of vanadic acid gives a green, flocculent precipitate when treated with **potassium ferrocyanide ;** and **tannic acid,** a bluish-black precipitate. When a conc. sulphuric acid soln. of vanadic acid is treated with **strychnine sulphate** it gives a bluish-violet coloration which soon becomes rose-coloured—this reaction is very sensitive ; with **aniline hydrochloride,** aniline black is formed. For reactions with salts of the lower oxides of vanadium, vide infra.

The physiological action of vanadium salts.—According to J. Priestley,[10] vanadium salts are poisonous, producing paralysis, convulsions, sleepiness, falling temp., and slow pulse. D. E. Jackson found that vanadium produces gastrointestinal irritation, increased intestinal peristalsis, and a rise of blood-pressure, more lasting but less pronounced than that caused by adrenaline. Constriction of the arterioles is present in kidney, intestine, and spleen, but not in the leg. This action is peripheral, not central. W. F. Dutton described the effects of the absorption of fumes from vanadium on workers. An early symptom of the effects is anæmia accompanied by emaciation and irritation of the throat and eyes, and the disease often terminates fatally. He advises thorough ventilation and the use of respirators as protective measures. J. Priestley found that with dogs the lethal dose is 0·00918–0·01466 grm. of the pentoxide per kilogram. The antidote is potassium ferrocyanide, and substances containing tannin. A. Gamgee and L. Larmuth studied the action of vanadium salts on frogs, and it was found that the toxicity of alkali orthovanadate is smaller than that of the pyro- or metavanadate. C. Binz and H. Schulz suggested that the members of the arsenic family owe their poisonous nature to the alternate oxidization and reduction which destroys

the albumen. S. Suzuki found that the presence of 0·1 per cent. of vanadium in a
water-culture medium acts banefully on barley, but 0·01 per cent. does no harm.
H. Weber said that the vanadium salts are antiseptic, and recommended a mixture
of sodium chlorate and a vanadium salt to which he applied the trade name *vanadin*,
but T. Bokorny said that the vanadium salts have no special antiseptic power.
F. Laran, and B. L. Lyonnet and co-workers recommended vanadium salts as a
therapeutic agent in tuberculosis, and anæmia.

The uses of vanadium.—Up to the early 'sixties of the nineteenth century
vanadium was a chemical curiosity. About that time, vanadic acid was found to
be more suitable than chromic acid as an oxidizing agent in some dyeing processes; [11] in the production of various shades of aniline dyes; [12] as a catalyst in
the oxidation of aniline hydrochloride to a fixed black for an indelible ink ; and as
a mordant in the transformation of vegetable cellulose to oxycellulose. The last-
named application, however, was superseded owing to the deleterious effect on
the fabric. It has been used as a photographic developer and sensitizer ; [13] as a
reducing agent ; [14] as a dryer for linseed oil paints ; [15] as a contact catalyst in
the oxidation of sulphur dioxide,[16] and other substances; in the purification of
hydrochloric acid from arsenic,[17] for the addition of vanadium dichloride causes
the precipitation of arsenic ; and vanadium carbide has been used in the preparation of incandescent [18] filaments. There are also some therapeutic applications
—*vide supra*, the physiological action of arsenic.[19] Perhaps the most important
application of vanadium is in the addition of a small proportion of that element to
steel, brass, etc. The general effect of vanadium is to toughen the alloy and increase
its resistance to repeated shocks, or varying stresses—*vide supra ;* [20] and it is used
in some rectifiers.[21]

REFERENCES.

1 A. W. Hull, *Phys. Rev.*, (2), **20**. 113, 1923; W. C. Brögger and G. Flink, *Zeit. Kryst.*, **9**.
232, 1884 ; J. W. Marden and M. N. Rich, *Journ. Ind. Eng. Chem.*, **19**. 786, 1927 ; H. Mache,
Sitzber. Akad. Wien, **106**. 590, 1897 ; H. E. Roscoe, *Phil. Trans.*, **158**. 1, 1868 ; **159**. 679, 1869 ;
160. 317, 1870 ; *Proc. Roy. Soc.*, **16**. 220, 1868 ; **18**. 37, 316, 1870 ; *Journ. Chem. Soc.*, **21**. 322,
1868 ; **23**. 344, 1870 ; **24**. 23, 1871 ; *Chem. News*, **17**. 135, 1868 ; **20**. 37, 1869 ; **21**. 183, 1870 ;
Phil. Mag., (4), **35**. 307, 1868 ; (4), **39**. 146, 1870 ; (4), **40**. 62, 1870 ; C. Setterberg, *Oefvers.
Vet. Akad. Förh.*, **39**. 10, 1862 ; L. Weiss and O. Aichel, *Liebig's Ann.*, **337**. 380, 1904 ; W. Muthmann, L. Weiss. and R. Riedelbauch, *ib.*, **355**. 58, 1907 ; O. Ruff and W. Martin, *Zeit. anorg.
Chem.*, **25**. 49, 1912 ; O. Ruff and L. Friedrich, *ib.*, **89**. 279, 1914 ; W. Prandtl and B. Bleyer,
ib., **64**. 217, 1909 ; W. Prandtl and H. Manz, *ib.*, **79**. 209, 1912 ; J. R. Rydberg, *Zeit. Phys.
Chem.*, **33**. 353, 1900 ; H. G. Grimm, *ib.*, **122**. 177, 1926 ; E. Donath and J. Mayrhofer, *Ber.*,
16. 1588, 1883 ; C. Matignon and E. Monnet, *Compt. Rend.*, **134**. 542, 1902 ; W. G. Mixter,
Amer. Journ. Science, (4), **34**. 141, 1912 ; W. R. Mott, *Trans. Amer. Electrochem. Soc.*, **34**. 255,
1918 ; G. K. Burgess and R. G. Waltenberg, *Journ. Franklin Inst.*, **176**. 737, 1913 ; *Brass World*,
9. 349, 1913 ; *Journ. Washington Acad.*, **3**. 361, 1913 ; *Zeit. anorg. Chem.*, **82**. 361, 1913 ;
P. W. Bridgman, *Proc. Amer. Acad.*, **62**. 207, 1927 ; L. Laissus, *Rev. Mét.*, **24**. 474, 1927 ;
W. von Bolton. *Zeit. Elektrochem.*, **11**. 45, 1905.

2 W. W. Coblentz, *Journ. Franklin Inst.*, **170**. 185, 1910 ; *Bull. Bur. Standards*, **2**. 470,
1907 ; 7. 215, 1911 ; H. von Wartenberg, *Verh. deut. phys. Ges.*, **12**. 105, 1910.

3 W. Biltz, *Zeit. anorg. Chem.*, **127**. 169, 1923 ; K. Someya, *ib.*, **161**. 46, 1927.

4 R. Thalén, *Om spectralanalyse*, Upsala, 1866 ; *Nova acta Upsala*, (3), **6**. 9, 1868 ; J. Parry
and A. E. Tucker, *Engg.*, **27**. 127, 429, 1879 ; **28**. 141, 1879 ; C. Porlezza and A. Donati, *Ann.
Chim. Applicata*, **16**. 622, 1926 ; E. Demarçay, *Spectres électriques*, Paris, 1895 ; F. Exner and
E. Haschek, *Wellenlängentabellen für spectralanalytische Untersuchungen auf Grund der ultra-
violetten Funkenspectren der Elemente*, Leipzig, 1902 ; *Wellenlängentabellen für spectralanalytische
Untersuchungen auf Grund der ultravioletten Bogenspectren der Elemente*, Leipzig, 1904 ; *Die
Spectren der Elemente bei normalen Druck*, Leipzig, 1912 ; *Sitzber. Akad. Wien*, **107**. 182, 1898 ;
A. Hagenbach and H. Konen, *Atlas der Emissionspectra*, Jena, 1905 ; J. M. Eder and E. Valenta,
Atlas typischer Spectren, Wien, 1911 ; *Sitzber. Akad. Wien*, **118**. 511, 1077, 1909 ; **119**. 519,
1910 ; T. Okaya, *Proc. Phys. Math. Soc. Japan*, (3), **1**. 332, 1919 ; A. de Gramont, *Bull. Soc.
Min.*, **21**. 94, 1898 ; *Analyse spectrale directe des minéraux*, Paris, 1895 ; *Compt. Rend.*, **126**.
1513, 1898 ; **150**. 37, 1910 ; **175**. 1129, 1922 ; J. N. Lockyer, *ib.*, **86**. 317, 1878 ; *Proc. Roy.
Soc.*, **27**. 279, 1878 ; **65**. 451, 1899 ; J. N. Lockyer and F. E. Bascandall, *ib.*, **68**. 189, 1901 ;
W. N. Hartley and H. W. Moss, *ib.*, **87**. A, 38, 1912 ; H. A. Rowland, *Astron. Astrophys.*, **12**.
321, 1893 ; *Phil. Mag.*, (5), **36**. 49, 1893 ; *Astrophys. Journ.*, **5**. 1, 1898 ; H. A. Rowland and

C. N. Harrison, *ib.*, **7.** 273, 1898 ; W. J. Humphreys, *ib.*, **6.** 169, 1897 ; W. M. Mitchell, *ib.*, **22.** 4, 1905 ; P. G. Nutting, *ib.*, **23.** 64, 220, 1906 ; G. E. Hale, W. S. Adams, and A. G. Gale, *ib.*, **24.** 185, 1906 ; H. Konen, *ib.*, **26.** 129, 1907 ; A. S. King, *ib.*, **28.** 300, 1908 ; **60.** 282, 1924 ; H. Shaw, *ib.*, **30.** 127, 1900 ; W. S. Adams, *ib.*, **30.** 86, 1909 ; A. M. Kilby, *ib.*, **30.** 243, 1909 ; R. Rossi, *ib.*, **34.** 21, 1911 ; H. D. Babcock, *ib.*, (1), **34.** 209, 1911 ; *Phys. Rev.*, (2), **22.** 201, 1923 ; A. Frerichs, *Ann. Physik*, (4), **81.** 807, 1926 ; B. Hasselberg, *Astrophys. Journ.*, **5.** 194, 1897 ; **6.** 22, 1897 ; *Behang Svenska Akad. Handl.*, **22.** 7, 1897 ; *Svenska Akad. Hand.*, **32.** 2, 1899 ; J. Formanek, *Die qualitative Spektralanalyse anorganischer und organischer Körper*, Berlin, 1905 ; H. Kayser, *Handbuch der Spectroscopie*, Leipzig, **6.** 750, 1912 ; C. C. Kiess and O. Laporte, *Science*, (2), **63.** 234, 1926 ; H. Nagakoa and Y. Sugiura, *Science Papers Japan Inst. Phys. Chem.*, **2.** 139, 1924 ; M. Kimura and G. Nakamura, *ib.*, **3.** 51, 1925 ; O. Lohse, *Sitzber. Akad. Berlin*, **179**, 1897 ; *Publ. Astrophys. Obs. Potsdam*, **12.** 41, 1902 ; M. Eppley, *Journ. Franklin Inst.*, **201.** 333, 1926 ; J. E. Purvis, *Trans. Phil. Soc. Cambridge*, **20.** 193, 1906 ; G. A. Hemsalech, *Phil. Mag.*, (6), **39.** 241, 1920 ; F. W. Dyson, *Phil. Trans.*, **206.** A, 403, 1906 ; R. J. Lang, *ib.*, 224, A, 371, 1924 ; *Nature*, **118.** 119, 1926 ; C. E. Gissing, *Spark Spectra of the Metals*, London, 1910 ; J. H. Pollock, *Proc. Roy. Soc. Dublin*, **11.** 331, 1909 ; W. F. Meggers, *Zeit. Physik*, **33.** 509, 1925 ; **39.** 114, 1926 ; *Journ. Washington Acad.*, **13.** 317, 1923 ; **14.** 151, 1924 ; C. C. Kiess and W. F. Meggers, *Bull. Bur. Standard-Scient. Papers*, **16.** 51, 1920 ; W. F. Meggers, C. C. Kiess, and F. M. Walters, *Journ. Amer. Opt. Soc.*, **9.** 355, 1924 ; M. A. Catalan, *Anal. Fis. Quim.*, **22.** 68, 72, 1924 ; K. Bechert and M. A. Catalan, *Zeit. Physik*, **37.** 658, 1926 ; A. Leide, *ib.*, **39.** 686, 1926 ; R. Mecke, *Zeit. Physik*, **42.** 390, 1927 ; O. Laporte, *Naturwiss.*, **11.** 779, 1923 ; *Phys. Zeit.*, **24.** 510, 1923 ; H. Gieseler and W. Grotrian, *Zeit. Physik*, **25.** 342, 1924 ; K. Bechert and L. A. Sommer, *ib.*, **31.** 145, 1925 ; W. Ludwig, *Zeit. wiss. Photochem.*, **16.** 157, 1917 ; R. C. Gibbs and H. E. White, *Proc. Nat. Acad.*, **12.** 448, 1926 ; *Phys. Rev.*, (2), **29.** 359, 426, 60 5, 655, 917, 1927 ; S. Goudsmit, *ib.*, (2), **31.** 946, 1928 ; H. N. Russell, *Astrophys. Journ.*, **66.** 184, 1927.

[5] V. Dolejsek, *Compt. Rend.*, **174.** 441, 1922 ; O. Stelling, *Zeit. phys. Chem.*, **117.** 175, 1925 ; H. Fricke, *Phys. Rev.*, (2), **16.** 202, 1920 ; K. Chamberlain, *ib.*, (2), **26.** 525, 1925 ; K. H. Kingdon, *ib.*, (2), **23.** 778, 1924 ; M. Levi, *Trans. Roy. Soc. Canada*, (3), **18.** 159, 1924 ; E. Hjalmar, *Phis. Mag.*, (6), **41.** 675, 1921 ; *Zeit. Physik*, **1.** 439, 1920 ; N. Stensson, *ib.*, **3.** 60, 1920 ; A. Leide, *ib.*, **39.** 636, 1923 ; B. B. Ray, *Phil. Mag.*, (6), **49.** 168, 1925 ; S. B. Hendricks and R. W. C. Wyckoff, *Journ. Phys. Chem.*, **31.** 703, 1927 ; M. J. Druyvesteyn, *Zeit. Physik*, **43.** 707, 1927 ; D. M. Bose, *Phys. Rev.*, (2), **27.** 521, 1926 ; *Zeit. Physik*, **35.** 213, 1925 ; D. Coster, *ib.*, **25.** 83, 1924 ; M. Siegbahm, *Jahrb. Rad. Elektron.*, **13.** 296, 1916 ; *Phil. Maj.*, (6), **37.** 601, 1919 ; R. Thoraeus, *ib.*, (7), **2.** 1007, 1926 ; G. Wentzel, *Naturwiss.*, **10.** 464, 1922 ; D. Coster, *Zeit. Physik*, **25.** 83, 1924 ; A. E. Lindh, *Zeit. Physik*, **31.** 210, 1925 ; B. Walter, *ib.*, **30.** 357, 1924 ; N. Seljakoff, A. Krasnikoff, and T. Stellezky, *ib.*, **45.** 548, 1927 ; R. Robl, *Zeit. angew. Chem.*, **39.** 608, 1926 ; H. N. Russell, *Astrophys. Journ.*, **66.** 233, 1927 ; R. N. Ghosh, *Journ. Indian Chem. Soc.*, **4.** 423, 1927.

[6] W. Muthmann and F. Fraunberger, *Sitzber. Akad. München*, **34.** 221, 1904 ; L. Marino, *Gazz. Chim. Ital.*, **34.** 230, 1904 ; *Zeit. anorg. Chem.*, **39.** 168, 1904 ; G. Tammann and J. Hinnüber, *ib.*, **160.** 256, 1927 ; T. F. Rutter, *ib.*, **52.** 368, 1907 ; *Die katalytischen Eigenschaften des Vanadins*, Leipzig, 1906 ; S. Fischer, *Trans. Amer. Electrochem. Soc.*, **30.** 175, 1916 ; L. Pissarjewsky, *Zeit. phys. Chem.*, **43.** 160, 1903 ; G. C. Schmidt, *ib.*, **106.** 105, 1923 ; J. W. Marden and M. N. Rich, *Journ. Ind. Eng. Chem.*, **19.** 786, 1927 ; G. Tammann and K. Schönert *Zeit. anorg. Chem.*, **122.** 27, 1922 ; P. Truchot, *Ann. Chim. Anal. Appl.*, **7.** 165, 1902 ; R. E. Myers, *Journ. Amer. Chem. Soc.*, **26.** 1130, 1904 ; A. Stahler and H. Wirthwein, *Ber.*, **38.** 3978, 1905 ; H. W. Underwood, *Chem. Met. Engg.*, **29.** 709, 1923 ; A. Piccini and N. Brizzi, *Zeit. anorg. Chem.*, **11.** 106, 1890 ; **19.** 394, 1899 ; A. Thiel and W. Hammerschmidt, *ib.*, **132.** 15, 1923 ; A. Bültemann, *Zeit. Elektrochem.*, **10.** 141, 1904 ; E. Renschler, *ib.*, **18.** 137, 1912 ; R. Luther, *ib.*, **13.** 294, 1907 ; W. F. Bleecker, *Met. Chem. Engg.*, **8.** 666, 1910 ; **9.** 209, 499, 1911 ; *U.S. Pat. No.* 1050796, 1913 ; L. Schicht, *Chem. News*, **41.** 280, 1880 ; **42.** 331, 1880 ; S. Cowper-Coles, *ib.*, **79.** 147, 1899 ; *Trans. Inst. Min. Met.*, **7.** 198, 1899 ; G. Gin, *Trans. Amer. Electrochem. Soc.*, **16.** 439, 1909 ; *Zeit. Elektrochem.*, **9.** 831, 1903 ; *German Pat.*, *D.R.P.* 154619, 1904 ; W. Borchers, *Elektrometallurgie*, Leipzig, 498, 1902 ; G. Gore, *Electrochemistry*, London, 101, 1906 ; C. Setterberg, *Oefvers. Vet. Akad. Förh.*, **39.** 10, 1882 ; K. F. Herzfeld, *Phys. Rev.*, (2), **29.** 703, 1927.

[7] K. Honda, *Science Rep. Tohoku Univ.*, **1.** 1, 1912 ; **2.** 25, 1913 ; **3.** 139, 223, 1914 ; **4.** 215, 1915 ; *Ann. Physik*, (4), **32.** 1027, 1910 ; M. Owen, *ib.*, (4), **37.** 657, 1912 ; P. Weiss and H. K. Onnes, *Compt. Rend.*, **150.** 687, 1910 ; P. Weiss and P. Collet, *ib.*, **178.** 2146, 1924 ; N. Perrakis, *Journ. Phys. Rad.*, **8.** 473, 1927 ; *Compt. Rend.*, **184.** 444, 1430, 1927 ; **185.** 111, 1927 ; P. Pascal, *ib.*, **147.** 742, 1908 ; W. Biltz, *Zeit. anorg. Chem.*, 127, 169, 1923 ; E. Wedekind, *Zeit. angew. Chem.*, **37.** 87, 1924 ; E. Wedekind and C. Horst, *Ber.*, **45.** 262, 1912 ; R. Dieterle, *Arch. Elektrotech.*, **9.** 314, 1920 ; I. Tamm, *Zeit. Physik*, **32.** 582, 1925 ; S. Freed, *Journ. Amer. Chem. Soc.*, **49.** 2456, 1927 ; D. M. Bose, *Zeit. Physik*, **43.** 864, 1927 ; D. M. Bose and H. G. Bhar, *ib.*, **48.** 716, 1928.

[8] W. Prandtl and H. Manz, *Zeit. anorg. Chem.*, **79.** 209, 1912 ; G. Tammann and K. Schönert, *ib.*, **122.** 27, 1922 ; W. Muthmann, L. Weiss, and R. Riedebauch, *Liebig's Ann.*, **355.** 58, 1907 ; L. Weiss and O. Aichel, *ib.*, **337.** 383, 1904 ; J. Aloy and A. Valdiguié, *Bull. Soc. Chim.*, (4), **35.** 792, 1924 ; O. Schmidt, *Zeit. phys. Chem.*, **118.** 193, 1925 ; C. Setterberg,

Oefvers. Vet. Akad. Förh., **39**. 10, 1882; H. E. Roscoe. Phil. Trans., **158**. 1, 1868; **159**. 679, 1869; **160**. 317, 1870; Proc. Roy. Soc., **16**. 220, 1868; **18**. 37, 316, 1870; Journ. Chem. Soc., **21**. 322, 1868; **23**. 344, 1870; **24**. 23, 1871; Chem. News, **17**. 135, 1868; **20**. 37, 1869; **21**. 183, 1870; Phil. Mag., (4), **35**. 307, 1868; (4), **39**. 146, 1870; (4), **40**. 62, 1870; H. W. Underwood, Chem. Met. Engg., **29**. 709, 1923; H. Huber, L. Kirschfeld, and A. Sieverts, Ber., **59**. B, 2891, 1926; L. Marino, Gazz. Chim. Ital., **39**. 152, 1904; H. Giebelhausen, Zeit. anorg. Chem., **91**. 251, 1915; N. Czako, Compt. Rend., **156**. 140, 1913; H. Moissan, ib., **122**. 1297, 1896; F. Fischer and F. Schrötter, Ber., **43**. 1442, 1454, 1910; M. Wunder and B. Janneret, ib., **152**. 1770, 1911; C. Matignon and E. Monnet, ib., **134**. 542, 1902; N. Domanicky, Journ. Russ. Phys. Chem. Soc., **48**. 1724, 1916; I. I. Tschukoff, Ann. Inst. Anal. Phys. Chem. Russ., **3**. 14, 1926; O. Schmidt, Zeit. phys. Chem., **118**. 193, 1925; A. Sieverts and A. Gotta, Zeit. anorg. Chem., **172**. 1, 1928.

⁹ H. Giebelhausen, Zeit. anorg. Chem., **91**. 251, 1915; R. J. Dunn and O. F. Hudson, Journ. Inst. Metals, **11**. 151, 1914; H. E. Roscoe, Phil. Trans., **158**. 1, 1868; **159**. 679, 1869; 160. 317, 1870; Proc. Roy. Soc., **16**. 220, 1868; **18**. 37, 316, 1870; Journ. Chem. Soc., **21**. 322, 1868; **23**. 344, 1870; **24**. 23, 1871; Chem. News, **17**. 135, 1868; **20**. 37, 1869; **21**. 183, 1870; Phil. Mag., (4), **35**. 307, 1868; (4), **39**. 146, 1870; (4), **40**. 62, 1870; G. Tammann and J. Hinnüber, Zeit. anorg. Chem., **160**. 256, 1927; R. M. Keeney, Mineral Ind., **26**. 720, 1917; H. Schirmeister, Beiträge zur Kenntnis der binären Aluminiumlegierungen hinsichtlich ihrer technischen Eigenschaften, Düsseldorf, 1914; Stahl Eisen, **35**. 649, 873, 996, 1915; R. Hohage and A. Grützner, ib., **44**. 1712, 1924; E. Maurer, ib., **45**. 1629, 1925; J. Aloy and A. Valdiguié, Bull. Soc. Chim.. (4), **35**. 792, 1924; G. Tammann and G. Siebel, Zeit. anorg. Chem., **148**. 297, 1925; J. O. Arnold and A. A. Reid, Journ. Iron Steel Inst., **83**. i, 249, 1911; **85**. i, 215, 1912.

¹⁰ H. Weber, Pharm. Ztg., **43**. 667, 1898; F. Laran, La Presse Médicale, i, 190, 1899; B. L. Lyonnet, F. Martz, and E. Martin, ib., i, 191, 1899; i, 190, 1899; Apoth. Ztg., **14**. 369, 1899; G. Witz and F. Osmond, Bull. Soc. Chim., (2), **45**. 309, 1886; A. Gamgee and L. Larmuth, Journ. Anat. Physiol., **11**. 235, 1877; L. Larmuth, ib., **11**. 251, 1877; J. Priestley, Phil. Trans., **166**. 495, 1876; Proc. Roy. Soc., **24**. 40, 1876; C. Binz and H. Schulz, Ber., **12**. 2199, 1879; T. Bokorny, Chem. Ztg., **28**. 596, 1804; S. Suzuki, Bull. Agric. Tokyo, **5**. 513, 1903; D. E. Jackson, Amer. Journ. Physiol., **29**. 23, 1911; W. F. Dutton, Eng. Min. Journ., **32**. 24, 1911.

¹¹ R. Pinkney, Brit. Pat. No., 2745, 1872; Chem. News, **33**. 116, 1876; J. Higgins, ib., **33**. 86, 1876; J. Lightfoot, Dingler's Journ., **203**. 483, 1872; E. Lauber and A. Steinheil, ib., **244**. 157, 1882; A. Guyard, Bull. Soc. Chim., (2), **25**. 58, 1876; Monit. Scient., (3), **6**. 355, 1876; G. Witz, ib., (3), **10**. 975, 1880; Compt. Rend., **83**. 348, 1876; **87**. 1087, 1878; **88**. 816, 1879; G. Witz and F. Osmond, ib., **95**. 42, 1882; S. Grawitz, ib., **88**. 389, 1879; F. L. Hess, Chem. Met. Engg., **23**. 1063, 1920; A. Rosenstiehl, Ann. Chim. Phys., (5), **8**. 561, 1876; Bull. Soc. Chim., (2), **25**. 291, 356, 1876; M. Hommey, Bull. Soc. Ind. Rouen, **4**. 263, 1876; Meister, Lucius, and Brüning, German Pat., D.R.P. 172654, 1903.

¹² R. Wagner, Dingler's Journ., **223**. 633, 1877; C. Appelbaum, ib., **271**. 423, 1889; R. Böttger, Jahresb. Phys. Ver. Frankfurt a. M., 18, 1872; G. Witz, Monit. Scient., (3), **10**. 975, 1880; C. A. Mitchell, Analyst, **28**. 146, 1903.

¹³ J. Gibbons, Chem. News, **30**. 267, 1874; R. E. Liesegang, Phot. Arch., **34**. 209, 1893; **36**. 282, 1895; M. Tobin, Apoth. Ztg., **14**. 661, 1899.

¹⁴ R. Luther and T. F. Rutter, Zeit. anorg. Chem., **54**. 1, 1907; R. Luther, Zeit. Elektrochem., **13**. 437, 1907.

¹⁵ F. H. Rhodes and K. S. Chen, Journ. Ind. Eng. Chem., **14**. 222, 1922.

¹⁶ E. de Haën, German Pat., D.R.P. 128616, 1902; F. W. Küster, Zeit. anorg. Chem., **42**. 459, 1904; A. Naumann, L. Moser, and E. Lindenbaum, Journ. prakt. Chem., (2), **75**. 146, 1907.

¹⁷ C. R. Böhm, Chem. Ztg., **31**. 1037, 1907; K. Thomas, Raw Material, **4**. 167, 1921; A. J. Ewins, Ind. Chemist, **1**. 3, 1925; G. M. Dyson, Chem. Age, **14**. 33, 1926.

¹⁸ Meister, Lucius. and Brüning, German Pat., D.R.P. 164355, 1905.

¹⁹ B. D. Saklatwalla, Journ. Ind. Eng. Chem., **14**. 968, 1922.

²⁰ Anon., Engg., **114**. 150, 1922; L. Moser, Oesterr. Chem. Ztg., **26**. 67, 1913; G. M. Dyson, Chem. Age, **14**. 33, 1926; B. D. Saklatwalla. Blast Furnace, **13**. 194, 202, 1925.

²¹ S. Ruben, U.S. Pat. No. 1649741, 1927.

§ 5. The Atomic Weight and Valency of Vanadium

Naturally, the at. wt. of vanadium was unknown so long as J. J. Berzelius'[1] hypothesis that vanadium dioxide, V_2O_2, was vanadium, was in vogue. From H. E. Roscoe's work on vanadium, it is possible to calculate from J. J. Berzelius' value for the ratio $V_2O_5 : V_2O_3$, the at. wt. 52·46; from his value for $VOCl_3 : 3AgCl$, 51·56; and from C. Czudnowicz's value for $V_2O_5 : V_2O_3$, 54·7. These numbers are too high. H. E. Roscoe showed that the error is most probably due to the presence of phosphoric acid in the vanadic acid employed, for this prevents the complete reduction of the pentoxide to the trioxide.

Vanadium acts in well-defined ways as a bi-, ter-, quadri-, and a quinque-valent element; but less clearly as a univalent element—*vide infra*, vanadium hemioxide—and as an element of a higher valency as a pentad—*vide infra*, the pervanadates. The compounds of bivalent vanadium show analogies with the salts of bivalent magnesium, chromium, manganese, iron, cobalt, and nickel—*e.g.* $RSO_4.7H_2O$, and some complex salts prepared by A. Piccini and L. Marino. The compounds of tervalent vanadium are analogous with the salts of tervalent alumi-nium, chromium, manganese, iron, and cobalt as exemplified by the alums prepared by A. Piccini, the complex fluorides of the type $(NH_4)_3RF_6$; and $CoRF_5.7H_2O$, prepared by E. Petersen, and A. Piccini and G. Giorgis. Quadrivalent vanadium furnishes an amphoteric oxide which can act both as a base and as an acid, forming hypovanadates; and the quadrivalency of the element is evident from H. E. Roscoe's determination of the vapour density of the tetrachloride, VCl_4. The subject was discussed by F. Parisi. Quinquevalent vanadium furnishes an oxide which acts as an acid radicle to form salts—vanadates—which C. F. Rammelsberg, J. Schabus, G. A. Kenngott, and A. Schafarik showed were, in many cases, isomorphous with the phosphates, and the arsenates. T. E. Thorpe's determination of the vapour density of the oxytrichloride, $VOCl_3$; and J. A. Hall's determination of the vapour density of the ester, $VO(C_2H_5O)_3$, agreed with this. According to D. I. Mendeléeff, the true analogies of vanadium are chromium and titanium on one hand, and columbium and tantalum on the other; vanadium exhibits a greater resemblance to the latter than to phosphorus.

H. E. Roscoe's value for the ratio $V_2O_5 : V_2O_3$ furnishes the at. wt. 51·382 (oxygen 16); and the ratio $VOCl_3 : 3Ag$ (107·88) gives, with chlorine 35·46, the at. wt. 51·046, and the ratio $VOCl_3 : 3AgCl$, 51·253. B. Brauner's best repre-sentative value from the early work so far considered is 51·33. W. Prandtl and B. Bleyer obtained from the ratio $VOCl_3 : 3AgCl$, 51·133, 50·965, and 51·069, and they considered that 51·069 was the best representative value; they also com-puted 51·356 from the ratio $V_2O_5 : V_2O_3$. F. W. Clarke's best representative value for the work so far considered is 51·037. D. J. McAdam decomposed anhydrous sodium metavanadate with hydrogen chloride and chlorine, and deter-mined the residual sodium chloride; they calculated from the ratio $NaVO_3 : NaCl$, 50·966 for the at. wt. of vanadium. H. V. A. Briscoe and H. F. V. Little obtained 50·941 from the ratio $VOCl_3 : 3Ag$, and 50·947 from the ratio $VOCl_3 : 3AgCl$. The general results show that with chlorine 35·457, the at. wt. of vanadium by H. E. Roscoe lies between 50·38 and 52·33; by W. Prandtl and B. Bleyer, between 50·87 and 51·2; by D. J. McAdam, between 50·94 and 50·99; and by H. V. A. Briscoe and H. F. V. Little, between 50·93 and 50·97. The best repre-sentative value is taken to be between 50·95 and 50·96; or **50·96.** The International Table for 1925 gives 51.

The **atomic number** of vanadium is 23. According to F. W. Aston,[2] vanadium has no **isotopes,** being a simple element with an at. mass of 51. The **electronic structure,** according to N. Bohr's scheme, is (2) (4, 4) (4, 4, 3) (2); R. Samuel and E. Markowicz gave (2) (2, 6) (2, 6, 3)(2). The subject was discussed by L. A. Sommer, M. L. Huggins, R. Ladenburg, C. D. Niven, D. M. Bose, S. Meyer, and H. Lessheim and co-workers; and G. Kirsch and H. Pettersson obtained no evidence of **atomic disintegration** when vanadium is bombarded with the long-range particles from the active-deposit of radium. H. Collins made some specu-lations on the structure of the atom of vanadium.

REFERENCES.

[1] J. J. Berzelius, *Lehrbuch der Chemie*, Dresden, 3. 1207, 1845: *Pogg. Ann.*, 22. 1, 1831; C. F. Rammelsberg, *ib.*, 98. 249, 1856; J. Schabus, *ib.*, 100. 297, 1856; G. A. Kenngott, *ib.*, 99. 95, 1856; C. Czudnowicz, *ib.*, 120. 17, 1863; H. E. Roscoe, *Phil. Trans.*, 158. 1, 1868; 159. 679, 1869; 160. 317, 1870; *Proc. Roy. Soc.*, 16. 220, 1868; 18. 37, 316, 1870; *Journ. Chem. Soc.*, 21. 322, 1868; 23. 344, 1870; 24. 23, 1871; *Chem. News*, 17. 135, 1868; 20. 37,

1869 ; **21.** 183, 1870 ; *Phil. Mag.*, (4), **35.** 307, 1868 ; (4), **39.** 146, 1870 ; (4), **40.** 62, 1870 ;
A. Schafarik, *Sitzber. Akad. Wien,* **33.** 1, 1858 ; **47.** 246, 1863 ; F. W. Clarke, *Amer. Chem. Journ.,*
3. 269, 1882 ; *Chem. News,* **63.** 76, 1891 ; *A Recalculation of the Atomic Weights,* Washington,
305, 1910 ; B. Brauner, *Handbuch der anorganischen Chemie,* Leipzig, **3.** ii, 679, 1907 ; A. Piccini,
Gazz. Chim. Ital., **27.** i, 416, 1897 ; A. Piccini and G. Giorgis, *ib.,* **22.** i, 55, 1892 ; A. Piccini
and L. Marino, *Zeit. anorg. Chem.,* **32.** 55, 1902 ; T. E. Thorpe, *Chem. News,* **24.** 135, 277, 1871 ;
Phil. Mag., (4), **42.** 305, 1871 ; H. V. A. Briscoe and H. F. V. Little, *Journ. Chem. Soc.,* **105.**
1310, 1914 ; J. A. Hall, *ib.,* **57.** 751, 1887 ; W. Prandtl and B. Bleyer, *Zeit. anorg. Chem.,* **65.**
152, 1910 ; **67.** 257, 1910 ; D. J. McAdam, *Journ. Amer. Chem. Soc.,* **32.** 1603, 1910 ; E. Petersen,
Ber., **21.** 3257, 1888 ; *Journ. prakt. Chem.,* (2), **40.** 52, 194, 271, 1889 ; D. I. Mendeléeff, *The
Principles of Chemistry,* London, **2.** 188, 1891 ; F. Parisi, *Gazz. Chim. Ital.,* **56.** 843, 1926 ;
57. 85.), 1927.

² H. Collins, *Chem. News,* **128.** 100, 1924 ; F. W. Aston, *Journ. Soc. Chem. Ind.—Chem.
Ind.,* **42.** 935, 1923 ; *Phil. Mag.,* (6), **47.** 385, 1924 ; (6), **49.** 1191, 1925 ; *Nature,* **112.** 449, 1923 ;
N. Bohr, *ib.,* **112.** Suppl., 1923 ; G. Kirsch and H. Pettersson, *ib.,* **112,** 394, 923 ; *Phil. Mag.,*
(6), **47.** 500, 1924 ; *Sitzber. Akad. Wien,* **132.** 299, 1924 ; **134.** 491, 1925 ; *Atomzertrummerung,*
Leipzig, 104, 1926 ; R. Samuel and E. Markowicz, *Zeit. Physik,* **38.** 22, 1926 ; L. A. Sommer,
ib., **37.** 1, 1926 ; M. L. Huggins, *Journ. Phys., Chem.,* **26.** 601, 1922 ; R. Ladenburg, *Naturwiss.,*
8. 88, 1920 ; S. Meyer, *ib.,* **15.** 623, 1927 ; C. D. Niven, *Phil. Mag.,* (7), **3.** 114, 1927 ;
D. M. Bose, *ib.,* (7), **5.** 1048, 1928 ; H. Lessheim, J. Meyer, and R. Samuel, *Zeit. Physik,* **43.**
199, 1927.

§ 6. Vanadium Hemioxide, Dioxide, and Trioxide

Vanadium furnishes the following well-defined oxides :

Vanadium dioxide, or hypovanadous oxide, V_2O_2, vanado-oxide.
Vanadium trioxide, or vanadous oxide, V_2O_3, vanadi-oxide.
Vanadium tetroxide, or hypovanadic oxide, V_2O_4, vanade-oxide.
Vanadium pentoxide, or vanadic oxide, V_2O_5, vanadan-oxide.

A hemioxide has been reported, and also a series of pervanadates. As indicated
below, there is some confusion in the nomenclature. The colour of the salt derived
from the dioxide is lavender or violet ; from the trioxide, green ; from the tetroxide,
blue ; and from the pentoxide, yellow.

J. J. Berzelius [1] reported a *purple oxide* to be formed by shaking vanadous hydroxide
with water for 24 hrs. in a vessel from which air is not all excluded ; a *green oxide*, by
melting a mixture of vanadium trioxide with six times its weight of the pentoxide, or a
mixture of equimolar parts of the tetra- and penta-oxides ; a *greenish-yellow oxide* by the
action of a neutral vanadous salt on a hypovanadic salt ; and an *orange-yellow oxide* by
exposing one of the previous oxides to air. These products doubtless represent intermediate stages in the oxidation of vanadium trioxide and one of the higher oxides. A. Ditte
reported the intermediate oxide, V_4O_7, *vanadium heptatetritoxide*, or $V_2O_3.V_2O_4$, or
$V_2O_2.V_2O_5$, as a dark blue crystalline mass formed by heating to redness in a porcelain
crucible lined with carbon a mixture of vanadium pentoxide, or ammonium metavanadate
and arsenic trioxide : or by reducing ammonium vanadate with sulphur dioxide at a red-
heat. There is nothing to show that this oxide is a chemical individual. O. Manasse reported the oxide, V_8O_{17}, or $3V_2O_4.V_2O_5$, to be formed by dissolving in alkali-lye the tetroxide
mixed with pentoxide ; A. Ditte reported V_4O_9, or $V_2O_4.V_2O_5$, by heating ammonium
metavanadate in air until the residue is almost melted, and by C. F. Rammelsberg,
by heating the pentoxide with lithium carbonate. J. T. Brierley obtained the hydrate
$V_2O_4.V_2O_5.2\frac{2}{3}H_2O$, by gently heating the salt $(NH_4)_2O.2V_2O_4.2V_2O_5.14H_2O$; and
J. J. Berzelius, and J. T. Brierley also reported $V_3O_7.4H_2O$, or $V_2O_4.2V_2O_5.8H_2O$, by slowly
heating vanadium trioxide in air. In all these cases, there is nothing to show that the
products are not intermediate stages in the oxidation of a lower to a high vanadium oxide.

H. E. Roscoe [2] suggested that the brown oxide which first forms on the surface
of vanadium when the finely divided metal is exposed to air for a long time, may be
vanadium suboxide, or **vanadium hemioxide**, V_2O, or, according to A. Werner's
nomenclature, *vanada-oxide*. According to W. Hittorf, the same oxide is formed
when vanadium pentoxide is reduced by the aluminium thermite process. J. Koppel
and A. Kaufmann, however, showed that the alleged suboxide is probably a mixture
of vanadium dioxide and vanadium.

According to H. E. Roscoe,[3] *hypovanadous oxide*, or *vanadium monoxide*, VO
or **vanadium dioxide**, V_2O_2, or VO, or, in A. Werner's nomenclature, *vanado-
oxide*, was regarded by J. J. Berzelius as elemental vanadium. By analogy with

the chromium oxides, A. Piccini called this compound *vanadous oxide*. There is therefore some confusion in the naming of these oxides. The analogy between chromic oxide, Cr_2O_3, and vanadium trioxide, V_2O_3, is not sufficient to overshadow the closer analogy between the vanadium compounds and those of, say, phosphorus, or nitrogen. The dioxide was prepared by A. Safarik, and H. E. Roscoe, by reducing the higher oxides with potassium, or by passing the vapour of vanadium oxytrichloride, mixed with an excess of hydrogen, through a combustion tube containing red-hot carbon. The dioxide remains as a grey metallic powder admixed with carbon. It is freed from chlorine by heating it to redness in hydrogen. L. Pauling discussed the space-lattice. The sp. gr. given by E. Wedekind and C. Horst is 5·758 at 14°. From W. G. Mixter's $(2V,5O) > 441$ Cals. ; and $(V_2O_2,3O) = 87·8$ Cals., it follows that $(2V,O_2) > 209$ Cals. E. Wedekind and C. Horst found the magnetic susceptibility to be $50·06 \times 10^{-6}$ units. In the compressed state, it conducts electricity. The dioxide is insoluble in water ; but it dissolves in dil. acids, forming a lavender or violet soln. of a **hypovanadous salt** without giving off hydrogen. A similar liquid is obtained by reducing a soln. of vanadium pentoxide in, say, sulphuric acid, with sodium amalgam, zinc or cadmium ; in the latter case the soln. should be warm, and a little platinum present. L. Schlucht reduced a soln. of vanadium pentoxide in dil. sulphuric acid electrolytically to the lavender-blue liquid ; J. T. Brierley similarly reduced a soln. of vanadium tetroxide ; and A. Piccini and L. Marino, a soln. of vanadium trichloride or pentoxide, with a platinum cathode, in which case, according to L. Marino, the yield is good in sulphuric acid soln. The results are not so good in hydrochloric acid or neutral soln. ; in the latter case, oxy-salts are formed. T. F. Rutter recommended a mercury cathode. If the lavender-blue soln. be treated with potassium or sodium hydroxide, brown or purple-red **hypovanadous hydroxide,** $V(OH)_2$, is precipitated. The hypovanadous salts are among the most powerful reducing agents of inorganic chemistry. The neutral and acidic soln. absorb oxygen very energetically ; they decompose water ; and rapidly bleach litmus, indigo-blue, and other vegetable colours. The hypovanadous hydroxide which is precipitated by alkali-lye immediately begins to decompose the water with the evolution of hydrogen and the formation of vanadous hydroxide, $V(OH)_3$. According to A. Piccini and L. Marino, when the soln. of a hypovanadous salt is treated with sodium carbonate, it gives a violet precipitate which decomposes at once. Sodium sulphide gives a violet precipitate which decomposes with evolution of hydrogen and hydrogen sulphide. With potassium nitrate and hydrochloric acid, there is an evolution of nitric oxide. From salts of tin, silver, gold, and platinum, the metal is precipitated by a soln. of a vanadous salt ; in the same way, copper is deposited quantitatively from its soln. It is worthy of note that chromous salts reduce cupric salts only to cuprous oxide. A. Piccini and L. Marino recommended the reducing action on a soln. of a copper salt as a test for hypovanadites ; T. F. Rutter, the reducing action on silver sulphate. L. Marino held that the latter test is not conclusive since vanadous salts also give a precipitate with silver sulphate whereas copper salts do not. T. F. Rutter, however, found that copper salts can be reduced by vanadous salts in acid soln. Hypovanadous salts precipitate arsenic from its soln. in hydrochloric acid—*vide supra*, the uses of vanadium. T. F. Rutter measured the oxidation potential—*vide supra*. E. Müller and A. Flath, R. Lang, and R. G. Gustavson and C. M. Knudson studied the electrometric titration of salts of bivalent vanadium with potassium permanganate. Results by the former, with 10 c.c. of a soln. containing about 0·1 grm. vanadium per litre, 85 c.c. of water, and 4 c.c. of conc. sulphuric acid,

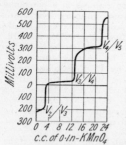

FIG. 4.—The Electrometric Titration of Hypovanadous Salts with Potassium Permanganate.

are indicated in Fig. 4. N. H. Furman titrated the salts with soln. of ceric sulphate.

J. J. Berzelius[4] obtained **vanadium trioxide,** *vanadous oxide,* or *vanadium sesquioxide,* V_2O_3, which, by analogy with chromic oxide, Cr_2O_3, was called by A. Piccini, *vanadic oxide.* A. Werner called it *vanadi-oxide.* J. J. Berzelius prepared this oxide by reducing vanadium pentoxide by hydrogen, at a red-heat, or, according to H. E. Roscoe, at a white-heat. If the pentoxide be crystalline, J. J. Berzelius said that the trioxide will also be crystalline ; and H. E. Roscoe added that the presence of one per cent. of phosphoric acid hinders the reduction. A. Ditte, A. Safarik, and C. Czudnowicz employed this process. J. J. Berzelius also obtained the trioxide by fusing the pentoxide in a carbon crucible ; A. A. Read, by heating the pentoxide to 1750° ; A. Ditte, by melting the pentoxide with an excess of potassium cyanide and extracting the mass with water ; A. Ditte, by heating ammonium metavanadate out of contact with air, either alone, or mixed with an excess of sulphur or of ammonium oxalate ; H. E. Roscoe, by passing a mixture of vanadium oxytrichloride, $VOCl_3$, and hydrogen through a red-hot tube ; E. Friederich and L. Sittig, by heating the pentoxide in hydrogen ; and E. Wedekind and C. Horst, by heating the solid oxychloride, VOCl, to a red-heat in a current of hydrogen until the brown mass is quite black in colour, and free from chlorine. The operation requires 12–16 hrs. G. Wegelin obtained a colloidal form by a prolonged grinding in an agate mortar.

Vanadium trioxide occurs a black powder, or in black lustrous crystals. V. M. Goldschmidt and co-workers said that the crystals are like those of corundum. A. Safarik gave 4·72 for the sp. gr. at 16° ; and W. Prandtl and B. Bleyer, 4·870. H. E. Roscoe said that this oxide is infusible, meaning, of course, that the m.p. is above the temp. of the ordinary furnaces available in his time. O. Ruff and W. Martin gave the m.p. at about 2000° ; and E. Friederich and L. Sittig, 1970°. E. Tiede and E. Birnbräuer made observations on this subject. W. G. Mixter's data $(2V,5O) > 441$ Cals. ; $(V_2O_3,2O) = 87·8$ Cals., corresponds with $(2V,3O) > 353$ Cals. H. E. Roscoe and L. Bleekrode said that the oxide is a good electrical conductor ; E. Friederich and L. Sittig gave 55×10^{-4} ohm for the resistance at 1100°. E. Wedekind and C. Horst found the magnetic susceptibility to be $13·88 \times 10^{-6}$ units. N. Perrakıs studied this subject. When the trioxide is heated in air, it oxidizes and burns like tinder. J. J. Berzelius said that it oxidizes the most readily in air, the lower the temp. at which it has been prepared, and after some months it forms small indigo-blue crystals of the tetroxide.

O. Schmidt studied the adsorption of hydrogen, argon, oxygen, nitrogen, ammonia, methane, ethane, ethylene, carbon monoxide, and carbon dioxide. H. von Wartenberg and co-workers found that at 2500°, vanadium trioxide is reduced by hydrogen at about 5 atm. press. H. Müller found that the values of $K = p_{H_2O}/p_{H_2}$ in the V_2O_4/V_2O_3-reaction : $V_2O_3 + H_2O \rightleftharpoons V_2O_4 + H_2$, at 493°, 538°, and 606°, are respectively 2·20, 2·63, and 5·03 ; and the calculated thermal values, respectively 121·8, 122·7, and 121·3. The trioxide colours water green ; and H. E. Roscoe represented the reaction which occurs when the trioxide is heated in chlorine : $3V_2O_3 + 6Cl_2 = V_2O_5 + 4VOCl_3$; ammonia transforms the white-hot trioxide into the nitride, VN. H. E. Roscoe said that the trioxide is insoluble in most acids and in alkali-lye. A. Safarik found that hot, dil. hydrochloric acid forms a dark green liquid ; and J. J. Berzelius said that with the exception of nitric acid, boiling acids do not dissolve the trioxide ; nitric acid forms a blue soln. and gives off nitric oxide. P. Sabatier and J. B. Senderens found that vanadium trioxide below 500° is not affected by nitrous oxide ; nor is it oxidized by nitric oxide ; but between 300° and 400°, nitrogen peroxide converts it into yellow pentoxide. E. Müller and H. Barck said that vanadium trioxide completely decomposes nitric oxide at 500°, forming vanadium tetroxide. P. Sabatier and A. Mailhe, and J. N. Pearce and A. M. Alvarado studied the catalytic activity of vanadium trioxide on the vapour of ethyl alcohol in forming ethylene. In the presence of **sulphuric** acid, the trioxide is oxidized to the pentoxide by potassium permanganate. J. J. Ber‹ zelius found that a mixed soln. of mercuric chloride and a vanadous salt gives with ammonia a mixed precipitate of *mercuric vanadite* and mercury diamminochloride. The precipitation is quantitative.

The analogies between vanadium trioxide and the oxides of tervalent aluminium, chromium, and iron have been indicated above. Salts of this basic trioxide oxide— **vanadous salts**—were obtained by H. E. Roscoe by reducing a sulphuric acid soln. of vanadium pentoxide by magnesium, or zinc ; by F. A. Gooch and R. W. Curtis, by reducing a soln. of vanadium pentoxide with hydriodic or hydrobromic acid ; by J. Locke and G. H. Edwards, by reducing vanadium oxydichloride with sodium amalgam ; and by A. Cioci, A. Piccini and N. Brizzi, E. Renschler, A. Bültemann, and T. F. Rutter, by the electrolytic reduction of a soln. of vanadium tetroxide or pentoxide in sulphuric acid. K. Someya discussed the violet colour of vanadous salt soln. The green soln. readily oxidizes in air. and it reduces soln. of silver and mercuric salts. L. Marino said that it does not reduce soln. of copper salts, but T. F. Rutter found that it does so. T. F. Rutter's observations are indicated in Table I. The vanadous salts are considered to be among the most powerful reducing agents in inorganic chemistry. They unite with oxygen with unusual vigour, and they decompose water with evolution of hydrogen even in the presence of acids and alkalies—these agents indeed accelerate the speed of the reaction. The vanadous salts relate vanadium with the magnesium series and with the chromium compounds. In the series, Ti, V, Cr, Mn, Fe, Co, Ni, titanous chloride is more difficult to prepare than the vanadous salt, and this in turn is more difficult to prepare than the chromous salt. Vanadous compounds are very unstable in aq. soln., while titanous salts decompose in the presence of water. When the green soln. is treated with aq. soln. of ammonia, or with the hydroxides or carbonates of the alkalies or alkaline earths, a flocculent, green precipitate of **vanadous hydroxide**, $V(OH)_3$, is produced. The presence of tartaric acid hinders the precipitation. The green hydroxide is oxidized to a brown hydroxide on exposure to air ; it is insoluble in an excess of alkali-lye, and with acids, it furnishes vanadous salts. Thus, E. Petersen found that with hydrofluoric acid it forms a soln. of vanadium trifluoride. A. Rogers and E. F. Smith prepared **ammonium vanaditoctotungstate**, $3(NH_4)_2O.V_2O_3.8WO_3.10H_2O$, in crystals freely soluble in water ; no precipitation occurs with an ammoniacal soln. of cupric sulphate. O. W. Gibbs obtained **mercurous vanaditoctotungstate** with a soln. of mercurous nitrate and ammonium divanaditotungstate, and he anticipated the existence of *platinum vanaditomolybdate* and a *platinum vanaditotungstate* analogous to the arsenitotungstate.

REFERENCES.

¹ J. J. Berzelius, *Akad. Handl. Stockholm*, 1, 1831 ; *Pogg. Ann.*, 22. 1, 1831 ; *Schweigger's Journ.*, 62. 323, 1831 ; 63. 26, 1831 ; A. Ditte, *Compt. Rend.*, 101. 1487, 1885 ; O. Manasse, *Liebig's Ann.*, 240. 23, 1886 ; C. F. Rammelsberg, *Sitzber. Akad. Berlin*, 3, 1883 ; J. T. Brierley, *Journ. Chem. Soc.*, 49. 30, 1886.

² H. E. Roscoe, *Phil. Trans.*, 158. 1, 1868 ; 159. 679, 1869 ; 160. 317, 1870 ; *Proc. Roy. Soc.*, 16. 220, 1868 ; 18. 37, 316, 1870 ; *Journ. Chem. Soc.*, 21. 322, 1868 ; 23. 344, 1870 ; 24. 23, 1871 ; *Chem. News*, 17. 135, 1868 ; 20. 37, 1869 ; 21. 183, 1870 ; *Phil. Mag.*, (4), 35. 307, 1868 ; (4), 39. 146, 1870 ; (4), 40. 62, 1870 ; W. Hittorf, *Phys. Zeit.*, 4. 196, 1903 ; J. Koppel and A. Kaufmann, *Zeit. anorg. Chem.*, 45. 352, 1905 ; A. Werner, *Neuere Anschauungen auf dem Gebiete der anorganischen Chemie*, Braunschweig, 12, 1905 ; London, 74, 1911.

³ H. E. Roscoe, *Phil. Trans.*, 158. 1, 1868 ; 159. 679, 1869 ; 160. 317, 1870 ; *Proc. Roy. Soc.*, 16. 220, 1868 ; 18. 37, 316, 1870 ; *Journ. Chem. Soc.*, 21. 322, 1868 ; 23. 344, 1870 ; 24. 23, 1871 ; *Chem. News*, 17. 135, 1868 ; 20. 37, 1869 ; 21. 183, 1870 ; *Phil. Mag.*, (4), 35. 307, 1868 ; (4), 39. 146, 1870 ; (4), 40. 62, 1870 ; A. Werner, *Neuere Anschauungen auf dem Gebiete der anorganischen Chemie*, Braunschweig, 12, 1905 ; London, 74, 1911 ; E. Müller and A. Flath, *Zeit. Elektrochem.*, 29. 500, 1923 ; R. Lang, *ib.*, 32. 454, 1926 ; J. J. Berzelius, *Akad. Handl. Stockholm*, 1, 1831 ; *Pogg. Ann.*, 22. 1, 1831 ; *Schweigger's Journ.*, 62. 323, 1831 ; 63. 26, 1831 ; J. T. Brierley, *Journ. Chem. Soc.*, 49. 822, 1886 ; L. Schlucht, *Berg. Hütt. Ztg.*, 39. 121, 1880 ; *Zeit. anal. Chem.*, 22. 241, 1883 ; E. Wedekind, *Zeit. angew. Chem.*, 37. 87, 1924 ; E. Wedekind and C. Horst, *Ber.*, 45. 262, 1912 ; 48. 102, 1915 ; A. Piccini, *Gazz. Chim. Ital.*,

27. i. 416, 1897; *Zeit. anorg. Chem.*, 19. 204, 1899; A. Piccini and L. Marino, *ib.*, 32. 55, 1902;
L. Marino, *ib.*, 50. 49, 1906; T. F. Rutter, *ib.*, 52. 368, 1907; *Zeit. Elektrochem.*, 12. 230, 1906;
Die katalytischen Eigenschaften des Vanadins, Leipzig, 1906; A. Safarik, *Liebig's Ann.*, 109.
85, 1859; W. G. Mixter, *Amer. Journ. Science*, (4), 34. 141, 1912; L. Pauling, *Journ. Amer.
Chem. Soc.*, 49. 765, 1927; N. H. Furman, *ib.*, 50. 755, 1675, 1928; R. G. Gustavson and
C. M. Knudson, *ib.*, 44. 2756, 1922.
⁴ J. J. Berzelius, *Akad. Handl. Stockholm*, 1, 1831; *Pogg. Ann.*, 22. 1, 1831; *Schweigger's
Journ.*, 62. 323, 1831; 63. 26, 1831; H. E. Roscoe, *Phil. Trans.*, 158. 1, 1868; 159. 679, 1869;
160. 317, 1870; *Proc. Roy. Soc.*, 16. 220, 1868; 18. 37, 316, 1870; *Journ. Chem. Soc.*, 21. 322,
1868; 23. 344, 1870; 24. 23, 1871; *Chem. News*, 17. 135, 1868; 20. 37, 1869; 21. 183, 1870;
Phil. Mag., (4), 35. 307, 1868; (4), 39. 146, 1870; (4), 42. 62, 1870; A. Werner,
Neuere Anschauungen auf dem Gebiete der anorganischen Chemie, Braunschweig, 12, 1905;
London, 74, 1911; A. Piccini, *Gazz. Chim. Ital.*, 27. i, 416, 1897; *Zeit. anorg. Chem.*, 19. 204,
1899; A. Piccini and L. Marino, *ib.*, 32. 55, 1902; L. Marino, *ib.*, 50. 49, 1906; A. Piccini
and N. Brizzi, *ib.*, 19. 394, 1899; A. Ditte, *Compt. Rend.*, 101. 1487, 1885; P. Sabatier and
J. B. Senderens, *ib.*, 114. 1431, 1892; 115. 236, 1892; 120. 618, 1895; P. Sabatier and A. Mailhe,
Ann. Chim. Phys., (8), 20. 289, 1910; R. Lang, *Zeit. Elektrochem.*, 32. 454, 1926; H. Müller,
W. Biltz's Festschrift, Hannover, 1927; L. Bleekrode, *Phil. Mag.*, (5), 5. 375, 439, 1878;
A. Safarik, *Sitzber. Akad. Wien*, 33. 1, 1858; 47. 246, 1863; E. Wedekind and C. Horst, *Ber.*,
45. 262, 1912; 48. 105, 1915; E. Wedekind, *Zeit. angew. Chem.*, 37. 87, 1924; A. A. Read,
Journ. Chem. Soc., 65. 313, 1894; A. Rogers and E. F. Smith, *Journ. Amer. Chem. Soc.*, 25.
1228, 1903; C. Czudnowicz, *Pogg. Ann.*, 120. 32, 1863; J. Locke and G. H. Edwards, *Amer. Chem.
Journ.*, 20. 594, 1898; *Zeit. anorg. Chem.*, 19. 398, 1899; E. Müller and H. Barck, *ib.*, 129. 309,
1923; A. Cioci, *ib.*, 19. 308, 1899; *Gazz. Chim. Ital.*, 29. i, 300, 1899; E. Petersen, *Journ. prakt.
Chem.*, (2), 40. 44, 1889; A. Bültemann, *Zeit. Elektrochem.*, 10. 141, 1904; E. Renschler, *ib.*,
18. 137, 1912; T. F. Rutter, *ib.*, 12. 230, 1906; *Zeit. anorg. Chem.*, 52. 368, 1907; *Die katalyschen
Eigenschaften des Vanadins*, Leipzig, 1906; O. Ruff and W. Martin, *Zeit. anorg. Chem.*, 25. 49,
1912; E. Friederich and L. Sittig, *ib.*, 145. 127, 1925; E. Tiede and E. Birnbräuer, *ib.*, 87.
129, 1914; W. Prandtl and B. Bleyer, *ib.*, 65. 152, 1910; K. Someya, *ib.*, 161. 46, 1927; *Science
Rep. Tohoku Univ.*, 16. 411, 1927; G. Wegelin, *Koll. Zeit.*, 14. 65, 1914; J. N. Pearce and
A. M. Alvarado, *Journ. Phys. Chem.*, 29, 256, 1925; H. von Wartenberg, J. Broy, and R. Reinicke,
Zeit. Elektrochem., 29. 214, 1923; E. Müller and A. Flath, *ib.*, 29. 500, 1923; R. G. Gustavson
and C. M. Knudson, *Journ. Amer. Chem. Soc.*, 44. 2756, 1922; F. A. Gooch and R. W. Curtis,
Zeit. anorg. Chem., 38. 246, 1904; *Amer. Journ. Science*, (4), 17. 41, 1904; W. G. Mixter, *ib.*,
(4), 34. 141, 1912; O. W. Gibbs, *Proc. Amer. Acad.*, 16. 114, 1880; 18. 236, 1883; 21. 97,
1886; O. Schmidt, *Zeit. phys. Chem.*, 133. 263, 1928; N. Perrakis, *Compt. Rend.*, 185. 111,
1927; V. M. Goldschmidt, T. Barth, and G. Lunde, *Skrift. Norske. Akad.*, 7, 1925.

§ 7. Vanadium Tetroxide and the Hypovanadates

J. J. Berzelius [1] obtained **vanadium tetroxide,** V_2O_4, and it has also been
called *vanadyl oxide,* $(VO)O$, or *vanadium dioxide,* VO_2, *hypovanadic oxide,* and,
according to A. Werner, *vanade-oxide.* J. J. Berzelius prepared this oxide by heating
to redness an intimate mixture of equimolar parts of vanadium tri- and penta-
oxides in the absence of air; or by heating the hydrated tetroxide in vacuo, or,
according to J. K. Crow, in an atm. of carbon dioxide. H. Buff and F. Wöhler
made the tetroxide by the electrolysis of molten vanadium pentoxide, and removing
the excess of pentoxide by boiling soda-lye. W. Prandtl heated the pentoxide
in a gas furnace for some hours, and found that a crust of the tetroxide is produced
by the reducing action of the gas. The unchanged pentoxide can be removed by
washing the product with aq. ammonia. A. Guyard reduced the pentoxide to
tetroxide by melting it with oxalic acid; E. Friederich and L. Sittig, by heating
it with carbon; A. Ditte, by heating it with phosphorus—but here a phosphate
if formed; A. Ditte, by heating the pentoxide in a current of sulphur dioxide
—the reaction is slow; and J. J. Berzelius, A. Ditte, and H. E. Roscoe, by heating
ammonium metavanadate out of contact with air. K. Someya found that bismuth
amalgam reduces vanadates to hypovanadates. H. E. Roscoe said that this
oxide is formed when the trioxide is exposed to air for some months. J. K. Crow
obtained the tetroxide by heating the oxychloride, $V_2O_4.4HCl.3H_2O$, in a current
of carbon dioxide. According to J. Koppel and E. C. Behrendt, quinquevalent
is reduced to quadrivalent vanadium by hydroxylamine hydrochloride, dextrose,
formaldehyde, alcohol, oxalic acid, hydrogen sulphide, and, best of all, by sulphur
dioxide.

Vanadium tetroxide obtained from the fused pentoxide appears as a black earthy mass; otherwise, it may appear as a dark blue crystalline powder. V. M. Goldschmidt examined the crystals, and found that the X-radiogram agreed with a space-lattice of the rutile type with $a=4.54$ A., $c=2.88$ A., or $a:c=1:0.633$. E. Wedekind and C. Horst gave 4.339 for the sp. gr. W. Prandtl said that in the absence of air it does not fuse at the m.p. of platinum, but in air, it slowly forms the pentoxide. K. Friederich gave 1967° for the m.p.; and E. Friederich and L. Sittig, 1640°. W. G. Mixter gave for the heat of formation $(V_2O_3,O)=59.6$ Cals.; and since $(2V,5O)>441$ Cals., and $(V_2O_4,O)=28.2$ Cals., $(2V,4O)>413$ Cals. He also gave $(V_2O_2,O_2)=204.2$ Cals. H. Müller gave $(V_2O_3,O)=61$ Cals.; K. Friederich gave 55 ohms for the electrical resistance per sq. mm., and E. Friederich and L. Sittig, for the sp. resistance, gave 450×10^{-4} ohms at 1100°. T. F. Rutter studied the oxidation and reduction potentials—*vide supra*. E. Wedekind and C. Horst found the magnetic suscepti- bility to be 3.73×10^{-6} units. N. Perrakis studied this subject. J. J. Berzelius found that when the tetroxide is heated to redness in a current of dry hydrogen it forms the trioxide. H. Müller found the equilibrium constant, K, in the reaction: $V_2O_4+H_2=V_2O_3+H_2O$ to be $K=[H_2O]/[H_2]=2.5$ over the range 500°–600°—*vide supra*, vanadium trioxide. He found for the values of $K=p_{H_2O}/p_{H_2}$ in the V_2O_5/V_2O_4-reaction: $V_2O_4+H_2O\rightleftharpoons V_2O_5+H_2$, at 496°, 530°, and 600°, respectively 7.6, 21.2, and 23.3; and the calculated thermal values of the reaction, respectively 118.2, 116.2, and 116.0 Cals. H. Buff and F. Wöhler found that exposure in air, or treatment with nitric acid, converts the tetroxide into the pentoxide. The tetroxide was found by J. K. Crow gradually to absorb water and oxygen from the air, and to be easily soluble in acids and alkali-lye. According to G. Gain, when an aq. soln. of vanadium sulphite is boiled, sulphur dioxide is evolved, and a pale red, crystalline powder is deposited, which, when dried on a porous tile, is the so-called *hypovanadic acid*, $H_4V_2O_6$; or *vanadyl hydroxide*, $VO(OH)_2$; or *dihydrated vanadium tetroxide*, $V_2O_4.2H_2O$. There are two isomeric forms of the dihydrate: one is the stable green hydrate, the other is unstable and red. When the red form is kept out of contact with the moisture of the air, it becomes olive-green. Each form loses a mol. of water at 140°–150°, forming a bluish-black monohydrate, $V_2O_4.H_2O$, and in hydrogen at 200°–250°, it forms the black tetroxide. The red dihydrate dissolves in sulphuric acid, forming an azure-blue soln., and the green dihydrate a green soln. The heats of soln. are respectively 12.62 and 10.89 Cals. Each soln. becomes colourless when neutralized with alkali-lye, and the heats of neutralization of the blue and green soln. are respectively 16.92 and 18.56 Cals. In passing from the red to the green dihydrate, there is therefore an absorption of 1.64 Cals. of energy. E. Parisi said that the transformation of the pink vanadyl compound into the olive-green modification is a consequence of the conversion of a part of the vanadium from the quadrivalent to the quinquevalent condition. The pink compound remains unchanged as regards colour and reducing power for potassium permanganate if it be kept in a tightly-stoppered bottle filled with water previously boiled, and sat. with carbon dioxide.

If a salt of the tetroxide, say the sulphate, or chloride, free from the pent- oxide, be treated with a cold soln. of sodium carbonate, J. J. Berzelius found that a greyish-white precipitate, which when washed and dried out of contact with air—say in vacuo—consists of *hydrated vanadyl hydroxide*, $(VO)(OH)_2.2\frac{1}{2}H_2O$, or *heptahydrated vanadium tetroxide*, $V_2O_4.7H_2O$. The supernatant liquid should be colourless. If it is blue, insufficient sodium carbonate has been added; if brown, too much sodium carbonate has been added, and some oxide has passed into soln.; and if green, vanadic acid is present. C. Czudnowicz said that the vanadyl salts are not precipitated by sodium carbonate; and A. Guyard, that the precipitate is sodium hypovanadate.

J. J. Berzelius found that the grey heptahydrate may contain a trace of carbon dioxide ; if any oxidation has occurred, it acquires a brown tinge, and then reddens blue litmus owing to the formation of vanadic acid. When heated in vacuo, it loses all its water, forming the anhydrous tetroxide. J. K. Crow showed that at 100°, in a current of carbon dioxide, the hydrate loses 4 mols. of water. The hydroxide is soluble in acids, forming vanadyl salts, and in alkali-lees, forming hypovanadates. Vanadium tetroxide is thus an amphoteric oxide. V. Auger found that when a mixture of sulphuric acid and vanadium tetroxide is heated, sulphur dioxide is evolved until one-third the vanadium is oxidized. J. Locke complains that vanadium tetroxide is sometimes compared with nitrogen tetroxide, and nitrous acid, NO.OH, with vanadous hydroxide, VO.OH, for little reason other than because they have similar formulæ. If this be sufficient for chemical analogy, why not put AlO.OH in the same class—for both hydroxides unite with alkalies, and both aluminium and vanadium form the alums ?

While anhydrous vanadium tetroxide dissolves slowly, the hydrated oxide dissolves quickly in acids, forming **hypovanadic or vanadyl salts.** Quadrivalent vanadium is amphoteric, for it unites either with bases or with acids to form salts. It acts as a base in the form of the bivalent radicle, VO, vanadyl, which is analogous with the bivalent radicle, UO_2, uranyl. The oxide of quadrivalent vanadium possesses very feeble acidic properties, and by a polymerization of many molecules the acidity seems to be so increased that it can form salts with bases ; as a result, a unimolecular anion of quadrivalent vanadium has not been obtained, and the vanadites hitherto investigated have the formula $R_2V_4O_9$. Quinquevalent vanadium compounds can be reduced to the quadrivalent form by hydroxylamine hydrochloride, formaldehyde, oxalic acid, sulphur dioxide, hydrogen sulphide, etc. J. J. Berzelius obtained the acidic soln. by reducing a soln. of vanadium pentoxide in acids by hydrogen ; nitrous acid ; sulphur dioxide ; phosphorous acid ; hydrogen sulphide—with the separation of sulphur ; hydrochloric, hydrobromic, or hydriodic acid—with the development of chlorine, bromine, or iodine ; and by the lower oxides of some metals, or the metals themselves. A. Guyard used oxalic, citric, or tartaric acid, sugar, alcohol, or methyl alcohol as reducing agent ; alcohol, hydrochloric acid, glucose, and formaldehyde act slowly, while hydroxylamine acts quickly. J. Koppel and E. C. Behrendt showed that the reaction : $V_2O_5+SO_2\rightleftharpoons SO_3+V_2O_4$, in sulphuric acid soln. is reversible. The reaction was examined by H. E. Roscoe, and C. Czudnowicz. H. E. Roscoe found that in acid soln., the lower oxides of vanadium are oxidized to the tetroxide by a current of air. The anhydrous salts are brown or green, the hydrated salts are blue. Most of them are soluble in water, forming blue soln., which on oxidation becomes green. Many of them were prepared by J. J. Berzelius, C. Czudnowicz, J. Koppel and co-workers, and A. Guyard. According to J. J. Berzelius, soln. of the salts become colourless when treated with ammonia, giving a brown precipitate which forms a brown soln. with water ; alkali hydroxides or carbonatos, as indicated above, precipitate the hydroxide. Ammonium sulphide gives a dark brown precipitate of vanadium sulphide, which forms a purple soln. with an excess of the precipitant. Potassium ferrocyanide gives a yellow precipitate insoluble in acids ; potassium ferricyanide, a yellowish-green gelatinous precipitate ; and tincture of galls, a bluish-black precipitate resembling ink. Hydrogen sulphide has no action on soln. of hypovanadic salts ; and zinc does not precipitate vanadium. T. F. Rutter's observations are indicated in Table I. A. Kurtenacker and F. Werner found that vanadyl sulphate quantitatively reduces hydroxylamine in strongly alkaline soln. to ammonia ; in neutral soln., nitrous oxide and nitrogen are formed ; in feebly acid soln., the catalytic decomposition furnishes ammonia, nitrous oxide, and nitrogen ; and in strongly acid soln. the action ceases. G. Canneri studied the complexes with citric and tartaric acids.

Vanadium tetroxide unites with the salifiable bases, forming **hypovanadates** —also called *vanadites.* The alkali hypovanadates are made by dissolving the tetroxide in alkali-lye ; the others, insoluble in water, are obtained as precipitates

TABLE I.—SOME REACTIONS WITH VANADOUS, HYPOVANADIC, AND VANADIC SALTS.

Reagent.	Vanadous, $V^{...}$	Hypovanadic, $V^{....}$	Vanadic, $V^{.....}$
Hydrogen dioxide	fast	fast	fast
Potassium permanganate . . .	fast	fast	slow
Chromic acid	fast	fast	none
Chloric acid	fast	slow	none
Vanadic acid	fast	none	none
Persulphuric acid	slow	slow	none
Iron alum	fast	none	none
Chlorine	fast	fast	none
Bromine	fast	slow	none
Oxygen	slow	none	none
Hydrochloroplatinic acid .	slow	none	none
Silver sulphate	slow	none	none
Copper sulphate	slow	none	none
Iodine	slow	none	none
Hydrogen sulphide	none	none	fast
Sulphurous acid	none	none	fast
Ferrous sulphate	none	none	fast
Hydrochloric acid	none	none	slow
Hydrobromic acid	none	none	slow
Hydriodic acid	none	slow	fast
Vanadic sulphate	none	none	fast
Vanadous sulphate	none	fast	fast

by double decomposition. The salts are dark brown, and when covered with water, or dissolved in it, they assume a green colour—the alkali salts soln. becomes colourless—being then oxidized to the vanadic state. The insoluble salts generally become soluble during the oxidation. The alkali hypovanadates in soln. are coloured blue by acids, forming double salts; purple-red, by hydrogen sulphide; and bluish-black, by tincture of galls. J. K. Crow found that lead acetate gives a brown precipitate ; with lead nitrate the precipitation is incomplete and a blue soln. is produced. Silver nitrate gives a black, crystalline precipitate—according to J. Koppel and R. Goldmann, the precipitate contains silver hypovanadate and vanadate, and silver.

A. Ditte reported that **ammonium hypovanadate,** $(NH_4)_4V_2O_6$, is formed in green crystals by treating a soln. of the oxyiodide, $V_2O_3I_2.2HI.8H_2O$, with ammonia; the green soln. becomes colourless when oxidized. J. J. Berzelius prepared **ammonium trihydrohypovanadate,** $(NH_4)H_3V_2O_6$, i.e. $(NH_4)_2O.2V_2O_4.3H_2O$, by adding an excess of aq. ammonia to a warm soln. of a hypovanadous salt so as to dissolve the precipitate first formed, and allowing the liquid to cool slowly. The crystals are redissolved in water, and the brown soln. again treated with ammonia. The crystalline ammonium trihydrohypovanadate is washed rapidly with ammonia and dried in vacuo. J. K. Crow washed the salt first with aq. ammonia, then with alcohol containing some acetic acid, and dried it over conc. sulphuric acid. The salt is readily oxidized. If the aq. soln. be evaporated in vacuo over calcium chloride, J. J. Berzelius observed that the brown product is insoluble in water. J. Koppel and R. Goldmann obtained the salt in glistening, brown needles or scales by adding a boiling soln. of the blue hypovanadous salt to aq. ammonia. The salt is soluble in water, but not soluble in alcohol, ether, or aq. ammonia. It readily gives off ammonia when exposed to air. J. Koppel and R. Goldmann prepared $Na_2O.2V_2O_4.4H_2O$, or *hemihydrated* **sodium trihydrohypovanadate,** $NaH_3V_2O_6.\frac{1}{2}H_2O$, in golden-yellow needles or scales by the method employed for the ammonium salt, or by cooling a hot soln. of the ammonium salt mixed with sodium hydroxide. J. K. Crow obtained the *dihydrate,* $NaH_3V_2O_6.2H_2O$, and also **potassium trihydrohypovanadate,** $K_2H_3V_2O_6$ with $\frac{1}{2}H_2O$ (I. Koppel and R. Goldmann) or $2H_2O$ (J. K. Crow), by J. J. Berzelius' process, in which a hot soln. of vanadyl sulphate or chloride is mixed with a slight excess of alkali-lye, and left to cool in a closed vessel. Brown, scaly crystals are deposited. They are washed first with potash-lye, then with alcohol, and dried in vacuo. Instead of alcohol, J. K. Crow used alcohol mixed with a little acetic acid. I. Koppel and R. Goldmann recommended the method employed for the ammonium salt. The brown product is permanent in air; is very soluble in water, forming a brown, opaque liquid—possibly a colloidal soln. The soln. is decolorized by exposure to air, forming potassium vanadate. An excess of potash-lye precipitates potassium vanadate from the brown soln. A. Ditte reported that when warm soln. of potassium iodide and soluble vanadium pentoxide are mixed together, iodine is liberated, and green lustrous crystals of the hypovanadate, $K_2O.2V_2O_4.H_2O$, are precipitated. If the mother-liquor is boiled and then conc. it deposits yellow crystals of potassium vanadate. If the iodide and vanadium pentoxide are fused together in a crucible out of contact with oxygen, iodine is liberated, and a brilliant black residue is left, which, when treated with warm water, yields a reddish-yellow soln., which deposits dark green crystals of the anhydrous hypovanadate, $K_2O.2V_2O_4$, leaving a yellow liquid, from which potassium vanadate can be crystallized.

J. Koppel and R. Goldmann were unable to prepare **silver hypovanadate,** but J. K. Crow obtained a black crystalline precipitate, $Ag_2O.V_2O_4$, by the action of silver nitrate on potassium hypovanadate. J. K. Crow, and I. Koppel and R. Goldmann obtained **barium trihydrohypovanadate,** $Ba(H_3V_2O_6)_2.H_2O$, by adding baryta-water to a soln. of vanadium tetroxide in hydrochloric acid until the liquid had an alkaline reaction. The brown precipitate is washed by decantation with hot water, and then on a filter-paper, and drying the product in a current of carbon dioxide at 120°. J. K. Crow said that the brown, amorphous compound is freely soluble in hydrochloric or nitric acid. J. K. Crow prepared what he regarded as **lead hypovanadate,** $PbO.V_2O_4$, by adding a soln. of lead acetate to a soln. of potassium hypovanadate—*vide supra.* A Rogers and E. F. Smith prepared **ammonium dihypovanadatotetradecatungstate,** $5(NH_4)_2O.2V_2O_4.14WO_3.13H_2O$, in black octahedral crystals freely soluble in water; no precipitation occurs with an ammoniacal soln. of cupric sulphate. O. W. Gibbs obtained **mercurous dihypovanadatoheptadecatungstate** from a soln. of mercurous nitrate and ammonium dihypovanadatoheptadecatungstate. J. J. Berzelius obtained a brown **manganese hypovanadate** by double decomposition; the product is oxidized by air to a yellow vanadate.

REFERENCES.

¹ J. J. Berzelius, *Akad. Handl. Stockholm,* 1, 1831; *Pogg. Ann.,* 22. 1, 1831; *Schweigger's Journ.,* 62. 323, 1831; 63. 26. 1831; A. Werner, *Neuere Anschauungen auf dem Gebiete der anorganischen Chemie,* Braunschweig, 12, 1905; London, 74, 1911; H. E. Roscoe, *Phil. Trans.,* 158. 1, 1868; 159. 679, 1869; 160. 317, 1870; *Proc. Roy. Soc.,* 16. 220, 1868; 18. 37, 316, 1870; *Journ. Chem. Soc.,* 21. 322, 1868; 23. 344, 1870; 24. 23, 1871; *Chem. News,* 17. 135, 1868; 20. 37, 1869; 21. 183, 1872; *Phil. Mag.,* (4), 35. 307, 1868; (4), 39. 146, 1870; (4), 42. 62, 1870; J. K. Crow, *Journ. Chem. Soc.,* 30. 454, 1876; K. Friederich, *Zeit. Physik,* 31. 813, 1925; E. Friederich and L. Sittig, *Zeit. anorg. Chem.,* 145. 127, 1925; W. Prandtl in L. Gmelin and K. Kraut, *Handbuch der anorganischen Chemie,* Heidelberg, 3. ii, 77, 1908; E. Wedekind and C. Horst, *Ber.,* 45. 262, 1912; 47. 105, 1915; E. Parisi, *Gazz. Chim. Ital.,* 56. 843, 1926; 57. 859, 1927; G. Canneri, *ib.,* 56. 637, 1926; E. Wedekind, *Zeit. angew. Chem.,* 37. 87, 1924; K. Someya, *Zeit. anorg. Chem.,* 138. 291, 1924; A. Kurtenacker and F. Werner, *ib.,* 160. 333, 1927; W. G. Mixter, *Amer. Journ. Science,* (4), 34. 141, 1912; T. F. Rutter, *ib.,* 12. 230, 1906; *Zeit. anorg. Chem.,* 52. 368, 1907; *Die katalyschen Eigenschaften des Vanadins,* Leipzig, 1906; A. Rogers and E. F. Smith, *Journ. Amer. Chem. Soc.,* 25. 1228, 1903; A. Rogers, *ib.,* 25. 298, 1903; E. F. Smith and F. F. Exner, *ib.,* 24. 573, 1902; J. Locke, *Amer. Chem. Journ.,* 20. 581, 1898; H. Buff and F. Wöhler, *Liebig's Ann.,* 110. 277, 1859; A. Guyard, *Bull. Soc. Chim.,* (2), 25. 350, 1876; C. Czudnowicz, *Pogg. Ann.,* 120. 40, 1862; H. Müller, *W. Biltz's Festschrift,* Hannover, 1927; C. C. Behrendt, *Verbindungen des vierwertigen Vanadins mit Schwefelsäure und schwefeliger Säure,* Berlin, 1902; J. Koppel and E. C. Behrendt, *Zeit. anorg. Chem.,* 154. 1903; J. Koppel and R. Goldmann, *ib.,* 36. 281, 1903; I. Koppel, R. Goldmann, and A. Kaufmann, *ib.,* 45. 345, 1905; E. Tiede and E. Birnbräuer, *ib.,* 87. 129, 1914; B. W. Gerland, *Ber.,*

9, 869, 1876; **10.** 1216, 1513, 1516, 2109, 1877; *Chem. News*, **34.** 2, 1876; **36.** 29, 271, 1877; A. Ditte, *Compt. Rend.*, **101.** 1487, 1885: **102.** 1310, 1886; **103.** 55, 1886; V. Auger, *ib.*, **173.** 306, 1921; G. Gain, *ib.*, **143.** 823, 1906; **146.** 403, 1907; N. Perrakis, *ib.*, **185.** 111, 1927; V. M. Goldschmidt, *Skrift. Norske Akad.*, **7**, 1925; 1, 1926.

§ 8. Vanadium Pentoxide

The end-product of the oxidation of vanadium, the lower oxides, the nitride or the sulphide, by roasting in air is vanadium pentoxide, V_2O_5, or *vanadic anhydride*, or, according to A. Werner,[1] vanadan-oxide. The pentoxide was also obtained by J. J. Berzelius and others, by oxidizing these substances with nitric acid or aqua regia, or by fusion with potassium nitrate, and washing the product with a dil. acid; it is formed by the hydrolysis of vanadium oxytrichloride, or oxytribromide; and by heating compounds of vanadium pentoxide with the volatile acids or bases. J. E. Teschemacker said that an impure vanadite occurs as *vanadium ochre* in the Cliffe Mine, Lake Superior; but W. T. Schaller said that the supposed mineral is cuprous oxide—a variety of cuprite or hydrocuprite. F. L. Hess described an opaque black mineral which he called **vanoxite**—compounded from vanadium oxide—occurring in the Utah-Colorado carnotite region. Its composition approximates *vanadyl vanadate*, $2V_2O_4.V_2O_5.8H_2O$.

The extraction of vanadium pentoxide from various minerals has been already discussed. H. E. Roscoe recommended purifying the dried pentoxide by moistening it with sulphuric acid, mixing it with hydrofluoric acid to remove the silica, and heating the mixture so as to drive off the sulphuric acid; to remove phosphates, the oxide is deflagrated with an equal weight of sodium in an iron crucible, and the residue washed with water until free from soluble alkali. The residue is treated with nitric acid, and converted into ammonium vanadate, which is purified by repeated crystallization. A. Safarik found that the pentoxide of a high degree of purity is produced when the oxytrichloride is decomposed by water; F. J. Pope described the preparation of a pure pentoxide from ammonium metavanadate. According to C. Matignon, in the decomposition of ammonium metavanadate by heat, any reduction of the resulting vanadium pentoxide may be avoided by proper working. The pure salt should be roasted in an oxidizing muffle with slowly-rising temp., and care exercised to prevent melting until the decomposition of the ammonium salt is complete. A platinum dish must be employed, since silicates are attacked and iron causes reduction. In the decomposition, an intermediate product may be isolated. By slow heating of a thin layer, the colour is seen to pass through yellow, brown, ruby-red, and a metallic steel-blue, and finally to become brick-red. The metallic-looking body had the formula $5V_2O_5.2VO_3.NH_4$.

A. Ditte assumed that there are three **allotropic forms** of the pentoxide. (1) A reddish-yellow, ochreous powder formed by heating ammonium vanadate in a closed vessel, treating the product with nitric acid, evaporating to dryness, and gently heating the residue. It absorbs water readily from the air, forming red $V_2O_5.H_2O$, and afterwards $V_2O_5.2H_2O$. The hydrates form a blood-red soln. with water. (2) A pale yellow powder obtained by heating ammonium vanadate at 440° for several hours in a current of dry air. It does not absorb moisture from the air, and is only slightly soluble in water with which it forms a yellow soln. A similar oxide, but with a reddish-yellow colour, is obtained by boiling ammonium vanadate with dil. nitric acid, and heating the resulting dihydrate to 350°–440°. (3) A dark brownish-red mass of needle-like crystals is obtained by heating ammonium vanadate out of contact with air, treating the residue with nitric acid, and heating the product until fused. The resulting pentoxide can be left in contact with water for several months when only 0·05 grm. per litre passes into soln. F. Ephraim doubted whether these different varieties are real allotropes; the differences may be a question of the average grain size.

The pentoxide prepared by roasting the hydrate, or the ammonium salt, is a reddish-yellow powder, and when hot, the powder is brick-red. J. J. Berzelius added that the colour is lighter the finer the grain-size of the powder. The molten oxide is yellowish-red, according to N. G. Sefström, and dark brown, according to J. F. W. Johnston. On cooling the fused pentoxide to the temp. at which it no longer appears red-hot in diffused daylight, J. J. Berzelius observed that heat is again developed and a glowing ring appears to pass inwards from the circumference to the centre of the mass, where the light is longest visible. The cold mass is reddish-brown, and, according to A. E. Nordenskjöld, it consists of a mass of acicular **crystals** belonging to the rhombic system. A. E. Nordenskjöld said that the crystals obtained by J. J. Berzelius were rhombic prisms with the axial ratios $a:b:c=0.3832:1:0.9590$; and with the cleavages on the (100)- and (010)-faces perfect; and the cleavage on the (001)-face distinct. F. Rinne studied the X-radiogram. According to J. J. Berzelius, if the pentoxide contains the tetroxide or a heavy metal oxide, it does not crystallize after fusion, but forms a cauliflower-like mass and appears black; if it contains only a little tetroxide, it may crystallize, but has then a darker colour, inclining to violet.

A. Safarik gave 3.49–3.56 for the **specific gravity** of crystallized vanadium pentoxide at 20°; W. Prandtl and B. Bleyer, 3.359; and E. Wedekind and C. Horst, 3.320. D. Balareff, and C. del Fresno studied the mol. vol. W. Prandtl gave for the **melting point** 690°, and T. Carnelley, 658°. J. J. Berzelius said that the pentoxide can be heated white-hot without losing oxygen provided no reducing gases have access to the compound; and A. A. Read found that the pentoxide is decomposed at 1750°, forming the trioxide. According to J. A. Norblad, the molten pentoxide contaminated with tetroxide may spit on cooling owing to the evolution of some oxygen. P. Hautefeuille said that the **spitting** is conditioned by the presence of alkali; the quantity of oxygen given off is proportional to the quantity of contained alkali. E. Tiede and E. Birnbräuer said that the pentoxide does not volatilize or melt when heated. W. Prandtl showed that the spitting which occurs when the molten alkali acid vanadates solidify is due to the reversible change of the acid vanadate to vanadylvanadate on solidification: $mM_2O.nV_2O_5 \rightleftharpoons mM_2O.(n-p)V_2O_5.pV_2O_4+\frac{1}{2}pO_2$, for oxygen is again absorbed and the acid vanadate regenerated on heating the vanadylvanadate in air. W. Prandtl showed that only the acid vanadates of the first group in the periodic system spit on solidification. The presence of a moderate proportion of boric oxide does not affect the spitting, but if much phosphate be present, no spitting occurs. J. J. Berzelius observed that vanadium pentoxide exhibited a calorescence when the undercooled liquid crystallizes. H. Moissan and A. Holt found that the pentoxide volatilizes when heated in the electric furnace. W. G. Mixter gave for the **heat of formation** $(2V.5O)>441$Cals; $(V_2O_3,O_2)=87.8$ Cals.; $(V_2O_4,O)=28.2$ Cals.; and $(V_2O_2,3O)=232.4$ Cals.; H. Müller calculated $(V_2O_4,O)=117$ Cals.; O. Ruff and L. Friedrich gave $(2V,5O)=437\pm7$ Cals.; and O. Ruff and W. Martin gave 2456 Cals. for the heat of combustion, and W. Muthmann and co-workers, 31.303 Cals. per eq. W. W. Coblentz examined the **ultra-red emission spectrum** of the pentoxide. According to J. Gibbons, alkali vanadates become green when in contact with organic substances and exposed to light, and as in the case of chromates (q.v.), glue under these conditions becomes insoluble in water. C. Renz found that brown vanadium pentoxide is **photosensitive**, for it becomes black with greater or less rapidity when exposed to light beneath glycerol, benzaldehyde, cinnamaldehyde, cuminol, or aqueous mannitol soln.; a lower oxide, initially vanadium tetroxide, is produced. Soln. of citric or tartaric acid in absolute alcohol become green and ultimately blue when illuminated in the presence of vanadium pentoxide; carbon dioxide is evolved freely. Similar decomposition is observed with mandelic acid, but, in this instance, the vanadium pentoxide is blackened. A. Karl said that vanadium oxide is triboluminescent. J. J. Berzelius found that the **electrical conductivity** of vanadium pentoxide is nil, but H. Buff and F. Wöhler, and L. Bleekrode said that when molten, the pentoxide is a good conductor ; and on electrolysis it forms the tetroxide. K. Friederich gave 31,000 ohms per sq. mm. for the electrical resistance of the pentoxide. The **electrolytic reduction** of vanadium pentoxide was examined by J. T. Brierley, A. Cioci, A. Bültemann, A. Piccini and N. Brizzi, and T. F. Rutter. A. C. Chapman and H. D. Law found that with a platinized platinum cathode the reduction did not reach the trioxide stage, but with a cathode of zinc, cadmium, or lead, the dioxide stage is reached. H. H. Willard and F. Fenwick studied the electrometric titration of vanadic acid when reduced by ferrous sulphate. For T. F. Rutter's observations on the **reduction potential,** *vide supra*, vanadium. E. Wedekind and C. Horst found the **magnetic susceptibility** to be 0.16×10^{-6} units. S. Meyer gave 0.95×10^{-6}, and S. Berkman and H. Zocher, 0.39×10^{-6}—*vide supra*, vanadium. N. Perrakis found that quinquevalent vanadium has a paramagnetism independent of temp. between 17° and 77° in vanadium pentoxide and in sodium vanadate, and between 17° and 45° in ammonium vanadate. The mean value (to within 10 per cent.) of the coefficient of atomic magnetization of quinquevalent vanadium derived from these determinations is 44.0×10^{-6}. Vanadium pentoxide has the same paramagnetism in the solid state as in soln. Like the atomic moment, the paramagnetism may have many different values in the same atom.

W. Biltz [2] triturated ammonium vanadate with dil. hydrochloric acid, and after washing the reddish-brown product with water found that the compound begins to pass through the filter. When the residue is treated with purified water, a reddish-yellow **colloidal solution** of vanadium pentoxide is formed. Soln. were also prepared by W. Biltz and W. Geibel, and H. Kuzel. E. Müller prepared the colloidal soln. by pouring molten vanadium pentoxide into distilled water. If the soln. is evaporated to dryness on the water-bath, the residue obtained is insoluble in water, but is much more reactive than the ordinary form of the acid. It is supposed that the production of the colloidal acid in the above manner is due to the rapidity with which the transition from the liquid to the solid state is effected. According to G. Wegelin, if the vapour of vanadium oxytrichloride is led into distilled water and the aq. soln. heated to its b.p., vanadic acid separates out in the form of reddish-brown flakes. If the precipitated acid is filtered and washed, it yields a colloidal soln. on further treatment with distilled water. If the soln. is evaporated to dryness at low temp., a resinous substance is obtained, which redissolves in water, forming a clear colloidal soln. J. D. Riedel obtained the colloidal soln. by gradually adding 50 grms. of isoamylorthovanadate to a litre of boiling water, and boiling the mixture until a homogeneous dark red soln. is obtained. When cold, the amylene is extracted with ether, and the ether removed by a current of air. About 8 per cent. of the vanadic acid is a non-colloidal soln. S. Ghosh and co-workers prepared colloidal gels by dialyzing soln. of the pentoxide. W. Prandtl and L. Hess prepared colloidal sols by the hydrolysis of butyl orthovanadate. G. Wegelin obtained the colloidal pentoxide by a prolonged grinding in an agate mortar. D. N. Chakravarti and N. R. Dhar found that colloidal soln. of vanadium pentoxide become more and more viscous, and finally set to a jelly as dialysis proceeds.

A. V. Dumansky found that the red, colloidal soln. contains negatively charged particles which gradually become smaller as the soln. ages. The electrical conductivity at first gradually falls and reaches a certain minimum value after some days, whilst the viscosity of the soln. increases ; there is, however, no constant relationship between these two properties. Dilution causes a gradual rise in the conductivity, which finally assumes a constant value ; this is doubtless due to the hydrolysis of the colloidal particles with the production of ions. The red colour of the sol finally changes to yellow, and yellow soln. are found to contain no colloidal particles when viewed in the ultra-microscope. The effect of temp. on the conductivity has also been studied. A rise of temp. is shown to produce an increase in conductivity ; on cooling, the conductivity of the soln. does not immediately regain its former value. According to H. Freundlich and W. Leonhardt, the colloidal particles carry a relatively large negative charge ; the colloidal soln. coagulates ferric and aluminium hydroxide hydrosols. When the colloidal soln. is stirred, it presents the appearance which would be observed by a liquid in which a mass of fine crystals is suspended. If examined between crossed Nicols, the slightest disturbance of the soln. causes illumination of the dark field. The anisotropy or birefringence of the hydrosol of vanadium pentoxide was examined by H. Freundlich and co-workers, H. R. Kruyt, and A. V. Dumansky. W. Reinders inquired whether the colloidal particles are themselves anisotropic, or whether the anisotropy is due to differences in the elastic properties of the soln. in different directions. He showed that freshly prepared colloidal soln. of vanadium pentoxide are not birefringent ; on keeping the soln. they slowly develop double refraction, and this is apparently due to the formation and increase in size of ultra-microscopic, crystalline needles. Hence, the colloidal particles of vanadium pentoxide are in reality micro-crystalline. H. Gessner assumed that the hydrosol prepared by W. Biltz has the constitution $(HVO_3)[V_2O_5.\frac{3}{3}NH_4.H_2O](NH_4VO_3)$. The conc. of molecularly dispersed vanadium pentoxide is always less than the solubility of crystalline vanadic acid, and furthermore decreases with increasing age of the sol ; at the same time, changes occur in the viscosity and conductivity. An equilibrium value is finally attained, and in a series of sols the equilibrium conc. of molecularly dispersed vanadium pentoxide decreases rapidly with increasing conc. of colloid. These phenomena are ascribed to the growth of rod-like particles in the original sol, which contains an unstable form of condensed vanadic acid in particles of irregular size. The larger particles adsorb dissolved vanadic acid and build it into their crystal structure, thus growing at the expense of the smaller particles. The coagulation experiments show that ageing increases the sensitivity of a sol towards electrolytes. Sols prepared by E. Müller's method of pouring fused vanadium pentoxide into water have the constitution $[V_2O_5.H_2O]VO_3'H^{\cdot}$; they behave in a very similar manner to the Biltz sols. J. Böhm examined the X-radiograms of aged sols. According to G. Wiegner and co-workers, vanadium pentoxide sols contain ultra-microns of elongated rod-like structures similar to fibrin sols ; in course of time these ultra-microns grow, this being accelerated by an increase in conc. of the sol. The tendency to coagulate is much increased after this growth, and can be brought about by filter-paper, boles, carbon, silk threads, and silicic acid and gelatin gels. This gelatinization is favoured or perhaps conditioned by vanadyl salts formed by the reduction of the vanadium pentoxide. The serum obtained from the gel coagulates more sol ; this is accounted for by its high content of vanadyl salts. Salts (contained in filter-paper) favour the reduction to vanadyl salts and therefore accelerate the coagulation. Vanadic acid stabilizes the sol. The dilution of the sol and consequently decreasing the conc. of the active vanadic acid ions brings about gelatinization. These results show a close analogy to fibrin sols. H. Zocher and K. Jacobsohn showed that some sols of vanadium pentoxide spontaneously separate into two phases—one isotropic and dilute, the other anisotropic and concentrated. J. Jochims observed that during the illumination, under the ultra-microscope, with a drop of a 1-2 per cent. of vanadium pentoxide sol, radially disposed, angular, rod-like particles appear, and the viscosity of the sol increases. The effect does not occur if the heat rays are filtered from the light. The same change is brought about by small quantities of sodium or calcium chloride, or potassium sulphate. Higher concentrations of the electrolyte cause the formation of a thixotropic gel—i.e. of a gel which can be liquefied by agitation. This subject was studied by J. Jochims.

D. N. Chakravarti and N. R. Dhar found that on the dialysis of soln. of vanadium pentoxide, the liquid becomes more and more viscous and finally gelatinizes. H. R. Kruyt showed that with an electric field parallel to the direction of the luminous beam, very little dispersion takes place, and the elongated particles apparently disappear. On the other hand, when the field is perpendicular to the luminous beam, the Tyndall effect is very pronounced. The optical properties were studied by R. H. Humphry, H. Freundlich and co-workers, H. Mottsmith and I. Langmuir, T. Schwedoff, S. Horiba and T. Kondo, etc. J. Errera found that a freshly made soln., containing 31 parts of oxide per 1000, had a sp. inductive capacity of 74·7, and this increased with age. A soln. five years old, containing 14 parts per 1000, had a sp. inductive capacity of 400. The liquid remaining after ultra-filtration gave a value of 82·9. After dilution the sol does not reach immediately a state of equilibrium, but a portion gradually passes into the molecular disperse state and, at the same time, diminution of the sp. inductive capacity takes place. By increasing the intensity of the oscillating circuit used as a source of alternating current, and therefore the strength of the electric field, the sp. inductive capacity increases, whereas for water under the same conditions it remains constant. With rise of temp. the sp. inductive capacity diminishes. The phenomena observed have the same origin as the optical anisotropy of vanadium pentoxide sols. R. Fürth and O. Blüh found that for a wave-length of 70 cms. a vanadium pentoxide sol three years old showed an increase in dielectric constant with increase in conc., but the converse was found in the case of a freshly made sol. The dielectric constant does not increase with the field strength; it is the polarization which increases. H. Freundlich and co-workers measured the rate of crystallization of sols of vanadium pentoxide; Wo. Ostwald, the viscosity; H. Freundlich and W. Seifriz, the elastic modulus; B. Lange, the polarization of light by sols; H. Freundlich and co-workers, R. H. Humphry, G. I. Pokrowsky, D. N. Chakravarti and N. R. Dhar, and A. Frey, the double refraction; A. Szegvari and E. Wigner, the electrical phenomena; H. Zocher, the structure of the sol; and H. Gessner, W. Reinders and G. van der Lee, N. R. Dhar and S. Ghosh, the ageing. H. Freundlich and co-workers showed that the ageing of the sol is dependent on a process of crystallization which proceeds according to a reaction of the second order; it is retarded by arsenic acid, while phosphoric acid is without influence. H. Lachs studied the scintillation effects with vanadium pentoxide as an ultra-microscopic colloid, and found that the effect diminishes with long standing owing to the development of crystals. A. Ivanitzkaja and M. Proskurnin studied the cataphoresis of the colloid. N. R. Dhar and S. Ghosh found that the hydroxide is peptized by alkali-lye with sugar, starch, or glycerol. The coagulation of the colloid by electrolytes, etc., was studied by W. Ostermann, G. Wiegner and co-workers, Wo. Ostwald, and N. G. Chatterji and N. R. Dhar.

Vanadium pentoxide is tasteless, and poisonous—*vide supra*, physiological action of vanadium. H. Lessheim and co-workers[3] discussed the electronic structure. The oxide reddens moist blue-litmus paper. J. J. Berzelius, and A. Ditte showed that the oxide is reduced to the trioxide when heated to redness in **hydrogen**; and E. Newbery and J. N. Pring, that it is reduced to the monoxide, at 2000° and 150 atm. press. H. Müller found the equilibrium constant, K, in the reaction $V_2O_5 + H_2 = V_2O_4 + H_2O$ to be $K = [H_2O]/[H_2] = 7·6 - 23·3$ over the range 540°–600°—*vide supra*, vanadium tetroxide. H. W. Underwood described the use of vanadium oxide as an oxidation catalyst. According to C. Reichard, soln. of vanadic acid, which are sulphur-yellow, are reduced only in the presence of a larger quantity of acid, and give first a pale bluish-green, then a pale green, and finally a dark green coloration. When the evolution of hydrogen is very feeble, a bluish coloration is first observed, which then passes through violet into green, a green precipitate finally being formed. Vanadates in concentrations above 1 per cent. give at first a violet, then a pale blue, and finally a greyish-blue coloration. J. J. Berzelius found that 100 parts of **water** at ordinary temp. dissolve 0·1 part of the pentoxide; and he added that if the powdered oxide be agitated with water, a yellow, turbid liquid is obtained from which the undissolved particles of acid are not deposited until after several days, and without being converted into the hydrate. When the yellow, turbid liquid is evaporated, it deposits most of the pentoxide in red rings round the sides of the basin, and a few crystals of a lower oxide of an orange colour are produced owing to the reducing action of the dust of atm. **air.** **A.** Ditte gave for the solubility of the fused oxide, 0·05 grm. per litre. J. Fritzsche mixed a boiling conc. soln. of an alkali vanadate with an excess of acid, dried the washed precipitate in air freed from ammonia, and obtained pale yellow, pulverulent *dihydrated vanadium pentoxide,* $V_2O_5.2H_2O$, or *pyrovanadic acid,* $H_4V_2O_7$. A similar product was obtained by C. von Hauer. The fresh precipitate dissolves in ammonia. According to A. Ditte, there are two forms of the dihydrate : (i) is obtained by exposing the reddish-yellow pentoxide (*vide supra*) to air, and it furnishes a blood-red limpid soln. with water ; (ii) is obtained by boiling a soln. of ammonium vanadate with a little nitric acid, and drying the washed precipitate in air. This form of the dihydrate does not alter in contact with water, and is only slightly soluble in water at 100°. According to B. W. Gerland, if copper vanadate be treated with an excess of sulphurous acid, orange-yellow crystals of *monohydrated vanadium pentoxide,* $V_2O_5.H_2O$, or *metavanadic acid,* HVO_3, are formed. K. A. Nenadkewitch found dark red aggregates of monohydrated vanadium pentoxide, $V_2O_5.H_2O$, at Tyuya-Mayum, Alai Mts., Turkestan. He called the mineral *alaite.* The same product is obtained by treating ammonium vanadate with copper sulphate, and washing the precipitate free from copper by sulphurous acid. A. Guyard suggested that B. W. Gerland's pentavanadic acid is really an ammonium vanadate. P. Düllberg reported that *ditritahydrated vanadium pentoxide,* $3V_2O_5.2H_2O$, or *hexavanadic acid,* $H_4V_6O_{17}$, can exist in aq. soln. in a very unstable form which readily furnishes the brown dihydrate. V. Auger found that vanadic acid incompletely reduces **hydrogen dioxide**—*vide infra,* pervanadic acid. The double reduction of V_2O_5 to V_2O_4, and of H_2O_2 to H_2O was studied by J. R. Cain and J. C. Hostetter, who attributed it to the formation of a persulphide and as catalyst in the sulphuric acid soln. The reaction was also studied by A. W. Hothersall, and A. C. Robertson.

For some chemical properties of the pentoxide see Table I. Vanadium pentoxide readily dissolves in the strong acids, forming **vanadic salts**—*vide infra,* the vanadium halides. Vanadium pentoxide and its salts are reduced to the tetroxide by **hydrogen chloride, bromide, or iodide.** Conc. **hydrochloric acid** slowly reduces the pentoxide and gives off chlorine, and F. A. Gooch and co-workers found that in aq. soln., the tetroxide is formed. The reaction was studied by J. J. Berzelius, E. Campagne, A. Ditte, C. Czudnowicz, R. Bunsen, C. F. Mohr, R. Holverscheit, A. Rosenheim, L. Milch, O. W. Gibbs, F. Ephraim, R. Finkener, **F. A.** Gooch and co-workers, A. Safarik, and E. F. Smith and J. G. Hibbs—*vide infra.* The reduction with **hydrobromic or hydriodic acid** was studied by P. E. Browning, A. Ditte, C. Friedheim and H. von Euler, A. E. Stoppel and co-workers, and R. Holverscheit. H. Ditz and F. Bardach said that the reduction with hydriodic acid proceeds to the trioxide stage, but G. Edgar could obtain only the tetroxide stage. F. Ephraim, and E. B. Auerbuch and K. Lange found that some vanadium volatilizes when the pentoxide is heated with hydrochloric acid. A. Ditte, and F. Ephraim found that when a mixture of vanadium pentoxide and **potassium chloride, bromide, or iodide** is fused, the halogen escapes and potassium hypovanadate is formed ; if **potassium fluoride** be employed and the residue extracted with water, potassium fluovanadate (*q.v.*) is produced ; similarly also with **sodium fluoride ;** while a soln. of sodium or **ammonium fluoride** dissolves vanadium pentoxide, and the soln. furnishes a series of fluovanadates. The reduction of vanadic acid by potassium iodide was found by I. Warynsky and B. Mdivani to be more readily affected in the presence of acetic acid than in the presence of the chloracetic acids, and most readily affected in the presence of trichloracetic acid. According to W. Prandtl and H. Manz, when a mixture of vanadium pentoxide and **calcium fluoride** is heated to redness, some vanadium is volatilized probably as a fluoride or oxyfluoride. This volatilization of vanadium from the fluoride was noted by A. Guyard, and by W. Manchot and H. Fischer.

A. Ditte said that the pentoxide is reduced to the trioxide when heated with

sulphur. The reduction of soln. of the pentoxide to the tetroxide stage by **hydrogen sulphide** was examined by G. Edgar, F. A. Genth, O. Manasse, B. W. Gerland, R. Holverscheit, C. Czudnowicz, A. Safarik, and C. F. Rammelsberg. The soln. is also reduced to the tetroxide stage by **sulphurous acid** as shown by J. J. Berzelius, A. Ditte, C. F. Rammelsberg, F. A. Genth, O. Manasse, B. W. Gerland, R. Holverscheit, and I. Koppel and E. C. Behrendt. Sulphur dioxide slowly reduces the vanadic-sulphuric acid soln. In the presence of sulphur, the reduction of quinquevalent vanadium gives at first a blue soln. of the hypovanadyl salt, and then at a later stage anhydrous vanadous sulphate is deposited and the soln. is entirely free from vanadium. According to V. Auger, a soln. of vanadic acid in **sulphuric acid** begins to decompose before the b.p. is reached. It loses oxygen, and after boiling for several hours an equilibrium is reached, two-thirds of the vanadium being reduced to the quadrivalent state, if the soln. contains less than one part of vanadium per thousand. With more conc. soln., as soon as the reduction has commenced, vanadyl hydrosulphate is first deposited and then vanadyl sulphate until the conc. is reduced to 1 : 1000. In all cases, reduction is incomplete. For the action of sulphuric acid, *vide infra*, the sulphates. J. R. Cain and J. C. Hostetter found that sulphuric acid soln. of quinquevalent vanadium are reduced to the quadrivalent form by soln. of the **persulphates.** B. W. Gerland studied the dialysis of soln. of the pentoxide in sulphuric acid. C. Matignon and F. Bourion observed that when the pentoxide is heated in the vapour of **sulphur monochloride,** vanadium tetrachloride and oxytrichloride are formed. G. Darzens and F. Bourion found that thionyl chloride forms an oxychloride when heated with **thionyl chloride.** A. Ditte showed that when the pentoxide is heated in a current of **ammonia,** it is reduced to the tetroxide stage. G. Gore found that vanadium pentoxide is insoluble in liquid ammonia ; and F. Ephraim and G. Beck observed that when exposed to ammonia gas, **vanadium monamminopentoxide,** $V_2O_5.NH_3$, is formed—possibly $NH_4(NH_2V_4O_{10})$. A. Ditte showed that in aq. soln., **ammonium salts**—chloride, perchlorate, iodate, carbonate, acetate, oxalate, nitrate, phosphate, arsenate, sulphate, chromate, molybdate, tungstate, and borate—form complex salts. I. Koppel and E. C. Behrendt found that **hydroxylamine** reduces soln. of vanadium pentoxide to the tetroxide stage ; and the reduction with hydroxylamine and **hydrazine** was studied by K. A. Hofmann and F. Küspert, K. A. Hofmann and V. Kohlschütter, and G. von Knorre and K. Arndt. J. J. Berzelius found that vanadium pentoxide is reduced by **nitrous acid.** Red **phosphorus** was found by A. Ditte to reduce the pentoxide to the tetroxide stage ; and by L. Rosenstein, to the tervalent state. J. J. Berzelius found that vanadium pentoxide is reduced by **phosphorous acid.** A. Guyard found that when the pentoxide is fused with **phosphoric acid,** it forms a glassy mass. O. Kallauner and I. Hruda found that the fusion point of china clay was lowered by admixture with vanadium pentoxide :

V_2O_5 .	0	1	5	10	20	40	60	80	100 per cent.
Fusion .	1770°	1750°	1730°	1710°	1670°	1435°	1180°	940°	675°

Vanadium pentoxide forms a series of heteropoly-acids and salts with **silicates** (6. 40, 47), **chromates, molybdates,** and **tungstates**—*vide infra*. J. A. Hedvall and N. von Zweigbergk studied the action of **barium dioxide** on vanadium pentoxide. A. Ditte found that **arsenic trioxide** reduces the pentoxide to $V_2O_3.V_2O_4$.

A. Guyard found that when fused with **boric oxide,** vanadium pentoxide forms a glassy mass ; and J. J. Berzelius found that vanadium pentoxide dissolves in molten **borax,** producing a yellow glass in an oxidizing atm., and a green one in a reducing atm. J. J. Berzelius, H. E. Roscoe, and J. F. W. Johnston found that when heated to whiteness with **carbon,** the pentoxide is reduced to the trioxide or to $V_2O_3.V_2O_4$. R. E. Slade and G. I. Higson found the equilibrium press. of the oxide with carbon is 1·5 mm. at 1340°. B. Mdivani found that the pentoxide is reduced to the trioxide when heated in **carbon monoxide ;** and to the dioxide when heated in **hydrogen cyanide** vapour. A. F. Benton studied the adsorption of carbon monoxide and **carbon dioxide** by vanadium pentoxide. G. Fester and G. Berraz used vanadium pentoxide, and silver and copper vanadates as catalysts in the oxidation of **alcohol**; W. P. Yant and C. O. Hawk, in the oxidation of methane; and K. Chakravarty and J. C. Ghosh, on carbon monoxide and hydrogen. A. Ditte found that **organic salts**—*e.g.* ammonium oxalate—reduce the pentoxide. The reduction of soln. of vanadic acid with **oxalic acid** or **oxalates** as studied by A. Rosenheim, and W. Halberstadt; and with **tartaric acid** and the **tartrates,** by P. E. Browning. A. Guyard, J. J. Berzelius, and I. Koppel and E. C. Behrendt observed that vanadic acid soln. are reduced by oxalic, tartaric, or **citric acid**; by **sugar, ethyl and methyl alcohol, glucose** and **formaldehyde.** J. J. Berzelius found that the pentoxide is insoluble in absolute alcohol, and sparingly soluble in aq. alcohol. W. Prandtl said that a colourless soln. in absolute alcohol can be obtained in ethyl vanadate by passing the vapour of alcohol into a mixture of alcohol with a fused mixture of vanadic and boric oxides so as to volatilize the boric oxide. A. Ditte found that when the pentoxide is heated with **potassium cyanide,** it is reduced to the trioxide; and W. E. Kay showed that the vapour of **carbon disulphide** reduces it to the trisulphide. P. Jannasch and H. F. Harwood found that when heated in the vapour of **carbon tetrachloride,** vanadium is quantitatively volatilized from vanadium pentoxide and the vanadates. H. D. Gibbs, S. Medsforth, J. M. Weiss and co-workers studied vanadium pentoxide as an oxidation catalyst of benzene, naphthalene, anthracene, and the methylbenzenes. K. Fuwa studied the colouring action of vanadium compounds on glass.

According to J. J. Berzelius, there is a vigorous reaction when vanadium pentoxide is heated with **potassium** and a mixture of the lower oxides is formed. Similar results were obtained by H. E. Roscoe with **sodium.** J. Locke and G. H. Edwards found that **sodium-amalgam** reduces a soln. of quinquevalent vanadium to the tervalent form. According to F. Hundeshagen, vanadic acid and other vanadic compounds do not precipitate **gold** from acidic, neutral, or alkaline soln.; in hydrochloric acid soln. or in presence of chlorides they exert a solvent action on gold, becoming thereby reduced to the vanadous or hypovanadous condition; if the soln. is then made neutral or alkaline, the whole of the gold is at once precipitated as a greyish-violet powder, which redissolves again on acidifying the soln. H. Moissan observed that **calcium** reduces the pentoxide to the lower oxide. The reduction of soln. of vanadic acid to the trioxide stage by **magnesium, zinc,** and **cadmium** was observed by C. Reichard, C. F. Rammelsberg, H. E. Roscoe, and F. A. Gooch and R. D. Gilbert. B. Glassmann, and A. C. Chapman and H. D. Law found that the pentoxide in sulphuric acid soln is reduced to the dioxide by zinc, and to the trioxide by magnesium. Zinc coated with cadmium acts far more rapidly than zinc coated with platinum. The reaction was also examined by B. Glassmann, and by F. A. Gooch and G. Edgar. K. Someya found that zinc-amalgam, and **bismuth-amalgam** reduce quinquevalent to quadrivalent vanadium salts; the reduction also occurs with **lead-amalgam.** According to L. W. McCay and W. T. Anderson, vanadic acid is reduced to quadrivalent vanadium by **mercury:** $HVO_3+Hg+3HCl=VOCl_2+HgCl+2H_2O$; or $2HVO_3+2Hg+3H_2SO_4=2VOSO_4+Hg_2SO_4+4H_2O$. K. Someya found that bismuth-amalgam reduces vanadium salts in sulphuric acid soln. to the quadrivalent form. C. W. Ridsdale, O. Lindemann, and D. T. Williams studied the reduction of vanadates by **ferrous salts.** Vanadium pentoxide dissolves in **alkali-lye,** forming **vanadates.**

REFERENCES.

[1] A. Werner, *Neuere Anschauungen auf dem Gebiete der anorganischen Chemie,* Braunschweig, 12, 1905; London, 74, 1911; J. J. Berzelius, *Lehrbuch der Chemie,* Dresden, 3. ii, 99, 1834; *Acad. Handl. Stockholm,* 1, 1831; *Schweigger's Journ.,* 62. 323, 1831; 63. 26, 1831; *Pogg. Ann.,* 22. 1, 1831; *Ann. Chim. Phys.,* (1), 47. 337, 1831; *Phil. Mag.,* (2), 10. 321, 1831; (2),

11. 7, 1832; S. Berkman and H. Zocher, *Zeit. Phys. Chem.*, **124.** 318, 1927; C. del Fresno, *Anal. Fis. Quim.*, **24.** 707, 1926; H. Müller, W. *Biltz's Festschrift*, 1927; J. Gibbons, *Proc. Manchester Lit. Phil. Soc.*, **14.** 41, 1875; *Mem. Manchester Lit. Phil. Soc.*, **5.** 276, 1876; *Chem. News*, **30.** 267, 1874; H. E. Roscoe, *Phil. Trans.*, **158.** 1, 1868; **159.** 679, 1869; **160.** 317, 1870; *Proc. Roy. Soc.*, **16.** 220, 1868; **18.** 37, 316, 1870; *Journ. Chem. Soc.*, **21.** 322, 1868; **23.** 344. 1870; **24.** 23, 1871; *Chem. News*, **17.** 135, 1868; **20.** 37, 1869; **21.** 183, 1870; *Phil. Mag.*, (4), **35.** 307, 1868; (4), **39.** 146, 1870; (4), **40.** 62, 1870; A. Safarik, *Sitzber. Akad. Wien*, **33.** 7, 1858; **47.** 256, 1863; F. L. Hess, *Bull. U.S. Geol. Sur.*, 750, 1924; F. J. Pope, *Berg. Hütt. Ztg.*, **58.** 556, 1899; *Trans. Amer. Inst. Min. Eng.*, **29.** 386, 1899; A. Ditte, *Compt. Rend.*, **101.** 498, 1885; N. Perrakis, *ib.*, **184.** 445, 1927; A. Karl, *ib.*, **146.** 1104, 1908; P. Hautefeuille, *ib.*, **90.** 744, 1880; H. Moissan and A. Holt, *ib.*, **135.** 78, 493, 1902; W. W. Coblentz, *Investigations of Infra-red Spectra*, Washington, 115, 1908; A. E. Nordenskjöld, *Oefvers. Akad. Förh.*, 299, 1860; *Pogg. Ann.*, **112.** 160, 1861; H. H. Willard and F. Fenwick, *Journ. Amer. Chem. Soc.*, **45.** 84, 1923; J. E. Teschemacker, *Amer. Journ. Science*, (2), **11.** 233, 1851; W. T. Schaller, *ib.*, (4), **39.** 404, 1915; C. Renz, *Helvetica Chim. Acta*, **4.** 961, 1921; L. Bleekrode, *Proc. Roy. Soc.*, **25.** 322, 1877; *Phil. Mag.*, (5), **5.** 375, 439, 1878; *Wied. Ann.*, **3.** 161, 1876; W. G. Mixter, *Amer. Journ. Science*, (4), **34.** 141, 1912; J. A. Norblad, *Acta Lund. Univ.*, **2.** 1, 1874; *Bull. Soc. Chim.*, (2), **23.** 64, 1875; F. Rinne, *Zeit. Kryst.*, **60.** 55, 1924; H. Buff and F. Wöhler, *Liebig's Ann.*, **110.** 275, 1859; W. Muthmann, L. Weiss, and R. Riedelbauch, *ib.*, **355.** 58, 1907; C. Matignon, *Chem. Ztg.*, **29.** 986, 1905; T. F. Rutter, *ib.*, **12.** 230, 1906; *Zeit. anorg. Chem.*, **52.** 368, 1907; *Die katalyschen Eigenschaften des Vanadins*, Leipzig, 1906; F. Ephraim, *Das Vanadin und seine Verbindungen*, Stuttgart, 48, 1904; N. G. Sefström, *Akad. Handl. Stockholm*, 255, 1830; *Schweigger's Journ.*, **62.** 316, 1831; *Pogg. Ann.*, **21.** 43, 1831; K. Friederich, *Zeit. Physik*, **31.** 813, 1925; T. Carnelley, *Journ. Chem. Soc.*, **33.** 273, 1878; A. A. Read, *ib.*, **65.** 313, 1894; J. T. Brierley, *ib.*, **49.** 822, 1886; J. F. W. Johnston, *Edin. Journ. Science*, (2), **5.** 166, 319, 1831; E. Wedekind, *Zeit. angew. Chem.*, **37.** 87, 1924; E. Wedekind and C. Horst, *Ber.*, **45.** 262, 1912; **47.** 105, 1915; W. Prandtl and B. Bleyer, *ib.*, **65.** 152, 1910; W. Prandtl, *ib.*, **38.** 657, 1905; W. Prandtl and H. Murschhauser, *ib.*, **56.** 173, 1907; *Zeit. anorg. Chem.*, **60.** 441, 1908; O. Ruff and L. Friedrich, *ib.*, **89.** 279, 1914; O. Ruff and W. Martin, *ib.*, **25.** 49, 1912; A. C. Chapman and H. D. Law, *Analyst*, **32.** 250, 1907; A. Cioci, *Gazz. Chim. Ital.*, **29.** i, 300, 1899; *Zeit. anorg. Chem.*, **19.** 308, 1899; A. Piccini and N. Brizzi, *ib.*, **19.** 394, 1899; J. A. Hedvall and N. von Zweigbergk, *ib.*, **108.** 119, 1919; E. Tiede and E. Birnbräuer, *ib.*, **87.** 129, 1914; A. Bültemann, *Zeit. Elektrochem.*, **10.** 141, 1904; D. Balareff, *Journ. prakt. Chem.*, (2), **102.** 283, 1921; J. Böhm, *Koll. Zeit.*, **42.** 276, 1927; H. G. C. Fairbanks, *Brit. Pat. No.* 287401, 1927; S. Meyer, *Wied. Ann.*, **68.** 325, 1899; **69.** 236, 1899; *Ann. Physik*, (4), **1.** 664, 1900.

² W. Biltz, *Ber.*, **37.** 1098, 1770, 1904; W. Biltz and W. Geibel, *Nachr. Gött.*, 141, 1906; H. Gessner, *Koll. Beihefte*, **19.** 213, 1924; H. Kuzel, *German Pat.*, *D.R.P.* 186980, 1906; E. Müller, *Zeit. Koll.*, **8.** 302, 1911; G. Wegelin, *ib.*, **11.** 25, 1912; G. Wiegner, J. Magasanik and H. Gessner, *ib.*, **30.** 145, 1922; R. Fürth and O. Blüh, *ib.*, **34.** 259, 1924; W. Reinders, *Proc. Acad. Amsterdam*, **19.** 189, 1916; H. R. Kruyt, *Versl. Akad. Amsterdam*, **18.** 1625, 1918; H. Diesselhorst and H. Freundlich, *Phys. Zeit.*, **16.** 419, 1915; H. Freundlich, *Zeit. Elektrochem.*, **22.** 27, 1916; H. Mottsmith and I. Langmuir, *Phys. Rev.*, (2), **20.** 95, 1922; T. Schwedoff, *Journ. Phys.*, (3), **1.** 49, 1892; J. Errera, *Bull. Soc. Chim. Belg.*, **33.** 422, 432, 1924; *Koll. Zeit.*, **31.** 59, 1922; **32.** 157, 373, 1923; H. Freundlich and F. Oppenheimer, *Ber.*, **58.** B, 143, 1925; H. Zocher, *Zeit. phys. Chem.*, **98.** 293, 1921; *Zeit. anorg. Chem.*, **147.** 91, 1925; H. Freundlich, H. Neukircher, and H. Zocher, *Koll. Zeit.*, **38.** 43, 48, 1926; H. Zocher and K. Jacobsohn, *ib.*, **41.** 220, 1927; J. Jochims, *ib.*, **41.** 215, 1927; H. Freundlich, F. Stapelfeldt, and H. Zocher, *Zeit. phys. Chem.*, **114.** 161, 190, 1925; H. Freundlich and E. Hase, *ib.*, **89.** 446, 1915; H. Freundlich and H. Dannenberg, *ib.*, **119.** 87, 1926; H. Freundlich and E. Schalek, *ib.*, **108.** 153, 1924; H. Freundlich and W. Seifriz, *ib.*, **104.** 233, 1923; H. Freundlich and S. K. Basu, *ib.*, **115.** 203, 1925; G. I. Pokrowsky, *Zeit. Physik*, **32.** 713, 1925; R. H. Humphry, *Proc. Phys. Soc.*, **35.** 217, 1923; N. G. Chatterji and N. R. Dhar, *Chem. News*, **121.** 253, 1920; D. N. Chakravarti and N. R. Dhar, *Journ. Phys. Chem.*, **30.** 1646, 1926; *Zeit. anorg. Chem.*, **152.** 393, 1926; S. Ghosh, D. N. Chakravarti, and N. R. Dhar, *ib.*, **152.** 399, 1926; N. R. Dhar and S. Ghosh, *ib.*, **152.** 409, 1926; *Journ. Phys. Chem.*, **30.** 1564, 1926; **31.** 187, 657, 1927; N. R. Dhar, *Journ. Indian Chem. Soc.*, **4.** 173, 1927; A. Szegvari and E. Wigner, *Koll. Zeit.*, **33.** 218, 1923; Wo. Ostwald, *ib.*, **36.** 99, 1925; **40.** 201, 1926; G. Wegelin, *ib.*, **14.** 65, 1914; A. Ivanitzkaja and M. Proskurnin, *ib.*, **39.** 15, 1926; H. Lachs, *Journ. Phys. Rad.*, **3.** 125, 1922; A. Szegvari, *Zeit. phys. Chem.*, **112.** 277, 1924; B. Lange, *ib.*, **132.** 1, 1928; J. D. Riedel, *Riedel's Ber.*, 13, 1914; *Pharm. Journ.*, **92.** 643, 1914; H. Freundlich and W. Leonhardt, *Koll. Beihefte*, **7.** 172, 1915; H. Gessner, *ib.*, **19.** 213, 1924; A. Frey, *ib.*, **20.** 209, 1925; A. V. Dumansky, *Journ. Russ. Phys. Chem. Soc.*, **54.** 703, 1924; *Koll. Zeit.*, **23.** 147, 1923; W. Ostermann, *Gött. Nachr.*, 1, 1904; W. Prandtl and L. Hess, *Zeit. anorg. Chem.*, **82.** 116, 1913; J. Böhm, *Koll. Zeit.*, **42.** 276, 1927; J. Jochims, *ib.*, **41.** 215, 1927; S. Horiba and T. Kondo, *Osaka's Sexagint*, **61.** 271, 1927; W. Reinders and G. van der Lee, *Rec. Trav. Chim. Pays-Bas*, **47.** 193, 1928.

³ A. Ditte, *Compt. Rend.*, **101.** 698, 1487, 1885; **102.** 1019, 1105, 1301, 1886; **103.** 55, 1886; **105.** 1067, 1887; **106.** 270, 1888; C. Matignon and F. Bourion, *ib.*, **133.** 631, 1904; V. Auger, *ib.*, **172.** 1355, 1921; **173.** 306, 1921; G. Darzens and F. Bourion, *ib.*, **153.** 270, 1912; E. Newbery and J. N. Pring, *Proc. Roy. Soc.*, **92.** A, 276, 1916; H. E. Roscoe, *Phil. Trans.*, **158.** 1, 1868;

159. 679, 1869 ; **160.** 317, 1870 ; *Proc. Roy. Soc.*, **16.** 220, 1868 ; **18.** 37, 316, 1870 ; *Journ. Chem. Soc.*, **21.** 322, 1868 ; **23.** 344, 1870 : **24.** 23, 1871 ; *Chem. News*, **17.** 135, 1868 ; **20.** 37, 1869 ; **21.** 183, 1872 ; *Phil. Mag.*, (4), **35.** 307, 1868 ; (4), **39.** 146, 1870 ; (4), **42.** 62, 1870 ; J. J. Berzelius, *Acad. Handl. Stockholm*, **1**, 1831 ; *Schweigger's Journ.*, **62.** 323, 1831 ; **63.** 26, 1831 ; *Pogg. Ann.*, **22.** 1, 1831 ; *Ann. Chim. Phys.*, (1), **47.** 337, 1831 ; *Phil. Mag.*, (2), **10.** 321, 1831 ; (2), **11.** 7, 1832 ; W. Prandtl, *Ber.*, **38.** 657, 1905 ; W. Prandtl and H. Manz, *ib.*, **44.** 2582, 1911 ; **45.** 1343, 1912 ; W. Manchot and H. Fischer, *Liebig's Ann.*, **357.** 129, 1907 ; W. Manchot, *Ber.*, **45.** 1154, 1912 ; B. Glassmann, *ib.*, **38.** 600, 1905 ; E. Campagne, *ib.*, **36.** 3164, 1903 ; G. von Knorre and K. Arndt, *ib.*, **33.** 38, 1900 ; C. Friedheim and H. von Euler, *ib.*, **28.** 2070, 1895 ; C. F. Rammelsberg, *ib.*, **1.** 158, 1868 ; *Sitzber. Akad. Berlin*, 787, 1880 ; K. Someya, *Zeit. anorg. Chem.*, **152.** 368, 382, 386, 391, 1926 ; J. Meyer, *ib.*, **161.** 321, 1927 ; J. F. W. Johnston, *Edin. Journ. Science*, (2), **5.** 166, 319, 1831 ; F. Ephraim, *Ber.*, **36.** 1177, 1903 ; *Zeit. anorg. Chem.*, **35.** 66, 1903 ; E. F. Smith and J. G. Hibbs, *ib.*, **7.** 41, 1894 ; *Journ. Amer. Chem. Soc.*, **17.** 682, 1895 ; F. A. Genth, *ib.*, (3), **12.** 32, 1876 : H. W. Underwood, *Chem. Met. Engg.*, **29.** 709, 1923 ; H. Müller, *W. Biltz's Festschrift*, Hannover, 1927 ; F. A. Gooch and L. B. Stockey, *Amer. Journ. Science*, (4), **14.** 369, 1902 ; *Zeit. anorg. Chem.*, **32.** 456, 1902 ; F. A. Gooch and R. W. Curtis, *ib.*, **38.** 246, 1904 ; *Amer. Journ. Science*, (4), **17.** 41, 1904 ; F. A. Gooch and G. Edgar, *ib.*, (4), **25.** 233, 1908 ; F. A. Gooch and R. D. Gilbert, *ib.*, (4), **14.** 205, 1902 ; *Zeit. anorg. Chem.*, **25.** 420, 1903 ; J. Locke and G. H. Edwards, *ib.*, **19.** 378, 1899 ; *Amer. Chem. Journ.*, **20.** 594, 1898 ; P. E. Browning, *Amer. Journ. Science*, (4), **2.** 185, 1896 ; *Zeit. anorg. Chem.*, **7.** 158, 1894 ; **13.** 113, 1896 ; I. Koppel and E. C. Behrendt, *ib.*, **35.** 154, 1903 ; A. Rosenheim, *ib.*, **4.** 368, 1893 ; *Ueber Vanadinwolframsäure*, Berlin, 1888 ; *Liebig's Ann.*, **251.** 197, 1889 ; K. A. Hofmann and V. Kohlschütter, *ib.*, **307.** 315, 1899 ; *Zeit. anorg. Chem.*, **16.** 463, 1898 ; H. Ditz and F. Bardach, *ib.*, **93.** 97, 1915 ; K. Someya, *ib.*, **138.** 291, 1924 ; **163.** 206, 1927 ; K. A. Hofmann and F. Küspert, *Ber.*, **31.** 64, 1898 ; B. Glassmann, *ib.*, **38.** 600, 1905 ; C. Reichard, *Chem. Ztg.*, **27.** 1, 1903 ; W. E. Kay, *Journ. Chem. Soc.*, **37.** 728, 1880 ; A. Safarik, *Journ. prakt. Chem.*, (1), **90.** 1, 1863 ; P. Jannasch and H. F. Harwood, *ib.*, (2). **80.** 127, 1909 ; D. T. Williams, *Journ. Soc. Chem. Ind.*, **21.** 389, 1902 ; A. W. Hothersall, *ib.*, **43.** 270, T, 1924 ; R. Finkener, *Dingler's Polyt. Journ.*, **276.** 479, 1890 ; E. B. Auerbach and K. Lange, *Zeit. angew. Chem.*, **25.** 2522, 1912 ; C. Czudnowicz, *Pogg. Ann.*, **120.** 17, 1863 ; C. W. Ridsdale, *Chem. News*, **57.** 83, 1888 ; B. W. Gerland, *ib.*, **34.** 2, 1876 ; **36.** 29, 271, 272, 1877 ; *Ber.*, **9.** 872, 1876 ; **10.** 1218, 1513, 1516, 1877 ; *Journ. prakt. Chem.*, (2), **4.** 139, 1871 ; *Bull. Soc. Chim.*, (2), **19.** 501, 1873 ; A. Guyard, *ib.*, (2), **25.** 350, 1876 ; H. Moissan, *ib.*, (3), **21.** 902, 1899 ; *Compt. Rend.*, **127.** 584, 1898 ; O. Lindemann, *Ueber die quantitative Bestimmung des Vanadins in Eisenerzen*, Jena, 1878 ; *Zeit. anal. Chem.*, **18.** 99, 1879 ; W. Halberstadt, *ib.*, **22.** 1, 1883 ; R. Holverscheit, *Ueber die quantitative Bestimmung des Vanadins und die Trennung der Vanadinsäure von Phosphorsäure*, Berlin, 1890 ; C. von Hauer, *Sitzber. Akad. Wien*, **39.** 454, 1860 ; G. Edgar, *Journ. Amer. Chem. Soc.*, **38.** 2369, 1916 ; *Zeit. anorg. Chem.*, **58.** 375, 1908 ; *Amer. Journ. Science*, (4), **25.** 332, 1908 ; F. A. Gorch and G. Edgar, *ib.*, (4), **25.** 233, 1908 ; L. W. McCay and W. T. Anderson, *Journ. Amer. Chem. Soc.*, **44.** 1018, 1922 ; G. Gore, *Proc. Roy. Soc.*, **20.** 441, 1872 ; **21.** 140, 1873 ; J. Fritzsche, *Bull. Acad. St. Petersburg*, (2), **9.** 202, 1851 ; P. Düllberg, *Zeit. phys. Chem.*, **45.** 129, 1903 ; A. C. Chapman and H. D. Law, *Analyst.*, **32.** 250, 1907 ; O. Manasse, *Des Vanadate der Erdalkalien*, Berlin, 1886 ; *Liebig's Ann.*, **240.** 23, 1887 ; R. Bunsen, *ib.*, **96.** 265, 1855 ; O. Kallauner and I. Hruda, *Sprech.*, **45.** 333, 345, 1922 ; B. Mdivani, *Ann. Chim. Anal.*, **12.** 305, 1907 ; T. Warynsky and B. Mdivani, *Monit. Scient.*, (2), **22.** 527, 1908 ; R. E. Slade and G. I. Higson, *B.A. Rep.*, 450, 1913 ; H. Lassheim, J. Meyer, and R. Samuel, *Zeit. Physik*, **43.** 199, 1927 ; F. Hundeshagen, *Chem. Ztg.*, **29.** 799. 1905 ; C. Reichard, *ib.*, **27.** 1, 1903 ; K. Fuwa, *Journ. Japan. Cer. Assoc.*, **236.** 1923 ; A. C. Robertson, *Proc. Nat. Acad.*, **13.** 192, 1927 ; H. D. Gibbs, *U.S. Pat. No.* 1463206, 1923 ; O. W. Gibbs, *Proc. Amer. Acad.*, **10.** 250, 1883 ; C. F. Mohr, *Lehrbuch der chemisch-analytischen Titrirmethode*, Braunschweig, 314, 1877 ; L. Milch, *Beiträge zur Kenntniss der Vanadins und Molybdans*, Berlin, 1887 ; K. A. Nenadkewitch, *Bull. Acad. St. Petersburg*, (6), **3.** 185, 1909 ; J. M. Weiss, C. R. Downs, and R. M. Burns, *Journ. Ind. Eng. Chem.*, **15.** 965, 1923 ; S. Medsforth, *Journ. Chem. Soc.*, **123.** 1452, 1923 ; F. Ephraim and G. Beck, *Helvetica Chim. Acta*, **9.** 38, 1926 ; A. F. Benton, *Journ. Amer. Chem. Soc.*, **45.** 887, 1923 ; L. Rosenstein, *ib.*, **42.** 883, 1920 ; J. R. Cain and J. C. Hostetter, *ib.*, **34.** 274, 1912 ; A. E. Stoppel, C. F. Sidener, and P. H. M. P. Brinton, *ib.*, **46.** 2448, 1924 ; W. P. Yant and C. O. Hawk, *ib.*, **49.** 1454, 1927 ; G. Fester and G. Barraz, *Anal. Asoc. Quim. Argentina*, **15.** 210, 1927 ; K. Chakravarty and J. C. Ghosh, *Journ. Indian Chem. Soc.*, **4.** 431, 1927.

§ 9. The Vanadates of Ammonium and the Alkalies

Vanadium pentoxide is amphoteric, and when it acts as an acidic oxide, it forms a series of salts called **vanadates**. Following H. E. Roscoe,[1] many of them may be regarded as derivatives of a series of hypothetical vanadic acids :

Orthovanadic acid	H_3VO_4
Pyrovanadic acid	$H_4V_2O_7$
Metavanadic acid	HVO_3

There is a number of vanadates of higher acidity, for which a satisfactory nomenclature has not been devised. C. F. Rammelsberg had a try. He classed the alkali vanadates :

Basic.	Neutral.	Acidic.
$M_8V_2O_9$		$M_2V_4O_{11}$ (tetra)
M_3VO_4 (ortho)	MVO_3 (meta)	MV_3O_8 (hexa)
$M_4V_2O_7$ (pyro)		

Following the method employed for the silicic acids, the orthopolyvanadic acids may be referred to the general formula $H_{n+2}V_nO_{3n+1}$: the loss of one mol. of water furnishes the protopolyvanadic acid—*i.e.* the *metapolyvanadic acids*—the loss of two mols. of water, deuteropolyvanadic acid ; etc. That is,

Orthopolyvanadic acid	.	.	.	.	$H_{n+2}V_nO_{3n+1}$
Protopolyvanadic acid	.	.	.	.	$H_nV_nO_{3n}$
Deuteropolyvanadic acid	.	.	.	.	$H_{n-2}V_nO_{3n-1}$
Triteropolyvanadic acid	.	.	.	.	$H_{n-4}V_nO_{3n-2}$
Tetreropolyvanadic acid	.	.	.	.	$H_{n-6}V_nO_{3n-3}$
Penteropolyvanadic acid	.	.	.	.	$H_{n-8}V_nO_{3n-4}$
Hexeropolyvanadic acid	.	.	.	.	$H_{n-10}V_{12}O_{3n-6}$

Hence pyrovanadic acid, $H_4V_2O_7$, becomes *orthodivanadic acid ;* P. Düllberg's *tetrabasic hexavanadic acid*, $H_4V_6O_{17}$—assumed to be present in aq. soln.—becomes *deuterohexavanadic acid ;* and T. Carnelley's salt, $6Tl_2O.7V_2O_5$, assumed to be a chemical individual, becomes the thallium salt of the imaginary *deuteroheptavanadic acid,* $H_{12}V_{14}O_{41}$.

J. J. Berzelius [2] observed that when a soln. of vanadic acid is treated with ammonia or an ammonium salt, **ammonium metavanadate,** NH_4VO_3, is precipitated ; and N. G. Sefström found that it is deposited when solid ammonium chloride, more than sufficient for saturation, is placed in a soln. of a vanadate. B. W. Gerland showed that if the soln. contains a potassium salt the precipitated metavanadate is contaminated with the alkali, but with sodium salts, the precipitate is not affected. M. Lachartre prepared ammonium metavanadate, NH_4VO_3, by saturating aq. ammonia with moist vanadium pentoxide, and crystallizing the products from dil. aq. ammonia. The sp. gr. is 2·326. One hundred parts of water dissolve 5·18 parts of the salt at 15° and 10·4 parts at 32° ; it is only slightly soluble in hot alcohol and in ether. When heated in a vacuum to 135°–210°, the salt yields anhydrous ammonium trivanadate ; above 210°, lower oxides of vanadium are formed. On boiling in aqueous soln., soluble ammonium divanadate and the insoluble hexavanadate are formed. Ammonium metavanadate forms colourless crystals which, according to J. A. Norblad, are isomorphous with the corresponding potassium salt. J. J. Berzelius obtained a variety with lemon-yellow crystals by digesting vanadium pentoxide in a closed vessel with ammonia, adding an excess of ammonia to the reddish-yellow liquid, and allowing the soln. to evaporate spontaneously. H. E. Roscoe, J. J. Berzelius, and J. A. Norblad found that the colourless crystals lose ammonia when heated and acquire a colour varying from lemon-yellow to reddish-brown. According to J. A. Norblad, when the salt is heated until ammonia is no longer evolved, a dark brown mixture of tetroxide and pentoxide is formed, which when treated with alkali-lye furnishes graphite-like prisms of the tetroxide, and a soln. of the pentoxide ; H. E. Roscoe found that when heated in oxygen, the pentoxide alone remains as a residue, and if heated in a covered crucible, a mixture of vanadium nitride, dioxide, trioxide, and one of the $V_2O_4.V_2O_5$ oxides is formed. The action of heat on ammonium metavanadate was studied by A. Ditte, C. Matignon, and F. Ephraim and G. Beck— *vide supra.* C. Matignon gave for the heat of formation $V_2O_{5solid}+H_2O_{liquid}+2NH_{3gas}=2NH_4VO_{3solid}+43\cdot6$ Cals. R. Robl observed no fluorescence with the salt in ultra-violet light. J. J. Berzelius said that the salt is only sparingly soluble in cold water, furnishing a colourless soln. : it is more soluble in boiling water, forming a yellow soln. The yellow colour is not due to the loss of ammonia because it is formed when the salt is placed in cold water in a closed vessel and the whole immersed in boiling water. C. von Hauer, and J. A. Norblad said that a hot soln. of the salt loses ammonia ; while A. Ditte found that after some hours' boiling, the aq. soln. deposits crystals of hexavanadate, and if it is to remain colourless, a large excess of ammonia must be present. A. Guyard said that it dissolves best in water at 70°. A. Ditte said that cold water dissolves 10 grms. per litre, and boiling water 60 grms. per litre. In the latter case, some of the salt is decomposed. C. Matignon found that helianthine is coloured red by the aq. soln. of ammonium metavanadate, but phenolphthalein gives no sharp reaction. J. J. Berzelius obtained a black, inky liquid with tincture of galls ; R. Wagner, with gallic acid ; and R. Böttger, with pyrogallol. R. Wagner, and J. Bellier observed colorations were produced by a number of organic compounds.

J. J. Berzelius prepared **ammonium deuterotetravanadate,** $(NH_4)_2O.2V_2O_5$ with 2 (or 3) mols. of H_2O, that is, $(NH_4)_2V_4O_{11}.2H_2O$; or *ammonium tetrahydrorthotetravanadate,* $(NH_4)_2H_4V_4O_{13}$, by evaporating an aq. soln. of ammonia sat. with vanadium pentoxide ; A. Guyard evaporated the soln. at 60°–70°. C. von Hauer, A. Ditte, J. J. Berzelius, and A. Guyard added conc. acetic acid to a hot aq. soln. of ammonium metavandate until the precipitate first formed redissolves, or until the liquid becomes permanently red. The liquid can be evaporated spontaneously while protected from dust, or over conc. sulphuric acid ; or it can be cooled for crystallization. The red or garnet-red rhombic prisms or plates have a golden reflex. J. A. Norblad said that the crystals lose water very slowly when exposed to air. A. Ditte, and J. A. Norblad said that the aq. soln. is unstable, and soon deposits plates of the hexavanadate—*vide infra.* According to M. Lachartre by the action of 4 per cent. acetic acid on boiling soln. of ammonium metavanadate, the tetravanadate, $2V_2O_5,(NH_4)_2O,3H_2O$, is obtained, which on desiccation loses $2H_2O$. The use of 10 per cent. acid gives the hexavanadate, $3V_2O_5(NH_4)_2O,2H_2O$, of sp. gr. 2·594, desiccation of which gives an anhydrous, red salt of sp. gr. 2·163. The previously-described, yellow, anhydrous trivanadate has a sp. gr. of 3·029. When the acetic acid is replaced by nitric, hydrochloric, or sulphuric acid, indefinite acid ammonium vanadates are formed, the composition varying with the concentration of the acid added. With a large excess of hydrochloric acid, reduction of the vanadate also takes place.

A. Ditte prepared what he called *ammonium sesquivanadate,* or **ammonium deuterohexavanadate,** $(NH_4)_4V_6O_{17}$, or $(NH_4)_2O.3V_2O_5$, with 4 or 6 mols. of H_2O, so that it may be *ammonium tetrahydrorthohexavanadate,* $(NH_4)_4H_4V_6O_{19}$, in ruby-red crystals, by crystallization from a soln. of vanadium pentoxide in a sat. soln. of ammonium oxalate. Some pale yellow crystals of an oxalatovanadate may be formed at the same time. The salt is easily soluble in cold water. J. A. Norblad prepared golden yellow, rhombic plates of **ammonium triterohexavanadate,** $(NH_4)_2V_6O_{16}$, or $(NH_4)_2O.3V_2O_5$, by dissolving ammonium deuterotetravanadate in luke-warm water, and heating the clear, red liquid on a water-bath. C. F. Rammelsberg made it by adding an excess of acetic acid to a soln. of ammonium metavanadate, and from the mother-liquid obtained in the preparation of the tetrerodecavanadate ; F. Ephraim and G. Beck, by heating the metavanadate to 202° ; and A. Ditte, by boiling an aq. soln. of the metavanadate for a long time, and by keeping at 70° a soln. of vanadium pentoxide in an aq. soln. of the metavanadate. A. Ditte said that the dry salt gives off no ammonia at 125°, a little at 160°, and all is expelled at 350°. It is almost insoluble in cold or hot water ; boiling water dissolves 1·5 grms. per litre. This salt is the most stable of all the ammonium vanadates. F. Ephraim and G. Beck observed the formation of no ammine when this salt is exposed to ammonia gas. A. Ditte's product was *pentahydrated* ; and that of C. von Hauer, *hexahydrated.* Neither J. A. Norblad, nor C. F. Rammelsberg could prepare the hexahydrate.

C. F. Rammelsberg prepared **ammonium tetrerodecavanadate,** $(NH_4)_4V_{10}O_{27}$.

$10H_2O$, or $2(NH_4)_2O.5V_2O_2.10H_2O$, by spontaneously evaporating a red soln. of ammonium metavanadate in acetic acid. The red prisms belong to the quadratic system. C. F. Rammelsberg thought that C. von Hauer's ammonium deuterotetravanadate may really be this salt. C. Matignon obtained **ammonium hexerododecavanadate,** $(NH_4)_2V_{12}O_{30}$, as a black, metallic powder, as an intermediate stage in the decomposition of ammonium metavanadate by heat. C. F. Rammelsberg reported what he called $\frac{5}{2}$-*acid ammonium vanadate*, that is, **ammonium penterotetradecavanadate,** $(NH_4)_6V_{14}O_{38}.4H_2O$, or $3(NH_4)_2O.7V_2O_5.4H_2O$, to be obtained as a yellowish-red powder from an acetic acid soln. of ammonium metavanadate. This salt is possibly C. von Hauer's deuterotetravanadate.

The oxidation of hydroxylamine and of hydrazine by vanadium sulphate was examined by K. A. Hofmann and F. Küspert, and G. von Knorre and K. Arndt. K. A. Hofmann and V. Kohlschütter prepared **ammonium amminodihydroxylaminometavanadate,** $(NH_4)VO_3(NH_2OH)_2(NH_3)$, by mixing 100 c.c. of aq. ammonia—sat. at 5°—with finely-powdered hydroxylamine hydrochloride (10 grms.); the mixture was cooled to 0° and ammonium metavanadate (3 grms.) gradually added and the mixture allowed to remain at 0° until yellow crystals separated; the lemon-yellow leaflets thus obtained were washed with conc. ammonia and dried in an atm. of ammonia over potassium hydroxide at as low a temp. as possible. The compound is quickly decomposed by water and dilute sodium hydroxide, dissolves in hydrochloric or sulphuric acid with the evolution of nitrous oxide, and when heated decomposes with a slight explosion. They also made **hydroxylamine diamminotrihydroxylaminometavanadate,** $(NH_4)VO_3(NH_2OH)_3(NH_3)$, in a similar manner to the preceding, but only 1·5 grms. of ammonium metavanadate were employed to 10 grms. of hydroxylamine hydrochloride; it crystallizes in slender yellow needles, is rapidly decomposed by moisture and carbonic anhydride, and contains 1 mol metavanadic acid, 3 mols hydroxylamine, and 2 mols ammonia. They also obtained what they thought to be **ammonium dihydroxylaminometavanadate,** $(NH_4)VO_3(NH_2OH)_{21}$, as an unstable, impure product.

C. F. Rammelsberg prepared **lithium orthovanadate,** Li_3VO_4, by heating a mixture of vanadium pentoxide and lithium carbonate, or nitrate, in stoichiometrical proportions. The resulting yellow powder was insoluble in water. A. Ditte obtained the *hexahydrate*, $Li_3VO_4.6H_2O$, by crystallization from the mother-liquor obtained in the preparation of the pyrovanadate. A. Rosenheim and W. Reglin obtained the *enneahydrate* in transparent, rhombohedral needles as indicated below, and this is probably the salt obtained by A. Ditte. The solubility coeff. of the ortho-salt is positive, the maximum solubility being 6·25 grms. of Li_3VO_4 per 100 grms. of soln. at 35·2°; above this temp. the monohydrate is stable and the temp. coeff. is negative. The solubility represented by S grms. of Li_3VO_4 in 100 grms. of soln. is:

	0°	23·0°	28·6°	30·2°	35·2°	38·4°	40°	45°	50°	60°
S .	2·40	4·60	5·25	5·91	6·25	5·09	4·20	3·90	2·80	2·60
Solid phase		$Li_3VO_4.9H_2O$						$Li_3VO_4.H_2O$		

A. Ditte found that when a soln. of lithium carbonate in an excess of a hot sat. soln. of lithium hydroxide is sat. with vanadium pentoxide, it furnishes white, microscopical crystals of *monohydrated* **lithium oxyorthovanadate,** $Li_2O.2Li_3VO_4.H_2O$; and if this salt is allowed to stand in contact with the mother-liquor for some time, transparent crystals of the *tetradecahydrate*, $Li_2O.2Li_3VO_4.14H_2O$, are formed. All the water of crystallization is expelled by heat. A. Rosenheim and W. Reglin obtained the *tetrahydrate* as a precipitate when a soln. of vanadium pentoxide in a large excess of a sat. soln. of lithium hydroxide is heated. It appears to have a negative temp. coeff. of solubility, but at low temp. when stirred with water it changes into the enneahydrated ortho-salt. By melting together stoichiometrical proportions of lithium nitrate and vanadium pentoxide, and crystallizing the aq.

soln. of the cold product, C. F. Rammelsberg obtained *tetrahydrated* **lithium pyro-vanadate**, $Li_2V_2O_7.4H_2O$, as a mass of white crystals. A. Ditte said that the *hexahydrate*, $Li_2V_2O_7.6H_2O$, is obtained as a white, crystalline mass from a soln. of the orthovanadate in one of lithium hydroxide. J. J. Berzelius, C. F. Rammelsberg, and A. Ditte warmed a red soln. of lithium tetravanadate with enough lithium carbonate to give a colourless soln. and obtained a yellowish-white, crystalline mass of **lithium metavanadate**, $LiVO_3.2H_2O$.

J. J. Berzelius prepared **lithium deuterotetravanadate**, $Li_2V_4O_{11}.9H_2O$, by the method employed for the potassium salt; and J. A. Norblad, by dissolving a fused mixture of lithium carbonate and vanadium pentoxide in hot water, mixing the soln. with acetic acid; evaporating the liquid to a syrup; adding alcohol; dissolving the dried mass in a little water; and crystallizing over conc. sulphuric acid. The orange-red crystals resemble those of potassium dichromate; they effloresce in dry air; they lose 8 mols. of water at 100°; and almost all the water at 225°. A. Ditte obtained a hydrate with 8 or 12 mols. of water according as the soln. was crystallized hot or cold. C. F. Rammelsberg prepared **lithium orthotetra-vanadate**, $Li_6V_4O_{13}.15H_2O$, as a white crystalline mass from a soln. of the orthovanadate in the least possible quantity of nitric acid. The salt is sparingly soluble in water. C. F. Rammelsberg evaporated a soln. of lithium vanadate acidified with nitric acid, and obtained red, probably triclinic, crystals of **lithium deutero-hexavanadate**, $Li_4V_6O_{17}.15H_2O$. A. Ditte obtained the same salt by boiling a soln. of lithium carbonate with an excess of vanadium pentoxide, acidifying the soln. with a few drops of acetic acid, and concentrating the liquid. The orange-red crystals were hexadecahydrated. C. F. Rammelsberg obtained a trihydrate and an enneahydrate. He also prepared **lithium deuteroctovanadate**, $Li_6V_8O_{18}.12H_2O$, in small, red, probably triclinic, crystals from a soln. of lithium ortho- or meta-vanadate acidified with acetic acid. By heating the mother-liquor from the octovanadate on a water-bath, orange-red crystals of **lithium triterodecavanadate**, $Li_6V_{10}O_{28}.14H_2O$, were formed. The salt is sparingly soluble in cold water. A soln. of lithium metavanadate in acetic acid furnished red, transparent, prismatic crystals of **lithium deuterododecavanadate**, $Li_{10}V_{12}O_{35}.30H_2O$, which rapidly effloresced in air. The salt is freely soluble in water.

C. Czudnowicz said that when vanadium pentoxide is melted with sodium carbonate each mol. of the former drives out 3 mols. of carbon dioxide, forming **sodium orthovanadate**, Na_3VO_4. H. E. Roscoe made a similar observation. J. A. Norblad melted stoichiometrical proportions of the two compounds, and obtained a dark green viscid mass which became white. It was soluble in water, not in alcohol. H. Baker, and J. A. Hall obtained 4- or 8-sided plates of the *heptahydrate*, $Na_3VO_4.7H_2O$, by crystallization from a soln. of 10 grms. of the dodecahydrate in 10 c.c. of sodium hydroxide soln. containing 7·5 grms. of NaOH, at 78°; and H. Baker prepared the *decahydrate*, $Na_3VO_4.10H_2O$, by crystallization by cooling a conc. soln. of the orthovanadate alone or mixed with sodium hydroxide. The solubility is greatly influenced by the temp. The crystals occur in dodecahedral or octahedral cubic crystals, and also in tabular, hexagonal crystals. The *dodeca-hydrate*, $Na_3VO_4.12H_2O$, was prepared by adding an excess of sodium hydroxide to a soln. of sodium pyrovanadate, or by digesting the cake obtained by heating a mixture of vanadium pentoxide and sodium carbonate, in water or dil. sodium hydroxide, and crystallizing the liquid. The salt is less soluble in soda-lye than in water. The hexagonal crystals develop overgrowths in a soln. of the phosphate. A. Ditte reported that the salt is the *tridecahydrate*, $Na_3VO_4.13H_2O$, but this is probably a mistake. H. E. Roscoe dissolved anhydrous orthovanadate in the smallest quantity of water possible, poured a layer of alcohol over the liquid, and in some hours found that the under layer furnished a mass of colourless needles of the *hexadecahydrate*, $Na_3VO_4.16H_2O$. The salt is readily soluble in water and the soln. has an acidic reaction. H. Baker found that the orthovanadates correspond in composition and crystalline form with the orthophosphates and orthoarsenates;

thus, $Na_3(P,V,As)O_4.12H_2O$ are hexagonal; $Na_3(P,V,As)O_4.10H_2O$ are cubic; $Na_3(V,P,As)O_4.8H_2O$ are rhombic; and $2Na_3(V,P,As)O_4.NaF.19H_2O$ are cubic. P. Düllberg studied the electrometric titration of soln. of vanadic acid with sodium hydroxide; he also made observations on the f.p. of the soln. He inferred from the results that the so-called orthovanadate is resolved in aq. soln. into pyrovanadate: $2Na_3VO_4+H_2O=Na_4V_2O_7+2NaOH$, forming the ions V_2O_7'''', and not HVO_4''. A. Rosenheim and K. H. Yang studied the alkalimetric titration of sodium ortho-vanadate, using phenolphthalein; and α-naphtholphthalein as indicators. The electrometric titration curve of $0.1N$-sodium orthovanadate, Na_3VO_4, with $0.4N$-HCl is shown in Fig. 5. A. Lottermoser placed a soln. of sodium vanadate in an inner anode cell, and $0.1N$-NaOH in the outer cathode cell, and, using a platinum cylinder as anode, on electrolysis he obtained an acid vanadate in the inner cell. A. Ditte obtained **sodium oxyorthovanadate,** $Na_2O.2Na_3VO_4.26(or\ 30)H_2O$, from a soln. of vanadium pentoxide in a great excess of soda-lye. If the soln. is evaporated slowly in vacuo, colourless prisms, with approximately 30 mols. of water of crystallization, are deposited; warm soln. deposit crystals with 26 mols H_2O. The salt melts in its water of crystallization, and the water escapes, leaving a white mass which gives an alkaline soln. with water. H. E. Roscoe melted a mol of vanadic pentoxide with 2 mols of sodium carbonate and obtained **sodium pyrovanadate,** $Na_2V_2O_7$. A. Ditte obtained

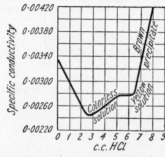

FIG. 5.—The Electrometric Titration Curve of Sodium Orthovanadate, Na_3VO_4.

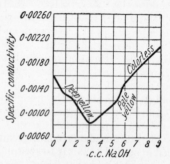

FIG. 6.—Electrometric Titration Curve of Hexavanadic Acid, $H_4V_6O_{17}$.

acicular crystals of the *octohydrate*, $Na_2V_2O_7.8H_2O$, by evaporating an aq. soln. of the salt to dryness, extracting the product with aq. alcohol, and cooling the soln. when sat. at 60°. H. E. Roscoe observed that if an aq. soln. be treated with alcohol, the *octodecahydrate*, $Na_2V_2O_7.18H_2O$, is formed; and the same salt is produced when an aq. soln. of the orthovanadate is allowed to stand, or is boiled: $2Na_3VO_4+H_2O=2NaOH+Na_4V_2O_7$. The hydrolysis is inde-pendent of the effect of any carbon dioxide. Alcohol precipitates an oily liquid from the soln., and this furnishes crystals of the octohydrate; J. A. Norblad obtained the salt by crystallization from a soln. of vanadium pentoxide or sodium vanadate in an excess of soda-lye. The six-sided plates or prisms were said by J. A. Norblad to be monoclinic, but C. F. Rammelsberg regarded them as hexagonal with the axial ratio $a:c=1:0.962$. S. Motylewsky gave 302 mgrms. for the drop-weight of the pyrovanadate when that of water is 100 mgrms. at 0°. The crystals effloresce in air. They are freely soluble in water but not in alcohol. Ammonium chloride precipitates ammonium metavanadate from the aq. soln. J. J. Berzelius prepared **sodium metavanadate,** $NaVO_3$, by allowing a soln. of the pentoxide in soda-lye to evaporate spontaneously; H. E. Roscoe, by treating a soln. of the pyrovanadate with carbon dioxide, and separating the sodium carbonate by crystallization; the mother-liquor contains the metavanadate, which is recovered by crystallization. J. A. Norblad used an analogous process, and also by boiling a soln. of sodium tetravanadate with dil. soda-lye until colourless. On evaporation straw-yellow or colourless, monoclinic, prismatic crystals are formed. The salt readily fuses, and when cold furnishes a white crystalline mass. If the aq. soln. be evaporated over sulphuric acid, it furnishes warty masses of prismatic crystals of the *monohydrate*, $NaVO_3.H_2O$, and all the water can be removed by keeping the crystals over sulphuric acid. If the mother-liquor from the monohydrate be treated with water and then with alcohol, an oily liquid is precipitated, and this furnishes crystals of the *dihydrate*, $NaVO_3.2H_2O$; if crystallized from a mixture of alcohol and water, the salt contains $2\frac{1}{2}$ mols of water; and if crystallized from a soln. of sodium carbonate, 3 or 4 mols of water according to the temp. S. Motylewsky gave 246 mgrms. for the drop weight of the metavanadate, when that of water at 0° is 100 mgrms. P. Düllberg inferred from the f.p. of soln. of the metavanadate, that the salt is really *sodium metatrivanadate*, $Na_3V_3O_9$. According to G. Canneri, the electrical conductivity of soln. of sodium metavanadate, acidified with increasing proportions of acetic acid, varies continuously at 30°, indicating that the condensation of the mols of the metavanadate is a continuous function of the conc. of the acetic acid. At the same time the colour of the soln. changes from yellow to orange-red. P. Pascal gave -30.2×10^{-5} for the mol. magnetic susceptibility of soln. of sodium metavanadate. F. Reichart and R. Wernicke found that soln. of ferric salts and of ferrous sulphate added in small quantities to alkaline soln. of sodium vanadate cause the precipitation of the vanadium as insoluble ferric vanadate, and by adsorption on the ferric hydroxide formed.

J. J. Berzelius prepared *enneahydrated* **sodium deuterotetravanadate,** $Na_2V_4O_{11}.9H_2O$, by treating a soln. of an excess vanadium pentoxide in one of sodium carbonate at 80°, with an excess of acetic acid, and concentrating the red soln. for crystallization by spontaneous evaporation. C. von Hauer said that an excess of acetic acid is to be avoided or hydrated vanadium pentoxide will be deposited. The transparent, orange-red crystals resemble manganous acetate. The crystals effloresce in dry air and become yellow without changing their form. J. A. Norblad said that the water of crystallization is all expelled at 200°. J. J. Berzelius, and C. von Hauer found the salt to be freely soluble in water, but insoluble in alcohol; one part of the salt will impart a distinct yellow colour to 156,000 parts of water. The anhydrous salt is a little soluble in warm water, and freely soluble in dil. acids. The salt is sensitive to light when in contact with organic matter. A. Ditte prepared the *pentahydrate*, $Na_2V_4O_{11}.5H_2O$, by evaporating in vacuo a soln. of vanadium dioxide in a boiling soln. of sodium carbonate. T. Carnelley reported **sodium orthotetravanadate,** $Na_6V_4O_{13}.2$ or $6H_2O$, analogous to sodium tetraphosphate, by crystallization from a soln. of the cold cake obtained by melting stoichiometrical proportions of sodium carbonate and vanadium pentoxide. The crystals are sparingly soluble in cold water. The aq. soln. furnishes a precipitate of the corresponding silver or thallium salt when treated with a soln. of the corresponding metal salt. J. A. Norblad reported what he called *sodium trivanadate*, that is, *enneahydrated* **sodium triterohexavanadate,** $Na_2V_6O_{16}.9H_2O$, by heating the red soln. of the tetravanadate on the water-bath: $2Na_2V_4O_{11}=2NaVO_3$ $+Na_2V_6O_{16}$; and A. Ditte obtained orange-red plates of the *trihydrate*, $Na_2V_6O_{16}.3H_2O$, by boiling for a long time soda-lye sat. with vanadium pentoxide. J. A. Norblad simultaneously obtained **sodium deuterohexavanadate,** $Na_4V_6O_{17}.$ $10H_2O$, in orange-red prismatic crystals in the preparation of enneahydrated sodium deuterotetravanadate. The crystals lose 7 mols. of water over conc. sulphuric acid, and melt at a red-heat. C. F. Rammelsberg obtained red, triclinic crystals of the *hexadecahydrate*, $Na_4V_6O_{17}.16H_2O$, which M. Websky found had the axial ratios $a:b:c=0.9189:1:1.025$, and $a=83°\ 52'$, $\beta=91°\ 19'$, and $\gamma=94°\ 31'$. The crystals effloresce in air. The water is all expelled when the salt is melted, and it is then brownish-black, and insoluble in water and in acids. S. Motylewsky gave 238 mgrms. for the drop-weight of the hexavanadate when that of water at 0° is 100 mgrms. A. Ditte reported garnet-red needles or six-sided plates of the *octodecahydrate*, $Na_4V_6O_{17}.18H_2O$, to be formed by evaporating and cooling a soln. of sodium metavanadate mixed with a little acetic acid. P. Düllberg inferred that the tetravanadate, $Na_2V_4O_{11}$, is really an acid salt of *deuterohexavanadic acid*, $H_4V_6O_{17}$, namely, **sodium hydrodeuterohexavanadate**, $Na_3HV_6O_{17}$; that the salt, $Na_4V_6O_{17}$, is **sodium dihydrodeuterohexavanadate**, $Na_2H_2V_6O_{17}$; and that the neutral $Na_4V_6O_{17}$ breaks up in aq. soln., forming $Na_3HV_6O_{17}$ and sodium hydroxide. From these hexavanadates, free hexavanadic acid is precipitated by the addition of mineral acids. It decomposes, especially if the soln. is heated or excess of mineral acid added, yielding the pentoxide, which separates as a brown precipitate. If a very large excess of acid has been added, the pentoxide passes into soln. again as a cation. The yellow hexavanadate ions, HV_6O_{17}''', are not permanent in the presence either of hydrogen or hydroxyl ions, and the rate of their disappearance corresponds with the velocity of a reaction of the first order. In contrast to the phosphates, the change of metavanadate into pyro- and ortho-vanadate takes place instantaneously. The electrometric titration curve of the deuterohexavanadic acid with soln. $H_4=0.01264N$-, and $0.00236N$-NaOH, is shown in Fig. 6. W. I. Baragiola obtained dark yellow **sodium tetreroctovanadate**, $Na_2V_8O_{21}.7\frac{1}{2}$(or $8\frac{1}{2}$)H_2O, by evaporating a boiling soln. of sodium metavanadate with a large excess of ammonium chloride; C. F. Rammelsberg, sparingly soluble **sodium tetrerodecavanadate**, $Na_4V_{10}O_{27}.3\frac{1}{2}H_2O$, from a warm conc. soln. of sodium pyrovanadate with a large excess of acetic acid; C. Friedheim and P. Michaelis, red, rhombic crystals of **sodium tetrerotetradecavanadate**, $Na_8V_{14}O_{39}.33H_2O$, from a soln. of equimolar parts of sodium metavanadate and dihydrophosphate; and C. Friedheim and P. Michaelis, red crystals of **sodium tetrerohexadeca-vanadate**, $Na_{10}V_{16}O_{45}.39H_2O$, from a soln. of about 1·5 parts of sodium meta-vanadate, and one part of sodium metaphosphate. C. F. Rammelsberg suggested that J. A. Norblad's trivanadate is really *sodium hexerohexadecavanadate*, $Na_6V_{16}O_{43}.24H_2O$.

J. A. Norblad's experiments on the amount of carbon dioxide displaced from potassium carbonate by potassium vanadate, or triterovanadate, gave no definite results. C. F. Rammelsberg prepared **potassium orthovanadate**, K_3VO_4, by fusing a mixture of stoichiometrical proportions of potassium carbonate and vanadium pentoxide; the pale yellow, crystalline mass is decomposed by water into the potassium pyrovanadate and hydroxide. E. Jänecke discussed the action of ammonia on this vanadate. A. Ditte found that a soln. of vanadium pentoxide in a soln. of 3 eq. of potassium hydroxide furnishes crystals of the *hexahydrate*, $K_3VO_4.6$(or $4\frac{1}{2}$)H_2O. A. Ditte reported **potassium oxyortho-vanadate**, $K_2O.2K_3VO_4.20H_2O$, from a soln. of 4 eq. of potassium hydroxide and one eq. of vanadium pentoxide evaporated to a syrup, and then treated with alcohol. The salt melts in its water of crystallization and becomes anhydrous. J. A. Norblad prepared monoclinic crystals of trihydrated **potassium pyrovanadate**, $K_4V_2O_7.3H_2O$, by boiling a soln. of potassium metavanadate and hydroxide, and evaporating the syrupy liquid over sulphuric acid. C. F. Rammelsberg prepared the same salt. The salt loses one-third its water over sulphuric acid, two-thirds at $100°$, and all when melted at $350°$. A. Ditte represented the salt as a *tetrahydrate*. J. J. Berzelius prepared **potassium metavanadate**, KVO_3, from a soln. of vanadium pentoxide in potash-lye by spontaneous evaporation, and extracting the excess of alkali from the product by cold water. J. A. Norblad mixed a soln. of vanadium pentoxide in conc. potash-lye with dil. acetic acid, and boiled the orange liquid until it became colourless, and repeated the treatment until a lemon-yellow liquid was obtained, which, on evaporation, furnished yellowish crystals. When these were recrystallized, colourless crystals of the metavanadate were obtained. The crystals became red, and at $100°$, brick-red. They melted at a red-heat. The crystals are sparingly soluble in cold water, freely soluble in hot water, and insoluble in alcohol. J. A. Norblad obtained the *monohydrate*, $KVO_3.H_2O$, by boiling a soln. of ammonium tetravanadate in potash-lye, and evaporating the colourless liquid over sulphuric acid ; or by crystallization from a soln. of the product obtained by fusing vanadium pentoxide with an excess of potassium nitrate. The colourless, needle-like crystals lose all their water at 110°. A. Ditte said that by varying the conditions he could make hydrates with $1\frac{1}{4}$, $1\frac{1}{2}$, 2, and $3H_2O$. C. F. Rammelsberg reported a *heptahydrate*, $KVO_3.7H_2O$, from a soln. of the product obtained by melting equimolar parts of vanadium dioxide and potassium carbonate.

J. A. Norblad obtained *tetrahydrated* **potassium deuterotetravanadate,** $K_2V_4O_{11}.4H_2O$, by mixing a hot soln. of potassium metavanadate in an excess of potash-lye with acetic acid so as to produce a dark red liquid. C. F. Rammelsberg used nitric acid. On cooling the boiling liquid, orange-yellow crystals are formed. J. J. Berzelius, C. Radau, and F. Ephraim also prepared this salt. A better yield is obtained if alcohol be added after the acid. The orange-yellow, rhombic crystals are stable in air, and they are freely soluble in water ; they lose no water over conc. sulphuric acid ; a part is lost at 100° ; and all at 200°. The salt melts below redness. J. J. Berzelius, and J. A. Norblad also prepared a *hemiheptahydrate*, $K_2V_4O_{11}.3\frac{1}{2}H_2O$, by adding alcohol to a dil. soln. of the tetrahydrate ; F. Ephraim, the *hexahydrate*, $K_2V_4O_{11}.6H_2O$, by evaporating the aq. extract of a fused mixture of a mol of vanadium pentoxide with 4 mols of potassium chloride ; and A. Ditte, the *decahydrate*, by cooling the garnet-red liquid obtained by sat. a soln. of potassium carbonate at 80° with vanadium pentoxide. If the crystallization occurs at a high temp. the *trihydrate* is formed ; if at a lower temp., the *octohydrate* ; and if at a lower temp. still, the *decahydrate*. C. F. Rammelsberg, and J. A. Norblad prepared tabular crystals of **potassium triterohexavanadate,** $K_2V_6O_{16}$, by heating a soln. of the tetravanadate on a water-bath until the yellow liquid becomes red : $2K_2V_4O_{11} = 2KVO_3 + K_2V_6O_{16}$. The salt is almost insoluble in water, and it is similar to the ammonium salt. J. A. Norblad obtained the *hexahydrate* $K_2V_6O_{16}.6H_2O$, from a soln. of the tetravanadate and acetic acid ; and A. Ditte reported the *monohydrate*, $K_2V_6O_{16}.H_2O$, in orange-yellow crystals from a soln. of vanadium pentoxide in potassium carbonate, mixed with acetic acid, and heated to about 70°. The cold mother-liquor afterwards deposits garnet-red crystals of the *pentahydrate*, $K_2V_6O_{16}.5H_2O$. C. F. Rammelsberg made **potassium deutero-hexavanadate,** $K_4V_2O_{17}.2H_2O$, in brownish crystals, by adding acetic acid to a soln. of potassium metavanadate. A. Ditte obtained it as a *hexahydrate*. F. Ephraim melted vanadium pentoxide with an excess of potassium chloride, and washed out the soluble salts. S. Motylewsky gave 168 mgrms. for the drop-weight of the hexavanadate when that of water at 0° is 100 mgrms. The greyish-brown, tabular crystals of **potassium tetreroctovanadate,** $K_2V_8O_{21}.1\frac{1}{2}H_2O$, are sparingly soluble in water. O. Manasse obtained **potassium tetrerodecavanadate,** $K_4V_{10}O_{27}.12H_2O$, by evaporating on a water-bath the mother-liquor employed in the preparation of potassium strontium vanadate (*q.v.*). C. F. Rammelsberg obtained a crystalline mass of **potassium orthoctovanadate,** $K_{10}V_8O_{25}.7H_2O$, by adding acetic acid to the mother-liquor obtained in preparing potassium pyrovanadate until colour disappears. C. Radau obtained **potassium triterodeca-vanadate,** $K_6V_{10}O_{28}.10H_2O$, by evaporating a hot soln. of 20 grms. potassium metavanadate with 22–23 c.c. of 30 per cent. acetic acid. The acid is diluted to prevent the separation of hydrated vanadium pentoxide. The dark red, monoclinic crystals have, according to A. Fock, the axial ratios $a : b : c = 0.5902 : 1 : 0.6040$, and $\beta = 117° 40'$, 100 parts of water dissolve 19·20 parts of salt at 17·5°. F. Ephraim reported that violet crystals of **potassium hepteroctodecavanadate,** $K_4V_{18}O_{47}$, are produced by washing the soluble salts from a fused mixture of a mol of vanadium pentoxide and 2 mols of potassium fluoride ; and he obtained **potassium deutero-tetracosivanadate,** $K_{22}V_{24}O_{71}.3\frac{1}{2}H_2O$, from a fused mixture of vanadium pentoxide and potassium chloride.

W. I. Baragiola prepared **ammonium sodium tetrerotetradecavanadate,** $\{(NH_4)_{0.545}Na_{0.455}\}_8V_{14}O_{39}.17\frac{1}{2}H_2O$, by crystallization from a conc. soln. of a mol of sodium metavanadate and 2 mols of ammonium chloride ; A. Ditte, **ammonium** sodium triterodecavanadate, $(NH_4)_{0 \cdot 66}Na_{0 \cdot 346}V_{10}O_{28}.15H_2O$, in orange plates, from a soln. of sodium silicate, ammonium metavanadate, and acetic acid ; W. I. Baragiola, ammonium potassium metatetravanadate $(NH_4)_{0 \cdot 5}K_{0 \cdot 5 \cdot 4}V_4O_{12} \cdot 1\frac{1}{2}H_2O$, by fractional crystallization from a boiling soln. of a mol of potassium metavanadate and ammonium chloride ; and ammonium potassium triterodecavanadate, $(NH_4)_{0 \cdot 25}K_{0 \cdot 756}V_{10}O_{28}.13H_2O$, if the ammonium chloride be present in great excess. C. Friedheim and P. Michaelis reported potassium sodium deuterohexavanadate, $(K_{0 \cdot 2}Na_{0 \cdot 8})_4V_6O_{17}.7H_2O$, to be obtained in red, prismatic crystals from a mixture of the mother-liquor of sodium tetrerohexadecavanadate, mixed with potassium chloride ; and red crystals of $(K_{0 \cdot 4}Na_{0 \cdot 6})_4V_6O_{17}.6H_2O$, from the mother-liquor of sodium tetrerotetradecavanadate mixed with an excess of potassium chloride.

G. Chabrié prepared cæsium metavanadate, $CsVO_3$, by boiling a mixture of 3·65 grms. of vanadium pentoxide, 6·5 grms. of cæsium carbonate, and 25 c.c. of water ; and cooling the filtered liquid.

REFERENCES.

[1] H. E. Roscoe, *Phil. Trans.*, **158.** 1, 1868 ; **159.** 679, 1869 ; **160.** 317, 1870 ; *Proc. Roy. Soc.*, **16.** 220, 1868 ; **18.** 37, 316, 1870 ; *Journ. Chem. Soc.*, **21.** 322, 1868 ; **23.** 344, 1870 ; **24.** 23, 1871 ; *Chem. News*, **17.** 135, 1868 ; **20.** 37, 1869 ; **21.** 183, 1877 ; *Phil. Mag.*, (4), **35.** 307, 1868 ; (4), **39.** 146, 1870 ; (4), **40.** 62, 1870 ; C. F. Rammelsberg, *Sitzber. Akad. Berlin*, **3**, 1883 ; *Wied. Ann.*, **20.** 928, 1883 ; T. Carnelley, *Journ. Chem. Soc.*, **26.** 322, 1873 ; P. Düllberg, *Zeit. phys. Chem.*, **45.** 129, 1903.

[2] J. J. Berzelius. *Acad. Handl. Stockholm*, **1**, 1831 ; *Schweigger's Journ.*, **62.** 323, 1831 ; **63.** 26, 1831 ; *Pogg. Ann.*, **22.** 1, 1831 ; *Ann. Chim. Phys.*, (1), **47.** 337, 1831 ; *Phil. Mag.*, (2), **10.** 321, 1831 ; (2), **11.** 7, 1832 ; H. E. Roscoe, *Phil. Trans.*, **158.** 1, 1868 ; **159.** 679, 1869 ; **160.** 317, 1870 ; *Proc. Roy. Soc.*, **16.** 220, 1868 ; **18.** 37, 316, 1870 ; *Journ. Chem. Soc.*, **21.** 322, 1868 ; **23.** 344, 1870 ; **24.** 23, 1871 ; *Chem. News*, **17.** 135, 1868 ; **20.** 37, 1869 ; **21.** 183, 1872 ; *Phil. Mag.*, (4), **35.** 307, 1868 ; (4), **39.** 146, 1870 ; (4), **42.** 62, 1870 ; N. G. Sefström, *Akad. Handl. Stockholm*, 255, 1830 ; *Schweigger's Journ.*, **62.** 316, 1831 ; *Pogg. Ann.*, **21.** 43, 1831 ; *Ann. Chim. Phys.*, (2), **46.** 105, 1831 ; *Phil. Mag.*, (2), **10.** 151, 1831 ; F. Ephraim and G. Beck, *Helvetica Chim. Acta*, **9.** 38, 1926 ; J. A. Norblad, *Acta Lund Univ.*, **2**, 1, 1874 ; *Bull. Soc. Chim.*, (2), **23.** 64, 1875 ; A. Guyard, *ib.*, (2), **25.** 355, 1876 ; J. Bellier, *ib.*, (3), **23.** 131, 1900 ; A. Ditte, *Compt. Rend.*, **101.** 698, 1487, 1885 ; **102.** 918, 1019, 1105, 1886 ; **103.** 56, 1886 ; **104.** 902, 1168, 1844, 1887 ; P. Pascal, *ib.*, **147.** 742, 1908 ; A. Lottermoser, *Zeit. Koll.*, **30.** 346, 1922 ; C. Matignon, *Chem. Ztg.*, **29.** 986, 1905 ; R. Wagner, *Dingler's Journ.*, **223.** 633, 1877 ; G. Canneri, *Gazz. Chim. Ital.*, **56.** ii, 779, 1923 ; R. Böttger, *Chem. Centrb.*, (3), **4.** 514, 1873 ; C. F. Rammelsberg, *Sitzber. Akad. Berlin*, **3**, 1883 ; *Wied. Ann.*, **20.** 938, 1883 ; C. von Hauer, *Sitzber. Akad. Wien*, **21.** 337, 1856 ; **39.** 455, 1860 ; K. A. Hofmann and V. Kohlschütter, *Zeit. anorg. Chem.*, **16.** 470, 1898 ; *Liebig's Ann.*, **307.** 315, 1899 ; M. Websky, *ib.*, **20.** 936, 1836 ; C. Radau, *Beitrag zur Kenntnis vanadinsaurer Salze*, Königsberg, 1888 ; *Liebig's Ann.*, **251.** 114, 1889 ; O. Manasse, *ib.*, **240.** 23, 1887 ; *Der Vanadate der Erdalkalien*, Berlin, 1886 ; K. A. Hofmann and F. Küspert, *Ber.*, **31.** 64, 1898 ; G. von Knorre and K. Arndt, *ib.*, **33**, 38, 1900 ; H. Baker, *Journ. Chem. Soc.*, **47.** 357, 1885 ; J. A. Hall, *ib.*, **51.** 94, 1887 ; T. Carnelley, *ib.*, **26.** 323, 1873 ; G. Chabrié, *Ann. Chim. Phys.*, (7), **26.** 228, 1902 ; C. Friedheim and P. Michaelis, *Zeit. anorg. Chem.*, **5.** 443, 1894 ; A. Scheuer, *ib.*, **16.** 292, 1898 ; F. Ephraim, *ib.*, **15.** 75, 1903 ; A. Rosenheim and K. H. Yang, *ib.*, **129.** 181, 1923 ; A. Rosenheim and W. Reglin, *ib.*, **120.** 111, 1922 ; W. I. Baragiola, *Ueber das Verhalten der normalen Natrium-Kaliumsalze des Wolframs, Molybdäns, und Vanadins gegen Ammoniumchlorid*, Berlin, 1902 ; J. Gibbons, *Chem. News*, **30.** 267, 1874 ; B. W. Gerland, *Journ. prakt. Chem.*, (2), **4.** 97, 1871 ; *Ber.*, **9.** 873, 1876 ; *Chem. News*, **34.** 2, 1876 ; **36.** 29, 271, 272, 1877 ; F. Reichart and R. Wernicke, *Anal. Soc. Quim. Argentina*, **7.** 110, 1912 ; M. Lachartre, *Bull. Soc. Chim.*, (4), **35.** 321, 1924 ; C. Czudnowicz, *Pogg. Ann.*, **120.** 17, 1863 ; A. Fock, *Zeit. Kryst.*, **17.** 1, 1890 ; P. Düllberg, *Zeit. phys. Chem.*, **45.** 175, 1904 ; S. Motylewsky, *Zeit. anorg. Chem.*, **38.** 410, 1904 ; R. Robl, *Zeit. angew. Chem.*, **39.** 608, 1926 ; E. Jänecke, *Zeit. Elektrochem.*, **33.** 518, 1927.

§ 10. The Vanadates of the Copper Family

C. Radau [1] found that when copper is precipitated in the presence of vanadic acid, it is always vanadiferous. B. W. Gerland said that copper orthovanadate, $Cu_3(VO_4)_2$, is precipitated when a soln. of copper sulphate is treated with ammonium metavanadate, **or** sodium deuterotetravanadate. The product contains a small excess of vanadium pentoxide. G. Tammann gave 450° for its temp. of formation from its component oxides. I. Kurbatoff obtained a dark green mineral which he called **usbekite,** from Karatschagir, Fergana, and its analysis approximated the *trihydrate,* $Cu_3(VO_4)_2.3H_2O$. A. E. Fersman gave the formula $4CuO.V_2O_5.3H_2O$. K. A. Nenadkewitsch found an olive-green mineral which he called *turanite* in the limestone of Tyuya-Muyun, Alai Mt., Turkestan. Its composition approximated **copper dihydroxyorthovanadate,** $Cu(OH)_2.3Cu_3(VO_4)_2$, or $5CuO.V_2O_5.2H_2O$. A. Carnot said that a warm soln. of vanadic acid gives a yellowish-brown precipitate of **copper pyrovanadate,** $Cu_2V_2O_7$, when poured into a soln. of cupric salt sat. with ammonia. A. Ditte found that a dil. soln. of copper sulphate gives a precipitate with ammonium vanadate which, on raising the temp., dissolves ; if the copper salt be in excess, the precipitate remains, and when the mother-liquor is boiled, it furnishes greenish-yellow plates of the *trihydrate,* $Cu_2V_2O_7.3H_2O$. C. Radau said that the precipitate is a mixture of the ortho- and pyro-vanadates. J. J. Berzelius said that the yellow precipitate obtained by adding alcohol to a mixture of a copper salt with an alkali vanadate is **copper metavanadate,** $Cu(VO_3)_2$. C. Radau obtained it from a boiling soln. of 10 grms. of potassium metavanadate in 250 c.c. of water, and of 17·5 grms. of hydrated copper sulphate in 250 c.c. of water, and allowed the mixture to stand for some time. The precipitate is contaminated with much alkali. A. Carnot also prepared this salt. G. Fester and G. Berraz used copper vanadate deposited on silica as a catalyst for oxidizing alcohol. C. Radau obtained **copper dioxyorthotetra-vanadate,** $8CuO.2V_2O_5$, or $CuO.Cu_3V_4O_{13}$, as an apple-green precipitate by adding copper sulphate to an acid vanadate ; and J. J. Berzelius, **copper deuterotetra-vanadate,** CuV_4O_{11}, from a mixture of copper sulphate and potassium deutero-tetravanadate.

C. Radau prepared **potassium copper triterohexavanadate,** $K_{0.66}Cu_{0.66})V_6O_{16}.$ $1\frac{1}{2}H_2O$, from a mixture of a boiling soln. of 10 grms. of potassium triterodecavana-date in 250 c.c. of water, and 15 grms. of hydrated copper sulphate in 250 c.c. of water, and allowing the clear liquid to evaporate spontaneously. A. Fock showed that the crystals are triclinic pinacoids with the axial ratios $a : b : c$ $=0.9382 : 1 : 1.1059$, and $a=98°$ 45′ ; $\beta=99°$ 38′ ; and $\gamma=85°$ 33′. C. Radau found that 100 c.c. of water at 18° dissolve 11·1 parts of the salt. In 1838, H. Hess described a mineral which he called **volborthite**—after A. Volborth. It is brown-yellow or olive-green, and occurs at Siserek and Nizhni Tagilsk, Ural, and several parts of Perm. Analyses by F. A. Genth correspond with **copper calcium hydroxy-orthovanadate,** $(Cu,Ca,Ba)_3(OH)_3VO_4.6H_2O$. A variety from Friedrichsrode, Thuringia, analyzed by H. Credner, was represented by C. F. Rammelsberg by $(Cu,Ca)_4V_2O_9.H_2O$, where Cu : Ca$=3 : 2$, or **copper calcium pyrovanadate,** $2(Cu,Ca)O.(Cu,Ca)_2V_2O_7.H_2O$; and A. d'Achiardi called it *calciovorborthite,* and M. Adam, *calcvorborthite.* J. Antipoff represented a variety from Turkestan by **copper calcium orthovanadate,** $Cu_3Ca_3(VO_4)_4.2H_2O$, or $(Cu,Ca)_3(VO_4)_2.H_2O$; and W. F. Hillebrand and H. E. Merwin gave for a variety from Utah, $5RO.V_2O_5.2H_2O$. Some arsenic and phosphoric oxides are present. Volborthite occurs in small six-sided plates often aggregated into globular forms. W. F. Hillebrand and H. E. Merwin said that the plates are probably monoclinic. The optic axial angle is $2V=68$ for Li-light ; 83° for Na-light ; and 19° for Tl-light. The optical character is positive for red-light, and negative for violet-light. The sp. gr. given by H. Credner is 3·495 for a green sample, and 3 860 for a grey one. The hardness is 3·0-3·5. W. F. Hillebrand said that the mineral has the indices of refraction $a=2.01$, $\beta=2.05$, and $\gamma=2.10$ for the Na-light. B. W. Gerland said the mineral dissolves if sulphur dioxide be passed through water with the mineral in suspension. F. Ephraim and G. Beck obtained **copper triterodecavanadate,** $3CuO.5V_2O_5.22H_2O$, by treating a soln. of the barium deuterohexavanadate with cupric sulphate. The salt, dehydrated at 220°, absorbs ammonia, forming the blue *dodecammine* at 245°, which forms a green *hexammine* between 190° and 210°, and the brown *diammine* between 120° and 145°.

H. E. Roscoe prepared **silver orthovanadate**, Ag_3VO_4, by mixing a freshly prepared soln. of the sodium salt with a neutral soln. of silver nitrate. If any free acid be present some pyrovanadate is formed. A. Ditte obtained the yellow precipitate from a soln. of ammonium vanadate and silver nitrate. The precipitate slowly dissolves in molten silver nitrate, and when the cold mass is leached with water, golden-yellow rhombohedral plates or six-sided prisms are formed. H. E. Roscoe found that the orthovanadate is freely soluble in aq. ammonia and nitric acid. E. C. Franklin and C. A. Kraus said that the orthovanadate is insoluble in liquid ammonia. A pale yellow precipitate of **silver pyrovanadate**, $Ag_4V_2O_7$, is formed when a soln. of sodium pyrovanadate is added to one of silver nitrate. W. Prandtl and L. Hess, and J. A. Hall also prepared this salt, and found that it furnishes ethyl orthovanadate when treated with ethyl bromide in ethereal soln. J. J. Berzelius said that a pale yellow or white precipitate of **silver metavanadate**, $AgVO_3$, is produced when a soln. of ammonium metavanadate is added to one of silver nitrate. It is not completely decomposed by hydrochloric acid. A. Ditte obtained acicular crystals of **silver ditritamminometavanadate**, $3AgVO_3.2NH_3.H_2O$ in yellow needles, by evaporating a soln. of silver pyrovanadate in aq. ammonia, over sulphuric acid. T. Carnelley prepared silver orthotetravanadate, $Ag_6V_4O_{13}$, by adding silver nitrate to a soln. of the sodium salt. The sp. gr. is 5·67 at 18°; and 100 parts of water at 14° dissolve 0·00467 part of the salt, and 0·00735 part at 100°. G. Fester and G. Berraz used silver vanadate deposited on fuller's earth as a catalyst in the oxidation of alcohol.

REFERENCES.

[1] C. Radau, *Beitrag zur Kenntniss vanadinsaurer Salze*, 1888; *Liebig's Ann.*, 251. 114,1889; P. N. Tschirvinsky, *Min. Mag.*, 20. 287, 1925; F. Ephraim and G. Beck, *Helvetica Chim. Acta*, 9. 38, 1926; I. Kurbatoff, *Centr. Min.*, 345, 1926; T. Carnelley, *Journ. Chem. Soc.*, 26. 323, 1873; A. E. Fersman, *Priroda*, 238, 1925; K. A. Nenadkewitsch, *Bull. Acad. St. Petersburg*, (6), 3. 185, 1909; H. Hess, *ib.*, (1), 4. 21. 1838; *Journ. prakt. Chem.*, (1), 14. 52, 1838; B. W. Gerland, *ib.*, (2), 4. 97, 1871; *Ber.*, 9. 873, 1876; *Chem. News*, 34. 2, 1876; 36. 29, 271, 272, 1877; H. Credner, *Pogg. Ann.*, 74. 546, 1848; E. C. Franklin and C. A. Kraus, *Amer. Chem. Journ.*, 20. 829, 1898; A. Ditte, *Bull. Soc. Chim.*, (2), 48. 651, 1887; *Chem. News*, 56. 23, 1887; *Compt. Rend.*, 104. 1705, 1887; A. Carnot, *ib.*, 104. 1803, 1850, 1887; 105. 119, 1887; *Chem. News*, 56. 16, 42, 279, 1887; J. J. Berzelius, *Acad. Handl. Stockholm*, 1, 1831; *Schweigger's Journ.*, 62. 323, 1831; 63. 26, 1831; *Pogg. Ann.*, 22. 1, 1831; *Ann. Chim. Phys.*, (1), 47. 337, 1831; *Phil. Mag.*, (2), 10. 321, 1831; (2), 11. 7, 1832; H. E. Roscoe, *Phil. Trans.*, 158. 1, 1868; 159. 679, 1869; 160. 317. 1870: *Proc. Roy. Soc.*, 16. 220, 1868; 18. 37, 316, 1870; *Journ. Chem. Soc.*, 21. 322, 1868; 23. 344, 1870; 24. 23, 1871; *Chem. News*, 17. 135, 1868; 20. 37, 1869; 21. 183, 1872; *Phil. Mag.*, (4), 35. 307, 1868; (4), 39. 146, 1870; (4), 42. 62, 1870; J. Antipoff, *Berg. Hütt. Ztg.*, 4. 255, 1908; F. A. Genth, *Proc. Amer. Phil. Soc.*, 17. 122, 1877; W. F. Hillebrand, H. E. Merwin, and F. E. Wright, *ib.*, 53. 31, 1914; W. F. Hillebrand and H. E. Merwin, *Amer. Journ. Science*, (4), 35. 441, 1913; C. F. Rammelsberg, *Handbuch der Mineralchemie*, Leipzig, 263, 1886; M. Adam, *Tableau minéralogique*, Paris, 33, 1869; A. Fock, *Zeit. Kryst.*, 17. 12, 1890; A. d'Achiardi, *I Metalli*, 2. 492, 1883; A. Scheuer, *Zeit. anorg. Chem.*, 16. 300, 1898; W. Prandtl and L. Hess, *ib.*, 82. 122, 1913; G. Tammann, *ib.*, 149. 168, 1925; J. A. Hall, *Journ. Chem. Soc.*, 51. 751, 1887; G. Fester and G. Berraz, *Anal. Asoc. Quim. Argentina*, 15. 210, 1927; A. E. Fersman, *Priroda*, 7, 1925; I. Kurbatoff, *Centr. Min.*, 345, 1926.

§ 11. The Vanadates of the Alkaline Earths

A. Ditte [1] prepared pale yellow plates of **strontium orthovanadate**, $Sr_3(VO_4)_2$, by heating vanadium pentoxide with potassium and strontium iodides, and washing away the soluble salts. O. Manasse could not obtain **barium orthovanadate**, $Ba_3(VO_4)_2$, because it immediately decomposed into the pyrovanadate and hydroxide. G. Tammann gave 300° for its temp. of formation from its component oxides. H. E. Roscoe made a similar observation with respect to **calcium orthovanadate**, $Ca_3(VO_4)_2$, precipitated by sodium orthovanadate from a soln. of calcium chloride. G. Tammann gave 375° for the temp. of formation from its component oxides. D. Balareff discussed the reaction. F. de Carli found that the reaction with barium oxide and vanadium pentoxide begins at 270°, and with calcium oxide, at 630°.

II. E. Roscoe obtained **calcium pyrovanadate,** $Ca_2V_2O_7.2\frac{1}{2}H_2O$, as a white amorphous precipitate by adding sodium pyrovanadate or orthovanadate to a soln. of calcium chloride. A. Ditte said that an excess of calcium chloride gives no precipitation with a soln. of ammonium metavanadate, but on adding ammonia, there is a white precipitate formed which, when boiled with the mother-liquor, forms needle-like crystals of the *dihydrate*, $Ca_2V_2O_7.2H_2O$. When heated, it loses its water without melting, and becomes yellow. It is freely soluble in dil. acids. F. Ephraim and G. Beck found that the pyrovanadate absorbs a little gaseous ammonia, but does not form a definite ammine. F. L. Hess and W. T. Schaller found that the *enneahydrate* occurs as a green efflorescence on the sandstone cliffs of Canon Pintado, Utah. It was called **pintadoite.** The analysis corresponds with $Ca_2V_2O_7.9H_2O$. The mineral is slightly pleochroic, and has a moderately high birefringence. It slowly dissolves in cold water. R. Robl observed a marked fluorescence when calcium pyrovanadate, or **strontium pyrovanadate,** SrV_2O_7, is exposed to ultra-violet light. H. E. Roscoe obtained **barium pyrovanadate,** $Ba_2V_2O_7$, in a similar manner ; and the precipitate obtained by J. J. Berzelius with baryta-water is thought to be the same thing. A. Carnot also prepared it by adding barium chloride to a boiling mixture, neutral or feebly ammoniacal soln. of a vanadate. The white precipitate becomes yellow when heated. R. Robl found that the salt fluoresces in the ultra-violet light of a quartz mercury lamp with light of wave-length $440\mu\mu$ to $280\mu\mu$.

A. Scheuer obtained pale yellow needles of trihydrated **calcium metavanadate,** $CaVO_3.3H_2O$, by adding alcohol to a soln. of calcium chloride and ammonium metavanadate. J. J. Berzelius, and J. A. Norblad found that the hot soln. just indicated gradually yields a yellowish-white mass of the *tetrahydrate*. O. Manasse found that the precipitate is mixed with some calcium chloride. J. A. Norblad said that the precipitate is stable in air but loses 2 mols. of water over conc. sulphuric acid ; and at 180°, all the water is expelled. The salt melts at a red-heat. It is more soluble in water than the strontium salt, and is not precipitated by alcohol from the dil. aq. soln. F. L. Hess and W. F. Foshag observed a yellow, triclinic mineral occurring in Utah ; they called it **rossite,** and considered it to be calcium metavanadate, $Ca(VO_3)_2.4H_2O$. The indices of refraction are $\alpha=1\cdot710$, $\beta=7\cdot170$, and $\gamma=1\cdot840$; the dispersion is strong; the optic axial angle $2V$ is large; the sp. gr. is $2\cdot45$; and the hardness 2 to 3. It is soluble in water. The so-called **metarossite** is partially dehydrated rossite, having the composition $Ca(VO_3)_2.2H_2O$. It is yellow, soft, and fibrous. It is biaxial ; $2V$ is large ; the dispersion is strong; the indices of refraction $\alpha=1\cdot840$, and β and γ exceed $1\cdot85$. J. J. Berzelius, J. A. Norblad, and O. Manasse obtained *tetrahydrated* **strontium metavanadate,** $SrVO_3.4H_2O$, in a similar way. Its properties are similar ; and it is sparingly soluble in water. A. Ditte obtained crystals of **barium metavanadate,** $BaVO_3$, by heating a mixture of vanadium pentoxide, sodium bromide, and a little barium bromide. A. Ditte obtained it by pouring an excess soln. of barium nitrate into a boiling soln. of ammonium metavanadate ; and on standing the whole precipitate crystallizes. The yellowish, prismatic crystals are sparingly soluble in water. J. J. Berzelius, and J. A. Norblad obtained a yellow, gelatinous precipitate by adding a soln. of ammonium metavanadate to one of barium chloride, and allowing the mixture to stand for some hours. A white, crystalline powder of the *monohydrate*, $BaVO_3.H_2O$, is formed. The aq. soln. on spontaneous evaporation yields small white crystals resembling the strontium salt. O. Manasse also obtained the barium salt. It is soluble in water.

F. Ephraim and G. Beck made crystals of **strontium orthotetravanadate,**

$3SrO.2V_2O_5.2H_2O$, by adding a soln. of strontium nitrate to a soln. of the potassium salt. O. Manasse prepared red crystals of *hexahydrated* **calcium deuterotetravanadate**, $CaV_4O_{11}.6H_2O$, by the spontaneous evaporation of equimolar parts of a soln. of calcium chloride and potassium deuterotetravanadate. J. J. Berzelius and C. von Hauer obtained the *enneahydrate*, $CaV_4O_{11}.9H_2O$, from soln. of calcium chloride and ammonium deuterotetravanadate. The orange-red crystals do not effloresce in air, and they are freely soluble in water. The salt melts easily, and after fusion it does not dissolve readily in water. J. A. Norblad reported a number of other hydrated forms. J. J. Berzelius, and C. von Hauer obtained *enneahydrated* **strontium deuterotetravanadate**, $SrV_4O_{11}.9H_2O$, from a soln. of the sodium salt and strontium chloride ; and A. Scheuer, by adding alcohol to the mother-liquor from the preparation of the pervanadate. J. Grailich said that the orange plates are monoclinic with the axial ratios $a : b : c = 0.842 : 1 : 1.045$, and $\beta = 98° 14'$. It is decomposed by the prolonged action of cold or hot water. J. J. Berzelius' *barium deuterotetravanadate* was shown by C. von Hauer to be the triterodecavanadate.

A. Ditte mixed an excess of ammonium metavanadate with calcium nitrate and a little nitric acid, and slowly evaporated the red soln. when golden-yellow crystals of **calcium triterohexavanadate**, $CaV_6O_{16}.12H_2O$, were obtained. They are freely soluble in water, and are transformed by boiling water into a yellow powder. According to W. F. Hillebrand and co-workers, a mineral which they called **hewettite**—after D. F. Hewett—occurs as an alteration product of patronite at Minarragen, Peru. It is mahogany-red and consists of minute rhombic needles of sp. gr. 2.554. The analysis corresponds with $CaO.3V_2O_5.9H_2O$, or **calcium dihydrodeuterohexavanadate**, $CaH_2V_6O_{17}.8H_2O$. The indices of refraction for Li-light are $\alpha = 1.77$; $\beta = 2.18$; and $\gamma = 2.35 - 2.40$. The pleochroism is strong—α is light cadmium yellow ; β, cadmium yellow ; and γ, orange. The mineral readily fuses to a dark red liquid, and is slightly soluble in water. Another dark red, earthy mineral of the same composition, occurring in Paradox Valley, Colorado, and in Eastern Utah, is similar to hewettite in composition. It occurs in minute rhombic plates. This dimorphous form of hewettite is called **metahewettite**. Its sp. gr. is 2.511, and for material with $3H_2O$, 2.942. The optical axial angle $2V = 52°$. The indices of refraction for Li-light are $\alpha = 1.70$; $\beta = 2.10$; and γ could not be determined. The pleochroism is intense : α and β are light orange-yellow, and γ is dark red. Both minerals are very sensitive to atm. humidity, and nearly all the water can be expelled without breaking the structure. The dehydration curves show a difference in the behaviour of the two minerals. A third mineral occurs as an orange-red or orange-yellow powdery efflorescence on the walls of the mine workings at Minasraga, Cerro de Pasco, Peru, and it is called **pascoite**. The analyses agrees with **calcium deuterohexavanadate**, $Ca_2V_6O_{17}.11H_2O$. The optical characters agree with the monoclinic symmetry. The optic axial angles are $2V = 50.5°$ for the Na-light, and $2V = 56°$ for Li-light ; the indices of refraction are $\alpha = 1.775$, $\beta = 1.815$, and $\gamma = 1.825$; the optical character is negative ; the dispension is strong ; and the sp. gr. is 2.457. The mineral melts readily to a dark red liquid ; and it is freely soluble in water. W. Lindgren and co-workers described black needles of a mineral from the shale of Minasragra, Cerro de Pasco, and they called it **melanovanadite**. Its composition agrees with **calcium hypovanadatovanadate**, $2CaO.3V_2O_5.2V_2O$. The monoclinic crystals have the axial ratios $a : b : c = 0.4737 : 1 : 0.5815$, and $\beta = 88° 37\frac{1}{2}'$. The sp. gr. is 3.477 at 15°, and the hardness 2.5. It is readily soluble in acids, forming a green soln. C. von Hauer made **strontium triterohexavanadate**, $SrV_6O_{16}.13\frac{1}{2}H_2O$, analogous to the corresponding calcium salt by boiling a dil. acetic acid soln. of strontium tetravanadate with strontium chloride, and evaporating the filtrate at a gentle heat, or over sulphuric acid. The salt can be recrystallized from acetic acid. The red crystals are stable in air ; and the four-sided plates belong to the triclinic system. Some measurements were made by A. Handl. The salt loses $8\frac{1}{2}$ mols. of water at

100°, and melts to a dark red liquid at dull redness. The aq. soln. suffers a little decomposition when heated. J. A. Norblad verified C. von Hauer's observations, but O. Manasse could not do so. A. Ditte obtained orange-red, rhombic crystals of the *tetradecahydrate* of barium **deuterohexavanadate**, $Ba_2V_6O_{17}.14H_2O$, by treating with barium nitrate a boiling soln. of ammonium vanadate in dil. acetic acid. F. Ephraim and G. Beck prepared the *dodecahydrate* of barium deuterohexavanadate, $2BaO.3V_2O_5.12H_2O$, by boiling a mixture of 30 grms. of ammonium metavanadate, 15 grms. of calcium oxide, and 200 c.c. of water until the smell of ammonia has gone; adding enough conc. hydrochloric acid to give the liquid a permanent yellow colour, and making the liquid up to 500 c.c. with $2N$-acetic acid. The liquid was then treated with a soln. of 30 grms. of barium chloride in 300 c.c. of water and 100 c.c. of $2N$-acetic acid, and allowed to stand for 2–3 hrs., when the salt appears as a crystalline precipitate the colour of dichromates. It does not form an ammine with ammonia.

O. Manasse prepared **calcium deuteroctovanadate**, $Ca_3V_8O_{23}.15H_2O$, from a soln. of eq. proportions of potassium tetravanadate, and calcium chloride in an excess of acetic acid; the filtrate furnishes red, tabular crystals of the salt. He likewise obtained **strontium deuteroctovanadate**, $Sr_3V_8O_{23}.4H_2O$, which lost 17·6 per cent. of water at 100°; 17·9 per cent. at 200°; and the rest at dull redness. O. Manasse obtained **strontium tetreroctovanadate**, $SrV_8O_{21}.11H_2O$, by adding alcohol to a soln. of the tetradecavanadate in hot water. The yellow powder loses 16·42 per cent. of water at 100°, and nearly all at 200°.

F. Ephraim and G. Beck made **calcium tetrerodecavanadate**, $2CaO.5V_2O_5.5H_2O$, by boiling a soln. of ammonium metavanadate with lime, and then acidifying the liquid with $2N$-acetic acid. On cooling the conc. soln. dichromate-yellow prisms were obtained. It does not form an ammine with ammonia. J. A. Norblad treated a soln. of potassium tetravanadate with barium chloride and allowed the filtrate to evaporate spontaneously when orange-red, prismatic crystals of **barium deuterodecavanadate**, $Ba_4V_{10}O_{29}.24H_2O$, were produced. O. Manasse could not confirm this. C. von Hauer, J. J. Berzelius, J. A. Norblad, and O. Manasse obtained **barium triterodecavanadate**, $Ba_3V_{10}O_{28}.19H_2O$, as a precipitate, by mixing hot soln. of potassium tetravanadate and barium chloride. The precipitate forms in a few hours small, yellow prisms. According to A. Fock, the triclinic crystals have the axial ratios $a:b:c = 0.7805:1:0.9528$, and $a = 106° 53'$, $\beta = 122° 13'$, and $\gamma = 71° 9'$. After the crystals had stood 12 days over conc. sulphuric acid, O. Manasse found that they had lost 11 per cent. of water; 15·07 per cent. in vacuo; and 16·74 per cent. after heating for a week at 100°. All is expelled at a dull red-heat when the salt fuses. C. von Hauer said that 100 parts of water at 20°–25° dissolve about 0·02 part of the salt, and dissolves more at a higher temp. The salt is decomposed by boiling water with the separation of the metavanadate. The salt can be recrystallized from acetic acid.

O. Manasse reported the formation of **calcium penterotetradecavanadate**, $Ca_3V_{14}O_{38}.7H_2O$, to be formed by crystallization from a soln. of the hexadecavanadate in hot water. The scarlet powder may not be a chemical individual. He also prepared **strontium tetrerotetradecavanadate**, $Sr_4V_{14}O_{39}.30H_2O$, by adding alcohol to a dil. soln. of eq. proportions of potassium tetravanadate and strontium chloride. J. A. Norblad regarded the orange-red plates as monoclinic. They lose 16·0–16·5 per cent. of water at 100°. O. Manasse reported **calcium hexerohexadecavanadate**, $Ca_6V_{16}O_{43}.26H_2O$, to be formed by adding acetic acid to a warm soln. of potassium tetravanadate and calcium chloride, and evaporating the liquid on the water-bath. The red crystals can be recrystallized from hot water, washed with alcohol, and ether, and dried in a current of dry air. The crystals lose 17·77 per cent. of water at 100°, and all at 180°. The crystals are decomposed by absolute alcohol.

O. Manasse prepared **potassium calcium deuterotetravanadate**, $(K_{0.8}Ca_{0.4})V_4O_{11}.4.4H_2O$, in yellowish-brown scales, by evaporating the mother-liquor from the preparation of calcium hexerohexadecavanadate. He also found that when eq. proportions of potassium tetravanadate and strontium chloride are allowed to crystallize together from 200 c.c. of hot water, reddish-yellow crystals of **potassium strontium tetrerotetradecavanadate**, $(K_{0.25}Sr_{0.375})_8V_{14}O_{39}.20H_2O$, which A. Fock said were triclinic, are formed. At 100°, 14·38 per cent. of water is given off, and at 200°, 17·74 per cent. Working with more dil. soln., the triacontahydrate is formed in monoclinic prisms which, according to A. Fock, have the axial ratios $a:b:c$ $=1:4729:1:1·3744$, and $\beta=96°\ 15'$. The salt can be recrystallized from water or acetic acid. If equimolar proportions of potassium tetravanadate and strontium chloride, and 180 c.c. of water be mixed with acetic acid, and allowed to crystallize, dark red crystals aggregates of $(K_{1.0}Sr_{0.5})_4V_{14}O_{37}.18H_2O$ are formed. A. E. Fersman described a mineral from Tyuya-Muyun, Fergana, which he called **tangeite**. K. A. Nenadkewitsch and P. A. Volkoff found that the analysis corresponds with **copper calcium vanadate**, $2CuO.2CaO.V_2O_5.H_2O$. The term tangeite is used for the crystalline form and Turkestan volborthite for the colloidal variety.

REFERENCES.

[1] O. Manasse, *Die Vanadate der Erdalkalien*, Berlin, 1886; *Liebig's Ann.*, **240**. 23, 1887; R. Robl, *Zeit. angew. Chem.*, **39**. 608, 1926; C. von Hauer, *Journ. prakt. Chem.*, (1), **76**. 156, 1859; *Sitzber. Akad. Wien*, **21**. 333, 1856; **39**. 451, 1860; A. Handl, *ib.*, **37**. 391, 1859; A. Ditte, *Compt. Rend.*, **96**. 1048, 1883; **104**. 1705, 1887; A. Carnot, *ib.*, **104**. 1803, 1850, 1887; **105**. 119, 1887; J. J. Berzelius, *Acad. Handl. Stockholm*, 1, 1831; *Schweigger's Journ.*, **62**. 323, 1831; **63**. 26, 1831; *Pogg. Ann.*, **22**. 1, 1831; *Ann. Chim. Phys.*, (1), **47**. 337, 1831; *Phil. Mag.*, (2), **10**. 321, 1831; (2), **11**. 7, 1832; H. E. Roscoe, *Phil. Trans.*, **158**. 1, 1868; **159**. 679, 1869; **160**. 317, 1870; *Proc. Roy. Soc.*, **16**. 220, 1868; **18**. 37, 316, 1870; *Journ. Chem. Soc.*, **21**. 322, 1868; **23**. 344, 1870; **24**. 23, 1871; *Chem. News*, **17**. 135, 1868; **20**. 37, 1869; **21**. 183, 1872; *Phil. Mag.*, (4), **35**. 307, 1868; (4), **39**. 146, 1870; (4), **42**. 62, 1870; F. Ephraim and G. Beck, *Helvetica Chim. Acta*, **9**. 38, 1926; J. A. Norblad, *Liebig's Ann.*, **240**. 41, 1887; *Acta Lund. Univ.*, **2**. 1, 1874; *Bull. Soc. Chim.*, (2), **23**. 64, 1875; A. Fock, *Zeit. Kryst.*, **17**. 1, 1890; F. de Carli, *Atti Accad. Lincei.* (6), **1**. 533, 1925; J. Grailich, *Krystallographisch-optische Untersuchungen*, Wien, 197, 1858; A. Scheuer, *Zeit. anorg. Chem.*, **16**. 304, 1898; G. Tammann, *ib.*, **149**. 68, 1925; **160**. 101, 1927; D. Balareff, *ib.*, **160**. 92, 1927; W. F. Hillebrand, H. E. Merwin, and F. E. Wright, *Proc. Amer. Phil. Soc.*, **53**. 31, 1914; F. L. Hess and W. T. Schaller, *Journ. Washington Acad.*, **4**. 576, 1914; W. Lindgren, *Proc. Nat. Acad.*, **7**. 249, 1921; W. Lindgren, L. F. Hamilton, and C. Palache, *Amer. Journ. Science*, (5), **3**. 195, 1922; A. E. Fersman, *Priroda*, 238, 1925; K. A. Nenadkewitsch and P. A. Volkoff, *Compt. Rend. Akad. Urss*, 43, 1926; F. L. Hess and W. F. Foshag, *Amer. Min.*, **11**. 66, 1926; *Proc. U.S. Nat. Museum*, **72**. 1, 1927.

§ 12. Vanadates of the Magnesium Family

J. J. Berzelius [1] reported **beryllium metavanadate** to be formed as a yellow powder sparingly soluble in water, by the action of ammonium metavanadate on a soln. of a beryllium salt; and with potassium tetravanadate and a beryllium salt soln., **beryllium tetravanadate** is formed as a yellow powder sparingly soluble in water. S. M. Tanatar and E. K. Kurowsky prepared a yellow amorphous precipitate by the action of sodium vanadate on a soln. of beryllium chloride; it contained $mBeCl_2.nBe_3(VO_4)_2.pBeO$; and with a soln. of beryllium nitrate, $mBe(NO_3)_2.nBe_3(VO_4)_2.pBeO$. P. H. M. P. Brinton found that the products obtained by the addition of soln. of soluble vanadates to soln. of beryllium salts are mixtures of variable composition, and not definite salts. The compound **beryllium metavanadate**, $Be(VO_3)_2.4H_2O$, has been obtained by boiling eq. quantities of beryllium hydroxide and vanadium pentoxide with water for about an hour; the soln. was filtered and concentrated to about 40 c.c., which usually yielded an orange-red syrup. This, while hot, was poured into a large volume of 95 per cent. alcohol, when a copious deposit of yellow particles was produced, which in twenty-four hours had settled to a thick layer of yellow crystals, which, microscopically, are yellow, waxy plates. The crystals are cubic, being cubes modified by the octahedron. Beryllium metavanadate is sparingly soluble in cold water, 1 per

1000, but readily so in hot water, and has a strong tendency to supersaturate. It is practically insoluble in chloroform, ether, or absolute alcohol, but is soluble in pyridine to about the same extent as in water. The crystals have a sp. gr. of 2·273, and lose the whole of their water of crystallization over sulphuric acid. F. Ephraim and G. Beck obtained **beryllium deuterohexavanadate**, $2BeO.3V_2O_4.11H_2O$, by treating the barium salt with beryllium sulphate. The dehydrated salt absorbs ammonia gas very slowly, forming the *dodecammine*, which forms the *hexammine* between 160° and 220°, and the *diammine* between 260° and 295°.

J. J. Berzelius prepared **magnesium metavanadate**, $Mg(VO_3)_2.6H_2O$, by boiling magnesia with vanadium pentoxide and water, and evaporating the filtrate. R. Sugiura and H. Baker could not obtain a definite salt by evaporating the aq. soln. F. de Carli found that the reaction between magnesium oxide and vanadium pentoxide begins at 455°. O. Manasse treated a conc. soln. of the filtrate with alcohol, and allowed the yellow, syrupy liquid to stand some days when aggregates of colourless, prismatic crystals were formed. The salt is freely soluble in water. A. Ditte found that when heated to redness the water of crystallization is driven off, and at a higher temp., fusion takes place. J. J. Berzelius reported *octohydrated* **magnesium deuterotetravanadate**, $MgV_4O_{11}.8H_2O$, to be formed in yellow plates by the spontaneous evaporation of an aq. soln. of potassium tetravanadate and magnesium sulphate ; if the salt be precipitated by alcohol, it appears as a yellow powder. C. von Hauer obtained it by mixing soln. of ammonium metavanadate with magnesium sulphate, and recrystallizing the precipitate from hot water. The salt is sparingly soluble in water. A. Ditte obtained the *enneahydrate*, $MgV_4O_{11}.9H_2O$, in red crystals, by treating a hot sat. soln. of ammonium meta-vanadate with an excess of magnesium chloride and acetic acid. O. Manasse reported **magnesium deuterohexavanadate**, $Mg_2V_6O_{17}.9\frac{1}{2}H_2O$, by treating a hot soln. of potassium tetravanadate with a small excess of magnesium sulphate. V. Cuttica and co-workers obtained the same compound as an *enneadecahydrate*, by the action of water on magnesium chlorovanadate. The yellowish-red crystals of O. Manasse's salt were found by A. Fock to be triclinic with the axial ratios $a:b:c=0·7928:1:0·9506$, and $a=114° 28'$, $\beta=108° 18'$, and $\gamma=74° 17'$. The salt is said to be isomorphous with the corresponding salts of barium, zinc, man-ganese, and cobalt. The salt loses all its water at 100°. R. Sugiura and H. Baker, and O. Manasse prepared **magnesium triterodecavanadate**, $Mg_3V_{10}O_{28}.28H_2O$, by boiling magnesia with vanadium pentoxide and water, and mixing the soln. with an excess of acetic acid. When the liquid is allowed to evaporate spontaneously, it furnishes two kinds of crystals : (i) brown, triclinic prisms with the axial ratios $a:b:c=0·997:1:1·009$, and $a=89° 24'$, $\beta=104° 20'$, and $\gamma=82° 22'$; the sp. gr. is 2·199 at 18°. (ii) Red, triclinic prisms with the axial ratios $a:b:c=0·788:1:0·676$, and $a=93° 35'$, $\beta=101° 30'$, and $\gamma=166° 55'$. The sp. gr. is 2·167 at 18°. A. Ditte could not prepare *ammonium magnesium vanadate*.

According to A. Ditte,[2] **zinc pyrovanadate**, $Zn_2V_2O_7$, is produced by melting vanadium pentoxide with a mixture of 5 parts of sodium bromide and one part of zinc bromide, and treating the product with water. The evaporation of the liquid gives orange-red prisms, freely soluble in water. C. Radau believed that the pro-duct is an acid vanadate. G. Tammann made some observations on the action of zinc oxide on vanadium pentoxide ; and F. de Carli found that the reaction begins at 260°. J. J. Berzelius obtained **zinc metavanadate**, $Zn(VO_3)_2.2H_2O$, by double decomposition ; and A. Ditte, by warming a mixture of soln. of ammonium metavanadate with an excess of zinc nitrate. The yellowish-white precipitate when kept warm in contact with its mother-liquor furnishes pale-yellow crystals. C. Radau said that the product is a mixture of an acid vanadate and pyrovanadate. J. J. Berzelius obtained an acid vanadate. F. Ephraim and G. Beck prepared **zinc deuterohexavanadate**, $2ZnO.3V_2O_5.15H_2O$, as in the case of the beryllium salt. It forms a *dodecammine* when the dehydrated salt is exposed to ammonia gas ; this becomes the *hexammine* at 170°, and the *diammine* at 235°. C. Radau reported **potassium zinc triterodecavanadate,** $K_2Zn_2V_{10}O_{28}.16H_2O$, to be formed by mixing boiling soln. of 20 grms. of potassium metavanadate in 400 c.c. of water, and 18 grms. of hydrated zinc sulphate in 250 c.c. of water. The evaporation of the filtrate furnishes pale red crystals which, according to A. Fock, are triclinic prisms with the axial ratios $a : b : c = 0.8025 : 1 : 0.9675$, and $a = 115° 2'$, $\beta = 109° 35'$, and $\gamma = 74° 57'$. They are isomorphous with the corresponding magnesium salt (q.v.). The salt is sparingly soluble in water, and freely soluble in acids.   C. Radau found that a mixture of soln. of 20 grms. of potassium metavanadate in 200 c.c. of water and 17 grms. of hydrated zinc sulphate in 200 c.c. of water and 20 c.c. of 25 per cent. acetic acid gives a liquid which furnishes red crystals of **potassium zinc tetrerotetradecavanadate,** $(K_{0.56}Zn_{0.22})_4V_{14}O_{39}.22\frac{1}{2}H_2O$.

J. J. Berzelius prepared **cadmium metavanadate,** $Cd(VO_3)_2$, by mixing a conc. soln. of an alkali vanadate and a cadmium salt ; the yellow precipitate gradually becomes white and crystalline.   A. Ditte made it by melting vanadium pentoxide with a mixture of 5 parts of sodium bromide and one part of cadmium bromide, and washing the product with water.   The fine needles melt at a red-heat. F. de Carli found that the reaction between vanadium pentoxide and cadmium oxide begins at 480°.   By boiling a soln. of ammonium metavanadate, cadmium nitrate and acetic acid, A. Ditte prepared red crystals of **cadmium triterohexavanadate,** $CdV_6O_{16}.2H_2O$.   F. Ephraim and G. Beck found that **cadmium deuterohexavanadate,** $2CdO.3V_2O_5.15H_2O$, is formed as in the case of the zinc salt.   It yields a *dodecammine*, which forms the *triammine* at about 200°, and the *diammine* at about 235°.   C. Radau prepared red crystals of **potassium cadmium deuterohexavanadate,** $K_2CdV_6O_{17}.9H_2O$, by crystallization from a filtered soln. of 12 grms. of potassium triterodecavanadate and 17 grms. of cadmium sulphate in 400 c.c. of water.   He also obtained **potassium cadmium triterodecavanadate,** $(KCd_{0.5})_3V_{10}O_{28}.10\frac{1}{2}H_2O$, from a soln. of 10 grms. potassium metavanadate in 200 c.c. of water, 17 grms. of cadmium sulphate in 250 c.c. of water, and 25 c.c. of 30 per cent. acetic acid.   The spontaneous evaporation of the red soln. furnishes orange-red crystals ; 100 parts of water at 18° dissolve 0.54 part of salt.

A. Carnot obtained **mercurous metavanadate** by treating a soln. of mercurous nitrate with ammonium metavanadate, and by almost neutralizing a soln. of vanadium pentoxide with ammonia and adding mercurous nitrate.   The orange yellow precipitate is decomposed by ammonia, and hydrogen sulphide.   J. J. Berzelius also obtained **mercurous tetravanadate,** as an orange-yellow precipitate, by treating a soln. of ammonium tetravanadate with mercurous nitrate.   By using soln. of mercuric salts, J. J. Berzelius obtained by double decomposition, **mercuric metavanadate,** as a lemon-yellow precipitate sparingly soluble in water ; and also yellow **mercuric tetravanadate.**

RFFERENCES.

[1] J. J. Berzelius, *Acad. Handl. Stockholm*, 1, 1831 ; *Schweigger's Journ.*, 62. 323, 1831; 63. 26, 1831 ; *Pogg. Ann.*, 22. 1, 1831 ; *Ann. Chim. Phys.*, (1), 47. 337, 1831 ; *Phil. Mag.*, (2), 10. 321, 1831 ; (2), 11. 7, 1832 ; A. Fock, *Zeit. Kryst.*, 17. 1, 1890 ; *Einleitung in die chemische Krystallographie*, Leipzig, 70, 1889 ; O. Manasse, *Die Vanadate der Erdalkalien*, Berlin, 1886 ; *Liebig's Ann.*, 240. 49, 1887 ; J. Grailich, *Krystallographisch-optische Untersuchungen*, Wien, 197, 1858 ; A. Ditte, *Compt. Rend.*, 104. 1705, 1844, 1887 ; R. Sugiura and H. Baker, *Journ. Chem. Soc.*, 35. 713, 1879 ; C. von Hauer, *Sitzber. Akad. Wien*, 21. 333, 1856 ; 39. 451, 1860 ; S. M. Tanatar and E. K. Kurowsky, *Journ. Russ. Phys. Chem. Soc.*, 41. 813, 1909 ; V. Cuttica, A. Tarchi and P. Alinari, *Gazz. Chim. Ital.*, 53. i, 189, 1923 ; F. Ephraim and G. Beck, *Helvetica Chim. Acta*, 9. 38, 1926 ; F. de Carli, *Atti Accad. Lincei*, (6), 1. 533, 1925 ; M. P. H. Brinton, *Journ. Amer. Chem. Soc.*, 38. 2361, 1916.

[2] J. J. Berzelius, *Acad. Handl. Stockholm*, 1, 1831 ; *Schweigger's Journ.*, 62. 323, 1831; 63. 26, 1831 ; *Pogg. Ann.*, 22. 1, 1831 ; *Ann. Chim. Phys.*, (1), 47. 337, 1831 ; *Phil. Mag.*, (2), 10. 321, 1831 ; (2), 11. 7, 1832 ; O. Manasse, *Die Vanadate der Erdalkalien*, Berlin, 1886 ; *Liebig's Ann.*, 240. 49, 1887 ; A. Fock, *Zeit. Kryst.*, 17. 1, 1890 ; *Einleitung in die chemische Krystallographie*, Leipzig, 70, 1889 ; A. Ditte, *Compt. Rend.*, 96. 1048, 1883 ; 104. 1705, 1887 ; A. Carnot, *ib.*, 105. 121, 1887 ; C. Radau, *Beitrag zur Kenntniss vanadinsauer Salze,* Königsberg, 1888 :

Liebig's Ann., 251. 114, 1889 ; F. de Carli, *Atti Accad. Lincei*, (6), 1. 533, 1925 ; G. Tammann, *Zeit. anorg. Chem.*, 149. 68, 1925 ; F. Ephraim and G. Beck, *Helvetica Chim. Acta*, 9. 38, 1920.

§ 13. The Vanadates of the Aluminium and Lead Families

J. J. Berzelius [1] obtained **aluminium metavanadate,** and aluminium tetra-vanadate by the method employed for the beryllium salts. The two aluminium salts are less soluble than those of beryllium. C. Renz obtained **indium meta-vanadate,** $In(VO_3)_3.2H_2O$, as a pale yellow precipitate, from a mixed soln. of indium chloride and sodium metavanadate.

T. Carnelley made a series of thallium vanadates. By melting together eq. proportions of sodium carbonate and vanadium pentoxide, at a dull red-heat, a red mass of **thallium orthovanadate,** Tl_3VO_4, is formed. There is a slight loss of thallium by volatilization. The sp. gr. is 8·6 at 17° ; the salt is only slightly soluble since 100 parts of water at 15° dissolve 0·1 part of salt, and at 100°, 0·17 part. By mixing aq. soln. of thallous sulphate and sodium orthovanadate, **thallium pyro-vanadate,** $Tl_4V_2O_7$, is precipitated ; and the same salt is obtained by fusing eq. proportions of sodium carbonate and thallium orthovanadate. The sp. gr. of the salt is 8·21 at 18·5° ; 100 parts of water at 14° dissolve 0·02 part of salt, and 0·026 part at 100°. By melting together eq. proportions of thallous carbonate and vanadium pentoxide, **thallium metavanadate,** $TlVO_3$, is formed in dark grey scaly crystals of sp. gr. 6·019 at 17°, 100 parts of water at 11° dissolve 0·0087 part of salt, and at 100°, 0·021 part. By mixing a boiling soln. of sodium pyrovanadate with a cold soln. of thallous sulphate, a white precipitate of **thallium orthotetravanadate,** $Tl_6V_4O_{13}$, is formed. The same salt is obtained by the action of sodium ortho-tetravanadate on a soln. of thallous sulphate. The sp. gr. of the yellow powder is 8·59 at 17·5° ; 100 parts of water dissolve 0·0293 part of salt at 14° and 0·0285 part at 100°. If thallous sulphate be added to a boiling soln. of sodium pyrovanadate in the presence of an excess of vanadium pentoxide, a white precipitate of **thallium orthodecavanadate,** $Tl_{12}V_{10}O_{31}$, is formed. 100 c.c. of water dissolve 0·0107 part of the pale yellow salt at 11°, and 0·0297 part at 100°. If a soln. of ammonium metavanadate be treated with an excess of thallous sulphate, and the precipitate be allowed to stand in contact with the mother-liquor, a reddish-white **thallium deuterotetradecavanadate,** $Tl_{12}V_{14}O_{41}$, is formed. V. Cuttica and co-workers made **thallous triterohexavanadate,** $Tl_2O.3V_2O_5$, by the action of water on the chlorovanadate.

J. J. Berzelius found that **yttrium metavanadate** is precipitated as a yellow powder when a yttrium salt soln. is treated with a metavanadate ; but with tetra-vanadates no precipitation occurs. A. Cleve treated a soln. of ytterbium nitrate with ammonium metavanadate and obtained a precipitate of **ytterbium oxyortho-decavanadate,** $Yb_2O_3.Yb_4V_{10}O_3$; and the mother-liquor deposits brown $Yb_2O_3.15V_2O_5$. P. T. Cleve prepared **didymium vanadate,** $DiVO_4$, by double decomposition ; and also **didymium metavanadate,** $Di(VO_3)_3$, he also found that neutral soln. of samarium salts and alkali metavanadate give pale yellow amorphous precipitates mainly samarium orthovanadate, but with sodium vanadate and samarium nitrate, a yellow precipitate of variable composition is obtained. The soln. on spontaneous evaporation at ordinary temp. gave red crystals of **samarium triterodecavanadate,** $Sa_2V_{10}O_{28}.20H_2O$, of sp. gr. 2·524 at 17·5°, and yellow crystals of $Sa_2V_{10}V_{28}.24H_2O$, of sp. gr. 2·624 at 17·5°. C. Bene-dicks obtained **gadolinium vanadate,** $Gd_2O_3.5V_2O_5.26H_3O$, in triclinic crystals with $a:b:c = 1·7083:1:0·9894$, and $\alpha = 84° 51$, $\beta = 94° 51'$, and $\gamma = 82° 13·5'$. Dark red dichroic crystals of **cerous orthovanadate,** $CeVO_4$, are produced when sodium orthovanadate is fused with cerous chloride; and **cerous triterodecavana-date,** $Ce_2V_{10}O_{28}.27H_2O$, has been prepared. G. Tammann gave 350° for the temp. of formation of cerous orthovanadate from its component oxides. G. Carobbi and

S. Restaino prepared cerium orthovanadate from soln. of cerium nitrate and sodium orthovanadate, and he found that cerium, lanthanum, didymium, and samarium can replace lead isomorphously in vanadates.

J. J. Berzelius [2] observed no precipitation of a *zirconium vanadate* occurs when a soln. of a zirconium salt is treated with an alkali metavanadate or tetravanadate ; and S. M. Tanatar and E. K. Kurowsky obtained mixed precipitates—*e.g.*, alkali vanadate and zirconium chloride gave **zirconium oxychlorovanadate** of the composition $mZrCl_4.nZr_3(VO_4).pZrO_2$. J. J. Berzelius found that with thorium salts, a yellow precipitate is formed. C. Volek prepared **thorium pyrovanadate,** $ThV_2O_7.6H_2O$, otherwise represented as **thorium hydrovanadate,** $Th(HVO_4)_2.5H_2O$, by treating a dil. soln. of thorium chloride with an 8 per cent. aq. soln. of ammonium metavanadate. The yellow precipitate is soluble in dil. acids. J. J. Berzelius said that **thorium metavanadate,** $Th(VO_3)_4.nH_2O$, is soluble in water. P. T. Cleve mixed a feebly acid soln. of thorium nitrate with sodium tetravanadate, evaporated the soln. on a water-bath, and obtained a brown powder of **thorium triterohexa-vanadate,** $Th(V_6O_{16})_2.8H_2O$.

J. J. Berzelius said that neither *stannous vanadate* nor *stannic vanadate* is precipitated when ammonium vanadate is added to a soln. of the corresponding salt of tin. F. de Carli found that the reaction between stannous oxide and vanadium pentoxide begins at 250°. According to W. Prandtl and O. Rosenthal, a series of **sodium stannatovanadates** are produced when a soln. of sodium orthovanadate and stannic chloride or sodium stannate is carefully neutralized. By cooling or diluting a soln. of stannic vanadate in hot conc. soda-lye, substances crystallizing in white needles are obtained ; similar products are formed when a soln. of sodium stannate and orthovanadate is crystallized ; and by cooling a fused mixture of stannic oxide, vanadium pentoxide, and sodium hydroxide. The compounds : **sodium stannatotrivanadate,** $Na_2SnO_3.3Na_3VO_4.32H_2O$; **sodium stannato-tetravanadate,** $Na_2SnO_3.4Na_3VO_4.48H_2O$; **sodium stannatopentavanadate,** $Na_2SnO_3.5Na_3VO_4.64H_2O$; and **sodium stannatohexavanadate,** $Na_2SnO_3.6Na_3VO_4.$ $80H_2O$, were obtained by varying the conc. and temp. of the reacting constituents. The salts all furnish transparent, doubly refracting, rhombic crystals of the aragonite habit.

H. E. Roscoe [3] prepared **lead orthovanadate,** $Pb_3(VO_4)_2$, by adding lead acetate to a soln. of sodium orthovanadate. The white precipitate is insoluble in water.

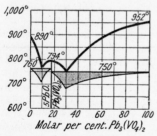

FIG. 7.—Freezing-point Curves of Lead Oxide and Orthovanadate.

G. Tammann gave 325° for the temp. of formation ; and F. de Carli said that the reaction between vanadium pentoxide and lead oxide begins at 560°. D. Balareff discussed the reaction. M. Amadori measured the f.p. of mixture of lead orthovana-date and lead oxide, and the results, summarized in Fig. 7, show the existence of only one basic salt —**lead pentoxyorthovanadate,** $5PbO.Pb_3(VO_4)_2$, melting at 794°. M. Amadori gave 1042° for the m.p. of lead orthoarsenate, and 952° for that of lead orthovanadate, and for mixtures with 25, 50, 75, and 90 per cent. of lead orthovanadate he found the f.p. to be 1018°, 994°, 968°, and 960° respectively. R. Robl observed no fluorescence with the salt in ultra-violet light.. There is no evidence on the f.p. curves of the formation of *lead oxyorthovanadate*, $PbO.Pb_3(VO_4)_2$. A. Ditte prepared **lead pyrovanadate,** $Pb_2V_2O_7$, by pouring ammonium metavana-date into an acetic acid soln. of lead nitrate, and boiling the mixture. The sulphur-yellow, prismatic crystals are soluble in hot dil. nitric acid. F. Ephraim and G. Beck made **lead orthohexavanadate,** $3PbO.2V_2O_5.2H_2O$, by treating manganese hexa-vanadate with lead nitrate. The dehydrated salt absorbs ammonia. H. E. Roscoe prepared what has been regarded as **lead oxypyrovanadate,** $PbO.2Pb_2V_2O_7$—possibly a mixture : $Pb_3(VO_4)_2.Pb_2V_2O_7$—by precipitation on mixing soln. of sodium pyrovanadate and lead acetate. The pale-yellow salt was found by T. Carnelley to melt at 731°. It is neither soluble in nor decomposed by water ; it is insoluble in acetic acid ; and decomposed by nitric acid. R. D. Thomson also described a lead vanadate.

C. Bergmann described a mineral from Lauterthal, Bavaria, which he named **dechenite**—after H. von Dechen. Analyses reported by C. Bergmann, H. Fischer and J. Nessler, and C. F. Rammelsberg agree with the formula for lead **metavanadate,** $Pb(VO_3)_2$. According to G. J. Brush, dechenite belongs to the same mineral species as eusynchite and aræoxene—*vide infra.* Lead metavanadate was made by J. J. Berzelius, H. E. Roscoe, and A. Carnot by treating ammonium or an alkali metavanadate with lead nitrate or acetate. The yellow precipitate becomes less voluminous when allowed to stand in contact with its mother-liquor for 24 hrs. Dechenite occurs botryoidal, nodular, in stalactitic masses sometimes with a columnar structure. The colour is deep red, yellowish-red or brownish-red. According to J. Grailich, the rhombic crystals of dechenite have the axial ratios $a : b : c = 0.8354 : 1 : 0.6538$. The artificial compound is white. The sp. gr. of dechenite is 5·60–5·81, and the hardness 3·5–4·0. T. Carnelley gave 849° for the m.p. of the salt. R. Robl observed no fluorescence with the salt in ultra-violet light. J. J. Berzelius found that the compound is sparingly soluble in water ; freely soluble in warm dil. nitric acid ; the soln. in conc. nitric acid, when warm, deposits a brown powder of vanadium pentoxide mixed with some lead. Conc. sulphuric acid decomposes the salt incompletely ; it is decomposed by molten potassium hydrosulphate but not by a soln. of potassium carbonate. A. Terreil noticed that a boiling 10 per cent. soln. of sodium sulphide decomposed dechenite and dissolved the vanadium pentoxide.

J. J. Berzelius treated a soln. of lead nitrate with potassium tetravanadate, and obtained a yellow precipitate of **lead deuterotetravanadate,** PbV_4O_{11} ; and A. Ditte obtained it by fusing vanadium pentoxide with a mixture of lead and sodium iodides. It is somewhat soluble in water ; freely soluble in dil. nitric acid ; and a boiling soln. of potassium carbonate extracts half the vanadium.

A. Damour [4] described a mineral from Sierra de Cordoba, Argentine, and he called it **descloizite**—after A. des Cloizeaux ; F. X. M. Zippe, G. Tschermak, and A. Schrauf, called it rhombic *vanadite* ; A. Frenzel, *tritochorite*—τρίτος, third ; and χωρεῖν, to follow—in allusion to the assumption that the mineral formed a third member of a series with eusynchite and aræoxene ; M. V. de Leon, *ramarite ;* and F. Pisani, *schaffnerite.* The mineral *vesbine,* found by A. Scacchi as yellow crusts in the crevices of the massive lava flows of 1631 at Vesuvius, was at first thought to be aluminium vesbiate—a salt of a new element, vesbium. F. Zambonini, and L. de Luise showed that it is probably a vanadate ; and F. Zambonini and G. Carobbi, that it is a hydrated cupro-descloizite approximating $(Pb,Cu)_3(VO_4)_2.$ $(Pb,Cu)(OH)_2.5H_2O$, and was formed through the agency of water during the solidification of the lava. Analyses of descloizite were reported by A. Damour, C. F. Rammelsberg, P. A. Wagner, W. F. Hillebrand, A. Döring, F. A. Genth, F. Pisani, M. V. de Leon, S. L. Penfield, O. Pufahl, A. Brunlechner, D. Lovisato, F. N. Guild, R. C. Wells, and A. Frenzel. The results in general agree with the formula $(Pb,Zn)_3(VO_4)_2.(Pb,Zn)(OH)_2$—*i.e.* **zinc lead hydroxyorthovanadate,** $(Pb,Zn)_2(OH)VO_4$; while C. F. Rammelsberg's *cuprodescloizite* agrees with $(Pb,Cu)_5(VO_4)_{22}.(Pb,Cu)(OH)_2$ — *i.e.* **copper lead hydroxyorthovanadate,** $(Pb,Zn)_2(OH)VO_4$. Some arsenic may replace vanadium. The colour of descloizite may be red, reddish-brown, brown, dark brown, and black ; cuprodescloizite is green, greenish-black, or yellowish brown. The mineral occurs massive, and with radiating fibres ; in stalactitic aggregates of crystals, or in short prismatic crystals belonging to the rhombic system. M. Websky thought the crystals were monoclinic, but A. des Cloizeaux showed that they are rhombic. According to G. vom Rath, the axial ratios $a : b : c = 0.6368 : 1 : 0.8045$. The (130)-face may be striated vertically. There is no cleavage. C. F. Rammelsberg gave 5·856–6·080 for the sp gr. ;

A. Döring, 5·93–6·14 ; S. L. Penfield, 6·202 ; F. A. Genth, 6·203 ; F. Pisani, 6·06 ;
W. F. Hillebrand, 5·88 ; D. Lovisato, 5·72 ; and M. V. de Leon, 6·01–6·10. The
hardness is 3·5. The optical character is negative. R. C. Wells gave 1·74 for the
index of refraction of cupro-descloizite, and 0·03–0·04 for the birefringence.
T. W. Case observed that descloizite is a poor conductor and is not appreciably
affected by light. E. E. Fairbanks gave 7·7 to 8·6 for the dielectric constant
(water 81). The mineral is soluble in cold dil. nitric acid.

H. E. Roscoe [5] described a mineral which he called **mottramite** and which
occurred as thin, crystalline incrustations in the keuper sandstones of Mottram
St. Andrews, and Alderley Edge, Cheshire ; he represented his analysis by
$(Pb,Cu)_3(VO_4)_5.2(Pb,Cu)(HO)_2$, **copper lead tetrahydroxyorthovanadate ;** and
C. F. Rammelsberg represented its composition by $R_3(VO_4)_2.3R(OH)_2$. It was
also analyzed by O. Pufahl. F. A. Genth found a mineral which he called
psittacinite—from *psittacinus*, siskin or parrot-green—occurring in the Silver Star
District, Montana, and elsewhere. Analyses reported by F. A. Genth, A. Döring,
C. F. Rammelsberg, and F. Pisani agree with formula $R_3(VO_4)_2.R(OH)_2.H_2O$, or
copper dihydroxyorthovanadate.

G. A. Kenngott,[6] and I. Domeyko described a lead copper vanadate occurring in the
Mina de la Marqueza, Chile. M. Adam called it *cuprovanadite,* and I. Domeyko, *chileite.*
Its existence as a definite mineral species has not been confirmed. Likewise also with the
vanadiolite of R. Hermann, found in small green crystals in the Slindianka River near
Lake Baikal, Siberia. C. F. Rammelsberg supposes it to be a mixture of augite and a
vanadate. T. Thomson described a lead vanadate occurring in Wicklow, Ireland, and
called it *wicklowite*—A. d'Achiardi called it *vichlovite.* F. Pisani described zinc lead
vanadate a mineral from Laurium, Greece ; W. P. Blake has also described a lead vanadate
from Castle Dome, Arizona. V. Dürrfeld described a hydrated zinc lead vanadate
mineral from Lahr, Baden ; he called it *hügelite*—after F. Hügel. The monoclinic crystals
have the axial ratios $a : b : c = 0.48954 : 1 : 0.38372,$ and $\beta = 60° 12' 6''$; it usually occurs
in microscopic needles irregularly arranged. The colour is orange-yellow or yellowish-
brown. The pleochroism is yellowish-green and greenish-yellow. The sp. gr. is 5.

H. Fischer and J. Nessler [7] found a massive or nodular mineral in Hofsgrund,
Baden, and they called it **eusynchite.** Its colour is yellowish-red, reddish-brown,
or green. Analyses, reported by C. F. Rammelsberg, C. Czudnowicz, C. Bergmann,
and J. Lang, agree with the formula for **zinc lead orthovanadate,** $(Pb,Zn)_3(VO_4)_2.$
The sp. gr. is 5·6–5·8 ; and the hardness, 3–4. The related mineral *araeoxene* from
Dahn, Rhenish, Bavaria, was described by F. von Kobell ; it is similar to eusynchite,
but contains some arsenic in place of vanadium. F. Sandberger, and F. Schumacher
regard araeoxene as a variety of descloizite. The mineral **brackebuschite**—named
after D. L. Brackebusch by A. Döring [8]—occurs in several localities in Cordoba,
Argentine. Analyses reported by A. Döring, and C. F. Rammelsberg gave a formula
close to that of descloizite, and the mineral is regarded as a **lead ferrous manganese
orthovanadate,** $(Pb,Mn,Fe)_3(VO_4)_2.H_2O.$ The mineral occurs in small, black,
prismatic crystals—possibly monoclinic. A. Damour considers that the manganese, iron, and copper present are only impurities.

REFERENCES.

[1] V. Cuttica, A. Tarchi, and P. Alinari, *Gazz. Chim. Ital.,* **53. i,** 189, 1923 ; J. J. Berzelius,
Acad. Handl. Stockholm, 1, 1831 ; *Schweigger's Journ.,* **62.** 323, 1831 ; **63.** 26, 1821 ; *Pogg. Ann.,*
22. 1, 1831 ; *Ann. Chim. Phys.,* (1), **47.** 337, 1831 ; *Phil. Mag.,* (2), **10.** 321, 1831 ; (2), **11.** 7,
1832 ; G. Tammann, *Zeit. anorg. Chem.,* **149.** 68, 1925 ; C. Renz, *Beiträge zur Kenntniss des
Indiums und Thalliums,* Breslau, 1902 ; *Ber.,* **34.** 2763, 1901 ; **36.** 1847, 2751, 4394, 1903 ; **37.**
2111, 1904 ; T. Carnelley, *Journ. Chem. Soc.,* **26.** 323, 1873 ; A. Cleve, *Zeit. anorg. Chem.,* **32.**
129, 1902 ; P. T. Cleve, *Nova Acta Upsala,* (3), **13.** 23, 30, 1887 ; *Chem. News,* **51.** 143, 1885 ;
52. 278, 1885 ; **53.** 92, 1886 ; *Bull. Soc. Chim.,* (2), **43.** 109, 364, 1885 ; G. Carobbi and S. Restaino,
Gazz. Chim. Ital., **56. i,** 59, 1926 ; C. Benedicks, *Zeit. anorg. Chem.,* **20.** 393, 1900.
[2] J. J. Berzelius, *Akad. Handl. Stockholm,* 1, 1831 ; *Schweigger's Journ.,* **62.** 323, 1831 ; **63.**
26, 1831 ; *Pogg. Ann.,* **22.** 1, 1831 ; *Ann. Chim. Phys.,* (1), **47.** 337, 1831 ; *Phil. Mag.,* (2), **10.**
321, 1831 ; (2), **11.** 7, 1832 ; F. de Carli, *Atti Accad. Lincei,* (6), **1.** 533, 1925 ; C. Volek, *Zeit.
anorg. Chem.,* **6.** 165, 1894 ; P. T. Cleve, *Bih. Svenska Akad. Handl.,* **2.** 6, 1874 ; *Bull. Soc. Chim.,*

(2), 21. 115, 1874; W. Prandtl and O. Rosenthal, *Ber.*, 40. 2125, 1907; S. M. Tanatar and E. K. Kurowsky, *Journ. Russ. Phys. Chem. Soc.*, 41. 813, 1909.
³ F. Ephraim and G. Beck, *Helvetica Chim. Acta*, 9. 38, 1926; H. E. Roscoe, *Phil. Trans.*, 158. 1, 1868; 159. 679, 1869; 160. 317, 1870; *Proc. Roy. Soc.*, 16. 220, 1868; 18. 37, 313, 1870; *Journ. Chem. Soc.*, 21. 322, 1868; 23. 344, 1870; 24. 23, 1871; *Chem. News*, 17. 135, 1868; 20. 37, 1869; 21. 183, 1870; *Phil. Mag.*, (4), 35. 307, 1868; (4), 39. 146, 1870; (4), 40. 62, 1870; J. J. Berzelius, *Acad. Handl. Stockholm*, 1, 1831; *Schweigger's Journ.*, 62. 323, 1831; 63, 26, 1831; *Pogg. Ann.*, 22. 1, 1831; *Ann. Chim. Phys.*, (1), 47. 337, 1831; *Phil. Mag.*, (2), 10. 321, 1831; (2), 11. 7, 1832; M. Amadori, *Gazz. Chim. Ital.*, 49. i, 38, 1919; G. Tammann, *Zeit. anorg. Chem.*, 149. 68, 1925; 160. 101, 1927; D. Balareff, *ib.*, 160. 92, 1927; T. Carnelley, *Journ. Chem. Soc.*, 33. 279, 1878; F. de Carli, *Atti Accad. Lincei*, (6), 1. 533, 1925; A. Ditte, *Compt. Rend.*, 96. 1050, 1883; 104. 1707, 1887; H. Herrenschmidt, *ib.*, 139. 635, 1924; A. Carnot, *ib.*, 105. 121, 1887; A. Terreil, *Bull. Soc. Chim.*, (2), 13. 115, 1870; G. J. Brush, *Amer. Journ. Science*, (2), 24. 116, 1857; C. Bergmann, *Pogg. Ann.*, 80. 393, 1850; R. D. Thomson, *Thomson's Records*, 1. 34, 1835; C. F. Rammelsberg, *Handbuch der Mineralchemie*, Leipzig, 92, 1875; 52, 1886; *Sitzber. Akad. Berlin*, 40, 1864; J. Grailich, *Krystallographisch-optische Untersuchungen*, Wien, 197, 1858; H. Fischer and J. Nessler, *Ber. Nat. Ges. Freiberg*, 1. 3, 1854; R. Robl, *Zeit. angew. Chem.*, 39. 608, 1926.
⁴ G. vom Rath, *Zeit. Kryst.*, 10. 464, 1885; F. N. Guild, *ib.*, 49. 324, 1911; M. Websky, *ib.*, 5. 542, 1881; *Sitzber. Akad. Berlin*, 672, 1880; C. F. Rammelsberg, *ib.*, 656, 1880; 1215, 1883; *Handbuch der Mineralchemie*, Leipzig, 92, 1875; 77, 1886; *Zeit. deut. geol. Ges.*, 32. 709, 1880; A. Döring, *Bol. Acad. Cienc. Cordoba*, 5. 471, 1883; M. V. de Leon, *Naturaleza*, 7. 65, 1884; F. Zambonini, *Mineralogia Vesuviana*, Napoli, 315, 1910; F. Zambonini and G. Carobbi, *Amer. Min.*, 12. 1, 1927; A. Scacchi, *Atti Accad. Napoli*, 8. 10, 1879; L. de Luise, *Notizie sulla eruzione Vesuviana del* 1906, Portici, 17, 1914; V. Dürrfeld, *Zeit. Kryst.*, 51. 278, 1912; 53. 182, 1913; D. Lovisato, *Atti Accad. Lincei*, (5), 13. 93, 1909; (5), 19. i, 326, 1910; A. Frenzel, *Tschermak's Mitt.*, (2), 3. 506, 1881; (3), 4. 97, 1881; A. Brunlechner, *Corinthia*, 2, 1892; W. F. Hillebrand, *Bull. U.S. Geol. Sur.*, 64, 1890; *Proc. Colorado Scient. Soc.*, 3. 193, 1890; *Amer. Journ. Science*, (3), 37. 434, 1889; S. L. Penfield, *ib.*, (3), 26. 364, 1883; R. C. Wells, *ib.*, (4), 36. 636, 1913; F. A. Genth, *Proc. Amer. Phil. Soc.*, 24. 36, 1887; F. Pisani, *Bull. Soc. Min.*, 12. 39, 1889; O. Pufahl, *Centr. Min.*, 289, 1920; F. X. M. Zippe, *Sitzber. Akad. Wien*, 44. 197, 1861; G. Tschermak, *ib.*, 44. 167, 1861; A. Schrauf, *Pogg. Ann.*, 116. 355, 1862; A. Damour, *Ann. Chim. Phys.*, (3), 41. 72, 1854; A. des Cloizeaux, *ib.*, (3), 41. 78, 1854; *Bull. Soc. Min.*, 9. 138, 191, 1886; P. A. Wagner, *South African Journ. Science*, 19. 142, 1922; *Chem. News*, 127. 100, 1923; E. E. Fairbanks, *Econ. Geol.*, 21. 399, 1926; T. W. Case, *Phys. Rev.*, (2), 9. 305, 1917.
⁵ H. E. Roscoe, *Proc. Roy. Soc.*, 25. 111, 1876; C. F. Rammelsberg, *Zeit. deut. geol. Ges.*, 32. 713, 1880; *Handbuch der Mineralchemie*, Leipzig, 189, 1886; F. A. Genth, *Proc. Amer. Phil. Soc.*, 14. 229, 1874; *Amer. Journ. Science*, (3), 12. 35, 1876; A. Döring, *Bol. Acad. Cienc. Cordoba*, 5. 506, 1883; F. Pisani, *Compt. Rend.*, 92. 1292, 1881; O. Pufahl, *Centr. Min.*, 289, 1920.
⁶ I. Domeyko, *Ann. Mines*, (4), 14. 150, 1848; F. Pisani, *Bull. Soc. Min.*, 12. 41, 1889; V. Dürrfeld, *Zeit. Kryst.*, 51. 278, 1912; 63. 183, 1914; A. d'Achiardi, *I Metalli*, 2. 568, 1883; M. Adam, *Tableau minéralogique*, Paris, 33, 1869; T. Thomson, *Outlines of Mineralogy, Geology, and Mineral Analysis*, London, 574, 1836; G. A. Kenngott, *Des Mohs'sche Mineralsystem*, Wien, 28, 1853; R. Hermann, *Journ. prakt. Chem.*, (2), 1. 445, 1870; C. F. Rammelsberg, *Zeit. deut. geol. Ges.*, 32. 713, 1880; W. P. Blake, *Min. Scient. Press.*, 43. 131, 1881.
⁷ H. Fischer and J. Nessler, *Ber. Nat. Ges. Freiberg*, 1. 3, 1854; *Neues Jahrb. Min.*, 570, 1855; F. Sandberger, *ib.*, i, 258, 1889; C. Bergmann, *ib.*, 397, 1857; F. von Kobell, *Journ. prakt. Chem.*, (1) 50. 496, 1850; C. Czudnowicz, *Pogg. Ann.*, 120. 26, 1863; C. F. Rammelsberg, *Handbuch der Mineralchemie*, Leipzig, 290, 1875; 91, 1886; *Sitzber. Akad. Wien*, 40. 1864; *Journ. prakt. Chem.*, (1), 91. 413, 1864; J. Lang, *Mitt. Baden Geol. Landesanst.*, 461, 1903; *Beitrag zur Kenntnis der Erzlagerstatten am Schaninoland*, Freiburg, 1903; F. Schumacher, *Zeit. prakt. Geol.* 19. 1, 1911; W. T. Schaller, *Journ. Amer. Chem. Soc.*, 33. 1833, 1911.
⁸ A. Döring, *Bol. Acad. Cienc. Cordoba*, 5. 501, 1883; C. F. Rammelsberg, *Zeit. deut. geol. Ges.*, 32. 711, 1880; A. Damour, *Ann. Chim. Phys.*, (3), 41. 72, 1854.

§ 14. Vanadates of the Bismuth and Chromium Families

The *arsenic vanadates* are treated in connection with vanadium arsenates. O. W. Gibbs [1] believed that a series of *antimony vanadates* corresponding with the arsenic vanadates are capable of existence. A soln. of potassium antimonal tartrate gives a yellowish-brown precipitate when treated with ammonium metavanadate, and this dissolves when the mixture is shaken. A. Frenzel found a mineral at the Pacher Mine, Schnerberg, Saxony, and he called it **pacherite**. Analyses by A. Frenzel, and W. T. Schaller agree with **bismuth orthovanadate**, $BiVO_4$. A. Frenzel obtained it by evaporating over sulphuric acid, a soln. containing bismuth nitrate and vanadium chloride.   Pacherite occurs in reddish-brown tabular, or acicular crystals which M. Websky found to be rhombic with the axial ratios $a : b : c$ =0·5317 : 1 : 2·5357.   The (001)-cleavage is perfect.   E. V. Shannon examined the crystals of a sample from Brazil.   G. Cesaro studied the optical properties. The sp. gr. is 6·249 at 24·5°, and the hardness 4.   The mineral is soluble in hydrochloric acid with the evolution of chlorine.   W. T. Schaller's analyses of bismuth ochres (q.v.) from California show that they are probably bismuth trihydroxyvanadate, $BiVO_4.Bi(OH)_3$, or $HO.Bi : VO_4.Bi(OH)_2$.   E. Zintl and L. Vanino prepared bismuth vanadate for therapeutic use by the addition of vanadates, at the ordinary or at raised temp., to soln. containing bismuth salts and substances which prevent the separation of basic bismuth compounds, such as acetic acid, mixtures of acetic acid and acetates, small quantities of mineral acids, polyhydric alcohols, or ketones. The product is subsequently heated in the air in case any reduction has taken place during the precipitation.

A. Carnot [2] found that chromium salts give a precipitate of chromium vanadate, $CrVO_4$, when treated with an alkali vanadate.   A. Ditte prepared ammonium vanadatochromate, $2(NH_4)_2O.V_2O_5.2CrO_3.7H_2O$, or chromatovanadate, by dissolving vanadium pentoxide in a soln. of ammonium chromate at 60°, and evaporating the red liquid in vacuo ; if the liquid be evaporated on a water-bath, crystals of ammonium hexavanadate are formed.   B. Glasmann evaporated an aq soln. of 2 mols each of chromic anhydride, ammonium metavanadate and ammonia at 60°, until a conc. soln. was obtained, and then evaporated it in vacuo.   Red prismatic crystals of ammonium vanadatochromate mixed with crystals of ammonium hexavanadate were formed.   B. Glasmann was unable to prepare any other vanadatochromate.

J. J. Berzelius [3] found that when vanadyl sulphate is treated with ammonium molybdate, a dark purple soln. is formed which, on exposure to air, becomes blue, and then yellow, without precipitation ; and that molybdenum salt soln. give a yellow liquid when treated with ammonium metavanadate.   O. W. Gibbs observed that when molybdic acid is added to a boiling soln. of ammonium metavanadate, complex vanadatomolybdates or molybdatovanadates are formed.   A number of these complexes have been reported by L. Milch, C. Friedheim and co-workers, H. von Euler-Chelpin, F. Toggenburg, H. Stamm, A. Isenburg, etc.   The tests for chemical individuality are not sufficient to decide the question.   Consequently, we are unable to distinguish between chemical individuals and mixtures.   The salts are prepared by adding molybdic acid to a soln. of a vanadate ; by adding vanadic acid to a soln. of molybdate or by mixing soln. of a vanadate and a molybdate. There is an extraordinarily wide variation in the composition of the salts—thus, there are nearly twenty ammonium vanadatomolybdates.   Their constitution has not yet been elucidated.   One series can be represented by $3R_2O.2V_2O_5.$ $4MoO_3.nH_2O$, where R denotes NH_4 or K.   This is one of the most stable of the series, and on the co-ordination theory they can be regarded as salts of the heteropolyacid, $H_{10}[(V_2O_6)_3H_2(Mo_2O_7)_3].nH_2O$, where the ammonium salt becomes $(NH_4)_9H[(V_2O_6)_3H_2(Mo_2O_7)_3].9H_2O$.   The three series, $2\frac{2}{3}R_2O.V_2O_5.6MoO_3.nH_2O$, where R_2 denotes $K_2.(NH_4)_2$, or Ba ; $2R_2O.V_2O_5.6MoO_3.nH_2O$, where R denotes Na or K ; and $3R_2O.V_2O_5.6MoO.nH_2O$, where R denotes NH_4 or K, may be derived from either of the heteropolyacids :

$$H_6\left[H_2\frac{(V_2O_6)}{(Mo_2O_7)_3}\right] \quad \text{or} \quad H_{10}\left[H_2\frac{(V_2O_6)}{(Mo_2O_7)} \atop O_2\right]$$

None of these acids has been isolated, but A. Ditte reported that if ammonium vanadatomolybdate is boiled with aqua regia containing an excess of nitric acid, a reddish, non-crystalline deposit is obtained, and if this is boiled with a large excess of nitric acid, it gradually changes into small, slender, transparent, orange-red needles of vanadatomolybdic acid, $V_2O_5.8MO_5.5H_2O$.   Vanadatomolybdic acid is only slightly soluble in boiling nitric acid, and is still less soluble in water. In this respect, it differs from phosphatomolybdic and arsenatomolybdic acids, which are readily soluble in water.

G. Canneri showed that within the limits imposed by the solubility of molybdic anhydride in soln. of the metavanadates of sodium, potassium, and ammonium, compounds of two types, differing in their physical properties, are formed. These crystallize respectively in large, orange-red prisms and in yellow, silky needles, or, sometimes, in pulverulent form. One and the same soln. may give both red and yellow crystals, either together or successively in either order. The value of the ratio $V_2O_5 : MoO_3$ varies gradually in the red crystals from $3 : 1$ to values corresponding with the maximum percentage of vanadium, this approaching the proportion occurring in polyvanadates. The ratio changes suddenly in value for the yellow crystals, which are poorer in vanadium. The various red crystals appear to consist of isomorphous mixtures, but the isomorphogenous terms cannot yet be defined, neither can their chemical natures be established ; it is, however, possible that they consist of polyvanadates and polymolybdates. Along with these isomorphous mixtures there exist certain well-defined compounds which are obtained under definite conditions. With these compounds difficulty is encountered in distinguishing between combined water and water of crystallization, but the salts are regarded as heteropolyaquates and are supposed to have formulæ based on the hypothesis of A. Rosenheim. According to W. Prandtl, molybdovanadates are double salts, and should hence be completely dissociated in soln. ; in sufficiently dil. soln., therefore, fractional precipitation of the different constituents should be possible, but this is not found to be the case.

G. Canneri found that the crystals formed by the system $NH_4VO_3 : MoO_3$ have the same pale-yellow colour and crystal habit in all cases, and consist of **ammonium hexavanadatopentamolybdate,** $4(NH_4)_2O.3V_2O_5.5MoO_3.10H_2O$. C. Friedheim and C. Castendyck obtained reddish-brown crystals of **ammonium tetravanadatodimolybdate,** $(NH_4)_2O.2V_2O_5.2MoO_3.8H_2O$, along with four other salts—*vide infra*—by fractional crystallization from a soln. of 800 grms. of ammonium silicatomolybdate and 180 grms. of ammonium metavanadate ; also yellowish-green crystals of **ammonium divanadatodimolybdate,** $(NH_4)_2O.V_2O_3.2MoO_3.4H_2O$, almost insoluble in water. H. von Euler-Chelpin obtained **ammonium divanadatotrimolybdate,** $(NH_4)_2O.V_2O_5.3MoO_3.17H_2O$, as a yellow crystalline powder, from a hot soln. of equimolar parts of molybdic acid and ammonium metavanadate ; and white needles of $2(NH_4)_2O.V_2O_5.3MoO_3.6H_2O$, from the mother-liquor in the preparation of the divanadatotetramolybdate, and also from a soln. of 4 mols of ammonium metavanadate and a soln. of ammonium paramolybdate. A. Isenburg also made this salt ; and W. Prandtl represented it by $(NH_4)_6V_6O_{18}.3(NH_4)_2H_4Mo_3O_{12}.12H_2O$. C. Friedheim and C. Castendyck obtained pale brown **ammonium hexavanadatotetramolybdate,** $2(NH_4)_2O. 3V_2O_5.4MoO_3.11H_2O$, by the fractional crystallization of the soln. employed for the tetravanadatodimolybdate ; L. Milch, and M. Liebert obtained **ammonium tetravanadatotetramolybdate,** $3(NH_4)_2O.2V_2O_5.4MoO_3.7\frac{1}{2}(9, or 11)H_2O$, by the action of a soln. of molybdic acid on an aq. soln. of ammonium metavanadate at about 70° ; and cooling the hot soln. or evaporating it over sulphuric acid. H. von Euler-Chelpin obtained it by the action of 4 mols of ammonium metavanadate on 3 mols of molybdic acid ; and A. Ditte from a hot soln. of vanadium pentoxide and ammonium molybdate. W. Prandtl represented this salt by the formula $(NH_4)_3HV_6O_{17}.6NH_4HMoO_4.7, 10,$ or $13H_2O$. The salt is readily soluble in water, from which soln. it can be recrystallized unchanged. It is decomposed by acids and alkali-lye, and the soln. gives a precipitate with salts of the alkaline earths, silver, mercury, lead, etc., but not by salts of the alkalies, copper, zinc, manganese, cobalt, and nickel. H. von Euler-Chelpin obtained **ammonium divanadatotetramolybdate,** $2(NH_4)_2O.V_2O_5.4MoO_3.7$ or $8H_2O$, from hot soln. of a mol of ammonium paramolybdate and 2 mols of ammonium metavanadate, by allowing it to stand

over sulphuric acid. M. Liebert obtained the same salt from the mother-liquor in the preparation of divanadatohexamolybdate. C. Friedheim and C. Castendyck obtained brownish-red needles of **ammonium tetracosivanadatopentamolybdate,** $4(NH_6)_2O.12V_2O_5.5MoO_3.24H_2O$, by fractional crystallization of the soln. employed for the tetravanadatodimolybdate; at the same time there is formed a yellow crystalline crust of **ammonium tetravanadatopentamolybdate,** $2(NH_4)_2O.2V_2O_5.$ $5MoO_3.8H_2O$. H. von Euler-Chelpin produced yellow crystals of the anhydrous salt from a soln. of 3 mols of molybdic acid and one mol of ammonium meta-vanadate; and M. Liebert, $3(NH_4)_2O.2V_2O_5.5MoO_3.8\frac{1}{2}H_2O$, from a boiling soln. of vanadium pentoxide in normal ammonium molybdate, and afterwards evaporated over conc. sulphuric acid. This salt was also obtained as a heptahydrate by A. Isenburg. H. von Euler-Chelpin prepared white needles of **ammonium octo-vanadatohexamolybdate,** $5(NH_4)_2O.4V_2O_5.6MoO_3.12$ or $14H_2O$, from a soln. of a mol of molybdic acid and 2 or 4 mols of ammonium metavanadate. W. Prandtl also prepared this salt, and he considered its composition is better expressed by $(NH_4)_3HV_2O_{17}.5NH_4HMoO_4.7H_2O$. O. W. Gibbs prepared *pentahydrated* **ammonium divanadatohexamolybdate,** $2(NH_4)_2O.V_2O_5.6MoO_3.5H_2O$, from a soln. of molybdic acid in a boiling soln. of ammonium metavanadate, and allowing the soln. to evaporate spontaneously. M. Liebert prepared the *hexahydrate* from a boiling soln. of ammonium paramolybdate and vanadium pentoxide. W. Prandtl represented it by the formula $(NH_4)_3HV_6O_{17}.6(NH_4)_2H_4Mo_3O_{12}.H_2O$; and O. W. Gibbs by $5(NH_4)_2O.2V_2O_5.12MoO_3.10H_2O$. A. Isenburg made $3(NH_4)_2O.$ $V_2O_5.6MoO_3.7H_2O$, by evaporating a soln. of 145 grms. of ammonium metavanadate and 765 grms. of ammonium paramolybdate in 2·5 litres of water. W. Prandtl represented it by $(NH_4)_6V_6O_{18}.6(NH_4)_2H_4Mo_3O_{12}.9H_2O$. F. Toggenburg prepared **ammonium hexavanadatoheptamolybdate,** $5(NH_4)_2O.3V_2O_5.7MoO_3.13$ or $16H_2O$, by dissolving 35·1 grms. of ammonium metavanadate and 50·4 grms. of molybdic acid in as little warm water as possible, mixing the liquid with 32·1 c.c. of aq. ammonia of sp. gr. 0·956, concentrating and cooling the hot, filtered liquid. It was also made by treating the dil. soln. of ammonium diphos-phatododecavanadatodododecamolybdate with aq ammonia. The yellow needles can be recrystallized from water without decomposition. The aq. soln. gives no precipitate with potassium chloride, but a white one with barium chloride. W. Prandtl represented it $(NH_4)_4V_6O_{17}.(NH_4)_2H_4Mo_3O_{12}.4NH_4HMoO_4.9$ or $12H_2O$. H. Stamm made **ammonium hexavanadatoctomolybdate,** $5(NH_4)_2O.3V_2O_5.$ $8MoO_3.14H_2O$, in rhombic crystals, from the mother-liquid after the preparation of ammonium diphosphatoctovanadatotetradecamolybdate. W. Prandtl repre-sented it $(NH_6)_4V_6O_{17}.2NH_4HMoO_4.2(NH_4)_2H_4Mo_3O_{12}.8H_2O$. O. W. Gibbs made **ammonium divanadatoctodecamolybdate,** $8(NH_4)_2O.V_2O_5.12MoO_3.15H_2O$, by saturating a boiling soln. of ammonium metavanadate with molybdic acid, and cooling the liquid slowly. The yellowish-green tabular crystals are decom-posed by boiling water. A. Isenburg made **ammonium octovanadatotrideca-molybdate,** $8(NH_4)_2O.4V_2O_5 : 13MoO_3.21H_2O$, by the spontaneous evaporation of a soln. of 2 mols of ammonium metavanadate and a mol of ammonium para-molybdate in 4 litres of hot water. W. Prandtl represented it $(NH_4)_3HV_6O_{17}.$ $2(NH_4)_2H_4Mo_3O_{12}.4NH_4HMoO_4.6H_2O$. L. Milch reported **ammonium hexavana-datotetracosimolybdate,** $10(NH_4)_2O.3V_2O_5.24MoO_3.10H_2O$, by concentrating on the water-bath a hot soln. of ammonium molybdate sat. with hydrated vanadium pentoxide. The salt can be purified by recrystallization. W. Prandtl represer?ted it by $(NH_4)_4V_6O_{17}.8(NH_4)_2H_2Mo_3O_{11}.2H_2O$.

G. Canneri found that the pale yellow crystals, formed in the system $KVO_3 : MoO_3$ at 30°, vary in composition with the conc. of the soln., forming compounds **potas-sium hexavanadatotetramolybdate,** $4K_2O.3V_2O_5.4MoO_3.7H_2O$, and **potassium tetravanadatohexamolybdate,** $3K_2O.2V_2O_5.6MoO_3.7H_2O$. While with the system $NaVO_3 : MoO_3$, **sodium hexavanadatoctomolybdate,** $4Na_2O.3V_2O_5.8MoO_3.10H_2O$, occurs in equilibrium with the red mixed crystals until the molybdenum has attained the ratio $V_2O_5 : MoO_3 = 112$, and it separates as a single phase when the proportion of molybdenum is still further increased. The red salt is **sodium hexavanadatomolybdate**, $2Na_2O.3V_2O_5.MoO_3.9H_2O$. It yields **barium octovanadatomolybdate**, $3BaO.4V_2O_5.MoO_3.12H_2O$, and **sodium hexavanadatodimolybdate**, $3Na_2O.3V_2O_5.2MoO_3.12H_2O$. H. von Euler-Chelpin prepared yellow crystals of **potassium divanadatotrimolybdate**, $K_2O.V_2O_5.3MoO_3.15H_2O$, from aq. soln. of potassium metavanadate and molybdic acid in equimolar proportions. He also obtained **potassium tetravanadatotetramolybdate**, $3K_2O.2V_2O_5.4MoO_3.7(8$ or $9)H_2O$, from a soln. of a mol of potassium metavanadate and 0·5 mol of molybdic acid; by treating with potassium chloride, a cold sat. soln. of ammonium tetravanadatotetramolybdate, or octovanadatohexamolybdate, or from a soln. of potassium hydroxide and ammonium tetravanadatotetramolybdate. M. Liebert obtained it from the mother-liquor in the preparation of potassium tetravanadatododecamolybdate. W. Prandtl represented it by the formula $K_3HV_6O_{17}.6KHMoO_4.7, 8$, or $10H_2O$. H. von Euler-Chelpin obtained olive-green crystals of **potassium tetravanadatopentamolybdate**, $2K_2O.2V_2O_5.5MoO_3.10H_2O$, mixed with yellow monoclinic crystals of potassium tetravanadatododecamolybdate, from a soln. of a mol of potassium metavanadate and 1·5 mols of molybdic acid in hot water. M. Liebert prepared lemon-yellow crystals of **potassium divanadatohexamolybdate**, $2K_2O.V_2O_5.6MoO_3.6H_2O$, from a hot, sat. soln. of potassium paramolybdate and hydrated vanadium pentoxide; H. von Euler-Chelpin also made it by mixing a soln. of equimolar parts of ammonium metavanadate and molybdic acid with a cold, sat. soln. of potassium chloride. H. Jacoby also prepared this salt. It is sparingly soluble in cold water, freely soluble in hot water, from which it crystallizes without decomposition. H. von Euler-Chelpin made $3K_2O.V_2O_5.6MoO_3.5H_2O$, from a hot soln. of a mol of potassium paramolybdate and 2 mols of potassium metavanadate; W. Prandtl represented it by $K_6V_6O_{18}.6K_2H_4Mo_3O_{12}.3H_2O$. H. von Euler-Chelpin also prepared **sodium divanadatohexamolybdate**, $2Na_2O.V_2O_5.6MoO_3.16H_2O$, from a soln. of equimolar parts of sodium metavanadate and molybdic acid; W. Prandtl represented it by $Na_2H_2V_6O_{17}.6Na_2H_4Mo_3O_{13}.26H_2O$. M. Liebert reported **potassium tetravanadatododecamolybdate**, $5K_2O.2V_2O_5.12MoO_3.12H_2O$, from a sat. soln. of normal potassium molybdate and hydrated vanadium pentoxide; and H. von Euler-Chelpin, from a soln. of two mols of sodium metavanadate and a mol of sodium paramolybdate mixed with potassium chloride. W. Prandtl represented it by $K_3HV_6O_{17}.6K_2H_4Mo_3O_{12}.6H_2O$, and he also obtained the anhydrous salt $K_3HV_6O_{17}.6K_2H_4Mo_3O_{12}$, as well as the mixed salt $(K,Na)_3HV_6O_{17}.6(Na,K)_2H_4Mo_3O_{12}.14H_2O$. M. Liebert reported **potassium divanadatododecamolybdate**, $3K_2O.V_2O_5.12MoO_3.15H_2O$, from a soln. of 3 mols of potassium carbonate, one mol of vanadium pentoxide, and 24 mols of molybdic acid. W. Prandtl prepared red pulverulent **potassium hexavanadatoicosimolybdate**, $10K_2O.3V_2O_5.21MoO_3.17H_2O$, or, as he writes it, $K_6V_6O_{18}.7K_2H_4Mo_3O_{12}.3H_2O$. from a soln. of 3 mols of vanadium pentoxide, and 18 mols of molybdic anhydride in potash-lye at ordinary temp., and then adding an excess of dil. acetic acid; he also reported $23K_2O.6V_2O_5.60MoO_3.57H_2O$, or, as he wrote it, $K_3HV_6O_{17}.10K_2H_4Mo_3O_{12}.8H_2O$, to be formed if a boiling soln. is used. A warm soln. of 3 mols of vanadium pentoxide and 6–8 mols of molybdic anhydride in potash-lye when treated with dil. acetic acid, furnishes yellowish-white needles of **potassium dodecavanadatohexadecamolybdate**, $9K_2O.6V_2O_5.16MoO_3.34H_2O$, or $K_3HV_6O_{17}.2KHMoO_4.2K_2H_4Mo_3O_{12}.6H_2O$. A soln. of 5 grms. each of vanadium pentoxide, and molybdic anhydride in potash-lye, feebly acidified with acetic acid, was found by W. Prandtl to furnish **potassium divanadatodimolybdate**, $3K_2O.V_2O_5.2MoO_3.8H_2O$, or $KVO_3.K_2MoO_4.4H_2O$, or $K_3V_3O_9.3K_2MoO_4.12H_2O$; if soda-lye be used instead of potash-lye, **sodium hexavanadatohexamolybdate**, $5Na_2O.3V_2O_5.6MoO_3.15H_2O$, or $Na_4V_6O_{17}.6NaHMoO_4.12H_2O$, was obtained. If the ratio $V_2O_5 : MoO_3$ be between the limits $3 : 6$ and $3 : 18$, **sodium hexavanadatoheptamolybdate**, $4Na_2O.3V_2O_5.7MoO_3.21H_2O$, or $Na_2H_2V_6O_{17}.$

$Na_2H_4Mo_3O_{12}.4NaHMoO_4.16H_2O$, is formed; with the ratio **3 : 8**, **sodium hexavanadatoctodecamolybdate**, $9Na_2O.3V_2O_5.18MoO_3.48H_2O$, or $Na_6V_6O_{18}.6Na_2H_4Mo_3O_{12}.36H_2O$ is formed.

H. von Euler-Chelpin reported **ammonium potassium tetravanadatotetramolybdate**, $2K_2O.(NH_4)_2O.2V_2O_5.4MoO_3.5H_2O$, in yellow prisms, from a soln. of 2 mols of ammonium metavanadate and a mol of molybdic acid with potassium chloride; on recrystallization, potassium tetravanadatotetramolybdate is formed. W. Prandtl represented its composition by $(K,NH_4)_3HV_6O_{17}.5(K,NH_4)HMoO_3.$ 6 or $13H_2O$. H. Jacoby made a similar salt. H. von Euler-Chelpin also made in yellow prismatic crystals **ammonium potassium hexavanadatopentamolybdate**, $3K_2O.(NH_4)_2O.3V_2O_5.5MoO_3.9H_2O$, from the mother-liquor in the preparation of the preceding salt. H. Jacoby also obtained white needles of $3\cdot5K_2O.0\cdot5(NH_4)_2O.$ $3V_2O_5.5MoO_3.16H_2O$, by treating the mother-liquor in the preparation of ammonium diphosphatododecavanadatodecamolybdate, with potassium chloride. H. von Euler-Chelpin obtained **ammonium sodium tetravanadatohexamolybdate**, $Na_2O.$ $(NH_4)_2O.2V_2O_5.6MoO_3.12H_2O$, from a soln. of a mol of molybdic acid and a mol of ammonium metavanadate mixed with sodium chloride and evaporated over a desiccating agent. The mother-liquor employed in the preparation of potassium tetravanadatododecamolybdate furnished pale yellow crystals of **sodium potassium tetravanadatododecamolybdate**, $4Na_2O.K_2O.2V_2O_5.12MoO_3.18H_2O$.

O. W. Gibbs found that a soln. of ammonium divanadatohexamolybdate gives no precipitate with copper sulphate. H. von Euler-Chelpin obtained an egg-yellow crystalline powder, **barium vanadatomolybdate**, $BaO.V_2O_5.MoO_3.7H_2O$, from the mother-liquor employed in the preparation of **barium octovanadatohexamolybdate**, $5BaO.4V_2O_5.6MoO_3.28H_2O$, by adding a 10 per cent. soln. of barium chloride to a soln. of 2 mols of ammonium metavanadate and a mol of molybdic acid. The pale yellow crystalline powder is soluble in hot water. H. von Euler-Chelpin obtained **barium tetravanadatohexamolybdate**, $3BaO.2V_2O_5.6MoO_3.8H_2O$, by crystallization from a soln. of ammonium barium divanadatotrimolybdate. O. W. Gibbs obtained **barium tetravanadatohexadecamolybdate**, $5BaO.2V_2O_5.16MoO_3.29H_2O$, by adding barium chloride to a dil. boiling soln. of vanadium pentoxide and an acid ammonium molybdate. W. Prandtl represented it by $Ba_2V_6O_{17}.6BaH_2Mo_4O_{14}.41H_2O$. M. Liebert prepared **barium hexavanadatoctodecamolybdate**, $7BaO.3V_2O_5.18MoO_3.36$ or $48H_2O$, by mixing with barium chloride a cold soln. of potassium tetravanadatododecamolybdate, or divanadatohexamolybdate. W. Prandtl represented it by $BaH_2V_6O_{17}.6BaH_4Mo_3O_{12}.24$ or $36H_2O$; and H. von Euler-Chelpin obtained it from the mother-liquor employed in the preparation of **ammonium barium divanadatotrimolybdate**, $(NH_4)_2O.BaO.$ $V_2O_5.3MoO_3.6H_2O$, which was obtained in yellow crystals, by treating a soln. of ammonium metavanadate and molybdic acid with barium chloride; or evaporating a soln. of 2 mols of ammonium metavanadate and one mol of molybdic acid over sulphuric acid. W. Prandtl represented it by the formula $(Ba,NH_4)HV_6O_{17}.5NH_4HMoO_4.6H_2O$. W. Prandtl prepared **barium hexavanadatoctodecamolybdate**, $9BaO.3V_2O_5.18MoO_3.32$ or $86H_2O$, or $Ba_3V_6O_{18}.6BaH_4Mo_3O_{12}.20$ or $74H_2O$, by adding barium chloride to a boiling soln. of 3 mols of vanadium pentoxide and 18 mols of molybdic anhydride in soda-lye treated with an excess of dil. acetic acid. L. Milch found that by dropping a soln. of barium chloride into a hot soln. of ammonium vanadatomolybdate, crystals of **ammonium barium dodecavanadatohexatricontamolybdate**, $5(NH_4)_2O.15BaO.$ $6V_2O_6.36MoO_3$, are formed. O. W. Gibbs made **mercurous vanadatomolybdate** by adding mercurous nitrate to a soln. of ammonium divanadatohexamolybdate.

According to J. J. Berzelius,[4] a yellowish-brown precipitate of **vanadyl tungstate** is formed when a soln. of a vanadyl salt and an alkali tungstate are mixed; the product is slightly soluble in water, and when kept under water, oxidation to the pentoxide occurs and the soln. acquires a yellow colour. Mixed soln. of tungstates and vanadates, or soln. of vanadium pentoxide in a soln. of a paratungstate, or a mixture of soln. of paratungstates and metavanadates, furnish a series of salts of heteropoly acids—the **vanadatotungstates** or **tungstatovanadates**. The salts have been studied by C. F. Rammelsberg, A. Ditte, O. W. Gibbs, A. Rosenheim and co-workers, and C. Friedheim and co-workers, but as in the case of the heteropolymolybdates, the subject is yet in rather an empirical stage. There are three fairly well-defined series : (i) The orange-red series, $5R_2O.3V_2O_5.6WO_3.nH_2O$, with NH_4, K, or Na in place of R. On the co-ordination theory, the formula is $R_5H_2[(WO_4)_3H_2(WO_3)_3].nH_2O$; (ii) The yellowish-red series $2R_2O.V_2O_5.4WO_3.nH_2O$, with $R=NH_4$, K, Na, CN_3H_6, Ag, $\frac{1}{2}Ba$, $\frac{1}{2}Ca$, and $\frac{1}{2}Sr$. The co-ordination formula is

$$R_4\left[H_2 \underset{(VO_3)_2}{\overset{(W_2O_7)_4}{}} \underset{(VO_3)_2}{} H_2\right]R_4.nH_2O$$

(iii) The purple-red series, $5R_2O.3V_2O_5.14WO_3.nH_2O$, with $R=NH_4$, K, Cs, CN_3H_6, and $\frac{1}{2}Ba$, has the co-ordination formula :

$$R_{20}H_{14}\left[\left\{\begin{matrix}(W_2O_7)_4H_2\\(V_2O_4)_2\end{matrix}\right\}-W_2O_7-\left\{\begin{matrix}(W_2O_7)_4H_2\\(V_2O_6)_2\end{matrix}\right\}-W_2O_7-\left\{H_2\begin{matrix}(W_2O_7)_4\\(V_2O_6)_2\end{matrix}\right\}\right]$$

It is doubtful if a **vanadatotungstic acid** has been prepared. O. W. Gibbs boiled a mixture of soln. of ammonium metavanadate and sodium paratungstate with nitric acid, and found that the orange-red liquid deposited a sulphur-yellow crystalline precipitate of a **divanadatotungstic acid,** $V_2O_5.10WO_3.22H_2O$, sparingly soluble in cold water. The mother-liquor furnished on evaporation needle-like crystals of **divanadatoctodecatungstic acid,** $V_2O_5.18WO_3.36H_2O$. A. Rosenheim could not confirm these statements, but he said that **octovanadatohexadecatungstic acid,** $4V_2O_5.16WO_3.41H_2O$, is obtained by suspending in water barium tungstate and vanadate in the proportions $V_2O_5 : 4WO_3$; precipitating the barium with sulphuric acid ; and concentrating the filtered liquid in vacuo over phosphoric pentoxide. The violet plates are sparingly soluble in cold water and freely soluble in hot water. 24 mols of water are lost at 100°–120°, and only one mol remains at 250°. C. Friedheim suggested that A. Rosenheim's product is a mixture of metatungstic acid and hydrated vanadium pentoxide.

C. F. Rammelsberg said that he obtained *ammonium hexavanadatotungstate,* $(NH_4)_2O.3V_2O_5.WO_3.6H_2O$, by treating commercial sodium vanadate (contaminated with tungstate) with acetic acid, and evaporating the red liquid spontaneously. The dark brown octahedra are decomposed by heat. F. Rothenbach evaporated a soln. of equimolar proportions of ammonium nitrate and sodium hexavanadatododecatungstate, over calcium chloride, and obtained octahedral crystals with the composition $34(NH_4)_2O.21V_2O_5.60WO_3.58H_2O$; the analysis would agree equally well with simpler proportions.

A. Rosenheim obtained garnet-red crystals of *hemipentahydrated* **ammonium divanadatotetratungstate,** $2(NH_4)_2O.V_2O_5.4WO_3.3\frac{1}{2}H_2O$, by boiling hydrated vanadium pentoxide with acid ammonium tungstate ; and C. Friedheim and E. Löwy obtained the *tetrahydrate* by evaporating a boiling soln. of a mol of ammonium paratungstate with 14 mols of ammonium metavanadate. A crop of orange-red, rhombohedral crystals appears after the deposition of a little ammonium metavanadate. C. Friedheim regarded both hydrates as ammonium hexavanadatododecatungstate, $6(NH_4)_2O.3V_2O_5.12WO_3.nH_2O$; and he obtained garnet-red octahedra of $4(NH_4)_2O.3V_2O_5.12WO_3.30H_2O$, by the action of vanadium pentoxide on a boiling soln. of ammonium paratungstate ; or from a mixture of acetic acid, ammonium metatungstate, and acid ammonium vanadate. A. Ditte obtained dark red octahedra of **ammonium divanadatopentatungstate,** $2(NH_4)_2O.V_2O_5.5WO_3.10H_2O$, from a soln. of vanadium pentoxide in ammonium tungstate. O. Friedheim said that this product is identical with the one described immediately preceding this. O. W. Gibbs assigned the formula $4(NH_4)_2O.V_2O_5.5WO_3.13H_2O$, to a salt obtained by boiling a soln. of ammonium metavanadate with ammonium paratungstate, and evaporating the orange-yellow liquid. The salt is sparingly soluble in cold water, and freely soluble in hot water ; the soln. gives precipitates with silver nitrate, mercurous nitrate, and potassium bromide. A. Rosenheim believed that this salt is really **ammonium octovanadatotetradecatungstate,** $7(NH_4)_2O.4V_2O_5.14WO_3.16H_2O$. Hydrochloric and nitric acids precipitate tungstic acid from the aq. soln.

A. Rosenheim reported **sodium divanadatotetratungstate,** $2Na_2O.V_2O_5.4WO_3.14\frac{1}{2}H_2O$, to be formed by boiling an excess of hydrated vanadium pentoxide with an aq. soln. of sodium paratungstate ; evaporating the deep orange liquid on a water-bath ; and allowing the syrupy liquid to crystallize over sulphuric acid. The deep red, triclinic crystals have the axial ratios $a:b:c=0.5184:1:1.0812$, and $a=106°\ 41'$, $\beta=90°\ 44'$, and $\gamma=85°\ 27'$. The crystals rapidly effloresce, and they are freely soluble in water. The aq. soln. precipitates tungstic acid when treated with mineral acids, it gives amorphous precipitates with mercurous and ferrous salts, and a deep red, crystalline precipitate with silver nitrate. C. Friedheim alleged that the correct formula for this compound is **sodium hexavanadato-dodecatungstate,** $6Na_2O.3V_2O_5.12WO_3.42H_2O$, and he represented the formation of the salt by the equation : $3Na_{10}W_{12}O_{41}+6V_2O_5=3Na_2W_4O_{13}+2Na_{12}V_6W_{12}O_{57}$. He added that it can be synthesized from sodium paratungstate and trivanadate. F. Rothenbach obtained a salt with the composition $4Na_2O.3V_2O_5.12WO_3.38H_2O$, in dark red octahedral crystals along with the triclinic divanadatotetratungstate. It can also be obtained by evaporating sodium metatungstate with an acetic acid soln. of sodium hexavanadate, and crystallizing. C. Friedheim and E. Löwy prepared **sodium hexavanadatohexatungstate,** $5Na_2O.3V_2O_5.6WO_3.38H_2O$, from a hot water soln. of 135 grms. of sodium paratungstate and 83 grms. of the meta-vanadate, by evaporation on a water-bath to a syrupy liquid, and fractional crystallization over sulphuric acid. The rhombohedral orange-brown crystals can be recrystallized from aq. soln. The salt retains 4 mols. of water at 120° ; and 100 parts of water at 13.8° dissolve 80 parts of the salt. The aq. soln. does not give a precipitate with potassium chloride, but silver nitrate, and barium chloride give precipitates quickly, and calcium chloride slowly. The salt fuses at a red heat, forming a glassy mass. C. Friedheim and E. Löwy reported that **sodium divanadatododecatungstate,** $7Na_2O.V_2O_5.12WO_3.29H_2O$, can be obtained from the mother-liquid from the preceding salt. It is decomposed by recrystallization forming **sodium divanadatotetradecatungstate,** $8Na_2O.V_2O_5.14WO_3.60(or\ 66)H_2O$.

A. Rosenheim obtained **potassium divanadatotetratungstate,** $2K_2O.V_2O_5.4WO_3.8H_2O$, by boiling a soln. of potassium paratungstate with hydrated vanadium pentoxide, and evaporating the deep red liquid to a syrupy consistency. It is freely soluble in water and the soln. behaves like the corresponding sodium salt. The yellowish-red or reddish-brown crystals are tabular, and rarely prismatic ; they belong to the triclinic system, and have the axial ratios $a:b:c=0.6993:1:0.6696$, and $a=95°\ 38'$; $\beta=93°\ 58'$; and $\gamma=90°\ 4'$. At 120°, 24 mols. of water are given off ; between 120° and 300°, 8 mols. are expelled ; and one mol. is retained very tenaciously. He therefore wrote the formula $8K_2O.4V_2O_5.16WO_3.9H_2O.24Aq$. A. Rosenheim found that along with the crystals of potassium metatungstate, and the preceding salt, there are present garnet-red, sparingly soluble, octahedral crystals of **potassium hexavanadatododecatungstate,** $4K_2O.3V_2O_5.12WO_3.30H_2O$. C. Friedheim and E. Löwy obtained a series of **sodium potassium hexa-vanadatohexatungstates** which are presumably solid soln. of $5Na_2O.3V_2O_5.6WO_3.nH_2O$ and $5K_2O.3V_2O_5.6WO_3.nH_2O$, in the proportions $5:1$, $1:4$, and $4:3$ by concentrating mixed soln. of the component salts over sulphuric acid. A. Rosenheim prepared **silver octovanadatohexadecatungstate,** $8Ag_2O.4V_2O_5.16WO_3.9H_2O$, by boiling a soln. of 3 : 7 sodium vanadate with hydrated vanadium pentoxide, and mixed with silver nitrate. The purple-red precipitate is soluble in cold water, but is decomposed by hot water. The mother-liquor, when evaporated in vacuo, gives red triclinic crystals of **silver tetravanadatohexatungstate,** $3Ag_2O.2V_2O_5.6WO_3.3H_2O$, almost insoluble in cold water, and decomposed by hot water. O. W. Gibbs reported **mercurcus vanadatotungstate** as a dark green precipitate from mercurous nitrate and octoammoniumdivanadatopentatungstate.

According to A. Rosenheim, **barium divanadatotetratungstate,** $2BaO.V_2O_5$. $4WO_3.11\frac{1}{4}$(or 13)H_2O, is obtained by boiling hydrated vanadium pentoxide with a soln. of acid sodium tungstate, and adding the calculated quantity of barium chloride. The pale yellow liquid furnishes orange-red crystals when evaporated over sulphuric acid. C. Friedheim prepared it by boiling vanadium pentoxide and barium paratungstate with water, and by boiling with water a mol of barium carbonate, 3 mols of vanadium pentoxide, and 10 mols of the 5 : 12 barium tungstate, or 6 mols of barium carbonate, 3 of vanadium pentoxide, and 12 of tungstic acid. C. Friedheim and E. Löwy obtained the salt by adding barium chloride to a soln. of sodium hexavanadatohexatungstate. The yellowish-red, rhombic crystals were reported by A. Rosenheim to have the axial ratios $a : b : c$ $=0.8332 : 1 : 1.4264$. The aq. soln. reacts like the alkali salts. It retains 9 mols. of water at $100°-120°$; and at $250°-300°$, one mol. of water is retained, and accordingly A. Rosenheim gave the formula $8BaO.4V_2O_5.16WO_3.9H_2O.44$Aq. C. Friedheim and E. Löwy said that the salt is $6BaO.3V_2O_5.12H_2O.34$(or 39)H_2O. A. Rosenheim obtained garnet-red octahedral crystals of **barium hexavanadatododecatungstate,** $4BaO.3V_2O_5.12WO_3.30H_2O$, in the preparation of the preceding salt from vanadium pentoxide and a boiling soln. of barium paratungstate. C. Friedheim obtained it by treating barium metatungstate with an acetic acid soln. of acid potassium vanadate. C. Friedheim obtained a purple-red barium salt of the same composition by adding insufficient dil. sulphuric acid to precipitate all the barium from a mixture of 4 mols of barium metatungstate and a mol of barium metavanadate suspended in water. A. Rosenheim reported that the crystals obtained by evaporating the clear liquor correspond with a mixture of barium vanadate BaV_8O_{21}, and tungstate, BaW_4O_{13}. A. Rosenheim also obtained a mixture from the liquid obtained by boiling barium paratungstate and ammonium metavanadate. O. W. Gibbs boiled a mixture of barium metatungstate and metavanadate and obtained deep red, quadratic plates mixed with crystals of ammonium metavanadate and tungstic acid.

C. Friedheim and E. Löwy treated sodium hexavanadatohexatungstate with calcium chloride and obtained yellow **calcium vanadatotungstate,** $2CaO.V_2O_5.2WO_3.12H_2O$. F. Rothenbach reported orange-yellow **barium vanadatotungstate,** $2Ba_2V_{10}O_{27}.3Ba_5W_{12}O_{41}$. $94H_2O$, to be formed from eq. soln. of sodium hexavanadatododecatungstate and barium chloride; orange-red cubes of **strontium vanadatotungstate,** $2Sr_2V_{10}O_{27}.3Sr_5W_{12}O_{41}.122H_2O$, were made in a similar way with strontium chloride; with magnesium sulphate, pale orange-yellow prismatic crystals of **sodium magnesium vanadatotungstate,** $Na_2MgV_6O_{17}$. $Na_{10}W_{12}O_{41}$; and with aluminium sulphate, dark garnet-red crystals of **sodium aluminium-vanadatotungstate,** $4Al_2V_{18}O_{48}.3Na_{13}Al_2W_{48}O_{156}.504H_2O$, were reported to be formed.

According to J. J. Berzelius,[5] uranium salts give a lemon-yellow precipitate of **uranium metavanadate** with alkali metavanadates, and of **uranium tetravanadate** with alkali tetravanadates. J. Antipoff reported a mineral from Ferghana, Turkestan, which was called **ferghanite.** Its analysis corresponded with **uranyl metavanadate,** $UO_2(VO_3)_2.6H_2O$. The mineral is biaxial with large optic axial angles; there is no pleochroism. The sp. gr. is 3·31; the hardness 2; the double refraction and index of refraction are small; and the radioactivity is 8 when that of uranium oxide is unity. F. L. Hess and W. T. Schaller found a brownish-yellow powder disseminated in the sandstone of Temple Rock, Utah. The mineral resembles carnotite and it was called **uranite.** The analysis agrees with $2UO_2.3V_2O_5.15H_2O$, or **uranyl deuterohexavanadate,** $(UO_2)_2V_6O_{17}.15H_2O$. The minute crystalline particles have a high birefringence. The mineral is not soluble in water, but it dissolves quickly in a soln. of ammonium carbonate.

C. Friedel and E. Cumenge[6] reported a mineral from Montrose Co., Colorado, which they called **carnotite**—after A. Carnot. Analyses by W. F. Hillebrand and

F. L. Ransome are indicated in Table II; other analyses were reported by C. Friedel and E. Cumenge, T. Crook and G. S. Blake, E. F. Wherry, W. F. Hillebrand, F. L. Hess, A. Schoep and E. Richet, A. Schoep, G. Canneri and V. Pestelli,

TABLE II.—ANALYSES OF COLORADO CARNOTITES.

Li_2O . .	trace	—	—	trace	—	—
Na_2O . .	0·14	0·09	0·07	0·13	0·02	0·01
K_2O . .	6·52	6·73	6·57	5·46	5·11	1·51
MgO . .	0·22	0·20	0·24	0·14	0·17	0·07
CaO . .	3·34	2·85	2·57	1·86	1·85	1·64
CuO . .	0·15	0·20	0·22	trace		trace
SrO . .	0·02	—	—	trace	trace	—
BaO . .	0·90	0·72	0·65	2·83	3·21	0·29
PbO . .	0·13	0·25	0·18	0·07	—	0·09
Al_2O_3 . .	0·09	—	0·08	0·29	—	0·08
Fe_2O_3 . .	0·21	1·77	0·72	0·42	3·36	0·25
CO_2 . .	0·56	0·33	—	—	—	—
SiO_2 . .	0·15	0·08	0·13	0·20	—	0·07
TiO_2 . .	0·03	0·10	—	—	—	0·08
P_2O_5 . .	0·80	0·35	0·40	0·05	trace	—
As_2O_5 . .	trace	0·25	—	—	—	—
V_2O_5 . .	18·49	18·35	15·76	18·05	17·50	7·20
SO_3 . .	—	0·12	0·18	—	—	—
MoO_3 . .	0·18	0·23	0·18	0·05	—	0·04
UO_3 . .	54·89	52·25	47·42	54·00	52·28	20·51
H_2O at 105°	2·43	2·59	1·85	3·16	4·52	1·85
H_2O at 350° .	2·11	3·06	2·79	2·21	3·49	1·64
H_2O over 350° .	—	—	—	—	—	0·19
Insoluble . .	7·10	8·34	19·00	10·33	—	—

P. Jannasch and H. F. Harwood, and E. Gleditsch. C. Friedel and E. Cumenge represented the analyses by the formula $K_2O.2UO_3.V_2O_5.3H_2O$, that is, **potassium diuranyl orthovanadate**, $K(UO_2)VO_4.1\frac{1}{2}H_2O$; and G. Canneri and V. Pestelli regarded it as a salt of **uranylvanadic acid** :

$$\left[V \begin{array}{c} UO_3 \\ O_3 \end{array}\right]H$$

E. Gleditsch found 0·03 per cent. of lithium and 0·15 per cent. of copper. W. F. Hillebrand believed that no definite representative formula can be assigned to carnotite, because it is a mixture of minerals. T. Crook and G. S. Blake, however, regard it as a definite mineral species. Some regarded the crystals of the lemon-yellow mineral as hexagonal. T. Crook and G. S. Blake suppose it to be rhombic. The optical character is negative ; the optical axial angle $2E=c.$ 90°. Pleochroism can be observed. E. S. Larsen gave for the indices of refraction $a=1·750$, $\beta=1·925$, and $\gamma=1·950°$. R. J. Strutt observed in the carnotite from Montrose $5·27×10^{-7}$ per cent. of radium bromide, 2·98 per cent. U_3O_8, and 0·01 c.c. of helium per gram. Observations on the radioactivity were made by B. B. Boltwood, E. Gleditsch, W. Marckwald and A. S. Russell, E. P. Adams, S. C. Lind and C. F. Whittemore, H. M. Plum, H. Schlundt, and A. G. Loomis and H. Schlundt. E. E. Fairbanks found the dielectric constant to be 9·3. The mineral is soluble in nitric acid. G. Canneri and V. Pestelli prepared **potassium uranylvanadate**, or *potassium-carnotite*, $K[V(UO_3)O_3]$, by adding uranic anhydride in the form of ammonium pyrouranate, to fused potassium metavanadate. The microscopic, rectangular, fluorescent plates belong to the rhombic system. The salts resemble the corresponding uranylphosphates. Unlike the vanadates, these artificial carnotites do not alter in colour when treated with acids. The analogous **sodium uranylvanadate**, $Na[V(UO_3)O_3]$, or *sodium-carnotite*, was similarly prepared.

K. A. Nenadkewitsch reported a *calcium-carnotite* from Tyuya-Muyun, Fergana, Turkestan, and he called it **tyuyamunite** or *tjuiamunite*. The analysis was (Ca,Sr)O, 5·99 per cent.; UO_3, 63·09; V_2O_5, 21·00; and H_2O, 7·04. E. Y. Rode also analyzed the mineral. A trace of thallium was also present. W. F. Hillebrand observed a similar mineral from Paradox Valley, Colorado. It is a hydrated **calcium diuranyl orthovanadate**—a kind of calcium carnotite. When treated with potassium mercuric iodide, as a separating liquid, the calcium is displaced by potassium and ordinary carnotite is formed; and F. L. Hess represented it by the formula $CaO.2UO_3.V_2O_5.9H_2O$. V. V. Dolivo-Dobrovolsky gave $a:b:c=1·303:1:2·337$ for the axial ratios of the rhombic crystals; the optic axial angle $2V = 48°$; the optical character is negative. F. L. Hess gave for the optical axial angle $2V=48°$; and W. F. Hillebrand, $2V=45°-51°$, and the indices of refraction $a=1·965-1·968$; $\beta=1·927-1·932$; while F. L. Hess gave $a=1·72$, $\beta=1·868$, and $\gamma=1·953$, and E. S. Larsen, $a=1·670$, $\beta=1·870$, and $\gamma=1·895$. The optical character is negative, and the pleochroism a, nearly colourless; β, canary-yellow; and γ, dark canary-yellow. P. Tschirwinsky found the hardness$=4$, and the sp. gr. 4·46. The mineral is radioactive. E. Y. Rode showed that the water makes the mineral of a zeolitic character. It is easily soluble in acids. The purple-red mineral **rauvite** was found by F. L. Hess and W. T. Schaller to have the composition $CaO.2UO_3.6V_2O_5.20H_2O$. The index of refraction is 1·88.

REFERENCES.

[1] O. W. Gibbs, *Proc. Amer. Acad.*, 2169, 1885; *Amer. Chem. Journ.*, 7. 209, 1885; A. Frenzel, *Neues Jahrb. Min.*, 514, 1872; 680, 1875; *Journ. prakt. Chem.*, (2), 4. 227, 361, 1871; M. Websky, *Tschermak's Mitt.*, (1), 2. 245, 1872; W. T. Schaller, *Bull. U.S. Geol. Sur.*, 610, 1916; *Journ. Amer. Chem. Soc.*, 33. 162, 1911; E. V. Shannon, *Proc. Nat. Museum U.S.A.*, 62. 9, 1923; G. Cesaro, *Bull. Acad. Belg.*, 142, 1905; E. Zintl and L. Vanino, *German Pat.*, *D.R.P.* 422947, 1924.

[2] A. Carnot, *Compt. Rend.*, 104. 1850, 1887; 105. 119, 1887; A. Ditte, *ib.*, 102. 1019, 1105, 1886; B. Glasmann, *Ueber die Trennung von Chrom und Vanadin und über Chromvanadate*, Bern, 1904.

[3] H. von Euler-Chelpin, *Ueber die Einwirkung von Molybdäntrioxyd und Paramolybdaten auf normal Vanadate, und eine neue Bestimmungsmethode von Vanadinpentoxyd und Molybdäntrioxyd neben einander*, Berlin, 1895; L. Milch, *Beiträge zur Kenntniss des Vanadins und Molybdän*, Berlin, 1887; M. Liebert, *Beiträge zur Kenntniss der sogenannten Vanadinmolybdänsäure*, Halle a. S., 1891; C. Friedheim and M. Liebert, *Ber.*, 24. 1173, 1891; C. Friedheim and C. Castendyck, *ib.*, 33. 1611, 1900; C. Castendyck, *Ueber Ammoniumsilicovanadinmolybdate, eine neue Klasse von chemischen Verbindungen*, Bern, 1900; O. W. Gibbs, *Amer. Chem. Journ.*, 5. 374, 1884; *Proc. Amer. Acad.*, 18. 232, 1883; A. Ditte, *Compt. Rend.*, 102. 757, 1886; F. Toggenburg, *Ueber Phosphorvanadinmolybdate*, Bern, 1902; H. Jacoby, *Ueber Phosphorvanadiummolybdate*, Bern, 1905; A. Isenburg, *Beiträge zur Kenntnis der Vanadinmolybdate*, Bern, 1901; H. Stamm, *Ueber Phosphorvanadinmolybdate*, Bern, 1905; J. J. Berzelius, *Acad. Handl. Stockholm*, 1, 1831; *Schweigger's Journ.*, 62. 323, 1831; 63. 26, 1831; *Pogg. Ann.*, 22. 1, 1831; *Ann. Chim. Phys.*, (1), 47. 337, 1831; *Phil. Mag.*, (2), 10. 321, 1831; (2), 11. 7, 1832; G. Canneri, *Gazz. Chim. Ital.*, 53. ii, 779, 1923; 55. ii, 390, 1925; W. Prandtl, *Zeit. anorg. Chem.*, 79. 97, 1912; A. Miolati and R. Pizzighelli, *Journ. prakt. Chem.*, (2), 77. 417, 1908; A. Rosenheim and J. Pinsker, *Zeit. anorg. Chem.*, 70. 73, 1911; A. Rosenheim and F. Kohn, *ib.*, 69. 247, 1911; A. Rosenheim, *ib.*, 70. 418, 1911; A. Rosenheim and J. Jaenicke, *ib.*, 77. 239, 1912.

[4] J. J. Berzelius, *Acad. Handl. Stockholm*, 1, 1831; *Schweigger's Journ.*, 62. 323, 1831; 63. 26, 1831; *Pogg. Ann.*, 22. 1, 1831; *Ann. Chim. Phys.*, (1), 47. 337, 1831; *Phil. Mag.*, (2), 10. 321, 1831; (2), 11. 7, 1832; C. F. Rammelsberg, *Ber.*, 1. 161, 1868; O. W. Gibbs, *Amer. Chem. Journ.*, 5. 380, 1884; *Proc. Amer. Acad.*, 18. 232, 1883; F. Rothenbach, *Ueber die Doppelsalze der Vanadin- und Wolframsäure*, Berlin, 1892; *Ber.*, 23. 3051, 1890; C. Friedheim, *ib.*, 23. 1505, 1890; *Zeit. anorg. Chem.*, 6. 287, 1894; C. Friedheim and E. Löwy, *ib.*, 6. 13, 1894; E. Löwy, *Ueber die Einwirkung der Parawolframate des Natriums, Kaliums und Ammoniums auf die entspechenden normalen Vanadate. Ein Beitrag zur Kenntnis der Doppelsalze der Vanadinsäure und Wolframsäure*, Hamburg, 1893; A. Rosenheim, *Ueber Vanadinwolframsäure. Ein Beitrag zur Kenntnis der complexen anorganischen Säuren*, Berlin, 1888; *Liebig's Ann.*, 251. 197, 1889; F. Rodolico, *Atti Accad. Lincei*, (6), 4. 471, 1926; A. Rosenheim and M. Pieck, *Zeit. anorg. Chem.*, 98, 223, 1916; W. Prandtl, *ib.*, 92. 198, 1915; A. Ditte, *Compt. Rend.*, 102. 1019, 1886; A. Rogers and E. F. Smith, *Journ. Amer. Chem. Soc.*, 25. 1224, 1903; A. Rogers, *ib.*, 25. 300, 1903.

[5] J. J. Berzelius, *Acad. Handl. Stockholm*, 1, 1831; *Schweigger's Journ.*, 62. 323, 1831;

63. 26. 1831; *Pogg. Ann.*, **22.** 1, 1831; *Ann. Chim. Phys.*, (1), **47.** 337, 1831; *Phil. Mag.*, (2), **10.** 321, 1831; (2), **11.** 7, 1832; J. Antipoff, *Berg. Journ.*, **4.** 255, 1908; F. L. Hess and W. T. Schaller, *Journ. Washington Acad.*, **4.** 576, 1914.

⁶ W. F. Hillebrand and F. L. Ransome, *Amer. Journ. Science*, (4), **10.** 138, 1900; W. F. Hillebrand, *ib.*, (4), **10.** 120, 1900; (4), **35.** 439, 1913; (5), **8.** 201, 1924; E. P. Adams, *ib.*, (4), **19.** 321, 1905; F. T. Wherry, *ib.*, (4), **33.** 575, 1912; B. B. Boltwood, *ib.*, (4), **18.** 97, 1904; T. Crook and G. S. Blake, *Min. Mag.*, **15.** 171, 1910; A. Schoep and E. Richet, *Bull. Soc. Géol. Belg.*, **32.** 85, 150, 340, 1923; P. Jannasch and H. F. Harwood, *Journ. prakt. Chem.*, (2), **80.** 134, 1909; G. Canneri and V. Pestelli, *Gazz. Chim. Ital.*, **54.** 641, 1924; F. L. Hess, *Eng. Min. Journ.*, **114.** 272, 1922; *Bull. U.S. Geol. Sur.*, 750, 1924; H. S. Galen, *ib.*, 315, 1907; E. S. Larsen, *ib.*, 679, 1921; W. T. Schaller, *ib.*, 750, 1924; F. L. Hess and W. F. Foshag, *Amer. Min.*, **11.** 66, 1926; *Proc. U.S. Nat. Museum*, **71.** 21, 1927; **72.** 12, 1927; F. L. Hess, *Eng. Min. Journ.*, **114.** 272, 1922; *Bull. U.S. Geol. Sur.*, 750, 1924; *Proc. U.S. Nat. Museum*, **71.** 21, 1927; F. L. Hess and W. T. Schaller, *Journ. Washington Acad.*, **4.** 576, 1914; E. Gleditsch, *Compt. Rend.*, **146.** 331, 1908; C. Friedel and E. Cumenge, *ib.*, **128.** 532, 1899; *Bull. Soc. Min.*, **22.** 26, 1899; *Bull. Soc. Chim.*, (4), **21.** 328, 1899; A. G. Loomis and H. Schlundt, *Journ. Ind. Eng. Chem.*, **8.** 990, 1916; H. Schlundt, *Journ. Phys. Chem.*, **20.** 485, 1916; R. J. Strutt, *Proc. Roy. Soc.*, **76.** 81, 1905; *Chem. News*, **91.** 299, 1906; W. Marckwald and A. S. Russell, *Ber.*, **44.** 771, 1911; K. A. Nenadkewitsch, *Bull. Acad. St. Petersburg*, (6), **6.** 945, 1912; P. Tschirwinsky, *ib.*, (6), **6.** 505, 1922; *Min. Mag.*, **20.** 287, 1925; S. C. Lind and C. F. Whittemore, *Journ. Amer. Chem. Soc.*, **36.** 2066, 1914; H. M. Plum, *ib.*, **37.** 1797, 1915; A. Schoep, *Bull. Soc. Géol. Belg.*, **33.** 85, 1923; V. V. Dolivo-Dobrovolsky, *Proc. Russ. Min. Soc.*, (2), **54.** 359, 1925; E. Y. Rode, *ib.*, (2), **54.** 377, 1925; E. E. Fairbanks, *Econ. Geol.*, **21.** 399, 1926.

§ 15. The Vanadates of the Manganese and Iron Families

A. Ditte[1] prepared brown needles of **manganese pyrovanadate,** $Mn_2V_2O_7$, by melting vanadium pentoxide with a mixture of equal parts of sodium and manganous bromides, and washing the cold product with water. It is decomposed by nitric acid with the separation of manganic oxide. A. Scheuer obtained reddish-brown six-sided plates of **manganese metavanadate,** $Mn(VO_3)_2$, by adding manganese sulphate to a soln. of ammonium metavanadate, and boiling the mixture for a long time. J. J. Berzelius obtained a hydrated form—presumably the *tetrahydrate*—by treating a mixed soln. of ammonium metavanadate and manganous chloride with alcohol, washing the precipitate in alcohol, dissolving it in water, and allowing the soln. to evaporate spontaneously. C. Radau obtained a reddish-brown precipitate of the tetrahydrate by mixing a soln. of potassium metavanadate in 250 c.c. of water with 20 grms. of manganese sulphate in 250 c.c. of water. The washed and dried product consists of microscopic needles. It loses 15·59 per cent. of water at 120°; 20·71 per cent. at 200°; and all is lost by fusing the salt. The tetrahydrate is sparingly soluble in cold water, but feebly soluble in hot water and in acids. F. Ephraim and G. Beck made **manganese deuterohexavanadate,** $2MnO.3V_2O_5.11H_2O$, by the action of the barium salt on manganese sulphate. The dehydrated salt forms a *dodecammine* with ammonia, and this passes to the *hexammine* at 130°, and the *diammine* at 240°. A series of **potassium manganese metavanadates** was prepared by C. Radau. Thus, $K_2Mn_7(VO_3)_{16}.25H_2O$, is produced when a soln. of 20 grms. of potassium metavanadate in 100 c.c. of water is mixed with 20 grms. of manganese sulphate in the same quantity of water; and when the aq. soln. of the precipitate is evaporated spontaneously, dark brown crystals with the composition $K_2Mn_{11}(VO_3)_{14}.48H_2O$ are formed. By evaporating the mother-liquor obtained in the preparation of manganese tetrahydrated metavanadate, C. Radau obtained crystals with the composition $2K_3VO_4$. $3Mn_3V_8O_{23}.27H_2O$. A mixture of potassium triterodecavanadate and manganese sulphate gives a salt $6K_2O.15MnO.35V_2O_5.98H_2O$. Ochre-yellow crystals of *pentadecahydrated* **potassium manganese triterodecavanadate,** $K_2Mn_2V_{10}O_{28}.15H_2O$, were obtained by mixing a soln. of 11·5 grms. of potassium triterodecavanadate in 100 c.c. of water with 5 grms. of manganese sulphate in the same amount of water. The *hexadecahydrate* was produced by mixing boiling soln. of 20 grms. of potassium metavanadate and 10 grms. of manganese sulphate each in 100 c.c. of water, and gradually adding 58 c.c. of 30 per cent. acetic acid. On crystallizing the filtered soln., red, triclinic crystals were obtained with the axial ratios $a : b : c = 0.7952 : 1 : 0.9678$, and $a = 114° 22'$; $\beta = 109° 35'$; and $\gamma = 74° 54'$. 100 c.c. of cold water at 18° dissolve only 1·7 grms. of the salt ; more is dissolved by hot water ; and the salt is freely soluble in acids. A mixture of potassium tetravanadate and manganese sulphate yields **potassium manganese penterotetradecavanadate,** $K_2Mn_3V_{14}O_{39}.21\frac{1}{2}H_2O$. G. Flink found a mineral at Langban, Sweden, which he called **pyrobelonite** —$\pi\hat{v}\rho$, fire, and $\beta\epsilon\lambda\acute{o}\nu\eta$, a needle—in allusion to the red, acicular crystals, which are really rhombic prisms with the axial ratios $a : b : c = 0.80402 : 1 : 0.65091$. The analysis corresponds with **lead manganese tetravanadate,** $Mn_7Pb_4V_4O_{21}.3H_2O$. The sp. gr. is 5·377 ; and the hardness 3·5.

J. J. Berzelius obtained a dark greenish-brown precipitate of **ferrous metavana-date,** by treating ferrous salts with potassium metavanadate ; it is soluble in hydrochloric acid, forming a green soln. Potassium tetravanadate under similar conditions furnishes green **ferrous tetravanadate,** which in 24 hrs. becomes yellow and crystalline. J. J. Berzelius also obtained **ferric metavanadate** as a straw-yellow precipitate slightly soluble in water by treating ferric sulphate with potassium metavanadate ; and straw-yellow **ferric tetravanadate** from potassium tetravanadate and ferric sulphate. J. J. Berzelius obtained straw-yellow, insoluble **cobalt metavanadate** from a soln. of cobalt nitrate and ammonium metavanadate. A. Carnot, and C. Radau also made a similar observation. J. A. Hedvall prepared green cobalt metavanadate, by heating mixtures of vanadium pentoxide and cobalt oxide. A. Ditte warmed a mixture of ammonium metavanadate with an excess of cobalt nitrate feebly acidified with nitric acid, and obtained garnet-red, rhombic prisms of the *hydrate* $Co(VO_3)_2.H_2O$. A. Carnot obtained this salt, $Co(VO_3)_2$, by treating an ammoniacal soln. of a cobalt salt with ammonium metavanadate. It absorbs oxygen from air and becomes brownish-red. J. J. Berzelius found that a soln. of a cobalt salt and an alkali tetravanadate gives a yellow precipitate of **cobalt tetravanadate** when treated with alcohol. The product is soluble in water. F. Ephraim and G. Beck obtained **cobalt deuterohexavanadate,** $2CoO.3V_2O_5.15H_2O$, by the action of cobalt sulphate on the barium salt. The compound dehydrated at 220° absorbs a small proportion of ammonia. A. Carnot obtained orange-yellow **cobaltic pentamminotriterodecavanadate,** $Co_2V_{10}O_{28}.5NH_3.9H_2O$, from a dil. acetic acid soln. of the cobaltammine and ammonium metavanadate ; when heated, it forms **cobalt teterodecavanadate,** $Co_2V_{10}O_{27}$. C. Radau prepared **potassium cobalt triterodecavanadate,** $K_2O.2CoO.5V_2O_5.16$(or $16\frac{1}{2}$)H_2O, from a soln. of potassium metavanadate and cobalt sulphate ; from a soln. of potassium triterodecavanadate and cobalt sulphate ; and from a soln. of potassium tetravanadate and cobalt sulphate. The reddish-yellow crystals belong to the triclinic system and have the axial ratios $a : b : c = 0.7861 : 1 : 0.9679$; and $a = 114° 49'$; $\beta = 109° 20'$; and $\gamma = 75° 5'$. 100 parts of water at 17·5° dissolve 0·48 part of the salt. C. Radau also prepared yellowish-brown acicular crystals of **potassium cobalt tetrerotetradecavanadate,** $K_2O.3CoO.7V_2O_5.21H_2O$, from a soln. of 20 grms. of potassium metavanadate in 400 c.c. of water and 18 grms. of cobalt sulphate in 250 c.c. of water by evaporation over a water-bath.

W. Vernadsky obtained a green or brown radioactive mineral from the Tyuya-Muyun mine, Fergana, which he called **kolovratite**—after L. C. Kolovrat. Analyses show 6·5–12·22 per cent. NiO ; and 6·20–11·55 per cent. V_2O_5. It was also mentioned by D. I. Shcherbakoff, S. P. Aleksandroff, and I. Kurbatoff. A. Ditte fused a mixture of vanadium pentoxide and nickel bromide with a large excess of potassium bromide, and obtained green, prismatic crystals of **nickel orthovanadate,** $Ni_3(VO_4)_2$. G. Tammann gave 515° for the temp. of formation. A. Ditte said that the salt does not melt at a red-heat, and is insoluble in nitric acid. J. J. Berzelius evaporated an aq. soln. of a nickel salt and alkali metavanadate and obtained a yellow, crystalline mass of **nickel metavanadate,** soluble in water and precipitated by alcohol from its aq. soln. A. Ditte obtained the metavanadate, $Ni(VO_3)_2$, in small, greenish-yellow prisms, by heating for a long time a soln. of ammonium metavanadate and nickel nitrate feebly acidified with nitric acid. J. J. Berzelius obtained yellow crystals of **nickel tetravanadate** by evaporating a soln. of alkali tetravanadate and a nickel salt. The salt is soluble in water, and is precipitated from its aq. soln. by alcohol. A. Ditte prepared the greenish-brown crystals of **nickel deuterotetravanadate**, $NiV_4O_{11}.3H_2O$, by evaporating the mother-liquor obtained in preparing the metavanadate. F. Ephraim and G. Beck prepared **nickel triterodecavanadate**, $3NiO.5V_2O_5.24H_2O$, by treating barium deutero-hexavanadate with nickel sulphate. The dehydrated salt forms a *dodecammine* at 108°; a *hexammine* at 160°; a *tetrammine* at 198°; and a *decammine* at 214°. C. Radau prepared greenish-yellow crystals of potassium **nickel dodecameta-vanadate**, $K_2Ni_5(VO_3)_{12}.27H_2O$, by mixing, at ordinary temp., soln. of 20 grms. of potassium metavanadate in 100 c.c. of water with 19 grms. of nickel sulphate; straw-yellow, acicular crystals of **potassium nickel deuterodecavanadate**, $K_2Ni_3V_{10}O_{29}.17H_2O$, from a soln. of 20 grms. of potassium metavanadate in 100 c.c. of water mixed with 20 grms. of nickel sulphate in 150 c.c. of water; greenish-yellow crystals of **potassium nickel triterodecavanadate**, $K_2Ni_2V_{10}O_{28}.16\frac{1}{2}H_2O$, from a boiling soln. of 920 grms. each of potassium metavanadate and nickel sulphate in 400 c.c. of water, and mixed with 80 c.c. of 25 per cent. acetic acid; and **potassium nickel penteroheptadecavanadate**, $K_2O.N_2O.7V_2O_5.23H_2O$, from a soln. of the preceding salt mixed with a nickel salt soln.; 100 parts of water at 17·5° dissolve 0·17 part of salt.

REFERENCES.

[1] J. J. Berzelius, *Acad. Handl. Stockholm*, 1, 1831; *Schweigger's Journ.*, **62**. 323, 1831; **63**. 26, 1831; *Pogg. Ann.*, **22**. 1, 1831; *Ann. Chim. Phys.*, (1), **47**. 337, 1831; *Phil. Mag.*, (2), **10**. 321, 1831; (2), **11**. 7, 1832; A. Ditte, *Compt. Rend.*, **96**. 1050, 1883; **104**. 1705, 1887; A. Carnot, *ib.*, **109**. 148, 1889; A. Scheuer, *Zeit. anorg. Chem.*, **16**. 304, 1898; *Ueber Uebervanadinsaure Salze*, Würzberg, 1897; C. Radau, *Beiträge zur Kenntniss vanadinsauer Salze*, Königsberg, 26, 1888; *Liebig's Ann.*, **251**. 114, 1889; G. Flink, *Geol. För. Förh. Stockholm*, **41**. 433, 1919; *Neues Jahrb. Min.*, i, 35, 1922; F. Ephraim and G. Beck, *Helvetica Chim. Acta.*, **9**. 38, 1926; J. A. Hedvall, *Zeit. anorg. Chem.*, **93**. 313, 1915; G. Tammann, *ib.*, **149**. 68, 1925; **160**. 101, 1927; I. Kurbatoff, *Centr. Min.*, 345, 1926; V. Vernadsky, *Compt. Rend. Acad. Russ.*, **37**, 1922; D. I. Shcherbakoff, *ib.*, 46, 1924; S. P. Aleksandroff, *Gornyi Zhurnal Moscow*, **100**. 1, 1924.

§ 16. The Hypovanadatovanadates

A series of mixed hypovanadates and vanadates have been reported and they have been called **vanadylvanadates, vanadicovanadates,** and **hypovanadatovana-dates.** J. J. Berzelius [1] noticed that when a soln. of hydrated vanadium tetroxide and ammonium carbonate is exposed to air in a tall narrow cylinder, dark green crystals collect at the bottom of the vessel. J. T. Brierley prepared **ammonium dihypovanadatotetravanadate**, $(NH_4)_2O.2V_2O_4.2V_2O_5.14H_2O$, by dissolving vanadium pentoxide in aq. ammonia, reducing two-thirds of the soln. with sulphur dioxide; mixing both fractions; making the liquid slightly alkaline with ammonia; acidifying with acetic acid, and adding alcohol. The dark green, crystalline precipitate is unstable. If ammonium chloride be added instead of acetic acid, and the liquid boiled for a long time, dark violet crystals of **ammonium dihypovana-datoctovanadate**, $3(NH_4)_2O.2V_2O_4.4V_2O_5.6H_2O$, are formed. O. W. Gibbs reported a green, crystalline powder of **ammonium hypovanadatoctovanadate**, $(NH_4)_2O.V_2O_4.4V_2O_5.8H_2O$, from a soln. of a vanadyl salt and ammonium metavanadate.

W. Prandtl melted 50 grms. of vanadium pentoxide, 6 grms. of sodium carbonate, and about one c.c. of syrupy phosphoric acid in a platinum crucible. Spitting occurs as the mass cools, and oxygen is given off; when the product is boiled with ammoniacal water, dark steel-blue, rhombic, pleochroic needles of **sodium hypovana-datodecavanadate**, $Na_2O.V_2O_4.5V_2O_5$, appear. The salt is insoluble in water; is

not changed by hot or cold nitric acid; ammoniacal hydrogen dioxide slowly oxidizes it to a vanadate; and conc. sulphuric acid forms a yellowish-brown soln. which is green when diluted. The salt melts at about 800° and absorbs oxygen from the air. With potassium carbonate under similar conditions, W. Prandtl prepared potassium hypovanadatodecavanadate, $K_2O.V_2O_4.8V_2O_5$. J. T. Brierley prepared **sodium dihypovanadatodivanadate,** $2Na_2O.2V_2O_4.V_2O_5.13H_2O$, in aggregates of microscopic, hexagonal prisms, by treating 12 grms. of vanadium pentoxide with an excess of a sat. soln. of sulphur dioxide, and, after adding a little sulphuric acid and boiling the liquid to drive off the excess of sulphur dioxide, mixing the hot blue liquid with a soln. of 6 grms. of vanadium pentoxide in soda-lye, and adding enough alkali to make the liquid alkaline. After standing a few days the soln. is acidified with acetic acid, mixed with a cold sat. soln. of sodium acetate, and the crystals washed first with a soln. of sodium acetate and then with alcohol. The salt is freely soluble in water, but not in a conc. soln. of alkali acetate. G. Canneri also obtained the sodium salts: $Na_2O : V_2O_4 : V_2O_5 = 1:1:5$; $1:1:4$; $2:1:4$; $3:1:5$; and $1:1:1$. J. T. Brierley obtained **potassium dihypovanadatovanadate,** $2K_2O.2V_2O_4.V_2O_5.6H_2O$, by working with potash-lye under similar conditions. The potassium salt is accompanied by dark violet octahedra of **potassium dihypovanadatoctovanadate,** $5K_2O.2V_2O_4.V_2O_5.H_2O$, and the same salt is obtained by boiling the mother-liquor from the sodium salt with potassium acetate. G. Canneri also prepared the potassium salts: $K_2O : V_2O_4 : V_2O_5 = 1:1:5$; $2:1:4$; and $1:1:1$.

O. W. Gibbs reported dark green crystals of **copper hypovanadatovanadate** to be formed by mixing a hydrochloric acid soln. of vanadyl chloride with a soln. of copper sulphate and sodium tetravanadate; and **silver hypovanadatovanadate,** $6Ag_2O.3VO_2.2V_2O_5.12WO_3.8H_2O$, by treating the corresponding ammonium salt with silver nitrate. W. T. Schaller described a dull green, massive, cryptocrystalline mineral from Minasraga, Peru, which he called **fernandinite**—after E. E. Fernandini. It rarely occurs in rectangular plates. The analysis corresponds with **calcium hypovanadatodecavanadate,** $CaO.V_2O_4.5V_2O_5.14H_2O$, or it can be regarded as a metavanadate, $H_4Ca(VO)_2(VO_3)_{10}.12H_2O$. W. T. Schaller described it as cryptocrystalline. The mineral is non-pleochroic, and the birefringence is medium. E. S. Larsen gave 2·05 for the index of refraction. It is sufficiently soluble in cold water to give a yellow soln., and it forms a green soln. with acids. W. Lindgren and co-workers described **melanovanadite** as a black mineral from Mina Ragra, Pasco, Peru. The analysis corresponds with $2CaO.2V_2O_4.3V_2O_5.nH_2O$. The monoclinic crystals have the axial ratios $a:b:c = 0.4737:1:0.5815$, and $\beta = 83° 37\frac{1}{2}'$. The sp. gr. is 3·477 at 20°; the hardness 2·5; the index of refraction $a = 1.74$; and the birefringence is strong. The pleochroism $a =$ dark yellowish-brown, β and $\gamma =$ dark reddish-brown.

O. W. Gibbs reported **ammonium dihypovanadato-divanadatoctocosimolybdate,** $11(NH_4)_2O.$ $2V_2O_4.V_2O_5.28MoO_3.20H_2O$, to be formed in greenish-yellow crystals by heating ammonium tetravanadate with an excess of a sat. soln. of ammonium paramolybdate, and evaporating the soln. The salt can be purified by recrystallization. When the soln. is treated with barium chloride, a precipitate of **barium hypovanadatovanadatomolybdate**—to which the formula $4BaO.3VO_2.2V_2O_5.30MoO_3.48H_2O$ has been assigned—is formed as a sparingly soluble, crystalline powder. An orange-yellow, crystalline precipitate is produced when the salt is boiled with silver nitrate; and with mercurous nitrate a crystalline precipitate of **mercurous hypovanadato-vanadatotungstate** is produced. O. W. Gibbs also obtained **ammonium hypovanadato-vanadatotungstate**—possibly $6(NH_4)_2O.3VO_2.2V_2O_5.12WO_3.12H_2O$ was assigned; **potassium hypovanadato-vanadatotungstate,** $6K_2O.3VO_2.2V_2O_5.12WO_3.nH_2O$; and **sodium hypovanadato-vanadatotungstate,** $6Na_2O.3VO_2.2V_2O_5.12WO_3.43H_2O$; when the soln. is treated with mercurous nitrate, **mercurous hypovanadato-vanadatotungstate** is formed.

REFERENCES.

[1] J. J. Berzelius, *Acad. Handl. Stockholm*, 1, 1831; *Schweigger's Journ.*, **62.** 323, 1831; **63.** 26, 1831; *Pogg. Ann.*, **22.** 1, 1831; *Ann. Chim. Phys.*, (1), **47.** 337, 1831; *Phil. Mag.*, (2), **10.** 321, 1831; (2), **11.** 7, 1832; O. W. Gibbs, *Proc. Amer. Acad.*, **21.** 50, 1886; *Amer. Chem. Journ.,*

5. 402, 1884 ; 7. 209, 1885 ; J. T. Brierley, *Journ. Chem. Soc.*, 49. 30, 822, 1886 ; W. Prandtl, *Ber.*, 38. 659, 1905 ; W. T. Schaller, *Journ. Washington Acad.*, 5. 7, 1915 ; E. S. Larsen, *Bull. U.S. Geol. Sur.*, 679, 1921 ; G. Canneri, *Gazz. Chim. Ital.*, 58. 6, 1928.

§ 17. Pervanadic Acid and the Pervanadates

L. C. A. Barreswil [1] observed that an acid soln. of ammonium metavanadate is coloured deep red by hydrogen dioxide, and the coloration is more stable than that produced with chromic acid. According to G. Werther, in the presence of ether, 0·000225 part of vanadium pentoxide produces a red colour, and 0·000012 part a pale rose-pink. The ethereal layer remains uncoloured. An excess of hydrogen dioxide decolorizes the red soln. produced when an acid is added to a mixture of hydrogen dioxide and an alkali vanadate. A. Scheuer evaporated a soln. of vanadium pentoxide in hydrogen dioxide in vacuo, and obtained a yellow crust of a **pervanadic acid,** which was not analyzed. It forms a red soln. with water ; and when treated with hydrochloric acid, it forms oxygen and chlorine. V. Auger said that pervanadic acid, like perchromic acid, catalytically decomposes hydrogen dioxide, at the same time, the pervanadic acid is reduced to a vanadyl salt, and this reaction becomes more rapid and more complete in the presence of an acid. Vanadyl salts, however, unlike chromium salts, are immediately oxidized to pervanadic acid in the presence of hydrogen dioxide, so that in the course of time the whole of the hydrogen dioxide introduced into an acid soln. of vanadic acid is completely destroyed and the reduction of the vanadic acid is more or less marked, according to the H˙-ion content of the soln. As shown by J. B. Cammerer, L. Pissarjewsky, and P. Düllberg, vanadium pentoxide dissolves in hydrogen dioxide, and after the catalytic decomposition of the latter there remains a yellow soln. in which L. Pissarjewsky assumed vanadic acid was present, and P. Düllberg, hexavanadic acid, $H_4V_6O_{17}$. J. Meyer and A. Pawletta called it **isopolyvanadic acid.** J. Meyer showed that the yellow soln. of vanadium pentoxide in hydrogen dioxide gradually decomposes liberating oxygen and depositing vanadium pentoxide. The rate of dissolution depends on the nature of pentoxide, the conc. of the soln. of hydrogen dioxide, and on the temp. The stability of the yellow soln. is small and is a function of the temp., and of the vanadium concentration ; a 0·1N-soln. becomes turbid in 8 hrs., while a 0·01N-soln. becomes turbid in some months—all at room temp. The mol. conductivity, μ, of soln. with m mols per litre is :

m	0·0002	0·002	0·02	0·025	0·05
μ	368·9	365·8	340·8	333·8	306·8

It is assumed that the vanadium goes into soln. as a peroxo-orthovanadic acid, $H_3[V(O_2)O_3]$, which gives off oxygen more rapidly than hydrogen dioxide. Hence the catalytic action of vanadic acid on hydrogen dioxide. J. Meyer and A. Pawletta represented the reaction with hydrogen dioxide and soln. containing vanadium pentoxide and sulphuric acid by $[VO_2]_2(SO_4)_3 + 6H_2O \underset{H_2SO_4}{\overset{H_2SO_4}{\rightleftharpoons}} 2VO_2(OH)_3 + H_2SO_4$. The vanadium compound indicated on the left is reddish-brown, and that on the right, bright-yellow. In agreement with this hypothesis, the vanadium radicle travels to the cathode on electrolysis. The product is not pervanadic acid, HVO_4, but a peroxidized vanadium sulphate $[V(O_2)]_2(SO_4)_3$, with quinquevalent vanadium as cation. They said that there is no satisfactory evidence of the existence of pervanadic acid, and J. Meyer denied the existence of the hexavanadic acid of P. Düllberg.

A. Scheuer obtained salts of the type RVO_4, **pervanadate,** or **permetavanadate** by the action of hydrogen dioxide on the alkali metavanadates. These compounds are regarded as salts of monobasic **pervanadic acid,** or **permetavanadic acid** HVO_4. The permetavanadate derivatives of the hypothetical acid :

$$HO.O—V{\ll}{}^O_O \quad or \quad {HO.O \atop O}{>}V{<}{}^O_O$$

are yellow and amorphous or microcrystalline ; they are insoluble in alcohol ; give off oxygen when treated with dil. sulphuric acid ; and behave towards hydrochloric acid as indicated above. A. Scheuer reported **ammonium pervanadate,** NH_4VO_4, to be produced as a yellow flocculent precipitate when a sat. soln. of ammonium metavanadate in a dil. sulphuric acid soln. of hydrogen dioxide is treated with alcohol ; **lithium pervanadate,** $LiVO_4$, was obtained by treating a soln. of lithium carbonate and ammonium metavanadate with hydrogen dioxide ; **sodium pervanadate,** $NaVO_4$ from a soln. of the alkali vanadate ; and similarly with **potassium pervanadate,** KVO_4. The heats of the reaction between a mol of potassium metavanadate and 1, 2, $3\frac{1}{2}$, and 4 mols of hydrogen dioxide are respectively 9·024, 17·772, 17·731, and 17·521 Cals. ; thus showing that increasing the proportion of hydrogen dioxide beyond 2 mols has no influence on the heat of reaction. Allowing for the heat of formation of hydrogen dioxide from water and oxygen, the heat of formation of the pervanadate is $KVO_3+O=KVO_4-14\cdot076$ Cals. In aq. soln., a more highly oxidized compound exists. This is either a salt KVO_5, or a complex $KVO_4.H_2O_2$. The heat of soln. is $-4\cdot155$ Cals. The electrical conductivity of soln. of the pervanadate shows that it is a salt of a monobasic acid. A mol of the salt KVO_4 in v litres has a conductivity of 134·8 for $v=128$; 138·0 for $v=256$; 139·2 for $v=512$; and 140·36 for $v=1024$; so that $\lambda H_{1024}-\lambda H_{128}=5\cdot56$. A soln. of ammonium pervanadate, free from hydrochloric acid, gives with silver nitrate a yellowish-brown precipitate of **silver pervanadate,** $AgVO_4$. Yellow, microcrystalline **calcium pervanadate,** $Ca(VO_4)_2$, was precipitated by adding alcohol to a sat. soln. of ammonium metavanadate in an acid soln. of hydrogen dioxide and calcium chloride. The precipitate is washed with a soln. of hydrogen dioxide free from sulphuric acid, and dried over calcium chloride. Similarly also with **strontium pervanadate,** $Sr(VO_4)_2$; **barium pervanadate,** $Ba(VO_4)_2$; **cadmium pervanadate,** $Cd(VO_4)_2$; and **lead pervanadate,** $Pb(VO_4)_2$.

When the alkali pervanadates are treated with alkali peroxides, P. Melikoff and L. Pissarjewsky obtained products which they regarded as salts—**perpyrovanadates**—of the hypothetical **perpyrovanadatic acid,** $H_4V_2O_{11}$, which contains 4 atoms of active oxygen per molecule : $H_4V_2O_{11}=H_4V_2O_7+4O$. By passing ammonia into a soln. of ammonium vanadate in hydrogen dioxide until the liquid smells strongly of that gas, and adding alcohol, yellow, rhombic prisms of **ammonium perpyrovanadate,** $(NH_4)_4V_2O_{11}$, are formed :

$$\overset{O}{\underset{O}{\cdot}}{>}V{\underset{ONH_4}{\overset{O.ONH_4}{\Big\langle}}}{-}O{-}{\underset{NH_4O}{\overset{NH_4O.O}{\Big\rangle}}}V{<}\overset{O}{\underset{O}{\cdot}}$$

The dry powder and the aq. soln. smell of ammonia ; the dry salt decomposes with the evolution of oxygen after it has stood a short time. Conc. sulphuric acid gives ozonized oxygen, dil. sulphuric acid, hydrogen dioxide. An insoluble precipitate is produced when the aq. soln. is treated with barium chloride or silver nitrate. By treating an aq. soln. of a mol of potassium pervanadate and an aq. soln. of hydrogen dioxide and 3 mols of potassium hydroxide, yellow crystals with the composition $3K_4V_2O_{12}.4KVO_4.4H_2O$, are obtained ; and the electrical conductivity of the soln. shows that it contains a salt of a tetrabasic acid. If this compound be treated with an excess of hydrogen dioxide and 4 to 5 mols of potassium hydroxide at 0°, the addition of two vols. of alcohol precipitates a dirty green compound which is washed with cold alcohol, and ether, and dried on a porous tile. The salt is **potassium perpyrovanadate,** $K_4V_2O_{13}.7H_2O$, or $K_8V_5O_{13}.14H_2O$. When heated it detonates. It slowly decomposes in aq. soln., giving off oxygen ; and if allowed to stand some time it deposits crystals of a product with a lower proportion of available oxygen, approximating $K_4V_2O_{12}.4H_2O$, or to $3K_4V_2O_{12}.4KVO_4.4H_2O$. L. Pissarjewsky found the conductivity of one-eighth of the mol $K_8V_5O_{26}$ in v litres to be in accord with $\lambda_{1024} - \lambda_{32} = 24 \cdot 16$, that is, with the assumption that it is a salt of a tetrabasic and of a monobasic acid.   The data are :

v	32	64	128	256	512	1024
λ	92·06	103·25	107·45	114·42	115·44	116·22

REFERENCES.

[1] L. C. A. Barreswil, *Ann. Chim. Phys.*, (3), **20**. 369, 1847; G. Werther, *Journ. prakt. Chem.*, (1), **83**. 195, 1861; *Ber.*, **15**. 2593, 1882; L. Pissarjewsky, *Journ. Russ. Phys. Chem. Soc.*, **34**. 210, 1902; **35**. 42, 1903; *Zeit. phys. Chem.*, **43**. 160, 1903; *Zeit. anorg. Chem.*, **32**. 341, 1902; P. Melikoff and L. Pissarjewsky, *ib.*, **19**. 405, 1899; J. Meyer, *ib.*, **161**. 321, 1927; A. Scheuer, *ib.*, **16**. 284, 1898; *Ueber Uebervanadinsäure Salze*, Würzberg, 1897; V. Auger, *Compt. Rend.*, **172**. 1355, 1921; J. Meyer and A. Pawletta, *Zeit. angew. Chem.*, **39**. 1284, 1926; *Zeit. phys. Chem.*, **125**. 49, 1927; *Zeit. anal. Chem.*, **69**. 15, 1926; P. Düllberg, *Zeit. phys. Chem.*, **45**. 129, 1903; J. B. Cammerer, *Chem. Ztg.*, **15**. 54, 1890.

§ 18. The Vanadium Fluorides and Oxyfluorides

According to E. Petersen,[1] when vanadium trioxide is dissolved in hydrofluoric acid, and the dark green liquid concentrated on the water-bath, the soln., when cooled, furnishes dark green, rhombohedral crystals of **vanadium trifluoride,** $VF_3.3H_2O$.   O. Ruff and H. Lickfett found that mixtures of different vanadium fluorides, difficult to separate, are obtained by the action of fluorine on vanadium, or vanadium chlorides ; better results are obtained by the action of anhydrous hydrogen fluoride on the anhydrous bromides or chlorides.   When hydrogen fluoride is passed over heated vanadium trichloride, a brown intermediate product is obtained at 120°–130° ; at 340°, the brown powder becomes green, but to remove all chlorine it is necessary to pass the gas for 6 to 8 hrs. with the temp. raised to a dark red-heat.   Vanadium trifluoride remains as a greenish-yellow powder of sp. gr. 3·3628 at 19° ; its m.p. lies above 800°, and it sublimes at a bright red-heat.   It is almost insoluble in water and the usual organic solvents ; but E. Petersen said that the salt is freely soluble in water, particularly hot water, and the soln. has an acid reaction ; showing that hydrolysis probably occurs.   If the aq. soln. be crystallized, a greyish-green product thought to be a basic salt is obtained.   The salt can, however, be recrystallized from hydrofluoric acid.   When exposed to air, the salt quickly effloresces ; and at 100° about one-third the water is lost, and the remainder at 130°.   Some oxygen is at the same time absorbed from the atm. ; when heated in air, vanadium pentoxide is formed ; and probably a little fluoride is lost by volatilization.   The salt is insoluble in alcohol.   The aq. soln. acts as a reducing agent—silver salts furnish silver, and mercuric and cupric salts form respectively mercurous and cuprous salts.   Many of the metal fluorides furnish complex salts. Soln. of alkali hydroxides and carbonates precipitate greyish-green vanadium trihydroxides.   The analysis of the salt agrees with the formula $VF_3.3H_2O$, which was written $V_2F_6.6H_2O$ by E. Petersen.

When ammonium fluoride is mixed with a soln. of vanadium trifluoride, E. Petersen found that a green precipitate of **ammonium hexafluovanadite,** $3NH_4F.VF_3$, or $(NH_4)_3VF_6$, is formed.   The green, microscopic octahedra are fairly soluble in water and in dil. acids ; but they are almost insoluble in alcohol, and in soln. of the alkali fluorides.   With a long-continued evaporation, the aq. soln. loses ammonia.   If the aq. soln. be evaporated on a water-bath, **ammonium pentafluovanadite,** $(NH_4)_2VF_5$, or $2NH_4F.VF_3$, is formed in emerald-green, octahedral crystals.   The salt is soluble in water, and it crystallizes unchanged from its aq. soln. ; it is sparingly soluble in alcohol.   The mother-liquor from the preceding salt furnishes a dark green aggregate of crystals of **ammonium tetrafluovanadite,** $NH_4F.VF_3$, or NH_4VF_4.   If a hydrofluoric acid soln. of potassium fluoride be treated with a soln. of vanadium trifluoride, a green crystalline powder of **potassium**

pentafluovanadite, $K_2VF_5.H_2O$, or $2KF.VF_3.H_2O$, is deposited and the supernatant liquor becomes colourless. The precipitate is washed with dil. hydrofluoric acid, and dried in air. It is easily soluble in water and dil. acids, and insoluble in a soln. of potassium fluoride. It loses no water at 100°, a little is lost at 130°, and all is lost at 170°. The sodium salt is represented by $5NaF.2VF_3.H_2O$, or **sodium henafluodivanadite,** $Na_5V_2F_{11}.H_2O$. It is formed like the potassium salt, and appears as a bright green, sparingly-soluble, crystalline powder. E. Petersen obtained what was thought to be **copper pentafluovanadite,** $CuVF_5$, by adding vanadium trifluoride to a soln. of copper carbonate in hydrofluoric acid. A. Piccini and G. Giorgis prepared **zinc pentafluovanadite,** $ZnF_2.VF_3.7H_2O$, in emerald green crystals sparingly soluble in cold water, and partly decomposed by hot water; it is easily oxidized in hydrofluoric acid soln. Green **cadmium pentafluovanadite,** $CdF_2.VF_3.9H_2O$, was prepared in a similar way. F. Ephraim and L. Heymann added the calculated proportion of thallous fluoride to a soln. of vanadium trioxide in hydrofluoric acid. The evaporation of the liquid furnished green, microscopic crystals of **thallous tetrafluovanadite,** $TlF.VF_3.2H_2O$. They are freely soluble in water. If an excess of thallous fluoride is used, or if conc. soln. of thallous fluoride and vanadic trifluoride are mixed, the cold, green microscopic crystals of **thallous pentafluovanadite,** $2TlF.VF_3.H_2O$, are formed. The salt is soluble in water, forming a green soln.; with conc. sulphuric acid, hydrogen fluoride is given off; cold, dil. nitric acid dissolves the salt and at the same time oxidizes it. Dil. hydrochloric acid precipitates thallous fluoride; alkali-lye blackens the salt without dissolution. E. Petersen prepared small, dark green, monoclinic prisms of **cobalt pentafluovanadite,** $CoVF_5.7H_2O$; and grass-green, monoclinic prisms of **nickel pentafluovanadite,** $NiVF_5.7H_2O$, were also prepared.

O. Ruff and H. Lickfett found that **vanadium tetrafluoride,** VF_4, is produced by the action of anhydrous hydrogen fluoride on vanadium tetrachloride, the reaction being started at $-28°$ and the temp. allowed to rise to $0°$ in the course of 2 hrs. It is a brownish-yellow, loose powder, which is very hygroscopic, deliquescing in the air to a blue liquid; readily soluble in water (blue soln.) and acetone (green soln.); the sp. gr. is 2·9749 at 23°. Above 325°, it decomposes into vanadium pentafluoride and vanadium trifluoride. According to J. J. Berzelius, the evaporation of the blue soln., obtained by dissolving vanadium tetroxide in hydrofluoric acid, furnishes a brown mass which is soluble in water. If the evaporation proceeds spontaneously, it leaves a green syrup from which green crystals are obtained. The crystals form a green soln. with absolute alcohol. A. Guyard said that the dark green residue obtained by evaporating the alcoholic soln. can be heated to a high temp. without decomposition and at a red-heat, it furnishes hydrogen fluoride, and then a yellow vapour of anhydrous **vanadium oxydifluoride,** VOF_2, or *vanadyl fluoride*. E. Petersen found that if the blue soln. of vanadium tetroxide in hydrofluoric acid be evaporated over sulphuric acid, blue pyramidal or prismatic crystals are formed of $VOF_2.nH_2O$, which corresponds with the composition of the complex fluorides derived from this oxydifluoride. According to O. Ruff and H. Lickfett, vanadium oxydifluoride is prepared by heating vanadyl dibromide in a current of anhydrous hydrogen fluoride, first at 150°–200° and then at 600°–700° for 6 hrs. It is yellow in colour, slightly soluble in acetone, but insoluble in other solvents. The sp. gr. is 3·3956 at 190°.

The salt **vanadium tetrafluoride,** VF_4, has not been prepared, but E. Petersen found that if ammonium pentafluohypovanadate be dissolved in conc.—35 per cent. —hydrofluoric acid, bluish-green microscopic prisms of what is probably $NH_4V_2F_9.nH_2O$, **ammonium enneafluohypovanadate,** are produced. They crumble to a greyish-green powder when dry and evolve the smell of hydrogen fluoride. When dried at 100° the salt becomes $2NH_4F.VOF_2$—*vide infra*. If a soln. of vanadium tetroxide in hydrofluoric acid be treated with an excess of a soln. of ammonium fluoride, E. Petersen found that small, blue, octahedral crystals of **ammonium vanadylpentafluoride,** $3NH_4F.VOF_2$, are formed. The crystals are cubic, but being optically anomalous, they are doubly refracting.   **A.** Piccini and G. Giorgis obtained the salt by reducing a hydrofluoric acid soln. of ammonium metavanadate with sulphur dioxide, neutralizing the liquid with ammonia, and adding a soln. of ammonium fluoride. The precipitate was moistened with a little water, pressed between bibulous paper, and dissolved in water. The first crop of crystals is ammonium vanadyltetrafluoride, and this is followed by the blue octahedra. A. Guyard proceeded similarly but used alcohol, and H. Baker, hydrogen sulphide, as the reducing agent instead of sulphur dioxide, and A. Piccini and G. Giorgis also reduced the vanadate electrolytically.   The salt is freely soluble in water ; sparingly soluble in alcohol ; and very sparingly soluble in soln. of alkali fluorides. E. Petersen, and A. Piccini and G. Giorgis obtained bluish-green, monoclinic prisms of **ammonium vanadyltetrafluoride**, $2NH_4F.VOF_2$, as just indicated ; and H. Baker obtained the *monohydrate*, $2NH_4F.VOF_2$; E. Petersen also obtained it by evaporating a soln. of the salt over sulphuric acid.   H. Baker said that the blue monoclinic crystals have the axial ratios $a:b:c=0.9653:1:-$.   The aq. soln. gives a precipitate with alcohol ; and is not attacked by sulphuric acid.   E. Petersen obtained dark blue crystals of **ammonium pentadecafluotetrahypovanadate**, $7NH_4F.4VOF_2$, mixed with some crystals of the pentafluohypovanadate, by evaporating over sulphuric acid a mixed soln. of equimolar proportions of ammonium fluoride and vanadium oxydifluoride.   J. J. Berzelius noticed that vanadium oxydifluoride forms blue crystals of complex salts, with sodium and potassium fluoride, and they are soluble in water but not in alcohol.   E. Petersen, and A. Piccini and G. Giorgis obtained sky-blue crystals of **potassium tetrafluohypovanadate**, $2KF.VOF_2$, by the methods used for the ammonium salt, keeping the oxydifluoride in excess.   E. Petersen showed that if the potassium fluoride be in excess, pale blue crystals of **potassium tridecafluotrihypovanadate**, $7KCl.3VOF_2$, are formed. They are washed with dil. hydrofluoric acid.   The salt is sparingly soluble in water, and in soln. of alkali fluorides ; but easily soluble in dil. acids.   It does not lose weight at 120°, but hydrogen fluoride is lost at higher temp. E. Petersen also obtained blue crystals of **sodium tetradecafluotrihypovanadate**, $8NaF.3VOF_2.2H_2O$, by the method used for the 7 : 3 potassium salt.   The salt suffers no loss at 100°, and at 170° the loss is only 3·28 per cent.   A. Piccini and G. Giorgis obtained blue crystals of **zinc tetrafluohypovanadate**, $ZnF_2.VOF_2.7H_2O$, by the electrolysis of a soln. of the calculated quantity of zinc oxide and vanadium pentoxide in hydrofluoric acid. The salt loses 6 mols. of water at 100°, and becomes colourless.   It is decomposed by hot water, and can be recrystallized from hot, dil. hydrofluoric acid.   The **cadmium tetrafluohypovanadate**, $CdF_2.VOF_2.7H_2O$, was prepared in a similar way.   F. Ephraim and L. Heymann prepared **thallous tetrafluohypovanadate**, $2TlF.VOF_2$, by reducing a soln. of vanadium pentoxide in hydrofluoric acid with sulphur dioxide, and adding an excess of thallous fluoride. The bluish-green precipitate is microcrystalline.   It gives off some hydrogen fluoride when exposed to air.   It is freely stable in cold water, but is decomposed by hot water.   The soln. reduces potassium permanganate.

Unsuccessful attempts have been made to isolate **vanadium pentafluoride**, VF_5. J. J. Berzelius found that with a mixture of sodium fluoride and vanadate, and sulphuric acid, hydrogen fluoride is given off, while vanadium pentoxide and sodium sulphate remain.   Warm hydrofluoric acid readily dissolves vanadium pentoxide, forming a colourless soln., which, when evaporated below 40°, leaves a colourless— E. Petersen said yellow or reddish-brown—mass of salt perfectly soluble in water. O. Ruff and H. Lickfett made the pentafluoride as a pure white sublimate when the tetrafluoride is heated in a current of nitrogen, the temp. being gradually raised from 300° to 650°, and the latter temp. maintained for two and a half hours.   At the ordinary temp., it possesses an appreciable vap. press., and in moist air becomes yellow, owing to the formation of oxyfluorides.   It is readily soluble in water, alcohol, chloroform, acetone, and light petroleum.   When heated in sealed glass tubes it does not melt, even above 200°, but it readily attacks the walls of the tube.

Its sp. gr. is 2·1766 at 19° and its b.p. 111·2° at 758 mm. It is the only vanadium compound in which five halogen atoms are bound to one vanadium atom. J. J. Berzelius said that the salt loses part of its acid when strongly heated, yielding a red mass which still forms a colourless soln. with water, and at a higher temp., the hydrofluoric acid is expelled leaving behind vanadium pentoxide. A number of complex salts of vanadium pentafluoride has been formed. According to E. Petersen, if the mother-liquor obtained in the preparation of potassium vanadyl-pentafluoride be allowed to stand for some hours, it deposits aggregates of needles and prisms of **potassium vanadyldodecafluovanadate**, $4KF.VF_5.VOF_3$. The salt is washed with dil. hydrofluoric acid, and dried in air. It is soluble in water and dil. hydrofluoric acid, but sparingly soluble in soln. of potassium fluoride.

According to O. Ruff and H. Lickfett, **vanadium oxytrifluoride**, VOF_3, is prepared from vanadyl trichloride in a manner similar to that described for the preparation of vanadium tetrafluoride; it may also be obtained by heating vanadium trifluoride to a red heat in a current of oxygen. It forms yellowish-white crusts, and is very hygroscopic, deliquescing in the air to a brownish-yellow soln. At 132°, when heated in glass tubes, it decomposes, red vanadium pentoxide being deposited; it then melts at about 300° and boils at 480°. In a current of oxygen, it sublimes at 130°. Its sp. gr. is 2·4591 at 20·5°. According to E. Petersen, if not too great an excess of ammonium fluoride be added to a soln. of vanadium pentoxide in hydrofluoric acid, and the soln. evaporated; or if ammonium vanadyltetra-fluoride be dissolved in hydrofluoric and heated on a water-bath, and the soln. cooled, colourless, four-sided prisms of **ammonium pentavanadylhydropentacosifluoride**, $HF.9NH_4F.5VOF_3$, are produced. H. Baker's ammonium fluoxyvanadate, $3(NH_4)HF_2.2VOF_3$ is probably identical with this salt. The salt is freely soluble in water, but sparingly soluble in alkali fluorides.

E. Petersen prepared **potassium vanadylpentafluoride**, $2KF.VOF_3$, by mixing a soln. of potassium fluoride with a hydrofluoric acid soln. of vanadium pentoxide, and washing the white crystalline precipitate with dil. hydrofluoric acid. The microscopic, four-sided prisms give off some hydrogen fluoride on exposure to air, and also at 100°. The colour becomes reddish-brown when the salt is confined over sulphuric acid. E. Petersen obtained **potassium divanadylhydrodecafluoride**, $3KF.HF.2VOF_3$, by cooling a soln. of the vanadyldodecafluovanadate, or vanadyl-pentafluoride from a soln. of hydrofluoric acid, heated on the water-bath. The microscopic, rectangular prisms are stable in air, but during their drying, they smell feebly of hydrogen fluoride. The salt suffers an insignificant change in weight at 100°. H. Baker reported *potassium divanadyltrihydrohenafluoride*, $3KF.3HF.2VOF_3$, to be formed from a soln. of potassium vanadylpentafluoride in hydrofluoric acid. E. Petersen suggested that this product is the same as his divanadylhydrodecafluoride. M. Travers obtained **sodium fluodivanadate**, $2Na_3VO_4.NaF.19H_2O$, in isomorphous association with sodium fluodisphosphate, $2Na_3PO_4.NaF.19H_2O$, by cooling the extract of bauxite with soda-lye.

The attempts to isolate *vanadyl fluoride* or **vanadium dioxyfluoride**, VO_2F, have not been successful, but complex salts have been prepared. A series of com-pounds of $VOF_3.VO_2F$ has also been reported. According to E. Petersen, and A. Piccini and G. Giorgis, when a soln. of vanadium pentoxide in hydrofluoric acid is mixed with enough ammonia for the soln. still to retain an acidic reaction, and evaporated, it furnishes *ammonium tetrafluodioxyvanadate*, or **ammonium vanadyl-tetrafluoride**, $3NH_4F.VO_2F$, or $(NH_4)_3(VO_2)F_4$—A. Werner gave $[O_2VF_4](NH_4)_3$. If the ammonia be in excess, some ammonium metavanadate is formed. E. Petersen dissolved vanadium pentoxide in a soln. of ammonium fluoride and extracted a little ammonium metavanadate from the vanadyltetrafluoride by hydrofluoric acid. H. Baker's pyramidal ammonium fluoxyvanadate, $12NH_4F.V_2O_5.2VOF_3$, is this salt. A. Piccini and G. Giorgis observed that the same compound is formed by the action of atm. oxygen on ammonium vanadylpentafluoride, or by adding ammonium fluoride to the same salt. The golden-yellow, octahedral crystals are cubic, but they have an anomalous double refraction. The salt loses ammonia when warmed to 100°. P. G. Melikoff and P. Kasanezky found that when ammonium vanadyltetrafluoride, $3NH_4F.VO_2F$, is treated with successive portions of hydrogen dioxide, *ammonium vanadyltrifluoride*, $2NH_4F.VO_2F$, is first formed ; and this behaves like a compound with the constitution $(NH_4O)_2VF_3$; the fluorine is gradually replaced by oxygen, and the end-product is a pervanadate—*vide infra*, the **potassium salt**. The formula of the vanadyltetrafluoride **is** therefore written :

$$\begin{matrix} NH_4O \\ NH_4O \end{matrix} {>} V {\begin{matrix} F{=}F{-}NH_4 \\ F \\ F \end{matrix}}$$

The intermediate products are :

$$\begin{matrix} NH_4O \\ NH_4O \\ F \end{matrix} {>} V {<} \begin{matrix} O \\ O \end{matrix} \qquad \begin{matrix} NH_4O \\ F \\ F \end{matrix} {>} V {<} \begin{matrix} O \\ O \end{matrix} \qquad \begin{matrix} NH_4O.O \\ HO \\ F \end{matrix} {>} V {<} \begin{matrix} O \\ O \end{matrix} \qquad \begin{matrix} NH_4O.O \\ NH_4O.O \\ F \end{matrix} {>} V {<} \begin{matrix} O \\ O \end{matrix}$$

F. Ephraim does not agree with this hypothesis. According to A. Piccini and G. Giorgis, when the aq. soln. of ammonium vanadyltetrafluoride is evaporated, a salt with less ammonium, namely, *ammonium pentafluotetroxydivanadate*, or **ammonium divanadylpentafluoride**, $3NH_4F.2VO_2F$, is formed in yellow plates which can be recrystallized from its aq. soln.; if the soln. in 10 per cent. hydrofluoric acid be slowly evaporated, the *monohydrate*, $3NH_4F.2VOF.H_2O$, is formed. When an aq. soln. of ammonium pentavanadylhydropentacosifluoride—*vide infra*—is allowed to crystallize, it furnishes **ammonium tetravanadylhydrododecafluoride**, $7NH_4F.HF.4VO_2F$, in white spherical aggregates, which form a yellow soln. with water. H. Baker's $6NH_4F.2VOF_3.V_2O_5.H_2O$ was thought by E. Petersen to be identical with this salt.

According to E. Petersen, if a soln. of vanadium pentoxide in hydrofluoric acid, warmed on the water-bath, be treated with potassium hydroxide until the liquid has a feeble acid reaction, golden-yellow crystals of **potassium vanadyltrifluoride**, $2KF.VO_2F$, or $(KO)_2VF_3$—A. Werner gave $[OVF_5]K_2$—separate as the soln. cools. The brown mass obtained by evaporating a soln. of vanadium pentoxide in hydrofluoric acid to dryness can be dissolved in hot water, and treated with a hot soln. of potassium fluoride ; on cooling the filtered liquid, the same salt is obtained. Hydrated vanadium pentoxide dissolves readily in a hot soln. of potassium fluoride containing a little hydrofluoric acid ; and the liquid, filtered from the white precipitate, furnishes crystals of the vanadyltrifluoride. F. Ephraim obtained the same salt by melting vanadium pentoxide with potassium fluoride, $6KF+V_2O_5 = K_2O+2K_2(VO_2)F_3$; and also by crystallization from a soln. of potassium fluoride and potassium divanadylpentafluoride. The six-sided, prismatic crystals are straw-yellow, or golden-yellow ; but if pure, F. Ephraim said that they would probably be white. Water splits this salt into the yellow divanadylpentafluoride ; but the soln. in potassium fluoride is colourless. E. Petersen said that salt can be dried over sulphuric acid ; and by careful heating it can be melted without decomposition. P. G. Melikoff and P. Kasanezky found that salt behaves like the ammonium salt towards hydrogen dioxide. The initial compound $(KO)_2VF_3$ passes to a pervanadate, KVO_4, or $6K_3HV_2O_{12}$, with the intermediate formation of

$$\begin{matrix} KO \\ KO \\ F \end{matrix} {>} V {<} \begin{matrix} O \\ O \end{matrix} \qquad \begin{matrix} KO.O \\ F \\ F \end{matrix} {>} V {<} \begin{matrix} O \\ O \end{matrix} \qquad \begin{matrix} KO \\ HO \\ F \end{matrix} {>} V {<} \begin{matrix} O \\ O \end{matrix} \qquad \begin{matrix} KO.O \\ KO.O \\ F \end{matrix} {>} V {<} \begin{matrix} O \\ O \end{matrix}$$

F. Ephraim does not accept this hypothesis. E. Petersen said that if an aq. soln. of potassium vanadyltrifluoride be crystallized, yellow aggregates of **potassium divanadylpentafluoride**, $3KF.2VO_2F$, are formed ; and A. Piccini obtained the **salt** by crystallizing the same compound from a soln. of potassium fluoride.

H. Baker reported *potassium divanadyldodecafluovanadate*, $6KCl.V_2O_5.2VOF_3.2H_2O$, to be formed from a soln. of vanadium pentoxide in one of potassium hydrofluoride, but E. Petersen suggested that it is really potassium divanadylpentafluoride. According to F. Ephraim, **barium vanadyl trifluoride,** $BaF_2.VO_2F$,

$$Ba<{\,_O^O}>V\!\!<^{\textstyle F}_{\textstyle F}_F$$

is obtained as a flocculent, light yellow precipitate on adding a soln. of vanadium fluoride to an excess of barium chloride. When calcium chloride is added to a soln. of an alkali vanadyl fluoride **calcium vanadyltrifluoride,** $CaF_2.VO_2F$, is formed. The complex fluoride then reacts with more chloride to produce a complex chloride : $2Ca(VO_2)F_3+3CaCl_2=3CaF_2+2Ca(VO_2)Cl_3$; in a similar manner, **magnesium vanadyltrifluoride,** and **ferric vanadyltrifluoride** are produced.

H. Baker prepared yellow, monoclinic prisms of **zinc oxydivanadyloctofluoride,** $ZnF_2.ZnO.2VOF_3.14H_2O$, by evaporating a soln. of zinc carbonate and vanadium pentoxide in hydrofluoric acid. The axial ratios are $a:b:c=0.93:1:0.83$, and $\beta=134°$. E. Petersen believed that this product is really **zinc vanadyltrifluoride,** $ZnF_2.VO_2F.7H_2O$, which was also prepared by A. Piccini and G. Giorgis. F. Ephraim and L. Heymann added a conc. aq. soln. of thallous fluoride to a soln. of vanadium pentoxide in hydrochloric acid, and obtained a flocculent precipitate of **thallous divanadylpentafluoride,** $3TlF.2VO_2F$, which soon crystallized. The salt is insoluble in water ; and readily soluble in dil. sulphuric acid.

A. Piccini and G. Giorgis obtained **sodium vanadaylvanadylheptafluoride,** $3NaF.VOF_3.VO_2F.H_2O$, on evaporating a soln. of 3 mols of sodium carbonate and 2 mols of vanadium pentoxide in hydrofluoric acid. After the precipitate has stood some days in contact with the mother-liquid, it forms yellow plates. H. Baker reported that **sodium fluodivanadate,** $2Na_3VO_4.NaF.19H_2O$, is formed when calculated proportions of vanadium trioxide, sodium carbonate, and sodium fluoride are melted together, and the aq. soln. of the cold mass allowed to crystallize. It is also obtained from a soln. of the theoretical proportions of sodium fluoride and orthovanadate or pyrovanadate and sodium hydroxide. The salt can be recrystallized from dil. soda-lye without decomposition. It forms octahedral, cubic crystals. P. Hautefeuille could not prepare **calcium fluorthovanadate** analogous to wagnerite by fusing calcium fluoride with vanadium pentoxide. F. Fischer and K. Thiele found that the bluish-green soln. of vanadic acid dissolves lead carbonate. M. Amadori studied the f.p. of mixtures of lead orthovanadate and lead fluoride, and the results are summarized in Fig. 8. There is one compound formed : **lead fluotriorthovanadate,** *fluovanadinite,* or *fluovanadatapatite,*

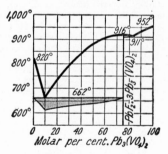

Fig. 8.—Freezing-point Curves of Lead Fluoride and Orthovanadate.

$PbF_2.3Pb(VO_4)_2$, or $Pb_5F(VO_4)_3$, or, according to A. Werner, $[Pb\{(PbVO_3.O)_2Pb\}]F_2$. M. Amadori found the m.p. of fluomimetite, $Pb_5Cl(AsO_4)_3$, to be 1042°, and of fluovanadinite, 916°, and for mixtures with 25, 50, and 75 per cent. of fluovanadinite, 1008°, 978°, and 944° respectively.

A. Ditte [2] has reported a number of fluovanadates whose nature has not been explained. F. Ephraim suggests that most of them are not chemical individuals, and when he tried, he could not verify A. Ditte's conclusion. A. Ditte found that a warm conc. soln. of ammonium fluoride dissolves a large quantity of soluble vanadium pentoxide, and the warm liquid deposits **ammonium tetrafluovanadate,** $V_2O_5.4NH_4F.4H_2O$, in pale-yellow crystals very soluble in water. When heated, they lose water and hydrogen fluoride, and yield **ammonium difluovanadate,** $V_2O_5.2NH_4F$. If the mother-liquor from the first crystals is mixed with excess of vanadium pentoxide, filtered and cooled, it deposits the tetrafluovanadate in almost white, brilliant, nacreous needles, readily soluble in cold water. With a cold soln. of ammonium fluoride and excess of vanadium pentoxide, the first product consists of indistinct yellow crystals of **ammonium octofluovanadate**, $V_2O_5.8NH_4F.4H_2O$, followed by crystals of the compound tetrafluovanadate.

A. Ditte also found that when sodium fluoride is heated in a closed crucible with an excess of vanadium pentoxide it yields a crystalline, red mass, and when this is treated with tepid water, it yields an orange soln., which deposits orange-red crystals of **sodium tetrafluohexavanadate**, $3V_2O_5.4NaF.18H_2O$. The mother-liquor when conc. yields lemon-yellow crystals of **sodium tetrafluovanadate**, $V_2O_5.4NaF$. With an excess of the alkaline fluoride, the product is pale-yellow, and is only slowly attacked by water. If extracted with warm water and the soln. evaporated in vacuo, the salt is obtained in transparent, orange-red crystals, and the mother-liquor yields small, yellowish-white crystals of **sodium octofluovanadate**, $V_2O_5.8NaF.3H_2O$.

A. Ditte observed that when an excess of vanadium pentoxide is fused with potassium fluoride in a platinum crucible, care being taken to prevent access of air, a brick-red crystalline mass is formed on cooling, and when this is treated with water, a residue of vanadium pentoxide is left, and a red soln. is obtained. The soln. first deposits a small quantity of potassium tetravanadate, formed in consequence of access of air, and then orange-red plates of **potassium difluohexavanadate**, $3V_2O_5.2KF.5H_2O$, which melts easily to a black liquid. The mother-liquor on further conc. deposits red, transparent prisms of **potassium difluovanadate**, $4V_2O_5.2KF.8H_2O$. Contact with air is more completely avoided by heating the crucible at the bottom of a long glass tube. Under these conditions, the aq. soln. first deposits potassium difluohexavanadate, then ruby-red prisms of the *hexahydrate*, $3V_2O_5.2KF.6H_2O$, and less soluble, lemon-yellow crystals of **potassium tetrafluohexavanadate**, $3V_2O_5.4KF$. All these compounds are soluble in conc. sulphuric acid, with evolution of hydrogen fluoride and formation of a red soln. which becomes pale-green when dil. with much water. When an excess of potassium fluoride is employed, the residue is pale-yellow, and on treatment with cold water first yields a sat. soln. of potassium fluoride, in which the vanadium compounds are practically insoluble. A further quantity of water forms a yellow soln., which deposits small plates of **potassium difluotetravanadate**, $3V_2O_5.2KF.8H_2O$, and the mother-liquor when conc. in vacuo yields **potassium difluohexavanadate**, $3V_2O_5.2KF.4H_2O$. The proportion of the residue least soluble in water has the composition of **potassium tetrafluodivanadate**, $V_2O_5.4KF.3H_2O$. With a large excess of potassium fluoride, the soln. yields successively large, thin, brilliant, orange-yellow lamellæ of the compound potassium difluohexavanadate ; white crystals with a greenish-yellow tinge of **potassium octofluodivanadate**, $V_2O_5.8KF.3H_2O$, and finally yellow crystals of dihydrated potassium tetrafluodivanadate. If air has free access and vanadium pentoxide is in excess, the residue is an orange-red mass with vitreous fracture, and when treated with hot water some vanadium pentoxide remains undissolved. The soln. first deposits potassium tetravanadate, and afterwards lemon-yellow crystals of **vanadium tetrafluodivanadate**, $V_2O_5.4KF$. Similar results are obtained with excess of potassium fluoride. Water first dissolves the excess of fluoride, and the soln. obtained by further treatment deposits yellowish-white crystals of dihydrated potassium octofluodivanadate. The action of potassium fluoride on vanadium pentoxide yields the compounds **potassium fluotetravanadate**, $2V_2O_5.KF$; **potassium difluohexavanadate**, $3V_2O_5.2KF$: **potassium fluodivanadate**, $V_2O_5.KF$; **potassium tetrafluohexavanadate**, $3V_2O_5.4KF$; **potassium tetrafluodivanadate**, $V_2O_5.4KF$; **potassium octofluodecavanadate**, $V_2O_5.8KF$, which may be regarded as analogous to potassium chlorochromate. Their soln. give no coloration and no precipitate with ammonia. If these compounds are regarded as derived from an oxyfluoride, the latter must be $V_2O_4F_2$. Possibly the compounds do not actually exist in the fused mass, but the aq. soln. contains several different compounds, giving rise to conditions of equilibrium in which the crystallizable salts described are formed. A soln. of potassium fluoride dissolves vanadium pentoxide, and the liquid deposits greenish-white crystals of potassium octofluodivanadate, which is but slightly soluble in excess of the alkaline fluoride. As the colourless soln. cools it becomes yellow, and deposits lemon-yellow crystals of potassium tetrafluodivanadate.

REFERENCES.

[1] E. Petersen, *Vanadinet og dets naermeste analoger ; en sammenlignenka hemisk undersögelse,* Copenhagen, 1888 ; *Chem. News,* **60**. 210, 1889 ; **61**. 61, 1890 ; *Ber.,* **21**. 3257, 1888 ; *Journ. prakt. Chem.,* (2), **40**. 47, 1889 ; J. J. Berzelius, *Acad. Handl. Stockholm,* **1**, 1831 ; *Schweigger's Journ.,* **62**. 323, 1831 ; **63**. 26, 1831 ; *Pogg. Ann.,* **22**. 1, 1831 ; *Ann. Chim. Phys.,* (1), **47**. 337, 1831 ; *Phil. Mag.,* (2), **10**. 321, 1831 ; (2), **11**. 7, 1832 ; A. Guyard, *Bull. Soc. Chim.,* (2), **25**. 351, 1876 ; A. Piccini and G. Giorgis, *Gazz. Chim. Ital.,* **18**. 186, 1888 ; **22**. i, 55, 1892 ; *Atti Accad. Lincei,* (6), **4**. i, 590, 1888 ; H. Baker, *Journ. Chem. Soc.,* **33**. 388, 1878 ; *Ber.,* **11**. 1722, 1878 ; *Liebig's Ann.,* **202**. 254, 1880 ; P. G. Melikoff and P. Kasanezky, *Journ. Russ. Phys. Chem. Soc.,* **36**. 77, 1904 ; *Zeit. anorg. Chem.,* **28**, 242, 1901 ; **41**. 442, 1904 ; F. Ephraim, *ib.,* **35**. 66, 1903 ; *Ber.,*

36. 1177, 1903 ; F. Ephraim and L. Heymann, *ib.*, **41.** 4460, 1909 ; A. Werner, *ib.*, **40.** 4449, 1907 ; *Zeit. anorg. Chem.*, **9.** 386, 1895 ; F. Fischer and K. Thiele, *ib.*, **67.** 313, 1910 ; M. Amadori, *Gazz. Chim. Ital.*, **49.** i, 38, 1919 ; *Rend. Accad. Lincei*, (5), **21.** ii, 768, 1912 ; (5), **27.** i, 143, 1918 ; *Atti. Ist. Venato*, **76.** ii, 419, 1917 ; *Rend. Ist. Lombardo*, **49.** 137, 1916 ; M. Amadori and E. Viterbi, *Mem. Accad. Lincei*, (5), **10.** 386, 1914 ; P. Hautefeuille, *Compt. Rend.*, **77.** 896, 1893 ; M. Travers, *Bull. Soc. Chim.*, (4), **33.** 297, 1923 ; O. Ruff and H. Lickfett, *Ber.*, **44.** 2539, 1911.

² A. Ditte, *Compt. Rend.*, **105.** 1067, 1887 ; **106.** 270, 1888 ; F. Ephraim, *Zeit. anorg. Chem.*, **35.** 66, 190 ; *Ber.*, **36.** 1177, 1903.

§ 19. The Vanadium Chlorides and Oxychlorides

H. E. Roscoe [1] prepared **vanadium dichloride,** VCl_2, by passing a mixture of hydrogen and vanadium tetrachloride through a glass tube heated to dull redness, when the dichloride collects in pale green crystals as a sublimate on the walls of the tube. If the current of gas is too rapid, or if insufficient hydrogen be present, some vanadium trichloride is formed ; and if the temp. is too high, some vanadium metal is formed which forms a silicide with the glass. H. Moissan and A. Holt observed the formation of the dichloride and silicon tetrachloride when vanadium silicide is heated in chlorine. J. Meyer and R. Backa obtained the dichloride by the action of hydrogen chloride on ferrovanadium at 300°–400°. A. Piccini and L. Marino obtained an aq. soln. of the dichloride by the electrolytic reduction of the trichloride, using a graphite anode. H. E. Roscoe found that the pale, apple-green, hexagonal plates have a sp. gr. 3·23 at 18° ; the salt volatilizes in hydrogen or carbon dioxide without decomposition. The hygroscopic crystals gradually deliquesce in air to a brown liquid owing to the absorption of water and oxygen. They are at first not wetted by water, but swim on that liquid ; however, they soon dissolve, forming a lavender-coloured soln. which decolorizes litmus, and indigo. According to A. Piccini and L. Marino, when the aq. soln. is evaporated, or when hydrochloric acid is added, hydrogen is evolved and the trichloride is formed. The reaction is very vigorous if a piece of platinum is present in the acid liquor. The dichloride is therefore a more vigorous reducing agent than chromous chloride. When the dichloride is heated to whiteness in nitrogen, some nitride is formed. For the action of heat, *vide infra*, vanadium trichloride. P. Pascal gave 139×10^{-5} for the mol. magnetic susceptibility of soln. of the dichloride. Alcohol forms a blue soln., and ether a green one. In aq. soln. the salt is oxidized to vanadium pentoxide by potassium permanganate.

According to H. E. Roscoe, **vanadium trichloride,** VCl_3, is formed when the tetrachloride is heated ; and when the tetrachloride is heated in a distillation flask, it boils with partial decomposition leaving a residue of the trichloride which can be dried in a current of carbon dioxide at 160°. The tetrachloride also decomposes slowly at ordinary temp. into the trichloride. The tetrachloride mixed with hydrogen furnishes a mixture of the trichloride and dichloride when passed through a red-hot tube. W. Halberstadt prepared the trichloride by warming the trisulphide in a current of chlorine. To remove sulphur chloride from the dark brown distillate, it is redistilled, and the red residue heated to 150° in a current of carbon dioxide. J. Meyer and R. Backa obtained the trichloride by the action of hydrogen chloride on vanadium at 300°–400° ; and also by passing carbon dioxide through the tetrachloride at 140°–150°. H. E. Roscoe showed that at ordinary temp., vanadium trichloride furnishes tabular crystals the colour of peach blossoms. The sp. gr. is 3·00 at 18°. It does not volatilize in dry hydrogen, but at a red-heat it forms the dichloride, and at a higher temp. still, the metal. On heating vanadium trichloride in a current of nitrogen to a dark red-heat, it is decomposed into vanadium tetrachloride, which distils off, and into vanadium dichloride, which remains behind. The quantity of vanadium tetrachloride, which is formed according to the equation : $2VCl_3 = VCl_4 + VCl_2$, is determined for each temp. by the partial press. of the chlorine, since, together with the above reaction, a second occurs, namely, $2VCl_4 = 2VCl_3 + Cl_2$. For the first reaction, the relation $[VCl_4]/[VCl_3]^2 = k_1$ holds, since the vap. press. of the VCl_2 in the presence of the solid is constant ; for the second reaction, the relation $[VCl_3]^2[Cl_2]/[VCl_4]^2 = k_2$ holds. Both these equilibria exist at the same time, and $[Cl_2]/[VCl_4] = k_1k_2$, that is, the quantity of vanadium tetrachloride formed by heating the trichloride is determined by the partial press. of the chlorine over the trichloride. It is consequently an easy matter to transform vanadium trichloride completely into the tetrachloride by heating it in a current of chlorine which is free from oxygen. Similar phenomena are observed when vanadium trichloride is heated at a dull red-heat in a current of carbon dioxide instead of nitrogen. Green vanadium dichloride, VCl_2, is formed according to the equation $2VCl_3 \rightleftharpoons VCl_4 + VCl_2$. If the heating is carried out at a bright red-heat the carbon dioxide is reduced by the vanadium dichloride, with the result that vanadium oxychloride, $VOCl$, and carbon monoxide are formed, as shown by the equation : $3VCl_2 + 2CO_2 = 2VOCl + VCl_4 + 2CO$. On still stronger heating, the reaction goes further, according to the equation : $4VCl_2 + 3CO_2 = V_2O_3 + 2VCl_4 + 3CO$, and pure vanadium trioxide is left behind. Thus it is quite unnecessary to reduce vanadium trichloride in a current of hydrogen in order to obtain the dichloride. According to H. E. Roscoe, vanadium trichloride is very hygroscopic, and deliquesces in air to a dark brown liquid which with a drop of hydrochloric acid becomes green. When heated in air, it develops red vapours of vanadium oxytrichloride, and some vanadium pentoxide remains. W. Biltz studied the thermal dissociation of the trichloride. J. Meyer and R. Backa prepared **vanadium hexamminotrichloride,** $[V(NH_3)_6]Cl_3$, by the action of liquid ammonia on the halide. The compound is decomposed by water, $[V(NH_3)_6]Cl_3 + 3H_2O = V(OH)_3 + 3NH_3 + 3NH_4Cl$; it is unstable in air : $[V(NH_3)_6]Cl_3 + O + 2H_2O = NH_4VO_3 + 3NH_4Cl + 2NH_3$, and in moist air forms the insoluble *hexahydrate,* $[V(H_2O)_6]Cl_3$. These compounds resemble the corresponding compounds of iron and aluminium rather than those of chromium and cobalt. The trichloride is soluble in alcohol and in ether, forming brown soln. The aq. soln. is oxidized to vanadium pentoxide by potassium permanganate. According to W. Halberstadt, when an aq. soln. of vanadium trichloride is boiled with sodium thiosulphate, its colour changes from brown to blue and green. If the thiosulphate is present in large quantities, a dark precipitate, consisting of sulphide and oxide, is thrown down. When an electric current is passed through an aq. soln. of vanadium trichloride acidified with hydrochloric acid, a red soluble substance is formed at the positive pole.

W. Halberstadt, and J. Locke and G. H. Edwards prepared the *hexahydrate,* $VCl_3.6H_2O$, by evaporating a soln. of vanadium trihydroxide in hydrochloric acid in vacuo, taking care to protect the soln. from atm. air during the operations. A. Piccini and N. Brizzi obtained the hexahydrate, by reducing a soln. of vanadium pentoxide in hydrochloric acid by means of the electric current. The green soln. of the trichloride so obtained is cooled with ice and salt, and precipitated by saturating it with hydrogen chloride. Vanadium trichloride, in acid or neutral soln., undergoes no change when kept in a sealed tube in an atm. of dioxide, and the crystalline salt remains unaltered for a considerable time in air kept dry by means of lime. The trichloride corresponds in composition with chromium trichloride, and resembles the violet modification of the latter both in chemical behaviour and when examined by the cryoscopic method.

J. Locke and G. H. Edwards obtained green crystals of **potassium tetrachlorovanadite,** $KVCl_4$, from a mixture of vanadium trichloride and potassium chloride dissolved in conc. hydrochloric acid. A. Stähler obtained what he regarded as **potassium pentachlorovanadite,** K_2VCl_5, analogous with the rubidium salt ; also ammonium pentachlorovanadite, $(NH_4)_2VCl_5$; **rubidium pentachlorovanadite,** $RbVCl_5$, was obtained by evaporating on the water-bath, in a current of hydrogen chloride, an aq. soln. of 3 grms. of hydrated vanadium trichloride and 2 grms. of rubidium chloride. The raspberry-red crystal powder was washed with absolute alcohol. It is sparingly soluble in water and in alcohol. By working in a similar manner cæsium pentachlorovanadite, Cs_2VCl_5, and **magnesium pentachloro-vanadite,** $MgVCl_5$, were obtained.

According to H. E. Roscoe, when the vapour of vanadium oxytrichloride is passed through a red-hot tube, in addition to the oxydichloride, **vanadium dioxy-chloride,** or *divanadyl chloride,* V_2O_2Cl, is formed as a brown, flocculent powder insoluble in water, and **vanadium oxychloride,** or *vanadyl chloride,* VOCl, as a yellow, crystalline powder resembling mosaic gold. The mol. formulæ are unknown. A. Safarik first prepared the former compound, and said that its sp. gr. is 3·64 at 20°; and when heated in air, it becomes blue, and then glows with the formation of vanadium pentoxide. It is freely soluble in nitric acid. E. Wedekind and C. Horst gave $27·17\times10^{-6}$ for the magnetic susceptibility.

H. E. Roscoe found that **vanadium tetrachloride,** VCl_4, is formed by heating vanadium or vanadium nitride to redness in a current of dry chlorine freed from air; and removing any oxytrichloride by fractional distillation in chlorine. It is also produced bv slowly passing the vapour of vanadium oxytrichloride mixed with chlorine through a red-hot layer of sugar-charcoal. The treatment was repeated two or three times with the product of the operation heated in a current of chlorine. Some trichloride always remains behind when the tetrachloride is vaporized. H. Moissan and A. Holt observed the formation of the tetrachloride when chlorine is passed over heated vanadium silicide; F. de Carli, over ferrovanadium; and J. Koppel and co-workers prepared it by passing dry chlorine over crude vanadium obtained by the alumino-thermite process, and removing the oxytrichloride by fractional distillation. W. Biltz and E. Keunecke gave directions for preparing the salt. C. Matignon and F. Bourion prepared the tetrachloride by passing a mixture of the vapour of sulphur monochloride and chlorine over heated vanadium pentoxide. The vapour of oxytrichloride first formed mixed with the sulphur monochloride vapour is made to pass through a 70-cm. tube heated to dull redness. The condensed product is then a mixture of sulphur monochloride and vanadium tetrachloride. This is separated by fractional distillation. J. Meyer and R. Backa made the tetrachloride by the action of chlorine on ferrovanadium at dull redness.

H. Lessheim and co-workers discussed the electronic structure of the tetra-chloride. H. E. Roscoe described vanadium tetrachloride as a dark reddish-brown, viscid liquid of sp. gr. 1·8584 at 0°, 1·8363 at 8°, and 1·8159 at 30°. For the action of heat, *vide supra,* vanadium trichloride. It does not freeze at −18°. J. Koppel and co-workers found that it solidifies in liquid air. W. Biltz and E. Keunecke gave −109° for the m.p. H. E. Roscoe found that the tetrachloride boils at 154° at 760 mm. press. O. Ruff and H. Lickfett gave 153·7° for the b.p. at 768 mm.; and W. Biltz and E. Keunecke, 148·5° at 755 mm. The vap. density is 6·78 between 205° and 215° when the theoretical value for VCl_4 is 6·68. The results are affected by the great tendency of the tetrachloride to split up into the trichloride and chlorine, even in the presence of an excess of chlorine. The tetrachloride decomposes slowly into the trichloride and chlorine, at ordinary temp., and more quickly at the b.p., or when the vapour is passed through a red-hot tube. This decomposition is accelerated by exposure to light. A. Voigt and W. Biltz found the electrical conductivity to be too small to measure. P. Pascal gave $66·2\times10^{-5}$ for the mol. magnetic susceptibility of an aq. soln. of vanadium tetrachloride (hydrolyzed to V_2O_4). The reduction of the vapour of the tetrachloride by hydrogen in the presence of iron was studied by N. Parravano and C. Mazzetti. It forms white fumes in air, and when thrown in water, it is at once decomposed, forming a blue soln. of oxychloride. The tetrachloride does not absorb chlorine at −18°; and when heated with bromine in a sealed tube at 180°, a solid mass is produced, which, when heated to 160° in a current of carbon dioxide, leaves a residue of the tribromide. J. Koppel and co-workers found that the tetrachloride yields a brown soln. with fuming hydrochloric acid. The tetrachloride reacts with alcohol, forming a blue soln.; and with ether, forming a deep red one. J. Koppel and co-workers found that the tetrachloride dissolves without change in chloroform, or in glacial acetic acid. W. Biltz and E. Keunecke found that the tetrachloride does not react with liquid hydrogen sulphide at $-78.5°$. H. E. Roscoe said that the tetrachloride is oxidized to vanadium pentoxide by a soln. of potassium permanganate.

According to H. E. Roscoe, when vanadium oxytrichloride and zinc are heated in a sealed tube at $400°$, zinc chloride, vanadium tetroxide, and a sublimate of **vanadium oxydichloride**, or *vanadyl dichloride*, $VOCl_2$, are produced; if the crystals are then heated to $130°$ in a current of carbon dioxide, any adherent vanadium oxytrichloride is removed. The oxydichloride is also formed as a by-product when the vapour of the oxytrichloride and hydrogen are passed through a red-hot tube. Some dichloride and trichloride are formed at the same time. The oxydichloride forms green tablets which deliquesce on exposure to moist air; it is slowly decomposed by water; and it is freely soluble in nitric acid. J. Koppel and co-workers found that the oxydichloride dissolved in absolute alcohol or acetic acid forms complex chlorides with 2–4 mols of pyridine or quinoline.

H. E. Roscoe was unable to prepare **vanadium pentachloride**, VCl_5, by the action of chlorine on vanadium tetrachloride at $-18°$, or by vaporizing the tetrachloride in an excess of chlorine. According to J. J. Berzelius, when vanadium pentoxide is dissolved in conc. hydrochloric acid, chlorine is evolved, and the pentoxide passes into soln. as if it were the tetroxide. The dark brown soln. does not dry up on evaporation, but furnishes a black liquid, soluble in water. If evaporated by heat, the liquid becomes blue. The blue soln. is also obtained if the vanadium pentoxide is associated with vanadium trioxide, sugar, alcohol, or hydrogen sulphide when it is attacked by the acid. The blue syrup obtained by evaporating the liquid shows no tendency to crystallize. It gives off hydrochloric acid at a gentle heat. A. Guyard, A. Safarik, and numerous others—*vide supra*, vanadium pentoxide—made observations on this subject. A. Ditte said that when the soln. of vanadic acid in hydrochloric acid is conc. by evaporation, the soln. becomes deep brown and deposits dark green, deliquescent crystals, which, when dried in vacuo over potassium hydroxide, have the composition of vanadium trioxydichloride, $V_2O_3Cl_3.4H_2O$; or, according to J. K. Crow, found that the brown deliquescent mass obtained by evaporating the soln. of vanadium pentoxide in hot conc. hydrochloric acid, has the composition: $V_2O_2Cl_4.5H_2O$, sometimes written $V_2O_4.4HCl.3H_2O$, or hydrated vanadium oxydichloride, $VOCl_2.2\frac{1}{2}H_2O$. E. F. Smith and J. G. Hibbs obtained the same substance as a reddish-brown, oily condensate by passing hydrogen chloride over sodium vanadate at $440°$. It dissolves in water, forming a blue soln., and, when treated with conc. hydrochloric acid, or alcohol, the soln. is brown. The change in colour is attributed to the existence of two different hydrates. A. Safarik said that the same product is obtained when vanadium tri- or penta-oxide is treated with hydrochloric acid; and F. Ephraim, that the product of the reaction is identical with that produced by the action of water on vanadium oxytrichloride—*vide infra*. B. Brauner reported the complex **platinum hexachloroxyhypovanadate,** $PtCl_4.VOCl_2.10\frac{1}{2}H_2O$

J. J. Berzelius, and J. F. W. Johnston prepared **vanadium oxytrichloride**, or *vanadyl trichloride*, $VOCl_3$—also called *vanadyl chloride*—by passing dry chlorine over heated vanadium trioxide, or a mixture of vanadium trioxide and carbon at a red-heat, and removed chlorine from the yellow liquid by a current of dry air. H. E. Roscoe added that the distillate is claret-red from admixed tetrachloride, but this can be removed by repeated distillation over sodium. A. Safarik obtained a similar product by the action of dry chlorine on a mixture of finely-divided vanadium pentoxide and lampblack—or, according to H. E. Roscoe, sugar-charcoal. The product is purified by fractional distillation. R. Edson and D. McIntosh used this process. L. l'Hôte obtained the oxytrichloride by passing chlorine over an intimate mixture of vanadium sulphide, lampblack, and oil; C. Matignon and F. Bourion, by passing sulphur chloride vapour over heated vanadium pentoxide, and F. Ephraim, by the action of hydrogen chloride on vanadium pentoxide at $60°$–$80°$:

$V_2O_5+6HCl \rightleftharpoons 2VOCl_3+3H_2O$—the water is removed by using a mixture of vanadium and phosphorus pentoxides—*vide supra.* H. V. A. Briscoe and H. F. V. Little prepared vanadium oxytrichloride by heating the pentoxide in a current of hydrogen so as to convert it into the trioxide, and afterwards heating the trioxide at dull redness in a current of chlorine, and collecting the oxytrichloride in a bulb, trapped with a U-tube containing conc. sulphuric acid, and cooled with ice : $3V_2O_3+3Cl_2 = 2VOCl_3+V_2O_5$. F. E. Brown and J. E. Snyder used a similar process. O. Ruff and H. Lickfett passed chlorine over the pentoxide at a dull red-heat and found oxygen was evolved and the oxytrichloride formed. They also chlorinated a mixture of vanadium pentoxide and sulphur at ordinary temp., and obtained the oxytrichloride. The same product was obtained by heating vanadium trichloride in oxygen. F. Ephraim said that a soln. of vanadium oxytrichloride is obtained by the action of conc. hydrochloric acid on vanadium pentoxide ; and J. Koppel and co-workers, by the action of a soln. of hydrogen chloride in acetic acid, ether, or alcohol on vanadium pentoxide or ammonium metavanadate. W. H. Furman, and L. E. Stout and G. C. Whitaker found that the acidified soln. can be kept some months without change.

A. Safarik, J. J. Berzelius, and H. E. Roscoe described vanadium oxytrichloride as a clear, mobile, pale yellow liquid at ordinary temp. A. Safarik gave 1·764 for the sp. gr. at 20° ; L. l'Hôte, 1·854 at 18° ; H. E. Roscoe, 1·841 at 14·5°, 1·836 at 17·5°, and 1·828 at 24° ; and T. E. Thorpe, 1·865 at 0°, and 1·631 at the b.p. O. Masson, and J. A. Groshans compared the mol. vol. and b.p. of the family of chlorides. H. E. Roscoe did not freeze the liquid at —15°. J. J. Berzelius said that the b.p. is over 100°. A. Safarik gave 127° ; H. E. Roscoe, 126·7° at 767 mm. ; L. l'Hôte, 126·5° ; and T. E. Thorpe, 127·19° at 760 mm. F. E. Brown and J. E. Snyder gave 124°–125° for the b.p. at 739 mm., or 127·19° at 760°. J. F. W. Johnston and A. Safarik found the vapour is greenish-yellow like that of chlorine. A. Safarik gave 6·41 for the vap. density at 227° when the theoretical value for $VOCl_3$ is 6·0 ; H. E. Roscoe gave 6·108 at 186° ; and T. E. Thorpe, 8·564. A. A. Agafonoff measured the electrical conductivity of aq. soln. of vanadium oxytrichloride which become turbid and intensely yellow when kept in sealed vessels. The electrical conductivity undergoes a corresponding change. Thus, at 18°, a freshly prepared soln. containing a mol of vanadium oxytrichloride in 74·06 litres of water has a conductivity of 179·77, which increases to 200·83 after 46 days, and diminishes to 178·34 after a further 9 days. On heating a soln. 42 days old to 30°, 60°, 70°, and 80°, and cooling again to 18°, the values obtained for the conductivity were 192·95, 214·98, 218·97, and 216·96 (or, when slowly cooled, 202·93) respectively. N. Perrakis measured the magnetic properties.

According to H. E. Roscoe, when the vapour of the oxytrichloride is mixed with hydrogen, and passed through a red-hot tube, vanadium trioxide, solid oxychlorides, and a little vanadium tetrachloride are formed. According to J. J. Berzelius, when the liquid is exposed to air, a dense yellowish-red cloud of vanadium pentoxide and hydrochloric acid is evolved ; and the liquid deliquesces rapidly, forming a dense red liquid covered with hydrated vanadium pentoxide ; a small quantity of water renders the liquid turbid, $2VOCl_3+3H_2O=6HCl+V_2O_5$; with a large proportion of water, it forms a pale yellow, transparent liquid having the taste of ferric chloride, and in a few days more, or when heated, the liquid becomes green, and then blue—chlorine is evolved and the liquid dissolves gold. A. Safarik said that when the pale yellow liquid is evaporated, it forms red hydrated vanadium pentoxide without becoming blue. F. E. Brown and J. E. Snyder found that the oxytrichloride dissolves chlorine readily at 0°, but the solubility decreases rapidly with rise of temp. ; bromine is miscible with all proportions of the oxytrichloride at room temp. ; and iodine is slightly soluble. F. Ephraim said that the soln. of the oxytrichloride in conc. hydrochloric acid is brown. F. E. Brown and J. E. Snyder found that sulphur is soluble in vanadium oxytrichloride, and after a time the liquid solidifies and sulphur dioxide is evolved ; O. Ruff and H. Lickfett represented the reaction $2VOCl_3 + S \rightarrow 2VCl_3 + SO_2$. F. E. Brown and J. E. Snyder found that **sulphuryl chloride** is miscible in all proportions with the oxytrichloride. Vanadium oxytrichloride was found by E. Uhrlaub, and H. E. Roscoe to absorb dry **ammonia** rapidly with the evolution of much heat and the formation of a white mass which partly sublimes; at a red-heat, vanadium nitride is formed. F. E. Brown and J. E. Snyder found that at room temp. the oxytrichloride is without action on red or white **phosphorus,** or **phosphorus pentoxide,** while **phosphorus trichloride** reduces vanadium oxytrichloride, forming a precipitate. The oxytrichloride is miscible in all proportions with **phosphorus oxychloride,** and then quickly reacts, forming a precipitate; and it has no action on **arsenic,** or on **bismuth.** H. E. Roscoe said that when the vapour of the oxytrichloride mixed with hydrogen is passed over red-hot **carbon,** dioxide is formed. According to F. E. Brown and J. E. Snyder, the following **hydrocarbons** are miscible in all proportions; they give red soln.; *n*-hexane, *n*-octane, benzene, toluene, petroleum ether, paraffin (when melted). Commercial kerosene and gasoline dissolve and then react, giving murky mixtures. Naphthalene and paraffin are soluble. The following liquid aldehydes react vigorously at room temp. giving insoluble products : anisic aldehyde, benzaldehyde, *n*-butyraldehyde, cinnamic aldehyde, *n*-heptaldehyde, salicylic aldehyde. β-hydroxybenzaldehyde and *o*-nitrobenzaldehyde, both solid, are soluble but not reactive. The following **organic halides** are miscible in all proportions : carbon tetrachloride, chloroform, ethyl bromide, ethyl chloride, ethyl iodide, *iso*-amyl bromide. J. Koppel and co-workers said that the oxytrichloride is insoluble in chloroform, while F. E. Brown and J. E. Snyder said that the two liquids are miscible in all proportions. J. J. Berzelius said that the trioxychloride forms with absolute **alcohol** a red, transparent mixture which changes colour more rapidly than the aq. soln., and ethyl chloride is formed. F. E. Brown and J. E. Snyder said that alcohol is miscible in all proportions with the oxytrichloride, and non-reactive. P. P. Bedson observed that when heated for 2 or 3 hrs. to 60°–°70° with **ether,** a complex $VOCl_3.(C_2H_5)_2O$ is formed. J. Koppel and co-workers found that the soln. in alcohol, ether, or **acetic acid** is dark red; and the alcoholic soln. forms complex salts with **pyridine.** F. E. Brown and J. E. Snyder found that the oxytrichloride is miscible in all proportions with **acetone,** and **acetic anhydride;** and it dissolves **benzophenone** without reaction. According to F. E. Brown and J. E. Snyder, no reaction occurs at ordinary temp. or at the b.p. with the following **metals :** potassium, sodium, copper, aluminium, tin, manganese, iron, nickel, or platinum. There was no evidence of soln. or reaction with the following **anhydrous salts :** aluminium chloride; ammonium molybdate; barium carbonate, chloride, nitrate, and sulphate; bismuth chloride, and sulphate; cadmium bromide, carbonate; calcium carbonate, chloride; ferric chloride; lead nitrate, sulphate; potassium acetate, bromate, bromide, carbonate, chlorate, chloride, chromate, dichromate, ferricyanide, hydroxide, iodide, nitrate, perchlorate, permanganate, pyroantimonate, pyrosulphate, sulphate, hydrosulphate hydrotartrate, thiocyanate; sodium acetate, arsenite, bromide, carbonate, chloride, hydroxide, iodide, nitrate, nitrite, sulphite; strontium carbonate, nitrate, and sulphate. It swells and blackens when boiled with the following **hydrated salts :** barium acetate, chlorate, and hydroxide; bismuth carbonate; potassium alum, antimonyl tartrate, chrome alum, ferrocyanide, oxalate, sodium carbonate, sodium cobaltinitrite, sodium tartrate; sodium ammonium hydrophosphate, hydroarsenate, dichromate, phosphate, hydrophosphate, dihydrophosphate, tartrate, tetraborate; strontium acetate, chloride, probably owing to the removal of water from the crystals and the subsequent hydrolysis of the oxytrichloride. According to J. J. Berzelius, the oxytrichloride can be boiled over potassium without decomposition, and H. E. Roscoe obtained a similar result with sodium and the heavy metals. J. J. Berzelius observed, however, that when potassium is strongly heated in the vapour of the oxytrichloride, it catches fire, producing the alkali chloride and vanadium oxide. H. E. Roscoe found that if the vapour mixed with hydrogen is passed over

heated sodium, a crust of sodium oxide is formed; and with magnesium, there
is a vigorous reaction, forming magnesium chloride and oxide. V. Cuttica and
co-workers found that when vanadium oxytrichloride is treated with magnesium
oxide at ordinary temp. it forms a complex **magnesium oxychlorovanadate,** and
with water it yields magnesium hexavanadate, $Mg_2V_6O_{17}.19H_2O$; when vanadium
oxytrichloride is heated in a sealed tube with copper oxide at 150°–160°, dark green
copper chlorometavanadate, $Cu(VO_3)_2CuCl$, i.e., $Cu=O_2=VOCl.CuVO_3$, is formed;
lead oxide likewise yields brick-red **lead chlorometavanadate,** $Pb(VO_3)_2.PbCl_2$,
i.e., $Pb=O_2=VOCl$, at ordinary temp. thallous oxide yields deep brown **thallous
chloro-dioxyvanadate,** $Tl_2O.VOCl_3$, or $(TlO)_2VCl_3$, which, when treated with water,
furnishes vanadyl chloride and the polyvanadate, $Tl_2O.3V_2O_5$. G. Carobbi fused
a mixture of lead vanadate, lead chloride, and praseodymium vanadate (10 : 2 : 1)
and obtained **lead praseodymium chlorovanadate,** $3(Pb,Pr)_3(VO_4)_2.PbCl_2$.

According to P. Hautefeuille,[2] **calcium chlorovanadate,** *calcium vanadato-
wagnerite,* $CaCl_2.Ca_3(VO_4)_2$, or $Ca_2Cl(VO_4)$, or $Ca(VO_4)(CaCl)$, is formed when a
mixture of calcium chloride and vanadium pentoxide is fused, and the product
washed with water. The white crystals are isomorphous with wagnerite, and have
a sp. gr. of 4·01. Magnesium chloride does not give *magnesium chlorovanadate,*
but rather magnesia, and a vanadium oxychloride; but when a mixture of lead
chloride, litharge, and vanadium pentoxide was similarly heated to dull redness,
and the excess of chloride washed away, yellow, transparent, six-sided prisms of
lead chlorotriorthovanadate, $3Pb_3(VO_4)_2.PbCl_2$, or $Pb_5Cl(VO_4)_3$, are formed.
A. Ditte also made observations on this subject. E. Weinschenk obtained a

similar product by heating lead chloride, ammonium metavanadate, and an excess of ammonium chloride in a sealed tube at 150°–180°.
H. E. Roscoe also obtained this compound by
fusing a mixture of lead orthovanadate and lead
chloride; and M. Amadori's study of the equilibrium conditions is summarized in Fig. 9.
G. Cesaro obtained crystals of the compound by
passing carbon dioxide into a soln. of the compound in alkali-lye.

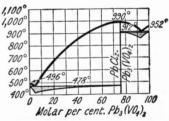

FIG. 9.—Freezing-point Curves of
Mixtures of Lead Chloride and
Orthovanadate.

The discovery of erythronium in the lead
mineral from Zimapan, Mexico, has been
previously described; it was shown that the
discoverer, A. M. del Rio, himself gave up the idea that a new element was
present, and believed that he had mistaken chromium for a new element.
For a time, therefore, this mineral was regarded as a lead chromate. Thus,
A. Brongniart called it *chromate de plomb brun.* After the rediscovery of
erythronium by N. G. Sefström, under the name vanadium, the mineral was
called *Vanadinbleierz* by G. Rose; and **vanadinite** by F. von Kobell. The same
mineral has also been called *vanadium spar,* and *vanadium lead spar.* Analyses
of the mineral from various localities have been reported by C. F. Rammelsberg,
D. Lovisato, H. T. Stearns, A. Frenzel, N. Collie, H. von Struve, A. E. Nordenskjöld, A. Döring, H. F. Keller, F. A. Genth, P. Jannasch, and N. S. Maskelyne.
The analyses show that the mineral is lead chlorotriorthovanadate. In some
cases part of the vanadic acid is isomorphously replaced by phosphoric acid, or
arsenic acid. A mineral with a high proportion of arsenic acid, from Lake Valley,
New Mexico, was called by F. A. Genth and G. vom Rath *endlichite*—after
F. M. Endlich. Some of the chlorine may be replaced; and lead may be partly
replaced by calcium.

The **colour** of vanadinite ranges through deep ruby-red, light-brownish-yellow,
straw-yellow, and reddish-brown. White crystals have not been observed; the
artificial crystals are yellow. It is therefore assumed that the colour is produced
by the vanadic acid; K. von Kraatz-Koschlau and L. Wöhler assumed that

the colour is produced by chromium but the hypothysis is non-proven. Vanadinite may occur in implanted globules or incrustations; and in prismatic **crystals** with smooth faces and sharp edges. The crystals are sometimes cavernous furnishing hollow prisms. The mineral also occurs in rounded forms, and in parallel groupings like pyromorphite. K. Vrba showed that the hexagonal crystals have pyramidal hemihedrism, and the axial ratio $a:c=1:0.71218$—the values range from the $1:0.71121$ to $1:0.7495$ of S. L. Penfield. M. Amadori gave for the artificial crystals $1:0.71115$. No **cleavage** or **twinning** has been observed. The apparent twinning about the (1010)-plane observed by R. W. Smith is produced by parallel growths. Crystals have been described by J. Barthoux, P. Comucci, J. D. Dana, W. Eissner, F. A. Genth, V. Goldschmidt, F. N. Guild, M. F. Heddle, A. L. Heisler, P. Krusch, A. Lacroix, D. Lovisato, W. F. Pettercd, F. P. Paul, K. A. Redlich, W. Rodenbender, W. T. Schaller, A. Sigmund, B. Silliman, G. Smith, L. J. Spencer, H. T. Stearns, C. A. Tenne and S. Calderon, P. A. Wagner, M. Websky, F. Zambonini, and V. R. von Zepharovich. J. Schabus, and C. F. Rammelsberg showed that the crystals are isomorphous with pyromorphite and mimetite. M. Amadori observed the formation of solid soln. with lead fluotriorthovanadate; and also with lead chlorotriorthophosphate; and G. Carobbi and S. Restaino observed the formation of solid soln. with sodium, lanthanum, and praseodymium replacing part of the lead isomorphously. Pseudomorphs of vanadinite after pyromorphite were observed by N. von Kokscharoff, and pseudomorphs of descloizite after vanadinite, by A. Brunlechner. W. Eissner measured the effect of temp. ranging from $-160°$ to $150°$ on the crystalangles of vanadinite and found the results can be represented by a straight line— about $13'$ are involved in the change. A break was observed at $710°$ with the artificial mineral, and this is taken to be a **transition temperature** for α-*vanadinite* and β-*vanadinite*. For the **specific gravity** C. F. Rammelsberg gave $6.635–6.89$; V. R. von Zepharovich, 6.98; D. Lovisato, 6.78 at $22.2°$; H. E. Roscoe, 6.707 at $12°$; H. von Struve, 6.863; H. F. Keller, 6.572; F. A. Genth, $6.862–7.809$; and P. Jannasch, 6.88. The **hardness** is $2.75–3.0$. T. Carnelley found that the **melting point** exceeds $802°$; M. Amadori, Fig. 9, gave $990°$. The m.p. of mixture of chlorovanadinite with the following percentage proportions of related compounds are:

	0	20	50	80	100 per cent.
Chloropyromorphite	990°	1012°	1056°	1116°	1156°
Chloromimetite	990°	1010°	1062°	1096°	1140°
Fluovanadate	990°	978° (25)	964°	942° (25)	916°

H. L. Bowman found the **index of refraction** of endlichite for the red C-line to be $\omega=2.341$, and $\epsilon=2.292$; and for the yellow D-line, $\omega=2.359$, and $\epsilon=2.311$; when the **birefringences** are $\omega-\epsilon=0.047$ respectively. For vanadinite, and redlight, $\omega=2.354$, $\epsilon=2.299$, and $\omega-\epsilon=0.055$. The optical character is negative. The pleochroism is ω, brownish-red, and ϵ, brownish-yellow. T. W. Case observed that the poor conductivity of vanadinite is not appreciably affected by light. E. E. Fairbanks gave $10.8–11.2$ for the **dielectric constant** (water 81). The mineral is insoluble in **water**; it forms lead chloride and a green soln. with **hydrochloric acid**; lead sulphate with **sulphuric acid**; and it readily dissolves in **nitric acid**, forming a yellow soln. A. Lacroix said that when vanadinite is evaporated with a drop of nitric acid on a glass slip, a deep red stain is produced. P. Jannasch and H. F. Harwood found that if **carbon tetrachloride** vapour is passed over the heated mineral, all the vanadium is volatilized, and lead chloride remains.

REFERENCES.

[1] H. E. Roscoe, *Phil. Trans.*, **158**. 1, 1868; **159**. 679, 1869; **160**. 317, 1870; *Proc. Roy. Soc.*, **16**. 220, 1868; **18**. 37, 316, 1870; *Journ. Chem. Soc.*, **21**. 322, 1868; **23**. 344, 1870; **24**. 23, 1871; *Chem. News*, **17**. 135, 1868: **20**. 37, 1869; **21**. 183, 1870; *Phil. Mag.*, (4), **35**. 307, 1868; (4), **39**. 146, 1870; (4), **40**. 62, 1870; J. J. Berzelius, *Acad. Handl. Stockholm*, 1, 1831; *Schweigger's Journ.*, **62**. 323, 1831; **63**. 26, 1831; *Pogg. Ann.*, **22**. 1, 1831; *Ann. Chim. Phys.*, (1), **47**. 337,

1831; *Phil. Mag.*, (2), **10**. 321, 1831; (2), **11. 7**, 1832; A. Piccini and L. Marino, *Zeit. anorg. Chem.*, **32**. 67, 1902; A. Piccini and N. Brizzi, *ib.*, **19**. 394, 1899; J. Meyer and R. Backa, *ib.*, **135**. 177, 1924; W. Biltz and E. Keunecke, *ib.*, **147**. 171, 1925; W. Biltz, *ib.*, **109**. 132, 1919; A. Voigt and W. Biltz, *ib.*, **133**. 277, 1924; R. Edson and D. McIntosh, *Trans. Roy. Soc. Canada*, (3), **9**. 81, 1915; E. Wedekind, *Zeit. angew. Chem.*, **37**. 87, 1924; E. Wedekind and C. Horst, *Ber.*, **45**. 262, 1912; W. Halberstadt, *ib.*, **15**. 1619, 1882; A. Stähler, *ib.*, **37**. 4411, 1904; J. A. Groshans, *ib.*, **19**. 974, 1886; *Phil. Mag.*, (5), **20**. 197, 1885; O. Masson, *ib.*, (5), **30**. 412, 1890; J. Locke and G. H. Edwards, *Amer. Chem. Journ.*, **20**. 594, 1898; F. de Carli, *Atti Congr. Chim. Para Appl.*, 399, 1923; H. Moissan and A. Holt, *Ann. Chim. Phys.*, (7), **27**. 277, 1902; O. Ruff and H. Lickfett, *Ber.*, **44**. 506, 1911; C. Matignon and F. Bourion, *Compt. Rend.*, **138**. 631, 1904; P. Pascal, *ib.*, **147**. 742, 1908; N. Perrakis, *ib.*, **184**. 1430, 1927; A. Ditte, *ib.*, **102**. 1310, 1886; L. l'Hôte, *ib.*, **101**. 1151, 1885; *Ann. Chim. Phys.*, (6), **22**. 407, 1891; A. Guyard, *Bull. Soc. Chim.*, (2), **25**. 58, 381, 1876; A. Safarik, *Sitzber. Akad. Wien*, **33**. 16, 1858; **47**. 252, 1863; N. Parravano and C. Mazzetti, *Rec. Trav. Chim. Pays. Bas*, **42**. 821, 1923; V. Cuttica, A. Tarchi, and P. Alinari, *Gazz. Chim. Ital.*, **53**. i, 189, 1923; J. F. W. Johnston, *Edin. Journ. Science*, (2), **5**. 166, 319, 1831; J. Koppel, R. Goldmann, and A. Kaufmann, *Zeit. anorg. Chem.*, **45**. 346, 1905; F. Ephraim, *ib.*, **35**. 66, 1903; E. F. Smith and J. G. Hibbs, *ib.*, **7**. 41, 1894; *Journ. Amer. Chem. Soc.*, **16**. 578, 1894; F. E. Brown and J. E. Snyder, *ib.*, **47**. 2671, 1925; T. E. Thorpe, *Chem. News*, **24**. 287, 1871; *Journ. Chem. Soc.*, **37**. 384, 1880; J. K. Crow, *ib.*, **30**. 457, 1876; H. V. A. Briscoe and H. F. V. Little, *ib.*, **105**. 1310, 1914; P. P. Bedson, *ib.*, **29**. 309, 1876; *Liebig's Ann.*, **180**. 235, 1876; A. A. Agafonoff, *Journ. Russ. Phys. Chem. Soc.*, **35**. 649, 1903; E. Uhrlaub, *Die Verbindungen einiger Metalle mit Stickstoff*, Göttingen, 1859; *Pogg. Ann.*, **103**. 134, 1858; B. Brauner, *Monatsh.*, **3**. 58, 1882; N. H. Furman, *Journ. Amer. Chem. Soc.*, **50**. 755, 1674, 1928; L. E. Stout and G. C. Whitaker, *Journ. Ind. Eng. Chem.*, **20**. 210, 1928; G. Carobbi, *Atti Accad. Lincei*, (6), **1**. i, 311, 1925; H. Lessheim and R. Samuel, *Zeit. Physik*, **40**. 220, 1926; **42**. 614, 1927; H. Lessheim, J. Meyer and R. Samuel, *ib.* **43**. 199, 1927; *Zeit. anorg. Chem.*, **165**. 253, 1927.

² P. Hautefeuille, *Compt. Rend.*, **77**. 896, 1873; J. Barboux, *ib.*, **175**. 312, 1922; A. Ditte, *ib.*, **96**. 1048, 1883; E. Weinschenk, *Zeit. Kryst.*, **77**. 492, 1890; V. Goldschmidt, *ib.*, **32**. 563, 1900; K. Vrba, *ib.*, **4**. 353, 1800; F. A. Genth and G. vom Rath, *ib.*, **10**. 462, 1885; *Chem. News*, **53**. 218, 1886; *Proc. Amer. Phil. Soc.*, **22**. 363, 1885; F. A. Genth, *ib.*, **23**. 30, 1889; **24**. 23, 36, 1887; H. F. Keller, *ib.*, **24**. 38, 1887; M. Websky, *Zeit. Kryst.*, **5**. 542, 1881; F. N. Guild, *ib.*, **49**. 325, 1911; P. Jannasch, *ib.*, **32**. 561, 1900; F. P. Paul, *ib.*, **52**. 600, 1912; P. Jannasch and H. F. Harwood, *Journ. prakt. Chem.*, (2), **80**. 127, 1909; (2), **97**. 93, 1918; R. P. Greg and W. G. Lettsom, *Manual of the Mineralogy of Great Britain and Ireland*, London, 409, 1858; N. von Kokscharoff, *Materialien zur Mineralogie Russlands*, St. Petersburg, 2. 370, 1856; M. F. Heddle, *The Mineralogy of Scotland*, Edinburgh, 2. 161, 1901; V. R. von Zepharovich, *Lotos*, **38**. 51, 1890; *Zeit. Kryst.*, **20**. 294, 1892; *Mineralogisches Lexikon für des Kaiserthum Oesterreich*, Wien, **2**. 335, 1873; T. Thomson, *Outlines of Mineralogy, Geology, and Mineral Analysis*, London, 1. 573, 1836; F. von Kobell, *Grundzuge der Mineralogie*, Nürnberg, 283, 1838; A. Brongniart, *Traité élémentaire de minéralogie*, Paris, 2. 204, 1887; G. Rose, *Reise nach dem Ural, dem Altai, und dem Kaspischen Meere*, Berlin, **1**. 209, 1837; *Pogg. Ann.*, **29**. 455, 1833; A. Lacroix, *Minéralogie de la France et de ses colonies*, Paris, **4**. 413, 1910; *Bull. Soc. Min.*, **31**. 44, 1908; G. A. Kenngott, *Uebersicht der Resultate mineralogischer Forschungen*, Wien, **48**, 1854; H. E. Roscoe, *Phil. Trans.*, **158**. 1, 1868; **159**. 679, 1869; **160**. 317, 1870; *Proc. Roy. Soc.*, **16**. 220, 1868; **18**. 37, 316, 1870; *Journ. Chem. Soc.*, **21**. 322, 1868; **23**. 344, 1870; **24**. 23, 1871; *Chem. News*, **17**. 135, 1868; **20**. 37, 1869; **21**. 183, 1870; *Phil. Mag.*, (4), **35**. 307, 1868; (4), **39**. 146, 1870; (4), **40**. 62, 1870; J. D. Dana, *A System of Mineralogy*, New York, 774, 1892; C. F. Rammelsberg, *Handbuch der Mineralchemie*, Leipzig, 290, 1875; 258, 1880; *Sitzber. Akad. Berlin*, 661, 1880; *Pogg. Ann.*, **98**. 249, 1856; J. Schabus, *ib.*, **100**. 297, 1857; W. Eissner, *Die Aenderung der Winkel des Apatits, Vanadinits, Pyromorphits und Mimetesits, sowie des optischen Verhältnisse des Apatits im Temperaturbereich von —160° bis +650°, und der Dimorphismus der Apatitgruppe*, Leipzig, 16, 1913; A. Sigmund, *Tschermak's Mitt.*, (2), **23**. 87, 1904; K. A. Redlich, *ib.*, (2), **17**. 518, 1898; A. Frenzel, *ib.*, (2), **3**. 505, 1881; K. von Kraatz-Koschlau and L. Wöhler, *ib.*, (2), **18**. 42, 1899; W. F. Pettered, *Proc. Roy. Soc. Tasmania*, **67**, 1897; A. Brunlechner, *Carinthia*, **2**. 2, 1890; P. Krusch, *Zeit. prakt. Geol.*, **9**. 211, 1901; W. Rodenbender, *ib.*, **9**. 52, 1901; D. Lovisato, *Atti Accad. Lincei*, (5), **12**. 1, 391, 1902; (5), **13**. ti, 43, 1904; C. A. Tenne and S. Calderon, *Die Mineralfundstätten der Iberischen Halbinsel*, Berlin, 242, 1902; N. Collie, *Journ. Chem. Soc.*, **55**. 91, 1889; W. Flight, *ib.*, **25**. 1053, 1872; T. Carnelley, *ib.*, **33**. 289, 1878; A. Arzruni, *Zeit. deut. geol. Ges.*, **37**. 557, 1885; G. Cesaro, *Bull. Acad. Belg.*, 327, 1905; G. Smith, *Proc. Roy. Soc., New South Wales*, **27**. 368, 1893; A. E. Nordenskjöld, *Geol. För. Förh. Stockholm*, **4**. 267, 1879; L. J. Spencer, *Min. Mag.*, **15**. 36, 1908; H. L. Bowman, *ib.*, **13**. 324, 1903; S. L. Penfield, *Amer. Journ. Science*, (3), **32**. 441, 1886; B. Silliman, *ib.*, (3), **32**. 198, 1881; A. M. del Rio, *ib.*, **71**. 7, 1822; *Schweigger's Journ.*, **62**. 324, 1831; *Pogg. Ann.*, **22**. 2, 1831; *Ann. Ciencias Nat. Madrid*, 7. 30, 1804; *Ann. Mines*, (1), **4**. 499, 1819; N. G. Sefström, *Acad. Handl. Stockholm*, 255, 1830; *Schweigger's Journ.*, **62**. 316, 1831; *Pogg. Ann.*, **21**. 43, 1831; *Ann. Chim. Phys.*, (2), **46**. 105, 1831; *Phil. Mag.*, (2), **10**. 151, 1831; R. W. Smith, *Proc. Colorado Scient. Soc.*, **2**. 161, 1887; W. T. Schaller, *Bull. U.S. Geol. Sur.*, 262, 1895; *Journ. Washington Acad.*, **1**. 149, 1911; H. von Struve, *Proc. Russ. Min. Soc.*, **1**, 1857; A. Döring, *Bol. Acad. Cient. Cordoba*, **5**. 498, 1883; N. S. Maskelyne, *Ber.*,

5. 992, 1872 ; M. Amadori, *Gazz. Chim. Ital.*, **49.** i, 38, 69, 1919 ; *Rend. Accad. Lincei*, (5), **21.** ii, 768, 1912 ; (5), 27. i, 143, 1918 ; *Atti 1st. Veneto*, **76.** ii, 419, 1917 ; *Rend. 1st. Lombardo*, **49.** 137, 1916 ; M. Amadori and E. Viterbi, *Mem. Accad. Lincei*, (5), **10.** 386, 1914 ; H. T. Stearns, *Amer. Min.*, **8.** 127, 1923 ; G. Carobbi, *Atti Accad. Lincei*, (6), **1.** i, 311, 1925 ; G Carobbi and S. Restaino, *Gazz. Chim. Ital.*, **56.** i, 59, 1926 ; F. Zambonini, *Memoire per servire alla descrizione della carta geologica d'Italia*, Roma, 1919 ; P. A. Wagner, *Trans. Geol. Soc. South Africa*, **23.** 59, 1921 ; J. Barthoux, *Bull. Soc. Min.*, **47.** 36, 1924 ; E. E. Fairbanks, *Econ. Geol.*, **21.** 399, 1926 ; P. Comucci, *Atti Accad. Lincei*, (6), **3.** 335, 1926 ; T. W. Case, *Phys. Rev.*, (2), **9.** 305, 1917 ; R. L. Heisler, *Eng. Min. Journ.*, **85.** 246, 1908.

§ 20. The Vanadium Bromides

H. E. Roscoe [1] prepared **vanadium tribromide,** VBr_3, by passing dried bromine vapour, freed from air, over red-hot vanadium nitride, and removing the excess of bromine by a current of carbon dioxide ; the same product was obtained by A. Safarik, and H. E. Roscoe by passing bromine over a red-hot mixture of vanadium pentoxide and carbon. The first product is the oxytribromide, then the oxydibromide, and finally the tribromide, which soon chokes up the tube with a sublimate. J. Meyer and R. Backa said that the tribromide is best obtained by the direct union of the elements. O. Ruff and H. Lickfett obtained it by the action of bromine on vanadium carbide at a dull red-heat. According to H. E. Roscoe, vanadium tribromide is a dark grey, amorphous opaque solid ; it is very unstable, and gives off bromine at ordinary temp. ; in moist air it rapidly deliquesces to a brown liquid which furnishes green vanadyl salts when treated with hydrochloric acid. According to J. Locke and G. H. Edwards, vanadium trihydroxide dissolves completely in hydrobromic acid, and, if air be excluded, the evaporation in vacuo furnishes crystals of the *hexahydrate*, $VBr_3.6H_2O$. A. Piccini and N. Brizzi reduced electrolytically a soln. of vanadium pentoxide in conc. hydrobromic acid, and allowed the green liquid, mixed with more conc. hydrobromic acid, to crystallize in a desiccator over lime, and sulphuric acid. The green, hygroscopic, crystalline powder is freely soluble in water, alcohol, and ether. The salt is hydrolyzed by water. The conc. aq. soln. is yellow or brown ; and the acidic soln. green. The green soln. becomes blue on exposure to air. The alcoholic soln. is green. The aq. soln. gives a precipitate of thallous bromide when treated with a soln. of thallous sulphate. J. Meyer and R. Backa made **vanadium hexamminotribromide,** $[V(NH_3)_6]Br_3$, as in the case of the corresponding trichloride (*q.v.*). The properties of the two compounds are similar.

According to J. J. Berzelius, the blue soln. of vanadium tetroxide in hydrobromic acid turns green during its spontaneous evaporation ; and in vacuo, it dries to a blue gum-like mass which, when gently heated, becomes violet-brown, but continues to be completely soluble in water. Alcohol precipitates from the syrupy aq. soln. a gelatinous mass which dissolves as the alcohol evaporates. The **vanadium tetrabromide,** VBr_4, corresponding with the tetrachloride, has not been isolated. H. E. Roscoe found that when the tribromide is treated with an excess of bromine, there is no evidence of the formation of a higher bromide. R. F. Weinland and K. Feige prepared **vanadium heptabromoantimonite,** $VBr_4.SbBr_3.7H_2O$ —*vide* antimony.

A. Guyard found that if vanadium pentoxide be treated with a mixture of bromine, water, and alcohol, a vigorous reaction sets in, and the liquid can be evaporated to dryness below 80°, without decomposition ; and A. Ditte said that if a soln. of vanadium pentoxide in conc. hydrobromic acid be evaporated in vacuo, over sulphuric acid, and potassium hydroxide, crystals of **vanadium dihydrotrioxytetrabromide,** $V_2O_3Br_2.2HBr.7H_2O$, are formed. When treated with aq. ammonia, an ammonium hypovanadate, $(NH_4)_4V_2O_6$, is precipitated. A. Safarik made vanadium oxybromides by heating the more or less reduced pentoxide with bromine. H. E. Roscoe found that if vanadium oxytribromide be heated to 180° it quickly decomposes with bromine and **vanadium oxydibromide,** $VOBr_2$, which appears as a brownish-yellow powder resembling ochre. If further heated it loses all its bromine and forms vanadium pentoxide. According to O. Ruff and H. Lickfett, if bromine vapour or, better still, a mixture of bromine and sulphur bromide vapour is passed over a mixture of vanadium pentoxide and sulphur at a red-heat, the distillate does not consist of vanadium oxytribromide, $VOBr_3$, but of a product which, on being heated in a vacuum at 240°, leaves a residue of pure vanadium oxydibromide, $VOBr_3$, sulphur bromide and bromine distilling away. The oxydibromide deliquesces rapidly in air, and forms a blue soln. with water. O. Ruff and H. Lickfett observed that if vanadium oxydibromide be heated to 360°, part of the compound sublimes undecomposed, and part decomposes leaving a violet residue of **vanadium oxybromide**, $VOBr$; and if this compound be heated in vacuo, vanadium tribromide distils off leaving a residue of vanadium tribromide. The oxybromide yields violet, octahedral crystals of sp. gr. 4·0002 at 18°. The salt is very slightly soluble in water, acetic anhydride, ethyl acetate, and acetone.

H. E. Roscoe found that when the vapour of dry bromine is passed over vanadium pentoxide at a red-heat, the dense white vapours which are early produced, and which condense to a dark red liquid, are mainly **vanadium oxytribromide,** $VOBr_3$. The liquid should be rectified by heating under reduced press.—say at 45° and 100 mm.—so as to expel the bromine. The dark red liquid has a sp. gr. 2·9673 at 0°, and 2·9325 at 14·5°. It distils readily at 130°–136°. It slowly decomposes at ordinary temp., and suddenly at 180°, forming bromine and the oxydibromide. The liquid is very hygroscopic, and is rapidly decomposed in moist air.

According to A. Ditte, if a mixture of vanadium pentoxide, and calcium bromide with an excess of sodium bromide, be kept in a fused state for a short time, white crystals of **calcium bromotriorthovanadate,** $Ca_5Br(VO_4)_3$, or *calcium vanadatobromapatite,* $CaBr_2.3Ca_3(VO_4)_2$, are formed ; and by using P. Hautefeuille's process for the corresponding chloride, tabular crystals of **calcium bromovanadate,** $Ca_2Br(VO_4)$, or $Ca=VO_4-Ca-Br$, or *calcium vanadatobromowagnerite,* $CaBr_2.Ca_3(VO_4)_2$, are produced. Greyish-white hexagonal plates and prisms of **strontium bromotriorthovanadate,** $Sr_5Br(VO_4)_3$, or *strontium vanadatobromapatite,* $SrBr_2.3Ca_3(VO_4)_2$, and **strontium bromovanadate,** $Sr_2Br(VO_4)$, or *calcium vanadatobromowagneriie,* $SrBr_2.Ca_3(VO_4)_2$, were also produced. Hexagonal, greyish-white tablets of **barium bromotriorthovanadate,** $Ba_5Br(VO_4)_3$, or *barium vanadatapatite,* $BaBr_2.3Ba_3(VO_4)_2$, were obtained in an analogous manner. A. Ditte prepared golden-yellow, hexagonal plates of **lead bromotriorthovanadate,** $Pb_5Br(VO_4)_3$, or *lead vanadatobromapatite,* $PbBr_2.3Pb_3(VO_4)_3$, in a similar manner.

REFERENCES.

[1] H. E. Roscoe, *Phil. Trans.*, **158**. 1, 1868 ; **159**. 679, 1869 ; **160**. 317, 1870 ; *Proc. Roy. Soc.*, **16**. 220, 1868 ; **18**. 37, 316, 1870 ; *Journ. Chem. Soc.*, **21**. 322, 1868 ; **23**. 344, 1870 ; **24**. 23, 1871 ; *Chem. News*, **17**. 135, 1868 ; **20**. 37, 1869 ; **21**. 183, 1870 ; *Phil. Mag.*, (4), **35**. 307, 1868 ; (4), **39**. 146, 1870 ; (4), **40**. 62, 1870 ; J. J. Berzelius, *Acad. Handl. Stockholm*, 1, 1831 ; *Schweigger's Journ.*, **62**. 323, 1831 ; **63**. 26, 1831 ; *Pogg. Ann.*, **22**. 1, 1831 ; *Ann. Chim. Phys.*, (1), **47**. 337, 1831 ; *Phil. Mag.*, (2), **10**. 321, 1831 ; (2), **11**. 7, 1832 ; J. Locke and G. H. Edwards, *Amer. Chem. Journ.*, **20**. 594, 1898 ; A. Piccini and N. Brizzi, *Zeit. anorg. Chem.*, **19**. 398, 1899 ; J. Meyer and R. Backa, *ib.*, **135**. 177, 1924 ; R. F. Weinland and K. Feige, *Ber.*, **36**. 260, 1903 ; A. Safarik, *Sitzber. Akad. Wien*, **33**. 14, 1858 ; **47**. 251, 1863 : A. Guyard, *Bull. Soc. Chim.*, (2), **25**. 351, 1876 ; A. Ditte, *Ann. Chim. Phys.*, (6), **8**. 524, 1886 ; *Compt. Rend.*, **94**. 1592, 1882 ; **96**. 575, 846, 1883 ; **102**. 1310, 1886 ; P. Hautefeuille, *ib.*, **77**. 896, 1873 ; O. Ruff and H. Lickfett, *Ber.*, **44**. 2534, 1911.

§ 21. The Vanadium Iodides

J. J. Berzelius,[1] and H. E. Roscoe were unable to prepare **vanadium triiodide,** VI_3, by the action of iodine in the cold or at a higher temp. on vanadium pentoxide or trioxide, or nitride ; nor could J. Meyer and R. Backa prepare this compound.

A. Piccini and N. Brizzi, however, made the *hexahydrate*, $VI_3.6H_2O$, by dissolving vanadium pentoxide in hydriodic acid, and reducing the conc. soln. by electrolysis as in the analogous case of the tribromide or trichloride. The product is mixed with conc. hydriodic acid, and evaporated over calcium oxide, and sulphuric acid at 0°. If the aq. soln. be evaporated at ordinary temp., a brown residue is produced. The small, green, acicular crystals deliquesce in air to a brown liquid. The aq. soln. gives a precipitate of thallous iodide when treated with a soln. of thallous sulphate. The salt is soluble in alcohol.

A. Guyard observed no reaction occurs when vanadium pentoxide, iodine, water, and alcohol are digested together. According to J. J. Berzelius, the blue soln. of vanadium tetroxide in hydriodic acid rapidly becomes green on exposure to air, and when evaporated spontaneously, leaves a brown mass which is soluble in water, forming a dark brown soln., which gives off iodine when treated with sulphuric acid. By evaporating in vacuo the greenish-blue soln. of vanadium pentoxide in hydriodic acid, and removing the excess of iodine with powdered silver, A. Ditte obtained a black deliquescent mass of **vanadium trihydrotrioxypentaiodide**, $V_2O_3I_2.3HI.10H_2O$, and this, when kept some days in a desiccator, furnishes **vanadium dihydrotrioxytetraiodide**, $V_2O_3I_2.2HI.8H_2O.Aq.$; ammonia acts on this salt as in the analogous case of the bromine compound.

By fusing a mixture of vanadium pentoxide, calcium iodide and an excess of potassium iodide, A. Ditte obtained colourless, hexagonal needles of **calcium iodotriorthovanadate**, $Ca_5I(VO_4)_3$, or *calcium vanadatiodapatite*, $CaI_2.3Ca_3(VO_4)_2$; and similarly with **strontium iodotriorthovanadate**, $Sr_5I(VO_4)_3$, or *strontium-vanadatiodapatite*, $SrI_2.3Sr_3(VO_4)_2$; and brown hexagonal prisms of **barium iodotriorthovanadate**, $Ba_5I(VO_4)_3$, or *barium vanadatiodapatite*, $BaI_2.3Ba_3(VO_4)_2$.

REFERENCES.

[1] J. J. Berzelius, *Acad. Handl. Stockholm*, 1, 1831; *Schweigger's Journ.*, 62. 323, 1831; 63. 26, 1831; *Pogg. Ann.*, 22. 1, 1831; *Ann. Chim. Phys.*, (1), 47. 337, 1831; *Phil. Mag.*, (2), 10. 321, 1831; (2), 11. 7, 1832; H. E. Roscoe, *Phil. Trans.*, 158. 1, 1868; 159. 679, 1869; 160. 317, 1870; *Proc. Roy. Soc.*, 16. 220, 1868; 18. 37, 316, 1870; *Journ. Chem. Soc.*, 21. 322, 1868; 23. 344, 1870; 24. 23, 1871; *Chem. News*, 17. 135, 1868; 20. 37, 1869; 21. 183, 1870; *Phil. Mag.*, (4), 35. 307, 1868; (4), 39. 146, 1870; (4), 40. 62, 1870; J. Meyer and R. Backa, *Zeit. anorg. Chem.*, 135. 177, 1924; A. Guyard, *Bull. Soc. Chim.*, (2), 25. 351, 1876; A. Ditte, *Compt. Rend.*, 96. 846, 1883; 102. 1310, 1886; *Ann. Chim. Phys.*, (6), 8. 524, 1886; A. Piccini and N. Brizzi, *Zeit. anorg. Chem.*, 19. 398, 1899.

§ 22. The Vanadium Sulphides and Oxysulphides

There are three well-defined vanadium sulphides: V_2S_2, V_2S_3, and V_2S_5. J. J. Berzelius [1] mistook vanadium oxide, V_2O_2, for vanadium, and when he described the two sulphides VS_2 and VS_3, it must be understood that his V is to be replaced by V_2O_2. J. J. Berzelius said that both compounds can be produced by wet and dry methods. W. E. Kay examined J. J. Berzelius' wet processes, and in the case of $(V_2O_2)S_4$ he found that when prepared by treating a soln. of sodium vanadate with hydrogen sulphides—pouring the liquor into an excess of dil. acid, washing the precipitate in a soln. of hydrogen sulphide; drying it in an atm. of carbon dioxide; and washing out the excess of sulphur with hot carbon disulphide—the product does not correspond with V_2S_5 or with $V_2O_2S_5$, and no definite formula can be assigned to it. Likewise in the case of the lower sulphides prepared by treating a soln. of vanadium pentoxide in hydrochloric acid and hydrogen sulphide; the precipitate was dissolved in fresh ammonium hydrosulphide soln., and precipitated by pouring the soln. into an excess of dil. acid. The product corresponds neither with V_2S_3 nor with $V_2O_2S_3$. It is a mixture of variable composition. On the other hand, the sulphide prepared in the dry way by J. J. Berzelius was shown by W. E. Kay to be a true trisulphide, V_2S_3, and he added that if

J. J. Berzelius had analyzed the product completely he would probably have ascertained the true nature of vanadium and of its compounds.

W. E. Kay showed that when compared with the oxides, the sulphides of vanadium are compounds of inferior stability ; for whilst in the oxygen series the penta-compound is stable at redness in a neutral atm., in the sulphur series the penta- is converted into the tri-sulphide. Again, in hydrogen at intense redness, the trioxide is permanent ; whilst the trisulphide is, under similar conditions, reduced to disulphide.

F. Hewett described a black mineral occurring at Minasragra, Peru, and it was named **patronite**—after A. R. Patrona. The observation of J. J. Bravo, and W. F. Hillebrand show that the black mineral has a complex composition but contains a large proportion of a vanadium sulphide—perhaps VS_4.

W. E. Kay prepared **vanadium disulphide,** V_2S_2, by heating vanadium trisulphide at a red-heat for 4–8 days in an atm. of hydrogen. It forms a black or a brownish-black powder with a bronze lustre, and sp. gr. 4·2–4·4. The disulphide rapidly absorbs oxygen, and when heated in air, gives off sulphur dioxide and passes through the stages of blue and black oxide into the fused crystalline pentoxide. If it be heated in a limited supply of air, free sulphur is also given off, the oxygen being retained by the vanadium. Boiling hydrochloric acid, both conc. and dil., and boiling dil. sulphuric acid attack the disulphide but very slightly ; cold conc. sulphuric acid does not act upon it, but it is dissolved by the hot acid to a greenish-yellow soln. Dil. nitric acid attacks the trisulphide slowly, the soln. being coloured blue ; with the hot dil. acid the action is more rapid, whilst by the conc. hot acid the substance is violently oxidized, and the soln. contains vanadic sulphate. Soda-lye, and aq. ammonia attack the vanadium trisulphide but slightly, either in the cold or on heating ; yellow ammonium sulphide slowly dissolves the disulphide, forming a wine-red soln., whilst in the case of the freshly prepared colourless ammonium hydrosulphide the liquid acquires a purple tint. Potassium hydrosulphide acts slowly on the disulphide, yielding a violet-red soln. E. Wedekind and C. Horst gave $7·22 \times 10^{-6}$ for the magnetic susceptibility.

J. J. Berzelius said that the lower oxide of vanadium does not combine with sulphur when a mixture of the two is heated, or when the vapour of sulphur is passed over the heated oxide. If vanadium trioxide be heated to redness in a current of hydrogen sulphide, **vanadium trisulphide,** V_2S_3, as black powder, is formed ; if the tetroxide be employed, the hydrogen sulphide first reduces it to the trioxide : $V_2O_4 + H_2S = S + V_2O_3 + H_2O$; and this then passes to the trisulphide : $V_2O_3 + 3H_2S = 3H_2O + V_2S_3$. A. Safarik obtained a similar result with vanadium pentoxide ; and, according to W. E. Kay, any vanadium compound can be used. To prepare the trisulphide, W. E. Kay recommended heating the pentoxide in the vapour of carbon disulphide, when the trisulphide appears in greyish-black tablets resembling graphite. A. Safarik gave 4·7 for the sp. gr. of the powder at 21° ; and W. E. Kay gave 3·7 for the sp. gr. of the crystals and 4·0 for that of the powder. A. Karl said that vanadium sulphide is triboluminescent. E. Wedekind and C. Horst gave $8·95 \times 10^{-6}$ for the magnetic susceptibility. When the trisulphide is heated in air or oxygen the trisulphide is oxidized similarly to the disulphide, but much less readily. Sulphur dioxide is evolved, and the blue and black oxides formed, these gradually passing into the pentoxide. The trisulphide is but slightly attacked by dil. or conc. hydrochloric acid, either in the cold or on heating. Hot dil. sulphuric acid also acts upon it but slowly, but by the conc. and hot acid it is more rapidly dissolved. Dil. nitric acid acts upon the trisulphide slowly in the cold and more rapidly on heating, forming a blue soln., as in the case of the disulphide ; by the conc. acid it is readily oxidized in the cold, whilst in the case of the hot acid the oxidation proceeds with violence. Soda-lye, and aq. ammonia have a slight solvent action on the trisulphide. Yellow ammonium sulphide acts upon the substance slowly, forming a wine-red liquid ; whilst with the colourless ammonium hydrosulphide a purple-coloured soln. is obtained, identical in appearance with that formed in the case of the disulphide. The colour of the liquid produced on soln. in potassium hydrosulphide is violet-red.

J. J. Berzelius said that vanadium trisulphide unites with the more basic metal sulphides, forming **sulphovanadites.** The alkali sulphovanadites are said to be made by saturating an alkali vanadite with hydrogen sulphide ; by mixing the vanadite with an alkali monosulphide ; by dissolving hydrated vanadic trioxide in an alkali hydrosulphide ; or by mixing a vanadium salt with an alkali hydrosulphide. To avoid the formation of a sulphovanadate, the vanadium salt should be free from vanadate, and the alkali hydrosulphide free from an excess of sulphur. The insoluble sulphovanadites are obtained by double decomposition. J. J. Berzelius described *ammonium, potassium, and sodium sulphovanadites* as being soluble in water, forming purple soln. resembling those of potassium permanganate ; and they are rendered turbid by the heavy metal sulphides ; *barium, strontium, and calcium sulphovanadites* are said to be reddish-brown salts sparingly soluble in water. These products are probably oxysulphovanadates. They want re-examining.

According to W. E. Kay, if a mixture of vanadium trisulphide and sulphur be heated to 400°, in the absence of air, a black powder of **vanadium pentasulphide,** V_2S_5, is formed. The sp. gr. is 3·0. When the pentasulphide is heated in the air it gives off sulphur dioxide, and is converted into the black oxide, which, on further heating, passes into the fused pentoxide. If, however, the heat be very carefully applied, some free sulphur is first given off without this taking fire. Heated in a neutral atmosphere, the pentasulphide loses two atoms of sulphur, being converted into trisulphide. The pentasulphide is but slightly attacked by hot conc. hydrochloric acid, and by hot dil. sulphuric acid, whilst by conc. sulphuric acid it is slowly dissolved, forming a yellow soln. Hot dil. nitric acid dissolves the pentasulphide slowly, but completely ; whilst by the conc. acid it is more energetically oxidized. Ammonia does not easily attack the pentasulphide, but it is readily dissolved by soda-lye especially on heating, forming a yellow soln. In this respect it differs markedly from the other vanadium sulphides which dissolve but slightly in soda-lye. The pentasulphide is slowly acted upon by the alkaline sulphides. With colourless ammonium hydrosulphide the soln. has the purple colour also yielded by the other vanadium sulphides. To obtain this colour in perfection, it is necessary that the hydrosulphide soln. shall be completely sat. with sulphuretted hydrogen, and the colour is best obtained by passing hydrogen sulphide to excess through ammonia soln., containing the pentasulphide in suspension. If the hydrogen sulphide be not present in excess, the liquid has a rich carmine-red colour. The soln. of pentasulphide in yellow ammonium sulphide is a brownish-red, whilst that in potassium hydrosulphide is wine-red. E. Wedekind and C. Horst gave $12·55 \times 10^{-6}$ for the magnetic susceptibility.

J. J. Berzelius said that the higher sulphide combines with the more basic metal sulphides to form **sulphovanadates.** His salts were probably oxysulphovanadates. They were made by treating an aq. soln. of an alkali vanadate with hydrogen sulphide or ammonium hydrosulphite ; by dissolving vanadium pentoxide in alkali hydrosulphide soln. ; by dissolving the higher sulphide in soln. of alkali hydroxide, carbonate, or hydrosulphide ; by fusing vanadium oxide with potassium carbonate and sulphur ; and the insoluble sulphovanadates, by double decomposition. The dry sulphovanadates are blackish-brown. The potassium and sodium salts form reddish-brown aq. soln. ; the barium, strontium, and calcium salts are sparingly soluble ; and the others are insoluble. Acids precipitate the higher sulphide from soln. of the sulphovanadate, but the lower sulphide is decomposed at the same time making the soln. appear blue. Alcohol gives a dark red crystalline precipitate when added to the aq. soln.

Vanadium, unlike columbium and tantalum, forms a series of salt derivatives of sulphovanadic acid, and a number of well-crystallized salts have been prepared by wet and dry methods. G. Krüss and K. Ohnmais prepared a series of sulphovanadates, and oxysulphovanadates. They found that **ammonium orthosulphovanadate,** $(NH_4)_3VS_4$, is deposited in crystals when hydrogen sulphide is passed for several hours into an ice-cold sat. soln. of ammonium metavanadate in ammonium hydrate of sp. gr. 0·898, and the dark-violet soln., obtained in this way is kept for some days. It can be more conveniently prepared by adding a soln. of ammonium hydrosulphide to a soln. of potassium metavanadate or sodium pyrovanadate ; after a comparatively short time, ammonium sulphovanadate separates from the soln. in rhombic crystals with the axial ratios $a : b : c = 0.9825 : 1 : 1.742$, similar in appearance to those of potassium permanganate ; its sp. gr. is 1.6202. The aq. soln. gives precipitates of sulphides or sulphovanadates with soln. of salts of copper, silver, zinc, and manganese, but not with salts of magnesium or the alkaline earths. G. Krüss and K. Ohnmais did not isolate **potassium orthosulphovanadate,** K_3VS_4, but they obtained solid soln. or mixtures of ammonium and potassium orthosulphovanadates by treating a soln. of potassium vanadate in potash with hydrogen sulphide, and then mixing it under different conditions with a soln. of ammonium sulphovanadate in ammonium hydrosulphide ; the analyses of these mixtures showed that they contained the normal ammonium salt, and most probably also the normal potassium salt.

G. A. Goyder described a mineral from Burra, South Australia, which was at first thought to be a copper vanadite, but later was shown to be **cuprous ortho-sulphovanadate,** Cu_3VS_4. It was called sulvanite. It is bronze-yellow, with a metallic lustre. The sp. gr. is 4.0, and the hardness 3.5. It was also described by A. Dieseldorff. A. Carnot obtained what was thought to be impure cupric sulphovanadate by adding ammonium hydrosulphide to a soln. of a vanadate and a copper salt.

G. Krüss prepared **sodium oxytrisulphorthovanadate,** Na_3VS_3O, by melting a mixture of vanadium pentoxide and sodium carbonate with a large excess of sulphur, until all the free sulphur was vaporized or burnt. The cold powdered product was extracted first with alcohol, then with carbon disulphide, and again with alcohol. J. Locke obtained this salt by the action of hydrogen sulphide on red-hot sodium orthovanadate. The same salt was probably prepared by J. A. Norblad by melting a vanadiferous slag with sodium carbonate, sulphur, and carbon. G. Krüss said that the product is a reddish-brown crystalline powder, which melts with very little decomposition to a red liquid. It forms a red soln. with water ; this rapidly decomposes and becomes green. The salt is sparingly soluble in alcohol. G. Krüss and K. Ohnmais prepared the *pentahydrate*, $Na_3VS_3O.5H_2O$, in crystals when a soln. of soda-lye of sp. gr. 1.122 (30 c.c.) is sat. with hydrogen sulphide, mixed with an aq. soln. (6 c.c.) of sodium pyrovanadate (3 grms.), and hydrogen sulphide passed through the ice-cold mixture for 4 hrs. ; it forms small, dark reddish-brown, very deliquescent crystals, and gradually loses the whole of its water when heated.

G. Krüss and K. Ohnmais prepared **sodium trioxysulphorthovanadate,** $Na_3VSO_3.10H_2O$, as an oil when freshly-prepared sodium hydrosulphide is added to a boiling soln. of sodium pyrovanadate, the mixture boiled for a short time, and the ice-cold, filtered soln. treated with alcohol (3 vols.) ; after being repeatedly washed with cold alcohol, it solidifies to a mass of orange-red crystals. It melts at 18°, and its sp. gr. is 1.7727.

G. Krüss and K. Ohnmais prepared **potassium oxyhexasulphopyrovanadate,** $(NH_4)_4V_2S_6O$, by passing hydrogen sulphide into a soln. of ammonium metavanadate in aq. ammonia of sp. gr. greater than 0.898 ; on keeping the red soln. for some months at a low temp., a considerable quantity of the salt is deposited in crystals. It is rather darker in colour than the normal salt, and its sp. gr. is 1.7155. The aq. soln. gives precipitates of sulphides or sulphovanadates with soln. of salts of copper, silver, zinc, and manganese, but not with salts of mag-nesium or the alkaline earths. The corresponding **potassium oxyhexasulphopyro-vanadate,** $K_4V_2S_6O.3H_2O$, can be prepared by treating an ice-cold soln. of potas-sium vanadate in potash-lye of sp. gr. 1.472, with hydrogen sulphide in absence of air ; after a long time, the salt separates from the soln. in crystals resembling those of freshly-prepared potassium permanganate ; it has a sp. gr. of 2.1443. When carefully heated at 150°, it is converted into the anhydrous salt, $K_4V_2S_6O$, but if heated too quickly, it melts to a cherry-red liquid, and, on continued heating, is decomposed with liberation of sulphur. If the mother-liquor in the preparation of this salt be evaporated over phosphorus pentoxide, crystals of a *hemitrihydrate*, $2K_4V_2S_6O.3H_2O$, of sp. gr. 2·1195, are formed. J. Locke found that when sodium pyrovanadate is heated to 580°–700° in a current of hydrogen sulphide, there is formed **sodium dioxypentasulphopyrovanadate**, $Na_4V_2S_5O_2$, in crystals which, in colour and lustre, resemble potassium permanganate; when the hot salt soln. is exposed to the air, it gives off sulphur dioxide, and is converted into sodium hypovanadate. The salt is very hygroscopic, and dissolves in water, to form a deep reddish-purple soln., rapidly changing in colour as hydrogen sulphide is given off, and finally becoming colourless. This colour change is accompanied by a remarkable alteration in the colour of the free sulphovanadic acid, which separates on addition of hydrochloric acid. From the freshly prepared soln., the precipitate is black, and from the nearly oxidized soln. is pale orange. These acids are, however, so unstable as to render their isolation in a pure state practically impossible. Unsuccessful attempts were made to prepare analogous salts of the heavy metals, but lead .pyrovanadate alone yielded a definite compound—**lead pentoxydisulphopyrovanadate**, $Pb_2V_2S_2O_5$, as a black, lustrous, crystalline powder. L. Thompson's *argyllite* from Inverary, Scotland, is thought to be a lead sulphovanadate.

REFERENCES.

[1] W. E. Kay, *Journ. Chem. Soc.*, 37. 728, 1880; J. J. Berzelius, *Acad. Handl. Stockholm*, 1, 1831; *Schweigger's Journ.*, 62. 323, 1831; 63. 26, 1831; *Pogg. Ann.*, 22. 1, 1831; *Ann. Chim. Phys.*, (1), 47. 337, 1831; *Phil. Mag.*, (2), 10. 321, 1831; (2), 11. 7, 1832; A. Karl, *Compt. Rend.*, 146. 1104, 1908; E. Wedekind, *Zeit. angew. Chem.*, 37. 87, 1924; E. Wedekind and C. Horst, *Ber.*, 45. 262, 1912; A. Safarik, *Sitzber. Akad. Wien*, 47. 251, 1863; J. A. Norblad, *Acta Lund. Univ.*, 2. 1, 1874; *Bull. Soc. Chim.*, (2), 23. 64, 1875; F. Hewett, *Eng. Min. Journ.*, 82. 385, 1906; J. J. Bravo, *Informaciones y memorias*, Lima, 8. 171, 1906; W. F. Hillebrand, *Amer. Journ. Science*, (4), 24. 148, 1907; J. Locke, *Amer. Chem. Journ.*, 20. 373, 1898; G. Krüss and K. Ohnmais, *Ber.*, 23. 2511, 1890; *Liebig's Ann.*, 263. 39, 1891; G. Krüss, *Zeit. anorg. Chem.*, 3. 204, 1893; G. A. Goyder, *Trans. Roy. Soc. South Australia*, 24. 69, 1900; *Journ. Chem. Soc.*, 77. 1094, 1900; A. Dieseldorff, *Zeit. prakt. Geol.*, 9. 421, 1901; A. Carnot, *Compt. Rend.*, 105. 121, 1887; L. Thompson, *Journ. Acta Sciences*, 16. 260, 1862.

§ 23. The Vanadium Sulphates

A. Piccini [1] prepared **hypovanadous sulphate**, $VSO_4.7H_2O$, by reducing a sulphuric acid soln. of vanadium pentoxide by means of an electric current in the absence of air. The violet-blue soln., when evaporated in vacuo over sulphuric acid furnished violet, monoclinic crystals of the salt. The crystals are isomorphous with those of ferrous sulphate with which it forms solid soln., $(Fe,V)SO_4.7H_2O$; similarly also with magnesium sulphate, $(Mg,V)SO_4.7H_2O$. Hypovanadous sulphate also forms mixed crystals with chromium and other sulphates—for V. Auger's observations, *vide supra*. These are decomposed on exposure to air. Amethyst-blue crystals of **ammonium hypovanadous sulphate**, $(NH_4)_2SO_4.VSO_4.6H_2O$, or **ammonium sulphatohypovanadite**, $(NH_4)_2V(SO_4)_2.6H_2O$, by the electrolysis of a sulphuric acid soln. of vanadium pentoxide containing ammonium sulphate. It is not so easily oxidized as hypovanadous sulphate. The crystals are monoclinic and isomorphous with the double salts of magnesium sulphate. The corresponding **potassium hypovanadous sulphate**, or **potassium sulphatohypovanadate**, $K_2V(SO_4)_2.6H_2O$, was prepared in a similar way. It is not so highly coloured as the ammonium salt. All these salts dissolve in water, forming yellow or brownish-yellow soln. which in the presence of acids turn blue. Both the acidic and neutral soln. absorb oxygen from air with great rapidity. In a similar manner A. Piccini and L. Marino prepared **rubidium hypovanadous sulphate**, $Rb_2V(SO_4)_2.6H_2O$, or **rubidium sulphatohypovanadite** contaminated with some rubidium alum.

J. T. Brierley [2] tried to make **vanadous sulphate**, $V_2(SO_4)_3$, by reducing a dil.

sulphuric acid soln. of vanadium pentoxide by zinc, but he could not separate the resulting zinc and vanadous sulphates. A. Stähler and H. Wirthwein prepared the anhydrous salt by slowly heating hexahydrated hydrovanaditodisulphuric acid to 180° in an atm. of carbon dioxide. The microcrystalline powder forms a yellowish-brown soln. with hydrochloric acid, and a green soln. with dil. sulphuric acid. J. Meyer and E Markowicz obtained the *enneahydrate*, $V_2(SO_4)_3.9H_2O$, and the *deca-* or *enneahydrate*, $V_2(SO_4)_3.9$(or 10)H_2O, from soln. acidified with a little dil. sulphuric acid. The *trihydrate*, $V_2(SO_4)_3.3H_2O$, was also obtained from conc. sulphuric acid soln. J. T. Brierley reduced electrolytically a conc. soln. of the pentoxide in dil. sulphuric acid, using a platinum dish as cathode, and a platinum plate as anode, until a drop of the soln. shaken up with a little water gave a green coloration without any sign of blue. The conc. green trioxide soln. was then mixed with about twice its bulk of conc. sulphuric acid, and allowed to remain for 24 hrs. ; at the end of that time the whole of the trioxide separated in combination with sulphuric acid as a pale green, sandy crystalline precipitate, which was placed upon a porous tile, washed with conc. alcohol until the free sulphuric acid was entirely removed, and then dried over sulphuric acid in a desiccator filled with an inert gas. The product was **vanadous hydrodisulphate**, $V_2O_3.4SO_3.9H_2O$, or $HV(SO_4)_2.4H_2O$. Sulphate of tervalent vanadium dissolves in water, yielding a bright green soln., from which alkalies precipitate the hydrated trioxide as a dirty green, somewhat gelatinous mass, which is rapidly oxidized in the air. This green hydrated trioxide readily dissolves in a soln. of the foregoing green sulphate, forming a deep chocolate-coloured liquid, and on evaporation this liquid yields a shining green amorphous mass, which again dissolves in water, forming a brown soln. M. C. Boswell and J. V. Dickson found that vanadium sulphate is oxidized when fused with sodium hydroxide. A. S. Russell recommended vanadous sulphate in place of titanous sulphate as a reducing agent. It is rather more powerful in its action ; indeed, it reduces titanic sulphate in the cold. A $0.1N$-soln. in $10N$-H_2SO_4 is not measurably oxidized when kept in a burette for an hour. It reduces all organic and inorganic substances reduced by titanous sulphate.

According to J. Meyer and E. Markowicz, the sulphates of tervalent vanadium representing **hydrovanaditodisulphuric acid**, $HV(SO_4)_2.nH_2O$, may be arranged in two classes. (i) Those obtained by reducing vanadyl salts electrolytically, represented by J. T. Brierley's *tetrahydrate*, $HV(SO_4)_2.4H_2O$, or $[V(H_2O)_4](SO_4)(HSO_4)$, and its ammonium salt, $(NH_4)V(SO_4)_2.4H_2O$; the salts prepared by A. Stähler and H. Wirthwein, namely, the *hexahydrate*, $HV(SO_4)_2.6H_2O$, $[V(H_2O)_6](SO_4)(HSO_4)$—by the electrolytic reduction of blue vanadyl sulphate. The green, finely crystalline powder is insoluble in alcohol, ether, acetic acid, or 60 per cent. sulphuric acid ; the aq. soln. is green. There are also ammonium and rubidium salts. The hypothetical *dodecahydrate*, $HV(SO_4)_2.12H_2O$, or $[V(H_4O_2)_6](SO_4)(NH_4SO_4)$, is represented by ammonium vanadic alum ; and by G. Scagliarini and A. Airoldi's *vanadium pyridine sulphate*, $[V(C_5H_5N)(H_2O)_3(SO_4)](HSO_4)$. (ii) J. Meyer and E. Markowicz prepared a series of salts by adding variable quantities of sulphuric acid to a soln. of vanadium acetate in acetic acid. Thus, the *pentahydrate*, $HV(SO_4)_2.5H_2O$, or $[V(H_2O)_4](SO_4)(HSO_4).H_2O$, was found to lose a mol. of water when allowed to stand over phosphorus pentoxide at room temp. and furnish the *tetrahydrate*, $HV(SO_4)_2.4H_2O$, which is said not to be identical with J. T. Brierley's tetrahydrate, but rather an isomer. Aq. soln. of the salt furnishes the *hexahydrate*, $HV(SO_4)_2.6H_2O$, which is said not to be identical with A. Stähler and H. Wirthwein's hexahydrate, but rather an isomer several of which are possible— *e.g.* $[V(SO_4)_2(H_2O)_2]H.4H_2O$; $[V(SO_4)(H_2O)_4](HSO_4)$, etc. ; and also the *octohydrate*, $HV(SO_4)_2.8H_2O$, or $[V(H_4O_2)_4](SO_4)(HSO_4)$. A soln. in conc. sulphuric acid gives the *dihydrate*, $HV(SO_4)_2.2H_2O$. Vanadous sulphate forms a series of complex salts with the alkali sulphates, forming a series of **vanadium-alums**, $RV(SO_4)_2.12H_2O$. G. Canneri made a quinidine vanadium alum.

A. Piccini prepared **ammonium vanadous sulphate,** or *ammonium vanaditodi-sulphate, or disulphatovanadite,* $(NH_4)V(SO_4)_2.12H_2O$, by dissolving 5–10 grms. of ammonium metavanadate in sulphuric acid in the molar proportions 2 : 3 ; adding 100–200 c.c. of a sat. soln. of sulphur dioxide, and driving off the excess by heating the liquid on a water-bath ; making the liquid up to its original vol. with water, and electrolyzing the filtered soln. until the soln. is green without a trace of blue.   The filtered soln. is then evaporated in vacuo for crystallization.   A. Bültemann electrolyzed the soln. with a clean lead or platinum cathode and a porous diaphragm.   The current efficiency is quantitative with cathodic current density up to 0·05 amp. per sq. cm.   When crystallized from sulphuric acid, the crystals are blue, and when crystallized from neutral soln., red.   This salt was made by A. Rosenheim and H. yu Mong.   J. Meyer and E. Markowicz observed that the pure alum is blue, and that the red colour is produced by traces of adsorbed tervalent vanadium hydroxide or oxide.   R. Marc has previously shown that the adsorption of traces of foreign coloured substances by the surfaces of crystals may profoundly modify the colour. A. Piccini said that the violet or wine-red crystals are less intensely coloured than the corresponding chrome alum.   The diakisdodecahedral crystals belong to the cubic system.   The index of refraction for red-light is 1·5070 ; for yellow-light, 1·4751 ; for green-light, 1·4784 ; blue-light, 1·4839 ; and for violet-light, 1·4858. The crystals are extremely soluble in water ; 100 parts of water at 10° dissolve 39·76 parts of salt.   J. Locke gave 1·210 mols per litre at 25°.   The conc. aq. soln. is chrome-green, and on dilution with water it becomes greenish-yellowish brown, brownish-yellow, and finally pale yellow—if sulphuric or hydrochloric acid be added, the soln. becomes green.   When confined over sulphuric acid, at 25°–30°, about eight-ninths of the water of crystallization is lost ; at 230° all is lost ; and at 300°, the salt decomposes.   J. Locke gave 45° for the temp. at which the salt melts in its water of crystallization.   In addition to vanadium ammonia alum, or the *dodecahydrate,* $NH_4V(SO_4)_2.12H_2O$, J. T. Brierley obtained the *tetrahydrate,* $(NH_4)V(SO_4)_2.4H_2O$; and A. Stähler and H. Wirthwein found that hexahydrated hydrovanaditodisulphuric acid furnishes the *hexahydrate* of the ammonium salt, $(NH_4)V(SO_4)_2 6H_2O$.   By treating a soln. of vanadium pentoxide in dil. sulphuric acid in the molar proportion 1 : 2, reducing with sulphuric acid as in the case of the ammonium salt just described, adding sodium sulphate, and reducing electrolytically, A. Piccini found that the syrupy liquid so obtained can be crystallized by keeping it at 0° for a long time.   The cubic crystals of **sodium vanadous sulphate,** or *sodium disulphatovanadite,* $NaV(SO_4)_2.12H_2O$, melt at 9° in their water of crystallization.   This salt was made by A. Rosenheim and H. yu Mong.   A. Piccini prepared **potassium vanadous sulphate,** or *potassium disulphatovanadite,* $KV(SO_4)_2.12H_2O$, in a similar way.   This salt was made by A. Rosenheim and H. yu Mong, and E. Renschler.   A. Bültemann said that the crystals behave like those of the ammonium salt.   According to A. Piccini, the violet, diakisdodecahedral crystals belong to the cubic system ; they melt in their water of crystallization at 20°.   The sp. gr. is 1·782 at 20°/4°.   F. A. Henglein studied the mol. vol. of the potassium, rubidium, and cæsium salts.   They are freely soluble in water, and crystallize only at a low temp. below 10° ; 100 parts of water at 10° dissolve 1984 parts of salt.   The dil. soln. are yellow ; the conc. soln., brownish-yellow ; and the syrupy liquid, green.   In air, the soln. changes slowly.   The crystals lose a part of their water of crystallization when confined over sulphuric acid ; at 100°, 35 per cent. is lost in 12 hrs. ; and all is expelled at 230°.   The salt melts at 20° in its water of crystallization.   A. Piccini obtained **rubidium vanadous sulphate** or *rubidium vanaditodisulphate, or disulphatovanadite,* $RbV(SO_4)_2.12H_2O$, in a similar manner.   The cubic crystals are similar and show no cleavage.   A. Bültemann found that the crystals behave like those of the ammonium salt.   A. Piccini said that the sp. gr. is 1·915 at 20°/4°.   The index of refraction for red-light is 1·4689; for green-light, 1·4758; and for violet-light, 1·4799.   The absorption spectrum has bands in the red, green, and violet.   The crystals are less soluble than the ammonium salt, for 100 parts of water dissolve only 2·56 parts of salt at 10°. Dil. aq. soln. are yellow or brownish-yellow and become green when an acid is added. They do not change in weight with 24 hrs.' exposure to air; at 100°, they lose water and become yellowish-green; at 230°, the water is all expelled; and at 300°, decomposition occurs. J. Locke found that the salt melts at 64° in its water of crystallization. In addition to the *dodecahydrate* just described, A. Stähler and H. Wirthwein obtained the *hexahydrate*, $RbV(SO_4)_2.6H_2O$, as in the case of the corresponding ammonium salt. A. Piccini prepared **cæsium vanadous sulphate** or *cæsium disulphatovanadite*, $CsV(SO_4)_2.12H_2O$, by the method employed for the other alums. A. Bültemann said that the crystals from sulphuric acid soln. are amethyst-violet and from neutral soln., ruby-red. A. Piccini added that the diakisdodecahedral crystals are cubic, with no cleavage. The sp. gr. is 2·033 at 20°/4°. The index of refraction for red-light is 1·4757; for yellow-light, 1·4780; for green-light, 1·4807; and for violet-light, 1·4878. The crystals are sparingly soluble in cold water, for 100 parts of water at 10° dissolve only 0·464 part of salt. They are more soluble in hot water so that the salt is readily crystallized from aq. soln. The neutral soln. prepared by heat are always brownish-yellow, never green. They lose some water at 100°; all is lost at 230°; and decomposition occurs at 300°. J. Locke said that the salt melts at 82° in its water of crystallization. F. Ephraim studied the mol. vols. of the potassium, rubidium, and cæsium vanadium alums. A. Piccini prepared **thallium vanadous sulphate,** or *thallium disulphatovanadite*, $TlV(SO_4)_2.12H_2O$, by the method employed for the other alums. The reddish-violet, diakisdo-decahedral crystals belong to the cubic system. The sp. gr. is 2·342 at 20°/4°. The index of refraction for medium red-light is 1·5070; for green, 1·5138; and for violet, 1·5219. The salt readily dissolves in hot water, but less so in cold water. 100 parts of water at 10° dissolve 11·06 parts of the salt. The crystals gradually alter when exposed to air; and lose a part of their water over sulphuric acid; more is lost at 100°, and all at 230°. The residue is yellowish-green. J. Locke said that the salt melts at 48° in its water of crystallization.

According to I. Koppel and E. C. Behrendt,[3] vanadyl sulphates or hypovanadic sulphates are produced by reducing quinquevalent to quadrivalent vanadium with sulphur dioxide. The normal hydrated vanadyl sulphate or hypovanadic sulphate, $(VO)SO_4.nH_2O$, separates if the liquid contains up to 3 mols of sulphuric acid per mol of vanadium pentoxide reduced; and acid sulphates, $(VO)SO_4.mH_2SO_4.nH_2O$, if more sulphuric acid be present. There are two forms of normal **vanadyl sulphate**, $(VO)SO_4$, or $V_2O_4.2SO_3$, or VO_2SO_3—the one is soluble, the other insoluble. (i) The *soluble-form* was prepared by J. J. Berzelius by saturating dil. sulphuric acid with hydrated vanadium tetroxide, and evaporating the soln. to dryness at a gentle heat or in vacuo. If the soln. be allowed to evaporate spontaneously it appears green, and a green oxide separates out, the soln. then becomes blue. B. W. Gerland found that the insoluble form becomes soluble if heated with water in a sealed tube 150°–200° for some hours, and the solid can be obtained by the evaporation of the liquid over sulphuric acid. J. K. Crow obtained it by evaporating the soln. of the dihydrate; if the evaporation be slow, over conc. sulphuric acid, the insoluble sulphate may be formed. A. Guyard treated vanadium pentoxide with a mixture of alcohol, water, and sulphuric acid; or evaporated to dryness a conc. soln. of vanadic sulphate and alcohol. The blue, gum-like product is soluble in water and in alcohol. If heated for a long time at 100°, it becomes brown ; and if heated out of contact with air, vanadium pentoxide remains. It dissolves in fused potassium hydrosulphate. (ii) The *insoluble-form*, according to B. W. Gerland, is obtained by boiling the soluble form or one of the hydrates for a short time with sulphuric acid. The anhydrous sulphate is thus precipitated as a heavy, greyish-green, sandy powder. According to C. Eichner, if vanadium pentoxide be heated with sulphuric acid in the presence of sodium or potassium sulphate, a precipitate of vanadyl sulphate first appears, and the double sulphates of quadri- and quinquevalent vanadium with potassium or soda. If ammonium sulphate be present, ammonium vanadium sulphate is formed, and it decomposes at a high temp., and the products reduce quadrivalent vanadium to the tervalent state. I. Koppel and E. C. Behrendt said that the anhydrous sulphate undergoes a reversible transformation with boiling sulphuric acid : $V_2O_4 + SO_3 \rightleftharpoons SO_2 + V_2O_5$. According to B. W. Gerland, the microscopic crystals of the insoluble sulphate are quite insoluble in cold water even after several months' digestion ; water acquires a pale blue colour after it has been boiled for a long time with the anhydrous sulphate. The solvent action of the water is favoured if a little hydrochloric or sulphuric acid be present ; and all becomes soluble, if the salt be heated with a little water in a sealed tube at 150°-200° ; with more water a slight green sediment is formed. Dil. alkaline soln. decompose the anhydrous sulphate, forming a brown hydroxide which is readily soluble in acids.

The equilibrium conditions of the hydrates of vanadyl sulphate have not been worked out. A number of hydrates were reported by B. W. Gerland, and I. Koppel and E. C. Behrendt, but some of them may be mixtures representing arbitrary stages in the process of dehydration. For example, by drying the pentahydrate at 100°, B. W. Gerland obtained the *hemitrihydrate*, $2VOSO_4.3H_2O$, but I. Koppel and E. C. Behrendt obtained the *hemipentahydrate*, $2VOSO_4.5H_2O$, under this condition. B. W. Gerland obtained the *hemitridecahydrate*, $2VOSO_4.13H_2O$, by exposing the crystals of the hemiheptahydrate, to moist air ; and I. Koppel and E. C. Behrendt, by mixing vanadium pentoxide with less than 3 mols of sulphuric acid, reducing the soln. with sulphur dioxide, and evaporating the liquid over sulphuric acid. The dark blue, prismatic crystals effloresce in dry air.

J. J. Berzelius prepared the *dihydrate*, $VOSO_4.2H_2O$, by reducing a soln. of vanadium pentoxide in a warm mixture of equal parts of sulphuric acid and water, and evaporating the filtrate to a small vol. The pale blue crystalline crust is probably an acid salt because alcohol extracts acid from it ; the mother-liquor is decanted, and the crust washed with alcohol, and then left in alcohol for some time. The product is thus converted into a bulky sky-blue powder consisting of minute scaly crystals ; this is washed in alcohol, and dried in vacuo over sulphuric acid or calcium chloride. This salt was also prepared in a similar way by J. K. Crow, and I. Koppel and E. C. Behrendt ; but B. W. Gerland did not succeed in making this hydrate. I. Koppel and E. C. Behrendt did not make it by evaporating a soln. of the sulphate at different temp., or by dehydrating one of the higher hydrates. J. J. Berzelius said that in moist air, the dry salt deliquesces to a syrup, which, on exposure to air at ordinary temp., deposits rhombic crystals the colour of hydrated cupric sulphate. The presence of a slight excess of sulphuric acid facilitates the crystallization. When heated in a closed vessel, water, sulphur dioxide, and sulphur trioxide are successively evolved, and molten vanadium pentoxide remains. It dissolves very slowly in water at 10° ; but the process of dissolution is faster in water at 60°, and still more rapid in boiling water, forming a blue soln. It deliquesces in warm moist air. It is only slightly soluble in absolute alcohol, but quite soluble in alcohol of sp. gr. 0·835. B. W. Gerland prepared blue crystals of the *hemiheptahydrate*, $2VOSO_4.7H_2O$, by heating the insoluble normal sulphate with water in a sealed tube at 100°-200° ; evaporating the liquid to dryness over sulphuric acid ; and allowing it to stand for a week moistened with alcohol. J. K. Crow obtained this hydrate by evaporating a soln. of hydrated vanadium tetroxide in sulphuric acid ; treating the residue with absolute alcohol until all acid is removed, and pressing the deliquescent mass between filter-paper. I. Koppel and E. C. Behrendt could not obtain the heptahydrate in this way, but they prepared it by evaporating at 80° a soln. of vanadayl sulphate as nearly neutral as possible. The salt was recrystallized from water at 80°. If the soln. be evaporated at 90°, or if the heptahydrate be dried at 90°, dark blue crystals of the *trihydrate*, $VOSO_4.3H_2O$, are formed. According to B. W. Gerland, the liquid, obtained by heating the insoluble anhydrous sulphate with water in a sealed tube at 150°-200°, when evaporated over sulphuric acid furnishes a blue transparent, gummy mass which when moistened with alcohol and left under a loose cover, gradually assumes a crystalline form ; the analysis corresponds with the *pentahydrate*, $VOSO_4.5H_2O$. It can be recrystallized by evaporating the alcoholic soln. at a low temp. I. Koppel and E. C. Behrendt obtained it from the soln. obtained by allowing the hydrated acid sulphate to deliquesce in air ; the crystals are washed by alcohol, and ether. The salt effloresces in air. At 100°, it loses $2\frac{1}{2}$ mols of water; at 125°, it loses another mol of water ; and at 150°, it forms the monohydrate, $VOSO_4.H_2O$.

I. Koppel and E. C. Behrendt prepared **vanadyl dihydrotrisulphate,** $2(VO)SO_4.H_2SO_4$, by heating one of the hydrates at 200° ; or by heating the pentahydrate with four times its weight of conc. sulphuric acid at 190°. The green, sandy powder consists of microscopic, quadratic plates, and is sparingly soluble in water. The *hemihydrate*, $2(VO)SO_4.H_2SO_4.\frac{1}{2}H_2O$, was obtained as a grey, sandy powder consisting of microscopic, four-sided plates, by evaporating a soln. of the sulphuric acid soln. of the sulphate at 175°, or drying the pentahydrate at this temp. It is very slowly dissolved by water. B. W. Gerland, and I. Koppel and E. C. Behrendt prepared the *dihydrate*, $2(VO)SO_4.H_2SO_4.2H_2O$, by evaporating the sulphuric acid soln. of the sulphate at 150°, or drying the pentahydrate at this temp. The pale blue, quadratic plates are slowly dissolved by cold water, and rapidly by hot water. The crystals slowly deliquesce in air. The pale blue crystalline crust obtained by J. J. Berzelius in the preparation of dihydrated vanadayl sulphate, when washed with cold water or alcohol, and dried over sulphuric acid, furnishes the *trihydrate*, $2(VO)SO_4.2H_2SO_4.3H_2O$. B. W. Gerland obtained it by evaporating the blue soln. of vanadium tetroxide in dil. sulphuric acid to a syrup ; mixing it with conc. sulphuric acid ; and, when cold, removing the excess of acid, washing with cold water or alcohol, and drying in vacuo over sulphuric acid. The salt was also prepared by J. K. Crow. I. Koppel and E. C. Behrendt recommended washing the salt with alcohol, and ether. The pale blue needles absorb moisture from the air, forming a thick, blue liquid. At 100°, the salt slowly gives off water. It dissolves very slowly in cold water, more rapidly in hot water ; and it is very sparingly soluble in alcohol. J. K. Crow prepared the *pentahydrate*, $2(VO)SO_4.H_2SO_4.5H_2O$, by evaporating on a water-bath a soln. of vanadium tetroxide in sulphuric acid ; draining the pale blue crystals on a porous tile ; washing with ether, and pressing between bibulous paper. I. Koppel and E. C. Behrendt also prepared this salt. J. K. Crow found that the microscopic, pale blue, quadratic plates deliquesce in air to a blue syrup ; they dissolve slowly in cold water, and rapidly in hot water ; they are very sparingly soluble in absolute alcohol, and insoluble in ether. B. W. Gerland reported the *tetradecahydrate*, $2(VO)SO_4.H_2SO_4.14H_2O$, to be formed by evaporating a soln. of the trihydrate to a syrup ; mixing the residue with conc. alcohol, and repeatedly washing the residue with alcohol. A blue waxy mass is obtained. Neither J. K. Crow, nor I. Koppel and E. C. Behrendt could prepare this hydrate. W. T. Schaller described a *pentadecahydrate* occurring as a mineral in blue granular aggregates, spherulites, or mammillary masses as an efflorescence on patronite ; it has composition $V_2O_4.3SO_3.16H_2O$, or $2VOSO_4.H_2SO_4.15H_2O$, at Minasragra, Peru ; and he called it **minasragrite.** It is triclinic or monoclinic and pleochroic with α, deep blue ; β, pale blue ; and γ, colourless. The indices of refraction are $α=1.515$, $β=1.525$, and $γ=1.545$; E. S. Larsen gave $α=1.518$, $β=1.530$, and $γ=1.542$. The optical character is negative. It is very soluble in cold water.

J. J. Berzelius, A. Guyard, and B. W. Gerland made a complex salt with potassium sulphate. I. Koppel and E. C. Behrendt found that vanadyl sulphate forms complex salts with the sulphates of ammonium and the alkalies. If a soln. of vanadium pentoxide in an excess of dil. sulphuric acid be reduced with sulphur dioxide, and then treated with 2–3 mols of ammonium sulphate ; the mixture evaporated first on the water-bath and then at a higher temp., until crystallization sets in ; and the product washed with cold water, then with alcohol, and ether, and dried over conc. sulphuric acid, pale blue, microscopic tablets of ammonium

divanadyl trisulphate, $(NH_4)_2SO_4.2VOSO_4.H_2O$, are formed. The crystals are stable in dry air, but deliquesce in moist air ; they are slowly but copiously dissolved by cold water. If dried at 175° to constant weight, all the water of crystallization is expelled. The corresponding **potassium divanadyl trisulphate,** $K_2SO_4.2VOSO_4$, was obtained in a similar manner. It behaves very like the ammonium salt, and is freely soluble in water. Similarly with **sodium divanadyl trisulphate,** $Na_2SO_4.2VOSO_4.2\frac{1}{2}H_2O$.

By treating a conc. aq. neutral soln. of ammonium divanadayl trisulphate with alcohol, **ammonium vanadyl disulphate,** $(NH_4)_2SO_4.VOSO_4.3\frac{1}{2}H_2O$, is formed ; and the same salt is produced when a soln. of 11·7 grms. of ammonium metavanadate, 10 c.c. conc. sulphuric acid, and 100 c.c. of water is reduced with sulphur dioxide, and then treated with alcohol. The deep blue, oily liquid is separated from the upper layer, which also forms a precipitate. When the oil has stood for about 8 days, during which time it has been in contact with alcohol, renewed daily, it furnishes a dark blue microcrystalline powder which is freely soluble in water, and in a mixture of alcohol and conc. sulphuric acid. It loses all its water at 175°. By a similar method, **potassium vanadyl disulphate,** $K_2SO_4.VOSO_4.3H_2O$, was obtained with properties like those of the ammonium salt ; similarly with **sodium vanadyl disulphate,** $Na_2SO_4.VOSO_4.4H_2O$. According to A. Rosenheim and H. yu Mong, the ammonium, sodium, and potassium sulphates of quadrivalent vanadium decompose in boiling sulphuric acid : $2V^{iv} = V^{iii} + V^{v}$, yielding a crystalline sulphate, $V_2O_3(SO_4)_2$, and a series of insoluble double sulphates, $MV(SO_4)_2$. C. Eichner observed that the appearance of tervalent vanadium in these experiments is due to the presence of ammonium vanadate in the vanadium pentoxide—*vide supra*, the action of sulphuric acid on vanadium pentoxide in the presence of ammonium sulphate.

J. J. Berzelius evaporated a nitric acid soln. of vanadyl sulphate to dryness and obtained a red, deliquescent crystalline mass, which later observations show was **vanadium trioxydisulphate,** $V_2O_5.2SO_3$, or $V_2O_3(SO_4)_2$. C. J. Fritzsche made it by dissolving hydrated vanadium pentoxide in 20 parts of conc. sulphuric acid at 100°, and heated the mixture rapidly to drive off fumes of sulphur trioxide. The product is washed with conc. sulphuric acid, pressed on porous tiles to remove the excess of acid, and dried over sulphuric acid. B. W. Gerland made the same compound by heating the dioxytrisulphate to 326°. The sulphate was also made by L. Münzing, A. Guyard, and A. Rosenheim and H. yu Mong. The pale red crystals are stable in the absence of moisture ; and when heated in a retort they give off fuming sulphuric acid. They deliquesce in moist air and are decomposed by water with the separation of hydrated vanadium pentoxide. J. J. Berzelius found that when a soln. of vanadium pentoxide in conc. sulphuric acid is diluted with half its vol. of water, and the excess of sulphuric acid expelled at the lowest possible temp., **vanadium dioxytrisulphate,** $V_2O_5.3SO_3$, or $V_2O_2(SO_4)_3$, is formed. B. W. Gerland added a little perchloric acid in order to prevent reduction by the flame gases, and the formation of insoluble vanadyl sulphate. The ruby-red crystals are probably octahedra. In air, they rapidly deliquesce to a brown syrup which mixes with water or alcohol without turbidity. It passes into the trioxydisulphate at about 326°. A. Ditte said that the *tetrahydrate*, $V_2O_5.3SO_3.4H_2O$, or $V_2O_2(SO_4)_3.4H_2O$, or $V_2(OH)_4(SO_4)_3.2H_2O$, is formed in hygroscopic, small, yellow crystals from a soln. of vanadium pentoxide in hot conc. sulphuric acid. L. Münzing said that A. Ditte's salt is the same as that prepared by J. J. Berzelius—*vide supra* for V. Auger's observations. P. Pascal gave 115×10^{-5} for the mol. magnetic susceptibility of soln. of $V_2O_2SO_4$—*vide supra*, vanadium—and N. Perrakis also measured the magnetic properties. L. E. Stout and G. C. Whitaker, and N. H. Furman found the acidified soln. can be kept months without change. V. Auger and C. Eichner observed that when a sulphuric acid soln. of vanadium pentoxide is slowly reduced, there is a point at which the orange soln. becomes dark blue changing to a clear blue when the acid vanadyl sulphate is formed. If the orange soln.

and the blue soln. are mixed in equal proportions, an indigo-blue soln. is produced. The spectral observations of the soln. indicate that a *vanadic vanadyl sulphate* is formed, $HSO_4.VO(OH).SO_4.V(OH)_2.HSO_4$; but the salt could not be isolated.

B. W. Gerland found that **ammonium vanadium tetroxydisulphate**, or *ammonium tetroxydisulphatodivanadate*, $(NH_4)_2O.V_2O_5.2SO_3.4H_2O$, is formed from a mixture of conc. soln. of ammonium sulphate and vanadium dioxytrisulphate, evaporated over sulphuric acid. The reddish-brown needles are freely soluble in cold water without the separation of vanadium pentoxide. He made **potassium vanadium tetroxydisulphate**, or *potassium tetroxydisulphatodivanadate*, $K_2O.V_2O_5.2SO_3.6H_2O$, in an analogous manner. A. Werner and R. Huber obtained a complex of the type **vanadium chromic dichlorodecaquodisulphate**, $[CrCl_2(H_2O)_4](SO_4)_2[V(H_2O)_6]$, and with Cr, Fe, or Al in place of V; but J. Meyer and L. Speich did not obtain the corresponding selenate.

REFERENCES.

[1] A. Piccini, *Zeit. anorg. Chem.*, **19**. 204, 1899 ; A. Piccini and L. Marino, *ib.*, **32**. 55. 1902 ; V. Auger, *Compt. Rend.*, **173**. 306, 306, 1921.

[2] J. T. Brierley, *Journ. Chem. Soc.*, **49**. 822, 1886 ; A. S. Russell, *ib.*, **129**. 497, 1926 ; F. Ephraim, *Ber.*, **50**. 1088, 1917 ; A. Piccini, *Gazz. Chim. Ital.*, **27**. i, 418, 1897 ; *Zeit. anorg. Chem.*, **11**. 106, 1896 ; **13**. 441, 1897 ; A. Piccini and N. Brizzi, **19**. 394, 1899 ; A. Rosenheim and H. yu Mong, *ib.*, **148**. 25, 1925 ; J. Meyer and E. Markowicz, *ib.*, **157**. 211, 1926 ; J. Locke, *Amer. Chem. Journ.*, **26**. 166, 332, 1901 ; **27**. 455, 1902 ; M. C. Boswell and J. V. Dickson, *Journ. Amer. Chem. Soc.*, **40**. 1773, 1918 ; A. Stähler and H. Wirthwein, *Ber.*, **38**. 3978, 1905 ; A. Bültemann, *Zeit. Elektrochem.*, **10**. 141, 1904 ; F. A. Henglein, *ib.*, **30**. 5, 1924 ; E. Renschler, *ib.*, **18**. 137, 1912 ; G. Canneri, *Gazz. Chim. Ital.*, **55**. ii, 611, 1925 ; R. Marc, *Zeit. phys. Chem.*, **75**. 710, 1910.

[3] A. Rosenheim and H. yu Mong, *Zeit. anorg. Chem.*, **148**. 25, 1925 ; I. Koppel and E. C. Behrendt, *ib.*, **35**. 154, 1903 ; E. C. Behrendt, *Verbindungen des vierwertigen Vanadins mit Schwefelsäure und schwefeliger Säure*, Berlin, 1902 ; B. W. Gerland, *Chem. News*, **34**. 2, 1876 ; **36**. 29, 271, 1877 ; *Ber.*, **9**. 869, 1876 ; **10**. 1216, 1513, 1877 ; **11**. 104, 1878 ; A. Guyard, *Bull. Soc. Chim.*, (2), **25**. 352, 1876 ; P. Pascal, *Compt. Rend.*, **147**. 742, 1908 ; N. Perrakis, *ib.*, **184**. 1430, 1927 ; J. K. Crow, *Journ. Chem. Soc.*, **30**. 453, 1876 ; J. J. Berzelius, *Acad. Handl. Stockholm*, 1, 1831 ; *Schweigger's Journ.*, **62**. 323, 1831 ; **63**. 26, 1831 ; *Pogg. Ann.*, **22**. 1, 1831 ; *Ann. Chim. Phys.*, (1), **47**. 337, 1831 ; *Phil. Mag.*, (2), **10**. 321, 1831 ; (2), **11**. 7, 1832 ; C. J. Fritzsche, *Bull. Acad. St. Petersburg*, (3), **9**. 199, 1866 ; L. Münzing, *Die Verbindungen der Vanadinsäure mit Schwefelsäure*, Berlin, 1889 ; V. Auger, *Compt. Rend.*, **173**. 306, 1921 ; E. S. Larsen, *Bull. U.S. Geol. Sur.*, 679, 1921 ; W. T. Schaller, *Journ. Washington Acad.*, **5**. 7, 1915 ; **7**. 501, 1917 ; A. Werner and R. Huber, *Ber.*, **39**, 329, 1906 ; J. Meyer and L. Speich, *Zeit. anorg. Chem.*, **118**. 5, 1921 ; V. Auger and C. Eichner, *Compt. Rend.*, **185**. 208, 1927 ; C. Eichner, *ib.*, **185**. 1200, 1927 ; L. E. Stout and G. C. Whitaker, *Journ. Ind. Eng. Chem.*, **20**. 210, 1928 ; N. H. Furman, *Journ. Amer. Chem. Soc.*, **50**. 755, 1675, 1928 ; A. Ditte, *Compt. Rend.*, **96**. 846, 1883 ; **102**. 1310, 1886 ; *Ann. Chim. Phys.*, (6), **8**. 524, 1886.

§ 24. Vanadium Carbonates, Nitrates, and Phosphates

I. Koppel and co-workers [1] reported that **ammonium vanadyl carbonate**, $7VO_2.2(NH_4)_2O.16H_2O$, is obtained by dissolving ammonium metavanadate in the minimum quantity of sulphuric acid and reducing with sulphur dioxide, neutralizing with ammonia, and, after evaporating to a small bulk, dropping slowly into a cold sat. soln. of ammonium carbonate until the precipitate formed redissolves only slowly. The liquid is then filtered and conc. over sulphuric acid. It forms violet crystals somewhat sparingly soluble in water, soluble in alkalies to a brown soln., and in acids to a blue soln. ; even in closed vessels it decomposes slowly with evolution of ammonia.

J. J. Berzelius [2] found that when the hydrated lower oxides of vanadium, or vanadium tetroxide are dissolved in dil. nitric acid, a blue soln. is obtained which is not further oxidized by even boiling nitric acid ; but when spontaneously evaporated, the soln. becomes green and deposits red crystals which still retain a little nitric acid. According to A. Guyard, the tetroxide is oxidized by nitric acid to the pentoxide, and a mixture of nitric acid and alcohol does not reduce vanadium

pentoxide. He added that a soln. of **vanadyl nitrate** can be obtained by double
decomposition between silver or barium nitrate and vanadyl chloride or sulphate
respectively. If the soln. be evaporated, the nitrate is decomposed with the
separation of the pentoxide. J. J. Berzelius also found that dil. nitric acid dissolves
a little vanadic acid, forming a yellow soln. which, when spontaneously evaporated,
leaves a reddish mass from which water dissolves a little **vanadic nitrate**. J. Meyer
and R. Backa found that by moistening the hexamminotrichloride or tribromide
with nitric acid, **vanadium hexamminotrinitrate**, $[V(NH_3)_6](NH_3)_3$, is formed.
The properties resemble those of the hexamminotrichloride (q.v.). S. M. Tanatar
and E. K. Kurowsky prepared **beryllium oxynitratovanadate**, $Be(NO_3).mBe_3(VO_4)_2.$
$nBeO$.

When a mixture of vanadium tetra- and penta-oxides is boiled with a soln. of
an alkali phosphate, **hypovanadatovanadatophosphates**, or *vanadylvanadium-*
phosphates, are produced. They are also obtained by melting the mixed oxides
with alkali phosphates while air is excluded. J. J. Berzelius[3] evaporated a mixed
soln. of sodium hydrophosphate and vanadyl phosphate with nitric acid, and
obtained yellow crystalline masses which were slowly dissolved by water, and the
soln. dried to a yellow viscid mass, soluble in water. J. Howaldt, and J. Meisel
consider that the so-called vanadylvanadium phosphates or the hypovanadatovanadatophosphates are not usually chemical individuals, but rather isomorphous
mixtures of vanadates and phosphates in which the hypovanadate radicle plays the
part of a strong base like K_2O, or $(NH_4)_2O$. O. W. Gibbs prepared **sodium hypo-**
vanadatohexadecavanadatoicosiphosphate, $8Na_2O.V_2O_4.8V_2O_5.10P_2O_5.74H_2O$, by
cooling a boiling soln. of calcined ammonium metavanadate and sodium hydrophosphate. The green, scaly crystals are insoluble in water. W. T. Schaller
described green, rectangular plates of a mineral from Sincos, Peru, and he called
it **sincosite**. Its analysis corresponds with **calcium hypovanadatophosphate**,
$CaO.V_2O_4.P_2O_5.5H_2O$. The sp. gr. is 2·84. The crystals closely resemble those of
torbernite in shape, habit, and optical properties. Most of the crystals are uniaxial,
but some are biaxial ; nearly all become biaxial on keeping. The biaxial form
probably corresponds with a lower hydrate, which reverts to the uniaxial form when
stored in a desiccator over dil. sulphuric acid. E. S. Larsen also examined the
mineral. The indices of refraction are $\epsilon=1·655$ and $\omega=1·680$, or $\alpha=1·675, \beta=1·690$,
and $\gamma=1·693$. The optical axial angle $2E=16°$ to $83°$. The pleochroism is shown by
its colours, colourless, pale yellow, or greyish-green. O. W. Gibbs prepared **potassium**
hexahypovanadatododecavanadatotetracosiphosphate, $7K_2O.6V_2O_4.6V_2O_5.12P_2O_5.$
$40H_2O$, by cooling a boiling soln. of potassium tetravanadate and an excess
of potassium hydrophosphate. The dark green, cubic crystals are decomposed by water, and a hot aq. soln. yields green crystals of **potassium hepta-**
vanadatododecavanadatotetracosiphosphate, $7K_2O.7V_2O_4.6V_2O_5.12P_2O_5.52H_2O$.
It is related to uranite. It is strongly pleochroic ; the index of refraction
$\epsilon=1·655$ and $\omega=1·680$. The sp. gr. is 2·84, and the hardness low. It is soluble
in dil. acids. O. W. Gibbs obtained **mercurous hypovanadatovanadatophosphate**
by the action of mercurous chloride on ammonium hypovanadatohexacontavana-
datotetraphosphate.

E. F. Smith and F. F. Exner reported that **ammonium diphosphatovandito-**
tungstate, $(NH_4)_2O.P_2O_5.V_2O_3.WO_3.nH_2O$, occurs in the mother-liquor remaining
after digesting wolframite with aqua regia. The hydrated tungstic acid is dissolved
in aq. ammonia, and the ammonium paratungstate crystallized out. The fractional
crystallization of the mother-liquor furnishes this salt in black, octahedral crystals.
A. Rogers obtained **ammonium tetraphosphatododecavanaditotetratessaraconta-**
tungstate, $15(NH_4)_2O.2P_2O_5.6V_2O_3.44WO_3.106H_2O$, by boiling for 6 hrs. a mixture
of a gram of ammonium phosphate, 15 grms. of ammonium tungstate, 1·1 grms. of
vanadium trioxide, 25 c.c. aq. ammonia, and 700 c.c. of water, evaporating the soln.
to a sp. gr. 1·030, and allowing it to stand for some time. The black octahedra
are soluble in water ; insoluble in alcohol, ether, and benzene ; dil. nitric and hydro-

chloric acids produce **a** small change of colour **when** boiled with the crystals; and boiling conc. hydrochloric acid gives a yellow precipitate but no chlorine. A. Rogers and E. F. Smith made **ammonium stannic phosphatovanaditotungstate** by the action of a boiling soln. of 30 grms. of ammonium tungstate and 100 c.c. of water on an excess of stannic hydroxide, and then adding 2 grms. of ammonium phosphate and hydrated vanadium trioxide. Black, octahedral crystals are obtained on evaporating the soln.

According to J. J. Berzelius,[4] vanadium tetroxide dissolved in a slight excess of phosphoric acid furnishes a blue soln., which, when evaporated below 50°, furnishes small blue crystals of **vanadyl phosphate.** They are to be washed free from phosphoric acid by alcohol. The crystals deliquesce rapidly in air. The water is all expelled by heat leaving a white, porous, spongy, deliquescent mass which forms a blue soln. with water ; at a higher temp., the salt fuses, forming a black mass, thought to be *vanadyl pyrophosphate*, which is insoluble in water. The conc. soln. of vanadyl phosphate mixed with anhydrous alcohol, gives a gelatinous, greyish-blue precipitate which is thought to be a basic salt. It does not deliquesce in air and is partially dissolved by water. If this phosphate be dissolved in nitric acid, and the soln. evaporated, nitrous fumes are evolved, and the syrupy liquid, on cooling, forms a lemon-yellow, crystalline crust. The nitric acid is removed by washing with cold water. The salt is slowly soluble in water, forming a yellow soln. Water of crystallization is expelled by heat. J. J. Berzelius, and C. Friedheim and M. Szamatolsky made yellow crystals of **vanadyl orthophosphate,** $H_2(VO_2)PO_4.4\frac{1}{2}H_2O$, or $V_2O_5.P_2O_5.2H_2O.9Aq.$, by dissolving vanadium pentoxide in syrupy phosphoric acid, allowing the soln. to stand for about 12 hrs., and evaporating in vacuo. The vanadates, arsenates, and phosphates are replaced isomorphously in many minerals. This subject has been studied by M. Amadori with the lead minerals—*vide supra*. The m.p. of mixtures of lead orthophosphate and orthovanadate were found to be :

Vanadate	0	25	50	85	100 per cent.
M.p.	1114°	996°	980°	962°	952°

for mixtures of fluopyromorphite and fluovanadinite :

Fluovanadinite	0	25	50	75	90	100 per cent
M.p.	1098°	1052°	1012°	970°	935°	916°

and for mixtures of chloropyromorphite and chlorovanadinite :

Chlorovanadinite	0	20	50	80	100 per cent.
M.p.	1156°	1116°	1056°	1012°	990°

These results and optical observations agree with the complete isomorphism of these salts. N. Collie described a **calcium lead chlorovanadatophosphate** or a *calcium vanadatopyromorphite* occurring as a mineral in Leadhills.

A. Ditte reported the *vanadatophosphoric acids* or *phosphatovanadic acids :* $V_2O_5.P_2O_5.14H_2O$, and $2V_2O_5.3P_2O_5.9H_2O$; and O. W. Gibbs, $6V_2O_5.7P_2O_5.3H_2O.34Aq.$, but C. Friedheim could not confirm this, and assumed that the reports are based either on analyses of impure materials, or inadequate methods of analysis. According to C. Friedheim, the so-called vanadatophosphoric acids and their salts can be divided into two groups : The members of the one group, called the **luteo-vanadatophosphates**—from *luteus*, yellow—are yellow, and indefinitely crystalline. The alkali salts are not very soluble in water, and are decomposed by that liquid. They were made by J. J. Berzelius, O. W. Gibbs, A. Ditte, and C. Friedheim, (1) from a mixture of phosphoric acid and vanadium pentoxide ; (2) from phosphates and vanadates in an acid soln. ; (3) from phosphates and vanadium pentoxide ; and (4) from vanadates and phosphoric acid. For example, O. W. Gibbs, and C. Friedheim prepared **ammonium luteovanadatophosphate,** $(NH_4)_2O.V_2O_5.P_2O_5.H_2O$, or $(NH_4)H(VO_2)PO_4$, by evaporating a soln. of ammonium meta-vanadate with five or six times the theoretical amount of phosphoric acid introduced as ammonium phosphate and nitric acid. The pale yellow crystalline mass is sparingly soluble in water, and when the yellow soln. is heated, it decomposes, becoming orange or red in colour. Salts of silver, barium, mercury, and lead furnish mixed precipitates of phosphates and vanadates. C. Friedheim also prepared the hydrate $(NH_4)H(VO_2)PO_4.H_2O$. A soln. of ammonium metavanadate forms with dil. phosphoric acid a yellow or reddish-yellow **ammonium luteodivanadato-phosphate**, $(NH_4)_2O.2V_2O_5.P_2O_5.7H_2O$, or $(NH_4)(VO_2)_2PO_4.7H_2O$. It is soluble in a little water without decomposition.

By evaporating the mother-liquid left after the preparation of the purpureo-salt, A. Ditte obtained yellow six-sided prisms with the composition $5(NH_4)_2O.2V_2O_5.4P_2O_5.$ $24H_2O$; and a mixed hot soln. of ammonium hexavanadate and phosphate, yellow plates of $5(NH_4)_2O.3V_2O_5.2P_2O_5.24H_2O$. C. Friedheim could not verify this, and suggested that these formulæ are the result of inaccurate analyses. By fusing a mixture of phosphoric acid and vanadium pentoxide, J. J. Berzelius obtained a pale yellow glass soluble in water—if a trace of vanadium tetroxide be present, the colour is uranium-green.

C. Friedheim and K. Michaelis obtained a yellowish-green mass of **potassium vanadatophosphate**, $K_2(VO_2)PO_4$, by evaporating a soln. of equimolar proportions of potassium dihydrophosphates and metavanadate on a water-bath. The soln. gives precipitates with barium chloride and silver nitrate. They also prepared **potassium luteodivanadatodiphosphate**, $3K_2O.2V_2O_5.2P_2O_5.5H_2O$, from the mother-liquor of the purpureodocosivanadatodiphosphate. C. Friedheim and M. Szamatolsky prepared **potassium luteodivanadatophosphate**, $K_2O.2V_2O_5.$ $P_2O_5.7H_2O$, from a soln. of potassium metavanadate in dil. phosphoric acid. A. Rosenheim and K. H. Yang found that with soln. containing the different proportions of phosphoric acid, the solid phase had the molar composition $P_2O_5.V_2O_5.H_2O$:

H_3PO_4	22·7	31·7	42·0	46·5	57·0	84 per cent.
Solid phase	1·08:1:7·3	1·05:1:6·8	1·15:1:4·3	1·18:1:6·3	1·15:1:7·0	1·24:1:7·2

and by using soln. of phosphates and vanadates sufficiently dilute—say 2 to $3N$— it is possible to prepare **ammonium vanadatophosphate**, $(NH_4)_2O.V_2O_5.P_2O_5.3H_2O$; **ammonium divanadatophosphate**, $(NH_4)_2O.2V_2O_5.P_2O_5.7H_2O$; **potassium vana-datophosphate**, $2K_2O.V_2O_5.P_2O_5$; and $1\frac{1}{2}K_2O.V_2O_5.P_2O_5.2\frac{1}{2}H_2O$; and **potassium divanadatophosphate**, $K_2O.2V_2O_5.P_2O_5.7H_2O$. The sodium salts were not pre-pared. The electrical conductivity of the potassium divanadatophosphate gave from $v=128$, $\lambda=255$; $v=256$, $\lambda=285$; $v=512$, $\lambda=316$; and $v=1024$, $\lambda=328$.

O. W. Gibbs reported **silver luteodivanadatodiphosphate**, $2Ag_2O.V_2O_5.P_2O_5.$ $5H_2O$, to be formed by adding an excess of silver nitrate to a soln. of ammonium vanadatophosphate mixed with some ammonium phosphate. The sulphur-yellow, crystalline precipitate was washed with very dil. nitric acid. It is sparingly soluble in hot and cold water. He also obtained yellow **mercurous luteovanadatophosphate** in an analogous way.

The members of the other group, called the **purpureovanadatophosphates**—from *purpura*, purple—are deep red and form alkali salts which can be recrystallized from aq. soln. They are prepared by dissolving vanadium pentoxide in alkali phosphates or alkali vanadates in phosphoric acid, without heating the mixture to a high temp. For example, C. Friedheim and M. Szamatolsky dissolved vanadium pentoxide in a warm soln. of ammonium phosphate, and obtained garnet-red, octahedral crystals of **ammonium purpureododecavanadatophosphate**, $7(NH_4)_2O.12V_2O_5.P_2O_5.2H_2O.24Aq$. The salt is fairly soluble in water, and it can be crystallized from the soln. at 50°–60°. The soln. is decomposed by acids and alkali-lees ; and salts of the heavy metals give mixed precipitates.

A. Ditte's salt, $3(NH_4)_2O.4V_2O_5.P_2O_5.16H_2O$, is supposed by C. Friedheim to be the purpureo salt just described; and the same remark applies to O. W. Gibb's salt, $20V_2O_5.P_2O_5.6H_2O.53Aq$. J. J. Berzelius also obtained a red compound by evaporating the red soln. of vanadium pentoxide in phosphoric acid.

C. Friedheim and M. Szamatolsky obtained **potassium purpureododecavanadatophosphate**, $7K_2O.12V_2O_5.P_2O_5.26H_2O$, from the ammonium salt and potassium chloride ; and C. Friedheim and K. Michaelis, **potassium purpureodocosivanadatodiphosphate**, $13K_2O.22V_2O_5.2P_2O_5.58H_2O$, by warming a dil. soln. of potassium dihydrophosphate and metavanadate, mixed in the cold. On cooling the liquid, rectangular plates of dark brown crystals separate ; a second crop of crystals furnishes **potassium purpureopentacosivanadatodiphosphate**, $15K_2O.25V_2O_5.2P_2O_5.76H_2O$. C. Friedheim regarded the luteo-compounds as salts in which the vanadium acts as a base towards the stronger phosphoric acid :

$$\begin{array}{ccc} VO_2.O \diagdown & VO_2.O \diagdown & VO_2.O \diagdown \\ HO \;\; \diagup P=O & RO \;\; \diagup P=O & VO_2.O \diagup P=O \\ HO \diagup & HO \diagup & RO \diagup \end{array}$$

| Vanadylphosphate | Vanadatophosphate | Divanadatophosphate |

where R represents NH_4 or a univalent metal. The purpureo-compounds are considered to be acid vanadates in which the phosphoric acid is in part replaced by vanadic acid.

A series of salts of the heteropoly acids—**phosphatovanadatomolybdates**—were prepared by O. W. Gibbs,[5] H. Jacoby, F. Toggenburg, P. Schulz, A. Hinsen, H. Stamm, etc. The list is quite a long one. Unfortunately, the available tests for chemical individuality are quite inadequate. In some cases a product seems to have had a different composition every time it has been made and analyzed. In a number of cases, studied by H. Jacoby, and F. Toggenburg, the ratios $V_2O_5 : MoO_3$ is $3 : 15$, $4 : 14$, $5 : 13$, $6 : 12$, and $7 : 11$, so that the sum of the two components is 18. Very few regularities have been noticed, so that the subject is in an empirical stage. The only thing possible, therefore, is a tabulation of the results. It is convenient to refer them to decreasing proportions of molybdic acid, with decreasing proportions of vanadic and phosphoric acids as supplementary groups. J. R. Cain and J. C. Hostetter concluded that in the co-precipitation of vanadic acid and ammonium phosphomolybdate there is a partition of the vanadic acid between the soln. and the solid phase ; the maximum adsorption by the solid phase occurs between 40° and 50° with $2N$-HNO_3 soln. The effect of dilution is to lower the adsorption, and the effect is hindered in the presence of ammonium nitrate. The so-called ammonium phosphatovanadatomolybdates probably form a series of solid soln. in which the end members are ammonium phosphomolybdate and ammonium phosphovanadate. This is in agreement with the observations of E. T. Wherry on the optical properties of salts of complex acids.

O. W. Gibbs prepared **ammonium tetraphosphatodivanadatoctotessaracontamolybdate**, $7(NH_4)_2O.2P_2O_5.V_2O_5.48MoO_3.30H_2O$, as an orange-red, crystalline precipitate by boiling a soln. of ammonium phosphomolybdate and metavanadate in hydrochloric acid. It is sparingly soluble in cold water, and decomposed by hot water ; H. Jacoby could not obtain this salt, but obtained instead **ammonium tetraphosphatodivanadatodotessaracontamolybdate**, $7(NH_4)_2O.2P_2O_5.V_2O_5.42MoO_3.42H_2O$. P. Schulz prepared red crystals **ammonium diphosphatohexavanadatoctodecamolybdate**, $6(NH_4)_2O.P_2O_5.3V_2O_5.18MoO_3.40H_2O$, by adding 48 grms. of ammonium metavanadate to a soln. of phosphatomolybdic acid heated on a water-bath. When the cold soln. is treated with a sat. soln. of ammonium chloride, red crystals are formed. He also obtained $7(NH_4)_2O.P_2O_5.3V_2O_5.18MoO_3.31H_2O$, by mixing aq. soln. of the component salts. The salt can be crystallized unchanged from its aq. soln. With barium chloride, the aq. soln. gives the ammonium barium salt, $2(NH_4)_2O.4BaO.P_2O_5.17MoO_3.46H_2O$; and with ammonia, the aq. soln. is partially decomposed. F. Toggenburg produced **ammonium diphosphatohexavanadatoheptadecamolybdate**, $6(NH_4)_2O.P_2O_5.3V_2O_5.17MoO_3.40H_2O$, by dissolving 7·8 grms. of ammonium metavanadate, 3·84 grms. of molybdic acid in 500 c.c. of warm water, and then adding 21·35 c.c. aq. ammonia of sp. gr. 0·956. The red, octahedral crystals are soluble in water ; the conc. soln. gives a small precipitate with ammonia ; and with potassium chloride a crystalline precipitate slowly forms. A. Düsterwald could not make this by direct synthesis ; but he obtained **ammonium diphosphatoctovanadatoheptadecamolybdate,** $6(NH_4)_2O.P_2O_5.4V_2O_5.17MoO_3.40H_2O.$

H. Jacoby prepared red crystals of **ammonium diphosphatodecavanadatopentadecamolybdate,** $2(NH_4)_2O.P_2O_5.5V_2O_5.15MoO_3.32H_2O$, by evaporating the soln. produced by the action of a conc. soln. of mercuric chloride on a sat. soln. of the phosphatododecavanadatododecamolybdate. If the mother-liquor remaining after the preparation of the 42-molybdate be treated with ammonia, and the soln. rapidly cooled, brown crystals of **ammonium diphosphatohexavanadatopentadecamolybdate,** $6(NH_4)_2O.P_2O_5.3V_2O_5.15MoO_3.41H_2O$, are formed ; and H. Jacoby also obtained $5(NH_4)_2O.P_2O_5.3V_2O_5.15MoO_3.39H_2O$, by warming a soln. of yellow ammonium phosphatomolybdate with ammonium vanadate for a long time on a water-bath ; or by mixing 21·1 grms. of ammonium metavanadate, 64·8 grms. of molybdic acid, and 6·9 grms. of ammonium dihydrophosphate with water and adding 10·67 c.c. to aq. ammonia of sp. gr. 0·956 soln. furnishes ruby-red crystals. A. Düsterwald prepared **ammonium diphosphatohexavanadatopentadecamolybdate,** $5(NH_4)_2O.P_2O_5.3V_2O_5.15MoO_3.39H_2O$, as well as $6(NH_4)_2O.P_2O_5.3V_2O_5.15MoO_3.37H_2O$. P. Schulz obtained the *icosihydrate* by adding ammonium 3 : 7-molybdate to a boiling soln. of vanadium phosphate, and afterwards evaporating the liquid over sulphuric acid. H. Lahrmann also prepared this salt, and he showed that the composition was not changed by five fractional crystallizations. The sp. gr. of H. Jacoby's salt is 2·9045 ; and the sp. gr. of the deep brownish-red aq. soln., sat. at 18°, is 1·144, and 100 c.c. contain 24·45 grms. of salt. Hydrogen dioxide colours the soln. first black and then green ; boiling hydrochloric acid reduces the soln. ; conc. sulphuric acid gives a yellow soln. ; ammonia gives an orange-yellow liquid which with an excess of ammonia is gradually decolorized ; nitric acid gives a yellow soln., and then gives a precipitate of ammonium phosphatomolybdate ; alcohol precipitates a yellow, and ether a purple-red oily liquid ; soda-lye gives a yellow crystalline precipitate soluble in excess ; potassium chloride gives a red crystalline precipitate with conc. soln. ; barium chloride gives no precipitate with dil. soln. ; mercuric chloride gives no precipitate. Mercurous nitrate and lead acetate give yellow precipitates ; silver nitrate gives a brown one.

O. W. Gibbs dissolved yellow ammonium (1·22–1·24) phosphatomolybdate in a boiling soln. of ammonium metavanadate, and, when the soln. was allowed to stand for some hours, obtained ruby-red octahedral crystals of **ammonium diphosphatohexadecavanadatotetradecamolybdate,** $8(NH_4)_2O.P_2O_5.8V_2O_5.14MoO_3.$ $50H_2O$. It can be recrystallized from its aq. soln. in hot water ; and the soln. gives precipitates with potassium bromide, silver nitrate, barium chloride, mercurous nitrate, lead acetate, and trimethylammonium chloride. F. Toggenburg obtained red flakes of *octocosihydrated* **ammonium diphosphatoctovanadatotetradecamolybdate,** $6(NH_4)_2O.P_2O_5.4V_2O_5.14MoO_3.28H_2O$, as a by-product along with the diphosphatododecavanadatododecamolybdate ; from the mother-liquor in the preparation of the same salt ; and by evaporating on the water-bath a conc. aq. soln. of 40 grms. of the diphosphatododecavanadatododecamolybdate, 10·2 grms. of ammonium dimolybdate to about half its vol. The liquid is cooled with ice, and the crystals washed and drained on a porous tile. A second crop of crystals is produced by evaporating the mother-liquid. The red cubic or octahedral crystals decompose as they dissolve in water ; and the aq. soln. gives a precipitate with ammonia ; a white decomposition product with barium chloride ; and a red microcrystalline precipitate with potassium chloride. H. Stamm obtained a *pentadecahydrate* with the best crop of crystals. H. Lahrmann prepared $8(NH_4)_2O.P_2O_5.4V_2O_5.14MoO_3.24H_2O$, from a soln. of diphosphatohexavanadatopentadecamolybdate in 350 c.c. of water and 6 mols of aq. ammonia, by evaporation first over the water-bath, and finally over phosphoric pentoxide. The sp. gr. of the reddish-black, octahedral crystals is 3·012 at 24°. The salt is decomposed by water. A. Düsterwald could not make this salt by direct synthesis; but he obtained **ammonium diphosphato-hexavanadatotetradecamolybdate,** $5(NH_4)_2O.P_2O_5.3V_2O_5.14MoO_3.17H_2O$; and **ammonium diphosphatohexavanadatotridecamolybdate,** $5(NH_4)_2O.P_2O_5.3V_2O_5.13MoO_3.31H_2O$.

H. Stamm obtained **ammonium diphosphatodecavanadatotridecamolybdate,** $6(NH_4)_2O.P_2O_5.5V_2O_5.13MoO_3.29H_2O$, in the first crop of crystals resulting from the evaporation of a soln. of 300 grms. of ammonium diphosphatoctovanadato-tetradecamolybdate in a litre of hot water; the second crop of crystals were $6(NH_4)_2O.P_2O_5.4V_2O_5.12MoO_3.24H_2O$. The *dotricontahydrate* was obtained by mixing warm soln. of phosphatomolybdic acid and ammonium metanavadate and adding ammonia and phosphoric acid. The deep red crystals can be re-crystallized from water. The aq. soln. sat. at 18° has a sp. gr. 1·0797, and 100 c.c. contain 25·53 grms. of salt. With potassium chloride the soln. furnishes $5V_2O.(NH_4)_2O.P_2O_5.5V_2O_5.13MoO_3.25(29$ or $30)H_2O$; and barium chloride, $BaO : (NH_4)_2O : P_2O_5 : V_2O_5 : MoO_3 : H_2O$, $3 : 3 : 1 : 4 : 16 : 39$ and $4 : 2 : 1 : 5 : 13 : 45$; and with ammonia, it furnishes $8(NH_4)_2O.P_2O_5.5V_2O_5.4V_2O_5.13MoO_3.26(or\ 33)H_2O$. F. Toggenburg obtained **ammonium diphosphatocto-vanadatotridecamolybdate,** $6(NH_4)_2O.P_2O_5.4V_2O_5.13MoO_3.37H_2O$, as a by-product in the preparation of the $1 : 1 : 4 : 14 : 28$-salt by the recrystallization of the $8 : 1 : 6 : 12 : 64$-salt; also from 67·2 grms. of molybdic acid, 31·2 grms. ammonium metavanadate, in about 500 c.c. of hot water; the red soln. was mixed with 21·36 c.c. of ammonia of sp. gr. 0·956, and 22 c.c. of syrupy phosphoric acid. The soln., sat. at 18°, has a sp. gr. 1·090; and 100 c.c. contain 15·43 grms. of salt. The aq. soln. of the brownish-red, efflorescent, octahedral crystals behave very like the $7 : 1 : 7 : 11 : 36$-salt—*vide infra.* This salt is decomposed when an attempt is made to crystallize the aq. soln.

H. Jacoby, and A. Düsterwald prepared **ammonium diphosphatododecavana-datododecamolybdate,** $6(NH_4)_2O.P_2O_5.6V_2O_5.12MoO_3.41H_2O$, by warming a soln. of phosphatomolybdic acid and ammonium metavanadate on the water-bath; and evaporating the filtered soln. over sulphuric acid. It was also obtained by dissolving 288 grms. of molybdic acid and 234·4 grms. of ammonium meta-vanadate in about 500 c.c. of water; and after standing some hours in the cold, adding 110 c.c. of phosphoric acid containing 215 grms. P_2O_5 per litre. The liquid is diluted with water, warmed on a water-bath, and the filtered liquid allowed to crystallize over sulphuric acid. The ruby-red, octahedral crystals have a sp. gr. 2·4107; the sp. gr. of the soln., sat. at 18°, is 1·099. Hydrogen dioxide colours the soln. almost black, which becomes red, yellow, and green when boiled; with hydrochloric acid of sp. gr. 1·12, the colour becomes red, and then yellow, and when boiled, a reduction occurs; dil. sulphuric acid colours the soln. dark brown, then red, and with boiling yellow; conc. sul-phuric acid gives a yellow soln.: nitric acid colours the soln. red, then yellow, and it precipitates ammonium phosphatomolybdate; soda-lye gives orange-yellow precipitates with conc. soln.; phosphoric acid, diphosphatocto-vanadatohexamolybdate; absolute alcohol, orange-yellow and orange-red precipitates; trimethylamine, an orange-red precipitate; ether, a purple-red precipitate; potassium chloride and barium chloride, crystalline precipi-tates with conc. soln.; silver nitrate gives a brown precipitate; mercuric chloride forms diphosphatodecavanadatopentadecamolybdate; and lead acetate, an orange-red precipitate. When a soln. of 100 grms. of the salt in 100 c.c. of water is mixed with 40 c.c. of aq. ammonia of sp. gr. 0·96, an orange precipitate of $8(NH_4)_2O.P_2O_5.6V_2O_5.12MoO_3.64H_2O$, is formed; and, according to H. Stamm, brownish-red crystals of $7(NH_4)_2O.P_2O_5.6V_2O_5.12MoO_3.33H_2O$, are produced when a soln. of 35 grms. of $8(NH_4)_2O.P_2O_5.5V_2O_5.13MoO_3.30H_2O$, in the smallest possible amount of water is evaporated over sulphuric acid. A. Düsterwald prepared **ammonium diphosphatohexavanadatopentadecamolybdate,** $5(NH_4)_2O.P_2O_5.3V_2O_5.15MoO_3.39H_2O$. H. Lahrmann prepared **ammonium diphosphatoctovanadato-**

dodecamolybdate, $6(NH_4)_2O.P_2O_5.4V_2O_5.12MoO_3.24H_2O$, as an orange precipitate, from a soln. of a mol of the $5:1:3:15:39$-salt mixed with 2–4 mols of ammonia. The sp. gr. is 2·9073 at 24°. It is always insoluble in cold water. H. Stamm obtained the salt by adding ammonia to the $6:1:5:13:29$-salt. A mixture of 8 mols of ammonium metavanadate ; 2, of orthophosphoric acid ; 12, of molybdic acid ; and 4, of ammonia, was found by H. Lahrmann to furnish deep ruby-red crystals of $5(NH_4)_2O.P_2O_5.4V_2O_5.12MoO_3.39H_2O$, of sp. gr. 2·8272 at 24°. The sp. gr. of the aq. soln., sat. at 18°, is 1·0932 ; and 100 c.c. contain 26·24 grms. of salt. A. Düsterwald prepared **ammonium diphosphatodecavanadatohenamolybdate,** $5(NH_4)_2O.P_2O_5.5V_2O_5.11MoO_3.33H_2O$.

F. Toggenburg obtained brownish-red crystals of **ammonium diphosphatotetra-decavanadatohenamolybdate,** $7(NH_4)_2O.P_2O_5.7V_2O_5.11MoO_3.36(or\ 37)H_2O$, accompanied by the pale yellow spangles of $8:1:6:12:64$-salt ; and separated the two by repeated levigation. It was also obtained by heating 81 grms. of ammonium metavanadate and 79·2 grms. of molybdic acid in about a litre of water ; mixing the soln. with 33 c.c. of syrupy phosphoric acid (4 mols) ; evaporating the liquid to about one-third its vol. ; and crystallizing over sulphuric acid. The dark brown crystals can be crystallized unchanged from the aq. soln., the sp. gr. of the soln., sat. at 18°, is 1·074 ; and 100 c.c. contain 13·25 grms. of the salt. The aq. soln. is coloured black by hydrogen dioxide ; hydrochloric acid of sp. gr. 1·12, colours the soln. red, then yellow, and reduction occurs on boiling the mixture ; dil. sulphuric acid gives no precipitate, and when boiled, the soln. becomes red and then yellow ; conc. sulphuric acid gives a small, orange precipitate which does not dissolve when the mixture is boiled ; dil. nitric acid behaves like conc. sulphuric acid ; phosphoric acid has no influence on the salt ; conc. soda-lye gives an orange precipitate soluble in excess ; potassium chloride gives a red precipitate which slowly dissolves when the temp. is raised ; barium chloride gives an orange, crystalline precipitate with conc. soln. ; silver nitrate, mercurous nitrate, and mercurous chloride give brown or reddish-brown precipitates. When treated with aq. ammonia, the salt, $9(NH_4)_2O.P_2O_5.7V_2O_5.11MoO_3.39H_2O$, is formed in brownish-red octahedral crystals ; A. Hinsen prepared $6(NH_4)_2O.P_2O_5.7V_2O_5.11MoO_3.34(or\ 43)H_2O$, in brownish-red octahedra, from an aq. soln. of 100 grms. of ammonium $7:3$-molybdate and 104 grms. of ammonium vanadatophosphate ; when treated with ammonia, it furnishes $8(NH_4)_2O.P_2O_5.7V_2O_5.11MoO_3.30H_2O$. H. Jacoby prepared **ammonium diphosphatoctovanadatohenamolybdate,** $4(NH_4)_2O.P_2O_5.4V_2O_5.11MoO_3.37H_2O$, by mixing a soln. of a mol of the $6:1:6:12:41$-salt with 5 mols of orthophosphoric acid. Yellow crystals are obtained by evaporating the soln. over sulphuric acid. The first crop of crystals are those of pale red ammonium phosphatovanadate.

O. W. Gibbs reported that crystals of **ammonium diphosphatodecavanadato-decamolybdate,** $5(NH_4)_2O.P_2O_5.5V_2O_5.10MoO_3.24H_2O$, can be obtained from the mother-liquor obtained in the preparation of the $8:1:8:14:50$-salt ; but H. Jacoby could not verify this. A. Hinsen obtained **ammonium diphosphatohepta-decavanadatoenneamolybdate,** $6(NH_4)_2O.P_2O_5.7V_2O_5.9MoO_3.28(33\ or\ 37)H_2O$, by fractionally crystallizing a soln. obtained by boiling 259·38 grms. of ammonium phosphatomolybdate in 200 c.c. of water in which 80 grms. of ammonium metavanadate, or an acid vanadate was dissolved. The first crop of crystals is ammonium metavanadate, this is followed by the dark red octahedra of the required salt. It can be recrystallized from its aq. soln. with potassium chloride, the aq. soln. furnishes the potassium salt indicated below ; with barium chloride, the barium salt ; and with ammonia, the $8:1:7:11:30$-salt.

P. Schulz prepared **potassium diphosphatotetravanadatoicosimolybdate,** $5K_2O.P_2O_5.2V_2O_5.20MoO_3.53H_2O$, by dissolving 30 grms. of ammonium meta-vanadate in a boiling soln. of 132 grms. of phosphato (1 : 24) molybdic acid. On evaporating the pale red soln. over sulphuric acid, it furnishes pale red crystals of this salt. The aq. soln. gives with ammonium chloride $K_2O.5(NH_4)_2O.P_2O_5$.

$2V_2O_5.20MoO_3.52H_2O$; and with barium chloride, $2K_2O.2BaO.P_2O_5.2V_2O_5.$ $18MoO_3.47H_2O$. A. Düsterwald prepared **potassium diphosphatodecavana-datoctodecamolybdate**, $9K_2O.P_2O_5.5V_2O_5.18MoO_3.30H_2O$; and **potassium diphos-phatodecavanadatohenamolybdate**, $8K_2O.P_2O_5.5V_2O_5.11MoO_3.14H_2O$. W. Engel prepared by double decomposition with the sodium salts and potassium chloride: **potassium diphosphatododecavanadatododecamolybdate**, $6K_2O.P_2O_5.6V_2O_5.$ $12MoO_3.48H_2O$; **potassium diphosphatohexavanadatopentadecamolybdate**, $6K_2O.P_2O_5.3V_2O_5.15MoO_3.35H_2O$; **potassium diphosphatoctovanadatotetra-decamolybdate**, $6K_2O.P_2O_5.4V_2O_5.14MoO_3.31H_2O$; **potassium diphosphatotetra-decavanadatohenamolybdate**, $6K_2O.P_2O_5.7V_2O_5.11MoO_3.37H_2O$; and **potassium diphosphatoctodecavanadatoenneamolybdate**, $6K_2O.P_2O_5.9V_2O_5.9MoO_3.43H_2O$. F. Toggenburg prepared **potassium diphosphatodecavanadatotridecamolybdate**, $6K_2O.P_2O_5.5V_2O_5.13MoO_3.23H_2O$, by treating ammonium diphosphatodovanadato-tridecamolybdate with potassium chloride. The aq. soln. of the red, rhombic crystals furnishes a brick-red crystalline powder of **potassium diphosphatotetra-decavanadatohenamolybdate**, $7K_2O.P_2O_5.7V_2O_5.11MoO_3.22H_2O$, which is decom-posed by water. A. Hinsen prepared **potassium diphosphatoheptadecavanadato-enneamolybdate**, $7K_2O.P_2O_5.7V_2O_5.9MoO_3.25H_2O$, by evaporating an aq. soln. of 10 mols or potassium metavanadate and 4 mols of potassium phosphatomolybdate. The red, rhombic plates can be recrystallized from water.

P. Schulz prepared **ammonium potassium diphosphatotetravanadatoicosi-molybdate**, $5(NH_4)_2O.K_2O.P_2O_5.2V_2O_5.20MoO_3.52H_2O$, by treating a cold soln. of dodecammonium diphosphatohexavanadatododecamolybdate, with 1·5 vols. of a soln. of potassium chloride, and evaporating over sulphuric acid. He also prepared pale red crystals of **ammonium potassium diphosphatohexavanadatocto-decamolybdate**, $(NH_4)_2O.6K_2O.P_2O_5.3V_2O_5.18MoO_3.43H_2O$, from a cold soln. of tetradecammonium diphosphatohexavanadatododecamolybdate and 1·5 vols. of a soln. of potassium chloride. H. Jacoby obtained a red, crystalline powder of **ammo-nium potassium diphosphatohexavanadatopentadecamolybdate**, $(NH_4)_2O.4K_2O.$ $P_2O_5.3V_2O_5.15MoO_3.36H_2O$, by treating decammonium diphosphatohexavanadato-pentadecamolybdate, with a cold sat. soln. of potassium chloride; H. Stamm, pale red crystals of **ammonium potassium diphosphatoctovanadatotetradecamolybdate**, $(NH_4)_2O.5K_2O.P_2O_5.4V_2O_5.14MoO_3.31H_2O$, by evaporating the mother-liquor left during the preparation of **ammonium potassium diphosphatodecavanadatotri-decamolybdate**, $(NH_4)_2O.5K_2O.P_2O_5.5V_2O_5.13MoO_3.25(29$ or $30)H_2O$, by treat-ing dodecammonium diphosphatodecavanadatotridecamolybdate, or diphos-phatoctovanadatotetradecamolybdate, with a sat. soln. of potassium chloride; H. Jacoby, red crystals of **ammonium potassium diphosphatododecavanadato-dodecamolybdate**, $(NH_4)_2O.5K_2O.P_2O_5.6V_2O_5.12MoO_3.46H_2O$, by treating the corresponding ammonium salt with a soln. of potassium chloride; H. Jacoby, and F. Toggenburg, brick-red crystals of **ammonium potassium diphosphatotetra-decavanadatohenamolybdate**, $(NH_4)_2O.6K_2O.P_2O_5.7V_2O_5.11MoO_3.25H_2O$, from hexadecammonium diphosphatododecavanadatododecamolybdate and a soln. of potassium chloride; H. Jacoby, **ammonium potassium diphosphatododecavana-datodecamolybdate**, $(NH_4)_2O.6K_2O.P_2O_5.6V_2O_5.10MoO_3.38H_2O$, from the mother-liquor of the preceding salt; and A. Hinsen, **ammonium potassium diphosphato-tetradecavanadatoenneamolybdate**, $\{K_{0\cdot9}(NH_4)_{0\cdot1}O\}_{14}.P_2O_5.7V_2O_5.9MoO_3.29H_2O$, from a soln. of the corresponding ammonium salt and a sat. soln. of potassium chloride. W. Blum obtained no precipitate by adding cupric sulphate to a soln. of diammonium phosphatovanadatomolybdate.

W. Engel prepared **sodium diphosphatododecavanadatododecamolybdate**, $6Na_2O.P_2O_5.6V_2O_5.12MoO_3.48H_2O$, from 308·7 c.c. of a soln. of sodium tetra-molybdate with 0·1655 grm. MoO_3 per c.c., 30·87 c.c. of phosphoric acid with 0·2300 grm. P_2O_5 per c.c., and 95·94 grms. of sodium vanadate. The sp. gr. was 2·05575. He measured the conductivity of the aq. soln. of the salt. W. Engel prepared **sodium diphosphatohexavanadatopentadecamolybdate**, $6Na_2O.P_2O_5.$

$3V_2O_5.15MoO_3.48H_2O$, from a soln. of 123·6 c.c. of the sodium tetramolybdate soln. just indicated, 6·2 c.c. of the phosphoric acid soln., and 9·52 grms. of sodium vanadate. The sp. gr. was 2·4856. He also measured the conductivity of the aq. soln. W. Engel also prepared **sodium diphosphatoctovanadatotetradecamolybdate**, $6Na_2O.P_2O_5.4V_2O_5.14MoO_3.48H_2O$; from a soln. of 313·04 c.c. of sodium tetramolybdate with 0·1288 grms. MoO_3 per c.c., 12·46 c.c. of phosphoric acid with 0·2279 grm. P_2O_5 per c.c., and 25·596 grms. sodium vanadate $2Na_2O.3V_2O_5$. The sp. gr. of the salt was 2·59705. He also measured the electrical conductivity. J. Contzen prepared **sodium diphosphatodecavanadatotridecamolybdate**, $6Na_2O.P_2O_5.5V_2O_5.13MoO_3.43H_2O$, from 129·56 c.c. of phosphomolybdic acid with 0·1805 grm. of $P_2O_5.24MoO_3$ per c.c., 6·64 c.c. of phosphoric acid with 0·1197 grm. P_2O_5 per c.c., 100 c.c. of water, 3·392 grms. of soda, and 18·98 grms. of acid sodium vanadate, $2Na_2O.3V_2O_5.18H_2O$. The sp. gr. of the salt was 2·0413. W. Engel prepared **sodium diphosphatotetradecavanadatohenamolybdate**, $6Na_2O.P_2O_5.7V_2O_5.11MoO_3.44H_2O$, from a soln. of 369 c.c. of sodium tetramolybdate as previously employed, 18·69 c.c. of the phosphoric acid and 50·94 grms. of sodium vanadate. The sp. gr. of the salt was 2·54462. He also measured the electrical conductivity. A. Düsterwald prepared **sodium diphosphatoctovanadatopentadecamolybdate,** $6Na_2O.P_2O_5.4V_2O_5.15MoO_3$, associated with ammonium chloride. J. Contzen prepared **sodium diphosphatohexadecavanadatodecamolybdate**, $7Na_2O.P_2O_5.8V_2O_5.10MoO_3.44H_2O$, from 139·13 c.c. of the soln. of sodium molybdate, 139·13 c.c. of phosphoric acid, 48·43 grms. of acid sodium vanadate, and 14·57 grms, of molybdic acid. The black octahedral crystals have a sp. gr. 2·0308. W. Engel prepared **sodium diphosphatoctodecavanadatoenneamolybdate**, $6Na_2O.P_2O_5.9V_2O_5.9MoO_3.30H_2O$, from a soln. of 134·2 c.c. of the sodium tetramolybdate previously used, 8·31 c.c. of the phosphoric acid, and 25·45 grms. of the sodium vanadate. The sp. gr. of the salt was 2·4853. J. Contzen prepared **sodium diphosphatoicosivanadatoctomolybdate**, $7Na_2O.P_2O_5.10V_2O_5.8MoO_3.48H_2O$, from 27·82 c.c. of sodium molybdate, 118·63 c.c. of phosphoric acid, 60·54 grms. of acid sodium vanadate, and 20·18 grms. of molybdic acid. The black octahedral crystals have a sp. gr. 2·7983.

W. Engel prepared by double decomposition with the sodium salt and barium chloride : **barium diphosphatotetradecavanadatohenamolybdate**, $6BaO.P_2O_5.7V_2O_5.11MoO_3.44H_2O$; and **barium diphosphatoctodecavanadatoenneamolybdate**, $6BaO.P_2O_5.9V_2O_5.9MoO_3.56H_2O$. P. Schulz prepared dark red crystals of **potassium barium diphosphatotetravanadatoctodecamolybdate**, $2K_2O.2BaO.P_2O_5.2V_2O_5.18MoO_3.47H_2O$, by treating a cold soln. of decapotassium diphosphatotetravanadatoicosimolybdate, with 1·5 vols. of a cold soln. of barium chloride ; and pale red crystals of **ammonium barium diphosphatohexavanadatoheptadecamolybdate**, $2(NH_4)_2O.4BaO.P_2O_5.3V_2O_5.17MoO_3.46H_2O$, by the action of a cold soln. of barium chloride on one of tetradecammonium diphosphatohexavanadatoctodecamolybdate ; H. Stamm, dark brown crystals of **ammonium barium diphosphatoctovanadatotetradecamolybdate**, $3(NH_4)_2O.3BaO.P_2O_5.4V_2O_5.14MoO_3.39H_2O$, from the mother-liquor obtained in the preparation of the next two salts, or by treating the corresponding ammonium salt with a soln. of barium chloride ; H. Stamm, pale red crystals of **ammonium barium diphosphatodecavanadatotridecamolybdate**, $2(NH_4)_2O.4BaO.P_2O_5.5V_2O_5.13MoO_3.46H_2O$, by the action of barium chloride on dodecammonium diphosphatodecavanadatotridecamolybdate ; a 10 per cent. soln. of barium chloride converts dodecammonium diphosphatovanadatotetradecamolybdate into $3(NH_4)_2O.4BaO.P_2O_5.5V_2O_5.13MoO_3.40H_2O$; F. Toggenburg, a brick-red crystalline powder of **ammonium barium diphosphatoctovanadatotridecamolybdate**, $2(NH_4)_2O.4BaO.P_2O_5.4V_2O_5.13MoO_3.37H_2O$, by treating a conc. soln. of the corresponding ammonium salt with barium chloride ; H. Jacoby, reddish-brown crystals of **ammonium barium diphosphatododecavanadatododecamolybdate**, $(NH_4)_2O.5BaO.P_2O_5.6V_2O_5.12MoO_3.49H_2O$, by treating the corresponding ammonium salt with barium chloride ; F. Toggenburg, reddish-brown crystals of **ammonium barium diphosphatotetradecavanadatodecamolybdate,** $2(NH_4)_2O.4BaO.P_2O_5.7V_2O_5.10MoO_3.43H_2O$, from a conc. soln. of the heptadecammonium diphosphatotetradecavanadatohenamolybdate and barium chloride ; and A. Hinsen, reddish-brown **ammonium barium diphosphatododecavanadatooctomolybdate,** $\{(NH_4)_{0.167}Ba_{0.916}O\}_6.P_2O_5.6V_2O_5.8MoO_3.38H_2O$, by the action of barium chloride on dodecammonium diphosphatotetradecavanadatoenneamolybdate. O. W. Gibbs prepared orange **mercurous phosphatovanadatomolybdate** by the action of mercurous nitrate on a soln. of ammonium diphosphatohexadecavanadatoheptadecamolybdate. H. Lahrmann obtained orange-yellow **lead diphosphatoctovanadatopentadecamolybdate,** by the action of lead nitrate on the ammonium salt ; **lead diphosphatoctovanadatotetradecamolybdate** from lead nitrate and the ammonium salt ; and **lead diphosphatohexavanadatotridecamolybdate,** from the ammonium salt and lead nitrate ; F. Toggenburg, **lead diphosphatoctovanadatotridecamolybdate** from lead nitrate and the ammonium salt ; H. Lahrmann, and H. Stamm, **lead diphosphatoctovanadatododecamolybdate** from lead nitrate and the ammonium salt ; F. Toggenburg, **lead diphosphatotetradecavanadatohenamolybdate** from lead nitrate and the ammonium salt ; and S. Jacobowitz, dark red **lead diphosphatoctodecavanadatohexamolybdate** by the action of lead nitrate on a soln. of the ammonium salt.

O. W. Gibbs prepared **ammonium hexaphosphatodivanadatohexacontatungstate,** $10(NH_4)_2O.3P_2O_5.V_2O_5.60WO_3.60H_2O$, by adding hydrochloric acid to a boiling soln. of tungsten phosphate (22–24 : 1) and ammonium metavanadate in aq. ammonia. The lemon-yellow crystalline precipitate was washed with a dil. soln. of ammonium nitrate and dried. It is insoluble in cold water and sparingly soluble in hot water, it is soluble in a soln. of ammonium phosphate ; in aq. ammonia ; and in a soln. of ammonium carbonate. A. Rogers prepared **ammonium tetraphosphatohexadecavanadatotetratricontatungstate,** $13(NH_4)_2O.2P_2O_5.8V_2O_5.34WO_3.86H_2O$, by evaporating the filtrate from the mixture obtained by boiling for 6 hrs. a gram of ammonium phosphate, 15 grms. ammonium tungstate, 3 grms. of ammonium vanadate, 20 c.c. aq. ammonia, and 700 c.c. water. The dark red octahedral and cubic crystals are sparingly soluble in cold and hot water, and insoluble in alcohol, ether, carbon disulphide, benzene, and nitrobenzene. They are not attacked by dil. nitric and hydrochloric acids ; conc. hydrochloric acid forms a yellow precipitate, and gives off chlorine ; conc. nitric acid gives a yellow precipitate, alkali-lye, a yellow precipitate ; mercuric nitrate, a yellow precipitate ; silver nitrate, a dark red precipitate ; and in ammoniacal soln., the heavy metal salts give coloured precipitates. O. W. Gibbs dissolved ammonium phosphotungstate in a boiling soln. of ammonium metavanadate, and after the soln. had stood for some time, obtained orange or garnet-red crystals of **ammonium diphosphatohexavanadatohexadecatungstate,** $5(NH_4)_2O.P_2O_5.3V_2O_5.16WO_3.37H_2O$; the salt can be recrystallized from its aq. soln. O. W. Gibbs [6] prepared orange-red crystals of **potassium hexaphosphatoctovanadatoctodecatungstate,** $8K_2O.3P_2O_5.4V_2O_5.18WO_3.32H_2O$, by dissolving sodium phosphatotungstate in a boiling soln. of ammonium vanadate, and adding an excess of potassium bromide ; if an aq. soln. of this salt be crystallized, it furnishes orange-brown crystals of **potassium diphosphatodivanadatoheptatungstate,** $3K_2O.P_2O_5.V_2O_5.7WO_3.11H_2O$. When a boiling soln. of hydrated vanadium pentoxide in one of barium phosphatotungstate is cooled, red, octahedral crystals of **barium hexaphosphatotetravanadatohexacontatungstate,** $18BaO.3P_2O_5.2V_2O_5.60WO_3.144H_2O$, are formed. They are decomposed by hot water. A. Rogers obtained no precipitate by adding neutral soln. of copper nitrate to a soln. of $3(NH_4)_2O.2P_2O_5.8V_2O_5.34WO_3.86H_2O$; with mercurous nitrate, yellow precipitates of **mercurous phosphatovanadatotungstates** are produced with the various ammonium phosphatovanadatotungstates—*vide supra,* hypovanadatophosphates.

G. Canneri [7] suggested that the phosphatovanadatotungstates are members of three limiting series of solid soln. Soln. rich in tungstic acid—say 4·8 grms.

ammonium metavanadate in 200 c.c. of water to which are added 40 grms. of ammonium metatungstate, and phosphoric acid eq. to 14 grms. P_2O_5—yield red crystals of the type, **ammonium hydrophosphatodivanadatoctotungstate,** $(NH_4)_6H[P(W_2O_7)_4(V_2O_6)_2].nH_2O$; while soln. rich in vanadic acid—say 9·75 grms. ammonium metavanadate, 40 grms. ammonium metatungstate, and 9 grms. of P_2O_5—yield ruby-red or wine-red crystals of the type, **ammonium hydrophosphato-trivanadatohexatungstate,** $(NH_4)_6H[P(W_2O_7)_3(V_2O_6)_3].25H_2O$; and soln. still richer in vanadic acid—say 14·5 grms. ammonium metavanadate, 40 grms. of ammonium metavanadate, and 8·9 grms. of P_2O_5—yield reddish-brown, or pitch-black crystals of the type, **ammonium hydrophosphatotetravanadatotetratungstate,** $(NH_4)_6H[P(W_2O_7)_2(V_2O_6)_2].25H_2O$. F. Rodolico found for the limiting series, $(NH_4)_6H[P(W_2O_7)_x(V_2O_6)_y]$ with 40·06 per cent. WO_3, and 32·86 per cent. V_2O_5, the axial ratio $a : c = 1 : 0.9932$; and for the one with 64·22 per cent. WO_3 and 12·09 per cent. V_2O_5, $a : c = 1 : 1.0011$.

References.

[1] I. Koppel, R. Goldmann, and A. Kaufmann, *Zeit. anorg. Chem.*, **45**. 349, 1905.
[2] J. J. Berzelius, *Acad. Handl. Stockholm*, 1, 1831 ; *Schweigger's Journ.*, **62**. 323, 1831 ; **63**. 26, 1831 ; *Pogg. Ann.*, **22**. 1, 1831 ; *Ann. Chim. Phys.*, (1), **47**. 337, 1831 ; *Phil. Mag.*, (2), **10**. 321, 1831 ; (2), **11**. 7, 1832 ; A. Guyard, *Bull. Soc. Chim.*, (2), **25**. 352, 1876 ; J. Meyer and R. Backa, *Zeit. anorg. Chem.*, **135**. 177, 1924 ; S. M. Tanatar and E. K. Kurowsky, *Journ. Russ. Phys. Chem. Soc.*, **41**. 813, 1919.
[3] J. J. Berzelius, *Acad. Handl. Stockholm*, 1, 1831 ; *Schweigger's Journ.*, **62**. 323, 1831 ; **63**. 26, 1831 ; *Pogg. Ann.*, **22**. 1, 1831 ; *Ann. Chim. Phys.*, (1), **47**. 337, 1831 ; *Phil. Mag.*, (2), **10**. 321, 1831 ; (2), **11**. 7, 1832 ; O. W. Gibbs, *Amer. Chem. Journ.*, **7**. 222, 1886 ; *Proc. Amer. Acad.*, **21**. 50, 1886 ; J. Howaldt, *Ueber Vanadylverbindungen*, Bern, 1904 ; J. Meisel, *Ueber die sogennanten Vanadylvanadinphosphate und arsenate*, Bern, 1904 ; W. T. Schaller, *Amer. Journ. Science*, (5), **8**. 462, 1924 ; *Journ. Washington Acad.*, **12**. 195, 1922 ; E. F. Smith and F. F. Exner, *Journ. Amer. Chem. Soc.*, **24**. 573, 1902 ; A. Rogers, *ib.*, **25**. 298, 1903 ; A. Rogers and E. F. Smith, *ib.*, **25**. 1233, 1903 ; W. T. Schaller, *Journ. Washington Acad.*, **12**. 195, 1922 ; *Amer. Journ. Science*, (5), **8**. 462, 1924 ; E. S. Larsen, *Bull. U.S. Geol. Sur.*, 679, 1921.
[4] C. Friedheim, *Ber.*, **23**. 1530, 2600, 1890 ; *Zeit. anorg. Chem.*, **2**. 318, 1892 ; **5**. 437, 1894 ; C. Friedheim and K. Michaelis, *ib.*, **5**. 449, 1894 ; C. Friedheim and M. Szamatolsky, *Ber.*, **23**. 1531, 1890 ; M. Szamatolsky, *Ueber die sogennante Phosphorvanadinsäure und deren Verbindungen*, Borlin, 1890 ; A. Ditte, *Compt. Rend.*, **102**. 757, 1091, 1105, 1886 ; O. W. Gibbs, *Amer. Chem. Journ.*, **7**. 209, 1885 ; *Proc. Amer. Acad.*, **21**. 50, 1886 ; J. J. Berzelius, *Acad. Handl. Stockholm*, 1, 1831 ; *Schweigger's Journ.*, **62**. 323, 1831 ; **63**. 26, 1831 ; *Pogg. Ann.*, **22**. 1, 1831 ; *Ann. Chim. Phys.*, (1), **47**. 337, 1831 ; *Phil. Mag.*, (2), **10**. 321, 1831 ; (2), **11**. 7, 1832 ; E. Petersen, *Ber.*, **21**. 3258, 1888 ; A. Guyard, *Bull. Soc. Chim.*, (2), **25**. 354, 1876 ; M. Amadori, *Gazz. Chim. Ital.*, **49**. i, 38, 69, 1919 ; *Rend. Accad. Lincei*, (5), **21**. ii, 768, 1912 ; (5), **27**. i, 143, 1918 ; *Atti Ist. Veneto*, **76**. ii, 419, 1917 ; *Rend. Ist. Lombardo*, **49**. 137, 1916 ; M. Amadori and E. Viterbi, *Mem. Accad. Lincei*, (5), **10**. 386, 1914 ; N. Collie, *Journ. Chem. Soc.*, **55**. 94, 1889 ; A. Rosenheim and K. H. Yang, *Zeit. anorg. Chem.*, **129**. 181, 1923.
[5] O. W. Gibbs, *Amer. Chem. Journ.*, **5**. 374, 1884 ; *Proc. Amer. Acad.*, **18**. 232, 1883 ; F. Toggenburg, *Ueber Phosphorvanadinmolybdate*, Bern, 1902 ; H. Jacoby, *Ueber Phosphor-vanadinmolybdate*, Bern, 1900 ; H. Stamm, *Ueber Phosphorvanadinmolybdate*, Bern, 1905 ; P. Schulz, *Ueber Phosphorvanadinmolybdate*, Bern, 1904 ; A. Hinsen, *Ueber Ammonium phosphor-vanadinmolybdate*, Bern, 1904 ; H. Lahrmann, *Beiträge zur Kenntniss der Ammoniumphosphor-vanadinmolybdate*, Bern, 1904 ; W. Blum, *Journ. Amer. Chem. Soc.*, **30**. 1858, 1908 ; S. Jacobo-witz, *Beiträge zur Kenntnis der Ammoniumphosphorvanadinmolybdate*, Bern, 1909 ; J. R. Cain and J. C. Hostetter, *Journ. Amer. Chem. Soc.*, **43**. 2522, 1921 ; E. T. Wherry, *Journ. Franklin Inst.*, **169**. 487, 1910 ; J. Contzen, *Beiträge zur Kenntnis Natriumphosphorvanadinmolybdate*, Bern, 1906 ; A. Düsterwald, *Beiträge zur Kenntnis Ammoniumphosphorvanadinmolybdate*, Bern, 1906 ; W. Engel, *Ueber Natriumphosphorvanadinmolybdate*, Berlin, 1904 ; F. Rodolico, *Atti Accad. Lincei*, (6), **4**. 471, 1926 ; A. Rogers, *Journ. Amer. Chem. Soc.*, **25**. 298, 1903.
[6] O. W. Gibbs, *Amer. Chem. Journ.*, **5**. 395, 1884 ; *Proc. Amer. Acad.*, **18**. 232, 1883 ; A. Rogers, *Journ. Amer. Chem. Soc.*, **25**. 298, 1903 ; G. Canneri, *Gazz. Chim. Ital.*, **56**. 642, 871, 1926.
[7] G. Canneri, *Gazz. Chim. Ital.*, **56**. 642, 871, 1926 ; F. Rodolico, *Atti Accad. Lincei*, (6), **4**. 471, 1926.

CHAPTER LV

COLUMBIUM

§ 1. The History of Columbium and Tantalum

In 1801, C. Hatchett [1] described a heavy, black stone with golden streaks of mica. It had been sent along with various specimens of iron-ore to the British Museum from Massachusetts, and was labelled as having come from Nautneauge, the Indian name for a place which could not be identified because the locality had since been assigned a European name. Analysis showed that the ore contained iron along with about 75 per cent. of an unknown substance of a metallic nature which gave coloured precipitates with potassium ferrocyanide (olive-green), and tincture of galls (orange) ; and it formed a blue or purple glass when fused with ammonium phosphate. C. Hatchett said that it is one of those metallic substances which retain oxygen with great tenacity and are therefore difficult to reduce. It gave an acidic oxide which reddened litmus, expelled carbon dioxide from carbonates, and formed combinations with the fixed alkalies. Unlike other metallic acids, it refused to unite with ammonia. The oxide was not changed by nitric acid ; it formed colourless soln. with sulphuric and hydrochloric acids from which a white flocculent precipitate was obtained with the fixed alkalies, and ammonia ; water also precipitated it in a state of sulphate from the sulphuric acid soln. C. Hatchett concluded :

> These properties completely distinguish it from the other acidifiable metals—*viz.* arsenic, tungsten, molybdena, and chromium ; as to the other metals lately discovered, such as uranium, titanium, and tellurium, they are still farther removed from it. . . . This new metal differs from tungsten and other acidifiable metals by a more limited degree of oxidation ; for, unlike these, it seems to be incapable of retaining oxygen sufficient to enable the total quantity to combine with the fixed alkalies. . . . Considering, therefore, that the metal which has been examined is so very different from those hitherto discovered, it appeared proper that it should be distinguished by a peculiar name ; and, having consulted with several of the eminent and ingenious chemists of this country, I have been induced to give it the name **columbium**.

A year later, A. G. Ekeberg found a new element in some Finnish and Swedish—Kimito and Ytterby—minerals—tantalites and yttrotantalites—resembling columbite. This mineral had previously been regarded as a form of cassiterite or a form of wolfram. He called the new element **tantalum**—from Tantalus of Grecian mythology—in allusion to the tantalizing difficulties he encountered in trying to dissolve the mineral in acids ; and J. J. Berzelius investigated the oxides of tantalum. The mineral was also analyzed by A. F. Gehlen, H. A. von Vogel, and M. H. Klaproth. W. H. Wollaston suggested that tantalum and columbium were the same element ; but this hypothesis was not confirmed. T. Thomson, A. G. Ekeberg, J. J. Berzelius, and F. Wöhler observed that the sp. gr. of specimens of columbite from different localities varies considerably, and the earths derived from pyrochlore, and some Bavarian tantalites have some peculiar properties. In 1844, H. Rose announced the existence of two new elements in a sample of columbite from Bodenmais—one was similar to A. G. Ekeberg's tantalum ; and the other was called **niobium**—from Niobe, the mythological daughter of

Tantalus. C. Hatchett's columbium and H. Rose's niobium probably contained a little tantalum.

A couple of years later, H. Rose announced the existence of yet a third new element in the columbite of Bodenmais, and he called it *pelopium*—from Pelops, the mythological brother of Niobe. In 1853, H. Rose showed that the assumed pelopic acid and niobic acid are different states of oxidation of the element niobium ; and C. W. Blomstrand, and J. C. G. de Marignac showed that H. Rose's *Unterniobsäure* was really niobic acid, and his *Niobsäure* was a mixture of tantalic and niobic acids. C. W. Blomstrand also showed that H. Rose's *Unterniobchlorid* is really an oxychloride. J. C. G. de Marignac established the isomorphism of the fluorides of tantalum and columbium. R. Hermann showed that both niobic and tantalic acids are contained in tantalite from Kimito, Finland, and columbite from Bodenmais, Bavaria. Since niobium discovered by H. Rose in 1844 is the same element as columbium discovered by C. Hatchett over 40 years earlier, it was pointed out by J. L. Smith, and P. Nicolardot, very properly, that it is more fitting to retain the term columbium for the element, and abandon niobium. The latter term, however, is still retained in Germany.

In addition to the unverified *pelopium*, some other elements belonging to this family of the elements have been announced prematurely. Thus, in 1860, F. von Kobell announced the presence of a new element in different minerals ; and he called it *dianium* —after Diana of Greek mythology—and the mineral was called *dianite*. C. W. Blomstrand, and J. C. G. de Marignac, however, showed that dianium is really columbium. R. Hermann reported a new element *ilmenium*—from the Ilmen Mountains, Urals—in samarskite and in aschynite, but J. C. G. de Marignac showed that ilmenium is really a mixture of tantalum and columbium. R. Hermann also introduced *neptunium* as a new element which he obtained from the Connecticut mineral; but A. Larsson showed that neptunium, like dianium, is identical with columbium. E. F. Smith and co-workers also were unable to find R. Hermann's neptunium in any of the minerals they examined.

REFERENCES.

¹ C. Hatchett, *Nicholson's Journ.*, **1**. 32, 1802 ; *Phil. Trans.*, **92**. 49, 1802 ; W. H. Wollaston, *ib.*, **99**. 246, 1809 ; A. G. Ekeberg, *Akad. Nya Handl.*, **23**. 180, 1802 ; *Gilbert's Ann.*, **14**. 246, 1803 ; *Crell's Ann.*, i, 3, 1802 ; *Scherer's Journ.*, **9**. 598, 1803 ; *Nicholson's Journ.*, **3**. 251, 1802 ; *Phil. Mag.*, **14**. 346, 1802 ; *Ann. Chim. Phys.*, (1), **43**. 276, 1802 ; J. J. Berzelius, *ib.*, **41**. 2, 1824 ; *Afhand. Fys. Kem. Min.*, **4**. 148, 252, 262, 1815 ; **6**. 237, 1818 ; *Ann. Chim. Phys.*, (2), **3**. 140, 1816 ; (2), **29**. 300, 1825 ; A. F. Gehlen, *Schweigger's Journ.*, **6**. 256, 1812 ; H. A. von Vogel, *Denks. Akad. München*, 213, 1817 ; M. H. Klaproth, *Beiträge zur chemischen Kenntniss der Mineralkörper*, Berlin, **5**. 1, 1810 ; F. Wöhler, *Liebig's Ann.*, **31**. 120, 1839 ; *Pogg. Ann.*, **48**. 83, 1839 ; H. Rose, *ib.*, **63**. 317, 1844 ; **69**. 118, 1846 ; **70**. 572, 1847 ; **71**. 157, 1847 ; **72**. 155, 471, 1847 ; **73**. 313, 455, 1848 ; **74**. 85, 285, 1848 ; **90**. 456, 1853 ; **99**. 65, 481, 575, 1856 ; **100**. 146, 417, 551, 1857 ; **101**. 11, 1857 ; **102**. 55, 289, 1857 ; **104**. 310, 432, 581, 1858 ; **105**. 424, 1858 ; **111**. 193, 426, 1861 ; **112**. 468, 549, 1861 ; **113**. 105, 292, 1861 ; **118**. 9, 33, 406, 497, 1863 ; R. Hermann, *Journ. prakt. Chem.*, (1), **38**. 95, 1846 ; (1), **40**. 477, 1847 ; (1), **50**. 497, 1850 ; (1), **65**. 54, 1855 ; (1), **70**. 193, 1857 ; (1), **73**. 503, 1858 ; (1) **75**. 62, 1858 ; (1), **83**. 106, 1861 ; (1), **84**. 317, 1861 ; (1), **95**. 65, 103, 128, 1865 ; (1), **97**. 350, 1866 ; (1), **99**. 21, 779, 1866 ; (1), **100**. 385, 1867 ; (1), **102**. 399, 1867 ; (1), **103**. 127, 416, 1868 ; (1), **107**. 129, 1869 ; (2), **2**. 108, 1870 ; (2), **3**. 373, 1871 ; (2), **4**. 178, 1871 ; (2), **5**. 66, 1872 ; C. W. Blomstrand, *ib.*, (1), **93**. 44, 1866 ; *Acta Univ. Lund.*, **1**. 7, 1864 ; **2**. 3, 1865 ; *Liebig's Ann.*, **135**. 198, 1865 ; F. von Kobell, *Sitzber. Akad. München*, **50**. 377, 1860 ; *Journ. prakt. Chem.*, (1), **79**. 291, 1860 ; (1), **83**. 193, 449, 1861 ; *Liebig's Ann.*, **114**. 337, 1860 ; *Phil. Mag.*, (4), **21**. 415, 1861 ; J. C. G. de Marignac, *Arch. Sciences Genève*, (2), **23**. 249, 326, 1865 ; *Compt. Rend.*, **60**. 234, 1865 ; *Ann. Chim. Phys.*, (4), **8**. 5, 1866 ; (4), **9**. 249, 1866 ; J. L. Smith, *ib.*, (5), **12**. 253, 1877 ; E. F. Smith, *Proc. Amer. Phil. Soc.*, **44**. 151, 177, 1905 ; *Journ. Amer. Chem. Soc.*, **26**. 1235, 1904 ; **27**. 1140, 1216, 1369, 1905 ; **30**. 1637,- 1909 ; A. Larsson, *Zeit. anorg. Chem.*, **12**. 189, 1896 ; P. Nicolardot, *Bull. Soc. Chim.*, (4), **1**. 669, 1907 ; T. Thomson, *Records Gen. Science*, **4**. 407, 1836.

§ 2. The Occurrence of Tantalum and Columbium

Columbium and tantalum do not occur in nature in the free state. The minerals containing these elements are scarce. The two elements usually occur associated with one another, forming the acidic component of minerals with the basic element

calcium, the **rare** earths, uranium, manganese, and iron. **F. W.** Clarke and
H. S. Washington [1] estimated that columbium and tantalum constitute 0·003 per
cent. of the igneous rocks of the earth's crust; **J. H. L.** Vogt gave 0·000000n per
cent. The earth's crust probably contains a little more columbium than tantalum.
W. Vernadsky gave 0·0$_4$1 and 0·0$_4$48 for the percentage proportions and 0·0$_4$5 and
0·0005 for the atomic proportions respectively of columbium and tantalum. These
elements have not been reported in minerals derived from extra-terrestrial sources—
meteorites; but **H. A.** Rowland [2] placed columbium in the list of minerals whose
lines appear in the solar spectrum; and tantalum in the list of doubtful elements
shown in the solar spectrum. **M. N.** Saha also placed tantalum in the " doubtful "
list.

Rather more minerals are known containing columbium free from tantalum,
than tantalum minerals free from columbium. Both columbites and tantalites
often contain more or less titanium, zirconium, germanium, tin, and tungsten. The
columbium minerals samarskite, wöhlerite, pyrochlore, euxenite, yttrotantalite,
fergusonite, and the columbite of Greenland often contain columbium associated
with only traces of tantalum; while the other columbium minerals are associated
with a larger proportion of tantalum. The melanocerites of Norway, and skogbölite
contain only a very small proportion of columbium; and in the tantalites of
Finland and Sweden, yttrotantalite, tapiolite, ixiolite, and microlite, the tantalum
usually predominates. Most of these minerals have been described in connection
with the rare earths—**5.** 38, 3—or in connection with the columbatosilicates—**6.** 40,
48. The more important occurrences are as follow :

Adelpholite—see the rare earths ; aeschynite has 51·45 per cent. Cb$_2$O$_5$ and TiO$_2$,
etc.; ainolite, a Finnish cassiterite, contains a tantalite ; ampangabeite has 43·7 to 50·6
per cent. (Cb.Ta)$_2$O$_5$—D. Guimaraes described a variety containing rather more titanium ;
annerödite has 48·15 per cent. (TaCb)$_2$O$_5$; arrhenite is a variety of columbotitanite ;
betafite, a hydrated uranyl columbate with 35·5 per cent. Cb$_2$O$_5$ and traces of columbium;
blomstrandite—see tapiolite ; chalcolamprite has 59·93 per cent. Cb$_2$O$_5$; columbite or
niobite, 60·46–83·2 per cent. of Cb$_2$O$_5$ and Ta$_2$O$_5$; epistolite is a sodium titanosilico-
columbate, Na$_7$Ti(CbO)$_3$(SiO$_4$)$_5$.3½H$_2$O, or Na$_{10}$Cb$_4$Si$_9$O$_{33}$.10H$_2$O ; eschimite resembles
euxenite in many respects ; eschwegeite, a hydrated yttrium tantalocolumbotitanate,
2Ta$_2$O$_5$.4Cb$_2$O$_5$.10TiO$_2$.5Y$_2$O$_3$.7H$_2$O, described by D. Guimaraes [3] and named after
W. L. Eschwege ; eucolite has up to 2·35 per cent. Ta$_2$O$_5$ and 3·52 per cent. Cb$_2$O$_5$; eudeiolite
has 59·65 per cent. Cb$_2$O$_5$; eudialyte—see eucolite ; euxenite has 34·21 to 36·04 per cent. Cb$_2$O$_5$
and Ta$_2$O$_5$; fergusonite has 15·52–48·17 per cent. Cb$_2$O$_5$ and 6·40–49·36 per cent. Ta$_2$O$_5$;
haddamite—see the rare earths ; hatchettolite—see the rare earths ; hjelmite has 3·63–16·35
per cent. Cb$_2$O$_5$ and 54·52–72·16 per cent. Ta$_2$O$_5$; ilmenorutile is a complex titanocolumbo-
tantalates ; ishikawaite, a rare earth columbate ; ixiolite, a variety of tapiolite having,
7·63–19·24 per cent. Cb$_2$O$_5$ and 63·58–70·49 per cent. of Ta$_2$O$_5$; or an iron tantalite,
Fe(Cb,Ta)$_2$O$_6$, containing tin and manganese ; kochelite—see the rare earths ; koppite—
see the rare earths ; lavenite has up to 5·20 per cent. (Ta,Cb)$_2$O$_5$; mariupolite—a syenitic
rock carrying columbium and tantalum oxides ; microlite is a variety of pyrochlor or a
calcium tantalate ; mossite is an iron columbotantalate having 82·92 per cent. Cb$_2$O$_5$ and
Ta$_2$O$_5$; nohlite has 50·43 per cent. of (Ta,Cb)$_2$O$_6$; plumbionite has 46·15 per cent.
Cb$_2$O$_5$; polycrase has about 24–26 per cent. Cb$_2$O$_5$ and Ta$_2$O$_5$; polymignite is a titano-
zircontite having 1·35–42·17 per cent. Ta$_2$O$_5$ and 6·37–11·99 per cent. Cb$_2$O$_5$; pyrochlore
has 47·13–62·18 per cent. Cb$_2$O$_5$, 5·38–13·52 per cent. TiO$_2$, etc. ; risorite—see the rare
earths ; rogersite—see tapiolite ; rutherfordite—see the rare earths ; samarskite has
47·47–50·17 per cent. Cb$_2$O$_5$ and Ta$_2$O$_5$, etc. ; samiresite, a hydrated uranyl columbate
with 45·8 per cent. Cb$_2$O$_5$ and 3·7 per cent. Ta$_2$O$_5$; sanidinite is a calcium silicozirconate
with 1·68 per cent. Cb$_2$O$_5$ and 0·21 per cent. Ta$_2$O$_5$; sipylite—see the rare earths ;
skogbölite, a variety of tapiolite having 84·44 per cent. Cb$_2$O$_5$ and Ta$_2$O$_5$; strüverite—see
ilmenorutile ; tantalite, and neotantalite have 7–40 per cent. Cb$_2$O$_5$, 42·15–76·34 per cent.
Ta$_2$O$_5$, up to 6·20 per cent. TiO$_2$, etc. ; tapiolite has 11·22 per cent. Cb$_2$O$_5$ and 73·91 per
cent. Ta$_2$O$_5$; toddite—a variety of columbite ; tritonite contains 3·63 per cent. Ta$_2$O$_5$,
zirconia, etc. ; tyrite—see the rare earths ; uranotantalite is a uraniferous tantalate ;
vietinghofite has 51 per cent. (Cb,Ta)$_2$O$_5$; wöhlerite has 14·41 per cent. Cb$_2$O$_5$,
but C. F. Rammelsberg found no tantalum ; yttrogarnet contains 2·97 per cent. of Ta$_2$O$_5$
and Cb$_2$O$_5$; yttroilmenite is a columbate of the rare earths ; yttrotantalite has 13·15
per cent. Cb$_2$O$_5$, 49·36 per cent. Ta$_2$O$_5$, etc.

H. Rose found **columbium and** tantalum in *perowskite*, and in *pyrite ;* **H. Caron,**

and G. T. Prior, in cassiterite and other stanniferous minerals; **T. L. Phipson,**
L. Weiss, E. T. Wherry, W. F. Hillebrand, and A. Carnot, in *wolframite;* T. Scheerer,
in *pitchblende;* H. St. C. Deville, in *cryolite;* G. T. Prior, in the *guarimite* of Monte
Somma; and F. Zambonini, in the *dysanalyte* of Monte Somma; and also in *vesbine*
from Vesuvius; D. Guimaraes found the two oxides in a radioactive mineral from
Minas Geraes, Brazil; and G. Carobbi, in the *schulite* from Traversella.

REFERENCES.

¹ F. W. Clarke and H. S. Washington, *Proc. Nat. Acad. Sciences*, **8.** 112, 1922; *The Composition of the Earth's Crust*, Washington, 20, 1924; J. H. L. Vogt, *Zeit. prakt. Geol.*, **6.** 324, 1898; W. Vernadsky, *Essai de minéralogie descriptive*, St. Petersburg, **1.** 121, 740, 1914; *Geochimie*, Paris, 16, 1924; A. E. Fersman, *Bull. Acad. St. Petersburg*, (6), **6.** 367, 1912.
² H. A. Rowland, *Johns Hopkins Univ. Circ.*, 85, 1891; *Amer. Journ. Science*, (3), **41.** 243, 1891; *Chem. News*, **63.** 133, 1891; M. N. Saha, *Phil. Mag.*, (6), **40.** 808, 1920.
³ H. Rose, *Pogg. Ann.*, **48.** 555, 1839; **77.** 157, 1848; Anon., *Bull. Imp. Inst.*, **5.** 429, 1907; C. F. Rammelsberg, *ib.*, **150.** 208, 1873; T. Scheerer, *ib.*, **72.** 56, 1847; H. Caron, *Compt. Rend.*, **61.** 1064, 1865; A. Carnot, **79.** 637, 1874; T. L. Phipson, *ib.*, **65.** 419, 1867; H. St. C. Deville, *ib.*, **49.** 210, 310, 1859; *Ann. Chim. Phys.*, (3), **61.** 309, 1861; G. T. Prior, *Min. Mag.*, **12.** 96, 1899; **15.** 257, 1909; D. Guimaraes, *Bol. Inst. Brasil Science*, **2.** 114, 1926; F. Zambonini, *Mineralogia Vesuviana*, Napoli, 214, 1910; *Amer. Min.*, **12.** 1, 1927; W. F. Hillebrand, *Amer. Journ. Science*, (3), **27.** 357, 1884; L. Weiss, *Zeit. anorg. Chem.*, **65.** 286, 1910; E. T. Wherry, *Proc. U.S. Nat. Museum*, **47.** 501, 1914; G. Carobbi, *Gazz. Chim. Ital.*, **54.** 59, 1924.

§ 3. The Extraction of Columbium and Tantalum Oxides

The pentoxides of the two elements are together extracted from the minerals
and afterwards separated. The concentration of tantalum minerals was discussed
by A. W. Gregory.[1] If only columbium is required, the mineral selected will be
one containing as little tantalum as possible—*e.g.* some of the columbites of low
sp. gr.—whereas if tantalum alone is required tantalites of high sp. gr. or fergusonite
will be employed. A special treatment for removing titanium oxide may be
necessary. As in the analogous case with zirconium, the elements—particularly
columbium—seem to behave differently in the presence of titanium. As W. Crookes
expressed it, when associated with titanium, the individuality of the elements seems
to be destroyed. The reactions which the elements undergo when alone, do not
necessarily occur when titanium is present. It seems as if a complex salt of
titanium and columbium or tantalum is formed. The behaviour of aluminium
hydroxide in the presence of beryllium towards soln. of ammonium carbonate is
another example observed by C. A. Joy.

The opening of the mineral.—This can be effected by fusing the finely powdered
mineral at a bright red-heat with from 3 to 8 times its weight of *potassium hydrosulphate.* J. J. Berzelius employed a platinum crucible; and J. C. G. de Marignac,
an iron crucible. G. Chesneau fortified the potassium hydrosulphate with half its
weight of sulphuric acid. The cold mass is digested with water which precipitates
most of the columbium and tantalum as hydrated pentoxides. These are contaminated with silica, titania, zirconia, ferric, stannic, and tungstic oxides. L. Weiss and
M. Landecker said that the mixture filters badly, and the wash-water is liable to be
turbid. If the residue be digested with hydrochloric acid, some of the desired earths
pass into soln. J. J. Berzelius recommended washing the residue with boiling
water, and, after drying and calcining, heating it with a mixture of sulphuric and
hydrofluoric acids so as to drive off the silica. W. E. von John recommended
removing the silica by fusing the mixture with sodium hydroxide and washing the
product with luke-warm water. The sodium columbate and tantalate so produced
are not soluble in alkali-lye, whereas the silicate is soluble in that menstruum.
J. J. Berzelius recommended digesting the residue remaining after washing the cake,
resulting from the hydrosulphate fusion, digesting for some days with a warm soln.

of ammonium hydrosulphide so as to remove the stannic and tungstic oxides, and convert the iron oxide into the sulphide. The residue is washed with a dil. soln. of ammonium hydrosulphide, and the iron sulphide removed by treatment with hot, conc. hydrochloric acid. C. F. Rammelsberg, and R. D. Hall and E. F. Smith recommended dil. hydrochloric acid. R. F. Weinland and L. Storz said that the hydrochloric acid dissolves considerable quantities of the hydrated columbium and tantalum oxides. The iron is held very tenaciously, and L. Weiss and M. Landecker recommended removing the iron by dissolving the freshly precipitated hydrates in a mixture of oxalic and tartaric acids, adding ammonia, and passing a current of hydrogen sulphide which precipitates only the iron. The complex columbic and tantalic oxalates crystallize well from the filtrates, and yield columbic and tantalic oxides on ignition. They also recommended removing all the impurities excepting titanic oxide by suspending the mixture in sulphuric acid, adding hydrogen dioxide, and saturating the soln. with sulphur dioxide. The columbic and tantalic acids are precipitated with any insoluble sulphates. These are removed by dissolving the earth acids with warm sulphuric acid and hydrogen dioxide. According to O. Hahn and H. Gille, the solubilities of titanic, columbic, and tantalic acids have not confirmed the efficacy of the process of L. Weiss and M. Landecker. Titanic and columbic acids are practically completely soluble in acid hydrogen dioxide, but tantalic acid when precipitated hot is almost insoluble, and when precipitated cold is only partly soluble. In mixtures, the different acids influence one another differently according to the conditions. Tantalic acid lowers the solubility of columbic acid, whilst titanic acid may increase the solubility of tantalic acid or may itself be rendered less soluble. The ultra-microscope indicates that in acid hydrogen dioxide soln., titanic acid forms a true soln., whilst columbic and tantalic acids form colloidal soln. H. Rose said that the ammonium hydrosulphide process for removing tin and tungsten is not satisfactory, and he recommended fusing the earth-acids with three times its weight of a mixture of sodium carbonate and sulphur in a porcelain crucible; washing the cold product with water, and then with hydrochloric acid. The sodium salts remaining were then fused with potassium hydrosulphate, and the cold cake treated with water. M. E. Pennington removed the tin and tungsten as sulphosalts after fusion with sodium thiosulphate. R. D. Hall and E. F. Smith said that the tin and tungsten are rapidly removed by crystallizing the complex fluorides a couple of times from hydrofluoric acid. H. W. Foote and R. W. Langley purified the mixture of earth-acids by fusion with six times its weight of ammonium hydrofluoride; adding hot water, and enough hydrofluoric acid to give a clear soln. Ammonia is then added, and the precipitate washed with ammoniacal water. It is then heated with a little conc. sulphuric acid to drive off the fluorine. The residue is again treated with water and ammonia to obtain the purified earth acids. H. Biltz and C. Kircher removed sulphur by heating the oxide in ammonia, and afterwards heating the product in oxygen. The above method with some modifications was also used by F. Ott, W. Muthmann and co-workers, R. Hermann, R. D. Hall, E. F. Smith, M. E. Pennington, C. W. Blomstrand, W. B. Giles, G. Chesneau, E. Wedekind and W. Maas, O. W. Gibbs, H. Biltz and L. Gonder, W. P. Headden, T. B. Osborne, J. L. Smith, J. C. G. de Marignac, G. T. Prior, O. Ruff and E. Schiller, R. J. Meyer and O. Hauser, and G. W. Sears and L. Quill.

G. W. Sears opened columbite and tantalite by fusion with sodium pyrosulphate —7 grms. per gram of ore—and compared the results obtained by working at 770°–900°, and using hydrofluoric acid, and sulphuric acid as solvents. The compounds formed by the fusion are probably tantalates and columbates rather than sulphates or complex sulphates. The results show that variations in the proportions of flux, and of the time of heating have little influence on the solubility of the product. Conc. sulphuric acid is more effective than hydrofluoric acid in separating columbium and tantalum by dissolving the columbium and leaving the tantalum undissolved; indeed, a complete separation of the two elements can be obtained by treating the fusion made at 825°–875°. The soln. of columbium is unaffected by cold $6N$-H_2SO_4, but is almost completely precipitated from hot soln.

The powdered mineral columbite—was opened up by O. W. Gibbs by evaporating it to dryness with a soln. of three times its weight of *potassium hydrofluoride* ; dissolving the mixture in hot water and hydrofluoric acid. On cooling, crystals of potassium oxyfluocolumbate separate out, and by recrystallization can be freed from iron and manganese. The mineral can also be fused with the potassium hydrofluoride, treated with water, and the filtered soln. evaporated to dryness, and the fluorine expelled by heating the residue with sulphuric acid. When the soln. is boiled with water, the earth-acid hydrates are precipitated. W. M. Barr used potassium hydrofluoride for opening up euxenite, and æschynite ; J. L. Smith, for samarskite ; and H. W. Foote and R. W. Langley, for stibiotantalite. M. E. Pennington said that the decomposition of columbite by this process is faster than is the case with the potassium hydrosulphate fusion process. W. B. Giles emphasized the difficulties attending this process.

W. B. Giles recommended opening up columbite by fusion with *potassium carbonate :*

The powdered mineral is mixed with two and a quarter parts of potassium carbonate and introduced into a steel crucible fitted with a lid, which is in turn placed in a plumbago crucible, also fitted with a cover, which is then filled up partly with powdered and partly with lumps of wood charcoal. After placing the whole in a furnace and exposing it for an hour to a most intense heat, the mass, owing to the action of the reducing gases, will contain the heavier metals, either as such (tin, copper) or else as lower oxides (iron, manganese), whilst the tantalum and niobium may be extracted as soluble potassium compounds with water. The soln. is then treated as usual for their separation.

A. Joly heated powdered hjelmite with a mixture of one-fifth its weight of dry *sodium carbonate*, and one-eighth its weight of sugar charcoal for 5 to 6 hrs. in a graphite crucible at a high temp. The tantalum, columbium, and titanium were converted into carbides and nitrides. The product was digested with boiling, conc. hydrochloric acid. The dried residue was heated in a current of chlorine. The residue was treated with boiling hydrochloric acid ; and the soln. treated with water to precipitate the mixed earth-acids. The mixture can be purified by dissolving it in hydrochloric acid at 70°–80°, and the soln. treated with sulphur dioxide to re-precipitate the earth-acids. H. S. Cooper treated materials containing tantalum and iron with chlorine at a temp. exceeding 450° so as to form chlorides of these elements ; the tantalum chloride is then hydrolyzed in a soln. containing 5 per cent. hydrochloric or sulphuric acid, or a 20 per cent. of sodium chloride, so as to prevent the hydrolysis of the iron chloride.

M. E. Pennington tried fused *borax* for opening up the mineral with poor results. J. Morozewicz found that mariupolite is decomposed by dil. hydrochloric acid, and the rare earths pass into soln. The tantalic and columbic acids can be separated from the insoluble residue when treated with hydrofluoric and sulphuric acids. A. G. Ekeberg, E. S. Simpson, W. B. Giles, and H. Rose opened the mineral by fusion with *alkali hydroxide* in a nickel, iron, silver, or gilded platinum crucible ; extracted the product with water acidified with hydrochloric acid, and boiled the soln. with dil. acid to precipitate the tantalic and columbic acids. H. Moissan heated columbite mixed with *carbon* in an electric furnace for 7 or 8 mins. and obtained a regulus containing tantalum and columbium and 2·18–2·34 per cent. of carbon, but no graphite. The alloy was converted into the potassium fluosalts and separated as indicated below. F. L. Hahn and W. Franke opened up columbates and tantalates by heating them at 250°–300° with carbon tetrachloride, and extracting the product with acid.

The separation of titanium from the columbium and tantalum oxides.—This is a difficult separation. (1) H. Rose recommended washing the product obtained from the potassium hydrosulphate fusion with cold water, and R. Hermann, with hot water ; but J. C. G. de Marignac, and L. Weiss and M. Landecker showed that the results are very bad. (2) J. C. G. de Marignac found that the fractional crystallization of the double fluorides of potassium from hydrofluoric acid is a long operation, and is not suitable for small quantities. G. Krüss and L. F. Nilson, M. E. Pennington, H. Lange, and E. F. Smith and co-workers did not get good results by this process. E. F. Smith showed that the process separates the potassium fluocolumbates and fluotantalates, and that the titanium accumulates with the fluocolumbate. R. D. Hall and E. F. Smith obtained good results by crystallization from a mixture of hydrogen dioxide and hydrofluoric acid ; and L. Weiss and M. Landecker, from a hydrochloric acid soln. of the complex fluorides. W. Muthmann and co-workers boiled with hydrochloric acid the cake obtained from the potassium hydrosulphate fusion. (3) G. Krüss and L. F. Nilson boiled the mixture of complex fluorides with water for about 12 hrs., restoring, from time to time, the water lost by evaporation. The insoluble acid salt is said to be free from titanium. The liquid is evaporated for crystallization and the crystals washed with cold water, dissolved in hot water, and the operation repeated. (4) M. E. Pennington obtained unsatisfactory results by volatilization in a current of hydrogen fluoride ; but C. W. Blomstrand obtained fair results by the fractional volatilization of the chlorides—titanium tetrachloride being more volatile than the pentachlorides of columbium and tantalum. A. Knop passed chlorine over a red-hot mixture of the oxides with carbon ; and R. D. Hall heated the mixed oxides in a current of carbon tetrachloride or of sulphur monochloride. E. F. Smith said the results are not satisfactory. (5) F. Ott precipitated the columbic oxide by adding sulphuric acid to the soln. in hydrochloric acid and obtained a product which he believed to be free from titanium. (6) According to L. Weiss and M. Landecker, a compound of titanium and columbium oxides appears to be formed in alkaline fusion of mixtures containing titanium ; this is hindered by the addition of an oxidizing agent to the alkali. For quantitative estimation, sodium nitrate is used. After dissolving in water and filtering, very little titanium remains in soln., and this is completely precipitated by hydrogen sulphide without carrying down the other earth-acids. Sodium peroxide and borax gave incomplete separations. A mixture of six parts potassium cyanide and one part potassium hydroxide effects complete separation, the titanium becoming insoluble. Sodium carbonate and sulphite, and various acid mixtures, fail to give a complete separation. (7) E. Demarçay boiled a soln. of the potassium oxyfluo-salts just neutralized with ammonia, and found that the titanium is not precipitated. R. D. Hall obtained good results by repeating the operation three times. E. F. Smith did not get good results by fractional precipitation with ammonia ; R. D. Hall and E. F. Smith, with other bases, with potassium iodate, sodium hydrophosphate, or formoxime. (8) H. Lange found that if the precipitated mixture of titanic, columbic, and tantalic acid be treated twice with a warm, 20 per cent. soln. of ammonium salicylate, with constant stirring, the titanic acid is quantitatively removed. The subject was discussed by A. R. Powell and W. R. Schoeller.

The separation of the columbium and tantalum.—H. W. Foote and R. W. Langley found that a fair estimate be made of the relative proportions of a mixture of columbic and tantalic oxides from the sp. gr. which are respectively 4·552 and 8·710. J. C. G. de Marignac's process for the separation of tantalum and columbium is based on the different solubilities of potassium fluotantalate, K_2TaF_6, and potassium fluocolumbate, $K_2CbOF_5.H_2O$, or $K_4CbOF_7.H_2O$; one part of the latter salt is soluble in 12–13 parts of cold water, while one part of the former is soluble in 150–157 parts of cold water. The separation is tedious, and is considered as follows :

It is convenient to use four platinum dishes—" A " dish, 7·5 cms. in diameter ; " B " dish, 9 cms. ; " C " dish, 6 cms. ; and " D " dish, 5 cms. in diameter—for the separation. Fuse the (weighed) mixed oxides of columbium and tantalum in a platinum crucible with eight times their weight of potassium carbonate. When solution is complete, cool the mass. Digest the cake in water. If any remains insoluble, filter, ignite the residue, and fuse with a little potassium carbonate. Add the aq. extract to the main soln. Boil the mixture with dil. hydrochloric acid to precipitate the columbic and tantalic acids. Collect the precipitate on a filter-paper ; wash into, say, dish " C." The filter-paper, folded inside out, is placed in dish " D," covered with hot water, and a few drops of hydrofluoric acid are added. Warm the mixture on a hot plate for a few minutes. Pour the soln. into dish " C." Repeat the washing of the filter-paper with very dil. hydrofluoric acid, and finish by washing the paper four times with hot water. *First Crop of Crystals.*—The dish " C " now contains all the columbium and tantalum oxides. Put the dish on a hot plate. If soln. be not complete in a few minutes, add another drop of hydrofluoric acid, but avoid an excess of this acid. Add slowly, with constant stirring, a boiling aq. soln. of 0·7 grm. of potassium fluoride to the boiling soln. in basin " C." Evaporate the contents to about 10 c.c. Wash down the sides of the basin with a few drops of hot water. Cool the vessel slowly to about 15°. Decant the clear soln. containing the columbium and part of the tantalum, through a 7-cm. filter-paper into dish " B." Wash the felted mass of crystals of potassium fluotantalate four times with cold water. *Second Crop of Crystals.*—Evaporate the mixed filtrate and washings down to about 5 c.c. Cool the soln. slowly as before. Decant the soln. through a 5·5-cm. filter-paper into dish " A." Wash the crystals four times with cold water. If flat plates of potassium-columbium oxyfluoride are present, wash the mass until they are removed. *Third Crop of Crystals.*—Evaporate the soln. to dryness on a water-bath. Cool, add one drop of hydrofluoric acid. Run 1–5 c.c. water from a burette into the soln. Heat the vessel quickly to dissolve the residue. Add 0·1 grm. of potassium fluoride dissolved in 1 c.c. of water. Note the volume of the soln. for " correction a." Cool the soln. for about an hour at 15° or less ; filter it into a small platinum dish ; and wash three or four times with a few drops of water at 15° or less. Note the vol. of the liquid used for the washing—" correction b." In making the corrections allow for a, 1 c.c. of water dissolves 0·002 grm. of Ta_2O_5 ; and for b, 1 c.c. of water dissolves $0·00091 Ta_2O_5$.

Modifications of the process were used by E. S. Simpson, C. F. Rammelsberg, M. E. Pennington, A. Tighe, O. Ruff and E. Schiller, E. Meimberg, R. F. Weinland and L. Storz, W. Muthmann and co-workers, and W. E. von John. R. D. Hall and E. F. Smith thus described the process they used for the separation of the mixture of tantalum and columbium obtained from columbite :

The moist metallic acids, after having been washed with dil. sulphuric acid, were brought into a large platinum dish, and dissolved in fairly conc. hydrofluoric acid. This soln. was then filtered, through a hot water funnel, from undecomposed mineral, and from potassium silicofluoride (due to the presence of some potassium sulphate in the moist oxides). The hydrofluoric acid soln. were collected in large rubber dishes, and sufficient potassium hydroxide was introduced to convert the tantalum into potassium tantalum fluoride, most of which separated out and was removed by filtration. This precipitate was dried as far as possible by suction. It was washed once, and then allowed to dry in the air. It weighed 11 kilograms. The mother-liquor from the potassium tantalum fluoride was evaporated in stages, potassium hydrate being added. The columbium separated usually in hexagonal, hard, short crystals, such as separate from a strongly acid soln. containing an insufficient amount of potassium fluoride. The total residue obtained in this way amounted to about 8 to 10 kilograms. These residues were decomposed by treating them with twice their own weight of sulphuric acid, heating gently until the bulk of the hydrofluoric acid was expelled, and then evaporating until the mass fumes strongly, and maintaining the temp. until the excess of sulphuric acid had been almost completely driven out. Several hours were required for this. It is necessary in order to get rid of the hydrofluoric acid. The residual mass was boiled with water to extract the bases which dissolved as sulphates. The insoluble hydroxides were thoroughly washed and dissolved in hydrofluoric acid. The first crop of crystals, obtained by evaporation with potassium hydroxide, was removed, and the mother-liquor then evaporated to dryness with sufficient potassium hydroxide to change all of the metallic acids into double fluorides. A portion of these crystals (first crop) was dissolved in water, and the tantalum removed by adding dil. potassium hydroxide to the soln., which, after the formation of a permanent precipitate, was boiled for some time. The precipitate consisted mainly of potassium tantalum oxyfluoride. It was filtered out, and the filtrate evaporated to dryness. The residue was baked for some time at 200°. By this procedure some hydrofluoric acid was expelled, and, on taking up the residue with water and boiling, more potassium tantalum oxyfluoride separated. By repetition of the process all of the tantalum was removed from the soln. The only test relied upon for the detection of tantalum was the soln. of this precipitate in a drop of hydrofluoric acid and evaporation to crystallization. If needles separated, their solubility in water was used to ascertain whether they were potassium tantalum fluoride or potassium columbium oxyfluoride. It is true that this test consumes considerable time, yet it is the only satisfactory means of determining with which of the metals the chemist is dealing. The formation of a precipitate by protracted boiling of a dil. soln. of potassium tantalum fluoride is not conclusive, for G. Krüss and L. F. Nilson have shown that potassium columbium oxyfluoride deposits under like conditions a small amount of a salt containing less fluorine. Further, the double fluoride must be re-crystallized several times, so that it will be sufficiently free from acid. Tantalum, if it is present in small amounts, may be precipitated by boiling.

H. Rose separated the mixture by fusing it with sodium hydroxide; dissolved the cake in water, and precipitated the two oxides by passing a current of carbon dioxide through the soln.; boiled the precipitate with soda-lye, and then with a dil. soln. of sodium carbonate until the filtrate scarcely shows any opalescence when treated with dil. sulphuric acid. The columbic acid passes into soln. and the tantalic acid remains as an insoluble sodium compound. W. B. Giles obtained a satisfactory separation by a repetition of the treatment; C. W. Blomstrand did not obtain good results. A. G. Ekeberg, R. Hermann, F. Oesten, C. W. Blomstrand, etc., tried modifications of this process. L. Weiss and M. Landecker said that columbic and tantalic acids are best separated from one another by fusing with sodium carbonate and nitrate, dissolving in warm water, cooling, and precipitating the tantalum with carbon dioxide. Slight variations in the conditions diminish the accuracy of the separation. A. R. Powell and W. R. Schoeller advocated the separation of these two elements by the fractional hydrolysis of the oxalates in the presence of tannin and a feebly acid soln.

The conversion of the salts into the pentoxides.—The complex fluosalts are heated with sulphuric acid at about 400° to drive off the fluorine. The product is then treated with a large excess of boiling water so as to form hydrated columbic or tantalic acid. This process was used by W. Muthmann and co-workers, and C. W. Balke. The sulphuric acid which contaminates the precipitate cannot be removed by prolonged washing, but F. Wöhler, H. Rose, and W. Muthmann and co-workers found that if the product be mixed with ammonium carbonate and heated, and the operation repeated a few times, the sulphuric acid is expelled—*vide infra*, columbium pentoxide. H. Rose recommended washing the hydrates with an ammoniacal soln. of ammonium chloride to eliminate the sulphuric acid. The ammonium chloride is used to prevent the peptization of the colloidal hydrates.

REFERENCES

1 H. Moissan, *Bull. Soc. Chim.*, (3), 27. 430, 1901; *Compt. Rend.*, 133. 20, 1901; 134. 212, 1902; G. Chesneau, *ib.*, 149. 1132, 1909; E. Demarçay, *ib.*, 100. 740, 1885; W. B. Giles, *Chem. News*, 95. 1, 37, 1907; 99. 1, 1909; E. S. Simpson, *Bull. West. Australia Geol. Soc.*, 23. 71, 1906; *Chem. News*, 99. 243, 1909; W. E. von John, *ib.*, 100. 154, 1909; J. L. Smith, *ib.*, 48. 13, 29, 1883; *Amer. Chem. Journ.*, 5. 44, 73, 1885; R. D. Hall and E. F. Smith, *Chem. News*, 92. 220, 232, 242, 252, 262, 276, 1905; *Proc. Amer. Phil. Soc.*, 44. 177, 1905; E. F. Smith, *ib.*, 44. 157, 1905; *Journ. Amer. Chem. Soc.*, 20. 292, 1898; R. D. Hall, *Observations on the Metallic Acids*, Easton, Pa., 1904; *Journ. Amer. Chem. Soc.*, 26. 1238, 1904; W. M. Barr, *ib.*, 30. 1669, 1908; C. W. Balke and E. F. Smith, *ib.*, 30. 1638, 1908; C. W. Balke, *The Double Fluorides of Tantalum*, Easton, Pa., 1908; R. F. Weinland and L. Storz, *Zeit. anorg. Chem.*, 54. 230, 1907; O. Hahn and H. Gille, *ib.*, 112. 283, 1920; O. Ruff and E. Schiller, *ib.*, 72. 329, 1911; L. Weiss and M. Landecker, *ib.*, 64. 68, 1909; *German Pat.*, D.R.P. 221429, 1909; M. Landecker, *Untersuchungen über die quantitative Bestimmung der Erdsäuren*, München, 1911; J. C. G. de Marignac, *Arch. Sciences Genève*, (2), 23. 249, 326, 1865; (2), 31. 89, 1868; *Compt. Rend.*, 60. 234, 1865; *Ann. Chim. Phys.*, (4), 8. 5, 1866; (4), 9. 249, 1866; (4), 13. 28, 1868; A. G. Ekeberg, *Akad. Nya. Handl.*, 23. 180, 1802; *Gilbert's Ann.*, 14. 246, 1803; *Crell's Ann.*, i, 3, 1802; *Scherer's Journ.*, 9. 598, 1803; *Nicholson's Journ.*, 3. 251, 1802; *Phil. Mag.*, 14. 346, 1802; *Ann. Chim. Phys.*, (1), 43. 276, 1802; C. F. Rammelsberg, *Journ. prakt. Chem.*, (1), 107. 343, 1869; *Pogg. Ann.*, 144. 64, 1871; F. Oesten, *ib.*, 99. 617, 1856; 100. 340, 1857; 103. 91, 1858; H. Rose, *ib.*, 99. 69, 1856; 100. 146, 418, 1857; 113. 301, 1861; C. W. Blomstrand, *Journ. prakt. Chem.*, (1), 99. 40, 1866; *Acta Univ. Lund*, 1. 7, 1864; 2. 3, 1865; *Liebig's Ann.*, 135. 198, 1865; F. Wöhler, *ib.*, 31. 120, 1839; R. Hermann, *Journ. prakt. Chem.*, (1), 68. 65, 1856; (1), 70. 398, 1857; (1), 5. 66, 1872; (2), 15. 105, 1877; W. Crookes, *Select Methods in Chemical Analysis*, London, 139, 1905; M. E. Pennington, *Journ. Amer. Chem. Soc.*, 18. 40, 1896; *Chem. News*, 75. 8, 18, 31, 38, 1897; *Derivatives of Columbium and Tantalum*, Easton, Pa., 1895; F. Ott, *Zeit. Elektrochem.*, 18. 349, 1912; *Elektrolytische Reduktion der Niobsäure*, München, 1911; O. W. Gibbs, *Amer. Journ. Science*, (2), 37. 355, 1864; H. W. Foote and R. W. Langley, *ib.*, (4), 30. 393, 1911; C. A. Joy, *ib.*, (2), 36. 83, 1863; *Chem. News*, 8. 183, 197, 1863; T. B. Osborne,

ib., **53**. 43, 1886; *Amer. Journ. Science*, (3), **30**. 229, 1885; W. P. Headden, *ib.*, (3), **41**. 91, 1891; F. Russ, *Zeit. anorg. Chem.*, **31**. 50, 1902; J. J. Berzelius, *Afhand. Fys. Kem. Min.*, **4**. 148, 252, 262, 1815; **6**. 237, 1818; *Ann. Chim. Phys.*, (2), **3**. 140, 1816; (2), **29**. 300, 1825; G. T. Prior, *Min. Mag.*, **15**. 83, 1910; H. Biltz and L. Gonder, *Ber.*, **40**. 4963, 1907; H. Biltz and C. Kircher, *ib.*, **43**. 1639, 1910; A. Knop, *ib.*, **29**. 1347, 1887; G. Krüss and L. F. Nilson, *ib.*, **20**. 1684, 1887; *Oefvers. Akad. Förh.*, **5**, 1887; A. Joly, *Ann. École Norm.*, (2), **6**. 738, 1877; J. Morozewicz, *Bull. Akad. Cracovie*, 207, 1909; R. J. Meyer and O. Hauser, *Die Analyse der seltenen Erden mit der Erdsäuren*, Stuttgart, 296, 1912; W. Muthmann, L. Weiss and R. Riedelbauch, *Liebig's Ann.*, **355**. 60, 1907; H. Lange, *Zeit. Naturwiss.*, **82**. 5, 27, 1910; E. Wedekind and W. Maas, *Zeit. angew. Chem.*, **23**. 2315, 1915; E. Meimberg, *ib.*, **26**. 83, 1913; A. Tighe, *Journ. Soc. Chem. Ind.*, **25**. 681, 1907; G. W. Sears and L. Quill, *Journ. Amer. Chem. Soc.*, **47**. 922, 1925; G. W. Sears, *ib.*, **48**. 343, 1926; *School Science*, **18**. 145, 1918; A. R. Powell and W. R. Schoeller, *Zeit. anorg. Chem.*, **151**. 221, 1926; *Journ. Chem. Soc.*, **119**. 1927, 1921; A. W. Gregory, *Brit. Pat. No.* 25127, 1925; H. S. Cooper, *U.S. Pat. No.* 1507987, 1924; F. L. Hahn and W. Franke, *German Pat.*, *D.R.P.* 437561, 1925.

§ 4. Columbium

H. Rose [1] attempted to isolate columbium by reducing potassium oxypenta-fluocolumbate with sodium, but he obtained only a lower oxide, not the element. J. C. G. de Marignac found that zinc does not reduce the boiling soln. to the metal; a mixture of zinc and sodium behaves like sodium; iron filings at a white-heat reduce the salt incompletely; there is an explosion with magnesium at a red-heat; aluminium gives an alloy; and when a molten mixture of potassium fluoride and fluocolumbate is electrolyzed, using platinum electrodes, the platinum is vigorously attacked but no columbium is formed. M. E. Pennington heated a mixture of 2 parts of columbium pentoxide, 10 of cryolite, and 10 of aluminium filings with an excess of sodium chloride in a graphite crucible for 8 hrs., and obtained a number of metallic buttons of an aluminium-columbium alloy. H. St. C. Deville also found that when columbium pentoxide is heated with carbon and sodium carbonate, a carbonitride is formed.

The preparation of columbium.—H. E. Roscoe obtained the metal as a bright, steel-grey, shining, metallic crust, by passing a mixture of the vapour of the penta-chloride and hydrogen through a red-hot glass tube, and strongly igniting the crust in a current of hydrogen in a porcelain tube until no hydrogen chloride is evolved. Air must be excluded. C. W. Blomstrand obtained a similar product by reducing the same chloride with hydrogen. J. C. G. de Marignac regarded this product as a hydride—*vide infra*. H. Moissan obtained columbium by heating a mixture of columbium pentoxide and sugar-charcoal in an electrical tube furnace at a high temp. in the absence of air. The product contained 2·3–3·4 per cent. of carbon as carbide. H. Goldschmidt and C. Vautin reduced columbium pentoxide by powdered aluminium in the thermite process, and obtained an alloy of columbium and aluminium. L. Weiss and O. Aichel, and W. Muthmann and co-workers used misch-metall in place of aluminium as the reducing agent. W. von Bolton said that the product is a mixture of columbium and unreduced oxide, and he recommended the following process:

Purified columbium pentoxide was moulded into filaments (by mixing it with a little paraffin), and these were heated to whiteness for 4 or 5 hrs. in carbon powder. The filaments of tetroxide obtained in this way conduct electricity. When such a filament is heated to whiteness in a vacuum by a direct current it is but little changed, a small portion at the positive end only being reduced to metal. By using an alternating current, however, the filament is converted into the metal in a quarter of an hour. This method yields very small quantities of the metal. Larger quantities were prepared as follows: columbium pentoxide and powdered aluminium react together when the mixture is heated at one point, yielding a hard, metallic regulus of sp. gr. 7·5, and containing 2·8 per cent. to 3·2 per cent. of aluminium as well as some unchanged oxide. By heating this material in a vacuum (a current of 185 ampères at 40 volts for 15 hrs. is required for 20 grms. of metal) the whole of the impurities are vaporized, leaving columbium of a high degree of purity.

The preparation of columbium lamp-filaments has been described by the Wolfram·

Lampen A.G., and H. Kuzel. The last-named also prepared **colloidal solution** of columbium by the long-continued shaking of the finely divided metal with organic and inorganic acids, salts with an acidic reaction, phenols, alkali hydroxides, ammonia, organic bases, etc.

The physical properties of columbium.—H. E. Roscoe said that columbium has a steel-grey colour, and a bright metallic lustre. H. Moissan obtained columbium as a regulus ; L. Weiss and O. Aichel, and W. Muthmann and co-workers described columbium as a white metal with a yellow tinge, and showing no sign of a crystalline structure ; but W. von Bolton said that the metal is coarsely crystalline and consists of rhombic crystals. S. von Olshausen examined the **X-radiogram,** and inferred that it has four interpenetrating cubic lattices of side $a=4\cdot191$ A. The lustre is very stable, and W. Muthmann and co-workers found that it persists even after boiling the metal for a day with aqua regia. H. E. Roscoe gave $7\cdot06$ for the **specific gravity** of the metal at $15°/15°$; and J. C. G. de Marignac, $7\cdot37$; but these numbers are far too small. W. Muthmann and co-workers gave $8\cdot4000$ at $15°/15°$, and $8\cdot431$ at $19\cdot8°/19\cdot8°$. H. von Bolton gave for the highly purified metal $12\cdot7$, and after rolling into foil, $12\cdot75$. H. G. Grimm made observations on the ionic radius. H. Moissan described the metal he prepared as being somewhat hard, for it readily scratched glass and quartz ; L. Weiss and O. Aichel said the metal is brittle and has a hardness of 7 ; while W. von Bolton found that the **hardness** is about the same as that of wrought iron; it can be hammered into foil $0\cdot05$ mm. thick; and it is possible, though difficult, to draw it into wire ; it can be welded at a red-heat. W. Muthmann and co-workers gave $0\cdot0617$ for the **specific heat,** and $5\cdot8$ for the at. ht. W. von Bolton found the sp. ht. to be $0\cdot071$ between $21°$ and $100°$, and the at. ht. $6\cdot67$. H. Moissan said that the **melting point** is over $1800°$, and W. von Bolton found $1950°$ for the m.p. in vacuo. W. R. Mott gave $1950°$ for the m.p., and calculated $3700°$ for the **boiling point.** Columbium volatilizes to a considerable extent when heated in vacuo. W. Muthmann and co-workers found that the **heat of combustion** to the pentoxide is $44\cdot133$ Cals. per eq.

H. von Wartenberg [2] gave $1\cdot80$ for the **index of refraction ;** $2\cdot11$ for the **absorption coefficient,** and $41\cdot3$ per cent. for the **reflecting power** with yellow light of wave-length $579\mu\mu$. R. Thalén found the lines in the **spark spectrum** of columbium were too feeble to measure ; but measurements were made by E. Demarçay, W. M. Barr, G. Krüss and L. F. Nilson, F. Exner and E. Haschek, M. C. M. McDonald, and A. Hagenbach and H. Konen. The strongest lines in the visible spectrum are 4630 and 4573 in the blue ; and 4165 and 4059 in the violet. The **arc spectrum** was examined by J. R. Capron, M. A. Catalan, J. H. Hildebrand, J. M. Eder and E. Valenta, F. Exner and E. Haschek, and A. Hagenbach and H. Konen. The **ultra-violet spectrum** was examined by F. Exner and E. Haschek, and C. C. Kiess and O. Laporte ; the effect of *pressure* on the spectral lines by W. J. Humphreys ; the influence of a *magnetic field*—the **Zeeman effect**—by R. Jack, and W. F. Meggers and C. C. Kiess ; and the *ultimate rays,* by A. de Gramont. E. Paulson attempted to find **series spectra** in the lines of columbium represented by the existence of groups of lines showing a constant difference of frequency, but without success. H. E. White and R. C. Gibbs, and W. F. Meggers noted some regularities in the spark and arc spectrum of columbium. O. Laporte discussed this subject. J. Formanek observed no **absorption spectrum** with soln. of the salts when treated with alkanna. F. C. Blake and W. Duane,[3] A. Leide, M. Siegbahn, B. B. Ray, J. Schrör, B. Walter, and M. Siegbahn and E. Friman gave for the K-series of **X-ray spectra,** $a_2a'=0\cdot754$; $a_1a=0\cdot749$; $\beta_1\beta=0\cdot669$, $\beta_2\gamma=0\cdot657$; and D. Coster, H. Hirata, D. Coster and E. P. Mulder, M. Druyvesteyn, E. Hjalmar, and M. Siegbahn, for the L-series, $a_2a'=5\cdot717$; $a_1a=5\cdot7113$; $a_3a''=5\cdot6886$; $\beta_1\beta=5\cdot4796$; and $\beta_2\gamma=5\cdot2951$; and D. Coster and F. P. Mulder, the M-, and N-series. S J. M. Allen studied the absorption of the X-rays by columbium. M. Levin and R. Ruer found that ordinary columbic acid exhibits a feeble **radioactivity,** probably owing to the presence of radium or thorium impurities.

W. von Bolton [4] found that the sp. **electrical resistance** is 0.0_3187 ohm J. W. Marden and M. N. Rich gave 0.0_418 ohm. per c.c. According to M. E. Pennington, when an aq. soln. of the complex fluoride, $K_2CbOF_5.H_2O$, is electrolyzed, for 8 hrs. with a current of one ampère, almost immediately the bottom of the platinum dish was covered with a blue deposit. This gradually spread over the whole surface exposed to the action of the current, and became in a short time iridescent. As the deposit increased, the deep blue tint changed to more of a grey and remained so until the current was broken. It was washed quickly with water, then with alcohol, and it was dried on the hand. The blue compound is a lower oxide of columbium. With a current of 2 ampères, a white hydroxide was formed, and a dark brown ring appeared about the anode. Soln. of sodium columbate behaved similarly. F. Ott studied the **electrolytic reduction** of columbic acid, using, in most cases, a lead cathode. He found that when columbium pentachloride is reduced in hydrochloric or sulphuric acid soln., or in an alcoholic soln. of hydrogen chloride, reddish-brown to black soln. are obtained, which contain tervalent columbium. Sodium columbate in hydrochloric acid soln. yields on reduction a green soln., which contains quadrivalent columbium; fused potassium fluoxycolumbate, K_2CbOF_5, yields on electrolytic reduction a bluish-black product, which also contains quadrivalent columbium. When columbium pentafluoride is reduced in sulphuric acid soln. at a platinum cathode, a blue soln., which appears to contain a compound of quadrivalent and quinquevalent columbium (corresponding with the oxide, $Cb_3O_7=Cb_2O_5.CbP_2$), is obtained. Assuming that the potential of the hydrogen electrode is zero, F. Ott found the results summarized in Table I.

TABLE I.—THE ELECTROLYTIC REDUCTION OF COLUMBIC ACID.

Oxide.	Colour.	Potential (volt).	Conditions of reduction.	Cathode potential (volt).
Cb_4O_3	Blue or black	$+0.125$	$CbCl_5$ in HCl-soln. and Pb or Pt cathode	$0.5–0.59$
	Reddish-brown	$+0.125$	$CbCl_5$ in alcoholic HCl and Pb cathode	$0.5–0.6$
	Reddish-brown	$+0.075$	$CbCl_5$ in H_2SO_4 soln. and Pb cathode	$0.5–0.6$
CbO_2	Green	$+0.061$	Na columbate in HCl soln. and Pb cathode	$0.45–0.19$
	Blue-black	$+0.055$	Molten K_2CbOF_5	$0.46–0.19$
Cb_3O_7	Blue	-0.032	} $CbCl_5$ in H_2SO_4 soln. and Pt cathode	$0.2–0.3$
Cb_2O_5	Colourless	-0.5		

W. Muthmann and F. Frauenberger found that the electromotive force of the cell $Cb \mid H_2CrO_4, KOH \mid Cb$ is 2·4 volts. The electrode potential in 25 per cent. potashlye rose from -0.433 to -0.197 volt in one min.; in 10 per cent. ammonia, from -0.403 to $+0.322$ in 3 mins.; and in conc. potash-lye, from -0.683 to -1.097 volts in 10 hrs. Again, in 40 per cent. nitric acid, the potential fall from -0.167 to -0.683 volt in 5 mins.; in conc. chromic acid, from $+0.787$ to -1.403 volts in 14 hrs.; in perchloric acid, from $+0.987$ to -0.063 volt in 1 hr.; in potassium permanganate, from $+0.267$ to -0.913 volt in 1 hr.; in ammonium ceric nitrate from $+0.617$ to -0.843 volt in 5 hrs.; in thiocyanic acid, from -0.033 to -0.493 volt in 10 mins.; and in 16 per cent. sulphuric acid, from $+0.157$ to -0.213 volt in 10 mins. The maximum value is $+1.047$ volts, and the minimum value -4.03 volts. The metal acquires a bluish film when it is in the **passive state.** W. von Bolton found that columbium electrodes in 10 per cent. sulphuric acid do not allow a current to pass even at 120 volts, but with one columbium cathode, one phase of an alternating current will pass. This was utilized by E. W. von Siemens and J. G. Halske in the construction of an electrolytic rectifier. A. Günther-Schulze studied the **electrolytic valve action** of columbium, and inferred that it is due to the formation of a porous non-conducting skin on the metal, the gas formed at the same time is retained in the pores of the skin, and forming the non-conductor to which the valve action is due. U. Sborgi found differences in the behaviour of columbium in different electrolytes according to its compactness. The metal which is not very compact is used as the anode in $0.2N$- to N-H_2SO_4; there is a momentary current of 1-2 volts; the current then becomes almost zero, and if the voltage is increased up to 112 volts, each increase is attended by the passage of a current which is only momentary. Some bubbles of gas appear, and the electrode becomes covered with a greenish-yellow or blue iridescent film, which is insoluble in the common acids and alkalies, but dissolves in hydrofluoric acid. The same results are obtained with phosphoric acid, potassium hydroxide, sodium hydroxide, potassium carbonate, sodium sulphate, sodium oxalate, oxalic acid, and ammonium fluoride. In no case could a permanent passage of current be observed. In other electrolytes, however (hydrochloric acid, sodium chloride, nitric acid, sodium nitrate, acetic acid, potassium bromide and iodide), the metal dissolves with valency 5, columbic acid being precipitated; the electrode becomes disintegrated. The same occurs in hydrofluoric acid, but in this case columbic acid is not precipitated. An anode which has been used in sulphuric acid, and is covered with the film already mentioned, dissolves when made the anode in nitric acid; after a time the film disappears, and the electrode becomes grey from disintegration. When it is again placed in sulphuric acid no current passes. The columbium anode in all electrolytes (except hydrofluoric acid) becomes covered at the very beginning of electrolysis with a layer which hinders the passage of ions, although the degree of impermeability varies in different electrolytes. The behaviour of this metal differs from that of the ordinary passive metals in these respects, and also because soln. occurs when the current does pass. W. von Bolton observed that the **electrical spluttering** of columbium in vacuo makes it unsuited for incandescent filament lamps. K. Honda found columbium to be paramagnetic; and the **magnetic susceptibility** to be 1.3×10^{-6} units; M. Owen gave 1.75×10^{-6} units. K. Honda observed no change in the value between 0° and 400°. S. Meyer gave for the atomic magnetic susceptibility $+0.49 \times 10^{-6}$ per gram-atom, and for the magnetization number $+5.9 \times 10^{-6}$.

The chemical properties of columbium.—F. Fischer and F. Schrötter [5] observed no reaction between **argon** and columbium when the metal is sparked in the liquefied gas. When columbium is heated in a current of **hydrogen**, a hydride is formed— *vide infra.* W. Muthmann and co-workers found that columbium does not change on exposure to **air;** and W. von Bolton showed that when it is gradually heated to redness, the metal acquires a yellow film which changes to blue, and finally brownish-blue. This film protects the metal from being rapidly attacked by **oxygen.** The metal is converted into the pentoxide by oxygen at a red-heat. H. Moissan added that the powdered metal burns to the pentoxide at about 400° in oxygen, and at a higher temp. in air. Some nitride is formed in air—*vide infra.* W. von Bolton observed that the red-hot metal in a current of the vapour of **water** reacts vigorously with the evolution of hydrogen. H. Moissan said that steam is not decomposed at 600°. H. Moissan observed that, at ordinary temp., columbium becomes incandescent in the presence of **fluorine,** and a volatile fluoride is formed. H. E. Roscoe said that the metal takes fire when gently heated in **chlorine;** and H. Moissan added that chlorine attacks the metal at about 205°, and **bromine** at a higher temp., while **iodine** acts at the softening temp. of glass. W. M. Barr observed no perceptible action with bromine at ordinary temp. H. Moissan showed that **hydrogen chloride** is decomposed by columbium at a dull red-heat, forming a white sublimate. The metal is slowly attacked by **hydrofluoric acid;** L. Weiss and O. Aichel added that the attack is rapid at the temp. of the water-bath, and W. von Bolton, that the attack is accelerated in the presence of platinum. H. E. Roscoe, H. Moissan, W. von Bolton, and L. Weiss and O. Aichel observed that hot or cold **hydrochloric acid** has no action on columbium. H. Moissan found that at a red-heat **iodic acid** is reduced by columbium. W. von Bolton said that **sulphur** reacts violently when heated with columbium; similarly with **selenium.** H. Moissan found that the reaction with sulphur acts only superficially at about 600°, while selenium and **tellurium** have no action at this temp. ; nor is **hydrogen sulphide** decomposed by columbium at 600°, but **sulphur dioxide** is reduced with incandescence at this temp. H. E. Roscoe, H. Moissan, and L. Weiss and O. Aichel found that cold **sulphuric acid** has no action on columbium, but the hot, conc. acid attacks the metal slowly. W. von Bolton said that the purified metal is not attacked by boiling sulphuric acid.

According to L. Weiss and O. Aichel, some nitride, as well as oxide, is formed when columbium is heated in air. H. Moissan said that **nitrogen** alone does not act perceptibly at 500°–600°, but at 1200°, it forms a yellow nitride ; and W. Muthmann and co-workers added that at a bright red-heat, a black nitride is formed. H. Moissan found that at a red-heat **ammonia** is decomposed into its elements in the presence of finely divided columbium, which itself suffers no change in weight. W. von Bolton said that a strip of columbium heated to redness in ammonia acquires a brown film which gives off ammonia when treated with alkali-lye. H. Moissan showed that **nitrous oxide** is reduced by columbium at a dull red-heat ; and similarly with **nitric oxide**—the reduction is attended by a vigorous combustion, and a grey powder is formed free from nitrogen. H. E. Roscoe, H. Moissan, L. Weiss and O. Aichel, and W. von Bolton observed that **nitric acid** does not dissolve columbium, nor is the metal attacked by aqua regia. H. Moissan said that **phosphorus** does not attack columbium at 500°–600°, but **phosphorus pentoxide** is reduced at a dull red-heat ; **arsenic** and **antimony** do not act on columbium at 500°–600°, but **arsenic pentoxide** is reduced below this temp. The fused metal combines slowly with **carbon,** but even when the latter is in excess, a regulus containing graphite is not formed. At a red-heat, columbium reduces **carbon dioxide** to the monoxide.

According to H. Moissan, columbium does not form alloys with **sodium, potassium, magnesium,** or **zinc ;** and these metals can be distilled from columbium without combination. W. von Bolton said that the metal does not dissolve in **mercury.** Alloys with **aluminium** can be formed as indicated above, and were made by J. C. G. de Marignac by reducing the heptafluocolumbate with aluminium ; by M. E. Pennington, by reducing the pentoxide with aluminium ; and by W. von Bolton, and H. Goldschmidt and C. Vautin, by the alumino-thermite process. H. Moissan prepared **columbium trialuminide,** CbAl$_3$. Columbium unites with small quantities of molten iron, but W. von Bolton said that the two elements form alloys with all possible proportions. H. Moissan observed that when heated with **chromic oxide** in the electric furnace, a brittle chromium-columbium alloy is formed. Columbium reacts vigorously when heated with **lead mono- or di-oxide.** W. von Bolton found that aq. soln. of **alkali hydroxide** have no action on columbium, but the fused alkali dissolves the metal, forming a columbate. L. Weiss and O. Aichel said that **alkali carbonate** behaves like the hydroxide. H. Moissan showed that molten **alkali sulphate** is reduced to sulphide by columbium, and blue crystals insoluble in water are formed ; and that fused **oxidizing agents**—*e.g.* **potassium nitrate**—attack columbium. At a red-heat, columbium reduces **mercurous or mercuric chloride** to mercury and columbium chloride is formed.

Some reactions of analytical interest.—The reactions of tantalum and columbium present so many resemblances, that the two elements can be considered together. When **sulphuric acid** is added to a cold soln. of a dil. alkali tantalate or columbate, an amorphous precipitate of the hydrated pentoxide forms. The precipitate is soluble in hot, conc. sulphuric acid, and with columbium the cold soln. remains clear when diluted with water, whereas with tantalum, tantalic acid is re-precipitated. A conc. soln. of the alkali salt gives a precipitate of tantalic or columbic acid when treated with **hydrochloric acid**—the tantalic acid dissolves in an excess of the precipitant, but columbic acid dissolves only slightly. If the acid is poured off, the precipitate dissolves in water. The action of nitric acid resembles that of hydrochloric acid. If the hydrated pentoxide be dissolved in an

excess of hydrofluoric acid, and **potassium fluoride** be added, sparingly soluble
potassium fluotantalate, and readily soluble fluocolumbate are formed. On boiling
the aq. soln. of these salts sparingly soluble oxyfluotantalate is alone precipitated ;
the corresponding columbate is very soluble. Aq. **ammonia** or **ammonium
sulphide** precipitates either the hydrated pentoxide or an ammonium salt from a
soln. in hydrochloric acid, and the precipitate is soluble in hydrofluoric acid ; and
tartaric acid prevents the precipitation. Soln. of columbates, titanates, and
cerium salts give a yellow coloration with **hydrogen dioxide,** but not so with
soln. of tantalates. This is due to the formation of a yellow percolumbate (*q.v.*)
—the corresponding pertantalate is colourless. Acid soln. of columbates or tantalates give a yellowish-white precipitate with **potassium ferrocyanide**—the precipitation is hindered in the presence of arsenic, oxalic, citric, or tartaric acid ; **potassium
ferricyanide** gives no precipitate, or a precipitate is formed very slowly ; tincture
of galls, or **tannic acid** in acid soln. of the tantalates gives a light brown precipitate ;
with columbates, the precipitate is orange-red. A mixture of **zinc** and hydrochloric acid gives a blue coloration with soln. of the columbates, but no coloration
is observed with the tantalates. A. Stähler [6] said that the indigo-blue soln.,
obtained when a sulphuric acid soln. of columbium pentoxide is reduced with
zinc, reduces cupric sulphate to metallic copper, and is therefore more strongly
reducing than one containing tervalent titanium. M. E. Pennington gave a comparison of the reactions of the salts indicated in Table II.

TABLE II.—COMPARISON OF SOME REACTIONS OF THE FLUOCOLUMBATES, FLUOTANTALATES,
AND FLUOTITANATES.

Reagent.	$K_2CbOF_5.H_2O$	K_2TaF_7	K_2TiF_6
$Pb(C_2H_3O_2)_2$	White pp.	White pp.	White pp.
$HgCl_2$ . .	Slight pp. in 24 hrs.	—	—
$HgNO_3$.	Yellow pp.	Yellowish-green pp.	Yellowish-green pp.
K_2CrO_4 .	White pp. soluble in H_2O. Partly soluble in K_2CrO_4 soln.	—	Pp. soluble in water
$K_2Cr_2O_7$.	—	Precipitate after stand-ing	—
KCy . .	White pp. on boiling	White pp.	White pp.
K_4FeCy_6 .	Green-blue pp. on boil-ing	Yellow pp. on boiling	Precipitate on boil-ing
KCyS . .	White pp.	White pp. soluble in the cold. Comes down by boiling	—
KI . .	White, granular pp. Iodine is liberated	White granular pp.	No pp., but iodine is liberated
Na_2HPO_4 .	—	White pp. after stand-ing	White pp.
$AgNO_3$.	—	White pp. after standing	—
$NaHSO_3$.	White pp.	White pp.	White pp.
$Na_4P_2O_7$.	—	Slight cloudiness	Pp.
H_3PO_3 .	—	—	Pp.
$NaPO_3$.	—	Slight cloudiness	—
KBr . .	White pp.	—	—

R. D. Hall found that a soln. of **potassium iodate** gave a complete precipitation with a
soln. of potassium fluotitanate, but no precipitate with a soln. of the oxyfluocolumbate.
R. D. Hall and E. F. Smith showed that no precipitation occurs with either except in
acidic soln. when both are precipitated. No precipitation occurs with **potassium chlorate,
bromate, or perchlorate.** L. Weiss and M. Landecker observed that when boiled with
perchloric acid soln. of columbic and tantalic acids give a quantitative precipitate easily
filtered ; and **hydrofluosilicic** acid gives no precipitate. M. E. Pennington obtained white
precipitates when both columbate and tantalates are treated with **sodium hydrosulphite,
or thiosulphate.** R. D. Hall and E. F. Smith observed no precipitation when a soln. of

potassium fluotitanate, or oxyfluocolumbate is treated with *benzylaniline, diphenylamine, tribenzylamine, β-naphthylamine, α-naphthylamine, nitrophthalene, bromphenylhydrazine, nitrophenylhydrazine, benzidine, o-nitraniline, p-nitraniline, m-nitraniline, diphenyl, diphenyl carbonate, methyl carbonate, ethyl carbonate, piperine, monochlorhydrin, trichlorhydrin, dibromhydrin, nitrosodipropylene, nitrosodiethylene, nitrosodimethylene succinimide, methyl diphenylamine, tetranitromethylaniline, bromaniline.* No precipitation occurred with the fluotitanate and only a slight precipitation with the oxyfluocolumbate when treated with *m-bromaniline, o-chloraniline, dichloraniline, diethylaniline, p-chloraniline, dimethylaniline, p-xylidine, o-xylidine, m-xylidine, tetrahydroquinoline.* The precipitation was complete with soln. of the fluotitanate, and the pp. was soluble in excess with oxyfluocolumbate treated with *monomethylamine, dimethylamine, trimethylamine, tetramethylamine, mono-ethylamine, diethylamine, triethylamine, dipropylamine, amylamine, isobutylamine, allylamine, ethylenediamine, propylenediamine, secondary-butylenediamine, normal-butylenediamine, hexylamine, benzylamine, benzylmethylamine, piperidine, camphylamine, dibenzylamine, pyridine, di-isobutylamine, tripropylamine, diamylamine, heptylamine.* The precipitation was partial with the fluotitanate and incomplete with the oxyfluocolumbate when treated with *m-toluylenediamine, picoline, tri-isobutylamine, bornylamine, aniline, m-toluidine, monomethylaniline, mono-ethylaniline, isoquinoline, quinoline, hexamethylenetetramine, m-bromaniline, o-chloraniline,* as above. R. D. Hall and E. F. Smith also observed the reactions indicated in Table III. They added that strychnine, quinidine, cinchonidine,

TABLE III.—REACTIONS OF TANTALUM, COLUMBIUM, TITANIUM, AND TUNGSTEN SALTS WITH SOME ORGANIC COMPOUNDS.

Reagent.	Ta	Cb	Ti	W
Codeine	No colour	No colour	Faint pink, may be due to morphine	Light brown ; on standing, trace purple
Morphine	Faint yellow	—	Red to brown, very delicate	Grey-brown, becoming purple ; H_2O ppt.
Resorcinol	No colour	No colour	Red-brown, fairly delicate	No colour
Naphthol (β)	,,	Faint yellow-brown	Coffee-brown, very delicate	Brown, becoming dark blue
Naphthol (α)	,,	Faint brown	Green to dark greenish-brown	Deep blue, very delicate
Pyrogallol	,,	Yellow to light brown	Dull dark red	Deep red to brown to dirty blue
Salicylic acid	,,	Very faint yellow	Deep red	Reddish-yellow
Cinchonidine	,,	No colour	No colour	On standing a slight purple
Apomorphine	,,	Yellow-brown	Light red-brown	Purple to brown to green and blue
Narceine	,,	Brownish-yellow	Brown	Dirty dark green
Bebeerine	,,	No colour	Clear brown	Dark brown to green
Narcotine	,,	Yellow	Brown	Light brown to green

and atropine gave no colour with any of the elements tested. Narceine and bebeerine alone in sulphuric acid gave a considerable colour, and with them the amount of reagent must be very small, or it will obscure any change produced by the addition of the double fluoride. In this connection it is of interest to note that L. Lévy studied the colours produced by the phenol-like bodies, dissolved in conc. sulphuric acid, when brought in contact with the oxides of titanium, tin, tantalum, columbium, and other elements, with the following results : Columbium could be tested for in the presence of all the others by using codeine, as it gave a pink colour, while titanium yielded no colour, and tantalum but a faint green. Titanium could be tested for by using morphine, with which it gave a carmine colour, columbium no colour, and tantalum a yellow colour passing into brown. Tantalum with resorcinol gave a dirty green colour, changing to amethyst and rose, while titanium yielded a flesh-red colour, going to chocolate-brown, and columbium a yellowish tint. None of the results was duplicated save the morphine test for titanium, which proved exceedingly delicate, yet to have the colour show definitely in columbium the latter must contain 0·5 per cent. of TiO_2. Codeine gave no colour with columbium, nor did resorcinol with tantalum, therefore L. Lévy could not have had pure material for his test. Morphine answered as a test for titanium. None answered for columbium in the presence of titanium, or for tantalum in the presence of columbium. Resorcinol proved to be fairly delicate test for titanium ; it gave no colour with columbium, tantalum, or tungsten—vide Table III. J. H. de Boer observed a violet colour is produced by *alizarinsulphonic* acid with salts of zirconium, aluminium, thorium, cerium, yttrium, erbium, thallium, columbium, tungsten, molybdenum, uranium, and titanium. All disappear in the presence of conc. hydrochloric acid excepting with zirconium. F. Steidler found that various shades of brown are produced by tantalum or columbium salts with linen or artificial silk dyed with *turmeric*.

H. Geisow found that an alkaline soln. of formoxime precipitated zirconium and titanium but not columbium ; and R. D. Hall and E. F. Smith added that the alkaline soln. of formoxime gave no precipitate when added to a soln. of titanium as double fluoride, zirconium as double fluoride, or to a soln. of columbium double fluoride. Further, after the addition of the formoxime soln., ammonium hydroxide failed to give a precipitate with any of the soln. noted above. It did, however, give a precipitate with tantalum double fluoride, but this was only partial. The statement of H. Geisow that titanium and zirconium can be separated from columbium by means of an alkaline formoxime soln. was not verified. The precipitation with tantalum is only partial, and not complete as stated by him. J. H. Muller observed that soln. of alkali columbate, tantalate, thorate, and zirconate give quantitative precipitates with **salicylic acid**, whereas titanates, molybdates, and tungstates are not so precipitated.

The atomic weight and valency of columbium.—Columbium behaves as a quinquevalent element as shown by the vapour density determinations of columbium pentachloride, $CbCl_5$, and columbium oxytrichloride, $CbOCl_3$, by H. St. C. Deville and L. Troost,[7] and O. Ruff's observations on columbium pentafluoride, CbF_5. In the percolumbic acid, $HCbO_4.nH_2O$, of P. G. Melikoff and L. Pissarjewsky, there is probably an oxygen atom in a peroxide chain. Compounds of lower valency are illustrated by the tetroxide, Cb_2O_4 ; the trichloride, $CbCl_3$; the dioxide, Cb_2O_2 ; and the hydride, CbH. According to D. I. Mendeléeff, columbium and tantalum stand in close relationship with vanadium and phosphorus ; while columbium is also related to molybdenum, and tantalum to tungsten. A. Piccini emphasized the relationship of the peroxides in the periodic table.

H. Rose analyzed a compound of columbium which he assumed to be a chloride, but which C. F. Rammelsberg showed was more likely to be an oxychloride. If the former, the at. wt. of columbium was near 122, and if an oxychloride near 94. The product, however, was probably contaminated with tantalum. R. Hermann's analyses are of little value in fixing the at. wt. of columbium because of the presence of impurities in his products. C. W. Blomstrand calculated from the ratio $2CbCl_5 : Cb_2O_5$, 96·1 ; from $CbCl_5 : 5AgCl$, 99·2 ; and from $5AgCl : Cb_2O_5$, 97·7. These numbers are not very concordant. J. C. G. de Marignac calculated 93·53 from the ratio $2(CbOF_3.2KF.H_2O) : Cb_2O_5$; 93·93 from $CbOF_3.2KF.2H_2O : K_2SO_4$; 93·71 from $Cb_2O_4 : K_2SO_4$; 94·19 from $10Cl : Cb_2O_5$; 93·91 from $2CbCl_5 : Cb_2O_5$; and 94·48 from $CbCl_5 : 5Cl$. J. C. G. de Marignac, and B. Brauner assumed that 94 is the best representative value of these results. Subsequent observations make the values smaller than this. C. W. Balke and E. F. Smith calculated 93·5 from the ratio $2CbCl_5 : Cb_2O_5$; and F. W. Clarke estimated from these results that 93·528 is the best representative value. E. F. Smith and W. K. van Haagen calculated 93·13 from the ratio $NaCbO_3 : NaCl$. The International Table for 1925 gave 93·1 as the best representative value for the at. wt. of columbium.

The **atomic number** of columbium is 41. The **isotopes** have not been determined.[8] The **electronic structure,** according to N. Bohr, will be (2) (4, 4) (6, 6, 6) (4, 4, 3) (2). C. D. Niven, H. Lessheim and R. Samuel, and M. L. Huggins studied the electronic structure of the atoms of columbium.

REFERENCES.

[1] H. Rose, *Pogg. Ann.*, **104**. 310, 1858 ; J. C. G. de Marignac, *Arch. Sciences Genève*, (2), **31**. 96, 1868 ; *Compt. Rend.*, **66**. 180, 1868 ; H. St. C. Deville, *ib.*, **66**. 183, 1868 ; H. Moissan, *ib.*, **133**. 20, 1901 ; *Scient. Amer. Suppl.*, **55**. 22039, 1902 ; S. von Olshausen, *Zeit. Kryst.*, **61**. 463, 1925 ; A. Larsson, *Zeit. anorg. Chem.*, **12**. 189, 1896 ; H. G. Grimm, *Zeit. phys. Chem.*, **122**. 177, 1926 ; H. Goldschmidt and C. Vautin. *Journ. Soc. Chem. Ind.*, **17**. 543, 1898 ; H. E. Roscoe, *Chem. News*, **37**. 25, 1878 ; *Proc. Manchester Lit. Phil. Soc.*, **17**. 44, 1878 ; *Mem. Manchester Lit. Phil. Soc.*, **6**. 186, 1879 ; L. Weiss and O. Aichel, *Liebig's Ann.*, **337**. 385, 1904 ; W. Muthmann, L. Weiss, and R. Riedelbauch, *ib.*, **355**. 64, 1907 ; H. Kuzel, *Brit. Pat. No.* 25864, 1906 ; *German Pat.*, *D.R.P.* 194348, 194707, 1905 ; 186980, 200466, 1906 ; Wolfram-Lampen A.G., *ib.*, 200300, 1905 ; 197352, 1907 ; W. von Bolton, *Zeit. Elektrochem.*, **13**. 145, 1907 ; W. R. Mott, *Trans. Amer. Electrochem. Soc.*, **34**. 255, 1918 ; M. E. Pennington, *Journ. Amer. Chem. Soc.*, **18**. 40, 1896 ; *Chem. News*, **75**. 8, 18, 31, 38, 1897 ; *Derivatives of Columbium and Tantalum*, Easton, Pa., 1895 ; C. W. Blomstrand, *Journ. prakt. Chem.*, (1), **99**. 40, 1886 ; *Acta Univ. Lund*, **1**. 7, 1864 : **2**. 3, 1865 ; *Liebig's Ann.*, **135**. 198, 1865.

[2] H. von Wartenberg, *Verh. deut. phys. Ges.*, **12**. 105, 1910 ; J. H. Hildebrand, *Journ. Amer. Chem. Soc.*, **30**. 1672, 1908 ; W. M. Barr, *ib.*, **30**. 1668, 1908 ; R. Thalén, *Nova Acta Upsala*, (3), **6**. 9, 1868 ; M. A. Catalan, *Ann. Fis. Quim*, **15**. 487, 1917 ; **16**. 513, 1918 ; J. R. Capron, *Photographed Spectra*, London, 1877 ; E. Demarçay, *Spectres électriques*, Paris, 1895 ; W. J. Humphreys, *Astrophys. Journ.*, **6**. 169, 1897 ; F. Exner and E. Haschek, *Tabellen der Funkenspectra*, Wien, 1902 ; *Tabellen der Bogenspectra*, Wien, 1904 ; *Sitzber. Akad. Wien*, **108**. 825, 1899 ; J. M. Eder and E. Valenta, *ib.*, **119**. 519, 1910 ; A. Hagenbach and H. Konen, *Atlas der Emissionsspectra*, Jena, 1905 ; J. Formanek, *Die qualitative Spektralanalyse anorganischer und organischer Körper*, Berlin, 1905 ; R. Jack, *Proc. Roy. Irish Acad.*, **30**. 42, 1912 ; A. de Gramont, *Compt. Rend.*, **166**. 365, 1918 ; W. F. Meggers, *Journ. Washington Acad.*, **14**. 442, 1924 ; W. F. Meggers and C. C. Kiess, *Journ. Amer. Opt. Soc.*, **12**. 417, 1926 ; E. Paulson, *Phys. Zeit.*, **16**. 352, 1915 ; *Ann. Physik*, (4), **45**. 419, 1914 ; G. Krüss and L. F. Nilson, *Oefvers. Akad. Förh.*, **5**. 1887 ; *Ber.*, **20**. 1685, 1887 ; C. C. Kiess and O. Laporte, *Science*, (2), **63**. 234, 1926 ; O. Laporte, *Journ. Amer. Opt. Soc.*, **13**. 1, 1926 ; M. C. M. McDonald, *Trans. Roy. Soc. Canada*, (3), **21**. 223, 1927 ; H. E. White and R. C. Gibbs, *Phys. Rev.*, (2), **29**. 259, 1927 ; (2), **31**. 309, 520, 1928.

[3] F. C. Blake and W. Duane, *Phys. Rev.*, (2), **10**. 697, 1917 ; M. Siegbahn, *Jahrb. Rad. Elektron.*, **13**. 296, 1916 ; H. Hirata, *Proc. Roy. Soc.*, **105**. A, 40, 1924 ; M. Siegbahn and E. Friman, *Phil. Mag.*, (6), **32**. 39, 1916 ; *Ann. Physik*, (4), **49**. 616, 1916 ; J. Schrör, *ib.*, (=), **80**. 297, 1926 ; D. Coster, *Compt. Rend.*, **174**. 378, 1922 ; D. Coster and F. P. Mulder, *Zeit. Physik*, **38**. 264, 1926 ; E. Hjalmar, *Zeit. Physik*, **3**. 262, 1920 ; B. Walter, *ib.*, **30**. 357, 1924 ; M. Levin and R. Ruer, *Phys. Zeit.*, **10**. 576, 1909 ; B. B. Ray, *Phil. Mag.*, (6), **48**. 707, 1924 ; S. J. M. Allen, *Phys. Rev.*, (2), **28**. 987, 1926 ; A. Leide, *Zeit. Physik*, **39**. 686, 1926 ; M. Druyvesteyn, *ib.*, **43**. 707, 1927.

[4] W. von Bolton, *Zeit. Elektrochem.*, **13**. 145, 1907 ; W. Muthmann and F. Frauenberger, *Sitzber. Bayr. Akad.*, **201**, 1904 ; A. Günther-Schulze, *Ann. Physik*, (4), **23**. 226, 1907 ; (4), **25**. 775, 1907 ; (4), **65**. 223, 1921 ; E. W. von Siemens and J. G. Halske, *German Pat.*, *D.R.P.* 150833, 1902 ; K. Honda, *Ann. Physik*, (4), **32**. 1044, 1062, 1910 ; M. Owen, *ib.*, (4), **37**. 657, 1912 ; S. Meyer, *Wied. Ann.*, **68**. 324, 1899 ; M. E. Pennington, *Journ. Amer. Chem. Soc.*, **18**. 54, 1896 ; *Chem. News*, **75**. 8, 18, 31, 38, 1897 ; *Derivatives of Columbium and Tantalum*, Easton, Pa., 1895 ; F. Ott, *Zeit. Elektrochem.*, **18**. 349, 1912 ; *Elektrolytische Reduktion der Niobsäure*, München, 1911 ; U. Sborgi, *Gazz. Chim. Ital.*, **42**. ii, 331, 1912 ; J. W. Marden and M. N. Rich, *Journ. Ind. Eng. Chem.*, **19**. 788, 1927.

[5] W. Muthmann, L. Weiss, and R. Riedelbauch, *Liebig's Ann.*, **355**. 58, 1907 ; L. Weiss and O. Aichel, *ib.*, **337**. 385, 1904 ; F. Fischer and F. Schrötter, *Ber.*, **43**. 1442, 1454, 1910 ; W. von Bolton, *Zeit. Elektrochem.*, **13**. 145, 1907 ; H. Moissan, *Compt. Rend.*, **133**. 20, 1901 ; H. E. Roscoe, *Chem. News*, **37**. 25, 1878 ; *Proc. Manchester Lit. Phil. Soc.*, **17**. 44, 1878 ; *Mem. Manchester Lit. Phil. Soc.*, **6**. 186, 1879 ; W. M. Barr, *Journ. Amer. Chem. Soc.*, **30**. 1671, 1908 ; J. C. G. de Marignac, *Arch. Sciences Genève*, (2), **31**. 96, 1868 ; *Compt. Rend.*, **66**. 180, 1868 ; M. E. Pennington, *Journ. Amer. Chem. Soc.*, **18**. 54, 1896 ; *Chem. News*, **75**. 8, 18, 31, 38, 1897 ; *Derivatives of Columbium and Tantalum*, Easton, Pa., 1895 ; H. Goldschmidt and C. Vautin, *Journ. Soc. Chem. Ind.*, **17**. 543, 1898.

[6] L. Lévy, *Compt. Rend.*, **103**. 1074, 1195, 1886 ; *Chem. News*, **54**. 300, 1886 ; R. D. Hall and E. F. Smith, *ib.*, **92**. 220, 232, 242, 252, 262, 276, 1905 ; *Proc. Amer. Phil. Soc.*, **44**. 195, 1905 ; *Journ. Amer. Chem. Soc.*, **27**. 1384, 1905 ; J. H. Muller, *ib.*, **33**. 1506, 1911 ; R. D. Hall, *ib.*, **26**. 1238, 1904 ; *Observations on the Metallic Acids*, Easton, Pa., 1904 ; M. E. Pennington, *Derivatives of Columbium and Tantalum*, Easton, Pa., 1895 ; *Journ. Amer. Chem. Soc.*, **18**. 52, 1896 ; *Chem. News*, **75**. 8, 18, 31, 38, 1897 ; J. H. de Boer, *Chem. Weekbl.*, **21**. 404, 1924 ; H. Geisow, *Beiträge zur Kenntnis der seltenen anorganischen Säuren*, München, 1902 ; M. Landecker, *Untersuchungen über die quantitative Bestimmung der Erdsäuren*, München, 1909 ; L. Weiss and M. Landecker, *Zeit. anorg. Chem.*, **64**. 101, 1909 ; *Chem. News*, **101**. 2, 13, 26, 1910 ; A. Stähler, *Ber.*, **47**. 841, 1914 ; F. Steidler, *Microchemie*, **2**. 131, 1924.

[7] H. St. C. Deville and L. Troost, *Compt. Rend.*, **56**. 891, 1863 ; **60**. 1221, 1865 ; *Ann. Chim. Phys.*, (4), **8**. 46, 1866 ; O. Ruff, *Ber.*, **42**. 429, 1909 ; P. G. Melikoff and L. Pissarjewsky, *Journ. Russ. Phys. Chem.*, **35**. 457, 1903 ; *Zeit. anorg. Chem.*, **20**. 340, 1899 ; A. Piccini, *ib.*, **12**. 169, 1896 ; C. W. Blomstrand, *Acta Univ. Lund*, **1**. 7, 1864 ; **2**. 3, 1865 ; *Liebig's Ann.*, **135**. 198,

1865; *Journ. prakt. Chem.*, (1), **99**. 40, 1866; R. Hermann, *ib.*, (1), **68**. 73, 1856; J. C. G. de Marignac, *Arch. Sciences Genève*, (2), **23**. 249, 326, 1865; *Ann. Chim. Phys.*, (4), **8**. 5, 1866; C. W. Balke, *The Double Fluorides of Tantalum*, Easton, Pa., 1908; C. W. Balke and E. F. Smith, *Journ. Amer. Chem. Soc.*, **30**. 1638, 1908; E. F. Smith and W. K. van Haagen, *ib.*, **37**. 1738, 1915; R. D. Hall and E. F. Smith, *Chem. News*, **92**. 220, 232, 242, 262, 276, 1905; *Proc. Amer. Phil. Soc.*, **44**. 177, 1905; E. F. Smith, *ib.*, **44**. 151, 1905; H. Rose, *Pogg. Ann.*, **104**. 439, 1858; C. F. Rammelsberg, *ib.*, **136**. 358, 1869; D. I. Mendeléeff, *The Principles of Chemistry*, St. Petersburg, 604, 1903; London, **2**. 191, 1891; B. Brauner in R. Abegg, *Handbuch der anorganischen Chemie*, Leipzig, **3**. iii, 805, 1907; F. W. Clarke, *A Recalculation of the Atomic Weight*, Washington, 335, 1910.

[8] F. W. Aston, *Phil. Mag.*, (6), **49**. 1191, 1925; G. D. Niven, *ib.*, (7), **3**. 1314, 1927; N. Bohr, *Nature*, **112**. Suppl., 1923; M. L. Huggins, *Journ. Phys. Chem.*, **26**. 601, 1922; H. Lessheim and R. Samuel, *Zeit. Physik*, **42**. 614, 1927.

§ 5. Columbium Hydrides

According to J. C. G. de Marignac,[1] and W. von Bolton, the products obtained by C. W. Blomstrand, and H. E. Roscoe by reducing columbium oxytrichloride with hydrogen at a bright red-heat are hydrides. W. von Bolton also obtained a hard, brittle metal by charging a strip of columbium with hydrogen by making it the cathode in the electrolysis of dil. sulphuric acid. W. Muthmann and co-workers exposed finely powdered columbium at an elevated temp. to hydrogen, and obtained an alloy with 7·9 per cent. of hydrogen corresponding with **columbium hydride**, CbH. W. von Bolton obtained a dark grey product of a similar composition which neither gained nor lost hydrogen when reheated in that gas. According to J. C. G. de Marignac, this hydride is formed when a mixture of potassium fluocolumbate and sodium is heated while the mixture is protected by a layer of sodium chloride. G. Krüss and L. F. Nilson repeated the experiment, and washed the product first with water, then with alcohol, and finally with ether. After drying at 100°, analyses showed that the product contained 77·5 per cent. of CbH; 21·53 per cent. Cb_2O_5; and 0·97 per cent. of Fe_2O_3.

The product is a dark grey, or black glistening powder of sp. gr. 6·0–6·6. The sp. ht. and mol. ht. respectively between 0° and 100° are 0·0977 and 9·3; between 0° and 210·5°, 0·0925 and 8·8; between 0° and 301·5°, 0·0871 and 8·3; and between 0° and 440°, 0·0834 and 7·9. J. C. G. de Marignac said that the product does not alter when heated to dark redness in **hydrogen**, but at a white heat about 0·36 per cent. is lost, and the sp. gr. rises from 6·15 to 7·37—possibly by the formation of oxide from the presence of oxygen in the hydrogen. W. Muthmann and co-workers said that the hydride is stable in **air**; G. Krüss and L. F. Nilson found it to be hygroscopic. J. C. G. de Marignac, G. Krüss and L. F. Nilson, and W. von Bolton found that it burns with incandescence when heated below redness in air, forming columbium pentoxide and water. The blue flame of hydrogen can be seen burning on the surface of the hydride. When heated in dry **oxygen**, water is formed; when heated in **chlorine**, a volatile, yellow chloride is formed; it forms four different columbium chlorides when heated in **hydrogen chloride**. It is soluble in conc. **hydrofluoric acid** with the evolution of hydrogen, but is not attacked by hot or cold **hydrochloric acid**. It burns when heated with **sulphur**, forming a black columbium sulphide. It is not attacked by hot or cold dil. **sulphuric acid**, but it dissolves in the conc. acid. It is not attacked by hot or cold **nitric acid**, or by **aqua regia**. It dissolves in molten **potassium hydrosulphate**; while it is not attacked by boiling **alkali-lye**.

REFERENCES.

[1] J. C. G. de Marignac, *Arch. Sciences Genève*, (2), **31**. 89, 1868; C. W. Blomstrand, *Acta Univ. Lund.*, **1**. 7, 1864; *Liebig's Ann.*, **135**. 198, 1865; H. E. Roscoe, *Chem. News*, **37**. 25, 1878; *Proc. Manchester Lit. Phil. Soc.*, **17**. 44, 1878; *Mem. Manchester Lit. Phil. Soc.*, **6**. 186, 1879; W. von Bolton, *Zeit. Elektrochem.*, **13**. 148, 1907; G. Krüss and L. F. Nilson, *Oefvers. Akad. Förh.*, **5**, 1887; *Ber.*, **20**. 1691, 1887; W. Muthmann, L. Weiss, and R. Riedelbauch, *Liebig's Ann.*, **355**. 78, 1907.

§ 6. The Lower Oxides of Columbium

The best defined oxide of columbium is the *pentoxide*, Cb_2O_5, which is an acid anhydride furnishing a series of salts, the columbates. Above the pentoxides there are the percolumbates which are derivatives of *percolumbic acid*, $HCbO_4$; and below that the *tetroxide*, Cb_2O_4; *tritapentoxide*, Cb_3O_5; the *trioxide*, Cb_2O_3; and the *dioxide*, Cb_2O_2, have been reported. The reduction of an alkali columbate with zinc and sulphuric or hydrochloric acid furnishes a blue soln. The reduction with zinc was examined by H. Rose,[1] A. E. Nordenskjöld, J. C. G. de Marignac, T. B. Osborne, F. Wöhler, etc. According to F. Ott, hydrofluoric acid hinders the reaction; and F. D. Metzger and C. E. Taylor said that the reduction proceeds nearly to the Cb_2O_3 stage. The reduction with tin was examined by H. Rose, and F. von Kobell; with copper, by H. Rose, and C. W. Blomstrand; and by electrolysis, by F. Ott, and M. E. Pennington—*vide supra*.

According to M. Delafontaine,[2] H. Rose, and R. Hermann prepared **columbium dioxide**, Cb_2O_2, which they considered to be the metal. It was obtained by heating potassium oxyfluocolumbate with sodium under a layer of fused potassium chloride in a covered iron crucible; digesting the cold product with boiling water; and washing the black powder with dil. alcohol. M. Delafontaine represented the reaction: $2K_2CbOF_3+6Na=4KF+6NaF+Cb_2O_2$. H. Rose also made it from columbium chloride and sodium as well as by passing phosphorus vapour and hydrogen over heated sodium columbate; H. St. C. Deville and L. Troost, by passing the vapour of columbium oxytrichloride over heated magnesium: $2CbOCl_3+3Mg=3MgCl_2+Cb_2O_2$; and H. St. C. Deville, by heating to 1200° a mixture of potassium columbate with an excess of potassium carbonate in a graphite crucible along with a mixture of rutile and carbon to cut off the nitrogen of the air, and treating the cold mass with dil. hydrofluoric acid—the columbium dioxide remains undissolved. Columbium dioxide appears as a black powder, or, according to H. St. C. Deville and L. Troost, in black, cubic crystals. H. Rose gave 6·27 for the sp. gr., and said that it is a good electrical conductor. When heated in air, it oxidizes vigorously with incandescence, forming columbium pentoxide; when warmed in air-free chlorine it furnishes volatile columbium oxytrichloride. Warm hydrofluoric acid dissolves it with the evolution of hydrogen, and it is readily attacked in the cold by a mixture of hydrofluoric and sulphuric acids; but hydrochloric acid attacks it slowly with the evolution of hydrogen; aqua regia attacks it more slowly than hydrochloric acid; an excess of conc. sulphuric acid dissolves it slowly, forming a brown soln.; hot nitric acid does not dissolve it—L. Weiss and M. Landecker said that the pentoxide is formed; boiling alkali-lye converts it into alkali columbate, and a soln. of alkali carbonate acts similarly; and molten potassium hydrosulphate oxidizes it to columbium pentoxide. L. Weiss and M. Landecker found that when heated with potassium or ammonium nitrate it is oxidized to the pentoxide.

E. F. Smith and P. Maas reported a bluish-black powder of **columbium trioxide**, Cb_2O_3, to be formed by heating columbium pentoxide with five times its weight of magnesium at a low temp. and dissolving out the magnesium and magnesium oxide with dil. hydrochloric acid. When the trioxide is heated in air it passes into the pentoxide. K. Friederich gave 860 ohms per sq. mm. for the electrical resistance of the trioxide. The trioxide is insoluble in acids with the exception of hydrofluoric acid. The evidence is not conclusive. According to T. B. Osborne, if a gram of hydrated pentoxide be dissolved in the smallest possible amount of hydrofluoric acid, and heated for 45 mins. at 80° with zinc and 50 c.c. of conc. hydrofluoric acid, pentoxide is reduced to the trioxide. E. Friederich and L. Sittig obtained the hemitrioxide by reducing the pentoxide with hydrogen; they said that it has a hardness of 6·5; a m.p. of 1780°; and a sp. resistance of $800×10^4$ ohms at 1100°.

J. C. G. de Marignac reported **columbium tritapentoxide,** Cb_3O_5, to be formed by boiling the hydrated pentoxide with hydrochloric acid, and treating the filtrate with zinc. The brown soln. deposits this oxide as a brown precipitate, and the brown oxide is obtained when ammonia is added. This oxide was first obtained by F. Wöhler. J. C. G. de Marignac also found that when hydrated pentoxide is boiled with hydrochloric acid and filtered, the residue forms an almost clear soln. with water, and is coloured deep blue by zinc and, in time, a hydrated blue oxide is deposited. Both the blue and brown oxides yield the same columbate when melted with potassium hydrosulphate. If potassium oxyfluocolumbate be reduced with zinc and enough hydrochloric acid to dissolve all the zinc, and then titrated with permanganate soln., the pentoxide will be found to have lost about one-third of its oxygen. The evidence is therefore inconclusive.

According to H. Rose, columbium pentoxide is scarcely affected by hydrogen at a red-heat; but at a white-heat, F. Wöhler observed the formation of a bluish-black oxide, and M. Delafontaine found that at a white-heat, the pentoxide is reduced by dry hydrogen to **columbium tetroxide,** Cb_2O_4. F. Ott electrolyzed 20 grms. of molten potassium oxypentafluocolumbate with the platinum dish as cathode, and a current of 2 amps. and 10 volts for 2 hrs. The cold product was leached with water and the residue, dried at 100°, was columbium tetroxide. V. M. Goldschmidt examined the crystals; and L. Pauling discussed the structure of the crystal lattice. The black powder has a pale blue lustre; it is stable in air at ordinary temp.; it burns at a dull red-heat, forming the white pentoxide. M. Delafontaine said that it is insoluble in hot and cold water, hydrochloric, sulphuric, and nitric acids, in aqua regia, and, according to F. Ott, in hydrofluoric acid. It is very little affected by boiling alkali-lye—*vide supra,* the electrical properties of columbium. F. Ott also obtained some **evidence** of the existence of a *columbium tritaheptoxide,* Cb_3O_7.

REFERENCES.

[1] H. Rose, *Pogg. Ann.,* **112.** 480, 1861; F. Wöhler, *ib.,* **48.** 93, 1839; A. E. Nordenskjöld, *ib.,* **111.** 278, 1860; *Oefvers Akad. Förh.,* **17.** 35, 1860; *Journ. prakt. Chem.,* (1), **81.** 193, 1860; T. B. Osborne, *Amer. Journ. Science,* (3), **30.** 331, 1885; F. Ott, *Elektrolytische Reduktion der Niobsäure,* München, 1911; *Zeit. Elektrochem.,* **18.** 349, 1912; J. C. G. de Marignac, *Arch. Sciences Genève,* (2), **25.** 17, 1866; F. D. Metzger and C. E. Taylor, *Zeit. anorg. Chem.,* **62.** 383, 1909; *Chem. News,* **100.** 257, 270, 1909; *School Mines Quart.,* **30.** 323, 1909; C. W. Blomstrand, *Acta Univ. Lund.,* **1.** 7, 1864; *Liebig's Ann.,* **135.** 198, 1865; M. E. Pennington, *Journ. Amer. Chem. Soc.,* **18.** 40, 1896; *Chem. News,* **75.** 8, 18, 31, 1897; *Derivatives of Columbium and Tantalum,* Easton, Pa., 1895; R. Hermann, *Journ. prakt. Chem.,* (1), **111.** 380, 1871; F. von Kobell, *ib.,* (1), **79.** 291, 1860; *Anz. Gehl. München,* **50.** 377, 1860; *Phil. Mag.,* (4), **21.** 4, 15, 1861.

[2] H. Rose, *Pogg. Ann.,* **104.** 310, 1858; **112.** 484, 1861; F. Wöhler, *ib.,* **48.** 92, 1839; R. Hermann, *Journ. prakt. Chem.,* (1), **111.** 386, 1871; M. Delafontaine, *Arch. Sciences Genève,* (2), **27.** 167, 1866; J. C. G. de Marignac, *ib.,* (2), **23.** 249, 326, 1865; (2), **31.** 89, 1868; *Ann. Chim. Phys.,* (4), **8.** 15, 1866; (4), **13.** 28, 1868; H. St. C. Deville and L. Troost, *Compt. Rend.,* **60.** 1221, 1865; H. St. C. Deville, *ib.,* **66.** 183, 1868; E. Friederich and L. Sittig, *Zeit. anorg. Chem.,* **145.** 127, 1925; K. Friederich, *Zeit. Physik,* **31.** 813, 1925; L. Weiss and M. Landecker, *Zeit. anorg. Chem.,* **64.** 89, 1909; *Chem. News,* **101.** 2, 13, 26, 1910; M. Landecker, *Untersuchungen über die quantitative Bestimmung der Erdsäuren,* München, 1911; T. B. Osborne, *Amer. Journ. Science,* (3), **30.** 333, 1885; F. Ott, *Elektrolytische Reduktion der Niobsäure,* München, 1911; *Zeit. Elektrochem.,* **18.** 349, 1912; E. F. Smith and P. Maas, *Zeit. anorg. Chem.,* **7.** 96, 1894; V. M. Goldschmidt, *Skrift. Norske Akad.,* **7,** 1925; L. Pauling, *Journ. Amer. Chem. Soc.,* **49.** 765, 1927.

§ 7. Columbium Pentoxide, and Columbic Acid

The extraction of **columbium pentoxide,** Cb_2O_5, from various minerals has been already described. When columbium is heated in oxygen; or columbium hydride or one of the lower oxides is heated in air; or ammonium oxyfluocolumbate, or columbium oxysulphide is roasted in air, columbium pentoxide is formed. The product from the oxysulphide should be heated with ammonium carbonate a few times to remove sulphates. L. Weiss and M. Landecker [1] obtained it by calcining oxalatocolumbic acid. The same product is obtained when the compounds of columbium fluoride or oxyfluoride with the alkali fluorides are evaporated with sulphuric acid, washed with water and calcined ; or when the chloride or oxychloride is treated with water or dil. ammonia, and the precipitate calcined. F. Wöhler obtained the pentoxide by melting a columbate with potassium hydrosulphate ; washing the product with water, and calcining the product mixed with ammonium carbonate. According to J. C. G. de Marignac, the pentoxide is obtained by evaporating potassium oxypentafluocolumbate with sulphuric acid a few times, washing the product with water, and calcining it with ammonium carbonate to remove the sulphuric acid. A similar process was used by R. F. Weinland and L. Storz, G. Krüss and L. F. Nilson, R. D. Hall, G. Chesneau, and H. Biltz and L. Gonder. According to L. Weiss and M. Landecker, the calcination with ammonium carbonate does not remove all the sulphate ; and they recommended treating the product with a small excess of ammonia, washing with dil. ammonia, and calcining the product. O. Ruff and F. Thomas said that columbium pentoxide is best purified by heating it in a bomb tube with carbon tetrachloride and fractionally subliming the resulting chlorides.

O. Hauser and A. Lewite found that a **colloidal solution** of hydrated columbium pentoxide is readily formed by fusing the pentoxide with alkali hydroxide, and dialyzing the aq. soln. so as to obtain a neutral liquid. The hydrosol is stable, and can be kept for weeks in a stoppered flask. By concentration over sulphuric acid, a liquid with 2·571 grms. of Cb_2O_5 per litre can be obtained. The disperse phase is negatively charged, and the various precipitation reactions are described. It is specially noteworthy that they are very sensitive to sulphate, chloride, sulphite, or nitrate ions, and that the hydrosol of tantalic acid is readily precipitated by a current of carbon dioxide, whereas that of columbic acid remains stable, at all events for 24 hrs. The sensitiveness towards the nitrate ion explains why H. W. Foote and R. W. Langley were unable to obtain good results in the separation of columbium and tantalum by L. Weiss and M. Landecker's process, since, according to this method, potassium nitrate is added to the sodium carbonate used in the fusion. Satisfactory results are obtained when sodium carbonate is used.

According to W. Muthmann and co-workers, and F. Ott, columbium pentoxide appears as a white, amorphous powder without taste or smell, and when heated it remains almost white. F. Wöhler, H. Rose, L. Weiss and M. Landecker said that the colour is yellow, and when heated it becomes lemon-yellow. When heated to a high temp., H. Rose said that it acquires a crystalline structure. J. J. Ebelmen obtained rhombic prismatic **crystals** by fusing the pentoxide with boric oxide. A. E. Nordenskjöld, A. Knop, and W. Florence obtained rhombic crystals by fusing the oxide with borax ; but in that case, P. J. Holmquist said that the crystals retain a little sodium. A. Knop did not obtain crystals by fusing the pentoxide with microcosmic salt ; but P. J. Holmquist prepared small colourless crystals by fusing the pentoxide with potassium or sodium hydrosulphate. According to E. Mallard, the rhombic prisms have the axial ratios $a : b : c = 0.3557 : 1 : —$. E. M. Bonshtedt described crystals of columbite from Lipovka, Urals, with $a : b : c = 0.3936 : 1 : 0.35248$. The (100)- and (010)-**cleavages** are distinct ; the optical character is positive. The **specific gravity** depends on the mode of preparation ; C. W. Balke and E. F. Smith gave 4·48–4·51 for the pentoxide prepared by calcining the precipitate from the pentachloride and ammonia ; and 4·88–5·05 for that made by calcining the product from the hydrolysis of the pentachloride in moist air ; J. C. G. de Marignac gave 4·37–4·46 for that obtained by melting potassium oxyfluocolumbate with potassium hydrosulphate, and 4·51–4·53 for that obtained by calcining ammonium oxyfluocolumbate ; F. Ott, 4·4849 ; H. Geisow, 4·00 when calcined over the colourless gas-burner, and 4·43 when calcined over the blast gas-flame ; H. Rose likewise obtained numbers ranging from 4·601 to 5·262 ; and P. J. Holmquist, 4·568 for the crystals from the hydrosulphate fusion.

E. M. Bonshtedt gave 5·0 for the sp. gr. of crystals of columbite. D. Balareff, and C. del Fresno studied the mol. vol. G. Krüss, and L. F. Nilson found the **specific heat** and mol. heat respectively between 0° and 100°, to be 0·1184 and 31·7 ; betweeu 0° and 210·5°, 0·1184 and 31·7 ; between 0° and 301·5°, 0·1243 and 33·8 ; and between 0° and 440°, 0·1349 and 30·1. J. J. Berzelius, and H. Rose observed the **calorescence** of the heated oxide, and J. Böhm showed, by X-radiograms, that the phenomenon is connected with the passage from the amorphous to the crystalline state. A. A. Read said that the pentoxide does not alter in weight when heated to 1750°. W. Muthmann and co-workers gave 44·133 Cals. per gram-eq. for the **heat of formation.**

C. Renz found that columbium pentoxide is **photosensitive,** for it is reduced when exposed to light in the presence of certain organic liquids and reducing soln.—*e.g.* glycerol. The process is affected by the presence of impurities. The lower oxide regenerates the pentoxide when exposed to air. E. L. Nichols and H. L. Howes found that columbium oxide mixed with a little tantalum oxide exhibits **flame luminescence.** E. L. Nichols said that when columbium oxide, Cb_2O_5, is gradually introduced into a hydrogen flame, it glows with a pale greenish-blue colour when in the oxidizing portion, but in the reducing region the colour changes abruptly to deep red. The former phase is selective with luminescence bands superposed on the radiation due to temp., whilst the latter resembles that of a black body and is due to the formation of the oxide, Cb_2O_4, which is black at the temp. of incandescence. The formation of similar black suboxides was observed in the cases of titanium and tantalum. A. Karl said that the oxide is **triboluminescent.** K. Friederich gave $11·4 \times 10^6$ ohms per sq. mm. for the **electrical resistance** of the pentoxide. S. J. Kiehl and D. Hart found that soln. of columbium pentoxide in 3 to $10M$-H_2SO_4 can be completely reduced to the tervalent stage by a mercury cathode. S. Meyer gave for the magnetic susceptibility $-0·08 \times 10^{-6}$, and S. Berkman and H. Zocher, $-0·04 \times 10^{-6}$.

H. Rose said that columbium pentoxide is reduced and blackened when heated in **hydrogen ;** and M. Delafontaine found that the tetroxide is formed. H. von Wartenberg and co-workers found that the oxide is reduced by hydrogen at 5 atm. press. at 2500°, and E. Newbery and J. N. Pring, that over 2000° and 150 atm. press., columbium monoxide is formed. For the action of **hydrogen dioxide,** *vide* tantalum pentoxide. W. K. van Haagen and E. F. Smith found that **hydrogen fluoride** converts the pentoxide into fluoride. When heated with dry **hydrogen chloride,** R. D. Hall and E. F. Smith found that a volatile chloride is formed. M. E. Pennington said that the thoroughly calcined pentoxide is slowly soluble in conc. **hydrofluoric acid.** On the other hand, R. F. Weinland and L. Storz found that calcined columbium pentoxide is insoluble in hydrofluoric acid ; and F. Ott, that it is likewise insoluble in **hydrochloric acid.** H. Rose found that the red-hot pentoxide does not alter in weight when heated in a current of **sulphur dioxide,** and with **hydrogen sulphide,** the oxytrisulphide is formed. M. E. Pennington said that **hyposulphurous acid** colours the pentoxide yellow. H. Rose found that the uncalcined oxide dissolves in hot, conc. **sulphuric acid,** but the calcined oxide is scarcely soluble in that menstruum. S. J. Kiehl and D. Hart found that a sat. soln. contains 8·34 grms. of columbium pentoxide and 80·11 per cent. of anhydrous sulphuric acid in 100 grms. of soln. The soln. must be at least $3M$-H_2SO_4 and contain not more than $0·038M$-Cb_2O_5 to remain stable for 3 days. For higher conc. of the pentoxide, more conc. acid must be used. E. F. Smith and co-workers, and R. D. Hall observed that when heated with **sulphur monochloride** vapour, the oxytrichloride and then the pentachloride are formed ; F. Bourion observed that the reaction with a mixture of sulphur monochloride and chlorine begins at about 300°. H. Rose found that at a white-heat, **ammonia** converts the pentoxide into nitride. H. Rose said that there is a small loss of weight when the pentoxide is mixed with **ammonium chloride** and calcined—presumably a trace of volatile oxychloride is formed. M. E. Pennington observed that **phosphorus pentachloride,** in a sealed tube at 180°–235°, forms columbium pentachloride, and phosphoryl chloride. H. Rose showed that the vapour of **carbon disulphide** converts the white-hot pentoxide into the oxytrisulphide ; and M. Delafontaine and C. E. Linebarger, and R. D. Hall and E. F. Smith found that **carbon tetrachloride** vapour, or a mixture of carbon dioxide and chlorine, converts the pentoxide into the pentachloride and the oxytrichloride—E. Demarçay said that the attack begins at 210°, and P. Camboulives, at 215°. O. Ruff and F. Thomas said that the chlorination occurs readily at 200°–225°, but not so with tantalum pentoxide. It is not possible to separate the two by this reaction because, in the presence of columbium pentoxide, tantalum also is converted into the pentachloride. F. Ott found that the calcined pentoxide is insoluble in **alkali-lye ;** but it is converted into the alkali columbate by the fused hydroxide, or by fused **alkali carbonate.** L. Weiss and M. Landecker showed that it is soluble in a mixture of sodium carbonate and borax. As indicated above, it is dissolved by molten **boric oxide,** or **borax,** and most of the pentoxide crystallizes from the soln. on cooling. A. Knop found that it is dissolved by molten **glass,** but W. Muthmann and co-workers found that it is not affected by porcelain glazes at a red-heat. H. Rose, and L. Weiss and M. Landecker observed that the pentoxide dissolves in molten **potassium hydrosulphate,** and most of it crystallizes out on cooling. H. Rose said that when the pentoxide is fused with **ammonium hydrosulphate,** it forms a viscid mass soluble in water. H. Rose observed that when heated with **oxidizing agents**—molten potassium nitrate, a molten mixture of potassium chlorate and sodium carbonate, or a mixture of potassium chlorate and hydrochloric acid—no higher oxide is formed.

According to H. Rose, **hydrated columbium pentoxide,** $Cb_2O_5.nH_2O$, or *columbic acid,* $HCbO_3$, is formed when columbium oxytrichloride is hydrolyzed by water. If the oxytrichloride be treated with water, an amorphous, voluminous hydrate is formed which is difficult to wash, but if the oxytrichloride be exposed to air, water is gradually attracted from the atm. and a crystalline hydrate, easy to wash, is formed. B. Santesson treated a soln. of columbium oxyfluoride with dil. ammonia. C. W. Blomstrand boiled columbium pentachloride with water and obtained columbic acid ; and J. C. G. de Marignac digested the product with aq. ammonia. C. W. Balke and E. F. Smith found it very difficult to wash out the last traces of chlorine, and they recommended treating the pentachloride with dil. ammonia, acidifying the liquid with nitric acid, filtering, and washing. H. Rose decomposed a boiling aq. soln. of an alkali columbate with hydrochloric acid, and obtained a hydrate which retained hydrochloric acid very tenaciously. R. F. Weinland and L. Storz used a modification of this process ; and B. Santesson employed sulphuric in place of hydrochloric acid. H. Rose fused the pentoxide with potassium or ammonium hydrosulphate and treated the cold product with water. It retains sulphates very tenaciously, and the residue was therefore boiled with aq. ammonia **or** a soln. of sodium carbonate, and washed with dil. hydrochloric acid or a dil. soln. of ammonium chloride. L. Weiss and M. Landecker treated a soln. of columbium pentoxide in sulphuric acid with water or aq. ammonia. J. C. G. de Marignac, F. Wöhler, and R. F. Weinland and L. Storz obtained a **colloidal solution** of hydrated columbium pentoxide by boiling the precipitated pentoxide with hydrochloric acid.

Hydrated columbium pentoxide is a white, amorphous solid. H. Rose found the sp. gravity to be 4·3. When obtained by the hydrolysis of the halides, it shows the phenomenon of calorescence when heated—5. 33, 10—but not so when obtained from the fused potassium hydrosulphate. When dried at 100°, it contains variable amounts of water ; J. C. G. de Marignac found that it lost 4·47 per cent. at 150° ; 5·75 per cent. at 200° ; and 7·8 per cent. at 300°. B. Santesson observed that the hydrate prepared from the oxyfluoride contained 8·04–8·51 per cent. of water, and that prepared by treating alkali columbate with sulphuric acid, 13·79—14·00 per cent.—the theoretical value for $Cb_2O_5.7H_2O$ is 13·55 per cent. Hence the term " columbic acid " refers only to the acidic character of the hydrated pentoxide.

R. Robl observed no fluorescence when the so-called metacolumbic acid is exposed
to ultra-violet light. H. Rose, and L. Weiss and M. Landecker found that the
hydrated pentoxide is soluble in **hydrofluoric acid** ; and that it is more soluble than
tantalic acid in **hydrochloric acid** ; but it is at the best only sparingly soluble in
cold, conc. hydrochloric acid—R. F. Weinland and L. Storz found that only one
per cent. Cb_2O_5 passes into soln. J. C. G. de Marignac, and F. Wöhler said that
the hydrated pentoxide is only sparingly soluble in boiling hydrochloric acid, but
the residue becomes soluble in water by this treatment. R. F. Weinland and
L. Storz found that only 1·2 per cent. Cb_2O_5 dissolves in highly conc. **hydrobromic
acid** ; and only a trace dissolves in **hydriodic acid,** and at the same time a little
pentoxide is reduced. L. Weiss and M. Landecker said that the hydrated pentoxide
is insoluble in **perchloric acid** ; and that it dissolves in **sulphuric acid** more easily
than does tantalic acid. R. D. Hall and E. F. Smith said that it is insoluble in dil.
sulphuric acid. The sulphuric acid soln. gives a precipitate when diluted with water,
when treated with alkali sulphates, sulphur dioxide, etc. The properties of the
sulphuric acid soln. were studied by H. Rose, J. C. G. de Marignac, and L. Weiss
and M. Landecker. The last-named found that the solubility in acids is hastened if
hydrogen dioxide be present. L. Weiss and M. Landecker found that the hydrated
pentoxide dissolves in **nitric acid** more readily than does tantalic acid ; and the
solubility in aq. **ammonia** or **ammonium chloride** is hastened if hydrogen dioxide
be present. M. E. Pennington found that up to 2 per cent. of the hydrated pentoxide
dissolves in warm soln. of **ammonium sulphide** when digested therein for some time.
L. Weiss and M. Landecker found that the hydrated pentoxide is insoluble in phosphoric acid, and that its solubility in a soln. of sodium hydrophosphate is favoured
by the presence of hydrogen dioxide. Freshly precipitated hydrated pentoxide
is soluble in **oxalic acid,** or **tartaric acid**—the soln. of columbium pentoxide in
oxalic acid is not affected by many reagents which are active with soln. in other
solvents. R. D. Hall found that a soln. of **potassium oxalate** dissolves the hydrated
pentoxide. H. Lange found that with **ammonium salicylate** an insoluble, yellow
adsorption compound is formed. H. Rose found that a soln. of an alkali columbate
acidified with hydrochloric or sulphuric acid colours **turmeric** brown or reddish-
brown. L. Weiss and M. Landecker found that the hydrated pentoxide is soluble
in **hydrofluosilicic acid.** H. Rose, and F. Wöhler showed that the hydrated
pentoxide is readily soluble in soln. of **alkali hydroxides** or **carbonates.** L. Weiss
and M. Landecker showed that the presence of hydrogen dioxide hastens the process
of dissolution. If the precipitate has aged a few hours, it dissolves with greater
difficulty than the fresh precipitate. The hydrated pentoxide is insoluble in soln.
of **sodium** or **ammonium hydrocarbonate**—*vide supra,* analytical reactions of
columbium.

REFERENCES.

¹ F. Wöhler, *Pogg. Ann.,* **48.** 92, 1839 ; H. Rose, *Sitzber. Akad. Berlin,* **12,** 1859 ; *Pogg. Ann.,*
69. 123, 1846 ; **111.** 193, 426, 1860 ; **112.** 447, 473, 549, 1861 ; **113.** 105, 1861 ; A. E. Nordenskjöld,
ib., **114.** 612, 1861 ; *Oefvers. Akad. Förh.,* **17.** 35, 1860 ; M. Delafontaine, *Arch. Sciences Genève,*
(2), **27.** 167, 1866 ; J. C. G. de Marignac, *ib.,* (2), **23.** 249, 326, 1865 ; (2), **31.** 89, 1868 ; *Ann. Chim.
Phys.,* (4), **8.** 5, 1866 ; (4), **9.** 249, 1866 ; (4), **13.** 28, 1868 ; F. Bourion, *ib.,* (8), (2). 564, 1910 ;
J. J. Ebelmen, *ib.,* (3), **33.** 34, 1851 ; *Compt. Rend.,* **33.** 525, 1831 ; G. Chesneau, *ib.,* **149.** 1132,
1909 ; E. Demarçay, *ib.,* **104.** 111, 1887 ; A. Karl, *ib.,* **146.** 1104, 1908 ; P. Camboulives, *ib.,*
150. 175, 1910 ; H. Geisow, *Beiträge zur Kenntnis der seltenen anorganischen Säuren,* München,
1902 ; F. Ott, *Elektrolytische Reduktion der Niobsäure,* München, 1911 ; *Zeit. Elektrochem.,* **18.**
349, 1912 ; O. Hauser and A. Lewite, *Zeit. angew. Chem.,* **25.** 100, 1912 ; R. F. Weinland and
L. Storz, *Zeit. anorg. Chem.,* **54.** 230, 1907 ; L. Weiss and M. Landecker, *ib.,* **64.** 68, 1909 ; *Chem.
News,* **101.** 2, 13, 1910 ; R. Robl, *Zeit. angew. Chem.,* **39.** 608, 1926 ; M. Landecker, *Untersuchungen
über die quantitative Bestimmung der Erdsäuren,* München, 1911 ; C. W. Blomstrand, *Journ.
prakt. Chem.,* (1), **99.** 40, 1866 ; *Acta Univ. Lund.,* **1.** 7, 1864 ; **2.** 3, 1865 ; *Liebig's Ann.,* **135.**
198, 1865 ; W. Muthmann, L. Weiss, and R. Riedelbauch, *ib.,* **355.** 84, 1907 ; A. Knop, *ib.,* **159.**
56, 1871 ; *Zeit. Kryst.,* **12.** 610, 1887 ; K. Friederich, *Zeit. Physik,* **31.** 813, 1925 ; G. Krüss and
L. F. Nilson, *Oefvers. Akad. Förh.,* 5, 1887 ; *Zeit. phys. Chem.,* **1.** 391, 1887 ; *Ber.,* **20.** 1682,
1887 ; H. Biltz and L. Gonder, *ib.,* **40.** 4963, 1908 ; E. Newbery and J. N. Pring, *Proc. Roy. Soc.,*

92. A, 276, 1916 ; C. Renr, *Helvetica Chim. Acta*, **4.** 961, 1921 ; R. D. Hall, *Observations on the Metallic Acids*, Easton, Pa., 1904 ; *Journ. Amer. Chem. Soc.*, **26.** 1238, 1904 ; C. W. Balke and E. F. Smith, *ib.*, **30.** 1648, 1908 ; C. W. Balke, *The Double Fluorides of Tantalum*, Easton. Pa., 1908 ; E. F. Smith, *Journ. Amer. Chem. Soc.*, **20.** 292, 1898 ; *Proc. Amer. Phil. Soc.*, **44.** 157, 1905 ; R. D. Hall and E. F. Smith, *ib.*, **44.** 177, 1906 ; *Chem. News*, **92.** 220, 232, 242, 252, 262, 276, 1905 ; M. E. Pennington, *ib.*, **75.** 8, 18, 31, 38, 1897 ; *Derivatives of Columbium and Tantalum*, Easton, Pa., 1895 ; *Journ. Amer. Chem. Soc.*, **18.** 40, 1896 ; W. K. van Haagen and E. F. Smith, *ib.*, **33.** 1504, 1911 ; M. Delafontaine and C. E. Linebarger, *ib.*, **18.** 532, 1896 ; H. von Wartenberg, J. Broy, and R. Reinicke, *Zeit. Elektrochem.*, **29.** 214, 1923 ; A. A. Read, *Journ. Chem. Soc.*, **65.** 313, 1894 ; E. L. Nichols and H. L. Howes, *Phys. Rev.*, (2), **19.** 300, 1922 ; E. L. Nichols, *ib.*, (2), **25.** 376, 1925 ; E. Mallard, *Ann. Mines*, (8), **12.** 427, 1887 ; J. Böhm, *Zeit. anorg. Chem.*, **149.** 217, 1925 ; O. Ruff and F. Thomas, *ib.*, **156.** 213, 1926 ; P. J. Holmquist, *Bull. Geol. Inst. Upsala*, **3.** 207, 1897 ; W. Florence, *Neues Jahrb. Min.*, ii, 99, 1898 ; S. Meyer, *Wied. Ann.*, **68.** 325, 1899 ; **69.** 236, 1899 ; *Ann. Physik*, (4), **1.** 664, 668, 1900 ; S. Berkman and H. Zocher, *Zeit. phys. Chem.*, **124.** 318, 1927 ; C. del Fresno, *Anal. Fis.-Quim.*, **24.** 707, 1926 ; D. Balareff, *Journ. prakt. Chem.*, (2), **102.** 283, 1921 ; B. Santesson, *Om nagra af metallen Niobiums föreningar*, Upsala, 1875 ; *Bull. Soc. Chim.*, (2), **24.** 53, 1875 ; H. Lange, *Zeit. Naturwiss.*, **82.** 27, 1910 ; H. W. Foote and R. W. Langley, *Amer. Journ. Science*, (4), **30.** 401, 1911 ; E. M. Bonshtedt, *Bull. Russ. Acad.*, (6), **19.** 513, 1925 ; S. J. Kiehl and D. Hart, *Journ. Amer. Chem. Soc.*, **50.** 1608, 1928 ; J. J. Berzelius, *Lehrbuch der Chemie*, Dresden, 2. 393, 1834.

§ 8. Columbates or Niobates

According to A. Stähler,[1] the salt-forming properties of the lower oxides of columbium are more like the elements of the chromium family than are those of titanium and vanadium. Columbium pentoxide is an acid anhydride forming a number of salts. As an acid, said R. F. Weinland and L. Storz, columbic acid is about the same strength as silicic acid, and is stronger than titanic acid. The alkali columbates were made by H. Rose by fusing a mixture of the alkali carbonate with what he called *Unterniobsaure*, Nb_2O_3, but which J. C. G. de Marignac showed to be columbium pentoxide. C. F. Rammelsberg recalculated H. Rose's results for the acidic oxide Cb_2O_5. A. F. Gehlen had previously obtained small, soluble crystals of alkali columbate by fusing columbite or tantalite with sodium or potassium carbonate. C. W. Balke and E. F. Smith, and M. H. Bedford showed that the nature of the product depends on the proportion of the component salts. F. Russ showed that the columbates readily form complex acid salts ; and R. F. Weinland and L. Storz found that the oxygen can be partially displaced by chlorine or bromine. A potassium columbate of indefinite composition was obtained by A. F. Gehlen, W. von Bolton, H. Moissan, J. C. G. de Marignac, and W. Muthmann, by the action of molten alkali hydroxide, or a mixture of the alkali carbonate and nitrate on the metal. H. Rose also made potassium columbates by the action of fused potassium hydroxide or carbonate, or aq. soln. of these compounds on hydrated columbium pentoxide. F. Russ found that a mol of columbium pentoxide drives a mol of carbon dioxide from a mol of potassium carbonate, and 2·5 mols of carbon dioxide from 3 and 5 mols of potassium carbonate. In general, the alkali columbates can be obtained by fusing columbium pentoxide with the alkali carbonates, the product obtained depends on the relative proportions of pentoxide and carbonate employed ; if too little carbonate be used, sparingly soluble acidic columbates are formed, while if large excess of carbonate is used, potassium, rubidium, and cæsium carbonates give clear fusions, soluble in a relative small proportion of water, while with sodium carbonate, the fusion is not clear, and the resulting columbate is not soluble in the presence of an excess of the alkali carbonate, but it is completely soluble in water. A large number of columbates have been reported, but probably many of these are merely mixtures. H. Rose found that the aq. soln. of potassium columbates can be boiled without decomposition, and when the soln. is evaporated to dryness, it can be again dissolved in water. The aq. soln. are partly decomposed by carbon dioxide. The general properties of these salts have been considered in connection with the analytical reactions of columbium, and the properties of columbic acid. Complex columbates can be named by the system employed for the vanadates, etc.

The **ammonium columbates** have not been studied in detail; they are formed by double decomposition with the alkali columbates and ammonium salts. K. A. Hofmann and V. Kohlschütter reported **hydroxylamine columbate,** $3(NH_2OH).HCbO_3$, to be formed by digesting a mixture of potassium deuterohexacolumbate with conc. aq. ammonia and hydroxylamine chloride; washing the product successively with dil. aq. ammonia, alcohol, and ether; and drying for an hour in vacuo over sulphuric acid. The white powder explodes when heated in a tube. It is sparingly soluble in water; and when digested with water at ordinary temp. it is decomposed. Another hydroxylamine columbate was obtained with similar properties; but with the composition $5NH_2OH.Cb_2O_5.2H_2O$.

H. Rose did not make definite potassium columbates, but from the amount of carbon dioxide evolved when columbium pentoxide is fused with potassium carbonate, he inferred that **potassium orthocolumbate,** K_3CbO_4, is formed; and F. Russ obtained this salt by calcining the oxalatocolumbate, $3K_2O.Cb_2O_5.6C_2O_3.4H_2O$. P. J. Holmquist reported the possible formation of acicular, or cubic and hexahedral crystals, or crystal aggregates of **sodium pyrocolumbate,** $Na_4Cb_2O_7$, by melting a mixture of 3·88 grms. of sodium carbonate, 4·94 grms. of columbium pentoxide, and 1·6 grms. of sodium fluoride; and washing out the fluoride with water. The salt is decomposed by water. A. Lottermoser placed a soln. of the normal columbate in the inner anode compartment, and $0·1N$-NaOH in the outer cathode compartment, and on electrolysis with a platinum cylinder as anode, an acid columbate was formed in the inner cell. B. Santesson obtained **potassium pyrocolumbate,** $K_4Cb_2O_7$, by melting the tetracolumbate with an excess of potassium carbonate, and washing away the soluble matters with water.

Although J. C. G. de Marignac was unable to prepare definite sodium columbates, yet H. Rose described **sodium metacolumbate,** $Na_2O.Cb_2O_5.nH_2O$, or $NaCbO_3.nH_2O$, as best crystallized and the most stable of all the columbates. A. Joly studied the substitution of columbic anhydride for carbonic anhydride in sodium carbonate, and P. J. Holmquist obtained the anhydrous salt by melting equimolar parts of sodium carbonate and columbium pentoxide with sodium fluoride as a flux. The cold mass was washed with water to remove the excess of sodium fluoride. The white, pseudo-cubic crystals consist of twinned plates. The sp. gr. of the finest powder at 18° is 4·512, and that of coarser powder is 4·559. The hydrated salt was obtained by H. Rose by fusing columbium pentoxide or hydroxide, or an acidic sodium columbate with sodium hydroxide in a silver crucible. The residue was insoluble in an excess of alkali-lye, but soluble in water. The same salt was formed by H. Rose, and B. Santesson by heating an aq. soln. of sodium hydroxide with columbium hydroxide in suspension; although the columbium pentoxide did not dissolve, on removing the excess of sodium hydroxide, the residue was soluble in water, and, on evaporation, the soln. gave crystals of the metacolumbate. H. Rose obtained the same salt by fusing sodium with columbium oxide; evaporating the clear liquid obtained by extracting the cold cake with water; and crystallizing the soln. C. W. Balke and E. F. Smith showed that the formulæ of H. Rose and C. F. Rammelsberg respectively—$Na_2O.Cb_2O_5.6H_2O$ and $Na_2O.Cb_2O_5.9H_2O$—probably refer to impure products for the spontaneous evaporation of the aq. soln., yields triclinic crystals of the *heptahydrate,* $Na_2O.Cb_2O_5.7H_2O$, with axial ratios $a:b:c=0·9559:1:0·8394$, and $\alpha=71°\ 20'$; $\beta=105°\ 30'$; $\gamma=54°\ 7'$. T. Barth said that the crystals of sodium metacolumbate are pseudo-cubic and the X-radiogram shows that the space lattice has one mol in the parallelopiped; the edge of the pseudo-cube $a=3·890$ A. The salt is isomorphous with perowskite, $CaTiO_3$, and mixed crystals occur as the mineral *dysanalyte* which has a pseudo-cubic lattice with edge 3·826 A. The salt loses 22·93 per cent. of water at 100°; and forms a clear soln. with water. A. Joly also reported **potassium metacolumbate,** $KCbO_3$, to be formed by fusing equimolar parts of potassium carbonate and columbium pentoxide with calcium fluoride in a platinum crucible, and slowly cooling the molten mixture. The cold product was treated with boiling dil. sulphuric acid for some days to remove the calcium fluoride, and there remained straw-yellow rectangular plates which did not belong to the cubic system.

J. C. G. de Marignac reported **potassium orthotetracolumbate**, $K_6Cb_4O_{13}.13H_2O$, to be formed by the slow evaporation of an aq. soln. of the dodeca- or tetradeca-columbate with an excess of potash-lye. The rhombic crystals have the axial ratios $a:b:c=0.9770:1:1.1722$; and they rapidly effloresce in air; and lose 7 mols. of water at 100°. R. Hermann prepared two salts of nearly the same composition by evaporating in vacuo, over sulphuric acid, a soln. of columbic acid in boiling potash-lye. F. Russ obtained evidence of the formation of a more basic salt, $2K_2O.K_6Cb_4O_{13}$, by measuring the amount of carbon dioxide expelled from potassium carbonate by columbium pentoxide. B. Santesson, and F. Russ obtained crystalline **potassium deuterotetracolumbate**, $K_2Cb_4O_{12}.5\frac{1}{2}H_2O$, by melting equimolar parts of potassium carbonate and columbium pentoxide, and washing out the soluble matters with water.

J. C. G. de Marignac prepared **potassium orthohexacolumbate**, $K_8Cb_6O_{19}.16H_2O$, in well-defined crystals, by evaporating in vacuo an aq. soln. of a fused mixture of columbium pentoxide with 2 or 3 times its weight of potassium carbonate. W. E. von John also prepared this salt; C. W. Balke and E. F. Smith obtained it in monoclinic crystals with the axial ratios $a:b:c=0.7120:1:0.5547$, and $\beta=84°$ 19'. J. C. G. de Marignac said that the salt is isomorphous with the corresponding tantalate; it effloresces quickly in air; loses 12 mols. of water at 100°; dissolves completely in water, and on evaporation, the aq. soln. yields the tetradecacolumbate. C. W. Balke and E. F. Smith likewise prepared **rubidium orthohexacolumbate**, $Rb_8Cb_6O_{19}.14H_2O$, in monoclinic crystals with the axial ratios $a:b:c=0.8816:1:1.0491$; and $\beta=84°$ 7'; and the corresponding **cæsium orthohexacolumbate**, $Cs_8Cb_6O_{19}.14H_2O$, in monoclinic crystals whose angular measurements coincide, within the limits of experimental error, with those of the rubidium salt. Both salts form anisomorphous group with the corresponding tantalates. A. Santesson reported small crystals of sodium deuterohexacolumbate, $Na_4Cb_6O_{17}.9H_2O$, to be formed from a boiling aq. soln. of a fused mixture of columbium pentoxide and potassium hydroxide; but M. H. Bedford could not confirm this. J. C. G. de Marignac obtained **potassium triterohexacolumbate**, $K_2Cb_6O_{16}.5H_2O$, as a white precipitate by boiling a soln. of potassium oxytrifluocolumbate and hydrocarbonate.

R. Hermann reported **sodium orthocolumbate**, $Na_{10}Cb_8O_{25}.21H_2O$, to be precipitated when sodium hydroxide is added to a hot soln. of potassium oxyfluo-columbate, but this has not been confirmed. W. R. Schoeller and C. Jahn studied the sodium columbates. A. Joly melted a mixture of columbium pentoxide with twice its weight of potassium sulphate in a platinum crucible at a red-heat, and after washing the cold mass with water, obtained thin tablets of **potassium deuterocto-columbate**, $K_6Cb_8O_{23}$. C. W. Balke and E. F. Smith obtained crystalline needles of **rubidium deuterocolumbate**, $Rb_6Cb_8O_{23}.9\frac{1}{2}H_2O$, from a fused mixture of columbium pentoxide and rubidium carbonate, or by melting the orthohexa-columbate. H. Rose obtained a precipitate corresponding with **sodium tetrerocto-columbate**, $Na_2Cb_8O_{21}.5H_2O$, as a gelatinous precipitate, by passing carbon dioxide into a soln. of sodium metacolumbate.

H. Rose reported *sodium orthodecacolumbate*, $Na_{12}Cb_{10}O_{29}.40H_2O$, to be obtained by washing with water the product obtained by melting a mixture of sodium carbonate and columbium pentoxide; C. W. Blomstrand's analyses corresponded with **sodium orthotetradecacolumbate**, $Na_{16}Cb_{14}O_{43}.30H_2O$. R. Hermann did not obtain the same results. C. W. Balke and E. F. Smith, and J. C. G. de Marignac obtained **potassium orthotetradecacolumbate**, $K_{16}Cb_{14}O_{43}.32H_2O$, by slowly evaporating an aq. soln. of the orthohexacolumbate. The rhombic bipyramidal crystals have the axial ratios $a:b:c=0.9584:1:0.7083$. They can be re-crystallized from water without change, and they lose 23 mols. of water at 100°. When the aq. soln. is treated with carbon dioxide a more acid salt separates out. C. W. Balke and E. F. Smith said that this salt is probably the orthododeca-columbate.

C. W. Balke and E. F. Smith obtained crystalline **lithium orthododecacolumbate**, $Li_{14}Cb_{12}O_{37}.26H_2O$, by cooling a warm mixture of soln. of lithium nitrate made feebly alkaline with lithium carbonate and a conc. soln. of potassium triterohexacolumbate. M. H. Bedford recrystallized R. Hermann's sodium orthoctocolumbate, and showed that it is probably the *dotricontahydrated* **sodium orthododecacolumbite**, $Na_{14}Cb_{12}O_{37}.32H_2O$. The same salt was made by recrystallizing the aq. extract of a fused mixture of sodium hydroxide and columbium pentoxide. This gives the *hexatricontahydrate*; and if alcohol be added to the aq. soln., the *hemitricontahydrate* is precipitated. This salt was also made by C. W. Balke and E. F. Smith. The prismatic crystals are fairly stable, and freely soluble in water. The aq. soln. gives precipitates with silver, barium, and zinc salts. W. E. von John said that the salt is insoluble in soda-lye. C. W. Balke and E. F. Smith obtained **potassium orthododecacolumbate**, $K_{14}Cb_{12}O_{37}.27H_2O$, by adding alcohol to an aq. soln. of the orthohexacolumbate; and by crystallization from aq. soln. of the same salt; and **cæsium orthododecacolumbate**, $Cs_{14}Cb_{12}O_{37}.30H_2O$, was obtained in an analogous way.

H. Rose obtained what he regarded as **ammonium sodium tetreroctocolumbate**, $\{(NH_4)_{0.833}Na_{0.167}\}_2Cb_8O_{21}.5H_2O$, by adding ammonium chloride or sulphate to a soln. of sodium metacolumbate; and J. C. G. de Marignac, **sodium potassium orthohexacolumbate**, $(K_3Na)_2Cb_6O_{19}.9H_2O$, by adding sodium hydroxide to a soln. of potassium columbate.

A. Larsson prepared **copper metacolumbate**, $Cu(CbO_3)_2$, by melting with boric oxide the precipitate obtained by adding copper sulphate to a soln. of the sodium salt, and washing the product with dil. hydrochloric acid. The sp. gr. of the black crystal aggregates is 5·60. If the pale green precipitate be dried at 100°, C. F. Rammelsberg said that it is the *dihydrate*, and C. W. Balke and E. F. Smith, the *hemiheptahydrate*; and C. W. Balke and E. F. Smith obtained **silver metacolumbate**, $AgCbO_3.H_2O$, as a yellowish-white precipitate by adding silver nitrate to a soln of sodium metacolumbate. The salt darkens by exposure to light. M. H. Bedford reported white, insoluble **silver orthododecacolumbate**, $Ag_{14}Cb_{12}O_{37}.5H_2O$, to be formed by adding a dil. soln. of silver nitrate to the sodium salt.

P. J. Holmquist obtained **calcium orthocolumbate**, $Ca_3(CbO_4)_2$, contaminated with sodium columbate, by treating a soln. of the sodium salt in molten sodium carbonate with calcium carbonate, and washing the precipitate with dil. hydrochloric acid. A. Joly obtained **calcium pyrocolumbate**, $Ca_2Cb_2O_7$, by heating to redness a mixture of columbium pentoxide with a great excess of calcium chloride, and washing the product with dil. hydrochloric acid; A. Larsson digested with a soln. of calcium chloride the precipitate obtained by treating a soln. of potassium columbate with calcium chloride; and P. J. Holmquist, by melting 1·83 grms. of columbium pentoxide, 20 grms. of calcium chloride, and 7 grms. of sodium fluoride; or by treating a soln. of columbium pentoxide in molten potassium hydrosulphate with calcium sulphate; or by adding calcium carbonate to a molten mixture of columbium pentoxide and calcium chloride. The colourless prismatic crystals, or rhombic needles or plates have a sp. gr. 4·4840 at 17°. P. J. Holmquist obtained what he regarded as isomorphous mixtures with sodium metacolumbate. A. Joly obtained **calcium metacolumbate**, $Ca(CbO_3)_2$, by heating a mixture of columbium pentoxide and calcium fluoride (2 : 1) with an excess of potassium chloride at a red-heat for 4-5 hrs., and extracting the product with water. A. Larsson said that the product is a mixture of the pyrocolumbate with columbium pentoxide; he also obtained the metacolumbate by melting the pyrocolumbate with boric oxide, and boiling the product with dil. hydrochloric acid. P. J. Holmquist said that the tabular crystals have a sp. gr. of 4·484 at 17°, and A. Larsson, 4·12. T. L. Walker and A. L. Parsons described a calcium columbate, $CaO.Cb_2O_5.2H_2O$, or $Ca(CbO_3)_2.2H_2O$, occurring as a mineral in Monteagle, Ontario; and they called it

ellsworthite—after H. V. Ellsworth. The amber-yellow or dark chocolate-brown mineral occurs in masses with a conchoidal fracture. It is isotropic with a refractive index exceeding 1·74. The sp. gr. is 3·608–3·758 ; and the hardness 4. A. Larsson obtained **strontium and barium columbates** by treating a soln. of the potassium salt with strontium or barium chloride, and melting the product with boric oxide. He could not obtain satisfactory formulæ from the analyses. M. H. Bedford precipitated **barium orthododecacolumbate,** $Ba_7Cb_{12}O_{37}.18H_2O$, from a hot soln. of the sodium salt and a dil. soln. of barium chloride.

A. Larsson prepared **beryllium columbate,** in thin plates mixed with acicular crystals of columbium pentoxide, by treating a soln. of potassium columbate with beryllium chloride ; melting the product with boric oxide ; and washing with water. He likewise prepared magnesium metacolumbate, $Mg(CbO_3)_2$, in short, doubly refracting prisms. C. F. Rammelsberg represented the precipitate, before fusion with the boric oxide, as a *tetrahydrate ;* and C. W. Balke and E. F. Smith as a *heptahydrate.* A. Joly reported **magnesium orthocolumbate,** $Mg_3(CbO_4)_2$, to be formed in colourless, prismatic crystals, along with those of a more basic salt, **magnesium oxyorthocolumbate,** $MgO.Mg_3(CbO_4)_2$, by fusing in a platinum crucible a mixture of columbium pentoxide, or alkali columbate, and magnesium chloride covered with ammonium chloride. A. Larsson washed the product with boiling water, and with boiling hydrochloric acid ; he could not prepare the ortho-salt. The colourless or pale yellow, hexagonal plates have a sp. gr. 4·43. The oxyortho-columbate is not attacked by dil. acids, but hot conc. sulphuric acid, or a mixture of hydrofluoric and dil. sulphuric dissolves the salt. It is attacked by fused potassium hydrosulphate. A. Joly reported **magnesium pyrocolumbate,** $Mg_2Cb_2O_7$, to be formed in black rhombic prisms from a fused mixture of columbium pentoxide and magnesium chloride. According to A. Larsson, when the precipitate obtained by treating a soln. of potassium columbate with zinc chloride is fused with boric oxide, and the product washed with water, a brown aggregate of rhombic crystals of **zinc metacolumbate,** $Zn(CbO_3)_2$, is formed. The sp. gr. is 5·69 at 17° ; **cadmium metacolumbate,** $Cd(CbO_3)_2$, was obtained in an analogous manner. The sp. gr. is 5·93 at 17°. C. W. Balke and E. F. Smith found that the precipitate obtained with the cadmium salt is the *hemiheptahydrate.* M. H. Bedford prepared **zinc orthododecacolumbate,** $Zn_7Cb_{12}O_{37}.25H_2O$, by adding zinc sulphate to a soln. of the sodium salt. H. Rose, and C. F. Rammelsberg obtained yellow **mercurous metacolumbate,** $HgCbO_3.1\frac{1}{2}H_2O$, by adding mercurous nitrate to a soln. of the sodium salt.

C. W. Balke and E. F. Smith prepared **aluminium metacolumbate,** $Al(CbO_3)_3.6H_2O$, by adding a soln. of alum to one of the sodium salt. A. Larsson obtained crystalline **yttrium orthocolumbate,** $YCbO_4$, by treating a soln. of potassium columbate with yttrium chloride ; melting the precipitate with anhydrous yttrium chloride ; and washing the product with boiling hydrochloric acid. A. Joly also prepared the same salt in octahedral crystals. For tetragonal *fergusonite,* or, idealized, yttrium columbate, $YCbO_4$, *vide* **5.** 38. 3. T. Barth obtained it by fusing a mixture of yttria and columbium pentoxide. The X-radiograms of the crystals show that the tetragonal cell has $a=7.76$ A., and $c=1132$ A., or $a:c=1:1.46$. The mineral glows about 400°, and after fusion, the X-radiogram shows that the unit tetragonal cell has $a=77.4$ A., $c=11.31$ A., or $a:c=1:1.46$. Each cell contains eight molecules of $YCbO_4$. A. Larsson obtained **yttrium metacolumbate,** $Y(CbO_3)_3$, by melting the precipitate just indicated with boric oxide instead of yttrium chloride. Y. Shibata and K. Kimuru described a rare earth at Ishikawa, Japan, and they called it **ishikawaite.** The black crystals have 8·40 per cent. of rare earths ; 21·88 per cent. UO_2 ; 36 per cent. Cb_2O_5, and 15 per cent. Ta_2O_5. The axial ratios of the rhombic crystals are $a:b:c =0.9451:1:1.147$; the sp. gr. is 6·2 to 6·4 ; and the hardness 5 to 6.

R. D. Hall and E. F. Smith said that a **titanium columbate** is probably formed when different organic bases are added in excess to a mixed soln. of potassium fluotitanate and oxyfluocolumbate. For the mineral **epistolite—sodium silicato-titanatocolumbate,** *vide* **6.** 40, 47. A mineral from Vogtsburg, Baden, was regarded as cubic titanic oxide by F. A. Walchner, and *perowskite* by A. Breithaupt, but it was shown by A. Knop to be a **calcium iron titanatocolumbate,** approximating, according to the analyses of F. Seneca, A. Knop, F. W. Mar, O. Hauser, and F. Zambonini, $6RTiO_3.RCb_2O_6$, where $2Cb=3R$. The mineral was called **dysanalyte** —from δυσανάλυτος, difficult to undo—in allusion to the difficulty of the analysis. P. J. Holmquist obtained mixed crystals of $2NaCbO_3.Ca_2Cb_2O_7.Ce_6Cb_4O_{19}$. The iron-black, cubic crystals or cubo-octahedra were found by J. Söllner, and A. Ben Saude to be optically anomalous, and sections parallel to the (100)- and the (111)-faces show twinning analogous to perowskite. The hardness is 4–5, and the sp. gr. 4·02–4·18. G. A. König observed *hydrotitanite*—a mixture of ferric oxide and colloidal titanic oxide—to be a product of the weathering of dysanalyte. A. Larsson prepared **zirconium columbate,** $ZrO_2.5Cb_2O_5$, by adding zirconium chloride to a soln. of potassium columbate; melting the precipitate with boric oxide; and boiling the product with dil. hydrochloric acid. The sp. gr. of the acicular crystals is 5·14 at 17°. P. J. Holmquist obtained a similar product by melting together zirconia, columbium pentoxide, and sodium fluoride. For **wöhlerite,** see **sodium calcium silicatozirconatocolumbate,** *vide* **6.** 40, 48. A. Larsson made **thorium columbate,** $5ThO_2.16Cb_2O_5$, by the method employed for zirconium columbate. The prismatic crystals are probably rhombic, and have a sp. gr. 5·21 at 17°. P. J. Holmquist also prepared a thorium columbate by melting together thoria, columbium pentoxide, and sodium fluoride. A pale yellow isotropic mineral called **lyndochite** was found by W. G. Miller in the pegmatite dyke of Lyndoch, Ontario. The composition approximates to an isomorphous mineral of the euxenite-polycrase family being a thorium calcium columbate of the euxenite type with uranium as a minor constituent. H. V. Ellsworth observed that the crystals are like those of euxenite, and have nearly the same axial ratio. There are parallel growths and twinning. There is no cleavage. The sp. gr. is 4·909 at 17·88; and the hardness 6·5.

C. W. Blomstrand obtained **chromium columbate,** as a yellow precipitate, by treating a soln. of columbium oxychloride with potassium dichromate; and E. F. Smith obtained **tungsten columbate** or rather complexes of columbium pentoxide and tungsten trioxide. The so-called *uranopyrochlore,* or *hatchettolite* —of **5.** 38, 3—is a *calcium uranyl tantalocolumbate ;* **sodium uranyl columbate,** $7Na_2O.4UO_2.9Cb_2O_5$, was prepared by P. J. Holmquist by melting together 2·9 grms. of uranium tritoctoxide, 1·3 grms. of columbium pentoxide, and 5 grms. of sodium fluoride at a high temp. The orange-yellow tablets are isotropic; their sp. gr. is 5·156 at 20°, and 5·173 at 17°. H. V. Ellsworth described a uranium columbate from Sudbury, Ontario. He called it **toddite.** It contained 8·97 per cent. Ta_2O_5; 53·73 per cent. Cb_2O_5; 8·71 per cent. UO_2; and 2·37 per cent. UO_3. It is pitch-black, isotropic, and brittle; it has no cleavage, and its hardness is $6\frac{1}{2}$. A. Lacroix described a mineral from Ambalahazo and Ambolotora, Betafo, Madagascar; and he called it **betafite.** It is a hydrated yttrium uranyl columbate —the analysis is indicated below. The crystals are cubic octahedra, and the sp. gr. is 3·75–4·17 ; **samiresite** is from Samiresy, Madagascar, it is also a hydrated lead uranium columbate with the subjoined analysis; and it occurs in fragile octahedra resembling rubber in appearance ; and **ampangabeite,** from Ampangabe, Madagascar, is a hydrated uranium columbate, containing some iron, whose analysis is indicated below :

	Cb_2O_5	Ta_2O_5	TiO_2	UO_2 or UO_3	$(Ce,La.Di)_2O_3$	$(Y,Er)_2O_3$	PbO	H_2O
Betafite .	35·5	—	23·60	27·15	2·1	20·80	0·38	12·50
Samiresite .	45·80	3·70	6·70	21·20	0·2	—	7·35	12·45
Ampangabeite	34·80	8·90	4·90	19·40	0·60	4·00	·—	12·40

Betafite had also 0·37, SnO_2; 1·12, ThO_2; 1·50, Al_2O_3; 0·50, Fe_2O_3; 0·40, MgO ; 3·12, CaO. Samiresite had also 0·10, SnO_2; 0·74, Al_2O_3; 1·60, FeO ; and 0·30, K_2O. Ampangabeite had also 2·50, ThO_2; 2·10, Al_2O_3; 8·60, Fe_2O_3; and 1·50, CaO.

W. Vernadsky described a hydrated titanocolumbate containing 23·5 per cent. W_3O_8, 15 per cent. CaO, and also lead, iron, and rare earths; it was called **mendeléeffite**—after D. I. Mendeléeff; and was found at Uluntui, near Slyudianka, Lake Baikal, Siberia. It resembles betafite, but whereas the yellowish or greenish colour of that mineral suggests the presence of uranium trioxide, the reddish-brown colour of mendeléeffite suggests uranium dioxide. The greyish-black, cubic crystals of mendeléeffite—rhombic dodecahedra with small octagonal faces—have a sp. gr. 4·76, and a hardness of 4·5.

A. Joly reported **manganese metacolumbate**, $Mn(CbO_3)_2$, to be formed in rose-red rhombic prisms when a mixture of equal weights of columbium pentoxide and manganese fluoride is melted with an excess of potassium chloride at a red-heat for an hour, and slowly cooled. The sp. gr. is 4·94 at 18°. A. Larsson added manganese sulphate to a soln. of potassium columbates, melted the precipitate with boric oxide, and treated the product with dil. hydrochloric acid. The dirty yellow crystalline powder of **manganese triterodecacolumbate**, $Mn_3Cb_{10}O_{28}$, had a sp. gr. 4·97 at 17°. A. Joly made what was thought to be black prisms of **ferrous metacolumbate**, $Fe(CbO_3)_2$, by heating a mixture of 3 parts of columbium pentoxide, and 2 parts of ferrous fluoride with an excess of potassium chloride for 2 hrs. in a platinum crucible at a red-heat; and also by passing hydrogen chloride over a red-hot mixture of columbium pentoxide and ferric oxide. P. J. Holmquist thought that the crystals are possibly columbium pentoxide coloured with iron oxide; in the ideal case *columbite* or *niobite* is a ferrous manganese columbate, but in nature it is associated with more or less isomorphous *tantalite* so that both minerals are represented by $(Fe,Mn)\{(Ta,Cb)O_3\}_2$—*vide* tantalates. P. J. Holmquist made a **ferric columbate** by melting columbium pentoxide with calcium chloride and ferric oxide—the product may be a calcium columbate coloured with ferric oxide. H. Rose, and C. F. Rammelsberg described **ferric hexacolumbate**, $Fe_4Cb_6O_{21}.8H_2O$, by adding ferric chloride to a soln. of an alkali columbate. A. Larsson treated a soln. of potassium columbate with cobalt nitrate, melted the precipitate with boric oxide; and obtained **cobalt metacolumbate**, $Co(CbO_3)_2$, as a dark blue crystalline powder of sp. gr. 5·56 at 17°. A. Larsson obtained **nickel columbate** in an analogous way.

REFERENCES.

[1] R. F. Weinland and L. Storz, *Zeit. anorg. Chem.*, **54**. 230, 1907; F. Russ, *ib.*, **31**. 60, 1902; K. A. Hofmann and V. Kohlschütter, *ib.*, **16**. 473, 1898; A. Larsson, *ib.*, **12**. 188, 1896; M. H. Bedford, *Journ. Amer. Chem. Soc.*, **27**. 1216, 1905; C. W. Balke and E. F. Smith, *ib.*, **30**. 1650. 1908; C. W. Blomstrand, *Acta Univ. Lund.*, **1**. 7, 1864; **2**. 3, 1865; *Oefvers. Akad. Stockholm*, **21**. 541, 1865; *Skand. Naturforsk. Forh.*, **9**. 277, 1865; *Compt. Rend.*, **61**. 337, 852, 1865; *Liebig's Ann.*, **105**. 198, 1865; *Journ. prakt. Chem.*, (1), **99**. 41, 1866; H. Rose, *Pogg. Ann.*, **113**. 105, 292, 1861; C. F. Rammelsberg, *ib.*, **144**. 56, 191, 1871; **150**. 198, 1873; *Journ. prakt. Chem.*, (1), **108**. 77, 1869; A. F. Gehlen, *Schweigger's Journ.*, **6**. 258, 1812; W. von Bolton, *Zeit. Elektrochem.*, **13**. 147, 1907; W. Muthmann, L. Weiss, and R. Riedelbauch, *Liebig's Ann.*, **355**. 67, 1907; F. Seneca, *ib.*, **104**. 371, 1857; A. Stähler, *Ber.*, **47**. 841, 1914; H. Moissan, *Compt. Rend.*, **133**. 20, 1901; *Bull. Soc. Chim.*, (3), **27**. 431, 1902; B. Santesson, *ib.*, (2), **24**. 53, 1875; *Om nagra af metallen Niobiums föreningar*, Upsala, 1875; A. Joly, *Ann. École Norm.*, (2), **6**. 172, 1877; *Compt. Rend.*, **61**. 266, 1875; W. Vernadsky, *ib.*, **176**. 993, 1923; A. Lacroix, *ib.*, **154**. 1040, 1912; *Bull. Soc. Min.*, **35**. 233, 1912; J. C. G. de Marignac, *Ann. Chim. Phys.*, (4), **8**. 20, 1866; *Arch. Sciences Genève*, (2), **23**. 249, 326, 1865; W. E. von John, *Chem. News*, **100**. 154, 1909; R. Hermann, *Journ. prakt. Chem.*, (1), **111**. 373, 419, 1871; P. J. Holmquist, *Bull. Geol. Inst. Upsala*, **3**. 227, 1897; *Zeit. anorg. Chem.*, **18**. 84, 1898; O. Hauser, *ib.*, **60**. 237, 1908; F. Zambonini, *Mem. Accad. Napoli*, **14**. 134, 1908; F. A. Walchner, *Zeit. Min.*, **1**. 516, 1825; J. Söllner, *Centr. Min.*, 310, 1912; A. Knop, *Zeit. Kryst.*, **1**. 284, 1877; F. W. Mar, *Amer. Journ. Science*, (3), **40**. 403, 1890; A. Breithaupt, *Vollständiges Handbuch der Mineralogie*, Dresden, **3**. 774, 1847; G. A. König, *Proc. Acad. Philadelphia*, 82, 1876; A. Ben Saude, *Ueber den Perowskit*, Göttingen, 18, 1882; T. Barth, *Norsk Geol. Tids*, **8**. 1, 1925; W. R. Schoeller and C. Jahn, *Analyst*, **51**. 613, 1926; W. G. Miller, *Rept. Ontario Bur. Mines*, **7**. iii, 234, 1897; H. V. Ellsworth, *Amer. Min.*, **12**. 212, 1927; T. L. Walker and A. L. Parsons, *Univ. Toronto Geol. Studies*, **16**. 13, 1923; A. Lottermoser, *Koll. Zeit.*, **30**. 346, 1922; Y. Shibata and K. Kimura, *Journ. Japan. Chem. Soc.*, **43**. 301, 648, 1922; T. Barth, *Norsk. Geol. Tids.*, **9**. 23, 1926; H. V. Ellsworth, *Amer. Min.*, **11**. 332, 1926; R. D. Hall and E. F. Smith, *Proc. Amer. Phil. Soc.*, **44**. 209, 1905; E. F. Smith, *Journ. Amer. Chem. Soc.*, **20**. 292, 1898.

§ 9. Percolumbic Oxide and the Percolumbates

P. G. Melikoff and L. Pissarjewsky [1] prepared what they called **percolumbic acid**, or **metapercolumbic acid**, $HCbO_4.nH_2O$, or, with quinquevalent columbium,

$$\underset{O}{\overset{HO}{>}}Cb\underset{O}{\overset{O}{<}}$$

by heating columbium pentoxide with a 30 per cent. soln. of hydrogen dioxide; or by adding dil. sulphuric acid to potassium percolumbate, dialyzing out the sulphuric acid and potassium sulphate, concentrating the liquid on the water-bath, and drying the product over sulphuric acid. According to A. Piccini, some is formed by the action of hydrogen dioxide on potassium fluocolumbate. F. Ott obtained it by electrolyzing a soln. of columbium pentachloride in 80 per cent. sulphuric acid in a diaphragm cell. The columbium is oxidized by the ozone from the electrolysis of the dil. sulphuric acid in the anode compartment, forming an orange-yellow liquor. The dialyzed soln. just indicated is a **colloidal solution** of percolumbic acid; and the hydrosol is also formed by treating columbic acid with warm, 30 per cent. hydrogen dioxide when the yellow, gelatinous percolumbic acid first formed gradually passes into the hydrosol. The yellow, amorphous solid was found by P. G. Melikoff and L. Pissarjewsky to be more stable than pervanadic or pernitric acid. It decomposes at 100° with a change of colour; it is insoluble in water; and at ordinary temp. dil. sulphuric acid has no action, but when warmed the percolumbic acid is decomposed with the formation of hydrogen dioxide; with conc. sulphuric acid, ozonized oxygen is given off; and with hydrochloric acid, chlorine is formed. L. Weiss and M. Landecker found that the precipitation with hydroxylamine is not quantitative. According to R. D. Hall and E. F. Smith, when hydrogen dioxide is added to a hydrochloric acid soln. of columbic hydroxide, a yellow precipitate of **columbium perhydroxide,** $Cb_2O_5.H_2O_2.5H_2O$, is formed.

C. W. Balke and E. F. Smith prepared the **percolumbates** by adding hydrogen dioxide to a soln. of the alkali columbate in the presence of an excess of the alkali carbonate or hydroxide. The salts are most readily obtained from such soln. by the addition of an equal vol. of alcohol, when the percolumbate separates as a white powder which can be filtered and washed with alcohol and ether. The percolumbates are stable in air; they dissolve in warm water without decomposition, but oxygen escapes when their soln. are boiled. C. W. Balke and E. F. Smith found **sodium perorthocolumbate,** Na_3CbO_8, or, with quinquevalent columbium:

$$\begin{matrix} NaO-O \\ NaO-O \\ NaO-O \end{matrix}\!\!\Big> Cb<\overset{O}{\underset{O}{\cdot}}$$

is difficult to prepare on account of the low solubility of sodium carbonate; they obtained it by adding hydrogen dioxide and sodium hydroxide to a soln. of sodium columbate, treating the soln. with an equal vol. of alcohol, and washing with alcohol and ether. They obtained **potassium perorthocolumbate,** K_3CbO_8, as a white crystalline powder consisting of tetragonal crystals with the axial ratio $a:c=1:0.844$. P. G. Melikoff and L. Pissarjewsky obtained **potassium permeta-columbate,** $KCbO_4.nH_2O$, as a white amorphous precipitate by warming or allowing a soln. of the pyro-salt to stand for some time. They obtained **potassium perpyro-columbate,** $K_4Cb_2O_{11},3H_2O$,

$$\overset{O}{\underset{O}{\cdot}}\!\!> Cb<\overset{O.OK}{\underset{OK}{}}O\overset{KO.O}{\underset{KO}{}}\!\!> Cb<\overset{O}{\underset{O}{\cdot}}+3H_2O$$

by melting in a silver crucible a 1 : 8 mixture of columbium pentoxide and potassium hydroxide; treating the soln. in a little water with hydrogen dioxide; adding an equal vol. of alcohol to the soln. warmed on a water-bath ; washing the precipitate with alcohol and ether, and drying it on a porous tile.   The product can be dissolved in water, mixed with hydrogen dioxide and potassium hydroxide, and again precipitated by alcohol.   The properties of the salt resemble those of the perorthocolumbate, and C. W. Balke and E. F. Smith obtained the perorthocolumbate, not the perpyrocolumbate, when following P. G. Melikoff and L. Pissarjewsky's directions.   O. Böhm obtained solid soln. of isomorphous mixtures of potassium or sodium percolumbate, pertantalate, and perchromate.   According to C. W. Balke and E. F. Smith, **rubidium perorthocolumbate**, Rb_3CbO_8, is produced by a method analogous to that employed for the sodium and potassium salts ; and similarly also with **cæsium perorthocolumbate**, Cs_3CbO_8.

C. W. Balke and E. F. Smith prepared acicular crystals of **sodium calcium perorthocolumbate**, $NaCaCbO_8.4H_2O$, by adding a neutral or feebly alkaline soln. of calcium chloride to a soln. of potassium perorthocolumbate at 50°, and washing the precipitate successively with alcohol and ether ; **potassium calcium perorthocolumbate**, $KCaCbO_8.4H_2O$, was obtained in a similar way.   Likewise also with **sodium magnesium perorthocolumbate**, $NaMgCbO_8.8H_2O$; **potassium magnesium perorthocolumbate**, $KMgCbO_8.7H_2O$; **rubidium magnesium perorthocolumbate**, $RbMgCbO_8.7\frac{1}{2}H_2O$; and with **cæsium magnesium perorthocolumbate**, $CsMgCbO_8.H_2O$.

REFERENCES.

[1] P. G. Melikoff and L. Pissarjewsky, *Zeit. anorg. Chem.*, **20.** 340, 1899 ; *Journ. Russ. Phys. Chem. Soc.*, **35.** 457, 1903 ; O. Böhm, *Zeit. Kryst.*, **63.** 319, 1926 ; R. D. Hall and E. F. Smith, *Proc. Amer. Phil. Soc.*, **44.** 209, 1905 ; *Chem. News*, **92.** 220, 232, 242, 252, 262, 276, 1905 ; *Journ. Amer. Chem. Soc.*, **27.** 1400, 1905 ; C. W. Balke and E. F. Smith, *ib.*, **30.** 1646, 1908 ; A. Piccini, *Zeit. anorg. Chem.*, **2.** 22, 1892 ; L. Weiss and M. Landecker, *ib.*, **64.** 89, 1909 ; M. Landecker, *Untersuchungen über die quantitative Bestimmung der Erdsäuren*, München, 1911 ; F. Ott, *Elektrolytische Reduktion der Niobsäure*, München, 1911 ; *Zeit. Elektrochem.*, **18.** 349, 1912.

§ 10. Columbium Fluoride and Oxyfluorides

According to H. Rose,[1] hydrated columbium pentoxide dissolves easily in cold hydrofluoric acid—especially when the conc. or fuming acid is used—but no crystals are formed.   If the soln. be evaporated to dryness, hydrogen fluoride is given off, and when the residue is heated, white fumes of fluoride or oxyfluoride are given off.   Calcined columbium pentoxide does not dissolve in hydrofluoric acid, but if the mixture be evaporated to dryness, and heated, fumes of the fluoride are given off.   If a mixture of calcined columbium pentoxide, and hydrofluoric and sulphuric acids be heated in a platinum vessel, white fumes of fluoride or oxyfluoride are given off.   The action of fluorine on columbium has already been discussed. O. Ruff and J. Zedner prepared **columbium pentafluoride**, CbF_5, by the action of fluorine on columbium containing about 3 per cent. of aluminium.   The roughly-powdered metal contained in a boat is placed in a platinum tube 25 cms. long and 1·2 cms. diameter, the middle portion of which is inserted in an asbestos box ; the constricted end of the tube is cooled by a lead worm, and connected to a receiver, from which moisture is carefully excluded.   The fluorine when passed over the merely warmed columbium at once combined, and the reaction was finished when the tube began to cool.   The box was next heated at 250°, when the pentafluoride distilled into the cooled portion of the tube, the aluminium fluoride remaining behind.   On re-distillation in vacuo at 110°, it is obtained as colourless, strongly refractive, monoclinic prisms.   O. Ruff and E. Schiller prepared the pentafluoride by mixing the pentachloride with anhydrous liquid hydrogen fluoride cooled by a freezing mixture and purifying the product by fractional distillation.

The pentafluoride forms colourless refracting prisms of **specific gravity** 3·2932 at 18° ; the m.p. is 72°–73°.   O. Ruff and E. Schiller gave 75·5° ; O. Ruff and

J. Zedner said that the **boiling point** of the pentafluoride is **236°** at 760 mm.; and
O. Ruff and E. Schiller gave 229·2°–229·5°.   The **vapour pressure** p mm. is :

	184·5°	191·6°	194·5°	199·5°	204·5°	208·4°	212·5°	214·5°	216·5°
p . .	303·1	329·7	358·9	422·6	467·1	504·7	563·2	697·6	750·4

According to O. Ruff and co-workers, when the pentafluoride is heated above its
b.p., in **hydrogen,** it forms a blue lower fluoride ; below its b.p., it is not affected
by **oxygen.** The pentafluoride is very hygroscopic in moist **air.** When the pentafluoride is treated with **water,** it hisses vigorously and dissolves with hydrolysis—
hydrofluoric acid and an oxyfluoride are formed.   The pentafluoride, above its
m.p., reacts with **bromine,** and **iodine ;** it dissolves in **hydrochloric acid** with the
evolution of heat, and when the soln. is evaporated some hydrogen fluoride is given
off.   The pentafluoride above its m.p. reacts with **sulphur ;** cold, conc. **sulphuric
acid** dissolves a little pentafluoride, and when heated, hydrogen fluoride is given off.
An excess of **ammonium sulphide** precipitates the hydroxide.   Columbium pentafluoride is not so soluble in **sulphur monochloride** as is the tantalum salt ; **sulphur
dichloride** reacts vigorously in the cold with columbium pentafluoride ; **sulphuryl
chloride** dissolves it less easily than it does the tantalum salt : **nitrogen** is indifferent
towards the pentafluoride below its b.p. ; **ammonia** precipitates the hydroxide ;
cold fuming or conc. **nitric acid** dissolves the pentafluoride in the cold ; yellow
and red **phosphorus** have no action on the pentafluoride below its b.p. ; **phosphorus
trichloride** forms a yellow gelatinous mass which, when warmed, gives off phosphorus
trifluoride ; **phosphoryl chloride** readily dissolves the pentafluoride with the evolution of gas ; **arsenic** and **antimony** have no action below the b.p. of the pentafluoride ; **arsenic trichloride** dissolves no appreciable quantity of the pentafluoride,
but when warmed a gelatinous mass is formed ; **antimony pentachloride**
behaves like arsenic trichloride ; **toluene** dissolves the pentafluoride in the cold
and the soln. becomes yellow and brown when heated ; **paraffin** behaves similarly ;
carbon disulphide, and **chloroform** dissolve only a little pentafluoride when heated ;
carbon tetrachloride and **tetrachloroethane** react with the pentafluoride ; **acetic
acid** and **acetic anhydride** react with the pentafluoride when heated, and gas is
evolved ; **ether** and **alcohol** behave similarly ; **silicon tetrachloride** has no action
in the cold, but it has a solvent action when heated ; warm **silico-chloroform**
exerts a reducing action ; **titanium tetrachloride** dissolves less columbium pentafluoride than the tantalum salt ; **tin tetrachloride** dissolves very little pentafluoride when cold, but more is dissolved when the liquid is hot, and the solute
crystallizes out on cooling ; **gold, magnesium,** and **aluminium** are not changed by
the pentafluoride boiling in an atm. of nitrogen ; **copper,** and **silver** colour it blue ;
iron, dark blue ; **lead,** bluish-grey ; **zinc,** a deep blue ; **tin** gives a grey powder.
Cold soln. of **alkali hydroxide or carbonate** in excess give an insoluble, gelatinous
precipitate ; when hot, a columbate is formed ; **potassium fluoride** forms only a
trace of a complex fluoride ; fused **potassium hydrofluoride** forms potassium
oxypentafluocolumbate ; and **potassium chloride** has no action on the pentafluoride.

According to J. C. G. de Marignac, if **metal fluorides** be added to a soln. of
hydrated columbium pentoxide in hydrofluoric acid, complex salts with columbium
oxyfluoride are formed ; but if an excess of conc. hydrofluoric acid be present, complex
fluorides are produced.   B. Santesson obtained complex acid salts from a soln.
of a metal carbonate and hydrated columbium pentoxide in conc. hydrofluoric
acid.   According to J. C. G. de Marignac, **potassium heptafluocolumbate,** K_2CbF_7,
is formed by cooling a warm soln. of potassium oxyfluocolumbate in hydrofluoric
acid ; and G. Krüss and L. F. Nilson evaporated a soln. of potassium oxyfluocolumbate and potassium hydrofluoride in a little hydrofluoric acid—*vide infra,*
Table IV.   J. C. G. de Marignac found that the rhombic crystals have the axial
ratios $a : b : c = 0·6682 : 1 : 0·4699$, and are isomorphous with the corresponding
tantalum salt ; but, according to R. D. Hall, with potassium hexafluotitanate.

R. Hermann said that the crystals lose hydrogen fluoride at 80°; but J. C. G. de Marignac reported that they are stable at 100°, but decompose at a higher temp. In moist air, the crystals fume and gradually furnish the oxypentafluoride; the soln. in hot water yields the same salt when cooled.   M. E. Pennington prepared **rubidium heptafluocolumbate**, Rb_2CbF_7, by evaporating on a water-bath a soln. of columbium pentoxide in hydrofluoric acid mixed with rubidium fluoride. The white, microscopic prisms are soluble in water, and in dil. hydrofluoric acid, but not in alcohol.   C. W. Balke and E. F. Smith said that this process furnishes the oxypentafluocolumbate, but if the salt be crystallized three times from its soln. in 35 per cent. hydrofluoric acid, **rubidium hexafluocolumbate**, $RbCbF_6$, is formed in acicular crystals.   M. E. Pennington prepared **cæsium heptafluocolumbate**, Cs_2CbF_7; and C. W. Balke and E. F. Smith **cæsium hexafluocolumbate**, $CsCbF_6$, as in the case of the rubidium salts.   R. D. Hall and E. F. Smith tried to make *potassium perfluocolumbate* by the action of hydrogen dioxide on a soln. of the peroxyfluocolumbate in conc. hydrofluoric acid, but without success.

B. Santesson reported a series of acid salts to be formed from hydrofluoric acid soln. of eq. proportions of the metal fluoride and columbium pentoxide : **copper hydrofluocolumbate**, $Cu_2CbF_9.HF.9H_2O$, in dark blue tablets ; **zinc hydrofluocolumbate**, $Zn_5Cb_3F_{25}.5HF.28H_2O$, is insoluble in water, and decomposed by heat ; **cadmium hydrofluocolumbate**, $Cd_5Cb_3F_{25}.5HF.28H_2O$, in white, prismatic crystals ; **mercuric hydrofluocolumbate**, $Hg_3CbF_{11}.8H_2O$, in spherical aggregates of white, prismatic crystals ; **manganese hydrofluocolumbate**, $5MnF_2.3CbF_5,5HF.28H_2O$, in rose-coloured prisms ; **ferrous hydrofluocolumbate**, $Fe_3Cb_2F_{16}.4HF.19H_2O$, in yellowish prisms ; **cobalt hydrofluocolumbate**, $Co_5CbF_{19}.5HF.28H_2O$, in dark red prisms ; and **nickel hydrofluocolumbate**, $Ni_3Cb_2F_{16}.4HF.19H_2O$, in green, acicular crystals, and $Ni_5Cb_3F_{25}.5HF.28H_2O$, in dark green prisms.

A. Joly [2] reported **columbium oxytrifluoride**, $CbOF_3$, to be formed by keeping a molten, red-hot mixture of columbium pentoxide and calcium fluoride in an atm. of hydrogen fluoride for a long time.   The crystals resemble those of the corresponding zirconium salt.   *Columbium dioxyfluoride*, CbO_2F, is known only in combination with potassium fluoride—*vide infra*.   J. C. G. de Marignac reported **ammonium trioxytetradecafluotricolumbate**, $(NH_4)_5Cb_3O_3F_{14}.H_2O$, to be formed from a hydrofluoric acid soln. of potassium fluoride and an excess of columbium oxytrifluoride in hexagonal crystals with the axial ratio $a : c = 1 : 0.4575$.   P. Groth added that, like the potassium salt, the crystals are probably pseudo-hexagonal and made up of monoclinic units.   The salt loses water incompletely at 100°, and at the same time acid fumes are given off.   The salt is decomposed when heated with calcium oxide.   The mother-liquor remaining after the preparation of this salt with a very great excess of columbium oxytrifluoride, furnishes pseudo-tetragonal prisms of **ammonium oxytetrafluocolumbate**, $(NH_4)_2CbOF_4$, which are stable at 150°.   J. C. G. de Marignac also obtained **ammonium oxypentafluocolumbate**, $(NH_4)_2CbOF_5$, from a soln. of ammonium fluoride and hydrated columbium pentoxide in hydrofluoric acid.   A. Werner wrote the formula

$$\left[Cb\begin{matrix}O\\F_5\end{matrix}\right](NH_4)_2$$

The rhombic bipyramidal crystals have the axial ratios $a : b : c = 0.4184 : 1 : 1.0058$, and are isomorphous with ammonium dioxytetrafluotungstate. They are stable at 170°–180°, but if slowly heated, the whole of the columbium can be converted to the pentoxide; the reaction which occurs when heated with calcium oxide is symbolized: $5CaO + 2(NH_4)_2CbOF_5 = 4NH_4 + 2H_2O + 5CaF_2 + Cb_2O_5$.   J. C. G. de Marignac prepared **ammonium oxyhexafluocolumbate**, $(NH_4)_3CbOF_6$, from hydrofluoric acid soln. containing an excess of ammonium fluoride.   The octahedral or cubic crystals are isotropic, and do not lose weight at 100°.   The salt was also made by H. Baker, and A. Piccini and G. Giorgis.   J. C. G. de Marignac obtained crystals of **ammonium oxyhenafluodicolumbate**, $(NH_4)_3CbF_8.CbOF_3$, from a soln. of the oxypentafluocolumbate in warm hydrofluoric acid.

In his study of the complex fluorides of columbium, J. C. G. de Marignac reported that he obtained **sodium oxyfluocolumbates** as crystalline crusts of indefinite composition, and although no analyses are given, he assumed the existence of the two salts $2NaF.CbOF_3.2H_2O$ and $NaF.CbOF_3.H_2O$. C. W. Balke and E. F. Smith could not confirm J. C. G. de Marignac's assumption, but they prepared **sodium oxyhexafluocolumbate**, $3NaF.CbOF_3$, by evaporating a soln. of 30 grms. of columbium pentoxide and 24 grms. of sodium carbonate in hydrofluoric acid, and recrystallizing from hot water. J. C. G. de Marignac described and analyzed five potassium oxyfluocolumbates. O. Ruff and E. Schiller found the results indicated in Table IV for the percentage solubility of potassium oxyfluocolumbate

TABLE IV.—SOLUBILITY OF POTASSIUM OXYFLUOCOLUMBATE.

CbF_5	KF	HF	Solid phase.
5·19	2·98	0·35	$K_2CbOF_5.H_2O$
7·07	5·33	4·35	$K_2CbOF_5.H_2O+K_2CbF_7$
4·33	2·32	10·43	K_2CbF_7
1·16	5·54	−0·13	$K_2CbOF_5.H_2O$
2·67	6·04	5·39	$K_2CbOF_5.H_2O+K_2CbF_7$
30·39	14·68	0·35	$K_2CbOF_5.H_2O$
11·66	10·08	−1·53	$K_2CbOF_5.H_2O$

at 16°. (The negative sign is only apparent and is an effect of the mode of calculation.) J. C. G. de Marignac found that a soln. of potassium fluoride and columbium pentoxide in hydrofluoric acid furnishes **potassium oxypentafluocolumbate**, $K_2CbOF_5.H_2O$; and the same salt is produced when any of the other oxyfluocolumbates is crystallized from its aq. soln. The salt was analyzed by J. C. G. de Marignac, A. Piccini, and T. B. Osborne. G. Krüss and L. F. Nilson obtained the anhydrous salt by crystallizing an aq. soln. of potassium heptafluocolumbate, and drying the product at 100°. J. C. G. de Marignac added that the *monohydrate* loses almost all its water at 100°, and it can be heated to 180°–200° without decomposition; and only a little hydrogen fluoride is lost when the salt is fused at a red-heat. The monohydrate crystallized from its aq. soln., or dil. hydrofluoric acid in thin monoclinic plates with the axial ratios $a:b:c=0.992:1:0.980$, and $\beta=103° 46'$, isomorphous with potassium fluotitanate, and oxyfluotungstate. M. E. Pennington said that the electrical resistance of the aq. soln. is very high; and F. Ott found that no marked reduction occurs when the aq. or the hydrochloric acid soln. is electrolyzed, though hydrated columbium pentoxide separates on the anode; there is a reduction to columbium tetroxide at the cathode when the fused salt is electrolyzed. J. C. G. de Marignac said that at 17°–21°, 100 parts of water dissolve 7·7–8·3 parts of the salt, but W. Muthmann added that the solubility is less than this. R. D. Hall and E. F. Smith found that the solubility is depressed by hydrogen dioxide, and raised by hydrofluoric acid; and R. D. Hall that it is depressed by potassium bromide and iodide. J. C. G. de Marignac, and M. E. Pennington said that the soln. is not changed by heat, and if any tantalum salt is present as impurity it is precipitated; G. Krüss and L. F. Nilson added that if the soln. is boiled, **potassium hexoxypentafluotricolumbate**, $K_2Cb_3O_6F_5$, is precipitated as a white, crystalline powder: $3K_2CbOF_5+3H_2O=K_2Cb_3O_6F_5+4KHF_2+2HF$, which is not altered at 110°, and is freely soluble in hydrofluoric acid.

J. C. G. de Marignac found that crystals of **potassium oxyhexafluocolumbate**, K_3CbOF_6, can be obtained from soln. containing an excess of potassium fluoride; and C. W. Balke and E. F. Smith obtained it by crystallization from a soln. containing 40 grms. of the oxypentafluocolumbate and 30 grms. of potassium fluoride;

while H. Baker prepared it by melting columbium pentoxide with an excess of potassium hydrofluoride.

J. C. G. de Marignac said that although the crystals seem to be cubes, the optical properties do not correspond with the " cubic nor the square prismatic " systems ; and he was unable to determine their crystal system. C. W. Balke and E. F. Smith observed the crystals are optically anomalous ; but H. Baker obtained cubic crystals which were *isotropic*, and isomorphous with $3NH_4F.CbOF_3$, $3NH_4F.ZrF_4$, and $3KF.ZrF_4$. The salt is stable at 100°, and only suffers a small loss when melted at a red-heat. J. C. G. de Marignac's acicular salt, **potassium hydro-oxyheptafluo-columbate**, $K_3CbOF_6.HF$, crystallizes in slender needles from soln. containing an excess of potassium fluoride and hydrofluoric acid. C. W. Balke and E. F. Smith obtained the best results with soln. containing potassium fluoride, hydrofluoric acid, and columbium pentafluoride in the proportions 1·8 : 1·2 : 1. J. C. G. de Marignac found that the axial ratios of the monoclinic crystals are $a : b : c$ $=0.6279 : 1 : 0.4900$, and $\beta=93° 14'$; and C. W. Balke and E. F. Smith added that the crystals are isomorphous with $K_3SnF_7.HF$. J. C. G. de Marignac found that the salt is stable at 100° ; and loses hydrogen fluoride when melted at a red-heat. The " oblique, monosymmetrical " salt of J. C. G. de Marignac—**potassium trioxytridecafluotricolumbate**, $K_4Cb_3O_3F_{13}.2H_2O$—was obtained from soln. containing an excess of columbium oxytrifluoride. C. W. Balke and E. F. Smith obtained the best results with potassium and columbium fluorides in the molar proportions 1 : 4. The triclinic crystals lose some water at 110° and all at 180°. J. C. G. de Marignac, and C. W. Balke and E. F. Smith found that soln. containing insufficient potassium fluoride to form the oxypentafluocolumbate furnish mono-clinic crystals of **potassium trioxytetradecafluotricolumbate**, $K_5Cb_3O_3F_{14}.H_2O$, with the axial ratios $a : b : c=0.596 : 1 : 0.400$, and $\beta=104°. 28'$. Only part of the water is expelled at 100°. E. Petersen prepared **potassium decoxytrifluotetra-columbate**, $3KF.2Cb_2O_5.5H_2O$, by dissolving one part of columbium pentoxide in 3·25 parts of molten potassium fluoride, and extracting the soluble portion with water. A white crystalline powder remains. If the potassium fluoride be reduced to 1·3 parts, prismatic crystals of **potassium pentoxyfluodi-columbate**, $KF.Cb_2O_5.3H_2O$, are formed.

C. W. Balke and E. F. Smith obtained thin plates of **rubidium oxypentafluo-columbate**, Rb_2CbOF_5, from soln. containing 2 mols of rubidium fluoride, and one mol of columbium oxytrifluoride ; while soln. with a mol of columbium penta-fluoride and 4–10 mols of cæsium fluoride furnished trigonal prisms of **cæsium oxypentafluocolumbate**, Cs_2CbOF_5, with the axial ratio $a : c=1 : 0.949$. According to J. C. G. de Marignac, a soln. of copper fluoride and columbium pentoxide in hydro-fluoric acid furnishes blue monoclinic prisms of **copper oxypentafluocolumbate**, $CuCbOF_5.4H_2O$, with the axial ratios $a : b : c=0.7627 : 1 : 0.5629$, and $\beta=103° 20'$. They are sparingly soluble in water, and do not lose weight at 100°. P. J. Holmquist melted a mixture of 11·2 grms. of calcium oxide, 26·74 grms. of columbium pentoxide, and 9 grms. of sodium fluoride at a high temp. and obtained octahedral crystals of **sodium calcium octoxyfluodicolumbate**, or *calcium-pyrochlore*, $NaCaCb_2O_6F$, of sp. gr. 4·196 at 19·5° ; the index of refraction for yellow light was 2·148-2·150, and for green light, 2·1795. He could not make the calcium salt without sodium. J. C. G. de Marignac obtained crystals of **zinc oxypentafluocolumbate**, $ZnCbOF_5.6H_2O$, as in the case of the copper salt. The trigonal crystals have the axial ratio $a : c=1 : 0.519$, and $a=112° 6'$; they are isomorphous with zinc fluotitanate. C. W. Balke and E. F. Smith obtained rhombic crystals of **thallium oxypentafluocolumbate**, Tl_2CbOF_5, with the axial ratios $a : b : c=0.4261 : 1 : 1.0129$, from hydrofluoric acid soln. of thallous fluoride and columbium pentafluoride.

A. Piccini mixed a warm aq. soln. of potassium oxypentafluocolumbate with 3 per cent. hydrogen dioxide, and after crystallizing the product two or three times from its aq. soln., obtained white plates of **potassium peroxypentafluocolumbate**, $K_2CbO_2F_5.H_2O$. The same salt was made by C. W. Balke and E. F. Smith. The salt is stable in air ; it loses water at 100°, and oxygen at 150°. C. W. Balke and E. F. Smith also prepared **rubidium peroxypentafluocolumbate**, $Rb_2CbO_2F_5.H_2O$, in thin yellow plates ; and **sodium peroxypentafluocolumbate**, $Na_3CbO_2F_6.H_2O$, in yellow crystals.

REFERENCES.

[1] H. Rose, *Pogg. Ann.*, **108**. 465, 1859 ; O. Ruff and J. Zedner, *Ber.*, **42**. 492, 1909 ; O. Ruff and E. Schiller, *Zeit. anorg. Chem.*, **72**. 329, 1911 ; E. Schiller, *Ueber Tantal- und Niobpentafluorid sowie über die Reindarstellung der Tantal- und Niobsaure*, Danzig, 1911 ; B. Santesson, *Om nagra af metallen Niobiums föreningar*, Upsala, 1875 ; *Bull. Soc. Chim.*, (2), **24**. 53, 1875 ; J. C. G. de Marignac, *Ann. Chim. Phys.*, (4), **8**. 5, 1866 ; *Arch. Sciences Genève*, (2), **23**. 249, 326, 1865 ; G. Krüss and L. F. Nilson, *Oefvers. Akad. Förh.*, 5, 1887 ; *Zeit. Phys. Chem.*, **1**. 391, 1887 ; *Ber.*, **20**. 1682, 1887 ; R. D. Hall, *Observations on the Metallic Acids*, Easton, Pa., 1904 ; *Journ. Amer. Chem. Soc.*, **26**. 1238, 1904 ; C. W. Balke and E. F. Smith, *ib.*, **30**. 1648, 1908 ; C. W. Balke, *The Double Fluorides of Tantalum*, Easton, Pa., 1908 ; E. F. Smith, *Journ. Amer. Chem. Soc.*, **20**. 292, 1898 ; *Proc. Amer. Phil. Soc.*, **44**. 157, 1905 ; R. D. Hall and E. F. Smith, *ib.*, **44**. 177, 205, 1906 ; *Chem. News*, **92**. 220, 232, 242, 252, 262, 276, 1905 ; M. E. Pennington, *ib.*, **75**. 8, 18, 31, 38, 1897 ; *Derivatives of Columbium and Tantalum*, Easton, Pa., 1895 ; *Journ. Amer. Chem. Soc.*, **18**. 40, 1896 ; M. Delafontaine and C. E. Lineberger, *ib.*, **18**. 532, 1896 ; R. Hermann, *Journ. prakt. Chem.*, (1), **100**. 388, 1867.

[2] A. Joly, *Ann. École Norm.*, (2), **6**. 172, 1877 ; *Compt. Rend.*, **81**. 266, 1875 ; J. C. G. de Marignac, *Arch. Sciences Genève*, (2), **23**. 249, 326, 1865 ; (2), **31**, 89, 1868 ; *Ann. Chim. Phys.*, (4), **8**. 5, 1866 ; (4), **9**. 249, 1866 ; (4), **13**. 28, 1868 ; P. Groth, *Chemische Krystallographie*, Leipzig, **1**. 573, 1906 ; A. Werner, *Neuere Anschauungen auf dem Gebiete der anorganischen Chemie*, Braunschweig, 81, 1905 ; H. Baker, *Journ. Chem. Soc.*, 35. 761, 1879 ; A. Piccini and G. Giorgis, *Atti Accad. Lincei*, (4), **4**. 595, 1888 ; A. Piccini, *Zeit. anorg. Chem.*, **2**. 22, 1892 ; A. Larsson, *ib.*, **12**. 192, 1896 ; O. Ruff and E. Schiller, *ib.*, **72**. 329, 1911 ; G. Krüss and L. F. Nilson, *Oefvers. Akad. Förh.*, 5, 1887 ; *Zeit. phys. Chem.*, **1**. 391, 1887 ; *Ber.*, **20**. 1682, 1887 ; F. Ott, *Elektrolytische Reduktion der Niobsäure*, München, 1911 ; *Zeit. Elektrochem.*, **18**. 349, 1912 ; C. W. Balke and E. F. Smith, *Journ. Amer. Chem. Soc.*, **30**. 1648, 1908 ; R. D. Hall, *Observations on the Metallic Acids*, Easton Pa., 1904 ; *Journ. Amer. Chem. Soc.*, **26**. 1238, 1904 ; R. D. Hall and E. F. Smith, *Proc. Amer. Phil. Soc.*, **44**. 177, 1906 ; *Chem. News*, **92**. 220, 232, 242, 262, 276, 1905 ; M. E. Pennington, *Chem. News*, **75**. 8, 18, 31, 38, 1897 ; *Derivatives of Columbium and Tantalum*, Easton. Pa., 1895 ; *Journ Amer. Chem. Soc.*, **18**. 40, 1896 ; L. Muthmann, L. Weiss. and R. Riedelbauch, *Liebig's Ann.*, 355. 61, 1907 ; T. B. Osborne, *Amer. Journ. Science*, (3), **30**. 329, 1885 ; E. Petersen, *Journ. prakt. Chem.*, (2), **40**. 287, 1889 ; P. J. Holmquist, *Bull. Geol. Inst. Upsala*, **3**. 209, 1897 ; *Zeit. Kryst.*, **31**. 305, 1899.

§ 11. Columbium Chlorides and Oxychlorides

H. St. C. Deville and L. Troost [1] obtained what was regarded as a **violet-brown columbium dichloride**, $CbCl_2$, by passing the vapour of columbium oxytrichloride over magnesium ribbon—*vide supra*, columbium dioxide. H. E. Roscoe passed the vapour of columbium pentachloride through a red-hot tube and obtained a black crystalline deposit resembling iodine which was considered to be **columbium trichloride**, $CbCl_3$. It is not decomposed by water, or aq. ammonia ; it is oxidized by nitric acid to the pentoxide ; and when heated in carbon dioxide : $CbCl_3+CO_2$ $=CO+CbOCl_3$. F. Ott could not obtain the solid trichloride from aq. soln. He prepared the aq. soln. by electrolyzing a soln. of the pentachloride in cold, conc. hydrochloric acid with a lead or platinum cathode, and a platinum anode in a compartment cell using a current density of 0·1–2·0 amp. per sq. dm. The pentachloride is reduced to a reddish-violet or brown, or to a dark blue, almost black, liquid When the liquid is exposed to air, or treated with hydrogen dioxide or potassium permanganate, it is oxidized through the stages : green tetroxide, blue heptatritoxide, and colourless pentoxide. It is very slowly oxidized by iodine ; it reduces chromic acid to chromic oxide, and cupric to cuprous salts. Aq. ammonia gives a dark blue precipitate which is rapidly oxidized by air. According to A. Stähler, the electrolytic reduction of columbium pentachloride in hydrochloric acid soln. does not furnish a chloride of tervalent columbium. The brown soln. obtained by using an amalgamated lead cathode gives reactions like those of tervalent titanium ; with a platinum cathode, a blue soln. is obtained of a colloidal character.

It gives a purple liquid with gold chloride, and on boiling, deposits a precipitate resembling purple of Cassius.

If the soln. of the trichloride in conc. hydrochloric acid be evaporated in a heated desiccator in an atm. of carbon dioxide, or in vacuo, black **columbium hydroxydichloride**, $Cb(OH)Cl_2.2\frac{1}{2}H_2O$, is formed ; the soln. in dil. hydrochloric acid, likewise treated, furnishes blue **columbium trihydroxytrichloride**, $Cb_2(OH)_3Cl_3.3H_2O$. The black compound is stable for a short time in an atm. of carbon dioxide ; but in air, it absorbs water, and rapidly oxidizes to the pentoxide. The aq. soln. is green ; and the alcoholic soln. is blue. It is insoluble in ether. The aq. soln. gives a brown voluminous precipitate with ammonia, which rapidly oxidizes. With sulphuric acid, a blue hydroxide is formed which quickly turns white ; but hydrochloric acid is not changed. If a soln. of columbium pentachloride in dil. hydrochloric acid containing an excess of ammonium chloride be electrolyzed until all the solid is dissolved, and the soln. evaporated in a hot desiccator in an atm. of carbon dioxide, a blue solid, thought to be *ammonium chlorocolumbite*, is formed. When lithium chloride is treated in a similar manner, and the soln. evaporated in vacuo over phosphorus pentoxide, it furnishes a bluish-black mass, probably a mixture of lithium chloride and *lithium chlorocolumbite;* and similarly, what was probably impure *potassium chlorocolumbite* was formed.

The green liquid obtained by F. Ott by electrolyzing a hydrochloric acid soln. of sodium metacolumbate, was thought to contain **columbium tetrachloride**, $CbCl_4$. It readily oxidizes in air. H. S. Harned obtained derivatives of what he regarded as bivalent *chlorocolumbium*, $[Cb_6Cl_{12}]X_2$, by reducing columbium pentachloride with sodium amalgam—*vide* tantalum. The salts appear to be derivatives of a *columbium tritaheptoxide*, Cb_3O_7, evidence for the existence of which was obtained by F. Ott. The chief product of the reduction is **columbium tritaheptachloride**, $[Cb_3Cl_6]Cl.3\frac{1}{2}H_2O$, or $[Cb_6Cl_{12}]Cl_2.7H_2O$, which appears as an olive-green powder, or in black crystals, insoluble in cold water but forming an olive-green soln. with hot water. The $[Cb_6Cl_{12}]$ radicle is cationic, when treated with an eq. proportion of sodium hydroxide, **columbium tritahexachlorohydroxide**, $[Cb_3Cl_6]OH.4H_2O$, or $[Cb_6Cl_{12}]Cl_2.8H_2O$, is formed as a black microcrystalline precipitate, which when treated with hydrochloric acid precipitates a brown powder, $[Cb_6Cl_{12}]Cl_2.9H_2O$, which is thought to have a constitution different from that of the olive-green chloride. If the hydroxide be treated with hydrobromic acid, **columbium tritahexachlorobromide**, $[Cb_3Cl_6]Br.3\frac{1}{2}H_2O$, or $[Cb_6Cl_{12}]Br_2.7H_2O$, is formed as a black microcrystalline precipitate.

According to H. Moissan, **columbium pentachloride**, $CbCl_5$, is formed by the direct union of the element at 205° when much heat is developed ; W. von Bolton worked at a red-heat. H. Rose obtained the pentachloride by passing chlorine over an intimate mixture of the pentoxide and carbon at a high temp. H. Rose and R. Weber added that if the temp. be too high, the oxytrichloride is formed ; if carbon monoxide be present, the pentachloride does not sublime. H. Rose freed the pentachloride from the oxytrichloride by subliming it in a current of chlorine ; and C. W. Blomstrand, in a current of carbon dioxide. F. Ott described an apparatus for applying H. Rose's process. W. Biltz and A. Voigt obtained the pentachloride by passing chlorine over heated columbium sulphide, and after removing the sulphur chloride, distilling off the pentachloride. H. E. Roscoe obtained the pentachloride by passing the vapour of the oxytrichloride over red-hot carbon ; H. Biltz and L. Gonder, by passing air-free chlorine over heated columbium sulphide ; M. E. Pennington, by heating a mixture of the pentoxide and phosphorus pentachloride for 8 hrs. in a sealed tube at 210° ; E. Demarçay, P. Camboulives, and O. Ruff and E. Schiller by passing a mixture of chlorine and the vapour of carbon tetrachloride over red-hot columbium pentoxide—the reaction begins at 280°, and proceeds rapidly at 440° ; F. Russ, by passing the vapour of carbon tetrachloride over red-hot potassium oxalatocolumbate ; E. F. Smith, R. D. Hall, and C. W. Balke and E. F. Smith, by the action of the vapour of sulphur monochloride and chlorine over columbium pentoxide at 200° in a sealed tube, and subsequently separating the pentachloride by fractional distillation, or else by passing the mixed gases over the heated pentoxide ; and F. Bourion, by passing the vapour of sulphur dichloride and chlorine over the heated pentoxide.

In E. F. Smith and R. D. Hall's process for columbium chloride, a mixture of the vapour of sulphur monochloride from the flask A, Fig. 1, and dry chlorine coming along the tube

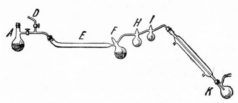

FIG. 1.—The Preparation of Columbium Pentachloride.

D, is passed over 10–20 grms. of strongly ignited columbium oxide in the combustion tube E. A voluminous oxychloride is first formed, and this is liable to choke the combustion tube containing the columbium oxide. The oxychloride is gradually converted into the volatile chloride which collects along with the sulphur chloride in the flask F. In 10–20 hrs. the stopcock connecting the system with the sulphur monochloride tube is closed, and the excess of sulphur monochloride is driven through the bulbs H and I and finally condensed in K. The columbium chloride is distilled from the bulb F to H, and finally from the bulb H to I, and the latter is finally sealed off. Tantalum pentachloride was prepared in a similar manner.

The sublimed pentachloride furnishes yellow, acicular crystals, which according to C. W. Balke and E. F. Smith, have a **specific gravity** 2·73–2·77 at 20°. Analyses were made by J. C. G. de Marignac, R. D. Hall, F. Bourion, and F. Ott. H. Rose's preparation was probably contaminated by much tantalum pentachloride. H. St. C. Deville and L. Troost found the **vapour density** to be 9·6 at 360° when the value calculated for $CbCl_5$ is 9·35. C. W. Balke and E. F. Smith obtained 9·45 between 280° and 300°. H. Rose gave 212° for the **melting point** and H. St. C Deville and L. Troost, 194°. The molten salt is red. H. Biltz and L. Gonder said that it readily volatilizes, and F. Wöhler added that the vapour is yellow. C. W. Balke and E. F. Smith said that it volatilizes much below its **boiling point,** 241° ; and H. St. C. Deville and L. Troost gave 240·5° for the b.p. R. Robl observed no fluorescence when columbium chloride is exposed to ultra-violet light. W. Biltz and A. Voigt found that when free from water, the **electrical conductivity** at 220°–235° is 0·000022, being about the same order as the best conductivity-water. The platinum electrodes were strongly attacked. W. Hampe had previously stated that the pentachloride is an insulator. C. W. Blomstrand, and H. E. Roscoe said that **hydrogen** at a red-heat reduces the pentachloride to the metal. F. Ott observed that the pentachloride fumes in moist **air,** and the surface was found by C. W. Balke and E. F. Smith to acquire a film of hydrated columbium pentoxide ; the reaction is completed after a few days' exposure to moist air. H. Rose also observed that the pentachloride is hydrolyzed by **water** to form the pentoxide and hydrochloric acid. According to O. Ruff and E. Schiller, the pentachloride reacts with liquid **hydrogen fluoride,** forming columbium penta-fluoride. H. Rose found that the salt is soluble in cold **hydrochloric acid,** which furnishes the hydrated pentoxide when boiled, or when diluted with water ; the salt is soluble in conc. **sulphuric acid** with the liberation of hydrochloric acid—the soln. becomes turbid when heated, and on cooling forms a gelatinous mass. F. Ott showed that hydrolysis occurs when the sulphuric acid soln. is diluted with water. H. Rose observed that the pentachloride can be heated in the vapour of **carbon disulphide** without blackening. E. F. Smith and R. D. Hall observed that the pentachloride is soluble in **sulphur monochloride,** and the hot, sat. soln. gives crystals of the pentachloride on cooling. When **ammonia** is passed into the ethereal soln., ammonium chloride and columbium pentatritanitride **are** formed. C. W. Balke and E. F. Smith, and R. D. Hall and E. F. Smith regard **carbon tetrachloride** as one of the best solvents for columbium pentachloride, and the yellow, hot soln. yield crystals of the salt on cooling ; **chloroform** rapidly dissolves the pentachloride, and the soln. decomposes when heated with the separation of a brown powder. H. Rose, and R. D. Hall and E. F. Smith found that when the soln. in **alcohol** is heated, alcohol, ethyl chloride, and hydrogen chloride are successively evolved ; when the alcoholic soln. is boiled, the hydrated pentoxide is precipitated. The pentachloride is soluble in **ether,** forming a yellow soln. which on evaporation yields a viscid liquid. The pentachloride forms addition products with **aniline, pyridine, piperidine,** etc. ; **benzene** reacts with the pentachloride, forming a gummy mass. H. Rose said that the pentachloride is soluble in a soln. of **potassium hydroxide** or **potassium carbonate.** O. Ruff and F. Thomas said that the pentachloride reacts with **tantalum pentoxide :** $Ta_2O_5 + 5CbCl_5 = 5CbO.Cl_3 + 2TaCl_5$.

R. D. Hall and E. F. Smith found that when columbium pentoxide is volatilized in dry hydrogen chloride, a white powder is formed approximating *columbium pentoxyhydrochloride,* $Cb_2O_5.nHCl$. It is insoluble in oxalic acid, and slowly dissolved by boiling, conc. sulphuric acid. E. F. Smith and P. Maas said that the white sublimate formed when columbium pentoxide is strongly heated in dry hydrogen chloride is *columbium tetroxyhydrochloride,* $Cb_2O_4.HCl.3H_2O$, but A. Larsson added that this is doubtful.

R. D. Hall and E. F. Smith said that the soln. of columbium pentachloride in **carbon tetrachloride** can be used for making complex salts with other **metal chlorides,** but no examples were indicated.

According to H. Rose and R. Weber, *columbyl chloride,* or **columbium oxytrichloride,** $CbOCl_3$, is produced at the same time as the pentachloride when an intimate mixture of the pentoxide and carbon is heated in a current of dry chlorine. The two compounds are easily separated owing to the greater volatility of the pentachloride. H. Rose separated them by fractional sublimation in chlorine ; H. St. C. Deville and L. Troost, in hydrogen. R. D. Hall and E. F. Smith removed the pentachloride by sublimation in a current of chlorine over heated columbium pentoxide ; and H. St. C. Deville and L. Troost made the oxytrichloride by passing the vapour of the pentachloride, in a current of carbon dioxide, over the red-hot pentoxide. M. Delafontaine and C. E. Lineberger, and R. D. Hall and E. F. Smith prepared this compound by heating the pentoxide in a current of carbon tetrachloride at 400° or a dull red-heat : $Cb_2O_5 + 3CCl_4 = 2CbOCl_3 + 3COCl_2$. The accompanying pentachloride is derived off by heating the product at as low a temp. as practicable in a current of carbon dioxide. R. D. Hall likewise obtained the oxytrichloride, mixed with the pentachloride, by the action of sulphur monochloride and chlorine over the pentoxide ; and F. Bourion used sulphur dichloride. H. St. C. Deville and L. Troost made the oxytrichloride by the action of dry chlorine on hot columbium dioxide.

F. Wöhler, and F. Bourion described the oxytrichloride as a white, crystalline mass ; and, according to R. D. Hall and E. F. Smith, when condensed on a hot surface, it forms a compact mass of acicular crystals. Analyses were made by H. Rose, C. W. Blomstrand, and H. St. C. Deville and L. Troost. The last-named found the **vapour density** to be 7·89 at 440°, and 7·87 at 860° in agreement with the theoretical value for $CbOCl_3$. The salt volatilizes at about 400° without melting. The vapour, said F. Wöhler, is colourless. C. W. Blomstrand found that the oxytrichloride is reduced to a blue product when heated in **hydrogen ;** but if not too strongly heated, H. Rose, and H. St. C. Deville and L. Troost found that it can be sublimed without decomposition. H. Rose, and R. Hermann observed that in moist **air,** the compound does not deliquesce, and it forms crystals of columbium pentoxide. It hisses in contact with **water,** and hydrolysis occurs with the separation of the hydrated pentoxide, and the evolution of much heat ; C. W. Blomstrand added that if the temp. be kept low, the soln. which is formed furnishes, on spontaneous evaporation, a gum-like mass—the hydrogel of the pentoxide.

R. D. Hall and E. F. Smith sublimed the oxytrichloride in a current of **chlorine**. H. Rose found that cold **hydrochloric acid** does not dissolve the oxytrichloride, nor does it form a gelatinous mass ; R. F. Weinland and L. Storz added that in hydrochloric acid, sat. at 0°, the eq. of about one per cent. Cb_2O_5 passes into soln. H. Rose found that boiling hydrochloric acid dissolves some oxytrichloride, and the soln. gives no turbidity with water, but it does so with sulphuric acid. C. W. Blomstrand said that dry **hydrogen sulphide** has no action in the cold ; but when warmed, some oxysulphide, hydrogen chloride, and water are formed ; **sulphur dioxide** has no action on the cold or hot oxytrichloride. H. Rose observed that conc. **sulphuric acid** slowly liberates hydrochloric acid, forming a turbid liquid, which becomes clear when heated and hydrogen chloride is evolved. C. W. Blomstrand said that when heated in **carbon disulphide** part of the oxytrichloride is blackened, and part volatilizes undecomposed. M. Delafontaine and C. E. Lineberger, and C. W. Blomstrand observed no reaction when the oxytrichloride is heated in a current of **carbon dioxide** ; the salt is readily soluble in **alcohol**, and ether produces in this soln., a yellowish-white precipitate. H. Rose said that no precipitate is produced by heating the alcoholic soln. with sulphuric acid, and when the liquid is distilled, some hydrogen chloride and ether are formed, and the liquid clears in the retort; R. F. Weinland and L. Storz said that the oxytrichloride forms complex salts with **pyridine** and **quinoline**. A soln. of **potassium hydroxide** dissolves the oxytrichloride in the cold ; but a soln. of **potassium carbonate** dissolves it only when boiling.

According to R. F. Weinland and L. Storz, the oxytrichloride forms complex salts with some **metal chlorides**. For instance, when a soln. of the hydrated pentoxide in conc. hydrochloric acid is mixed with an excess of ammonium chloride, crystals of unstable **ammonium oxypentachlorocolumbate**, probably $(NH_4)_2CbOCl_5$, are formed ; with rubidium chloride, yellow, octahedral crystals of **rubidium oxypentachlorocolumbate**, Rb_2CbOCl_5, are formed—soluble in hydrochloric acid, and less stable than the cæsium salt ; similarly, pale yellow octahedral crystals of **cæsium oxypentachlorocolumbate**, Co_2CbOCl_5, were produced. R. F. Weinland and M. Fiederer said that the salt is isomorphous with the chromium salt, $CrOCl_3.2CsCl$. The salts are stable in dry air.

REFERENCES.

¹ F. Bourion, *Ann. Chim. Phys.*, (8), 20. 565, 1910 ; H. St. C. Deville and L. Troost, *ib.*, (4), 8. 46, 1866 ; *Compt. Rend.*, 56. 891, 1863 ; 60. 1221, 1865 ; 64. 294, 1867 ; E. Demarçay, *ib.*, 104. 111, 1887 ; P. Camboulives, *ib.*, 150. 175, 1910 ; H. Moissan, *ib.*, 133. 20, 1901 ; *Bull. Soc. Chim.*, (3), 27. 431, 1902 ; F. Ott, *Elektrolytische Reduktion der Niobsäure*, München, 1911 ; *Zeit. Elektrochem.*, 18. 349, 1912 ; W. von Bolton, *ib.*, 13. 148, 1907 ; H. E. Roscoe, *Chem. News*, 37. 25, 1878 ; *Proc. Manchester Lit. Phil. Soc.*, 17. 44, 1878 ; *Mem. Manchester Lit. Phil. Soc.*, 6. 186, 1879 ; C. W. Blomstrand, *Acta Univ. Lund.*, 1. 7, 1864 ; *Liebig's Ann.*, 135. 198, 1865 ; H. Biltz and L. Gonder, *Ber.*, 40. 4969, 1907 ; W. Biltz and A. Voigt, *Zeit. anorg. Chem.*, 120. 71, 1921 ; F. Russ, *ib.*, 31. 78, 1902 ; E. F. Smith and P. Maas, *ib.*, 7. 96, 1894 ; A. Larsson, *ib.*, 7. 193, 1894 ; C. Renz, *ib.*, 36. 100, 1923 ; O. Ruff and E. Schiller, *ib.*, 72. 329, 1911 ; O. Ruff and F. Thomas, *ib.*, 156. 213, 1926 ; R. F. Weinland and L. Storz, *ib.*, 54. 225, 1907 ; *Ber.*, 39. 3057, 1906 ; R. F. Weinland and M. Fiederer, *ib.*, 39. 40C2, 1906 ; H. Rose, *Pogg. Ann.*, 104. 433, 1858 ; H. Rose and R. Weber, *ib.*, 90. 462, 1853 ; C. F. Rammelsberg, *ib.*, 144. 56, 191, 1871 ; 150. 198, 1873 ; F. Wöhler, *ib.*, 48. 83, 1839 ; *Liebig's Ann.*, 31. 120, 1839 ; R. D. Hall, *Observations on the Metallic Acids*, Easton, Pa., 1904 ; *Journ. Amer. Chem. Soc.*, 26. 1238, 1904 ; C. W. Balke and E. F. Smith, *ib.*, 30. 1648, 1908 ; C. W. Balke, *The Double Fluorides of Tantalum*, Easton, Pa., 1908 ; E. F. Smith, *Journ. Amer. Chem. Soc.*, 20. 292, 1898 ; *Proc. Amer. Phil. Soc.*, 44. 157, 1905 ; E. F. Smith and R. D. Hall, *ib.*, 44. 177, 1906 ; *Chem. News*, 92. 220, 232, 242, 252, 262, 276, 1905 ; M. E. Pennington, *ib.*, 75. 8, 18, 31, 38, 1897 ; *Derivatives of Columbium and Tantalum*, Easton, Pa., 1895 ; *Journ. Amer. Chem. Soc.*, 18. 40, 1896 ; M. Delafontaine and C. E. Lineberger, *ib.*, 18. 532, 1856 ; R. Hermann, *Journ. prakt. Chem.*, (1), 111. 396, 1871 ; W. Hampe, *Chem. Ztg.*, 11. 816, 846, 904, 934, 1109, 1158, 1887 ; J. C. G. de Marignac, *Ann. Chim. Phys.*, (4), 8. 5, 1866 ; (4), 9. 249, 1866 ; *Arch. Sciences Genève*, (2), 23. 249, 326, 1865 ; H. S. Harned, *Journ. Amer. Chem. Soc.*, 35. 1078, 1913 ; A. Stähler, *Ber.*, 47. 841, 1914 ; R. Robl, *Zeit. angew. Chem.*, 39. 608, 1926.

§ 12. Columbium Bromides, Iodides, and Oxybromides

According to H. Rose,[1] **columbium pentabromide**, $CbBr_5$, is formed along with the oxytribromide when bromine vapour is carried by a current of carbon dioxide over a red-hot mixture of columbium pentoxide and carbon. The two products are separated by fractional volatilization, the pentabromide being the more volatile. W. M. Barr also found that a little is produced when the oxytribromide is sublimed in an atm. of nitrogen or carbon dioxide. Columbium pentabromide is not produced when the vapour of sulphur monobromide is passed over the heated pentoxide, but it is formed when bromine vapour is passed over heated columbium metal obtained by the aluminothermite process. The crystalline product has the colour and appearance of red phosphorus; and when melted and cooled it yields garnet-red prisms. It melts at about 150°; and distils undecomposed in a current of nitrogen or carbon dioxide at about 270°. It fumes strongly in air; is very hygroscopic, and forms first the oxytribromide, and then the pentoxide. It is hydrolyzed by water with the development of much heat. It is also readily dissolved by anhydrous ethyl bromide, or alcohol with the development of heat.

H. Rose, and W. M. Barr obtained **columbium oxytribromide**, $CbOBr_3$, by passing the vapour of bromine over a red-hot mixture of columbium pentoxide and carbon, and removing the more volatile pentabromide by fractional distillation—*vide supra*. The pale yellow solid volatilizes without melting when heated in a current of bromine vapour. It is more difficult to sublime than the oxytrichloride; when heated in carbon dioxide, H. Rose said that it is transformed into the pentoxide. It fumes in moist air and forms the pentoxide; and it is hydrolyzed by water, forming the pentoxide and hydrobromic acid. It dissolves in conc. hydrochloric acid, and in hot conc. sulphuric acid. It dissolves with the development of heat in ethyl chloride, and in alcohol; R. F. Weinland and L. Storz found that the alcoholic soln. gradually forms hydrated columbium pentoxide and ethyl bromide. It forms a series of complex salts with pyridine, and quinoline. If columbic acid be suspended in conc. hydrobromic acid at 0°, and the soln. saturated with hydrogen bromide, and the soln. of the oxybromide be treated with the calculated quantity of a warm soln. of rubidium bromide and about 5 c.c of 80 per cent. hydrobromic acid, dark red octahedral crystals of **rubidium oxypentabromocolumbate**, Rb_2CbOBr_5, are formed. The crystals are very sensitive to moisture. Brick-red, octahedral cubic crystals of **cæsium oxypentabromocolumbate**, Cs_2CbOBr_5, were obtained.

W. M. Barr said that an impure, stable **columbium iodide** was prepared from the pentabromide. R. F. Weinland and L. Storz were unable to prepare columbium iodide, and they said that the complex salt of columbium pentaiodide and pyridine iodide reported by C. Renz is really pyridine periodide. R. F. Weinland and L. Storz were also unable to prepare oxyiodocolumbates analogous to the oxychloro- and oxybromo-columbates.

REFERENCES.

[1] H. Rose, *Pogg. Ann.*, **104**. 442, 1858; W. M. Barr, *Journ. Amer. Chem. Soc.*, **30**. 1671. 1908; C. Renz, *Zeit. anorg. Chem.*, **36**. 100, 1903; R. F. Weinland and L. Storz, *ib.*, **54**. 228, 1907; *Ber.*, **39**. 3057 1906.

§ 13. Columbium Sulphide, Oxysulphide, and Sulphates

According to W. von Bolton,[1] the direct union of heated columbium and sulphur furnishes **columbium sulphide**—according to R. Fittig, possibly CbS_2. G. Krüss and L. F. Nilson obtained a sulphide by heating the hydride in sulphur vapour H. Biltz and L. Gonder said that a brown product is obtained when the pentoxide is heated in a current of hydrogen sulphide ; and when the pentoxide is heated to bright redness in a mixture of the vapour of carbon disulphide and hydrogen sulphide —the product is washed with carbon disulphide, and dried over sulphuric acid in vacuo. The product was thought to be a mixture of CbS_2 and Cb_2S_5. Observations on this subject were made by H. Biltz and C. Kirchner. R. Robl observed no fluorescence when columbium sulphide is exposed to ultra-violet light. A. Karl said that the sulphide is triboluminescent.

According to H. Rose, columbium pentoxide at a white-heat is incompletely transformed by hydrogen sulphide into **columbium oxysulphide**—possibly Cb_2OS_3, or $Cb_2O_2S_3$—water, and sulphur ; sodium columbate, or a mixture of columbium pentoxide and sodium carbonate, behaves similarly. The impure oxysulphide is also formed by passing the vapour of carbon disulphide for 4 hrs. over white-hot columbium pentoxide, and cooling the product in an atm. of carbon dioxide ; and also by heating the oxytrichloride in dry hydrogen sulphide : $2CbOCl_3+4H_2S$ $=Cb_2OS_3+H_2O+6HCl+S$. Analyses were made by R. Hermann, H. Rose, C. F. Rammelsberg, H. Biltz and L. Gonder, and M. Delafontaine, but without conclusive evidence as to the formula. F. Russ obtained an impure oxysulphide by the action of the vapour of carbon disulphide on heated potassium oxalato-columbate. The composition is $K_{12}Cb_4O_3S_{10}$, or $6K_2S_2.Cb_4O_3S_7$; and since a little carbon was also present, it was thought that the $Cb_4O_3S_7$ would be better represented by $Cb_2O_2S_3$, or Cb_2OS_4. It is also suggested that the product represents an intermediate stage in the sulphuration of columbium pentoxide, and that with the right conditions, *columbium pentasulphide*, Cb_2S_5, as well as *potassium ortho-sulphocolumbate*, K_3SbS_4, might be formed.

The black or bluish-black crystalline oxysulphide acquires a steel lustre, never a brassy lustre, when rubbed in an agate mortar ; it is a good conductor of electricity. It loses about one-third of its sulphur when heated in a current of hydrogen ; it burns when heated in air, forming columbium pentoxide and sulphur dioxide ; chlorine converts it into the pentachloride—partially in the cold, completely when hot ; iodine and boiling water do not attack it, and iodine can be sublimed from its admixture with the oxysulphide ; boiling hydrofluoric acid attacks it slowly, but it is not attacked by boiling hydrochloric acid. Dil. sulphuric acid, hot or cold, has no action, but the conc. acid when heated forms a columbium sulphate ; nitric acid slowly transforms it into the pentoxide, and aqua regia acts similarly ; a boiling soln. of potassium sulphide has no action ; molten potassium hydroxide converts it into potassium sulphide and columbate ; and a mixture of sulphur and potassium carbonate acts similarly without forming a sulpho-salt.

The unsatisfactory nature of our knowledge of the columbium sulphides and oxysulphides applies also to the sulphates. F. Ott electrolyzed a soln. of columbium pentachloride in sulphuric acid and obtained liquids which may contain sulphates of tervalent and quadrivalent columbium. H. Rose obtained a soln. of **columbium sulphate** by dissolving the oxysulphide in aqua regia or in sulphuric acid, and by melting columbium pentoxide or a columbate with potassium hydrosulphate, and dissolving the cold product in water. C. W. Blomstrand obtained a white mass by treating an aq. soln. of columbium oxytrichloride with sodium sulphate. H. Geisow said that when the sulphuric acid soln. of the oxysulphide is evaporated, at 340°, **columbium tetroxysulphate**, $Cb_2O_5.SO_3$, or $Cb_2O_4(SO_4)$, or $O_2Cb.SO_4.CbO_2$, is formed ; and at 430°, $2Cb_2O_5.SO_3$, or $Cb_2O_5.Cb_2O_4(SO_4)$. F. Ott electrolyzed a soln. of 4·5 grms. of columbium pentachloride in 150 c.c. of hot conc. sulphuric acid with a lead cathode, in a compartment cell, and when the reduction had proceeded to tervalent columbium, added 10 grms. of ammonium sulphate, and continued the electrolysis until this salt had dissolved. The soln. was evaporated in vacuo, and the salt dried on a porous tile over phosphorus pentoxide. The resulting **ammonium hydropentasulphatocolumbite,** $(NH_4)_2SO_4.Cb_2(SO_4)_3.H_2SO_4.6H_2O$ appeared as a reddish-brown powder, which can be kept in dry air for some time. It forms a brown soln. with water, which by oxidation becomes successively blue, green, and colourless ; it is immediately coloured blue by ammonia, or hydrochloric acid ; it is virtually insoluble in alcohol and ether. The solubility of potassium sulphate prevented the formation of **potassium hydropentasulphatocolumbite** in a similar way. A. Stähler could not obtain a sulphate of tervalent columbium, **columbous sulphate,** $Cb_2(SO_4)_3$, by the electrolytic reduction of a sulphuric acid soln. of columbium pentachloride ; but S. J. Kiehl and D. Hart reduced a soln. of columbium oxide in 3 to $10M$-H_2SO_4 completely to the tervalent stage by a mercury cathode.

REFERENCES.

[1] W. von Bolton, *Zeit. Elektrochem.*, **13**. 148, 1907 ; F. Ott, *ib.*, **18**. 349, 1912 ; *Elektrolytische Reduktion der Niobsäure*, München, 1911 ; A. Karl, *Compt. Rend.*, **146**. 1104, 1908 ; H. Biltz and L. Gonder, *Ber.*, **40**. 4963, 1907 ; H. Biltz and C. Kirchner, *ib.*, **43**. 1645, 1910 ; F. Russ, *Zeit. anorg. Chem.*, **31**. 82, 1902 ; H. Rose, *Pogg. Ann.*, **111**. 193, 1860 ; C. W. Blomstrand, *Acta Univ. Lund.*, **1**. 7, 1864 ; *Liebig's Ann.*, **135**. 198, 1865 ; C. F. Rammelsberg, *Journ. prakt. Chem.*, (1), **108**. 95, 1869 ; R. Hermann, *ib.*, (1), **111**. 393, 1871 ; M. Delafontaine, *Arch. Sciences Genève*, (2), **27**. 173, 1866 ; H. Geisow, *Beiträge zur Kenntnis der seltenen anorganischen Säure*, München, 1902 ; R. Fittig, *Grundriss der anorganischen Chemie*, Berlin, 448, 1871 ; A. Stähler, *Ber.*, **47**. 841, 1914 ; R. Robl, *Zeit. angew. Chem.*, **39**. 608, 1926 ; S. J. Kiehl and D. Hart, *Journ. Amer. Chem. Soc.*, **50**. 1608, 1928 ; G. Knüss and L. F. Nilson, *Oefvers. Akad. Förh.*, **5**, 1887 ; *Zeit. phys. Chem.*, **1**. 391, 1887 ; *Ber.*, **20**. 1682, 1887.

§ 14. Columbium Carbonate, Nitrate, and Phosphate

No *columbium carbonate* has been reported although F. Russ,[1] and L. Weiss and M. Landecker obtained a series of complex oxalates. No *columbium nitrate* has been described. C. W. Blomstrand obtained what may have been *columbium phosphate*, as an insoluble precipitate, by adding sodium phosphate to an aq. soln. of columbium oxytrichloride.

REFERENCES.

[1] F. Russ, *Zeit. anorg. Chem.*, **31**. 70, 1902 ; L. Weiss and M. Landecker, *ib.*, **64**. 76, 1909 ; C. W. Blomstrand, *Acta Univ. Lund.*, **1**. 7, 1864 ; *Liebig's Ann.*, **135**. 198, 1865.

CHAPTER LVI

TANTALUM

§ 1. The Preparation of Tantalum

THE history and occurrence of the element tantalum have been described in connection with columbium. The metal of a high degree of purity has been obtained only in recent years. J. G. Children [1] obtained a reduction product of tantalum pentoxide as a reddish-yellow, brittle substance, which he obtained by strongly heating the pentoxide in an electric circuit. W. von Bolton obtained the element in the same way as he obtained columbium, namely, by electrically heating rods of the tetroxide in a vacuum furnace—*vide infra*, the action of oxygen on tantalum. J. J. Berzelius attempted to reduce tantalum pentoxide by heating it in a carbon crucible, but obtained a very poor result; and A. Joly heated a mixture of the pentoxide with carbon and sodium carbonate in a carbon crucible at a white heat, and obtained a mixture of tantalum carbide and nitride. H. Moissan obtained a better result by heating a mixture of a mol of tantalum pentoxide and 5 gram-atoms of carbon in a graphite crucible in an electric furnace. The product contained 0·5 per cent. of carbon alloyed with the tantalum probably as carbide. E. W. von Siemens and J. G. Halske recommended heating a theoretical mixture of oxide and carbon at a white-heat out of contact with air—say in an atm. of hydrogen—and removing the occluded hydrogen by heating the metal in vacuo.

H. Rose found that the passage of phosphorus vapour over sodium tantalate gave no metal; and E. F. Smith and P. Maas obtained none by the reducing action of magnesium or zinc on tantalum pentoxide. L. Weiss and O. Aichel ignited a mixture of the pentoxide and mischmetal as in the thermite process and obtained the metal. W. Muthmann and co-workers employed a similar process. W. von Bolton obtained a hard, brittle alloy by reducing the pentoxide with aluminium as in the thermite process; and W. K. van Haagen obtained a similar result. H. Rose obtained the metal by heating sodium with tantalum pentachloride in an iron crucible, but much chloride was lost by volatilization; if the pentachloride be heated with ammonia, tantalum nitride, not the metal, is formed.

J. J. Berzelius, H. Rose, and R. Hermann obtained the metal by heating sodium or potassium-heptafluotantalate with the alkali metal under a layer of alkali chloride in an iron crucible; and leaching out the soluble products in the water. J. C. G. de Marignac considered that the product so obtained is tantalum hydride. The process was employed by A. Siemens, and M. E. Pennington. J. W. Marden reduced the chloride by sodium in a closed vessel. The black powder containing some oxide, and hydrogen, is purified by pressing it into small cylinders and melting it in vacuo by an electric current as in the patented process of E. W. von Siemens and J. G. Halske. A. S. Cachemaille reduced the oxide by heating it with calcium and an alkali or alkaline earth halide in an iron bomb lined with lime.

H. Kuzel prepared **colloidal tantalum** by the process employed for columbium; and T. Svedberg obtained the colloidal soln. by the sIputtering of an arc of tantalum wires in isobutyl alcohol. The sol can be kept 2 or 3 weeks. It is brownish-black in transmitted light, and black in reflected light.

REFERENCES.

[1] W. von Bolton, *Zeit. Elektrochem.*, **11.** 47, 1905; *Zeit. angew. Chem.*, **36.** 1537, 1906
J. G. Children, *Phil. Trans.*, **105.** 363, 1815; J. J. Berzelius and J. G. Gahn, *Afh. Fys. Kemt
Min.*, **4.** 252, 1815; J. J. Berzelius, *Schweigger's Journ.*, **16.** 437, 1816; *Pogg. Ann.*, **4.** 10, 1825;
J. C. G. de Marignac, *Arch. Sciences Genève*, (2), **31.** 100, 1868; *Compt. Rend.*, **66.** 180, 1868;
H. Moissan, *ib.*, **134.** 211, 1902; *Bull. Soc. Chim.*, (3), **27.** 434, 1902; A. Joly, *ib.*, (2), **25.** 506,
1876; A. S. Cachemaille, *Brit. Pat. No.* 238663, 1924; A. Siemens, *Chem. News*, **100.** 223,
1909; *Proc. Roy. Inst.*, **19.** 590, 1909; E. W. von Siemens and J. G. Halske, *German Pat.*, *D.R.P.*
152848, 152870, 153826, 1903; 155548, 1904; 216706, 1907; 397641, 1922; H. Kuzel, *ib.*,
193379, 1905; 186980, 1906; *Brit. Pat. No.* 25864, 1906; H. Rose, *Pogg. Ann.*, **99.** 66, 1856;
100. 146, 1857; *Sitzber. Akad. Berlin*, 385, 1856; T. Svedberg, *Ber.*, **39.** 1712, 1906; L. Weiss
and O. Aichel, *Liebig's Ann.*, **337.** 387, 1904; W. Muthmann, L. Weiss, and R. Riedelbauch,
ib., **355.** 62, 1907; R. Hermann, *Journ. prakt. Chem.*, (2), **5.** 69, 1872; E. F. Smith and P. Maas,
Zeit. anorg. Chem., **7.** 96, 1894; W. K. van Haagen, *Tantalum and some of its Halides*, Easton
Pa., 1909; *Journ. Amer. Chem. Soc.*, **32.** 729, 1910; M. E. Pennington, *ib.*, **18.** 65, 1896; *Derivatives of Columbium and Tantalum*, Easton, Pa., 1895; *Chem. News*, **75.** 8, 18, 31, 38, 1897;
J. W. Marden, *U.S. Pat. No.* 1646734, 1927.

§ 2. The Physical Properties of Tantalum

W. Muthmann [1] and co-workers described tantalum as a white metal with a
greyish tinge; the lustre is bright and is little affected by exposure to air. According to W. von Bolton, the powder obtained by the sodium reduction when pressed
and melted in vacuo furnishes a platinum-grey metal. When heated in vacuo
over 1700°, the metal rapidly crystallizes. According to A. W. Hull, the **X-radiogram** of tantalum agrees with a body centred cubic lattice with side of length
3·272 A., and a distance between the nearest atoms of 2·833 A. Observations
were also made by E. C. Bain, and K. Becker and F. Ebert. Z. Jeffries and
R. S. Archer estimated the lowest recrystallization temp. to be 1000°. J. A. M. van
Liempt prepared single crystals by heating tantalum chloride vapour, and
hydrogen by a glowing tantalum wire. H. Moissan gave 12·8 for the **specific
gravity** of a metal with about half per cent. of carbon; W. Muthmann and
co-workers found the sp. gr. at 16° to be 14·491; T. Barratt and R. M. Winter,
16·67; F. W. Hinrichsen and N. Sahlbom gave 16·5; and W. von Bolton,
16·64 for bars of the metal. and 16·5 for the wire. When heated electrically in
vacuo for 12 hrs., the sp. gr. of the wires approaches that of the bars. W. von
Bolton gave 14·08 for the sp. gr. of 96·8 per cent. tantalum obtained by reducing
potassium heptafluotantalate. W. Muthmann and co-workers gave 12·61 for the
atomic volume; H. G. Grimm made observations on the ionic radius. W. Muthmann
and co-workers found that the **hardness** is between 6 and 6·5; and W. von Bolton,
that the hardness of tantalum containing a little oxygen approaches that of hardened
steel. E. W. Engle found that the hardness of tantalum on Brinell's scale is 46.
According to E. W. von Siemens and J. G. Halske, the presence of carbon (carbide),
hydrogen (hydride), oxygen (oxide), boron, aluminium, silicon, titanium, and tin
hardens the metal. H. Moissan described the metal he obtained with half per cent.
of carbon as being hard and brittle; W. von Bolton, and A. Siemens said that
the purified metal is soft, tough, and **malleable.** It can be hammered out into
thin sheets, or drawn into fine wire—filament wires, for instance, are only 0·03 mm.
in diameter. The metal, indeed, is as elastic and tough as soft steel. The
elastic modulus is nearly the same as that of steel, and approximates 19,000
kgrms. per sq. mm. for wires of 0·08 mm. diameter; wires 0·05 mm. thick have a
tensile strength of 150–160 kgrms. per sq. mm.; and wires 1 mm. thick, a tensile
strength of 93 kgrms. per sq. mm.—*i.e.* 57 tons per sq. inch. The elongation is
one to two per cent. For the **compressibility**, T. W. Richards gave $5·4 \times 10^{-7}$
megabars or $5·2 \times 10^{-7}$ kgrms. per sq. cm. over a press. range of 500 kgrms. per
sq. cm. at 20°; and P. W. Bridgman, working over the press. range of 12,000
kgrms. per sq. cm., found at 30°, $\delta v/v_0 = -10^{-7}(4·79 - 0·25 \times 10^{-5}p)p$; and at 75°,

$-10^{-7}(4\cdot92-0\cdot25\times10^{-5}p)p$, so that there is a close approach to constancy at the two temp. P. W. Bridgman also gave for the compressibility, β, at 30°, $0\cdot0_6479$; $\delta\beta/\beta\delta p = 0\cdot0_510$; $-\delta a/a\delta p = 0\cdot0_4126$; and $-\beta_0(\delta a/\delta ap) = 2\cdot63$, where a denotes the coeff. of thermal expansion. T. W. Richards estimated 455,000 for the **internal pressure** in megabars. L. H. Adams gave $0\cdot0_649$ for the compressibility, and $0\cdot01$ for the change of the compressibility with press.—megabar unit. J. Laissus discussed the diffusion of tantalum in iron.

W. von Bolton found the coeff. of **thermal expansion,** with a rod of 3 mm. diam. and 15 cms. long, was 0·0000079 between 0° and 50°. A. G. Worthing found for the thermal expansion at $T°$ K., $\delta l/l = 0\cdot0_5660(T-300)+0\cdot0_952(T-300)^2$; in agreement with J. Disch's value $0\cdot0_5646\theta+0\cdot0_990\theta^2$. J. Dewar found the relative **thermal conductivity** to be about three-quarters that of iron, and about one-eighth that of copper. T. Barratt and R. M. Winter gave 0·130 cal. per cm. per degree per second for the heat conductivity of tantalum at 17°, and 0·129 cal. at 100°. W. Muthmann and co-workers gave 0·03017 for the **specific heat** of the metal with 0·5 per cent. of iron ; and for the purified metal, 0·0346 ; W. von Bolton gave 0·0363 between 16° and 100° ; P. Nordmeyer and A. L. Bernoulli, 0·0326 between $-185°$ and 20° ; and J. Dewar, 0·033 between 14° and 100° ; 0·032 between $-78°$ and 14° ; and 0·028 between $-78°$ and $-183°$. The influence of temp. is not very great, but, according to F. Streintz, it is sufficient to show that the metal does not follow the ordinary sp. ht. rule. W. Muthmann and co-workers gave 6·32 for the **atomic heat** ; W. von Bolton, 6·57 ; and J. Dewar, 5·97. F. Simon and M. Ruhemann gave for C_p and C_v respectively 3·56 and 3·55 at 71·11° K. ; 3·81 and 3·80 at 77·55° K. ; and 3·82 and 3·81 at 78·01° K. W. von Bolton gave 2250°–2300° for the **melting point** ; A. G. Worthing, 3027° ; E. Tiede and E. Birnbräuer, 2475 ; M. von Pirani and A. R. Meyer, 2850°±40° ; W. E. Forsythe, 2802° ; and W. R. Mott, 2850°. A tantalum lamp filament with the ordinary load was found by M. von Pirani to melt at 2000°. W. R. Mott calculated 5300° for the **boiling point** of tantalum. E. Tiede and E. Birnbräuer said that it begins to volatilize at 2200°. W. Muthmann and co-workers gave for the **heat of combustion,** 837·9 cals., or 30·8 Cals. per gram-equivalent ; and J. E. Moose and S. W. Parr gave 1373 cals. for the heat of oxidation per gram.

H. von Wartenberg [2] found the **index of refraction** to be 2·05 ; the **absorption coefficient,** 2·31 ; and the **reflecting power,** R, 43·8 per cent. for yellow light with $\lambda = 579\mu\mu$. W. W. Coblentz gave for

λ	.	.	0·5	0·6	0·8	1·0	1·2	1·6	2·0	4·0	8·0	12·0
R	.	.	38·0	45·0	64·0	78·0	84·0	88·0	90·5	93·0	93·8	95·0

The spectral emissivity was studied by H. von Wartenburg, W. W. Coblentz, F. Henning, M. von Pirani, G. V. McCauley, and C. E. Mendenhall and W. E. Forsythe. A. G. Worthing gave :

$T°$ K. . . .	.	.	300°	1000°	1600°	2000°	2600°	3300°
Spectral emissivity $\{$ 0·665u	.	.	0·493	0·459	0·434	0·418	0·397	0·375
$\phantom{\text{Spectral emissivity}}\{$ 0·463μ	.	.	0·56	0·52	0·49	0·47	0·44	—
Brightness temp. (°K.)	.	.	—	966°	1506°	1851°	2339°	2870°
Colour temp. (°K.)	.	.	—	—	1642°	2075°	2705°	—
Total emissivity .	.	.	—	—	0·194	0·232	0·287	—
Radiation temp. (°K.)	.	.	—	—	1062°	1390°	1901°	—
Radiation intensity (watts per sq. cm.)	—	—	1·65	4·81	16·9	—

According to J. M. Eder and E. Valenta, the **spark spectrum** of tantalum is very poor in the visible region, and does not show any marked characteristics. The lines are feeble, or indistinct, and difficult to measure. Observations were reported by R. Thalén, E. Demarçay, F. Exner and E. Haschek. E. J. Allin and H. J. C. Ireton studied the spark spectrum under water. The **arc spectrum** of tantalum pentoxide between carbon electrodes was found by J. M. Eder and E. Valenta to be rich in lines in the extreme red region. The more intense lines are

6675·75, 6621·45, 6612·12, 5675·10, 6516·33, 6514·57, 6505·70, 6485·60, 6450·56, 6430·98, 6389·66, 6361·06, 6356·32, 6325·23, 6309·78, 6268·87, and 6256·81. Measurements were also reported by C. Rütten and H. Morsch, F. Exner and E. Haschek, and H. Morsch. W. J. Humphreys observed the effect of pressure on the spectral lines. H. Konen and H. Finger found that the spark spectrum between tantalum electrodes under liquids—especially water—is continuous. E. Paulson reported the existence of a **series spectra** represented by groups of lines showing a constant difference of frequency, but H. Josewsky could not verify this. W. W. Coblentz examined the **ultra-red emission spectrum** of tantalum. J. Formanek observed no **absorption spectrum** with soln. of tantalum salts, and no reaction with tincture of alkanna. A. L. Helfgott studied the radiation of tantalum. J. Lifschitz observed the spectrum of the **voltaluminescence,** *i.e.* the glow which occurs when an electric current is passed under certain circumstances through an electrolytic cell—with direct or alternating current, and tantalum electrodes.

M. Siegbahn [3] gave for the K-series of the **X-ray spectrum,** $\beta_6 = 1·3267$; $\beta_7 = 1·2600$; $\gamma_5 = 1·1700$. B. R. Stephenson and J. M. Cork gave values for wave-lengths α', α, β, and γ. J. Schrör, B. B. Ray, and A. Duvallier studied these rays. J. Schrör, P. Auger and A. Duvallier, G. Réchou, E. Hjalmar, Y. Nishina, M. J. Druyvesteyn, U. Dehlinger, M. Siegbahn, H. Hirata, I. Wennerlöf, D. Coster, A. Duvallier, and E. Hjalmar gave for the L-series, $\alpha_2\alpha_1 = 1·52933$; $\alpha_1\alpha = !·51824$; $\beta_1\beta = 1·32351$; $\beta_2\gamma = 1·28065$; $\gamma_1\alpha = 1·13471$; $\eta = 1·435$; $\gamma_2\theta = !·101$; $\beta_4v = 1·341$: $\beta_3\phi = 1·303$; and $\gamma_3\chi = 1·094$. A. Duvallier, Y. Nishina, E. Hjalmar, J. H. van der Tuuk, and G. Wentzel reported for the M-series, $\alpha = 7·237$, $\beta = 7·0115$, etc.; Y. Nishina, J. Thibaud and A. Soltan, and J. C. Boyce studied the N-series; and Y. Nishina, the O-series. G. Hagen, and F. Kirchner studied the Compton effect with tantalum. G. von Hevesy and J. Böhm discussed the analysis of tantalum minerals by means of the X-ray spectrum. J. E. P. Wagstaff gave $4·75 \times 10^{12}$ for the **vibration frequency.**

S. Dushman and co-workers [4] studied the **emission of electrons** from tantalum at 200° K. O. W. Richardson, and S. Dushman and co-workers gave $i = 60·2T^2e^{-b/T}$ for the general equation for the emission of electrons from a metal when i denotes the electronic current; T, the absolute temp.; e, the base of natural logarithms; and b, a constant of the emitting substance. The constant b is related to ϕ, the work done by an electron in escaping from the surface, by the equation $b = \phi/k$, where k is a constant. Electropositive elements with a low value of ϕ will give a higher electronic emission than substances with a high value of ϕ; but metals with a high value of ϕ, and a high m.p. can be used at a higher temp. when the electronic emission is greater. Some values of ϕ in eq. volts are as follows :

	W	Pt	Ta	Mo	C	Cu	Fe	Th	K
ϕ	4·478	4·8	4·31	4·18	4·14	4·05	3·2	2·69	1·30

G. Hagen, and F. Kirchner studied the scattering of X-rays and the Compton effect. F. Rother found that the emission of electrons between tantalum electrodes occurs between 2×10^6 and 9×10^6 volts per cm.; S. C. Roy studied the photo-electric emission of electrons as a function of the temp.; and O. Rietschel, the effect of press. W. H. Rodebush estimated the rate of evaporations of electrons from a hot tantalum filament. N. Piltschikoff stated that the so-called **Moser's rays**—the rays emitted from metal surfaces—are emitted by tantalum; they restore silver bromide reduced by positive rays. M. Levin and R. Ruer observed that tantalic acid can affect a photographic plate probably owing to the presence of thorium or radium impurities. C. Renz found that while tantalum pentoxide is reduced with considerable difficulty by chemical means, it is markedly **photosensitive** in the presence of certain organic liquids—*e.g.* glycerol—and is reduced to a lower oxide. H. Klumb, and R. Shurmann investigated the influence of gases on the photoelectric emission of tantalum.

J. J. Berzelius [5] said that the impure tantalum which he prepared had poor **electrical conductivity** ; whilst H. Rose's sample was regarded as a good conductor, and H. Moissan's sample, with half per cent. of carbon, was called a non-conductor. W. W. Coblentz found the tantalum filament of an unused tantalum lamp had a diameter 0·048, and an **electrical resistance** of 0·85 ohm per cm. W. von Bolton said that the average sp. resistance is 0·165 with a temp. coeff. of about 3 per cent. between 0° and 100°. P. W. Bridgman found the coeff. for two different samples to be 0·00293 and 0·00335 ; L. Holborn gave 0·00347 ; and F. Streintz, 0·003. Observations were made by A. Schulze. E. W. von Siemens and J. G. Halske found the conductivity to be 6·85 when that of mercury is unity. M. von Pirani found that wires of various thickness varied in their sp. resistance from 0·173 to 0·188 ohm, but after heating to 1900° in a high vacuum for from 100 to 200 hrs. they all possessed the same sp. resistance, namely, 0·146 ohm, and the temp. coeff. between 0° and 100° was 0·33 per cent. A. Siemens said that the temp. of tantalum filament consuming 1·5 watt per candle-power is about 1850°, and its resistance is about six times its resistance at 100° so that the temp. coeff. between 100° and 1850° may be taken as 0·29 per cent. The difference between these results is caused by alterations in the structure of the wires during their manufacture, and the heating in vacuo served a similar purpose to the annealing of steel. According to E. W. Engle, tantalum has a greater resistance but a smaller temp. coeff. than molybdenum or tungsten. J. W. Marden and M. N. Rich gave $0·0_414$ ohm per c.c. A. G. Worthing gave for the resistance, R ohms, in absolute temp. ;

T		1600°	1800°	2000°	2200°	2400°	2600°	2800° K.
R		67·6	74·1	80·5	86·9	92·9	99·1	105·0 ohms

and for $(dR/dT)(T/R)$, 0·785. M. von Pirani found the following ratios for the resistance, R at $\theta°$, between —180° to 2000°, to that at 20°, R_{20} :

		—180°	0°	100°	200°	600°	1000°	1400°	1600°	2000°
R/R_{20}		0·34	0·94	1·27	1·59	2·76	3·86	4·64	5·32	6·34

H. Pécheux found a tantalum wire, almost free from columbium, and 0·5 metre long, had $R=16·38(1+0·0025\theta+0·0000004\theta^2)$ microhm. P. W. Bridgman found for the effect of press., p, on the resistance, R, between 0 and 12,000 kgrms. per sq. cm. to be :

		0°	25°	50°	75°	100°
	$p=0$	$-0·0_51487$	$-0·0_51497$	$-0·0_51507$	$-0·0_51518$	$-0·0_51530$
R	$p=12,000$	$-0·0_51373$	$-0·0_51391$	$-0·0_51409$	$-0·0_51426$	$-0·0_51442$
	Average	$-0·0_51430$	$-0·0_51444$	$-0·0_51458$	$-0·0_51472$	$-0·0_51486$

A. G. Worthing observed that the ratio of the thermal and electrical conductivities, in C.G.S. units, is 27 at 1600° K.; 33 at 1800° K.; 46 at 2000° K.; and 56 at 2100° K. L. Grunmach and F. Weidert showed that the increase in the electrical resistance by transverse magnetization is less than is the case with many other metals—copper, silver, lead, zinc, tin, lead, bismuth, palladium, and platinum. R. Holm studied the contact resistance of two tantalum plates pressed together.

H. Pécheux found that the **thermoelectric force** of a *platinum-tantalum* couple with the tantalum almost free from columbium and platinum at a temp., $\theta°$, between 0° and 400°, is $dE/d\theta=2·20+0·0246\theta$ microvolts. This value is increased by preheating the tantalum, and decreased when increasing proportions of columbium are present. Purified tantalum stands between palladium and platinum with 10 per cent. rhodium ; if the tantalum be contaminated with columbium, it stands between platinum and palladium. A. G. Worthing found that the *tungsten-tantalum* couple at a high temp. is four times as sensitive as the platinum-Rd couple ; the coeff. of Thomson's effect in microvolts per degree is —5 at 1600° K. ; —6 at 1800° K. ; —8 at 2000° K. ; and —9 at 2100° K. S. Morugina also studied this couple—*vide* tungsten. W. W. Coblentz found for the thermoelectric force of the *copper-tantalum* couple between —400° and 400° about 4·1 microvolt per degree, *i.e.*, nearly the same as that of the copper-constantin couple. R. L. Pearson's value was too low.

According to W. von Bolton, tantalum stands in the **electrochemical series,** in dil. nitric acid, between silver and platinum—rather closer to the former than to the latter. G. von Hevesy found the **potential difference** between tantalum and its pentoxide is 0·00 volt ; W. Muthmann and F. Fraunberger gave —0·5 volt for the potential difference between tantalum and N-KCl ; while G. von Hevesy found —0·04 volt with respect to the calomel electrode. G. von Hevesy showed that the metal readily assumes the **passive state.** G. C. Schmidt showed that tantalum gives a low potential after it has been polished, but the metal regains its normal potential in about 20 mins. G. von Hevesy and R. E. Slade showed that the potential difference between tantalum and a 0·006 mol soln. of tantalum penta-fluoride is for the passive metal 1·537 volts, and for the active metal 0·165 volt —hydrogen zero. They added that in its most passive state, tantalum has *ein edleres Potential* than silver by about one volt, whilst an active metal has a potential close to that of copper. H. Kuessner found that a tantalum anode in 16N-KOH is converted into the pentoxide and the electrochemical valency is 5. The pentoxide forms a layer on the anode which permits a small current to pass. Increasing the applied voltage does not increase this current beyond 0·02-0·03 amp. per sq. cm. The tantalum anode in hydrofluoric acid acquires a coating of oxide which is broken at 220 volts. ; and W. von Bolton found that in sulphuric acid, the tantalum anode acquires a film of oxide which stops the current. Hence, tantalum acts as a rectifier when used as an anode in an electrolyte, for it will allow of the passage of the positive current only in one direction. E. Müller measured the potential of a hypochlorite anode with a tantalum cathode of other metals. G. Osterheld showed that the **overvoltage** of the tantalum cathode in 2N-sulphuric acid is 1·14 volts. As a reducing electrode in the case of benzophenone, caffeine, and nitro-benzene, tantalum yields very poor results—*vide infra*, tantalum hydride. P. K. Frölich and G. L. Clark gave for the hydrogen overvoltage of the metals in increasing order : Pd, Pt, Ta, Ni, Co, Fe, Zn, Cu, Au, and Hg. The metal over-voltages decrease in the same order. A. Thiel and W. Hammerschmidt studied this subject. The **electrolytic valve action** was studied by A. Günther-Schulze, E. Newbery, E. W. Engle, E. M. Dunham, and E. H. Robinson said that the tantalum rectifier resembles the aluminium rectifier ; dil. sulphuric acid is a satisfactory electrolyte, and lead as the other electrode. A current freely passes from the acid to the anode, but only to a small extent in the reverse direction unless the e.m.f. applied exceeds 40-200 volts, depending on the conditions. The addition of a small proportion of ferrous sulphate to the acid very much improves the rectification. Soda-lye, as electrolyte, corrodes the tantalum. N. A. de Bruyne and R. W. W. Sanderson studied the electrostatic capacity of tantalum anodes in dil. sulphuric acid of sp. gr. 1·285 at 18°. W. von Bolton found that the electrical spluttering of a tantalum filament in vacuo is very small ; H. R. von Traubenberg studied the loss of weight of the tantalum electrode in the oscillatory spark discharge in oxygen and nitrogen ; and H. Finger showed that the electrical spluttering of the tantalum under water is very slow. C. Zwikker studied the thermal emission of electrons. R. H. Fowler studied the electron theory of thermionic emission of tantalum.

E. W. Siemens and J. G. Halske [6] found tantalum to be paramagnetic. M. Owen showed that the **magnetic susceptibility** of tantalum is $0·81 \times 10^{-6}$ units, and it decreases with rise of temp. K. Honda gave $0·93 \times 10^{-6}$ at 18°, and $0·8 \times 10^{-6}$ at 800°. S. Meyer gave for the at. magnetic susceptibility $1·02 \times 10^{-6}$ units ; and the at. magnetization number, $58·0 \times 19^{-6}$. D. M. Bose and H. G. Bhar studied the susceptibility of tantalum salts.

REFERENCES

¹ K. Becker and F. Ebert, *Zeit. Physik*, **16**. 165, 1923; H. Moissan, *Compt. Rend.*, **134**. 211, 1902; *Bull. Soc. Chim.*, (3), **27**. 434, 1902; A. Siemens, *Proc. Roy. Inst.*, **19**. 590, 1909; *Chem. News*, **100**. 223, 1909; E. W. von Siemens and J. G. Halske, *German Pat.*, *D.R.P.* 200174, 200175, 1907; 229617, 1908; *Brit. Pat. No.* 6651, 1908; H. G. Grimm, *Zeit. phys. Chem.*, **122**. 177, 1926; L. Weiss and O. Aichel, *Liebig's Ann.*, **337**. 287, 1904; W. Muthmann, L. Weiss and R. Riedelbauch, *ib.*, **355**. 62, 1907; J. Disch, *Zeit. Physik.* **5**. 173, 1921; W. von Bolton, *Zeit. Elektrochem.*, **11**. 47, 503, 1905; F. Streintz, *ib.*, **11**. 274, 1905; M. von Pirani and A. R. Meyer, *ib.*, **17**. 919, 1911; M. von Pirani, *Verh. deut. phys. Ges.*, **12**. 301, 1910; P. Nordmeyer and A. L. Bernoulli, *ib.*, **5**. 175, 1907; F. W. Hinrichsen and N. Sahlbom, *Ber.*, **39**. 2605, 1906; W. W. Coblentz, *Investigations of Infra-red Spectra*, Washington, 92, 1908; W. E. Forsythe, *Astrophys. Journ.*, **34**. 353, 1911; *Elec. World*, **59**. 833, 1902; T. W. Richards, *Journ. Amer. Chem. Soc.*, **37**. 1643, 1915; **46**. 1419, 1924; **48**. 3063, 1926; T. W. Richards and E. P. Bartlett, *ib.*, **37**. 470, 1915; J. E. Moose and S. W. Parr, *ib.*, **46**. 2656, 1924; P. W. Bridgman, *Proc. Amer. Acad.*, **58**. 166, 1923; E. C. Bain, *Trans. Amer. Inst. Min. Met. Eng.*, **68**. 625, 1922; E. W. Engle, *ib.*, **71**. 691, 1925; W. R. Mott, *Trans. Amer. Electrochem. Soc.*, **34**. 255, 1918; J. Dewar, *Chem. News*, **100**. 224, 1909; A. W. Hull, *Phys. Rev.*, (2), **17**. 571, 1921; *Science*, (2), **52**. 227, 1920; T. Barratt and R. M. Winter, *Ann. Physik*, (4), **77**. 1, 1925; *Proc. Phys. Soc.*, **26**. 247, 1914; Z. Jeffries and R. S. Archer, *Chem. Met. Engg.*, **26**. 343, 1922; A. G. Worthing, *Phys. Rev.*, (2), **21**. 705, 1923; (2), **28**. 190, 1926; E. Tiede and E. Birnbräuer, *Zeit. anorg. Chem.*, **87**. 129, 1914; J. A. M. van Liempt, *Bull. Amer. Inst. Min. Eng.*, 15, 1927; L. H. Adams, *Journ. Washington Acad.*, **17**. 529, 1927; T. Simon and M. Ruhemann, *Zeit. phys. Chem.*, **129**. 334, 1927; J. Laissus, *Rev. Mét.*, **24**. 345, 1927.

² H. von Wartenberg, *Verh. deut. phys. Ges.*, **12**. 104, 1910; M. von Pirani, *ib.*, **12**. 301, 1910; W. W. Coblentz, *Bull. Bur. Standards*, **5**. 374, 1909; **7**. 197, 1911; *Journ. Franklin Inst.*, **170**. 169, 1910; F. Henning, *Jahrb. Rad. Elektron.*, **17**. 30, 1920; *Zeit. Instr.*, **30**. 61, 1910; G. V. McCauley, *Astrophys. Journ.*, **37**. 164, 1913; C. E. Mendenhall and W. E. Forsythe, *ib.*, **37**. 380, 1913; A. G. Worthing, *ib.*, **34**. 352, 1911; *A Determination of the Melting Points of Tantalum and Tungsten*, Philadelphia, 1911; *Phys. Rev.*, (2), **28**. 174, 190, 1926; *Journ. Amer. Opt. Soc.*, **13**. 635, 1926; F. Exner and E. Haschek, *Wellenlängentabellen für spectranalytische Untersuchungen auf Grund der ultravioletten Funkenspectren der Elemente*, Leipzig, 1902; *Wellenlängentabellen für spectralanalytische Untersuchungen auf Grund der ultravioletten Bogenspectren der Elemente*, Leipzig, 1904; *Die Spectra der Elemente bei normalen Druck*, Leipzig, 1912; *Sitzber. Akad. Wien*, **107**. 813, 1898; J. M. Eder and E. Valenta, *ib.*, **118**. 1902, 1909; **119**. 582, 1910; *Atlas typischer Spectren*, Wien, 1911; H. Josewsky, *Zeit. wiss. Photochem.*, **17**. 79, 1917; A. G. Worthing, *Phys. Rev.*, (2), **28**. 174, 190, 1926; *Journ. Amer. Opt. Soc.*, **13**. 635, 1926; H. Morsch, *Das Bogenspektrum von Tantal*, Bonn, 1905; C. Rütten and H. Morsch, *Zeit. wiss. Photochem.*, **3**. 195, 1905; H. Finger, *ib.*, **7**. 355, 1906; *Verh. deut. phys. Ges.*, **11**. 369, 1909; H. Konen and H. Finger, *Zeit. Elektrochem.*, **15**. 166, 1909; E. Paulson, *Ann. Physik*, (4), **45**. 419, 1914; *Phys. Zeit.*, **16**. 352, 1915; R. Thalén, *Nova Acta Upsala*, (3), **6**. 9, 1868; E. Demarçay, *Spectres électriques*, Paris, 1895; W. J. Humphreys, *Astrophys. Journ.*, **6**. 169, 1897; J. Lifschitz, *Proc. Acad. Amsterdam.*, **26**. 561, 1923; J. Formanek, *Die qualitative Spektralanalyse anorganischer und organischer Körper*, Berlin, 151, 1905; H. Kayser, *Handbuch der Spectroscopie*, Leipzig, **6**. 566, 1912; J. Carrera, *Compt. Rend.*, **176**. 740, 1923; E. J. Allin and H. J. C. Ireton, *Trans. Roy. Soc. Canada*, (3), **21**. 127, 1927; A. L. Helfgott, *Zeit. Physik.* **49**. 555, 1928.

³ M. Siegbahn, *Jahrb. Rad. Elektron.*, **13**. 296, 1916; **18**. 240, 1921; M. Siegbahn, *Ann. Physik*, (4), **49**. 611, 616, 1906; *Phil. Mag.*, (6), **32**. 39, 1916; D. Coster, *Compt. Rend.*, **174**. 378, 1922; A. Duvallier, *ib.*, **183**. 193, 1926; P. Auger and A. Duvallier, *ib.*, **176**. 1297, 1923; G. Réchou, *ib.*, **180**. 1107, 1925; H. Hirata, *Proc. Roy. Soc.*, **105**. A, 40, 1924; G. von Hevesy and J. Böhm, *Zeit. anorg. Chem.*, **164**. 69, 1927; E. Hjalmar, *Zeit. Physik*, **3**. 262, 1920; **7**. 341, 1921; **15**. 65, 1923; I. Wennerlöf, *ib.*, **41**. 524, 1927; M. J. Druyvesteyn, *ib.*, **43**. 707, 1927; J. H. van der Tuuk, *ib.*, **44**. 737, 1927; G. Wentzel, *Naturwiss.*, **10**. 369, 1922; Y. Nishina, *Phil. Mag.*, (6), **49**. 521, 1925; B. B. Ray, *ib.*, (6), **48**. 707, 1924; J. E. P. Wagstaff, *ib.*, (6), **47**. 84, 1924; G. Hagen, *Ann. Physik*, (4), **78**. 407, 1925; F. Kirchner, *ib.*, (4), **78**. 421, 1925; J. Schrör, *ib.*, (4), **80**. 297, 1926; B. R. Stephenson and J. M. Cork, *Phys. Rev.*, (2), **27**. 138, 1926; J. C. Boyce, *ib.*, (2), **23**. 575, 1924; V. Dehlinger, *Zeit. Kryst.*, **65**. 615, 1927; J. Thibaud and A. Soltan, *Journ. Phys. Rad.*, (6), **8**. 484, 1927.

⁴ N. Pilschikoff, *Phys. Zeit.*, **7**. 69, 1906; M. Levin and R. Ruer, *ib.*, **10**. 576, 1909; S. Dushman, H. N. Rowe, and C. A. Kidner, *Phys. Rev.*, (2), **21**. 207, 1923; S. Dushman, H. N. Rowe, J. W. Ewald, and C. A. Kidner, *ib.*, (2), **21**. 207, 1923; (2), **25**. 338, 1925; S. Dushman and J. W. Ewald, *Phys. Rev.*, (2), **20**. 109, 1922; *Gen. Elect. Rev.*, **26**. 154, 1923; S. C. Roy, *Proc. Roy. Soc.*, **112**. A, 599, 1926; C. Renz, *Helvetica Chim. Acta*, **4**. 961, 1921; W. H. Rodebush, *Journ. Amer. Chem. Soc.*, **45**. 997, 1923; R. Shurmann, *Zeit. Physik*, **13**. 17, 1923; F. Rother, *Ann. Physik*, (4), **81**. 317, 1926; O. W. Richardson, *Phil. Mag.*, (6), **26**. 345, 1913; *Phys. Zeit.*, **14**. 793, 1913; *The Emission of Electrons under the Influence of Chemical Action*, London, 1921; F Kirchner, *Ann. Physik*, (4), **78**. 421, 1925; G. Hagen, *ib.*, (4), **78**. 407, 1925; O. Rietschel, *ib.*, (4), **80**. 71, 1926; H. Klumb, *Zeit. Physik.* **47**. 652, 1928.

⁵ P. W. Bridgman, *Proc. Amer. Acad.*, **52**. 573, 1917; **58**. 185, 1923; L. Holborn, *Ann.*

Physik, (4), **59**. 145, 1919 ; J. J. Berzelius, *Schweigger's Journ.*, **16**. 437, 1816 ; *Pogg. Ann.*, **4**. 10, 1825 ; H. Rose, *ib.*, **99**. 66, 1856 ; **100**. 146, 1857 ; A. Schulze, *Zeit. Metallkunde*, **15**. 155, 1923 ; **16**. 48, 1924 ; A. Siemens, *Chem. News*, **100**. 223, 1909 ; E. W. von Siemens and J. G. Halske, *German Pat.*, *D.R.P.* 200174, 200175, 1907 ; 229617, 1908 ; W. von Bolton, *Zeit. Elektrochem.*, **11**. 47, 1905 ; F. Streintz, *ib.*, **11**. 274, 1905 ; H. Kuessner, *Ueber das anodische Verhalten des Molybdans, Mangans, Chroms, und Tantals*, Halle a. S., 1910 ; *Zeit. Elektrochem.*, **16**. 772, 1910 ; M. von Pirani, *ib.*, **13**. 344, 753, 1907 ; *Verh. deut. phys. Ges.*, **12**. 335, 1910 ; G. von Hevesy, *Phil. Mag.*, (6), **23**. 643, 1912 ; G. von Hevesy and R. E. Slade, *Zeit. Elektrochem.*, **18**. 1001, 1912 ; G. Osterheld, *ib.*, **19**. 585, 1913 ; A. Günther-Schulze, *Ann. Physik*, (4), **23**. 246, 1907 ; (4), **65**. 223, 1921 ; *Zeit. Physik*, **6**. 237, 1921 ; **9**. 225, 1922 ; P. K. Frölich and G. L. Clark, *Zeit. Elektrochem.*, **31**. 649, 1925 ; E. Müller. *ib.*, **31**. 323, 1925 ; H. R. von Traubenberg, *Phys. Zeit.*, **13**. 415, 1912 ; L. Grunmach and F. Weidert, *ib.*, **7**. 729, 1906 ; *Ber. deut. phys. Ges.*, **4**. 359, 1907 ; S. Morugina, *Zeit. tech. Physik*, **7**. 486, 1926 ; R. Holm, *ib.*, **8**. 151, 1927 ; E. Newbery, *Proc. Roy. Soc.*, **114**. A, 486, 1925 ; J. W. Marden and M. N. Rich, *Journ. Ind. Eng. Chem.*, **19**. 786, 1927 ; W. Muthmann and F. Fraunberger, *Sitzber. Akad. München*, (2), **34**. 201, 212, 1904 ; H. Pécheux, *Compt. Rend.*, **153**. 1140, 1911 ; A. G. Worthing, *Phys. Rev.*, (1), **23**. 152, 1912 ; (2), **28**. 190, 1926 ; *Elect. World*, **59**. 861, 1912 ; R. L. Pearson, *Electrician*, **63**. 594, 1909 ; E. H. Robinson, *Expl. Wireless*, **2**. 889, 1925 ; W. W. Coblentz, *Bull. Bur. Standards*, **6**. 107, 1909 ; H. Finger, *Zeit. wiss. Photochem.*. **7**. 355, 1909 ; *Verh. deut. phys. Ges.*, **11**. 369, 1909 ; G. C. Schmidt, *Zeit. phys. Chem.*, **106**. 105, 1923 ; L. Holborn, *Zeit. Physik*, **8**. 58, 1921 ; C. Zwikker, *Versl. Akad. Amsterdam*, **35**. 336, 1926 ; A. Thiel and W. Hammerschmidt, *Zeit. anorg. Chem.*, **132**. 15, 1923 ; N. A. de Bruyne and R. W. W. Sanderson, *Trans. Faraday Soc.*, **23**. 42, 1927 ; E. W. Engle, *Trans. Amer. Inst. Min. Eng.*, **71**. 691, 1925 : E. M. Dunham, *Science*, (2), **65**. 525, 1927 ; R. H. Fowler, *Proc. Roy. Soc.*, **117**. A, 549, 1928 ; H. Moissan, *Compt. Rend.*, **134**. 211, 1902 ; *Bull. Soc. Chim.*, (3), **27**. 434, 1902.

[6] E. W. Siemens and J. G. Halske, *Das Tantalmetal*, Charlottenberg, 1912 ; M. Owen, *Ann. Physik*, (4), **37**. 657, 1912 ; K. Honda, *ib.*, (4), **32**. 1027, 1910 ; *Science Rep. Tohoku Univ.*, **1**. 1, 1912 ; **2**. 25, 1913 ; **3**. 139, 293, 1914 ; **4**. 215, 1915 ; S. Meyer, *Wied. Ann.*, **68**. 324, 1899 ; D. M. Bose and H. G. Bhar, *Zeit. Physik*, **48**. 716, 1928.

§ 3. The Chemical Properties of Tantalum

The chemical reactions of tantalum are very similar to those of columbium ; but it is not so strong a reducing agent. Tantalum readily absorbs hydrogen when heated to redness ; thus, it forms a hydride (*q.v.*) with **hydrogen** and becomes very brittle. W. von Bolton [1] found that most of the absorbed hydrogen can be expelled by heating the product in vacuo. G. Oesterheld observed that, like palladium, a tantalum cathode easily absorbs hydrogen when used as cathode in the electrolysis of sulphuric acid. A. Sieverts and E. Bergner found that tantalum absorbs **argon** to a small extent, and a little more **helium** is absorbed than is the case with argon. F. Fischer and F. Schrötter observed no reaction when tantalum is sparked below liquid argon. J. J. Berzelius found that tantalum powder glows when heated to redness in **air ;** and A. Siemens said that the black powder and thin wires can be ignited by applying to them the flame of a match. When the metal is heated in air, it shows at about 400° a yellow, and then a blue tint like steel, and when the heating is continued, it burns to the pentoxide. H. Moissan said that the ignition temp. in dry **oxygen** is 600°. A. Siemens, and W. von Bolton found that when a tantalum filament contaminated with oxide is heated in a high vacuo, the combined oxygen will be expelled ; and it is possible to detect when a filament contains oxide by very gradually heating it up, when the parts containing the oxide will appear brighter than the other parts owing to the greater electrical resistance of the oxide. In a few minutes the glow of the filament becomes quite uniform owing to the expulsion of the oxygen. If the oxygen press. is below 20 mm., the tantalum does not form an oxide. Hence by electrically heating the oxide under reduced press., and pumping off the oxygen as it is given off, it is possible to isolate the metal. Red-hot tantalum decomposes **water,** and the escaping hydrogen inflames ; below about 300°, tantalum is not affected by water ; moisture has no action on the metal. W. Guertler and T. Liepus observed no action with sea-water, aerated sea-water, or aerated rain-water during 4 weeks' exposure ; nor did a soln. of **hydrogen dioxide** in alkali-lye attack the metal in 48 hrs.

According to H. Moissan, **fluorine** unites with finely powdered and warm tantalum with incandescence ; and J. J. Berzelius found that the hot metal burns vigorously in **chlorine,** and H. Moissan showed that the attack by chlorine is slow at 150°, faster at 200°, and rapid at 250°. W. Guertler and T. Liepus observed no action with sat. chlorine-water in 48 hrs. W. K. von Haagen showed that **bromine** scarcely attacks the hot metal, but if the temp. is high enough, the pentabromide sublimes ; and, added H. Moissan, the action is fast at the softening temp. of glass, and much heat is developed. The vapour of **iodine** does not attack the metal ; and when powdered tantalum is heated with **iodine pentoxide,** iodine vapours are copiously evolved. J. J. Berzelius, E. W. Engle, and H. Rose observed that tantalum dissolves slowly in warm **hydrofluoric acid,** and W. von Bolton noted that corrosion figures are produced ; while if the metal in contact with platinum be dipped in this acid, it rapidly dissolves with the evolution of hydrogen. H. Kuessner found that tantalum goes anodically into soln., and at the same time becomes passive owing to the formation of a film of oxide, observed by G. von Hevesy and R. E. Slade—*vide supra*. H. Rose, and H. Moissan found that a warm mixture of hydrofluoric and nitric acids dissolves tantalum rapidly with the production of red fumes. H. Moissan observed that **hydrogen chloride** attacks the heated metal forming a white sublimate, which darkens as the temp. rises, and hydrogen is evolved. Boiling **hydrochloric acid** has no action on tantalum ; W. Guertler and T. Liepus observed no action during 48 hrs.' exposure, to 10 and 36 per cent. acid ; and A. Siemens, and W. von Bolton reported that since tantalum resists all acids, alkalies, and moisture at temp. below 300°, it is good for making chemical apparatus which do not require a high temp., and for instruments liable to rust if made of steel. H. Moissan observed that unlike columbium when tantalum is heated with an aq. soln. of **potassium chlorate** there is no action.

W. von Bolton showed that at 100° **sulphur** has no perceptible action on tantalum, but when heated to higher temp. union occurs ; J. J. Berzelius found that his impure tantalum could be inflamed in sulphur vapour ; and H. Moissan obtained a somewhat similar result. W. Guertler and T. Liepus observed that 10 and 50 per cent. soln. of **sodium sulphide**—with or without alkali-lye—do not attack tantalum during 48 hrs. H. Moissan added that **hydrogen sulphide** has no action at 600° ; and **sulphur dioxide** is reduced at approximately 500°, forming sulphur and tantalum pentoxide. Boiling **sulphuric acid** does not attack the compact metal ; but H. Moissan said that the boiling, conc. acid slowly attacked the tantalum he prepared, and was coloured brown. W. Guertler and T. Liepus observed that 10 per cent. sulphuric acid has no action during 48 hrs., and similarly also with 20 per cent. acid sat. with sodium sulphate. W. von Bolton observed that **selenium** behaves like sulphur towards tantalum. H. Moissan said that tellurium has no action at 700° ; but W. von Bolton said that a greyish-black telluride is formed. W. Muthmann and co-workers said that **nitrogen** reacts with tantalum at a red-heat, forming a nitride ; H. Moissan said that the attack is only slight at 1200°. On the other hand, W. von Bolton showed that at a dull red-heat, tantalum absorbs nitrogen greedily, and the metal becomes very brittle. H. Moissan showed that at a red-heat, **ammonia** is decomposed while the metal acquires a dark colour, without changing in weight. W. Guertler and T. Liepus observed no reaction with 10, 50, and 70 per cent. ammonia during 48 hrs. At 500°, tantalum reacts vigorously with **nitrogen trioxide and pentoxide.** Boiling **nitric acid,** or aqua regia was found by W. von Bolton to have no action on the metal. W. Guertler and T. Liepus also observed that 10 and 50 per cent. soln. of the acid have no action during 48 hrs., and similarly also with aqua regia. H. Moissan showed that molten **potassium nitrate** attacks tantalum more slowly than it does columbium. The vapour of **phosphorus** does not attack tantalum at the softening temp. of glass ; and **phosphorus pentoxide** is reduced by the red-hot metal, forming phosphorus. The vapour of **arsenic** or **antimony** does not attack tantalum at the softening temp. of glass, but **arsenic pentoxide** is reduced.   **W. von Bolton** found that a trace of **boron** or **carbon** makes the metal hard without harming its ductility, but more carbon makes the metal brittle.   A soln. of **carbon dioxide** in air was found by W. Guertler and T. Liepus to have no action on tantalum in 48 hrs.; and similarly also with soln. of **acetic, citric, and tartaric acids.   Silicon** and **titanium,** like carbon, make the metal brittle.   H. Moissan studied the carbide (*q.v.*), and O. Hönigschmid, the silicide (*q.v.*).

H. Moissan found that molten **sodium** or **potassium** does not alloy with tantalum.   W. von Bolton, L. Jordan and co-workers, and H. Moissan said that **silver** does not alloy with tantalum, and if molten tantalum be poured on a block of silver, the molten metal sinks into the silver without dissolving a trace; **magnesium** was found by E. F. Smith and P. Maas to form an alloy;   W. von Bolton said that **zinc** forms no compound; and W. von Bolton, and G. Tammann and J. Hinnüber said that **mercury** forms no amalgam; and O. Brunck observed no alloying occurs when zinc is deposited electrolytically on tantalum; **cadmium** behaves similarly.   E. F. Smith and P. Maas obtained an alloy by reducing the oxide with **aluminium** powder; and tantalum produced by the alumino-thermite process contains some aluminium.   J. C. G. de Marignac obtained **aluminium tritatantalide,** Al_3Ta, by melting a mixture of potassium fluotantalate and aluminium filings (1 : 1·5) in a carbon crucible, and treating the regulus with cold hydrochloric acid. The black, crystalline powder has a sp. gr. 7·02.   It is but slightly affected when warmed in air; it is attacked by cold hydrofluoric acid; and is slightly affected by boiling hydrochloric acid.   Boiling, conc. sulphuric acid attacks it, but it resists cold dil. sulphuric or nitric acid, or aqua regia.   It is attacked by molten potassium hydrofluoride.   H. Schirmeister found that the mechanical properties of aluminium alloys, containing the following percentage proportions of tantalum, were :

Tantalum.	0·0	0·3	0·8	1·5	2·2	2·5 per cent.
Tenacity	9·5	10·0	10·6	10·3	10·3	10·4
Elongation	41	38	38	38	39	39
Hardness	26	—	30	—	28	—

W. von Bolton found that **molybdenum** and **chromium** are readily soluble in molten tantalum.   J. J. Berzelius heated **manganese** oxide with tantalum and found that when the product is treated with hydrochloric acid, manganese passes into soln., and the tantalum remains as a black powder.   Five to 10 per cent. of **iron** forms a hard, ductile alloy.   H. Moissan also obtained an alloy with iron. J. J. Berzelius obtained an alloy by heating tantalum with ferric oxide.   L. Guillet studied the tantalum-steels, but found that they possessed no mechanical properties inviting special attention; he showed that the normal steels are all pearlitic in character; the quantity of pearlite is in proportion to the carbon content, but is better distributed as the percentage of tantalum increases.   The mechanical properties show that the tantalum produces a slight increase in the breaking load, the limit of elasticity, and the resistance to shock, and a slight decrease in the elongation. The effect produced by 1 per cent. of tantalum can, however, be obtained by addition of other substances, particularly nickel.   The transformation points between 600° and 675° are scarcely visible on the curve, but those between 770° and 790° on heating, and between 730° and 750° on cooling, are very clear; the last transformation, at about 900°, is rather slow.   The quenched steels have the same structure as the ordinary steels.   The influence of the tantalum on the mechanical properties is somewhat more evident with the quenched than with the ordinary steels.   E. W. von Siemens and J. G. Halske found that **nickel** alloyed with 5–10 per cent. of tantalum is more ductile and acid-resisting than nickel alone; with 30 per cent. of tantalum, the alloy is tough, and easily worked, and is not attacked by aqua regia and other acids.   A wire 0·5 mm. diameter breaks with a load of 2000 kgrms. per sq. mm.   W. von Bolton found that a boiling soln. of **alkali hydroxide** has no action on tantalum; but H. Moissan, and W. von Bolton showed that the fused hydroxide decomposes the metal, forming hydrogen and a tantalate. A. L. Bernoulli found that tantalum dissolves anodically in conc. potash-lye, and, added F. W. Hinrichsen and N. Sahlbom, with a high anodic tension. W. Guertler and T. Liepus found that 10 and 50 per cent. soln. of sodium hydroxide have no action during 48 hrs. According to W. von Bolton, when tantalum powder is heated with **lead oxide** or **lead dioxide** metallic lead is formed ; **manganese dioxide** at a red-heat is reduced by tantalum. For the action of tantalum on **manganese and iron oxides,** *vide supra.* H. Moissan showed that **mercurous or mercuric chloride** is reduced by tantalum. W. Guertler and T. Liepus observed no action with a soln. of mercuric chloride at 90° ; nor with an aq. soln. of **magnesium chloride.** The reactions of tantalum of analytical interest have been indicated in connection with columbium.

The uses of tantalum.—Tantalum is used as a filament in the manufacture of incandescent lamps. The characteristic difference between carbon and tantalum filaments was illustrated by A. Siemens,[2] and W. von Bolton by representing the normal resistance of both filaments by 100 when they are giving a light of one candle for 1·5 watts. The resistance of tantalum alters directly and that of carbon inversely as the temp. so that the former is better able to resist over-heating. S. L. Malowan said that a tantalum lamp with a very thin filament burns with an efficiency of 1·5 watts per Hefner candle, and has a life of 1000 hrs. ; at 2 watts per Hefner candle the temp. of the wire is 2201°. Tungsten filaments have largely replaced tantalum. A. Siemens, and M. von Pirani showed that tantalum can be used in making rustless instruments where great hardness and ductility are required—*e.g.* dental and surgical instruments ; pen nibs ; normal weights ; clock springs ; gramophone needles ; etc. It can be used as cathode in electrolytic analysis, etc. ; thus, according to C. W. Balke, it can be used for the deposition of zinc since it does not alloy with the metal, and if used for the electrodeposition of gold and silver, these metals can be dissolved from the cathode with aqua regia which does not attack the tantalum. It is also available as a rectifier, *e.g.* in charging accumulators from an alternating current supply since two tantalum electrodes in a single cell will convert an alternating current into a direct one. It has some advantages over platinum as an anticathode on account of its smaller tendency to splutter. In steels, S. L. Malowan said that tantalum raises the breaking and elasticity limits. O. Brunck discussed the application of tantalum as a substitute for platinum, where resistance to acids or aqua regia are required. Its sensitiveness towards hydrofluoric acid, and, when heated, towards oxygen limit its use. E. Groschuff and F. Mylius found that a tantalum crucible lost slightly in weight with hot nitric or hydrochloric acid ; the loss was ten times greater when the crucible was heated with sulphuric acid at 200° ; and it was completely destroyed by a conc. soln. of potash-lye at 130°.

The atomic weight and valency of tantalum.—In spite of a few more or less ill-founded reports to the contrary, tantalum almost uniformly behaves as a quinquevalent element. In the per-acids and per-salts also, as in the case of colum-bium, the element is quinquevalent. J. J. Berzelius [3] at first regarded tantalum tetroxide as the metal, and he represented the pentoxide by the formula TaO_2 ; later, he measured what he regarded as the at. wt. by treating tantalic acid with baryta-water, and by the action of chlorine on the sulphide, and obtained 183·7–184·6 on the assumption that the at. wt. of oxygen is 16. The proximity of these numbers to the at. wts. employed at the present day is purely a coincidence since a different formula was employed—Ta_2O_3 for what is now known to be Ta_2O_5. H. Rose obtained results similar to those of J. J. Berzelius ; and likewise also C. W. Blomstrand. These numbers were afterwards recalculated for quinquevalent tantalum where the oxide becomes Ta_2O_5.

From H. Rose's ratios $2TaCl_5 : Ta_2O_5 : 10AgCl$, it follows that the at. wt. of tantalum is 175·0 ; from C. W. Blomstrand's ratios, $2TaCl_5 : Ta_2O_5$, 173·7 ; $TaCl_3 : 5AgCl$, 178·4 ; and from $10AgCl : Ta_2O_5 : 2TaCl_5$, 176·2. J. C. G. de

Marignac's ratio $2K_2TaF_7 : Ta_2O_5$, the at. wt. of tantalum becomes 183·7 ; from $K_2TaF_7 : K_2SO_4$, 181·8 ; $K_2SO_4 : Ta_2O_5$, 182·76 ; $2(NH_4)_2TaF_7 : Ta_2O_5$, 182·76 ; $10AgCl : Ta_2O_5$, 182·26 ; and from $TaCl_5 : 5AgCl$, 181·00. F. W. Hinrichsen and N. Sahlbom calculated 181·0 from the ratio $2Ta : Ta_2O_5$. From these results, B. Brauner inferred that the at. wt. of tantalum is 181·4 ; and F. W. Clarke, 181·019. A. Joly obtained 182 by treating ammonium heptafluotantalate with sulphuric acid, and calcining the product for the pentoxide—$2(NH_4)_2TaF_7 : Ta_2O_5$. E. F. Smith added that the double salts are not suited for at. wt. determinations because of the uncertainty as to their composition after each crystallization. C. W. Balke calculated 181·52 from the ratio $2TaCl_5 : Ta_2O_5$; G. W. Sears and C. W. Balke obtained 180·90-181·36 from the ratios $2TaCl_5 : Ta_2O_5$ and $TaCl_5 : 5AgCl$; while W. H. Chapin and E. F. Smith obtained 181·68-181·91 from the ratio $2TaBr_5 : Ta_2O_5$. The International Table for 1926 gave 181·5 for the best representative value.

The **atomic number** of tantalum is 73. F. W. Aston [4] has not yet succeeded in determining the **isotopes** of tantalum. N. Bohr's **electronic structure** of the atom is (2) (4, 4) (6, 6, 6) (8, 8, 8, 8,) (4, 4, 3) (2). The subject was discussed by L. A. Sommer, C. D. Niven, H. G. Grimm, and M. L. Huggins.

REFERENCES.

[1] J. J. Berzelius, *Schweigger's Journ.*, 16. 437, 1816 ; *Pogg. Ann.*, 4. 10, 1825 ; H. Rose, *ib.*, 99. 70, 1856 ; A. Siemens, *Chem. News*, 100. 223, 1909 ; J. C. G. de Marignac, *Arch. Sciences Genève*, (2), 31. 101, 1868 ; W. von Bolton, *Zeit. Elektrochem.*, 11. 47, 1905 ; H. Kuessner, *ib.*, 16. 772, 1912 ; G. von Hevesy and R. E. Slade, *ib.*, 18. 1001, 1912 ; O. Hönigschmid, *Monatsh.*, 28. 1017, 1907 ; J. Sieverts and E. Bergner, *Ber.*, 45. 2576, 1912 ; A. L. Bernoulli, *ib.*, 39. 2606, 1906 ; F. W. Hinrichsen and N. Sahlbom, *ib.*, 39. 2600, 1906 ; F. Fischer and F. Schrötter, *ib.*, 43. 1442, 1454, 1914 ; W. Muthmann, L. Weiss, and R. Riedelbach, *Liebig's Ann.*, 355. 62, 1907 ; H. Schirmeister, *Beiträge zur Kenntnis der binären Aluminiumlegierungen hinsichtlich ihrer technischen Eigenschaften*, Düsseldorf, 1914 ; *Stahl Eisen*, 35. 649, 873, 996, 1915 ; H. Moissan, *Compt. Rend.*, 134. 211, 1902 ; *Bull. Soc. Chim.*, (3), 28. 434, 1909 ; E. W. von Siemens and J. G. Halske, *German Pat.*, *D.R.P.* 277242, 1913 ; *Met.*, 11. 65, 1914 ; W. K. von Haagen, *Tantalum and some of its Halides*, Easton, Pa., 1909 ; *Journ. Amer. Chem. Soc.*, 32. 729. 1910 ; G. Oesterheld, *Zeit. Elektrochem.*, 19. 585, 1913 ; E. F. Smith and P. Maas, *Zeit. anorg. Chem.*, 7. 99, 1894 ; H. Goldschmidt and C. Vautier, *Journ. Soc. Chem. Ind.*, 17. 543, 1908 ; O. Brunck, *Chem. Ztg.*, 36. 1233, 1912 ; L. Guillet, *Compt. Rend.*, 145. 327, 1907 ; W. Guertler and T. Liepus, *Zeit. Metallkunde*, 17. 310, 1925 ; E. W. Engle, *Trans. Amer. Inst. Min. Eng.*, 71. 691, 1925 ; L. Jordan, L. H. Grenell, and H. K. Herschmann, *ib.*, . , 1927 ; G. Tammann and J. Hinnüber, *Zeit. anorg. Chem.*, 160. 249, 1927.

[2] A. Siemens, *Chem. News*, 100. 223, 1909 ; W. von Bolton, *Zeit. Elektrochem.*, 11. 48, 723, 1905 ; E. Groschuff and F. Mylius, *ib.*, 21. 286, 1915 ; E. W. von Siemens and J. G. Halske, *Das Tantalmetal*, Charlottenburg, 1912 ; *German Pat.*, *D.R.P.* 152848, 152870, 153826, 154998, 156714, 161081, 163414, 1903 ; 181050, 1904 ; 188466, 1905 ; 184349, 197382, 1906 ; 211165, 1908 ; Westinghouse Electric and Manufacturing Co., *U.S. Pat. No.* 1588518, 1926 ; Deutsche Gasglühlicht A.G., *ib.*, 182683, 194653, 1905 ; Wolfram-Lampen A.G., *ib.*, 200300, 1905 ; E. de Haen, *ib.*, 197074, 1906 ; E. W. Engle, *Trans. Amer. Inst. Min. Met. Eng.*, 71. 691, 1925 ; O. Brunck, *Chem. Ztg.*, 36. 1233, 1912 ; S. L. Malowan, *Edelerden. Erz*, 4. 26, 1923 ; *Canadian Chem. Met.*, 7. 255, 1923 ; C. W. Balke, *Journ. Ind. Eng. Chem.*, 15. 560, 1923 ; *Chem. Met. Engg.*, 27. 1271, 1923 ; H. Kuzel, *German Pat.*, *D.R.P.* 194348, 194707, 1905 ; 200466, 1906 ; J. Lux, *ib.*, 194371, 1906 ; F. J. Planchon, *ib.*, 194893, 1907 ; M. von Pirani, *Zeit. angew. Chem.*, 25. 2107, 1912 ; G. W. Sears, *School Science*, 18. 145, 1918 ; L. Moser, *Oesterr. Chem. Ztg.*, 26. 67, 1923.

[3] J. J. Berzelius, *Schweigger's Journ.*, 16. 439, 1816 ; *Svenska Akad. Handl.*, 334, 1824 ; *Pogg. Ann.*, 4. 6, 1825 ; H. Rose, *ib.*, 99. 78, 575, 1856 ; J. C. G. de Marignac, *Ann. Chim. Phys.*, (4), 9. 251, 1866 ; *Arch. Sciences Genève*, (2), 26. 89, 1866 ; *Compt. Rend.*, 63. 85, 1866 ; A. Joly, *Ann. École Norm.*, (2), 6. 141, 1877 ; E. F. Smith, *Proc. Amer. Phil. Soc.*, 44. 155, 1905 ; *Chem. News*, 92. 220, 232, 242, 252, 262, 276, 1905 ; *Journ. Amer. Chem. Soc.*, 44. 151, 1905 ; C. W. Balke, *The Double Halides of Tantalum*, Easton, Pa., 1908 ; *Journ. Amer. Chem. Soc.*, 32. 1127, 1910 ; G. W. Sears and C. W. Balke, *ib.*, 37. 833, 1915 ; W. H. Chapin and E. F. Smith, *ib.*, 33. 1504, 1911 ; W. K. von Haagen, *ib.*, 32. 729, 1910 ; *Tantalum and some of its Halides*, Easton, Pa., 1909 ; F. W. Clarke, *Journ. Amer. Chem. Soc.*, 33. 261, 1911 ; *A Recalculation of the Atomic Weights*, Washington, 337, 1910 ; B. Brauner in R. Abegg, *Handbuch der anorganische Chemie*, Leipzig, 3. iii, 839, 1907 ; F. W. Hinrichsen and N. Sahlbom, *Ber.*, 39. 2600, 1906 ; C. W. Blomstrand, *Acta Univ. Lund*, 1. 7, 1864 ; *Liebig's Ann.*, 135. 198, 1865.

[4] F. W. Aston, *Phil. Mag.*, (6), 49. 1191, 1925 ; N. Bohr, *Nature*, 112. Suppl., 1923 ;

L. A. Sommer, *Zeit. Physik*, **37**. 1, 1926 ; H. G. Grimm, *Zeit. phys. Chem.*, **101**, 403, 1922 ;
M. L. Huggins, *Journ. Phys. Chem.*, **26**. 601, 1922 ; C. D. Niven, *Phil. Mag.*, (7), **3**. 1314, 1927.

§ 4. Tantalum Hydride

J. C. G. de Marignac [1] said that when sodium heptafluotantalate is reduced with
sodium under a layer of alkali chloride, **tantalum hydride** is the main product.
According to W. von Bolton, if a strip of tantalum be used as cathode in the
electrolysis of dil. sulphuric acid, there is an evolution of hydrogen, and about
0·3 per cent. is absorbed by the metal. At the same time, the metal becomes brittle.
The hydrogen can be expelled only with difficulty, it is only partially removed by
fusion. G. Oesterheld also observed that when tantalum is used as a reducing cathode
it loses its elastic properties and becomes crystalline and brittle. M. von Pirani
observed that tantalum at a red-heat occludes about 55 times its vol. of hydrogen
—0·3 per cent.—and at a yellow heat about 740 vols. A crystalline hydride is
formed, whose electrical resistance is about $2\frac{1}{2}$ times that of the metal. When the
hydride is heated in vacuo, there remains 0·1 per cent. which is expelled only with
long continued fusion in vacuo. A. Sieverts and E. Bergner showed that the
solubility of hydrogen in tantalum from 1330° upwards is for the same hydrogen
press. smaller with rise of temp., and is approximately proportional to the square
root of the press. Below 500°, the gas-free metal is indifferent towards hydrogen.
The saturation of the metal at the lower temp. is more quickly attained if the
tantalum be first charged at a higher temp. W. Muthmann and co-workers
observed that powdered tantalum in a stream of hydrogen takes up at 1000°,
1·0–1·5 per cent. in 2 hrs. ; 2·1 per cent. in 12 hrs. ; and at 1200°, the product
corresponds with $TaH_{12\cdot5}$. The black, pulverulent hydride has similar chemical
properties to those of columbium hydride.

REFERENCES.

[1] J. C. G. de Marignac, *Arch. Science Genève*, (2), **31**. 100, 1868 ; *Compt. Rend.*, **66**. 180, 1868 ;
W. von Bolton, *Zeit. Elektrochem.*, **11**. 50, 1905 ; M. von Pirani, *ib.*, **11**. 55, 1905 ; G. Oesterheld,
ib., **19**. 585, 1913 ; W. Muthmann, L. Weiss, and R. Riedelbauch, *Liebig's Ann.*, **355**. 91, 1905 ;
A. Sieverts and E. Bergner, *Ber.*, **44**. 2347, 2402, 1911 ; *Journ. Soc. Chem. Ind.*, **30**. 1217, 1911.

§ 5. The Lower Tantalum Oxides

R. Hermann [1] melted a mixture of potassium heptafluotantalate and potassium
under a layer of fused sodium chloride in a well-closed iron crucible. The cold
product is washed with water, and repeatedly boiled with potash-lye. The residual
tantalum dioxide, Ta_2O_2, is readily removed from the admixed tantalum by
levigation, and dried over sulphuric acid. There is a doubt about the chemical
individuality of the product. The black powder has a sp. gr. 7·35 ; it burns like
tinder when heated in air, forming the pentoxide ; it dissolves in hydrofluoric acid
with the evolution of hydrogen. K. Friederich and L. Sittig doubted the
individuality of the dioxide Ta_2O_4. There are considerable doubts about *tantalum
trioxide*, Ta_2O_3, which R. Hermann thought was present in the columbites, which
when separated appears as the pentoxide, thus, according to W. K. van Haagen and
E. F. Smith, the pentafluoride is produced when hydrogen fluoride is passed over
a tantalate at a white-heat. K. Friederich gave 100 ohms per sq. mm. for the
electrical resistance of the trioxide ; but K. Friederich and L. Sittig doubted the
chemical individuality of the trioxide.

According to O. Brunck, the film of oxide formed on a tantalum anode in the
electrolysis of metal salt soln. is probably **tantalum tetroxide,** Ta_2O_4.
J. J. Berzelius and J. G. Gahn obtained what was probably this oxide, in an impure
state, by heating tantalum pentoxide for an hour in a closed carbon crucible ;

W. von Bolton, by electrically heating to 1700° rods of tantalum pentoxide embedded in carbon ; and E. F. Smith and P. Maas, by heating the pentoxide mixed with five parts by weight of magnesium, and treating the product with dil. hydrochloric acid to remove magnesium and magnesia, there remained a blue, dark grey, dark brown, or black mass, which, when rubbed in a mortar, does not give a metallic lustre. W. von Bolton said that it scratches glass, and is a good electrical conductor—J. J. Berzelius and J. G. Gahn said that it is a non-conductor and when heated in oxygen forms the pentoxide. It gives no carbon dioxide when fused with potassium nitrate ; it forms a tantalate when fused with potassium hydroxide ; and it is not attacked by acids, or by aqua regia.

REFERENCES.

[1] R. Hermann, *Journ. prakt. Chem.*, (2), 5. 69, 1892 ; W. von Bolton, *Zeit. Elektrochem.*, 11. 45, 1905 ; J. J. Berzelius and J. G. Gahn, *Afh. Fys. Kemi Min.*, 4. 252, 1815 ; J. J. Berzelius, *Schweigger's Journ.*, 16. 437, 1816 ; *Pogg. Ann.*, 4. 10, 1825 ; E. F. Smith and P. Maas, *Zeit. anorg. Chem.*, 7. 98, 1894 ; A. G. Ekeberg, *Akad. Nya Handl.*, 23. 180, 1802 ; *Nicholson's Journ.*, 3. 251, 1802 ; *Gilbert's Ann.*, 14. 246, 1803 ; K. Friederich, *Zeit. Physik.* 31. 813, 1925 ; K. Friederich and L. Sittig, *Zeit. anorg. Chem.*, 145. 127, 1925 ; W. K. van Haagen and E. F. Smith, *Journ. Amer. Chem. Soc.*, 33. 1505, 1911 ; O. Brunck, *Chem. Ztg.*, 36. 1233, 1912.

§ 6. Tantalum Pentoxide and Tantalic Acid

According to J. J. Berzelius [1] powdered tantalum begins to glow when heated below redness in air, forming **tantalum pentoxide**, Ta_2O_5 ; and H. Moissan said that the metal begins to burn in dry oxygen below 600°. W. Muthmann and co-workers said that when the powdered metal is rapidly heated to redness in oxygen, it becomes incandescent, and the pentoxide is formed ; the oxidation of the metal begins below redness but is not completed at that temp. The calcination of the hydroxide—*vide infra*—or one of the lower oxides (*q.v.*) furnishes the pentoxide. W. K. van Haagen obtained the pentoxide by roasting the sulphide, or treating it with nitric acid ; by treating the pentafluoride or a fluotantalate with conc. sulphuric acid, washing with boiling water and calcining ; hydrolyzing the pentachloride or pentabromide with water and calcining ; or by treating these substances with oxidizing agents. The preparation of the pentoxide from the tantaliferrous minerals has been described in connection with columbium. O. Ruff and F. Thomas said that tantalum pentoxide is best purified by converting it into potassium fluotantalate or sodium tantalate and treating the product repeatedly with conc. sulphuric acid.

According to W. Muthmann and co-workers, tantalum pentoxide is a white powder which remains white when hot, but then has a faint yellow tinge ; if titanium oxide be present, the colour of the cold oxide may be yellow and when hot, orange. M. Delafontaine said that the yellow colour of H. Rose's product was due to the presence of some columbium pentoxide. H. Rose, and G. Tammann said that if the oxide be strongly heated it becomes crystalline ; and H. Rose said that the oxide obtained from fused potassium hydrosulphate is a microcrystalline powder after it has been calcined with ammonium carbonate. J. J. Ebelmen found that prismatic **crystals** are produced by strongly heating the oxide with boric oxide ; and E. Mallard obtained colourless, rhombic needles by heating it with microcosmic salt in a porcelain oven ; the axial ratios were $a : b : c = 0.8288 : 1 : 0.8239$. P. J. Holmquist prepared rhombic plates appearing like hexagonal plates owing to twinning, by heating the pentoxide with boric oxide in a porcelain oven. Observations on the crystals were also made by A. E. Nordenskjöld and J. J. Chydenius. According to H. Rose, the product obtained by calcining tantalic acid, precipitated from tantalum pentachloride by water, is amorphous, and has a **specific gravity** 7·28 ; that obtained from **tantalic acid** which has been slowly formed by exposure to a moist atm., is crystalline and has a sp. gr. 7·284 ; that obtained by fusion with potassium hydrosulphate and calcination with ammonium carbonate is crystalline and has a sp. gr. 7·055–7·066, and after heating 45 mins. at a white-heat, it has a sp. gr. 7·986. After heating in a porcelain oven, at about 1600°, the sp. gr. is 8·257. Hence, the sp. gr. of the product depends on its mode of formation, or on the temp. at which it has been heated. W. K. van Haagen's product had a sp. gr. 7·58 when obtained by calcining the product from the hydrolysis of the pentabromide. J. C. G. de Marignac's product from fused potassium hydrosulphate had a sp. gr. 7·6 ; and that obtained by calcining the product of the action of sulphuric acid on ammonium fluotantalate, 8·01. F. W. Hinrichsen and N. Sahlbom gave 7·53 for the sp. gr.; W. Muthmann and co-workers, 7·5108–7·5867 at 20°; H. St. C. Deville and L. Troost, 7·35 ; C. W. Balke, 7·91–8·62 ; and P. J. Holmquist gave 7·7775 for the crystals obtained by calcination with boric oxide. D. Balareff, and C. del Fresno studied the mol. vol. O. Hahn and K. E. Pütter found that tantalic acid is not volatile, and the loss observed when commercial tantalic acid is heated, is due to the alkali which it contains. For the **flame luminescence,** *vide* columbium pentoxide. A. Karl said that the oxide is triboluminescent.

E. Tiede and E. Birnbräuer said that the pentoxide does not vaporize, and does not melt at 1650°. J. J. Berzelius observed the **calorescence** of the heated oxide, and J. Böhm showed by X-radiograms that the effect is due to the passage from an amorphous to the crystalline state. W. Muthmann found the **heat of formation** to be 837·9 cals., or 30·8 Cals. per gram-equivalent. J. E. Moose and S. W. Parr gave 1375 cals. per gram. H. Rose said that the **electrical conductivity** of the pentoxide is nil ; but this statement does not apply to the heated oxide. K. Freiderich gave ∞ ohms per sq. mm. for the electrical resistance of the pentoxide. G. von Hevesy showed that the **electrode potential** Ta : Ta_2O_5 against the normal calomel electrode is 0·003 to 0·007 volt. S. Berkman and H. Zocher gave $-0·07 \times 10^{-6}$ for the **magnetic susceptibility.**

H. Rose said that tantalum pentoxide remains white after it has been heated to redness in **hydrogen.** H. von Wartenberg and co-workers did not reduce tantalum pentoxide by hydrogen at 2500° and 5 atm. press. E. F. Smith and P. Maas observed that the heated pentoxide is not attacked by **chlorine** unless it be mixed with carbon ; similar remarks apply to the action of **bromine.** According to H. Rose, and W. K. van Haagen, **iodine** does not react with the pentoxide in a sealed tube at 280° ; nor does the vapour react with a heated mixture of the pentoxide and carbon. Unlike columbium pentoxide, tantalum pentoxide is not attacked when strongly heated in **hydrogen chloride,** or in **hydrogen bromide.** W. K. van Haagen and E. F. Smith found that **hydrogen fluoride** converts the tantalum into volatile fluoride. J. J. Berzelius said that the pentoxide is insoluble in **acids—hydrochloric acid** and **hydrofluoric acid**—but M. E. Pennington found it soluble in conc. hydrofluoric acid. Although H. Rose stated that the pentoxide can be completely volatilized by heating it to redness with admixed **ammonium fluoride.** O. Ruff and E. Schiller said that no tantalum fluoride is formed, and no tantalum is lost by volatilization. In the absence of carbon, E. F. Smith and P. Maas found that the red-hot pentoxide is not affected by the vapour of **sulphur ;** J. J. Berzelius noted that only a trace of sulphide is formed when **hydrogen sulphide** is heated in a current of hydrogen sulphide ; H. Biltz and C. Kirchner agreed with this state-ment, and added that the pentoxide at 720° is coloured superficially grey by hydrogen sulphide. E. F. Smith observed that the **sulphur monochloride** dissolves tantalum oxide when the mixture is heated. J. J. Berzelius said that the pentoxide is not soluble in conc. **sulphuric acid ;** and M. E. Pennington found that it is not coloured by **hyposulphurous acid.** H. Rose, and A. Joly observed that when the pentoxide is heated in **ammonia** gas, the nitride is formed. J. J. Berzelius said that the pentoxide is insoluble in nitric acid. M. E. Pennington observed that in a sealed tube at 180°–245°, **phosphorus pentachloride** converts the pentoxide into the pentachloride. J. J. Berzelius and J. G. Gahn found that **carbon** at a white-heat converts the pentoxide into tantalum and its tetroxide. H. Moissan observed the

3 M

formation of a carbide—*vide supra*—when the pentoxide is reduced at a high temp. by carbon. R. E. Slade and G. I. Higson found the equilibrium press. of the oxide mixed with carbon to be less than 0·1 mm. at 1270°. M. Delafontaine and E. C. Linebarger showed that the heated pentoxide is attacked by the vapour of **carbon tetrachloride,** and P. Camboulives added that if air be excluded the formation of tantalum pentachloride begins at 250°. O. Ruff and F. Thomas said that tantalum pentoxide is not affected by carbon tetrachloride at 200°–225°. H. Rose observed that **carbon disulphide** reacts with red-hot tantalum pentoxide, forming the disulphide. E. F. Smith and P. Maas observed that a brownish-black mass with about 3·5 per cent. of **magnesium** is produced when the pentoxide is heated with magnesium in a current of hydrogen; they also tested the action of **aluminium**—*vide supra*, tantalum aluminide. According to L. Weiss and M. Landecker, molten **potassium hydroxide** dissolves the pentoxide, forming a mass which is soluble in water—*vide infra* for the action of the **alkali carbonates** and hydroxides. H. Rose also observed that the strongly calcined pentoxide dissolves with difficulty in fused **potassium hydrosulphate,** and a large excess of the latter —say 1 : 10—is required to open up the pentoxide. L. Weiss and M. Landecker opened up the oxide with this reagent, and also with a molten mixture of sodium carbonate and **borax.** H. Rose found that if the pentoxide is not too strongly calcined, it dissolves in molten **ammonium hydrosulphide.** J. A. Hedvall and N. von Zweigbergk studied the action of **barium dioxide** on the pentoxide. J. J. Berzelius and J. G. Gahn observed no reaction when the pentoxide is heated with **mercuric sulphide.** O. Ruff and F. Thomas found that tantalum pentoxide reacts with **columbium pentachloride,** forming tantalum pentachloride and columbium oxychloride.

According to H. Rose, in the hydrolysis of tantalum pentachloride by water, an amorphous precipitate is produced if water be mixed with the pentachloride, and if the pentachloride be exposed to a moist atm., the product is crystalline. It requires a prolonged washing with water to remove the hydrochloric acid ; dil. aq. ammonia removes the acid much more quickly. When dried in air, the **tantalum hydroxide** contains over 20 per cent. water, *i.e.* $Ta_2O_5.5H_2O$, and when dried at 100°, 6–8 per cent., thus approximating $Ta_2O_5.H_2O$, or **metatantalic acid,** $HTaO_3$. H. Rose also obtained tantalic acid by treating a soln. of sodium tantalate with sulphur dioxide, and washing the product with cold water—aq. ammonia extracts a little sulphuric acid ; by fusing the pentoxide with potassium hydrosulphate, and washing the product with water, then with aq. ammonia to remove sulphates, and finally with water. The peptization of the precipitate during the washing is prevented by using $\frac{1}{2}$ per cent. aq. ammonia, or one per cent. acetic acid.

According to O. Hauser and A. Lewite, **colloidal tantalum hydroxide** is produced by melting a mixture of tantalum pentoxide and sodium hydroxide in a silver crucible ; dissolving the cold mass in water ; and dialyzing the soln. with parchment for about 10 days. The properties of the sol resemble those of the sol of columbium hydroxide, but unlike the latter, the hydroxide is completely precipitated by carbon dioxide ; it is also precipitated by ammonium oxalate.

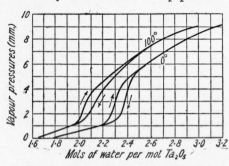

FIG. 1.—Vapour Pressures of Hydrated Tantalum Pentoxide.

G. Jander and H. Schulz showed that there is a continuous variation in the water content with varying vap. press., Fig. 1 ; and that the rehydration, and redrying curves resemble those obtained with hydrated silica. The hysteresis cycle at 100° is smaller than that at 0°, and is displaced more towards the side of lower water content. **The** hydrated oxide remained white and chalky under all conditions.

Tantalum hydroxide appears as a white, amorphous, or crystalline powder. **At** a dull red-heat the water is expelled, and, as noted by J. J. Berzelius, a calorescence occurs, which H. Rose found to be less marked if the precipitate has been previously washed with hot water. L. Weiss and M. Landecker found that the hydroxide is less soluble in dil. **acids** than is the case with columbium hydroxide ; H. Rose said that at the moment of formation it is soluble in different acids, the presence of **hydrogen dioxide** accelerates the speed of dissolution of the hydroxide in acids, aq. ammonia, in soln. of ammonium chloride, or sodium hydroxide, carbonate, hydrosulphate. The dissolved hydroxide is reprecipitated when the hydrogen dioxide is decomposed. A. A. Noyes found that tantalic acid is only slightly soluble in hydrogen dioxide ; W. B. Giles, that it is completely dissolved when suspended in dil. sulphuric or hydrochloric acid and hydrogen dioxide ; and O. Hahn and H. Gille, that when precipitated from hot soln. it is almost insoluble, but from cold soln. it is slightly soluble in acid hydrogen dioxide. As indicated by H. Rose, and C. W. Balke, it forms a clear soln. with **hydrofluoric acid ;** R. F. Weinland and L. Storz found that only a trace dissolves in cold, highly conc. **hydrochloric acid,** so that dil. soln. of tantalates become opalescent when treated with the conc. acid ; with dil. acids there is no precipitate on warming. The hydroxide is insoluble in **perchloric acid.** A little hydroxide dissolves in boiling, conc. sulphuric acid, and the soln. becomes turbid when poured into water, but the tantalum is not completely precipitated by the dilution even if the soln. be boiled. The action of **nitric acid** is like that of hydrochloric acid, but the solvent action is smaller. The hydroxide is insoluble in **phosphoric acid ;** and also in **phosphorus, and hypophosphorus acids.** The freshly precipitated hydroxide is soluble in **oxalic and tartaric acids ;** and, added J. J. Berzelius and J. G. Gahn, and R. D. Hall, in a soln. of **potassium oxalate.** Tantalic acid readily dissolves in **hydrofluosilicic acid.** Freshly precipitated tantalum hydroxide is easily soluble in aq. soln. of **alkali hydroxide,** and it dissolves in a soln. of **sodium carbonate** less easily than does columbium hydroxide ; it is insoluble in soln. of sodium hydrocarbonate, or of ammonium carbonate. The solubility is perceptibly smaller if the hydroxide has been allowed to stand more than a few hours, at room temp., without being covered with an aq. soln., and disappears after warming the hydroxide to about 110°. H. Rose said that tantalic acid does not displace carbon dioxide from a soln. of the alkali carbonates. H. Lange found that a soln. of **ammonium salicylate** gives a flesh-coloured precipitate insoluble in hot water, and in a soln. of ammonium salicylate—*vide* Tables II and III, **9.** 55, 4. E. Wedekind and H. Fischer found that colloidal tantalic acid does not adsorb prussian blue.

REFERENCES.

¹ J. J. Berzelius and J. G. Gahn, *Afh. Fys. Kemi Min.*, **4.** 252, 1815 ; J. J. Berzelius, *Lehrbuch der Chemie*, Dresden, 3. 158, 1834 ; *Schweigger's Journ.*, 16. 437, 1816 ; *Pogg. Ann.*, 4. 10, 1825 ; H. Rose, *ib.*, **74.** 285, 1848 ; **99.** 66, 1856 ; **100.** 145, 422, 1857 ; A. E. Nordenskjöld and J. J. Chydenius, *ib.*, 110. 645, 1860 ; *Oefvers. Akad. Förh.*, 3, 1860 ; *Chem. News*, 4. 102, 1861 ; W. Muthmann, L. Weiss, and R. Riedelbach, *Liebig's Ann.*, 355. 84, 1907 ; W. K. van Haagen, *Tantalum and some of its Halides*, Easton, Pa., 1909 ; *Journ. Amer. Chem. Soc.*, 32. 729, 1910 ; M. Delafontaine, *Arch. Sciences Genève*, (2), **27.** 167, 1866 ; M. Delafontaine and E. C. Linebarger, *Journ. Amer. Chem. Soc.*, 18. 535, 1896 ; M. E. Pennington, *ib.*, 18. 64, 1896 ; *Chem. News*, 75. 8, 18, 31, 38, 1897 ; *Derivatives of Columbium and Tantalum*, Easton, Pa., 1895 ; C. W. Balke, *Double Fluorides of Tantalum*, Easton, Pa., 1908 ; C. W. Balke and E. F. Smith, *Journ. Amer. Chem. Soc.*, 30. 1648, 1908 ; W. K. van Haagen and E. F. Smith, *ib.*, 33. 1504, 1911 ; E. F. Smith, *ib.*, 20. 289, 1898 ; R. D. Hall, *ib.*, 26. 1241, 1904 ; *Observations on the Metallic Acids*, Easton, Pa., 1904 ; J. E. Moose and S. W. Parr, *Journ. Amer. Chem. Soc.*, 46. 2656, 1924 ; E. F. Smith and P. Maas, *Zeit. anorg. Chem.*, 7. 96, 1894 ; J. Böhm, *ib.*, 149. 217, 1925 ; R. F. Weinland and L. Storz, *ib.*, 54. 224, 1907 ; O. Ruff and E. Schiller, *ib.*, 72. 355, 1911 ; G. Jander and H. Schulz, *ib.*, 144. 225, 1925 ; L. Weiss and M. Landecker, *ib.*, 64. 98, 1909 ; *Untersuchungen über die quantitative Bestimmung der Erdsäuren*, München, 1911 ; K. Friederich, *Zeit. Physik*, 31. 318, 1925 ; G. Tammann, *Ann. Physik*, (4), **9.** 249, 1902 ; H. Lange, *Zeit. Naturwiss.*, 82. 29, 1910 ;

P. J. Holmquist, *Bull. Geol. Inst. Upsala*, 3. 205, 1897 ; E. Mallard, *Ann. Mines*, (8), 12. 427, 1887 ; J. J. Ebelmen, *Ann. Chim. Phys.*, (3), 33. 34, 1851 ; J. C. G. de Marignac, *ib.*, (4), 9. 254, 1866 ; *Compt. Rend.*, 63. 85, 1866 ; *Arch. Sciences Genève*, (2), 26. 89, 1866 ; H. St. C. Deville and L. Troost, *Compt. Rend.*, 64. 294, 1867 ; P. Camboulives, *ib.*, 150. 175, 1910 ; A. Karl, *ib.*, 146. 1104, 1908 ; F. W. Hinrichsen and N. Sahlbom, *Ber.*, 39. 2600, 1906 ; G. von Hevesy, *Zeit. Elektrochem.*, 18. 456, 1912 ; E. Wedekind and W. Maas, *Zeit. angew. Chem.*, 23. 2315, 1910 ; O. Hauser and A. Lewite, *ib.*, 25. 102, 1912 ; A. Joly, *Ann. École Norm.*, (2), 6. 151, 1877 ; *Bull. Soc. Chim.*, (2), 25. 506, 1876 ; H. Moissan, *ib.*, (3), 27. 434, 1902 ; *Compt. Rend.*, 134. 211, 1902 ; J. A. Hedvall and N. von Zweigbergk, *Zeit. anorg. Chem.*, 108. 119, 1919 ; O. Ruff and F. Thomas, *ib.*, 156. 213, 1926 ; J. Böhm, *ib.*, 140. 217, 1925 ; O. Hahn and K. E. Pütter, *ib.*, 127. 153, 1923 ; O. Hahn and H. Gille, *ib.*, 112. 283, 1920 ; E. Tiede and E. Birnbräuer, *ib.*, 87. 129, 1914 ; H. von Wartenberg, J. Broy, and R. Reinecke, *Zeit. Elektrochem.*, 29. 214, 1923 ; A. A. Noyes, *Tech. Quart.*, 17. 214, 1904 ; *Chem. News*, 93. 180, 1906 ; W. B. Giles, *ib.*, 95. 1, 1907 ; R. E. Slade and G. I. Higson, *B.A. Rep.*, 450, 1913 ; S. Berkman and H. Zocher, *Zeit. phys. Chem.*, 124. 318, 1927 ; C. del Fresno, *Anal. Fis. Quim.*, 24. 707, 1926 ; D. Balareff, *Journ. prakt. Chem.*, (2), 102. 283, 1921 ; E. Wedekind and H. Fischer, *Ber.*, 60. B, 544, 1927 ; H. Biltz and C. Kirchner, *ib.*, 43. 1636, 1910.

§ 7. The Tantalates

Tantalic acid forms a series of salts called **tantalates**. Many of these occur in nature , others can be prepared by first making an alkali tantalate, and treating a soln. of that salt with soln. of other metal salts. Some tantalates are also obtained by fusing the metal chloride with tantalum pentoxide. The alkali tantalate $R_2O : Ta_2O_5=4 : 3$ seems to be the most stable form. G. Jander and H. Schulz [1] said that this ratio should be 7 : 5 not 4 : 3. The tantalates, insoluble in water, can be dissolved in molten ammonium or potassium hydroxide, and, if they have not been calcined, in boiling sulphuric acid. The oxygen of the tantalates can be partially replaced by chlorine or bromine—*vide infra*, the oxyhalides.

According to H. Rose, tantalum hydroxide precipitated by ammonia from acid soln. always contains ammonia ; and when a soln. of sodium tantalate is treated with ammonium chloride, and the precipitate washed with cold water, **ammonium triterohexatantalate**, $(NH_4)_2Ta_6O_{16}.5H_2O$, or $(NH_4)_2O.3Ta_2O_5.5H_2O$, is formed. In the presence of alkali hydroxide or carbonate, the precipitation is slow in the cold, rapid when heated. The salt is a little soluble in water.

A. Joly observed that at a red-heat calcined tantalum pentoxide or tantalic acid unites with molten sodium hydroxide with incandescence ; the resulting sodium tantalate does not dissolve in the matrix. H. Rose, and J. J. Berzelius observed that with potassium hydroxide the product is completely soluble in water. According to A. Joly, when the pentoxide is fused with sodium carbonate, carbon dioxide is expelled less readily than from potassium carbonate ; and less readily, again, than is the case with columbium pentoxide. The amount of carbon dioxide expelled depends on the duration and temp. of fusion. In one case, A. Joly obtained a loss corresponding with the formation of *sodium orthotantalate*, $3Na_2O.Ta_2O_5$, or Na_3TaO_4 ; and H. Rose, using potassium carbonate, obtained a loss eq. to the formation of $10K_2O.3Ta_2O_5$. F. Oesten reported an acid tantalate—Na_2O, 2·23 per cent. ; Ta_2O_5, 97·77 per cent.—or more probably a mixture of tantalates to be formed by melting tantalic acid with potassium hydrocarbonate (1 : 5), washing and drying the resulting sulphatotantalic acid ; treating the product with cold soda-lye for a long time, and washing the mass with hot water. H. Rose also noticed that a tantalate with a low proportion of soda is produced by washing the metatantalate with water for a long time. All this means that the alkali tantalates are slowly hydrolyzed by water. A. Lottermoser obtained acid sodium tantalate by the method he used for the acid columbate.

H. Rose reported **sodium hexerotetradecatantalate**, $2Na_2O_5.7Ta_2O_5.10H_2O$, to be precipitated when carbon dioxide is passed into an aq. soln. of the orthohexatantalate, and drying the pale yellow product at 100° ; hydrogen sulphide gives a similar result, but acts more quickly than carbon dioxide. W. R. Schoeller and C. Jahn studied the sodium tantalates. By repeatedly heating potassium orthohexatantalate with ammonium chloride, and extracting the mass with water, H. Rose obtained what he regarded as **potassium penterotetradecatantalate**, $3K_5O.7Ta_2O_5$. By treating with carbon dioxide an aq. soln. of tantalum pentoxide in molten potassium hydroxide, H. Rose obtained **potassium deuterotetratantalate**, $K_2O.2Ta_2O_5.3H_2O$, or **potassium deuterohexatantalate**, $2K_2O.3Ta_2O_5.6H_2O$.

According to J. C. G. de Marignac, when sodium orthohexatantalate is heated alone, or, according to H. Rose, when it is heated with ammonium carbonate, and extracted with water, **sodium metatantalate**, $NaTaO_3.2H_2O$, is formed. H. Rose obtained the same salt by mixing an aq. soln. of the orthohexatantalate with its own vol. of alcohol, washing the precipitate with conc. alcohol; calcining; and washing the product with a very dil. soln. of ammonium carbonate—if water alone be used, peptization occurs. The metatantalate is also produced by fusing tantalic acid with twice its weight of sodium carbonate, extracting the excess of alkali with water; washing the residue with hot water; drying; and calcining the product. J. C. G. de Marignac reported **potassium metatantalate**, $KTaO_3$, to be formed by calcining the orthohexatantalate alone, or, according to H. Rose, with ammonium carbonate, and extracting the product with water. C. W. Balke and E. F. Smith obtained **cæsium orthododecatantalate**, $7Cs_2O.6Ta_2O_5.38H_2O$, as a precipitate, by treating an aq. soln. of the orthohexatantalate with alcohol.

According to H. Rose, when tantalum pentoxide is fused with twice its weight of sodium hydroxide, and the excess of alkali removed from the cold mass with cold water, the residue containing all the tantalum dissolves in hot water, and on cooling this soln., small crystals of **sodium orthohexatantalate**, $4Na_2O.3Ta_2O_5.25H_2O$, or $Na_8Ta_6O_{19}.25H_2O$, are formed. J. C. G. de Marignac also prepared this salt, but said that some acid salt is present, and added that the salt of a high degree of purity was produced by H. Rose by extracting the cold, fused mass, just indicated, with water; washing the residue until the wash-water no longer colours litmus blue, or silver nitrate brown; and drying in vacuo over sulphuric acid. The salt was analyzed by H. Rose, J. C. G. de Marignac, and R. Hermann. G. Jander and H. Schulz said that the ratio should be 7 : 5 not 4 : 3; and they represented the salts as derivatives of **hydropentatantalic acid**, $H_7[Ta(TaO_4)_4]$. The acid is probably a complex one in which the oxygen atoms of orthotantalic acid have been replaced by the TaO_4-groups. The sodium salt is **sodium pentatantalate**, $7Na_2O.5Ta_2O_5.24H_2O$, or $K_7[Ta(TaO_4)_4].24H_2O$. They prepared the alkali tantalates by fusing the hydroxides with tantalum pentoxide and crystallizing from water; tantalic acid is precipitated from the aq. soln. by acids, including carbonic acid, but the precipitate is soluble in excess of strong acid. Different proportions of potassium hydroxide and tantalum pentoxide always lead to the same crystalline tantalate; from highly conc. soln. crystals of different form were obtained, but these were readily converted into the first form, and probably differed only in water of crystallization. By the addition of sodium hydroxide to aq. potassium tantalate two sodium salts, also differing only in water of crystallization, were obtained, namely, the *heptahydrate*, $Na_7[Ta(TaO_4)_4].11H_2O$, and the *icosihydrate* $Na_7[Ta(TaO_4)_4].20H_2O$. The **lithium pentatantalate**, $Li_7[Ta(TaO_4)_4].20H_2O$, was similarly prepared. According to J. C. G. de Marignac, the colourless, hexagonal plates of the sodium salt have the axial ratio $a : c = 1 : 1 \cdot 0167$. H. Rose found that all but 2–4 per cent. of water is expelled at 100°, and E. Wedekind and W. Maas suggested that 4 or 5 mols. of water are constitutional. H. Rose suggested that when the salt is so heated, it is resolved into an acid salt and sodium hydroxide. The decomposition proceeds more readily in the presence of ammonium chloride, and the acid salt acts on the sodium carbonate and carbon dioxide is expelled. The moist product colours red litmus blue. If the salt be rapidly heated, the water is all expelled, and if heated with ammonium carbonate, it gives only a small loss in weight, and the moist product does not colour red litmus blue. E. Wedekind and W. Maas prepared a salt similar to that obtained by H. Rose. They added that 10·5 mols. of water are lost at 105°–110°; another mol. at 190°; and the last mol.

requires a much higher temp. They therefore represented it by the formula
$Na_4HTa_3O_{10}.12\cdot32H_2O$, or, probably,

$$\begin{matrix}(HO)_2 \\ (NaO)_2\end{matrix} \gg Ta.O.\overset{\overset{OH}{|}}{\underset{\underset{O}{|}}{Ta}}.O.Ta \ll \begin{matrix}(OH)_2 \\ (ONa)_2\end{matrix} \quad +10H_2O$$

When dehydrated, the hexatantalate is formed. H. Rose found that 100 parts of water at 13·5° dissolve 0·203 part of salt, and when boiling, 0·617 part. The salt suffers some hydrolysis, and colours red litmus blue. J. C. G. de Marignac found that when this compound is boiled with water a more acid salt is formed. H. Rose added that sulphur dioxide precipitates all the tantalum from the aq. soln., while hydrogen sulphide or carbon dioxide precipitates acid salts—*vide supra*. The salt is only sparingly soluble in alcohol ; and when alcohol is added to the aq. soln., a precipitate is formed, which, when dried at 100°, has the composition : $Na_2O.Ta_2O_5.2H_2O$ W. E. von John observed that the salt is insoluble in soda-lye. J. C. G. de Marignac, and H. Rose prepared **potassium orthohexatantalate**, $4K_2O.3Ta_2O_5.16H_2O$, from a molten mixture of tantalum pentoxide with potassium hydroxide or carbonate. Analyses of the salt were made by H. Rose, J. C. G. de Marignac, and R. Hermann. As indicated above, G. Jander and H. Schulz's analysis agrees with **potassium pentatantalate**, $K_7[Ta(TaO_4)_4].12H_2O$, and its mode of preparation is there indicated. G. Jander and H. Schulz said that in the alkali tantalates the ratio $M_2O : Ta_2O_5$ is 7 : 5, and the basicity of the tantalic acid is at least six, according to the variation of the conductivity with the dilution. Potassium tantalate may be represented as $K_7[Ta(TaO_4)_4]$ with a mol. wt. of about 1440. 0·5N-soln. of potassium tantalate had a diffusion coeff. of 0·24 when dissolved in 0·1N-KOH, or 0·1N-KNO_3, and a high value in water. The mol. wt. of potassium tantalate is therefore 1750. The crystals of the salt were found by J. C. G. de Marignac to be monoclinic prisms with the axial ratios $a : b : c = 0\cdot7164 : 1 : 0\cdot5475$, and $\beta = 95° 19'$. The salt is partially decomposed at 100° into an acid salt and potassium hydroxide ; and after the salt has been heated to redness, water abstracts one-fourth of the alkali and leaves the metatantalate behind. A similar result was obtained by H. Rose after heating the salt with ammonium carbonate. J. C. G. de Marignac found that the salt can be dissolved in warm water without decomposition, and it recrystallizes from the soln. on evaporation in vacuo—but not so readily as before. If the aq. soln. be boiled or evaporated in air, hydrolysis occurs, and an acidic salt is precipitated. H. Rose found that the longer the salt is boiled with water the greater the proportion of alkali extracted. W. E. von John said that the salt is soluble in potash-lye. According to J. Morgenroth and F. Rosenthal, potassium hexatantalate does not kill the trypanosomes of mice, though it seems to inhibit their transmission from one form to another,· and it also inhibits the poisonous action of antimony compounds on the trypanosomes of mice, and on mice themselves. C. W. Balke and E. F. Smith obtained colourless, transparent, monoclinic pyramids of **rubidium orthohexatantalate**, $Rb_4Ta_6O_{19}.14H_2O$, by fusing a mixture of 15 grms. of tantalum pentoxide and 25 grms. of rubidium carbonate, extracting the cold mass with a little warm water, and cooling. The axial ratios are $a : b : c = 0\cdot8822 : 1 : 1\cdot0510$, and $\beta = 95° 58'$; and the crystals are isomorphous with the corresponding columbium salt. Monoclinic prisms of **cæsium orthohexatantalate**, $Cs_4Ta_6O_{19}.14H_2O$, were produced in a similar way ; they are isomorphous with the corresponding columbate. H. Rose treated a soln. of sodium orthohexatantalate with silver nitrate and obtained a white precipitate, which has a yellow tinge when dry ; it is **silver orthohexatantalate**, $Ag_4Ta_6O_{19}$. At 100°, it becomes dark yellow, brown, and finally black ; and loses 2·1–2·3 per cent. in weight when calcined. Hydrogen reduces the silver but not the tantalum pentoxide at a red-heat ; ammonia dissolves the salt completely ; and it is decomposed by nitric acid with the separation of tantalum pentoxide.

J. J. Berzelius [2] obtained a calcium tantalate of an undetermined composition by digesting tantalic acid with calcium chloride. The mineral **pyrrhite** was described in connection with the rare earths—**5**. 38, 3. R. Brauns represented his incomplete analysis as if the mineral were **calcium orthotantalate,** $Ca_3(TaO_4)_2$, associated with some acid radicle. It forms yellowish- or brownish-red, isotropic octahedra ; the sp. gr. is 4·13 ; the hardness, 5·5 ; and the index of refraction, over 1·83. The mineral **microlite** has been discussed from the point of view of the rare earths—**5**. 38, 3. W. C. Brögger, and E. S. Simpson reported a number of additional analyses ; and the idealized formula is $Ca_2Ta_2O_7$, **calcium pyrotantalate,** where some tantalum is replaced by columbium. R. J. Strutt found that it also contained helium—0·5 c.c. per gram—radium—3·7×10⁻⁸ per cent. $RaBr_2$— thorium, and uranium—1·89 per cent. U_3O_8. The radioactivity is 0·101 when that of U_3O_8 is unity ; and the ratio Ra : U=1·96. E. S. Larsen gave 1·930 for the index of refraction. A. Joly obtained the pyro-salt by heating the meta-salt with calcium chloride for 7–8 hrs. ; and P. J. Holmquist, by melting a mixture of calcium chloride and tantalum pentoxide. The prismatic and acicular crystals belong to the cubic system, and they may have an abnormal double refraction. A. Joly said rhombic—if so, the salt is dimorphous. The crystals of microlite are cubic, and the sp. gr. is 5·17–5·65, and the hardness 6. The mineral **pyrochlore** has been discussed from the point of view of the rare earths—**5**. 38, 3—and, according to T. L. Walker and A. L. Parsons, it is also to be regarded as an impure **calcium metacolumbate,** $Ca(CbO_3)_2$, with part of the columbium replaced by tantalum— *vide infra,* fluotantalates. A. Joly synthesized calcium metatantalate by heating the pentoxide with calcium chloride for some hours at a bright red-heat, and obtained a crystalline mass of this salt on the bottom and walls of the crucible. The brown octahedral crystals of pyrochlore belong to the cubic system ; the sp. gr. is 4·2– 4·4 ; the hardness 5·0–5·5 ; and the m.p., 1340°—*vide* **5**. 38, 3. E. S. Larsen gave μ=1·96 for the index of refraction ; and S. Kreutz found for light of wave-length $\lambda \times 10^{-5}$ cm., the following values for the indices of refraction, μ :

λ	7·00	6·86	6·56 (C)	5·89 (D)	5·18 (b)	4·86 (F)
$\mu\{$ I	1·9818	1·9831	1·9866	1·9995	2·0234	2·0363
II	2·0076	—	—	2·0248	—	2·0363

The differences between I and II are due to non-homogeneity of the material, a subject discussed by O. Mügge, and V. M. Goldschmidt as an example of what they call the *Isotropisierung* of mineral—a result of changes induced by the presence or proximity of radioactive minerals. The related minerals, *marignacite, loranscite,* and *wiikite,* were discussed in connection with the rare earths—**5**. 38, 3. E. S. Larsen gave 2·0 for the index of refraction of wiikite. T. L. Walker and A. L. Parsons described an amber-yellow or dark chocolate, massive mineral from Hybla, Ontario, which they called **ellsworthite**—after H. V. Ellsworth. The mineral is isotropic; the sp. gr. 3·608 (yellow), and 3·758 (brown) ; and the hardness, 4. The analyses are represented by the idealized formula of *dihydrated* calcium metacolumbate, $Ca(CbO_3)_2.2H_2O$, but considerable $(UO_2)''$, Fe'', and traces of other elements replace Ca ; much Ti ; some Ta, Si, U'''', and traces of other elements replace the Cb ; and a little fluorine is present. E. T. Wherry applied the at. vol. replacement theory—*cf.* **6**. 40, 44. J. J. Berzelius and J. G. Gahn obtained what was probably **barium orthohexatantalate,** $Ba_4Ta_6O_{19}.6H_2O$, by the action of barium chloride on tantalic acid ; and H. Rose, by the action of barium chloride on soln. of sodium orthohexatantalate, washing the precipitate with cold water, and drying at 100°. The salt is strongly calorescent when calcined. It is but slightly soluble in cold water. It is decomposed by fusion with potassium hydroxide.

H. Rose added magnesium sulphate to a soln. of sodium orthohexatantalate, and obtained a flocculent precipitate which became crystalline on standing for half an hour. It was washed with cold water and dried at 100°, when the analysis corresponded with **magnesium orthohexatantalate,** $Mg_4Ta_6O_{19}.9H_2O$. It showed no calorescence when heated. A. Joly made hexagonal crystals of what he regarded as $4MgO.Ta_2O_5$—magnesium dioxyorthotantalate—by a method employed for the corresponding dioxyorthocolumbate. H. Rose prepared mercurous ortho-hexatantalate, $4Hg_2O.3Ta_2O_5.5H_2O$, by adding a freshly prepared soln. of mercurous nitrate to one of sodium orthohexatantalate, washing with cold water, and drying at 100°. The yellow mass becomes brown at 100°; it is decomposed by warm nitric acid. Mercuric nitrate gives a white precipitate of presumably mercuric orthohexatantalate, $4HgO.3Ta_2O_5.nH_2O$, under similar conditions; mercuric chloride gives a precipitate very slowly, and if alkali hydroxide is present some mercury oxychloride is also formed.

J. J. Berzelius precipitated aluminium tantalate by adding an aluminium salt to a soln. of alkali tantalate. T. Barth [3] obtained yttrium tantalate, $YTaO_4$, as in the case of the columbate (q.v.). The X-radiogram shows that unit tetra-gonal cell has $a=7.75$ A.; $c=11.41$ A.; and $a:c=1:1.47$. The mineral koppite has been described from the point of view of the rare earths—5. 38, 3. It is a calcium rare earth columbatotantalate, but an approximate formula has not been derived from the analysis. It was examined by J. Soellner, and H. V. Ellsworth and J. F. Walker. E. S. Larsen gave 2.12–2.18 for the index of refraction, and the radioactivity was examined by G. Meyer. Vide 5. 38, 3, for polycrase, and euxenite. The neotantalite of 5. 38, 3, is a related mineral for which E. S. Larsen gave the refractive index 1.96. E. F. Smith said that complex tantalotungstates are obtained from soln. of tungstates and tantalates.

The mineral hatchettlolite has been discussed from the point of view of the rare earths—5. 38, 3—and T. L. Walker and A. L. Parsons [4] regard it as an impure monohydrated calcium uranium metacolumbate, $R(CbO_3)_2.H_2O$. Varieties from Hybla, Ontario, had 9.27–13.58 per cent. of uranium, and 0.42–0.52 per cent. ThO_2, and a radioactivity of 0.830–1.125 (euxenite unity).

The mineral fergusonite was previously described from the point of view of the rare earths—5. 38, 3. It is a calcium rare earth orthocolumbatotantalate, $(Y,Er,Ce)(Cb,Ta)O_4.Ca_2Cb_2O_7$, or $12R(Cb,Ta)O_4.(Th,U)(Si,Sn)O_4$. Additional analyses were made by A. Lacroix,[5] and Y. Shibata and K. Kimura. J. Schetelig, and A. Lacroix studied the radioactivity of the mineral; and E. S. Larsen gave 2.19 for the index of refraction. The related mineral risörite—5. 38, 3—is a complex uranium orthotantalate with admixed metatitanate; and it has also been described by J. Schetelig. E. S. Larsen gave 2.04–2.08 for the index of refraction. The related rutherfordite, and kochelite were also described 5. 38, 3. Similar remarks apply to sipylite, for which E. S. Larsen gave the refractive index 2.05–2.07. The mineral euxenite has been described from the point of view of the rare earths—5. 38, 3. T. L. Walker and A. L. Parsons [6] represented the idealized mineral by the formula $RO.2Cb_2O_5.H_2O$, calcium yttrium uranyl deutero-tetra-columbate—or, according to G. Tschermak, since the ratio $Cb_2O_5 : TiO_2$ is near $1 : 2$, calcium yttrium uranyl titanocolumbate, $Y_2Ti_4O_{11}.2(Ca,Fe)(Cb_2O_5).(UO_2)Cb_2O_5$. Part of the columbium is replaced by tantalum. Additional analyses were reported by R. C. Sabot, W. G. Miller and C. W. Knight, J. Schetelig, and A. Betim. P. Tschirwinsky and N. A. Orloff found 0.1 per cent. of scandium, L. F. Nilson, 0.003–0.01 per cent. A. Betim found some gallium. The crystals were examined by R. C. Sabot, H. Ungemach, J. Schetelig, and A. Betim. The radioactivity was examined by T. L. Walker and A. L. Parsons, A. Lacroix, and A. Betim; the spark spectrum by P. Tschirwinsky and N. A. Orloff, A. Betim, and L. F. Nilson. C. Grossmann examined the products of the weathering of euxenite. The related mineral polycrase was described in connection with the rare earths—5. 38, 3; and a similar remark applies to blomstrandine, and priorite. E. S. Larsen gave 1.70 for the index of refraction of polycrase. A. Lacroix examined the radioactivity of priorite, and J. Schetelig analyzed the mineral.

G. A. Goyder [7] described a mineral occurring in the stanniferous sands of Greenbushes, West Australia. He called it stibiotantalite in allusion to its composition. Analyses by G. A. Goyder, and S. L. Penfield and W. E. Ford agree with the formula **antimonyl metacolumbatotantalate,** $(SbO)(Ta,Cb)O_3$. The dark brown, hemimorphic crystals are rhombic with the axial ratios $a:b:c$ $=0·7995:1:0·8448$. There is polysynthetic twinning about the (100)-plane; the prismatic crystals may show vertical striations like columbite. The hemimorphism is in the direction of the a-axis. The (100)-cleavage is perfect; the (010)-cleavage is indistinct. The optical character is positive. The optical axial angle for Li-, Na-, and Tl-light is respectively $2V=73°\ 40'$, $75°\ 5'$, and $77°\ 38'$ for material of sp. gr. 6·818, and $2V=70°\ 0'$, $73°\ 35'$, and $77°\ 50'$ for material of sp. gr. 6·299. The sp. gr. of the mineral with 36·35 per cent. Ta_2O_5 and 18·98 per cent. Cb_2O_5 is 6·72; and with 11·16 per cent. Ta_2O_5 and 39·14 per cent. Cb_2O_5, 5·98. The index of refraction and birefringence are:

Ray		Sp. gr. 6·818				Sp. gr. 6·299		
	a	β	γ	$\gamma-a$	a	β	γ	$\gamma-a$
Li .	2·3470	2·3750	2·4275	0·0805	2·3686	2·3876	2·4280	0·0594
Na .	2·3742	2·4039	2·4568	0·0826	2·3977	2·4190	2·4588	0·0691
Tl .	2·4014	2·4342	2·3876	0·0862	2·4261	2·4508	2·4903	0·0642

A. Joly [8] prepared **manganese metatantalate,** $Mn(TaO_3)_2$, as in the case of the corresponding metacolumbate; and likewise, he prepared **ferrous metatantalate,** $Fe(TaO_3)_2$. The mineral **æschynite** described in connection with the rare earths —**5**. 38, 3—is a calcium rare earth iron metacolumbate associated with thorium titanate, $2R(CbO_3)_3.2ThTiO_4.TiO_2$. E. S. Larsen gave 2·205–2·26 for the index of refraction. F. Zambonini [9] described a mineral from Craveggia, Piedmont, which he called **strüverite**—after G. Strüver. For a micaceous mineral of the same name, *vide* sismondite, **6**. 40, 41. Analyses were reported by F. Zambonini and G. T. Prior, A. Lacroix, S. J. Johnstone, and R. C. Wells. The results agree with the assumption that the mineral is a **ferrous columbatotantalate,** associated with the titania—$Fe\{(Ta,Cb)O_3\}_2.4$ to $6TiO_2$. According to F. Zambonini, the iron-black crystals are tetragonal with the axial ratio $a:c=1:0·6456$. The sp. gr. is 5·54– 5·56; and the hardness 6·0–6·5. This mineral may be taken to represent the tantalum-end of a series with **ilmenorutile** at the columbium end. Analyses of ilmenorutile were reported by W. C. Brögger, N. von Kokscharoff, and F. Zambonini and G. T. Prior. The sp. gr. is 5·074–5·133. A. Lacroix described a mineral from Ampangabe, Madagascar, which was called **ampangabeite—5**. 38, 3. Its composition corresponds with **uranium iron metacolumbate,** $R(CbO_3)_3.3H_2O$, where RO represents oxides of uranium, thorium, rare earths, calcium, and iron. Analyses were reported by G. Tschernick, [10] A. Lacroix, L. Duparc and co-workers, R. C. Sabot. The colour ranges from a pale yellowish-brown (sp. gr. 3·3484) to a brownish-black (sp. gr. 4·6441). The prismatic crystals are optically isotropic; the hardness is about 4. The crystals were examined by R. C. Sabot, A. Lacroix, and H. Ungemach. E. S. Larsen gave 2·13 for the index of refraction. The radioactivity is very marked. The mineral is soluble in hydrochloric acid.

The mineral **betafite** from Madagascar has been described from the point of view of the rare earths—**5**. 38, 3—a similar remark applies to **samiresite**. Both minerals were analyzed by A. Lacroix. [11] T. L. Walker and A. L. Parsons represented betafite by the formula $2RO.3Cb_2O_5.3H_2O$, **calcium uranium iron deuterohexacolumbate.** There is 16·2–18·3 per cent. of titania present, so that the mineral may be **calcium uranium iron titanocolumbate.** Up to about one per cent. of tantalum is present. The crystals were examined by H. Ungemach. E. S. Larsen gave 1·915–1·925 for the index of refraction of the isotropic crystals. A. Lacroix found the mineral to be radioactive. The sp. gr. is 4·17. T. L. Walker and A. L. Parsons represented samiresite by the formula $RO.2Cb_2O_5.5H_2O$, **uranium iron deuterotetracolumbate**—about 6·70–8·76 per cent. of titania is present, and 3·7 per cent. of tantalia. A. Lacroix found the mineral to be radioactive. E. S. Larsen gave 1·92–1·96 for the index of refraction. The mineral **blomstrandite** was described in connection with the rare earths—**5**. 38, 3. T. L. Walker and

A. L. Parsons represented the idealized mineral by $RO.2Cb_2O_5.3H_2O$, *i.e.* **uranium rare earth deuterotetracolumbate.** It is more likely to be a **uranium rare earth titanocolumbate,** since, from the analysis reported by A. Lacroix, 10·8 per cent. of titania is present.

W. J. Vernadsky [12] described a radioactive mineral from Ulunti, Lake Baikal, Siberia. It is related to betafite, and was called **mendeléeffite**—after D. I. Mendeléeff. The incomplete analysis corresponds with a **calcium uranium titanocolumbate.** The greyish-black cubic crystals appear in the form of rhombic dodecahedra with small octahedral faces. The sp. gr. is 4·46–4·76 ; and the hardness 4·5. The mineral **samarskite** has been described from the point of view of the rare earths—**5.** 38, 3. It is considered to be **calcium ferrous uranyl rare earth pyrocolumbatotantalate,** $(Fe,Ca,UO_2)R(Cb,Ta)_6O_2$; additional analyses were given by Y. Shibata and K. Kimura, A. Lacroix, and L. M. Dennis and J. Papish. The rhombic crystals were described by Y. Shibata and K. Kimura, who gave for the axial ratios $a:b:c=0.5456:1:0.5178$. E. S. Larsen gave 2·10–2·25 for the index of refraction. A. Lacroix examined the radioactivity of the mineral. The variety *yttrotantalite* has a refractive index, 2·15 ; and *hjelmite* has $a=2.30$, and $\gamma=2.40$ for Li-light or $\omega=2.30$ and $\epsilon=2.40$. *Nohlite, loranscite, rogersite, plumboniobite, annerödite,* and *ishikawaite* were previously described—**5.** 38, 3.

The history of C. Hatchett's [13] ore of columbium and A. G. Ekeberg's **tantalite** has been discussed in connection with columbium. R. Jameson called the ore of columbium, **columbite ;** F. S. Beudant, *baierine*—from Bavaria ; W. Haidinger, *niobite ;* T. Thomson, *torrelite*—after J. Torrey ; A. Breithaupt, *greenlandite ;* C. U. Shepard, *hermannotite*—after R. Hermann ; R. Hermann, *ferroilmenite ;* F. von Kobell, *dianite ;* A. E. Nordenskjöld, *mangantantalite ;* A. Arzruni, *manganotantalite ;* A. Lacroix, *manganocolumbite ;* G. Rose, *mengite ;* T. Thomson, *ferrotantalite ;* J. F. L. Hausmann, *siderotantalite ;* W. Haidinger, *ildeforsite ;* and A. Breithaupt, *Harttantalerz.* The *paracolumbite* of C. U. Shepard was afterwards shown by him to be menaccanite. Numerous analyses have been reported.[14] A selection of recent analyses is shown in Table I.

TABLE I.—ANALYSES OF COLUMBITES AND TANTALITES.

—	1	2	3	4	5	6	7	8	9	10
Cb_2O_5	68·94	68·00	67·20	66·60	64·60	63·90	63·77	55·79	48·87	37·49
Ta_2O_5	10·00	9·88	10·10	1·74	12·60	13·74	11·33	15·21	30·58	42·95
TiO_2	Trace	0·53	0·92	5·22	—	0·80	1·50	5·19	—	0·66
SnO_2	0·38	0·88	0·96	0·36	0·40	0·54	0·45	0·56	0·91	—
FeO	15·99	5·45	5·96	8·61	15·00	5·92	11·38	10·90	2·95	2·50
MnO	3·56	14·79	15·08	9·06	7·30	14·95	8·79	10·24	15·70	13·02
Sp. gr.	5·59	5·201	5·421	5·147	6·62	5·496	5·272	5·431	6·26	—

—	11	12	13	14	15	16	17	18	19	20
Cb_2O_5	34·60	27·22	8·63	5·49	6·97	5·56	4·32	3·69	1·97	5·18
Ta_2O_5	46·02	53·47	69·55	76·08	77·24	78·28	79·50	81·40	83·57	77·23
TiO_2	1·52	1·30	1·50	2·84	0·81	1·33	0·92	0·58	Trace	1·38
SnO_2	0·38	0·44	5·29	0·22	1·18	0·28	0·32	0·12	0·10	0·32
FeO	13·32	11·91	10·84	14·16	13·60	13·35	13·42	12·55	13·28	14·84
MnO	4·31	5·66	4·19	1·21	1·02	1·22	1·56	1·73	1·19	0·42
Sp. gr.	6·444	6·725	6·954	7·019	7·180	7·468	7·794	7·878	7·985	7·190

In Table I, No. 1 is from Ishikawa, Japan, by Y. Shibata and K. Kimura ; Nos. 2 and 3, from Old Mike Mica Mine, Custer Co., by W. P. Headden ; No. 4, from Hybla, Ontario, by T. L. Walker and A. L. Parsons ; No. 5, from Ampangabe, Madagascar, by A. Lacroix ; No. 6, as No. 3 ; No. 7, from Ambatofotsikely, Madagascar, by L. Duparc and co-workers, and R. C. Sabot ; No. 8, from Orust, Sweden, by G. K. Almström ; No. 9, from Lyndoch, Ontario, by T. L. Walker and A. L. Parsons ; No. 10, from S. Norway, by W. C. Brögger ; Nos. 11 to 20 are by W. P. Headden—No. 11 is from Harney City, Pennington Co. ; No. 12 is from Tin Mountain, Custer Co. ; Nos. 13 to 20 are from Old Mike Mica Mine, Custer Co. ; No. 20 is a tapiolite. No. 4 had 1·25 per cent. zirconia. SnO_2 is inclusive of WO_3. No. 3 had 2·02 per cent. U_3O_8. Rare earths, lime, silica, and water have been omitted.

When the proportion of columbium oxide predominates the mineral can be called *columbite*, and with tantalum oxide predominant, *tantalite*. In these analyses, the manganous oxide ranges from 1·14 to 19·86 per cent. ; ferrous oxide, from 1·17 to 16·67 per cent. ; columbium pentoxide, from 2·50 to 77·97 per cent. ; and the tantalum pentoxide from 0·83 to 84·44 per cent. The compositions of the idealized manganese and ferrous tantalates and columbates are :

	FeO	MnO	Cb_2O_5	Ta_2O_5
$Fe(CbO_3)_2$ . . .	21·20	—	78·80	—
$Fe(TaO_3)_2$ . . .	13·96	—	—	86·04
$Mn(CbO_3)_2$ . .	—	20·99	79·01	—
$Mn(TaO_3)_2$ . .	—	13·80	—	86·20

Columbite and tantalite are therefore to be regarded as solid soln. of these four compounds, and they are symbolized $(Ge,Mn)\{(Cb,Ta)O_3\}_2$; ranging by insensible gradations from nearly pure **manganese ferrous metacolumbate** (columbite) to nearly pure **manganese ferrous metatantalate** (tantalite). In the mangano-columbite from Branchville, the iron is nearly all replaced by manganese, and also in the manganotantalite from Sanaska. H. V. Ellsworth described a mineral *toddite* from Sudbury, Canada. It appears to be a variety of columbite with some iron and manganese replaced by uranium. The amount of stannic oxide in these minerals ranges up to 5·38 per cent. ; silica, up to 0·4 per cent. ; titania, up to 6·20 per cent. ; zirconia, up to 1·25 per cent. ; tungstic oxide, up to 0·76 per cent. ; uranic oxide, up to 2·02 per cent. ; rare earths, up to 2·12 per cent. ; alumina, up to 1·65 per cent. ; magnesia, up to 0·42 per cent. ; and calcium oxide, up to 0·56 per cent. T. L. Walker and A. L. Parsons found 3·34 per cent. of thoria in colum-bite from Hybla, Ontario—analysis No. 4, Table I. E. S. Simpson reported 0·02 per cent. nickel oxide in a sample from West Australia ; A. E. Nordenskjöld, 0·14 per cent. of cupric oxide in a sample from Kimito, and A. Stelzner, 0·34 per cent. in a sample from Sierra de Cordoba, Argentine ; C. W. Blomstrand, 0·12 per cent. of lead oxide in a sample from Greenland ; and K. von Chrustschoff, 0·02 per cent. germania in a sample from Finland. G. Eberhard observed that special lines of scandium could be obtained with a columbite from South Dakota ; Moss, Norway ; and Orijarvi, Finland. W. Ramsay and co-workers found much hydrogen and no helium in a North American columbite ; helium was obtained from other samples, and also from tantalite from Fahlun. H. Erdmann obtained over 0·0007 per cent. of ammonia from columbite from Fahluns.

Columbite and tantalite may be iron-black, greyish-black, brownish-black, or reddish-brown in **colour,** and they often show an iridescent surface. The minerals may occur massive ; more usually in short prisms, or thin tablets. A. Schrauf [15] in his *Monographie des Columbits* investigated the habit of the crystals ; and observations on this subject were also made by H. W. Foote, and W. C. Brögger. The rhombic **crystals** were found by E. S. Dana to have the axial ratios $a : b : c$ =0·82850 : 1 : 0·88976 ; A. Schrauf obtained 0·40744 : 1 : 0·33467 with a different orientation of the crystals. W. C. Brögger found that as the proportion of tantalum in columbite increases, the a-axis increases, and the c-axis decreases ; O. J. Lee and E. T. Wherry's observations are in agreement with this. The proportion of tantalum oxide increases with the sp. gr. as indicated below, and taking obser-vations by A. des Cloizeaux, N. von Kokscharoff, E. S. Dana, J. D. Dana, and A. Arzruni in order,

Sp. gr. .	5·39	5·37	5·65	5·95	7·3
Ta_2O_5 .	—	—	9·2	29·0	79·8 per cent.
$a : b : c$	0·829 : 1 : 0·878	0·830 : 1 : 0·882	0·829 : 1 : 0·890	0·829 : 1 : 0·878	0·830 : 1 : 0·873

G. Rose observed the **twinning** of the crystals. Contact twins about the (021)·plane are common ; they are often heart-shaped, and show delicate, feathery striations on the (100)-face. Twinning about the (530)-, (051)-, or the (023)-plane is rare. There are also penetration twins. The **cleavage** on the (100)-face is distinct ; that on the (010)-face is less clear. The **corrosion figures** of some columbites obtained by L. Michel, and O. Mügge are in agreement with the rhombic bipyramidal symmetry. Some variations show a feeble **pleochroism,** others a strong one. A manganotantalite from Amelia, Virginia, showed α to be pale red ; β, blood-red ; and γ, deep blood-red. The optic axial angle $2V$ is large ; the optical character positive ; and E. S. Larsen found for columbite from Canon City, Colorado, the **refractive index** 2·45 with the **birefringence** strong ; a ferro-columbite from Haddon, Connecticut, also had a strong birefringence, and the index of refraction for Li-light, 2·40 ; a tantalite from Dakota had the indices of refraction $\alpha=2\cdot26$, $\beta=2\cdot32$, and $\gamma=2\cdot43$; while a manganotantalite from Amelia, Virginia, had $\alpha=2\cdot19$, $\beta=2\cdot25$, and $\gamma=2\cdot34$. Observations on the crystals were also made by W. P. Blake, O. B. Böggild, E. M. Bonshtedt, H. L. Bowman, A. Breithaupt, H. J. Brooke, A. des Cloizeaux, L. Duparc and co-workers, E. S. von Federoff, F. A. Genth, E. Hussak, P. Jereméeff, K. Jimbo, A. Lacroix, C. C. von Leonhard, H. C. Lewis, G. vom Rath, A. F. Rogers, R. C. Sabot, W. T. Schaller, C. U. Shepard, J. F. Smith, G. H. Tipper, H. Ungemach, T. Wada, and C. H. Warren. According to A. Breithaupt, G. Rose, and P. Jereméeff, columbite and wolframite are isomorphous ; while P. Groth and A. Arzruni said that although the angles of the rhombic minerals are similar, the minerals are not isomorphous. W. C. Brögger showed that the minerals of the columbite and æschynite groups are related ; and he discussed the relation between columbite, tantalite, brookite, rutile, tapiolite, wolframite, hübnerite, etc. G. T. Prior gave the following comparison of the topic parameters :

	Mol. vol.	χ	ψ	ω
Brookite, $Ti_3Ti_3O_{12}$ . .	117·54	4·450	5·288	4·994
Tantalite, $Fe_2Ta_4O_{12}$ . .	124·64	4·581	5·530	4·920
Hübnerite, $Mn_3W_3O_{12}$ . .	126·40	4·647	5·599	4·859

Measurements of the **specific gravity** were recorded along with most of the analyses, and the results range from 5·15 to 8·2. The results depend on the proportion Cb : Ta. This is brought out by J. C. G. de Marignac's Table II ; and

TABLE II.—RELATION BETWEEN THE SPECIFIC GRAVITY AND COMPOSITION OF COLUMBITES AND TANTALITES.

Origin of columbite.	Sp. gr.	Per cent. Ta_2O_5
Arksat fiord, Greenland	5·36	3·3
Acworth, New Hampshire . . .	5·65	15·8
La Vilate, Limoges	5·70	13·8
Bodenmais	5·74	13·4
Haddam, Connecticut	5·85	(10·0)
Bodenmais	5·92	27·1
Haddam	6·05	30·4
Bodenmais	6·06	35·4
Haddam	6·13	31·5
Sweden (tantalite)	7·03	65·6

H. W. Foote and R. W. Langley proposed estimating the proportions of columbium and tantalum pentoxides from the sp. gr. of the mixture. The **hardness** is about 6. G. Spezia was able to **melt** columbite in the coal-gas flame fed by a blast of warm air. The **optical properties** were examined by A. Schrauf, O. Mügge, and J. Königsberger. T. W. Case said that the poor electrical conductivity of columbite is not appreciably affected by light. A. L. Fletcher found a sample from Arendal,

Norway, melted but did not flow freely at 1350° ; a sample from Warwick. New Jersey, softened but did flow at 1500°, and another sample from Moss, Norway, melted at 1310° but did not flow freely ; and at 1400°, the powder aggregated into drops. E. T. Wherry found columbite and tantalite to be good radio-detectors. F. Pisani showed that columbite from Bavaria had no effect on a photographic plate exposed for 24 hrs. D. Mawson and T. H. Laby found that columbite from Barrier Ranges, N.S.W., is not **radioactive** ; but E. T. Wherry observed that a Pennsylvanian columbite was radioactive, and V. M. Goldschmidt obtained a similar result with a Norwegian columbite. T. L. Walker and A. L. Parsons found that columbite from Hybla, Ontario, had a radioactivity of 0·830 when that of euxenite was unity. A. Schrauf said that columbite has no **electrical conductivity**, and is **paramagnetic**. According to C. F. Plattner, tantalite and columbite dissolve slowly in molten borax, and in molten microcosmic salt. The minerals resist attack by the ordinary acids ; they are decomposed by fused potassium hydrosulphate. J. L. Smith opened up the mineral with hydrofluoric acid ; W. K. van Haagen and E. F. Smith, with hydrogen fluoride at a white-heat; and E. F. Smith, with sulphur monochloride—*vide supra*, the extraction of columbium and tantalum pentoxides.

According to E. Mäkinen,[16] the tantalite occurring in the pegmatite of Tammela and Kimito, Finland, was described by P. A. Gadd, in 1767, as a stanniferous garnet containing iron and manganese. In 1802, A. G. Ekeberg discovered the presence of tantalum, and named the mineral *tantalite*. The mineral was also analyzed by M. H. Klaproth in 1810, and L. N. Vauquelin in 1819. The mineral was also described by J. F. L. Hausmann, and by J. J. Berzelius. Some differences in colour, sp. gr., and composition were emphasized by N. Nordenskjöld, H. J. Holmberg, and A. E. Nordenskjöld. There was (i) the tantalite from Skogböle—*Tantalite mit zimtbraunen Pulver ;* (ii) the tantalite from Kimito—*kimitotantalite ;* (iii) the tantalite from Tammela or tammelatantalite—or the tantalite of A. G. Ekeberg. Some tantalite from Skogböle, in Kimito, was found by J. J. Berzelius to be stanniferous, and some was free from tin ; and A. E. Nordenskjöld called the stanniferous tantalite from Skogböle *ixionlite* or **ixiolite**—from Ixion, an associate of the mythological Tantalus. It is identical with the *cassiterotantalite* of J. F. L. Hausmann, and the *kimitotantalite* of N. Nordenskjöld. The other variety comparatively free from tin was called **skogbölite**, and it is what is ordinarily called tantalite ; it is the tantalite of A. G. Ekeberg ; the tantalite with the cinnamon-brown powder of A. G. Ekeberg, and J. J. Berzelius ; and the *tammelatanalite* of N. Nordenskjöld. Both skogbölite and ixiolite furnish rhombic crystals. In 1861, A. E. Arppe described a tantalite from Sukula which had a composition very like that from Tammela, but furnishes tetragonal crystals, and A. E. Nordenskjöld called it **tapiolite**—after one of the gods of Finnish mythology. V. M. Goldschmidt discussed the X-radiogram of tapiolite. Analyses of skogbölite were reported by R. Hermann, and H. Rose ; and of ixiolite by A. E. Nordenskjöld, R. Hermann, and C. F. Rammelsberg. P. Groth and K. Mieleitner regard ixiolite as a stanniferous columbite or tantalite ; but the 13 per cent. SnO_2 reported by A. E. Nordenskjöld was not confirmed by C. F. Rammelsberg. E. S. Simpson described ixiolite from West Australia ; and W. J. Vernadsky and A. E. Fersman, from the Ilmen mountains, Russia. Like columbite, therefore, ixiolite is ferrous manganous metacolumbatotantalate, $(Fe,Mn)\{(Ta,Cb)O_3\}_2$. Skogbölite may be represented by the same formula, although, according to the analysis of A. E. Nordenskjöld, it approximates closely to ferrous metantalate, $Fe(TaO_3)_2$. Analyses of tapiolite were reported by C. F. Rammelsberg, A. E. Nordenskjöld, W. C. Brögger, W. P. Headden, and E. S. Simpson. It too can be regarded as a ferrous manganous metacolumbatotantalate, approximating to ferrous metacolumbatotantalate. This remark applies also to the mineral **mossite** obtained in black crystals by W. C. Brögger from Moss, Norway. According to W. T. Schaller, mossite is only a columbiferous tapiolite. V. M. Goldschmidt discussed the X-radiogram. E. S. Simpson described *Manganomossite* from Yinnietharra, Western Australia ; it appears to be a *mangano-columbite*. N. Nordenskjöld reported *adelpholite*— 5. 38, 3—as a tetragonal hydrated ferrous manganese columbatotantalate from Finland. It was also described by E. Mäkinen, and A. E. Nordenskjöld. The sp. gr. is 3·8; and the hardness, 3·5–4·5. P. Groth and K. Mieleitner regard it as a product of the weathering of columbite.

Skogbölite furnishes black, opaque, rhombic crystals which, according to N. Nordenskjöld, have the axial ratios $a : b : c = 0·81696 : 1 : 0·65106$. The cleavage of the prismatic crystals is indistinct. The sp. gr. is 7·8–8·0 ; and the hardness, 6·0–6·5. The greyish-black or steel-grey, rhombic crystals of ixiolite, have, according to A. E. Nordenskjöld, the axial ratios $a : b : c = 0·5508 : 1 : 1·2460$. W. J. Vernadsky and A. E. Fersman gave 0·545 : 1 : 0·201. The crystals are sometimes twinned about the (103)-plane. The sp. gr. is 6·87–7·1 : and the hardness, 6·0–6·5. A. E. Nordenskjöld gave for the axial ratio of the black, tetragonal crystals of tapiolite $a : c = 1 : 0·6464$; E. Mäkinen gave 1 : 0·6499 ; and W. C. Brögger, 1 : 0·65251. The crystals sometimes appear to be monoclinic owing to distortion. The cleavage is not distinct ; the sp. gr. is 7·36–7·496 ; and the hardness, 6. E. S. Larsen found the indices of refraction of tapiolite for Li-light to be $\omega = 2·27$, and $\epsilon = 2·42$; and the pleochroism is strong, ω being pale yellow or reddish-brown, and ϵ almost opaque. The black, prismatic crystals of mossite are tetragonal, and, according to W. C. Brögger, have the axial ratios $a : c = 1 : 0·6438$. Twinning occurs about the (101)-plane, and, in some cases, the twins simulate rhombic forms. There is no cleavage ; the sp. gr. is 6·45. The relation between the axial ratios of the three rhombic minerals may be represented :

Columbite.	Skogbölite.	Ixiolite.
$a : b : c$	$a : b : c$	$\frac{2}{3}a : b : \frac{2}{3}c$
0·8285 : 1 : 0·8898	0·8170 : 1 : 0·8681	0·8262 : 1 : 0·8307

P. Groth proposed A. Schrauf's relation for columbate while doubling the *a*-and *c*-axes, and gave the ratios $a : b : c = 0·8047 : 1 : 0·7159$ for columbite, and 0·8170 : 0·6511 for skogbölite ; but, added E. S. Dana, the similarity is more apparent than real, because nearly all the prominent planes of each mineral are wanting on the other, and the habits are very different. Tantalite itself corresponds closely with the columbite in both habit and angle. E. S. Simpson discussed the relation between the sp. gr. and composition of tapiolite, mossite, strüverite, and ilemenorutile ; and the subject was examined by T. Crook and S. J. Johnstone, and W. T. Schaller. W. C. Brögger suggested that ferrous metatantalate is dimorphous, forming tetragonal tapiolite, and rhombic tantalite.

J. A. Hedvall prepared **cobalt metatantalate**, $Co(TaO_3)_2$, by heating mixtures of cobalt oxide and tantalum pentoxide.

REFERENCES.

[1] H. Rose, *Pogg. Ann.*, 100. 340, 559, 1857 ; 101. 11, 1857 ; 102. 57, 1857 ; F. Oesten, *ib.*, 100. 340, 1857 ; J. J. Berzelius, *ib.*, 4. 10, 1825 ; *Schweigger's Journ.*, 16. 437, 1816 ; J. J. Berzelius and J. G. Gahn, *Afh. Fys. Kemi Min.*, 4. 252, 1815 ; J. C. G. de Marignac, *Arch. Sciences Genève*, (2), 26. 89, 1866 ; *Ann. Chim. Phys.*, (4), 9. 259, 1866 ; *Compt. Rend.*, 63. 85, 1866 ; W. E. von John, *Chem. News*, 100. 154, 1909 ; A. Joly, *Ann. École Norm.*, (2), 6. 168, 1877 ; *Bull. Soc. Chim.*, (2), 25. 506, 1876 ; E. Wedekind and P. Maas, *Zeit. angew. Chem.*, 23. 2315, 1910 ; L. Weiss and M. Landecker, *Zeit. anorg. Chem.*, 64. 65, 1909 ; W. R. Schoeller and C. Jahn, *Analyst*, 51. 613, 1926 ; A. Lottermoser, *Koll. Zeit.*, 30. 346, 1922 ; R. Hermann, *Journ. prakt. Chem.*, (2), 5. 83, 1872 ; C. W. Balke, *The Double Fluorides of Tantalum*, Easton, Pa., 1908 ; C. W. Balke and E. F. Smith, *Journ. Amer. Chem. Soc.*, 30. 1666, 1909 ; J. Morgenroth and F. Rosenthal, *Zeit. Hyg., Infect. Krankh.*, 68. 506, 1911 ; *Berlin Klin. Woch.*, 46. 2, 1911 ; G. Jander and H. Schulz, *Koll. Zeit.*, 36. 109, 1925 ; *Zeit. anorg. Chem.*, 144. 225, 1925.
[2] W. C. Brögger, *Vid. Selsk. Skrift.*, 54, 1921 ; V. M. Goldschmidt, *ib.*, 5, 1924 ; E. S. Simpson, *Proc. Austral. Assoc.*, 12. 310, 1909 ; *Min. Mag.*, 18. 108, 1917 ; *Chem. News*, 99. 77, 1909 ; R. J. Strutt, *Proc. Roy. Soc.*, 76. A, 88, 1905 ; E. S. Larsen, *Bull. U.S. Geol. Sur.*, 679, 1921 ; W. T. Schaller, *ib.*, 610 (105), 1916 ; S. Kreutz, *Bull. Acad. Cracovie*, 54. A, 227, 1915 ; O. Mügge,

TANTALUM

Centr. Min., **721**, 753, 1922; T. L. Walker and A. L. Parsons, *Univ. Toronto Geol. Stud.*, **16**, 1923; R. Brauns, *Die Mineralien der niederrheinischen Vulkangebiete*, Stuttgart, 1922; J. J. Berzelius and J. G. Gahn, *Afh. Fys. Kemi Min.*, **4.** 252, 1815; J. J. Berzelius, *Schweigger's Journ.*, **16.** 437, 1816; *Pogg. Ann.*, **4.** 10, 1825; H. Rose, *ib.*, **102.** 59, 1857; A. Joly, *Ann. École Norm.*, (2), **6.** 151, 1877; *Bull. Soc. Chim.*, (2), **25.** 506, 1876; E. T. Wherry, *Amer. Min.*, **9.** 17, 1924; P. J. Holmquist, *Bull. Geol. Inst. Upsala*, **3.** 181, 1897; *Synthetische Studien über die Perowskit- und Pyrochlormineralien*, Upsala, 1897.

[3] J. Soellner, *Mitt. Baden. geol. Landesanst.*, **8.** 191, 1915; G. Meyer, *Ber. Nat. Ges. Freiberg*, **20.** 1, 1914; E. S. Larsen, *Bull. U.S. Geol. Sur.*, 679, 1921; E. F. Smith, *Proc. Amer. Phil. Soc.*, **44.** 158, 1905; T. Barth, *Norsk. Geol. Tids.*, **9.** 23, 1926; H. V. Ellsworth and J. F. Walker, *Sum. Rep. Geol. Sur. Canada*, 230, 1926.

[4] T. L. Walker and A. L. Parsons, *Univ. Toronto Geol. Stud.*, 16, 1923.

[5] E. S. Larsen, *Bull. U.S. Geol. Sur.*, 679, 1921; A. Lacroix, *Minéralogie de Madagascar*, Paris, **1.** 372, 1922; **2.** 128, 1922; **3.** 319, 1923; Y. Shibata and K. Kimura, *Japan. Journ. Chem.*, **2.** 1, 1923; J. Schetelig, *Vid. Selsk. Skript.*, 1, 1922; O. Hauser, *Zeit. anorg. Chem.*, **60.** 230, 1908.

[6] T. L. Walker and A. L. Parsons, *Univ. Toronto Geol. Stud.*, 16, 1923; C. Grossmann, *Compt. Rend.*, **159.** 777, 1914; A. Betim, *ib.*, **161.** 177, 1915; A. Lacroix, *Minéralogie de Madagascar*, Paris, **2.** 128, 1922; **3.** 319, 1923; H. Ungemach, *Bull. Soc. Min.*, **39.** 5, 1916; W. G. Miller and C. W. Knight, *Amer. Journ. Science*, (4), **44.** 243, 1917; E. S. Larsen, *Bull. U.S. Geol. Sur.*, 679, 1921; R. C. Sabot, *Études cristallographiques et optiques d'un certain nombre de minéraux des pegmatites de Madagascar et des minéraux de Oural*, Genève, 1916; P. Tschirwinsky and N. A. Orloff, *Centr. Min.*, 257, 1922; J. Schetelig, *Die Mineralien der südnorwegischen Granitpegmatitgänge*, Christiania, 1906; L. F. Nilson, *Ber.*, **13.** 1439, 1880; *Compt. Rend.*, **91.** 118, 1880.

[7] G. A. Goyder, *Journ. Chem. Soc.*, **63.** 1076, 1893; S. L. Penfield and W. E. Ford, *Amer. Journ. Science*, (4), **22.** 61, 1906.

[8] E. S. Larsen, *Bull. U.S. Geol. Sur.*, 679, 1921; A. Joly, *Compt. Rend.*, **81.** 269, 1875.

[9] F. Zambonini, *Atti Accad. Napoli*, (3), **13.** 35, 1907; F. Zambonini and G. T. Prior, *Min. Mag.*, **15.** 62, 1908; S. J. Johnstone, *ib.*, **16.** 224, 1912; R. C. Wells, *Amer. Journ. Science*, (4), **31.** 432, 1911; A. Lacroix, *Bull. Soc. Min.*, **35.** 194, 1912; N. von Kokscharoff, *Materialen zur Mineralogie Russlands*, **5.** 194, 1866; W. C. Brögger, *Die Mineralien der südnorweischen Granitpegmatitgänge*, Kristiania, 46, 1906.

[10] A. Lacroix, *Minéralogie de Madagascar*, Paris, **1.** 391, 1922; *Compt. Rend.*, **154.** 1044, 1912; *Bull. Soc. Min.*, **35.** 194, 1912; L. Duparc, R. C. Sabot, and L. Wunder, *ib.*, **36.** 9, 1913; R. C. Sabot, *Études cristallographiques et optiques d'un certain nombre de minéraux des pegmatites de Madagascar et des minéraux de l'Oural*, Genève, 1916; E. S. Larsen, *Bull. U.S. Geol. Sur.*, 679, 1921; H. Ungemach, *Bull. Soc. Min.*, **39.** 5, 1916; G. Tschernick, *ib.*, **49.** 127, 1926.

[11] A. Lacroix, *Compt. Rend.*, **154.** 1640, 1912; *Bull. Soc. Min.*, **35.** 233, 1913; *Minéralogie de Madagascar*, Paris, **1.** 379, 1922; **2.** 128, 1922; **3.** 319, 1923; T. L. Walker and A. L. Parsons, *Univ. Toronto Geol. Stud.*, 16, 1923; E. S. Larsen, *Bull. U.S. Geol. Sur.*, 679, 1921.

[12] E. S. Larsen, *Bull. U.S. Geol. Sur.*, 679, 1921; L. M. Dennis and J. Papish, *Journ. Amer. Chem. Soc.*, **43.** 2131, 1921; A. Lacroix, *Minéralogie de Madagascar*, Paris, **1.** 376, 1922; **2.** 128, 1922; **3.** 319, 1923; *Bull. Soc. Min.*, **34.** 67, 1911; Y. Shibata and K. Kimura, *Japan. Journ. Chem.*, **2.** 15, 1923; W. J. Vernadsky, *Compt. Rend.*, **176.** 993, 1923.

[13] C. Hatchett, *Phil. Trans.*, **92.** 49, 1802; A. G. Ekeberg, *Akad. Nya Handl.*, **23.** 80, 1802; *Gilbert's Ann.*, **14.** 246, 1803; *Crell's Ann.*, i, 3, 1802; *Scherer's Journ.*, **9.** 598, 1803; *Nicholson's Journ.*, **3.** 251, 1802; *Phil. Mag.*, **14.** 346, 1802; *Ann. Chim. Phys.*, (1), **43.** 276, 1802; F. S. Beudant, *Traité élémentaire de minéralogie*, Paris, **2.** 655, 1832; R. Jameson, *A System of Mineralogy*, Edinburgh, **2.** 582, 1805; J. F. L. Hausmann, *Handbuch der Mineralogie*, Göttingen, **2.** 960, 1847; W. Haidinger, *Handbuch der bestimmenden Mineralogie*, Wien, 548, 1845; A. Breithaupt, *Vollständiges Handbuch der Mineralogie*, Dresden, 874, 1847; *Vollständige Charakteristik des Mineralsystems*, Dresden, 230, 1832; *Berg. Hütt. Ztg.*, **17.** 61, 1858; T. Thomson, *Records Gen. Science*, **4.** 408, 416, 1836; C. U. Shepard, *Amer. Journ. Science*, (2), **12.** 209, 1851; (2), **50.** 90, 1870; (3), **11.** 140, 1876; (3), **20.** 156, 1880; R. Hermann, *Journ. prakt. Chem.*, (2), **2.** 118, 1870; (2), **4.** 209, 1871; A. E. Nordenskjöld, *Geol. För. Förh. Stockholm*, **3.** 284, 1877; G. K. Almström, *ib.*, **44.** 482, 1922; G. Rose, *Pogg. Ann.*, **23.** 366, 1831; *Reise nach dem Ural, dem Altai, und dem kaspischen Meere*, Berlin, **2.** 83, 1842; A. Arzruni, *Proc. Russ. Min. Soc.*, (2), **23.** 181, 1887; A. Lacroix, *Minéralogie de la France et de ses colonies*, Paris, **4.** 314, 1910; F. von Kobell, *Sitzber. Akad. München.*, **50.** 375, 1860; *Journ. prakt. Chem.*, (1), **79.** 291, 1860; (1), **83.** 110, 1861; A. Fersman, *Compt. Rend. Acad. Russ.*, 10, 1925; R. T. Schaller, *Bull. U.S. Geol. Sur.*, 610 (105), 1916.

[14] H. A. von Vogel, *Denks. Akad. München*, 213, 1817; *Schweigger's Journ.*, **21.** 60, 1817; J. G. Gahn and J. J. Berzelius, *ib.*, **16.** 263, 293, 1816; *Afh. Fis. Kemi Min.*, **4.** 172, 205, 1815; C. F. Rammelsberg, *Handbuch der Mineralchemie*, Leipzig, 393, 1860; *Sitzber. Akad. Berlin*, 163, 1872; *Pogg. Ann.*, **144.** 56, 1871; T. Thomson, *Records Gen. Science*, **4.** 407, 1836; H. Müller, *Journ. Chem. Soc.*, **11.** 244, 1859; *Korresp. Ver. Regensburg*, **6.** 33, 52, 1852; *Journ. prakt. Chem.*, (1), **58.** 180, 1853; R. Hermann, *ib.*, (1), **38.** 121, 1846; (1), **44.** 208, 1848; (1), **65.** 75, 1855; (1), **68.** 94, 1856; (1), **70.** 207, 1857; (1), **97.** 350, 1866; (2), **2.** 108, 1870; (2), **4.** 205, 1871; (2), **13.** 386, 1875; *Bull. Soc. Nat. Moscow*, **38.** 291, 302, 346, 1865; C. F. Chandler,

Miscellaneous Chemical Researches, Göttingen, 32, 1856 ; *Pogg. Ann.*, **118**. 348, 1863 ; **H. Rose,** *ib.*, 63. 317, 1844 ; **71**. 157, 1847 ; **104**. 85, 1858 ; A. von Awedejeff, *ib.*, **63**. 328, 1844 ; J. Jacobson, *ib.*, 63. 329, 1844 ; G. Jenzsch, *ib.*, **97**. 107, 1856 ; F. Oesten, *ib.*, **118**. 356, 1863 ; A. Schlieper, *ib.*, 63. 330, 1844 ; C. M. Warren, *ib.*, **118**. 349, 1863 ; C. Grewingk, *ib.*, **70**. 572, 1847 ; C. Bromeis, *ib.*, **71**. 168, 1847 ; A. E. Nordenskjöld, *ib.*, **107**. 374, 1859 ; **122**. 610, 1864 ; *Oefvers Akad. Förh.*, **20**. 448, 1863 ; *Beskrifning öfver de i Finland funna Mineralier*, Helsingfors, 39, 1855 ; *Geol. För. Förh. Stockholm*, 3. 284, 1877 ; R. J. Haüy, *Traité de minéralogie*, Paris, 4. 388, 1822 ; A. Damour, *Compt. Rend.*, 25. 673, 1847 ; **28**. 353, 1849 ; *Ann. Mines*, **(4)**, **13**. 337, 1848 ; **(4)**, **14**. 423, 1848 ; W. C. Brögger, *Vid. Selsk. Skrift*, 6, 1906 ; *Die Mineralien der südnorwegischen Granitpegmatitgänge*, Christiania, 1906 ; J. C. G. de Marignac, *Arch. Sciences Genève*, (2), **25**. 26, 1866 ; *Ann. Chim. Phys.*, (4), **8**. 68, 1866 ; K. von Chrustschoff, *Proc. Russ. Min. Soc.*, (2), **31**. 417, 1894 ; A. Arzruni, *ib.*, (2), 23. 181, 1887 ; G. P. O. Tschernik, *ib.*, (2), **34**. 653, 694, 1902 ; *Bull. Acad. St. Petersburg*, (6), **2**. 242, 1908 ; T. Wada, *The Minerals of Japan*, Tokyo, 83, 1904 ; A. Stelzner, *Tschermak's Mitt.*, (1), 3. 233, 1873 ; A. Lacroix, *Minéralogie de Madagascar*, Paris, 1. 371, 1922 ; *Bull. Soc. Min.*, 35. 180, 1912 ; 41. 186, 1918 ; G. Tschernick, *ib.*, 49. 127, 1926 ; L. Duparc, R. Sabot, and M. Wunder, *ib.*, 36. 9, 1913 ; R. C. Sabot, *Études cristallographiques et optiques d'un certain nombre de minéraux des pegmatites de Madagascar et des minéraux de L'Oural*, Genève, 1916 ; A. G. Mailland, *Bull. Geol. Sur. West Australia*, 23, 1906 ; E. S. Simpson, *Proc. Anstral. Assoc.*, 11. 449, 1907 ; G. T. Prior, *Min. Mag.*, 13. 217, 1903 ; G. K. Almström, *Geol. För. Förh. Stockholm*, 44. 482, 1922 ; G. Chesneau, *Compt. Rend.*, 149. 1132, 1909 ; J. Schetelig, *Vid. Selsk. Skr.*, 1, 1922 ; H. Buttgenbach, *Bull. Soc. Geol. Belg.*, 46. 229, 1923 ; J. L. Smith, *Amer. Journ. Science*, (3), **13**. 360, 1877 ; W. P. Headden, *ib.*, (3) 41. 89, 1891 ; (5), 3. 293, 1922 ; *Proc. Colorado Scient. Soc.*, 8. 57, 1905 ; L. Weiss and M. Landecker, *Zeit. anorg. Chem.*, **64**. 96, 1909 ; G. A. Koenig, *Proc. Acad. Philadelphia*, 39, 1876 ; F. A. Genth, *ib.*, 52, 1889 ; F. P. Dunnington, *Amer. Chem. Journ.*, **4**. 138, 1883 ; *Amer. Journ. Science*, (3), **24**. 153, 1882 ; W. J. Comstock, *ib.*, (3), **19**. 131, 1880 ; T. B. Osborne, *ib.*, (3), **30**. 336, 1885 ; E. J. Hallock, *ib.*, (3), **21**. 412, 1881 ; C. A. Schaeffer, *ib.*, (3), **28**. 430, 1884 ; *Trans. Amer. Inst. Min. Eng.*, **8**. 233, 1884 ; C. W. Blomstrand, *Acta Lund. Univ.*, 2. 3, 1866 ; *Journ. prakt. Chem.*, (1), **99**. 41, 1866 ; *Proc. Russ. Min. Soc.*, (2), **23**. 188, 1887 ; T. W. Case, *Phys. Rev.*, (2), **9**. 305, 1917 ; A. Cossa, *Atti Accad. Lincei*, (4), 3. 111, 1887 ; J. V. Janowsky, *Sitzber. Akad. Wien*, **80**. 34, 1879 ; G. Eberhard, *Sitzber. Akad. Berlin*, 851, 1908 ; H. Erdmann, *Ber.*, 29. 1710, 1896 ; W. Ramsay, J. N. Collie, and M. Travers, *Journ. Chem. Soc.*, **67**. 684, 1895 ; W. Ramsay, and M. Travers, *Proc. Roy. Soc.*, **60**. 443, 1897 ; T. L. Walker and A. L. Parsons, *Univ. Toronto Geol. Stud.*, 16, 1923 ; Y. Shibata and K. Kimura, *Japan. Journ. Chem.*, 2. 13, 1923 ; H. V. Ellsworth, *Amer. Min.*, 11. 332, 1926 ; G. Tschernick, *Bull. Soc. Min.*, 49. 127, 1926.

¹⁵ E. S. Larsen, *Bull. U.S. Geol. Sur.*, 679, 1921 ; A. Schrauf, *Sitzber. Akad. Wien*, 44. 464, 1861 ; *Atlas der Krystallformen der Mineralreiches*, Wien, 49, 1877 ; O. J. Lee and E. T. Wherry, *Amer. Min.*, 4. 80, 1919 ; E. T. Wherry, *ib.*, 10. 28, 1925 ; *Mineral Collector*, 14. 17, 1907 ; E. M. Bonshtedt, *Bull. Acad. Union Rep. Soiret*, 19. 513, 1925 ; W. C. Brögger, *Vid. Selsk. Skrift.*, 1, 1887 ; 6, 1906 ; *Die Mineralien der südnorwegischen Granitpegmatitgänge*, Christiania, 1906 ; E. S. Dana, *Amer. Journ. Science*, (3), **13**. 390, 1877 ; (3), **32**. 386, 1886 ; J. D. Dana, *ib.*, (1), **32**. 149, 1837 ; *A System of Mineralogy*, New York, 736, 1892 ; H. W. Foote, *Amer. Journ. Science*, (4), 1. 460, 1896 ; W. P. Headden, *ib.*, (3), 24. 372, 1882 ; (3), 41. 89, 1891 ; *Proc. Colorado Scient. Soc.*, 2. 31, 1882 ; 8. 57, 1905 ; C. U. Shepard, *Amer. Journ. Science*, (1), 16. 220, 1829 ; (1), 34. 402, 1838 ; C. H. Warren, *ib.*, (4), 6. 123, 1898 ; W. T. Schaller, *ib.*, (4), 24. 154, 1907 ; W. P. Blake, *ib.*, (3), 41. 403, 1891 ; H. W. Foote and R. W. Langley, *ib.*, (4), 30. 393, 1910 ; *Chem. News*, 103. 53, 1911 ; D. Mawson and T. H. Laby, *ib.*, 92. 39, 1905 ; G. Rose, *Reise nach dem Ural, dem Altai, und dem kaspischen Meere*, Berlin, 2. 85, 1842 ; *Sitzber. Akad. Berlin*, 433, 1844 ; *Pogg. Ann.*, 64. 171, 336, 1845 ; H. Rose, *ib.*, 71. 157, 1847 ; E. S. von Federoff, *Das Kristallreich*, Petrograd, 859, 1920 ; C. F. Plattner, *Probierkunst mit dem Lötrohre*, Leipzig, 211, 321, 1907 ; N. von Kokscharoff, *Materialen zur Mineralogie Russlands*, St. Petersburg, 10. 261, 1891 ; A. des Cloizeaux, *Ann. Mines*, (5), **8**. 398, 1855 ; P. Groth and A. Arzruni, *Pogg. Ann.*, 149. 240, 1873 ; A. Arzruni, *Proc. Russ. Min. Soc.*, (2), 23. 181, 1887 ; P. Jereméeff, *ib.*, (2), 7. 301, 1872 ; (2), 23. 351, 1887 ; *Gornyi Journ.*, 3. 263, 1887 ; O. Mügge, *Neues Jahrb. Min.*, i, 147, 1898 ; L. Milch, *ib.*, i, 159, 1900 ; A. L. Fletcher, *Proc. Roy. Dublin Soc.*, (2), 13. 443, 1913 ; C. C. von Leonhard, *Taschenbuch Min.*, 13. 27, 1819 ; G. vom Rath, *Verh. Nat. Ges. Rheinl.*, 36. 115, 1879 ; G. H. Tipper, *Rec. Geol. Sur. India*, 50. 255, 1919 ; H. Laubmann and H. Steinmetz, *Zeit. Kryst.*, 55. 573, 1920 ; V. M. Goldschmidt, *ib.*, 44. 559, 1908 ; G. Struver, *ib.*, 10. 85, 1885 ; *Atti Accad. Lincei*, (4), 1. 8, 1884 ; A. Cossa, *ib.*, (4), 3. 111, 1887 ; A. Piccini, *ib.*, (5), 7. i, 246, 1898 ; D. Lovisato, *ib.*, (5), 7. i, 246, 1898 ; H. Traube, *Die Minerale Schlesiens*, Breslau, 71, 1881 ; A. Lacroix, *Minéralogie de la France et de ses colonies*, Paris, 4. 614, 1910 ; *Compt. Rend.*, 154. 1041, 1912 ; *Minéralogie de Madagascar*, Paris, 1. 367, 1922 ; *Bull. Soc. Min.*, 35. 184, 1912 ; 41. 186, 1918 ; H. Ungemach, *ib.*, 39. 25, 1916 ; F. Pisani, *ib.*, 27. 58, 1904 ; L. Duparc, R. C. Sabot, and M. Wunder, *ib.*, 36. 9, 1913 ; R. C. Sabot, *Études cristallographiques et optiques d'un certain nombre de minéraux des pegmatites de Madagascar et des minéraux l'Oural*, Genève, 1916 ; H. J. Brooke, *Phil. Mag.*, (3), 10. 187, 1831 ; T. Wada, *The Minerals of Japan*, Tokyo, 83, 1904 ; K. Jimbo, *Beiträge zur Mineralogie von Japans*, Tokio, 2, 1906 ; E. Hussak, *Tschermak's Mitt.*, (2), **18**. 351, 1899 ; A. F. Rogers, *School Mines Quart.*, **31**. 208, 1910 ; **H.** C. Lewis, *Proc. Acad. Philadelphia*, 51, 1882 ; F. A. Genth, *ib.*, 52, 1889 ; **E. S. Simpson.**

Rept. Dept. Mines Western Australia, 120, 1923 ; H. L. Bowman, Min. Mag., **12. 97**, 121, 1902 ;
13. 119, 1903 ; G. T. Prior, ib., **13.** 220, 1903 ; A. Breithaupt, Berg. Hütt. Ztg., **17.** 61, 1858 :
Journ. prakt. Chem., (1), **4.** 268, 1835 ; O. B. Böggild, Medd. Grönland, **32.** 208, 1905 ; J. C. G. de
Marignac, Arch. Sciences Genève, (2), **25.** 25, 1866 ; Ann. Chim. Phys., (4), **8.** 49, 1865 ; G. Spezia,
Atti Accad. Torino, **22.** 419, 1887 ; J. L. Smith, Amer. Chem. Journ., **5.** 50, 1884 ; J. F. Smith,
Amer. Min., **4.** 121, 1919 ; E. F. Smith, Journ. Amer. Chem. Soc., **20.** 289, 1898 ; W. K. von
Haagen and E. F. Smith, ib., **33.** 1504, 1911 ; J. Königsberger, Centr. Min., 565, 597, 1908 ;
T. L. Walker and A. L. Parsons, Univ. Toronto Geol. Stud., 16, 1923 ; T. W. Case, Phys. Rev.,
(2), **9.** 305, 1917 ; L. Michel, Neues Jahrb. Min., i, 159, 1900.
    [16] J. A. Hedvall, Zeit. anorg. Chem., **93.** 313, 1925 ; E. S. Larsen, Bull. U.S. Geol. Sur.,
679, 1921 ; W. T. Schaller, ib., 509, 1912 ; Journ. Washington Acad., **1.** 477, 1911 ; E. Mäkinen.
Bull. Comiss. Geol. Finland, 35, 1913 ; P. A. Gadd, Indica mineralogiæ in Fennia subgentilimo,
Abö, 1767 ; A. G. Ekeberg, Akad. Nya Handl., **23.** 80, 1802 ; Gilbert's Ann., **14.** 246, 1803 ;
Crell's Ann., i, 3, 1802 ; Scherer's Journ., **9.** 598, 1803 ; Nicholson's Journ., **3.** 251, 1802 ; Phil.
Mag., **14.** 346, 1802 ; Ann. Chim. Phys., (1), **43.** 276, 1802 ; J. J. Berzelius, Afh. Fys. Kemi
Min., **4.** 262, 1815 ; **6.** 237, 1818 ; Schweigger's Journ., **16.** 447, 1816 ; A. E. Nordenskjöld,
Beskrifning öfver de i Finland funna Mineralier, Helsingfors, 87, 1855 ; Pogg. Ann., **101.** 625,
1857 ; **122.** 604, 1864 ; Acta Soc. Fenn., **5.** 164, 1858 ; **20.** 445, 1863 ; N. Nordenskjöld, ib.,
1. 119, 1832 ; Pogg. Ann., **50.** 656, 1840 ; Bidrag till kännedom af Finlands Mineralier och
Geognosie, Stockholm, 1820 ; H. J. Holmberg, Proc. Amer. Min. Soc., 153, 1862 ; M. H. Klaproth,
Beiträge zur chemischen Kenntnis der Mineralkörper, Berlin, **5.** 1, 1810 ; J. F. L. Hausmann,
Leonhard's Taschenbuch, **6.** 1812, 1812 ; L. N. Vauquelin, ib., **13.** 27, 1819 ; H. Rose, Pogg.
Ann., **104.** 85, 1858 ; T. Crook and S. J. Johnstone, Min. Mag., **16.** 231, 1912 ; E. S. Simpson,
ib., **18.** 117, 1917 ; Rep. Austral. Assoc., **12.** 314, 1909 ; Chem. News, **99.** 77, 1909 ; A. E. Arppe,
Acta Soc. Fenn., **6.** 589, 1861 ; R. Hermann, Journ. prakt. Chem., (2), **4.** 201, 1871 ; Erman's
Arch., **10.** 260, 1852 ; C. F. Rammelsberg, Ber., **4.** 875, 1871 ; **5.** 17, 1872 ; Sitzber. Akad. Berlin,
164, 1871 ; 181, 1872 ; Handbuch der Mineralchemie, Leipzig, **357**, 1875 ; W. P. Headden,
Proc. Colorado Scient. Soc., **8.** 167, 1906 ; W. C. Brögger, Oefvers Svenska Akad., 330, 1890 ;
Vid. Selsk. Skrift., 1, 1897 ; 6, 1906 ; Die Mineralien der südnorwegischen Granitpegmatitgänge,
Christiania, 1906 ; E. S. Dana, A System of Mineralogy, New York, 238, 1892 ; P. Groth and
K. Mieleitner, Mineralogische Tabellen, München, 65, 1921 ; P. Groth, Tabellarische Uebersicht
der Mineralien, Braunschweig, 86, 1898 ; W. J. Vernadsky and A. E. Fersman, Bull. Acad.
St. Petersburg, (6), **4.** 511, 1910 ; A. Schrauf, Sitzber. Akad. Wien, **44. 464**, 1861 ; V. M. Gold-
schmidt, Skrift. Norske Akad., 1, 1926.

§ 8. Pertantalic Acid and the Pertantalates

According to P. G. Melikoff and L. Pissarjewsky,[1] when potassium metapertantalate is treated with dil. sulphuric acid, a white precipitate of **metapertantalic
acid**, $HTaO_4.nH_2O$, is formed. It is more stable than percolumbic acid (q.v.),
but its properties are otherwise similar. The constitution of $HTaO_4.nH_2O$ is
supposed to be:

$$\begin{matrix} O \\ O \end{matrix} > Ta < \begin{matrix} OH \\ O \end{matrix}$$

P. G. Melikoff and L. Pissarjewsky evaporated to dryness on a water-bath a soln. of
1·5 grms. of sodium orthohexatantalate in 30 c.c. of 2 per cent. hydrogen dioxide ;
dissolved the residue in water ; added a little hydrogen dioxide to the filtrate, and
then an equal vol. of alcohol. The white amorphous precipitate appeared to be
sodium metapertantalate—the analysis corresponded with $NaTaO_4.NaTaO_5.13H_2O$.
By treating sodium orthohexatantalate with the 2 per cent. hydrogen dioxide,
and sodium hydroxide ; mixing the filtrate with an excess of hydrogen dioxide ;
and, after cooling with ice-water, adding an equal vol. of alcohol, a precipitate
sodium orthopertantalate, $Na_3TaO_8.H_2O$, is deposited. This was dried on a porous
tile. The monohydrate is a white, amorphous powder sparingly soluble in water.
When the aq. soln. is warmed, oxygen is given off ; dil. sulphuric acid furnishes
hydrogen dioxide, and the conc. acid, ozonized oxygen. C. W. Balke prepared the
tetradecahydrate. G. Böhm modified E. H. Riesenfeld's formula for the perchromates
to adopt it to P. G. Melikoff and L. Pissarjewsky's formula for the pertantalates :

$$\begin{matrix} O \\ O \end{matrix} > Ta < \begin{matrix} O-ONa \\ O-ONa \\ O-ONa \end{matrix} \qquad \begin{matrix} O \\ O \end{matrix} > Cr < \begin{matrix} O-ONa \\ O-ONa \\ O-ONa \end{matrix}$$

Pertantalate.   Perchromate.

they found that potassium or sodium pertantalate, percolumbate, and perchromate are isomorphous. The subject was discussed by G. Böhm. P. G. Melikoff and L. Pissarjewsky prepared **potassium orthopertantalate**, K_3TaO_8, by fusing tantalum pentoxide and potassium hydroxide (1 : 3) in a silver crucible, dissolving the cold cake in a little water, and proceeding with hydrogen dioxide as in the case of the sodium salt. The resulting *hemihydrate* has analogous properties. C. W. Balke obtained the anhydrous salt, and said that it is isomorphous with the corresponding perchromate. C. W. Balke and E. F. Smith added an excess of hydrogen dioxide to a soln. of 4 grms. of rubidium orthohexatantalate and 10 grms. of rubidium carbonate. The crystalline powder of **rubidium orthopertantalate**, Rb_3TaO_8, was washed with alcohol and ether, and dried in air. It is less soluble than the corresponding percolumbate. In a similar manner, **cæsium orthopertantalate**, Cs_3TaO_8, was prepared. P. G. Melikoff and L. Pissarjewsky prepared what was probably **calcium, strontium, and barium orthopertantalates** by the method employed for the potassium salt; and when the potassium salt was treated with calcium chloride, **potassium calcium orthopertantalate**, $KCaTaO_8$. $4\frac{1}{2}H_2O$, was formed in rhombic crystals; and C. W. Balke and E. F. Smith prepared acicular crystals of **sodium calcium orthopertantalate**, $NaCaTaO.4\frac{1}{2}H_2O$, and also **sodium magnesium orthopertantalate**, $NaMgTaO_8.8H_2O$; **potassium magnesium orthopertantalate**, $KMgTaO_8.7H_2O$; and **rubidium magnesium orthopertantalate**, $RbMgTaO.8H_2O_8$, in a similar manner. The needle-like crystals of the potassium salt are more soluble in water than the corresponding calcium salt.

REFERENCES.

[1] P. G. Melikoff and L. Pissarjewsky, *Zeit. anorg. Chem.*, **20**. 345, 1899; C. W. Balke, *The Double Fluorides of Tantalum*, Easton, Pa., 22, 1905; *Journ. Amer. Chem. Soc.*, **27**. 1156, 1905; C. W. Balke and E. F. Smith, *ib.*, **30**. 1666, 1909; G. Böhm, *Zeit. Kryst.*, **63**. 319, 1926; E. H. Riesenfeld, *Ber.*, **41**. 3941, 1908.

§ 9. Tantalum Fluorides, Fluotantalates, and Oxyfluotantalates

H. Moissan [1] observed that warm tantalum powder burns in fluorine, forming fumes which condense on a cold surface. As previously indicated, J. J. Berzelius, H. Rose, W. von Bolton, and H. Kuessner obtained a soln. of the metal in hydrofluoric acid, and when evaporated, H. Rose said that tantalum fluoride is formed; while G. von Hevesy and R. E. Slade obtained the oxyfluoride. O. Hahn and K. E. Pütter found that soln. of tantalic acid in hydrofluoric acid are hydrolyzed during evaporation and the residue shows no volatility when heated. Dil. hydrofluoric acid was found by O. Ruff and E. Schiller slowly to dissolve tantalum pentoxide if the mixture is heated in a platinum flask provided with a reflex condenser. H. Rose said that no tantalum is volatilized if sulphuric acid be present, but in its absence, some tantalum is volatilized when the soln. is evaporated, and if tantalum pentoxide be heated with ammonium fluoride, it can be completely volatilized. These statements were contradicted by J. C. G. de Marignac, and by O. Ruff and E. Schiller. J. J. Berzelius, H. Rose, J. C. G. de Marignac, and O. Ruff and E. Schiller noticed that hydrofluoric acid forms a clear soln. with tantalum hydroxide, and if the soln. be evaporated alone, hydrolysis occurs, and an oxyfluoride is deposited; but if ammonium or alkali fluorides be present, complex fluotantalates are formed.

O. Ruff and E. Schiller prepared **tantalum pentafluoride**, TaF_5, by the action of fluorine on tantalum containing about 3 per cent. of aluminium, as in the case of the corresponding columbium salt. The product was purified by distillation in vacuo at 90°–100°. The same salt was prepared by the action of dried hydrogen fluoride on tantalum pentachloride, cooled by a freezing mixture of ice and salt. When the evolution of hydrogen chloride has ceased, the hydrofluoric acid is distilled off, and then the tantalum pentafluoride. Moisture must be excluded. O. Hahn and K. E. Pütter obtained the pentafluoride by heating barium fluotantalate. According to O. Ruff and E. Schiller, the tantalum pentafluoride product appears in tetragonal prisms with a strong double refraction. The **specific gravity** is 4·981 at 15°, and 4·744 at 19·5°. The **melting point** is 96·8°; and the **boiling point** at 760 mm. is 229·2°–229·5°. The **vapour pressure,** p mm., is:

	183°	198·5°	204°	212·5°	227·5°	228·9°
d . .	368·2	447·3	485·8	540·8	720·7	753·7

R. Lorenz and W. Herz discussed certain regularities in the relation $(T_2-T_1)/(\theta_2-\theta_1)$=constant, where T_1 and T_2 represent absolute temp. corresponding with vap. press., p_1 and p_2, and θ_1 and θ_2 are the b.p. at the same two press.

The boiling pentafluoride is not affected by **hydrogen** or by **oxygen.** It is very hygroscopic in **air,** and it dissolves with a hissing noise in **water.** The boiling aq. soln. is clear, but on evaporation, an oxyfluoride is formed, which, when roasted in air, passes quantitatively into the pentoxide. G. von Hevesy and R. E. Slade found that it is less readily hydrolyzed by water than is the case with tantalum pentachloride, or the pentafluoride of columbium or vanadium. O. Ruff and E. Schiller showed that the boiling pentafluoride does not react with **bromine** or **iodine.** The pentafluoride dissolves in **hydrochloric acid** with the evolution of a little heat. The boiling pentafluoride does not react with **sulphur ;** cold **sulphuric acid** dissolves only a little pentafluoride, but more dissolves in the hot acid, and hydrofluoric acid escapes ; **sulphuryl chloride** dissolves the fluoride without any visible sign of chemical action, and when the soln. is evaporated, the residue contains sulphur, chlorine, fluorine, and tantalum. Cold **sulphur monochloride** dissolves only a little sulphofluoride ; there is a vigorous reaction with **sulphur dichloride** in the cold—gas is evolved, and the liquid becomes **warm ;** but no reaction occurs with **hydrogen sulphide.** The boiling pentafluoride is not attacked by **nitrogen ; ammonium hydroxide,** or a soln. of **ammonium sulphide,** precipitates tantalum hydroxide. Cold fuming **nitric acid** does not dissolve the pentafluoride so readily as water—the soln. remains clear when diluted and when warmed, but on standing in a warm place, it slowly deposits a crystalline oxyfluoride. Boiling tantalum pentafluoride has no action on **phosphorus ;** with **phosphorus trichloride,** in the cold, a jelly is formed, and when warmed, phosphorus trifluoride is produced ; and with **phosphoryl chloride,** in the cold, there is a vigorous reaction, gas is evolved, and a colourless soln. is produced which, on evaporation, furnishes an oxychloride. The boiling pentafluoride does not act on **arsenic** or **antimony.** Cold **arsenic trichloride** dissolves very little when cold ; and when warmed, a white jelly is formed ; **antimony pentachloride** behaves similarly. The cold pentafluoride is indifferent towards many organic substances—*e.g.* **toluene,** and **paraffin,** but when heated, a brown decomposition product is formed ; warm **carbon disulphide** dissolves a little pentafluoride ; **carbon tetrachloride** gives a brown mass ; **tetrachloroethane** gives a black mass ; **chloroform** dissolves a little, without visible change ; **acetic acid,** and **acetic anhydride,** readily dissolve the pentafluoride without visible reaction ; absolute **alcohol** readily dissolves it with the generation of some heat ; and **ether** reacts vigorously with the evolution of hydrogen fluoride. C. W. Balke obtained complex salts with **methylamine, ethylamine, triethylamine, pyridine, and quinoline fluorides.** O. Ruff and E. Schiller observed that at a high temp. **glass** decomposes the pentafluoride, forming tantalum pentoxide and silicon tetrafluoride. Very little pentafluoride is dissolved by **silicon tetrachloride ;** while **titanium tetrachloride** reacts vigorously ; and **tin tetrachloride** dissolves very little in the cold, but more is dissolved by the hot liquid, and crystals are deposited when the soln. is cooled.

The vapour of the pentafluoride does not attack **copper, silver, gold, magnesium, zinc, aluminium,** and **iron ;** while a black powder is formed with **tin,** and **lead.** A cold conc. soln. of **alkali hydroxide or carbonate** reacts vigorously with the pentafluoride, forming an insoluble oxyfluoride ; while cold, dil. soln. precipitate a hydroxyfluoride, and if hot, the hydroxide. Molten **potassium hydrofluoride** forms a pentafluotantalate; hot **potassium fluoride** reacts very slowly with the pentafluoride; while **potassium chloride** reacts neither when cold nor when hot. C. W. Balke obtained a series of complex salts with the alkali fluorides.

H. O. Hahn and K. E. Pütter observed that with hydrofluoric acid, tantalum pentafluoride forms **hydrohexafluotantalic acid,** $HTaF_6.6H_2O$. C. W. Balke prepared **lithium hexafluotantalate,** $LiTaF_6.2H_2O$, by evaporating on a water-bath a soln. of 10 grms. of lithium carbonate in one of 40 grms. of tantalum pentoxide in conc. hydrofluoric acid, and cooling the soln. The colourless, monoclinic prisms can be crystallized from conc. hydrofluoric acid. The axial ratios of the crystals are $a:b:c=0.5703:1:1.6235$, and $\beta=92°\ 14'$. The crystals gradually lose their lustre in air. The mother-liquor left after the preparation of sodium heptafluotantalate furnish cubic crystals of **sodium hexafluotantalate,** $NaTaF_6$. C. W. Balke obtained crystals of **cæsium hexafluotantalate,** $CsTaF_6$, by mixing soln. of the constituent fluorides, and recrystallizing from hydrofluoric acid; and by recrystallizing the heptafluotantalate, 2 or 3 times from hydrofluoric acid. The trigonal crystals have the axial ratio $a:c=1:1.0467$, and $a=95°\ 40'$. By recrystallizing rubidium heptafluotantalate a number of times, C. W. Balke and E. F. Smith obtained impure **rubidium tridecafluoditantalate,** $Rb_3Ta_2F_{13}$, as a granular mass.

J. J. Berzelius prepared crystals of **ammonium heptafluotantalate,** $(NH_4)_2TaF_7$, by adding ammonia to a hydrofluoric acid soln. of tantalic acid, until a precipitate begins to form, and evaporating the clear liquid. J. C. G. de Marignac said that the tetragonal plates have the axial ratio $a:c=1:1.804$. The crystals do not lose appreciably in weight when heated to 100° for an hour, but when kept for a longer time at that temp. they do lose weight. They decrepitate when rapidly heated. At a higher temp., J. C. G. de Marignac observed that ammonium fluoride is sublimed. J. C. G. de Marignac found the salt to be freely soluble in water, from which soln. it can be crystallized unchanged. If the aq. soln. be warmed for a short time, hydrolysis occurs, and tantalum hydroxide separates out. O. Hahn and K. E. Pütter also prepared the ammonium heptafluotantalate, $NH_4F_2.TaF_5$, or NH_4TaF_7. If a soln. of sodium fluoride and a large excess of tantalum pentafluoride be evaporated and cooled, J. C. G. de Marignac, and C. W. Balke found that six-sided plates of **sodium heptafluotantalate,** $Na_2TaF_7.H_2O$, are formed. According to J. C. G. de Marignac, the rhombic bipyramids have the axial ratios $a:b:c=0.838:1:1.274$. The crystals lose water at 100°, and suffer no other change at 130°–150°. When recrystallized from water, the octofluotantalate is formed. J. J. Berzelius prepared **potassium hydroheptafluotantalate,** $KHTaF_7$, by cooling a boiling sat. soln. of hydrofluoric acid and potassium tantalate; and from a hydrofluoric acid soln. of the heptafluotantalate. J. C. G. de Marignac said that this salt is not formed by recrystallizing a soln. of the heptafluotantalate and tantalum pentafluoride. J. J. Berzelius prepared **potassium heptafluotantalate,** K_2TaF_7, by adding potassium hydroxide to a hot soln. of tantalic acid in hydrofluoric acid until a precipitate begins to form, and cooling the clear soln. W. H. Chapin obtained the salt from a soln. of potassium carbonate in a hydrofluoric soln. of tantalum hydroxide; H. Rose, by treating tantalum hydroxide with a soln. of potassium fluoride; and A. Piccini, from a soln. of potassium oxyfluotantalate in conc. hydrofluoric acid. Analyses were made by J. J. Berzelius, H. Rose, J. C. G. de Marignac, R. Hermann, A. Piccini, and W. H. Chapin. The small, acicular crystals were found by J. C. G. de Marignac to belong to the rhombic system, to have the axial ratios $a:b:c=0.6682:1:0.4610$; and to be isomorphous with the corresponding heptafluocolumbate. H. Behrens said the birefringence is feeble. H. Topsöe gave 4·56 for the sp. gr., and F. W. Hinrichsen and N. Sahlbom, 5·24. The salt decrepitates when heated and then fuses, and, according to H. Rose, and J. C. G. de Marignac, it does not decompose in a platinum crucible at a white heat

nor even when heated with potassium pyrosulphate. **J. J.** Berzelius said that the
salt is freely soluble in cold water, more so in hot water ; and C. W. Balke and
E. F. Smith said that it is less soluble if hydrofluoric acid be present, and, added
J. C. G. de Marignac, 100 parts of water containing a little hydrofluoric acid dissolve 0·5 part of salt at 15° ; and with rather more hydrofluoric acid, 0·675–0·67 part.
O. Ruff and E. Schiller represented the equilibrium conditions at 18°–18·5°, and
at 85°–90° by

	Conc.	TaF$_5$	0·25	0·10	0·09	1·33	1·24	5·35	0·036
18°		KF	0·12	4·79	6·73	0·56	0·52	2·25	21·93
		HF	0·029	0·074	0·015	4·47	4·2	24·3	10·44
	Solid phase		$K_wTa_xO_yF_z + K_2TaF_7$			K_2TaF_7			

	Conc.	TaF$_5$	2·18	0·9	5·73	6·00	10·91	1·18
85°		KF	1·69	5·27	2·41	2·52	4·59	22·42
		HF	0·85	1·17	4·47	4·2	24·3	10·44
	Solid phase.		$K_wTa_xO_yF_z + K_2TaF_7$		K_2TaF_7			

The solubility is thus shown to increase with an increasing conc. of hydrofluoric
acid, and afterwards to decrease. H. Rose said that the aq. soln. reddens blue-
litmus ; and decomposes when boiled with the separation of an oxyfluoride as shown
by J. J. Berzelius, J. C. G. de Marignac, C. W. Balke and E. F. Smith, and
M. E. Pennington. The electrolysis of the soln. was found by M. E. Pennington
to yield some tantalum hydroxide. C. W. Balke, M. E. Pennington, and E. F. Smith
prepared **rubidium heptafluotantalate**, Rb_2TaF_7, from a soln. of the component
salts with a small excess of hydrofluoric acid. It can be recrystallized from water
containing a little hydrofluoric acid. The white needles are more soluble than the
potassium salt—100 parts of water dissolve 2·5 parts of salt. The aq. soln. is
hydrolyzed when boiled. C. W. Balke found **cæsium heptafluotantalate**, $CsTaF_6$,
to be also more soluble than the potassium salt. It cannot be recrystallized from
water without hydrolysis. J. C. G. de Marignac **prepared copper heptafluotantalate**, $CuTaF_6.4H_2O$, from a soln. of the component salts by evaporation over
sulphuric acid. The blue, rhombic prisms are freely soluble in water ; and lose
some water and hydrofluoric acid at 100°. O. Hahn and K. E. Pütter prepared
barium fluotantalate, $3BaF_2.2TaF_5$. J. J. Berzelius prepared **calcium fluotantalate** by evaporating a soln. of calcium tantalate in hydrofluoric acid ; likewise also **magnesium fluotantalate**. J. C. G. de Marignac also obtained the
magnesium salt by evaporating a soln. of the component salts. Similarly with
zinc heptafluotantalate, $ZnTaF_7.7H_2O$, which forms deliquescent, rhombic plates.
F. Ephraim and L. Heymann obtained **thallium heptafluotantalate**, Tl_2TaF_7,
from a soln. of the component salts in hydrofluoric acid. The rectangular plates
do not form a clear soln. with water, and when boiled tantalum hydroxide is
deposited. It is sparingly soluble in cold, readily soluble in hot hydrofluoric acid.
It is decomposed by conc. sulphuric acid.

C. W. Balke obtained **ammonium octofluotantalate**, $(NH_4)_3TaF_8$, by concentrating a soln. of the component salts with ammonium fluoride in excess.
J. C. G. de Marignac prepared **sodium octofluotantalate**, Na_3TaF_8, from a soln.
of the orthohexatantalate in dil. hydrofluoric acid ; and by crystallization from
an aq. soln. of the heptafluotantalate. H. Rose obtained it from a soln. of the
component salts, and C. W. Balke from a soln. with $NaF : TaF_5 = 4 : 1$. The needle-
like crystals, according to C. W. Balke, are rhombic, and have the axial ratios
$a : b : c = 0.6017 : 1 : 0.2799$. The crystals are stable in air ; they fume but do not
melt easily when heated in a platinum crucible. H. Rose added that the salt is
freely soluble in water and the soln. reddens blue litmus. C. W. Balke found that

100 parts of water at 25° dissolve 4·83 parts of salt. When the aq. soln. is boiled, the oxyfluoride does not separate, but hydrofluoric acid passes off with the steam. The calcined residue blues a soln. of red litmus. M. E. Pennington said that white needles of **cæsium icosifluotantalate**, $Cs_{15}TaF_{20}$, are formed from a soln. of the component salts. It is sparingly soluble in water, and the aq. soln. is not decomposed on the water-bath. J. D. M. Smith regards this compound as evidence of a co-valency of 20 in tantalum, but N. V. Sidgwick says that the compound may really be $R_3[TaF_8].12CsF$.

J. C. G. de Marignac obtained an amorphous, white tantalum oxyfluoride by evaporating in vacuo a soln. of tantalum hydroxide in hydrofluoric acid. G. von Hevesy and R. E. Slade likewise obtained it by evaporating a soln. of tantalum in hydrofluoric acid. It is almost insoluble in water. The composition varies with the mode of preparation, but **tantalum oxytrifluoride**, $TaOF_3$, appears in a number of complex salts. A. Joly obtained **ammonium oxyhexafluotantalate**, $3NH_4F.TaOF_3$, from a hot soln. of tantalum hydroxide in conc., aq. ammonium fluoride. The octahedral crystals are freely soluble in water ; and the aq. soln. becomes turbid when heated. If an excess of hydrofluoric acid be present in crystallizing the salt, **ammonium oxyhydroheptafluotantalate**, $3NH_4F.TaOF_3.HF$, is formed. A. Joly obtained regular octahedra of **potassium oxyhexafluotantalate**, $3KF,TaOF_3$, in a similar way. J. C. G. de Marignac, and C. W. Balke and and E. F. Smith obtained **potassium pentoxytetradecafluotetratantalate**, $4KF.Ta_2O_5.2TaF_5$, by boiling an aq. soln. of potassium heptafluotantalate. G. Krüss and L. F. Nilson represented its composition by $KF.TaOF_3$. It is insoluble in boiling water ; freely soluble in hydrofluoric acid.

A. Piccini prepared **potassium peroxypentafluotantalate**, $2KF.TaO_2F_3.H_2O$, by cooling a warm soln. of potassium heptafluotantalate in 4 per cent. hydrogen dioxide, feebly acidified with hydrofluoric acid ; and C. W. Balke and E. F. Smith, by dissolving the heptafluotantalate in hot, dil., aq. hydrofluoric acid, and mixing the soln. with an equal vol. of 3 per cent. hydrogen dioxide. The tabular crystals can be recrystallized from a hydrofluoric acid soln. of hydrogen dioxide. The salt gives off water at 100°, and oxygen at a higher temp. ; it is freely soluble in water. Aq. ammonia does not precipitate tantalum hydroxide, but a precipitate is formed if alcohol be added. It is decomposed by hydrofluoric acid ; and the sulphuric acid soln. decomposes potassium permanganate. In a similar way, C. W. Balke and E. F. Smith prepared **rubidium peroxypentafluotantalate**, $2RbF.TaO_2F_3.H_2O$, in tabular crystals.

REFERENCES.

¹ O. Ruff and E. Schiller, *Zeit. anorg. Chem.*, 72. 355, 1911 ; *Ber.*, 42. 494, 1909 ; E. Schiller, *Ueber Tantal- und Niobpentafluorid, sowie über die Reindarstellung der Tantal- und Niobsäure,* Danzig, 1911 ; J. C. G. de Marignac, *Ann. Chim. Phys.*, (4), 9. 249, 1866 ; *Compt. Rend.*, 63. 85, 1866 ; *Arch. Sciences Genève*, (2), 26. 89, 1866 ; H. Topsöe, *ib.*, (2), 45. 76, 223, 1872 ; H. Moissan, *Bull. Soc. Chim.*, (3), 27. 434, 1902 ; *Compt. Rend.*, 134. 211, 1902 ; A. Piccini, *Zeit. anorg. Chem.*, 2. 24, 1892 ; O. Hahn and K. E. Pütter, *ib.*, 127. 153, 1923 ; R. Lorenz and W. Herz, *ib.*, 143. 336, 1925 ; R. Lorenz, *ib.*, 138. 104, 1924 ; J. J. Berzelius, *Pogg. Ann.*, 4. 6, 1825 ; H. Rose, *ib.*, 99. 70, 1856 ; R. Hermann, *Journ. prakt. Chem.*, (2), 5. 81, 1872 ; G. von Hevesy and R. E. Slade, *Zeit. Elektrochem.*, 18. 1001, 1912 ; H. Kuessner, *ib.*, 16. 772, 1910 ; W. von Bolton, *ib.*, 11. 47, 1905 ; W. H. Chapin, *The Halide Bases of Tantalum,* Easton, Pa., 1909 ; W. H. Chapin and E. F. Smith, *Journ. Amer. Chem. Soc.*, 33. 1499, 1911 ; C. W. Balke and E. F. Smith, *ib.*, 27. 1154, 1905 ; C. W. Balke, *ib.*, 32. 1129, 1911 ; *The Double Fluorides of Tantalum,* Easton, Pa., 1908 ; M. E. Pennington, *Derivatives of Columbium and Tantalum,* Easton, Pa., 1895 ; *Chem. News,* 75. 8, 18, 31, 38, 1897 ; *Journ. Amer. Chem. Soc.*, 18. 48, 1896 ; C. W. Balke, M. E. Pennington, and E. F. Smith, *ib.*, 27. 1150, 1905 ; H. Behrens, *Anleitung zur mikrochemischen Analyse,* Hamburg, 104, 1895 ; A. Joly, *Ann. École. Norm.*, (2), 6. 162, 1877 ; *Compt. Rend.*, 81. 1266, 1875 ; N. V. Sidgwick, *Journ. Soc. Chem. Ind.—Chem. Ind.*, 42. 1203, 1923 ; J. D. M. Smith, *ib.*, 42. 1073, 1923 ; O. Ruff and W. Plato, *Ber.*, 37. 675, 1904 ; G. Krüss and L. F. Nilson, *ib.*, 20. 1690, 1887 ; F. W. Hinrichsen and N. Sahlbom, *ib.*, 39. 2600, 1906 ; F. Ephraim and L. Heymann, *ib.*, 42. 4461, 1909.

§ 10. Tantalum Chlorides and Oxychlorides

The normal chloride is tantalum pentachloride, $TaCl_5$. O. Ruff and F. Thomas [1] found that when tantalum pentachloride and aluminium are heated in an evacuated bomb-tube at 300°, complete reduction to tantalum does not occur even when the aluminium is in excess. If rather less than the calculated amount of aluminium be used for **tantalum tetrachloride,** $TaCl_4$, and the excess of the pentachloride and aluminium chloride be distilled off at 250°, the tetrachloride is formed, but whether it is a compound of quadrivalent tantalum, or a complex of the tri- and penta-chlorides is not clear. If the product be heated further, more pentachloride is given off, and the residue becomes richer in tantalum. Thus, at 350°–400°, **tantalum trichloride,** $TaCl_3$, is formed ; and at 600°, **tantalum dichloride,** $TaCl_2$. At 680°–700° the product is richer in tantalum, and is pyrophoric. The dichloride dissolves in water with the evolution of hydrogen, and the formation of an oxychloride of tervalent tantalum. The trichloride dissolves without the evolution of gas. K. Lindner and H. Feit prepared the dichloride by heating the pentachloride with metallic lead at 600° in an atm. of hydrogen. The residue was extracted with hydrochloric acid in a reflux apparatus, and, after removing the lead with hydrogen sulphide, evaporating the soln. in vacuo. The green crystals were represented by the formula Ta_3Cl_6, or $(TaCl_2)_3$. According to K. Lindner, E. Haller, and H. Helwig, tantalum pentachloride is reduced by powdered metals to the dichloride and, since the reaction proceeds less violently than with the molybdenum and tungsten compounds, the addition of powdered quartz may be omitted. Aluminium, zinc, and lead are efficient. The residues are extracted exhaustively with hydrochloric acid. The isolation of the compound $HTa_3Cl_7.4H_2O$, a blackish-green, unusually stable, crystalline powder, from the extracts is a matter of some difficulty, since it only separates from very conc. soln. and its crystallization is greatly impeded by the presence of dissolved aluminium chloride. It is prefer-able, therefore, to use zinc which can be removed as sulphide after addition of sodium acetate to the solution ; or else lead, the dissolved traces of which can be precipitated directly with hydrogen sulphide. Molten tantalum pentachloride cannot be reduced electrolytically between carbon poles, since the substance is an insulator. Electrolysis takes place after addition of alkali chlorides, and the dichloride is formed to some extent ; but the method has no preparative value.

O. Ruff and F. Thomas said that the green soln. of tantalum trichloride in **hydrochloric or sulphuric acid** slowly oxidizes in air with the separation of tantalic acid. It is oxidized by **hydrogen dioxide,** by an aq. soln. of **chlorine, by nitric acid,** and by a soln. of **potassium permanganate.** An aq. soln. of **sodium hydroxide,** added in small quantities, gives a green flocculent precipitate soluble in excess, forming a fine green soln. ; **sodium sulphide** produces a precipitate soluble in excess —when shaken in a test-tube the soln. is brown, but on standing, it becomes green —the precipitation is incomplete ; aq. **ammonia** behaves like sodium hydroxide, but the precipitate is not soluble in excess, and the green precipitate rapidly oxidizes and becomes brown ; **ammonium sulphide** gives a dark green precipitate which dissolves in conc. hydrochloric acid without giving off gas ; a soln. of **sodium phosphate, potassium ferrocyanide, sodium borate,** or of **potassium fluoride** gives a gelatinous precipitate, the filtrate is green, and the precipitate is probably flocculated tantalic acid ; **sodium carbonate, and hydrocarbonate** precipitate tantalous hydroxide incompletely ; **sodium thiosulphate** gives a precipitate soluble in excess ; **potassium oxalate** gives a dark olive-green precipitate—the precipitation is complete—soluble in conc. hydrochloric acid giving a pale green soln. of a complex salt ; and **potassium cyanide** in small quantities precipitates a dark green cyanide which is soluble in more potassium cyanide and is decomposed by conc. hydrochloric acid giving off hydrogen cyanide. According to C. Chabrié, the *dihydrate* of tantalum dichloride, $TaCl_2.2H_2O$, is formed when tantalum penta-chloride is reduced with sodium amalgam. It is an emerald-green, microcrystalline powder, with a spectrum like that of tantalum pentoxide. When freshly prepared, it is soluble in water. The pentoxide was moulded into filaments (by mixing it with a little paraffin), and these were heated to whiteness for 4 or 5 hrs. in carbon powder. The filaments of tetroxide obtained in this way conduct electricity. When such a filament is heated to whiteness in a vacuum by a direct current it is but little changed, a small portion at the positive end being reduced to metal. By using an alternating current, however, the filament is converted into the metal in a quarter of an hour. This method yields very small quantities of the metal. Larger quantities were prepared as follows : columbium pentoxide and powdered aluminium react together when the mixture is heated at one point, yielding a hard, metallic regulus of sp. gr. 7·5, and containing 2·8 per cent. to 3·2 per cent. of aluminium as well as some unchanged oxide. By heating this material in a vacuum (a current of 185 ampères at 40 volts for 15 hrs. is required for 20 grms. of metal) the whole of the impurities are vaporized, leaving columbium alone. According to W. H. Chapin, C. Chabrié used the at. wt. for tantalum 183 instead of 181, and so obtained a wrong formula. It can be represented as a **tantalum heptatrita-chloride,** $Ta_3Cl_7.3\frac{1}{2}H_2O$, or $Ta_6Cl_{12}Cl_2.7H_2O$. It furnishes a hydroxide : $[Ta_6Cl_{12}](OH)_2$, and is insoluble in hydrochloric acid. K. Lindner compared this salt with molybdous chloride, $(MoCl_2)_3$, and regarded it as a complex $H[Ta_3Cl_7(H_2O)]$, in which the water can be replaced by alcohol to form $H[Ta_3Cl_7(C_2H_5OH)]$. There is also **ammonium amminochlorotantalite,** $NH_4[Ta_3Cl_7(NH_3)]$—*vide infra.*

J. J. Berzelius obtained **tantalum pentachloride,** $TaCl_5$, as a yellowish-white powder, by burning tantalum in chlorine ; and H. Moissan said the attack begins at 150°, and at 250° is attended by incandescence, and the sublimation of the pentachloride. K. Lindner and H. Feit obtained it as a bright yellow powder by passing chlorine over tantalum at 600°. K. Lindner, E. Haller, and H. Helwig found that tantalum is converted into the pentachloride by carbonyl chloride vapour. H. Rose and R. Weber, and W. Biltz and A. Voigt made it by heating a mixture of the pentoxide and carbon in a current of dry chlorine. M. E. Pennington observed that it is formed when the pentoxide and phosphorus pentachloride are heated in a sealed tube at 210°–245°, and the product fractionated by distillation under a reduced press. E. Demarçay, R. D. Hall and E. F. Smith, M. Delafontaine and C. E. Linebarger, and O. Ruff and E. Schiller obtained it by heating the pentoxide in a current of carbon tetrachloride ; and F. Bourion, O. Ruff and E. Schiller, and R. D. Hall, by heating the pentoxide in a current of the vapour of sulphur monochloride and chlorine—*vide* columbium pentachloride. Tantalum pentachloride was analyzed by H. Rose, C. W. Blomstrand, R. D. Hall, H. St. C. Deville and L. Troost, M. E. Pennington, and F. Bourion. H. St. C. Deville and L. Troost found the **vapour density** to be 12·8 at 360°. The salt is a pale yellow solid—rather paler than columbium pentachloride. W. Biltz and A. Voigt obtained it as a snow-white mass of crystals. The sublimate appears in orange-yellow needles or prisms. H. Rose gave 221° for the **melting point ;** and H. St. C. Deville and L. Troost, 211·3°. H. Rose said that it begins to volatilize at 144°, and, according to H. St. C. Deville and L. Troost, its **boiling point** is 241·6°, at 753 mm. press. K. Lindner and H. Feit gave 233°. W. Hampe found that molten tantalum pentachloride has a good **electrical conductivity,** but W. Biltz and A. Voigt found that at 230°–240°, the conductivity is 0.30×10^{-6} mho. The platinum electrodes were strongly attacked. G. W. Sears said that the pentachloride is quite stable in dry air, but H. Rose found that it readily attracts moisture from **air,** and gives off the vapour of hydrogen chloride without becoming deliquescent. When freshly prepared, it hisses in contact with **water,** and is hydrolyzed into tantalum and hydrochloric acid. The hygroscopicity, and tendency to hydrolysis, are so great that G. W. Sears considers that the pentachloride is not suitable for use in at. wt. determinations. It does not occlude **chlorine.** O. Ruff and E. Schiller found that the pentachloride is converted by **hydrogen fluoride** into the penta-fluoride (*q.v.*). H. Rose found that **hydrochloric acid** dissolves the pentachloride

In the cold, and after standing some time, it gives a gelatinous liquid ; boiling hydrochloric acid dissolves it incompletely, but the soln. does not gelatinize on cooling. The addition of water makes the soln. opalescent. R. F. Weinland and L. Storz said that it is freely soluble in alcohol or acetic acid sat. with hydrogen chloride. O. Ruff and F. Thomas found that the pentachloride is not reduced when heated with **sulphur.** H. Rose showed that at a red-heat, **hydrogen sulphide** forms tantalum disulphide and hydrochloric acid ; with conc. **sulphuric acid,** hydrogen chloride is given off, and the salt passes into soln. which becomes very turbid when heated. The pentachloride is stable in dry **nitrogen ;** with aq. **ammonia** in the cold, the tantalum is completely precipitated as hydroxide. K. Lindner and H. Feit found that when ammonia is passed into a sat. soln. of the tetrachloride in carbon disulphide, a yellow **tantalum amminopentachloride** is formed; and a yellow product is produced when ammonia is passed into a boiling soln. of tantalum pentachloride in carbon tetrachloride ; and when alcoholic soln. of ammonia and tantalum penta-chloride are mixed, a crystalline substance is formed. These three products were too unstable for **analysis.** O. Ruff and F. Thomas said that the pentachloride is reduced to a lower chloride when heated with red **phosphorus,** but not so with **arsenic, antimony, or bismuth.** H. Rose observed no reaction with the vapour of **carbon disulphide** and the heated pentachloride. The pentachloride is soluble in absolute **alcohol,** and the boiling soln. gives a precipitate with sulphuric acid. When the alcoholic soln. is distilled, alcohol and hydrogen chloride are evolved at 83°–85°, but no tantalum is volatilized. K. Lindner and H. Feit found that it is soluble in **chloroform, ethyl bromide, carbon tetrachloride,** and particularly **carbon disulphide.** It forms complex salts with **pyridine.** O. Ruff and F. Thomas found that the pentachloride is reduced to a lower chloride when heated with **magnesium, zinc, tin,** or **aluminium,** but not so with **mercury.** H. Rose found that a boiling soln. of **potassium hydroxide** dissolves a little pentachloride, but not so with a soln. of **potassium carbonate.** No complex salts have been obtained with the **alkali chlorides.**

H. St. C. Deville and L. Troost observed the formation of no oxychloride when the vapour of tantalum pentachloride is passed over the heated pentoxide ; but when the pentachloride, prepared from the pentoxide, is sublimed in vacuo, at 500°, O. Ruff and F. Thomas observed the formation of **tantalum dioxychloride,** TaO_2Cl. According to F. R. Weinland and L. Storz, colourless crystals of complex salts of **tantalum oxytrichloride,** $TaOCl_3$, with pyridine and with quinoline can be prepared by the action of the base on tantalum pentachloride dissolved in alcohol, and containing some hydrochloric acid. They also obtained a complex with pyridine and **tantalum trioxytetrachloride,** $Ta_2O_3Cl_4$.

K. Lindner and H. Feit saturated an aq. soln. of the dichloride with hydrogen chloride, and on evaporation obtained dark green, six-sided crystals of what they regarded as $H[Ta''_3Cl_7.H_2O].3H_2O$, analogous to the corresponding molybdenum compound. O. Ruff and F. Thomas said that when a hydrochloric soln. of tantalum trichloride is evaporated under reduces press., a crystalline compound of tervalent tantalum is formed, viz., **tantalum oxyheptachloride,** $Ta'''_3Cl_7O.3H_2O$. It is the same as that obtained by K. Lindner and H. Feit, who were mistaken in assuming that it contained bivalent tantalum from its reducing action on potassium per-manganate, and silver salts. Only 3 mols. of water are lost when it is heated, and the evolution of a little hydrogen chloride on further heating, is ascribed to traces of water having been retained by the salt. K. Lindner and H. Feit found that the oxychloride forms complexes with alcohol, and with pyridine. When treated with dil. potash-lye, and afterwards with acetic acid, a dark brown amorphous precipitate of **tantalum oxydihydroxypentachloride,** $[Ta_3Cl_5(H_2O)_5]OH.Aq.$, or, according to O. Ruff and F. Thomas, $[Ta_3Cl_5O(OH)_2.3H_2O].3H_2O$, is formed. K. Lindner added : *das letzte Wort in dieser Wertigkeitsfrage ist wohl noch nicht gesprochen.*

REFERENCES.

[1] W. H. Chapin, *The Halide Bases of Tantalum*, Easton, Pa., 1909 ; *Journ. Amer. Chem. Soc.*, **32**. 329, 1910 ; G. W. Sears, *ib.*, **39**. 1582, 1917 ; M. Delafontaine and C. E. Linebarger, *ib.*, **18**. 532, 1896 ; M. Delafontaine, *Arch. Sciences Genève*, (2), **27**. 167, 1866 ; M. E. Pennington, *Journ. Amer. Chem. Soc.*, **18**. 64, 1896 ; *Chem. News*, **75**. 8, 18, 31, 38, 1897 ; R. D. Hall, *Observations on the Metallic Acids*, Easton, Pa., 1904 ; *Journ. Amer. Chem. Soc.*, **26**. 1243. 1904 ; R. D. Hall and E. F. Smith, *ib.*, **27**. 1393, 1905 ; *Proc. Amer. Phil. Soc.*, **44**. 202, 1905 ; *Chem. News*, **92**. 220, 232, 242, 252, 262, 276, 1905 ; H. St. C. Deville and L. Troost, *Compt. Rend.*, **64**. 294, 1867 ; E. Demarçay, *ib.*, **104**. 111, 1887 ; C. Chabrié, *ib.*, **144**. 804, 1907 ; H. Moissan, *ib.*, **134**. 211, 1902 ; *Bull. Soc. Chim.*, (3), **27**. 434, 1902 ; E. Schiller, *Ueber Tantal- und Niobpentafluoride, sowie über die Reindarstellung der Tantal- und Niobsäure*, Danzig, 1911 ; O. Ruff and E. Schiller, *Zeit. anorg. Chem.*, **72**. 355, 1911 ; *Ber.*, **42**. 494, 1909 ; F. Bourion, *Ann. Chim. Phys.*, (8), **20**. 566, 1910 ; H. Rose and R. Weber, *Pogg. Ann.*, **69**. 115, 1846 ; **90**. 458, 1853 ; H. Rose, *ib.*, **99**. 76, 1856 ; J. J. Berzelius, *ib.*, **4**. 6, 1825 ; R. F. Weinland and L. Storz, *Zeit. anorg. Chem.*, **54**. 240, 1907 ; W. Biltz and A. Voigt, *ib.*, **120**. 71, 1921 ; O. Ruff and F. Thomas, *Ber.*, **55**. B, 1466, 1922 ; *Zeit. anorg. Chem.*, **148**. 1, 19, 1925 ; K. Lindner, E. Haller, and H. Helwig, *ib.*, **130**. 209, 1923 ; K. Lindner and H. Feit, *ib.*, **132**. 10, 1924 ; **137**. 66, 1924 ; K. Lindner, *ib.*, **160**. 57, 1927 ; **162**. 203, 1927 ; *Ber.*, **55**. B, 1458, 1922 ; C. W. Blomstrand, *Acta Lund. Univ.*, **1**. 7, 1864 ; **2**. 3, 1865 ; *Liebig's Ann.*, **135**. 198, 1865 ; W. Hampe, *Chem. Ztg.*, **11**. 816, 846, 904, 934, 1109, 1158, 1887.

§ 11. Tantalum Bromides and Oxybromides

W. H. Chapin [1] reduced tantalum pentabromide with sodium amalgam as in C. Chabrié's method for tantalum dichloride, and obtained a product whose composition corresponded with **tantalum heptatritabromide,** $Ta_3Br_7.3\frac{1}{2}H_2O$, which he represented by the formula $[Ta_6Br_{12}]Br_2.7H_2O$. The green powder, under the microscope, consists of hexagonal crystals ; at 100°, only a little hygroscopic moisture is given off ; at 120°, the compound decomposes, forming an insoluble compound which is anhydrous after being heated to 150°–250°. The salt is freely soluble in water, forming a green soln. which is stable in air, and colours silk, and paper. The rise of the b.p. in propyl alcohol corresponds with a mol. wt. of 2275 when the theoretical value for $[Ta_6Br_{12}]Br_2$ is 2332 ; while the lowering of the f.p. of water corresponds with a mol. wt. of 720, which is only one-third of the theoretical. Bromine-water decolorizes the liquid, and sulphur dioxide restores the colour ; and hydrochloric acid forms $[Ta_6B_{12}]Cl_2.7H_2O$. In the cold, aq. ammonia changes the colour of the liquid, and when heated, yields a brown precipitate of tantalum hydroxide. The salt is freely soluble in alcohol, and in pyridine, and these soln. are decomposed when heated. With sodium hydroxide, $[Ta_6Br_{12}](OH)_2.5H_2O$ is formed ; silver nitrate precipitates only one-seventh of the bromine so that 2 mols. of bromine are supposed to be bound in the mol. different to the other twelve. K. Lindner represented the bromide as an acid, $H[Ta_3Br_7(H_2O)]$; and the chlorobromide, $H[Ta_3Cl_6Br(H_2O)]$.

W. K. van Haagen reduced tantalum pentabromide by passing the vapour mixed with hydrogen through a red-hot glass tube, and obtained a small yield of a green compound, with marked tinctorial properties when dissolved in water. He thought that it is *tantalum tribromide*, $TaBr_3$, but W. H. Chapin showed that it is more probably the pentatritabromide.

W. K. van Haagen said that when bromine vapour is passed over tantalum at ordinary temp., the metal is not attacked ; but at an elevated temp., a pale yellow sublimate of **tantalum pentabromide,** $TaBr_5$, is formed. This compound was made by H. Rose, by passing bromine vapour over a red-hot mixture of tantalum pentoxide and carbon—taking care that moisture and air are excluded. W. H. Chapin and E. F. Smith employed a similar process. W. K. van Haagen resublimed the product three times in an atm. of purified and dried carbon dioxide. According to W. K. van Haagen, the yellow tabular crystals have a **specific gravity** 4·67 ; the **melting point** is about 240°, and they form a transparent red-liquid ; the **boiling point** is about 320°, but volatilization begins below the m.p. The yellow vapour looks like chlorine. The compound can be sublimed in **hydrogen** without decomposition, but at a higher temp., there is a partial reduction to a lower chloride. The compound fumes strongly in **air.** H. Rose found that the salt is hydrolyzed by **water,** forming tantalum hydroxide and hydrobromic acid. When distilled with **hydrogen iodide,** some pentaiodide is formed; and with **potassium iodate** some iodine is set free. The pentafluoride is freely soluble in methyl or ethyl **alcohol** with the development of so much heat that the alcohol may boil. The soln. is pale yellow—water decolorizes the soln. but gives no precipitate. The salt is freely soluble in **ethyl bromide,** and the soln. becomes warm—the red soln. deposits golden-yellow crystals when cooled or evaporated in vacuo. The pentabromide is not reduced by **silver** to a lower bromide; and it reacts vigorously when mixed with **silver fluoride,** but tantalum fluoride is not produced—possibly a complex salt is formed.

W. K. van Haagen observed that no tantalum oxybromide is formed during the sublimation of tantalum pentabromide, but W. H. Chapin and E. F. Smith said that **tantalum oxytribromide,** $TaOBr_3$, is possibly formed by heating tantalum pentoxide in an atm. of hydrogen bromide, and in the distillation of the penta-bromide. W. H. Chapin found that when the tritaheptabromide is treated with $0.1N$-NaOH, in the cold, and the precipitate washed with ether, and dried in vacuo, dark green, hexagonal plates of **tantalum hydroxyhexabromide,** $Ta_3(OH)Br_6.5H_2O$, or $[Ta_6Br_{12}](OH)_2.10H_2O$, are formed. They are stable in air below 100°; but on a water-bath at 100°, part becomes insoluble, and some tritaheptabromide is formed; at 250°, the water is all expelled; and at 500°, the hydroxyl-group is driven off. The salt is sparingly soluble in water, soluble in alcohol, and insoluble in ether; it dissolves in acids, and with hydriodic acid forms $[Ta_6Br_{12}]I_2.7H_2O$. R. F. Weinland and L. Storz could not prepare complex salts with tantalum oxytribromide owing to the insolubility of tantalum pentabromide in hydrobromic acid. W. H. Chapin said that the lower chloride he prepared furnishes complex salts.

W. H. Chapin obtained a mixed salt, **tantalum hexabromochloride,** $Ta_3ClBr_6.3\frac{1}{2}H_2O$, or $[Ta_6Br_{12}]Cl_2.7H_2O$, by evaporating a hydrochloric acid soln. of the hydroxide or of the tritaheptabromide. According to K. Lindner and H. Feit, if tantalum pentachloride be reduced with lead, at 600°, in an atm. of hydrogen, and the product dissolved in hydrobromic acid, the soln. furnishes green crystals of **tantalum oxybromohexachloride,** $H[Ta_3Cl_6Br.H_2O].3H_2O$—or better, according to O. Ruff and F. Thomas, $[Ta_3Cl_6Br.O].3H_2O$—when evaporated in vacuo. This compound forms a complex salt with pyridine and in the presence of an excess of hydrobromic acid, a complex salt of pyridine with **tantalum tribromohexachloride,** $(Ta_3Cl_6Br_3)(C_5H_5N)$.

REFERENCES.

[1] W. H. Chapin, *The Halide Bases of Tantalum,* Easton, Pa., 1909; *Journ. Amer. Chem. Soc.,* 32. 324, 1910; W. H. Chapin and E. F. Smith, *ib.,* 33. 1499, 1911; W. K. van Haagen, *ib.,* 32. 729, 1910; *Tantalum and some of its Halides,* Easton Pa., 1909; H. Rose, *Pogg. Ann.,* 99. 87, 1856; C. Chabrié, *Compt. Rend.,* 144. 804, 1907; K. Lindner and H. Feit, *Zeit. anorg. Chem.,* 137. 66, 1924; K. Lindner, *ib.,* 162. 203, 1927; R. F. Weinland and L. Storz, *ib.,* 54. 233, 1907; O. Ruff and F. Thomas, *ib.,* 148. 23, 1925

§ 12. Tantalum Iodides and Oxyiodides

[1] W. K. van Haagen[1] observed no reaction occurs when iodine and tantalum are heated in a sealed tube at 280° for 8 hrs.; and H. Rose said that no tantalum iodide is formed when iodine vapour acts on a red-hot mixture of tantalum pentoxide and carbon. H. Moissan was unable to prepare this iodide; W. K. van Haagen found that by distilling tantalum bromide over granular silver iodide, iodine is set free, but if silver iodate be present, **tantalum pentaiodide,** TaI_5, is formed:

$7TaBr_5 + 5AgIO_3 = TaI_5 + 3Ta_2O_5 + 5AgBr + 15Br_2$. The liberated bromine reacts on the pentaiodide, reforming the pentabromide. The pentaiodide is best made by slowly distilling the pentabromide in a current of dried hydrogen iodide, when it appears as a brownish-black sublimate consisting of lamellar crystals resembling those of iodine. The crystals melt to a brown liquid; the vapour looks like bromine vapour. The salt resembles the pentabromide in its relations to moist air and water, but it reacts more slowly. W. H. Chapin did not succeed in reducing the pentaiodide to a lower iodide by means of sodium-amalgam. No *tantalum oxyiodide* was observed by W. K. van Haagen when the pentaiodide was heated in a current of dry air.

W. H. Chapin made hexagonal prisms of **tantalum hexabromoiodide,** $Ta_3Br_6I.3\frac{1}{2}H_2O$, or $[Ta_6Br_{12}]I_2.7H_2O$, by dissolving the hydroxyhexabromide in hydriodic acid, and crystallizing the soln.

REFERENCES.

[1] W. K. van Haagen, *Journ. Amer. Chem. Soc.*, 32. 729, 1910; *Tantalum and some of its Halides*, Easton, Pa., 1909; W. H. Chapin, *The Halide Bases of Tantalum*, Easton, Pa., 1909; *Journ. Amer. Chem. Soc.*, 32. 329, 1910; H. Moissan, *Compt. Rend.*, 134. 211, 1902; *Bull. Soc. Chim.*, (3), 27. 434, 1902; H. Rose, *Pogg. Ann.*, 99. 76, 587, 1856; R. F. Weinland and L. Storz, *Zeit. anorg. Chem.*, 54. 240, 1907.

§ 13. Tantalum Sulphides and Sulphates

J. J. Berzelius [1] said that tantalum at a red-heat burns with great vigour in sulphur vapour, forming **tantalum disulphide,** TaS_2; and W. von Bolton heated a mixture of the two elements under a layer of potassium chloride and observed that the elements unite vigorously. J. J. Berzelius and J. G. Gahn observed no sulphide is formed by heating a mixture of tantalum pentoxide with sulphur, with mercuric sulphide, or potassium sulphide; or by heating the pentoxide in a current of hydrogen sulphide. H. Rose obtained the sulphide by passing hydrogen and the vapour of carbon disulphide over the white-hot pentoxide; but not by heating tantalum pentachloride in the vapour of carbon disulphide. H. Rose made the sulphide by passing a slow current of dry hydrogen sulphide over heated tantalum pentachloride; H. Biltz and C. Kirchner prepared the disulphide by passing a dry mixture of hydrogen sulphide and carbon disulphide over heated tantalum pentoxide. The pentoxide is attacked at 650°, but the pure sulphide is best obtained at temp. higher than 900°. It is stable at all temp. up to 1300°, and above 1200° it begins to change from the amorphous to the crystalline condition. Analyses were made by J. J. Berzelius, H. Rose, R. Hermann, and H. Biltz and C. Kirchner. Tantalum disulphide appears as a dark grey or black, crystalline mass. R. Robl observed no fluorescence when the disulphide is exposed to ultra-violet light. A. Karl found the sulphide to be triboluminescent. H. Rose found that the trisulphide loses very little sulphur when heated in **hydrogen.** It burns to the pentoxide when heated in **air,** but the last traces of sulphur dioxide can be removed only by calcination with admixed ammonium carbonate. Hot or cold **water** has no action. The disulphide absorbs moisture very readily, and holds it very tenaciously, and when heated in water vapour forms hydrogen sulphide and tantalum pentoxide. In the cold, **chlorine** has no action, but when heated, it forms sulphur monochloride and tantalum pentachloride; **iodine** can be sublimed from the disulphide without change; and when heated with iodine and water no reaction occurs; **hydrofluoric acid** decomposes it so slowly that no smell of hydrogen sulphide can be detected; and **hydrochloric acid** has no action. Boiling, conc. **sulphuric acid** slowly decomposes the sulphide; boiling **nitric acid** decomposes it slowly, forming, according to W. von Bolton, tantalum pentoxide; **aqua regia** is not much faster than nitric acid in its action of the sulphide. Molten **potassium hydroxide** forms potassium sulphide and tantalate ; and analogous products are obtained when the sulphide is fused with a mixture of sulphur and **sodium carbonate ;** and a conc. soln. of **potassium polysulphide** does not dissolve tantalum disulphide.

O. Ruff and E. Schiller obtained a complex product, thought to be *tantalum sulpho-fluoride,* from a soln. of tantalum pentafluoride in sulphur monochloride ; and a *tantalum fluochlorosulphide* from a soln. of the pentafluoride in sulphuryl chloride.

J. J. Berzelius [2] said that tantalum sulphate remains when tantalum sulphide is roasted in air ; and when tantalum hydroxide is treated with conc. sulphuric acid. R. Hermann reported **tantalum oxysulphate,** $3Ta_2O_5.SO_3.9H_2O$, or $2Ta_2O_5.Ta_2O_4(SO_4).9H_2O$, to remain as a residue when the product of fusing tantalum pentoxide with potassium hydrosulphate is extracted with water. W. Muthmann and co-workers said that this compound does not lose its sulphate-radicle when roasted at a red-heat for a long time. It is soluble in hydrochloric acid, but separates when the dil. soln. is boiled.

W. H. Chapin said that crystalline **tantalum bromosulphate,** $[Ta_6Br_{12}]SO_4.nH_2O$, is formed when the corresponding bromide is treated with silver nitrate. If the product obtained by reducing tantalum pentachloride with lead at 600° be treated with dil. sulphuric acid, K. Lindner and H. Feit said that the soln. furnishes crystals of **tantalum chlorosulphate,** $H_2[Ta_3Cl_6SO_4]$, or, as represented by O. Ruff and F. Thomas, $Ta_3Cl_6.SO_4.OH$.

The *tantalum carbonate, nitrate, or phosphate* has not yet been prepared.

REFERENCES.

[1] J. J. Berzelius and J. G. Gahn, *Afh. Fys. Kemi Min.,* **4.** 252, 1815 ; J. J. Berzelius, *Pogg. Ann.,* **4.** 6, 1825 ; H. Rose, *ib.,* **99.** 575, 1856 ; *Gilbert's Ann.,* **73.** 139, 1823 ; W. von Bolton, *Zeit. Elektrochem.,* **11.** 50, 1905 ; R. Robl, *Zeit. angew. Chem.,* **39.** 608, 1926 ; H. Biltz and C. Kirchner, *Ber.,* **43.** 1639, 1910 ; R. Hermann, *Journ. prakt. Chem.,* (1), **70.** 195, 1857 ; E. Schiller, *Ueber Tantal- und Niobpentafluoride soure über die Reindarstellung der Tantal- und Niobsäure,* Danzig, 1911 : O. Ruff and E. Schiller, *Zeit. anorg. Chem.,* **72.** 355, 1911 ; *Ber.,* **42.** 494, 1909 ; A. Karl, *Compt. Rend.,* **146.** 1104, 1908.

[2] J. J. Berzelius, *Pogg. Ann.,* **4.** 5, 1825 : R. Hermann, *Journ. prakt. Chem.,* (1), **70.** 201, 1857 ; W. Muthmann, L. Weiss. and R. Riedelbauch, *Liebig's Ann.,* **355.** 62, 1907 ; W. H. Chapin, *The Halide Bases of Tantalum,* Easton, Pa., 1909 ; *Journ. Amer. Chem. Soc.,* **32.** 329, 1910 ; K. Lindner and H. Feit. *Zeit. anorg. Chem.,* **137.** 66, 1924 ; O. Ruff and F. Thomas, *ib.,* **148.** 1, 19, 1925.

INDEX